published by mcr:music

© the|unsigned|guide/UK 2006

UK ISBN: 0 9544601 3 8

Published by mcr:music Ltd., 3rd Floor, 24-26 Lever Street, Manchester, M1 1DZ.

Editorial Tel: +44 (0)161 907 0030
Subscriptions Tel: +44 (0)161 907 0029
Advertising Tel: +44 (0)161 234 6815

www.theunsignedguide.com

PUBLISHERS MESSAGE

Welcome to the first UK Edition of The Unsigned Guide. The first North West edition was published early in 2003 and with two further editions printed in 2004 (North West) and 2005 (Greater London), we are extremely pleased to now make this UK Edition available to a wider fraternity of bands, musicians and managers from across the UK to include full coverage of the industry throughout Northern Ireland, Scotland, England & Wales. If you are serious about your music, The Unsigned Guide is essential. It's as simple as that.

For the past 12 months our research teams have been busy compiling this edition to bring you by far the most comprehensive UK unsigned band resource ever produced. The book you are now holding is the result of tens of thousands of telephone conversations, emails & letters.

We would like to extend our genuine thanks to everyone who has helped us compile The Unsigned Guide and we hope you find it helpful in your quest for professional development over the coming year or so.

Remember, we never claim to deliver the 'get signed quickly' formula because it simply doesn't exist. There are no secrets in this industry, just hard work, commitment and creativity. The rest will unfold organically if it's meant to be.

Watch out for valuable, practical advice from Radio 1's OneMusic team, PRS-MCPS Alliance, Musicians' Union and BPI. You could certainly do worse than heed the advice these organisations impart.

We're also looking forward to some very exciting developments in 2006 here at The Unsigned Guide with the introduction of up-to-the-minute data-downloads via www.theunsignedguide.com as well as a band management software package which will change the lives of many unsigned bands for the better, for ever!

Finally, we truly hope our work compiling the brand new UK edition of The Unsigned Guide lives up to your expectations and, as ever, we wish you all the very best for the coming twelve months.

mcr:music
Publisher

A few words from our sponsor:

SOUNDCONTROL
The UK's Number One Musical Instrument Retailer

Sound Control is the UK's single largest musical instrument retailer with 25 stores across the country from Dundee and Glasgow to London and Southampton. Established over 20 years ago, and with a wealth of expertise in the world of music equipment, we have never lost sight of the individual needs of our customers. This has been achieved through our unique approach to new customers, whilst maintaining our commitment to developing and strengthening partnerships with our existing clients.

We recognise that our most important resource is our staff. Through our structured program of comprehensive training, combined with their proficiency as musicians with live and recording experience, we are in a unique position to offer you the best possible advice, along with our competitive pricing policy.

Now, as the largest music retailer in Europe, Sound Control can offer musicians an unrivalled service, with the largest single stockholding, huge buying power and widest range of experience. Call us now on 08700 67 1234 or visit our web site at www.soundcontrol.co.uk.

Editors: Stephen Loukes, Lee Donnelly
Production Manager: Ben Holden
Research Manager: Louise Dodgson, Kate Doyle
Production Assistants: Paul McManus, Mark Bristol
Research: Chris Dart, Nikki Irabor, Sian Roberts, Harriet Gill, Cynthia Park, Kara James, Joe Hughes, Emily Churchill, Robin Walls, Jessica Thompson, Tom Moran, Lee Shelton, Georgia Fitzgerald, Yolanda Johnson, Helen Windebank, Neil Wright, Helen Bowling, Adele Millward, Daniel Scott, Kelly Robson, Sarah Murray, Mark Coleman, Laura Hamilton, Matt Adams, Ian Kilner, Tom Booton, Mark Russell
Design: Ben Holden, Mark Bristol
Photography: Mark Bristol
Print Management: Steve Wilkin (Unwin Bros. Ltd.)
Advertising: Joe Lyon

Special thanks to Nigel McCune (Musicians' Union), Matt Fernand (BBC Radio 1), Stuart Belsham & team (MCPS-PRS Alliance), Mark Flanagan & Andy Gillespie at Sound Control, Mike Senior (Bright Partnership), Helen Worthington, Anna Lomas (SPICE), Matt Phillips (BPI), Sandra Gourley (NIMIC) & Grant Tyrie.

CONTENTS

Introduction

the|unsigned|guide

The UK Music Industry: Unsigned and Unwrapped.

The Unsigned Guide is produced entirely with unsigned bands and artists in mind and our researchers have spent thousands of hours (literally!) compiling this accurate and specific information so that you, the unsigned band, can spend more time doing what you do best, making music, not collecting telephone numbers.

We have always taken a proactive stance on researching the areas of the music industry which we feel are of particular use and interest to unsigned and emerging talent and that has still been very much the case during the production of this first UK edition.

On the request of many bands, managers and other readers and users of The Unsigned Guide, we have included some new sections such as Press & PR companies, Independent Promoters (in addition to in-house venue promoters), Distributors and a Recommended Reading List. We have also included a section written specifically for The Unsigned Guide by BBC Radio 1's OneMusic team which offers a truly professional and realistic take on the current UK music industry from the perspective of an unsigned or emerging artist, band, manager or producer. Similarly, the PRS-MCPS Alliance Admissions Team have produced a hugely useful FAQ section which amongst other things, should help you to gauge the point at which you should consider approaching collection societies with a view to applying for membership. On an extremely practical level, both of these sections are hugely informative and well written and you should definitely take the time to read them.

As publishers of The Unsigned Guide, mcr:music have always worked very closely with unsigned bands & artists and we operate with a genuine interest in grass-roots music. As an unsigned band you are the future of the music industry, this much is a fact. Some bands will break through, some won't, another fact. However, the fundamental reason we have taken the time to update our research and produce this UK edition is that at least now everyone has a fighting chance of getting out there and getting heard. We can't write and play the songs for you, but we can make sure you have the relevant tools and contact details available to you and we have provided this information in the form of the very book you are reading.

We suggest that you use The Unsigned Guide as a day-to-day source of reference information as well as a practical hands-on guide to developing your understanding of the music industry. The UK edition of The Unsigned Guide contains essential information and contact details relevant to most aspects of the industry. From basic recording agreements, how to best promote and market your sound through the media, suggested publishing and recording A&R contacts, how to book better gigs, radio stations that play demos on-air as well as details of key music industry and advisory organisations.

At the beginning of each sectiwon, we have included a relevant introduction containing straight-talking, practical information with references to specific organisations and companies that may be able to help you. Read each section foreword carefully before you make your calls or plan your campaigns, they have been written by the Musicians' Union and other experienced industry contributors. A solid entry-level understanding of the particular industry sector you are concentrating on (for example, management, the media or live performance) will save you a great deal of time and effort in the long run.

From our experience, we find that arguably the most overlooked factor in the development of an unsigned band is management or at least some form of representation, creatively and/or on a business level. Management is certainly an area we cover in more detail later in the book, but initially there are three basic options:

i) Self-management, ii) Employing the services of a management company or iii) lining-up a suitably interested friend with enthusiasm and a few contacts to do the job. The choice is obviously entirely yours, but until you generate commercial interest, it is highly unlikely that you will be an attractive proposition for labels, publishers or indeed management companies.

However, from the outset we would recommend putting someone in place to help you manage the direction and development of your band. You will need them to take responsibility for tasks such as approaching venues and promoters to book your gigs, to undertake basic marketing and press work, arranging for a decent website to be built and to find you decent deals in terms of, for example, recording studio bookings or CD duplication. They should also take charge of presenting your demos to a professional standard to the wider industry (including managing follow-up phone calls and emails) and hopefully to begin entry-level contract negotiations on your behalf. In no uncertain terms, you should be looking for someone who can industriously and methodically manage your band affairs.

As a small word of advice, we strongly suggest you don't play at management, it's an expensive hobby. Don't be flash and don't pretend that you've seen it, done it. Chances are you haven't. Get the best you can out of your manager and make sure an inter-band agreement exists as soon as possible. Simple rules are, don't pay over the odds and don't necessarily believe everything a manager tells you.

We encourage you to use The Unsigned Guide to plan your next set of live shows. As well as working with your local promoters and venues to develop your hometown fan-base, try to look further a field to other promoters for bookings in other towns and cities. On occasions, diligent promoters should be willing to offer a non-local travelling unsigned band (i.e. you cannot guarantee to attract a local audience) the opportunity to play on the same bill as two or three established local acts. A promoter that applies his unsigned trade ethically will be prepared to do this if the economics stack-up and the other bands' local audience will cover his risk (i.e. the costs attached to the gig such as venue hire, secu-

rity, engineer, PA, etc.) with a reasonable margin for his efforts. When contacting out-of-town venues and promoters always be aware of this and we guarantee that you will build a far better set of live contacts than if you try to 'fudge' the fact that there "might" be people turning up to see you when in actual fact you know it is highly unlikely that they will. If your performance is well received, by playing the game with an honest approach it is more likely you will be re-booked the next time you choose to take to the road. Additionally, if you do get to the stage in your professional career when you start touring through bookings with an agent, it will only bolster your reputation as a straight-talking band.

Whilst you are gigging, make sure to promote yourselves as effectively as you can. Although it is extremely difficult to do this in the early days, a combination of good old-fashioned hard work and a few creative moves should start the ball rolling. Be sure to employ as many conventional marketing techniques as you can including well-designed print with solid distribution as well as appropriate new media marketing (email and internet presence). In addition to good word-of-mouth promotion and any press coverage you may be able to secure, you should find that if your music is interesting and draws public attention, you will begin to find the word of the band spreading nicely. The fact is that the sum of the parts will equal the whole where your promotion is concerned and you will find that you simply alienate one method at the expense of another by not covering all possible marketing channels.

You should also be working hard to build solid working relationships with your promoters, venues and local journalists. Speak to retailers about stocking your CDs and make every effort to be creative in promoting what you do. At grass-roots level, it is only you who can kick things into gear by actively promoting what you do and without doubt you must build a strong local fan-base before moving on to develop wider audiences.

Although each section of The Unsigned Guide has been compiled individually, you will need to cross-reference particular sections and use information from multiple sections simultaneously. It is of limited use spending time covering one section, just to ignore others. The industry works as a whole, relying on each component part to work with another. You must treat your campaigns in the same way. Don't eliminate certain aspects of the industry on the belief that another will carry you through - it won't.

INTRODUCTION

To start with, you must research all aspects of the music industry, from management to recording, live performance and marketing. Your band is a business and a poorly managed business will fail - with debts.

Be under no illusions, the road is hard and well travelled - after all it can be a great way to earn a living. Competition is fierce, there are thousands of unsigned bands and artists across the UK so you will need to be dedicated, hard working and prepared to put the hours in. The Unsigned Guide can only help you if you are ready to help yourselves.

The Music Services/Retail section will amongst other things, help you to find the best recording studios and rehearsal rooms in your area as well as recommended mastering and product duplication facilities to instrument repair and equipment hire shops, record shops, minibus/splitter hire companies and music related insurance services.

The Media section will help you to produce an effective band biography, press release and electronic press kit as well providing details of the most suitable radio stations and presenters, press titles, magazines and websites to contact.

You should use the A&R sections to plan the record companies and publishers you need to approach with your demos, most of which will also highlight their preferred musical genre as well as where and how they suggest you submit your material.

In addition, The Unsigned Guide has a section to help you with the creative and design side of your work, with contact details for graphic designers, photographers and print houses for production of posters, flyers, tickets and other artwork. If you feel confident enough to produce your own artwork, keep it simple and effective. Don't overdo it, in many cases less is more.

Look out for the Industry Organisations section which lists dates of important music industry events & festivals, as well as contact information for industry organisations and advisory groups such as AIM (Association of Independent Music) and Musicians' Union. You should use the diary to keep a note of forthcoming dates including gigs, studio bookings and rehearsals. You should also keep track of when and where demo recordings have been sent, allowing reasonable time for follow-up calls. Plan and orchestrate your campaigns thoroughly, make realistic timing estimates and stick to them.

In conjunction with the Musicians' Union, we have developed a section to provide artists with legal advice including issues such as inter-band agreements, sample clearance and assistance with contract negotiation (see www.musiciansunion.org.uk).

The Unsigned Guide also contains a detailed section listing useful web resources such as industry reference and consumer music sites as well as information on how to post your music on the internet and some of the best sites to help you.

Finally, the Tuition & Training section contains information about organisations that provide music related training as well as details of the range of courses available. More specialist schools and independent regional music teachers are also included for your information.

Feedback

The Unsigned Guide is published on an annual basis and so your feedback is essential. We have already begun to develop a network of bands, musicians and managers that regularly use and depend on the information we collect, so we whole-heartedly encourage readers to input on how the book is presented and the type of information you consider to be most useful.

Let us know about the venues that were supportive, which recording studios did another great job on your demo and which radio stations or magazines were enthusiastic about your songs. You will find feedback sheets at the back of book. Fill them in and send them back to us or email your comments to mail@theunsignedguide.com. Finally, if there are any details which you think we have over-looked or not covered in enough detail, let us know. We'll do our best to include them in subsequent editions.

Thanks for reading and we wish you all the best for the coming year.
The Editor

The Unsigned Guide
3rd Floor
24-26 Lever Street
Manchester
M1 1DZ
Tel: +44 (0) 161 907 0030

One·music

BBC Radio 1's OneMusic team offer some wise words of advice

As Radio 1's site for up & coming DJs and unsigned musicians, OneMusic is pleased to be associated with the Unsigned Guide. It's a brilliant idea. Whether you're looking for that multi-album deal or aiming for underground success through your own releases, you'll find the contacts you need to help you out. The next stage is to figure out how to make the best of them - which is what OneMusic is for.

> "There are no rules to getting into the music industry. Most bands go into it and they don't know anything – we didn't know anything. We're all encouraged to think that mistakes are bad – 'don't make mistakes! Mistakes are bad!' That's absolute crap. Mistakes are how you learn. Do as much as you can."
>
> **Fran Healey - Travis**

We interview many of the artists who feature on Radio 1 about their experiences working their way up through the industry. Then we post those on the site so you can see how other people have done it. We also talk to the people behind the scenes who help keep successful bands going. We've included a few quotes from some of the people we've spoken to here, so you can see that the information we're giving you is the proper thing.

The thing we've found from talking to all these people is that there aren't really any shortcuts and there's no guaranteed route to success. Ask any 10 successful artists how they got to be where they are and they'll all have a different story. That's what makes this business so exciting - and also so frustrating.

It really is about the music.
Whatever you may have heard, making great music is still the best way to get on in the music business. It costs tens or even hundreds of thousands of pounds to bring an unsigned band or producer to the nation's attention. If your music isn't at the stage where you can persuade a few people to spend a couple of quid to come and see you at your local venue, why would a label risk spending all that cash on your act?

> "I worked at EMI for 3 years. When you sign an artist and you're at a major record label, it doesn't cost 20 grand. It costs a million pounds. If you're making music it's very important that you take that on board. You think 'Why aren't I big? My music's all right.' All right's never good enough. The truth of the matter is that if you are that star that you believe you are, you will get signed and it will happen"
>
> **Trevor Nelson - Radio 1**

That's not a bad thing. It means that the most important thing you can do as a musician is exactly the thing you want to do - make great music! If you can make your 12" so good that all the DJs want it, or play a gig so awesome that your whole town is talking about you then you're on your way.

How to get heard
There are plenty of people out there looking for the Next Big Thing. Companies rely on new acts in order to keep their businesses going and you can be sure that if you're making enough of a noise - by playing packed gigs or shifting singles by yourself - then someone will come and find you.

That brings us to the next important point: the people you need to impress aren't the mysterious industry people who keep promising to come to your gigs and never show up. They're the people around you. If you can persuade them to come to your gigs in their hundreds, or to fill the floor when the DJ drops your tune then that's the best way to impress the music industry. And the way to do that is to make great music.

> "We developed enough of a following to make people sit up and take notice. There were too many people interested in us for us to be ignored."
>
> **Frankie - Ex-Bassist, The Darkness**

Who does what for a band?

It's useful to have an idea of all the different people that help make a signed act work. Firstly, these are the sort of people you can approach for help. Many of them will get involved with unsigned acts if they think that there's a future in it for them. Record labels get thousands of demos but not many people think of approaching people in other areas of the business, so you're in with more of a chance of getting through to them.

Secondly, it helps to see the different elements that make the business work so that you can apply them to your own music. Have a look down the list and it should help separate out all the different elements that getting your music noticed involves.

A&R. Contrary to what most people think, most of an A&R person's time isn't spent signing new bands, it's spent looking after the ones they've already signed. As a signed band, your A&R person is your main representative within the label. They'll be fighting your corner for marketing and recording budgets. We have loads of help with approaching A&R people on the OneMusic site.

Marketing. This is usually done by the record company and refers to all the forms of publicity that you have to pay for: adverts in magazines, in shops and on billboards, music videos etc. You can't really approach a marketing department as an unsigned act - we just mention it here so you know what it is.

PR. PR is basically everything else - all the promotional stuff that isn't charged for directly. That would mean radio & TV appearances and airplay, press reviews and interviews. Generally a band will hire their own PR people and will usually have one for each medium - a 'plugger' for TV and another

for radio, a press officer to handle print media and sometimes a new media plugger for websites. PR companies and press agencies will occasionally work with an unsigned act and there's more on approaching them on the OneMusic site.

Lawyer. Almost all contracts in the music business require some degree of negotiation, and lawyers are the people who'll do all that on an artist's behalf. So they're talking to A&R people, managers and everyone else all day and as a result are incredibly well connected. New acts mean new business for them, so many have a list of unsigned acts that they're helping out and some even have compilation CDs of promising music that they give out to their contacts.

Publisher. Bands don't generally make their money from record sales, especially in their early days. By the time the label have charged back all the costs of making and marketing a record it can take years before an act sees any income from actually selling records. Publishing is where all the money really is - it's paid out for use of music on radio, TV and film and in pubs, clubs and even hairdressers. Publishers can take a longer view of an act's career and so are traditionally more prepared to take on an unsigned act and develop them than labels are. We have a lot more on that subject on OneMusic.

Booking Agent. Often just referred to as an 'agent', this is the person who will handle a band's live commitments. It's their job to book tours, negotiate the band's fees and also try and get them the best billings at festivals. It's very rare for an agent to get involved with an unsigned act, though.

Manager. It's a manager's job to make all this stuff work together. They have to ensure that an act's touring schedule fits in with the release of the record and that all the other PR and marketing happens at the right time, too. Someone has to have an overview - what if a TV recording clashes with a major festival spot?

Management

Managers are often an act's first contact within the 'industry' so we think they deserve a section of their own. A manager's relationship with a band, especially in their early days, is extremely intensive - they're usually acting as PR and booking agent as well as helping the band with the business side. If they're going to pour time and effort into your act they need to really get on with you as people and love your music.

Also, managers earn their money as a percentage of an act's income. As you're probably painfully aware,

the|unsigned|guide

The Unsigned Guide/UK/2006. Material published in this directory may not be reproduced (in any form) without written consent.

the income for an unsigned act is pretty much nil. So a manager has to risk working with you for free to start with, in the hope that they'll get their reward when you're successful. That's why finding one is so hard. It's not like hiring a plumber where pretty much anyone who's competent will do - you need the right one for your act.

> "New talent does not lie undiscovered, there are too many very aggressive A&R people out there fighting each other to find it. Lawyers will let A&R people know about any new acts they are representing, as will managers. Journalists are an obvious place to go, both local and regional. A&R people also check out recording studios around the country and rehearsal studios and local music venues, asking the owners if anyone good has been in."
>
> ## Mike Smith - Head of Acquisitions (A&R basically), EMI Publishing

There are always managers looking for acts to work with but it's important to have a perspective on it. Most bands think they need a manager long before they actually do. Generally speaking, if you've got to the stage where you're ready for professional management then one will come and find you.

Initially though, there's nothing required of a manager that you can't do yourselves, or that a well-organised and personable friend can't do on your behalf.

Remember that most professional managers started out by helping a band that was just starting out and ended up doing it for a living when the band made it big. Which means there are plenty of bands who've got signed while being managed by their friends, and plenty of people who've helped get a band signed without having a clue what they were doing when they started doing it.

Demos
Of all the things in music this is probably the most contentious. Is it really worth sending demos if no-one listens to them? Certainly if you do it right then they can help, but they're not enough on their own. Have you ever read a biography of a band that went 'We started out, did a couple of gigs and then sent our first demo to a major who signed us on the spot'? It just doesn't happen like that.

> "If the better known managers don't come calling, try the next level down. For instance, management companies often have new staff joining the company who are on the lookout for new talent. Apart from that anyone - as long as they're committed enough and actually believe insomnia to be a good thing - is fair game for management. Coldplay and more recently The Strokes have both been steered by people who were simply mates of the band and have learnt their craft on the job."
>
> ## Steve Lamacq - Radio 1

Randomly sending out demos to people is a waste of your time and that of the people you send them to. But if you can pick a few key people and work on building a relationship with them, then you can use demo recordings to your advantage. Find out a few names of people who are involved with your favourite acts and use this book to find their contact details. Then keep them up to date with new recordings, gig fliers and other promotional stuff. We're got plenty more about that on OneMusic, too.

Learn from others' mistakes
There are a couple of things we see from demos we're sent at OneMusic. The first is that many people don't draw a line between recordings to sell (ie albums and EPs) and recordings to send out to people. If you're going to record a load of tracks to sell at gigs then do just that with them. But don't send them out as demos because they aren't the same thing.

When you make an album you need to make the music flow from track to track. We ask people to specify their two favourite tracks for the OneMusic site and for people sending in album-length CDs, it's almost never the first two tracks that they specify. This can only be a bad thing - you always want to have your best tunes first.

If you want to record loads of songs, why not send them out at a rate of two a month? That way your name is more likely to stick in someone's mind and you have an excuse to phone them regularly. Trust us; you don't need a posh package every time you send out a demo. Just a plastic wallet with a bit of laser-printed paper will do it if the music is great. Sell the expensive stuff and make the stuff you give away cheap and specific for the purpose.

INTRODUCTION

> "I would never advise a songwriter to send in something cold. If a song comes in addressed to 'the A&R department,' it tells you quite a few things. First of all it tells you that this is very much an amateur artist. Secondly, it tells you that they've got no contacts in the industry at all and thirdly it tells you they didn't have the common sense to pick up the phone and find out a name. So immediately you are not that kindly disposed to it."
>
> Ellis Rich - CEO, Independent Music Group

Target the right places

The second thing we see is that most people send demos to the wrong places. If you're making dance or hip hop, the thing that'll get your music signed is the heat you're causing in the clubs. So rather than sending promos to labels, get them to DJs and promoters. Likewise, many bands start sending stuff to national radio stations, where competition for airtime is extremely fierce. Target local stations and local press first. Aim to hit the people who will come to your gigs and help build that all-important buzz around your act.

Almost all successful bands start out by doing a small release on a local label before moving on to a bigger one. The reason is fairly obvious: if you can show that your music sells with limited promotional resources then it'll reassure a bigger label that you're worth risking all that money we talked about earlier. You can work a small release with some distribution behind it to build from local to national press and that'll open the door to out-of-town gigs. So target small labels before approaching the big fish.

> "I personally think you should send a maximum of three tracks, or maybe your one absolute best track to date. If I see a CD with 25 tracks on it, once I've listened to the first three I start to get bored; it's a lot to take in. But with one track you get an immediate response"
>
> Sarah Lockhart - A&R, EMI

Finally, it's almost never worth producing recordings to sell yourself unless you're really prepared to hammer it and put in the hours of phone bashing to promote the release properly. If you can't get a local deal and don't have the time to keep hassling radio

WHAT'S ONEMUSIC?

OneMusic is the source of information for music makers, DJs and people wanting to work in the music industry. There's creative and business advice in our How To... section. Or you can read features with leading artists - we ask them for their tips on making music and getting it heard. Whether you're aiming for major label stardom or planning your own underground releases, we have the information you need.

If you want to be an A&R person, manager, studio engineer or work in music PR then we've interviewed some leading professionals for our Industry Jobs section. There's advice on getting started, finding work placements and exactly what the job entails.

And whatever you want to do, if you can't find what you need on the site, you can just email us and we promise to reply within 24 hours. So if you want to find out how to get on in music, where else are you going to go? www.bbc.co.uk/radio1/onemusic is the only URL you need!

If you're a rapper, producer or DJ and you're into hip hop, RnB or Drum n Bass we also have the only site in the UK with advice specifically for Urban musicians. It's called 1XMusic and you'll find it at www.bbc.co.uk/1xtra/1xmusic

producers and journalists, give your music away. Trying to sell it just puts a barrier between it and the rest of the world. It's extremely cheap to make short runs of CDs which you can then use as bribes: "first 30 people through the door get a free CD," "if you give me your email address I'll give you a free EP."

> "Anyone sending out CDs should save a bit of money by not sending them to people who aren't going to be remotely interested. We also get people ringing up asking what kind of music we sign - well if you don't know that you shouldn't be sending us your music."
>
> Andy Ross - A&R legend

The Internet
There's no doubt that the 'net has brought about a revolution in the music industry, but does that apply to unsigned bands? Well, yes and no. The problem is that most people get confused about what the 'net is for. The 'net is an extremely useful distribution tool. You can sell or give away music without the expense of having to produce CDs or vinyl. But it's not a promotional tool any more than having your name in the phone book is.

There are plenty of ways to get your music onto the 'net - either by making your own web-site or by signing up to one of the many that host unsigned music. The problem is that loads of bands have already done that so there are millions of tracks available for free. Try typing 'unsigned music download' into a search engine and see how many hits you get.

> "Although the web is good for keeping fans in touch with what is going on, there is no substitute for playing live and having a good record to push. Our site serves as a point of contact for anyone interested in the band after seeing us live or hearing us on the radio or reading about us in magazines etc."
>
> James Davies - Trip (OneMusic artist)

Remember that most people who get on the net already know what they want before they go there, anyway. So if they've never heard of your act, they're unlikely to stumble across it. Of course if they have heard of your music then the 'net is a great place for them to find more of it. But they need to be typing your name into that search engine, which means they need to have heard it first.

The 'net does have some promotional uses. You can use message boards on relevant websites to promote your act. Make sure your gigs and releases are mentioned on the right listings sites and use email and your own web-site to keep your fans informed of what you're up to. But it's part of a wider plan not an end in itself.

Go get 'em
The people behind this Guide are very keen that the people who buy it get what they need. The contacts in here represent the ones you need as an unsigned musician - it's up to you how to use them. Our advice is that it's all about thinking globally but acting locally. There are loads of people knocking on the front door of the industry so avoid getting lost in the crowd. Find yourself a side window to climb in through.

> "I think that perseverance is the first virtue you need to have in order to succeed in this business. You need to keep at it and people will find you. Try and create your own buzz because if you're good, that news travels quickly. Before you know it, label representatives will come and see what all the fuss is about."
>
> Ian McAndrew - Manager, Travis & Craig David

There are two myths about the industry that need exploding. One is that there are men in suits who run things from plush offices. Forget it - they don't exist. The other is that really talented people go unnoticed. They don't. There are plenty of reasons why they don't necessarily go all the way, and that's because there are so many things that can go wrong between picking up your first instrument and releasing your first album. But if you're really in with a shout of success then you will be found. And if no one's come along yet, that's because you're not quite ready. So keep writing, work on building a following and be prepared for the long haul. This thing's going to take years.

Ultimately, the sooner you take control of your musical career, the more control you'll have as you progress and the more chance you have of ending up where you want to be. The more you find out about the business the better placed you'll be to know what's a good deal or a bad one, a move that's going to help you get on and one that's going to go nowhere. Learning about the business side doesn't make you a bad person, or any less creative. It just puts you in the driving seat.

Matt Fernand, BBC Radio 1 OneMusic.

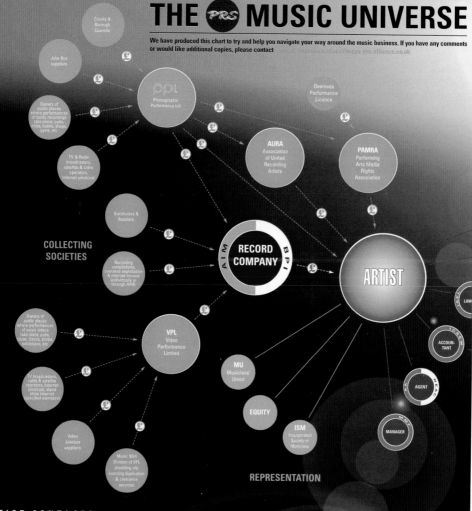

THE ⊙PRS MUSIC UNIVERSE

We have produced this chart to try and help you navigate your way around the music business. If you have any comments or would like additional copies, please contact and-communications@mcps-prs-alliance.co.uk

COLLECTING SOCIETIES

REPRESENTATION

ARTIST CONTACTS

AA - AGENTS' ASSOCIATION (GREAT BRITAIN), 54 Keyes House, Dolphin Square, London SW1V 3NA. Tel:020-7834-0515 Fax:020-7821-0261 Web:www.agents-uk.com An organisation formed to represent and enhance the interests of entertainment agents.

ICAEW - INSTITUTE OF CHARTERED ACCOUNTANTS IN ENGLAND & WALES, Chartered Accountants Hall, Moorgate Place, London EC2P 2BJ. Tel:020-7920-8504 Fax:020-7920-8687 Web:www.icaew.co.uk An association that represents the music industry accounting profession.

APRS - ASSOCIATION OF PROFESSIONAL RECORDING SERVICES, PO Box 22, Totnes TQ9 7YZ. Tel:01803-868-600 Fax:01803-868-444 Web:www.aprs.co.uk Sets an industry standard on behalf of its members: recording studios, producers, engineers, etc.

CPA - CONCERT PROMOTERS' ASSOCIATION, 8 St. Mark's Road, Henley-on-Thames, Oxon RG9 1LJ. Tel:01491-575060 Fax:01491-414082 Email:carolcomm-cpa@virgin.net

IAEL - INTERNATIONAL ASSOCIATION OF ENTERTAINMENT LAWYERS, 45-51 Whitfield Street, London W1T 4HB. Tel:020-7907-3000 Fax:020-7907-3111 Web:www.iael.org Representing music industry solicitors/lawyers internationally.

MMF - MUSIC MANAGERS FORUM, 1 York Street, London W1U 6PA. Tel:0870-850-7800 Fax:020-7603-4411 Web:www.ukmmf.net Represents the interests of artist managers.

LAW SOCIETY (OF ENGLAND & WALES) - 113 Chancery Lane, London WC2A 1PL. Tel:020-7242-1222 Fax:020-7831-0344 Web:www.lawsociety.org.uk Sets professional standards and improves the law. Keeps records on every solicitor and practice.

NEAC - NATIONAL ENTERTAINMENT AGENTS COUNCIL, PO Box 112, Seaford, East Sussex BN25 2DQ. Tel:0870-755-7612 Fax:0870-755-7613 Web:www.neac.org.uk Providing guidance and a code of conduct for agents

AIM - ASSOCIATION OF INDEPENDENT MUSIC, Lamb House, Church Street, Chiswick, London W4 2PD. Tel:020-8994-5599 Fax:020-8994-5222 Web:www.musicindie.com The first industry trade body set up to specifically represent, promote and protect the interests of all independent music companies

BPI - BRITISH PHONOGRAPHIC INDUSTRY, Riverside Building, County Hall, Westminster Bridge Road, London SE1 7JA. Tel:020-7803-1300 Fax:020-7803-1310 Web:www.bpi.co.uk Association of UK record companies.

EQUITY - (BRITISH ACTORS EQUITY ASSOCIATION), Guild House, Upper St.Martins Lane, London WC2H 9EG. Tel:020-7379-6000 Fax:020-7379-7001 Web:www.equity.org.uk Association protecting the rights of actors in the UK

ISM - INCORPORATED SOCIETY OF MUSICIANS, 10 Stratford Place, London W1C 1AA. Tel:020-7629-4413 Fax:020-7408-1538 Web:www.ism.org Professional association for performers, composers & teachers.

MU - MUSICIANS' UNION, 60-62 Clapham Road, London SW9 0JJ. Tel:020-7582-5566 Fax:020-7582-9805 Web:www.musiciansunion.org.uk Negotiates & provides a variety of agreements and services for musicians and composers.

AURA - ASSOCIATION OF UNITED RECORDING ARTISTS, Peter Hurrey, 1 York Street, London W1U 6PA. Tel:0870-850-5200 Fax:0870-850-5201 Web:www.aurauk.com Represents professional recording artists & studio producers.

PAMRA - PERFORMING ARTS MEDIA RIGHTS ASSOCIATION, 161 Borough High Street, London SE1 1HR. Tel:020-7940-0400 Fax:020-7407-2008 Web:www.pamra.org.uk Collects & distributes performance income to its members.

PPL - PHONOGRAPHIC PERFORMANCE LTD, 1 Upper James Street, London W1F 9DE. Tel:020-7534-1000 Fax:020-7534-1111 Web: www.ppluk.com Collecting society licensing broadcast & public performance of sound recording in the UK.

VPL - VIDEO PERFORMANCE LIMITED, 1 Upper James Street, London W1F 9DE. Tel:020-7534-1400 Fax:020-7534-1414 Web: www.vpluk.com UK collection agency licensing the broadcast & public performance of music videos.

Please note there are a number of other specialist music industry organisations that are not shown above. See publications such as Music Week Directory or British Music Yearbook for details.

BRITISH ACADEMY OF COMPOSERS & SONGWRITERS - *British Music House, 25-27 Berners Street, London W1T 3LR. Tel:020-7636-2929 Fax:020-7636-2212 Web: www.britishacademy.com* Europe's leading composers' organisation (all genres).
MU - MUSICIANS' UNION, *60-62 Clapham Road, London SW9 0JJ. Tel:020-7582-5566 Fax:020-7582-9805 Web:www.musiciansunion.org.uk* Negotiates & provides a variety of agreements and services for musicians and composers.
BRITISH MUSIC RIGHTS, *British Music House, 26 Berners Street, London W1T 3LR. Tel:020-7306 4446 Fax:020-7306 4449 Web:www.bmr.org* An 'umbrella' organisation which lobbies on behalf of MPA, MCPS, PRS, & British Academy Of Composers & Songwriters.
ASCAP - AMERICAN SOCIETY OF COMPOSERS AUTHORS & PUBLISHERS, *8 Cork Street, London W1X 1PB. Tel:020-7439-0909 Fax:020-7434-0073 Web:www.ascap.com* American performing rights society.
BMI - BROADCAST MUSIC INC. *84 Harley House, Marylebone Road, London NW1 5HN. Tel:020-7486-2036 Fax:020-7224-1046 Web:www.bmi.com* American performing rights organisation.
MCPS - MECHANICAL COPYRIGHT PROTECTION SOCIETY, *29/33 Berners Street, London W1T 3AB. Tel:020-7580-5544 Fax:020-7306-4455 Web:www.mcps.co.uk* Collecting royalties on behalf of writers & publishers whenever their works are recorded.
MPA - MUSIC PUBLISHERS' ASSOCIATION, *3rd Floor, Strandgate, 20 York Buildings, London WC2N 6JU. Tel:020-7839-7779 Fax:020-7839-7776 Web:www.mpaonline.org.uk* Promoting and protecting the interests of music publishers.
PRS - PERFORMING RIGHT SOCIETY, *29/33 Berners Street, London W1T 3AB. Tel:020-7580-5544 Fax:020-7306-4455 Web:www.prs.co.uk* Collecting royalties on behalf of music creators & publishers for public performance & broadcast.
SESAC - SOCIETY OF EUROPEAN SONGWRITERS & COMPOSERS, *67 Upper Berkeley Street, London W1H 7QX. Tel:020-7616-9284 Fax:020-7563-7029 Web: www.sesac.com* American performing right collection society.
ICAEW - INSTITUTE OF CHARTERED ACCOUNTANTS IN ENGLAND & WALES, *Chartered Accountants Hall, Moorgate Place, London EC2P 2BJ. Tel:020-7920-8504 Fax:020-7920-8697 Web:www.icaew.co.uk* An association that represents the music industry accounting profession.
IAEL - INTERNATIONAL ASSOCIATION OF ENTERTAINMENT LAWYERS, *45-51 Whitfield Street, London W1T 4HB. Tel:020-7907-3000 Fax:020-7907-3111 Web:www.iael.org* Representing music industry solicitors/lawyers internationally.
LAW SOCIETY (OF ENGLAND & WALES) - *113 Chancery Lane, London WC2A 1PL. Tel:020-7242-1222 Fax:020-7831-0344 Web:www.lawsociety.org.uk* Sets professional standards and improves the law. Keeps records on every solicitor and practice.

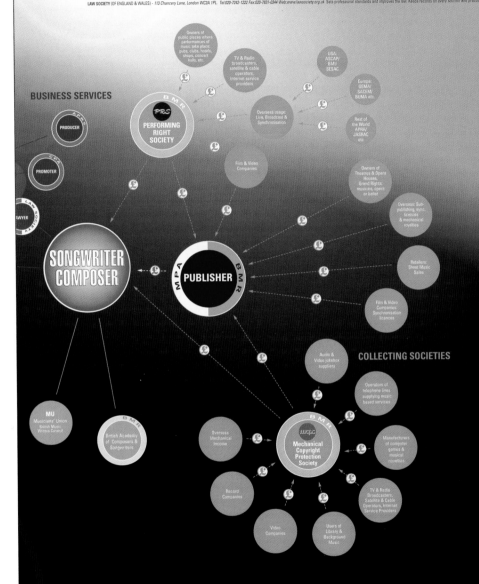

MAP 1: UK RECORD COMPANY
(AND ASSOCIATED BUSINESS/PERSONNEL)

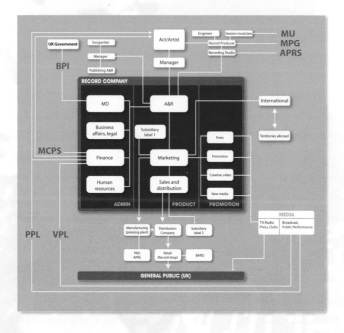

MAP 2: UK MUSIC PUBLISHING COMPANY
(AND ASSOCIATED BUSINESS/PERSONNEL)

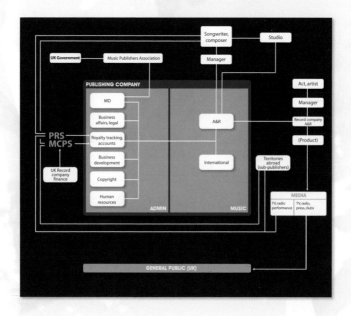

MAP 3: ARTIST MANAGEMENT
(AND ASSOCIATED BUSINESS/PERSONNEL)

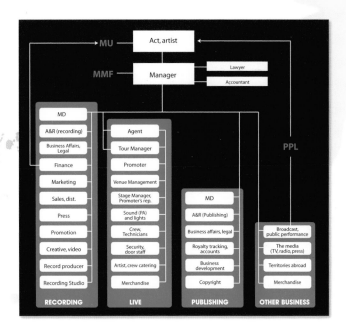

MAP 4: UK LIVE PERFORMANCE
(AND ASSOCIATED BUSINESS/PERSONNEL)

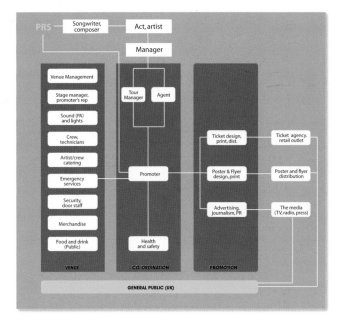

BPI
25 Saville Row
London
W1X 1AA

www.bpi.co.uk

Section 1
Record Companies

the|unsigned|guide

1.1 Record Companies Foreword

It is reasonable to say that most unsigned bands and artists producing original material will be looking to sign a recording contract which is often easier said than done, particularly in today's volatile economic climate. With more and more job losses across the wider music industry, constant swings in consumer trends and the increasingly rapid development of digital distribution, it is becoming harder and harder for bands and artists to secure good recording contracts.

It is fundamental that your campaign (in a bid to get signed) is well executed and you must to be totally dedicated and committed to the cause. It's all very easy to quickly become disillusioned with the whole process and give in. If you're in this business for a deal, you can't even begin to think that things will develop overnight - no matter how good or unique you think you sound. It's an extremely difficult task to undertake (although good talent will always usually out itself in the end) and over the years we've heard countless stories about artists that feel they've being misled, misinformed and/or mistreated by labels in the past, even before a deal is struck. The truth of the matter is that the real work only starts when a label has sufficient belief in you to justify their investment.

> **You should make the effort to profile A&R staff and research the labels they represent.**

Research and awareness of how the recording industry operates are the key factors where hunting down a contract is concerned. Although recording companies are ultimately responsible for producing and promoting your releases, A&R staff are likely to be your first point of contact. A&R will make

decisions, often over a period of time as to your suitability to signing to the label they represent. It is the A&R staff that you need to make sure are hearing your music.

You should make the effort to profile A&R staff and research the labels they represent. A&R will specialise in certain musical genres as will often the labels they represent. It is pointless to waste time and money sending your demos to A&R and record labels who don't operate in your genre. Similarly, just because a label has signed artists or bands in the past who play in a similar genre as you, it doesn't mean they are always looking for the same types of bands a second or third time around.

Just as other businesses do, record companies have to take risks when introducing new products to the marketplace and they will always be subject to natural market forces (supply and demand), changes in research and development (for example new technologies) and swings in consumer trends.

Record labels will research and monitor consumer activity as a part of their overall business strategies and you must adopt the same principles in the way you operate when approaching the recording industry. In the same way that as a band, you should concentrate on getting the sound you want, both recorded and live, your manager should be equally trusted in firstly ensuring your material is heard by the labels that are most likely to want to deal with you and secondly that those labels also have the funds available to back your releases, both in terms of production and marketing.

For example, a small independent label may show interest you and make preliminary offers to produce and press your material but without a significant marketing spend how will anyone hear about your release so they can buy it? Similarly, if you are signed by a label which doesn't necessarily see you as a high priority (although to lesser or greater extent you will be priority if they have invested funds in you), you may find that your releases, if any at all, are inadequately financed in terms of marketing and so are destined to sell poorly even before you record them. As soon as preliminary discussions are underway with a recording company, make sure your manager investigates the label's short and medium term intentions with regards to marketing and promoting your releases. We would strongly recommend seeking legal opinion even if negotiations reach this stage.

The media obviously has an enormous impact on the record industry and shifts in audience trends affect the types of bands labels may be looking to sign. It must be a fundamental part of your research to establish firstly which A&R are shopping for new bands and secondly the type of music and bands they are looking for.

We suggest you use this section to identify the types of labels and styles of A&R that you think match your music most accurately and you must find the relevant contacts at each of the labels you intend to approach. Fewer and fewer bands secure deals with significant advances and evermore is the case that with more bands and artists submitting material, labels can afford for potential signings to work harder for their contract and you may only find that a low key deal comes your way in the early stages, if at all. Ultimately you should be submitting your demos recorded to the highest possible standard and not to rely on any sympathetic industry ears, there aren't any.

Research the labels that may have been recently established (either as independents or major-subsidiaries). The reason they will have been set-up is to release records with a view to making money. The theory stands that funds will be available to newly established labels to develop new signings and so you may ultimately have a greater chance of being signed.

The music industry is subject to market forces in exactly the same way as any other commercial organisation or business and without making bottom-line sales there will be no funds to take-on new signings.

A&R departments may also suggest to their label that your material is licensed as part of a compilation or that they will only offer you a deal or option

on the success of a first release. The success of this release will rely heavily on media promotion and without it the release may not perform well and therefore the release deal fails.

> **It must be a fundamental part of your research to establish firstly which A&R are shopping for new bands and secondly the type of music and bands they are looking for.**

You must be aware of all these aspects of the industry before you approach recording companies. In summary, you (or your manager) should at very least be partly familiar with how recording companies and associated organisations operate before you go looking. We thoroughly recommend you embark on a course of further reading to develop you understanding of this sector of the music industry. You should take the time to browse through the recommended reading list we have included later in this book.

In certain circumstances, your representative (with regards to instigating recording contracts) may be a broker or agent - an individual or company that will attempt to seek and negotiate a contract on your behalf. If you approach a broker, or are approached, you should be aware in precise terms, of the nature of the engagement. In every instance, seek independent legal direction or alternatively for Musicians' Union members, your regional office will operate a support service to guide you.

This section of The Unsigned Guide contains contact details for 593 UK record companies. Browse the listings and classify your own genre of music and match it with those labels/A&R contacts you think may be interested. Prepare a short, straight-to-the-point biography, include a couple of good pictures of the band or suitable artwork, press cuttings/details of media coverage, dates of a couple of forthcoming gigs (London & elsewhere) and most importantly make sure your demo is professionally recorded, well mixed and well presented.

> **Make sure your demo is professionally recorded, well mixed and well presented.**

Check beforehand how labels ideally want demos submitted. Check the format and the maximum number of tracks they are looking for. If you design a sleeve or inlay card, make it simple and easy to

RECORDING COMPANIES

read. More importantly, make sure there is a contact name and at least a telephone number on the sleeve and on the recording itself (CD/MD/DAT etc.). Equally as important is that you make sure your material is 'requested mail'. If a label doesn't want to know, it will be for a reason and that will usually be that funds are not available and/or that they are not looking to sign new artists. Sending unsolicited material will often mean you waste the price of producing yet another demo. Additionally, some labels will ask for a website address where your music is available. Make sure the site is easily accessible and that the recording is of a good standard.

Finally, make sure you keep a contacts database of all the labels that have received your demo pack. Every time you send a new demo, make a short follow-up call (or email) to each A&R contact, ask their opinions and be straight to the point, don't pester and be productive with each call.

In the event that a preliminary contract in any form with any third party is drafted (as with inter-band agreements) it goes without saying that you should always look to seek legal advice from a music lawyer or for Musicians' Union members, your regional office will operate a support service to help you through the next stages.

Visit **www.musiciansunion.org.uk** for more information.

1.2 Recording Agreements: Part 1

The following should apply to you as a solo artist or member of a band:

1. Exclusivity

It has always been the argument of record companies that establishing new artists is a costly and lengthy business. Consequently, any recording agreement you are offered which involves considerable amounts of money is likely to be exclusive, comprehensive and long term. How desirable this is, from the artist's point of view, will be discussed below.

2. How will I be paid?

Recording artists are paid on the basis of a royalty from record sales and at the beginning of each contract year cash advances on account of future royalties.

Royalties

These vary according to the strength of your bargaining position but 10%-14% (sometimes higher) of retail selling price is about average for a new band. RSP is the selling price in the shops, minus VAT and a percentage packaging charge which record companies require artists to contribute towards marketing costs. The end result is that if a CD retails for £12, a band could earn between 70p and £1.00 per CD sold. The cost of recording and other advances you have received will be subtracted first from any royalties due.

Musicians Union Advice

You should try and secure higher royalties after a certain sales figure has been reached. Try to increase your rate of royalty throughout each new year of the contract.

Aim for payment on 100% of sales and not lower figures such as 90% as some companies will offer. Insist on a full royalty for 12" CD singles as they are no longer merely promotional records.

Some record companies insist on paying only a half rate royalty for "TV advertised" product. The Musicians Union feel that this subject should be left open for discussion at the appropriate time.

Advances

These are a financial sign of good faith from the record company and the money you will live on until your royalties arrive. They should always be non-returnable (i.e. only recoupable from future record royalties). They may be paid at the beginning of each contract year or half at the beginning of the year and half after delivery of your record commitment for that year.

Musicians Union Advice

There is no such thing as a standard advance. However, if the contract is a long term one an advance should be large enough to provide the members of the band with a reasonable living wage until initial costs have been met and royalty income is being received. It should also be commensurate with the exclusive right to your recording services that the record company will demand.

3. When will I be paid?

Most companies will render a statement of account to their artists twice yearly within sixty or ninety days of the end of June and December. If your royalty earnings are greater than 1) recording costs and 2) any advances paid by the company, then this statement will be accompanied by a cheque.

Musicians Union Advice

We feel that only the cost of recording time and personal advances should be offset against royalty income. You should try and get references to nebulous "other costs" deleted from an agreement offered to you, or at least make them subject to joint agreement. Also, try and avoid cross collateralisation of advances against non-royalty income such as PPL money (artists' share of "airplay" revenue).

4. How long will the agreement be for?

A typical record deal with a major record company might be for one year plus four options, calling for five albums in total. However, recent judgments in the British courts seem to have frowned upon the restrictive nature of long term recording agreements and especially with small labels who are unable to guarantee sufficient annual advances you should be trying for as short a deal as possible.

Musicians Union Advice

If a guaranteed annual advance is insufficient for the members of the band to live on then you should only commit yourself to one album. There should be a time limit of one year within which this should be recorded and released.

Even with larger companies who can afford advances if recordings have not been released in the major markets of the world within a certain time you should be able to terminate the agreement. Finally, it is wise to leave out extra records such as "live" and "greatest hits" albums from an agreement in order to use them as a bargaining tool later on.

5. Who owns the recordings?

It is important to remember that because the record company has initially commissioned and paid for the recordings, in the eyes of the law they are the owners and not you. A recording agreement will require you to give consent for the company to exploit your performances contained on the recordings by selling records and authorising others to broadcast them, etc.

Musicians Union Advice

We feel that these consents ought to apply only to record sales and the right to give others permission to broadcast recordings. Vague "audio visual rights" or "other uses" should be subject to negotiation from time to time and not just signed away.

Also you should ensure that any session musician you use signs the appropriate MU consent form to avoid potential future problems.

6. What will the record company require of me?

- That you record exclusively for them (although you should be allowed to do non featured session work with other artists provided you credit your record label on the sleeve).

- That any tracks recorded for them will not be re-recorded for any other company for several years after the end of the agreement.

- That you do not have any outstanding agreements with any other record label.

- That you give permission for them to use photographs and biographical details for publicity purposes.

- That you will be prepared to devote a reasonable amount of time to interviews and promotional activities.

Musicians Union Advice

It should be made clear in the agreement that the record company will cover the reasonable cost of promotional activities, interviews, etc. Also, permission for photographs and biographical details should not be extended to "merchandising rights". These should be left quite separate from the recording agreement.

This information has been kindly provided by Musician's Union.

For more information, please contact:

Musician's Union
London Office
60-62 Clapham Road
London
SW9 0JJ

email: dp1@musiciansunion.org.uk
tel: 020 7582 5566

Visit **www.musiciansunion.org.uk** for more information.

1.3 Recording Agreements: Part 2

1. Producers
An experienced producer is more important for certain types of bands than others, but if you wish to use a well known producer you will have to pay for the privilege. Many producers now work on the basis of a royalty payment combined with an initial fee which is an advance against that royalty. Once again, unfortunately, the record company may insist that the producer royalty comes out of your own royalties.

Musicians Union Advice
Ideally, the record company would cover the cost of the producer. If they will not agree to this (and most won't), we suggest that the band tries to limit their contribution to a producer royalty to 2% and that the record company pays the balance, if any.

2. Videos
With videos also, it pays to keep an eye on the budget as most bands ultimately foot the bill. The record company will initially pay the cost, but they will usually want to recoup 50% of these expenses from future record royalties and the other 50% from any commercial exploitation, i.e. sales of compilation videos through record shops, etc.

Musicians Union Advice
It is important that the contract allows for you to share in income from any exploitation of videos where the company itself receives revenue.

3. Tour support
Most bands start off playing in small venues and sometimes the record company will help to subsidise a tour when fees received fall short of the high cost of putting a band on the road these days. This money is known as "tour support". Once you are playing larger venues it should no longer become necessary.

Another, more odious, form of tour support is when your record company is approached by a promoter, asking them if they would like to "buy you on" to a tour with an established artist.

Musicians Union Advice
We in the Union are not alone in the music industry in condemning the "buy on" and we feel that, over the years, it has been tolerated rather than encouraged. We believe that it is time for some honest discussion on the subject, as it means that, effectively only bands with major record deals can secure support slots with established artists.

4. What will the company pay for?
Initially, all recording expenses, although these will be fully recoupable from future record royalties.

The reasonable expenses incurred by you while attending press interviews, promotional activities, etc.

Record sleeve artwork, advertising, promotion, marketing and distribution costs should not be recoupable in any way.

5. Other points to bear in mind
Try and secure some kind of control over budgets, choice of producers, choice of material and studios, etc. Try and ensure that your masters only need to be "technically" acceptable rather than "commercially acceptable in the opinion of the record company", also that there is a firm commitment from them to release within a certain time period.

Be sure to pay particular attention to the royalty rates being offered for digital sales or downloads, particularly ensuring deductions for packaging or new technology don't appear in the small print.

Do not use any non Musicians Union members on your recordings and ensure that all musicians are either i) signed to the label or ii) paid as session musicians, in which case they should have signed the appropriate consent forms.

Beware of using someone else's copyright material in your recordings or your sleeve artwork without first obtaining their permission. Be aware that, in most cases, if the band splits you will still be signed individually to the record company.

> **Recording Agreements are highly complex, legally binding documents. You should always consult a music business lawyer before signing such an agreement.**

If anyone other than your record company records a performance of yours (e.g. a live gig), you will be in breach of contract if you knowingly allow it. If you "guest" on another artist's record make sure you get the permission of your record label first.

Recording Agreements are highly complex, legally binding documents. You should always consult a music business lawyer before signing such an agreement. One option always open to Musicians Union members is the free 'Contract Advisory Service'. Information on this service is available through your branch Secretary.

This information has been kindly provided by Musicians' Union.

For more information, please contact:

Musicians' Union
London Office
60-62 Clapham Road
London
SW9 0JJ

email: dp1@musiciansunion.org.uk
tel: 020 7582 5566

Visit **www.musiciansunion.org.uk** for more information.

1.3 RECORD COMPANIES

!K7 Records London
1 Devonport Mews, Devonport Road, London, W12 8NG
tel: 0208 762 9910
fax: 0208 762 9912
web: www.k7.com
contact: Katherine, Berni
genre: Club Music/Hip-Hop/R&B
info: !K7 Records are interested in hearing from musicians, DJs and producers working with Club Music. Rapster Records, a division of !K7 Records, releases Hip-Hop and R&B music. Demo submissions for both labels can be made to the address above.

1 Man Army Records
Bristol/Bath
email: info@1manarmyrecords.co.uk
web: www.1manarmyrecords.co.uk
genre: Electronic Dance Music
info: 1 Man Army Records is an independent label based in Bristol and Bath, promoting and releasing new forms of electronic dance music. Email for contacts and postal address.

23rd Precinct Recordings
23 Bath Street, Glasgow, G2 1HU
tel: 0141 332 4806
fax: 0141 353 3039
email: billy@23rdprecinct.co.uk
web: www.23rdprecinct.co.uk
genre: All Music Types Accepted
info: Send demos on CD to the address above, plus an email to let the label know your material is on its way. The label is run from the 23rd Precinct shop, Scotland's first independent Dance music store. For catalogue information visit the website. See also 23rd Precinct Music in the Publishing Companies listings.

3 Beat Music Ltd.
5 Slater Street, Liverpool, L1 4BW
tel: 0151 709 3355
fax: 0151 707 0227
email: mike@3beat.co.uk
web: www.3beat.co.uk
contact: Mike
genre: House
info: Send demos (on CD or MD) with biog and contact details to the address above. 3 Beat also run a label management company representing Border Community, DK Records, Polaroid, Deep Records.

3rd Stone Records Ltd.
PO Box 8, Corby, Northamptonshire, NN17 2XZ
tel: 01536 202 295
fax: 01536 266 246
email: adasam@adasam.co.uk
web: www.adasam.co.uk
contact: Steve Kalidoski
genre: All Music Types Accepted
info: Send demo on CD or tape to the address above. Make sure to write contact number directly onto the CD or tape.

4AD
17-19 Alma Road, London, SW18 1AA
tel: 020 8870 9724
fax: 020 8874 6600
email: 4ad@4ad.com
web: www.4ad.com
contact: Chris Sharp, Ed Horrox
genre: Everything except mainstream Pop
info: See the 4AD website for an idea of the types of acts the label represents. Send demos on CD, vinyl or cassette to the address above. No music via email. Part of the Beggars Group.

4Real Records
Myrtle Cottage, Rye Road, Hawkhurst, Kent, TN18 5DW
tel: 01580 754 771
fax: 01580 754 771
email: info@4realrecords.com
web: www.4realrecords.com
contact: Terry Scully
genre: Pop/Dance
info: Send demos to Terry at the address above.

57 Records UK
89 Romanby Road, Northallerton, North Yorkshire, DL7 8FH
email: richard@57records.co.uk
web: www.57records.co.uk
contact: Richard Doney
genre: Guitar Based
info: Send demos on CD to the address above. You are advised to check the 57 Records website before submitting any material.

A2 Records (Assassination Music)
Ardquoy, Pinstone Way, Gerrards Cross, Buckinghamshire, SL9 7BJ
tel: 01494 862 770
fax: 01494 862 770
email: richard@a2records.com
web: www.a2records.com
contact: Rupert Withers
genre: All Music Types Accepted

Abacabe Records
10 Messaline Avenue, London, W3 6JX
tel: 020 8723 7376
fax: 020 8723 7380
email: fran@bluesinbritain.org
web: www.bluesinbritain.org
contact: Fran Leslie
genre: Blues
info: Handles UK based Blues artists. Associated with 'Blues in Britain' magazine. Send demos to the address above.

Abstract Sounds
10 Tiverton Road, London, NW10 3HL
tel: 020 7286 1106
fax: 020 8289 8679
email: abstractsounds@btclick.com
contact: Edward Christie
genre: Punk/Dance/Indie/Rock
info: Abstract Sounds is made up of 3 labels, Get Back (Punk/Indie), North South (Dance) and Abstract Sounds (Punk/Indie). Also see associated Metal label, Candlelight Records.

Acid Jazz Records
146 Bethnal Green Road, London, E2 6DG
tel: 020 7613 1100
email: info@acidjazz.co.uk
web: www.acidjazz.co.uk
contact: Richard Searle
genre: All Music Types Accepted
info: Send demos and any other relevant information to the address above. Acid Jazz listen to all material they receive and try to respond to as many as possible.

4AD

17-19 Alma Road
London SW18 1AA

P : 020 8870 9724
F : 020 8874 6600

e : 4ad@4ad.com
w : www.4ad.com

A&R : Ed Horrox
Dist : Vital

ACM Records
The Apollo Unit 3, 18 All Saints Road, London, W11 1HH
tel: 020 7221 2275
email: mike@acm-records.co.uk
web: www.acm-records.co.uk
contact: Mike, Tony Cornnell
genre: All Music Types Accepted
info: In-house label linked with ACM production company with recording studio deal with many styles of music and artist development. For further details of studio, see listing in relevant section.

Adrift Records
The Old Bakehouse, Hale Street, Staines, Middlesex, TW18 4UW
tel: 01784 458 700
fax: 01784 458 333
email: info@adriftrecords.com
web: www.adriftrecords.com
contact: Julian Shay
genre: House/Breaks
info: Send demos on CD to the address above. Make sure to include full contact details.

Afro Art
109 Dukes Avenue, Muswell Hill, London, N10 2QD
tel: 020 8374 4411
fax: 020 8374 4410
email: afroart@ukonline.co.uk
web: www.afroartrecords.com
contact: Paul Murphy, Simone Beedle
genre: Jazzy House/Broken Beat/Afro-beat/Latin/Nu Jazz
info: Home to Spiritual South.

Akoustik Anarkhy (aA)
Manchester
email: hello@akoustikanarkhy.co.uk
web: www.akoustikanarkhy.co.uk
contact: Noel Vasquez
genre: All Music Types Accepted
info: aA's roots lie in releasing Leftfield Guitar music, though the current roster encompasses all from Baroque Pop to Hip-Hop Beats. See also listing in Promoter section.

All Around The World
9-13 Penny Street, Blackburn, Lancashire, BB1 6HJ
tel: 01254 264 120
fax: 01254 693 768
email: info@aatw.com
web: www.aatw.com
contact: Jo Farrer
genre: Commercial Dance
info: Submit demos on CD or vinyl (but preferably CD) to the address above. Include SAE if you would like your demo returned.

Amber Artists
PO Box 1, Chipping Ongar, Essex, CM5 9HZ
tel: 01277 365 046
email: recordcompany@amberartists.com
web: www.amberartists.com
contact: Paul Tage
genre: Pop
info: Deal with Adult Contemporary Pop. Call Paul with details of your music, follow with demo on request.

Ambience Records Ltd.
Bethal House, Newton Place, Lee-on-the-Solent, Hampshire, PO13 9JL
tel: 07769 558 807
email: info@ambiencerecords.co.uk
web: www.ambiencerecords.co.uk
contact: Ross Gill
genre: Alternative/Hip-Hop
info: Record label and production company. So far the roster mainly consists of Guitar based Indie bands, but the label are keen to receive material from other genres.

The Animal Farm
Atomic Studios, Block B, Tower Bridge Business Complex, 100 Clements Road, London, SE16 4DG
tel: 020 7237 8768
email: info@theanimalfarm.co.uk
web: www.theanimalfarm.co.uk
contact: Ville Leppanen
genre: Acoustic/Pop/Rock/Punk/Metal/Guitar Based
info: Send demos to the above address. Please do not email MP3s. Also have recording facilities available. See listing for Atomic Studios in relevant section.

Aquasonic Records
PO Box 26308, London, N8 8WR
tel: 020 7281 6111
email: info@aquasonic.co.uk
web: www.aquasonic.co.uk
contact: Rickki Blue
genre: Soulful Drum&Bass
info: Send demos, preferably on CD, to the address above.
No unsolicited large music files via email please. Aquasonic Records do listen to all submissions and will generally offer feedback, but allow a couple of weeks for a reply.

Ariwa Sounds Ltd.
34 Whitehorse Lane, London, SE25 6RE
tel: 020 8653 7744
fax: 020 8771 1911
web: www.ariwa.com
contact: Neil Fraser
genre: Reggae/Dub/Roots

Artful
Unit 41, Waters Workshop, 249-251 Kensal Road, London, W10 5DB
tel: 020 8968 1231
fax: 020 8964 1181
email: info@fullfill.co.uk
web: www.fullfill.co.uk
contact: Danielle Chambers, Steve
genre: All Music Types Accepted
info: Send demos to the address above, include an SAE if you would like your material returned. Artists from the label's roster include Gary Numan, Marc Almond, Future Sound of London and The Fall.

Artificial Bliss Recordings Ltd.
12 Lucas Gardens, Luton, Bedfordshire, LU3 4BE
tel: 01582 503 168
email: info@artificialbliss.com
web: www.artificialbliss.com
contact: Simon Mitchell, Simon Curry, Chris Curry
genre: Funk/Electronic/Hip-Hop/Ambient/Chill/Progressive/Breakbeat/Urban/House/Trance/Drum&Bass
info: Send demo to the above address.

Astir Records
34 Galpins Road, Thornton Heath, Surrey, CR7 6EA
tel: 07976 234 885
fax: 07031 150 872
email: info@astirrecords.co.uk
web: www.astirrecords.co.uk
contact: Sohail
genre: World/Ethnic
info: Send demos on CD to the address above. Astir Records' priority is real musicians rather than manufactured acts.

ATG Records
1/1, 573 Pollockshaws, Glasgow, G41 2QQ
tel: 07958 696 010
email: dogg@atgrecords.com
web: www.atgrecords.com
contact: Dogg
genre: Ambient/Chillout/Electronica/Rock/Funk/Metal
info: Email ATG Records with an introduction to your band and your music, follow with a demo and brief biog. Make sure to include contact details.

Atlantic Records UK
The Electric Lighting Station, 46 Kensington Court, London, W8 5DA
tel: 020 7938 5500
fax: 020 7368 4900
web: www.warnermusic.com
contact: A&R Dept.
genre: All Music Types Accepted
info: Formerly East West Records, Atlantic Records is still part of the Warner group. Send demos on CD to the address above.

Audiobulb Records
PO Box 3496, Sheffield, S10 3ZR
email: contact@audiobulb.com
web: www.audiobulb.com
contact: David William
genre: Ambient/Electronic/IDM (Intelligent Dance Music)
info: Audiobulb Records release exploratory Electronic music, glitch, minimal ambient, idiosynctratic beats and IDM from artists around the world. Releases are in the form of commercial CDs and MP3 downloads via the website. Send demos in form of links to MP3 tracks hosted on your own website. Audiobulb will request full demos from artists whose work interests them. Please do not send MP3 files via email.

LISTEN.....

AUDIOBULB RECORDS
EXPLORATORY ELECTRONIC MUSIC
WWW.AUDIOBULB.COM // CONTACT@AUDIOBULB.COM

Audiorec Records
21 Silicon Centre, 26-28 Wadsworth Road, Greenforth, Middlesex, UB6 7JZ
tel: 020 8810 7779
email: info@audiorec.co.uk
web: www.audiorec.co.uk
contact: Jyotindra Patel
genre: Indian
info: Send demos on CD to the address above.

Authentic Music
9 Holdom Avenue, Bletchley, Milton Keynes, MK1 1QR
tel: 01908 364 200
fax: 01908 648 592
email: info@authenticmedia.co.uk
web: www.authenticmedia.co.uk
contact: Dave Bruce, Gaz Russell
genre: Christian Music of any genre
info: Submit demos to the address above.

Award Records
76 Buchanan Street, Blackpool, FY1 3BN
tel: 01253 623 901
fax: 01253 294 652
email: info@unionmusic.co.uk
contact: Mr A. Chadwick
genre: All Music Types Accepted
info: Send demos on any format to the address above.

B2 Records
53 Corbet Avenue, Sprowston, Norwich, NR7 8HS
tel: 01603 444 859
contact: Kingsley Harris
genre: Guitar Based/Pop
info: Linked to NR One Records. Send demo to the above address.

Back to Basics Recordings
PO Box 41, Tipton, West Midlands, DY4 7YT
tel: 0121 520 1150
fax: 0121 520 2150
email: contact@back2basicsrecords.co.uk
web: www.back2basicsrecords.co.uk
contact: A&R Dept.
genre: Drum&Bass

Backs Records Ltd.
St. Mary's Works, St. Mary's Plain, Norwich, Norfolk, NR3 3AF
tel: 01603 624 290
fax: 01603 619 999
email: derek@backsrecords.co.uk
contact: Derek Chapman
genre: All Music Types Accepted
info: Send demos to the address above. Include biog and press cuttings. Linked with Haven Records, see listing for further information.

Bad Robot
5 Clairmont Terrace, Ashbrook, Sunderland, SR2 7LB
tel: 07843902955
email: info@badrobot.co.uk
web: www.badrobot.co.uk
contact: Paul Le Hat
genre: All Music Types Accepted

Baked Goods
c/o Baked Goods Distribution, Unit 201, Ducie House, 37 Ducie Street, Manchester, M1 2JW
tel: 0161 244 5841
fax: 0161 236 33514
email: info@baked-goods.com
web: www.baked-goods.com
contact: Shlom
genre: All Music Types Accepted
info: Send demos to the address above.

Barely Breaking Even Records
PO Box 25896, London, N5 1WE
tel: 020 7607 0597
fax: 020 7607 4696
email: leeb@bbemusic.com
web: www.bbemusic.com
contact: A&R Dept.
genre: Techno/Garage/Hip-Hop/Dance/Jazz/Funk
info: Send demo on CD to the address above.

Baroque Records
14 Florence Close, Coventry, CV12 0BY
tel: 02476 361 001
fax: 02476 361 818
email: info@baroquerecords.co.uk
web: www.baroquerecords.co.uk
contact: Keith McDonnell
genre: House/Breakbeat
info: Independent UK House label. Send demos on CD to the address above. Material can also be submitted via MP3, but please email and advise in advance. Also see listing for Electrofly in Record Companies section.

Beggars Banquet
17-19 Alma Road, London, SW18 1AA
tel: 020 8870 9912
fax: 020 8871 1766
email: beggars@beggars.com
web: www.beggars.com
contact: Roger Trust
genre: Alternative Guitar Based
info: Send demos to the address above. No music via email please. Other labels in the Beggars Group include Matador, XL Recordings, Too Pure and 4AD.

Bella Union
14 Church Street, Twickenham, Middlesex, TW1 3NJ
tel: 020 8744 2777
fax: 020 8891 1895
email: fiona@bellaunion.com or simon@bellaunion.com
web: www.bellaunion.com
contact: Fiona Glyn-Jones, Simon Raymond
genre: All Music Types Accepted

Berlin Records
Caxton House, Caxton Avenue, Bispham, Blackpool, Lancashire, FY2 9AP
tel: 01253 508 670
fax: 01253 508 670
email: berlinstudios@virgin.net
contact: Ron Sharples
genre: All Music Types Accepted
info: Ron Sharples also runs Berlin Recording Studio, along with www.unsignedartists.net. Bands and acts can pay £25/year to have their profiles and tracks uploaded on to the website and can sell CDs online .

BHI Records
21b Mitcham Lane, Streatham, London, SW16 6LQ
tel: 020 8677 4651
email: info@bhirecords.co.uk
web: www.bhirecords.co.uk
genre: All Music Types Accepted
info: Use online form on the above website to submit your details and track in MP3 format.

Big Bear Records
PO Box 944, Birmingham, West Midlands, B16 8UT
tel: 0121 454 7020
fax: 0121 454 9996
email: records@bigbearmusic.com
web: www.bigbearmusic.com
contact: Jim Simpson
genre: Blues/Jazz/Swing

Big Dada Recordings
PO Box 4296, London, SE11 4WW
tel: 020 7820 3535
email: info@bigdada.com
web: www.bigdada.com
contact: Will Ashon
genre: Hip-Hop/Leftfield Hip-Hop/Grime
info: Big Dada is the Hip Hop off-shoot of Ninja Tunes and home to Roots Manuva.

Big Help Music Ltd.
Deppers Bridge Farm, Deppers Bridge, Sutham, Warwickshire, CV47 2SZ
tel: 01926 614 640
email: dutch@bighelpmusic.com
web: www.bighelpmusic.com
genre: Rock/Singer-Songwriter/Pop
info: Big Help Music have a dedicated A&R team that seek out acts to sign. Do not accept unsolicited demos. Also provide management services. See listing in relevant section for details.

Big Red Records
Surrey
tel: 07708 187 704
email: demos@bigredrecords.co.uk
web: www.bigredrecords.co.uk
contact: Josh
genre: All Music Types Accepted
info: Independent label based in South London. Aims to sign artists that are serious about their music and want a long term music career, not just a few single releases.

Birdwar Records
PO Box 174, Leeds, LS12 5WU
email: info@birdwar.com
web: www.birdwar.com
genre: All Music Types Accepted
info: Birdwar is a new label set up with the view to release new and exciting music of any genre. They operate an open demo submissions policy. Send material to the address above.

Biteback Records
Newcastle
tel: 0191 265 9987
email: info@bitebackrecords.co.uk
web: www.bitebackrecords.co.uk
contact: Neal Gaunt, David Glover, Oliver Kennard
genre: Acoustic/Alternative Country/Rock/Singer-Songwriter
info: Contact by telephone or email for demo submission details.

Black Magic Records
5, 296 Earls Court Road, London, SW5 9BA
tel: 020 7565 0806
fax: 020 7565 0806
email: blackmagicrecords@talk21.com
web: www.blackmagicrecords.com
contact: Mataya Clifford
genre: World/Urban/Dance/R&B/Reggae
info: Email Black Magic Records with details of your music. Follow with demo on request.

Blacklist Entertainment
Fulham Palace, Bishops Avenue, London, SW6 6EA
tel: 020 7751 0175
fax: 020 7736 0606
email: jayne@blacklistent.com
web: www.blacklistent.com
contact: Jayne Meegan
genre: All Music Types Accepted
info: Send CD demos to the address above.

Blah Blah Recordings
The Basement, 146 Shirland Road, London, W9 2BT
tel: 07734 812 232
email: alan@blahblahrecordings.com
genre: All Music Types Accepted
info: Send demos to the address above.

Blasé
1-3 French Place, London, E1 6JB
tel: 07867 552 931
email: info@blaserecords.com
web: www.blaserecords.com
contact: Jeanga
genre: Electronica
info: Send demos on CD to the address above, or email Blasé with details of your website.

Blast First
429 Harrow Road, London, W10 4RE
tel: 020 8964 2001
fax: 020 8964 3722
email: blastfirst@mutehq.co.uk
web: www.mute.com
contact: Paul Smith
genre: All Music Types Accepted
info: Affiliated with Mute Records. Contact via email, as phone number is for the Mute Records office. Email for Blast First is checked once weekly.

BleatBeat Records
Ronavik, Aith, Bixter, Shetland, ZE1 0SL
tel: 07881 820 094
email: mail@bleatbeat.co.uk
web: www.bleatbeat.co.uk
contact: Marvin Smith
genre: All Music Types Accepted
info: Bleat Beat Records is a small independent label operating from the Shetland Islands.

Blue Beat
Matlock, Brady Road, Lyminge, Kent, CT18 8HA
tel: 01303 863 185
fax: 01303 863 185
email: info@expressmusic.co.uk
web: www.bluebeat.co.uk
contact: A&R, Siggy Jackson
genre: Blue Beat/Ska/Reggae
info: Demos are accepted in any format. Send SAE for return of demos.

Blue Cat Records
17 Shaw Road, Heaton Moor, Stockport, SK4 4HA
tel: 0161 432 0050
email: mary@bluecatmusic.co.uk
web: www.bluecatmusic.co.uk
contact: Mary O'Meara
genre: All Music Types Accepted
info: Send a demo and biog to the address above. The label accept demos from bands of all genres but their output so far has mainly been Indie Rock.

Blueblood Records
PO Box 416, Bristol, BS99 2DE
tel: 0117 907 9358
fax: 0117 907 9358
email: info@bluebloodrecords.com
web: www.bluebloodrecords.com
contact: Martin Fairclough
genre: Blues/Roots
info: Send demos to the address above. Blueblood have digital distribution service.

Blues Matters Records
PO Box 18, Bridgend, Mid Glamorgan, CF33 6YW
tel:	01656 745 028
email:	info@bluesmatters.com
web:	www.bluesmatters.com
contact:	Alan Pearce
genre:	Blues/Rhythm & Blues
info:	One of the leading UK Blues labels.

Bolts Records
PO Box 346, Enfield, Middlesex, EN3 5EL
tel:	020 8292 5073
email:	nicky@massmediauk.net
contact:	Nicky Price
genre:	House/Hi-NRG/All Genres Of Dance Music
info:	Send demos on CD to the address above. No material

can be returned.

Born To Dance
PO Box 50, Brighton, BN2 6YP
tel:	01273 301 555
fax:	01273 305 266
email:	gav@borntodance.com
web:	www.borntodance.com
contact:	Gavin McAll, Natasha Brown
genre:	House
info:	Born To Dance release funky, uplifting, vocal House

with commercial crossover and a Latin twist. Submit demos on CD
to the address above. Full details of the labels associated high spec
London based studio can be found on the Born To Dance website. Very
keen to license and distribute tracks. Artists have featured on many
compilations.

Boss Music
7 Jeffreys Place, Camden, London, NW1 9PP
tel:	020 7284 2554
fax:	020 7284 2560
email:	info@bossmusic.net
contact:	Andy Ross
genre:	Rock/Pop/Guitar Based
info:	Send demo to the address above. No MDs please.

Include biog and photo.

Botchit & Scarper
PO Box 16047, London, NW1 7ZH
tel:	020 7729 8030
fax:	020 7729 8121
email:	info@botchit.com
web:	www.botchit.com
contact:	Martin Love
genre:	Breaks
info:	Send demos to the address above. Associated with the

Drum&Bass labels Emotif and DZR.

Boulevard Music
16 Limetrees, Llangattock, Crickhowell, Powys, NP8 1LB
tel:	01873 810 142
fax:	01873 811 557
email:	silvergb@aol.com
web:	www.silverword.co.uk
contact:	Kevin King
genre:	All Music Types Accepted
info:	Send demos on CD to the address above, maximum of

three tracks. Include any other relevant information that supports the
marketability of your music. Part of the Silverword group which run a
number of labels and music publishing companies.

Brewhouse Music
Breeds Farm, 57 High Street, Wicken, Cambridgeshire, CB7 5XR
tel:	01353 720 309
email:	enquiries@brewhousemusic.co.uk
web:	www.brewhousemusic.co.uk
contact:	Eric Cowell
genre:	Traditional/Folk/Classical
info:	Brewhouse comprises of 3 labels. Send demos to the

above address. Also run a studio suitable for Spoken Word projects.
Contact for further details.

Brille Records Ltd.
North Studio, Ground Floor, Walker House, Boundry Street, London,
E2 7JE
tel:	020 7324 7260
email:	info@brillemusic.com
web:	www.brillerecords.com
contact:	Leo Silverman
genre:	All Music Types Accepted
info:	Send demos to the above address.

Bronze Records
17 Priory Road, London, NW6 4NN
email:	info@bronzerecords.co.uk
web:	www.bronzerecords.co.uk
contact:	Gerry Bron
genre:	All Music Types Accepted
info:	Newly reformed independent label, always on the

lookout for new and interesting acts and musicians. Gerry also has a
management company.

BS1 Records
124 Cheltenham Road, Bristol, BS6 5RW
email:	info@bs1records.com
web:	www.bs1records.com
genre:	Drum&Bass
info:	Email link to MP3 tracks to the above address.

Bucks Music Group
Onward House, 1 Uxbridge Street, London, W8 7TQ
tel:	020 7221 4275
fax:	020 7229 6893
email:	info@bucksmusicgroup.co.uk
web:	www.bucksmusicgroup.co.uk
contact:	Ronen Guha
genre:	All Music Types Accepted
info:	Comprises several labels, including Fly Records and

Cube Soundtracks.

b-unique
PO Box 31449, London, SW6 3XB
email:	info@b-uniquerecords.com
web:	www.b-uniquerecords.com
contact:	A&R Dept.
genre:	All Music Types Accepted
info:	Home to the Kaiser Chiefs.

Burning Shed
Windsor House, 74 Thorpe Road, Norwich, NR1 1BA
tel:	01603 767 726
email:	info@burningshed.com
web:	www.burningshed.com
contact:	Pete Morgan
genre:	Ambient/Electronic
info:	Send demos to the address above.

Buzz Records
126 Elderslie Street, Glasgow, Scotland, G3 7AW
tel:	0141 221 3060
email:	dave@radiotones.com
web:	www.thebuzzgroup.co.uk
contact:	Dave Arcari
genre:	All Music Types Accepted
info:	The roster is currently full, but feedback will be happily

given.

Cacophonous
231 Portobello Road, London, W11 1LT
tel:	020 7792 9791
fax:	020 7792 9871
email:	julie@visiblenoise.com
web:	www.cacophonous.com
contact:	Julie Weir
genre:	Grind/Extreme Metal/Noise Core
info:	Extreme Metal, Grind Core, Noise Core and Blast Beat.

Send demos to the address above. Associated with Visible Noise
Records.

Calamity Records
PO Box 540, Edgware, Middlesex, HA8 4AQ
tel: 020 8958 3639
email: dan@calamityrecords.net or demo@calamityrecords.net
web: www.calamityrecords.net
contact: Dan Gordon
genre: Indie/Punk/Emo/Alternative Rock
info: Please do not send MP3 attachments.

Candece Records
PO Box 22864, London, NW9 9WU
tel: 020 8204 0603
fax: 020 8204 0603
email: ladycarolle@hotmail.com
contact: Lady Carolle, Miles Collington
genre: R&B/Soul/Jazz/Funk
info: Send demos on CD to the address above, maximum of 4 tracks.

Candid Productions Ltd.
16 Castelnau, London, SW13 9RU
tel: 020 8741 3608
fax: 020 8563 0013
email: info@candidrecords.com
web: www.candidrecords.com
contact: Alan Bates
genre: Latin/Jazz/Blues/World

Candlelight Records
10 Tiverton Road, London, NW10 3HL
tel: 020 7286 1106
email: abstractsounds@btclick.com
web: www.candlelightrecords.co.uk
contact: A&R Dept.
genre: Metal
info: Successful Metal label associated with the Abstract Sounds label.

Candy Cover
10 Berrystead, Hartford, Northwich, Cheshire, CW8 1NG
tel: 07751 244 738
email: andy@candycover.co.uk
web: www.candycover.co.uk
contact: Andy Pierce
genre: Indie/Pop
info: Seeks bands and artists to promote to bigger and better things. Demos should be sent to Andy Pierce at the above address.

Candy Productions Ltd.
PO Box 260, Birkenhead, CH42 9WH
tel: 0151 652 4495
email: cath@candyproductions.co.uk
web: www.candyproductions.co.uk
contact: Cath, Andy
genre: Alternative/Leftfield
info: Accept Alternative and Leftfield music of all genres except Pop and Dance. Send demos in CD format with current biog and any gig listings to the above address. Currently the band Soviet Underdog are on their roster, but they are actively scouting at the moment for more bands and artists.

Captains of Industry
PO Box 404, Durham, DH1 2ZR
tel: 0191 386 6174
email: info@captainsof.com
web: www.captainsof.com
genre: Indie/Rock/Punk/Metal
info: Send CD and photo where possible to above address.

Cargo Records
17 Heathmans Road, Parsons Green, London, SW6 4TJ
tel: 020 7731 5125
fax: 020 7731 3866
email: info@cargorecords.co.uk
web: www.cargorecords.co.uk
contact: Phil Hill, A&R Dept
genre: All Music Types Accepted

Caritas Records
28 Dalrymple Cresent, Edinburgh, Lothian, EH9 2NX
tel: 0131 667 3633
fax: 0131 667 3633
email: caritas-records@caritas-music.co.uk
web: www.caritas-music.co.uk
contact: Katharine Douglas
genre: Classical/Folk

Carlin Music
Ironbridge House, 3 Bridge Approach, London, NW1 8BD
tel: 020 7734 3251
fax: 020 7439 2391
email: cpm@carlinmusic.co.uk
web: www.carlinmusic.co.uk
contact: Nick Farries A&R Dept.
genre: All Music Types Accepted

Catskills Records
PO Box 3365, Brighton, BN1 1WQ
tel: 01273 626 245
fax: 01273 626 246
email: info@catskillsrecords.com
web: www.catskillsrecords.com
contact: Jonny
genre: All Music Types Accepted
info: Send demos on CD to the address above.

Celtic Soul Music
The Old Inn, Portnacroish, Appin, Argyll, PA38 4BL
tel: 01631 730 469
web: www.celtic-soul-music.com
genre: Celtic
info: Independent record label promoting Celtic music. Also run musicians cooperative dealing with any genre. Please contact for information.

Century Media
6 Water Lane, Kentish Town Road, NW1 8NZ
tel: 020 7482 0161
fax: 020 7482 3165
email: adam@centurymedia.net
web: www.centurymedia.net
contact: Andy
genre: Metal
info: Please send demos FAO A&R to the address above.

Champion Records
181 High Street, London, NW10 4TE
tel: 020 8961 5202
fax: 020 8965 3948
email: mel@championrecords.co.uk
web: www.championrecords.co.uk
contact: Mel Medalie, Raj Porter
genre: House/Garage
info: Send demos on CD to the address above or submit via email directly to Raj Porter. In either case please include a contact email address.

Chemikal Underground
PO Box 3609, Glasgow, G42 9TP
tel: 0141 550 1919
fax: 0141 550 1918
email: via website
web: www.chemikal.co.uk
contact: Paul Savage
genre: Alternative
info: Send demos to the address above.

Cherry Red Records
3a Long Island House, Warple Way, London, W3 0RG
tel: 020 8740 4110
fax: 020 8740 4208
email: infonet@cherryred.co.uk
web: www.cherryred.co.uk
contact: Matt Bristow, Toby Wright
genre: Soul/Sixties Pop/Indie/Punk/Rock

Chilli Discs
The Arts Centre, 9 Myrtle Street, Liverpool, L7 7GJ
tel: 0151 252 4245
fax: 0151 252 4399
email: chillidiscs@hotmail.com
web: www.chillidiscs.co.uk
contact: Steve Reynolds, Alex Dunford, Mark Brocklesby
genre: All Music Types Accepted
info: Send demo on CD, maximum of 3 tracks, to the address above. Include a short biog.

Chips Records
Manchester
email: lee@chipsrecords.co.uk
web: www.chipsrecords.co.uk
contact: Lee Mann
genre: Electric Pop/Rock
info: Email the label for a postal address, or send MP3s via the above email address.

Chocolate Fireguard
PO Box 461, Huddersfield, HD5 8WL
tel: 01484 432 657
fax: 01484 327 026
email: info@chocolatefireguard.co.uk
web: www.chocolatefireguard.co.uk
contact: A&R
genre: Soul/Rock/Hip-Hop/Funk/Dance
info: Have a look at Chocolate Fireguard's website before submitting a demo to make sure the label is right for you.

Citinite
PO Box 27294, London, N11 1XG
email: info@citinite.com
web: www.citinite.com
contact: Manuel Sepulveda
genre: Electronic Dance Music
info: Send demos, preferably on CD or MD, to the address above. Cassettes are also accepted but please do not send DAT tapes, web links, FTP files or MP3s via email. Include contact details on the body of the CD, MD or cassette and a short biog. Maximum of four tracks, with what you consider to be your best work at the start. Tracks not containing samples are preferred, if a track does contain samples indicate this on your demo. All demos are listened to but submissions cannot be returned. Citinite will reply if they are interested in releasing your music - please don't chase the label for a response. Looking towards music influenced by Electro, New Wave, Chicago and Detroit styles.

Cleveland City
52a Clifton Street, Chapel Ash, Wolverhampton, West Midlands, WV3 0QT
tel: 01902 838 500
fax: 01902 839 500
email: info@clevelandcity.co.uk
web: www.clevelandcity.co.uk
contact: Lee
genre: All Music Types Accepted
info: Send original tracks and remixes to the above address.

C'mon Records
Llanfyllin, Powys, SY22 5JG
tel: 01691 649 044
email: contact@cmonrecords.co.uk
web: www.cmonrecords.co.uk
genre: R&B/Classical/Dance/Folk/Punk/Indie/World/Rock
info: Email C'mon Records with an introduction and a track of your music. The label will be in touch if they are interested in hearing more of your music. Also linked with recording studio (The Beehouse), equipment hire company (MantraSound), and mastering and duplication services (Mantra CD & Recording). See listings in relevant sections.

Commercial Recordings
12 Lisnagleer Road, Dungannon, County Tyrone, BT70 3LN
tel: 028 8776 1995
email: info@commercialrecordings.com
web: www.commercialrecordings.com
genre: Country/Irish

Complicit Recordings Ltd.
PO Box 348, Brighton, BN2 5YF
fax: 01273 739 329
email: info@complicit.net
web: www.complicit.net
contact: James Jephcott, Jenny Black
genre: House/Progressive House/Tribal House
info: Send fully mastered demos to the address above. Make sure to write contact details on the actual demo, and make sure to pay the full postage. Please allow a few weeks for a response. Complicit Recordings has a sister label, Explicit Recordings, which releases Hard House and Trance. See listing for further details.

Concept Music Ltd.
Shepherds Building, Charecroft Way, Shepherds Bush, London, W14 0EH
tel: 020 7751 1755
fax: 020 7751 1566
email: info@conceptmusic.com
web: www.conceptmusic.com
contact: Max Bloom
genre: All Music Types Accepted
info: Complete artist development. Send demos on CD to the address above, or email MP3s to above address.

Cone Records
PO Box 42, Todmorden, OL14 7DH
tel: 01422 881 815
email: info@conerecords.com
web: www.conerecords.com
contact: Steve Fenton, Steve Fenton
genre: Experimental/Breaks/Fusion
info: Send demos to the address above, along with biog. CD or vinyl accepted. No MP3s or other music files will be accepted via email. Cone Records also run a recording studio, Calder Recordings. See relevant section for details.

Congo Music Ltd.
17a Craven Park Road, London, NW10 8SE
tel: 020 8961 5461
fax: 020 8961 5461
email: congomusic@hotmail.com or congomusic@tiscali.com
web: www.congomusic.com
contact: Root Jackson
genre: All Music Types Accepted

Connect Records
3 Shelton Square, City Centre, Coventry, CV1 1DG
tel: 02476 550 555
email: sales@djbargains.co.uk
web: www.djbargains.co.uk
contact: Matt Green, Simon Blackett
genre: All Genres Of Dance Music/Electronic
info: DJs and producers can send demos on CD to the address above. See website for details of Connect Records DJ Agency, online record and DJ equipment shops.

Conquer Records
PO Box 33904, London, NW9 7ZU
tel: 020 8537 9400
email: podol@conquerec.com
web: www.conquerec.com
contact: Tomasz
genre: Industrial/Metal/Death Metal/Grind
info: Send demo to the address above. Include biog, photo and any press.

Console Sounds Ltd.
Po Box 7515, Glasgow, G41 3ZW
tel: 0141 636 6336/07703 324322
fax: 0141 636 6336
email: steviesole@solemusic.co.uk
web: www.solemusic.co.uk or www.consolesounds.co.uk
contact: Stevie Sole Middleton, Chris Harris, Geoff Montford
genre: Americana/Rock/Electronica
info: Send demos to the address above. Associated with Solemusic Industries Ltd. For DJ bookings please check www.steviesole.com, or contact Geoff Montford.

Cooking Vinyl
10 Allied Way, London, W3 0RQ
tel: 020 8600 9200
fax: 020 8743 7448
email: info@cookingvinyl.com
web: www.cookingvinyl.com
contact: Tom Wheeley
genre: All Music Types Accepted
info: Send demos on CD to the address above. Mark FAO Tom Wheeley, A&R Department. No other music formats or videos please. Make sure to include a contact email address.

Cookshop Music
18 Crown Street, Brighton, BN1 3EH
tel: 01273 725 803
fax: 01273 725 803
email: info@cookshopmusic.co.uk
web: www.cookshopmusic.co.uk
contact: James Dean, Emily Cracknell
genre: Experimental/Downbeat/Leftfield
info: Contact Cookshop Music directly via email or phone, or send demos to the address above. All submissions are listened to but cannot be returned. Supporting new talent is very much a priority for the label.

Coombe Records
London
email: info@coomberecords.com
web: www.coomberecords.com
contact: George
genre: Electronica/Mellow Acoustic
info: Email Coombe Records with details of your band, music and any upcoming gigs, and previous or forthcoming releases.

Cornishmusic.com
Canonstown, Hayle, Cornwall, TR27 6NB
tel: 01736 740 503
email: cornishmusic@btinternet.com
web: www.cornishmusic.com
contact: Tim Chapple, Susan Chapple
genre: All Music Types Accepted
info: Cornishmuisc.com was set up in 2002 to promote contemporary and traditional Cornish music. Send demos on CD to the address above, mark FAO Susan Chapple, A&R. Alternatively, email or telephone to introduce yourself and your music.

Cowgirl Records
27 Old Gloucester Street, London, WC1N 3XX
tel: 07949 839 852
email: peter.gold@cowgirlrecords.com or laurence.jones@cowgirlrecords.com
web: www.cowgirlrecords.com
contact: Peter Gold, Laurence Jones
info: Will accept demos in any format via post or email address.

CP Recordings Ltd.
PO Box 2253, Stoke On Trent, ST4 7WP
tel: 07734 949 115
email: cprecordings@cprecordings.com
web: www.cprecordings.com
contact: David Oldfield
genre: Breaks/Progressive House/Tech-House
info: Send a good quality demo to the address above. If submitting material electronically, send at minimum 128kbps.

C-Pij Records
Greater London
email: contact@ninawalsh.com
web: www.c-pij.co.uk or www.ninawalsh.com
contact: Nina Walsh
genre: Experimental Electronics/Electro-Folk
info: Contact C-Pij Records via their website for demo submission information.

CRAMP (Crediton Rural Arts & Music Project)
Dean Street, Crediton, Devon, EX17 3ER
tel: 01392 668 824/07837 659 363
email: info@crampdevon.org
web: www.crampdevon.org
contact: Marie Belsten
genre: All Music Types Accepted
info: CRAMP is a community project for the Devon area. Eclectic range of musical styles and acts. Local bands and musicians can submit demo FAO Marie to the above address. CRAMP are also involved in other community based activities including promoting gigs and running workshops. See entry in Useful Regional Organisations for further details.

Crash Records
PO Box 13, Chinnor, Oxfordshire, OX39 4WD
email: info@crash-records.co.uk
web: www.crash-records.co.uk
contact: Michele
genre: All Music Types Accepted
info: Crash Records are particularly interested in hearing from bands and musicians who have a good work ethic, enthusiasm and loads of energy, are gigging hard and have the right attitude. All musical styles listened to but originality is important. Send demos to the address above.

Critical Mass Recordings
63 Hartland Road, London, NW6 6BH
tel: 020 7625 5552
fax: 020 76255553
email: info@criticalmassrecordings.com
web: www.criticalmassrecordings.com
contact: Alex Payne
genre: Dance
info: Deal with cross section of Dance genres. Send demo to the address above.

Crucial Recordings
PO Box 31685, Brixton, London, SW2 2YT
email: crlabelinfo@crucial-records.com
web: www.crucial-records.com
contact: Dan G, Pauly E
genre: All Music Types Accepted
info: Crucial Records are interested in musicians with a political and social conscience, absolutely no exceptions. The label will respond to submissions only if interested in pursuing a long term developmental relationship. Contact firstly via email address above.

Cruise International Records
Leeds
tel: 0113 266 9189/07970 182 621
email: info@cruiseinternationalrecords.co.uk
web: www.cruiseinternational.co.uk
contact: Michael Cruise
genre: All Music Types Accepted
info: Contact Cruise via email initially, and send demo upon request. Cruise International are also linked with Crystal Sound, a recording studio also offering mastering services. See entries in relevant sections for further details.

Cuba Recordings
PO Box 44139, London, SW6 7XR
email: info@cubarecordings.com
web: www.cubarecordings.com
contact: Bobby M
genre: All Music Types Accepted
info: Cuba Recordings is an independent label focusing on quality rather than any specific genre. Releases have covered all variations of House Music as well as Electro, Breaks, Trip-Hop and more but they are open to any good music. Demos are best submitted by post to the address above, marked FAO A&R department. Alternatively, email a link to your material to demos@cubarecordings.com.

Cube Records Ltd.
Onward House, 11 Uxbridge Street, London, W8 7TQ
tel: 020 7221 4275
fax: 020 7229 6893
email: info@bucksmusicgroup.co.uk
web: www.bucksmusicgroup.com
contact: Ronen Guha
genre: All Music Types Accepted
info: Part of the Bucks Music group. Have recently set up offshoot label Cube Soundtracks, which focuses on music from independent British films.

Cultural Foundation
Rosedale, North Yorkshire, YO18 8RL
tel: 01751 417 147
fax: 01751 417 804
email: info@cultfound.org
web: www.cultfound.org
contact: Peter Bell
genre: All Music Types Accepted
info: Deal with a very wide range of music. Specialise in North East and Yorkshire based bands.

dA Records Ltd.
Briar Bank Studios, 10 Beach Road, Penarth, CF64 1JX
tel: 02920 705 137
email: info@darecords.com
web: www.darecords.com
contact: Danny Chang, Peter Ferris
genre: Commercial
info: Call the label and speak to Danny or Peter. Follow with demo on request.

DB Records
PO Box 19318, Bath, BA1 6ZS
tel: 01225 782 322
email: info@dbrecords.co.uk
web: www.dbrecords.co.uk
contact: David Bates
genre: All Music Types Accepted
info: Send demos to David at the address above. It is vital that you include contact details (email, name and phone number or address).

DC Recordings
231 Portobello Road, London, W11 1LT
tel: 020 7792 9791
fax: 020 7792 9871
email: james@dcrecordings.com
web: www.dcrecordings.com
contact: James Dyer
genre: Breaks & Beats/Soundtracks/Funk/Hip-Hop/Electro
info: Email with details of your music. Follow with demo on request.

Dead Digital
The Basement, Islington Mill, James Street, Salford, Manchester, M3 5HW
tel: 07815 451 394
email: info@deaddigital.com
web: www.deaddigital.com
contact: Maurice Carlin
info: Off-beat electro/wired analogue and misshapen guitar sounds. UK independent with an ear for a cool tune. New and innovative tracks veering towards a Pop tangent stand the best chance of a repeated listen.

Dead Earnest
PO Box 10170, Dundee, DD4 8WW
tel: 01382 776 595
email: deadearnest@btopenwotld.com
web: www.deadearnest.btinternet.co.uk
contact: Andy Garibaldi
genre: All music types accepted except rap
info: Send demos on CD or cassette to the address above.

Dead Happy Records
3b Castledown Avenue, Hastings, East Sussex, TN34 3RJ
tel: 01424 434 778
email: vibezone@excite.com
web: www.deadhappyrecords.co.uk
contact: Dave Arnold
genre: Indie/Trance/Dance
info: Send demos on any format to the address above. Include covering letter and biog, and make sure to write your contact details on the actual demo.

Deadly Beef Burger Records
Nottingham, Nottinghamshire, NG2 4AB
tel: 0115 910 0843
email: fokkewolf@deadlybeefburger.com
web: www.deadlybeefburger.com
genre: All Music Types Accepted
info: Please make contact first before sending any music.

Deep Structure
London
tel: 07984 707 806
web: www.blumarten.com
contact: Leo Wyndham, Chris Marigold
genre: Electronic
info: Deep Structure is a specialist Electronic label set up by Leo Wyndham and Chris Marigold of Blu Mar Ten (Good Looking Records, Exceptional Records). Recent releases include Drum&Bass 12"s by Social Security (Hospital Records, Creative Source). Submit demos via email. MP3s must be under 4Mb.

DeepBlue Recordings
PO Box 3590, West Midlands, DY6 7ZG
tel: 07958 914 205
fax: 07050 692 953
email: deepbluerecords@hotmail.com or info@solarstone.org.uk
web: www.deepbluerecords.co.uk
contact: Andy Bury, Rich Mowatt
genre: Trance/Progressive House
info: DeepBlue is predominantly a Trance label, but does release some Progressive House. Send demos on CD to the address above. Alternatively, email links to MP3s of your material to either of the above addresses. Please do not email actual MP3 files.

Deep-Water Recordings
120a Hartopp Road, Bathysphere, The Depot, 31 Rutland Street, Leicester, LE1 1RE
tel: 0116 261 6832
fax: 0116 270 2706
email: deepwater@bathysphere.co.uk
web: www.deep-water.net
genre: Downtempo Electronica
info: Send demos on CD or MD to the address above. Include a brief biog.

Defected
12 D'Arblay Street, London, W1F 8DU
tel: 020 7439 9995
fax: 020 7432 6470
email: andyd@defected.co.uk
web: www.defected.co.uk
contact: Simon Dunmore, Andy Daniel
genre: House/Garage/Dance
info: Send demos on CD to the address above.

Deft Recordings
Nottingham
tel: 07990 830 473
email: iain@deft-recordings.com
web: www.deft-recordings.com
contact: Iain Harper
genre: Deep, Soulful House
info: Home to Schmoov!, Reza, Flatpack, Kitster, Sueno Soul and Martin McFly.

Delphian Records
290 Colinton Mains Road, Edinburgh, EH13 9BS
tel: 0845 644 9308
fax: 07092 165 783
email: info@delphianrecords.co.uk
web: www.delphianrecords.co.uk
contact: Paul Baxter
genre: Classical
info: Demo material should always be submitted on CD format. Sample material is unable to be returned.

Deltasonic Records
102 Rose Lane, Mossley Hill, Liverpool, L18 8AG
tel: 0151 724 4760
fax: 0151 724 6286
email: info@deltasonic.co.uk
web: www.deltasonic.co.uk
contact: A&R
genre: Alternative
info: All demos will be listened to but reply not guaranteed. CDs are the preferred format, no cassettes please. Press, photos and biog are useful, but not essential.

Demi Monde Records
Foel Studio, Llanfair, Caereinion, Powys, SY21 0DS
tel: 01938 810 758
fax: 01938 810 758
email: foel.studio@dial.pipex.com
web: www.demimonde.co.uk
contact: Dave Anderson
genre: 70's Psychedelia
info: Focus on Psychedelia and 70s influenced music. Send demos to the address above. Also run publishing company under same name, and recording studio, Foel Studio. See entries in relevant sections for details.

Democracy Records
Upper York Street, Earlsdon, Coventry, Warwickshire, CV1 3GQ
tel: 02476 223 892
fax: 02476 223 892
email: admin@glasshouseproductions.co.uk
web: www.democracymusic.com
contact: Amos Sanderson, Sharon Jones
genre: Indie Pop/World/Reggae/Ragga/Garage/Dance/ Hip-Hop/Urban/Soul/R&B
info: Part of the Glasshouse Productions group, encompassing music publishing, an entertainment agency and training for sound engineers. Send demo with photo, biog, press cuttings and details of forthcoming gigs to the address above.

Demolition Records
Henry Study House, 139 Bede Burn Road, Jarrow, Tyne & Wear, NE32 5AZ
tel: 0191 423 9313
email: info@demolitionrecords.com
web: www.demolitionrecords.com
genre: Rock/Metal
info: Current artists include David Lee Roth and Twisted Sister. Please remember to include contact details with all demos plus photos and biogs.

Deprivation Records
Midlands
tel: 07811 197 561
email: jukesy@deprivationrecordings.co.uk
web: www.deprivationrecords.co.uk
contact: Adam Jukes
genre: Techno/Hard House
info: Deprivation are always on the look out for new artists on the Hard House/Techno scene. Contact the label by email for further information.

Detail Recordings
181 Olive Grove Road, Sheffield, S2 3GE
tel: 0114 201 2661
email: info@detailrecordings.co.uk
web: www.detailrecordings.co.uk
contact: Adam Clark
genre: All Music Types Accepted
info: Check the website for information on past releases. Send demos to the above address.

Detour Music Ltd.
PO Box 18, Midhurst, West Sussex, GU29 9YU
tel: 01730 815 422
fax: 01730 815 422
email: detour@btinternet.com
web: www.detour-records.co.uk
contact: David Holmes
genre: Power Pop
info: Mod and Scooterist label. Send demos to the address above.

Dicelines
Studio 2, 1st Floor, Argyle House, 1103 Argyle Street, Glasgow, G3 8ND
tel: 07931 381 780
email: info@dicelines.com
web: www.dicelines.com
contact: Ally Gray
genre: Rock
info: A label, promoter and management company. See listing in Promoter section for further information.

Different Drummer
PO Box 2571, Birmingham, B30 1BZ
tel: 0121 603 0033
email: info@differentdrummer.co.uk
web: www.differentdrummer.co.uk
contact: Richard Whittingham
genre: All Genres of Dance Music
info: No Guitar based music please.

DiN Records
email: info@din.org.uk
web: www.din.org.uk
contact: Ian Boddy
info: Specialises in Ambient Electronica. Bands should get in contact via email to discuss demos.

Distinct'ive Records
35 Drury Lane, London, WC2B 5RJ
tel: 020 7240 1399
fax: 020 7240 1261
email: info@distinctiverecords.com
web: www.distinctiverecords.com
contact: Richard Ford
genre: Dance
info: Send demos to the address above. Distinct'ive have a particular interest in House and Breakbeat.

The Divine Art Record Company
8 The Beeches, East Harlsey, Northallerton, North Yorkshire, DL6 2DJ
tel: 01609 882 062
email: info@divine-art.com
web: www.divine-art.com
contact: Stephen Sutton
genre: Experimental/Classical/Leftfield
info: Do not ask artists to work exclusively with label. Deal with Classical music, in the widest sense of the word, including Experimental and Contemporary "art-music" but no Pop, Rock, Dance, Rap or any other type of current "popular" music.

Domino Recording Co.
PO Box 47029, London, SW18 1WD
tel: 020 8875 1390
fax: 020 8875 1391
email: pauls@dominorecordco.com
web: www.dominorecordco.com
contact: Paul Sandall, Flash Taylor
genre: Alternative
info: Domino Records listen to all material submitted, but cannot reply to everyone. If the label is interested they will be in touch. Please do not follow your submission with phone calls or emails.

Dorado Records
76 Brewer Street, London, W1F 9TX
tel: 020 7287 1689
fax: 020 7287 1684
email: contact@dorado.net
web: www.dorado.net
contact: Ollie Buckwell, Marcus Dubois
genre: Acid Jazz/Drum&Bass/Jazz
info: See also listing for DJ and Electronic arm of the label, Filter Records. See listing for Filter Records for further information.

Double Dragon Music
120-124 Curtain Road, London, EC2A 3SQ
tel: 020 7739 6903
fax: 020 7613 2715
email: info@doubledragonmusic.com
web: www.doubledragonmusic.com
contact: Tav, Gavin
genre: Alternative Guitar Based/Rock
info: Double Dragon are always for demos showing strong songwriting. Demos should be marked FAO Milo A&R.

Down By Law Records
PO Box 20242, London, NW1 7FL
email: info@proofsongs.co.uk
genre: All Music Types Accepted
info: Send 3 track demo on CD to the address above. Include an SAE if you would like your material returned.

Downbeat Records
61-62 Thornton Street, Newcastle Upon Tyne, Tyne & Wear, NE1 4AW
tel: 0191 222 1213
email: info@altvinyl.com
web: www.altvinyl.com
contact: Graham Thrower
genre: Singer-Songwriter/Acoustic/Lo-Fi
info: Send demos to the address above. Linked with Alt.Vinyl label and record shop. See entries for further details.

the|unsigned|guide

The Unsigned Guide/UK/2006. Material published in this directory may not be reproduced (in any form) without written consent.

Dragonfly Records
67-69 Chalton Street, London, NW1 1HY
tel: 020 7554 2100
fax: 020 7554 2100
email: dragonfly@dragonflyrecords.co.uk
web: www.dragonflyrecords.co.uk
contact: Humphrey
genre: Trance

Dream Driven Recordings
180 Salmon Street, Kingsbury, London, NW9 8NX
tel: 07766 825 843
email: info@dreamdriven.com
web: www.dreamdriven.com
contact: David McHugh
genre: Post-Rock
info: Small label into Post/Drone Rock styles, as well as Experimental and instrumental guitar based music.

Drenched Recordings
Flat 7, The Vaults, 1 Tariss Street, Manchester, M1 2FF
tel: 07977 920 660
fax: 07092 357 295
email: info@drenchedrecordings.com
web: www.drenchedrecordings.com
contact: James Ellis
genre: Deep House
info: Send demos on CD to the address above. Include a biog and discography. Drenched Records back catalogue is available via the label's website.

Drop Music
67 Henrietta Street, Nottingham, NG6 9JB
tel: 0115 877 0658
fax: 0115 877 0658
email: info@dropmusic.co.uk
web: www.dropmusic.co.uk
contact: Laurence Ritchie
genre: Deep House/Funky House
info: Send demos to the above address.

DTPM Recordings
First Floor, 40a Great Eastern Street, London, EC2A 3EP
tel: 020 7749 1199
email: guy@dtpm.net
web: www.dtpmrecordings.net
contact: Guy Williams
genre: House
info: Submit demos on CD to the address above, or send MP3 via email.

Dubcupboard
Flat 2, 35 Greenleaf Road, Walthamstow, London, E17 6QN
tel: 020 8520 3426
email: dubcupboard@btinternet.com
web: www.geocities.com/dubcupboard/music.html
contact: Kenny
genre: Drum&Bass/Jungle/Breaks & Beats
info: Online record label specialising in Dub infected Jungle.

E3 Records
PO Box 156, Wallasey, Cheshire, CH45 9XA
tel: 0151 638 2009
email: info@e3-records.com
web: www.e3-records.com
contact: Bex Whitfield
genre: All Music Types Accepted
info: Send demo, biog and full contact details including postal and email addresses to the above address. Demos will be accepted on CD, MP3, cassette and video formats.

Earache Records Ltd.
PO Box 144, Nottingham, NG3 4GE
tel: 0115 950 6400
fax: 0115 950 8585
email: mail@earache.com
web: www.earache.com
contact: Ali Marr
genre: Metal
info: Submit your demo on MP3 via the Earache website, or send a CD to the address above.

East Central One
Creetings House, All Saints Road, Creeting St. Mary, Ipswich, IP6 8PR
tel: 01449 720 988
fax: 0207 726 027
email: enquiries@eastcentralone.com
web: www.eastcentralone.com
contact: Steve Fernie
genre: All Music Types Except Dance
info: Email Steve with a biog and history of your act. Follow with demo on request.

Eastside Records
Top Floor, Outset Building, 2 Grange Road, London, E17 8AH
tel: 020 8509 6070
fax: 020 8509 6021
email: info@eastside-records.co.uk
web: www.eastside-records.co.uk
contact: Alexis Michaelides
genre: R&B/Hip-Hop/Garage
info: Please send demo to above address with contact details. Also accept MP3s via email.

Eat Sleep Records
3rd Floor, 1a Adpar Street, London, W2 1DE
email: info@eatsleeprecords.com
web: www.eatsleeprecords.com
contact: Chris Baker
genre: All Music Types Accepted
info: FAO A&R. Should be CD format with 3 or 4 tracks, along with contact details and some information on the band. Their aim is to sign up bands that they really believe in, be that a Folk band, a Garage Rock band or a Singer-Songwriter. Linked with other labels Full Time Hobby, Hassle Records and Sorepoint Records. See listings for further details.

Effin
PO Box 114, Bury District Office, BL9 8FG
tel: 0161 280 0908
fax: 0161 280 0908
email: info@alive.org.uk
web: www.alive.org.uk
contact: Peter Ross
genre: Rock/Pop
info: Send demo to the address above.

Elbandito Recordings
email: info@elbandito.co.uk
web: www.elbandito.co.uk
genre: Hip-Hop/Ambient/Lo-Fi/Acoustic
info: The type of music Elbandito Records are particularly interested in Ambient, 'Mash-ups and Glitch', Lo-Fi Acoustic and 'Mock-Hop' (there are some examples of Mock-Hop linked to the website). A sense of humour evident in the music is also an advantage. Email Elbandito Records to introduce yourselves and your music, follow with demo on request.

Electriks
3rd Floor, 24-26 Lever Street, Manchester, M1 1DZ
tel: 0161 278 5650
email: huw@electriks.co.uk
web: www.electriks.co.uk
contact: Huw Morgan
genre: Dance
info: Send demos on vinyl or CD to the address above. For more information on Electriks events, including Electric Chair, see the website.

Electrofly Ltd.
14 Florence Close, Bedworth, Coventry, CV12 0BY
tel: 02476 365 552
fax: 02476 361 818
email: info@electrofly.co.uk
web: www.electrofly.co.uk
contact: Keith McDonnell
genre: Breakbeat
info: Send demos on CD to the address above. Material can also be submitted via MP3, but please email and advise in advance. Also see listing for Baroque Records.

Elefanttree Records
71 High Street East, Wallsend, Tyne & Wear, NE28 7RJ
tel: 0191 262 4999/07910 250 286
contact: Alan Blevins
genre: All Music Types Accepted
info: Looking for "completely different" music and original songs. Publishing is available, as well as an in-house producer and a practice facility. This is the studio where Sting, Jimmy Nail, and many Thrash Metal artists began. Elefanttree Records are highly respected in the music industry and have secured major contracts for working bands.

Ellorac Records
PO Box 22864, London, NW9 9WU
tel: 020 8204 0603
fax: 020 8204 0603
email: ladycarolle@hotmail.com
contact: Lady Carolle, Miles Collington
genre: Soul/Funk

Elsewhen Records
59 Lateward Road, Brentford, TW8 0PL
tel: 020 8400 5932
email: info@elsewhen.org.uk
web: www.elsewhen.org.uk
contact: Sam
genre: Chillout/Lounge/Jazzy
info: Submit demos on CD to the address above or send an MP3 via email.

Emerald Music (Ireland) Ltd.
120a Coach Road, Temple Patrick, County Antrim, BT39 0HA
tel: 028 9443 2619
fax: 028 9443 2162
email: info@emeraldmusic.co.uk
web: www.emeraldmusiconline.com
contact: George Doherty
genre: Irish/Scottish Club/Irish/Scottish Traditional

EMI Records
EMI House, 43 Brook Green, Hammersmith, London, W6 7EF
tel: 020 7605 5000
fax: 020 7605 5050
web: www.emichrysalis.co.uk
genre: All Music Types Accepted
info: EMI Records suggest you submit your material through an established industry source (such as a Manager, Lawyer, Publisher or Producer) who have had previous contact with the company.

Eminence Records
18-24 John Street, Luton, Bedfordshire, LU1 2JE
tel: 01582 817 032
email: joanna@eminenceleisure.co.uk
web: www.eminence-records.co.uk
contact: Joanna
genre: All Music Types Accepted
info: Send demo on CD with photo and any recent gig dates. Part of the Eminence Group, who also book over 600 late night entertainment venues.

End Recordings
18 West Central Street, London, WC1A 1JJ
tel: 020 7419 9199
fax: 020 7419 9099
email: ryan@endclub.com
web: www.endclub.com
contact: Ryan
genre: Techno/House/Breakbeat
info: Label arm of The End club. Send demos on CD to Ryan at the address above. 3 or 4 tracks preferred.

Endorphin Records
134 Replingham Road, Southfields, London, SW18 5LL
email: jackenraptured@hotmail.com.
contact: Jack Trevillion
genre: Ambient Dance/Remix Projects/Experimental Dance/ Electronic With Beats
info: Send demo on CD to the address above, include contact details and a short biog. Artists can send demos cold or email first to introduce themselves. Endorphin Records listens to all material submitted and will always reply (usually within one month). The label specialises in the above genres and will accept submissions of any type of Dance music. See also sister label, Enraptured Records.

Enraptured Records
134 Replingham Road, Southfield, London, SW18 5LL
email: jackenraptured@hotmail.com
web: www.enrapturedrecords.com
contact: Jack Trevillion
genre: Ambient/Guitar Based/Experimental/Electronica/ Electronic
info: Enraptured Records is interested in music with a cutting edge, leftfield sound that stands out from the crowd. Send demo on CD to the address above, include contact details and a short biog. Artists can send demos cold, or email first to introduce themselves. Enraptured Records listen to all material submitted and will always send a reply (usually within one month). See also sister label, Endorphin Records.

Escape Music Ltd.
16 Westmoor Gables, Princes Road, Heaton Moor, Stockport, SK4 3NQ
tel: 0161 431 9165
fax: 0161 431 9165
email: escapemusic@dial.pipex.com
web: www.escape-music.com
contact: Halil Turk
genre: Heavy Metal/Hard Rock

Estate Recordings
Subtub Music Ltd., 18 Sparkle Street, Manchester, M1 2NA
tel: 0161 273 3435
fax: 0161 273 3695
email: info@estaterecordings.com
web: www.estaterecordings.com
contact: Tim Giles
genre: UK Hip-Hop
info: Send demos on CD, MD or tape to the address above. Demos are responded to where possible, but please allow a couple of weeks.

Ether Music
Broadway Studios, 28 Tooting High Street, London, SW17 0RG
tel: 020 8378 6956
fax: 020 8378 6959
email: contact@etheruk.com
web: www.etheruk.com
genre: Soul/Jazz/Funk/Latin/World/Dance
info: Send a demo on CD to the address above, mark FAO A&R.

Eukatech Records
PO Box 602, London, WC2 9AJ
email: hq@eukatechrecords.com
web: www.eukatech.co.uk
contact: Rory Viggers
genre: Electronic/Techno/House
info: Send demos on CD to the address above. The label is run from a specialist House, Tech-House and Techno online music store.

Evil Genius Records
36 Hill Road, London, N10 1JG
email: emjayzed@yahoo.co.uk
contact: Matthew Julian
genre: Beats/Hip-Hop/Rap/Breaks
info: Send good quality demos to the address above.

Evil Twin Records
Suite 29, 10 Mark Rutherford Road, Bedford, MK42 0HZ
email: passionhifi@ntlworld.com
web: www.eviltwinrecords.com
contact: A&R
genre: Hip-Hop
info: The label deals mainly with Hip-Hop acts but all musicians showing real talent will be considered, regardless of genre. Evil Twin is currently a leading light in British Hip-Hop, with producers and artists from the UK and America working together to create something that they believe is unique.

Exceptional Records
PO Box 16208, London, W4 1ZU
email: info@exceptionalrecords.co.uk
web: www.exceptionalrecords.co.uk
contact: Bob Fisher
genre: Electronica
info: Submit demos on CD to the address above, or send an MP3 via email. The label advises you to check their website before sending material to make sure that your music suits their style.

Exercise1
London
tel: 07814 341 906
email: office@exercise1.net
web: www.exercise1.net
contact: Tom Madders, Nik Pearson, Lucas Stidson
genre: All Music Types Accepted/Alternative
info: Label that was started by a group of like minded individuals putting on a club night eventually signing their favourite acts. They listen to all demos. Firstly submit your track onto the forum section of website. If you prefer not to do this, either email for a postal address or send MP3s (not too big please!) or links.

Eye Industries
(Rear of) 71a Masbro Road, London, W14 0LS
tel: 020 7471 3205
fax: 020 7471 3206
email: info@eyeindustries.com
web: www.eyeindustries.com
contact: Marco
genre: All Music Types Accepted
info: The majority of Eye Industries releases so far have been Dance tracks, but the label accepts demos from musicians of all genres. Send a CD to the address above (maximum 4 tracks). Alternatively, email an MP3 to above address. Eye Industries also operate an artist management company. See listing in relevant section for further information.

F4 Records
8 Brewery Yard, Deva Centre, Trinity Way, Manchester, M3 7BB
tel: 0161 839 3930
fax: 0161 839 3940
email: info@f4records.co.uk
web: www.f4records.co.uk
contact: Anthony Wilson, Tom Clarke
genre: All Music Types Accepted/All Music Types Accepted
info: Send demos to the address above.

Faith & Hope
23 New Mount Street, Manchester, M4 4DE
tel: 0161 839 4445
fax: 0161 839 1060
email: yoyo@faithandhope.co.uk
web: www.faithandhope.co.uk
contact: A&R
genre: Alternative Pop
info: Send demos on CD or tape to the address above or email MP3s (no bigger than 4Mb) to music@faithandhope.co.uk.

Fantastic Plastic
The Church, Archway Close, London, N19 3TD
email: info@fantasticplastic.co.uk
web: www.fantasticplastic.co.uk
contact: Darren Robson
genre: Alternative Guitar Based
info: Send demos on CD to the address above, maximum of 4 tracks. Include contact details, biog, upcoming live dates and if possible, photos and press clippings. If you would like your material returned also include SAE. If Fantastic Plastic are interested in your band they will contact you. Please do not follow with calls or emails. For further details refer to full demo submission policy on website.

Farfield Records
40 Harrison Road, Southampton, SO17 3TJ
tel: 02380 362 171
fax: 02380 362 171
web: www.ambientmusic.co.uk
contact: Nick Webb
genre: Ambient
info: Check to see if Farfield are accepting demos before sending any material. To submit a demo, complete the form on Farfield Records website, available via the 'Contacts' page.

Farmfresh Records
PO Box 573, Newcastle Upon Tyne, NE5 2WP
tel: 07779 342 183
email: farmfresh@recordinglabel.co.uk
web: www.farmfreshrecords.co.uk
contact: Dave Curry, Claire Riley
genre: All Music Types Accepted
info: A small independent label based in Newcastle and Brighton promoting folk and Electronica. Farmfresh run a regular promotions unit called Live Stock, showcasing in both cities. To submit demos and biogs, send to the address above.

Fat Cat Records
PO Box 3400, Brighton, BN1 4WG
tel: 01273 747 433
fax: 01273 777 718
email: demo@fat-cat.co.uk
web: www.fat-cat.co.uk
contact: Dave, Alex
genre: Leftfield/All Music Types Accepted
info: Send demos on CD, MD or DAT to the address above. The Fat Cat Records website contains a DIY resource for new bands and labels that aims to provide a forum of information, ideas and resources.

www.fathippyrecords.co.uk

Fat Hippy Records
c/o Captain Tom's, 11-15 Ann Street, Aberdeen, AB25 3LH
email: info@fathippyrecords.co.uk
web: www.fathippyrecords.co.uk
contact: Tom
info: Independent label set up to help emerging artists put out their music.

Fat Northerner Records
Langley Lane Farm, Langley Lane, Middleton, Manchester, M24 5LJ
tel: 0161 682 4994
email: staff@fatnortherner.com
web: www.fatnortherner.com
contact: Dan Thomas, Ruth Daniel
genre: All Music Types Accepted
info: Fat Northerner Records is a Manchester based independent record label that aims to bring outstanding and original new music of all genres to people around the world, discover and professionally develop new talent and develop new opportunities for bands and artists.

Fat Records
Battersea Business Centre, Unit 36, 99-109 Lavender Hill, London, SW11 5QL
tel: 020 7924 1333/020 7924 1833
email: info@thefatclub.com
web: www.thefatclub.com
contact: Paul Arnold, Emily Walker
genre: Breakbeat
info: Send demos to the address above. Chew The Fat, run by the Fat Records team, is London's longest running Breakbeat club night. For more information see the website above.

Fellside Recordings
PO Box 40, Workington, Cumbria, CA14 3GJ
tel: 01900 615 56
fax: 01900 615 85
email: info@fellside.com
web: www.fellside.com
contact: Paul Adams
genre: Folk
info: Affiliated with Lake Recordings (Jazz).

FFVinyl
Warwick Hall, Off Banastre Avenue, Cardiff, CF14 3NR
tel: 02920 694 450
email: press@ffvinyl.com
web: www.ffvinyl.com
contact: Martin Bowen
genre: Guitar Based
info: Send demos to the address above, include details of your website if possible. The majority of the label's output has so far been by local South Wales acts, but will consider signing bands from further afield if they are deemed a high enough standard.

Fiction Records
72-80 Black Lion Lane, London, W6 9BE
tel: 02074715400
email: fictionrecords@wmmusic.com
web: www.fictionrecords.com
contact: Alex Close, Jim Chancellor
genre: Guitar Based
info: Send a 3 track demo on CD to the address above. Make sure your contact details are marked on the format. Include a list of forthcoming gigs. Fiction listen to everything they receive but cannot respond to everyone. If they are interested they will be in touch. You are advised to check the website before submitting any material to get an idea of Fiction's preferred style.

Fiddler Crab Music
Ipswich
email: info@fiddlercrabmusic.co.uk
web: www.fiddlercrabmusic.co.uk
contact: Sam Clodd
genre: All Music Types Accepted
info: Fiddler Crab are interested in all styles of music, although it must be original. Mainly interested in acts based in the East and South East of England. Email for details of demo submission address. Fiddler Crab Music also promote unsigned gigs from all over the country. See listing in relevant section for details.

Fierce Panda
PO Box 21441, London, N7 6WZ
tel: 020 7609 2789
email: mrbongopanda@aol.com
web: www.fiercepanda.co.uk
contact: Simon Williams
genre: All Music Types Accepted
info: No more than 3 tracks (ideally 2) on CD or cassette from bands and acts with previous or forthcoming London gigs. Include full track listing, biog and contact details. Fierce Panda listen to all submissions but cannot guarantee a reply to every one.

Filter Records
76 Brewer Street, London, W1F 9TX
tel: 020 7287 1689
fax: 020 7287 1684
email: ollie@dorado.net
web: www.dorado.net.
contact: Ollie Buckwell
genre: Breakbeat/House
info: The more DJ and Electronic orientated side of Dorado Records. See Dorado listing for more information.

Filthy Little Angels
7 Howgill Close, Nelson, BB9 0SX
tel: 07866 107 682
email: info@filthylittleangels.com
web: www.filthylittleangels.com
contact: Woon
genre: Alternative Guitar Based/Electronic/Punk/Alternative Electronic
info: Submit demo and biog to the above address. All formats accepted.

Firefly Recordings
PO Box 30179, London, E17 5FE
tel: 07720 64 4204
email: info@fireflyrecordings.com
web: www.fireflyrecordings.com
contact: Chris Evans
genre: Hardcore/Alt. Country/Twisted folk/Punk/Emo
info: Firefly Records observe a strict no Ska policy. Send demos to the address above.

First Time Records
Sovereign House, 12 Trewartha Road, Praa Sands, Penzance, Cornwall, TR20 9ST
tel: 01736 762 826
fax: 01736 763 328
email: panamus@aol.com
web: www.panamamusic.co.uk
contact: Roderick Jones
genre: All Music Types Accepted
info: Send a demo to the address above. First Time Records, as a development label, specialises in working with new bands and musicians. Part of the Panama Music Group.

First Word Records
PO Box 592, Leeds, LS5 3WS
tel: 0113 275 4793
email: info@firstwordrecords.co.uk
web: www.firstwordrecords.com
contact: Aly, Andy
genre: Hip-Hop/Jazz/Breaks
info: Send demo on CD and biog to the address above. If you would like your CD returned please enclose a SAE.

Firstlove Musik
15 Graham Avenue, Mitcham, Surrey, CR4 2HJ
tel: 07963 569 788
email: self_taught2000@hotmail.com
genre: R&B/Neo-Soul/Hip-Hop
info: Send demo (on CD or cassette) to the address above, along with a biog and any other relevant information.

Flash Point Records
167 Adamshill Road, Sydenham, SE26 4AZ
web: www.flashpointrecords.co.uk
contact: Jupe, Marc
genre: Hard House
info: Send demos on CD to the address above.

Folksound Records
250 Earlson Avenue North, Coventry, CV5 6GX
tel: 02476 711 935
email: rootsrecs@btclick.com
contact: Graham Bradshaw
genre: Folk
info: Call Folksound Records to introduce yourself and your music. Follow with demo on request.

For Us Records
130 Talbot Road, London, W11 1JA
tel: 020 7229 8541
fax: 020 7221 1146
email: backroom@roughtrade.com
web: www.roughtrade.com
contact: Billy
genre: All Music Types Accepted
info: For Us Records is the Rough Trade record shop's in-house label. They release one-off singles on 7" vinyl, and albums that have either not been released on vinyl, or are new acts or generally interesting projects. Most of the releases are likely to be limited to 500-1500. Send 1 track on CD to the address above. Releases are stocked in the Rough Trade shops, as well being distributed by Cargo. For more information about the record shops, see the above website.

Forecast Records
3rd Floor, 24-26 Lever Street, Manchester, M1 1DZ
tel: 0161 234 6812
email: info@forecastrecords.co.uk
web: www.forecastrecords.co.uk
contact: Ben Holden
info: Forecast are looking for the most original and dynamic music from all genres with a preference towards exhilarating contemporary Indie and heartfelt acoustica. Everything is listened to and feedback guaranteed. Send tracks on CD along with biog to address above, or email music files (no more than 2) to demos@forecastrecords.co.uk.

Fortune & Glory
Osmond House, 78 Alcester Road, Moseley, Birmingham, B13 8BB
tel: 0121 256 1310
fax: 0121 256 1318
email: hendricks@fortuneandglory.co.uk
web: www.fortuneandglory.co.uk
contact: Hendricks
genre: Alternative/Indie Guitar Music/Rock

Fox Records
62 Lakerise, Romford, Essex, RM1 4EE
tel: 01708 760 544
fax: 01708 760 563
email: foxrecords@talk21.com
web: www.foxrecordsltd.co.uk
contact: Colin Brewer, Linda Ryle
genre: Rock/R&B/Pop/Dance
info: Send demo, biog and photo to the address above. The label is interested in music with chart and commercial potential. See also Management Company listings.

Freakaboom
PO Box 21545, London, E10 5FX
email: info@freakaboom.com
web: www.freakaboom.com
contact: Justin Owen
genre: Breakbeat
info: Producers, artists and DJs can submit demos to the address above.

Freedag Records
39 Palmerson Place, Edinburgh, EH12 5AU
tel: 0131 202 6236
fax: 0131 202 6238
email: talent@freedagmusicgroup.com
contact: David Murray
genre: Alternative/Indie/Acoustic
info: Indie record label rapidly expanding in to other areas. Promise to listen to all demos sent in by post to the above address or via email on MP3. 5 tracks maximum. Also include a biog and a photo. Full UK coverage.

Freerange Records
PO Box 52106, London, E9 7WX
tel: 020 8533 8100
email: info@freerangerecords.co.uk
web: www.freerangerecords.co.uk
contact: Jamie Odell
genre: Funky House/Electronic/House
info: Interested in most types of Electronic house based funk music although it must be original. Send demos to the address above.

Fresh Records/Freskanova
PO Box 4075, Whitchurch on Thames, Reading, RG8 7FU
tel: 0118 984 3468
fax: 0118 984 3463
email: vicki@freshmusic.co.uk
web: www.freshmusic.co.uk
contact: Vicky Aspinall
genre: All Music Types Accepted

Full Cycle Records
Unit 23, Easton Business Centre, Felix Road, Bristol, BS5 0HE
tel: 0117 941 5824
fax: 0117 941 5823
email: info@fullcycle.co.uk
web: www.fullcycle.co.uk
contact: Gerard
genre: Drum&Bass
info: Send demos on CD to the address above.

Full Time Hobby
3rd Floor, 1a Adpar Street, London, W2 1DE
tel: 020 7535 6739
fax: 020 7563 7283
email: info@fulltimehobby.co.uk
web: www.fulltimehobby.co.uk
contact: Chris Baker
genre: All Music Types Accepted
info: Send 3 or 4 track CD demo to the above address. Linked with labels Eat Sleep Records, Hassle Records and Sorepoint Records. See listings for further details.

Fulmination Records
PO Box 2333, Stoke-On-Trent, ST2 9YP
email: submissions@fulminationrecords.co.uk
web: www.fulminationrecords.co.uk
contact: Simon Walklate/A&R Department
genre: Rock/Metal
info: Mainly deal with Rock and Metal bands, however any Alternative genres are accepted. Make initial contact via email. CD demos are preferred. Email biog including a list of past and upcoming live dates. Fulmination Records will reply for more information if they are interested.

Funkee Fish Records
PO Box 145, Stoke Gabriel, Totnes, Devon, TQ9 6ZX
tel: 07814 544 611
email: info@funkeefish.com
web: www.funkeefish.com
contact: Jenny
genre: Instrumental/Jazz/Fusion/Acoustic/Folk/Singer-Songwriter
info: Funkee Fish is an independent label that specialises in Acoustic, Folk, Singer-Songwriter, Instrumental, Jazz and Fusion, but they are open to all genres. The aim of the label is to give musicians the freedom to write and record quality emotive music, not to mould them into a money making product. Email before submitting any material. Every demo is listened to and the label guarantee a response. Funkee Fish also have their own 24 track recording studio with experienced in-house engineers and session musicians. See listing in relevant section for details.

Fusetrax
33 Lockes Yard, 4 Great Marlborough Street, Manchester, M1 5AL
email: info@fusetrax.co.uk
web: www.fusetrax.co.uk
contact: Chris Newbold
genre: Breakbeat
info: Fusetrax deal mainly in the field of Breakbeat (mostly bass heavy Nu-Skool with oodles of dirty Funk!), although they are fundamentally quite eclectic. Send a demo on CD to the address above. For more information on Fusetrax's successful club night, Fuse, see the website above.

Fusion Records
9 Telford Walk, Off Ayers Road, Old Trafford, Manchester, M16 3AN
tel: 07867 616 178
email: overyonder3@msn.com
contact: Trevor Orr
genre: Jungle/Commercial Reggae/Soul
info: Send demos to Fusion.

Futureproof Records
PO Box 31631, London, W11 1UA
tel: 020 7792 8597
fax: 020 7221 3694
email: info@futureproofrecords.com
web: www.futureproofrecords.com
contact: Phil, Murrey
genre: Hip-Hop/Dance/Electronica/Urban/R&B/Soul
info: Send demos on CD or vinyl to the address above. The label advises you to check their website before submitting any material.

Gargleblast Records
8 Dornoch Court, Bellshill, Lanarkshire, ML4 1HN
tel: 01689 842 899
email: info@gargleblastrecords.com
web: www.gargleblastrecords.com
contact: Shaun Tallamy
genre: All Music Types Accepted
info: Gargleblast are currently looking for new artists for their roster and welcome demos of every musical style, from anywhere in the country. Demos accepted on CD, MP3 and vinyl formats. Send to the above addresses with copy of biog.

Ghost Town Records
31 Glenfield Road, Nelson, Lancashire, BB9 8AP
tel: 01282 616 861
email: info@ghosttownrecords.co.uk
web: www.ghosttownrecords.co.uk
contact: Joanne St. Clair
genre: Urban Folk
info: Ghost Town do not accept unsolicited demos. Make initial contact using the above email address.

Glasswerk Records
38b Ventnor Road, Wavertree, Liverpool, L15 4JF
tel: 0151 707 9044
email: ar@glasswerk.co.uk
web: www.glasswerk.co.uk
contact: Mat Ong
genre: All Music Types Accepted
info: Independent specialist single releases and compilation albums from upcoming artists. All genres. Demos on CD only with press pack, biography and gig dates.

Glitch Records
Nottingham
email: alexandercalver@hotmail.com
contact: Alex Calver
genre: Hard Dance/Techno
info: Email Glitch Records to introduce yourself and your music. Follow with demo on request.

Glitterhouse Records
123c Cadogan Terrace, Victoria Park, London, E9 5HP
email: tris@glitterhouserecords.co.uk
web: www.glitterhouserecords.co.uk
contact: Tris Dickin
genre: Electronica/Future Sound/Alt. Country/Dub
info: Send demo on CD and biog to the address above. Make sure to write your contact details on the actual disc.

Global Warming
PO Box 5192, Hatfield Peverel, Chelmsford, Essex, CM3 2QH
web: www.globalwarmingrecords.com
contact: Trevor
genre: All Music Types Accepted
info: Send demo on CD to the address above. Follow with an email a few weeks after submission.

God Made Me Hardcore
Studio 200, Cable Street Studios, 566 Cable Street, London, E1W 3HB
email: info@iamhardcore.biz
contact: Andy
genre: Electronic Dance Music
info: Send an email to the address above to introduce yourself and your music. Follow with demo on request. No MP3s please.

Golf Records
PO Box 6, Wallingford, Oxfordshire, OX10 9DA
tel: 01491 825 029
fax: 01491 826 320
email: info@plastichead.com
web: www.golfrecords.co.uk
genre: Metal/Punk/Hardcore
info: Send demos on CD to the address above, include biog, photo and contact details. Mark FAO A&R. Golf Records is home to, amongst others, Less Than Jake.

Gotham Records
PO Box 6003, Birmingham, B45 0AR
tel: 0121 477 9553
fax: 0121 693 2954
email: barry@barrytomes.com
web: www.gotham-records.com
contact: Barry Tomes
genre: Reggae/Pop/Dance/Rock
info: Send finished masters to the address above. Mark the envelope 'Requested Material.'

Grand Central Records
10 Stephen Mews, London, W1T 1AG
email: ali@grandcentralrecords.com
web: www.grandcentralrecords.com
contact: Alastair Little
genre: Beats/Folk/Dancehall/Ragga/Hip-Hop/Soul/Electronica
info: Send CD only, include biog, press and photos if possible.

Greentrax Recordings
Cockenzie Business Centre, Edinburgh Road, Cockenzie, East Lothian, EH32 0XL
tel: 01875 814 155
fax: 01875 813 545
email: greentrax@aol.com
web: www.greentrax.com
contact: Ian Green
genre: Scottish Traditional

Groovin' Records
PO Box 39, Hoylake, CH47 2HP
tel: 0151 632 6156
email: groovin.records@virgin.net
web: www.groovinrecords.co.uk
contact: Al
genre: Rhythm & Blues/Folk/Blues/Funk/Soul
info: Email Groovin' Records to introduce yourself and your material. Be as specific as you can about the type of music you play.

Gut Records
Byron House, 112a Shirland Road, Maida Vale, London, W9 2EQ
tel: 020 7266 0777
fax: 020 7266 7734
email: paul@gutrecords.com
web: www.gutrecords.com
contact: Paul Martin, Lucy
genre: All Music Types Accepted
info: Submit demos on CD to the address above.

Hackpen Records Ltd.
PO Box 1746, Andover, SP10 1BA
email: info@hackpenrecords.com
web: www.hackpenrecords.com
contact: Steve Crabtree
genre: All Music Types Accepted
info: Send demos to the address above.

Halo Records UK Ltd.
88 Church Lane, East Finchley, London, N2 0TB
tel: 020 8444 0049
fax: 020 8883 5453
email: info@halo-uk.net
web: www.halo-uk.net
contact: Jo
genre: All Music Types Accepted
info: Send demos with biography and photo to address above. All genres considered but Halo mainly deal with Rock bands.

Handspun Records
45 Pembridge Road, London, W11 3HG
tel: 020 7792 2523
email: anthony@haveaniceday.net
contact: Anthony Cooper
genre: Upbeat Ambient Grooves
info: Tracks will be selected for inclusion on compilation CDs that will be sold via fashion retailers. Send demos on CD to the address above.

Happy Face Records
The Old Smithy, Post Office Lane, Kempsey, Worcestershire, WR5 3NS
tel: 01905 820 659
fax: 01905 820 015
email: studio@oldsmithy.com
web: www.oldsmithy.com
contact: Janet Allsopp
genre: All Music Types Accepted

Harbour Town Records
PO Box 25, Ulverston, Cumbria, LA12 7UN
tel: 01229 588 290
fax: 01229 588 290
email: records@hartown.demon.co.uk
web: www.harbourtownrecords.com
contact: Gordon Jones
genre: Traditional/Singer-Songwriter/Acoustic/Roots/Folk
info: Send demo, biog and any other relevant information to the address above. CD duplication facilities.

Harmonia Mundi UK Ltd.
45 Vyner Street, London, E2 9DQ
tel: 020 8709 9509
fax: 020 8709 9501
email: info.uk@harmoniamundi.com
web: www.harmoniamundi.com
contact: Ian Fenton
genre: Classical/World/Jazz

Hassle Records
3rd Floor, 1a Adpar Street, London, W2 1DE
tel: 020 7535 6739
fax: 020 7563 7283
email: info@hasslerecords.com
web: www.hasslerecords.com
genre: Garage Rock/Punk/Metal
info: Current roster includes Juliette and The Licks. Send 3 or 4 track demo to the above address. Linked with other labels Sorepoint Records, Eat Sleep Records and Full Time Hobby. See listings for further details.

Haven Records
St Mary's Works, St Mary's Plain, Norwich, Norfolk, NR3 3AF
tel: 01603 626 221
fax: 01603 619 999
email: derek@backsrecords.co.uk
contact: Derek Chapman
genre: Singer-Songwriter
info: Affiliated with Backs Records. See listing for further informaion.

Headhunter Records
Stanley Street Lane, Kinning Park, Glasgow, G41 1EZ
tel: 0141 429 7111
email: info@headhunterrecords.co.uk
web: www.headhunterrecords.co.uk
contact: Andrew
genre: All Music Types Accepted
info: An independent record company based in Glasgow, who cover all aspects of music and video recording, as well as production, duplication and distribution. Also offer 24 hour rehearsal and recording facilities. See listings in relevant sections for details.

Heat Recordings
63 Hartland Road, London, NW6 6BH
tel: 0207 625 5552
email: info@heatrecordings.com
web: www.heatrecordings.com
contact: Alex Payne
genre: Leftfield Dance/House
info: Send demos on CD to the address above. Include email contact details and mark FAO Alex Payne. Heat Recordings is associated with the more Alternative label, Critical Mass Recordings.

Heavenly Recordings
47 Frith Street, London, W1D 4SE
email: info@heavenlyrecordings.com
web: www.heavenly100.com
contact: Spencer Smith
genre: Indie
info: Heavenly's signings include Beth Orton, Doves, Ed Harcourt, The Vines, 22-20s & Nada Surf. Check website or send email regarding current demo policy.

Heavy Metal Records
152 Goldthorn Hill, Penn, Wolverhampton, WV2 3JA
tel: 01902 345 345
fax: 01902 345 155
email: info@heavymetalrecords.co.uk
web: www.heavymetalrecords.co.uk
contact: Paul Birch
genre: Heavy Metal/Punk/Rock
info: Send demos FAO Paul Birch to the above address. Linked with Revolver Records. See listing for further details.

Highblue
13 Lenthall Street, Liverpool, L4 5TN
tel: 0151 222 5262/07740365898
email: management@highblue.co.uk
web: www.highblue.co.uk
contact: D.P. Ryan
genre: All Music Types Accepted
info: Demos can be sent to either the above postal or email address.

Holier Than Thou Records Ltd.
46 Rother Street, Stratford on Avon, Warwickshire, CV37 6LT
tel: 01789 268 661
email: httrecords@aol.com
web: www.holierthanthourecords.com
contact: David Begg
genre: Rock/Alternative
info: Send demos on CD to the address above. Unfortunately, demos cannot be returned but the A&R team aim to respond to all submissions within 5 weeks. Email via the Holier Than Thou website. Holier Than Thou are also involved in management and run a distribution company. See listings in relevant sections for more details.

Honey Records
92 Vauxhall Road, Liverpool, L3 6DL
email: info@honeyrecords.co.uk
web: www.honeyrecords.co.uk
contact: Mat Flynn
genre: All Music Types Accepted
info: Although Honey Records' roster has mainly dealt with Rock and Indie in the past, they are very keen to receive demos of a wide variety of genres. Send demos to the above address with contact information.

Honeypot Records
8a Suddell Road, Darwen, BB3 3HD
tel: 01254 771 658
fax: 01254 771 658
email: natashahoneypot@hotmail.com
contact: Natasha Jones
genre: All Music Types Accepted
info: Send 3 track demo on CD to the above address.

Hope Recordings
Loft 5, The Tobacco Factory, Raleigh Road, Southville, Bristol, BS3 1TF
tel: 0117 953 5566
fax: 0117 953 7733
email: info@hoperecordings.co.uk
web: www.hoperecordings.co.uk
contact: Leon Alexander, Luke Allen
genre: Electronic Dance Music
info: Send demos to the address above. Part of the Hope Music Group. Also run an artist management company, see listing in relevant section for further information.

Hospital Records
182-184 Dartmouth Road, London, SE26 4QZ
tel: 020 8613 0400
fax: 020 8613 0401
email: info@hospitalrecords.com
web: www.hospitalrecords.com
contact: Chris Goss
genre: Drum&Bass
info: Send demo on CD to the address above. Maximum of 3 tracks. Mark FAO A&R. No MP3s please.

Hotshot Records/House of the Blues
29 St. Michael's Road, Leeds, Yorkshire, LS6 3BG
tel: 0113 274 2106
fax: 0113 278 6291
email: dave@bluescat.com
web: www.bluescat.com
contact: Dave Foster
genre: Singer-Songwriter/Blues
info: Contact Dave for details of demo submission. No unsolicited demos.

HOWL Records
Belfast
email: records@howlclub.com
web: www.howlclub.com
contact: Helen, Carol
info: HOWL records was formed in 2003 as a side project to Belfast's HOWL Club. You are advised to check the HOWL website to get an idea of the type of music the label is interested in.

Human Condition Records
120a West Granton Road, Edinburgh, EH5 1PF
tel: 0131 551 6632
fax: 0131 551 6632
email: jamie@humancondition.co.uk
web: www.humancondition.co.uk
contact: Jamie Watson
genre: Guitar Based
info: No Metal, Folk or Dance music, but otherwise fairly open. Also run Chamber Recording Studio in Edinburgh. Visit the website for more information .

Hydrogen Dukebox
89 Borough High Street, London, SE1 1NL
email: info@hydrogendukebox.com
web: www.hydrogendukebox.com
genre: Electronic

Hysteria Records
PO Box 346, Enfield, Middlesex, EN3 5EL
tel: 020 8292 5073
email: info@massmediauk.net
contact: Nicky Price
genre: Dance
info: Send demos on CD. Material cannot be returned.

Iffy Biffa Records
Welland House Farm, Spalding Marsh, Spalding, Lincolnshire, PE12 6HF
tel: 07711 513 791
email: mark@iffybiffa.co.uk
web: www.iffybiffa.co.uk
contact: Mark Bunn
genre: Rock/Indie
info: Send demos to the address above. Iffy Biffa Records aim to provide all artists with a fair recording deal and the optimum promotion of their repertoire, and to create and explore exciting avenues in the industry.

done up to here

Illicit Recordings
2a Southam Street, London, W10 5PH
tel: 020 8960 3253
fax: 020 8968 5111
web: www.illicitrecordings.com
contact: Ian Clifford
genre: Dance/Hip-Hop/Breakbeat
info: Send demo to the address above. Do not follow with phone calls or emails please, Illicit Recordings will contact you if they are interested.

Incentive Music
21 The Grand Union Centre, West Row, London, W10 5AS
tel: 020 8964 2555
email: incentive@incentivemusic.co.uk
web: www.incentivemusic.co.uk
contact: Oliver Newman, Kalvin Ryder
genre: Urban/Dance/Trance/Pop-Trance
info: Send demos on CD to the address above, or submit MP3s via email.

Independiente Ltd.
The Drill Hall, 3 Heathfield Terrace, Chiswick, London, W4 4JE
tel: 020 8747 8111
fax: 020 8747 8113
email: info@independiente.co.uk
web: www.independiente.co.uk
contact: Gerard Philips, Julian Hargreaves
genre: Alternative/Guitar Based
info: Send demos to the address above, ideally with a picture or details of band website.

Inigo Recordings
642 Wandsworth Road, London, SW8 3JW
email: info@inigorecordings.com
web: www.inigorecordings.com
contact: Alex
genre: Funky House/Electro/Breakbeat
info: Send demos to the above address. Inigo also run recording studios and a bar with live music from DJs and bands. See entries in relevant sections for further details.

Innocent
Crown House, 72 Hammersmith Road, London, W14 8UD
tel: 020 7605 5000
fax: 020 8968 6533
email: innocent@vmg.co.uk
web: www.the-raft.com
contact: Joe Kentish
genre: Pop
info: Call Innocent and speak to anyone in the A&R Department. Follow with demo on request.

Inspirition
3 Coles Lane, Chewton Mendip, BA3 4NF
tel: 01761 241 243/0779 656 2811
email: inspirition.music@virgin.net
web: www.in-spirit-i-on.gmxhome.de
contact: Isabel
genre: Alternative/Rock/Jazz
info: Record company and music education. Trains children and adults in musicality and performance. Telephone Isabel for more details.

Instant Hit
PO Box 34, Ventnor, PO38 2YR
tel: 01983 857 079
genre: All Music Types Accepted
info: Contact by telephone before sending any material. Instant Hit only work with local artists.

In-Tec Records
Reverb House, Bennett Street, London, W4 2AH
tel: 020 8742 7693
fax: 020 8994 8617
email: intec@intecrecords.com
web: www.intecrecords.com
contact: Mark
genre: Techno/House
info: Intec Records was launched in 1999 by Carl Cox and DJ C1. Send demos on CD, maximum of 5 tracks, to the address above. Mark FAO A&R Department.

Integral Records
Top Floor, 65 Dalmally Street, Glasgow, G20 6RN
tel: 0141 945 1734
email: pomeg@icqmail.com
web: www.pomeg.co.uk
genre: Experimental/Electro-Folk/Indie/Electronica/Acoustic
info: The label is interested in many styles of music, mainly left of the mainstream. Home to Pomegranate.

Integrity Records Ltd.
40 Mill Street, Bedford, Bedfordshire, MK40 3HD
tel: 01234 267 459
fax: 01234 212 864
email: nick@integrityrecords.co.uk
web: www.integrityrecords.co.uk
contact: Nick Tarbitt
genre: All Music Types Accepted
info: Send demos on CD or cassette to Nick at the address above. Maximum of 4 tracks. If you would like your material returned, include SAE. Integrity guarantee to listen and respond to all demos.

Invicta Hi-Fi
5th Floor, Gostins Building, 32-36 Hanover Street, Liverpool, L1 4LN
tel: 0151 709 5264
email: admin@invictahifi.co.uk
web: www.invictahifi.co.uk
contact: A&R,
genre: Band Based Music
info: Invicta is an underground Pop label, specialising mainly in Electronica. Send 3 track demos on any format (but preferably CD) with picture and biog to the address above.

IRL (Independent Records Ltd.)
PO Box 30884, London, W12 9AX
tel: 020 8746 7461
fax: 020 8749 7441
email: info@independentrecordsltd.com
web: www.independentrecordsltd.com
contact: Tom Haxell
genre: All Music Types Accepted
info: Send demos to the address above.

Iron Man Records
PO Box 9121, Birmingham, B13 8AU
tel: 0871 226 0910
email: via website
web: www.ironmanrecords.co.uk
contact: Mark Badger
info: Iron Man Records is an independent record label. Iron Man Records also operates as a live music promoter under the name Badger Promotions. Iron Man Records/Badger Promotions put together and maintain a scene report for Birmingham and the surrounding area documenting everything to do with the current Birmingham music scene. Iron Man Records runs a small internet based mail order distribution service to help make available and promote new music. Send SAE for a list. The Iron Man Records/Badger Promotions website aims to provide a resource base for local bands and anyone else outside Birmingham. The site collates useful addresses, links, fanzine lists, venue contact details and information on releasing your own records.

Irritant Records
North London
email: traffic@irritantrecords.com
web: www.irritantrecords.com
contact: Andy
genre: Electronic
info: Irritant Records is interested in hearing any kind of twisted Electronic music. The current mailing address for demo submissions is available from the website. Sub-label Secret Weapon deals with all types of Hardcore, Gabba and Rave.

ISHQ Records
PO Box 6992, Birmingham, B9 5FS
tel: 0121 773 8807
fax: 0121 766 7780
email: info@ishqrecords.com
web: www.ishqrecords.com or www.ballysagoo.com
contact: Sita Pall
genre: Indian
info: ISHQ Records is interested in releasing Indian Music with a Western crossover. Send demos to the address above, include a brief covering letter and a short biog (no longer than an A4 sheet please). Include contact details other than a telephone number, and make sure your details are written clearly on the actual demo. Singers, MCs and rappers can submit home recordings, but DJs and producers are expected to submit high quality recordings on CD. If you are worried about protecting your work, send a 1 minute piece of no more than 3 tracks. It can take up to 14 days to confirm receipt of your demo. Thereafter ISHQ Records will respond within 8 weeks. If the label have not contacted you after this time, please contact them by email, letter or fax.

Island Records
364-366 Kensington High Street, Hammersmith, London, W14 8NS
tel: 020 7471 5300
fax: 020 8748 1998
web: www.islandrecords.co.uk
genre: All Music Types Accepted
info: Send demos on CD to the address above, mark FAO A&R Manager. Island Records is part of the Universal Music group of companies. No unsolicited materials.

Isobar Records
56 Gloucester Place, London, W1U 8HJ
tel: 020 7486 3297
fax: 020 7486 3297
email: info@isobarrecords.com
web: www.isobarrecords.com
contact: Peter Morris
genre: Trance/Dance
info: Remixers and vocalists should send demos on CD to the address above.

Issue Records
PO Box 25821, London, N5 2ZA
tel: 07951 707 149
email: leroy@issue-records.co.uk
web: www.issue-records.co.uk
contact: Leroy Goodey
genre: Dance
info: Send demo to the above address. Deal with Rock/Dance music in the style of The Prodigy and Leftfield.

ITN Corporation
PO Box 1795, Sheffield, S3 7FF
tel: 0114 272 8726
email: itn@itncorp.demon.co.uk
web: www.inthenursery.com
contact: Nigel Humberstone
genre: Soundtracks
info: No unsolicited demos. Call or email first before submitting any material.

It's Time
London
tel: 07881 650 883
email: nick@itstimerecords.co.uk
web: www.itstime.co.uk
contact: Nick Elliot
genre: Alternative/Singer-Songwriter/Acoustic
info: It's Time is about real musicians and songwriters, those who have something to say and want to retain some control over how they say it and when. Dedicated to improving artists and music. Music development and management. Nick is also a music photographer, see relevant section.

Jackstar Recordings
Top Floor, 195 High Street, Penge, London, SE20 7PF
tel: 07789 204 776
email: jackstar80@hotmail.com
web: www.jackstar-recordings.com
contact: Paul Langley
genre: Hard Techno
info: Send demos on CD to the address above. Include at least 4 tracks and a biog.

Jam Today Records
61 Springfield Way, Cranfield, Bedford, MK43 0JN
tel: 01234 757 784/07717 670 141
email: jamtodayrecords@aol.com
contact: Keni Stevens
genre: Hip-Hop/Urban/Soul/R&B
info: Jam Today guarantee to listen to all demos received. Send FAO Keni Stevens to the address above. Enclose SAE if you require any items returned. Jam Today also provide a consultancy service offering advice about aspects of the music business such as contracts and royalty payments. Contact for further information.

Joesoap Records Ltd.
Kilmeny, 31 Bennochy Road, Kirkcaldy, Fife, KY2 5QY
tel: 01592 564 670/07739 553 097
email: info@joesoaprecords.co.uk
web: www.joesoaprecords.co.uk
contact: Paul Finnie
genre: Guitar Based/Mainstream
info: Send demo to the above address.

Joof
PO Box 4032, Worthing, West Sussex, BN13 3WE
email: label@joof.uk.com
web: www.joof.uk.com
contact: Glenn Mack
genre: Trance
info: Joof deals exclusively with Trance artists. Send demos to the above address.

RECORD COMPANIES

JSNTGM (Just Say No to Government Music)
PO Box 1025, Blackpool, FY3 0EB
email:	andy@jsntgm.com
web:	www.jsntgm.com
contact:	Andy Higgins
genre:	Alternative/Indie/Punk
info:	Small, hard-working label has been in existence since

the early 90s, working with different bands (Hooton 3 Car, Four Letter Word, Erase Today, Travis Cut, SICK56, Dina, Z/28) and musicians, setting up gigs, writing fanzines and releasing vinyl, cassettes and CDs. JSNTGM write the 'Blackpool Rox II' fanzine, in which all demos they receive get reviewed. Currently organising music, art and political activities as part of the Arts Council funded 'Ugly Truth About Blackpool' project.

JUDmusic Records
48 Brynnffynnon Road, Y-Felinheli, LL56 4SJ
tel:	01248 671 663
email:	george@stiwdioeglwys.fsnet.co.uk
web:	www.stiwdioeglwys.co.uk
genre:	R&B/Urban/Hip-Hop/Drum&Bass
info:	Send demos to the address above. Please ensure that

the recording is of the best possible quality. Also run a Welsh language label, Recordiau Menai Records, a publishing company (JUDmusic Publishing) and a production studio (Stiwdio Eglwys). See relevant sections for more information.

Jump Records
Unit 2, Briar Rhydding, Baildon, West Yorkshire, BD17 7JW
tel:	01274 596 547/07976 201 847
email:	banksy@jumprecords.com
web:	www.jumprecords.com
contact:	A&R
genre:	All Music Types Accepted
info:	Jump Records for various ways to promote your music.

Free and fee web promotion options. Also run recording and rehearsal studios. See separate entries for details.

Just Music
PO Box 19780, London, SW15 1WU
tel:	020 8741 6020
fax:	020 8741 8362
email:	justmusic@justmusic.co.uk
web:	www.justmusic.co.uk
contact:	A&R
genre:	Ambient/Electronica/Acoustic
info:	The label's output is largely, but not exclusively,

instrumental. Send demos on CD to the address above. You are advised to visit the Just Music website before submitting any material. Demos should be addressed to A&R.

Kahvi
email:	nik@kahvi.org
web:	www.kahvi.org
contact:	Nik/A&R
genre:	Relaxing/Experimental/IDM (Intelligent Dance Music)/
	Ambient/Chillout
info:	Kahvi is run entirely online. See website for further

information.

Kickin' Music Ltd.
Unit 8, Acklam Workshops, 10 Acklam Road, London, W10 5QZ
tel:	020 8964 3300
fax:	020 8964 4400
email:	info@kickinmusic.com
web:	www.kickinmusic.com
contact:	Christian Larsson
genre:	Dance/Reggae/Rock
info:	Kickin' Music is an umbrella organisation for a number

of labels representing different Dance music genres. Kickin' Records (House), Slip 'n' Slide (House), Slip 'n' Slide Blue (Chilled House), Stoned Asia (Asian/Chillout/Downbeat) and Hardleaders (Drum&Bass). Send demos on CD to the address above. See also Haripa Music Publishing.

Killin Time Records
PO Box 121, Stevenage, Hertfordshire, SG2 8XG
tel:	01438 232 195
email:	mark@killintimerecords.co.uk or
	keith@killintimerecords.co.uk
web:	www.killintime.co.uk
contact:	Mark Sutton, Keith Bryant
genre:	Neo-Folk/New Metal/Progressive Metal/Thrash Metal/
	Metal
info:	Send demos to the address above. Include biog and

photo.

Kinetix
Spire-Ark, West Clayton, Chorley Wood, Hertfordshire, WD3 5EX
tel:	01923 285 281
fax:	01923 285 286
email:	info@kinetex.org
web:	www.kinetix.org
contact:	Jon Sharp
genre:	All Genres Of Dance Music

Kinsella Music
68 Schools Hill, Cheadle, Cheshire, SK8 1JD
email:	kevkinsella@aol.com
contact:	Kev Kinsella
genre:	All Music Types Accepted
info:	Everything except Country&Western, but mainly Dance

music at the moment. Send demos to the address above. Contact Kev Kinsella with queries.

Kitchenware Records
7 The Stables, St. Thomas' Street, Newcastle-upon-Tyne, NE1 4LE
tel:	0191 230 1970
fax:	0191 232 0262
email:	info@kitchenwarerecords.com
web:	www.kitchenwarerecords.com
contact:	Nicki Turner
genre:	All Music Types Accepted
info:	Artists/bands should send a package of 2 or 3 songs,

photo & biog to Nicki Turner at the Kitchenware address. Associated with Kitchenware Management.

Klone Records
15 Falcon Road, Tempo House, London, SW11 2PJ
tel:	020 7228 6821
fax:	020 7228 6972
email:	post@klonerecords.com
web:	www.klonerecords.com
contact:	Anne Plaxton
genre:	NRG Pop
info:	Send demos to the address above. Include as much

information as possible, including a photo.

Koolworld Records
PO Box 884, Luton, Bedfordshire, LU2 7ZX
tel:	01582 734 001
email:	info@koolworld.co.uk
web:	www.koolworld.co.uk
contact:	Dave Wooster
genre:	Dance
info:	Contact by telephone, post or email. Demos must be in

CD format.

Kubist Records
PO Box 34150, London, NW10 5DS
tel:	01273 727 400
web:	www.kubist.co.uk
contact:	Ben, Chris
genre:	Progressive House/Breakbeat
info:	Send demos on CD to the address above, or email MP3s

to either Chris or Ben.

Kudos Records Ltd.
77 Fortress Road, London, NW5 1AG
tel:	020 7482 4555
fax:	020 7482 4551
email:	info@kudosrecords.co.uk
web:	www.kudosrecords.co.uk
contact:	Rosie Frao
genre:	Techno/House/Leftfield/Jazz/Hip-Hop
info:	Deals with most independent music. Kudos is primarily

a distributor, acts and labels can submit material to Rosie Frao at the address above.

Last Breath Records
35a Miller Street, Inverness, IV2 3DN
tel:	01463 718 681
email:	sharkrmack@hotmail.com
web:	www.lastbreathrecords.co.uk
contact:	Ross Mackay
genre:	Hip-Hop/Rap
info:	Send demos FAO Ross Mackay to the above address.

Lazy Mist Recordings
PO Box 16235, Glasgow, G13 3YQ
tel:	07947 382 960
email:	lazymist@rowanarts.co.uk
web:	www.rowanarts.co.uk
contact:	Keith Johnston
genre:	Pop/Rock
info:	Branching out from Traditional based releases to more

contemporary music. Want to hear from as many bands all over the country as possible. Email or post tracks to the addresses above.

Leaf Recordings
Suite 216, Bon Marche Building, 241 Fearndale Road, London, SW9 8BJ
tel:	020 7733 1818
fax:	020 7733 5818
email:	leaf@posteverything.com
web:	www.theleaflabel.com
contact:	Tony Morley
info:	Not dedicated to any particular genre, but do release

Experimental music. Send demos to the address above.

Lewis Recordings
PO Box 37163, London, E4 7WR
tel: 020 8523 9578
email: info@lewisrecordings.com
web: www.lewisrecordings.com
contact: Mike Lewis
genre: Hip-Hop
info: Lewis Recordings deal mainly with Hip-Hop but the company have signed a Japanese Electronic group. Send demos on CD to the address above, mark FAO Mike Lewis.

Line Out Records
98 Aldebury Road, Maidenhead, Berkshire, SL6 7HE
tel: 01628 627 289
email: bob@lineoutrecords.com
web: www.lineoutrecords.com
contact: Bob Barker
genre: Synthpop/Electronic Braindance/ IDM (Intelligent Dance Music)/Darkwave/Industrial
info: Line Out encourages all the musicians involved to work with each other on group projects as much as their solo work and as a label are very live focused. The best way to get in contact is to attend one of Line Out's gigs - details of which details on the website. Alternatively, send a demo to the address above, including a covering letter and biog.

Linn Records Recording Services
Glasgow Road, Waterfoot, G76 0EQ
tel: 0141 303 5029
fax: 0141 303 5007
email: records@linn.co.uk
web: www.linnrecords.com
contact: A&R
genre: Classical/Jazz/Folk

Lo Recordings
2b Swanfield Street, London, E2 7DS
tel: 0207 613 1813
email: info@hub100.com
web: www.lorecordings.com
contact: Jon Tye
genre: Electronica
info: Lo Recordings is interested in all genres of Electronica. Send demos on CD to the address above, or electronically on MP3.

Loca Records
PO Box 233, Brighton, BN2 3FD
tel: 07904 184 203
email: info@locarecords.com
web: www.locarecords.com
contact: David, Marcus
genre: Electronic/Post Rock
info: Loca Records only accept demos on CD sent to the address above. Include contact details, biog and any other relevant information. The label will contact you if they are interested. You are advised to check the Loca Records website downloads before submitting any material. No MP3s via email please.

Lockjaw Records
1 Oaklands, Cradley, Malvern, WR13 5LA
tel: 01886 880 035
fax: 01886 880 135
email: info@lockjawrecords.co.uk
web: www.lockjawrecords.co.uk
contact: Jack Turner, Sam Turner
genre: Leftfield/Alternative Rock/Punk Rock/Emo
info: Send demos to the address above. No sound files via email please.

Locomoto Recordings
Thames Works, Church Street, Chiswick, London, W4 2PE
tel: 0208 994 0711
fax: 0208 995 6609
contact: Pete Armitage
genre: Blues/Rhythm & Blues/Rock
info: Call Locomoto Recordings to introduce yourself and your music, follow with demo on request.

Long Lost Brother Records
43 Mountfield Road, London, NW4 4SS
tel: 020 8342 8400
email: info@longlostbrother.co.uk
web: www.longlostbrother.co.uk
contact: Kevin Simpsons
genre: All Music Types Accepted
info: Send demos on CD to the address above.

Loose Music
Unit 205, 5/10 Eastman Road, London, W3 7YG
tel: 0208 749 9330
fax: 0208 749 2230
email: info@loosemusic.com
web: www.loosemusic.com
contact: Tom Bridgewater
genre: Guitar Based/Americana
info: No unsolicited submissions please. Email Loose Music to introduce yourself and your music, follow with demos on request. Absolutely no MP3s via email.

Lost Dog Recordings
PO Box 7534, Glasgow, G42 AY
email: info@lostdogrecordings.com
web: www.lostdogrecordings.com
contact: Jonathon Stone
genre: Electronica/Leftfield/Electro-Rock
info: Send a demo on CD to the address above, follow with an email two weeks later. It is recommended that you listen to music on the website before submitting material. No MP3s via email please. All demos received will have an entry (with comments) on the Lost Dog Recordings website. No pub Rock!!

Lumenessence
PO Box 11, Brighton, BN2 9ZS
tel: 01273 690 149
fax: 01273 690 149
email: people@lumenessence.co.uk
web: www.lumenessence.co.uk
contact: Mark Williams
genre: All Music Types Accepted
info: Call or email Lumenessencee, follow with demo. The label are interested in hearing from vocalists, producers, DJs and acts doing something a little different.

Lush Blush
21 Beechfield Road Longsight Industrial Estate, Bury, Manchester, BL9 9QT
tel: 07974750152
email: andy@testa-rossa.com
web: www.testa-rossa.com
contact: Andy Rossa
genre: Commercial Dance
info: Send a demo on CD to the address above

Majic Music
PO Box 66, Manchester, M12 4XJ
tel: 0161 225 9991
fax: 0161 225 9991
email: info@sirenstorm.com
web: www.sirenstorm.com
contact: Mike Coppock
genre: Dance/Folk/Eurasian Fusion
info: Send demos on CD to the address above. Majic Music also offer a web design service, contact the label for more information.

Mantis Recordings
PO Box 6244, Derby, DE1 1YA
tel: 01332 371 782
email: info@mantis-recordings.com
web: www.mantis-recordings.com
contact: Andy Mantis
genre: Experimental/House/Hip-Hop/Electronic
info: Email Mantis Recordings in advance of sending any material. Also offer music consultancy services, contact for further information.

RECORD COMPANIES

Many Moods - The Record Company
PO Box 1245, Bradford, BD12 0WY
tel: 0870 068 9404/07761 337 620
email: andy@manymoods.co.uk
web: www.manymoods.co.uk/records
contact: Andy Taylor
genre: All Music Types Accepted
info: Many Moods label was formed as a natural progression from the production company. Demos should be sent to the address above marked FAO Andy, or alternatively email with links to artist's website.

Matador Records
PO Box 20125, London, W10 5WA
tel: 020 8969 5533
fax: 020 8969 6633
email: mike@matadorrecords.com
web: www.matadorrecords.com
contact: Mike
genre: All Music Types Accepted
info: Contact via email before sending demo.

Matchbox Recordings Ltd.
33 Bath Street, Abingdon, Oxfordshire, OX14 3RH
tel: 01235 559 800
email: info@matchboxrecordings.co.uk
web: www.matchboxrecordings.co.uk
contact: Dale Olivier
genre: Indie/Pop/Rock
info: Specialise in releasing new music compilations, EPs, singles and albums featuring new Indie bands and artists. Also operate an internet radio station, Matchbox Radio 24, which is accessible through the Matchbox Recordings website. UK Discs, in association with Matchbox Radio 24, provide a CD and inlay artwork duplication service and free radio advertising for unsigned bands, as well as offering manufacture at special rates for unsigned bands. See entry in relevant section for further details.

Mate Recordings International
PO Box 106, Manchester, M32 8RG
tel: 0161 611 8062
email: info@materecordings.com
web: www.materecordings.com
contact: Andy Woods
genre: Northern Disco/Electronic Pop/Avant Garde Electronica
info: Mate Recordings is a record label based both in Manchester and Helsinki, celebrating irregular and international underground modern movements in music and electronic arts. Send demos on CD to the address above, include a short biog.

MCI
33 Foley Street, London, W1W 7TL
tel: 020 7612 3000
fax: 020 7612 3301
email: adrian.sear@demonmusicgroup.co.uk
contact: Adrian Sear
genre: Non-commercial

Mekong Delta
Demos, 17 Trevethick Street, Gateshead, Tyne & Wear, NE8 4XP
email: info@mekongdelta.co.uk
web: www.mekongdelta.co.uk
contact: Matt Young
genre: Ambient/Post-Rock/Lo-Fi/Electronica
info: Website has jukebox of the best music released to date. Initial contact should be made via email. If Mekong Delta are interested in receiving a demo, they will reply.

Memnon Entertainment Ltd.
3rd Floor, Habib House, 9 Stevenson Square, Manchester, M1 1DB
tel: 0161 238 8516
fax: 0161 236 6717
email: memnon@btconnect.com
web: www.memnonentertainment.com
contact: Rudi Kidd
genre: Soul/Garage/Urban/Hip-Hop/Jazz/R&B

Memphis Industries Ltd.
8 Ripplevale Grove, London, N1 1HU
tel: 020 7607 2610
fax: 020 7619 0477
email: matt@memphis-industries.com
web: www.memphis-industries.com
contact: Matt Jacob, Ollie Jacob
genre: All Music Types Accepted
info: Send demos on CD to the address above, maximum of 4 tracks. Include brief biog. All submissions are listened to.

Mercury Records
1 Sussex Place, Hammersmith, London, W6 9XS
tel: 020 8910 5333
fax: 020 8910 5895
web: www.mercuryrecords.co.uk
contact: A&R Manager
genre: All Music Types Accepted
info: Send demos on CD to the address above, mark FAO A&R Manager. Mercury Records is part of the Universal Music Group of Companies.

Merry-Go-Round Records
43-45 Tunstall Road, London, SW9 8BZ
tel: 020 7738 7777
fax: 020 7738 7007
email: info@thedairy.co.uk
web: www.thedairy.co.uk
contact: Mary Evans
genre: All Music Types Accepted

Metal Queen Promotions
63 Pembroke Road, Norwich, Norfolk, NR2 3HD
tel: 07946 688 562
email: diego@mqprojects.co.uk
web: www.mqprojects.co.uk
contact: Diego Lowa
genre: Experimental/Lo-Fi/Indie Rock/Electronica
info: Metal Queen Promotions are a non-profit making organisation, releasing a series of eclectic compilation CDRs featuring local and national artists. The music policy is fairly vague - anything with a heart and a bit of intelligence is considered, although the preferred genres are those stated above. Demos are always welcome. Email contact is preferred to phone calls in the first instance. Metal Queen Promotions also promote the annual Norwich Pop Underground Convention (NPUC) every June. Visit the website for more information.

Mi5 Recordings
Houldsworth Mill Business Centre, Houldsworth Street, Reddish, Stockport, SK5 6DA
tel: 0870 787 5698
fax: 0871 433 8757
email: info@mi5recordings.co.uk
web: www.mi5recordings.co.uk
contact: Andrew Calvert
genre: All Music Types Accepted

Mighty Atom Records
First Floor, Dylan Thomas House, 32 Alexandra Road, Swansea, SA1 5DT
tel: 01792 476 567
fax: 01792 476 564
email: info@mightyatom.co.uk
web: www.mightyatom.co.uk
contact: Jo Gibb, Elliot Davies
genre: Rock/Metal
info: Send demos on CD to the address above. Follow with a phone call to let the label know you have submitted material. If Mighty Atom Records are interested in your band, they will be in touch via phone or email.

Millennium Records
6 Water Lane, Camden, London, NW1 8NZ
tel: 020 7482 0272
fax: 020 7267 4908
email: mail@millenniumrecords.com
web: www.millenniumrecords.com
contact: Ben Recknagel
genre: Indie/Dance
info: Millennium also run Yellow Sunshine Explosion label (Goa and Progressive Trance). See website for details.

Mimashima Records
Po Box 1083, Liverpool, L69 4WQ
tel: 0151 222 5785
fax: 0151 222 5785
email: mail@mimashimarecords.co.uk
web: www.mimashimarecords.co.uk
contact: Noel Fitzsimmons
genre: Psychobilly/Ska/Punk/Alternative
info: Underground label specialising in the genres listed. Send 3 track demo (preferably on CD) with biog and photo to the address above. Include SAE if you want your material returned.

Mohock Records
Sovereign House, 12 Trewartha Road, Praa Sands, Penzance, Cornwall, TR20 9ST
tel: 01736 762 826
fax: 01736 763 328
email: panamus@aol.com
web: www.panamamusic.co.uk
contact: Roderick Jones
genre: Roots/Folk
info: Send demos to the address above. Part of the Panama Music Group.

The genre-free independent label with a Virtual Venue for unsigned artists. We sign artists on the basis of audience response.

You get:
- Full length track promotion – FREE
- Your music rated & reviewed on-line – FREE
- Listener feedback – FREE
- A global audience and new fans – FREE

Plus:
- 50% of revenue when you sell downloads
- A chance to be the next MVine signing

Visit the Virtual Venue for more info – we're on your side.

www.mvine.com

Moksha Recordings
PO Box 102, London, E15 2HH
tel: 020 8555 5423
fax: 020 8519 6834
email: info@moksha.co.uk
web: www.moksha.co.uk
genre: Alternative/Dance/Hip-Hop
info: Send 3 track demo to the address above. Include details of any upcoming live dates. Mark FAO A&R.

MoMT Records
13 Chesterfield Road, Newbury, Berkshire, RG14 7QB
tel: 01635 46119
email: Ian@momt.co.uk
web: www.momt.co.uk
contact: Ian Proudfoot
genre: All Genres Of Electronic Music
info: MoMT Records are interested in bands that produce mainly electronic music. This includes everything from Electronica to Drum&Bass. Industrial to Post Rock. A better idea of the bands they like can be found on MoMT Record's website. Email Ian at the address above to give MoMT Records an idea of yourselves and your music, follow with demo on request. MoMT are always looking for bands that are doing something a little bit different from the crowd. They feel originality and ideas are often more inspiring than musicianship.

Moof Records
87 Baston Road, Bromley, Hayes, BR2 7BS
tel: 07861 161 909
email: info@moofrecords.co.uk
web: www.moofrecords.co.uk
contact: Jason Temple
genre: Post Rock/Guitar Based/Indie/Acoustic
info: Accept demo on any format except cassette. Also send any additional information such as biog, photos or a website link.

Mook Records
PO Box 155, Leeds, LS7 2XN
email: mail@mookhouse.ndo.co.uk
web: www.mookhouse.ndo.co.uk
contact: Phil Mayne
genre: Alternative Indie
info: Send demo on CD or cassette to the address above. Include brief biog and press clippings. If you would like your material returned, enclose SAE. Mook Records operate from a rehearsal/ recording studios and produce most releases in-house. For more information on the House Of Mook Studios see listings in the relevant sections.

Moon Rock Music
PO Box 883, Merseyside, L69 4RH
tel: 0151 922 5657
email: contacts@moonrock.mersinet.co.uk
web: www.moonrock.mersinet.co.uk
contact: Billy Stratton, Linda Stratton
genre: Singer-Songwriter
info: Send demos on CD to the address above.

Moteer Records
10 Taylor Street, Prestwich, Manchester, M25 1FP
email: craig@moteer.co.uk
web: www.moteer.co.uk
contact: Craig Tattersall, Andrew Johnson
genre: Electronica
info: Send demo to the above address.

Mother Tongue
35 Marsden Street, London, NW5 3HE
tel: 07973 137 554
email: julian@mothertongue.tv
web: www.mothertongue.tv
contact: Julian de Takats
genre: Alternative Pop
info: Send demos with contact details to the address above.

Moving Shadow Ltd.
PO Box 2251, London, SE1 2FH
tel: 0207 252 2661
email: info@movingshadow.com
web: www.movingshadow.com
contact: Gavin Johnson
genre: Drum&Bass
info: Send demo, preferably on CD and minimum of 2 tracks to the address above.

Mr Bongo/Disorient
2nd Floor, 24 Old Steine, Brighton, BN1 1EL
tel: 01273 600 546
fax: 01273 600 578
email: info@mrbongo.com
web: www.mrbongo.com
genre: Latin/House
info: Send demos on CD to the address above. Disorient is a division of Mr Bongo that releases House music.

Mr Pand Records
Plymouth
email: mr_pand@hotmail.com or mrpand@gmail.com
web: www.mrpandrecords.tk
contact: Anthony Pand, Paul
genre: Alternative Guitar Based/Hip-Hop
info: Email Anthony for more information on the label. Send MP3 demos via email to the GMail account listed above. Mr Pand Records also have a 16 track recording studio. See listing in relevant section for details.

MusicZombie Records
PO Box 180, Letchworth Garden City, Hertfordshire, SG6 3ZN
tel: 07961 985 959
email: records@musiczombie.com
web: www.musiczombie.com
contact: Rich Underwood
genre: All Music Types Accepted
info: Accept demos for all musical genres from Metal and Punk to Pop and Electronica. Musiczombie also promote gigs, run an agency for unsigned bands, as well as an online shop at www.mzstore.com.

Mute Records
429 Harrow Road, London, W10 4RE
tel: 020 8964 2001
fax: 020 8968 4977
email: jgladwell@mutehq.co.uk
web: www.mute.com
contact: Joff Gladwell
genre: Alternative/Electronic
info: Send demo, preferably on CD, to the address above. Maximum of 4 tracks. No MP3s or other sound files via email please. Mute will be in contact with you if they are interested, do not follow with phone call. If you want to make sure that your material has been received, please send it by registered post.

Mvine Ltd.
82 Chestnut Grove, New Malden, KT3 3JS
tel: 0845 890 0521
email: info@mvine.com
web: www.mvine.com
contact: Kerry Harvey-Piper
genre: All Music Types Accepted
info: An independent genre-free label with a web-based virtual venue for original unsigned artists. Upload 3 songs for public A&R, receive feedback from the audience, expand your fan base and sell your tracks as downloads (proceeds are split 50/50). You may progress through to becoming a Featured Artist and a potential signing to the label. Visit the website for full details of all free services for artists.

My Kung Fu
133 The Coal Exchange, Mount Stuart Square, Cardiff Bay, CF10 5ED
tel: 02920 190 151
email: hamster@my-kung-fu.com
web: www.my-kung-fu.com
contact: Carl Morris.
genre: Leftfield
info: Send 3 or 4 track demo on CD to the address above. Mark FAO Hamster. No email attachments please, but you can send a link to where your music is available on the web.

N2 Records
Unit B, The Courtyard, 42 Colwith Road, London, W6 9EY
tel: 07900 431 131
fax: 020 8741 3289
email: info@n2organisation.com
web: www.n2organisation.com
contact: Trevor Porter, Oliver Smallman
genre: All Music Types Accepted
info: Send demos to the address above.

N2K Records
The Studios, 8 Horton Place, Kensington, London, W8 4LZ
tel: 020 7937 0272
email: marketing@n2k.ltd.uk
genre: All Music Types Accepted
info: Send a demo on CD to the address above, along with an email telling the label that you are submitting your material.

The Naim Label
Southampton Road, Salisbury, Wiltshire, SP1 2LN
tel: 01722 426 600
email: thenaim.label@naim-uk.com
web: www.thenaimlabel.co.uk
contact: Anna Tooth
genre: World/Acoustic/Guitar Based/Jazz/Classical

Nation Records Ltd.
19 All Saints Road, London, W11 1HE
tel: 020 7792 8167
fax: 020 7792 2854
email: akination@btopenworld.com
web: www.nationrecords.co.uk
contact: Aki Nawaz
genre: World/Roots/Dance
info: Deals with a fusion of World music, Dance, Earth and Roots. Send demo on any format except MD to the address above. Nation Records is home to, amongst others, Asian Dub Foundation, Natasha Atlas and Transglobal Underground.

Needles Records
PO Box 22864, London, NW9 9WU
tel: 020 8204 0603
fax: 020 8204 0603
email: ladycarolle@hotmail.com
contact: Lady Carolle/Miles Collington
genre: Soul/Funk

Negative Records
27 Wolsey Road, London, N1 4QG
web: www.negativerecords.com
contact: Diggory Kenrick, Dan Penniman
genre: Garage Rock/Punk/Americana/Dub/Indie
info: Negative Records is a 'small but perfectly-formed' London label specialising in prime quality Rock'n'Roll, Dub, Experimental and Garage Rock. Send demos and biog to the address above but please consider the label's current output before submitting your demo. Unfortunately, Negative Records cannot guarantee a response.

Nemo Records
25 Grosvenor Road, Heaton Moor, Stockport, Cheshire, SK4 4EE
email: benphuzz@hotmail.com
contact: Ben Taylor, Tony Pinkham
genre: Funk/Rock/Beats
info: Nemo Records has a substantial A&R contact network and PR/Promotions team (ex Sony). The label hosts monthly showcase nights and can offer studio sessions with a Wiiija Records producer. Send demos to the address above. See also Management Companies and Promoter sections.

Neon Records
Studio Two, 19 Marine Crescent, Glasgow, G51 1HD
tel: 0141 429 6366
fax: 0141 429 6377
email: mail@go2neon.com
web: www.go2neon.com
contact: Robert Noakes, Elaine Craig
genre: All Music Types Accepted
info: Send demos on request on CD to the address above. Email first.

Nervous Records
5 Sussex Cresent, Northholt, Middlesex, UB5 4DL
tel: 020 8423 7373
fax: 020 8423 7773
email: info@nervous.co.uk
web: www.nervous.co.uk
contact: Roy Williams
genre: Rockabilly/Psychobilly

Nettwerk Productions UK
Clearwater Yard, 35 Inverness Street, London, NW1 7HB
tel: 020 7424 7500
email: info@nettwerk.com
web: www.nettwerk.com
genre: All Music Types Accepted
info: Send demos on CD to the address above. See also Management Company listings.

New State Entertainment Ltd.
Unit 2a, Queens Studio, 121 Salisbury Road, London, NW6 6RG
tel: 0207 372 4474
fax: 0207 372 4484
email: info@newstate.co.uk
web: www.newstate.co.uk
contact: Tim Binns
genre: All Genres Of Dance Music
info: New State Entertainment has a number of different label divisions, representing different genres of Dance music - Mob Records (Underground Electronic Funk), Skyline Records (House), Maelstrom Records (Tech-Trance and Tech-House), Tundra Recordings (Chillout) and Nebula Music (all genres). Links to individual label websites can be found on the New State website. Send demos on CD to the address above.

New World Music Ltd.
Harmony House, Hillside Road East, Bungay, Suffolk, NR35 1RX
tel: 01986 891 600
fax: 01986 891 601
email: info@newworldmusic.co.uk
web: www.newworldmusic.co.uk
contact: A&R
genre: World/Relaxation
info: Send demo on CD along with biog to the address above.

Newmemorabilia Ltd.
Po Box 121, Manchester, M19 2XE
email: info@thelovers.co.uk or t.hingley@ntlworld.com
web: www.thelovers.co.uk or www.tomhingley.co.uk
contact: Tom Hingley
genre: All Music Types Accepted
info: Send demos and biog to the address above. The label was set up by Tom Hingley, lead singer and co-manager of The Inspiral Carpets and represents both him as a solo artist and his new band The Lovers. Tom helped run the Cow records label and currently lectures in Music Business and Songwriting, as well as acting as a music industry consultant. Newmemorabilia Ltd. is also a publishing and management company.

Nice 'N' Ripe Records
FX Promotions, Unit 27 Grenville Workshops, 502 Hornsey Road, London, N19 4EF
tel: 020 7281 8363
fax: 020 7281 7663
email: nicenripe@fxpromotions.demon.co.uk
web: www.fxpromotions.demon.co.uk/nicenripe
genre: All Genres Of Urban Dance Music
info: Send demos on CD to the address above, mark FAO A&R Department.

Nikt Records
PO Box 5, Cwmbach, Whitland, SA34 0WA
tel: 01994 484 466
email: cadillacranch@telco4u.net
web: www.nikturner.com
contact: Nik Turner
genre: Funk/Fusion/Latin/Hip-Hop/Jazz/World
info: Send demos to the above address. Nikt Records is run by Nik Turner, founding member of Prog Rock legends Hawkwind. Also runs another record label (Riddle Records), publishing company (Hello Qtie), Money Talks Management, Money Talks Agency, Riddle Hallucinations Video Production, and Cadillac Ranch Recording Studios. See entries in relevant sections for further details.

Ninja Tunes
PO Box 4296, London, SE11 4WW
tel: 020 7820 3535
email: ninja@ninjatune.net
web: www.ninjatune.net
contact: A&R
genre: Downtempo Electronica/Leftfield/Nu Jazz/Hip-Hop/Breakbeat
info: Send demos to the address above. See entry for Big Dada regarding Ninja's specialist Hip-Hop inprint.

No Dancing Records
PO Box 125, Belfast, BT7 3EW
email: info@nodancing.co.uk
web: www.nodancing.co.uk
contact: Jimmy
genre: Indie/Rock/Leftfield
info: Email the label with an introduction, follow with a demo (no more than 3 tracks) to the address above.

No Front Teeth
PO Box 27070, London, N2 9ZP
tel: 07949 770 864
email: nftzine@hotmail.com
web: www.nofrontteeth.co.uk
contact: Marco
genre: Punk Rock
info: Send a demo on CD to the address above. No Front Teeth is also a regularly updated Punk Rock webzine with reviews, interviews and news.

Noisy Nympho Recordings Ltd.
171 Carlisle Street, Splott, Cardiff, South Glamorgan, CF24 2PE
tel: 02920 453 846
email: liv@noisynympho.com
web: www.noisynympho.com
contact: Liv
genre: Indie/Jazz-Rock/Rock/Punk/Funk
info: Noisy Nympho are looking for passionate, professional acts. Genres are not strict, but tracks must have potential. Send demo FAO Liv to the above address.

Nomadic Music Ltd.
Unit 18a/b, 101 Farm Lane, London, SW6 1QJ
tel: 020 7386 6800/07813 212 933
email: liam@nomadicmusic.net
web: www.nomadicmusic.net
contact: Liam Keightley
genre: All Music Types Accepted
info: Nomadic Music is a record label, production company and music publisher. They are totally committed to artist development and have 3 recording studios. The company is genuinely independent both financially and creatively. Their mission is to work with the best music regardless of genre although the label does not take urban music. Also provide artist management services. Contact for further details.

Northern Ambition
PO Box 250, Sale, M33 7WW
email: info@northernambition.com
web: www.northernambition.com
contact: Rob Allen
genre: Electronica/Folk/Indie/Alternative
info: The label has no pre-requisites as far as the type of music it's looking for. Guitars and Synths are equally welcome as long as the songs they strum/beep are brilliant. Send demos to the address above, with details of any upcoming Manchester gigs.

Now Music
15 Tabbs Lane, Scholes, Yorkshire, BD19 6DY
tel: 01274 851 365
fax: 01274 874 329
email: john@now-music.com
web: www.now-music.com
contact: John Wagstaff
genre: Pop
info: Comprises of 2 labels, Flair (Pop) and Wag (all genres).

NR One Records
53 Corbet Avenue, Sprowston, Norwich, NR7 8HS
tel: 01603 444 859
email: info@nrone.co.uk
web: www.nrone.co.uk
contact: Kingsley Harris
genre: All Music Types Accepted
info: Label promoting music from East Anglia. Send demo to the above address. See also listing for East Anglian Music Archive in Useful Regional Organisations section.

NRK Sound Division
Unit 5.3, Central Trading Estate, Bath Road, Bristol, BS4 3EH
tel: 0117 300 5497
fax: 0117 300 5498
email: nrk@nrkmusic.com
web: www.nrkmusic.com
contact: Redg Weeks
genre: House
info: Send demos on CD to the address above. NRK will not accept MP3s. Home to Nick Holder, Joey Negro and Miguel Migs.

Nubass Records
Unit 155, 23 New Mount Street, Manchester, M4 4DE
tel: 0161 953 4700
email: greg_walsh40@hotmail.com
contact: Greg Walsh
genre: Urban
info: Send demo on CD to the address above.

Nude Records

Zeppelin Building, 59 - 61 Farringdon Road, London, EC1M 3JB
tel: 020 7691 8689
fax: 020 7691 8688
email: ben@nuderecords.com
web: www.nuderecords.com
contact: Ben James
genre: Alternative/Indie/Singer-Songwriter
info: The recently re-vamped Nude Records are looking for acts to release singles and albums.

Off Beat Scotland

107 High Street, Royal Mile, Edinburgh, EH1 1SW
email: info@offbeat.co.uk
web: www.offbeat.co.uk
contact: Iain McKinna
genre: All Music Types Accepted
info: A music production company dedicated to recording singer/songwriters, solo artists and bands as well as producing and composing new and original music for CD, Film, Theatre and TV and Radio. Offbeat started in 1993 and since then have produced over 50 CD albums for major and independent labels and self funded artists. Have also composed music for leading ad agencies and film companies.

One Little Indian Records

34 Trinity Crescent, London, SW17 7AE
tel: 020 8772 7600
fax: 020 8772 7601
email: info@indian.co.uk
web: www.indian.co.uk
contact: Derek Birkett
genre: Alternative/Indie
info: Send demo on CD to Derek at the address above. Include any other relevant information.

Outafocus Recordings

146 Bethnal Green Road, London, E2 6DG
tel: 020 7613 1100
email: info@outafocus.co.uk
web: www.outafocus.co.uk
contact: Danny Core
genre: Alternative Guitar Based
info: Send demo on CD to the address above. Maximum of three tracks please, mark FAO A&R. If you would like material returned, include SAE.

Over Records

London
email: joel@over-records.com
web: www.over-records.com
contact: Joel Derby
genre: Ambient/Experimental
info: Over Records plans to release new material by a diverse range of artists and to issue spoken word and multimedia material in the near future. Interested artists should email in the first instance.

P3 Music

4 St. Andrews Street, Alyth, Perthshire, PH11 8AT
tel: 01828 633 790
fax: 01828 633 798
email: james@p3music.com
web: www.p3music.com
contact: James Taylor, Alison Burns
genre: Pop/Rock/Classical/Folk/Jazz/Blues
info: Send demo on CD and press pack to the address above.

Pafos Records

119 Stridingedge, Washington, Tyne & Wear, NE37 1HJ
tel: 0191 431 2179/07861 145 687
email: marc@pafosrecords.com
web: www.pafosrecords.com
contact: Marc
genre: Hip-Hop/All Genres Of Dance Music
info: Pafos is a Dance label that likes to incorporate all forms of dance music from Trance to Hip-Hop. Subsidiary label, Northeast Records also deal with Dance and a Dance events/promotions company running out of the same office called Saints or Sinners.

Palooka UK

68b Melrose Place, Coatbridge, North Lanarkshire, ML5 1RJ
tel: 07833 641 597
email: bobby@palookauk.co.uk
web: www.palookauk.co.uk
contact: Bobby
genre: Indie

Park Records

PO Box 651, Oxford, Oxfordshire, OX2 9RB
tel: 01865 241 717
fax: 01865 204 556
email: info@parkrecords.com
web: www.parkrecords.com
contact: John Dagnell
genre: Folk/Folk Rock
info: Send demos on CD along with biog to John Dagnell. Park Records is home to, amongst others, Steeleye Span, Maddy Prior, Kathryn Tickell, Lindisfarne, Kirsty McGee, Abbie Lathe, Jeard Kenney and Rock Salt And Nails. See also listing in Press & PR section.

Parlophone

43 Brook Green, London, W6 7EF
tel: 020 7605 5416
fax: 020 7605 5074
email: nathan.thompson@emimusic.com
web: www.parlophone.co.uk
contact: Nathan Thompson, Jimmy Smith
genre: All Music Types Accepted
info: Part of the EMI group.

Parlour 9 Recordings

3 Sycamore Court, Burnt Ash Road, London, SE12 8RB
tel: 07980 720 185
email: contact@parlour9.co.uk
web: www.parlour9.co.uk
contact: Gavin Melnyk
genre: Alternative
info: Parlour 9 operates with a Punk, DIY ethic and is interested in many styles of music from Techno to Punk, as long as it has integrity. Releases under the moniker 'Lo-fi Superior Recordings'. Check the website for details.

Paul Rodriguez Music

15 Stanhope Road, London, N6 5NE
tel: 020 8802 5984
fax: 020 8809 7436
email: paul@paulrodrigueznus.demon.co.uk
contact: Paul Rodriguez
genre: Drum&Bass/Classical/Jazz/Dance
info: Umbrella group encompassing labels Amalie Records (Classical), No Tiez (Drum&Bass), Scorcher Records (Dance) and Loose Tie (A general label dealing mainly with Jazz music). Do not accept unsolicited material. Email with details of your music. Follow with demo on request.

PDC Entertainments

245a Shakespeare Road, London, SW9 8RR
tel: 020 7733 0600
contact: Elijah Kerr
genre: Urban/Hip-Hop/R&B
info: Send demo FAO Elijah Kerr. All submissions will receive a reply.

Penny Black Recordings

Unit 16, The Truman Brewery, 91 Brick Lane, London, E1 6QL
tel: 020 7375 2297
fax: 020 7375 2296
email: lena@dreadrecordingsuk.com
web: www.dreadrecordingsuk.com
contact: Lena
genre: Drum&Bass
info: Penny Black, Dread Recordings and UFO Recordings are all located on the same premises. They have been formed by Drum&Bass guru Ray Keith.

Phush Consumables

109 Newport Road, Manchester, M21 9NW
tel: 07779 012 292
email: phush1@gmail.com
web: www.hippocamp.net
contact: Xander Cook
genre: Electronic
info: Send a demo on CD to the address above. For more information on Phush Consumables events, see the above website. The label is a affiliated with www.hippocamp.net.

Phuture Lounge Records

69 Independent Place, Downs Park Road, London, E8 2HE
email: tom@wocmanagement.com
web: www.phuturelounge.com
contact: Tom McCarthy
genre: R&B/Soul/Broken Beat/Hip-Hop
info: Established to provide a platform for forward thinking musicians, writers and vocalists. Artists on the label include Vaceo, Mpho Skeef, LTA, Michelle Amador and Oezlem. Label is housed in Phuturistix Studio Complex in Manchester, however send demos to the address above. Phuture Lounge guarantee that they will listen to all submissions, but are unable to respond to every demo they receive.

Parlophone

contact:
james.smith@emimusic.com
nathan.thompson@emimusic.com
Tel: 0207 605 5000

PIAS Recordings
338a Ladbrooke Grove, London, W10 5AH
tel: 020 8324 2500
fax: 020 8324 0010
email: pias@piasrecordings.com
contact: Claire Feist
genre: All Music Types Accepted
info: Send demos to the address above, include biog and photo. CDs only, maximum of 4 tracks.

Planet Mu Records
PO Box 276, Worcester, WR5 2XJ
email: mike@planet-mu.com
web: www.planet-mu.com
contact: Mike Paradinas
info: Submit demos on CD, vinyl, MD or cassette to the address above. Do not send by registered post or any other method that requires a signature. No MP3s please.

Planet Records
11 New Market Street, Colne, Lancashire, BB8 9BJ
tel: 01282 866 317
fax: 01282 866 317
email: pendlehawkmusic@ntlworld.com
web: www.pendlehawkmusic.co.uk
contact: Adrian Melling
genre: Folk/Roots/Blues
info: Planet Records also organise live music once a month at Jim's Acoustic Café in Colne. Send demo to above address. Also run a distribution service, Pendle Hawk Distribution and recording studio, Pendlehawk Studios. Enquire for further information.

Planetghost Music
PO Box 118, Leeds, LS9 6WX
email: info@planetghost.co.uk
web: www.planetghost.co.uk
contact: George
genre: Electronic/Alternative/Industrial/Gothic/Metal
info: Send demos on CD or DAT to the address above. Please do not send MP3s. If Planetghost Music are interested they will get back to you.

Plank Records
9 The Shaftesbury Centre, 85 Barlby Road, London, W10 6BN
tel: 0208 962 6244
email: bushwacka@plank.co.uk
web: www.plank.co.uk
contact: Lewis Copeland
genre: Dance
info: Plank Records, formed in 1995, is made up of 3 different labels - Plank (Breakbeat), Oblong (House) and New Icon (Downtempo, Nu Jazz). Send demos on CD to the address above, or submit MP3s/Real files via email.

Plastic Fantastic Records
35 Drury Lane, Covent Garden, London, WC2B 5RH
tel: 020 7240 8055
email: shop@plasticfantastic.co.uk
web: www.plasticfantastic.co.uk
contact: Justin Garrett
genre: Progressive House
info: Over 70 releases with artists ranging from Peace Division, Mooncat and Francesca Farfa.

Plastic Raygun
3 North Chambers, Castle Arcade, CF10 1BX
tel: 02920 403 222
fax: 02920 403 222
email: info@plasticraygun.com
web: www.plasticraygun.com
genre: Breakbeat/Alternative Electronic
info: Send a demo on CD to the address above, with contact details written clearly on the actual CD. Plastic Raygun endeavour to respond to all submissions.

Platipus Records
Unit 206, Old Gramophone Works, 326 Kensal Road, London, W10 5BZ
tel: 020 8969 9009/020 8969 5333
fax: 020 8969 8044
email: info@platipus.com
web: www.platipus.com
contact: Jeremy
genre: Trance
info: Send demos on CD to the address above.

Playaville Ltd.
Imperial House, 64 Willoughby Lane, Tottenham, London, N17 0SP
tel: 0870 766 8303
email: info@playaville.com
web: www.playaville.com
contact: Stevie Nash
genre: Commercial/Pop/R&B/Hip-Hop
info: Send demos FAO Stevie to the address above. Playaville also provide music video production and recording services. See entry in relevant section for further details.

Player Records & Management
Round Foundry Media Centre, Foundry Street, Leeds, LS11 5QP
tel: 0870 420 2370
fax: 0870 420 2380
email: andy.benge@playerrecords.com
web: www.playerrecords.com
contact: Andy Benge
genre: House
info: Artists and DJs send demos on DAT, MD or CD to the address above. Remixes can also be submitted. See also management listing.

Players
Subtub Music Ltd., 18 Sparkle Street, Manchester, M1 2NA
tel: 0161 273 3435
fax: 0161 273 3695
email: info@players-uk.com
web: www.players-uk.com
contact: Tim Giles
genre: Dub/Electronic/Hip-Hop/Funk/Nu Jazz/Latin
info: Send demos on CD, MD or tape to the address above. Demos are responded to where possible, but please allow a couple of weeks.

Plum Projects
8 Perseverance Place, Richmond, Surrey, TW9 2PN
tel: 0208 288 0531
email: unsg@plumprojects.com
web: www.plumprojects.com
contact: Slim
genre: Leftfield Dance
info: Plum Projects is primarily an online record label, but will consider releasing tracks on hard format if they get a good response on the site. Email the label, follow with demo on request.

Pogo Records
White House Farm, Shropshire, TF9 4HA
tel: 01630 647 374
fax: 01630 647 612
contact: Keith Phillips
genre: Punk
info: Send demos to the address above. Part of the RTL Group.

Poisoned Whiskey Records
42 Parry Street, Ton Pentre, RCT, South Wales, CF41 7AJ
email: marcus@poisonedwhiskeyrecords.com or marcusmarcus666@hotmail.com
web: www.poisonedwhiskeyrecords.com
genre: Rock/Instrumental/Emo/Indie/Hardcore/Electronica/Metal/Punk
info: Send demos to the address above. No Pop, Ska-Punk, Dance, Funk Rock, Pub Rock or Trad-Punk.

Polydor UK
364 - 366 Kensington High Street, London, W14 8NF
tel: 0207 471 5400
web: www.umusic.com
contact: Ben Parmar
genre: All Music Types Accepted
info: Send 3 track demo on CD to the address above.

Poptones
3 Berkley Grove, London, NW1 8XY
tel: 020 7483 2541
fax: 020 7722 8412
email: info@poptones.co.uk
web: www.poptones.co.uk
contact: A&R
genre: Alternative Guitar Based
info: Send demos to the address above. Do not send any material via email. Poptones is run by former Creation Records boss Alan McGee.

Pork Recordings
PO Box 18, Hull, HU1 3YU
tel: 01482 441 455
fax: 01482 441 455
email: support@pork.co.uk
web: www.pork.co.uk
contact: Porky
genre: Electronic/Leftfield
info: Send demos on CD, cassette or DAT to the address above.

Positiva
EMI House, 43 Brook Green, London, W6 8EF
tel: 020 7605 5000
fax: 020 7605 5186
web: www.positivarecords.com
contact: Jason Ellis, Ben Cherrill
genre: Dance
info: Positiva only accept mastered demos. Cannot guarantee a response to every submission.

President Records Ltd.
Units 6 & 7, 11 Wyfold Close, London, SW6 6SE
tel: 020 7385 7700
fax: 020 7385 3402
email: hits@president-records.co.uk
web: www.president-records.co.uk
contact: David
genre: All Pop Genres Accepted
info: Send demos on CD or cassette to the address above.
Submit 2 or 3 tracks, unless you have a completed album.

Prison Records
13 Sandys Road, Worcester, WR1 3HE
tel: 01905 613 023
fax: 01905 613 023
email: split.music@virgin.net
web: www.prison-records.com
contact: Chris Warren
genre: All Music Types Accepted
info: Send demo to address above.

Prolifica Records
Unit A105, Saga Centre, 326 Kensal Road, London, W10 5BZ
tel: 020 8964 1917
email: info@prolifica.net
web: www.prolifica.net
contact: Colin
genre: All Music Types Accepted
info: Send demos on CD to the address above.

Proof Records
PO Box 20242, London, NW1 7FL
tel: 020 7485 1113
email: info@proofsongs.co.uk
contact: A&R
genre: Dance/All Music Types Accepted
info: Send demos on CD, no more than 3 tracks, to the
address above. If you would like your material returned enclose SAE.
Although they specialise in Dance, they are very keen to hear new
music from any genre. Affiliated with Proof Songs music publishers, see
listing in relevant section.

Provocateur Records
31 Fordwich Road, Fordwich, Canterbury, Kent, CT2 0BW
tel: 01227 711 008
fax: 01227 712 021
email: jazz@provocateurrecords.co.uk
web: www.provocateurrecords.co.uk
contact: Jo Lilley
genre: Jazz
info: 'Provocateur is one of Europe's most sophisticated
independents, specialising in the fascinating border territories at the
edges of contemporary jazz.' (The Guardian).

Psychiatric Records
Glasgow
email: demos@psychiatricrecords.com
web: www.psychiatricrecords.com
contact: Gordon Kennedy
genre: Leftfield
info: Psychiatric Records are looking for music that is "weird
and wrong". Email contact should be made before demo is sent. Please
send email links to your music rather than large attachments. Artists
currently associated with Psychiatric include Colditz, The Pendulums,
Rutabaga and Kill Binary Kill.

Pure Gold Records
Sovereign House, 12 Trewartha Road, Praa Sands, Penzance, Cornwall,
TR20 9ST
tel: 01736 762 826
fax: 01736 763 328
email: panamus@aol.com
web: www.panamamusic.co.uk
contact: Roderick Jones
genre: Country/MOR
info: Send demos to the address above. Part of the Panama
Music Group.

Quartz Records Ltd.
PO Box 6912, Birmingham, West Midlands, B27 7BB
tel: 0121 770 8544
fax: 0121 770 8544
email: music@jamaicapleasuregroup.com
web: www.jamaicapleasuregroup.com
contact: Bernie Dixon
genre: Rock/Reggae/Easy Listening/Pop/R&B/Hip-Hop/Jazz
info: Biographies and pictures should be included with
demos.

Radiotone
PO Box 43103, London, E17 8WD
email: info@radiotone.co.uk
web: www.radiotone.co.uk
contact: Steve Cooper
genre: Alternative Guitar Based/Electronic/Pop
info: Send demos on CD to the address above. No Hard Rock
please.

Rainy Day Records
Sovereign House, 12 Trewartha Road, Praa Sands, Penzance, Cornwall,
TR20 9ST
tel: 01736 762 826
fax: 01736 763 328
email: panamus@aol.com
web: www.panamamusic.co.uk
contact: Roderick Jones
genre: All Music Types Accepted
info: The label release compilation albums covering all
musical genres. Send demos to the address above. Part of the Panama
Music Group.

Ram Records
PO Box 70, Hornchurch, Essex, RM11 3NR
tel: 01708 455 851
fax: 01708 441 270
email: info@ramrecords.com
web: www.ramrecords.com
contact: Scott Bourne
genre: Drum&Bass
info: Send demos on CD or MD to the address above.

Ramp Recordings Ltd.
Phoenix House, Bridge Street, Stowmarket, Suffolk, IP14 1BP
tel: 07793 404 222
email: contact@ramprecordings.com
web: www.ramprecordings.com
contact: Tom Kerridge
genre: All Music Types Accepted
info: The label specialises in Hip-Hop, Deep House and
Broken Beats, but is open to submissions from any type of music.
Artists currently on the roster include Count Bass D and Declaime.

Recordiau Awen Records
2 Bryn Robert Cottages, Old Llandegfan, Ynys Mon, LL59 5PW
tel: 01248 715324
email: charlie@awen.fsnet.co.uk
genre: Welsh Language/All Music Types Accepted
info: Angelsey-based record company, mainly operating in
the Welsh market. Also run publishing company (Cyhoeddiadau Pandy
Publishing) and recording studio (Stiwdio Pandy). See relevant sections
for details.

Recordiau Menai Records
48 Brynffynnon Road, Y-Felinheli, LL56 4SJ
tel: 01248 671 663
email: george@stiwdioeglwys.fsnet.co.uk
web: www.stiwdioeglwys.co.uk
genre: Welsh Language
info: Send demos to the address above. Please ensure that
the recording is of the best possible quality. Also run an Urban label,
JUDmusic Records, a publishing company (JUDmusic Publishing) and
a production studio (Stiwdio Eglwys). See relevant entries for more
information.

The Red Flag Recording Company
1 Star Street, London, W2 1QD
tel: 020 7258 0093
fax: 020 7402 9238
email: info@redflagrecords.com
web: www.redflagrecords.com
contact: Ben Leahy
genre: Guitar Based
info: Send demos on CD to the address above. Include biog,
photo and any press.

Red Lightnin'
42 The Street, North Lopham, Diss, Norfolk, IP22 2LU
tel: 01379 687 693
fax: 01379 687 559
email: peter@redlightnin.com
web: www.redlightnin.com
contact: Peter Shertser
genre: Blues
info: Red Lightnin' is a dedicated Blues label. Please check
their website before sending any material.

Red Recordings
PO Box 5641, Milton Keynes, Buckinghamshire, MK10 9ZH
tel:	0870 383 1511
fax:	07092 041 494
email:	jay@redrecordings.com
web:	www.redrecordings.com
contact:	Jay Walker
genre:	Progressive/House/Tribal House
info:	Demos are preferably to be in CD format, but MP3s are
accepted if this is not possible.

Red Records
412 Beersbridge Road, Belfast, BT5 5EB
tel:	028 9065 4450
fax:	028 9047 1625
web:	www.red-records.com
contact:	Michael
genre:	Chillout
info:	Send demos on CD to the address above. The label
cannot return any submissions. Affiliated with Belfast based recording
studio, Mach 2. See listing in relevant section for further information.

Redemption Ltd.
23a Church Street, Bloxwich, Wallsall, West Midlands, WS3 3HE
tel:	01922 494 056
email:	info@redemption.co.uk
web:	www.redemption.co.uk
genre:	Dance
info:	Specialise in Dance music. Send demos to the address
above. Also see distributors section for information about national and
international distribution.

Relentless Records
43 Brook Green, Hammersmith, London, W6 7EF
tel:	020 8964 6720
fax:	020 8964 6087
email:	a&r@relentless-music.com
web:	www.relentless-records.net
contact:	Glynn Aikins
genre:	All Music Types Accepted
info:	Home to Joss Stone, KT Tunstall and many others. Send
demos on CD to the address above.

Rephlex
PO Box 2676, London, N11 1AZ
tel:	020 8368 5903
email:	info@rephlex.com
web:	www.rephlex.com
contact:	A & R Dept.
genre:	Electronic Braindance

Reptor Productions
Po Box 198, Abergele, Conwy, LL22 9WZ
tel:	01745 343 777
email:	douglaslacey@reptorproductions.co.uk
web:	www.reptorproductions.co.uk
contact:	Douglas Lacey, Lynn Jones
genre:	All Music Types Accepted
info:	Send demos to the above address. Reptor also broadcast
an online radio show called Reptor Radio featuring unsigned bands. See
website for details.

Resist Music Ltd.
138b West Hill, London, SW15 2UE
tel:	020 8780 0305
fax:	020 8788 2889
web:	www.resist-music.co.uk
contact:	Robin, Ben
genre:	All Genres Of Dance Music
info:	Send demos to the address above.

Resurrection Records
228 Camden High Street, London, NW1 8QS
tel:	020 7813 2917
email:	katrina@resurrection-rec.demon.co.uk
web:	www.resurrectionmusic.com
contact:	Andy
genre:	Gothic
info:	Send demos to the address above. For more information
on the Resurrection Records record shop, see the relevant section.

Retribute Records
PO Box 76, New Ferry, Wirral, CH63 9WU
email:	retribute@aol.com
web:	www.retributerecords.com
contact:	Chris
genre:	Industrial/Extreme Metal/Metal/Heavy Metal
info:	All forms of heavy music. Send demos on CD or cassette
to the address above. Include biog and photograph. No sound files via
email please. See also demo submission policy on website for further
information.

Reveal Records
63 St. Peter's Street, Derby, DE1 2AB
tel:	01332 349 244
fax:	01332 349 141
email:	sales@revealrecords.com
web:	www.reveal-records.com
info:	Send demo to the above address.

Reverb Records
Reverb House, Bennett Street, London, W4 2AH
tel:	020 8747 0660
fax:	020 8747 0880
email:	records@reverbxl.com
web:	www.reverbxl.com
contact:	Tony Murphey
genre:	All Music Types Accepted
info:	Send demo on CD to the address above. Include biog,
press cuttings and details of upcoming gigs.

Revolver Records
152 Goldthorn Hill, Penn, Wolverhampton, West Midlands, WV2 3JA
tel:	01902 345 345
fax:	01902 345 155
email:	paul.birch@revolverrecords.com
web:	www.revolverrecords.com
contact:	Peter Black
genre:	Jazz/R&B/Guitar Based/Alternative/Metal/Rock/Punk
info:	The main focus of the label is Rock, but will consider
material from the Jazz and R&B genres. Include SAE if you would like
your material returned. Linked with Heavy Metal Records. See listing
for further details.

RF Records
City College Manchester, City Campus, Room 30, Chorlton Street,
Manchester, M1 3HB
tel:	0161 279 7302
fax:	0161 279 7725
email:	pellis@ccm.ac.uk
web:	www.rfrecords.com
contact:	Chris Williams
genre:	All Music Types Accepted
info:	RF Records will upload demos they receive onto their
website and highlight their favourite every month.

Riddle Records
PO Box 5, Cwmbach, Whitland, SA34 0WA
tel:	01994 484 466
email:	cadillacranch@telco4u.net
web:	www.nikturner.com
genre:	Jazz/Funk/Fusion/World/Latin/Hip-Hop
info:	Send demos to the address above. Riddle Records
is owned by Nik Turner, founding member of Prog Rock legends
Hawkwind. Also runs another record label (Nikt Records), publishing
company (Hello Qtie), Money Talks Management, Money Talks Agency,
Riddle Hallucinations Video Productions and Cadillac Ranch Recording
Studios. See entries in relevant sections for further details.

Ridge Records
1 York Street, Aberdeen, AB11 5DL
tel:	01224 573 100
fax:	01224 572 598
email:	office@ridge-records.com
web:	www.ridge-records.com
contact:	Mike Smith
genre:	Celtic Rock

Riot Club
Unit 4, 27a Spring Grove Road, Hounslow, Middlesex, TW3 4BE
tel:	020 8572 8809
email:	riot@riotclub.co.uk
web:	www.riotclub.co.uk
contact:	A&R
genre:	Punk/Indie
info:	Send demo to the above address. Riot Club also have
rehearsal facilities, as well as management services. See entries in
relevant sections for further details.

Road Goes On Forever Records
PO Box 109, Washington, Tyne & Wear, NE37 3YF
tel:	0191 415 9991
fax:	0191 415 9992
email:	info@rgfrecords.co.uk
web:	www.rgfrecords.co.uk
contact:	John Tobler
genre:	Jazz/Folk/Blues/Country

Roadrunner Records
Ealing Studios, Ealing Green, London, W5 5EP
tel: 020 8567 6762
fax: 020 8567 6793
email: rrguest@roadrunnerrecords.co.uk
web: www.roadrunnerrecords.co.uk
contact: Mark Palmer
genre: Rock/Metal
info: Send demos on CD, to the address above. Videos can also be submitted.

Rock Action Records
PO Box 15107, Glasgow, G1 1US
email: info@rockactionrecords.co.uk
web: www.rockactionrecords.co.uk
contact: Craig
genre: Electronic/Alternative/Leftfield/Rock
info: Send demos to the address above. Rock Action Records, set up and run by Mogwai, cannot guarantee an individual response to submissions.

Rock 'n' Roll Unlimited
214 Bolton Road West, Ramsbottom, Bury, ML0 9PE
tel: 07974 215 220
email: info@rocknrollunlimited.com
web: www.rocknrollunlimited.com
contact: Simon Collier
genre: Rock 'n' Roll/Hard Rock/Punk
info: Send an email to Simon, introducing yourselves and your music.

Rough Trade Records
66 Golbourne Road, London, W10 5PS
tel: 020 8960 9888
fax: 020 8968 6715
email: james.endeacott@roughtraderecords.com
web: www.roughtraderecords.com
contact: James Endeacott
genre: Indie/Rock
info: Also incorporates Tugboat and Blanco Y Negro.

RTL Records
White House Farm, Shropshire, TF9 4HA
tel: 01630 647 374
contact: Xavier Lee
genre: All Music Types Accepted
info: RTL comprises of 5 record labels. Depending on the genre, a different person should be contacted. Xavier should be contacted for Rock, Tanya Woof for MOR, Catrin Lemat for Classical, and Ron Dickson for any other music. All available information should be included when sending a demo.

RuffLife UK
PO Box 38115, London, W10 6XG
tel: 020 8932 2860
email: international@ruffnation.com
web: www.ruffnation.com
genre: Hip-Hop/Rock
info: Send demos on CD to the address above.

Rumour Records
Tempo House, 15 Falcon Road, London, SW11 2PJ
tel: 020 7228 6821
fax: 020 7228 6972
email: info@rumour.demon.co.uk
web: www.rumourrecords.co.uk
contact: Oscar Engells
genre: Pop/Techno/Garage/Drum&Bass/Hard House/Trance
info: Send demos on CD to the address above. Include biog and any other relevant information. Also run Klone Records (Pop).

S. S. S.
Flat 2, 21 Lichfield Road, Great Yarmouth, Norfolk, NR31 0EQ
tel: 01493 665 300
email: barock@hotmail.co.uk
genre: Rock and non-formulaic dance music
info: S. S. S. is an umbrella company for BaRock and S. S. S. labels. BaRock is mainly working within the Rock genre, while S. S. S. covers the Dance scene. Have helped lots of local bands and are interested in sourcing original and new sounds.

S:alt Records
PO Box 51343, London, N1 0ZF
email: info@saltrecords.com
web: www.saltrecords.com
contact: Roberto Concina
genre: Electronic/Nu Jazz/Alternative Rock
info: Send demos on CD to the address above, email in advance so the label know to expect your submission. S:alt Records will listen to music from most genres, but want to hear something interesting.

Sain
Canolfan Sain, Llanwnda, Caernarfon, LL54 5TG
tel: 01286 831 111
fax: 01286 831 497
email: sain@sainwales.com
web: www.sainwales.com
contact: Dafydd Roberts
genre: Classical/Folk/Rock

Sanctuary Group
Sanctuary House, 45-53 Sinclair Road, London, W14 0NS
tel: 020 7602 6351
fax: 020 7603 5941
web: www.sanctuarygroup.com
contact: John Williams, Kerry Chapman
genre: All Music Types Accepted

Saturn Return Records
PO Box 1083, Liverpool, L69 4WQ
tel: 0151 222 5785
email: mail@saturnreturnrecords.co.uk
web: www.saturnreturnrecords.co.uk
contact: Noel Fitzsimmons
genre: Mainstream Dance/House
info: Send 3 track demo (preferably on CD) with biog and photo to the address above. Please include an SAE if you would like your material returned.

Schnitzel Records
PO Box 37291, London, SW11 5TX
email: info@schnitzel.co.uk
web: www.schnitzel.co.uk
contact: A&R Dept.
genre: Indie Pop/Alternative
info: Email first with an introduction to yourselves and your music. Follow with demo on request.

Scotdisc
BGS Productions Ltd., Newtown Street, Kilsyth, Glasgow, G65 0LY
tel: 01236 821 081
fax: 01236 826 900
email: info@scotdisc.co.uk
web: www.scotdisc.co.uk
contact: D.B. Stevenson
genre: Scottish

Scrap Records
Brighton
tel: 07859 909 595
email: dirtysquatters@hotmail.com
web: www.scraprecords.com and www.dirtysquatters.com
contact: Gary, Milla
genre: Hip-Hop/Industrial/Punk/Thrash Metal/Drum&Bass
info: Many genres but tends to focus on more Hardcore music with issues.

Scue Records Ltd.
6 Auckland Road, Clapham Junction, London, SW11 1EP
tel: 07900 0988 472
email: info@scue.co.uk
web: www.scue.co.uk
contact: Steve Jennings
genre: Acoustic/Singer-Songwriter
info: A label with both UK and Australasian interests who are very open to new, talented artists. Submit demos via their website.

Seamless Recordings Ltd.
192-194 Clapham High Street, London, SW4 7UD
tel: 020 7498 5551
fax: 020 7498 2333
email: amber@bargrooves.com
web: www.seamlessrecordings.com
contact: Amber Spence-Holmes
genre: House
info: Demos can be submitted on any format, but CD is preferable. Mark FAO Seamless Recordings A&R Department.

Secret Tree Ltd.
5-6 Northumberland Buildings, Queens Square, Bath, BA1 2JE
tel: 07974 956 228
email: sales@secrettree.net
web: www.secrettree.net
contact: Ben Hawkes, John Chinnick
genre: Alternative
info: Any genre considered but must be different, alternative and passionate. Online music retail selling a wide variety of alternative releases. Will be selling unsigned artists' work under the 'Visible Underground' banner. For further information regarding Visible Underground see listing in Management Companies section.

Seeca Music Ltd.
Mortlake Business Centre, 20 Mortlake High Street, London, SW14 8JN
tel: 020 8487 8622
fax: 020 8487 8621
email: info@seeca.co.uk
web: www.seeca.co.uk
contact: Will Desborough
genre: Post Hardcore/Indie/Rock/Guitar Based
info: Seeca are working with a new distribution model that exploits the opportunities of digital technology. Seeca will release singles by download only. Albums will be released by download and as a physical product. Seeca are really interested in hearing guitar based music with a cutting edge. Send 3 tracks on CD to the above postal address or via email. Please also include any press, biog and pictures.

Seldom Records
London, W14 4AP
email: music@seldomrecords.co.uk
web: www.seldomrecords.co.uk or www.myspace.com/seldomrecords
contact: Charlie Light
genre: Alternative/Eclectic
info: Seldom Record's aim is quite simply to release the music they like, helping to push true artists and musicians out to a larger audience. They are a non-profit label and hence all revenue goes into the development and promotion of artists. Demos are preferred on CD format but please feel free to submit others. Follow your submission with an email. Check website for up to date address details before posting anything.

Serious One Records
PO Box 346, Enfield, Middlesex, EN3 5EL
tel: 020 8292 5073
email: nicky@massmediauk.net
contact: Nicky Price
genre: Pop
info: Send demos on CD to the address above. No material can be returned.

Shadow Inc Records
139 Abercorn Crescent, South Harrow, HA2 OPY
tel: 07950 663 338
email: shadowinc_records@yahoo.co.uk
contact: Marcus Nils
genre: Pop/R&B/Hip-Hop/Grind
info: All types of music are accepted.

Shadowless Records
Unit 33, 1st Floor, 65-66 Caroline Street, Birmingham, B3 1UG
tel: 07958 281 379
email: tomo@shadowless.com
web: www.shadowless.com
contact: Tomo
genre: R&B/Grime/Drum&Bass/Urban/Hip-Hop/Garage
info: Tomo is part of an act called Gamma who have released records on Big Dada and has remixed Roots Manuva, as well as appearing on various compilations. Shadowless also provide recording facilities. See entry in relevant section for further details.

ShanelsWorldRecords
London
tel: 07800 764 915
email: info@shanelsworld.com
web: www.shanelsworld.com
genre: Rap/Commercial/Urban/Hip-Hop
info: Submit MP3s and web links via email at the address above, along with a short biog.

Sharpe Music
9a Irish Street, Dungannon, County Tyrone, BT70 1DB
tel: 028 8772 4621
fax: 028 8775 2195
email: info@sharpemusicireland.com
web: www.sharpemusicireland.com
contact: Raymond Stewert
genre: Country/Irish
info: Send demos to the address above.

Shifty Disco
1st Floor, 9 Park End Street, Oxford, Oxfordshire, OX1 1HH
tel: 01865 798 791
email: info@shiftydisco.co.uk
web: www.shiftydisco.co.uk
contact: Dave Newton
genre: All Music Types Accepted
info: Send demo and biog to the address above. As well as their album releases Shifty Disco release weekly singles, available to download from their site.

Shock Records
PO Box 301, Torquay, Devon, TQ2 7TB
tel: 01803 614 392
email: info@shockrecords.co.uk
web: www.shockrecords.co.uk
contact: Graham Young
genre: Hard Dance/Hard House/Trance

Shoeshine Records
PO Box 15193, Glasgow, G2 6LB
email: info@shoeshine.co.uk
web: www.shoeshine.co.uk
genre: Melodic Indie Guitar
info: Send demos on CD to the address above marked FAO A&R. Linked with Spit & Polish Records. See separate listing.

sijis Records
PO Box 31656, London, W11 1YG
email: info@sijis.com
web: www.sijis.com
contact: Jon Hayes
genre: Experimental/Electronica/Indietronica
info: Set up to promote and enhance the international Experimental music scene.

Silent Revolution Ltd.
7 Hawksmoor Mews, 200 Cable Street, London, E1 0DG
tel: 07749 498 538
email: silentrevolution@hotmail.com
web: www.silentrevolutionrecords.co.uk
contact: Valerio Meletti
genre: Folk/Mainstream/Alternative
info: Record label with strong links in Italy and Belgium. Always looking for new talent.

Silicon Hustler
15 Salisbury Terrace, Liverpool, L15 4HD
tel: 0870 744 3931
fax: 07092 333 396
email: info@siliconhustler.com
web: www.siliconhustler.com
contact: Gary Ladd
genre: Electro/Electro Punk
info: Send a demo on CD to the address above, or submit MP3s via email.

Silverword Music Group
16 Limetrees, Llangattock, Crickhowell, Powys, NP8 1LB
tel: 01873 810 142
fax: 01873 811 557
email: silverwordgroup@aol.com
web: www.silverword.co.uk
contact: Kevin King
genre: All Music Types Accepted
info: Send demos on CD to the address above, maximum of 3 tracks. Include any other relevant information that supports the marketability of your music. Please make sure contact details are on actual CD and include a SAE. Silverword Music Group also incorporates several labels, distribution and a management company. See listings in relevant sections for further details.

Sink & Stove
PO Box 992, Bristol, BS99 5ZN
email: info@sinkandstove.co.uk
web: www.sinkandstove.co.uk
contact: Benjamin Shillabeer
genre: Alternative/Post-Rock/Indie/Electronica/Experimental Pop/Punk
info: Sink & Stove are a cutting edge, independent, dynamic underground label. The music represented is diverse but united by innovation, attitude and intelligence. Current artists include The Organ, The Playwrights, Controller. Controller, and You & The Atom Bomb.

Skam Records
PO Box 76, Manchester, M45 7XW
email: shop@skam.co.uk
web: www.skam.co.uk
contact: Andy Maddocks
genre: Dance
info: Experimental Dance label. Send demos to the address above. Skam cannot guarantee a reply to every submission but do listen to all material they receive.

Skint/Loaded Records
PO Box 174, Brighton, BN1 4BA
tel: 01273 738 527
fax: 01273 208 766
email: mail@skint.net
web: www.skint.net
contact: A&R Dept.
genre: Dance/Alternative Guitar Based
info: Send demo on CD to the address above. Make sure to write full contact address on the actual format. Allow up to 2 months for a response (by post). Skint cannot return any material they receive.

Slam Productions
3 Thesiger Road, Abingdon, Oxfordshire, OX14 2DX
tel: 01235 529 012
fax: 01235 529 012
email: info@slamproductions.net
web: www.slamproductions.net
contact: George Haslam
genre: Contemporary Jazz/Improvised
info: Information included with a demo should be written on a single sheet.

Sleep When You're Dead Records
South London
tel: 07840 218 806
email: team@sleepwhenyouaredead.com
web: www.sleepwhenyouaredead.com
contact: Michael Wisby
genre: Rock/Alternative/Grunge/Punk
info: Independent record label based in South London. Aims to sign artists that are serious about their music and want a long term music career, not just a few single releases. Email with details of your act and send demo on request.

Smooch Records
2 Seabank Road, Colwyn Bay, LL28 4BT
tel: 07788 181 750
email: geoffpburke@yahoo.com
contact: Geoff Burke
genre: Dance/Commercial/Soul/Jazz
info: Email Geoff with details of your act. Send demo upon request. Looking for artists in London, North Wales and North West regions.Smooch also provide Management services. See listing in relevant section for further details.

Snapper Music
1 Star Street, London, W2 12D
tel: 0207 563 5500
email: admin@snappermusic.co.uk
web: www.snappermusic.com
contact: Tom Gallagher
genre: Rock/Metal
info: Send demo on CD to the address above, include brief biog.

Solar Creations
PO Box 9691, Birmingham, B27 7ED
tel: 0121 707 8504
email: scott@solarcreations.net
web: www.solarcreations.net
contact: Scott Roe
genre: Indie Rock
info: Send demos in CD format FAO Scott to the above address or via website. Solar Creations also provide management and PR services, as well as organising live music at The Actress & The Bishop, Birmingham.

Solarise Records
PO Box 31104, London, E16 4UE
tel: 07980 453 628
email: info@solariserecords.com
web: www.solariserecords.com
contact: Paul
genre: All Music Types Accepted
info: Solarise are an independent online record label that showcases, promotes and sells CDs and MP3s of any talented, independent and original musicians from all over the world and from any genre. Send demos to the address above.

Solemusic Industries Ltd.
Unit B1, Glenwood Business Park, Glasgow, G45 9UG
tel: 0141 636 6336/07703 324322
fax: 0141 636 6336
email: steviesole@solemusic.co.uk
web: www.solemusic.co.uk
contact: Stevie Sole Middleton, Chris Harris, Geoff Montford
genre: Vocal House
info: Send demos to the address above. Solemusic incorporates 2 other Dance labels, Tronicsole (House) and Clubsole (Funky Dancefloor House). See separate listings for further details.

Solent Records
68-60 Corner House, Lugley St, Newport, Isle of Wight, PO30 5ET
tel: 01983 525 110
web: www.solentrecords.co.uk
genre: Mainstream
info: Small label only interested in artists from the South of England i.e Isle of Wight, Sussex.

FOOTWEAR

www.f-sharp.co.uk

Soma Quality Recordings Ltd.
2nd Floor, 342 Argyle Street, Glasgow, G2 8LY
tel: 0141 229 6220
email: glenn@somarecords.com
web: www.somarecords.com
contact: Glenn Gibbons
genre: Dance
info: Send demo on CD to the address above, follow with an email.

Some Bizarre
London
tel: 020 7836 9995
fax: 020 7836 9909
email: info@somebizarre.com
web: www.somebizarre.com
contact: Stevo
genre: Alternative
info: Email or telephone for demo submission address. Send 3 track demo on CD to the address above. Include short biog. Some Bizarre consider themselves to be an especially bold and adventurous label.

Sonar Records Ltd.
82 London Road, Coventry, CV1 2JT
tel: 02476 220 749
email: office@sonar-records.demon.co.uk
web: www.cabinstudio.co.uk
contact: Jon Lord
genre: Guitar Based
info: Sonar Records run a 24 track studio, and generally release material from artists who record in it. See listing for Cabin Studio in the relevant section for more information regarding the recording facilities.

Sonic 360
33 Riding House Street, London, W1W 7DZ
tel: 020 7636 3939
email: zen@sonic360.com
web: www.sonic360.com
contact: Zen
genre: Eclectic/Electronica/Alternative/Indie/Rock
info: Email Sonic 360 with details of your band and your music, follow with demo. Sonic 360 was set up in 2000 by producer Chris Allison, who has worked with, amongst others, Coldplay, The Beta Band and Dot Allison). The label also manages 2 subsidiary labels, Head + Arm and Sombrero, along with Sonic 360 Music, a publishing company. For more information regarding Sombrero, Head + Arm and Sonic 360 Music, see the Sonic 360 website.

Sonic Vista Recordings
85 Inmans Road, Hedon, Hull, HU12 8NQ
tel: 01482 896 330
email: sonicvistarecordings@ernest1.karoo.co.uk
contact: Terry Dunn
genre: Alternative
info: Send hard copy of demo along with press pack or biog to the above address.

Sony BMG
Bedford House, 69-79 Fulham High Street, London, SW6 3JW
tel: 0207 384 7500
fax: 0207 371 9298
web: www.sonybmg.com
contact: A & R Dept.
genre: All Music Types Accepted
info: Prefer to have demos submitted via an established industry professional (Lawyer, Manager or Agent).

Sorepoint Records
3rd Floor, 1a Adpar Street, London, W2 1DE
tel: 020 7535 6739
fax: 020 7563 7283
email: info@sorepointrecords.com
web: www.sorepointrecords.com
contact: Chris Baker
genre: Metal/Emo/Post-Punk
info: Send demos FAO A&R Department to the address above. 3 or 4 tracks on CDR, along with contact details and some information on the band. Deal with the heavier end of music. Sore Point is also linked with other labels Full Time Hobby, Hassle Records and Eat Sleep Records. See listings for further details.

Sorted Records
PO Box 5922, Leicester, LE1 6XU
email: sortedrecords@hotmail.com
web: www.sorted-records.org.uk
contact: Dave Dixey
genre: Indie/Leftfield
info: Send demos on CD to the address above.

Soul Brother
1 Keswick Road, East Putney, London, SW15 2HL
tel: 0208 875 1018
fax: 0208 871 0180
email: soulbrother@btinternet.com
web: www.soulbrother.co.uk
genre: Soul/Jazz
info: Soul Brother licence certain tracks. Send demos to the address above.

Soul Jazz Records Ltd.
7 Broadwick Street, Soho, London, W1F 0DA
tel: 020 7734 3341
fax: 020 7494 1035
email: info@soundsoftheuniverse.com
web: www.souljazzrecords.co.uk
contact: Karen
genre: Punk/Disco/Electro/Hip-Hop/Funk/Brazilian/ Deep House/Roots Reggae/Latin
info: For more information on the associated Sounds of the Universe record shop, see the relevant section.

Soul2Soul
The Yard, 45 Fouberts Place, London, W1 7QF
tel: 020 7439 6060
email: info@soul2soul.co.uk
web: www.soul2soul.co.uk
genre: Garage/Soul/R&B/Dance
info: Associated with Funki Dred Records Ltd. (Dance/ Garage).

Soultown 45 Records
PO Box 346, Enfield, Middlesex, EN3 5EL
tel: 020 8292 5073
email: nicky@massmediauk.net
contact: Nicky Price
genre: R&B/Dance
info: Send demos on CD to the address above. No material can be returned.

Sound Surgery Records
Top Floor No. 4, 16 Salisbury Road, Hove, East Sussex, BN3 3AD
tel: 07092 300 741
email: soundsurgery@email.com
web: http://clik.to/soundsurgery
contact: Mark Wilson
genre: Breakbeat
info: Demos and DJ mixes can be submitted on CD, MD or cassette. Check the website for a current mailing address. Demos cannot be returned.

Sounds Devious
London
email: info@soundsdevious.com
web: www.soundsdevious.com
contact: Nihal de Silva
genre: Urban/Drum&Bass/Hip-Hop
info: DJs, producers and MCs can submit demos to the label. Email for a postal address.

Southern Fried Records
Fulham Palace, Bishops Avenue, London, SW6 6EA
tel: 020 7384 73 73
fax: 020 7384 7392
email: info@southernfriedrecords.com
web: www.southernfriedrecords.com
contact: A&R
genre: All Music Types Except Thrash Metal or Goth
info: Send demos on CD to the address above.

Soviet Union Records
67 Ashbourne Grove, Whitefield, Manchester, M45 7NL
tel: 0161 959 0748
email: sovrec@yahoo.co.uk
web: www.manchestermusic.co.uk
contact: Mike Gray
genre: Alternative/Indie

Spank Records
36 Windsor Street, Liverpool, L8 1XS
tel: 0151 707 2925
fax: 0151 707 2925
email: mail@spankrecords.com
web: www.spankrecords.com
contact: Jon Hall
genre: Alternative Guitar Based/Indie/Metal/Rock
info: Send a 3/4 track demo on CD or cassette (preferably CD) to the address above. Make sure to write contact details and track listing on the actual CD or cassette. Spank Records do listen to all material, but cannot respond to everything they receive. If you would like to follow up your submission, allow a week after posting then email. No sound files via email please.

Spiky Black Cat Records
PO Box 499, London, WC1H 9ZA
tel: 07833 673 805
email: records@spikyblackcat.co.uk
web: www.spikyblackcat.co.uk
contact: Romek Szczesniak
genre: Alternative/Goth/Punk/Rock
info: Send demos on CD to the address above. A selection of material submitted will be reviewed on the Spiky Black Cat website. The label issues a compilation CD of their best artists entitled 'Cat Scratchings'.

Spiralscope Records
127b Oswald Road, Chorlton, Manchester, M21 9GE
tel: 0161 860 7788
email: info@spiralscoperecords.com
web: www.spiralscoperecords.com
contact: Naomi Davey
info: Demos should be sent on CD or cassette. Biogs are not essential, but full contact details should be included.

Spit & Polish Records
PO Box 15193, Glasgow, G2 6UB
email: info@shoeshine.co.uk
web: www.shoeshine.co.uk
genre: Americana/Country
info: Send demo to the above address marked FAO A&R. Linked with Shoeshine Records. See separate listing.

Splank! Records
3rd Floor, 24-26 Lever Street, Manchester, M1 1DZ
tel: 07812 564 799
email: jonny@splankrecords.co.uk
web: www.splankrecords.co.uk
contact: Jonny Strinati
genre: Breakbeat/Nu-Skool Breaks
info: Demos on CD or vinyl are welcome. Send to the address above, make sure to include full contact details.

Stanze Interiors
436-438 Green Lanes, Palmers Green, London, N13 5XG
tel: 020 8882 0005
fax: 020 8882 0620
email: info@soundstate.com
web: www.stanze.co.uk or www.soundstate.com
contact: Arkin Jones
genre: Vocal House/Soulful House/Jazz
info: Soundstate Recordings are interested in House music with vocals, preferably Soulful, Gospel or Jazz based. Send a demo on CD and biog to the address above. Original music is preferred but covers will be considered. Soundstate Recordings are a small independent label and so cannot expect large returns, but the label will help get your music played by some of the world's biggest DJs, with the aim of helping you establish yourself as an artist. Soundstate Recordings is a division of Numb Nums Recordings Ltd.

Stereoscout/Loverboy Records
14 Victoria Road, Douglas, Isle Of Man, IM2 4ER
tel: 01624 677 214
email: dave@stereoscout.com
web: www.stereoscout.com
contact: Dave
genre: Singer-Songwriter/Indie
info: Stereoscout deal with Singer-Songwriters and Loverboy deal with more band orientated music. Mainly concerned with artists based on the Isle Of Man.

StickyLicky Records UK
Band-Idol, PO Box 4234, Wolverhampton, WV6 8WZ
tel: 01902 834 7777
email: admin@stickylickyrecords.com
web: www.stickylickyrecords.com
contact: Roland Stow, Steve Hough, Bob Evans
genre: Rock/Indie/Pop/Punk/Punk Rock/
Any Material With Chart Potential
info: StickyLicky Records UK are currently on the look out for new acts. Send a demo, press pack (including biog), photo and gig listings to the address above. Follow your submission with a phone call after 3 weeks.

Stressed Records
3 Rose Close, Chellaston, Derby, DE73 1XP
tel: 01332 703 249
email: info@stressedrecords.co.uk
web: www.stressedrecords.co.uk
contact: Phil
genre: Metal/Alternative Guitar Based/Rock/Punk
info: Send demo to the above address.

Stunted Records
6 Cliff Gardens, Scunthorpe, DN15 7PJ
tel: 01724 358 966
email: john@stuntedrecords.co.uk
web: www.stuntedrecords.co.uk
contact: John Clay
genre: Rock/Metal
info: Send demos to the above address.

Sublime Recordings
77 Preston Drove, Brighton, BN1 6LD
tel: 01273 560 605
fax: 01273 560 606
email: info@sublimemusic.co.uk
web: www.sublimemusic.co.uk
contact: A&R Dept.
genre: All Music Types Accepted
info: Send a 3 track demo on CD to the address above. The only additional information required is a contact telephone number and email address. Sublime Recordings can release one-off singles.

Suburb The Record Label
138-140 Southwark Street, London, SE1 0SW
tel: 0207 593 1555
email: info@suburbtherecordlabel.co.uk
web: www.suburbtherecordlabel.co.uk
contact: Phil Parker
genre: Ambient/Electronica/Leftfield/Experimental Electronic/ Hip-Hop
info: Suburb also offer graphic design services. See listing in relevant section for details.

Subversive Records
Hawethorn House, Forth Banks, Newcastle Upon Tyne, NE1 3SG
tel: 0191 221 1666
fax: 0191 221 1777
email: info@subversiverecords.co.uk
web: www.subversiverecords.co.uk
contact: Terry Hollingsworth
genre: All Music Types Accepted
info: Send 3 track demo on CD to Terry Hollingsworth at the address above. Make sure to write a contact number on the CD. All material will be listened to. Affiliated with the Metal/Rock/Indie label State of Decay (www.stateofdecay.com), as well as 10xBetter, artist management and PR company. See listings for further details.

Sudden Def Recordings
PO Box 39038, London, E9 5WQ
tel: 07771 848 710
email: info@suddendef.com
web: www.suddendef.com
contact: Bridge Atterbury
genre: Drum&Bass
info: Send demos on CD to the address above, or alternatively submit an internet link via email or transferred over AOL Instant Messenger (SuddenDef01). The label listen to all demos and are well known for encouraging and helping to bring through new talent both domestically and internationally.

Sugar Shack Records Ltd.
PO Box 73, Fishponds, Bristol, BS16 7EZ
tel: 0117 985 5092
fax: 0117 985 5092
email: mike@sugarshackrecords.co.uk
web: www.sugarshackrecords.co.uk
contact: Mike Darby, John Berridge
genre: Rock/Guitar Based
info: Send 3 track CD to the address above. See also listing for Sugar Shack Management in relevant section.

Sunday Best Recordings
Studio 10, 25 Denmark Street, London, WC2H 8NJ
tel: 020 7240 2248
email: info@sundaybest.net
contact: Sarah Bolshi, Rob Da Bank
genre: Electronic/Leftfield/Dance
info: Sunday Best release alternative music that crosses a variety of genres. Send an email to introduce yourself and your music, follow with demo on request. The label also hosts regular club nights, for dates and information on forthcoming events, check the regularly updated Sunday Best website. Sunday Best also promote annual Dance festival, Bestival.

Supercharged/Against The Grain
PO Box 137, Brighton, BN1 4YF
tel: 01273 628 181
email: info@superchargedmusic.com
web: www.superchargedmusic.com
contact: Lloyd Seymour
genre: Breakbeat
info: Send demos on CD to the address above. Supercharged/ Against The Grain promise to listen to and reply to all submissions. The label is home to Krafty Kuts and The Freestylers.

Superglider Records
First Floor, 123 Old Christchurch Road, Bournemouth, BH1 1EP
email: mail@superglider.com
web: www.superglider.com
info: Although Superglider Records are not actively seeking demos, they do listen to everything received with great interest. You are advised to listen to the MP3s on the label's website, to get an idea of the type of music they release before submitting any material.

Supreme Dream Records
PO Box 136, Cheadle, Cheshire, SK8 3YL
tel: 0161 490 7585
fax: 0161 490 7586
email: info@supremedreamrecords.com
web: www.supremedreamrecords.com
contact: Imran Mohammed
genre: Asian Fusion/R&B/House
info: Send a demo on CD to the address above.

Survival Records Ltd.
PO Box 2502, Devizes, Wiltshire, SN10 3ZN
tel: 01380 860 500
fax: 01380 860 596
email: survivalrecords@globalnet.co.uk
web: www.survivalrecords.co.uk
contact: Anne-Marie Heighway
genre: Celtic
info: Send demos to the above address. For full details and history of the company visit the website.

Switchflicker
2nd Floor, 24-26 Lever Street, Manchester, M1 1DZ
email: jayne@switchflicker.co.uk
web: www.switchflicker.co.uk
contact: Jayne Compton
genre: Electronica/Alternative
info: Send demos on any format to the address above.

Taffpop Records
1 The Kingsway, Swansea, SA1 5JQ
tel: 07963 372 818
email: artists@taffpop.com
web: www.taffpop.com
contact: Andy
genre: Metal/Disco/Dance/Leftfield/Hip-Hop/Punk/Pop/Indie
info: Send demos and any other relevant information to the address above. Also have facilities for CD duplication. Contact for further details.

Tailor Made Music/Liquid Asset
PO Box 2311, Romford, Essex, RM5 2DZ
tel: 01708 734 670
fax: 01708 734 671
email: del@dancelabel.com
web: www.dancelabel.com
contact: Del Blewitt
info: A group of labels (home to the Suburban Base hardcore label) and consultancy agency. Also release compilations in a variety of genres, including the Euphoria (Dance), Electric (80s Pop), Mod and Pure Groove compilations.

The Talent League
9 Douglas Square, Green Way, London, SM4 5MP
tel: 020 8685 0870
email: sam@thetalentleague.co.uk
web: www.thetalentleague.co.uk
contact: Samantha Crompton
genre: All Music Types Accepted
info: All music styles considers, contact Samantha for further details of demo submission. The Talent League also provides Management and Distribution services, as well as promoting gigs. See entries in relevant sections for further details.

Tangerine Records
PO Box 289, Hyde, Cheshire, SK14 1WS
tel: 0161 367 2706
email: info@tangerine-records.com
contact: Alex Harper
genre: Guitar Based/Electronic
info: Send a demo and biog to the address above. Alex Harper is also a freelance producer. For more information see www.alexharper.com.

Tenor Vossa Records Ltd.
PO Box 34803, London, W8 7OZ
tel: 020 7221 0511
email: tenor.vossa@virgin.net
web: www.tenorvossa.co.uk
genre: Space Rock/Haunting Soundscapes/Alt. Country
info: Send demos to the address above. Accept most music types. Associated with TV Records who have the same contact details.

Tetrachrome Recordings
PO Box 173, Manchester, M21 9YS
tel: 0161 286 6445
fax: 0161 286 6445
email: info@tetrachrome-recordings.com
web: www.tetrachrome-recordings.com
contact: James
genre: Electronic Dance Music
info: Send demos to the address above.

Third Eye
9 Walpole Road, Bournemouth, Boscombe, BH1 4HA
email: wilson_jh@hotmail.com
contact: Jay, Chris
genre: All Music Types Accepted
info: Send demo to the above address FAO Jay or Chris.

Thursday Club Recordings (TCR)
310 King Street, London, W6 0RR
tel: 020 8748 9480
fax: 020 8748 9489
email: info@tcr.uk.com
web: www.tcr.uk.com
contact: A&R
genre: Breakbeat
info: Send demos on CD to the address above, follow with an email. TCR is the UK's longest running Breaks label.

Toddler Records
22 Henry Street, Redcar, Cleveland, TS10 1BJ
tel: 01642 507 734
email: michael.todd43@ntlworld.com
web: www.toddlerrecords.com
contact: Michael Todd
genre: Punk/Indie
info: Send demos to the address above. All submissions are listened to.

Too Dark Records
PO Box 12516, Birmingham, B32 9AJ
tel: 07941 335 661
email: malabu@hotmail.com
web: www.toodarkrecords.com
contact: Malabu
genre: Hip-Hop/R&B
info: Too Dark compile mix-tapes of the artists and producers they work with. To be considered for inclusion, send demo to the above address.

Too Pure Records
17-19 Alma Road, London, SW18 1AA
tel: 020 8870 9912
fax: 020 8871 1766
email: jasonwhite@beggars.com
web: www.toopure.com
contact: Jason White
genre: Indie Guitar Music
info: Send material on CD, cassette or vinyl. Mark all submissions FAO Too Pure. No music via email please. Part of the Beggars Group (www.beggars.com).

Too Tone Records
London
tel: 07739 799 003
email: info@tootone.com
web: www.tootone.com
contact: David Franks
genre: Hip-Hop/Rap/R&B
info: Email Too Tone with details of yourself and your music, follow with demo on request.

ToppaTop Records
55 Great Hampton Street, Hockley, Birmingham, B18 6EL
tel: 07859 907 221/07859 907 220
email: toppatop@btconnect.com
contact: Paul Smith
genre: Urban/Hip-Hop/R&B
info: Also run video production and modelling agencies. Contact for further information.

TOV Music Group
PO Box 42109, London, SW8 2WT
tel: 020 7498 3888
fax: 020 7622 1030
email: info@tovmusic.com
web: www.tovmusic.com
contact: A&R
genre: Drum&Bass
info: Send demos on CD to the address above, with your email address written clearly on the actual disc. Mark FAO TOV Music A&R. No sound files via email please.

the|unsigned|guide

The Unsigned Guide/UK/2006. Material published in this directory may not be reproduced (in any form) without written consent.

TPF Records
Welsh Hills Works, Jenkin Street, Porth, Rhondda, CF39 9PP
tel: 01443 688 500
email: via website
web: www.thepopfactory.com
genre: All Music Types Accepted
info: TPF Records is part of The Pop Factory complex that also comprises various recording studio spaces, venue and video production facilities. See relevant sections for more details.

Transcopic Ltd.
9 Greenland Street, London, NW1 0ND
email: jamie@transcopic.com
web: www.transcopic.com
contact: Jamie Davies
genre: Indie Rock/Alternative
info: Send demos on CD, vinyl or cassette to the address above. Transcopic do listen to all material sent but cannot guarantee a reply. If they like your music they will be in touch. Transcopic was founded by Graham Coxon.

Transient Records
Unit 5, Waldo Works, Waldo Road, London, NW10 6AW
tel: 020 8964 8890
fax: 020 8960 5741
email: music@transient.com
web: www.transient.com
contact: Glenn Mack
genre: Trance/Psychedelic Trance
info: Associated with Joof and Automatic. Send demos to the address above.

Trash Talk
39 Northfield Road, Sheffield, S10 1QP
tel: 0114 268 4604
email: info@trashtalkrecords.co.uk
web: www.trashtalkrecords.co.uk
contact: Dave Johnson
genre: Funky House
info: Send demos on CD to the address above.

Travelled Music
The Tileworks, Paxton, Berwick upon Tweed, TD15 1TJ
tel: 01289 386737
email: alan@travelledmusic.co.uk
web: www.travelledmusic.co.uk
contact: Alan Thompson
genre: Electronic/Rock/Pop/Folk
info: Managers of Ordinary Son. Any interested bands should include in their demo packs biographies, and details of past gigs.

Tru Thoughts
PO Box 2818, Brighton, BN1 4RL
tel: 01273 694 617
email: info@tru-thoughts.co.uk
web: www.tru-thoughts.co.uk
contact: Robert Luis
genre: Jazz/Breakbeat/Downbeat/Soul/Hip-Hop/Funk
info: Send demos on CD to the address above, with contact details (preferably an email address) written clearly on the actual format. Make sure the best three tracks are at the start of your demo and include a brief written description of each one. The label advise you to listen to their current and previous releases before submitting any material. If you are submitting material to the label, Tru Thoughts would prefer if you became a registered member on their website so they can keep you informed of upcoming events and releases. Associated with the Zebra Traffic website, see listing for further details.

Tumi Music Ltd.
8-9 New Bond Street Place, Bath, Somerset, BA1 1BH
tel: 01225 462 367
fax: 01225 444 870
email: info@tumimusic.com
web: www.tumimusic.com
contact: Mo Fini
info: Deal exclusively with Cuban and Latin music. Artists represented by Tumi Music include Yusa, Papa Noel, Jovenes Clasico Del Son, Candido Fabre and Son 14.

Twisted Nerve
Unit 6 & 7, 8 Lower Ormond Street, Manchester, M1 5QF
email: info@twistednerve.co.uk
web: www.twistednerve.co.uk
genre: All Music Types Accepted
info: Send demos (preferably on CD, but will accept DAT, MD or cassette) to the address above. Include only what you feel are your best tracks. Make sure that a contact email or telephone number is written on the actual CD, MD, DAT or cassette. Twisted Nerve will contact you if they like your material but allow at least a few weeks for a reply. For more information on submitting demos to Twisted Nerve, see www.twistednerve.co.uk/demos

U-Freqs
56 Oakfield Court, Haslemere Road, Crouch End, London, N8 9QY
email: stevino@u-freqs.com
web: www.u-freqs.com
contact: Stevino
genre: Alternative
info: The label are looking for anything strange, odd, weird, quirky or shocking - using traditional instruments or electronic equipment. Their motto - "scouring the dregs of humanity for the one genius tune in everyone." Send demos to the address above. You are advised to check the label's back catalogue before submitting any material.

Underdogg Entertainment Ltd.
41 Lynnhurst, Tannochside, Uddington, Glasgow, G71 6SA
tel: 01698 308 692
email: hydro@underdoggentertainment.com
web: www.underdoggentertainment.com
contact: Adnan Ahmed
genre: R&B/Alternative Rock/Hip-Hop/Rap
info: Alternative label, events and distribution company.

Undiscovered Music
5 Sprules Road, London, SE4 2NL
tel: 020 7639 1664
fax: 020 7207 2907
email: a-r@undiscovered.co.uk or licensing@undiscovered.co.uk
web: www.undiscovered.co.uk
contact: Angelo Tardio
genre: Reggae/Electro/House/R&B/Lounge/Chillout/Hip-Hop
info: Demos should be sent to the label's Italian office at Via Icaro 15, 80072 Lucrino Naples, Italy (Tel: +39 081 855 5311).

Unique Corp Ltd.
1 Pennine Parade, Pennine Drive, London, NW2 1NT
tel: 020 8458 6006
fax: 020 8458 6660
email: info@uniquecorp.co.uk
web: www.uniquecorp.co.uk
contact: A&R
genre: Dance/Urban/Pop/R&B
info: Send demos on CD to the address above.

Universal
364 - 366 Kensington High Street, London, W14 8NS
tel: 020 7471 5300
fax: 020 8910 3224
email: louis.bloom or joel.harrisson@umusic.com
web: www.umusic.com
contact: Louis Bloom (Universal) or Joel Harrison (Island)
genre: All Music Types Accepted
info: Do not accept unsolicited demos.

Urbcom
5th Floor, 28 Landos Court, Gunson Street, Manchester, M40 7WT
tel: 0161 202 5261/07813 845 822
fax: 0161 202 5261
email: info@urbcom.net
web: www.urbcom.net
contact: Mark Lingard
genre: Electronic/Dance/Industrial
info: Demos preferably submitted in CD-R format. Biogs and photos should also be included.

V/Vm Test Records
email: vvm@goldserve.net
web: www.brainwashed.com/vvm
contact: James
genre: Alternative
info: Email the label for a demo submission address, follow with a CD. Make sure to write your contact information on the actual disc. No sound files via email please. You are advised to check the MP3s on the V/Vm Test Records website before sending in any material.

V2 Records
131-133 Holland Park Avenue, London, W11 4UT
tel: 020 7471 3000
fax: 020 7603 4796
web: www.v2music.com
contact: A&R, Oliver Hodge
genre: All Music Types Accepted
info: Send demos on CD to the address above.

Valentine Records
Flat 10, 12 Palantine Road, Manchester, M20 3JA
email: info@valentinerecords.co.uk
web: www.valentinerecords.co.uk
contact: Dave Fox
genre: Electronic/Alternative
info: Before you submit a demo, Valentine Records advise you to listen to some of the acts already signed (sound clips are available on the website), to decide if your music really fits in with the general direction of the label. CD or MD, please write contact details (including email address) on the actual disc. Valentine Records do listen to all material they receive, but cannot reply to everyone.

Valve Recordings
Unit 24, Ropery Business Park, Hope & Anchor Lane, London, SE7 7RX
tel: 020 8853 4900
fax: 020 8853 4908
email: info@valverecordings.com
web: www.valverecordings.com
contact: Adam
genre: Drum&Bass
info: Send demos with a covering letter to the address above. Mark FAO Adam or Mike.

Vampire Records
20 Tanners Hill, Deptford, London, SE8 4JP
tel: 020 8691 6666
fax: 020 8692 9999
email: info@vampiremusic.co.uk
web: www.vampiremusic.co.uk
contact: Bryan Harman
genre: Dance
info: Also incorporates recording studios, rehearsal rooms, equipment hire service, music shop, mastering and duplication services, and tuition. For further details see entries in relevant sections for Vampire Music.

Varial Records
email: info@varialrecords.net
web: www.varialrecords.net
contact: Mat Carter
genre: Downtempo/Dub House/Electro/Techno/Electronica
info: Email Varial Records an introduction to yourself and your music, follow with a demo on request.

Verity Records
69 -79 Fulham High Street, London, SW6 3JW
tel: 020 7384 7500
contact: A&R Dept.
genre: All Music Types Accepted
info: Send demo to the above address.

Vertical Records
The Art House, 752 Argyle Street, Glasgow, G3 8UH
tel: 0141 847 0002
fax: 0870 762 7126
email: info@verticalrecords.co.uk
web: www.verticalrecords.co.uk
contact: Donald Shaw
genre: Celtic/Roots/Acoustic
info: Send demos to the address above.

The Viper Label
PO Box 48, Liverpool, L17 7JE
email: theviperlabel@hotmail.com
web: www.the-viper-label.co.uk
contact: Paul Hemmings
genre: Alternative Guitar Based
info: Independent label whose aims are to release interesting and exciting Contemporary and archive music worldwide. Releases have included 'The Unearthed Liverpool Cult Classic' series (definitive collection of Liverpool Music from the 70s to the present day), 'Captain Beefheart Live in the UK 72-80', 'The Lost LA's albums', and 'The Great Liverpool Acoustic Experiment' (collection featuring Space, The Christians, The Hokum Clones, Ian McNabb). For full discography and information about future releases, please contact Viper.

Viral Music Management Ltd.
158 Bidduiph Road, Mossley, Congleton, CW12 3LS
email: darren@viralmusic.co.uk
web: www.viralmusic.co.uk
contact: Darren Pearce
genre: All Music Types Accepted
info: Online record label. Send demo to address above.

Viral Wax Recordings
2 Cedarwood Glade, Stainton, Middlesborough, TS8 9DJ
email: info@viralwaxrecordings.com
web: www.viralwaxrecordings.com
genre: Breakbeat/Leftfield/Experimental/Electronic
info: Send demos to the address above, CD and MD only (no MP3s). Please mark details on the actual format. No more than 5 tracks. Send an SAE if you want your tracks returned.

Visceral Thrill Recordings
8 Deronda Road, London, SE24 9BG
tel: 020 8647 7990
fax: 020 8671 5548
contact: David Massey
genre: All Music Types Accepted
info: Send demos on CD to the address above. Include a maximum of 4 tracks.

Visible Noise ✏
231 Portobello Road, London, W11 1LT
tel: 0207 792 9791
fax: 0207 792 9871
email: julie@visiblenoise.com
web: www.visiblenoise.com
contact: Julie Weir
genre: Rock/Metal
info: Send good quality demos with biog and photo to the address above (No MP3s via email please). Visible Noise signings include Lost Prophets, Number One Son and Bullet For My Valentine.

Vokal Records
PO Box 2742, Romford, RM7 1AS
email: info@vokalrecords.com
web: www.vokalrecords.com
genre: Urban/Asian
info: Send demos to the above address.

Voltage Records
Voltage Studios, St. Stephen's Mill, Ripley Street, Bradford, BD5 7JW
tel: 01274 393 998
email: info@voltagerecords.com
web: www.voltagerecords.com
contact: Tim Walker
genre: Guitar Based/Electronica
info: Send a demo on CD to the address above. For more information on the label's recording studio, Voltage Studio, see www.voltagestudios.com.

Voluptuous Records
29 Wentworth Park, Finchley, London, N3 1YE
email: carl@formidable-mgmt.com
contact: Carl
genre: All Music Types Accepted
info: Send 2 or 3 track demo CD to the address above. Any music with commercial potential will be considered.

Vox Pop Music
18 Sparkle Street, Manchester, M1 2NA
tel: 0161 273 3435
fax: 0161 273 3695
email: info@voxpop45.com
web: www.voxpop45.com
contact: Tim Giles
genre: Deep Funk/Soul/Northern Soul
info: Vox Pop is predominantly a reissue label but would release new material as well, as long as it sounds authentic. Send demos to the address above. A division of Sub Tub Music Ltd.

Wafer Thin Records
PO Box 81, Birmingham, B30 2LF
tel: 0121 444 5887
email: waferthin@hotmail.com
web: www.waferthin.org
contact: Rob Peters
genre: Acoustic/Singer-Songwriter
info: Send demos to the address above.

Wafty Crank
24 Lime Tree Avenue, York, North Yorkshire, YO32 4BE
tel: 07753 327 826
email: tim.johnson@waftycrank.co.uk
web: www.waftycrank.co.uk
contact: Tim Johnson
genre: Punk/Hip-Hop/Ska
info: Currently working with 5 local acts. Wafty Crank also put on gigs in York and offer a web and graphic design service. See entries in relevant sections for further details.

Wag Records
15 Tabbs Lane, Scholes, Yorkshire, BD19 6DY
tel: 01274 851 365
fax: 01274 874 329
email: john@now-music.com
web: www.now-music.com
contact: John Wagstaff
genre: Pop

Wall of Sound Recordings Ltd.
Office 2, 9 Thorpe Close, London, W10 5XL
tel: 020 8969 1144
fax: 020 8969 1155
email: general@wallofsound.co.uk
web: www.wallofsound.net
contact: Alvin Collis, Mark Jones
genre: Hip-Hop/Dance/Alternative/Indie
info: Send demos on CD to address above. Maximum of 5 tracks. Wall Of Sound is affiliated with 2 other labels, Bad Magic (Hip Hop) and We Love You (Singer-Songwriter). Contact information for both affiliate labels as above.

Warp Records Ltd.
PO Box 25378, London, NW5 1GL
tel: 020 7284 8350
fax: 020 7284 8360
email: info@warprecords.com
web: www.warprecords.com
contact: Ngaio Davies, Chloe
genre: Electronic
info: Contact Warp Records with details of yourself and your music, follow with demo on request. Home to, amongst others, Aphex Twin and Boards Of Canada. Warp have an associated Hip-Hop label called Lex Records.

Warped Records
17 Waterloo Gardens, London, N1 1TY
tel: 020 7609 1616
fax: 020 7700 1700
contact: Merton
genre: World
info: Send demo to the address above. Maximum of 3 tracks.

Wasp Factory Recordings
1st Floor, 65-67 High Street, Cheltenham, GL50 1DU
tel: 01242 521 713
email: enquiries@wasp-factory.com
web: www.wasp-factory.com
contact: Mark Eris
genre: Industrial/Post Rock/Electronic
info: Send demos on CD to the address above. Include details of upcoming live dates. The label was winner of the UK's Young Music Professionals Award 2003.

Wave Records Ltd.
PO Box 7794, Long Eaton, Nottingham, NG10 4YE
tel: 0115 973 0519
fax: 0115 946 0929
email: info@wave-records.com
web: www.wave-records.com
contact: Jon Garton
genre: House/Trance/Hard Dance
info: All demos welcome, submit to the address above.

Whoop! Records
PO Box 14408, London, SW17 9ZS
tel: 020 8875 0381
fax: 020 8875 0385
email: contact@whoop.co.uk
web: www.whoop.co.uk
contact: Joel Xavier
genre: House/Funky House
info: Email the label with an introduction to yourselves and your music. Follow with a demo on request. Whoop! Records' sub label, Kinky Vinyl, releases Funky House. See also Management Company listings.

Wicked World
Suite 1-3 Westminster Building, Theatre Square, Nottingham, NG1 6LG
tel: 0115 950 6400
fax: 0115 950 8585
email: mail@earache.com
web: www.earache.com/wickedworld.html
contact: Dan Tobin
genre: Underground Metal
info: Send demos to the address above. You can also send details of where your music is available online, but no MP3s via email please. Wicked World is a subsidiary of Earache Records.

Wildwood Acoustic
PO Box 137, Kendall, Cumbria, LA8 0XD
tel: 01539 824 008
email: wildwood@georgelloyd.com
web: www.georgelloyd.com
contact: A&R Dept.
genre: Acoustic/World
info: Phone before sending demos. Part of the Lloyd Music Group Ltd.

Wingtip Records Ltd.
757 Southchurch Road, Southend-on-Sea, Essex, SS1 2PP
tel: 01702 469 229
email: wingtiprecords@aol.com
web: www.wingtiprecords.com
contact: Ray Brown
genre: All Music Types Accepted
info: Send CD to the address above. Include biog, photos and any other relevant information.

Woodland Records Ltd.
111 The Custard Factory, Digbeth, Birmingham, B9 4AA
tel: 0121 693 0013
fax: 0121 693 0013
email: info@woodlandrecords.com
web: www.woodlandrecords.com
contact: Perry Hamus
genre: Jazz/Lounge/Latin/Nu Jazz/Deep House/ Leftfield Funky House/Broken Beat
info: Woodland Records aims to push Leftfield music forms. Send demos on CD or vinyl to the address above. If you would like your material returned, please include SAE. The label guarantee to listen and respond to all submissions. Licensing enquiries are welcome.

World Circuit Ltd.
138 Kingsland Road, London, E2 8DY
tel: 020 7749 3222
fax: 020 7749 3222
email: post@worldcircuit.co.uk
web: www.worldcircuit.co.uk
contact: Julie
genre: World

Wrath Records
The Cardigan Centre, 145-149 Cardigan Road, Leeds, LS6 1LJ
email: info@wrathrecords.co.uk
web: www.wrathrecords.co.uk
contact: Steven Morricone
genre: Guitar Based/Indie Rock
info: Wrath Records is based around a co-operative of musicians and generally release their own music. However as the label expands, there may be the opportunity to release other material. The general approach is expansion through co-operation. Demo submissions are always welcome and a selection are reviewed on the Wrath Records website. Listen to snippets on the website to judge if your material is suitable before sending to Wrath.

XL Recordings
1 Codrington Mews, London, W11 2EH
tel: 020 8870 7511
fax: 020 8871 4178
email: xl@xlrecordings.com
contact: Matt Thornhill
genre: Electronic/Alternative
info: Mark demos FAO A&R and write 'Demo from [your band]' on the outside of the package.

Xtrax London
PO Box 966, London, SE11 5SA
tel: 020 7582 5380
fax: 020 7582 5380
email: xtraxuk@dircon.co.uk
contact: Alan X
genre: Dance
info: Xtrax London deals exclusively with Dance music. Send appropriate demos to the address above.

Year Zero
378 Oldfield Lane North, Greenford, Middlesex, UB6 8PU
tel: 020 8575 8753
email: larryleigh@hotmail.com
contact: Lawrence Leigh
genre: Indie Guitar Music
info: Send demo on CD or cassette to the address above. Include biog and photo.

Yperano
PO Box 17222, London, W12 8ZG
email: info@yperano.com
web: www.yperano.com
contact: A&R Dept.
genre: Metal/Rock
info: Always on the look out for unsigned bands. Send demos to the address above. Include lyrical content and a photo of your band.

Zarg Records
White House Farm, Shropshire, TF9 4HA
tel: 01630 647 374
fax: 01630 647 612
contact: Ron Dickson
genre: Rock/Rock Horror/Heavy Rock
info: Demos are accepted on CD and MD, accompanied by any information available. Associated with the publishing company RTL Music, so songwriters can also send in their work. Currently signed to the label are Nightmare, Suburban Studs and Orphan.

Zebra Traffic
P.O. Box 2818, Brighton, BN1 4RL
tel: 01273 669 070
fax: 01273 694 589
email: mail@zebratraffic.co.uk
web: www.zebratraffic.co.uk
contact: Tom Simpson
genre: UK Hip Hop
info: See the website for demo submission details. Linked with Tru Thoughts label, see listing for details.

Zenith Café
Barhams, Bakers Lane, Linton, Cambridge, Cambridgeshire, CB1 6NF
tel: 01223 897 800
email: info@zenithcafe.co.uk
web: www.zenithcafe.co.uk
contact: Danny
genre: All Music Types Accepted
info: Zenith Café accepts demos on CD or DVD from within all genres of music. Prefer bands to include a biog with the demo pack.

Zenith Records
163 Gerrard Street, Birmingham, West Midlands, B19 2AH
tel: 0121 554 7424
fax: 0121 551 9250
email: info@earthproductions.co.uk
web: www.earthproductions.co.uk
contact: Ron Thompson
genre: All Music Types Accepted
info: Zenith deal with all types of music, but their main interests lie in Dance, Reggae and R&B. Send demos to the address above.

ZTT Records
The Blue Building, 8-10 Basing Street, London, W11 1ET
tel: 020 7221 5101
fax: 020 7221 3374
email: info@ztt.com
web: www.ztt.com
contact: Paul Barton
genre: All Music Types Accepted
info: Send demo on CD and biog to the address above. Include an SAE if you would like your material returned.

ZYX Records UK Ltd.
Unit 11, Cambridge Court, 210 Shepherds Bush Road, London, W6 7NJ
tel: 0207 371 6969
fax: 0207 371 6688
email: lauren.lorenzo@zyxrecords.freeserve.co.uk
web: www.zyxrecords.de
contact: Lauren Lorenzo
genre: All Music Types Accepted

Section 2
Publishing Companies

the|unsigned|guide

2.1 Publishing Companies Foreword

As a songwriter you may be interested in business, but chances are your talent is best spent creating. So if your time is predominantly spent writing, someone needs to take care of the business side of things and this is where the publishing companies come into play.

In a nutshell, the role of the publishing company is to generate as much revenue as they can by granting licenses for other people to use your material. When you sign a publishing contract, you are signing over your copyright to a third party who you contract to sell your songs on your behalf.

1. Copyright
Copyright is a 'property' right. This means that the owner of the right, who can be the author or any person to whom the author has assigned it, has the exclusive right to authorise or prevent others from using a 'musical work' in various ways. These 'restricted acts' are:

- Making a copy of the work, which includes recording it

- Publishing the work

- Performing the work in public (live or through recordings)

- Broadcasting the work

- Making an arrangement of the work.

A 'musical work' consists entirely of music and the words of a song are a 'literary work'. Both are protected in the same way.

> **Under UK law, copyright does not exist until a musical or literary work is recorded in writing or otherwise.**

If a song is co-composed, the Musicians' Union strongly advises contributors to sign and date a short agreement setting out the name of the song, the names of their contributors and their respective shares in the song. Also you will need to state whether the shares are in respect of words only, music only, or in words and music. For example, John Smith 25% (Words) + Phil Allen 75% (Words/Music).
Without a 'Song Share Agreement' a publisher, or the courts, may infer equal contributions, and the potential for dispute between contributors (e.g. if the song writing partnership splits up) is greatly increased.

Under UK law, copyright does not exist until a musical or literary work is recorded in writing or otherwise. This means that there is no copyright in ideas until they take some material form, usually a manuscript or recording (e.g.CD/DAT).

Unlike some other countries, registration is not required for copyright protection. However, in cases where there is a dispute about the 'originality' or 'authorship' of a particular work, it can help to produce evidence establishing the date when the work was created. One practical way of doing this is to deposit a copy with a responsible person, such as solicitor and obtain a dated receipt. Alternatively, you could send yourself a copy of the recording or manuscript of the work by Special Delivery/Registered Post and leave it, unopened, in a safe place.

Copyright in a musical work lasts for seventy years after the end of the year in which the author dies. At the end of this period the musical work then becomes public property. It should be noted that there is no copyright in a title of a song or the name of a band. If there is reason to believe that you think that it represents your work or group, a legal action for 'passing off' is possible, although obtaining proof can be quite difficult.

2. Do I need my songs to be published by a 'publisher' to earn money from them?

The short answer to this is not necessarily. If one of your songs comes out on record and you do not have a music publisher, then your name should appear under the title of the song on the record label, and underneath this should be the words 'Copyright Control, or if you are a member, 'MCPS'. This will alert others to the fact that you are the copyright owner of the song and have not assigned it to any music publisher.

Additional Sources of Revenue

Synchronisation Fees
These are one off payments made to copyright holders by the producer of a film or a television company for the right to incorporate songs into a film soundtrack or television programme. This fee can be negotiated directly with the producer, or providing you are a member, you could ask the MCPS to do it on your behalf.

Sheet Music
Some songs still sell well in sheet music form. Composers are entitled to a royalty payment from such sales.

3. Why sign with a publisher then?
Both the PRS and MCPS have worldwide affiliates, so that fees and royalties can be collected for you wherever your song is played or recorded throughout the world. However, many composers/songwriters still choose to sign with a music publisher and give up a portion of their royalties by doing so. Here are some of the reasons why:

Advances
Publishers will often pay a writer annual advances on account of future royalties. If you can delay signing with a publisher until after you have had several strong performing songs, these annual advances might be very sizeable.

Administration & Collection
Further down the line, many writers and artists decide to form their own publishing companies and merely wish to seek the administration services of a large corporate publisher. In return for a small share of earnings from royalties the larger company will take over the day-to-day business of administering the catalogue.

Record Deals & Promotional Assistance
Sometimes, where a composer/performer is having trouble finding a record deal, a music publisher may be quicker to spot their talent. The publisher may provide free demo time and help to try and secure a record deal for the songwriters/artists. In this instance, you should not expect the annual advances to be as large.

Covers
Not all songwriters and musicians are looking to perform their own material. Consequently, for a non-performing composer/song writer, it can be useful to team up with a music publisher who will try to promote your music and place it with major recording artists. However, some publishers are better than others at doing this, so talk to other writers, look through trade magazines and web sites etc. to check on a publisher's success rate.

4. What is negotiable in a publishing deal?

Length of Contract
A publishing contract could be just for one song or it could cover everything you write for a number of years. If a publishing company is offering advances, it will probably want a blanket deal for a number of years. The Musicians' Union suggest a maximum of three years.

Assignment of Copyright
It is not always necessary to assign the copyright in your songs to a publisher for the full copyright life. Instead, you could try for the length of the agreement (for example three years) plus a number of extra years, known as a retention period. This could be anything up to twenty-five years, depending upon your bargaining power.

Royalties & Advances
At least 70% in favour of the songwriter seems to be the going rate for new writers nowadays. This should cover mechanicals (MCPS royalties), synchronisation fees and any other uses and PRS. Sheet music sales normally yield a royalty of about 10%-15% of retail selling price. Some songwriters are successful in securing increases in their percentages throughout each new year of the agreement, but

the agreement needs to provide for this possibility. Always consult an independent legal advisor regarding such matters.

Accounting
Tends to be twice yearly, at the end of March and the end of September. Make sure there is a Right of Audit in the agreement giving you the right to inspect the publisher's books or have them inspected on your behalf.

Protection of Copyright
This role now becomes that of the publisher and not you. If anyone infringes the copyright, the publisher will split the damages with you.

Reversion & Determination Clauses
An important clause for a songwriter. You should ensure that if the publisher has failed to exploit the song within a given period of time, or is for example made bankrupt, you will get your songs back.

What are Moral Rights?
The new Copyright Act has granted to songwriters and composers:-

1. The right to claim authorship of their work

2. The right to object to any modification or distortion of their work. Beware of any clause in a publishing agreement requiring you to waive completely your rights in this area.

Statements
You will probably receive statements on twice-annually basis. A good statement will provide clear details of the following items:-

- Source of income (e.g. PRS, Mechanicals, etc.)
- Total royalty received by publisher
- Songwriter's share
- Date of receipt by publisher

5. Self Publishing
At a certain stage in your career you may wish to set up your own publishing company. Information is available from the PRS and MCPS about the criteria necessary to join these organisations as a publisher member.

Self Publishing Advantages:
You will keep 100% of royalties earned from your songs and retain 100% of copyright.

Self Publishing Disadvantages:
The larger the amount of work involved if the songs become successful, the necessity to 'do your own deals' with foreign sub-publishers and the investment money necessary to start your own company. These disadvantages could be overcome by entering into an administration-type deal as earlier discussed.

This information has been kindly provided by Musicians' Union.

Visit **www.musiciansunion.org.uk** for more information.

MU members can view a sample Music Publishing Agreement, with explanatory notes, on the MU website.

NB. Publishing agreements are highly complex, legally binding documents. You should always consult a music business solicitor before signing such an agreement. One option always available to MU members is the Union's free contract advisory service. Information is available through your branch secretary.

2.2 PUBLISHING COMPANIES

23rd Precinct Music
23 Bath Street, Glasgow, G2 1HU
tel: 0141 332 4806
fax: 0141 353 3039
email: billy@23rdprecinct.co.uk
web: www.23rdprecinct.co.uk
genre: Dance
info: Send demos on CD to the address above, plus an email to let 23rd Precinct Music know that your material is on its way. The label is run from the 23rd Precinct shop, Scotland's first independent Dance music store. For catalogue information visit the website. See also 23rd Precinct Recordings in the Record Companies listings.

4807 Music
15 Stanhope Road, London, N6 5NE
tel: 020 8340 7797
fax: 020 8340 6923
email: paul@paulrodriguezmus.demon.co.uk
contact: James Usher, Lucy Rodriguez
genre: Library

A7 Music
PO Box 2272, Rottingdean, Brighton, BN2 8XD
tel: 01273 304 681
fax: 01273 308 120
email: info@a7music.com
web: www.a7music.com
contact: Steve B
genre: All Music Types Accepted
info: Send demos on CD (no more than three tracks) to the address above.

Abacabe Music
10 Messaline Avenue, London, W3 6JX
tel: 020 8723 7376
fax: 020 8723 7380
email: fran@bluesinbritain.org
web: www.bluesinbritain.org
contact: Fran Leslie
genre: Blues
info: Abacabe Music is the publishing arm of 'Blues in Britain' magazine, who every year release a compilation of the best in British Blues, including unsigned acts. Send demos to Fran at the address above.

Acorn Publishing
1 Tylney View, London Road, Hook, Hampshire, RG27 9LJ
tel: 07808 377 350
email: publishingacorn@hotmail.com
web: www.acorn-music.com
contact: Mark Olrog
genre: All Music Types Accepted
info: Email Mark at the address above with details of your act. Send demo on request. The website also provides a variety of alternative services such as downloadable music.

Adventures in Music Publishing
PO Box 261, Wallingford, Oxfordshire, OX10 0ZY
tel: 01491 832 183
fax: 01491 832 183
email: info@adventuresin-music.com
web: www.adventuresin-music.com
contact: Paul Conroy
genre: All Music Types Accepted
info: Call or email Paul with details of your act. Send demos on request.

Afrikan Cowboy Publishing
33 Colomb Street, London, SE10 9HA
tel: 020 8305 2448
email: afrikancowboyltd@aol.com
contact: Dean Hart
genre: R&B/Instrumental/Dance/Rock/Pop
info: Send music only. Maximum of 3 tracks to the postal address above.

Air-Edel Associates Ltd.
18 Rodmarton Street, London, W1U 8BJ
tel: 020 7486 6466
fax: 020 7224 0344
email: air-edel@air-edel.co.uk
web: www.air-edel.co.uk
contact: Mark Lo
genre: All Music Types Accepted
info: Deal mainly with film and television music. Send demos to address above.

All-Media Music Ltd.
15 Stanhope Road, London, N6 5NE
tel: 020 8340 7797
fax: 020 8340 6923
email: allmediamusic@paulrodriguezmus.demon.co.uk
contact: Lucy Rodriguez
genre: Television/Film soundtrack and theme music
info: Deals mainly with music for television, but will accept other projects. Include SAE if you would like your demo returned. No unsolicited material.

Amphonic Music Ltd.
Kerchesters, Waterhouse Lane, Kingswood, Surrey, KT20 6HT
tel: 0800 525 132
fax: 01737 833 812
email: promotions@amphonic.co.uk
web: www.amphonic.com
contact: Ian Dale
genre: Television/Film soundtrack and theme music
info: Deal primarily with music for television, radio and corporate videos. Will accept demos, and have regular listening sessions for unsigned material. Mainly use instrumental music.

Anglia Music Company
39 Tadorne Road, Tadworth, Surrey, KT20 5TF
tel: 01737 812 922
fax: 01737 812 922
email: angliamusic@ukgateway.net
contact: Norma Camby
genre: MOR/Easy Listening
info: Send demo with one or two tracks to Norma Camby at the address above.

Angus Publications
14 Graham Terrace, Belgravia, London, SW1W 8JH
tel: 07850 845 280
web: www.billmartinsongwriter.com
contact: Bill Martin
genre: Pop
info: Send demos FAO Bill to the address above.

Ape Music Publishing
5 Ossington Street, London, W2 4LZ
tel: 020 7034 0849
fax: 020 7727 8751
email: info@apemusicpub.com
web: www.apemusicpub.com
contact: Mikail Graham
genre: Rock/Pop/R&B
info: Refer to guidelines on website before sending demo.

Arena Music Co Ltd.
Hatch Farm Studios, Chertsey Road, Addlestone, Surrey, KT15 2EH
tel: 01932 828 715
fax: 01932 828 717
email: brian.adams@dial.pipex.com
web: www.thestoreformusic.com
contact: Brian Adams
genre: All Music Types Accepted
info: Send demos to Brian at the address above.

Arketek
53 Edge Street, Nutgrove, St. Helens, Merseyside, WA9 5JX
email: alan@arketek.com
web: www.arketek.com
contact: Alan Ferreira
genre: Television/Film soundtrack and theme music
info: Arketek Music specialise in obtaining usage of songs in film and TV, and are highly successful in obtaining song placements with US TV and film companies. Have obtained usages for Buffy the Vampire Slayer, Charmed and Roswell High. Please submit for TV and film work on CD only. No returns.

Artic King Music
Cambridge House, Card Hill, Forest Row, Sussex, RH18 5BA
tel: 01342 822 619
email: info@modernwoodmanagement.co.uk
web: www.modernwoodmanagement.co.uk
contact: Mickey Modern
genre: All Music Types Accepted
info: Send demos to the address above.

Associated Music International Ltd.
34 Salisbury Street, London, NW8 8QE
tel: 020 7402 9111
fax: 020 7723 3064
email: marc@amimedia.co.uk
web: www.amimedia.co.uk
contact: Marc Sheinman
genre: All Music Types Accepted
info: Send demos to Marc Sheinman (A&R Department) at the address above.

Avid
10 The Metro Centre, Dwight Road, Tolpits Lane, Watford, Hertfordshire, WD18 9UF
tel: 01923 281 281
fax: 01923 281 200
email: info@avidgroup.co.uk
web: www.avidgroup.co.uk
contact: Richard Lim
genre: Jazz/Nostalgia/Easy Listening
info: Generally do not deal with unsigned acts but if music is suitable and of good quality then it will be considered. Also distribute music.

Bacon Empire Publishing Ltd.
271 Royal College Street, London, NW1 9LU
tel: 020 7482 0115
fax: 020 7267 1169
email: maurice@baconempire.com
contact: Maurice Bacon
genre: All Music Types Accepted
info: Send demos to the address above.

Barry Collings Entertainments
21a Clifftown Road, Southend-on-Sea, SS1 1AB
tel: 01702 330 005
fax: 01702 333 309
email: bcollent@aol.com
web: www.barrycollings.co.uk
contact: Barry Collings
genre: Commercial
info: Send demos to the address above. Also operate as an artist management company.

BAT Music
The Coach House, Swinhope Hall, Swinhope, Market Rasen, Lincolnshire, LN8 6HT
tel: 01472 399 011
fax: 01472 399 025
contact: Bernard Theobald
genre: All Music Types Accepted
info: Send demos to address above.

BDM Music Ltd.
PO Box 460, North Shields, Tyne & Wear, NE30 4WA
tel: 0191 296 5577
email: ray@lindisfarne.co.uk
contact: Ray Laidlaw
genre: All Music Types Accepted
info: Send demos FAO Ray to above address.

Big Bear Music
PO Box 944, Edgbaston, Birmingham, West Midlands, B16 8UT
tel: 0121 454 7020
fax: 0121 454 9996
email: agency@bigbearmusic.com
web: www.bigbearmusic.com
contact: Jim Simpson
genre: Jazz/Blues/Swing
info: Send demos to Jim Simpson at the address above.

Big City Triumph Music
3 St. Andrew Street, Lincoln, Lincolnshire, LN5 7NE
tel: 01522 539 883
fax: 01522 528 964
email: steve.hawkins@easynet.co.uk
web: www.icegroup.co.uk
contact: Steve Hawkins
genre: Pop/Rock
info: Send demos to the address above.

Big Life Music
67-69 Chalton Street, London, NW1 1HY
tel: 020 7554 2100
fax: 020 7554 2154
email: reception@biglife.co.uk
web: www.biglife.co.uk
contact: Tim Parry
genre: All Music Types Accepted
info: Send demos to address above.

Big Red Car
22 Somerford House, Cirencester, Gloucestershire, GL7 1TW
tel: 01285 658 487 or 01285 642 289
fax: 01285 658 487
email: paul@sirensound.com
contact: Paul Turney
genre: All Music Types Accepted
info: Send demos to the address above. Include SAE if you would like your demo returned.

Big Top Music
14 Havensfield Drive, Clarendon Park, Upper Tean, Staffordshire, ST10 4RR
tel: 01538 723 890
email: p_quinton@btopenworld.com
web: www.bigtopmusic.com
contact: Paul Quinton
genre: Indie
info: Call or email Paul with details of your act. Send demo on request.

Blue Melon Publishing
240-240a High Road, Harrow Weald, Middlesex, HA3 7BB
tel: 020 8863 2520
fax: 020 8863 2520
email: steve@bluemelon.co.uk
web: www.bluemelon.co.uk
contact: Steven Glen, Mark Albert
genre: All Music Types Accepted
info: Send demos, preferably via email, to address above. Blue Melon also own download website (www.buyhear.com) features new and unsigned artists. See entry in relevant section for further details.

Blue Mountain Music
8 Kensington Park Road, London, W11 3BU
tel: 020 7229 3000
fax: 020 7221 8899
email: afua@bluemountainmusic.tv
web: www.bluemountainmusic.tv
contact: Afua
genre: All Music Types Accepted
info: Send a demo CD, any number of tracks, to the above address. Make sure to include a biog. Happy to deal with unsigned artists. Publishers for U2 and Bob Marley.

BMG Zomba
20 Fulham Broadway, London, SW6 1AH
tel: 020 7835 5300
fax: 020 7835 8318
email: musicresearch@bmgzomba.com
web: www.bmgzomba.com
genre: Television/Film soundtrack and theme music
info: BMG Zomba deal with writers composing music suitable for TV and film placement. Send demos to the above address.

Bob Lamb Music
122a Highbury Road, Kings Heath, Birmingham, West Midlands, B14 7QP
tel: 0121 443 2186
email: boblamb@recklessltd.freeserve.co.uk
contact: Bob Lamb
genre: All Music Types Accepted
info: Send demos and biography to Bob Lamb at the address above.

Bootleg Recordings
Westminster House, 6 Westminster Road, Failsworth, Manchester, M35 9LQ
tel: 0161 202 0202
fax: 0161 833 9933
email: allanrobinson@abci.fsnet.co.uk
contact: Allan Robinson
genre: All Music Types Accepted
info: Send demos to the address above. Email MP3s to Allan.

Boulevard Music Publishing
16 Lime Trees Avenue, Llangattock, Crickhowell, Powys, NP8 1LB
tel: 01873 810 142
fax: 01873 811 557
email: silverwordgroup@aol.com
web: www.silverword.co.uk
contact: Kevin Holland King
genre: Pop/Hip-Hop/Urban/MOR/Easy Listening/Country/ Instrumental
info: Send 3 track CD demo, and biog to the address above. Include a SAE if you would like your demo returned. Will accept most genres.

Bryan Morrison Music
1 Star Street, London, W2 1QD
tel: 020 7706 7304
fax: 020 7706 8197
email: bryanmorrisonmusic@btconnect.com
contact: Bryan Morrison
genre: All Music Types Accepted
info: Send demos to the address above.

Bucks Music
Onward House, 11 Uxbridge Street, London, W8 7TQ
tel: 020 7221 4275
fax: 020 7229 6893
email: info@bucksmusicgroup.co.uk
web: www.bucksmusicgroup.com
genre: All Music Types Accepted
info: Send demos marked 'Demo Submission' to the address above.

Bug Music Ltd.
Long Island House, Unit GB, Warple Way, London, W3 0RG
tel: 020 8735 1868
fax: 020 8743 1551
email: info@bugmusic.co.uk
web: www.bugmusic.com
contact: Mark Anders
genre: All Music Types Accepted
info: Send demos to the address above marked FAO A&R Department.

Campbell Connelly & Co. Ltd.
8-9 Frith Street, London, W1D 3JB
tel: 020 7434 0066
fax: 020 7439 2848
email: linda.whittle@musicsales.co.uk
web: www.musicsales.com
contact: Linda Whittle
genre: All Music Types Accepted
info: Send demos to the above address.

Candid Productions
16a Castelnau, Barnes, London, SW13 9RU
tel: 020 8741 3608
fax: 020 8563 0013
email: info@candidrecords.com
web: www.candidrecords.com
contact: Alan Bates
genre: Jazz/World
info: Send demo FAO Alan Bates. Candid deal mainly with Jazz music, but welcome demos from all genres.

Carlin Music Corporation
Iron Bridge House, 3 Bridge Approach, Chalk Farm, London, NW1 8BD
tel: 020 7734 3251
fax: 020 7439 2391
email: simonabbott@carlinmusic.com
web: www.carlinmusic.com
contact: Simon Abbott
genre: All Music Types Accepted
info: Send demos to Simon Abbott in A&R. Carlin guarantee a reply but it may take up to three months.

Catskills Music Publishing
PO Box 3365, Brighton, BN1 1WQ
tel: 01273 626 245
email: info@catskillsrecords.com
web: www.catskillsrecords.com
contact: Khalid, Amr, Jonny
genre: All Music Types Accepted/Dance
info: Send demos FO Jonny to address above. Catskills specialise mainly in Dance-orientated music. Associated with Catskills Records. See relevant section for details.

Celtic Music
Hookstone Park, Harrogate, Yorkshire, HG2 7DB
tel: 01423 888 979
fax: 01423 540 970
email: mail@celtic-music.co.uk
web: www.celtic-music.co.uk
contact: Dave Bulmer
genre: Country/Nostalgia/Classical/Traditional/Blues/ Jazz/Folk
info: Send demos to the address above.

Chain Music
24 Cornwall Road, Cheam, Surrey, SM2 6DT
tel: 020 8643 3353
fax: 020 8643 9423
email: gchurchill@c-h-a-ltd.demon.co.uk
contact: Carole Howells
genre: All Music Types Accepted
info: Send demos to the address above.

Champion
181 High Street, Harlesden, London, NW10 4TE
tel: 020 8961 5202
fax: 020 8965 3948
email: raj@championrecords.co.uk
web: www.championrecords.co.uk
contact: Raj Porter
genre: Singer-Songwriter/House/Garage
info: Send demos FAO Raj Porter.

Chesnut Music
Smoke Tree House, Tilford Road, Farnham, Surrey, GU10 2EN
tel: 01252 794 253
fax: 01252 792 642
email: admin@keynoteaudio.co.uk
contact: Tim Wheatley
genre: All Music Types Accepted
info: Send demos to the address above.

Chisholm Songs
36 Follingham Court, Drysdale Place, London, N1 6LZ
tel: 020 7684 8594
email: deschisholm@hotmail.com
contact: Desmond Chisholm
genre: Pop/Funk/Soul/R&B
info: Send demos to Desmond Chisholm. Desmond also runs an artist management company.

Chrysalis Music Ltd.
The Chrysalis Building, 13 Bramley Road, London, W10 6SP
tel: 020 7221 2213
fax: 020 7465 6178
email: phil.catchpole@chrysalis.com
web: www.chrysalis.com
contact: Phil Catchpole
genre: All Music Types Accepted
info: Send demos to Phil Catchpole at the above address.

Complete Music Ltd.
3rd Floor, Bishops Park House, 25-29 Fulham High Street, London, SW6 3JH
tel: 020 7731 8595
fax: 020 7371 5665
email: info@complete-music.co.uk
web: www.complete-music.co.uk
contact: Kareem Taylor
genre: Commercial
info: Will accept anything with 'chart appeal', from Pop and R&B, to one-off Dance tracks, to Guitar-based music and Rock. Send demos (CD, no more than 3 tracks) FAO Kareem Taylor.

Concept Music Publishing Ltd.
Shepherds Building Central, Office LG4, Charecroft Way, London, W14 0EH
tel:	020 7751 1755
fax:	020 7751 1566
email:	info@conceptmusic.com
web:	www.conceptmusic.com
contact:	Roseann
genre:	All Music Types Accepted
info:	Demos can be sent to the address above.

Cooking Vinyl Ltd.
10 Allied Way, London, W3 0RQ
tel:	020 8600 9200
fax:	020 8743 7448
email:	info@cookingvinyl.com
web:	www.cookingvinyl.com
contact:	Tom Wheeley
genre:	Rock/Folk/Indie/Country
info:	Send demos with biography and any press cuttings to the address above.

Cordella Music Ltd.
35 Britannia Gardens, Hedge End, Hanmpshire, SO30 2RN
tel:	0845 061 6616
fax:	01489 780 909
email:	barry@cordellamusic.co.uk
web:	www.cordellamusic.co.uk
contact:	Barry Upton
genre:	Pop/Commercial/Dance
info:	Cordella have worked with Steps, Sonia and The Cheeky Girls. Send demo to address above.

Cornerways Music
Ty'r Craig, Longleat Avenue, Craigside, Llandudno, LL30 3AE
tel:	01492 549 759
fax:	01492 541 482
email:	lorenzprods@aol.com
contact:	Gordon Lorenz
genre:	MOR/Easy Listening
info:	Call or email with details of your act. Send demo on request. Deal exclusively with Easy Listening music.

Creative World Entertainment Ltd.
PO Box 2206, Lichfield, Staffordshire, WS14 0GZ
tel:	01543 253 576
fax:	01543 255 184
email:	mail@creative-world-entertainment.co.uk
web:	www.creative-world-entertainment.co.uk
contact:	Mervyn Spence
genre:	All Music Types Accepted
info:	Send demos to the address above. Creative World regret that they are unable to return demos.

Creole Music Ltd.
The Chilterns, France Hill Drive, Camberley, Surrey, GU15 3QA
tel:	01276 686 077
fax:	01276 686 055
email:	creole@clara.net
contact:	Bruce White
genre:	Reggae
info:	Send demos to the address above. Deal almost exclusively with Reggae, although if Creole feel that the music is of a good standard although unsuitable for them, they may pass it on to other publishers.

Cutting Edge Music Holding Ltd.
2nd Floor, 53 Frith Street, London, W1D 4SN
tel:	020 7292 9616
email:	simon@cutting-edge.uk.com
web:	www.cutting-edge.uk.com
contact:	Simon White
genre:	Television/Film soundtrack and theme music
info:	Call Simon with details of your act. Send demo on request.

Cyhoeddiadau Pandy Publishing
Pandy Mill, Pentraeth, Ynys Mon, LL75 8BJ
tel:	01248 450 007
email:	stiwdiopandy@btopenworld.com
genre:	All Music Types Accepted
info:	Primarily operate within the Welsh market. Also run a record label (Recordiau Awen Records) and a recording studio (Stiwdio Pandy). See relevant sections for details.

Damn The Man Music Ltd.
3-5 Wigan Road, Westhoughton, Bolton, BL5 2BN
tel:	01942 859 158
fax:	01942 859 416
email:	damntheman@btinternet.com
web:	www.damntheman.co.uk
contact:	Martin Rigby
genre:	All Music Types Accepted
info:	Online publishing company. Email MP£s or send a demo, biog, gig listings and photo to the above address.

DB Music
PO Box 19318, Bath, BA1 6ZS
tel:	01225 782 322
email:	info@dbrecords.co.uk
web:	www.dbrecords.co.uk
contact:	David Bates
genre:	All Music Types Accepted
info:	Send demos to David at the address above.

De Haske Music (UK) Ltd.
Fleming Road, Earlstrees, Corby, Northamptonshire, NN17 4SN
tel:	01536 260 981
fax:	01536 401 075
email:	music@dehaske.co.uk
web:	www.dehaske.co.uk
contact:	Mark Coull
genre:	Brass/Concert bands/Woodwind and Brass
info:	Send demos to the address above.

De Wolfe Music Ltd.
2nd Floor, Shropshire House, 11-20 Capper Street, London, WC1E 6JA
tel:	020 7631 3600
fax:	020 7631 3700
email:	warren@dewolfemusic.co.uk
web:	www.dewolfe.co.uk
contact:	Warren De Wolfe
genre:	Television/Film soundtrack and theme music
info:	Send demos to Warren De Wolfe at the address above.

Dejamus Ltd.
Suite 11, Accurist House, 44 Baker Street, London, W1U 7AZ
tel:	020 7486 5838
fax:	020 7487 2634
email:	stephenjames@dejamus.co.uk
contact:	Stephen James
genre:	Commercial
info:	Dejamus deal with Pop music, from Guitar-based to Dance. They are interested in anything with chart appeal. Send demos to Stephen at the address above. He will usually reply within 4 weeks.

Demi Monde Records & Publishing
Foel Studio, Llanfair, Caereinion, Powys, SY21 0DS
tel:	01938 810 758
fax:	01938 810 758
email:	dave.anderson or demi.monde@dial.pipex.com
web:	www.demimonde.co.uk
contact:	Dave Anderson
genre:	70's Psychedelia/Rock
info:	Send demos to the address above. Also run record label under same name, and a recording studio, Foel Studio. See entries in relevant section for details.

DEP International Ltd.
1 Andover Street, Birmingham, West Midlands, B5 5RG
tel:	0121 633 4742
fax:	0121 643 4904
email:	enquiries@ub40.co.uk
web:	www.ub40.co.uk
contact:	Carol Beirne
genre:	All Music Types Accepted
info:	Send demos to Carol at the address above.

DMC Ltd.
PO Box 89, Slough, Berkshire, SL1 8NA
tel:	01628 667 124
fax:	01628 605 246
email:	info@dmcworld.com
web:	www.dmcworld.com
genre:	Garage/Techno/Dance/House/Drum&Bass
info:	Send demos to Peter at the address above.

DOR Encryption
PO Box 1797, London, E1 4TX
tel:	020 7702 7842
email:	encryption@dor.co.uk
web:	www.dor.co.uk
contact:	Martin Parker
genre:	Experimental
info:	Contact Martin Parker via email with details of your act. Do not send unsolicited demos as Martin is unlikely to respond.

Earache Songs UK Ltd.
PO Box 144, Nottingham, Nottinghamshire, NG3 4GE
tel:	0115 950 6400
fax:	0115 950 8585
email:	mail@earache.com
web:	www.earache.com
contact:	Digby Pearson
genre:	Extreme Metal/Metal
info:	Send demos to the address above. Do not send any MP3s.

Eaton Music Ltd.
39 Lower Richmond Road, Putney, London, SW15 1ET
tel: 020 8788 4557
fax: 020 8780 9711
email: eatonmus@aol.com
web: www.eatonmusic.com
contact: Terry Oates
genre: Television/Film soundtrack and theme music
info: Send demos to the address above.

Emerald Music (Ireland) Ltd.
120a Coach Road, Templepatrick, Co. Antrim, BT39 0HA
email: info@emeraldmusic.co.uk
web: www.emeraldmusiconline.com
contact: Martin McBurney
genre: Irish/Scottish
info: Send demos to the above address.

EMI Music Publishing Ltd.
127 Charing Cross Road, London, WC2H 0QY
tel: 020 7434 2131
fax: 020 7434 3531
email: dpemberton@emimusicpub.com
web: www.emimusicpub.com
contact: David Pemberton
genre: All Music Types Accepted
info: EMI Music Publishing does not accept unsolicited material. Contact David through legal or managerial representation, and arrangements can be made to forward a demo.

Endomorph Music
Leeds
tel: 0113 274 2106
email: clio@bluescat.com
web: www.bluescat.com
contact: Clio Bradbury
genre: Jazz/Funk/Dub
info: Contact Clio with details of your music before sending demo. No MP3s please. Associated with Activate Records. Endomorph Music also has its own recording studio, Studio Phat. For more information email Skip, Dave or Jim at skip@bluescat.com.

Eschenbach Editions
28 Dalrymple Crescent, Edinburgh, EH9 2NX
tel: 0131 667 3633
fax: 0131 667 3633
email: eschenbach@caritas-music.co.uk
web: www.caritas-music.co.uk
contact: James Douglas
genre: Classical/Folk
info: Contact James with details of your music before sending demo.

Esquire Music Company
185a Newmarket Road, Norwich, Norfolk, NR4 6AP
tel: 01603 451 139
contact: Peter Newbrook
genre: Jazz
info: Send demos to the address above.

Express Music Ltd.
Matlock, Brady Road, Lyminge, Kent, CT18 8HA
tel: 01303 863 185
fax: 01303 863 185
email: sjackson@expressmusic.uk.com
contact: Siggy Jackson
genre: Reggae/Roots/World
info: Send demos to Siggy Jackson at the address above. Include SAE if you wish to have your material returned.

Faith & Hope
23 New Mount Street, Manchester, M4 4DE
tel: 0161 839 4445
fax: 0161 839 1060
email: yoyo@faithandhope.co.uk
web: www.faithandhope.co.uk
genre: All Music Types Accepted
info: Address demos to A&R Department.

Flowsound
2 Rosebery Avenue, Tottenham, London, N17 9RY
tel: 020 8808 8554
email: rickdavey@flowsound.com
web: www.flowsound.com
contact: Rick Davey
genre: Reggae/African/Dance
info: Rick will accept all types of music, but mainly deals with Reggae. Send demo with any additional information such as biog, photos and press FAO Rick Davey at the above address.

Folktrax & Soundpost Publications
Heritage House, 16 Brunswick Square, Gloucester, GL1 1UG
tel: 01452 415 110
email: peter@folktrax.freeserve.co.uk
web: www.folktrax.org
contact: Peter Kennedy
genre: Folk/Traditional
info: Send demos to the address above.

Frisky Frank Music
Olympic Heights, 1 The Retreat, Birchington, Kent, CT7 9HS
tel: 01843 846 848
fax: 01843 846 848
contact: Frank
genre: Pop
info: Send demo and picture to Frank at the above address.

Frontline Music Publishing
PO Box 31, Bushey, Hampshire, WD23 2PT
tel: 01923 244 673
fax: 01923 244 693
email: info@purplecitymusic.com
contact: Jordan Jay
genre: All Music Types Accepted
info: Send demo on CD (no more than three tracks) to the address above.

Full 36ixty
PO Box 902, Suite 306, Bradford, BD1 9AH
tel: 07792 499 198
email: info@full360ltd.com
web: www.full360ltd.com
contact: Katherine Canoville, Paul Brook
genre: All Music Types Accepted
info: Call or email with details of your act. Send demo on request.

Futureproof Music Ltd.
PO Box 31631, London, W11 1UA
tel: 020 7792 8597
fax: 020 7221 3694
email: info@futureproofmusic.com
web: www.futureproofmusic.com
contact: Phil Legg
genre: Funk/Soul/Dance/Urban/Hip-Hop/R&B
info: Send demos to the address above.

George Martin Music Ltd.
Lyndhurst Hall, Lyndhurst Road, Hampstead, London, NW3 5NG
tel: 020 7794 0660
email: music@georgemartinmusic.com
web: www.georgemartinmusic.com
contact: Giles Martin, Adam Sharp
genre: Pop/Rock
info: George Martin Music will not accept unsolicited music. Get in touch with Giles or Adam through some sort of representation such as manager, agent or lawyer, then arrangements to submit a demo will be made.

Glasshouse Productions
Upper York Street, Earlsdon, Coventry, Warwickshire, CV1 3GQ
tel: 02476 223 892
fax: 02476 229 341
email: admin@glasshouseproductions.co.uk
web: www.glasshouseproductions.co.uk
contact: Amos Anderson
genre: All Music Types Accepted
info: Send 3 track demo, biog, and CV to the address above. Include as much information as you can about yourselves, your music and what you want from Glasshouse. Include SAE if you would like your demo returned.

Good Groove Songs Ltd.
Unit 217, Buspace Studios, Conlan Street, London, W10 5AP
tel: 020 7565 0050
fax: 020 7565 0049
email: tracey@goodgroove.co.uk
contact: Tracey Fox
genre: All Music Types Accepted
info: Send demos to the address above.

Grade One Music Ltd.
34 Salisbury Street, London, NW8 8QE
tel: 020 7402 9111
fax: 020 7723 3064
email: eliot@amimedia.co.uk
web: www.amimedia.co.uk
contact: Eliot Cohen
genre: Pop/Indie
info: Send demos to Eliot Cohen at the address above.

Grand Central Music Publishing Ltd.
10 Stephen Mews, London, W1T 1AG
email:	ali@grandcentralrecords.com
web:	www.grandcentralrecords.com
contact:	Alastair Little
genre:	Ragga/Beats/Electronica/Folk/Dancehall/Hip-Hop/ Soul
info:	Send demo FAO Alastair Little.

Grass Roots Music Publishing
29 Love Lane, Rayleigh, Essex, SS6 7DL
tel:	01268 747 077
contact:	Gerald Mahlowe
genre:	All Music Types Accepted
info:	Send demo (no more than three tracks) to the address above.

Gut Records
A&R Department, 112a Shirland Road, London, W9 2EQ
tel:	020 7266 0777
fax:	020 7266 7734
email:	aandr@gutrecords.com
web:	www.gutrecords.com
contact:	Paul Martin, James O'Driscoll
genre:	All Music Types Accepted
info:	Send a demo, no more than 3 tracks on CD to the address above. Include short biog and picture if possible. See the Gut Recordings website for profiles of individual A&R staff.

Halcyon Music Ltd.
233 Regents Park Road, Finchley, London, N3 3LF
tel:	0700 078 3633
fax:	0700 078 3634
contact:	Alan Williams
genre:	Pop/MOR/Easy Listening
info:	Halcyon sign individual songs, rather than writers. Will accept unsolicited demos sent to the address above.

Haripa Music Publishing Ltd.
Unit 8, Acklam Workshops, 10 Acklam Road, London, W10 5QZ
tel:	020 8964 3300
email:	info@kickinmusic.com
web:	www.kickinmusic.com
contact:	Matt Ward
genre:	Dance/Electronica
info:	Send demos to the address above. Part of record label and publishing group, Kickin' Music Ltd. See listing in Record Companies section.

Heavy Truth Music Publishing
PO Box 8, Corby, Northamptonshire, NN17 2XZ
tel:	01536 202 295
email:	info@heavytruth.com
web:	www.heavytruth.com
genre:	All Music Types Accepted
info:	Send demo to address above. Heavy Truth will be in touch if it appeals to them.

Hello Qtie
PO Box 5, Whitland, SA34 0WA
tel:	01994 484 466
email:	cadillacranch@telco4u.net
web:	www.nikturner.com
genre:	Fusion/Hip-Hop/Jazz/Funk/World/Latin
info:	Hello Qtie is run by Nik Turner, who is a founding member of Prog Rock legends Hawkwind. Send demos to the address above, and Nick will do his best to help you out. Hello Qtie may not be a position to offer a publishing deal, but Nik is time served in the industry, and is happy to offer advice. Also run 2 record labels (Riddle Records and Nikt Records), Money Talks Management, Money Talks Agency, Riddle Hallucinations Video Productions, and Cadillac Ranch Recording Studios. See entries in relevant sections for further details.

Henry Hadaway Organisation
Suite No. 1, 1-13 Cricklewood Lane, Cricklewood, London, NW2 1ET
tel:	020 8830 8813
fax:	020 8830 8801
email:	info@hho.co.uk
web:	www.hho.co.uk
contact:	Henry Hadaway
genre:	All Music Types Accepted
info:	Send demo, biog and recent photo to the address above. Also deal with licensing for DVDs. Publishing, distribution, digital distribution and finished products. Also provide audio and visual licensing.

Horatio Nelson Records & Tapes Ltd.
PO Box 1123, London, SW1P 1HB
tel:	020 7828 6533
fax:	020 7828 1271
contact:	Derek Boulton
genre:	Jazz/MOR/Easy Listening
info:	Send demos to the address above.

Horus Music
PO Box 12780, Birmingham, B42 9AX
tel:	07814 050 007
email:	info@horusmusic.co.uk
web:	www.horusmusic.co.uk
contact:	Nick Dunn
genre:	All Music Types Accepted
info:	Send demo FAO Nick Dunn at the above address. Also offer artist management services. See listing in relevant section for further details.

Humph Music
15 Stanhope Road, London, N6 5NE
tel:	020 8340 7797
fax:	020 8340 6923
email:	paul@paulrodriguezmus.demon.co.uk
contact:	Paul Rodriguez
genre:	Jazz
info:	Call or email with details of your act and send demo on request. Humph will not accept unsolicited demos.

Immaculate Misconception
Basement Studios, Park House, 15-19 Greenhill Crescent, Watford, Hertfordshire, WD18 8PH
tel:	01923 220 169
contact:	Tony Smith
genre:	All Music Types Accepted
info:	Send demos on CD with biog to Tony at the address above.

Inception Music Publishing
Unit 1, Meadow Street, Heol-y-Gors, Townhill, Swansea, SA1 6RZ
tel:	01792 581 500
fax:	01792 581 500
email:	inceptionmusic@btconnect.com
contact:	Paul Scott
genre:	All Music Types Accepted
info:	Send demos with biography and any other relevant information to Paul Scott at the address above. Paul also runs a studio and will include studio time in a publishing deal. He is well connected in the industry and if he feels that he cannot help you but somebody else can, he is happy to pass your details on.

Inky Blackness Ltd.
PO Box 32089, Camden Town, London, NW1 0NX
tel:	07958 520 580
email:	inky@inkyblackness.co.uk
web:	www.inkyblackness.co.uk
contact:	Ian Tregoning
genre:	Electronic/Television/Film soundtrack and theme music
info:	Send demos to the address above.

Iota Music Publishers
Kerchesters, Waterhouse Lane, Kingswood, Surrey, KT20 6HT
tel:	01737 832 837
fax:	01737 833 812
email:	aaron@soundstage.co.uk
web:	www.amphonic.com
contact:	Ian Dale
genre:	Composers
info:	Specialise in production music. Composers should send demos to the address above.

Isa Music
1 Ravenstone Drive, Gissnoch, Glasgow, G46 6AL
tel:	0141 637 6010
fax:	0141 637 6010
email:	lismor@lismor.com
web:	www.lismor.com
contact:	Ronnie Simpson
genre:	Traditional
info:	Send demos to the address above.

J.Albert & Son (UK) Ltd.
Unit 29, Cygnus Park, Dalmeyer Road, London, NW10 2XA
tel:	020 8830 0330
fax:	020 8830 0220
email:	james@albertmusic.co.uk
web:	www.albertmusic.co.uk
contact:	James Cassidy
genre:	All Music Types Accepted
info:	Send demos to James Cassidy at the address above.

Jamdown Music Ltd.
PO Box 45992, London, W3 7YL
tel:	020 8930 1073
email:	othman@jamdown-music.com
web:	www.jamdown-music.com
contact:	Othman Mukhlis
genre:	All Music Types Accepted
info:	Send demos to Othman Mukhlis.

MAILING LISTS

Available for all sections of this directory.

CALL 0161 234 6812

John Stedman Music Publishing
PO Box 1584, London, N3 3NW
tel: 020 8346 8663
fax: 020 8346 8848
email: john@jsprecords.com
web: www.jsprecords.com
contact: John Stedman
genre: Blues/Jazz
info: Contact John Stedman Music Publishing via email or phone. Send demo on request.

JUDmusic Publishing
48 Brynffynnon Road, Y-Felinheli, LL56 4SJ
tel: 01248 671 663
email: george@stiwdioeglwys.fsnet.co.uk
web: www.stiwdioeglwys.co.uk
genre: All Music Types Accepted
info: Send demos to the address above. Please ensure that the recording is of the best possible quality. Also run 2 record labels (JUDmusic Records and Recordiau Menai) and a production studio (Stiwdio Eglwys). See relevant entries for more information.

Just Publishing
PO Box 19780, London, SW15 1WU
tel: 020 8741 6020
fax: 020 8741 8362
email: justmusic@justmusic.co.uk
web: www.justmusic.co.uk
contact: Serena Benedict
genre: Downtempo/Chill/Ambient/Electronica/Acoustic
info: Send demos to the address above.

Kamara Music Publishing
PO Box 56, Boston, Lincolnshire, PE22 8JL
tel: 07976 553 624
email: chriskamara@megahitrecordsuk.co.uk
web: www.megahitrecordsuk.co.uk
contact: Chris Kamara
genre: R&B/Pop/Commercial
info: Send demo with photos and biog to the address above.

Kerroy Music Publishing
PO Box 22, Icklesham, East Sussex, TN36 4WB
tel: 07802 714 019
fax: 01424 813 881
email: kerroy@beamingbroadband.com
contact: Iain Kerr
genre: All Music Types Accepted
info: Send demos to the address above.

Kevin King Music Publishing
16 Limetrees Avenue, Llangattock, Crickhowell, Powys, NP8 1LB
tel: 01873 810 142
fax: 01873 811 557
email: kevinkinggb@aol.com
web: www.silverword.co.uk
contact: Kevin King
genre: All Music Types Accepted
info: Send demos to the address above. Associated with SMG Distribution, who work in conjunction with THE Distribution throughout the UK. Distribute to WHSmith, HMV, Amazon and CD Zone, among others. Email SMGdistribution@aol.com. Media promotion of new releases through Promo UK. Email promogb@aol.com for more information.

Kirklees Music
609 Bradford Road, Bailiff Bridge, Brighouse, West Yorkshire, HD6 4DN
tel: 01484 722 855
fax: 01484 723 591
email: sales@kirkleesmusic.co.uk
web: www.kirkleesmusic.co.uk
contact: Graham Horsfield
genre: Brass/Classical/Traditional
info: Send demos to the address above. Specialists in Brass Band music.

Kite Music Ltd.
Binny Estate, Ecclesmachan, West Lothian, Edinburgh, EH52 6NL
tel: 01506 858 885
fax: 01506 858 155/01506 858 931
email: kitemusic@aol.com
web: www.kitemusic.com
contact: Billy Russell
genre: Pop/R&B
info: Send demos to the address above.

Le Matt Music
White House Farm, Pipe Gate, Shropshire, TF9 4HA
tel: 01630 647 374
fax: 01630 647 612
contact: Catherine Le Matt
genre: All Music Types Accepted
info: Send demo, biography and photo to the address above. Include SAE if you would like your demo returned.

Leaf Songs Ltd.
Reverb House, Bennett Street, London, W4 2AH
tel: 020 8747 0660
fax: 020 8747 0880
email: liam@leafsongs.com
web: www.leafsongs.com
contact: Liam Teeling
genre: All Music Types Accepted
info: Send demos to the address above.

Lee Music Publishing
White House Farm, Market Drayton, Shropshire, TF9 4HA
tel: 01630 647 374
fax: 01630 647 612
contact: Keith Phillips
genre: All Music Types Accepted
info: Send demos to the address above. Include details of venues played and other deals you are involved with. Include SAE if you would like any demo returned.

Loaded Lime Music
PO Box 156, Wallasey, Cheshire, CH45 9XA
tel: 0151 638 2009
fax: 0151 638 2009
email: info@loadedlime.com
contact: Bex Williams
genre: All Music Types Accepted
info: Send demos with full contact details to the above address.

Lockup Music Publishing Ltd.
10 Tenison Road, Cambridge, CB1 2DW
tel: 01223 352 744
fax: 01223 565 917
email: info@lockupmusic.co.uk
web: www.lockupmusic.co.uk
contact: Anneli Stockwell
genre: Dance
info: Send MP3 or CD marked FAO Annalie, with a photo and a biog.

Lupus Music
1 Star Street, London, W2 1QD
email: lupusmusic@btconnect.com
genre: All Music Types Accepted
info: Send demos to the address above.

Maori Music Publishing
The Bungalow, Cadman Lane, Snaith, East Yorkshire, DN14 9JR
tel: 01405 869 700
email: maori@cadmanlane.co.uk
web: www.confidentialrecords.fsnet.co.uk/maori.htm
contact: Nev Barker
genre: All Music Types Accepted
info: Send demo to the address above.

Mcasso Music
32 Great Marlborough Street, London, W1F 7JB
tel: 020 7734 3664
email: music@mcasso.com
web: www.mcasso.com
contact: Mike Connaris
genre: Television/Film soundtrack and theme music
info: Send demos to the address above.

MCS Ltd.
32 Lexington Street, London, W1F 0LQ
tel: 020 7255 8777
fax: 020 7255 8778
email: guy@mcsmusic.com
web: www.mcsmusic.com
contact: Guy Fletcher
genre: All Music Types Accepted
info: Send good quality demo plus biography to Guy at the address above.

Melody Lauren Music
Unit B2, Livingston Court, 55-63 Peel Road, Harrow, Middlesex, HA3 7QT
tel: 020 8427 2777
fax: 020 8427 0660
email: anthony@wienerworld.com
web: www.wienerworld.com
contact: Anthony Broza
genre: All Music Types Accepted
info: Send demos to the address above.

Memnon Entertainment Ltd.
3rd Floor, Habib House, 9 Stevenson Square, Manchester, M1 1DB
tel: 0161 238 8516
fax: 0161 236 6717
email: memnon@btconnect.com
web: www.memnonentertainment.com
contact: Rudi Kidd
genre: All Music Types Accepted
info: Send demos and biog to the address above.

Mesh Music
13 Sandys Road, Worcester, WR1 3HE
tel: 01905 298 09
fax: 01905 613 023
email: meshmusic@prison-records.com
web: www.prison-records.com
genre: All Music Types Accepted
info: Send demos to the address above. Also associated with Split Music.

Millennium Songs Ltd.
6 Water Lane, London, NW1 8NZ
tel: 020 7482 0272
fax: 020 7267 4908
email: millennium@millenniumrecords.com
web: www.millenniumrecords.com
contact: Ben Recknagel
genre: Dance
info: Send demos to the address above.

Minaret Music
59 Glenthorne Road, London, W6 0LJ
tel: 020 8748 4499
fax: 020 8748 6699
email: minaretmusic@dial.pipex.com
contact: Peter Robinson
genre: Soul/R&B
info: Send demos to the address above.

Mint Music Ltd.
227 Goldhawk Road, London, W12 8ER
tel: 020 7351 9379
email: info@mintmusic.info
contact: Jim Ingle
genre: All Music Types Accepted

Moggie Music
101 Hazelwood Lane, Palmers Green, London, N13 5HQ
tel: 020 8886 2801
fax: 020 8882 7380
email: artistes@halcarterorg.com
web: www.halcarterorg.com
contact: Abbie Carter
genre: All Music Types Accepted
info: Send demo, biography and photo to the address above.

MoonRock Music
PO Box 883, Liverpool, L69 4RH
tel: 0151 922 5657
fax: 0151 922 5657
email: bstratt@mersinet.co.uk
web: www.moonrock.mersinet.co.uk
contact: Billy Stratton
genre: Singer-Songwriter
info: Send demos to the address above.

Mother Tongue
35 Marsden Street, London, NW5 3HE
email: info@mothertongue.tv
web: www.mothertongue.tv
contact: Julian de Takats
genre: Alternative Pop
info: Send demos to the address above.

Moving Shadow Music
PO Box 2251, London, SE1 2FH
tel: 020 7252 2661
fax: 0870 051 2594
email: info@movingshadow.com
web: www.movingshadow.com
contact: Gav Johnson
genre: Drum&Bass/Breaks
info: Send demos to the address above.

MSR Music Ltd.
78 Alcester Road, Moseley, Birmingham, B13 8BB
tel: 0121 256 1313
email: john@msrmusicltd.co.uk
web: www.msrmusicltd.co.uk
contact: John Hemming
genre: Rock/World/Alternative

Mule UK Music
Suite 306, Parkgate House, Parkgate, Bradford, BD1 5BS
tel: 01274 730 663/07792 499 198
email: mulemusic@hotmail.com
web: www.mulemusic.co.uk
contact: Katherine Canoville
genre: Eclectic/Diverse
info: Call or email with details of your act. Send demo on request.

Multiplay Music
19 Eagle Way, Harrold, Bedfordshire, MK43 7EW
tel: 01234 720 785
fax: 01234 720 664
email: info@multiplaymusic.com
web: www.multiplaymusic.com
contact: Kevin White
genre: Rock/Pop/Singer-Songwriter
info: Send demos to Kevin White at the address above. Include SAE if you would like your demo returned.

Murfin Media International
The Old Smithy, Post Office Lane, Kempsey, Worcestershire, WR5 3NS
tel: 01905 820 659
fax: 01905 820 015
email: muffmurfin@btconnect.com
contact: Muff Murfin
genre: Commercial
info: Send demos to the address above.

The Music Factor Ltd.
15 Stanhope Road, London, N6 5NE
tel: 020 8340 7797
fax: 020 8340 6923
email: themusicfactor@paulrodriguezmus.demon.co.uk
contact: Paul Rodriguez
genre: All Music Types Accepted
info: Call Paul or Lucy with details of your act. Send demo on request.

Music Factory Mastermixes
PO Box 503, Rotherham, S62 6WX
tel: 01709 710 022
fax: 01709 523 141
email: info@musicfactory.co.uk
web: www.musicfactory.co.uk
contact: Andy Pickles
genre: All Music Types Accepted
info: Send demos to the email address above. Reply guaranteed.

Music For Films
34 Batchelor Street, London, N1 0EG
tel: 020 7278 4288
email: rgoldmff@aol.com
contact: Robert Gold
genre: All Music Types Accepted
info: Send demos to the address above.

Musicalities Ltd.
Snows Ride Farm, Snows Ride, Windlesham, Surrey, GU20 6LA
tel: 01276 474 181
fax: 01276 452 227
email: info@musicalities.co.uk
web: www.musicalities.co.uk
contact: Ivan Chandler
genre: All Music Types Accepted
info: Contact Musicalities with details of your act. Send demo upon request. Please consult website before submitting any material.

Mute Song
Lawford House, 429 Harrow Road, London, W10 4RE
tel: 020 8964 2001
fax: 020 8968 6983
email: info@mutehq.co.uk
web: www.mutelibtech.com
contact: Andrew King
genre: Alternative
info: Send demos to the address above.

Native Songs
32 Ransomes Dock, 35-37 Parkgate Road, London, SW11 4NP
tel: 020 7801 1919
fax: 020 7738 1819
email: info@nativemanagement.com
web: www.nativemanagement.com
contact: Anna Carpenter
genre: Pop/Singer-Songwriter
info: Contact Native Songs via email with details of your act. Follow with demo on request.

Natural State
PO Box 2614, Eastbourne, East Sussex, BN21 7DQ
tel: 01323 721 603
email: info@obedientbone.com
contact: Simon Veiler
genre: All Music Types Accepted
info: Send demos and any other information FAO Simon at the address above. If you need material returning, please send a SAE. Natural State also run a management company. See entry in relevant section for details.

Neon Music
Studio 2, 19 Marine Crescent, Kinning Park, Glasgow, G51 1HD
tel: 0141 429 6366
fax: 0141 429 6377
email: mail@go2neon.com
web: www.go2neon.com
contact: Robert Noakes
genre: All Music Types Accepted/Roots/Singer-Songwriter
info: Send demos FAO Robert Noakes at the above address. Mainly deal with Singer-Songwriter and Roots music, although Neon Music will listen to all demos received.

Nervous Music Publishing
5 Sussex Cresent, Northolt, Middlesex, UB5 4DL
tel: 020 8423 7373
fax: 020 8423 7773
email: info@nervous.co.uk
web: www.nervous.co.uk
contact: Roy Williams
genre: Rockabilly
info: Send demos to the address above.

Newmemorabilia Ltd.
PO Box 121, Manchester, M19 2XE
tel: 07973 861 540
fax: 0161 872 4529
email: info@thelovers.co.uk or t.hingley@ntlworld.com
web: www.thelovers.co.uk or www.tomhingley.co.uk
contact: Tom Hingley
genre: Indie/Guitar Based
info: Send demos and biog to the address above. Newmemorabilia Ltd. is also a record label and management company set up by Tom Hingley, lead singer and co-manager of the Inspiral Carpets. Tom currently lectures in Music Business and Songwriting, as well as acting as a music industry consultant. For more information see the websites above and refer to entry in Record Companies section.

No Known Cure Publishing
45 Kings Road, Dover Court, Harwich, Essex, CO12 4DS
tel: 07760 427 306
email: tomsong1@hotmail.com
contact: T.F. McCarthy
genre: All Music Types Accepted
info: Send demos to the address above.

Nomadic Music Ltd.
Unit 18a/b, 101 Farm Lane, London, SW6 1QJ
tel: 020 7386 6800
email: liam@nomadicmusic.net
web: www.nomadicmusic.net
contact: Liam Keightley
genre: All Music Types Accepted
info: Nomadic Music comprises of a record label, production company and music publishers, as well as running three recording studios. Totally committed to artist development and have three recording studios. The company is genuinely independent both financially and creatively. Their mission is to work with the best music regardless of genre, although does not take on much Urban material.

NorthStar Music Publishing
PO Box 868, Cambridge, CB1 6SJ
tel: 01787 278 256
fax: 01787 279 069
email: info@northstarmusic.co.uk
web: www.northstarmusic.co.uk
contact: Grahame Maclean
genre: All Music Types Accepted
info: Send demos to the address above.

Notting Hill Publishing Co.
Bedford House, 8b Berkley Gardens, London, W8 4AP
tel: 020 7243 2921
fax: 020 7243 2894
email: info@nottinghillmusic.com
web: www.nottinghillmusic.com
contact: David Loader
genre: All Music Types Accepted
info: Send demos to the address above.

Orestes Music Publishing Ltd.
13 Alliance Court, Alliance Road, London, W3 0RB
tel: 020 8993 7441
fax: 020 8992 9993
email: orestes@dorm.co.uk
web: www.orestesmusic.co.uk
contact: John O'Reilly
genre: All Music Types Accepted
info: Contact Orestes, preferably via email, with details of your music. Follow with demos on request.

P & P Songs Ltd.
Hope House, 40 St. Peter's Road, London, W6 9BD
tel: 020 8237 8400
fax: 020 8741 0825
email: firstname@pandpsongs.com
web: www.windsweptpacific.com
contact: Peter McCamley
genre: All Music Types Accepted
info: Send demos with as much contact information as possible to the address above. Include SAE for reply. Uk branch of the Windswept Pacific publishing group.

Palan Music Publishing Ltd.
Greenland Place, 115-123 Bayham Street, London, NW1 0AG
tel: 020 7446 7444
fax: 020 7446 7421
email: paulp@palan.com
web: www.palan.com
contact: Paul
genre: Rock/Alternative
info: Send demos to the address above.

Your wish list and our check list = 100% compatibility and here's the top 10 to prove it.

☑ *hit potential songs*   ☑ *dance floor fillers*

☑ *catchy choruses*   ☑ *pop/soul*

☑ *sweet melodies*   ☑ *r 'n' b/funk*

☑ *radio friendly tunes*   ☑ *sample & profanity free*

☑ *wide appeal*   ☑ *MIDI files available*

Now say goodbye to that genie and contact us instead

PLUS MUSIC PUBLISHING

36 Follingham Court,
Drysdale Place
London N1 - 6LZ
Tel: 020 7684 8594
E-mail: deschisholm@hotmail.com

Palm Pictures & Blue Mountain Music
8 Kensington Park Road, London, W11 3BU
tel:	020 7229 3000
fax:	020 7221 8899
email:	bluemountain@islandlife.co.uk
web:	www.bluemountainmusic.tv or
	www.palmpictures.com
contact:	Afua Acheampong
genre:	All Music Types Accepted
info:	Send demos to the address above.

Panama Music Library
Sovereign House, 12 Trewartha Road, Praa Sands, Penzance, Cornwall, TR20 9ST
tel:	01736 762 826
fax:	01736 763 328
email:	panamus@aol.com
web:	www.panamamusic.co.uk
contact:	Roderick Jones
genre:	Television/Film soundtrack and theme music
info:	Panama supply recorded mood music libraries to

television, radio, audio-visual, advertising and film industries worldwide. Send demos to the address above. The Panama Group also includes many publishing arms including Promo Sonor International, Caribbean Music Library amongst others. See website for more details.

Parliament Music Ltd.
PO Box 6328, London, N2 0UN
tel:	020 8444 9841
fax:	020 8442 1973
email:	info@parliament-management.com
genre:	All Music Types Accepted
info:	Send demos to the address above on CD format.

Paul Rodriguez Music Ltd.
15 Stanhope Road, London, N6 5NE
tel:	020 8340 7797
fax:	020 8340 6923
email:	paul@paulrodriguezmz.demon.co.uk
contact:	Paul Rodriguez
genre:	Dance/Drum&Bass
info:	Call or email with details of your act and send demo on request.

Peermusic UK Ltd.
Peer House, 8-14 Verulam Street, London, WC1X 8LZ
tel:	020 7404 7200
fax:	020 7404 7004
email:	info@peermusic.com
web:	www.peermusic.com
contact:	Nigel Elderton
genre:	All Music Types Accepted
info:	Send demos to the address above.

Perfect Songs
8-10 Basing Street, London, W11 1ET
tel:	020 7229 1229
fax:	020 7221 3374
email:	paul@spz.com
web:	www.spz.com
contact:	Paul Barton
genre:	All Music Types Accepted
info:	Send demos to Paul at the address above.

Perfect Space Music Publishing
Ichthus House, 1 Northfield Road, Aylesbury, Buckinghamshire, HP20 1PB
tel:	01296 583 700
email:	info@reallyfreemusic.co.uk
web:	www.reallyfreemusic.co.uk
contact:	Peter Wheeler
genre:	World
info:	Send demos to the address above. Perfect Space are

open to music which does not fall into the mainstream or traditional genres of Popular music such as Pop, Rock, Punk and Dance.

Phab Music
High Notes, Sheerwater Avenue, Woodham, Surrey, KT15 3DS
email:	phabmusic@yahoo.co.uk
contact:	Phillip Bailey
genre:	Alt. Country/Country/Punk/Rockabilly
info:	Post CDs to the address above. Include a photo and biog

where possible.

Plan C Music Ltd.

Covetous Corner, Hudnall Common, Little Gaddesden, Hertfordshire, HP4 1QW

tel:	01442 842 851
fax:	01442 842 082
contact:	Christian Ulf-Hansen
genre:	Pop/Rock/Singer-Songwriter
info:	Send demos to the address above.

Playwrite Music Ltd.

1 Star Street, London, W2 1QD

tel:	020 7258 0093
email:	info@playwrite.uk.com
contact:	Nicky McDermott
genre:	All Music Types Accepted
info:	Contact Nicky with details of your act and send demos

on request.

Plus Music Publishing

36 Follingham Court, Drysdale Place, London, N1 6LZ

tel:	020 7684 8594
email:	deschisholm@hotmail.com
web:	www.plusmusic.co.uk
contact:	Desmond Chisholm
genre:	Pop/Soul/R&B/Funk
info:	Send demos with SAE to the address above.

Pogo Records Publishing

White House Farm, Pipe Gate, Shropshire, TF9 4HA

tel:	01630 647 374
fax:	01630 647 612
contact:	Katherine Le Matt
genre:	All Music Types Accepted
info:	Send demo and as much information as possible,

including biog, photos and videos or DVDs if available, to address above. If your material is not suitable for Pogo, they will pass onto other labels within their group. Include SAE if you would like your demo returned.

Post House Music

Fairways, Benover Road, Yalding, Kent, ME18 6ES

tel:	01622 814 154
email:	phmusic@onetel.co.uk
contact:	Pauline Southcombe
genre:	All Music Types Accepted
info:	Send demos to the address above. Include SAE if you

want your material returned.

Primo Music Ltd.

39 Bettespol Meadows, Redbourn, Hertfordshire, AL3 7EN

tel:	01582 626 015
email:	tony@primomusic.co.uk
contact:	Tony Peters
genre:	All Music Types Accepted
info:	Send demos to the address above.

Proof Songs

PO Box 20242, London, NW1 7FL

tel:	020 7485 1113
email:	info@proofsongs.co.uk
contact:	Justin Perry
genre:	All Music Types Accepted
info:	Send demos on CD (no more than 3 tracks) to the

address above. Include SAE if you would like your demo returned. Proof Songs are open to most types of music and listen to all demos they receive. Affiliated with Proof Records, see listing in relevant section.

Pure Groove Music

679 Holloway Road, London, N19 5SE

tel:	020 7263 4660
fax:	020 7263 5590
email:	mickshiner@puregroove.co.uk
web:	www.puregroove.co.uk
contact:	Mick Shiner
genre:	Dance/Alternative/Urban
info:	Send demos to the address above, and follow with a

phone call to make sure your material has arrived.

R37 Publishing

PO Box 1083, Liverpool, L69 4WQ

tel:	0151 222 5785
email:	mail@mimashimarecords.co.uk
web:	www.mimashimarecords.co.uk
contact:	Noel Fitzsimmons
genre:	All Music Types Accepted
info:	Send demos to the address above. Also associated

with Mimashima and Saturn Return Records. See relevant sections for details.

Raven Black Music

Oxford Innovation Centre, Mill Street, Oxford, OX2 0JX

tel:	01989 767 868
fax:	01865 793 165
email:	raven@tourdates.co.uk
web:	www.tourdates.co.uk
contact:	Dean G. Hill
genre:	Rock
info:	Submit demos FAO Dean G. Hill at the above address.

Contact by email for demo feedback. Raven Black Music also manage and promote unsigned bands, and run the above listings website. See entries in relevant sections for details.

Raw 42

3rd Floor, Prospect House, 11-13 Lonsdale Garden, Tunbridge Wells, Kent, TN1 1NU

tel:	01892 616 042
email:	info@raw42.com
web:	www.raw42.com
contact:	Ian Sims
genre:	All Music Types Accepted
info:	Raw 42 are an independent A&R service for unsigned

musicians. Please submit MP3s only via the Raw 42 website.

Real World Publishing

Box Mill, Mill Lane, Box, Corsham, Wiltshire, SN13 8PL

tel:	01225 743 188
fax:	01225 744 369
email:	publishing@realworld.co.uk
web:	www.realworld.co.uk
contact:	Chris Lavington
genre:	Folk/World/World Fusion
info:	Please email before sending demos. Will also consider

other genres on a one to one basis. Linked with WOMAD (World of Music, Arts & Dance) festival. For further details see www.womad.org.

Red Bus Music International Ltd.

34 Salisbury Street, London, NW8 8QE

tel:	020 7402 9111
fax:	020 7723 3064
email:	eliot@amimedia.co.uk
web:	www.amimedia.co.uk
contact:	Eliot Cohen
genre:	All Music Types Accepted
info:	Will accept unsolicited demos, but advise telephoning

before sending any material.

Renaissance Music

South Lodge, Littleworth, Partridge Green, Sussex, RH13 8JX

tel:	01403 711 507
fax:	01403 711 507
email:	peter@renaissance2.plus.com
contact:	Peter Reilly
genre:	All Music Types Accepted
info:	Contact Renaissance Music via telephone or email. Send

demo on request.

Reverb Music

Reverb House, Bennett Street, London, W4 2AH

tel:	020 8747 0660
fax:	020 8747 0880
email:	rob.adamson@reverbxl.com or
	tony.murphy@reverbxl.com
web:	www.reverbxl.com
contact:	Rob Adamson, Tony Murphy
genre:	All Music Types Accepted
info:	Send demos FAO Tony Murphy at the address above.

Revolver Records

152 Goldthorn Hill, Penn, Wolverhampton, West Midlands, WV2 3JA

tel:	01902 345 345
fax:	01902 345 155
email:	paul.birch@revolverrecords.com
web:	www.revolverrecords.com
contact:	Peter Black
genre:	All Music Types Accepted
info:	Send demos to the address above. Also run Revolver

Records. See entry in Record Companies section for further details.

Right Music

177 High Street, Harlesden, London, NW10 4TE

tel:	020 8961 3889
fax:	020 8951 9955
email:	info@rightrecordings.com
web:	www.rightrecordings.com
contact:	John Kaufman
genre:	All Music Types Accepted
info:	Send demos to the address above. John will contact you

if he is interested in your act.

Rise International Music Ltd.
PO Box 6529, Southgate, London, N14 7LQ
tel: 07939 288 735
fax: 020 8368 0782
email: mario3@btinternet.com
contact: Mark Rise
genre: All Music Types Accepted
info: Send demos to the address above.

Rive Droite Music Ltd.
Home Park House, Hampton Court Road, Kingston-upon-Thames, Surrey, KT1 4AE
tel: 020 8977 0666
fax: 020 8977 0660
email: rivedroite@rivedroitemusic.com
web: www.rivedroitemusic.com
contact: Ian Mack
genre: All Music Types Accepted
info: Send demos to the address above. Include SAE if you would like material returned.

Rockit Music Publishers
149 Station Street, Cheslyn Hay, Walsall, Staffordshire, WS6 7EH
tel: 01922 416 950
email: rockitmusicuk@aol.com
web: www.rockitmusicuk.com
contact: Anthony Raybould
genre: All Music Types Accepted
info: Send CD with brief information about the writer FAO Anthony Raybould at the above address.

Roedean Music Ltd.
16-17 Grafton House, 2-3 Golden Square, London, W1F 9HR
tel: 020 7434 7286
fax: 020 7437 3852
contact: Tony Hall
genre: Soul/R&B
info: Send demos to the address above.

Roll Over Music
29 Beethoven Street, London, W10 4LJ
tel: 020 8969 0299
fax: 020 8968 1047
email: info@rollover.co.uk
web: www.rollover.co.uk
contact: Bruin Housley, Laura Lee
genre: All Music Types Accepted
info: Send demos (maximum of 4 tracks) to the address above. Roll Over also run a recording studio. Contact for further details.

RTL Music Publishing
White House Farm, Shropshire, TF9 4HA
tel: 01630 647 374
fax: 01630 647 612
contact: Mick Lawson
genre: All Music Types Accepted
info: Send demos with biography and photo to the address above. If you would like your demos to be returned please include a SAE.

Rufus Music
146 Bethnal Green Road, London, E2 6DG
tel: 020 7613 1100
email: rufus@acidjazz.co.uk
contact: Danny Corr
genre: All Music Types Accepted
info: Deal mainly with any type of music. Send demos to the address above.

Rumour Music Publishing
Tempo House, 15 Falcon Road, London, SW11 2PJ
tel: 020 7228 6821
fax: 020 7228 6972
email: post@rumour.demon.co.uk
web: www.rumourrecords.co.uk
contact: Anne Plaxton
genre: Dance
info: Send demos to the address above.

The Running Media Group
Suite 237, 78 Marylebone High Street, London, W1U 5AP
tel: 07973 129 068
email: bob@runningmedia.com
web: www.runningmedia.com
contact: Bob Miller
genre: All Music Types Accepted
info: Send demos to the address above on CD format.

Rykomusic Ltd.
329 Latimer Road, London, W10 6RA
tel: 020 8960 3311
fax: 020 8960 4334
email: info@rykodisc.co.uk
web: www.rykodisc.co.uk
contact: Chris Twinam
genre: All Music Types Accepted
info: Send demos to the address above.

Satellite Music Ltd.
34 Salisbury Street, London, NW8 8QE
tel: 020 7402 9111
fax: 020 7723 3064
email: satellite_artists@hotmail.com
web: www.amimedia.co.uk
contact: Eliot Cohen
genre: Commercial/Pop
info: Send demos to the address above.

Seeca Records Ltd.
Mortlake Business Centre, 20 Mortlake High Street, London, SW14 8JN
tel: 020 8487 8622
fax: 020 8487 8621
email: info@seeca.co.uk
web: www.seeca.co.uk
contact: Will Desborough
genre: Indie/Post Hardcore/Guitar Based/Rock
info: Seeca are working with a new distribution model that exploits the opportunities of digital technology. Seeca will release singles by download only and albums will be released by download and as a physical product. Seeca are really interested in hearing Guitar-based music with a cutting edge. Send 3 tracks on CD to the above postal address or via email. Please also include any press, biog and pictures.

SGO Music Publishing Ltd.
PO Box 2015, Salisbury, SP2 7WU
tel: 01264 811 154
fax: 01264 811 172
email: sgomusic@sgomusic.com
web: www.sgomusic.com
contact: Stuart Ongley
genre: All Music Types Accepted
info: Will not accept unsolicited demos. Contact Stuart Ongley before sending any material.

Shalitglobal Publishing
7 Morr Street, London, W1D 5NB
tel: 020 7851 9155
fax: 020 7851 9156
email: info@shalitglobal.com
web: www.shalitglobal.com
contact: Jonathon Shalit
genre: All Music Types Accepted
info: Send demo with full contact details and photo to the address above. Part of Shalitglobal management.

Shanna Music Ltd.
PO Box 31, Bushey, Hertfordshire, WD23 2PT
tel: 01923 244 673
fax: 01923 244 693
email: info@purplecitymusic.com
contact: Barry Blue
genre: All Music Types Accepted
info: Send demo on CD (no more than three tracks) to address above.

Sherlock Holmes Music Ltd.
Unit 1, Chapel Road, Portslade, Brighton, BN41 1PF
tel: 01273 424 703
fax: 01273 418 856
email: mail@sherlockholmesmusic.co.uk
web: www.sherlockholmesmusic.co.uk
contact: Nick Baxter
genre: Dance
info: Independent UK music publisher. Representing many UK dance acts including Underworld, and many overseas acts such as Ian Van Dahl, and compositions by Sir Bob Geldolf, Justin Hayward and many more. They will sign up songwriters and catalogues and copyright their works, oversee exploitation, license uses, log uses, arrange worldwide representation, register works and ensure appropriate collection of fees and royalties. Have representatives throughout the world ensuring proper administration of works, wherever they are used. Have been awarded Ivor Novello as well as many gold and platinum discs. Send demos to the above address.

Single Minded Music Publishing
11 Cambridge Court, 210 Shepherds Bush Road, London, W6 7NJ
tel: 0870 011 3748
fax: 0870 011 3749
email: tony@singleminded.com
web: www.singleminded.com
contact: Tony Byrne
genre: All Music Types Accepted
info: Send demos to the address above.

Skint Music Publishing
PO Box 174, Brighton, BN1 4BA
tel: 01273 738 527
fax: 01273 208 766
email: mail@skint.net
web: www.skint.net
contact: Tim Jeffries
genre: Dance/Alternative Guitar Based/All Music Types Accepted
info: Send demo on CD to the address above. Make sure to include full contact address on the actual disc. Allow up to two months for a response. Skint cannot return any material they receive.

Sleeping Giant Music Publishing
34 Great James Street, London, WC1N 3HB
tel: 020 7405 3786
fax: 020 7405 5245
email: info@prestige-elite.com
web: www.prestige-elite.com
contact: Keith Thomas
genre: Blues/Pop/Rock/Soul/Jazz/Reggae
info: Send demos to the address above.

SLNB
143 Westmead Road, Sutton, Surrey, SM1 4JP
tel: 020 8395 3045
fax: 020 8395 3046
email: slnbmusic@blueyonder.co.uk
web: www.slnb.com
contact: Steve McIntosh
genre: R&B/Commercial/Pop
info: Send demos on CD to the address above. Include SAE for reply.

Solent Songs
68-70 Lugley Street, Newport, Isle of Wight, PO30 5ET
tel: 01983 524 110
fax: 08707 620 132
email: songs@solentrecords.co.uk
web: www.solentrecords.co.uk
contact: John Waterman
genre: Commercial
info: Send demos to the address above. Solent Songs are mainly interested in artists based on the South coast.

Solida-Soulville Music Publishing
PO Box 7874, London, SW20 9XD
tel: 07050 605 219
fax: 07050 605 239
email: info@pan-africa.org
contact: Oscar Sam Carrol Jr.
genre: Pop/Urban/R&B/Hip-Hop
info: Send demos to the address above.

The Song Corporation
Business Centre, 5 Blackhorse Lane, London, E17 6DS
tel: 020 8527 0447
email: publishing@songcorporation.com
web: www.songcorporation.com
genre: All Music Types Accepted
info: Send demo and biog to above address. Also have recording studio and CD duplication service. See entries in relevant sections.

Songs In The Key of Knife
c/o Hospital Records, 182-184 Dartmouth Road, London, SE26 4QZ
tel: 020 8613 0400
fax: 020 8613 0401
email: info@hospitalrecords.com
web: www.hospitalrecords.com
contact: Chris
genre: Drum&Bass/Dance
info: Send demos by post only.

Sony ATV Music Publishing UK Ltd.
13 Great Marlborough Street, London, W1F 7LP
tel: 020 7911 0200
email: flash_taylor or simon_aldridge@uk.sonymusic.com
web: www.sonymusic.co.uk
contact: James Dewar, Ed Howard, Flash Taylor, Simon Aldridge
genre: All Music Types Accepted
info: Send demos with full contact details to the address above. Mark FAO Flash Taylor for bands and Simon Aldridge for writers, both in the A&R department. Include SAE if you would like your demo returned.

Sound Image
Unit 2b, Bankquay Trading Estate, Slutchers Lane, Warrington, Cheshire, WA1 1PJ
tel: 01925 445 742
fax: 01925 445 742
contact: Steve Millington, Steve Oates
genre: All Music Types Accepted
info: Send demos to the address above. Also run management company and recording studio (Frog Studios). See entries in relevant sections for further details.

South Star Music
PO Box 1350, Southampton, SO15 5WX
tel: 07789 882 368
email: admin@southstarmusic.co.uk
contact: Stewart Dugdale
genre: R&B/Pop/Rock/Soul
info: Send demo to above address. 3 track disc including biog, picture and any press. Also involved in songwriting, management and have studios on site.

Split Music
13 Sandys Road, Worcester, WR1 3HE
tel: 01905 298 09
fax: 01905 613 023
email: split.music@virgin.net
genre: All Music Types Accepted
info: Send demos to the address above.

Stickysongs Ltd.
Sticky Studios, Kennel Lane, Windlesham, Surrey, GU20 6AA
tel: 01276 479 255
email: admin@stickycompany.com
web: www.stickycompany.com
contact: Jake Gosling
genre: All Music Types Accepted
info: Send demo and biography to the address above. Also offer recording services.

Stop, Drop & Roll Music Ltd.
Colbury Manor, Jacobs Gutter Lane, Eling, Southampton, SO40 9FY
tel: 0845 658 5006
fax: 0845 658 5009
email: jessica.stone@stopdroproll.com
web: www.stopdroproll.com
contact: Jessica Stone
genre: Indie/Pop/Urban/R&B
info: Send demos on CD to the address above.

Storm Songs
2nd Floor, 1 Ridgefield, Manchester, M2 6EG
tel: 0161 839 5111
fax: 0161 839 1487
email: mike@storm-music.com
web: www.storm-music.com
contact: Mike Ball
genre: All Music Types Accepted
info: Send demos to the address above.

Strange Art Music
1 Lagado Close, Lilliput Road, Lilliput, Poole, Dorset, BH14 8LD
tel: 01235 771 577
email: strangeartmusic@yahoo.com
genre: All Music Types Accepted
info: Send demos to the address above. Strange Art specialise in music for the Southeast Asian and American market.

Structure Music
PO Box 26273, London, W3 6FN
tel: 0870 207 7720
fax: 0870 208 8820
email: info@structuremusic.co.uk
web: www.structuremusic.co.uk
contact: Olly Groves
genre: Dance/Singer-Songwriter/Television/Film soundtrack and theme music
info: Send demos to the address above.

Sublime Music Publishing
77 Preston Drove, Brighton, BN1 6LD
tel: 01273 560 605
fax: 01273 560 606
email: info@sublimemusic.co.uk
web: www.sublimemusic.co.uk
contact: Patrick Spinks
genre: All Music Types Accepted
info: Send CD (no more than three tracks) to the address above.

Sugarstar Music
IT Centre, York Science Park, York, YO10 5DG
tel: 0845 644 8424
fax: 07092 228 681
email: mark@sugarstar.com
web: www.sugarstar.com
contact: Mark J. Fordyce
genre: All Music Types Accepted
info: Specialise in song placements for film, TV and games. Send demos on CD only to the address above. Sugarstar regret that they are unable to return demos.

SW Music
48 Fernside Road, Poole, Dorset, BH15 2JJ
tel: 01202 773 103/01202 681 419
fax: 01202 681 419
email: david.dacosta@ntlworld.com
contact: Dave Dacosta
genre: All Music Types Accepted
info: Send demos to the address above.

Tairona Songs Ltd.
PO Box 102, London, E15 2HH
tel: 020 8555 5423
fax: 020 8519 6834
email: tairona@moksha.co.uk
web: www.moksha.co.uk
contact: Charles Cosh
genre: Alternative
info: Send demos to the address above.

Taste Music Ltd.
PO Box 31797, London, SW15 2XG
tel: 020 8780 3311
fax: 020 8785 9892
email: laurie@tastemusic.com
web: www.tastemusic.com
contact: Laurie Latham Jnr.
genre: Rock
info: Taste Music work with Muse, amongst others. Send demos to the address above. Please limit CDs to 3 tracks. Please do not submit any MP3s.

TMC Publishing
PO Box 150, Chesterfield, Derbyshire, S40 0YT
tel: 01246 236 667
email: tony@tmcrecords.co.uk
web: www.tmcrecords.co.uk
contact: Tony
genre: All Music Types Accepted
info: Contact by email first before sending a demo.

Toby Darling Ltd.
37-39 Southgate Street, Winchester, Hampshire, SO23 9EH
tel: 01962 844 480
fax: 01962 854 400
email: info@tobydarling.com
web: www.tobydarling.com
contact: Toby Darling
genre: Alt. Country/Acoustic
info: Send demos to the address above.

Tonecolor
Matlock, Brady Road, Lyminge, Folkestone, Kent, CT18 8HA
tel: 01303 863 185
fax: 01303 863 185
email: siggyjackson@onetel.net.uk
contact: Siggy Jackson
genre: Reggae/Punk/Jazz
info: Send demos to the address above. Include SAE if you would like your demo returned.

Tribal Songs
66c Chalk Farm Road, London, NW1 8AN
tel: 020 7482 6944
email: tribal.songs@tribaltreemusic.co.uk
web: www.tribaltreemusic.co.uk
genre: All Music Types Accepted
info: Send demo to the above address. See also listing for Tribal Tree Music in Useful Regional Organisations section for further information regarding services they provide to musicians and bands.

Trinifold Music
12 Oval Road, Camden, London, NW1 7DH
tel: 020 7419 4300
fax: 020 7419 4325
email: trinuk@globalnet.co.uk
contact: Robert Rosenberg
genre: Rock
info: Send demos to the address above.

Truelove Music
19f Tower Workshops, Riley Road, London, SE1 3DG
tel: 020 7252 2900
fax: 020 7252 2890
email: tlm@truelove.co.uk
web: www.truelove.co.uk
contact: John Truelove
genre: Electronic/Techno/House
info: Send demos to the address above.

Tsunami Sounds Ltd.
Muscott House, Meadrow, Godalming, Surrey, GU7 3HN
tel: 01483 410 100
fax: 01483 410 100
email: info@tsunami.co.uk
web: www.tsunami.co.uk
genre: Composers
info: Independent music publishing company. Also specialise in music production for the advertising, television, film and computer game industries.

TUMI (Music) Ltd.
8-9 New Bond Street Place, Bath, Somerset, BA1 1BH
tel: 01225 464 736
fax: 01225 444 870
email: info@tumimusic.com
web: www.tumimusic.com
contact: Mo Fini
genre: Latin American/Cuban
info: Send demos to the address above.

Tunetrader
PO Box 647, Portsmouth, PO1 2ZT
tel: 0845 226 2162
fax: 0845 762 0204
email: nick@tunetrader.com
web: www.tunetrader.com
contact: Nick Hooper
genre: Specialise in licensing independent music for placement in television, film and advertising.

Unique Corp Ltd.
1 Pennine Parade, Pennine Drive, London, NW2 1NT
tel: 020 8458 6006
fax: 0208 458 6660
email: info@uniquecorp.co.uk
web: www.uniquecorp.co.uk
contact: Richard Mayes
genre: Urban/R&B/Pop
info: Send demos to the address above.

Utopia Publishing
Utopia Village, 7 Chalcot Road, London, NW1 8LH
tel: 020 7586 3434
fax: 020 7586 3438
email: utopiarec@aol.com
contact: Phil Wainman
genre: Rock/Pop
info: Send 3 track demos to the address above.

Walk On The Wild Side
8 Deronda Road, London, SE24 9BG
tel: 020 8674 7990
fax: 020 8671 5548
contact: Dave Massey
genre: All Music Types Accepted
info: Send demos to the address above.

Wall Of Sound Music
Office 2, 9 Thorpe Close, London, W10 5XL
tel: 020 8969 1144
fax: 020 8969 1155
email: general@wallofsound.uk.com
web: www.wallofsound.net
contact: Alvin Collis
genre: Dance/Hip-Hop/Indie
info: Send demos to the address above.

Watercolour Music
Ardgour, PH33 7AB
tel: 01397 701 352/07833 597 458
email: watercolourmusic@aol.com
web: www.watercolourmusic.com
contact: Nick Turner
genre: Singer-Songwriter/Indie
info: Send demos electronically to the email address above. Alternatively send a CD with a biog to the postal address marked FAO Nick Turner.

Websongs Ltd.
Troupe Studios, 106 Thetford Road, New Malden, Surrey, KT3 5DZ
tel: 020 8949 0928
email: kip.trevor@websongs.co.uk
web: www.websongs.co.uk
contact: Kip Trevor
genre: Rock/Metal/All Music Types Accepted
info: Send demos, no more than three tracks, to the address above.

Westbury Music Ltd.
Suite B, 2 Tunstall Road, London, SW9 8DA
tel: 020 7733 5400
fax: 020 7733 4449
email: enquiries@westburymusic.net
web: www.westburymusic.net
contact: A&R Department.
genre: Reggae/Hip-Hop/Garage/Dance
info: Call the A&R department with details of your act. Send demo on request.

Whitebuck Music Publishing
122 Mosley Common Road, Worsley, Manchester, M28 1AN
tel: 0161 790 4640
fax: 0161 703 8521
email: whitesfarmstudio@aol.com
contact: Gary White
genre: All Music Types Accepted
info: Send demos to the address above. Associated with Whitebuck recording studio. Contact for details.

Wintrup Songs
31 Buckingham Street, Brighton, East Sussex, BN1 3LT
tel: 01273 880 439
email: a.mcgowan3@ntlworld.com
contact: Allan McGowan
genre: All Music Types Accepted
info: Mainly deal with royalty collection, although do accept some demos. Contact Allan with details of your act and follow with demo on request.

Wipe Out Music Ltd.
PO Box 1NW, Newcastle, NE99 1NW
tel: 0191 266 3802
fax: 0191 266 6073
email: enquiries@wipeoutmusic.com
web: www.wipeoutmusic.com
contact: John Espen
genre: Indie/Punk
info: Only interested in very off the wall, weird, noisy Indie and Punk. No unsolicited demos.

Zomba Music Publishers
20 Fulham Broadway, London, SW6 1AH
tel: 020 7384 7500
fax: 020 7835 5261
email: mike.mauley@bmgzomba.co.uk
web: www.bmgzomba.co.uk
contact: Mike Mauley
genre: All Music Types Accepted
info: Send CD demo with biography to the address above.

Section 3
Music Services/Retail

the|unsigned|guide

3.1 Music Services/Retail Foreword

Many of the sub-sections listed in Music Services/ Retail will have been covered, in part, by forewords in other sections of this directory. As with other sections you will find contact details and a short summary of the types of services each organisation supplies. Amongst others, these include recording studios, rehearsal rooms, designers, mastering & duplication (See the hugely useful Musicians Union information in the foreword to Section 6 - Advisory/ Industry Organisations regarding 'Releasing your Own Product') plus the information below regarding different types of Production Agreements. There is also information and contacts provided for sectors of the industry including video promo facilities, photographers, music & instrument shops, printers, lawyers/legal advice plus insurance services. All the entries have been researched as unsigned friendly, affordable and based in the North West.

Before you book studio or rehearsal space for example, make a few calls and get the best price you can. Similarly spend time researching the most suitable printers or insurance companies. Prices and services offered will vary between suppliers so don't jump at the first quote you get and always keep receipts. This section will probably be the most frequently visited during any of your campaigns. So please use the feedback sheets provided at the back of this directory to let us know which of the companies listed have been particularly helpful, or not, if the case arises.

Production Agreements

Over the last 10-15 years there has been a significant increase in the amount of Production Agreements being offered to artists. This is partly due to recording studios branching out and finding new ways of using their facilities to make money. Also, record companies are increasingly looking to license fin-

ished products, rather than bear the costs and hassle of putting artists in the studios themselves.

What is a Production Agreement (or Deal)?

The terms of a Production Deal can vary enormously and, of course, it is essential that an artist receives independent legal advice from an experienced music industry solicitor prior to signing. In this section we will look at the terms and considerations of the three different types of Production Deal, which are currently the most commonplace in the music industry.

Studio Demo Agreement

a. This first type of agreement is one which enables the studio to use its 'downtime' and gives the artist a chance to make a demo without having to pay for the studio time upfront.

b. Generally the studio does not take any copyright in the masters recorded.

c. In return for this 'free' studio time, the studio will want to make a charge, which will be payable sometime in the future - usually after the artist gets a record deal. Also, the studio will want an override royalty, usually on all releases up to and including the first album. A 1% or 2% royalty, based on retail price, would be usual.

d. Sometimes, the producer also wants to produce the first album released on a third party label.

Studio Demo Agreement - A Summary

The Studio Demo Agreement crosses over to other types of Production Deals, where the studio claims rights in what is recorded and then agrees either to release the work independently, or (more often) to find a third party company to release the product. All other types of production agreements actually rely on some form of license arrangement. Usually the artist will assign copyright to the original production company, which in turn licenses these rights to another company, which then releases the artists product. In effect, this then creates a 'middleman' - with two interested parties now taking their share of the profit before passing the balance of earnings on.

Manager's Production Company Agreement

a. In this instance the manager will offer the artist his or her facility for recording demos or may do a deal with an outside studio (as in Studio Demo Agreement above). In doing so, s/he will then take a complete assignment of rights for one or more albums. The resulting demo tapes are then taken to record companies in the normal way, but here the artist does not sign direct, in fact it is the Manager's Production Company which signs the record deal.

b. This type of deal is generally only justifiable if the manager also has a studio and producer with whom s/he works closely and who can jointly add something to the artist's music. The manager in this case normally does a deal based on a 50/50 split of his/her net receipts and should also pay over 50% of any advances s/he receives. (Note: Some deals may be based on a retail or dealer price base, if the company is more sophisticated.)

Manager's Production Company Agreement - A Summary

If this type of deal is offered, there are two key aspects to consider. Firstly, does the manager and his/her team actually have the skill and facilities to enhance what you, the artist, is doing? Or would you be better off signing directly with a more skilled and well-equipped third party company? If the answer is 'yes' to the second question, do not sign with the manager's company.

Secondly, a conflict may arise between the manager's financial responsibility to the artist which includes both handling the artist's finances and acting as an impartial advisor on all aspects of the artist's career - and his/her financial interest in the production company. The only way to resolve this probable conflict is for the manager to agree to waive his/her commission completely in respect of any income earned through the production company.

Independent Production Company Agreement

This third type of Production Deal is the same, in essence, as that offered by a manager. An Independent Production Company signs the artist for between 1-3 albums (note: do not sign for more albums than this without proper guarantees of full advances and increased royalties) and then pays income based on 50%/50% of net receipts. The important difference here is that because the production company is independent, the agreement can be fully negotiated without conflict.

Consideration of the production company's resources and the skills of its producer will be crucial in deciding whether it's better to sign this sort of agreement rather than go direct to the third party record company. It is worth bearing in mind that production companies can often write material for recording and record it to a standard ready for commercial release. Without this, many third party record companies may not be interested at all.

Conclusion

The three types of Production Deals described above (and any hybrids) are all based on Standard Recording Agreements - and therefore the principles in the Musicians' Union notes regarding Recording Agreements still apply.

Finally, be aware of any company which requires its artists to sign away their publishing rights especially if the manager of the band is an interested party.

This information has been kindly provided by Musicians' Union.

For more information, please contact:

Musicians' Union
London Office
60-62 Clapham Road
London
SW9 0JJ

email: dp1@musiciansunion.org.uk
tel: 020 7582 5566

Visit www.musiciansunion.org.uk for more information.

MUSIC SERVICES/RETAIL

MUSIC SERVICES/RETAILS

3.2 ARTWORK, CREATIVE & DESIGN

EAST of ENGLAND 93 GREATER LONDON 94 MIDLANDS 101 NORTHEAST 105 NORTHWEST 109
SOUTHEAST 117 SOUTHWEST 120 YORKSHIRE 124 NORTHERN IRELAND 128 SCOTLAND 129 WALES 132

EAST of ENGLAND

2G Ltd.
Newton Hall, Town Street, Newton, Cambridge, CB2 2PE
tel: 01223 871 001
email: design@think2g.com
web: www.think2g.com
contact: Lisa
info: Provide creative design, marketing and cost effective design solutions. Ideas that excite and inspire including photography and web design options.

4i Design
29a Chapel Street, Exning, Newmarket, CB8 7HA
tel: 01638 611 183
fax: 01638 610 973
email: thestudio@4i-design.co.uk
web: www.4i-design.co.uk
info: Small, established and reputable graphic design agency with a colourful variety of clients and designers alike. From stunning unique style design and album branding, to posters, flyers, and adverts.

AD Design
297 Hills Road, Cambridge, CB2 2QS
tel: 01223 711 569
email: andy@think-ad.co.uk
web: www.think-ad.co.uk
contact: Andy Davis
info: Innovative design solutions helping you to stand out from the crowd! Specialise in all kinds of printed media, plus website design and production.

Adept Design (Norfolk) Ltd.
15 White Hart Street, Aylsham, Norwich, Norfolk, NR11 6HG
tel: 01263 734 198
email: admin@adeptdesign.co.uk
web: www.adeptdesign.co.uk
contact: Derek Blois
info: All types of print and web based media produced.

Anamorphic
The Old School House, The Street, Melton, Suffolk, IP12 1PL
tel: 01394 382 820
email: dave@anamorphic-design.co.uk
web: www.anamorphic-design.co.uk
info: Website designer. Has previously worked with unsigned bands.

Cameron Design & Marketing Ltd.
40 Camel Road, Littleport, Ely, Cambridgeshire, CB6 1PU
tel: 01353 860 006
email: camerongraphics@btconnect.com
web: www.cameron.uk.com
info: Full design and marketing services.

CBA
51 London Road, Stapleford, Cambridge, CB2 5DG
tel: 01223 845 550
email: studio@cbg-design.co.uk
web: www.cba-design.co.uk
info: CBA can provide marketing literature, website and new media.

Colby Marketing
133a Magdalen Road, Norwich, Norfolk, NR3 4LB
tel: 01603 418 681
email: sales@colbymarketing.co.uk
contact: Edward Colby
info: Colby Marketing specialise in print based media, and can collaborate in order to produce websites.

Creative Sponge
1 Netherconesford, King Street, Norwich, NR1 1PW
tel: 01603 622 766
email: sally@creativesponge.co.uk
web: www.creativesponge.co.uk
contact: Sally Hubble
info: Award winning design agency.

Custance Design Associates
Blacksmiths Cottage, Rede, Bury St. Edmunds, Suffolk, IP29 4BE
tel: 01284 789 341
email: custancedesign@intamail.com
contact: Robert Custance
info: Custance can produce logos, posters and flyers, as well as web design in collaboration with a hosting company.

Custardfish
10 St. Margaret's Square, Ipswich, Suffolk, IP4 2BS
tel: 01473 280 001
email: info@custardfish.com
web: www.custardfish.com
info: Full print and design services including flyers, posters, CD artwork and website design. Specialise in illustrations and multimedia work.

Design 4 Online
Baray, Davids Lane, Benington, Boston, PE22 0BZ
tel: 01205 760 241
email: enquiries@design-4-online.co.uk
web: www.design-4-online.co.uk
contact: Matthew Brown
info: Web and graphic designers.

Design Consultancy IQUK
114a London Road, Chatteris, Cambridgeshire, PE16 6SF
tel: 01354 692 793
email: db@iquk.com
web: www.iquk.com
contact: Danny Baverstock
info: Full colour design for web and print. Previous experience of working with bands.

DGDesign
13 Holmesway, Peterborough, PE4 7XZ
tel: 01733 761 337
email: darren@grigas-design.com
web: www.grigas-design.com
info: Provides anything promotional for upcoming gigs such as flyers and posters. Also have online design service.

Dizzyhippo
167 Cemetery Road, Ipswich, IP4 2HL
tel: 01473 420 233
email: info@dizzyhippo.com
web: www.dizzyhippo.com
info: Provide variety of graphic design services, as well as print facility.

Dolby Gallery
West Street, Oundle, Peterborough, PE8 4EF
tel: 01832 273 801
email: dolbygallery@design-factory.co.uk
web: www.dolbygallery.com
contact: Simon Dolby
info: Creative graphic designers, painters and illustrators. Established 16 years.

MUSIC SERVICES/RETAIL

Double S Design
67 Severn Road, Ipswich, IP3 0PU
tel: 01473 728 617
email: info@doublesdesign.com
web: www.doublesdesign.com
info: Comprehensive service including a wide range of print options and web design including Flash. Lots of experience with the youth market.

Eclipse Design
Unit 6, Fletcher Way, Weston Road, Norwich, NR3 3ST
tel: 01603 409 060
email: info@eclipse-design.co.uk
web: www.eclipse-design.co.uk
contact: Ben
info: Eclipse Design will produce creative print and web based media including illustration and web hosting.

Elsey Adcock Associates Ltd.
Ground Floor, 3 Cromwell Court, Grey Friars Road, Ipswich, IP1 1XG
tel: 01473 226 448
email: iinfo@elsey-adcock.co.uk
web: www.elseyadcock.co.uk
info: Provides website design and all printing design.

Firebrand
25 Prince's Street, Ipswich, IP1 1PH
tel: 01473 233 281
fax: 01473 230 667
email: wendy@firebrandweb.com
web: www.firebrandweb.com
contact: Wendy Offord
info: Small, enthusiastic design consultancy specialising in design for anything music related. Aim to create a design for your band as individual as the music. Can work to budget.

Firebrand Communications Ltd.
25 Princes Street, Ipswich, IP1 1PH
tel: 01473 233 281
email: info@firebrandweb.com
web: www.firebrandweb.com
info: Full service design and advertising design.

Hectic Designs
March, Cambridgeshire
tel: 01354 650 991
email: info@hecticdesigns.com
web: www.hecticdesigns.com
contact: Ben Taylor
info: Design for web and print. Ben is in an unsigned band himself, and is sensitive to the needs of musicians.

Impact Design
5 Huntingfield Road, Bury St. Edmunds, Suffolk, IP33 2JE
tel: 01284 769 138
email: keithmulley@btconnect.com
contact: Keith Mulley
info: Graphic designers. Can design band logos, CD covers and t-shirts. Can provide service over the internet to anywhere in the country.

Indent Graphic Services
15a Town Green, Wymondham, Norfolk, NR18 0PN
tel: 01953 601 303
email: info@indentgraphics.net
web: www.indentgraphics.net
contact: John Stamp
info: Indent will produce quality print based media and websites. One in-house designer is in a band himself, so the company are informed about the needs of bands and musicians.

James Kindred Designs
Ipswich
tel: 01473 232 042/07921 517 912
email: jameskindred@mac.com
web: www.jameskindred.co.uk
contact: James Kindred
info: Single freelance designer who has previously provided artwork and photography for bands. Ideal for smaller scale projects.

Javelin Graphics
17 Mill Road, Wells-Next-The-Sea, Norfolk, NR23 1HE
tel: 01328 710 349
email: jmjoslin@tiscali.co.uk
web: www.johnjoslin.co.uk
contact: John Joslin
info: All types of print based media produced including posters, flyers, CD artwork, stationery and websites.

Karen Rowe Design
12 Hares Walk, Sudbury, CO10 1BL
tel: 01787 371 375
info: Provide graphic design and advertising.

Out of House
18 Grantchester Road, Trumpington, Cambridge, CB2 2LH
tel: 01223 840 872
email: post@outofhouse.co.uk
web: www.outofhouse.co.uk
contact: Rob Kinnear
info: Small design agency with impressive client list. Great deal of experience, plus impressive portfolio and track record of delivering results for clients of all sizes.

Phex Design
7 St. Anne's Crescent, Gorleston, Great Yarmouth, Norfolk, NR31 7LF
tel: 07789 818 966
email: dan@phexdesign.com
web: www.phexdesign.com
info: Specialises in web design and has previously worked with unsigned bands, as well as constructing a music tablature database.

Proaction Design Ltd.
12 Manor Mews, Bridge Street, St. Ives, Cambridgeshire, PE27 5EG
tel: 01480 464 444
email: proactiondesign@aol.com
web: www.proaction-design.com
contact: Martin Young
info: Graphic design, print, internet, display etc. Has worked with small bands/promotions previously.

School House Studios
Borley Mill, Borley, Sudbury, CO10 7AB
tel: 01787 375 475
email: martin@visualcomm.co.uk
web: www.visualcomm.co.uk
contact: Martin Reed
info: School House Studios can produce creative design, photography, print, multimedia and websites.

Starfish Ltd.
Unit 4, Curtis Road, Norwich, NR6 6RB
tel: 01603 414 888
email: info@starfishlimited.com
web: www.starfishlimited.com
info: Graphic design company who specialise in design and artwork for CD covers and all music and audio-visual related packaging. Budget jobs to large scale complicated packages, original ideas or working from your visuals, all in industry standard software formats.

Vincent Creatives
49 Vinery Road, Cambridge, CB1 3DN
tel: 01223 240 996
email: info@vincent-creatives.com
web: www.vincent-creatives.com
info: Graphic design including website design and Flash animation.

GREATER LONDON

10 Talents
Suite 9, Green Court House, 200 Mile End Road, London, E1 4LD
tel: 07941 741 534
email: 10talents@bsgmusic.com
web: www.bsgmusic.com
info: Full design facilities from logos to complete packages. 10 Talents can also help with PR and marketing.

12 Point
401 Coppergate House, 16 Brune Street, London, EC1 7NJ
tel: 020 7721 8630
email: studio@twelve-point.co.uk
web: www.twelve-point.co.uk
contact: Mark Brett
info: A creative studio combining all aspects of design, artwork and new media, taking projects right through to the printed document.

1977 Design Creative
Aberdeen House, Highbury Grove, London, N5 2EA
tel: 020 7226 9444
email: info@19-77.com
web: www.19-77.com
contact: Paul Bailey
info: Cover all aspects of design, including CD artwork and website design.

300 Million
1 Roseoman Place, Finsbury, London, EC1R OJY
tel: 020 7833 3838
fax: 020 7833 1888
email: lotsofideas@300million.com
web: www.300million.com
contact: Nigel Davis
info: Provide brand design for both web and print. 300 Million are especially sympathetic to the needs of unsigned acts as several of the staff have formed their own unsigned band. See the website for details.

4sight Visuals
199 Creighton Avenue, London, N2 9BN
tel: 020 8883 9327/07813 336 408
email: info@4sightvisuals.co.uk
web: www.4sightvisuals.co.uk
contact: Dan Clark
info: Graphic design for both web and print, including DVD, logo and flyer design. Regularly work with unsigned acts.

9thplanet

9th Planet Design
45-46 Charlotte Road, London, EC2A 3PD
tel: 020 7739 3658
email: neildell@9thplanetdesign.com
web: www.9thplanetdesign.com
contact: Neil Dell
info: With 20 years experience designing for the music industry (and many other client groups), 9th Planet Design can offer a fast, efficient and professional service supplying competitively priced website and print design. Projects can be finished to print, disc or PDF for items including single sided one-colour flyers, CDs (booklet, tray inlays and on-body), posters and 4 colour books. Some recent music industry clients include Ace Records, Becalmed, Demon Music Group, Hux/BBC, RPM, Sanctuary and Universal.

a fish in sea
14a Ullswater Road, London, SE27 0AL
tel: 020 8761 1046
email: info@afishinthesea.co.uk
web: www.afishinsea.co.uk
contact: Michael Mursell
info: Provide graphic design services, mainly for print.

Abstract Graphics
Studio House, 142 Merton Hall Road, Wimbeldon, London, SW19 3PZ
tel: 020 8543 2636
email: info@abstractgraphics.co.uk
web: www.abstractgraphics.co.uk
contact: Miles
info: Provide web, print and logo design services.

Active Webdezign
Studio 1A, Sussex Ring, London, N12 7HY
tel: 020 8446 1515
email: info@webdezign.co.uk
web: www.webdezign.co.uk
contact: Mike Yan
info: Provide print and web design services.

AEDIS
2 Gees Court, St. Christopher's Place, London, W1U 1JA
tel: 020 7616 0180
fax: 0870 243 8597
email: info@aedis-uk.com
web: www.aedis-uk.com
contact: Robin Stevens
info: Provide print and web design services. AEDIS have experience designing CD artwork.

Airheads
1st Floor, 131-179 Belsize Road, London, NW6 4AB
tel: 020 7328 8796
email: info@airheads.co.uk
web: www.airheads.co.uk
contact: Bunny or Jason
info: Cover all aspects of design work including web design, airbrush design, customised clothing and CD artwork.

Amadi Design
Studio 8, Tottenham Green Enterprise Centre, Town Hall Approach Road, London, N15 4RX
tel: 020 8375 3465
email: info@amadidesign.co.uk
web: www.amadidesign.co.uk or www.logokitchen.com
contact: Lola
info: Have previous experience working with bands' design requirements for CD artwork, web design, flyers and merchandise.

Andrew Rae
London
tel: 07765 008 636
email: a@andrewrae.org.uk
web: www.andrewrae.org.uk
info: Illustration and animation. Clients include MTV, 333 and Transparent Sound.

Ark Creative Ltd.
146 Bertram Road, Enfield, Middlesex, EN1 1LS
tel: 020 8292 7274
email: enquiries@ark-creative.co.uk
web: www.ark-creative.co.uk
contact: Nathan Black
info: Web designers who have previous music experience. Resources include new media and marketing. There is an additional Oxford branch, call the above number for details.

Aybul Design
112 The Vale, Southgate, London, N14 6AY
tel: 020 8920 5643
fax: 020 8920 6531
email: info@aybul.com
web: www.aybul.co.uk
contact: Bill
info: Provide web and print design services.

Baby Elephant
74a Hoxton Street, London, N1 6LP
tel: 020 7739 0469
email: mail@baby-elephant.co.uk
web: www.baby-elephant.co.uk
contact: Neil Hobson
info: Offer graphic and website design services. Baby Elephant have experience working in the music industry. Previous clients include Kerrang and Kiss 100 radio, as well as CD artwork design for different artists. Affordable rates for unsigned bands.

BakerSmith Design
8 The Glass House, 3 Royal Oak Yard, London, SE1 3GE
tel: 0870 712 3545
email: claire@bakersmith.co.uk
web: www.bakersmith.co.uk
contact: Claire
info: Provide print and web design services. Also have office based in the South West. See listing for further details.

Barneby Ltd.
17 Willis Road, London, E15 3HH
tel: 020 8519 6599
email: nicky.barneby@btinternet.com
info: Provide editorial design service, including leaflets and brochures.

Blade Design
Holborn Studios, 49-50 Eagle Wharf Road, London, N1 7ED
tel: 020 7253 6070
fax: 020 7253 4484
email: info@bladeweb.co.uk
web: www.bladeweb.co.uk
contact: Steve
info: Blade provide a professional print design service for the music industry. They do not regularly work with unsigned acts, but are willing to if the band have established managerial representation. Previous clients include Jools Holland, amongst many others.

Bleach
Unit 1, 5 Foxton Square, London, N1 6NU
tel: 020 7426 0111
email: info@drinkbleach.co.uk
web: www.drinkbleach.co.uk
contact: Rob
info: As a totally integrated agency, Bleach offer a full range of creative design solutions to achieve results and get recognition. Specialist services include identity for print and packaging, and new media web design with moving graphics. They have worked with a number of bands and record labels including Icarus, Spiritual South, Oblique, Apollo, Nova, Safe House Records, Incentive Records and Demon Music.

Bloodybigspider
4 Renmuir Street, London, SW17 9SS
tel: 020 8772 4549
email: info@bloodybigspider.com
web: www.bloodybigspider.com
contact: Stephen Holmes
info: Provide print design services. Have worked with independent labels and bands in the past.

Blue Design Ltd.
8 The Glass House, 3 Royal Oak Yard, London, SE1 3GE
tel: 020 7378 1814
fax: 020 7378 1811
email: studio@bluedesign.ltd.uk
web: www.bluedesign.ltd.uk
contact: Chris Goddard
info: Blue Design aim to give you the high level exposure for all promotional channels, whether it be a poster campaign, event material or PR photography. Are happy to work with artists from any genre.

Brother Russia
London
tel: 07779 290 953
email: design@brotherrussia.co.uk
web: www.brotherrussia.co.uk
contact: Alistair
info: CD artwork, website design, design for print including posters, flyers and t-shirts graphics. For details of photography services see relevant section.

Capricorn Multimedia
49 Golders Gardens, London, NW11 9BS
tel: 020 8209 0948
email: info@capricorn-multimedia.co.uk
web: www.capricorn-multimedia.co.uk
contact: Ryan Lazarus
info: Full CD artwork reproduction and design service. CD duplication and mastering facilities available. Also provide music video production, incorporating animation and visual effects. See relevant sections for more information.

Century 23 (London)
3rd Floor, 54-55 Margaret Street, London, W1W 8SH
tel: 020 7612 8174
email: andrew@century-23.com
web: www.century-23.com
info: Century 23 have been working in close association with the live music, clubbing, entertainment, and leisure industries across Britain for 7 years providing both design and printed promotional products. Band friendly. Most of the team are members of bands or DJ. Contact for prices on flyers, posters, tickets, design, runs of CDs and vinyl. Also have offices in Belfast and Edinburgh.

Clavicorn Ltd.
35-37 Grosvenor Gardens, London, SW1W 0BS
tel: 020 7953 4024
email: info@clavicorn.com
web: www.clavicorn.com
contact: Jonathan
info: Provide print and web design services, including built-in database systems for your website.

The Clubb
Unit 21, Cremer Business Centre, 37 Cremer Street, London, E1 8HD
tel: 020 7336 6147
email: design@theclubb.co.uk
web: www.theclubb.co.uk
contact: Carly
info: Provide a mainly print-based design service, including posters and flyers. Occasionally design for the web.

Conker Design Ltd.
280 Fulham Road, London, SW10 9EW
tel: 020 7795 1002
email: studio@conkerdesign.co.uk
web: www.conkerdesign.co.uk
contact: Marcus
info: Provide full print and web design service, including registration and site maintenance.

Creographics
261 Haydons Road, Wimbledon, London, SW19 8TY
tel: 020 8540 5959
fax: 020 8715 8959
email: info@creographics.com
web: www.creographics.com
contact: Andy Matthews
info: Provide print and logo design services.

Crumpled Dog Design
18 Phipp Street, London, EC2A 4NU
tel: 020 7739 5553
email: christian@crumpled-dog.com
web: www.crumpled-dog.com
info: Provide web and promotional literature design services.

Darwin Press
77a Blackheath Road, Greenwich, London, SE10 8PD
tel: 020 8691 1357
fax: 020 8961 6556
email: sales@darwinpress.co.uk
web: www.darwinpress.co.uk
info: Provide print design services for posters, flyers and occasionally CD inlays.

Deadbeat Music
London
tel: 020 8765 9678
email: tim@deadbeatmusic.co.uk
web: www.deadbeatmusic.co.uk
contact: Tim Mitra
info: Website design. Experience of working with bands and musicians. Tim also helps bands to record professional demos using his studio at home. He can also assist with songwriting skills. See website for details or contact Tim on the above number.

Deep Creative
12a Imperial Studios, 3-11 Imperial Road, London, SW6 2AG
tel: 020 7751 0824
fax: 020 7751 0823
email: deeper@deep.co.uk
web: www.deep.co.uk
info: Provide web and print design services.

Design4Music
7 Ground Floor, Portland Mews, Soho, London, W1F 8JQ
tel: 020 7734 5676
fax: 020 7734 5323
email: info@design4music.com
web: www.design4music.com
info: Provide a full design and marketing service for individuals and businesses within all sectors of the music industry.

Designwize GWA
268 Church Road, Leyton, London, E10 7JQ
tel: 020 8539 6977
email: designwizegwa@aol.com
info: Graphic design for web and print.

D-Face
Studio 104, The Base Station, 326 Kensal Road, London, W10 5BZ
tel: 020 8959 3125/07817 806 011
fax: 020 8959 3125
email: design@d-face.co.uk
web: www.d-face.co.uk
contact: Donna
info: Specialists in design for music and video packaging. Also provide a web design service. Previous clients include Zomba Records.

DL Graphics
Ground Floor, 64 Old Street, London, EC1V 9AN
tel: 020 7566 0057
fax: 020 7566 0058
email: info@dl-graphics.com
web: www.dl-graphics.com
contact: Derek Turpin
info: Provide print and full web design services (including assistance in the registration process) to accommodate any budget. In-house poster printing service, which allows DL Graphics to oversee your project from original idea all the way through to the finished product.

DogStar Design
39 Doughty Street, London, WC1N 2LF
tel: 020 7430 7766
fax: 020 7430 7767
email: enquiries@dogstardesign.co.uk
web: www.dogstardesign.co.uk
info: A multi-disciplined design communications agency.

Eat More Chickens
London
email: info@eatmorechickens.net
web: www.eatmorechickens.net
info: Young and forward-thinking design collective who work in all media. Flexible yet distinctive, and able to provide original animation, illustration, layout and design work for posters, record sleeves, ad campaigns, moving image and the web.

Eliot Thoburn
tel: 020 7033 9299/07989 697 898
email: ethoburn@btinternet.com
web: www.peepshow.org.uk
info: Illustration. Clients include Loaded, Shoreditch Twat, Loaded, 333 and Channel Four.

Emmi
London
email: hello@emmi.co.uk
web: www.emmi.co.uk
info: Freelance designer, Emmi Salonen, designs CD and LP covers, posters, business cards and entire identities for bands and musicians. Prices negotiable.

Excerpt
tel: 07976 453 580
email: tom@excerpt.org.uk
web: www.excerpt.org.uk
info: Experienced freelancers specialising in promos, photography and print design.

Fat Beehive
Second Floor, 59 Rivington Street, Shoreditch, London, EC2A 3QQ
tel: 020 7739 8704
fax: 020 7613 3303
email: info@fatbeehive.com
web: www.fatbeehive.com
contact: Matt Taylor, Tom Morton
info: Provide web design services. Previous clients include Silverback Records.

Firedog Design
32 Lexington Street, London, W1F 0LQ
tel: 020 7292 6270
email: info@firedog-design.co.uk
web: www.firedog-design.co.uk
contact: Fraser Black
info: Agency that works to develop growing and yet to be discovered brands. They offer the complete range of creative services, from CD sleeves to e-flyers at reasonable prices. Experience in working with the music industry, counting BMG Europe amongst their clients.

Fletcher Ward Design
27 Albemarle Street, London, W1S 4HZ
tel: 020 749 14399
email: fwd@fletcherwarddesign.co.uk
web: www.fletcherwarddesign.co.uk
contact: Brian Ward
info: Primarily provide print design, although they have also designed websites.

Form
Ground Floor, 47 Tabernacle Street, London, EC2A 4AA
tel: 020 7014 1430
fax: 020 7014 1431
email: studio@form.uk.com
web: www.form.uk.com
contact: Paul
info: Graphic design consultancy working mainly in the music industry. Previous clients include Island and Polydor Records, but they are equally willing to work with unsigned acts.

Full Stop
37a Park Road, London, N8 8TE
tel: 020 8374 3166/07713 648725
email: clare@fullstopdesign.co.uk
web: www.fullstopdesign.co.uk
contact: Clare Mellor
info: Provide full print and logo design services, from original idea to finished product. A small creative company who offer reasonable prices and are keen to work with unsigned acts.

Green Ink
28 Hanbury Street, Spitalfields, London, E1 6QR
tel: 020 7247 7248
fax: 020 7247 7293
email: design@green-ink.co.uk
web: www.green-ink.co.uk
info: Specialise in music packaging design and DVD and CD-Rom design. Previous clients include Oasis, Faith No More and Echo & The Bunnymen.

Highrise Media
Studio A116, Faircharm Trading Estate, 8-12 Creekside, London, SE8 3DX
tel: 020 8469 9300
fax: 020 8469 9301
email: mail@highrisemedia.com
web: www.highrisemedia.com
contact: Andre Lecointe
info: Web and graphic design services. Music videos and film production. See relevant section for more details.

Hip Replacement
London
tel: 07980 663 246
email: leebaxter@hip-replacement.com
web: www.hip-replacement.com
contact: Lee Baxter
info: Web design and graphic design for print, photography and video service. Has worked with musicians and labels previously.

IMS Ltd.
Unit C, Southwark Bridge Business Centre, 79-81 Union Street, London, SE1 1SG
tel: 020 7407 5566
fax: 020 7407 5577
email: info@ims-limited.net
web: www.ims-limited.net
contact: Manish Chandarana
info: Provide print, logo and web design services. IMS also have an in-house printing service, and can produce tickets, flyers, posters, t-shirts and balloons. Prices start from £10.

Insect
1st Floor Studio, 2-8 Scrutton Street, London, EC2A 4RT
tel: 0871 208 0083
fax: 0870 036 908
email: info@insect.co.uk
web: www.insect.co.uk
info: Sleeve design, website design and art direction. Previous clients include Haven, Therapy! and Kelli.

Invisible Ink
Erico House, 93-99 Upper Richmond Road, London, SW15 2TG
tel: 020 8785 5625
email: info@invisible-ink.biz
web: www.invisible-ink.biz
contact: Richard Miller
info: Provide print and web design services. Have previously designed CD covers and flyers for unsigned bands.

JJ Lacey
London
tel: 07773 860 497
email: jasonjlacey@hotmail.com
contact: Jason Lacey
info: Offers music promotion services to artists and bands. Packages available including album cover and logo design, full video and video samples for promotional material, styling and photography, as well as verification and adjustments of recordings. See listings in relevant sections for further details.

Kate Moross
86 Islington High Street, London, N1 8EG
tel: 07811 152 543
email: kate@katemoross.com
web: www.katemoross.com
info: Graphics, illustration and ideas. Providing, high quality and concept driven graphic design and illustration.

Kut & Payste Media
26-28 Hatherley Mews, Walthamstow, London, E17 4QP
tel: 020 8520 5933
fax: 020 8520 9401
email: info@kutandpayste.com
web: www.kutandpayste.com
contact: Freddie B-Apeagyei
info: Offer design, reprographic, printing, multimedia, internet, digital video and broadcast services. Have previously worked with Coldplay on 'Safety' single artwork.

Lateral Net Ltd.
Charlotte House, 47-49 Charlotte Road, London, EC2A 3QT
tel: 020 7613 4449
fax: 020 7613 4645
email: studio@lateral.net
web: www.lateral.net
info: Provide full web design service.

Luke Best
London
tel: 020 7033 9299/07973 622 458
email: luke@lukebest.com
web: www.lukebest.com
info: Illustration and animation. Clients include MTV, Channel Four, Diesel, Toyota, The Fades and Agent Blue.

Marcus Smithwick Graphic Design
1 Altior Court, 74-76 Shepherds Hill, London, N6 5RJ
tel: 020 8341 7970
email: marcus.smithwick@mac.com
contact: Marcus Smithwick
info: Graphic design for web and print.

Mary & Mick
11 Allerford Court, Bromley Road, London, SE6 2XL
tel: 020 8461 2197
email: info@maryandmick.com
web: www.maryandmick.com
info: Provide print design services, including flyers and CD artwork.

Miles Donovan
London
tel: 07715 103 673
email: m@milesdonovan.co.uk
web: www.milesdonovan.co.uk
info: Illustration. Clients include Warner Brothers, J Records, Maverick, Fact Magazine, Straight no Chaser and The Face.

Montelimar
Studio 1, 99 Arundell Avenue, Liverpool, L17 2AT
tel: 07963 111 730
email: contact@montelimar.co.uk
web: www.montelimar.co.uk
contact: David Lake
info: Provide record sleeve design for small labels and unsigned acts, as well as original art on canvas. See the website for examples of Montelimar's work.

Motorik Design
359 Bethnal Green Road, London, E2 6LG
email: motorikdesign@yahoo.couk
contact: B. Kersey
info: Design for record sleeves, promotional material, as well as work carried out using Flash.

Net Solutions (London) Ltd.
40 Rosebery Avenue, London, SW14 8LW
tel: 020 8255 2483
fax: 020 8255 4022
email: info@netsols.co.uk
web: www.netsols.co.uk
contact: Steve Hacon
info: Provide web design services. Also offer website maintenance and re-design packages. Prices start at £25 per hour.

No Holes Bard
Studio 9, 25 Horsell Road, Highbury, London, N5 1XL
tel: 020 7697 8222
email: info@noholesbard.com
web: www.noholesbard.com
contact: James
info: Provide web design services.

Outburst Creative
16 Rosebery Avenue, London, EC1R 4TD
tel: 020 7713 6500
fax: 020 7713 6501
email: info@outburstcreative.ocm
web: www.outburstcreative.com
contact: James Wheele
info: Provide web and print design services at affordable prices.

Peepshow Collective
London
tel: 020 7033 9299
email: info@peepshow.org.uk
web: www.peepshow.org.uk
info: Illustration, styling, design, art direction and animation. An extensive portfolio can be found at the website above. Clients include: MTV, Absolut Vodka, Evisu, Diesel, Toyota, Orange, Puma, Rolling Rock, Dazed and Confused, Levis, Channel Four, Sony, Warner Brothers, Firetrap, BBC, Harvey Nichols, Loaded, The Face and Fosters.

Pen & Pixel
London
tel: 020 7993 2549
email: penandpixel@penandpixel.com
web: www.penandpixel.com
info: CD artwork and design for print and web. Previous clients include Snoop Doggy Dogg, Master P and Korn. Also have offices in California and New York.

Preloaded
16-24 Underwood Street, London, N1 7JQ
tel: 020 7684 3505
fax: 020 7684 3500
email: rob@preloaded.com
web: www.preloaded.com
contact: Rob
info: Provide web and print design services. Previous clients include Universal, EMI and Decca Music, BBC, Coca-Cola, MTV, Channel Four and E-sure.

Prophet Media
London
tel: 020 8673 6596/07968 035 627
email: stuart@prophetmedia.co.uk
web: www.prophetmedia.co.uk
info: Website design and coding, CD cover design, hosting, flyer design and cost effective printing.

The Red Box Group
London
tel: 0870 746 5192
fax: 0870 746 5193
email: adam@redboxgroup.net
web: www.redboxgroup.net
contact: Adam Jennings
info: The Red Box group of companies have been providing digital support for the arts since 1996. They offer web consultancy, design and development; DVD and CD-ROM content and front end creation; flyer, poster and CD sleeve design and EPKs (Electronic Press Kits). Previous clients have included Universal, Warner and Sony.

Red C
2 Cloth Court, London, EC1A 7LS
tel: 020 7796 2929
fax: 0870 460 5914
email: info@red-c.co.uk
web: www.red-c.co.uk
contact: Torsten Stauch
info: Can provide dynamic websites designed to fit in with your existing image. The sites are built so they can be easily updated, allowing you to add new gig dates and other information. Red C will also submit your website to search engines, including Google, AOL and MSN.

Sho Design Group
57 Farringdon Road, London, EC1M 3JB
tel: 020 7993 5472
email: info@sho-mail.com
web: www.sho-studio.com
contact: Richard
info: Provide branding, print and web design services. Previous clients include Echo Records and Warner Music UK.

Siab Studios
London
tel: 07773 535 170
email: info@siabstudios.co.uk
web: www.siabstudios.co.uk
contact: Colin Warhurst, Antony O'Hanlon
info: Offer a number of services for unsigned bands including photography, logo design and CD cover and insert designs, as well as affordable music video production. Siab also run a scheme allowing young media talent to gain experience by matching clients and inexperienced but enthusiastic talent together. Clients visiting the site have a choice of utilising the full resources of Siab Studios and/or allowing raw talent a chance to create work for them, usually at a cheaper rate, or even free of charge, in order for them to gain experience.

Sien
74a St Mary's Road, London, NW10 4AX
tel: 020 8965 6138
email: info@sien.co.uk
web: www.sien.co.uk
contact: Jonathan Spybey
info: Web and graphic design specialists. Can produce artwork for album covers. Have worked with unsigned bands in the past.

Singernet Ltd.
102 Springbank Road, Lewisham, London, SE13 6SX
tel: 020 8697 7466
email: info@singernet.co.uk
web: www.singernet.co.uk
contact: Suzie Singer
info: Provide web design services.

Skylab Design & Communication Ltd.
Suite 5, The Sanctuary, 23 Oakhill Grove, Surbiton, Surrey, KT6 6DU
tel: 020 8390 0100
email: info@skylabdesign.co.uk
web: www.skylabdesign.co.uk
contact: Dale Westcott
info: Provide web, print, logo and advertising design services. Previous clients include Warner and Sony.

Slim Designs
91-95 Brick Lane, Old Truman Brewery, London, E1 6QL
tel: 020 7375 3995/07811 607 969
email: info@slimdesigns.com
web: www.slimdesigns.com
contact: Nick Slim
info: Illustration and design for print. Can also offer printing and photography services. See listing in relevant sections for details.

want to take the world by storm?

so let Small Japanese Soldier help you.

we're an aggressive guerrilla design unit that can take care of your sleeve design, promotion and image.

all you have to be is unsigned.

call andy on 020 7421 9400
or email andy@smalljapanesesoldier.com
when you think you're ready.

Small Japanese Soldier
32-38 Saffron Hill, London, EC1N 8FH
tel: 020 7421 9400
fax: 020 7421 9334
email: jungle@smalljapanesesoldier.com
web: www.smalljapanesesoldier.com
contact: Andy Hunns, Liz Brown
info: Provide a CD artwork design service. Regularly work in the music industry. Previous clients include Thea Gilmore, Black Box Recorder, Matthew Ryan, The Glitterati and Alabama 3.

Snowstation
52 Putney Park Lane, London, SW15 5HQ
tel: 020 7706 4926
email: info@snowstation.co.uk
web: www.snowstation.co.uk
info: Provide web design services. Previous clients include One Little Indian.

Solid Sand Studios
The Gatehouse, Unit 31, 313-315 Kingsland Road, London, E8 4DL
email: info@solidsandstudios.com
web: www.solidsandstudios.com
info: Innovative design solutions built around creative thinking, including range of new media services.

Specialmoves
3rd Floor, Northburgh House, London, EC1V OAT
tel: 020 7253 3399
email: info@specialmoves.com
web: www.specialmoves.com
contact: James Nord
info: Provide web design service. Would be willing to wok with unsigned bands, contact primarily with details.

Spirit IC
New Hibernia House, Buttermarket, London Bridge, London, SE1 9AG
tel: 020 7378 0000
email: touch@spiritic.co.uk
web: www.spiritic.co.uk
info: Provide web and print design services.

Strange Corporation
11-15 Betterton Street, Soho, London, WC2H 9BP
tel: 0870 241 7451
email: results@strangecorp.com
web: www.strangecorp.com
contact: Jamie Sergeant
info: Provide web, DVD and video design services. Have designed record sleeves on several occasions. Previous clients include BMG Music. See also listing for office based in Poole.

Stuart Lang
7 Poland Street, London, W1F 8PU
tel: 07967 179 644
email: stuart@bearmail.co.uk
contact: Stuart Lang
info: Stuart has previously worked with unsigned bands, designing logos, websites, flyers and other print. Contact him directly to view previous work and discuss your needs.

The Studio
72a Old Dover Road, Blackheath, London, SE3 8SY
tel: 020 8853 8531
fax: 020 8853 8532
email: design@thestudio-london.com
web: www.thestudio-london.com
contact: Sally Smith
info: Provide web, print and product design services.

Suburb Design
138-140 Southwark Street, London, SE1 0SW
tel: 020 7593 1555
email: info@suburbdesign.co.uk
web: www.suburbdesign.co.uk
contact: Phil Parker
info: Provide web and print design services. They also have a record label. See relevant section for details.

Tomas
London
email: info@tomas.uk.com
contact: Tom
info: Artwork for promos and album covers. Also provide band photography service. See listing in relevant section for details.

Undertow Design
Unit 7, 9-10 College Terrace, London, E3 5EP
tel: 020 8983 4718
email: info@undertow-design.co.uk
web: www.undertow-design.co.uk
contact: Steven Wilkins
info: Provide print design services, including CD artwork. Has worked with many record labels.

The Unknown
Unit 204, Holywell Centre, 1 Phipp Street, London, EC2A 4PS
tel: 020 7739 1000
fax: 020 7739 8609
email: jaffa@the-unknown.co.uk
web: www.the-unknown.co.uk
contact: Jaffa
info: Provide record cover design services for the music industry. Previous clients include Soft Cell, Daniel Bedingfield and A Man Called Adam. While The Unknown work most frequently with signed bands, they occasionally take on unsigned projects.

v2vclubmedia
PO Box 44176, London, SW6 1WA
tel: 020 7381 6987/07903 300 744/07957 467 361
email: info@v2vclubmedia.com
web: www.v2vclubmedia.com
contact: Denton, Denise
info: v2vclubmedia work exclusively within the music industry. Offer print design including flyers, posters, brochures and business cards, plus design for web, multimedia and logos.

Vampire Music
20 Tanners Hill, Deptford, London, SE8 4JP
tel: 020 8691 6666
fax: 020 8692 9999
email: info@vampiremusic.co.uk
web: www.vampiremusic.co.uk
info: Graphic design for CD packaging, flyers, tickets, posters, leaflets, labels and logos. Vampire Music also incorporates recording studios, rehearsal rooms, mastering and duplication services, a music shop, as well as equipment hire and tuition. See entries in relevant sections for details.

Version Ltd.
15 Holywell Row, London, EC2A 4JB
tel: 020 7684 5470
email: info@versioncreative.com
web: www.versioncreative.com
contact: Anthony Oram
info: Provide design services for web, print and enhanced CDs.

View
The Penthouse, Long Island House, London, W3 ORG
tel: 020 8740 9751
fax: 020 8740 9857
email: view@view.uk.com
web: www.view.uk.com
contact: Tim Watson
info: Provide web and print design services.

Wall Design & Art Direction
Studio 2, Ground Floor, 42 Kinsway Place, London, EC1R OLU
tel: 020 7251 2004
email: info@wallcreative.com
web: www.wallcreative.com
contact: Sheridan Wall
info: Provide print, logo and web design services. Wall Design are keen to take on more work within the music industry, and regularly design CD artwork. Previous clients include Longpigs and Beverly Knight.

We Made This
28a Jelf Road, London, SW2 1BJ
tel: 020 7737 3580
email: heythere@we-made-this.com
web: www.we-made-this.com
info: Specialise in design for print, especially in materials with a tactile surface. Logos and identities.

WhiteLight Design
233 Woodhouse Road, London, N12 9BD
tel: 020 8361 8302
fax: 020 8361 0753
email: studio@wlight.com
web: www.wlight.com
contact: Michelle Collins
info: Award-winning graphic design consultancy whose previous work includes Oasis and Sex Pistols book designs, plus many other music industry related projects. They offer photography, web design, CD artwork design plus flyers, passes and promotional item design and print.

Whizzywig Ltd.
Holy Well House, Wellington Passage, Wansted, London, E11 2AL
tel: 020 8989 3341
fax: 020 8989 4114
email: enquiries@whizzywig.co.uk
web: www.whizzywig.co.uk
contact: Peter Batt
info: Provide full print and web design services, including site maintenance. Specialise in magazines and brochure design.

Zero Degreez Designs
9 Rochester Close, Streatham, London, SW16 5DL
email: designer@zerodegreezdesign.com
web: www.zerodegreezdesign.com
contact: Katherine Taylor
info: Provide web and print-based design services, and can provide IT support service for the creation of databases. Offer competitive prices and aim for 100% customer satisfaction.

MIDLANDS

80-20 Creative Marketing Services
5 King Charles Court, Vine Street, Evesham, WR11 4RF
tel: 01386 765 777
email: info@80-20.co.uk
web: www.80-20.co.uk
info: Creative design and marketing company who can produce websites and print based media such as logos and posters.

The Ad-Lib Partnership
Havana House, Sabrina Avenue, Worcester, WR3 7AZ
tel: 01905 611 128
email: design@ad-lib.co.uk
web: www.ad-lib.co.uk
contact: John Summers
info: Range of design services including artwork, packaging, print and web design.

All Computer Solutions
51 Copthill Farm Cottage, Deeping Road, Uffington, Stamford, PE9 4TD
tel: 01780 480 948
email: webmaster@business-call.co.uk
contact: James
info: Previous experience of working with musicians. Able to provide web and graphic design and some media design. See www.business-call.co.uk for an example of their work.

Ambrow Ltd.
Carlton Business & Technology Centre, Station Road, Carlton, Nottingham, NG4 3AA
tel: 0115 840 5555
email: sales@ambrow.com
web: www.ambrow.com
contact: Andrew Potts
info: Purely internet based design company. Can provide small numbers of CD duplication.

Artworks Unlimited
Birmingham
tel: 0121 453 5264/07788 931 511
email: info@artworks-unlimited.co.uk
web: www.artworks-unlimited.co.uk
contact: Paul Shotan
info: Design for web and print. Logos and custom screen savers. Artworks Unlimited also offer video production. See relevant section for details.

Bigfish Creative Consultants Ltd.
58 Friar Gate, Derby, DE1 1DF
tel: 01332 370 022
email: andy@bfcc.co.uk
web: www.bfcc.co.uk
info: Also provide graphic design and can provide printing. Also include most new media design such as DVDs, music videos and web design. Contact for further information.

Blue Moon Creative
The Barn, 36 High Street, Pershore, WR10 1DP
tel: 0800 298 5795
email: info@blue-moon.co.uk
web: www.blue-moon.co.uk
contact: Clare
info: Full design service including printed media such as posters, and also web design and production.

Blue Spheres
Unit 2, Wrens Court, 55 Lower Queen's Street, Sutton Coldfield, B72 1RT
tel: 0121 362 1670
fax: 0121 362 1674
email: sarah@bluespheres.net
web: www.bluespheres.net
info: Specialise in web design and development.

Bluflame Design Ltd.
5 Birmingham Road, Walsall, WS1 2LT
tel: 01922 645 656
email: vicki@bluflame.co.uk
web: www.bluflame.co.uk
info: Can produce literature, advertising and print, as well as web design.

Brian Beddowes
Studio 7, 90 Litchfield Road, Sutton Coldfield, West Midlands, B74 2SY
tel: 07799 883 984
email: brianbeddowes@hotmail.com
web: www.brianbeddowes.co.uk
info: CD and promotional print artwork. Printing also taken care of. Also provides band photography service. See relevant section for more details.

Bruce Davis Associates Ltd.
Meadow House, Ingon Lane, Snitterfield, Stratford-upon-Avon, CV37 0QF
tel: 01789 731 007
info: Wide range of integrated and strategic business solutions, including: full e-commerce websites, brand management, internet and print marketing, advertising and publication design.

Catfight Records
Brimingham
email: hookup@catfightrecords.co.uk
web: www.catfightrecords.co.uk
info: Catfight Records offer exclusive domain packages from £70 (no additional fees) including a registered domain name, gig list page, photo gallery, downloads (such as wallpaper, MP3 samples and lyrics), email forwarding and search engine submittal. Alternatively, you can have your site hosted by Catfight Records from £50 consisting of home page, biog, news section, downloads, gallery (10 images) and contact page. No pop-ups on either package.

Coleman Moore Partner Agency Network Ltd.
Duston House, Duston, Northampton, NN5 6JN
tel: 01604 598 989
email: talktous@colemanmoore.com
web: www.colemanmoore.com
contact: Laura Marlowe
info: Full marketing support for all types of promotion. New media and print management.

Crave Creative
Acorn House, 22 High Street, Sutton Coldfield, B72 1UX
tel: 0121 321 1088
email: info@cravecreative.co.uk
web: www.cravecreative.co.uk
contact: Luke Chapman
info: Leading edge, bespoke solutions to meet your demands. Web design, e-commerce, multi-media, marketing, animation, as well as traditional design to print e.g. posters and flyers.

Creative Insight
31 Coleshill Street, Sutton Coldfield, B72 1SD
tel: 0121 321 2828
email: sales@creativeinsight.co.uk
web: www.creativeinsight.co.uk
contact: Jane Turner
info: Can create promotional literature and brand identity, as well as traditional print based media such as posters and flyers. Web design and PR facilities also available.

CW Creative Media
37 Prospect Hill, Redditch, B97 4BS
tel: 01527 582 920
email: nick.powell@cwcm.co.uk
web: www.cwcm.co.uk
contact: Nick Powell
info: Provide a fully comprehensive design service spanning graphic design to media and web design. The company cover printing and CD replication as well.

Darkwaveart
33 Carter Gate, Lace Market, Nottingham, NG1 1GL
tel: 07775 506 479
email: matt@darkwaveart.co.uk
web: www.darkwaveart.co.uk
contact: Matthew Vickerstaff
info: Professional artwork for CD sleeves, posters, flyers, press kits, demos and t-shirt design.

Digital Paint
Barratt House, Kingsthorp Road, Northampton, NN2 6EZ
tel: 0845 120 0278
email: wayde@digitalpaint.co.uk
web: www.digitalpaint.co.uk
contact: Wayde Rathbone
info: Previous experience with working for unsigned bands. Mainly web based design, but will team up with another company for any graphic design.

Double Yellow
tel: 0116 212 6857/07817 753 489
email: info@doubleyellow.co.uk
web: www.doubleyellow.co.uk
contact: Rakesh Vaghela
info: Can create portfolios for bands, also artwork, photography and web design services available.

Dragonfly Presentation Graphics
Island House, Arthur Street, Barwell, Leicester, LE9 8GZ
tel: 01455 852 522
email: info@dragonflypg.co.uk
web: www.dragonflypg.co.uk
contact: Chris Whitby
info: Design and print, exhibition and display stands and backgrounds.

Dreamscape Design
5 Gwendoline Avenue, Hinckley, LE10 OEY
tel: 01455 616 543
email: info@dreamscapedesign.co.uk
web: www.dreamscapedesign.co.uk
contact: Neville Langston
info: Will cover some graphic design, but specialise in web development and hosting.

DV8 Design Solutions
The Atrium, 20 Wollaton Street, Nottingham, NG1 5FW
tel: 0115 934 7303
email: create@dv8design.co.uk
web: www.dv8design.co.uk
contact: Wayne France
info: Have worked with bands previously including the Fab 4, plus lots more. Can produce assist with branding, websites and CD covers and inlays.

E-foreknowledge
17-21 Vaughton Street South, Birmingham, B12 OYN
tel: 0800 075 2020
email: info@e-foreknowledge.com
web: www.e-foreknowledge.com
info: Graphic design services, as well as printing.

Erato Graphics
8 Hucknall Road, Newstead Village, Nottingham, NG15 0BD
tel: 01623 450 005
email: info@eratographics.co.uk
web: www.eratographics.co.uk
contact: Greg Shackleford
info: All levels of design and artwork, traditional and web based designs. Competitive fees.

Eventure
3-7 Middle Pavement, Nottingham, NG1 7DX
tel: 0115 941 7744
email: marks@evenutureinternet.com
web: www.eventureinternet.com
contact: Mark Storey
info: Graphic and web design company with services in marketing and e-commerce.

F1 Design
Kingsly Road, Lincoln Fields, Lincoln, LN6 3TA
tel: 01522 508 080
fax: 01522 508 085
email: info@f1design.co.uk
web: www.f1design.co.uk
contact: Paul Mason
info: Provide graphic and web design as well as corporate branding, CD duplication and web programming. Can also provide advertising and marketing services.

Fireloop Creative
Crown Studios, 24a King Street, Lye, Stourbridge, DY9 8UT
tel: 01384 349 324/07876 523 370
email: creative@fire-loop.co.uk
web: www.fire-loop.co.uk
info: Design for web and print. CD-Rom authoring. Illustration, animation and 3D graphics. Video and photography services.

Foil
The Warehouse, 1a Stamford Street, Leicester, LE1 6NL
tel: 0116 233 3413
email: info@foildesign.com
web: www.foildesign.com
contact: Richard Dawson
info: Complete design service including literature, print, point of sales and advertising plus website design.

Freetimers Internet
115 Adnitt Road, Northampton, NN1 4NQ
tel: 01604 638 421
email: enquiries@freetimers.com
web: www.freetimers.com or www.dzine-creative.com
contact: Greg Poulson
info: Comprehensive design company covering web, 3D, graphic and media design. Provides marketing and video services as well.

FunkyHead
Wigston, Leicestershire, LE18 1LH
tel: 0116 210 2130
email: info@funkyhead.co.uk
web: www.funkyhead.co.uk
contact: Colin Tennant
info: Custom graphics for may items including bass drum heads.

G.I.P.P.A.
Office 6, The Balcony, The Cattle Market, Hereford, HR4 9HX
tel: 01432 270 752/07779 611 685
email: gippa@freedesignonline.co.uk
web: www.gippa.co.uk
contact: Brendan Stephens
info: Graphics and illustrations for the Performing Arts. Also offer photography services. See listing in relevant section for details.

Get Your Band On
Leicester Creative Business Depot, 31 Rutland Street, Leicester, LE1 1RE
email: via website
web: www.getyourbandon.com
info: Web design services for bands. Variety of packages available. Will also revamp and upgrade existing websites to make them more eye-catching, and include features such as streamed sound and video. Also provide hosting and web domain registering. Other services include design and production of printed publicity materials and promotional packs. See also listings for photography and video promo services, as well as entries for affiliated company, Pink Angel Promotions.

Graphica Lincoln
Greystones, Holmes Lane, Dunholme, Lincoln, LN2 3QT
tel: 01673 862 424
email: sales@graphicalincoln.co.uk
web: www.graphiclincoln.co.uk
info: Design for print, advertising, posters, CD-Roms and websites.

Haas Information Management Ltd.
27-29 Millstone Lane, Leicester, LE1 5JN
tel: 0116 262 7833
email: info@haas-im.com
web: www.haas-im.com
info: Specialise in website design.

The Holman Group
46-47 Water Street, Birmingham, B3 1HP
tel: 0121 212 3575
fax: 0121 212 3585
email: info@holmangroup.co.uk
web: www.holmangroup.co.uk
contact: Lee Holman
info: Provide graphics, illustration, branding, new media and advertising.

HTDL
The Courtyard, 132 Widney Lane, Solihull, B91 3LH
tel: 0121 711 4878
email: post@htdl.co.uk
web: www.htdl.co.uk
info: Can assist with design, marketing and branding.

Imprint
Wrightsway, Outer Circle Road, Lincoln, LN2 4JY
tel: 01522 539 570
email: guy@imprintcolourprinters.com
web: www.imprintcolourprinters.com
contact: Guy Greaves
info: Graphic design for print including posters, flyers and CD artwork.

Inter Flash Design Ltd.
250-258 Barr Street, Birmingham, B19 3AG
tel: 0800 781 8827
fax: 0121 554 0004
email: info@interflashdesign.co.uk
web: www.interflashdesign.co.uk
info: Graphic and web design company that can also provide lighting and digital media design. Company can also deliver advertising and marketing services.

Iris Production
The Hollymoor Centre, Manor Park Grove, Northfield, Birmingham, B31 5ER
tel: 07811 435 186
email: info@iris-production.co.uk
web: www.iris-production.co.uk
contact: Scott Vale
info: Web design services. Also provide graphic design for use on posters, t-shirts and CD artwork. Iris Production offer video promo and CD duplication services. See entries in relevant sections for further details.

Jackson Hammond Design
1 Lyme Drive, Parklands, Newcastle Road, Trent Valet, Stoke On Trent, ST4 6NW
tel: 01782 711 741
fax: 01782 717 119
email: sheila@jacksonhammond.co.uk
web: www.jacksonhammond.co.uk
contact: Sheila Hammond
info: Everything design oriented including websites, posters and flyers.

Jason Church
241 Lichfield, Tamworth, B78 3QF
tel: 07900 545 470
email: info@jasonchurch.co.uk
web: www.jasonchurch.co.uk
contact: Jason Church
info: Creative solutions for print and web, brochures, leaflets, CD-Roms and websites.

John Harlow Associates
33 Oxford Street, Leamington Spa, CV32 4RA
tel: 01926 451 421
email: sales@pageslimited.co.uk
info: All types of print and web based design.

Katapult Ltd.
Vernon House, Vernon Street, Derby, DE1 1FR
tel: 01332 294 416
email: info@katapult-studios.com
web: www.katapult-studios.com
contact: Dawn Lockett
info: Provide graphic design and printing, as well as CD duplication, motion graphics and music videos. See listings in relevant sections for details.

Lime Lizard Design Ltd.
Meriden Hall, Main Road, Meriden, Coventry, CV7 7PT
tel: 01676 525 173
email: richard@limelizard.co.uk
web: www.limelizard.co.uk
contact: Richard Hickman
info: Can produce all types of print based media. Also provide custom-made web design service.

Martin Hyde
Derby
tel: 01332 664 438/07775 758 131
email: martin@martinhyde.co.uk
web: www.martinhyde.co.uk
info: Graphic design for all print requirements including CD artwork, flyers and posters. Multimedia and web design.

Matrix Print Consultants Ltd.
11 Desborough Road, Rothwell, Kettering, NN14 6JG
tel: 01536 713 811
email: sales@matrixprint.com
web: www.matrixprint.com
contact: Gary Elliott
info: Creative design and artwork, illustration, photography, posters, flyers, CD artwork, publishing and copywriting.

MUSIC SERVICES/RETAIL

Metafocus Ltd.
2 Broadway, Lace Market, Nottingham, NG1 1PS
tel: 0115 947 0011
fax: 0115 947 0014
email: info@metafocus.co.uk
web: www.metafocus.co.uk
info: Graphic and web design services as well as associated printing service. Also incorporate media design, marketing, advertising, PR and branding capabilities.

Michael Associates
1 Hazeldene Road, Hamilton, Leicester, LE5 1UA
tel: 0870 766 8281
fax: 0871 242 4413
email: info@michaelassociates.co.uk
web: www.michaelassociates.co.uk
contact: Michael Cheung
info: We provide web design, hosting, email distribution, Search Engine Optimization promotion, marketing, graphic design and printing.

Milkshake Creative Design & Illustration
tel: 07890 349 440/07779 047 694
email: general@milkshakedesign.net
web: www.milkshakedesign.net
info: Milkshake creative design and illustration was conceived to create the best possible solutions for all given criteria. With over 5 years industry experience including working with bands and promoters, they have gained a strong, unique style which provides their clients with a vibrant stance that enables them to be noticed ahead of the others. Can provide logos, flyers, posters, websites, press packs and merchandise.

Mooli
10 Forest Road, Loughborough, LE11 3NP
tel: 01509 240 040
email: them@mooli.com
web: www.mooli.com
info: Comprehensive design service with graphic and web design, as well as media design. Also include CD duplication and distribution.

Mustard Merchandise
Studio A307, LCB Depot, Rutland Street, Leicester, LE1 1RE
tel: 0116 261 6895
fax: 0116 261 6896
email: sales@mustardmerchandise.co.uk
web: www.mustardmerchandise.co.uk
info: Offer complete design service, including large print formatting for corporate or small scale projects. Also produce personalised merchandise.

Nebron Graphic
Burslem Enterprise Centre, Moorland Road, Burslem, Stoke-on-Trent, ST6 1JQ
tel: 01782 827 723
email: info@nebron.co.uk
web: www.nebron.co.uk
contact: Dave Beardmore
info: Can provide type-setting, printed media and illustration to produce posters, flyers and artwork.

Net Syndicate Ltd.
The Mill, Lodge Lane, Derby, DE1 3HB
tel: 0845 009 5560
email: info@netsyndicate.co.uk
web: www.netsyndicate.co.uk
contact: Phil Wilkinson
info: Provide graphic, web and video flash design. Associated with a separate printing company.

Netsource Solutions Ltd.
9 Gate Lane, Sutton Coldfield, B73 5TR
tel: 0121 621 3600
email: enquiries@netsourcesolutions.com
web: www.netsourcesolutions.com
info: Graphic, web and media and video design, as well as CD Roms.

Netsposure
Empire House, Beauchamp Avenue, Kidderminster, DY11 7AQ
tel: 01562 825 455
fax: 01562 746 681
email: info@netsposure.co.uk
web: www.netsposure.co.uk
info: Purely web based and online design company that can also provide online promotion as well as 'Search' marketing.

Nexus Creative Ltd.
The Cider Mill & Stables, Court Farm, Church Lane, Norton, Worcester, WR5 2PS
tel: 01905 821 919
fax: 01905 821 313
email: paul@nexuscl.com
web: www.nexuscl.com
contact: Paul Bradley
info: Graphic and website design company that can provide printing and new media design as well. Encompasses advertising and marketing, as well as CD duplication services. See listing in relevant section for further details.

Orchard Art & Design
16 Daffodil Place, Walsall, WS5 3DX
tel: 01922 632 447
email: enquiries@orchardartanddesign.co.uk
web: www.orchardartanddesign.co.uk
contact: Mel
info: Various kinds of print based design work undertaken including posters, flyers and leaflets.

The Organisation for Electronic Commerce Ltd.
19 West Rock, Saltisford, Warwick, CV34 4SG
tel: 0845 230 4570
fax: 01926 490 106
email: info@ofec.co.uk
web: www.ofec.co.uk
contact: Edward Williams
info: Deliver web and graphic design solutions, as well as Flash design and distribution for online sales, downloads and CDs.

Original Yeti Media
71 Chruch Street, Butt Lane, Stoke on Trent, ST7 5NX
tel: 01782 777 466
email: theoriginalyeti@hotmail.com
web: www.theoriginalyeti.co.uk
contact: Mark Cruxton
info: Graphic design, advertising and web related material.

Page Marketing Ltd.
5 Walker Grove, Stapleford, Nottingham, NG9 7GY
tel: 0115 949 9114
email: info@pagewebdesign.co.uk
web: www.pagewebdesign.co.uk
contact: Richard Mill
info: Graphic and web design services.

Paperdoll Media
West Bromwich
tel: 07786 706 454
email: gpatel@paperdollmedia.co.uk
web: www.paperdollmedia.co.uk
info: Design for print, web and illustration. DVD and CD-Rom authoring. Demo studio available. See relevant section for details.

Perspektiv Ltd.
34 Stoney Street, Nottingham, NG1 1NB
tel: 0115 950 0510
fax: 0115 948 1868
email: info@perspektiv.co.uk
web: www.perspektiv.co.uk
info: Graphic and web design with printing facilities and some media design. Can provide marketing.

Phoot Creative
17 Victoria Road, Meole Brace, Shrewsbury, SY3 9HX
tel: 01743 350135
email: info@phoot.com
web: www.phoot.com
contact: Steve Ashdown
info: PR and advertising related web and graphic design.

Premier Shops Ltd.
Office 9, Burton House Business Centre, 83 Burton Road, Derby, DE1 1TJ
tel: 01332 743 853
email: email@premiershops.net
web: www.premiershops.net
info: Complete design service including web design.

Puppygreen Web & Prints Design
27 Great Farley Drive, Northfield, Birmingham, B31 5HG
tel: 0870 042 8375
email: info@puppygreen.com
web: www.puppygreen.com
contact: Matt Simpson
info: Will cover all areas of web and graphic design.

R2
28 Lincoln Road, Olton, Birmingham, B27 6PA
tel: 0121 708 0488
email: team@r2-webdesign.com
web: www.r2-webdesign.com
contact: Simon Thomas
info: Covers web and graphic design, as well as electronic media and print marketing.

Rock Kitchen Ltd.
31 Lower Brown Street, Leicester, LE1 5TH
tel: 0116 233 7500
email: greatideas@rkh.co.uk
web: www.rkh.co.uk
contact: David Moore
info: Graphic design solutions, as well as PR and advertising related material.

Seventy Three Design
57 Milton Street, Northampton, NN2 7JG
tel: 01604 792 988
email: vicki@seventy-three.co.uk
web: www.seventy-three.co.uk
contact: Vicki Lovegrove
info: Graphic design service including posters, leaflets and promotional literature.

Shine Design Ltd.
37 New Street, Kenilworth, CV8 2EY
tel: 01865 875 032
contact: Jon
info: Shine is creative graphic design company offering brilliant ideas. Production of album covers, promotional posters, websites and merchandise.

Smart Management UK Ltd.
47 Racecourse Crescent, Shrewsbury, SY2 5BW
tel: 0845 226 0266
email: simon@smartuk.net
web: www.smartuk.net
info: Smart Management are currently working with unsigned bands and are keen to continue. They offer exclusive website design, unique digital and printed media, and cost effective advertising.

Spud Design
76 Millfield Road, Bromsgrove, B61 7BL
tel: 01527 579 980
email: info@spud-design.co.uk
web: www.spud-design.co.uk
contact: Justin Hegenbarth
info: Spud Design specialises in branding but can produce all kinds of print based media, as well as websites. The company is enthusiastic to work with bands and musicians, especially with regards to CD covers and artwork.

Stayfree Studios
Lillie House, 1a Conduit Street, Leicester, LE2 0JN
tel: 0116 223 0303
email: music@stayfree.co.uk
web: www.stayfreemusic.co.uk
info: Provide web design and hosting for bands. Also offer recording and rehearsal studios. See listings for further details.

Studio Digital Ltd.
Windsor Court, Windsor Business Park, Trent Valley Road, Lichfield, WS13 6EU
tel: 01543 416 912
fax: 01543 416 914
email: info@studiodm.co.uk
web: www.studiodm.co.uk
contact: Domonic McGrail
info: Include graphic design, prints and advertising. Also linked with Dupe.co.uk, company providing CD duplication. See listing in relevant section for details.

Think Incorporated
21 Prince Rupert Mews, Beacon Street, Lichfield, WS13 7DD
tel: 01543 418 935
email: info@thinkincorporated.com
web: www.thinkincorporated.com
info: Web design, print design, branding, screensavers, online games and typography.

Tribe 13
Leicester
tel: 07830 351 244
email: enquiries@tribe13.co.uk
web: www.tribe13.co.uk
info: Logos, CD artwork and design for print. Tribe 13 can also provide professional copy for press releases.

Two Dag Design
22a King Street, King Street, Southwell, Nottinghamshire, NG25 0EN
tel: 01636 819 093
email: info@twodag.co.uk
web: www.twodag.co.uk
contact: Tom Reed
info: Design company specialising in music related design, implementation and print. Main services include web design, graphic design, web hosting, signage, flyers, promotional items, php driven forums and database driven mailing list services.

Upper Level Designs
Unit 13, Trench Lock 3, Summerfield Road, Telford, TF1 5ST
tel: 01952 223 333
email: info@upperlevel.co.uk
web: www.upperlevel.co.uk
info: Will cover most areas of web and graphic design plus printing and production. Can also provide CD duplication, enquire for details.

Vanity Pure Design
24 Hampshire Road, Derby, DE21 4EG
tel: 01332 727 317
email: info@vanity-puredesign.co.uk
web: www.vanity-puredesign.co.uk
contact: Helen Dunmore
info: Web and graphic design company with previous music industry experience. Can provide 3D modelling as well.

Workshop Design Co.
14-18 St. Mary's Gate, Nottingham, NG1 1PF
tel: 0115 947 3495
email: john@workshopdesign.co.uk
web: www.workshopdesign.co.uk
info: Award winning designer. Can produce all types of print based media as well as websites and advertising management.

Xervia
139 Queens Road, Leicester, LE2 3FL
tel: 0845 045 0705
fax: 0116 210 5013
email: info@xervia.com
web: www.xervia.com
info: Comprehensive design company with previous music experience delivering web and graphic design, printing, media design, marketing and CD duplication. See listing in Mastering & Duplication section for further information.

Yellowdoor Design
434 Hinckley Road, Leicester, LE3 0WA
tel: 0116 223 6846
email: sales@yellowdoor.co.uk
contact: Rick Tuck
info: Can produce anything and everything to do with graphics! All types of print based media undertaken and the possibility of associated web design.

Ying Yang
96 Down Street, Leicester, LE4 6JG
tel: 0870 746 1334
email: info@itnc.co.uk
web: www.itnc.co.uk
info: Cover most areas of web design and graphic design with access to printing facilities. Associated with Interpro Technet Consultancy.

1079 Graphics
187 Baldoon Sands, Middlesborough, Cleveland, TS5 8UB
tel: 01642 278 007
email: 1070graphics@postmaster.co.uk
contact: Steve
info: Provide design for flyers, posters, CD covers, leaflets and business cards.

2B Graphics Partnership
Unit 3A, Stockfield Hall Farm, Stocksfield, NE43 7TN
tel: 01661 844 703
email: enquiries@2bgraphics.com
web: www.2bgraphics.com
contact: Andrew Beniams
info: Provide website design, hosting and promotional literature.

Alpha Communications
1 Red Hill Villas, Durham, County Durham, DH1 4BA
tel: 0191 375 0101
email: info@alpha.coop
web: www.alpha.coop
info: Have worked with unsigned bands before. Specialise in promotional material, website design and display materials.

MUSIC SERVICES/RETAIL

OI!

TROUBLE GETTING NOTICED?

A strong brand is an important factor in helping you to stand out from your competitors.

We will work closely with you to understand your ambitions and the way in which you want to be seen by the outside world.

The aim? To develop a brand that is totally you.

OUR PRODUCTS INCLUDE:

BRAND DEVEOPMENT

GRAPHIC DESIGN

WEB DESIGN

ECOMMERCE APPLICATIONS

PRINTING

INTERACTIVE CD'S & DVD'S

HAPPY PEOPLE

WANT SOME?

CARROTMEDIA
creative people

www.carrotmedialtd.com
0191 226 7328

Arnett Design To Print
36 Dunmoor Grove, Ingleby Barwick, Stockton-on-Tees, Cleveland, TS17 0QW
tel: 01642 751 032
info: Provides design for print, CD covers, poster and other promotional materials. Have worked with unsigned bands before.

The Art Department
2 Park Avenue, Wallsend, Tyne & Wear, NE28 8DE
tel: 0191 295 1000
email: creativity@the-art-department.com
web: www.the-art-department.com
contact: Alyson Rhodes
info: Long established design agency which can produce all types of media. Experienced in designing websites for musicians.

Bitingedge
32 Queens Gardens, Blyth, Northumberland, NE24 5HH
tel: 01670 360 413
email: unleash@bitingedge.net
web: www.bitingedge.net
contact: James Mallon, Mick Sharpe
info: All forms of design and print.

Blumilk
17 Riverside Studios, Amethyst Road, Newcastle Business Park, Newcastle Upon Tyne, NE4 7YL
tel: 0191 241 3555
email: mark@blumilk.com
web: www.blumilk.com
contact: Mark Knight
info: Have previously worked with Demolition Records. Provide web and flyer design.

Carrot Media Ltd.
Suite 2, John Buddle Work Village, Buddle Road, Newcastle Upon Tyne, NE4 8AW
tel: 0191 226 7328
fax: 0191 226 7329
email: ideas@carrotmedialtd.com
web: www.carrotmedialtd.com
contact: Justin Turner
info: Provides logo and flyer design, as well as printing. Also design websites and can sell music online.

Christina Unwin
30 Southside, Shadforth, Durham, County Durham, DH6 1LL
tel: 0191 372 3939
email: christina@wave.demon.co.uk
contact: Christina
info: Provides graphic design illustrations. Practices exhibition design. Christina has previously designed for CD covers and would like to cover this field further.

Comeupsmiling Ltd.
Meadow View, Thirsk Road, Yarm, TS15 9HE
tel: 01642 787 722
email: chris@comeupsmiling.com
web: www.comeupsmiling.com
info: Specialise in web design with a variety of packages available.

The Consultancy
Grange Business Centre, Belasis Avenue, Billingham, TS23 2AA
tel: 01642 353 100
email: info@theconsultancy.co.uk
web: www.theconsultancy.co.uk
contact: Richard Thornton
info: All types of media designed and produced including videos, DVDs and websites.

Corporate Element
25 Rydal Road, Lemington, Newcastle Upon Tyne, NE15 7LR
tel: 0191 264 3770
email: info@corporateelement.com
web: www.corporateelement.com
contact: Mark Pattinson
info: Corporate Element cover all areas of design communication.

Dot Net Heads Ltd.
20 The Copse, Blaydon on Tyne, Tyne and Wear, NE21 5PH
tel: 0800 310 1395
email: info@dotnetheads.com
web: www.dotnetheads.com
info: Website design, promotions and hosting packages.

DSB Graphics
17 Mill Lane, Billingham, Cleveland, TS23 1HH
tel: 0191 423 2964
email: daveburden53@hotmail.com
info: Graphic design service for CD covers, posters and flyers.

Freedom Web Design
28 Malvern Street, South Shields, Tyne and Wear, NE33 5LE
tel: 0191 423 4251
email: enquiries@freedom-webdesign.co.uk
web: www.freedom-webdesign.co.uk
contact: Steven Elliott
info: Low cost, professional website development and services.

Fusion Creative Services Ltd.
35 Woodland Road, Darlington, DL3 7BJ
tel: 01325 252 484
email: mike@fusioncreative.co.uk
web: www.fusioncreativeservices.co.uk
contact: Mike Brough
info: Experienced creative design agency offering graphic, web and packaging design services.

Fyfe Anderson Design Consultants
Suites 1-4, 14 Blandford Square, Newcastle upon Tyne, Tyne & Wear, NE1 4HZ
tel: 0191 230 4955
email: dave@fyfeanderson.com
web: www.fyfeanderson.com
contact: David Fyfe
info: Has worked with bands before and can produce all kinds of print and web based media.

Genius Entertainment
PO Box 111, Derwentside, DH9 8YR
tel: 01207 236 555
email: info@genius-entertainment.com
web: www.genius-entertainment.com
contact: Adam Chetter
info: Web design. Also provide other services including event management and PR services. See website for further details.

GWB Advertising
3rd Floor, Wingrove House, Ponteland Road, Newcastle Upon Tyne, Tyne & Wear, NE5 3DP
tel: 0191 271 1441
email: art@gwb-advertisng.co.uk
web: www.gwb-advertising.co.uk
contact: Gary Burnie
info: Provide CD cover designs, flyers, web designs and posters.

Halogen Design Ltd.
Suite 9, John Buddle Work Village, Buddle Road, Newcastle Upon Tyne, NE4 8AW
tel: 0191 226 7321
email: info@halogendesign.co.uk
web: www.halogendesign.co.uk
info: Full service graphic design agency.

JPA Technical Literature
10 Portland Terrace, Newcastle Upon Tyne, NE2 1QQ
tel: 0191 281 8393
email: design@jpatl.com
web: www.jpatl.com
contact: Neil Storey
info: Comprehensive service including posters, flyers, web design and album artwork.

June Elliot Freelance Design
Unit 12, Delaval Trading Estate, Seaton Delaval, Whitley Bay, NE25 0QT
tel: 07855 776 230
email: june@surfaceink.co.uk
info: Provide web, CD, flyer, leaflet and poster design.

L & K Graphics Ltd.
Rockhouse, Wheatsheaf Corner, Houghton Le Spring, Tyne & Wear, DH4 4QX
tel: 0191 385 6591
email: lkgraphics@btconnect.com
contact: Keith Morrell
info: Design service only, no print facilities. Interested in working with bands and musicians.

Marcus Byron
Elmhow, Belmont Gardens, Haydon Bridge, Hexham, Northumberland, NE47 6HG
tel: 01434 688 393
email: studio@marcusbyron.co.uk
web: www.marcusbyron.co.uk
contact: Marcus Byron
info: Graphic design and illustration.

MD Creative
12 Mosely Street, Newcastle Upon Tyne, NE1 1DE
tel: 0191 230 8046
email: info@mdcreative.co.uk
web: www.mdcreative.co.uk
contact: Mark Denny
info: General graphic design company.

Neptune Technical Solutions
78 Neptune Road, Newcastle Upon Tyne, NE15 7QN
tel: 0191 267 5786
email: info@nts-online.co.uk
web: www.nts-online.co.uk
info: Full design and website development. Album cover design as well.

Onebestway
1st Floor, 63 Westgate Road, Newcastle Upon Tyne, Tyne and Wear, NE1 1SG
tel: 0191 230 5558
email: mike@onebestway.com
web: www.onebestway.com
contact: Michael Owen
info: Provide web design and have previous experience of working with unsigned bands.

Paul Samat
66 Haughton Green, Darlington, County Durham, DL1 2DF
tel: 07973 384 085
email: info@paulsamat.co.uk
web: www.paulsamat.co.uk
contact: Paul Samat
info: Experienced in field of design and print. Have designed CD covers and posters for unsigned band in the past.

The Point Design
Studio 4, The Old Forge, Hoult Estate, Walker Road, Newcastle Upon Tyne, NE6 2HL
tel: 0191 224 4483
email: info@thepointdesign.co.uk
web: www.thepointdesign.co.uk
contact: Jane Saddler
info: Graphic design company offering wide range of print services including posters and CD artwork, as well as web design.

Product Agency
61 High Bridge, Newcastle Upon Tyne, Tyne & Wear, NE1 6BX
tel: 0191 230 3834
email: johnnyproductagency.com
web: www.productagency.com
info: Covers any type of design related to music promotion.

Propa Graphics
61 Highbridge, Newcastle Upon Tyne, Tyne & Wear, NE1 6BX
tel: 0191 261 5413
email: cat@propagraphics.com
web: www.propagraphics.com
contact: Cat Noon
info: Propa Graphics often work with bands and provide a full service covering all forms of print and web based media including album artwork, illustration and animation.

Pure Design
13 Queens Gardens, Newcastle Upon Tyne, Tyne & Wear, NE12 9PL
email: joan.nicklin@blueyonder.co.uk
contact: Joan Nicklin
info: Provide CD cover design, web design and publicity materials.

Reactive Design
Moreland Street, Hartlepool, Cleveland, TS24 7NL
tel: 01429 862 911
email: info@reactivedesign.co.uk
web: www.reactivedesign.co.uk
contact: Andrew Kennedy
info: Designs for CD covers and flyers.

Silver Cat New Media Design
50 Intrepid Close, Seaton Carew, Hartlepool, Cleveland, TS25 1GE
tel: 07776 236 234
email: enquiries@silvercatmedia.co.uk
web: www.silvercatmedia.co.uk
info: Provides website design, album cover artwork and logo design.

Solid Images Design
5 Fallodon Avenue, Shilbottle, Alnwick, Northumberland, NE66 2UP
tel: 01665 575 400
email: info@solidimages.com
web: www.solidimages.com
info: Have undertaken promotional work for Marilyn Manson, Bjork and Joe Satriani.

Spot on Displays Ltd.
42 Stations Road, Stanley, DH9 0JL
tel: 01207 236 909
fax: 01207 284 636
email: sales@spotondisplays.com
web: www.spotondisplays.com
info: Effective, eye-catching and informative design coupled with high quality production. Can produce a vast range of large format exhibition graphics, banners and signage, as well as leaflets and posters.

A2DESIGNC0
01618324740

GUERRILLA GRAPHIX® MCR

Stonebrook Print and Design Services Ltd.
2 Buddle Street, Wallsend, NE28 6EH
tel: 0191 263 3302
email: sales@stonebrook.co.uk
web: www.stonebrook.co.uk
info: Full creative and concept design service including posters, flyers and leaflets.

The Studio Cooperative
Cathedral Buildings, Dean Street, Newcastle Upon Tyne, NE1 1PG
tel: 0191 211 1976
email: info@thestudiocooperative.co.uk
web: www.thestudiocooperative.co.uk
contact: Steve Pardue, Bruce Allinson
info: The Studio Cooperative is a collective of creatives. Can assist with range of media including digital and print based products.

Tangletree
6 Storey Lane, Blaydon-On-Tyne, NE21 4NF
tel: 0191 414 5172
email: steve@tangletree.com
web: www.tangletree.com
info: Provide poster and flyer design, CD cover design, CD printing and t-shirts. Have worked with unsigned bands before.

Therefore Creative
Churchill House, 12 Mosely Street, Newcastle upon Tyne, NE1 1DE
tel: 0191 286 9833
email: eric@there-fore.com
web: www.there-fore.com
info: Therefore Creative has expanded their design services to incorporate HTML email marketing.

Urban River Creative
Windsor Hall, Burrow Street, South Shields, NE33 1PP
tel: 0191 423 5688
email: info@urbanriver.com
web: www.urbanriver.com
contact: Paul Slater Slater
info: Provide print and design, promotion services and music streaming.

Via Creative Consultants
The Innovation Centre, Vienna Court, Kirkleatham Business Park, Redcar, TS10 5SH
tel: 01642 777 848
email: mail@viacreative.co.uk
web: www.viacreative.co.uk
info: Provides graphic designing, marketing and media consultants.

Wansford Associates
9 Queen Street, Newcastle Upon Tyne, NE1 3UG
tel: 0191 350 6161
email: info@wansford.biz
web: www.wansford.biz
contact: Lee Morton
info: Provide website design and internet marketing.

Yonline Ltd.
Suite 1.3, Howard House Commercial Centre, Howard Street, North Shields, Tyne & Wear, NE30 1AR
tel: 0191 259 0001
fax: 0191 259 0021
email: info@yonline.co.uk
web: www.yonline.co.uk
info: Design for websites, adverts and album covers.

NORTHWEST

A to M Design
75 Lever Street, Manchester, M1 1FL
tel: 07803 011 391
email: hello@a-to-m.com
web: www.a-to-m.com
contact: Nick Jones, Mike Fallows, Ben Lamb, Andy Smith
info: Design for album sleeves, websites, posters, logos, typography, artwork, graphics, photography and flyers. Reasonable rates.

A2 Design Co
Unit 8, Brewery Yard, The Deva Centre, Trinity Way, Salford, M3 7BB
tel: 0161 832 4740
fax: 0161 832 4750
email: info@a2designco.com
contact: Jason Nicholls
info: Design for print, music, new media and corporate ID. Has previously worked with bands.

Axis Graphic Design Ltd.
9 Silverdale Road, Manchester, M21 0SH
tel: 0161 882 0004
fax: 0161 882 0005
email: info@axisgraphicdesign.co.uk
web: www.axisgraphicdesign.co.uk
contact: Alan Ward
info: Small design company with an international reputation. Design for the arts.

B.Z. Marketing & Design
Riverside House, River Lane, Saltney, Chester, CH4 8RQ
tel: 01244 689 999
email: info@bzmarketing.co.uk
web: www.bzmarketing.co.uk
info: Posters, flyers and web design. BZ will work to your needs, whatever they are!

Balance Advertising & Design Consultants
Design House, 5 Fazakerley Street, Liverpool, L3 9DL
tel: 0151 236 5788
email: paul@balanceadc.com
web: www.balanceadc.com
contact: Paul Collins
info: Cutting edge design and advertising. See website or call in for more details. Have previously worked with bands and DJs.

Balboa Graphics
8 Kremlin Drive, Stoneycroft, Liverpool, L13 7BY
tel: 0151 259 1676
email: info@balboagraphics.com
web: www.balboagraphics.com
info: Graphic design, web hosting and design services. Linked with Bump Studios who offer mastering and duplication facilities. See entries in relevant sections for details.

Bay Type
Manderley House, Heysham, LA3 1LN
tel: 07710 405 864
fax: 07710 405 864
email: r.cleet@btinternet.com
contact: Roger Cleet
info: Creative digital artwork and print. Have worked with bands previously.

Bolland & Lowe
33-45 Parr Street, Liverpool, L1 4JN
tel: 0151 707 8108
email: creative@bollandlowe.co.uk
web: www.bollandlowe.co.uk
info: Identities, logos, web design and design for packaging and print including CD covers. Experience with working for the music industry, having designed the identity for Liverpool and Manchester's contingent to the SxSW festival.

Bump Studios
8 Kremlin Drive, Stoneycroft, Liverpool, L13 7BY
tel: 0151 259 1676
email: info@bumpstudios.co.uk
web: www.bumpstudios.co.uk

Burn
Studio 154, Liverpool Palace, 9 Slater Street, Liverpool, L1 4BW
tel: 0151 707 6707
email: info@burneverything.co.uk
web: www.burneverything.co.uk
contact: David Hand, Sam Wiehl
info: Graphic design, web design and illustration. Experience of working with bands, and can offer a creative approach.

Catapult Enterprises
Liverpool
tel: 07773 134 485
email: info@catapultenterprises.co.uk
web: www.catapultenterprises.co.uk
contact: Tony Elliott
info: Wide range of services from websites to backdrops, including advertising, promotion, packaging, logo design, illustration and photography. They offer a full promotional service and advice on how bands can market themselves.

Coleman Taylor Graphic Design
Haiben House, 10 Haiben Close, Grasscroft, Saddleworth, OL4 4DU
tel: 01457 872 666
email: info@colemantaylor.co.uk
web: www.colemantaylor.co.uk
contact: Paul Guilfoyle
info: Web design, posters, flyers and CD artwork.

Band Websites
Promo Photography
Logos
Gig Posters
Flyers

web: www.cozzcreates.com
email: info@cozzcreates.com

Cozz Creates
Trinity, Manchester
tel: 07976 001 343
email: cozz@cozzphotography.co.uk
web: www.cozzwebdesign.com
contact: Adam Costello
info: Affordable, quirky website design, that is right for your band. Features include e-commerce, .gif animation, java and html. Can also offer logo design, photography, flyers, posters, badges and t-shirts.

Creative Media Advertising Ltd.
Overton House, West Road, Congleton, Cheshire, CW12 1JY
tel: 01260 292 600
email: ideas@creativenet.co.uk
web: www.creativenet.co.uk
contact: Paul Hartley
info: Web design services. Creative Media will invest time and effort at all stages, from original concepts to final result.

D.N.A.
5th Floor, 121 Princess Street 121 Princess Street, Manchester, M1 7AD
tel: 0161 236 9445
email: lee@dna.tc
web: www.dna.tc
contact: Lee Whitfield
info: Specialises in web design and CD artwork for bands. Would like to hear from new bands with their ideas.

Dave Rothwell
53 Mossdale Drive, Rainhill, Prescot, L35 4NF
tel: 0151 426 7684
email: dave@visualjaz.com
web: www.visualjaz.com
info: Exclusive limited edition fine art prints. Commisions for CD artwork and promotional print.

Design Mouse
59 Draperfield, Chorley, Lancashire, PR7 3PL
tel: 01257 267 936
email: info@designmouse.net
contact: Amanda Gray
info: Graphic design for print. Covers anything from flyers, posters and leaflets to CD artwork and logo design.

Digital Artwork
First Floor, 21 Albion Street, New Brighton, Cheshire, CH45 9LE
tel: 0151 638 6755
email: pw@digitalartwork.demon.co.uk
contact: Peter Whitfield
info: Digital art, design for print, 3D design and illustration.

Dinosaur
21 Back Turner Street, Manchester, M4 1FR
tel: 0161 831 0831
email: info@dinosaur.co.uk
web: www.dinosaur.co.uk
contact: Mark Beaumont
info: Graphic design and advertising for the music, cultural and youth industries. Previous clients range from independent labels to EMI Music Publishing.

Ditto Design, Copy & Print
12a Crescent Road, Windermere, Cumbria, LA23 1EA
tel: 01539 444 456
email: ditto@btinternet.com
web: www.ditto-design.com
contact: John Rimmer
info: Photocopying, graphic design, T-shirts, posters and flyers.

Dominic Thomas Design
Manchester
tel: 0161 432 8055
email: info@dominicthomas.com
web: www.dominicthomas.com
contact: Dominic Thomas
info: Manchester based art director and graphic designer. Portfolio includes various design led campaigns for numerous clients including Adidas, Badly Drawn Boy, Future Kings of Spain and Kings of Convenience.

Dreambomb
Manchester Craft & Design Centre, 17 Oak Street, Northern Quarter, Manchester, M4 4JD
tel: 07950 804 415
web: www.dreambomb.com
contact: Alexis
info: Graphic art and web design. Graffiti-inspired artwork and clothing.

album sleeve | poster
website | promotional design
from inception to production

flag. *nurturing bright ideas*

t: 0161 274 3958   e: info@flagdigital.com   w: www.flagdigital.com

D-Room
14 Bark Street East, Bolton, BL1 2BQ
tel: 01204 382 599
fax: 01204 382 599
email: info@d-room.co.uk
web: www.d-room.co.uk
contact: Tony Lythgoe
info: D-Room have a lot of experience working with bands and musicians and are happy to discuss any ideas you have. Can provide artwork and design solutions for album covers and other promotional material, as well as projection and stage design. See website for details of other services available, including video and website production.

Elements Creative Ltd.
5 Kenyon Road, Swinley, Wigan, WN1 2DH
tel: 01942 242 420
fax: 01942 242 458
email: media@elementscreative.com
web: www.elementscreative.com
contact: Paul McManus
info: Graphic design company specialising in printed media and website design, including work for the music industry.

Emo Design
35 Serpentine Road, Kendal, Cumbria, LA9 4PE
tel: 01539 734 710
email: ben@emodesign.com
web: www.emodesign.com
contact: Ben Dodgson
info: Creative design solutions for print and the internet. Emo work with fellow designers, photographers and illustrators to produce innovative and interesting results.

Explosive Graphics
Unit 8, The Schoolhouse, Trafford Park, Manchester, M17 1DZ
tel: 0161 877 1177
email: sales@exg.co.uk
web: www.exg.co.uk
contact: John Bendik
info: Mainly produces large format graphics. Have worked previously with bands.

Flag
Manchester
tel: 0161 274 3958
email: info@flagdigital.com
web: www.flagdigital.com
info: Album sleeve, poster, website, and promotional design from inception to production.

Fluidmedia.net Ltd.
Croft Studios, Hollins Lane, Accrington, Lancashire, BB5 2LB
tel: 01254 394891
email: general@fluidmedia.net
web: www.fluidmedia.net
contact: Jon Greenwood
info: Web design, flyer, poster and print design, as well as CD covers, CD and DVD duplication, and recording services.

Foursides
Manchester
tel: 07929 189 751
email: info@foursides.co.uk
web: www.foursides.co.uk
contact: Matt Fawbert
info: Specialises in striking, innovative web design. Offer a personal service and unique design ideas combined with quality construction and affordable rates. Specialise in working with unsigned bands.

Go Cre8
Mariners House, Queens Dock Business Centre, 67-83 Norfolk Street, Liverpool, L1 0BG
tel: 0845 226 3086
email: info@gocre8.co.uk
web: www.gocre8.co.uk
contact: Darryn
info: Web design and graphic design services. Also offer web hosting and maintenance. Also offer CD mastering and duplication facilities. See entry in relevant section for further details.

Greenhouse Creative
Conavon Court, 12 Blackfriars Street, Manchester, M3 5BQ
tel: 0161 214 0010
fax: 0161 214 0011
email: info@greenhousecreative.co.uk
web: www.greenhousecreative.co.uk
contact: Craig Green
info: Can provide any graphic or web design solutions.

Howard Yaffe Graphics
10 Avondale Street, Cheetham Hill, Manchester, M8 0NB
tel: 0161 740 0866
fax: 0161 740 0866
email: h.yaffe@ntlworld.com
contact: Howard Yaffe
info: Graphic design, artwork, logos, leaflets and brochures.

Hydrant Design Associates
15 St. James' Road, Carlisle, Cumbria, CA2 5NX
tel: 01228 598 697
email: info@hydrant.co.uk
web: www.hydrant.co.uk
contact: Leo White
info: Graphics, web and multimedia design with a friendly, personal approach. Specialise in environmentally and ethically aware design solutions. Hydrant Design Associates have a genuine interest in new music.

I Profile
69 Radcliffe Road, Bolton, Lancashire, BL2 1AW
tel: 01204 370 506
email: info@i-profile.co.uk
web: www.i-profile.co.uk
contact: Paul Hibbert
info: Creative web design. Also run online collectors record store, see www.bandhits.co.uk.

Image Creative
The Bank, 4 Lane Ends, 155 Victoria Road East, Thornton Cleveleys, FY5 5HH
tel: 01253 338 260
email: ic@imagecreative.co.uk
web: www.imagecreative.co.uk
info: Creative consultants. Provide graphic design, PR, events organisation and marketing. Have worked with bands previously.

Influence Design Group
Unit 235, Ducie House, Ducie Street, Manchester, M1 2JW
tel: 0870 228 2272
fax: 0161 443 322
email: damyon@influencedesign.com
web: www.influencedesign.com
contact: Damyon Anderson Garrity
info: ID, branding and promotion for acts across all genres.

InnerDark Studios
Manchester
tel: 07740 907 181
email: contact@innerdarkstudios.com
web: www.innerdarkstudios.com
contact: Ash Tidball
info: Websites tailored to client's requirements, designed to stand out. Both Flash and HTML available.

Jack Croal Design
Manchester
tel: 07747 116 927
email: jackcroal@easynet.co.uk
contact: Jack Croal
info: Print graphics, posters and record sleeves. Vast experience of working with bands and musicians.

Juno Ltd.
Gostin Building, Hanover Street, Liverpool, L1 4LN
tel: 0151 707 2200
fax: 0151 707 1695
email: info@junostudio.co.uk
web: www.junostudio.co.uk
contact: Liz, Scott
info: Create designs for the music industry and bands including The Zutons, Dead 60s and many others.

JWG Creative Media Ltd.
Latham Close, Bredbury Industrial Park, Bredbury, Stockport, SK6 2SD
tel: 07939 213 427
email: jonathan.green@jwgcreativemedia.co.uk
web: www.jwgcreativemedia.co.uk
contact: Jonathan Green
info: Creative solutions to musicians and industry professionals. Services include videos, promos and stage visuals (produced in association with Menagerie). Web and print design services also available.

Leafdesign

A stylish, concept driven approach to getting your band recognised.

For further information
contact Hayley on: 07739423133
or email: leafdesign@hotmail.com

MUSIC SERVICES/RETAIL

Leaf Design
5 Catterick Road, Didsbury Village, Manchester, M20 6HN
tel: 07739 423 133
email: leafdesign@hotmail.com
contact: Hayley Leaf
info: A stylish, concept driven approach to getting your band recognised. Specialising in album sleeves, CD artwork, logos, flyers, posters and literature for the music industry.

Lisa Graphics
305 Whalley Road, Accrington, Lancashire, BB5 5AD
tel: 01254 232 653
fax: 01254 871 560
email: bill@lisa-graphics.co.uk
web: www.lisa-graphics.co.uk
contact: Bill Southall
info: Print and web design. See website for numerous examples of their work.

Love Creative
72 Tib Street, Manchester, M4 1LG
tel: 0161 907 3150
fax: 0161 907 3155
email: a.sim@@lovecreative.com
web: www.lovecreative.com
contact: Alistair Sim
info: Graphic design, poster and flyer design, advertising, plus CD and album artwork.

MAD (Marketing, Advertising & Design)
Trafford House, Chester Road, Manchester, M32 0RS
tel: 0161 848 0578
email: marketing@madagency.co.uk
web: www.madagency.co.uk
contact: Mandy Rathmill
info: Design for all print and digital media.

Manchester Printing Company Ltd.
75 Lever Street, Manchester, M1 1FL
tel: 0161 236 4646
fax: 0161 236 6590
email: sales@manchesterprinting.com
web: www.manchesterprinting.com
contact: Debbie Davies
info: In-house printers and designers skilled in producing original and distinctive concepts and ideas. Solutions to cover any aspect of print and design required. Call for a no obligation quote, or to discuss any future print or design requirements. Manchester Printing Company are always keen to encourage up and coming talent. Welcome all enquiries, no matter how small.

Marlin Design & Marketing Ltd.
Unit A, Longford Trading Estate, Thomas Street, Manchester, M32 OJT
tel: 0161 864 1134
fax: 0161 864 5240
email: info@marlindesign.co.uk
web: www.marlindesign.co.uk
contact: Julie Phealan
info: Graphic design and logos.

mcr:music Ltd.
3rd Floor, 24-26 Lever Street, Manchester, M1 1DZ
tel: 0161 907 0030
email: stef@mcrmusic.co.uk
web: www.mcrmusic.co.uk
info: Print and promo services for unsigned bands. Extensive print distribution networks.

Melanie Knott
Manchester
tel: 07734 820 182
email: underfallingfrescoes@hotmail.com
contact: Melanie Knott
info: Art commissions, illustrations and band artwork. Contact Melanie for further details.

Mike's Studio
Liverpool
tel: 0151 494 3352
email: ideas@mikesstudio.co.uk
web: www.mikesstudio.co.uk
info: Freelance graphic designer, mainly for print. Experience working in the music industry including cover design for Kathryn Williams. Work with Merseyside based individuals and organisations, including small projects with small budgets.

Minuteman Press
42 Bridge Street, Bolton, BL1 2EG
tel: 01204 397 434
fax: 01204 397 435
email: mmpbolton@btconnect.com
contact: Adam Farmer
info: Artwork for CD covers, posters and flyers. Can incorporate your own images (from disk, hand drawn sketches or photographs). Full print facilities also available. Band friendly.

MELANIE KNOTT

ARTWORK
AND
ILLUSTRATION

underfallingfrescoes@hotmail.com
www.myspace.com/melanie_knott
telephone: 07734820182

An award winning creative design agency,
specialising in conceptual brand communication.

Oneighty Creative Limited.
The Gate House, Appleby Street,
Blackburn, Lancashire BB1 3BL

Url_www.oneightycreative.com

Eml_info@oneightycreative.com

oneighty°

Musicstream Ltd.
Hesketh House, 3a School Road, Sale, Cheshire, M33 7XY
tel:	0161 973 9004
email:	info@mustream.com
web:	www.mustream.com
contact:	Tom Carson
info:	Design for websites available. Musicstream also provide

distribution services, as well as merchandise manufacture. See listings
in relevant sections for further details.

NCV Design
Pendle Way, Whalley Road, Barrow, Lancashire, BB7 9AS
tel:	01254 822 135
fax:	01254 822 135
email:	nigel@ncvdesign.co.uk
web:	www.ncvdesign.co.uk
contact:	Nigel Vaughan
info:	Graphic design and illustration. Specialise in airbrushed

album covers.

Nonconform Design Ltd.
62 Hope Street, Liverpool, L1 9BZ
tel:	0151 707 0334
email:	projects@nonconform.co.uk
web:	www.nonconform.co.uk
contact:	Andrew Weatherstone
info:	Experienced designers for clients which include

record labels and artists. Call and speak to Nonconform about your
requirements and they'll do their best to help!

Oneighty Creative Ltd.
The Gatehouse, Appleby Street, Blackburn, Lancashire, BB1 3BL
tel:	01254 689955
fax:	01254 690967
email:	info@oneightycreative.com
web:	www.oneightycreative.com
info:	Award-winning creative brand specialists focussing in

creative marketing solutions for small to blue chip sized businesses.

Origin Creative Design
Chetham House, Bird Hall Lane, Cheadle Heath, Stockport, Cheshire,
SK3 0ZP
tel:	0161 495 4808
fax:	0161 495 4592
email:	paul@origincreativedesign.com
web:	www.origincreativedesign.com
contact:	Mark Bottomley
info:	Origin are designers and printers who have worked for

clients including Wigan Jazz Festival.

Paul Astill & Associates
3rd Floor, 24 Lever Street, Manchester, M1 1DZ
tel:	0161 237 1799
email:	paul@astillassociates.com
web:	www.astillassociates.com
contact:	Paul Astill
info:	A multidisciplinary graphic design studio specialising

in the entertainment and leisure sectors. Produce bespoke graphics
and identity for a diverse range of clients from national and local bars,
restaurants and clubs to city wide festivals. Stylish, concept driven
approach ranging from conventional branding solutions, graphics and
websites to unique attention grabbing objects and mailers.

Paul Parkinson
No.2 Hazelbadge Road, Poynton, Stockport, Cheshire, SK12 1HE
tel:	01625 872 151
email:	typographics@hotmail.com
contact:	Paul Parkinson
info:	Design for print including work with bands and

musicians.

Piranha Advertising & Marketing Solutions
The Chambers, 53 Guildhall Street, Preston, PR1 3NU
tel:	01772 888 331
email:	preston@piranha-solutions.com
web:	www.piranha-solutions.com
contact:	Paul Airey
info:	Piranha provide the latest design, production and

marketing techniques on the internet.

Plast-C
33-45 Parr Street, Parr Street Studios, Liverpool, L1 4JN
tel:	0151 709 3940
info:	Design services for the music industry.

astill associates

graphic design: logo / packaging / promotion / branding / print / digital / web / signage
www.astillassociates.com / 0161 237 1799

Premier Creative Print Ltd.
Unit 3, Burnden Industrial Estate, Manchester Road, Bolton, BL3 2NG
tel: 01204 388 299
fax: 01204 532 454
email: info@premiercreative.co.uk
web: www.premiercreative.co.uk
contact: Dale Fragal
info: Development of existing ideas or designs from brief. Full printing facilities available.

Primary Communications
Astley House, 29 Queens Road, Chorley, Lancashire, PR7 1JU
tel: 01257 232 155
email: jackie@primarygraphics.co.uk
web: www.primarygraphics.co.uk
contact: Jackie
info: Advice on all aspects of design and marketing.

The Purple Turtle
Unit 1a, Trafalger House, Trafalger Street, Burnley, BB11 1RA
tel: 01282 433 351
email: david@thepurpleturtle.co.uk
web: www.thepurpleturtle.co.uk
contact: David Harrison
info: Large format poster printers, graphic designers and digital printers.

PWD Creative Solutions Ltd.
1st Floor, The Old Fire Station, Station Road, Amber Bridge, Preston, PR7 6TN
tel: 01772 312 554
fax: 01772 312 163
email: info@pwdesignuk.co.uk
web: www.pwdesignuk.co.uk
contact: Paul Williams
info: Specialise in design and print, short run digital colour and logo design.

Roy Anderson
3 - 5 Holland Street, Liverpool, L7 0JG
tel: 0151 259 5331
email: roy.anderson13@btinternet.com
info: Contemporary art, including paintings and sculptures, adapted to suit your needs.

Sarah Unwin
20 Tweedle Hill Road, Blackley, Manchester, M9 8LP
tel: 07963 552 794
email: sarahlouiseunwin@yahoo.com
info: Design for flyers, CD covers, vinyl sleeves, branding, posters and other promotional material, as well as canvas art. Specialises in traditional mediums such as pencil, paint and collage work. Sarah is open to experimentation with mediums and concepts.

Scene Print & Design Ltd.
Studio 3, Travers House, Hope Street, Leigh, Lancashire, WN7 1AJ
tel: 01942 608 759
email: info@scenegraphics.co.uk
web: www.scenegraphics.co.uk
contact: Barry Hutchings
info: All aspects of print and multimedia design. Have worked with bands previously.

Sirenstorm Media
PO Box 66, Manchester, M12 4XJ
tel: 0161 225 9991
email: info@sirenstorm.com
web: www.sirenstorm.com
contact: Tony Spalding
info: Print, flyers, posters, CD covers and websites. Sirenstorm have a positive interest in new bands and artists.

Smiling Wolf
62 Hope Street, Liverpool, L1 9BZ
tel: 0151 707 6253
email: howl@smilingwolf.co.uk
web: www.smilingwolf.co.uk
contact: Simon Rhodes
info: Highly creative multimedia design company. Soundscapes to corporate identity.

Spiral Media Consultancy Ltd.
8 Trinity Chambers, Ivy Street, Birkenhead, Wirral, CH41 5EF
tel: 0151 666 8250
email: sales@spiralmedia.co.uk
web: www.spiralmedia.co.uk
contact: Margaret Evans
info: Graphic design for literature, flyers, corporate ID, illustration, signs and web design.

Stan Chow (Chinkyafro)
Unit 55, 4th Floor, 24 Lever Street, Manchester, M1 1DZ
tel: 07939 598 936
email: stan.chow@virgin.net
web: www.chinkyafro.com
contact: Stan Chow
info: Stan has designed flyers for club nights for the past 6 years. He is also Creative Director of El Presidente Industries (which is a small independent label), involving the design of posters, stickers, flyers, logos, sleeves and the whole 'corporate' image. Has designed for Andy Votel, most notably illustrating Alfie's last album cover 'A Word In Your Ear'. Other clients have included GQ Magazine, Elle, Cosmopolitan, Sunday Times Magazine, Durex, Selfridges, and numerous book covers for a variety of publishers.

Steve McGrail Design & Illustration
36 Park Road North, Newton-le-Willows, WA12 9TD
tel: 01925 223 259
email: postmaster@stevemcgrail.plus.com
info: Design and illustration for print, from concept to finish.

T3
Adamson House, Pomona Strand, Old Trafford, Manchester, M16 0TT
tel: 0161 872 7170
fax: 0161 872 7144
email: gareth@t3-net.com
web: www.t3-net.com
contact: Gareth Griffiths
info: Design for print and web. Would be interested to hear from good up and coming bands.

Talbot Malone Design
The New Media Centre, Old Road, Warrington, Cheshire, WA4 1AT
tel: 01925 633 339
email: design@talbotmalone.co.uk
web: www.talbotmalone.co.uk
contact: Geoff, Dave
info: Posters, websites, flyers, CD artwork and logos.

Tangent Design Ltd.
37-41 Longshut Lane West, Stockport, SK2 6RX
tel: 0161 237 3007
email: dave@tangent-design.com
web: www.tangent-design.com
contact: Dave Marsh
info: Graphic design for print and screen-based design.

Taplin Design
7 Brentwood Avenue, Urmston, Manchester, Lancashire, M41 0XD
tel: 0161 610 8308
fax: 0161 610 8308
email: d.taplin1@ntlworld.com
contact: Dave Taplin
info: Graphic design for print. Taplin Design are interested in working with local bands.

Tennant Design
21 Spinners Yard, Fisher Street, Carlisle, Cumbria, CA3 8QJ
tel: 01228 514 668
email: enquiries@tennantdesign.co.uk
web: www.tennantdesign.co.uk
contact: Ivan Tennant
info: Creative solutions at affordable rates.

Tetsuo Advertising & Design
426 Wilbraham Road, Chorlton, Manchester, M21 0AS
tel: 07725 018 755
contact: Sean Lumby
info: Small individual design service providing promotional packs for record companies, sleeve artwork, posters and non-web based advertising.

Thread Creative Studio
Arch 29, North Campus Incubator, Sackville Street, Manchester, M60 1QD
tel: 0871 230 7174
email: info@threadcreative.co.uk
web: www.threadcreative.co.uk
contact: Ben
info: Complete design service including brand design, web design and graphic design.

Velvet Skies Webdesign
Manchester
tel: 07799 125 502
email: markbristol@hotmail.co.uk
web: www.velvetskieswebdesign.com
contact: Mark Bristol
info: Velvet Skies can bring your website aspirations to life. Very competitive rates, for example a basic 4 page website is priced between £100 and £200 depending on the content. Can incorporate photography, animation and film to set your image ahead of the rest.

West-Head
125 Aigburth Road, Liverpool, L17 4JU
tel: 07791 700 872
email: granty@thezutons.net
web: www.thezutons.net/westhead
contact: Neil Grant
info: Web design, flash animation, CD-ROM authoring, illustration and graphic design for print.

Williams and Crosby
The Stables, King Edward Street, Macclesfield, SK10 1AQ
tel: 01625 666 900
fax: 01625 666 908
email: mail@wandc.com
web: www.wandc.com
contact: Ed Williams
info: Corporate identity, brochures, web design, exhibition design, multimedia and packaging.

Zelus Graphics
The Cottage, Eversley Park, Chester, CH2 2AJ
tel: 01244 378 276
fax: 01244 399 331
email: mike@zelus.co.uk
web: www.zelus.co.uk
contact: Mike Haughton
info: Design for printed media including posters and album artwork.

SOUTHEAST

Aardvark Design Studio
129 Warren Road, Banstead, Surrey, SM7 1LT
tel: 01737 350 948/01737 218 340
email: mail@aardvark.co.uk
web: www.aardvark.co.uk
contact: Steven Heath Smith
info: Aardvark Design Studios are willing to turn their hand to any project. They work closely with clients to produce effective solutions.

Adooda Web Design Ltd.
26 The Old Town Hall, 142 Albion Street, Southwick, Brighton, BN42 4AX
tel: 01273 594 000
fax: 01273 594 949
email: info@adoodawebdesign.co.uk
web: www.adoodawebdesign.co.uk
contact: Mike
info: Web design, web hosting and search engine optimisation. Previous music experience.

Alphanet Media Ltd.
95 Ditchling Road, Brighton, East Sussex, BN1 4ST
tel: 01273 623 009
email: info@alpha-net.co.uk
web: www.alpha-net.co.uk
info: Web and graphic design company with marketing delivery.

Altered Media
Fleet, Hampshire
email: info@altered-media.com
web: www.altered-media.com
info: Specifically design websites for bands with features including facility to display photos, share music and video tracks, as well as update gigs and news pages. Also offer logo, leaflet and promotional material design.

Bespoke Internet
Barham Court Business Centre, Teston, Maidstone, ME18 5BZ
tel: 0845 644 3991
email: enquiries@bespokeinternet.com
web: www.bespokeinternet.com
info: Web, graphic and print design company. Close links with the music industry.

Big Fat Web Hosting
PO Box 4462, Worthing, West Sussex, BN11 3YF
tel: 0871 872 5324
email: mike@bigfatwebhosting.co.uk
web: www.bigfatwebhosting.co.uk
contact: Mike Jackson
info: Web design and hosting for bands. Features available in packages include video and music downloading and streaming, photo gallery and messageboard. 500MB hosting costs £49 per year. Web design service from £149.99.

Cherry Creative
99 Shalmsford Street, Chartham, Canterbury, CT4 7RQ
tel: 01227 738 953
email: carolyn.cherry@cherrycreative.co.uk
web: www.cherrycreative.co.uk
info: Web, graphic and print design company.

Clare Richardson Design for Web & Print
54 Oxford Road, Newbury, Berkshire, RG14 1PG
tel: 01635 551 555
email: ctr@clarezone.co.uk
web: www.clarezone.co.uk
info: Website designer who has recently completed a project for the composer of the Alan Parsons Project. See www.poe-cd.com.

Close To Water
Media House, 41 Crayford Way, Kent, DA1 4JY
tel: 01322 555 087
fax: 01322 552 333
email: solutions@ctow.co.uk
web: www.ctow.co.uk
info: Provide full design service, including web and promotional printing.

Courtney Website Design & Hosting
29 Highgrove Road, Portsmouth, Hampshire, PO3 6PP
tel: 02392 785 546
email: courtneydesign@aol.com
web: www.courtneyuk.com
info: Web design company affiliated with local musicians.

d2j Studios
Unit 4, Templefields Enterprise Centre, South Road, Harlow, Essex, CM20 2AR
tel: 01279 431 161
email: d2jstudios@hotmail.com
contact: Mick Donoghue, Paul Donoghue
info: Artwork for CDs and vinyl. D2j Studios also offer recording and rehearsal facilities. See entries in relevant sections for details.

D-Code
30a Headley Road, Liphook, Hampshire, GU30 7NP
tel: 07867 515 574
email: bookings@theliveroom.co.uk
web: www.d-code.org.uk
contact: Will Yates
info: Graphic design packages, as well as web design, photography, interactive CD-Rom production, and some video facilities. Linked with The Liveroom, recording and rehearsal studios. See entries in relevant sections for details.

Def-Sta Projects
149 Elm Grove, Brighton, East Sussex, BN2 3ES
tel: 07880 735 416
email: jonathan@def-sta.com
web: www.def-sta.com
info: Previous experience of working with bands and musicians. Specialising in web, print and project management.

deliberateDESIGN
1 Page Place, Folkstone, Kent, CT19 6HX
tel: 01303 258 237
email: jhjackson@ntlworld.com
web: www.deliberatedesign.co.uk
info: Web design company.

Delta Traffic
13a Richmond Road, Brighton, BN2 3RL
tel: 01273 297 927
email: alex@deltatraffic.co.uk
web: www.deltatraffic.co.uk
info: Website hosting and design.

Dot Café
19 Dunstans Street, Canterbury, CT2 8BH
tel: 01227 478 778
email: info@dotcafedesigns.com
web: www.dotcafedesigns.com
info: Web, graphic and print design company that can provide production as well.

E-Clipz Studios
3 Whitby Parade, Whitby Road, South Ruislip, Middlesex, HA4 9EA
tel: 0870 609 2853
email: info@eclipz.co.uk
web: www.eclipz.co.uk
contact: Abena Mills, Kianna Elfaham
info: Graphic design, web and multimedia studio. Promoters' packages and artist branding.

Electric Putty Ltd.
7 Prestonville Road, Brighton, BN1 3TL
tel: 01273 746 333
email: us@electricputty.co.uk
web: www.electricputty.co.uk
contact: Melanie Burke
info: Web design, programming and consultancy services.

eplatforms Ltd.
Brighton Media Centre, 15-17 Middle Street, Brighton, East Sussex, BN1 1AL
tel: 01273 201 161
fax: 0870 005 3017
email: info@eplatforms.com
web: www.eplatforms.com
info: Graphic and web design company who have worked with Zulu Records.

Esoteric Anodyne Ltd.
PO Box 203, Brighton, BN1 4WE
tel: 01273 680 013
fax: 0870 705 2732
email: info@esotericanodyne.com
web: www.esotericanodyne.com
info: Web design company. Able to follow through from initial design to employment.

GETSETup.Net
3 Field Gate Drive, Kingsclere, Newbury, Berkshire, RG20 5SQ
tel: 0870 011 1447
email: neil@getsetup.net
web: www.getsetup.net
info: Purely web design company with previous music clients. Can also produce e-newsletters.

Giant Fiery Hand
Brighton
email: andrew@giantfieryhand.com
web: www.giantfieryhand.com
info: Experienced designers. Can modify existing artwork or create new concepts and design. Illustration and CD mastering as well.

Global Initiative
52 Cornmarket Street, Oxford, OX1 3HJ
tel: 01865 304 005
fax: 01865 304 001
email: ideas@global-initiative.com
web: www.global-initiative.com
contact: Gareth Nixon
info: Design company specialising in 'experience consultancy' which encompasses all aspects of graphic and web design.

Helmstone Communications Ltd.
18 Guildford Road, Brighton, East Sussex, BN1 3LU
tel: 01273 747 447
email: info@helmstone.com
web: www.helmstone.com
contact: Tony Nisbett
info: Graphic and web design company with previous music industry experience.

Indigo New Media
Maddison Suite, Wenta Business Centre, Colne Way, Watford, WD24 7ND
tel: 0870 744 7884
email: lookandsee@indigonewmedia.net
web: www.indigonewmedia.net
info: Web design and online marketing for bands. Indigo New Media set up the Damien Rice fan website, see www.damienrice.co.uk.

Internet Design Brighton
7 Thornhill Close, Hove, East Sussex, BN3 8JL
tel: 01273 277 151
email: office@id-brighton.co.uk
web: www.id-brighton.co.uk
contact: Gary Cook
info: Have designed several websites for bands. Also offer some print design.

John Bassett
Hastings, East Sussex
email: john@johnbassett.co.uk
web: www.johnbassett.co.uk
info: Website design in both Flash and HTML. Graphic design for CD artwork, logos, flyers and other promotional print. Can create animated GIF or Flash banner ads for bands - costs for this from £5. Also provide audio mastering. See relevant section for more details.

Liquid Light Digital Ltd.
22a Dukes Lane, Brighton, BN1 1BG
tel: 01273 739 709
web: www.liquidlight.co.uk
info: Previously worked with EMI and various other companies providing web design solutions. Follow through from initial design to development and employment.

Mark Design
Suite 103, Brighton Media Centre, 15-17 Middle Street, Brighton, East Sussex, BN1 1AL
tel: 01273 201 358
email: info@mark-design.co.uk
web: www.mark-design.co.uk
contact: Gus Mark
info: Web and graphic design company that offer a comprehensive service.

MB Commerce Ltd.
34-36 St. George's Road, Kemptown, Brighton, East Sussex, BN2 1ED
tel: 0845 665 1006
fax: 01273 606 130
email: info@mbcommerce.co.uk
web: www.mbcommerce.co.uk
contact: Christian Thrower
info: Web and graphic design company. Running for 5 years, with previous knowledge of the music industry.

Mick Collins
Parndon Mill Lane, Harlow, Essex, CN20 ZHP
tel: 01279 414 181
email: aaah@blueyonder.co.uk
web: www.graphic-designer.co.uk
info: Guitarist who provides web site design.

mpjdesign
Wareton, Calcott Hill, Sturry, Canterbury, Kent, CT3 4ND
tel: 01227 713 181
web: www.mpjdesign.com
info: Web, print and graphic design company. Marketing solutions are also available, as well as design for French language.

Neujuice
Gloucester House, 45 Gloucester Street, Brighton, BN1 4EW
tel: 01273 688 872
email: info@neujuice.com
web: www.neujuice.com
contact: Nick Davis
info: Previous music experience. Creative design and marketing for your band. Offer stimulating and friendly environment to develop effective design across digital and print media.

New World Web Design
Gosport, Hampshire
email: info@newworldwebdesign.co.uk
web: www.newworldwebdesign.co.uk
contact: Craig Jones
info: Web design, hosting and promotion services. Also linked with Rock Links who provide a duplication service. Contact for further information.

NMG Design
20 Kingsbury Street, Brighton, BN1 4JW
tel: 07989 541 487
email: nealgrundy@hotmail.com
web: www.nmgdesign.co.uk
contact: Neal Grundy
info: Design for promotional print and CD artwork. Can provide all necessary photography services involved. See relevant section for more details.

Nothing To See Here
Brighton
tel: 01273 626 274
email: steve@nothing-to-see-here.com
web: www.nothing-to-see-here.com
info: Nothing To See Here are a collective of design, new media and video specialists. Design for web and print including logos, identities and CD artwork. Also produce video promos. See relevant section for more details.

On-Screen Graphics
225 Cowley Road, Oxford, Oxfordshire, OX4 1XG
tel: 01865 204 417
email: info@onscreengraphics.co.uk
web: www.onscreengraphics.co.uk
contact: Phil Robson
info: Previous experience with local music bands and events. Fully flexible and comprehensive design service.

Optical Arena
Unit 8, Beaconsfield Workshop, Ditchling Rise, Brighton, East Sussex, BN1 4QL
tel: 01273 819 507
email: info@opticalarena.co.uk
web: www.opticalarena.co.uk
info: Previous advertising and CD cover for music events. Web and graphic design.

MUSIC SERVICES/RETAIL

Planet Gromit
PO Box 926, Canterbury, Kent, CT1 9AD
tel: 01227 732 546
email: info@planetgromit.com
web: www.planetgromit.com
info: Mainly web and multimedia design. Company has previously designed for Madonna, Robbie Williams and Paul McCartney.

Quirky Motion
Floor 5, The Amphenol Business Complex, Thanet Way, Whitstable, Kent, CT5 3WF
tel: 0870 787 4181/07811 638 649
email: thechaps@quirkymotion.com
web: www.quirkymotion.com
contact: John Lumgair
info: Animation, illustration and video production. For more details see the Video Production listings.

Red Ant Design
23 Union Street, Maidstone, Kent, ME14 1EB
tel: 01622 664 333
email: sales@redantdesign.com
web: www.redantdesign.com
info: Web and content management company.

Red Design
Studio 1.1, 11 Jew Street, Brighton, BN1 1UT
tel: 01273 704 614
fax: 01273 704 615
email: info@red-design.co.uk
web: www.red-design.co.uk
info: Provided CD artwork and design for FC Kahuna, Fatboy Slim, McFly, Thirteen Senses and David Gray.

Redcat Media Ltd.
1-13 Lord Montgomery Way, Portsmouth, Hampshire, PO1 2AH
tel: 0845 644 6720
email: andy@redcatmedia.net
web: www.redcatmedia.net
contact: Andy Jacobs
info: Web and graphic design, as well as new media and marketing consultancy.

Redhead Design
Gloucester House, 45 Gloucester Street, Brighton, BN1 4EW
tel: 01273 602 440
email: info@redheaddesign.com
web: www.redheaddesign.com
contact: Laura Danby
info: Provide website design and corporate identity, brochures, packaging, along with magazine and book design.

Redwire
Parndon Mill, Harlow, Essex, CN20 2HP
tel: 01279 414 181
email: aaah@blueyonder.co.uk
web: www.graphic-designer.co.uk
contact: Mick Collins
info: Mick is a guitarist himself, and can provide a variety of music related designs.

The Silent Coup
Unit 3, Grange Farm Units, Nelsons Lane, Hurst, Berkshire, RG10 0RR
tel: 0118 934 0934/07094 601 059
email: admin@the-silent-coup.org
web: www.the-silent-coup.org
info: Website design and build including easy to update homepage with band news, summary of upcoming shows and events, links to tracks available to download and buy from external sites,and automated mailing list with a signup form for your fans. Complete graphic design and printing for CD packaging. Also provide rehearsal and recording facilities, as well as tuition services. See relevant sections for more information. Offer demo and website inclusive packages, call for details.

Sliced Ltd.
91 Western Road, Brighton, East Sussex, BN1 2NW
tel: 01273 776 373
fax: 01273 706 030
email: info@slicedcreative.co.uk
web: www.slicedcreative.co.uk
contact: Nick
info: Web and graphic design company who provide web based CMS package and custom designs.

Squiff Creative Media
30 Lawrence Road, Tilehurst, Reading, Berkshire, RG3 06N
tel: 0118 941 5545
email: info@squiffweb.co.uk
web: www.squiffweb.co.uk
info: Provides record sleeves, illustrations, logos, web design, and DVD production and video editing.

Sussex Web Services
75 Bridgemere Road, Eastbourne, East Sussex, BN22 8TF
tel: 0845 166 8801
email: info@sussexwebservices.co.uk
web: www.sussexwebservices.co.uk
info: Affordable web design service for the creative industries.

Tangerine
Leewood Farm, 1 Harthall Lane, Kings Langley, Hertfordshire, WD4 8JJ
tel: 01923 261 266
fax: 01923 261 266
email: studio@designbytangerine.co.uk
web: www.designbytangerine.co.uk
info: Design for web and print including all CD and DVD artwork. Website database design. Can also provide mastering and duplication facilities, as well as printing. See relevant sections for details.

TDSF Web Development
185 Cheriton Road, Folkestone, Kent, CT19 5JP
tel: 01303 857 006
email: enquiries@tdsf.co.uk
web: www.tdsf.co.uk
info: Web design company that will go from the design concept through to launch.

Telset
Studio 201, 22 Eden Street, Kingston Upon Thames, Surrey, KT1 1DN
tel: 0870 415 1515
email: info@telset.net
web: www.telset.net
contact: Mark Howard
info: Web design and hosting services. Also design CD artwork at set rate of £75.

Think Marketing
The Old Stables, Well Street, Burghclere, Newbury, Berkshire, RG20 9ND
tel: 01635 276 066
email: team@think.co.uk
web: www.think.co.uk
contact: Richard Bowden
info: Print, web and graphic design company with marketing consultancy.

Think Tank Group UK Ltd.
The Old Brewery, 75 Stour Street, Canterbury, Kent, CT1 2NR
tel: 01227 789 797
email: info@thinktankgroup.co.uk
web: www.thinktankgroup.co.uk
contact: Alex Ridings
info: Web design company that provides all aspects of website design and creation including marketing and web hosting.

ujerr.com
52 Demesne Furze, Headington, Oxford, Oxfordshire, OX3 7XF
tel: 01865 744 922
email: info@ujerr.com
web: www.ujerr.com
contact: David Upjohn
info: Previous experience with bands. Purely web based design and web marketing.

Zen Design
John Dickinson Centre, London Road, Apsley, Hemel Hempstead, HP3 9QU
tel: 01442 234 812/01442 234 813
fax: 07092 390 011
email: info@zendesignltd.co.uk
web: www.zendesignltd.co.uk
contact: Angela Morgan
info: Zen Design offer a complete service for the whole spectrum of graphic and web design. Their graphic design department covers all aspects of graphics that are needed for the music industry including CD covers, website design, posters and logos. Zen's web design team will help you choose your web domain and will also host your site. They create a range of websites, from offering your band simple web presence to complete Flash dynamic sites with music, multimedia videos and e-commerce.

SOUTHWEST

2fish Productions Ltd.
264 Southampton Road, Portsmouth, PO6 4QD
tel: 02392 327 365
fax: 02392 327 365
email: uguide@2fi.sh
web: www.2fi.sh
contact: Darren Bovis-Coulter
info: Web and graphic design company who have worked with many local bands, and have been involved with developing music websites. Also assist with band promotion and back drops.

Aardvark Creative
19 Sailsbury Street, St. George, Bristol, BS5 8EE
tel: 0117 378 9008
email: info@aardvark-creative.com
web: www.aardvark-creative.com
contact: Cerise Reed
info: Have extensive experience working with record labels including EMI. Also worked with bands previously.

BakerSmith Design
Unit D6, Devon Business Park, Saunders Way, Collumpton, Devon, EX15 1BS
tel: 0870 712 3545
web: www.bakersmith.co.uk
info: Provide print and web design services. Also have an office based in London. See listing for further details.

Band-space.com
99 Eggbuckland Road, Higher Compton, Plymouth, PL3 5JR
tel: 07762 661 615
email: mail@band-space.com
web: www.band-space.com
info: Specialises in website design for unsigned bands. Complete site featuring band information, biog, MP3s, news, gig and contact details available from £99.

Big Happen
Bristol
tel: 07909 974 064
email: nathan@bighappen.com
web: www.bighappen.com
info: Design and illustration for print and the web. Logos, CD covers and album artwork.

Bleeding Skull
Cornwall
email: scott@bleedingskull.net
web: www.bleedingskull.net
info: Bleeding Skull Design specialise in dark designs which suit Metal, Grunge, Doom, Gothic and Hardcore bands, although are willing to design for any genre.

Bright Spark Marketing Group
178-180 Hotwell Road, Bristol, BS8 4RP
tel: 0117 311 1995
email: mail@bsmg.co.uk
web: www.bsmg.co.uk
info: Web and graphic design services.

Caroline Duffy
32 Bull Lane, Crews Hole, Bristol, BS5 8AB
tel: 0117 955 6184
email: caroline@carolineduffy.co.uk
web: www.carolineduffy.co.uk
contact: Caroline Duffy
info: Innovative, forward thinking design studio capable of producing posters, flyers and album artwork.

Chalk-dk
5 Framlington Court, Libertus Road, Cheltenham, GL51 7EG
tel: 01242 255 787
email: info@chalk-dk.com
web: www.chalk-dk.com
info: Designs suitable for logos, branding, graphics and web.

Character Graphics
56 Station Road, Taunton, TA1 1NS
tel: 01823 279 008
email: characters@btinternet.com
contact: John
info: Low cost art and design available. Also print flyers and posters.

Clockworx
Units A&B, Nimrod Way, Wimborne, BH21 7SH
tel: 01202 865 115
email: fred@clockworxdesign.com
web: www.clockworxdesign.com
contact: fred
info: Worked with musicians before. Will do anything from CD covers to 48 page brochures.

Crescent Design
5 Royal Cresent, Cheltenham, GL50 3DA
tel: 01242 253 020
email: mgf@crescent-design.com
web: www.crescent-design.com
contact: Mark Freshney
info: Eager to work with bands and musicians on all aspects of design.

Crunch Creative Design Ltd.
231 Citadel Road East, Plymouth, PL1 2NG
tel: 01752 601 434
web: www.crunchcreative.co.uk
info: Crunch Creative are a multi-disciplined design agency specialising in strategic solutions for brand identity, advertising, marketing, web and new media, print and illustration.

Cut The Mustard
33 Belmont Road, St. Andrews, Bristol, BS6 5AW
tel: 0117 908 1176/07779 269 236
email: info@cutthemustard.net
web: www.cutthemustard.net
info: Original artwork in print. Painting, graphic design and web design.

De-Sign
F2 Hazledene Court, 152 Richmond Park Road, Bournemouth, BH8 8TW
tel: 01202 524 594
email: richkean@de-signgraphics.co.uk or richkean@yahoo.co.uk
web: www.de-signgraphics.co.uk
info: Specialists in logo and identity, plus website design.

Design Unltd
5 Penrose Villas, Plymouth, PL4 7BD
tel: 01752 296 627
email: hello@designunltd.co.uk
web: www.designunltd.co.uk
contact: Matt Sanwell
info: Creative graphic design studios producing many forms of design and print. Enthusiastic about working with bands and musicians.

Direction Advertising & Design
1st Floor, 123 Old Christchurch Road, Bournemouth, BH1 1EP
tel: 01202 298 258
email: enquiries@direction123.com
web: www.direction123.com
info: Company has worked with bands before and can offer logo design, branding, web design and new media services.

Earth Gallery
Fore Street, Bampton, Tiverton, EX16 9ND
tel: 01398 332 100/01398 351 489
fax: 01398 332 100
email: info@earthgallery.biz
web: www.earthgallery.biz
contact: Marlon / Sophie
info: Gallery and studio which provide fine art, graphic design, web design, and CD covers. Also provide photography services, logo design and digital art.

Emma Luczyn
Top Floor Flat, 34 Belmont Road, St. Andrews, Bristol, BS6 5AS
tel: 07787 521670
email: emmaluczyn@gmail.com
web: www.emmaluczyn.co.uk
contact: Emma Luczyn
info: Offer contemporary graphic design at a reasonable price. Mostly design for print, specialising in promotional material and advertising.

Feel Happy Corp.
TFF, 34 Belmont Road, St. Andrews, Bristol, BS6 5AS
tel: 07787 521 670
email: emmaluczyn@gmail.com
web: www.emmaluczyn.co.uk
contact: Emma Luczyn
info: Graphic design services. Previously carried out work for Knowledge and Blowback magazines.

Forest Graphics
4 Forest View, Crossways, Dorchester, DT2 8UR
tel: 01305 854 291
email: info@forestgraphics.co.uk
web: www.forsetgraphics.co.uk
info: Can offer web design, logos, photography, video editing, 360 panoramic views and print material.

Fuzed Design
99 Eggbuckland Road, Higher Compton, Plymouth, PL3 5JR
tel: 07762 661 615
email: paul@fuzeddesign.co.uk
web: www.fuzeddesign.co.uk
contact: Paul Springett
info: Web and graphic design.

feel happy corp

Suppliers of top-notch graphics for whatever your genre of music.

Submit your orders through www.emmaluczyn.co.uk contacts page.

Generator
Innovation Centre, St.Cross Park, Newport, Isle of Wight, PO30 5WB
tel: 01983 550 395
email: studio@generatorgraphics.co.uk
web: www.generatorgraphics.co.uk
info: Have worked with musicians before and have an understanding of the industry.

Glass Tone Design
Unit 3a, Riverside Business Park, Bath, BA2 3DW
tel: 01225 487 700
email: info@glasstone.co.uk
web: www.glasstone.co.uk
contact: Greg Brooker
info: Designers who can work on all graphic needs, including band logos, CD inlays, flyers and t-shirts. Glass Tone also provide recording, rehearsal, management, PA hire and mastering services. In addition to this they organise live events in Bath and Bristol. Refer to entries in appropriate sections.

Global Design & Print Ltd.
76 Shelly Road East, Bournemouth, BH7 6HB
tel: 01202 727 070
email: production@theglobalgroup.uk.com
web: www.theglobalgroup.uk.com
contact: Natasha Kubiak
info: Worked with bands before. Full production including websites CDs and general artwork.

Green Ginger Studios
Unit 8a, The Old Dairy, Sancreed, Penzance, TR20 8QP
tel: 01736 811 118
email: simon@blueiris-eclipse.co.uk
contact: Simon
info: Design studios with print capabilities. Have worked with local bands before. Design is more 'Art' based, rather than commercial.

Image & Music
Cornwall
tel: 01503 272 633/07779 703 281
email: cdart@imageandmusic.co.uk
web: www.imageandmusic.co.uk
info: CD artwork from £280. Call or email for a full quote. Web design also available.

Joyaa
Blue In Green Studios, Dartmoor
tel: 01364 661 420
email: omniio@homecall.co.uk
web: www.joyaa.com
info: CD artwork, either constructing design from components provided by client or completely from scratch. DVD editing. Joya works from, and in close association with, Blue In Green Studios. See Recording Services section for more details.

Jump Media
3 Church Road, Penryn, TR10 8DA
tel: 01326 375 422
fax: 01326 378 735
email: info@jumpmedia.co.uk
web: www.jumpmedia.co.uk
contact: Robert Hatcher
info: Sophisticated web design, logo and identity design. Full range of print also available for exhibition.

Kolor Skemes
Unit 8, Morlands Industrial Estate, Morland Road, Highbridge, TA9 3ET
tel: 01278 795 047
email: alan@kolorskemes.com
web: www.kolorskemes.com
contact: Alan Smith
info: Fresh, friendly and creative graphic design service. Designed to be different.

Lake House Design
Haddon Lake House, Old Park Road, Ventnor, Isle of Wight, PO38 1XR
tel: 01983 855 151
email: phillippa@lakehousedesign.co.uk
web: www.lakehousedesign.co.uk
info: Web design, graphics, photo realistic illustration. New business willing to work with musicians.

Lumby-Futrille
Langport, Somerset, TA10 9QT
tel: 01458 250 284
email: design@lumbyfutrille.co.uk
web: www.lumbyfutrille.co.uk
info: Can assist with web design, identity, promotional literature and logos.

MetalMusicSites.com
397a Ham Green, Holt, BA14 6PX
email: info@metalmusicsites.com
web: www.metalmusicsites.com
contact: Samuel Vincent
info: Offer all inclusive web design packages for bands, musicians and other music based communities.

Monkey Puzzle Repro Art
Unit 5, Mount Pleasant Eco Park, Chapel Hill, Porth Towen, TR4 8HL
tel: 01209 890 333
contact: Eve Jemmett
info: Mostly design posters for exhibitions but are happy to work with bands in the area. Can do short printing runs also.

Montpellier Marketing Communications Group Ltd.
Glendale House, 11 Montpellier Terrace, Cheltenham, GL50 1UX
tel: 01242 262 977
email: info@montpelliercreative.com
web: www.montpelliercreative.com
contact: Roger Tailor
info: Have worked with bands in the past. Can create record sleeves and websites.

Morganian
4 Millbrook Road, Paignton, Devon, TQ3 3AU
tel: 01803 551 344
email: morganian@btinternet.com
web: www.morganian.co.uk
info: Provides web design, photography, plus CD cover design.

Mouseworx
Unit 3, Halthaies Workshops, Bradninch, Exeter, EX5 4LQ
tel: 01392 881 777
email: andy@mouseworx.biz
web: www.mouseworx.biz
contact: Andy Collins
info: Mouseworx has over 20 years graphic design experience and can produce logos, leaflets, posters, flyers and websites.

Ocular Arts
The Tramshed, Walcot Street, Bath, BA1 5BD
tel: 0870 7667 601
email: info@oculararts.com
web: www.oculararts.com
info: Provide graphic design, promotional literature, photography, illustration and web design.

Orgill Advertising
19-20 Scott Business Park, Beacon Park Road, Plymouth, PL2 2PB
tel: 01752 201 601
email: info@orgilladvertising.co.uk
web: www.orgilladvertising.co.uk
contact: Sarah Proffer
info: Creative thinking and design from a company which has 20 years experience. Can help with marketing and PR, as well as produce a wide range of print based media.

Out Of Hand
Bristol
tel: 0117 907 1280
email: info@outofhand.co.uk
web: www.outofhand.co.uk
info: Design for promotional print material including flyers and posters. Also develop with logos, websites and e-flyers. Can assist with hand-to-hand flyer distribution, as well as providing print services. See relevant section for details.

Oxygen Creative Services
Lowman Green, Tiverton, EX16 4LB
tel: 01884 255 999
email: steve@oxygencreative.co.uk
web: www.oxygencreative.co.uk
contact: Steve
info: Creative design including websites, logos and graphics.

Pixelfarmer
1 West Court, Newquay, TR7 1UG
tel: 07790 770 434
email: info@pixelfarmer.co.uk
web: www.pixelfarmer.co.uk
contact: Rob Suckley
info: Web and graphic design.

Revolting
36 Sopers Lane, Poole, BH17 7ES
tel: 0845 443 5457
email: studio@wearevolting.co.uk
info: Design for print and web. Art direction for photo shoots. Photography and illustrations.

RT Media Ltd.
Enterprise House, Aviation Park West, Bournemouth International Airport, Bournemouth, BH23 6NW
tel: 01202 594 748
email: info@rtmedia.com
web: www.rtmedia.com
contact: Ross Thornley
info: Graphic and web design. Also offer PR and marketing services, enquire for further details.

Rumba Graphic Design
24 Park Street, Bristol, BS1 5JA
tel: 0117 907 5323
email: simon@rumbadesign.co.uk
web: www.rumbadesign.co.uk
contact: Simon Rees
info: Experienced design company. Willing to work with bands and musicians.

Sandstorm Media
Creative Planet, Hackpen Lane, Wroughton, Wiltshire, SN4 9NS
tel: 01793 845588
email: info@sandstormmedia.co.uk
web: www.sandstormmedia.co.uk
contact: Tom Ward
info: Sandstorm provide both postproduction facilities and studio workspaces. We have 3 different workspaces on site, the largest has an internal space of 1 acre. Our company's primary activity is postproduction for commercials and music videos. Services include 3D, VFX, editing (for video, HD and film), colour grading and DVD authoring.

Skyla Graphics
Bournemouth
tel: 07977 915 889
email: skyla@skylagraphics.co.uk
web: www.skylagraphics.co.uk
contact: Claire
info: Design for CD artwork, flyers and posters. Demo and promotional packages, plus logos and website design. Skyla Graphics offer full publicity and graphic support to unsigned and emerging bands. For more details of Skyla Graphics' photography services see relevant section.

Spend Spend Spend
tel: 01392 437 861
email: tom@spend-spend-spend.com
web: www.spend-spend-spend.com
contact: Tom Vinelott
info: Website design, as well as graphic work suitable for CDs, posters and flyers. Tom also offers photography services. See listing in relevant section.

Storm Creative Ltd.
7b Boyces Avenue, Clifton, Bristol, BS8 4AA
tel: 0117 915 9692
email: sales@stormcreative.gb.com
web: www.stormcreative.gb.com
info: Provide web design, graphic design, as well as logos.

Strange Corporation
Unit 4, The Old Generator House, Bourne Valley Road, Poole, Dorset, BH12 1DZ
tel: 01202 755 580
email: results@strangecorp.com
web: www.strangecorp.com
info: Provide web, DVD and video design services. Have designed record sleeves on several occasions. Previous clients include BMG Music. See also listing for office located in London.

Top Copy Ltd.
1 Ensbury Park Road, Moordown, Bournemouth, BH9 2SQ
tel: 01202 523 233
email: office@topcopy.ltd.uk
web: www.topcopy.ltd.uk
contact: Becky/Neville
info: Happy to hear from bands to discuss artwork.

Trevor Peters Design
Units 18-19, Portway Business Centre, Old Sarum, Salisbury, SP4 6QX
tel: 01722 412 227
email: tpd@tpdesign.co.uk
web: www.tpdesign.co.uk
info: Graphic designers specialising in logos, web design and identity.

WOW Creative Services
Suite 22-23, Newburn Centre, Newburn Crescent, Swindon, SN1 5EW
tel: 01793 719 033
email: sandyg@wowcreative.com
web: www.wowcreative.co.uk
contact: Natasha
info: Graphic design, web design, plus print material such as flyers and posters.

YORKSHIRE

.bindoff
23 Linton Crescent, Leeds, LS17 8PZ
tel: 0113 268 1526
email: hello@bindoff.co.uk
web: www.bindoff.co.uk
contact: Matt
info: Develop websites, as well as offering e-marketing, new media and CD Rom authoring.

3 Squared
St James' House, Vicar Lane, Sheffield, S1 2EX
tel: 0114 223 8333
email: info@3squared.co.uk
web: www.3squared.co.uk
contact: Tim Jones
info: Web based design studio able to produce websites, screensavers, MP3s and CD Roms. Have worked within the music industry previously.

4:3 Creative
Globe Works, Penistone Road, Sheffield, S6 3AE
tel: 0114 270 0600
info: Can design CD covers, posters, flyers, t-shirts and websites. Worked with musicians before and very willing to do so again.

Adam Storch
83 Southfield, Hull, Hessle, HU13 0ET
tel: 01482 641 547
email: adamstorch03@hotmail.com
contact: Adam
info: Graphics based design company with print facilities and contacts to allow web design and construction.

Army Of Cats
Leeds
email: vote_tyler_durden_86@hotmail.com
web: www.armyofcats.com/art/
contact: Graham Pilling
info: Graham is happy to take commissions for work of any kind, including cartoons, tattoo designs, poster and flyer designs, record sleeves, greetings cards, website graphics and paintings. Also run a record label, Obscene Baby Auction. See relevant section for more details.

Aspect Design & Marketing
22 Victoria Avenue, Harrogate, HG1 5PR
tel: 01423 501 161
email: creativity@aspectgraphics.co.uk
web: www.aspectgraphics.co.uk
contact: Jonathon Rayfield
info: Graphic design company which can also produce websites and professional photographs.

B-17 Design Publicity & Marketing
6 First Avenue, Doncaster, DN9 3GA
tel: 01302 802 079
email: graham@b-17.co.uk
contact: graham dobson
info: Produces all types of design for print including posters and flyers.

Bigcheese Design Consultancy
Church House, 178a Batley Road, Wakefield, WF2 0AJ
tel: 01924 788 778
email: chris@bigcheesedc.com
web: www.bigcheesedc.com
contact: Chris Lee
info: Can produce almost anything within print based media e.g. posters, flyers and album artwork.

Blimey Charlie Productions
61 Brinckman Street, Barnsley, South Yorkshire, S70 1JQ
tel: 01226 202 676
email: webmaster@bcp.8m.net
web: http://bcp.8m.net/
contact: Munk
info: Blimey Charlie offer design services of all types to promote your band including CD sleeves, posters, websites or t-shirt design. In return, they ask that you organise a gig in your area. Blimey Charlie will then provide 2 bands plus your band with flyers, (which you will distribute), posters and a webpage to promote the event. Your act will then be placed on a list of bands that are available when another band organises a gig in their area. That way, bands can help each other to get gigs. For further information on this scheme, contact by telephone or email.

Bluestone Design Group Ltd.
The Bank House, Bridge Road, Boston Spa, Wetherby, LS23 6HD
tel: 0845 166 2085
email: via website
web: www.bluedesign.co.uk
info: Creating inspiration not indifference. Can assist anywhere the client needs a visual presence e.g. CD covers, e-marketing, web development, posters and flyers.

boda
15 Queen Square, Leeds, LS2 8AJ
tel: 0870 950 3084
email: jess@theboda.co.uk
web: www.theboda.co.uk
contact: Jessica
info: Print graphics including posters, flyers and record sleeves.

Brainstorm Design
Suite 9, Howcroft House, 919 Bradford Road, Birstall, WF17 9JY
tel: 01924 472 010
email: david@brainstormdesign.co.uk
web: www.brainstormdesign.co.uk
contact: David Whitworth
info: Web design and printed graphics at reasonable prices. Keen to work with bands and musicians.

breed Creative

Breed Creative
Rotherham
email: unsigned@breedcreative.com
web: www.breedcreative.com
info: Design for print, web and clothing. Breed Creative have a particular interest in unsigned bands, and host 3 new tracks a month on their site. To have your music considered email Breed Creative for a submission address.

Bubble Creative Design Ltd.
The Hollies, Old Lane, Bramhope, Leeds, LS16 9AZ
tel: 0113 203 7173/07855 701 891
email: info@bubblecreative.com
web: www.bubblecreative.com
contact: Joanne, Ross
info: Specialise in producing websites and promotional material for the music industry.

Cube Graphics Ltd.
28 Ground Floor, Shaftsbury Avenue, Roundhay, Leeds, LS8 1DT
tel: 07971 684 962
email: candice@cubegraphics.co.uk
web: www.cubegraphics.co.uk
info: Graphic design and illustration. Cube Graphics is a small company of 2 designers offering a personal approach to every design brief for an affordable fee.

Danny Blackman
Leeds
tel: 07790 946 714
email: tbp278@hotmail.com
web: www.dannyblackman.co.uk
info: Design for web and print. Danny can provide both bespoke web design and cheaper template pages primarily for bands but also promotors, venues and record labels. Based between Leeds and Manchester.

DCH Design
68 Beckside, Beverley, North Yorkshire, HU17 0PD
tel: 01482 866 977
email: david@dchdesign.co.uk
web: www.dchdesign.co.uk
contact: David
info: All aspects of design including graphic and web design. Has worked with bands before. Experience in promotion and advertising.

Def1nitive Design & Media Ltd.
Unit A3, Wyther Lane Industrial Estate, Wyther Lane, Kirkstall, Leeds, LS5 3AP
tel: 0113 224 2211
web: www.def1nitive.com
info: A friendly, national, award winning creative agency serving the UK, with original ideas from print to new media.

The Design & Print Project Ltd.
2 The Courtyard, 27 The Village, Haxby, York, YO32 3HS
tel: 01904 768 899
email: info@thedpproject.com
web: www.thedpproject.com
info: Family run graphic design company offering design and printing of posters and flyers, as well as web design and construction.

Design Forum
Airedale House, 423 Kirkstall Road, Leeds, LS4 2EZ
tel: 0113 242 1155
email: via website
web: www.design-forum.net
contact: Nigel Widdowson
info: Full service graphic design agency offering a range of design services for both print and new media.

The Design Union
Leeds
tel: 0870 420 2456
email: hello@thedesignunion.com
web: www.thedesignunion.com
contact: Mark
info: The Design Union is a small responsive company, which provides dedicated web based solutions for a multitude of clients.

designSmiths
Studio 6, Springfield Mills, Bagley Lane, Farsley, Pudsey, LS28 5LY
tel: 0113 236 1796
email: andrew@wearesmiths.com
web: www.wearesmiths.com
contact: Andrew Critchett
info: Graphic design, artwork, posters and website design.

Drawingboard Productions
Leeds
tel: 07748 800 661
email: info@drawingboardproductions.co.uk
web: www.drawingboardproductions.co.uk
info: Design for promotional and marketing material in print and on the web. DVD authoring and enhanced CD contents. Can also provide recording services. See relevant section for details.

Eclipse Design & Advertising Ltd.
Eclipse Design, 2 North West Business Park, Servia Hill, Leeds, LS6 2QH
tel: 0113 244 3733
email: andrewp@eclipsedesign.uk.com
web: www.eclipsedesign.uk.com
contact: Andrew Pearson
info: Multi-disciplinary design and promotional agency, able to create the right sort of image, producing everything from a basic logo, flyers and covers to support items such as posters and t-shirts. Experienced in working with bands including 10,000 Things for whom they produced the logo.

Emozi Digital Art
2 Hell Wath Grove, Ripon, HG4 2JT
tel: 01765 607 603
email: emozi@btinternet.com
contact: Jean-Paul Looney
info: Emozi can produce all types of printed graphics including posters and album sleeves, as well as providing digital services such as image manipulation and photo retouching.

The Factory
3rd Floor, Castleton Mill, Armley Road, Leeds, LS12 2DS
tel: 07866 310 538
email: working@the-factory.co.uk
web: www.the-factory.co.uk
contact: Tim Chorlton
info: Affordable and creative design, marketing and photography. Have produced posters and photography for bands previously.

Feel Design Ltd.
2 South Barn, Midgeley Lane, Goldsborough, North Yorkshire, HG5 8NJ
tel: 01423 860733
email: info@feeldesign.co.uk
web: www.feeldesign.co.uk
contact: James Blundell
info: Established multimedia/web/graphics company with clients ranging from small businesses up to large companies including British Telecom. One-stop shop for websites, CD/promotional design and video/DVD production.

Gate 9 (Design)
9 St. Helen's Gate, Almondsbury, Huddersfield, HD4 6SD
tel:	01484 422 233
email:	info@gate9.com
web:	www.gate9.com
info:	Full design and print service available.

the **Graphic Attic Ltd**

The Graphic Attic
12 Dragon Parade, Harrogate, HG1 5HX
tel:	01423 509 170
fax:	01423 538 328
email:	info@graphicattic.co.uk
web:	www.graphicattic.co.uk
contact:	Ian Ladley
info:	Offers a range of design services to suit any budget

including web design and poster and flyer printing.

Green Graphics
17 Shepherds Grove, Deighton, Huddersfield, HD2 1JY
tel:	07859 067 067
email:	greengraphics1@ntlworld.com
contact:	Wayne Green
info:	Green Graphics specialise in advertising and

illustrations. High impact and low cost.

The Ground Floor Design Ltd.
Springhead Mills, Springhead Road, Oakworth, Keighley, BD22 7RX
tel:	0845 009 1733
email:	info@thegroundfloor.co.uk
web:	www.thegroundfloor.co.uk
info:	Design service covering all media including print, CD

artwork and web design.

Howarth McSwain Ltd.
Provincial House, Solly Street, Sheffield, S1 4BB
tel:	0114 221 8811
web:	www.hmdesigners.com
info:	Howarth McSwain can produce all styles of illustration

for album sleeves and posters.

Jahdo
8 Heath Street, Bingley, BD16 2NX
tel:	07906 937 654
email:	info@jahdo.com
web:	www.jahdo.com
contact:	Oliver Bond
info:	Web design company who can produce websites to WC3

standard. Bespoke design service with 10 years net experience.

Jammy
St. Michael's Hall, 11 Bennett Road, Leeds, LS6 3HN
tel:	0113 278 4110
email:	info@jammydesign.com
web:	www.jammydesign.com
contact:	Sarah Jarman
info:	Design solutions for promotional flyers, posters and

album artwork. Have worked with bands before.

Jooce Ltd.
Unit 3a, Wharfdale Road, Euroway Industrial Estate, Bradford, West Yorkshire, BD4 6SG
tel:	01274 686 574
email:	info@jooce.fslife.co.uk
contact:	Steve Evans
info:	Can produce many types of print based media including

posters, flyers and album artwork.

Leading Website Design
4 Fernbank Drive, Bingley, BD16 4HB
tel:	01274 788 045
email:	info@leadingwebsitedesign.co.uk
web:	www.leadingwebsitedesign.co.uk
contact:	Sean
info:	Professional and affordable internet specialists who can

provide web design and hosting, e-commerce solutions and custom internet applications.

Luke Drodz
Leeds
email:	lukedrodz@hotmail.com
info:	All manner of hand-drawn design and artwork from gig

posters to album covers. Works on sliding scale to client's budgets and needs. For examples of Luke's artwork see www.tastyfanzine.org.uk.

Massive Media
The Design Exchange, Little Germany, Bradford, BD1 5BD
tel:	0800 011 2830
email:	info@massive.co.uk
web:	www.massive.co.uk
contact:	Johnny Ratcliffe
info:	Dedicated to e-business and web design. Also run an

online music magazine, www.thebeatsurrender.co.uk

Mint Creative Solutions
The Studio, 16 Leamington Drive, Apperley Bridge, Bradford, BD10 9ST
tel:	0870 043 3840
email:	info@designbymint.com
web:	www.designbymint.com
info:	Creative and innovative solutions for design, print, web

and multimedia.

Orijin Business Solutions
8-8a Cow Pasture Road, Ilkley, West Yorkshire, LS29 8SR
tel:	01943 608 181
email:	adam@orijinbusiness.com
web:	www.orijinbusiness.com
contact:	Adam
info:	Web and graphic design, advertising design and general

web-related assistance.

Pencil Marks Design Ltd.
The Stables, Troy Road, Horsforth, Leeds, West Yorkshire, LS18 5SY
tel:	0113 281 9000
email:	design@pencilmarks.co.uk
web:	www.pencilmarks.co.uk
info:	Worked with bands many times and can produce

posters, flyers, leaflets and websites. See the website above for relevant email addresses and telephone numbers.

Peter Turpin Associates
George Cayley Drive, Clifton Moor, York, YO30 4XE
tel: 01904 479 511
email: enquiry@pturpin-associates.co.uk
web: www.pturpin-associates.co.uk
contact: Simon Buckle
info: Creative designs and quality printing. Can also design and build websites.

Phorm Design
36b Shambles Street, Barnsley, S70 2SQ
tel: 01226 770 303
email: simon@phormdesign.co.uk
web: www.phormdesign.co.uk
contact: Simon Griffiths
info: Phorm Design has created posters and flyers for many of the larger bars and clubs in Sheffield. It also has an associated photo studio and has worked with clients such as Hed Kandi and Misteeq.

Picturedrum Strategic Design Consultants
292 Tadcaster Road, York, YO24 1ET
tel: 01904 700 673
email: info@picturedrum.com
web: www.picturedrum.com
contact: Ashley McGovern
info: Picturedrum has a wealth of experience working with bands and specialises in website design and design to print.

Polyweb Design
Unit 2-3, 12 Whingate, Leeds, LS12 3BL
tel: 0113 263 1698
email: steve@polywebdesign.com
web: www.polywebdesign.com
contact: Steve
info: Website design, hosting and much more all at competitive prices.

Questar Communications Ltd.
Linden House, 34 Moorgate Road, Rotherham, S60 2AG
tel: 01709 371 100
email: info@questar.co.uk
web: www.questar.co.uk
info: Questar is a multimedia graphics design company who offer web design and development services, as well as PR, promotions and new media options.

Revelator
80 Market Street, Brass Castle Hill, Pocklington, York, YO42 2AB
tel: 01759 307 707
email: info@revelator.co.uk
web: www.revelator.co.uk
info: Design for web and print. Experienced in CD artwork design. Also offer band photography services. See entry for Mark Pierce Photography in relevant section for details.

Richard Carr
12 Beckbridge Green, Normanton, West Yorkshire, WF6 1QL
tel: 07834 825 304
email: richcarr02@hotmail.com
info: Designer looking to work with bands and musicians. Fully qualified in web and graphic design.

S & L Designs
Raylor Centre, James Street, York, YO10 3DW
tel: 01904 438 703
email: action@s-ldesigns.co.uk
web: www.s-ldesigns.co.uk
info: Willing to work with bands. See the website for further details.

S.P.J. Marketing
Oak Lodge, 48 Wroot Road, Finningley, Doncaster, DN9 3DR
tel: 01302 772 288
fax: 01302 772 208
email: simon@spjmarketing.co.uk
web: www.spjmarketing.co.uk
contact: Simon Judge
info: Graphic design and print. Some experience in the music industry.

Spiltmilk
Higgin Chamber, Boulderclough, Luddendenfoot, Halifax, HX2 6JS
tel: 01422 881 353
email: lee@spiltmilk-ad.com
contact: Lee
info: Can provide print and web design and illustrations.

Synthetic Dominion Ltd.
4 Old Vicarage Close, Cottingley, Bingley, BD16 1RZ
tel: 0870 751 2868
email: info@sydo.net
web: www.sydo.net
info: Multi-disciplined graphic design company who can design and produce posters, flyers, album artwork and websites.

Thain Design
4 Gordon Avenue, Harrogate, North Yorkshire, HG1 4RD
tel: 01423 886 021
email: jeremy.thain@btinternet.com
contact: Jeremy Thain
info: Print and web design. Keen to work with bands and musicians.

Triangle Multimedia
1a Whip-Ma-Whop-Ma Gate, York, YO1 8BL
tel: 01904 610 783
email: music@trianglemultimedia.com
web: www.trianglemultimedia.com
contact: Mike Brown
info: Creative web design including e-commerce sites, web hosting, domain names, web promotions and marketing.

Wafty Crank
24 Lime Tree Avenue, York, North Yorkshire, YO32 4BE
tel: 07753 327 826
email: tim.johnson@waftycrank.co.uk
web: www.waftycrank.co.uk
contact: Tim Johnson
info: Offer website design and graphic design services for bands and musicians. Wafty Crank also run a record label, as well as promoting gigs in York. See entries in relevant sections for further details.

Website World
13 Furnival Gate, Sheffield, S1 4HW
tel: 0114 275 0923
email: info@website-world.co.uk
web: www.website-world.co.uk
info: High street store providing custom websites from £295.
Free website price guide, website re-design service and after sales
support packages.

Wonkey Monkey
127 Lanetop, Linthaite, Huddersfield, HD7 56G
tel: 01484 321 111
email: info@wonkeymonkey.com
web: www.wonkeymonkey.com
info: Has worked with local unsigned bands in the past and
is in a band himself. Very willing to work with bands and musicians
again. Able to offer web design and graphic design.

NORTHERN IRELAND

Atto
1 Exchange Place, Belfast, County Antrim, BT1 2NA
tel: 028 9027 8338
email: info@helloatto.com
web: www.helloatto.com
info: Worked with bands before, including graphic and web
design.

Bradbury Design
Bradbury Bureau, Equality House, 6-14 Donegall Pass, Belfast, BT7 1BS
tel: 028 9023 3535
fax: 028 9057 2057
email: production@bradbury-graphics.co.uk
web: www.bradbury-graphics.co.uk
info: Full range of design and print options. Happy to work
with any bands from the area.

Catalyst
Unit 114, Enkalon Industrial Estate, 25 Randalstown Road, Antrim,
BT41 4LD
tel: 028 9448 8251
email: info@catalyst.co.uk
web: www.catalyst.co.uk
contact: Mark
info: Website design, brochures and image consultants.

Century 23 (Belfast)
2nd Floor, 111a Woodstock Road, Belfast, BT6 8AB
tel: 0871 700 0080
email: andrew@century-23.com
web: www.century-23.com
info: Century 23 have been working in close association with
the live music, clubbing, entertainment, and leisure industries across
UK for 7 years providing both design and printed promotional products.
Band friendly. Most of the team are members of bands or DJ. Contact
for prices on flyers, posters, tickets, design, runs of CDs and vinyl. Also
have offices in Edinburgh and London.

Circle Creative Communications
75 Holywood Road, Belfast, BT4 3BA
tel: 028 9047 3747
email: info@circlecc.com
web: www.circlecc.com
contact: Julianne Parkhill
info: All aspects of graphic and website design, and CD cover
artwork.

Coppernoise
8 Cromac Avenue, Belfast, County Antrim, BT7 2JA
tel: 028 9031 1933
email: info@coppernoise.com
web: www.coppernoise.com
contact: stuart
info: Services offered by Coppernoise include graphic and
web design, event management, marketing support, PR and printing.

Cornell Design
Cornell House, 9 Hanover Street, Craigavon, County Armagh, BT1 1LT
tel: 028 3833 9100
email: neil@cornelldesignstudios.com
web: www.cornelldesignstudios.com
contact: Neil
info: Cornell Design welcomes work from musicians. Graphic
and web design, CD cover artwork.

Creative Media
Church House, 24 Dublin Road, Omagh, BT78 1HE
tel: 028 8225 5720
email: info@creativemediani.com
web: www.creativemediani.com
contact: Nuala
info: Design for posters, flyers and other promotional items.

Cybear Design
10 Kildoag Road, Killaloo, Londonderry, BT47 3TQ
tel: 028 7134 4505
email: design@cybears.co.uk
contact: Adrian Brothers
info: Wide range of print based media, as well as web design
and digital photography.

D.N.A.
17a Market Street, Magherafelt, County Londonderry, BT45 6EE
tel: 028 7963 1920
email: mail@dnacreatives.com
web: www.dnacreatives.com
contact: Fiona Coleman
info: Will work with bands for artwork, logos, websites and
posters.

Design Ethos
2 Lord Wardens View, Bangor, County Down, BT19 1GN
tel: 028 9127 5002
email: studio@designethos.co.uk
web: www.designethos.co.uk
contact: Avril Graham
info: Design Ethos have worked with bands in the past. Can
produce CD artwork, websites, flyers and general design requirements.

Design Works
5 Marcus Street, Newry, County Down, BT34 1ET
tel: 028 3083 3536
email: info@designworks-ni.com
web: www.designworks-ni.com
contact: Colin Cranney
info: Happy to work with bands and musicians, graphic
design, web design and DVD duplication.

Dickson Design Group
87 Jericho Road, Crossgar, Downpatrick, BT30 9LQ
tel: 028 4483 1183
email: info@dickson-design.co.uk
web: www.dickson-design.co.uk
contact: John Dickinson
info: Can assist with graphic design, websites, CD artworkt
and marketing.

Directions Advertising & Design
8 Favour Royal Road, Aughnacloy, County Tyrone, BT69 6BR
tel: 028 8555 7643
email: directions_ad@btconnect.com
contact: Joan
info: Has worked with bands before and would be happy to
again.

Doghouse
29a Mill Street, Comber, Newtownards, County Down, BT23 5EG
tel: 028 9187 3655
email: info@doghousecreative.co.uk
contact: Kieth
info: Mainly specialise in print based design, but has
produced CD artwork in the past.

Donaghy Design
Unit 51, Dungannon Business Park, Coalisland Road, Dungannon,
County Tyrone, BT71 6JT
tel: 028 8772 7835
email: all@donaghydesign.com
contact: Paul Donaghy
info: Previous experience of working with bands and
musicians. Contact Paul with details of your requirements.

Dooloop Design
60 Glenview Drive, Lurgan, Craigavon, County Armagh, BT66 7ET
tel: 028 3832 3778
email: info@dologos.com
web: www.dologos.com
contact: Johnathon
info: All aspects of design covered. Dooloop Design are happy
to work with bands and musicians.

Frank
135 Cromac Street, Belfast, BT2 8JE
tel: 028 9024 1033
email: frank@frankbelfast.com
web: www.frankbelfast.com
contact: Damion Cranney
info: Offer complete range of graphic design services
incorporating identity and interactive work.

GraphXstudio
31 Regent Street, Newtownards, BT23 4AD
tel: 028 9180 0944
email: george@graphxstudio.co.uk
web: www.graphxstudio.co.uk
contact: George
info: Previous experience of working with unsigned bands and always keen to take on new bands. Web and graphic design, as well as animation. All genres catered for. Can also provide video and DVD production. See relevant section for details.

Hamill Design
2b Heron Wharf, Heron Road, Belfast, BT3 9LE
tel: 028 9022 8080
email: info@hamilldesign.com
web: www.hamilldesign.com
contact: Kenney
info: Hamill Design are happy to work with musicians. Able to produce CD covers and general artwork.

Hamilton Design Practice
11 Lombard Park, Lisburn, BT28 2UJ
tel: 028 9267 7834
email: w.hamilton@btconnect.com
web: www.hamiltondesign.info
contact: W. Hamilton
info: Design work for posters, flyers and logos.

Hexagon Design
2 Redburn Square, Holywood, BT18 9HZ
tel: 028 9042 4090
email: info@hexagondesign.com
web: www.hexagondesign.com
contact: Paul Beattie
info: Design suitable for editorials, CD covers, plus general artwork. Hexagon have previous experience of working with local musicians.

Komodo
79 Magheraconluce Road, Hillsborough, County Down, BT26 6PR
tel: 028 9268 8285
email: info@komodorecordings.com
web: www.komodorecordings.com
info: Graphic design and printing services. Can provide artwork for merchandise items such as t-shirts, stickers and banners. Komodo also have recording facilities, mastering and duplication services, drum tuition, as well as organising gigs. See entries in relevant sections for further details.

Lermagh Design
4 Iona Park, Londonderry, County Londonderry, BT48 9LH
tel: 028 7136 5300
email: seamus@lermagh.com
web: www.lermagh.com
contact: Seamus
info: General design for promotional print.

Leslie Stannage Design
71-75 Donegall Pass, Belfast, BT7 1DR
tel: 028 9022 4455
email: info@l-s-d.com
web: www.l-s-d.com
contact: Roisin Mcauley
info: Carry out design work for a number of clients. Can fulfil print, web and general artwork requirements.

Mint Marketing
61 Carrickfergus Road, Ballynure, Ballyclare, County Antrim, BT39 9QJ
tel: 028 9334 2804
email: suzanne@mintmarketing.co.uk
web: www.mintmarketing.co.uk
contact: Suzanne
info: Graphic design, web design and illustrations.

New Creation.com
163-169 Donegall Road, Belfast, County Antrim, BT12 5NA
tel: 028 9026 7950
email: info@newcreation.com
web: www.newcreation.com
contact: Ronnie Maghie
info: Design agency who can also assist with advertising and new media.

Ronin GS
Cotton Court Building, Waring Street, Belfast, County Antrim, BT1 2DW
tel: 028 9032 2355
email: chris@ronin-gs.com
web: www.ronin-gs.com
contact: Chris
info: CD cover design and artwork. Previous work includes record sleeves for 'Bellcrash'.

Zoo Creative
Unit 7b, Hyde Business Park, Pennyburn Industrial Estate, Londonderry, BT48 0LU
tel: 028 7128 1355
email: ask@zoocreative.co.uk
web: www.zoocreative.co.uk
contact: Helen Quin
info: Specialise in logos, web design and printing services.

SCOTLAND

0141 Design
38 Carmunnock Road, Glasgow, G44 4UE
tel: 0141 440 7241
email: info@0141design.co.uk
web: www.0141design.co.uk
info: Will meet all graphic design and new media needs.

153 Ltd.
14 Brackendene, Houston, Johnstone, PA6 7DE
tel: 01505 615 360
email: tnb1@153.co.uk
web: www.153.co.uk
info: Web design and authoring. Can set up websites to all standards from basic requirements to advanced portals capable of taking online payments.

39 Steps
1st Floor, 22 Fleshmarket Close, Edinburgh, EH1 1DY
tel: 0131 220 3851
email: rendezvous@39stepsstudio.com
web: www.39stepsstudio.com
info: Provide designs for print and web.

The Ad Shed Ltd.
Unit 15K, The Control Tower, Perth Airport Business Park, Scone, Perth, PH2 6PL
tel: 01738 553 555
email: info@theadshed.co.uk
web: www.theadshed.co.uk
contact: Crawford Mollison
info: Graphic design and advertising.

Artist Les Clark
2 Broomhill Terrace, Aberdeen, Aberdeenshire, AB10 6JN
tel: 01224 313 332
info: All aspects of artwork and graphic design covered, as well as flyers and paintings too.

Artista
1 Cathcart Street, Ayr, Ayrshire, KA7 1BJ
tel: 01292 619 000
info: Design suitable fot posters, flyers and leaflets.

ArtWorks
Dryad Annfield, Kingskettle, Cupar, KY15 7TN
tel: 01337 831 172
email: mike@art-works.uk.com
web: www.art-works.uk.com
info: Covers all aspects of artwork and design, offering creative and illustrative solutions

Barkhaus Creative Solutions
13 West Terrace, South Queensferry, EH30 9LL
tel: 0131 331 3476
email: info@barkhaus.co.uk
web: www.barkhaus.co.uk
info: Provide print designs for flyyers, posters, leaflets. Also offer web design and hosting.

Bluekazoo Internet Services Ltd.
143 Constitution Street, Edinburgh, EH6 7AD
tel: 0131 555 1284
email: enquiries@bluekazoo.co.uk
web: www.bluekazoo.co.uk
contact: Mark Palmer
info: Affordable web design with a variety of packages available. Sites can incorporate Flash animation, message boards and facility for HTML newsletters.

Border Marketing
54 Island Street, Galashiels, TD1 1NU
tel: 01896 759 583
email: info@bordermc.co.uk
web: www.bordermc.co.uk
info: Promo materials, web design and development, and internet broadband hosting.

Brever Web Design
60a Craigour Drive, Edinburgh, EH17 7NT
tel: 0845 129 8534
email: info@breverwebdesign.com
web: www.breverwebdesign.com
info: Graphic design for print including tickets, flyers, posters, album covers and on-body CD design. Custom web design from £350. Initial consultation and quote free. Enhanced CD authoring, including songs, lyrics, pictures and biog. Audio recording and video production services provided. See relevant sections for more details.

Bulletproof ID
19 Mercat, 1103 Argyle Street, Glasgow, G3 8ND
tel: 0141 222 2079
email: info@bulletproofid.com
web: www.bulletproofid.com
info: All areas of printed and website design covered.

Century 23 (Edinburgh)
17-19 Maritime Lane, Edinburgh, EH6 6RZ
tel: 0871 700 0080
email: andrew@century-23.com
web: www.century-23.com
contact: Andrew
info: Century 23 have been working in close association with the live music, clubbing, entertainment, and leisure industries across Britain for 7 years providing both design and printed promotional products. Band friendly . Most of the team are members of bands or DJ. Contact for prices on flyers, posters, tickets, design, runs of CDs and vinyl. Also have offices in Belfast and London.

Channel 6 Multimedia
2 Torphichen Place, Edinburgh, EH3 8DU
tel: 0131 229 1109
email: bands@ch-6.co.uk
web: www.ch-6.co.uk
info: Can offer design for websites and web flyers. Work with range of clients, both small and large.

Colour Jam
Rosenhiem, Arradoul, Buckie, Moray, AB56 5AQ
tel: 01542 834 490
email: email@colourjam.com
web: www.colourjam.com
contact: Chris
info: Provides next generation websites and graphic design. Created the Highland Ultimate Band List website, see listing in Web Resources section.

Contact Multimedia
tel: 07811 038 793
email: info@cmmc.co.uk
web: www.cmmc.co.uk
info: Variety of services including web construction and design, presentations and showreels. See website for examples of work.

CYP-PS
34 Pinebank, Livingston, EH54 6EU
tel: 07810 431 590
email: www.cyp-ps.co.uk
web: info@cyp-ps.co.uk
info: All forms of web and print based design and production. Small business offering an individual approach and fair prices.

D8Web
93 Hope Street, Glasgow, G2 6LD
tel: 0141 572 0810
email: info@d8web.co.uk
web: www.d8web.co.uk
contact: James Young
info: Have provided promotional material for Belle and Sebastian. Create artwork for album covers, posters and anything music related.

Design Folk
27 Portland Road, Kilmarnock, KA1 2BT
tel: 01563 571 220
email: john@designfolk.com
info: Design for logos, CD covers, flyers, magazines, posters and adverts.

Design For Business
28 Langdykes Drive, Cove Bay, Aberdeen, AB12 3HW
tel: 01224 875 080
email: jb@design-for-business.com
web: www.design-for-business.com
info: Posters, flyers and leaflets.

Designers On The Run
Studio G7, 30-38 Dalmay Street, Leith, Edinburgh, EH6 8RG
tel: 07984 601 114
email: info@designersontherun.com
web: www.designersontherun.com
info: Design for web, print and advertising. Promotional literature also available.

Designs by Descent
7 Martins Lane, The Green, Aberdeen, AB11 6NR
tel: 01224 213 677
email: info@designsbydescent.co.uk
web: www.designsbydescent.co.uk
info: Provide identity, branding, flash animation and web design.

D-Tech
Rylenorden & Clyde Yacht Club, Rhu, Helensburgh, Dunbartonshire, G84 8NG
tel: 01436 821 501
email: info@dtechuk.com
web: www.dtechuk.com
info: All aspects of graphic design provided.

Duncan Weddell Web Services
Duncanlaw Farm, Gifford, Haddington, EH41 4PQ
tel: 0845 838 6295
email: info@duncanweddell.co.uk
web: www.duncanweddell.co.uk
info: With over 7 years commercial experience, having worked with clients including as Honda, Bank of Scotland and Famous Grouse. Free quotes available.

Dunning Design
120 Carstairs Street, Glasgow, G40 4JD
tel: 0845 055 1350
email: chris@dunningdesign.com
web: www.dunningdesign.com
info: Every type of design covered including graphic, web, multimedia and 3D.

Eden Consultancy Group
Denny Business Centre, Carronbank Crescent, Denny, FK6 6GA
tel: 0845 226 3240
email: info@edenconsultancygroup.co.uk
web: www.edenconsultancygroup.co.uk
info: Website design and magazine advertising.

Eskimo Design
48 Palmerston Place, Edinburgh, EH12 5DE
tel: 0131 625 5620
email: info@eskimoonline.com
web: www.eskimoonline.com
info: Web and printed literature design.

FGC Web Design
20 Applecross Road, Kirkintilloch, Glasgow, G66 3TJ
tel: 0141 578 1256
email: enquiries@fgcwebdesign.co.uk
web: www.fgcwebdesign.co.uk
info: Professional web design and hosting at affordable rates.

Grafyte Studios
15 William Street, Dundee, DD1 2ND
tel: 01382 220 649/07834 118 644
email: alex@grafytestudios.co.uk
web: www.grafytestudios.co.uk
contact: Alex Cowles
info: Provide entertainment website and media design services.

Grant Innes Graphic Design
100 Forfar Road, Dundee, DD4 7BG
tel: 01382 452 297
email: grantinnes@hotmail.com
info: All printed design provided.

Graphic Partners
Gladstone Court, 179 Canongate, Edinburgh, EH8 8BN
tel: 0131 557 3558
email: info@graphicpartners.co.uk
web: www.graphicpartners.co.uk
info: Multimedia design, branding and concepts. Previous clients have included Clash Magazine and Walkers.

Hamilton Design Ltd.
Royal Highland Centre, Ingliston, Newbridge, EH28 8NB
tel: 0131 335 0313
email: hamilton.design@virgin.net
web: www.hamiltondesignltd.com
info: Design for all print products and websites.

Hicksville Ltd.
1 Bruntsfield Place, Edinburgh, EH10 4HN
tel: 0131 229 9050
email: howdy@welcometohicksville.com
web: www.welcometohicksville.com
info: Hicksville is a creative agency offering graphic, print, logo and web design services, as well as illustration and photography..

The Hub Agency
The Wheatsheaf, Spiers Wharf, Port Dundas, Glasgow, G4 9TB
tel: 0141 333 0313
email: enquiries@thehubagency.com
web: www.thehubagency.com
info: Print and advertising design.

Iweave Ltd.
4 Brentham Crescent, Stirling, FK8 2AZ
tel: 01786 450 606
web: www.iweave.co.uk
contact: Bob Jones
info: Web design only, including ipix photography and database creation.

Junction Box Media Ltd.
1 Riverside Court, Island Bank Road, Inverness, IV2 4XB
tel: 01463 717 789
email: chris@junctionbox.com
web: www.junctionbox.com
info: Wesbite solutions for a variety of clients. Can build sites that both look good, and provide excellent functionality.

L & M Web Development
64 Haig Street, Grangemouth, FK3 8QF
tel: 0800 019 9322
email: lee@lmwebdevelopment.co.uk
web: www.lmwebdevelopment.co.uk
info: Offer 20% discount to bands and musicians. Wide variety of designs from internet web designs to album covers.

Lawrence Creative
1 Newton Place, Glasgow, G3 7PR
tel: 0141 333 9009
email: info@lawrencecreative.com
web: www.lawrencecreative.com
info: Experienced company offering website and new media design.

Lewis Creative Consultants
4 Quayside Mills, Leith, Edinburgh, EH6 6EX
tel: 0131 554 1286
email: postman@lewis.co.uk
web: www.lewis.co.uk
info: All aspects of print and web design covered.

Mackins
Dundee
tel: 0845 200 4582
email: info@mackins.co.uk
web: www.mackins.co.uk
info: Web design including Flash animation and 3D rendering.

Ocean 70
The Pentagon Centre, 50 Washington Street, Glasgow, G3 8AZ
tel: 0141 221 2337
email: explore@ocean70.com
web: www.ocean70.com
info: All areas of artwork and design covered.

Randak Design Consultants Ltd.
90 Mitchell Street, Glasgow, G1 3NQ
tel: 0141 221 2142
email: info@randakdesign.com
web: www.randakdesign.com
info: All areas of printed and web based media covered.

Redwing Design
7 Main Street, Stathaven, ML10 6AJ
tel: 01357 521 242
email: info@redwingdesign.net
web: www.redwingdesign.net
contact: Laughlin Allen
info: Offer website designs and advertising services for clients of all sizes.

Saunders Design Consultantcy
7 Borden Road, Glasgow, G13 1RB
tel: 0141 560 2693
web: www.saundersandsaunders.com
info: Graphic designers who can assist with web, print, logos and any other requirements.

Sensor Studios
38 Drumlanrig Street, Dumfriesshire, DG3 5LJ
tel: 01848 331 765
email: neil@sensorstudios.com
web: www.sensorstudios.com
contact: Neil Allardice
info: Offer range of design services including website, print, CD covers, skins, desktop wallpapers and e-cards.

Shacknasty Designs
16 Robertson Crescent, Neilston, Glasgow, G78 3HD
tel: 0141 560 5471
email: info@shacknastydesigns.com
web: www.shacknastydesigns.co.uk
contact: Millie
info: Creative and comprehensive design service incorporating print management, web graphics and logo design.

Smile Design
Aigan View, Benrinnes Drive, Tom-Na-Bent, Aberlour, AB38 9NQ
tel: 01340 871 725
email: help@smiledesign.co.uk
web: www.smiledesign.co.uk
contact: Zoe
info: Website design. Can also design publicity material and logos.

Sound Doctor
54 George Street, Cellardyke, Fife, KY10 3AU
tel: 07867 763 582
email: info@sounddoctor.co.uk
web: www.sounddoctor.co.uk
contact: John Wills
info: Web design service. Can also provide audio streaming websites, allowing musicians and bands to stream music on their sites without paying a monthly charge to their service providers. Sound Doctor is run by experienced musicians who are happy to assist and advise unsigned bands. Also offer sound mastering service. See entry in relevant section for details.

Source Graphic Design
36 Dalmeny Street, Edinburgh, EH6 8RG
tel: 0131 555 4334
email: info@designbysource.com
web: www.designbysource.com
info: Flyers, posters, leaflets, illustrations, folders and packs.

Tayfusion
Spalding House, 90-92 Queen Street, Broughty Ferry, Dundee, DD5 1AJ
tel: 01382 778 931
email: info@tayfusion.com
web: www.tayfusion.com
info: Web design services. Provide high quality video and music streaming and online jukeboxes.

TBDA (Scotland) Ltd.
112 John Player Building, Stirling Enterprise Park, Stirling, FK7 7RP
tel: 01786 446 004
email: tbda@tbdascot.co.uk
web: www.tbdascot.co.uk
contact: Tanya Hine
info: Web design and graphic design for print including logos and adverts.

Traffic Design Consultants Ltd.
Suite 311, The Pentagon Centre, 36 Washington Street, Glasgow, G3 8AZ
tel: 0141 204 4490
email: scott@traffic-design.co.uk
web: www.traffic-design.co.uk
contact: Scott Witham
info: Designs for print, album covers, logos and flyers.

Trinity Artwork
17 Henderson Terrace, Leuchars, St. Andrews, Fife, KY16 0EP
tel: 01334 839 176
email: info@trinity-artwork.com
web: www.trinty-artwork.com
contact: John Ryan
info: John is a musician himself. Offers web and graphic design.

Verde Design & Print
C11 Charlotte Street, Perth, PH1 5LW
tel: 01738 625 491
email: info@verdedesign.co.uk
web: www.verdedesign.co.uk
info: Illustration and design comprising web and printing requirements.

Walrus & Carpenter Ltd.
Unit 0/2, 216 Main Street, Glasgow, G40 1JU
tel: 0141 554 9945
fax: 0141 554 9945
email: info@wnc.uk.net
web: www.wnc.uk.net
info: As well as providing web and graphic design solutions, Walrus & Carpenter also offer video production. See listing in relevant section for further details.

Web Age Ltd.
The Walled Garden, Sundrum, Ayr, KA6 5LA
tel: 0870 011 6621
email: info@webage.co.uk
web: www.webage.co.uk
info: Have created a number of sites for unsigned bands. Able to create most media requirements for bands including videos.

Weesleekit
Unit 5, Ladyknowe, Moffat, Dumfriesshire, DG10 9DY
tel: 01683 221 991
email: steve@weesleekit.com
web: www.weesleekit.com
info: Collective of 3 designers based in Dumfries and Galloway. Personal and flexible service where you work directly with a designer. For examples of work, refer to above website.

West Coast Graphics
17 Struan Road, Glasgow, G44 3AT
tel: 0141 633 5307
email: don.westcoast@mac.com
info: All areas of printed media covered.

Zombie Works
1/1 The Angel Building, 12 Paisley Road West, Glasgow, G51 1LE
email: gareth@zombie-works.co.uk
web: www.zombie-works.co.uk
contact: Gillian, Gareth
info: Zombie Works is an online musicians' resource, producing high quality promotional material for bands and musicians. Provide bands and musicians with everything they need to get noticed and ensures that the right image is presented when they do. Services include photography, promo packs, video duplication and web design. See listings in relevant sections for further details.

Zoo Design
15 Terrace Road, Carnoustie, Angus, DD7 7AE
tel: 01241 410 844
email: sue@zoodesign.co.uk
web: www.zoodesign.co.uk
info: Flyers, posters, CD cover design, as well as general artwork and web design.

WALES

6721
Cambrian Buildings, Mount Stuart Square, Cardiff, CF10 5FL
tel: 02920 406 721
fax: 02920 405 100
email: math@6721.co.uk
web: www.6721.co.uk
contact: Matthew Talfan
info: Provide web, media and graphic design, as well as marketing options.

Absolute Creative Solutions Ltd.
11 Earle Place, Cardiff, CF5 1NZ
tel: 02920 228 975
fax: 02920 228 975
email: admin@absolutecreativesolutions.co.uk
web: www.absolutecreativesolutions.co.uk
info: Previous music and club experience. Web and graphic design with printing provided.

AJ Typesetters Fairways
Carmel Hill, Carmel, Holywell, CH8 8NZ
tel: 01352 710 345
fax: 01352 711 789
email: ajtypesetter@btinternet.co.uk
web: www.ajtypesetters.co.uk
contact: Jeff Jones
info: Web and graphic design and printing services.

AP: Design Matters
31 Llanfair Road, Pontcanna, Cardiff, CF11 9PZ
tel: 02920 210 570
email: info@ap-designmatters.co.uk
web: www.ap-designmatters.co.uk
contact: Anwen Pegrum
info: Design for all print including CD covers, posters and flyers. Website design, building and hosting.

Ape Design
tel: 07974 671 023
email: jon@apedesign.com
web: www.apedesign.com
contact: Jon Clee
info: Design for record and CD artwork, posters, flyers, logos and t-shirts. Also provide web graphics and t-shirts. Clients include BBC Radio1, Green Man Festival, Welsh Music Foundation, Echo, Chrysalis Music, Boobytrap, Plastic Raygun, Slowgraffiti, mykungfu, Dockrad and Complete Control Music.

Argraff
Rhos Y Corn, St. David's Road, Aberyswyth, Ceredigion, SY23 1EU
tel: 01970 611 153
fax: 01970 624 913
email: argraff@arywe.co.uk
info: Graphic design and printing service.

Black Sheep Design Consultants Ltd.
103 Bute Street, Cardiff, CF10 5AD
tel: 02920 490 722
fax: 02920 490 723
email: greatdesigns@blacksheep.info
web: www.blacksheep.info
contact: Jack Bland
info: Extensive design service incorporating web, media and graphic design along with printing, CD duplication and marketing options.

Bluesky Media Ltd.
19-21 Uplands Cresent, Uplands, Swansea, West Glamorgan, SA2 0NX
tel: 01792 473 235
fax: 01792 472 303
email: paul@bluesky-media.net
web: www.bluesky-media.net
info: Cover web, media and graphic design.

Burning Red
Suite 111, 61 Wellfield Road, Cardiff, CF24 3DG
tel: 029 2025 3915
email: info@burningred.co.uk
web: www.burningred.co.uk
info: From promotional flyers to full content management driven websites.

Chameleon Creations
14 Henrietta Street, Swansea, SA1 4HW
tel: 01792 520 073
fax: 01792 551 407
email: studio@chameleoncreationsdesign.com
web: www.chameleoncreationsdesign.com
contact: Katherine Hammill
info: Graphic and web designers. Also offer printing services. The company has lots of CD and DVD design experience.

Chameleonic Design
33 Rookwood Street, Cardiff, CF11 6PH
tel: 07967 000 823
email: nic@chameleonic-design.com
web: www.chameleonic-design.com
contact: Nic Finch
info: Chameleonic Design specialise in creating identities, logos, flyers, record covers, illustration and websites for established record labels and club promoters, as well as fledgling independent record labels, magazines and promotion companies, and bands directly. Previous clients have included Faith & Hope Records, SFDB Records, Dojo Studios and nightclubs across the UK.

Colourbox
82 Mansel Street, Swansea, West Glamorgan, SA1 5TY
tel: 01792 272 716
fax: 01792 272 716
email: studio@colourbox.info
web: www.colourbox.info
info: Design company with previous music experience designing for DJs. Deliver web design, as well as Flash animation and printing.

Daiatlas Ltd.
Home Farm, Dyffryn, Cardiff, South Glamorgan, CF5 6SU
tel: 02920 592 085
fax: 02920 593 462
email: info@daiatlas.co.uk
web: www.daiatlas.co.uk
contact: Daniel Jones
info: Lots of previous music experience. Provide graphics, web development and printing. Also provide a web marketing service.

David Ganderton
8 Cae Maen Llwyd, Cefn Hengoed, Hengoed, Mid Glamorgan, CF82 7LS
tel: 01143 819 148
email: david.ganderton@virgin.net
info: Graphic designs company.

Designis
109 Bishop Hannon Drive, Cardiff, South Glamorgan, CF5 3QU
tel: 02920 568 570
email: designers@dsl.pipex.com
web: www.designis.co.uk
contact: Isabelle Butcher
info: Purely graphic design and printing.

Designworld
59 Cowbridge Road East, Cardiff, CF11 9AE
tel: 02920 389 840
fax: 02920 235 334
email: info@design-world.org.uk
web: www.design-world.org.uk
contact: Karen Wright
info: Creative design group offering a wide range of graphic design requirements including website creation and design for print.

Digital Create
South Wales
email: info@digitalcreate.co.uk
web: www.digitalcreate.co.uk
contact: Adam Bowman
info: New media and software design company, providing design services to new and up and coming bands. Website design and build, audio streaming and delivery online. E-commerce applications.

Elfen
20 Harrawby Lane, Cardiff Bay, Cardiff, CF10 5GN
tel: 02920 484 824
email: post@elfen.co.uk
web: www.elfen.co.uk
info: Elfen offer a complete package including CD artwork, design for posters and flyers and website design.

Escape
Wommanby House, Jones Court, Wommanby Street, Cardiff, CF10 1BR
tel: 02920 645 210
fax: 02920 644 238
email: info@escapetodesign.com
web: www.escapetodesign.com
contact: Pete Surma
info: Involved in web, graphic and new media design. Also encompass printing and marketing.

The Flying Fish
Crud Yr Awel, 1 Gelnclettwr Cottage, Pontshaen, Llandysul, SA44 4TX
tel: 01545 590 404
fax: 01545 590 466
email: viv@the-flying-fish.com
web: www.the-flying-fish.com
contact: Vivian Mullett
info: Previous music experience in designing CD covers, and also provide printing and illustrating services.

Fractally Yours
29 Victoria Avenue, Craig-y-Don, Llandudno, LL30 1DQ
tel: 01492 871 822
email: delora@fractallyours.com
web: www.fractallyours.com
contact: Delora
info: Original designs, based on mathematical formulae. Each one is entirely individual. See gallery on website for examples of work.

g.dsign
62 West Street, Gorseinon, Swansea, West Glamorgan, SA4 4AF
tel: 01792 549 172
email: info@gdsign.co.uk
web: www.gdsign.co.uk
info: Previous music experience. Provide illustrations and original artwork.

GMID
3 Prospect Place, Swansea, West Glamorgan, SA1 1 QP
tel: 01792 641 350
fax: 01792 301 548
email: studio@gmid.net
web: www.gmid.net
contact: Graham Morse
info: Previous experience with music design. Design company covering graphic, web and new media design.

The Info Group
The Village Studio, Heol-y-Coed, Rhiwbina, Cardiff, CF14 6HP
tel: 02920 694 040
email: info@the-info-group.co.uk
web: www.the-info-group.co.uk
contact: David Hopkins
info: Provide web, graphics, printing and media, and also have PR experience.

jaffa;design
11 Elm Walk, Mynydd Isa, Flintshire, CH7 6XZ
tel: 01978 844 482
email: jaffadesign@btinternet.com
web: www.jaffadesign.uk.com
info: Purely graphic design company.

Jon Parsons
143 Robert Street, Milford Haven, Dyfed, SA73 2HS
tel: 01646 694 328
fax: 01646 694 328
email: jon.parsonsgraphic@talk21.com
info: Previous music experience. Purely graphics and printing.

Koncept Photography
37 Heol y Coed Rise, Brackla, Bridgend, CF31 2QD
tel: 07788 755 434
email: darren@konceptphotography.com
web: www.konceptphotography.com
contact: Darren Dobbs
info: Design for print and web. Flyers, posters and CD covers. Live photography services available. See website for examples of Darren's work.

Limegreentangerine
Studio 57, 57 Cowbridge Road East, Cardiff, CF11 9AE
tel: 02920 232 222
fax: 02920 235 222
email: info@limegreentangerine.co.uk
web: www.limegreentangerine.co.uk
info: Limegreentangerine is a multi-faceted design studio offering creative solutions at realistic prices. Specialists in branding, strategy, identity, literature, email promotions, print, new media, CD-Roms, web design, Flash websites, banner ads, brochures and screensavers.

Lynton Black Media
12 Waterhall Road, Cardiff, CF5 3LL
tel: 02920 195 300
email: lbm@lyntonblack.net
web: www.lyntonblack.net
info: Design and production of promotional material, marketing and web based media for bands and musicians.

Mary Wycherley
Cardiff
tel: 07838 191 912
email: molejwych@yahoo.com
info: Graphic design and artwork for promotional print and CD covers. Can also supply band photography. See relevant section for details.

Matrix Design Communication
Head Office, Unit 46, Addison Road Workshops, Addison Road, Port Talbot, SA12 6HZ
tel: 01639 895 694
fax: 01639 895 639
email: sales@design-matrix.co.uk
web: www.design-matrix.co.uk
info: Design for print including CD inlays, posters, flyers and brochures. Signs and banners. In-house printing.

Matthew Miles
28b St. Woolo's Road, Newport, Gwent, NP20 4GN
email: design@matthewmiles.co.uk
web: www.matthewmiles.co.uk
info: Design for print including flyers, posters and CD artwork. Can source website construction and design companies on request. Matthew has experience working within the music industry, including club flyer design and record shop branding.

Millimagic
28 Gelligaer Street, Cathays, Cardiff, CF24 4LA
tel: 02920 223 857
email: ameliananankivell@yahoo.com
web: www.milli.com
contact: Amelia Nankivell
info: Provides original artwork and design for creative individuals and small companies. Logos, flyers, illustrations, t-shirt and sleeve design. Web and graphic design with previous music experience.

Peter Gill & Associates Ltd.
256 Cowbridge Road East, Cardiff, CF5 1XG
tel: 02920 377 312
email: info@petergill.com
web: www.petergill.com
info: Design company that encompasses all aspects of design.

Polar 10 Ltd.
4 Pencisely Rise, Cardiff, South Glamorgan, CF5 1DX
tel: 02920 215 110
fax: 02920 215 122
email: info@polar10.com
web: www.polar10.com
contact: Mark Edwards
info: Multi-disciplined design company focussing on powerful visual concepts covering all aspects of design and production.

Precision Print Ltd.
Rear of 1, Pentrepoeth Road, Morriston, Swansea, SA6 6AA
tel: 01792 414 040
fax: 01792 414 242
email: info@precisionprint.co.uk
web: www.precisionprint.co.uk
info: Experienced graphic designers who can assist with all forms of printed media and website design. Also offer printing services. See listing in relevant section for further information.

Ridler Webster Ltd.
The Watermill, Felindre, Swansea, West Glamorgan, SA5 7NA
tel: 01792 700 070
fax: 01792 700 011
email: lance@ridlerwebster.co.uk
contact: Lance Webster
info: Previous experience of working with record companies. Purely graphic designs.

Sightwaves
Newton, Mid Wales
email: steve@sightwaves.co.uk
web: www.sightwaves.co.uk
info: Photography and graphic design for print such as posters, brochures, catalogues and CD artwork. Layout and production of all related artwork.

Signal Graphic Design Ltd.
Lletty Scncyn, Llanerfyl, Welshpool, Powys, SY21 0HA
tel: 01938 811 811
info: Web and graphic design, specialising in advertising.

Starfish Design
PO Box 121, Conwy, Gwynedd, LL30 9AH
tel: 01492 573 212
email: sales@starfishonline.co.uk
web: www.starfishonline.co.uk
contact: Rachel Roberts
info: Previous music experience. Focus on graphic and web design, marketing and advertising.

Stolen Name
Cardiff
email: info@stolen-name.co.uk
web: www.stolen-name.co.uk
info: Art and design services. CD covers, logos, promotional artwork and website design. Cater for bands and individuals looking for a small and unique website to showcase their work, as well as community sites and small shops and online catalogues. All websites are tailored to individual requirements and budgets.

Sweet
20 Mount Stuart Square, Cardiff, CF10 5DP
tel: 02920 436 304
email: studio@sweetcreative.co.uk
web: www.sweetcreative.co.uk
contact: Fay Blakeley
info: Graphic and web design plus printing, marketing and advertising services.

Syniad2 Ltd.
Metropole Chambers, Salubrious Passage, Swansea, West Glamorgan, SA1 3RT
tel: 01792 301 400
fax: 01792 301 405
email: info@syniad2.co.uk
web: www.syniad2.co.uk
contact: Robert Vaughan
info: Web and graphic design company with previous experience of working with bands and musicians.

Teamwork Design
5 Schooner Way, Cardiff, CF10 4DZ
tel: 02920 473 455
email: lee@teamworksdesign.com
web: www.teamworksdesign.com
contact: Mike Robinson
info: Design company with previous music experience. Also provide web design and printing services.

Waters Designs Ltd.
Digital Technium, University of Wales, Singleton Park, Swansea, SA2 8PP
tel: 01792 513 773
fax: 01792 513 774
email: info@waters-designs.com
web: www.waters-designs.com
info: Web and graphic design with printing and multimedia solutions.

Web Media Works Ltd.
72-78 Morfa Road, Swansea, SA1 2EP
tel: 01729 470 394
fax: 01792 455 176
email: info@webmediaworks.co.uk
web: www.webmediaworks.co.uk
contact: Tariq El-Hoffs
info: Web and graphic design company that also deliver animation, software and media development. Also provide printing and CD replication.

Wheelbarrow Studios
Weedon House, Risca, Newport, NP11 6HA
tel: 01633 619 902
email: info@wbarrow.co.uk
web: www.wbarrow.co.uk
contact: Terry Evans
info: Graphic, web and new media designers with previous music experience.

Wyattgraphics
5 Wren Close, St. Mellons, Cardiff, South Glamorgan, CF3 0PD
tel: 02920 337 603
web: www.wyattgraphics.co.uk
info: Design company with previous music experience. Company includes web and graphic design. Large format printing is readily available.

Zodshop
Criafolen Goch, Abercych, Boncath, Carmarthenshire, SA37 0LH
tel: 01239 711 638
email: neil@zodshop.freeserve.co.uk
web: www.zodshopdesign.co.uk
contact: Neil Buckland
info: Complete design packages for print and web. Zodshop are an environmentally sensitive design company that is run from a studio powered by renewable resources. All aspects of the job, from design to finish, are carried out using the most environmentally friendly procedures. Winner of the Wales Environmental Awards 2004 for Best Use of Energy In Business.

3.3 DISTRIBUTORS

Absolute Marketing & Distribution Ltd.
The Old Lampworks, Rodney Place, London, SW19 2LQ
tel:	020 8540 4242
email:	info@absolutemarketing.co.uk
web:	www.absolutemarketing.co.uk
contact:	Simon Wills
genre:	All Music Types Accepted
info:	Open to all music genres, although handle a lot of

Dance music. Usually deal with signed artists on labels but are open to receiving well presented and quality independent submissions.

Arabesque
Network House, 29-39 Stirling Road, London, W3 8DJ
tel:	020 8992 7732
fax:	020 8992 0340
email:	sales@arab.co.uk
web:	www.arab.co.uk
contact:	Brian Horn
genre:	Rock/Pop/Dance
info:	National and international distribution.

Audigist Digital Distribution
31 Row Street, Macclesfield, Cheshire, SK11 6UT
tel:	07939 216 031
email:	accounts@audigist.com
web:	www.audigist.com
genre:	All Music Types Accepted
info:	Audigist are an online MP3 sales company. Sign up

is free and artists receive 75p for each download. Check website for details or to sign up today.

Aura Surround Sound Ltd./Mo's Music Machine
Unit 11, Forest Business Park, Argall Avenue, Leyton, London, E10 7fB
tel:	020 8520 7264
email:	ronny@mosmusic.co.uk
web:	www.mosmusic.co.uk
contact:	Ronny Anderson
genre:	All Genres Of Dance Music accepted
info:	Large distributor of CDs (all genres) and vinyl (mainly

Dance, specialise in Old Skool).

Awal UK
PO Box 183, Sheffield, S2 4WX
tel:	0114 279 6511 (Ext 3303)
email:	info@awal.co.uk
web:	www.awal.co.uk
contact:	Paul Bower
genre:	All Music Types Accepted
info:	Digital distributor working with labels and unsigned

bands and musicians. Currently represent over 200 organisations. Assist in the aggregation, encoding and sale of music and spoken word content through digital providers such as iTunes, Napster, HMV and Virgin. For further information contact Paul Bower.

Backs Distribution
St. Mary's Works, St. Mary's Plain, Norwich, Norfolk, NR3 3AF
tel:	01603 624 290
fax:	01603 619 999
email:	info@backsrecords.co.
web:	www.shellshock.co.uk
contact:	Derek Chapman
genre:	All Music Types Accepted
info:	National distribution for all types of music.

Baked Goods Distribution
Unit 201, Ducie House, 37 Ducie Street, Manchester, M1 2JW
tel:	0161 244 5841
fax:	0161 236 3351
email:	simon@baked-goods.com
web:	www.baked-goods.com
contact:	Simon Tonkinson
genre:	Everything except mainstream Pop
info:	National and international distribution.

Blues Matters Records Distribution
PO Box 18, Bridgend, Mid Glamorgan, CF33 6YW
tel:	01656 745 028
email:	info@bluesmatters.com
web:	www.bluesmatters.com
contact:	Alan Pearce
genre:	Blues
info:	The leading UK Blues magazine, independent Blues

label and distributor.

Cadillac Jazz Distribution
15 Kings Exchange, Tileyard Road, London, N7 9AH
tel:	020 7619 9111
fax:	020 7619 0901
email:	john@cadillacjazz.co.uk
web:	www.cadillacjazz.co.uk
contact:	John Jack
genre:	Jazz
info:	Specialist in Jazz. Affiliated with labels, Cadillac Jazz

Records and Ogun Records.

Cargo Records
17 Heathmans Road, Parsons Green, London, SW6 4TJ
tel:	020 7731 5125
email:	info@cargorecords.co.uk
web:	www.cargorecords.co.uk
contact:	Craig Gogay
genre:	All Music Types Accepted
info:	Large distributor. Accept all types of music. National and

international distribution.

CM Distribution
North Works, Hook Stone Park, Harrogate, HG2 7DB
tel:	01423 888 979
fax:	01423 885 761
email:	cm@northworks.co.uk
genre:	Folk
info:	Specialists in Celtic orientated music, Folk, Blues and

Roots. Nationwide distribution.

Coalface Music Ltd.
Warwick Hall, Banastre Avenue, Heath, Cardiff, CV14 3NR
tel:	01443 675 568
email:	coalfaceorder@ffvinyl.com
web:	http://shop.bighairwhiteboy.co.uk/acatalog/
contact:	Martin
genre:	All Music Types Accepted
info:	Online store that represents Welsh labels. Also run a

label, FFVinyl. See listing in relevant section for details.

Confidential Records
Cadman Lane (off Pontefract Road), Snaith, East Yorkshire, DN14 9JR
tel: 01405 869 700
email: confidential@confidentialrecords.fsnet.co.uk
web: www.confidentialrecords.fsnet.co.uk
contact: Nev Barker
genre: All Music Types Accepted
info: Traditional and internet distribution. Always interested in new acts. Recording studio available at reduced rates for those that use Confidential to distribute. Up to 90% royalties and 75% of publishing royalties for artists. PRS and MCPS registration. Artists get an internet page (with MP3 and link to their own site where applicable). Also offer advice on marketing and promotion.

Copperplate Distribution
68 Belleville Road, London, SW11 6PP
tel: 020 7585 0357
fax: 020 7585 0357
email: copperplate2000@yahoo.com
web: www.copperplatedistribution.com
contact: Alan O'Leary
genre: All Music Types Accepted
info: Will accept all types of music, but specialise in Folk. Nationwide distribution.

Crusader Marketing Co. Ltd.
173-175 Terminus Road, Eastbourne, East Sussex, BN21 3NX
tel: 01323 749 997
fax: 01323 749 911
email: enquiries@oldtownmusic.co.uk
web: www.oldtownmusic.co.uk
contact: Peter Riley
genre: Blues/Nostalgia/Rock'n'Roll/Nostalgia/50s Retro/ Jazz

Deal Real
3 Marlborough Court, London, W1F 7EF
tel: 020 7287 7245
fax: 020 7287 7246
email: info@dealreal.co.uk
web: www.dealreal.co.uk
contact: Sef Khama
genre: R&B/Breaks & Beats/Funk/Hip-Hop
info: Premier Hip-Hop store with national distribution.

Devilfish Distribution Ltd.
Unit GH, Cooper House, 2 Michael Road, London, SW6 2AD
tel: 020 7384 1524
email: info@devil-fish.com
web: www.devil-fish.com
contact: Mark MacDonald
genre: Drum&Bass
info: National and international distribution.

Discovery Records Ltd.
Banda Trading Estate, Nurssteed Road, Devizes, Wiltshire, SN10 3DY
tel: 01380 728 000
fax: 01380 722 244
email: info@discovery-records.com
web: www.discovery-records.com
contact: Mike Cox
genre: All Music Types Accepted
info: Discovery pride themselves on making available unusual music, hard to find imports and specialist titles on record labels from around the world.

EmuBands
Studio 2, 1st Floor, Argyle House, 1103 Argyle Street, Glasgow, G3 8ND
email: info@emubands.com
web: www.emubands.com
contact: Ally Gray
genre: All Music Types Accepted
info: EmuBands is a service for unsigned bands offering web hosting and design, digital distribution into the leading download services e.g. iTunes, Napster, and online merchandise design and retailing. Open to submissions from any band or musician.

EPM
Unit 204, The Saga Centre, 326 Kensal Road, London, W10 5BZ
tel: 020 8964 4900
fax: 020 8964 9752
email: jonas@electronicpm.co.uk
web: www.epm-musiconline.com
contact: Jonas Stone
genre: Electronica
info: Digital distribution on both national and regional level. Specialising in Electronic music.

Essential Music

Stars Building, 10 Silverhill Close, Nottingham, NG8 6QL
tel: 0115 951 9864/0870 830 0683
fax: 0870 8300 0679
email: acts@african-caribbean-ents.com
web: www.african-caribbean-ents.com
contact: Isaac
genre: Reggae/African/Afro-beat/Blues/R&B/Gospel
info: National and international distribution.

F Minor

8 Commercial Mews North, 45A Commercial Road, Eastbourne, East Sussex, BN21 3XF
tel: 01323 738 763
fax: 01323 738 763
email: sales@fminor.com
web: www.fminor.com
contact: Paul Callaghan
genre: All Music Types Accepted
info: Specialise in vinyl but also carry an extremely comprehensive CD range as well. Cover all genres except Classical.

Flowsound

2 Rosebery Avenue, Tottenham, London, N17 9RY
tel: 020 8808 8554
fax: 020 8808 8554
email: rickflowsounddavey@amserve.com
contact: Rick Davey
genre: Dance/Reggae
info: Online distribution.

Forte Music Distribution

45 Buckland Road, Lower Kingswood, Tadworth, Surrey, KT20 7DN
tel: 01737 833 858
email: info@fortedistribution.co.uk
web: www.fortedistribution.co.uk
contact: Scott Stewart
info: National and regional independent distribution.

Holier Than Thou

46 Rother Street, Stratford Upon Avon, Warwickshire, CV37 6LT
tel: 01789 268 661
email: httrecords@aol.com
web: www.holierthanthou.co.uk
contact: David Begg
genre: Rock
info: HTT will release and distribute an artist's soundtrack, on the condition that the soundtrack is of a commercially viable standard. For full details of all services visit the website.

Iron Man Records

PO Box 9121, Birmingham, B13 8AU
tel: 0871 226 0910
email: via website
web: www.ironmanrecords.co.uk
contact: Mark Badger
info: Iron Man Records runs a small internet based mail order distribution to help make available and promote new music. Send SAE for a list. Iron Man Records is a small independent record label, linked with Badger Promotions who organise gigs throughout Birmingham and the surrounding area. See listing in relevant section for details.

K-Tel Entertainment (UK) Ltd.

12 Fairway Drive, Greenford, London, UB6 8PW
tel: 020 8747 7550
fax: 020 8575 2264
email: info@k-tel-uk.com
web: www.kteluk.com
contact: Janie Weber
genre: 50s Retro/Rock 'n' Roll/Country
info: Specialists in 50s, 60s, 70s and Rock'n'Roll music.

Kudos Distribution

77 Fortess Road, Kentish Town, London, NW5 1AG
tel: 020 7482 4555
fax: 020 7482 4551
email: mailorder@kudosrecords.co.uk
web: www.kudosrecords.co.uk
contact: Danny Ryan
genre: All Music Types Accepted
info: Deal with all kinds of music. National and international distribution to a wide range of shops from small independents upwards.

Lasgo Chrysalis Ltd.

Unit 2, Chapmans Park Industrial Estate, 378-388 High Road, London, NW10 2DY
tel: 020 8459 8800
fax: 020 8451 5555
email: info@lasgo.co.uk
web: www.lasgo.co.uk
contact: Paul Burrows
genre: All Music Types Accepted
info: Wholesale distributor of CDs, DVDs, books and vinyl to the traditional and non-traditional music market worldwide.

Mania Entertainment Group Ltd.

Media House, 34 Salisbury Street, London, NW8 8QE
tel: 020 7402 9111
fax: 020 7723 3064
email: peter@mania.net
web: www.mania.net
contact: Joanne Goldring-Cohen
genre: All Music Types Accepted
info: Online distribution.

Media UK Distribution

Sovereign House, 12 Trewartha Road, Praa Sands, Penzance, Cornwall, TR20 9ST
tel: 01736 762 826
fax: 01736 763 328
email: panamus@aol.com
web: www.songwriters-guild.co.uk
contact: Roderick Jones
genre: All Music Types Accepted/70's Psychedelia
info: Affiliated to The Guild Of International Songwriters & Composers. Record, video, DVD and AV distribution company.

Midland Record Co. Ltd.

Chase Road, Brownhills, Walsall, WS8 6JT
tel: 01543 378 222
fax: 01543 360 988
email: steve@midlandrecord.co.uk
contact: Steve Skidmore
genre: All Music Types Accepted
info: Distribute CDs and DVDs.

Musicstream Ltd.

Hesketh House, 3a School Road, Sale, Cheshire, M33 7XY
tel: 0161 973 9004
email: info@mustream.com
web: www.musream.com
contact: Tom
genre: All Music Types Accepted
info: Sales and distribution specialists for single, album and music DVDs. Deal with everything from major chains to small, independent stores. Can also organise promotion through street teams. Contact for further details. Merchandising services also available, as well as website design. See listings in relevant sections for details.

Musoswire

PO Box 100, Gainsborough, DN21 3XH
tel: 01427 628 826
email: dan@musoswire.com
web: www.musoswire.com
contact: Dan Nash
genre: All Music Types Accepted
info: Excellent service enabling artists to sell their work online at minimal cost. All genres of music are welcome and artists get continued personal involvement. Offer provisions for large and short-run duplication, CD cover design, band photography, web design and hosting. See also listing in Web Resources section for details of services provided to musicians.

Nervous Records

5 Sussex Crescent, Northolt, UB5 4DL
tel: 020 8423 7373
fax: 020 8423 7773
email: info@nervous.co.uk
web: www.nervous.co.uk
contact: Roy Williams
genre: Psychobilly/Rock'n'Roll/Rockabilly
info: Nervous are forward thinking and do not want these genres to be viewed as nostalgia only. Always interested in distributing new acts.

New Note Distribution Ltd.

Pinnacle Building, Teardrop Centre, London Road, Swanley, Kent, BR8 TS
tel: 01322 616 050
fax: 01322 615 658
email: info@newnote.com
web: www.newnote.com
contact: Graham Griffiths, Eddy Wilkinson
genre: World/Jazz/Classical/Latin
info: National distribution.

Norman Records

Unit 1, Armley Park Court, Stanningley Road, Leeds, LS12 2AE
tel: 0113 231 1114
email: phil@normanrecords.com
web: www.normanrecords.com
contact: Phil
genre: Electronica/Indie
info: National distribution.

With **over 25 years** of experience we sell **directly** to over **400 stores**, including HMV, Virgin and MVC

We export worldwide via distribution partners, and supply information to over 160 UK and European internet sites.

Contact us on:
020 8390 3322
info@novadist.net

One of the fastest growing CD and DVD distributors in the UK.

www.novadist.net

Nova Sales & Distribution (UK) Ltd.
Isabel House, 46 Victoria Road, Surbiton, Surrey, KT6 4JL
tel: 020 8390 3322
fax: 020 8390 3338
email: info@novadist.net
web: www.novadist.net
contact: Wilf Mann
genre: All Music Types Accepted
info: Nationwide distribution, all types of music accepted.

Nu Urban Music
Unit 3, Rivermead Industrial Estate, Pipers Way, Thatcham, Berkshire, RG19 4EP
tel: 01635 587 900
fax: 01635 292 314
email: info@nu-urbanmusic.co.uk
web: www.nu-urbanmusic.co.uk
contact: Tobie Scapes
genre: Urban
info: National and international distribution. Specialists in Drum&Bass.

Pinnacle Records
Hether Court, 6 Maidstone Road, Sidcup, Kent, DA14 5HH
tel: 020 8309 3600
fax: 020 8309 3892
email: enquiries@pinnacle-records.co.uk
web: www.pinnacle-records.co.uk
contact: James Bassett
genre: All Music Types Accepted
info: National and regional distribution.

Prime Direct Distribution
Unit 7, 99 Oldham Street, Manchester, M4 1LW
tel: 0161 817 3330
fax: 0161 817 2319
email: richard@primedirectdist.co.uk
web: www.primedirectdist.co.uk
contact: Richard Stewart
genre: Dance
info: Formerly Prime Distribution. Independent distributor with good contacts across the country. Offices in London, the Midlands and Manchester.

Proper Music Distribution Ltd.
The New Power House, Gateway Business Centre, Kangley Bridge Road, London, SE26 5AN
tel: 0870 444 0799
email: properinfo@proper.uk.com
web: www.properdistribution.com
contact: Malcolm Mills
genre: All Music Types Accepted
info: Cover the whole UK music market from market traders to supermarkets.

Redemption Ltd.
23a Church Street, Bloxwich, Walsall, West Midlands, WS3 3HE
tel: 01922 494 056
email: info@redemption.co.uk
web: www.redemption.co.uk
genre: Dance
info: National and international distributors. Also see Record Companies section for further details on Redemption.

Roots Records
250 Earlsdon Avenue North, Coventry, West Midlands, CV5 6GX
tel: 02476 711 935
email: rootsrecs@btclick.com
contact: Graham Bradshaw
genre: Acoustic/Folk
info: Nationwide distribution to most types of outlets.

Select Music & Video Distribution Ltd.
3 Wells Place, Redhill, RH1 3SL
tel: 01737 645 600
fax: 01737 644 065
email: aanderson@selectmusic.co.uk
web: www.selectmusic.co.uk
contact: Anthony Anderson
genre: Classical
info: The UK's leading independent distributor of Classical music on CD and DVD. Part of the Naxos Group, Select distributes many of today's leading Classical labels including Naxos, Hyperion, BIS, Naïve, BBC Legends, Collegium, Gimell and, on the DVD side, BBC-Opus Arte, TDK, Arthaus and Euroarts.

Shellshock Distribution
23a Collingwood Road, London, N15 4LD
tel: 020 8800 8110
fax: 020 8800 8140
email: info@shellshock.co.uk
web: www.shellshock.co.uk
contact: Gareth Ryan
genre: All Music Types Accepted
info: Deal with most types of music, particularly Rock, Metal and Electronica. Nationwide distribution.

Shetland Music Distribution (SMD)
128 Sandveien, Lerwick, Shetland Islands, ZE1 0RW
tel: 07880 950 248
genre: All Music Types Accepted
info: SMD are willing to consider any music to be distributed within the Shetland Isles. Also encourage the distribution of music made in the Shetlands.

Silverword Music Group (Silverwood Distribution)
16 Limetrees, Llangattock, Crickhowell, Powys, NP8 1LB
tel: 01873 810 142
email: silverwordgroup@aol.com
web: www.silverword.co.uk
contact: Kevin Holland King
genre: Folk/MOR/Easy Listening/Singer-Songwriter/ Acoustic/Guitar Based
info: Encourages emerging artists. UK and internet distribution. Package deals for new bands and artists at reasonable prices. Silverword Music Group also incorporates a record label and management company. See entries in relevant sections for further details.

Snapper Music Plc.
Unit 3, The Coda Centre, 189 Munster Road, London, SW6 6AW
tel: 020 7610 0330
fax: 020 7610 0355
email: admin@snappermusic.co.uk
web: www.snappermusic.com
contact: Johnny Wilks
genre: Blues/Rock/Pop/Indie
info: Snapper Music deal with established acts. Sub-label Believe Music signs new artists.

Soul Trader
Unit 43, Imex-Spaces Business Centre, Ingate Place, London, SW8 3NS
tel: 020 7498 0732
fax: 020 7498 0737
email: soultrader@btconnect.com
contact: Marc Lessner
genre: Hip-Hop/Leftfield Dance/Indie/R&B
info: Supplies large and small independents. Mainly deal with finished products from unsigned artists.

Southern Record Distribution
70 Lawrence Road, London, N15 4EG
tel: 020 8802 3000
email: info@southern.com
web: www.southern.com
genre: Electronica/Drum&Bass/IDM (Intelligent Dance Music)
info: Drum&Bass specialists. National distribution. Deal largely with UK labels as opposed to bands.

SRD
70 Lawrence Road, London, N15 4EG
tel: 020 8802 3000
fax: 020 8802 2222
email: info@southern.com
contact: Mark Harris
genre: All Music Types Accepted

Stern's Distribution
74-75 Warren Street, London, W1T 5PF
tel: 020 7387 5550
fax: 020 7388 2756
email: sales@sternsmusic.com
web: www.sternsmusic.com
contact: Ian Thomas
genre: Reggae/World/African/Afro-beat/Latin
info: Specialists in World, African, Latin and Reggae. National distribution.

Supabeats
Greater London
tel: 020 8469 9300
email: info@supabeats.com
web: www.supabeats.com
contact: Michelle Messam
genre: All Music Types Accepted
info: Online music distribution service.

The Talent League
9 Douglas Square, Green Way, Norten, London, SM4 5MP
tel: 020 8685 0870
email: sam@thetalentleague.co.uk
web: www.thetalentleague.co.uk
contact: Samantha Crompton
genre: All Music Types Accepted
info: National and international distribution. All types of music. The Talent League also run a management company, record label, as well as promoting gigs. See entries in relevant sections for further information.

Thames Distribution Ltd.
12 Mill Farm Business Park, Millfield Road, Hounslow, TW4 5PY
tel: 020 8898 2227
fax: 020 8898 2228
email: thames@thamesdistributionmusic.com
contact: Roger Gibbon
genre: All Music Types Accepted
info: National and international distribution.

Tuned Distribution
Unit 26, Acklam Workshops, 10 Acklam Road, London, W10 5QZ
tel: 020 8969 1355
fax: 020 8962 1342
email: info@tuned-distribution.co.uk
web: www.tuned-distribution.co.uk
contact: Lee Muspratt
genre: Dance
info: Vinyl specialists in Dance related genres including House, Hard House, Trance and Progressive.

Unique Records & Distribution
Unit 12, Lodge Bank Industrial Estate, Off Crown Lane, Horwich, Bolton, BL6 5HY
tel: 01204 479 005
email: hi@uniquedist.co.uk
web: www.uniquedist.co.uk
contact: Alan Smith
genre: All Music Types Accepted
info: Unique are wholesalers so do not sell directly to the public, but offer a good variety of services to those who wish to start a label and are always interested in listening to new material.

3.4 EQUIPMENT HIRE

EAST of ENGLAND 141 GREATER LONDON 142 MIDLANDS 146 NORTHEAST 150 NORTHWEST 151 SOUTHEAST 156 SOUTHWEST 160 YORKSHIRE 162 NORTHERN IRELAND 165 SCOTLAND 165 WALES 169

EAST of ENGLAND

ADEC Equipment Bank (Arts Development in East Cambridgeshire)
Babylon Gallery, Waterside, Ely, Cambridgeshire, CB7 4AU
tel: 01353 616 995
email: info@adec.org.uk
web: www.adec.org.uk
contact: Joanne
info: Huge range of equipment for hire through the ADEC Equipment Bank. Full list can be found on website. Available to venues, schools, colleges, theatre and drama groups, music societies and community groups. Offer significant reductions compared to commercial hire rates. See also listing in Useful Regional Organisations section for details of other services offered by ADEC.

B & H Sound Services
The Old School, Crowland Road, Eye, Peterborough, PE6 7TN
tel: 01733 223 535
fax: 01733 223 545
email: sound@bhsound.co.uk
web: www.bhsound.co.uk
contact: Peter Lister
info: Small vocal PAs to large concert rigs. Delivery and engineer also available.

Ken Stevens
MUSIC AND INSTRUMENTS

Ken Stevens Music & Instruments
Sussex Street, Cambridge, CB1 1PW
tel: 01223 367 758
fax: 01223 362 480
email: help@kenstevens.co.uk
web: www.kenstevens.co.uk
info: Range of musical instruments for sale or hire. See website for details.

Laser Lighting & Sound
39A Woodbridge Road East, Ipswich, IP4 5NQ
tel: 01473 721 690
fax: 01473 270 790
email: sales@laserlighting.co.uk
web: www.laserlighting.co.uk
contact: Allen Stimson
info: Full live audio equipment available for dry hire or with engineer. Delivery also provided.

Millers Music Centre
Sussex Street, Cambridge, CB1 1PW
tel: 01223 354 452
fax: 01223 362 480
email: help@millersmusic.co.uk
web: www.millersmusic.co.uk
info: Wide range of instruments for sale or hire. Call for quote.

Missile Entertainment
54 Kingsway, Ipswich, Suffolk, IP3 9EN
tel: 0800 783 5535/07885 286 222
email: info@missileentertainment.com
web: www.missileentertainment.com
info: Missile Entertainment hire PA rigs from 5kW to 20kW.

Patchwork Music
113 Cambridge Road, Milton, Cambridge, CB4 6AT
tel: 07974 424 063
email: toby@patchworkmusic.co.uk
web: www.patchworkmusic.co.uk
contact: Toby Mills
info: Live audio equipment available for dry hire or with technician. Delivery provided.

PDS Sound & Lighting
21 Ivatt Way Business Park, Westwood, Peterborough, PE3 7PG
tel: 01733 261 199
email: info@pdssoundandlighting.com
web: www.pdssoundandlighting.com
contact: Rob
info: PDS are a friendly and helpful company who can provide both lighting and sound equipment for hire and sale. They offer technical support or dry hire, and can deliver and collect equipment if requested.

Pearce Hire
Unit 27, Second Drove Industrial Estate, Fengate, Peterborough, PE1 5XA
tel: 01733 554 950
fax: 01733 892 807
email: info@pearcehire.co.uk
web: www.pearcehire.co.uk
contact: Andy White
info: A full dry hire service provided on PAs and rigs up to 35kW. See website for full details.

Pyramid Audio
26 Field Cottages, Timworth, Bury St. Edmunds, Suffolk, IP31 1JB
tel: 01284 728 936
email: pyramidaudio@supanet.com
contact: Ian
info: PA and sound equipment hire from 200W to 40kW. Dry hire or engineers available. Pyramid also offer a delivery and collection service if required.

The Soundhouse
Unit 6, Capital Trading Estate, Whapload Road, Lowestoft, Suffolk, NR32 1UL
tel: 01502 513 050
email: martywoods@btopenworld.com
contact: Marty or Jon
info: Small vocal PAs to large scale equipment for hire. Delivery, engineer and repairs also available.

Steve's PA Hire
Maybank, Buxton Road, Spixworth, Norwich, NR12 7BJ
tel: 01603 405 563
email: steve@stevespahire.co.uk
web: www.stevespahire.co.uk
contact: Steve
info: Complete sound system hire service for all concert events. Delivery and collection. Dry hire available if requested.

Tyco Integrated Systems
Bridge House, Saxon Way, Bar Hill, Cambridge, CB3 8TY
tel: 01954 784 040
info: Large live audio systems available for hire.

GREATER LONDON

10 Out Of 10
14 Forest Hill Business Centre, Clyde Vale, London, SE23 3JF
tel: 0845 123 5664
fax: 020 8699 8968
email: sales@10outof10.co.uk
web: www.10outof10.co.uk
info: Sound and lighting equipment for sale and hire. See website for rates.

A1 Pro Equipment Hire
153 London Road, Ewell, KT17 2BT
tel: 0800 018 7278
email: info@a1proents.com
web: www.a1proents.com
info: Musical equipment and PA systems for hire. Soundsystems, disco and karaoke.

Abbey Music
Lodge Hill, Abbeywood, London, SE2 0AY
tel: 020 8312 4916
email: info@abbeymusicstudios.co.uk
web: www.abbeymusicstudios.co.uk
info: Sound system hire for any sized venue. Dry hire for smaller items. 30k PA available suitable for use at small festivals and concerts. Contact Abbey Music for prices. Also have rehearsal and recording studios. See relevant sections.

All Safe And Sound
London Business Innovation Centre, Mollison Avenue, Enfield, Middlesex, EN3 7XU
tel: 020 8350 7607
email: info@allsafeandsound.co.uk
web: www.allsafeandsound.co.uk
info: Outdoor PA, audio-visual and lighting hire. Dry hire available.

Amazon Sound
2 Fife Road, London, N22 5EG
tel: 07971 203 821
email: greg@amazonsound.demon.co.uk
info: PA systems for hire.

AT Sound Hire
264 Woodcote Road, Wallington, Surrey, SM6 0QE
tel: 020 8669 9984
email: info@atsound.co.uk
web: www.atsound.co.uk
info: AT Sound Hire usually hire to events organisers rather than individual bands, but may be able to help you depending on your particular needs.

Atlantic Hire Services
4 The Limes, North End Way, London, NW3 7HG
tel: 020 8209 0025
info: PA, backline, lighting and studio equipment for hire.

Audio & Acoustics
United House, North Road, London, N7 9DP
tel: 020 7700 2900
fax: 020 7700 6900
email: aaaco@aol.com
info: PA systems for hire. Dry hire available.

Audio Energy
16 Concord House, Park Lane, Tottenham, London, N17 0JQ
tel: 0845 644 2820
fax: 0845 644 2821
email: info@audioenergy.co.uk
web: www.audioenergy.co.uk
contact: Chad Jenner
info: PA hire with or without engineer.

Audio Village Ltd.
1 Nesta Road, Woodford Green, IG8 9RG
tel: 020 8504 2820
email: vernon@audiovillage.tv
web: www.audiovillage.tv
info: Audio Village provide full service audio equipment hire, including engineer and drop off/pick up.

Audio Visual Machines
Phoenix House, 2 Upper Teddington Road, Kingston, Surrey, KT1 4DY
tel: 020 8746 2744
email: info@avmachines.com
web: www.avmachines.com
info: PA and plasma screens for hire.

Audiohire
133-137 Kilburn Lane, London, W10 4AN
tel: 020 8960 4466
email: admin@audiohire.co.uk
web: www.audiohire.co.uk
info: PA, lighting and recording equipment for hire as well as selected instruments.

Autography Sound Recording Ltd.
2 Spring Place, London, NW5 3BA
tel: 020 7485 4515
fax: 020 7284 1233
email: hire@autograph.co.uk
web: www.autograph.co.uk
info: PA systems for hire. Call for details.

Better Sound Ltd.
31 Cathcart Street, Kentish Town, London, NW5 3BJ
tel: 020 7482 0177
fax: 020 7482 2677
email: admin@bettersound.co.uk
web: www.bettersound.co.uk
contact: Peter Dodson
info: Better Sound hire equipment such as microphones, recorders and small mixers. Dry hire only. Delivery in and around London. Repairs also available.

Britannia Row Productions Ltd.
9 Osiers Road, Wandsworth, London, SW18 1NL
tel: 020 8877 3949
fax: 020 8874 0182
email: info@britanniarow.com
web: www.britanniarow.com
contact: Bryan Grant
info: PA equipment available for hire. Delivery service and repairs.

Capital Hire
Unit P1, Metropolitan Business Centre, Enfield Road, London, N1 5AZ
tel: 0800 195 6954
email: sales@capitalhire.com
web: www.capitalhire.com
info: Staging, PA and DJ equipment for hire. Drop off/pick up available. See website for prices and an online order form.

Capital Sound Hire Productions
Abacus House, 60 Weir Road, London, SW19 8UG
tel: 020 8944 6777
fax: 020 8944 9477
email: info@capital-sound.co.uk
web: www.capital-sound.co.uk
contact: Paul Timmins
info: Equipment hire for live shows.

Centre Stage
Unit 1B, Atlas Business Centre, Oxgate Lane, London, NW2 7HJ
tel: 020 8208 1033
fax: 020 8208 1055
email: centre.stage@virgin.net
contact: Graham Baker
info: Live sound equipment available for hire.

Chilli Sound Systems
300 Caledonian Road, Islington, London, N1 1BB
tel: 07973 500 651
email: info@chillisound.co.uk
web: www.chillisound.co.uk
info: PA systems for Dance music events available for hire. Also have office based in Brighton. See entry in South East region for details.

Class Ltd.
837 Garratt Lane, London, SW17 0PG
tel: 020 8944 1400
email: sales@classdisco.co.uk
web: www.classdisco.co.uk
info: PA systems and lighting equipment for hire.

DB Audio
Unit 1b, Atlas Business Centre, Oxgate Lane, London, NW2 7HJ
tel: 020 8208 1771
info: Range of audio equipment for hire.

Decibel Audio Ltd.
Unit 19, Greenwich Business Park, Norman Road, Greenwich, London, SE10 9QF
tel: 0845 128 4185
fax: 0845 128 4187
email: info@decibel-audio.co.uk
web: www.decibel-audio.co.uk
contact: Ali Ghassemi
info: Range of live audio equipment available for hire.

THE HAMMOND HIRE COMPANY

WITH OVER 31 YEARS OF EXPERIENCE

WE ARE EUROPES LEADING VINTAGE KEYBOARD COMPANY HIRE REPAIRS AND SALES 24 HOURS A DAY 7 DAYS A WEEK

020 7288 0037

organs@www.hammondhire.com

www.hammondhire.com

Delta Sound Inc. (UK) Ltd.
Unit 2, St. George's Estate, Richmond Road, Kingston upon Thames, Surrey, KT2 5BQ
tel: 020 8481 0500
fax: 020 8481 0501
email: enquire@deltasound.co.uk
web: www.deltasound.co.uk
contact: Paul Keating
info: Dry hire and delivery of live audio equipment.

Dobson Sound Productions
66 Windsor Avenue, London, SW19 2RR
tel: 020 8545 0202
fax: 020 8543 3646
contact: Paul Dobson
info: Dry hire and delivery service for live audio equipment.

E1 Audio
30 Jackman House, London, E1 2PU
tel: 020 7511 9686/07790 003 931
email: info@e1audio.co.uk
web: www.e1audio.co.uk
info: Sound, lighting and PA systems for hire. Dry hire and drop off/pick up available. E1 hire out a 2kW 4 speaker rig, which fits in the back of a car.

Early Riser Disco Centre
50-52 Beulah Road, London, E17 9LQ
tel: 020 8520 3401
email: sales@earlyriser.co.uk
web: www.earlyriser.co.uk
info: PA, disco and karaoke equipment available.

Ed Bassett Music Ltd.
23 The Swan Centre, Rosemary Road, London, SW17 0AR
tel: 020 8947 0025/07836 553 765
email: mail@edbassett.com
web: www.edbassett.com
info: PA systems for hire.

Encore Group Ltd.
Unit 8, Perivale New Business Centre, 19 Wadsworth Road, Perivale, Greenford, UB6 7LF
tel: 020 8991 2612
fax: 020 89912616
email: mick@encore.demon.co.uk
contact: John Tinline
info: Live audio equipment for dry hire, delivery service available.

Entec Sound & Light
517 Yeading Lane, Northolt, Middlesex, UB5 6LN
tel: 020 8842 4004
fax: 020 8842 3310
email: sales@entec-soundandlight.com
web: www.entec-soundandlight.com
contact: Dick Hayes
info: Dry hire and delivery available on live sound equipment. DB AudioTechnics partner.

FX Music
Unit 1B, Atlas Business Centre, Oxgate Lane, Staples Corner, London, NW2 7HJ
tel: 020 8208 1771
fax: 020 8208 1883
email: sales@fx-music.co.uk
web: www.fx-music.co.uk
contact: Dave Beck
info: Sound equipment hire, mainly for big events. Delivery service and dry hire also available.

FX Rentals
38-40 Telford Way, London, W3 7XF
tel: 020 8746 2121
email: info@fxgroup.net
web: www.fxgroup.net
info: FX Rentals has the largest stock of audio equipment for hire in Europe. Supply range of audio equipment, PA, instruments, studio and audio-visual gear, as well as backline, recorders, microphones, video and location equipment. Available 24 hours a day. Call for details of pricing. Discounts on hire charges are available to regular customers, in addition to discounts for longer hires.

Gighire
Unit 8, Print Village, 58 Chadwick Road, London, SE15 4PU
tel: 020 7732 4141
fax: 020 7732 7337
email: info@noise.demon.co.uk
web: www.systemsetc.co.uk
contact: Bernard Mani
info: Full hire and sales service for audio and visual equipment. Dry hire and delivery also available.

The Hammond Hire Company
Islington, London
tel: 020 7288 0037
email: organs@hammondhire.com
web: www.hammondhire.com
contact: Tiny Evans
info: Hammond Hire is the specialist UK company for Hammond Tonewheel Organs, classic keyboards and analogue synths.

Harris Hire
London
tel: 020 8663 1807
fax: 020 8658 2803
email: info@harris-hire.co.uk
web: www.harris-hire.co.uk
info: Extensive range of instruments and backline for hire.

IFH Hire
49 Liddington Road, London, E15 3PL
tel: 020 8536 0649
fax: 07092 022 897
email: ian@soundengineer.co.uk
web: www.soundengineer.co.uk
info: PA, mics, speakers, amps and mixers for hire. Dry hire available.

John Henry's
16-24 Brewery Road, London, N7 9NH
tel: 020 7609 9181
fax: 020 7700 7040
email: info@johnhenrys.com
web: www.johnhenrys.com
contact: John Henry
info: Massive range of live audio equipment available for hire. Provided equipment for Later with Jools Holland and Top of the Pops amongst others. See website for more details.

Keith Monks Sound Systems
Brodrick Hall, Brodrick Road, London, SW17 7DY
tel: 020 8682 3456
email: info@cunnings.co.uk
web: www.cunnings.co.uk
info: Wide range of audio equipment for hire. Sales and installations as well. See the website for detailed listings.

KMR Audio Ltd.
1375 High Road, Whetstone, London, N20 9LN
tel: 020 8445 2446
fax: 020 8369 5529
email: sales@kmraudio.com
web: www.kmraudio.com
contact: Niki Melville-Rogers
info: Provided audio equipment for Live 8. Offers both dry hire or with engineer. Sales, repair and delivery also available.

Knight Sound & Light
98-100 Uxbridge Road, London, W7 3SU
tel: 020 8579 0144
email: info@knightsoundandlight.com
web: www.knightsoundandlight.com
info: PA and recording equipment for hire. Dry hire and drop off/pick up available.

Lymelyte Concert & PA Media
4 The Marbles, 20 Grosvenor Terrace, London, SE5 0DD
tel: 020 7708 2544
email: info@lymelyteconcert.com
web: www.lymelyteconcert.com
info: Range of PA equipment for hire.

Martin Bradley Sound & Light
69a Broad Lane, Hampton, TW12 3AX
tel: 020 8979 0672
email: ms1bradley@aol.com
info: Sound equipment for live music events. Complete Audio service including engineer and drop off/pick up.

MCQ Entertainments Ltd.
218 Walworth Road, London, SE17 1JE
tel: 020 7701 3204
fax: 020 7237 6290
email: mcqentltd@btconnect.com
web: www.mcqentltd.co.uk
info: DJ equipment for hire.

Music Bank (Hire) Ltd.
1st Floor, Building D, Tower Bridge Business Complex, 100 Clements Road, London, SE16 4DG
tel: 020 7252 0001
fax: 020 7231 3002
email: nunu@musicbank.org
web: www.musicbank.org
contact: Nunu Whiting
info: Live audio equipment and backline available for hire. Also run rehearsal rooms, Waterloo Sunset Studios, and transport hire, Direct Tour Hire. See listings in relevant sections for details.

The Music Room
The Old Library, 116-118 New Cross Road, London, SE14 5BA
tel: 020 7252 8271
fax: 020 7252 8252
email: sales@musicroomsolutions.com
web: www.musicroom.web.com
info: Sound systems and instrument hire, as well as lighting, DJ equipment and audio visual services for gigs and rehearsals. Complete production and/or dry hire available. For details of The Music Room's rehearsal studio and recording facilities see the relevant sections.

OCR Roadcrew
75 Totteridge Road, Enfield, Middlesex, EN3 6NG
tel: 07899 913 595
contact: Simon Williamson
info: Full production equipment. No dry hire. Delivery service provided.

Orbital Sound Ltd.
57 Acre Lane, Brixton, London, SW2 5TN
tel: 020 7501 6868
email: hire@orbitalsound.co.uk
web: www.orbitalsound.co.uk
info: PA systems for hire.

The PA Company
Unit 7, The Ashway Centre, Elm Crescent, Kingston Upon Thames, Surrey, KT2 6HH
tel: 020 8546 6640
fax: 020 8547 1469
contact: Doug Beveridge
info: Dry hire or with engineer. Hire on small PAs to larger events. Delivery service available.

Pandora Productions
Unit 38, Hallmark Trading Centre, Fourth Way, Wembley, Middlesex, HA9 0LB
tel: 020 8795 2432
fax: 020 8795 2431
email: pandoraprods@btconnect.com
info: Sound and lighting equipment for hire. Dry hire available.

Pro Acoustic
180 Finchley Road, London, NW3 6BP
tel: 020 7794 5151
email: info@proacoustic.co.uk
web: www.proacoustic.co.uk
info: PA, sound equipment and lighting for hire.

PW Enterprises
3 Barnfield Avenue, Shirley, Croydon, CR0 8SF
tel: 020 8654 8546
fax: 020 8654 8546
info: Sound and lighting equipment for hire. Dry hire available. Call for more details.

Rapture PA & Sound Systems
46 Merton Road, London, SE25 5ND
tel: 020 8764 3486
email: rapturemac@hotmail.com
info: PA (10kW) and DJ equipment available for hire, for both indoor and outdoor venues.

re:creation sound
Unit B2, 83 Copers Cope Road, Beckenham, Kent, BR3 1NR
tel: 020 8658 2260
fax: 020 8658 2261
email: office@recreationsound.co.uk
web: www.recreationsound.co.uk
info: PA systems, audio-visual and lighting for gigs and outdoor events.

RG Jones Sound Engineering
26 Endeavor Way, Wimbledon, London, SW19 8UH
tel: 020 8971 3100
fax: 020 8971 3101
email: enquiries@rgjones.co.uk
web: www.rgjones.co.uk
contact: John Carroll
info: Anything from small PAs to large scale festival equipment. Full service provided including engineer, delivery, sales and repair.

RNSS Ltd.
South Bank Centre, Belvedere Road, London, SE1 8XX
tel: 020 7593 0011
fax: 020 7928 9059
email: office@rnss.net
web: www.rnss.net
contact: Andy Cotton
info: Live audio equipment available for hire with engineer including delivery and service.

Rooz Studios
2a Corsham Street, London, N1 6DP
tel: 020 7490 1919
info: A range of equipment available for hire. Rooz also run a rehearsal studio complex, as well as tour bus hire service. See entries in relevant sections for further details.

Roy Truman Sound Services
Unit 23, Atlas Business Centre, Oxgate Lane, London, NW2 7HJ
tel: 020 8208 2468
fax: 020 8208 3320
email: rtss@london.com
contact: Elisabeth Wirrer
info: A range of PAs and audio equipment available for hire with or without engineer. Delivery service.

SBN International
38 Hayward Court, Studley Road, Stockwell, London, SW4 6QW
tel: 07854 168 848
email: sbnjinkz2sbn@hotmail.com
contact: Jinkz
info: Sound engineer who can work live or in the studio.

Sensible Rentals Ltd.
Rebond House, 98-124 Brewery Road, London, N7 9PG
tel: 020 7700 6655
fax: 020 7609 9478
email: info@sensiblerentals.com
web: www.sensiblerentals.com
contact: Johnny Henry
info: Live audio equipment available for hire with delivery service. Engineers and repairs also offered.

Sound Directions Ltd.
18 Colville Road, London, W3 8BL
tel: 020 88963 555
email: info@sounddirections.co.uk
web: www.sounddirections.co.uk
info: Sound Directions distribute specialist speaker systems and media playback devices for background to foreground music, public address, information points, audio marketing, and other audio applications.

The Sound Division Group
Montague House, 389 Liverpool Road, Islington, London, N1 1NP
tel: 020 7609 3999
fax: 020 7609 1310
email: hire@soundivision.com
web: www.soundivision.co.uk
contact: Chris Baxter
info: Full range of audio production equipment available for hire including delivery service.

Sound Force UK
44 Church Road, Crystal Palace, London, SE19 2ET
tel: 0870 609 2497
fax: 020 8771 1555
email: soundforce.london@virgin.net
web: www.soundforceuk.co.uk
info: Sound Force UK hire a wide range of equipment including amps, speakers and processors. Dry hire. Drop off/pick up service, as well as set up.

SRD Group Ltd. (London)
78 York Street, London, W1H 1DP
tel: 020 7043 4136
fax: 020 7101 0378
email: info@srdgroup.co.uk
web: www.srdgroup.co.uk
contact: Stuart Roberts
info: Small vocal PAs to large scale outdoor equipment available for hire. Repairs offered. No delivery. Also branch based in Kent. See listing in South East region for details.

Studiohire
8 Dalham Mews, London, NW3 5DB
tel: 020 7431 0212
fax: 020 7431 1134
email: mail@studiohire.net
web: www.studiohire.net
info: Backline, PA (range of sizes), lighting and instrument hire. Studiohire have an enormous stock of vintage analogue synthesizers, pianos and organs available for hire. Dry hire and drop off/pick up available.

Systems Etc Ltd.
Unit 8, Print Village, Chadwick Road, London, SE15 4PU
tel: 020 7732 3377
fax: 020 7732 7337
email: info@noise.demon.co.uk
web: www.systemsetc.co.uk
info: Systems Etc specialise in system hire, sound installation, as well as sound and lighting sales from home systems to major events. System Etc is also a live events co-ordinator.

Terminal Studios Hire
4-10 Lamb Walk, London Bridge, London, SE1 3TT
tel: 020 7403 3050
fax: 020 7407 6213
email: pa@terminal.co.uk
web: www.terminal.co.uk
contact: Charlie Barrett
info: Full range of audio equipment available for hire from small PAs to large scale systems. Delivery, sales and repairs also available. Terminal also run rehearsal rooms. See listing in relevant section for details.

Thames Audio Ltd.
3 Kimber Road, London, SW18 4NR
tel: 020 8870 4456
fax: 020 8870 7456
email: info@thamesaudio.co.uk
web: www.thamesaudio.co.uk
contact: Peter Cox
info: Range of PAs available with or without engineer. Sales, delivery and repair also available.

Tickle Music Hire
The Old Dairy, 133-137 Kilburn Lane, London, W10 4AN
tel: 020 8964 3399
fax: 020 8964 0343
email: slae@ticklemusichire.com
web: www.ticklemusichire.com
contact: Jerry Evans
info: Huge range of audio equipment available for hire from small vocal PAs to synths and amps. Check website for details.

Trafalgar Lighting
9-10 Northway, London, N9 0AD
tel: 020 8887 0082
fax: 020 8887 0072
email: hire@trafalgarlighting.co.uk
web: www.trafalgarlighting.co.uk
contact: Allen Paulus
info: Some PAs but mostly lighting available for hire. Delivery, installation and sales also offered.

Ultrasound Professional Audio Systems
60 Reynolds Avenue, Romford, RM6 4NS
tel: 020 8599 6690
fax: 07092 221 523
email: sales@ultrasoundpro.com
web: www.ultrasoundpro.com
contact: Vince Gray
info: Full range of audio equipment available for hire with or without engineer. Delivery service.

Up All Night Music
Top Floor, 20 Denmark Street, London, WC2H 8NA
tel: 020 7419 4696/020 7419 4697
fax: 020 7419 4698
email: info@upallnightmusic.com
web: www.upallnightmusic.com
info: PA, sound and stage crew. Full details of packages available can be found on the website. Up All Night Music also promote gigs at several venues in London, as well as providing management services to up and coming acts. Refer to relevant sections for further details.

Vampire Music
20 Tanners Hill, Deptford, London, SE8 4PJ
tel: 020 8691 6666
fax: 020 8692 9999
email: info@vampiremusic.co.uk
web: www.vampiremusic.co.uk
info: Vampire Music has a fully comprehensive service and are constantly upgrading their equipment. In addition to PA and backline hire, they can supply a full range of drum kits, guitar and bass amplifiers, microphones, effects and processing units, DAT machines, stage monitoring, mixing desks, pro-turntables and CD decks. Dry hire available. Vampire Music also incorporates recording studios, rehearsal rooms, music shop, CD duplication, as well as design and tuition services. See entries in relevant sections for details.

Vegas Sound House
Unit 39, Silicone Business Centre, 28 Wadsworth Road, Perivale, Middlesex, UB6 7JZ
tel: 020 8998 9122
fax: 020 8991 2661
email: loz@vegassoundhouse.com or matt@vegassoundhouse.com
web: www.vegassoundhouse.com or www.lozvegasmusic.co.uk
info: Equipment hire including range of backline, drums and PA. Mobile recording unit also available. Low rental rates are offered to bands who use the on-site rehearsal facilities regularly. Vegas Sound House also run a music shop under the same name, recording and rehearsal studios 'Loz Vegas Studios', promotions and booking agency 'Music Scene UK', 'Music Providers' management, 'Some Think Media' media design company, as well as running the Drum Academy. See entries in relevant sections for further information.

Wax Unlimited
9 Northwold Road, London, N16 7HL
tel: 020 7275 7513
email: wax@waxattacks.com
info: PA and sound system hire. Drop off and pick up available.

MUSIC SERVICES/RETAIL

Willpower PA Systems
Unit 4, Acorn Production Centre, 105 Blundell Street, London, N7 9BN
tel: 020 7609 9870/020 7607 4343
email: norton@willpowerpa.com
web: www.willpowerpa.com
info: PA systems for hire.

Wing Hire
442 Upper Elmers End Road, Beckenham, Kent, BR3 3HQ
tel: 020 8650 118
email: info@wingmusic.co.uk
web: www.wingmusic.co.uk
contact: Barry Mitchell
info: Equipment available for hire includes PA systems, lighting, record decks and microphones. Dry hire available.

MIDLANDS

Accusound
19 Bitteswell Road, Lutterworth, Leicestershire, LE17 4EL
tel: 01455 552 306
fax: 01455 559 448
email: griff@accusound.com
web: www.accusound.com
contact: Griffith Jones
info: Manufacturer of mics for acoustic instruments. Available for hire.

Ace PA Hire
Unit 10, Tame Road Industrial Estate, Tame Road, Birmingham, B6 7DS
tel: 0121 327 9276
email: acepahire@aol.com
web: www.acepahire.co.uk
contact: Paul Bavin
info: Range of live audio equipment available for hire. See website or contact for more details.

Acoustic Arrangements
14 Hammond Business Centre, Hammond Close, Attleborough Fields Industrial Estate, Nuneaton, Warwickshire, CV11 6RY
tel: 02476 343 434
fax: 02476 348 383
email: hire@a-a.uk.com
web: www.a-a.uk.com
contact: Glyn Chapman
info: Full audio and visual equipment available for hire. Engineer and delivery service also available.

Andrew Sound
4 Robinson Road, Bedworth, CV12 0EL
tel: 02476 364 235
fax: 02476 364 235
email: info@andrewsound.co.uk
web: www.andrewsound.co.uk
info: Small scale vocal PAs for hire. See website or contact for more details.

Andy Simpson Audio
109 Tilehouse Green Lane, Knowle, Solihull, West Midlands, B93 9EN
tel: 07761 275 490
email: andy@andysimpsonaudio.com
web: www.andysimpsonaudio.com
info: Andy is a freelance sound engineer and is available for hire to engineer live or in the studio.

ASM Pro Audio Solutions
3 Shelton Square, Coventry, CV1 1DG
tel: 02476 550 555
email: sales@djbargains.co.uk
web: www.djbargains.co.uk
info: Full range of live audio equipment available for sale or hire. Contact or see website for more details.

Audio Crafts PA Hire
112 Main Street, Newton Linford, Leicester, LE6 0AF
tel: 0116 210 9401
info: Range of live audio equipment available for hire. Suitable for bands and concerts. Contact for more details.

Birmingham Disco Centre
311-315 Marsh Lane, Birmingham, B23 6JD
tel: 0121 454 7039
email: sales@birminghamdisco.co.uk
web: www.birminghamdisco.co.uk
info: Sales, hire and installation of live audio and lighting equipment. Contact for more details.

Birmingham Sound Hire
Robannas Studios, Robanna House, Cliveland Street, Newtown, Birmingham, B19 3SN
tel: 0121 359 3071
email: equipment@birminghamsoundhire.co.uk
web: www.birminghamsoundhire.co.uk
info: Range of live audio equipment available for hire including backline. Delivery and engineer also available.

Cee-lite & Sound
Unit 52, Imex Business Park, Ormond Street, Fenton, Stoke on Trent, ST4 3NP
tel: 01782 596 666
email: sales@cee-lite.com
web: www.cee-lite.com
contact: Mr. Harrison
info: Large range of audio and audio-visual equipment available for hire from small PAs to large scale lighting rigs. See website for further details.

Central Theatre Supplies
1186 Stratford Road, Hall Green, Birmingham, B28 8AB
tel: 0121 778 6400
fax: 0121 702 2046
email: iank@centraltheatresupplies.co.uk
web: www.centraltheatresupplies.co.uk
contact: Ian
info: Small vocal PAs and reasonably big outdoor equipment available for hire.

Chameleon Pro Audio & Lighting
Unit 10, Orton Industrial Estate, London Road, Coalville, LE67 3JA
tel: 01530 831 337
email: info@chameleon-pa.co.uk
web: www.chameleon-pa.co.uk
contact: Stewart Duckworth
info: Range of PAs available for hire, as well as lighting rigs. Delivery and service also offered. Contact for more details.

The Cloud One Group
24 Proctor Street, Birmingham, B7 4EE
tel: 0121 333 7711
email: admin@cloudone.net
web: www.cloudone.net
info: Full range of live audio equipment available for hire. Sales, delivery, repairs and engineers also available. Cloud one also specialise in flight cases.

CrewCo Control
55 Main Street, Long Compton, Warwickshire, CV36 5JS
tel: 0845 458 9400
fax: 0845 458 9411
email: contactus@crewco.net
web: www.crewco.net
info: PA systems and lighting for hire. Dry hire only.

East Midlands Sound & Lighting
Unit 21, Old Moat House, off Springfield Road, Grantham, Lincolnshire, NG31 7DG
tel: 01476 579 574
fax: 01476 565 762
email: info@emslonline.co.uk
web: www.emslonline.co.uk
contact: Simon Morley
info: Small vocal PAs to large outdoor systems available for hire. Delivery, service, sales and repairs also offered.

ESS PA Hire
Unit 14, Bleak Hill Way, Hermitage Lane Industrial Estate, Mansfield, Nottinghamshire, NG18 5EZ
tel: 01623 647 291
fax: 01623 622 500
email: philmcdaniel@orange.net
contact: Phil McDaniel
info: Equipment hire mainly for major live events. Backline hire also available.

Fabtronic Sound & Lighting
Unit 8, William Street, Northampton, NN1 3EW
tel: 01604 368 100
fax: 01604 368 900
email: info@fabtronic.co.uk
web: www.fabtronic.co.uk
contact: Murray Dunkley
info: Massive range of live audio equipment, as well as lighting available for hire with or without engineer. Delivery, sales and repair also offered.

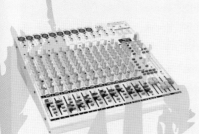

Hi-Q Sound
Unit 15, Monks Way, Monks Road, Lincoln, LN2 5LN
tel:	01522 567 670
email:	sales@hiqsound.co.uk
web:	www.hiqsound.co.uk
contact:	Mark Hudson
info:	Design and installation of pro live audio equipment. Hire

also available with or without engineer. Contact or see website for more details.

Inta Sound PA
Unit 15, Highgrove Farm Industrial Estate, Pinvin, Pershore, Worcestershire, WR10 2LF
tel:	01905 841 591
fax:	01905 841 590
email:	sales@intasoundpa.co.uk
web:	www.intasoundpa.co.uk
contact:	Francis Dale
info:	Full audio-visual rentals with or without engineer.

Repairs, sales and delivery also offered.

Juice Lighting & Sound
9-10 Gresley Close, Drayton Field Industrial Estate, Daventry, Northamptonshire, NN11 8RZ
tel:	01327 876 883
fax:	01327 310 094
email:	sales@juicesound.co.uk
web:	www.juicesound.co.uk
contact:	John Silk
info:	Manned audio and visual systems for hire. Delivery and

repair also available.

LNP Sound
PO Box 1121, Sutton Coldfield, West Midlands, B75 6ZQ
tel:	0121 308 0834
email:	pahire@lnpsound.com
web:	www.lnpsound.com
contact:	Paul Spicer
info:	Audio equipment available for hire from small vocal PAs

to equipment suitable for up to 600 people. Delivery and engineer also available.

Magnet Backline Hire
Unit 2, Davisella House, Newark Street, Sneinton, Nottingham, NG2 4PP
tel:	0115 924 3324
email:	rob@magnetstudios.co.uk
web:	www.magnetstudios.co.uk
contact:	Rob Reid
info:	Range of backline, as well as PA and lighting for hire.

Magnet also run rehearsal rooms, and offer splitter van rental service. See listings in relevant sections for details.

Marina Promotions
19 Rose Avenue, Coundon, Coventry, CV6 1DD
tel:	02476 597 825
fax:	02476 597 825
email:	mick@marinapromotions.co.uk
web:	www.marinapromotions.co.uk
contact:	Mick Painter
info:	Audio-visual equipment available for hire. Delivery

service and engineer provided, as well as staging.

MCL Birmingham
69 Dartmouth Middleway, Birmingham, B7 4UA
tel:	0121 333 3333
fax:	0121 333 3347
email:	hire@mcl-birmingham.com
web:	www.mclav.com
contact:	Chris Cheatle
info:	Audio-visual equipment stockists. Dry hire, or with

engineer. Delivery service also available.

Midland Sound & Lighting Ltd.
33 Dukes Close, Thurmaston, Leicester, LE4 8EY
tel:	0116 269 7636
fax:	0116 269 7616
email:	andysam@sayfree.co.uk
contact:	Andy Salmon
info:	Audio-visual equipment for hire, sales and installation.

Nightair Productions
Unit 1, Eastfield Side, Sutton-in-Ashfield, Nottinghamshire, NG17 4JW
tel: 01623 557 040
fax: 01623 555 586
email: sales@nightair.co.uk
web: www.nightair.co.uk
contact: Andrew Monk
info: Anything from small PAs to full production equipment.
Delivery, repairs and engineers available.

Nightfire Acoustic Technology
30a Cartlton Road, Worksop, Nottinghamshire, S80 1PH
tel: 01909 474 977
fax: 01909 475 139
email: iannightfire@pa-direct.co.uk
web: www.pa-direct.co.uk
contact: Ian Warrener
info: 10kW audio rig available for hire.

Omega Sound Systems
Windsor Business Park, Trent Valley Road, Lichfield, Staffordshire,
WS13 6EU
tel: 01543 257 280
fax: 01543 257 228
contact: Paul Harvey
info: Live audio equipment available for hire with engineers.
Delivery service also available.

Pacific Sound & Lighting Ltd.
Rich Bitch Recording Studios, 505 Bristol Road, Selly Oak, Birmingham,
B29 6AU
tel: 0121 471 3110
fax: 0121 471 3103
email: philip_gowers@yahoo.co.uk
contact: Philip Gowers
info: Full production equipment available for hire from small
PAs to staging and lighting.

Pheonix Soundworks
The Square, Earls Barton, Northampton, NN6 0NA
tel: 01604 466 499
fax: 01273 275 768
email: sales@phoenixsoundworks.com
web: www.phoenixsoundworks.com
contact: Duncan Marlow
info: Primarily dry PA hire with delivery service but can
provide engineer if needed.

Press Red
5 Jasmine Close, The Rock, Telford, TF3 5EJ
tel: 01952 403 884
fax: 01952 401 375
email: rentals@pressred.biz
web: www.pressred.biz
contact: Derek Tallent
info: Range of live audio equipment available for hire.
Delivery and repair also offered.

Pro Live Audio
19 Blakelow Drive, Etwall, Derby, DN65 6NN
tel: 01283 730 925
email: enquiries@proliveaudio.co.uk
web: www.proliveaudio.co.uk
contact: John Knapp
info: Large range of live audio equipment available for hire
with engineer and delivery service also offered. See website for more
details.

Raw Power Pro Sound Ltd.
Unit 14, Crofton Close, Allenby Industrial Estate, Lincoln, LN3 4NT
tel: 01522 529 786
fax: 01522 569 486
email: sales@rawpower.co.uk
web: www.rawpower.co.uk
contact: Paul Quinney
info: Full range of audio and visual equipment available for
hire. Small PAs to large outdoor equipment, with or without engineer.
Sales and delivery also offered.

Ricochet Music Rooms
Unit A, 117 Stafford Street, Walsall, WS2 5DX
tel: 01922 613 063
info: Dry PA hire. Rehearsal rooms also available. See relevant
section for more details.

RMPA (Worcester)
42 Lower Ferry Lane, Callowend, Worcester, WR2 4UN
tel: 01905 831 877
fax: 01905 830 906
email: rmpaworcester@aol.com
web: www.rmpa.co.uk
contact: Rick Bailey
info: Have provided audio equipment for the Acoustic stage at
Glastonbury for the last 10 years. See website for more details.

MSL AND MIDLAND SOUND and LIGHTING LIMITED

Professional Sound Systems

Hire - Sales - Installation - Services

Tel: 01162 697 636
Fax: 01162 697 616
Mobile: 07970 620 893
Email: andysam@stayfree.co.uk

MSL

Salop Music Centre
St. Michael's Street, Shrewsbury, SY1 2DE
tel: 01743 364 111
email: hire@salopmusic.co.uk
web: www.salopmusic.co.uk
contact: Rob Mulliner
info: Wide range of live audio equipment available for hire.
Contact or see website for more details.

Sherborne Sound
15 Bingham Road, Radcliffe on Trent, Nottingham, NG12 2FY
tel: 0115 933 2111
web: www.sherbornesound.co.uk
contact: Kevin Beevers
info: Small vocal PAs available for hire.

Solo Lighting & Sound
137 Derby Road, Stapleford, Nottingham, NG9 7AS
tel: 0115 917 1718
email: info@solomusicstore.co.uk
web: www.solomusicstore.co.uk
contact: Andy Kulesza
info: Full range of live audio and visual equipment available
for hire including staging, DJ and karaoke equipment, backline and
effects. Contact for more details.

The Sound Bunker
Unit 12, Victoria Business Centre, Neilston Street, Leamington Spa,
Warwickshire, CV31 2AZ
tel: 01926 832 929/07944 310 095
email: thesoundbunker@yahoo.co.uk or
thesoundbunker@btconnect.com
info: PA hire with or without engineer, and backline hire. The
Sound Bunker is also a rehearsal studio. See relevant section for more
details.

MUSIC SERVICES/RETAIL

SSE Audio Group
Burnt Meadow House, Burnt Meadow Road, North Moons Moat, Worcestershire, B98 9PA
tel: 01527 528 822
fax: 01527 528 840
email: hire@sseaudio.com
web: www.sseaudio.com
contact: Rich Rowley
info: Offer a wide range of audio equipment to hire for touring, festivals and events. Stage and set design, equipment manufacture, sales and repair also available.

Stage Audio Services
Unit 2, Bridge Street, Wordsley, Stourbridge, West Midlands, DY8 5YU
tel: 01384 263 629
fax: 01384 263 620
email: kevinmobers@aol.com
contact: Kevin Mobberley
info: Full range of live audio equipment available for hire with engineer. Delivery service provided.

Stagepoint Productions
Holly Farm Business Park, Honily, Kenilworth, Warwickshire, CV8 1NP
tel: 01926 484 591
fax: 01926 484 253
email: sales@stagepoint.co.uk
web: www.stagepoint.co.uk
contact: Paul McVeigh
info: Full production equipment available for hire from small vocal PAs to large scale outdoor systems with delivery and engineer. Staging and lighting also available.

Steve's Sound Systems
15 Beechfields, Barlaston, Stoke On Trent, ST12 9AP
tel: 01782 373 480
info: Wide range of live audio equipment available for hire. Contact for more details.

Sub Zero Music
The Leisure Factory, 20-22 Mount Pleasant, Bilston, West Midlands, WV14 7LJ
tel: 01902 405 511
fax: 01902 401 418
email: music@therobin.co.uk
contact: Mike Hamblett
info: PA hire with engineer and delivery service. Backline also available.

TourTech
3 Quarry Park Close, Moulton Park Industrial Estate, Northampton, NN3 6QB
tel: 01604 494 846
fax: 01604 642 454
email: tourtecuk@aol.com
web: www.tourtech.co.uk
contact: Dick Rabel
info: PA systems for hire with or without engineer. Delivery, sales and repair also available.

Waveform Productions
Waterworks Road, Worcester, WR1 3EZ
tel: 07729 011 398
email: info@waveformproductions.co.uk
web: www.waveformproductions.co.uk
info: Full range of equipment available for hire and installation. See website for more details

Zique Audio
Highfield Works, John Street, Hinckley, Leicestershire, LE10 1UY
tel: 01455 610 364
fax: 01455 610 164
email: garry@msn.com
contact: Gary Hargraves
info: Audio equipment for live gigs available for hire. No dry hire.

NORTHEAST

Aurora Light & Sound
15 Kingston Terrace, Sunderland, SR6 9QJ
tel: 07971 035 746
email: auroralightandsound@hotmail.com
info: Range of live audio equipment available for hire up to 30kW with engineer, sales, installation and repair also offered. Contact for more details or see website.

Brooklyn Sound Systems
46 Glendale Road, Tollesby, Middlesbrough, TS5 7QB
tel: 01642 816 179
web: www.brooklynsound.co.uk
info: Range of small vocal PAs available for hire. Free site survey or appraisal offered. See website for details.

Burrells Audio Ltd.
21a Seaside Lane, Easington, Peterlee, County Durham, SR8 3PG
tel: 0191 527 9865
web: www.burrellsaudio.co.uk
info: Live audio equipment available for hire from small vocal PAs to large outdoor equipment. Sales, repair, delivery and engineer also available.

Dreamhouse Audio
Station House, Cockfield, Bishop Auckland, County Durham, DL13 5HH
tel: 01388 718 020
fax: 01388 718 020
email: info@dhaudio.co.uk
web: www.dhaudio.co.uk
contact: Graham Kay
info: Full touring rigs available for hire. Engineers and splitter van hire also offered.

Hi-Lights Theatre Services
Unit 18e, White Rose Way, Follingsby Park, Gateshead, Tyne & Wear, NE10 8YX
tel: 0191 495 0608
fax: 0191 469 2027
email: martin@hi-lights.tv
web: www.hi-lights.tv
contact: Martin Warden
info: Anything from a microphone to large outdoor staging and audio equipment available for hire! With or without engineer. Delivery service.

Lorne Street Studios
19 Lorne Street, Middlesbrough, TS1 5QY
tel: 01642 246 090
email: stesmith@yahoo.co.uk
info: PA and backline hire with engineer. Recording and rehearsal facilities available. See relevant section for more details.

Midnight Electronics
Off Quay Building, Foundry Lane, Newcastle Upon Tyne, NE6 1LH
tel: 0191 224 0088
fax: 0191 224 0080
email: hires@midnightelectronics.co.uk
web: www.midnightelectronics.co.uk
contact: Dave Cross
info: Dry hire and installation of live audio equipment.

MT Audio Systems
70 Bloomfield Road, Darlington, County Durham, DL3 6RZ
tel: 01325 252 106
fax: 01325 252 106
email: mtaudio@ntlworld.com
web: www.mtaudio.net
contact: Mal Turner
info: Full range of live audio and visual equipment available for hire or sale. Generators and staging. Also provide a delivery service.

New York Productions
Units 16 & 11, Shaw Building, Deptford Terrace, Sunderland, SR4 6DD
tel: 0191 565 1222
fax: 0191 565 1333
email: dave@newyorkproductions.co.uk
web: www.newyorkproductions.co.uk
contact: Dave Arkley
info: Full production equipment available for hire from small PAs to staging and lighting. Delivery service and engineers provided.

Nitelites Ltd.
Unit 3E, Howden Green Industrial Estate, Norman Terrace, Wallsend, Tyne & Wear, NE28 6SX
tel: 0191 295 0009
fax: 0191 295 0009
email: nitelites@onyxnet.co.uk
contact: Jim Moore
info: Small PAs to full production equipment including staging and lights. No dry hire.

PFL Audio
Tweedmouth Industrial Estate, Berwick Upon Tweed, TD15 1XF
tel: 01289 308 030
info: PA hire and lighting hire.

Studio 64
90 Corporation Road, Middlesbrough, TS1 2RE
tel: 01642 860 006
web: www.studio64.org.uk
info: 300W Peavey unit available for hire at £40 per day. More powerful units are available on request. Studio 64 also provide recording, rehearsal, CD duplication and tuition services. See relevant sections for more details.

Teeside Sound & Lighting
75 Durham Street, Hartlepool, TS24 0HP
tel: 01429 232 676
info: Small vocal PAs available for hire, as well as lighting rigs. Contact for more details.

Titus Live
PO Box 304, Newcastle Upon Tyne, Tyne & Wear, NE3 4WE
tel: 07900 601 142
email: tituslive@yahoo.co.uk
web: www.tituslive.co.uk
contact: Pak Chum
info: Small vocal PAs available for hire up to 4kW. Engineers also provided. See website for more details.

Travelled Music
The Tile Works, Paxton, Berwick Upon Tweed, TD15 1TJ
tel: 01289 386 737
email: info@travelledmusic.co.uk
web: www.travelledmusic.co.uk
contact: Alan Thompson
info: Offer PA and instrument hire. Travelled Music also provide management, promotion, CD duplication and merchandising services. See listings in relevant sections for details.

NORTHWEST

3D Set Design
Unit 8, Temperance Street, Ardwick, Western Park, Manchester, M12 6HR
tel: 0161 273 8831
fax: 0161 273 6786
email: twalsh@3dsetco.com
web: www.3dsetco.com
contact: T. Walsh
info: Stage and set design and hire.

AC Sound Hire
33 The Circuit, Alderley Edge, SK9 7LS
tel: 01625 583 265
email: acsoundhire@aol.com
web: www.acsoundhire.com
contact: Colin
info: Specialise in the design, supply, hire and installation of high output PA and music systems for indoor and outdoor events. Can supply systems from 100W to 30kW.

ACM Ltd.
Rutland House, 38b Rutland Street, Swinton, Manchester, M27 6AU
tel: 0161 950 2020
email: chrismperry@btopenworld.com
contact: Chris Perry
info: Sound and lighting equipment with engineers. No dry hire. Delivery available. Call for quote.

Adlib Audio Hire Ltd.
Adlib House, Fleming Road, Speke, Liverpool, L24 9LS
tel: 0151 486 2214
fax: 0151 448 1454
email: hire@adlibaudio.co.uk
web: www.adlibaudio.co.uk
contact: Mark Roberts
info: PA equipment and engineer hire. Deposits required for dry hire.

Akwil Projects Ltd.
Akwil House, 493-495 Chester Road, Manchester, M16 9HF
tel: 0161 872 7337
fax: 0161 872 8945
email: sales@akwil.com
contact: Eddie Akka, Andrew Akwil
info: Sound equipment including PAs, speakers, amps (up to 2KW) and stage monitors. Specialist sound and lighting installation. Automation for bars, clubs, restaurants and hotels. Can provide engineers. Call for details of full range and quote.

Apogee Telecom
Unit 311, Silk House, Park Green, Macclesfield, Cheshire, SK11 7QJ
tel: 0870 420 5461
fax: 01625 429 888
email: uk@apogee-telecom.com
web: www.apogee-telecom.com
contact: Carlos Benesovsky
info: Large range of live audio equipment available for hire. Engineers and delivery service also available.

Aquarius Acoustics
Unit 1, Stanley Street, Colne, Lancashire, BB8 9DD
tel: 01282 859 797
fax: 01282 863 250
email: dave@aquariusacoustics.com
web: www.aquariusacoustics.com
contact: Dave Pickering
info: PA equipment hire. Front of house and monitors. Engineers available. Deposit required. Delivery service available.

Arranpaul Audio
Unit 2, Cocker Avenue, Poulton Industrial Estate, Poulton-le-Fylde, FY6 8JU
tel: 01253 890 590
fax: 01253 890 290
email: info@arranpaulaudio.co.uk
contact: Paul Rogerson
info: Sound and lighting equipment for hire. Can provide engineers. Delivery, set up and pick up service. Can supply moving lights as well. Call for quote.

Audile
Unit 110, Cariocca Business Park, Hellidon Close, Ardwick, Manchester, M12 4AH
tel: 0161 272 7883
email: rob@audile.co.uk
web: www.audile.co.uk
contact: Rob Ashworth
info: Sound, lighting and video equipment. Delivery and engineers available. See website for details of range. Call Audile for quote.

Audiotec
193 Duckworth Street, Darwen, BB3 1AU
tel: 01254 773 865
email: info@audioteconline.co.uk
web: www.audioteconline.co.uk
contact: Brian
info: DJ equipment and lighting systems for hire. Delivery available. Deposit and ID required. Also have outlet in Chorley (Tel. 01257 274 339).

Audioworks
Unit 2a, Bentham Business Park, Bentham, Lancaster, LA2 7NB
tel: 07957 856 384/01524 261 628
fax: 01524 241 619
email: enquiries@audioworks.co.uk
web: www.audioworks.co.uk
contact: Martin Hodgson
info: Audio visual equipment hire including sound systems and associated items, video and projection systems and LCD projectors. Delivery depends on equipment rented and area.

Big Fish Corporation
Beehive Mill, Jersey Street, Manchester, M4 6JG
tel: 0161 950 4250
fax: 0161 228 0357
email: wayne@bigfish21.fsnet.co.uk
contact: Wayne Chappell
info: Backline equipment and PA hire. Engineers available, but will dry hire. Deposit required. Delivery service. Big Fish also provide rehearsal studios. See listing in relevant section for details.

Concert Systems
Unit 4D, Stag Industrial Estate, Atlantic Street, Altrincham, Cheshire, WA14 5DW
tel: 0161 927 7700
fax: 0161 927 7722
email: hire@concert-systems.com
web: www.concert-systems.com
contact: Paul Tandy
info: Hire sound equipment, lighting, stage rigging. Can deliver nationally.

Donut Sound
1 Falmouth Road, Crewe, Cheshire, CW1 3QS
tel: 01270 215 649
fax: 01270 215 649
email: pauldonlon@compuserve.com
contact: Paul Donlon
info: Sound equipment hire including PA systems, mics, mixing desks and amplifiers. Delivery and collection and set up available. Dry hire or engineers can be provided. Deposit is required (usually 10% of cost of hire). Call for quote.

Drinkle & Mann Ltd.
Unit 2, Peel Green Trading Estate, Green Street, Eccles, Manchester, M30 7HF
tel: 0161 707 7588
fax: 0161 707 7599
email: name@drinkle-mann.co.uk
web: www.drinkle-mann.co.uk
contact: Colin Hulme
info: Sound equipment and engineer hire. Delivery available. Deposits required.

Firehouse Studios
Rear of the Market Hall, Market Square, Millom, Cumbria, LA18 4HZ
tel: 07732 927 603
email: firehouse@firehousestudios.co.uk
web: www.firehousestudios.co.uk
contact: Barry
info: PA hire up to 18kW, as well as recording equipment. Contact Barry for further information. Firehouse also run rehearsal and recording studios. Refer to entries in relevant sections for details.

Heroes PA Hire
4 Courtsway West, Greasby, Wirral, CH49 2NF
tel: 0151 678 3968
fax: 0151 678 3968
web: www.bedlam.uk.com/heroes/
contact: Pete Goulborn
info: Sound and lighting equipment hire and tour management. Dry hire on smaller systems only. Very experienced in the music industry. Band friendly.

Hi Q Sound Systems
Albion Street, Pendlebury, Manchester, M27 4FG
tel: 0161 793 6222
fax: 0161 793 0586
contact: Dave Williams
info: PA systems up to 3.5kW and lighting. Engineers available. Call for quote.

Hillock Productions
Long Meadow, Tirley Lane, Utkinton, Tarporley, CW6 0JZ
tel: 07860 917 446
web: www.hillockproductions.com
contact: Frank
info: Wide range of live audio equipment available for hire with engineer. Delivery also provided.

Hippo PA Hire
8 Marchwell Road, Ellesmere Port, CH65 5BR
tel: 0151 200 5071
email: hippo.pa@ntlworld.com
contact: Tony, Steve
info: PAs (4kW front, 1kW foldback). Full service provided including delivery, set up and engineer. No dry hire.

HSL Productions
Unit 0, Ribble Business Park, Challenge Way, Blackburn, BB1 5RB
tel: 01254 698 808
fax: 01254 698 835
email: contact@hslproductions.com
web: www.hslproductions.com
contact: Sean McGlone,
info: PAs up to 500kW and lighting systems. Engineers can be supplied if needed. Delivery service. Deposit required.

Impact Hire
Unit 5, Lower Level, Warwick Mill, Carlisle
tel: 01228 670 048
web: www.impacthire.co.uk
contact: Noel Graham
info: Wide range of live audio equipment available for hire from small vocal PAs to large scale touring rigs. Lighting also available.

Impulse Lighting
Unit 14, Parkside Industrial Estate, Edgelane Street, Royton, Oldham, OL2 6DS
tel: 0161 652 9888/07774 655 119
fax: 0161 652 9963
email: info@impulse-lighting.com
web: www.impulse-lighting.com
contact: Pete
info: From 1kW to 20kW PA and intelligent lighting systems hired. Dry hire or engineer supplied. Sales (new and ex-rental) and repairs.

Intrak
6 Delany Drive, Freckleton, Preston, PR4 1SJ
tel: 01772 633 697
email: intrak@iname.com
web: www.intrak.co.uk
contact: John, Kath
info: 32 channel PA systems up to 25kW and lighting systems. Engineers available. Can deliver in the North West.

Jigsaw Sound & Lighting
343 Lyelake Lane, Bickerstaff, Ormskirk, L39 0EY
tel: 01695 721 795
fax: 07092 316 986
email: enquiries@jigsaw-hire.co.uk
contact: Jon Ashburner
info: Dry hire service. PA systems up to 30kW and lighting equipment. Delivery available. Jigsaw offer a complete service to bands, from set up to pick up.

MUSIC SERVICES/RETAIL

Kelco Technical
Unit 1, Business Park, Old Trafford, Manchester, M16 0GY
tel: 0161 848 7500
fax: 0161 848 7400
email: john@kelco.co.uk
web: www.kelco.co.uk
contact: John
info: Sound equipment including PAs, amps, mics, speakers and cables. Lighting and special effects (including confetti cannons and smoke machines) also available. Can provide engineers. Delivery across the UK. Call for brochure.

Kirkpatrick Sound Engineering
1 Clover Drive, Pickmere, Knutsford, WA16 0WF
tel: 01565 733 200
email: roy@kirkpatrick4sound.fsbusiness.co.uk
web: www.kirkpatrick4sound.co.uk
contact: Mr Kirkpatrick
info: PA hire up to 1kW with engineer. Induction loops and audio-visual systems, PA and sound reinforcement systems. Design, installation and hire. Roy has 35 years experience in sound engineering.

Lancaster Music Co-Op
1 Lodge Street, Lancaster, LA1 1QW
tel: 01524 388 544
email: musiccoop@musiccoop.co.uk
web: www.musiccoop.co.uk
contact: Ian, Tom, Dave
info: Amps, PA systems, mics and Drum kits. ID required. Drum kit at £15 per day, PA from £25 per day, guitar amp from £5 per day, bass amp at £8 per day and mics at £3 per day. Also sell a range of accessories.

Lancelyn Theatre Supplies
Poulton Road, Bebington, Wirral, CH63 9LN
tel: 0151 334 8991
fax: 0151 334 4047
email: northwest@lancelyn.co.uk
web: www.lancelyn.co.uk
contact: Bob Baxter
info: Lighting, sound and special effects hire. Engineers available, can deliver. Brochure available on request by phone, or can be downloaded from website. Lancelyn also have access to recording studios.

Lea Royse
14 Mardale Drive, Bolton, BL2 5HX
tel: 07976 701 367
email: learoyse@aol.com
info: Sound engineer. Can supply rig up to 3kW. Lea will deliver, set up and pack away the rig himself.

Lee Engineering
Palantine House, Scotforth Road, Lancaster, Lancashire, LA1 4SA
tel: 01524 846 078/01524 846 070
fax: 01524 846 178
email: hire@leeeng.co.uk
web: www.leeeng.co.uk
contact: Phil Leedal
info: Sound, lighting and video equipment for hire. Can also provide sound and lighting engineers. Delivery on request, subject to availability.

Linney PA
5 Elliscales Avenue, Dalton-in-Furness, Cumbria, LA15 8BW
tel: 01229 466 716
email: alex@linneypa.co.uk
web: www.angelfire.com/electronic/linneypa/
contact: Alex
info: Provides a range of full sound systems complete with engineers, from 100W to 15,000W. Dry hire of smaller sound systems and separate items of audio equipment. Troubleshooting and repair of sound systems or individual components. Engineers with up to 15 years experience in live and studio sound.

Liteopia Ltd.
16 Broomville Avenue, Sale, Manchester, M33 3DD
tel: 0161 973 6527/07967 009 208
email: hire@liteopia.co.uk
web: www.liteopia.co.uk
contact: Simon Chaplin
info: Lighting and sound hire. Dry hire or engineers can be supplied depending on requirements. Delivery and pick up available. Also sales of music technology equipment including keyboards, synths, mixers, and software.

Lomax Electrical
35 North Parade, Hoylake, Wirral, CH47 3AJ
tel: 0151 632 0032
email: steve@lomaxelectrical.co.uk
web: www.lomaxelectrical.co.uk
contact: Steve Lomax
info: PA systems up to 1kW and lighting. Engineers can be provided. Delivery available. Call for a quote.

Low Fold Professional Audio
Shireshead Old Church, Stony Lane, Forton, Preston, PR3 1BV
tel: 01524 792 020
fax: 01524 792 305
email: info@lowfold.com
web: www.lowfold.com
contact: Mark Burford
info: PA and recording equipment available for hire. Full details of pricing available on website.

Mac Sound Hire
1&2 Attenburys Park Estate, Altrincham, Cheshire, WA14 5QE
tel: 0161 969 8311
fax: 0161 962 9423
email: info@macsound.co.uk
web: www.macsound.co.uk
contact: Julie Murray
info: Full audio equipment hire. Normally used for theatre and orchestral. Repairs also available.

Manchester Light & Stage Company
78 North Western Street, Ardwick, Manchester, M12 6DY
tel: 0161 273 2662
fax: 0161 273 2664
email: info@manchesterlightandstage.com
web: www.manchesterlightandstage.com
contact: Jim
info: Running since 1974. Wide range of stage and lighting equipment available.

Margin Music
3 Market Place, Macclesfield, Cheshire, SK10 1EB
tel: 01625 619 013
email: marginmusic@aol.com
web: www.marginmusic.co.uk
contact: Alan White
info: Large range of lighting equipment for hire, plus PAs up to 1kW. Dry hire only.

MCL Manchester
18 Lord Byron Square, Stowell Technical Park, Salford Quays, Manchester, M50 2XH
tel: 0161 745 9933
fax: 0161 745 9975
email: jmcaffer@mclav.com
web: www.mclav.com
contact: Jamie McAffer
info: Audio visual equipment hire. Will deliver. Delivery and collection charges may apply depending on distance travelled. Deposit is required. Call for quotation.

Mega Watt Sound
Tall Trees, 136a Roe Lane, Southport, Merseyside, PR9 7PJ
tel: 01704 220 639
fax: 01704 506 390
email: mws.com@virgin.net
contact: Stuart Watt
info: Sound system and PA hire. Engineer always supplied, no dry hire. Deposit required. Call Stuart for quote.

Noisebox
New Islington Mill, Regeant Trading Estate, Salford, Manchester, M5 4DE
tel: 0161 798 5677
fax: 0161 798 5677
email: steve.noise@btclick.com
contact: Steve Lloyd
info: PA hire, with or without engineer. DJ equipment and some recording equipment. Delivery and pick up available. Recording studio available.

Northern Lights
89 Scotforth Road, Lancaster, Lancashire, LA1 4SD
tel: 01524 845 584
fax: 01524 845 584
email: n.lights@fsbdial.co.uk
contact: Ray Wilkinson
info: Sound, lighting and special effects including pyrotechnic equipment and bubble machines. Can also provide operators. Delivery available on request. It is advised to book equipment 1 month in advance, although cancellations sometime allow for last minute hire.

Paradise Electrics
3 Paradise Street, Blackburn, BB2 1LW
tel: 01254 680 101
email: crikeymick@hotmail.com
contact: Michael Clarke
info: PA and lighting hire. Lighting rig and sound systems up to 6kW. No dry hire. Deliver, set up and pick up covered by engineer.

Play PA
241 Heysham Road, Morecambe, LA3 1NN
tel: 01524 417 529/07768 591 051
email: jamesatplayattic@aol.com
contact: James Dorrington
info: Will hire anything from small pub systems up to 10kW rigs. No dry hire. James is an experienced engineer and has worked at gigs across the country.

Powerhouse Sound Systems
27 Bolton Road, Bury, BL8 2AB
tel: 0161 764 9360
fax: 0161 763 5080
email: sales@doctorrock.co.uk
contact: Keith
info: PA systems from 300W to 1.2kW. Engineer, drop off and pick up service supplied for larger systems. Systems up to 10kW available.

Premier Sound & Light
The Citadel, Bella Street, Bolton, BL3 4DU
tel: 01204 621 95
email: stevebarlow@ic24.net
info: PA hire, DJ equipment and lighting. Dry hire. No delivery.

Reidy's
7-13 Penny Street, Blackburn, BB1 6HJ
tel: 01254 265 212
email: sales@reidys.com
web: www.reidys.com
contact: Paul, Jason, Chris
info: PAs up to 5kW and lighting. Call for details of full range and quote.

Rhythm of Life Ltd.
Rhythm House, King Street, Carlisle, CA1 1SJ
tel: 01228 515 141
fax: 01228 515 161
email: hire@rhythm.co.uk
web: www.rhythm.co.uk
contact: Ian Howe
info: Live audio and visual equipment available for hire. Full service available including delivery, repairs and engineering. Also sales, installation, and event management.

Rio Systems Ltd.
4 Elder Road, St. John's Industrial Estate, Lees, Oldham, OL4 3DZ
tel: 0161 626 0000
email: pete@riosys.co.uk
contact: Pete
info: Pro audio-visual systems. Call for advice and a quote.

Rocky's Audio
96b North Western Street, Ardwick, Manchester, M12 6JL
tel: 0161 273 1609
email: geoff@rockysaudio.freeserve.co.uk
web: www.rockysaudio.freeserve.co.uk
contact: Gavin
info: PA hire, sales, installation and repair. Full delivery, set up and engineering service available. Can provide a range of systems from small vocal PAs to full stage systems.

Romers
Unit 8, Scotshaw Brook Industrial Estate, Branch Road, Lower Darwen, Blackburn, BB3 0PR
tel: 01254 595 16
fax: 01254 680 570
email: sales@romers.co.uk
web: www.romers.co.uk
contact: John Caton
info: PA equipment hire. Dry hire or can provide engineers. Delivery available. Call for quote.

Smithfield Electronics
3 Ermine Road, Hoole, Chester, CH2 3PN
tel: 01244 400 300
email: chris@smithfield-online.com
web: www.smithfield-online.com
contact: Joanne
info: Full range of sound and lighting equipment available. £50 deposit required, along with 3 forms of ID. Can supply engineers. Delivery, pick up and set up at extra charge. Also sell, repair and install equipment.

Sound Right PA Systems
H2 Brookside Business Park, Middleton, Manchester, M24 1GS
tel: 0161 653 2022
email: soundright.pasystems@virgin.net
contact: John Anson
info: PAs up to 10kW, lighting, staging and theming. Can provide engineer. Larger systems not available on dry hire. Call Sound Right for quote.

Southside PAs
220 Church Lane, Woodford, Stockport, SK7 1PQ
tel: 0161 439 8982
contact: Mike Smith
info: 2.5kW and 5kW PAs for hire with engineer. No dry hire.

Spectrum Sound Systems
Unit 40, Argyle Industrial Estate, Appin Road, Birkenhead, Wirral, CH41 9HH
tel: 0151 650 1156/0151 678 3747
fax: 0151 650 1156/0151 678 3747
email: enquiries@spectrumsoundsystems.co.uk
contact: Adrian Bryan
info: PAs up to 40kW. Can provide engineer. Delivery available. Deposit and ID required. Work alongside Reflex Lighting to provide complete staging package.

Stagebox
187-189 Central Drive, Blackpool, FY1 5ED
tel: 01253 291 119/01253 620 023
email: steve@stagebox.com
web: www.stagebox.com
contact: Steve
info: PA systems up to 15kW and lighting. Can provide engineers. Delivery available. Call Steve for quote. Stagebox is a shop and smaller PA hire service, Stagebox Systems is for larger hire.

Stardream Audio Visual (SAV)
Party House, Mowbray Drive, Blackpool, FY3 7JR
tel: 01253 302 602
fax: 01253 301 000
email: sales@stardream.co.uk
web: ww.stardream.co.uk
contact: Steve Salisbury
info: Hire and installation of live audio-visual equipment from small vocal PAs to large venues.

STS Touring Productions Ltd.
Unit 103 & 104, Cariocca Business Park, 2 Hellidon Close, Ardwick, Manchester, M12 4AH
tel: 0161 273 5984
fax: 0161 272 7772
email: paul@ststouring.co.uk
web: www.ststouring.co.uk
contact: Pete Dutton
info: PA and backline equipment hire. Full technical support (lighting, sound and backline engineers). Will deliver, charges apply. Deposits usually required. Brochure available on request.

Studiocare Professional Audio
Unit 9, Century Building, Summers Road, Brunswick Business Park, Liverpool, L3 4BL
tel: 0151 236 7800
fax: 0151 284 0300
email: hire@studiocare.com
web: www.studiocare.com
contact: Andrew, Luke
info: Outboard equipment, microphones, PA systems, Pro Tools recording systems and instruments. Delivery and collection available. Sales and service centre for large range of recording and PA equipment. Contact Rick Whalley for sales or Steve Metcalfe for second hand purchases.

Swan's Music Ltd.
The Belan, Moss Lane, Mobberley, Cheshire, WA16 7BS
tel: 01565 873 044
fax: 01565 873 044
email: hire@swansmusic.co.uk
web: www.swansmusic.co.uk
info: Large range of instruments for hire including pianos, organs and drum kits, plus PA and audio equipment. Call Swan's Music for further details and conditions of rental.

MUSIC SERVICES/RETAIL

The Musical Instrument Hire Specialists

Piano Tuning
Repair And Refurbishment
Removal And Transportation

Extensive Selection Of Pianos
Instruments And Backline
Equipment For Hire

Recent clients include:
Jamie Cullum
Ryan Adams
Procul Harem
Coldplay
Rat Pack
Divine Comedy

The Belan
Moss Lane
Mobberley
WA16 7BS
Tel: 01565 873 044
Fax: 01565 873 044
Mob: 07710 341 394

www.swansmusic.co.uk
hire@swansmusic.co.uk

Tube UK Ltd.
77 Cariocca Business Park, Hellidon Close, Manchester, M12 4AH
tel: 0161 275 9990
email: info@tubeuk.com
web: www.tubeuk.com
contact: Melvin Coote
info: Equipment supply and engineering for all music events including gigs and festivals. Long term hire option is available.

Venue Sound & Light Hire Company
59 Old Lansdowne Road, Didsbury, Manchester, M20 2WY
tel: 0161 980 6430/0161 434 9322
email: jjs44nci@hotmail.com
contact: John Saffer
info: PAs up to 1kW. Ideal for local bands requirements. Dry hire only. Lighting available.

VME

VME Ltd.
Unit D, Marlborough Close, Park Gate Industrial Estate, Knutsford, Cheshire, WA16 8XN
tel: 01565 652 202
fax: 01565 652 203
email: sales@vme-uk.com
web: www.vme-uk.com
contact: Tani Davie
info: Anything from small vocal PAs to large scale outdoor equipment available for hire with or without engineer, and equipment for sale. Delivery service available.

Wigwam Acoustics Ltd.
Unit 402, Phoenix Close Industrial Estate, Heywood, Lancashire, OL10 2JG
tel: 01706 363 800
fax: 01706 363 810
email: rental@wigwamhire.co.uk
web: www.wigwam.co.uk
info: PA equipment and engineer hire. Delivery available with charge. Deposits vary with equipment. Price list available on request, or telephone for a quote. Also have equipment for sale.

SOUTHEAST

24/7 Studios
6 Hertford Street, Cowley, Oxford, OX4 3AJ
tel: 01865 435 981/07768 410 080
email: robin@247studios.co.uk
web: www.247studios.co.uk
info: Bass amp, guitar combo and Marshall Valve JCM 900 available for rental. Rates can be viewed on the website. 24/7 also have recording and rehearsal studios. See relevant entries for details.

AC Light & Sound Hire
Wheatley, Oxford
tel: 01865 875 519
email: contact@acdisco.com
web: www.acdisco.com
info: Range of live audio equipment available for hire from small vocal PAs to large outdoor events. See website for details.

AIM Sound Services
1 Gaunts Way, Letchworth Garden City, Hertfordshire, SG6 4PQ
tel: 01462 685 796
email: info@aimsound.co.uk
contact: Andrew Moore
info: Range of live audio equipment available for hire. Delivery service and engineers also offered.

AOTN Sound & Lighting
Hastings
tel: 07976 323 294
email: info@aotn.net
web: www.aotn.net
contact: Lloyd
info: Provide sound and lighting requirements for events ranging from exhibitions to music festivals. Previous clients include South Coast Dance Weekender, Blazing Squad and Eddie Izzard.

Arena Entertainment Systems
16 St. Leonard's Close, Denton, Newhaven, BN9 0RW
tel: 01273 514 161
fax: 01273 812 218
email: arenainfo1@aol.com
web: www.arenaentertainmentsystems.com
contact: Matt Constable
info: Dry hire or with engineer. Small band rigs to large outdoor systems. Delivery and pick up service provided. Lighting rigs available.

Audio Plus
Unit 3, Central Park, Military Road, Colchester, Essex, C01 2AA
tel: 01206 369 966
fax: 01206 549 966
email: sales@audio-plus.co.uk
web: www.audio-plus.co.uk
info: PA systems for hire. Dry hire available.

Band-X
19 Barden Road, Speldhurst, Kent, TN3 0PZ
tel: 07707 574 534/07811 939 518
email: band-x@bluebottle.com
web: www.band-x.org.uk
contact: Matt Burgess
info: PA and instrument hire available at reasonable prices. Dry hire. Collection and delivery service on a 10 mile radius of Tunbridge Wells. Band-X are also involved with artist management. See entry in relevant section for details.

Bluemoon Sound & Light
4 Surrenden Close, Brighton, East Sussex, BN1 8EB
tel: 07919 486 752
web: www.bluemoonhire.com
contact: John Whippy
info: Wide range of live audio equipment available for hire. Delivery and lighting also available. See website for quotes.

The Chaps PA Co.
The Limes, 78 Bute Road, Wallington, Surrey, SM6 8AB
tel: 07835 481 538
email: danielwhite1@mac.com
contact: Daniel White
info: Delivery service of PA and live sound equipment. Splitter van available.

Chilli Sound Systems
Flat 2, 14 Devonshire Place, Brighton, East Sussex, BN2 1QA
tel: 07973 500 651
email: info@chillisound.co.uk
web: www.chillisound.co.uk
info: PA systems available for hire. Cover South East of England. Also office based in London. See listing in Greater London section for details.

Control Sound
5 Cherwell Close, Didcot, Oxon, OX11 7UF
tel: 01235 816 400
fax: 01235 816 400
email: martin@controlsound.com
web: www.controlsound.com
contact: Martin Noyce
info: Dry hire, repairs and delivery for a range of live sound equipment.

Cosmic Electronics Ltd.
62-66 Ongar Road, Brentwood, Essex, CM15 9AX
tel: 01277 216 078
email: sales@cosmic-uk.com
web: www.cosmic-uk.com
info: PA systems for hire. See website for details of equipment available and price listings.

CRS Media Technology Ltd.
Pinehurst, Filshem Valley, St. Leonard's On Sea, East Sussex, TN38 0PB
tel: 01424 444 141
fax: 01424 202 030
email: roland@crsmedia.co.uk
web: www.crsmedia.co.uk
contact: Roland Clarke
info: PA and sound equipment available for hire with delivery service and repairs. Stocks DB AudioTechnics.

D.P.A. Sound
11 Fairview Close, Tonbridge, Kent, PN9 2UU
tel: 07973 147 909
email: info@dpasound.co.uk
web: www.dpasound.co.uk
contact: Andrew
info: PA and recording equipment for hire. Installation service available.

D-Tek
PO Box 2190, Woodford Green, Essex, IG8 8YG
tel: 0700 034 7267
email: john@d-tek.co.uk
web: www.d-tek.co.uk
contact: John Dean
info: Live sound and visual equipment available for dry hire with delivery service.

Dimension Audio Hire
Unit E2, Sussex Manor Business Park, Gatwick Road, Crawley, West Sussex, RH10 9NH
tel: 01293 582 000
email: mail@dimension.co.uk
web: www.dimension.co.uk
info: PA and sound equipment for hire. Dry hire available.

Euro Hire Sound & Light
Unit 6, Bessemer Park, Bessemer Road, Basingstoke, Hampshire, RG21 3NB
tel: 01256 461 234
fax: 01256 461 226
email: jools@eurohire.co.uk
web: www.eurohire.co.uk
contact: Mervin Goerge
info: Dry hire and delivery available on live audio equipment. Staging, lighting and backline hire also available.

Event Sound & Light
Unit 34 Waterhouse Business Centre, Croma Way, Waterhouse Lane, Chelmsford, Essex, CM1 2EQ
tel: 01245 392 260
fax: 01245 392 261
email: sci@eventsoundandlighting.com
web: www.eventsoundandlighting.com
contact: Nigel Hills
info: Full range of production equipment from small PAs to large scale outdoor rigs including stage, lighting and backline. Delivery, sales and repair also available.

GPA Hire
Unit 5, Holmshaw Business Park, Layhams Road, Keston, Kent, BR2 6AR
tel: 01959 577 761
fax: 01959 577 763
email: info@gpahire.com
web: www.gpahire.com
contact: Gary Young
info: Provided live audio equipment for Leftfield, Massive Attack and Ian Brown. Dry hire or with engineer.

Gravesend Sound & Lighting (GSL)
128b Milton Road, Gravesend, DA12 2PG
tel: 01474 566 024/07970 102 030
email: info@gsl-online.co.uk
web: www.gsl-online.co.uk
info: GSL hire out a comprehensive range of audio and lighting equipment. Disco and karaoke equipment. 500W sound system to a 50kW concert rig with full lighting system and various engineers.

Hocken Audio Visual Ltd.
5 Waterhouse Lane, Kingswood, Tadworth, Surrey, KT20 6EB
tel: 01737 370 371
fax: 01737 370 372
email: info@hockenav.co.uk
web: www.hockenav.co.uk
contact: Martin Smith
info: Full audio-visual equipment available for hire for live use. Dry or with engineer. Sales and repairs also offered.

Jedi Lighting & Sound
Unit 14, 4th Avenue, Bluebridge Industrial Estate, Halstead, Essex, CO9 2SY
tel: 01787 475 999
fax: 01787 475 999
web: www.lightingandsound.co.uk
contact: Rosslin or Andrew
info: Sales and hire of audio equipment and lighting. Delivery also offered. See website for more details.

K2 Music Ltd.
Unit 70, Fresh Wharf Estate, Fresh Wharf Road, Barking, Essex, IG11 7BW
email: info@k2musicltd.co.uk
web: www.k2musicltd.co.uk
contact: Steve Gee
info: Equipment hire and repair services. K2 also provide rehearsal facilities, tuition, as well as a music shop. See listings in relevant sections for details.

Komotion Ltd.
Reading, RG4
tel: 07092 334 420
email: info@komotion.ltd.uk
web: www.komotion.ltd.uk
contact: Nick and Rob
info: Fully managed sound systems from 3.5kW to concert standard. Delivery service also available.

Maple Equipment Hire
Unit 39-43, Grainger Road Industrial Estate, Southend On Sea, SS2 5DD
tel: 01702 613 066
email: maplestudios@hotmail.com
contact: Glyn Morgan
info: Audio equipment hire from small vocal PAs to large scale festivals. Dry hire or with engineer. Sales, repair and delivery also available.

MUSIC SERVICES/RETAIL

ML Executive Sound Design
Unit 2, Crayford Commercial Centre, Greyhound Way, Crayford, Kent, DA1 4HF
tel: 01322 552 828
email: mlexecutives@btclick.com
web: www.mlexecutives.com
info: PA and backline for hire. Dry hire available.

ML Sound Advice
Unit 2, Crayford Commercial Centre, Greyhound Way, Crayford, Kent, DA1 4HF
tel: 01322 552 828
fax: 01322 552 929
email: gareth@mlsoundadvice.com
web: www.mlsoundadvice.com
contact: Gareth
info: Audio equipment supplied for everything from showcases to arenas. Large amount of backline and rare equipment available. Also do stage design and in-ear monitors. No dry hire.

MM Productions
Unit 10, Smeaton Close, Severalls Industrial Estate, Colchester, Essex, CO4 9QY
tel: 01206 845 947
email: enquiries@mmproductions.co.uk
web: www.mmproductions.co.uk
contact: Martin Hunt
info: Small to large PAs and audio equipment available for hire. Delivery and engineers also offered. See website for more details.

Model Music
Newbury, Berkshire
tel: 0870 808 0100/07747 848 896
fax: 0870 808 0098
email: info@modelmusic.co.uk
web: www.modelmusic.co.uk
info: Offer PA, backline and lighting hire, with or without crew. Many different hire package configurations available. See website for full details. Work closely with Pan Artist who help unsigned acts.

Moonlite Productions
12 Chequers End, Winslow, Buckingham, MK18 3HT
tel: 07966 331 000
email: info@moonlite.co.uk
web: www.moonlite.co.uk
contact: James Lyengar
info: Full audio-visual equipment for hire and sale. Staging, lighting, screens, pyrotechnics and cameras also available.

The Music Centre
35-37 Tavistock Road, Bedford, MK40 2RB
tel: 01234 349 593
email: mic@musiccentre.co.uk
web: www.musiccentre.co.uk
contact: Mick
info: Range of small PAs available for hire. See website for more details.

The Noizeworks
Unit 2, Bakers Court, Coppen Road, Dagenham, Essex, RN8 1HJ
tel: 0870 240 3119
email: noizeworks@tesco.net
web: www.thenoizeworks.co.uk
info: Noizeworks hire out PA systems, wireless microphones, monitoring, and DJ and live recording equipment. Dry hire and crewing/engineering services available.

Page One (System Technology)
78 Glebe Lane, Maidstone, Kent, ME16 9BA
tel: 01622 728 200
fax: 01622 720 950
web: www.pageonesystems.com
info: Small PAs available for hire with delivery service.

Panache Audio
Unit A5, Spectrum Business Centre, Medway City Estate, Strood, Kent, ME2 4NP
tel: 01634 720 700
fax: 01634 720 333
email: dave@panacheaudio.info
web: www.panacheaudio.info
contact: Dave Ong
info: Full production equipment available for hire. Delivery service also provided.

Peter Maciuk Installations Ltd.
Unit 2, Old Chair Wharf, Station Approach, Dorking, Surrey, RH4 1EF
tel: 01306 883 781
fax: 01306 740 964
email: info@pmihire.co.uk
web: www.pmihire.co.uk
contact: Peter Maciuk
info: Live audio equipment hire with or without engineer. Delivery and repair service also available.

Playback Systems
Unit 1b South, New England House, Brighton, BN1 4GH
tel: 01273 671 297
email: info@playbacksystems.com
web: ww.playbacksystems.com
contact: Charles Foley
info: Large range of PA equipment available for hire from 1kW to 40kW. Playback also provide recording and rehearsal facilities. See entries in relevant sections for further details.

Powerbase Sound Hire
Unit 1B, Little Caring Farm, Caring Road, Leeds, Kent, ME17 1TH
tel: 01622 861 626
fax: 01622 861 626
email: andy@powerbasesoundhire.com
web: www.powerbasesoundhire.com
contact: Andy Holliday
info: Full audio equipment hire with or without engineer. Lighting and delivery also available.

Satlinks
Chorlton House, 45 Station Road, Henley on Thames, RG9 1AT
tel: 01491 681 089
web: www.nowdance.com
info: High quality audio-visual equipment available for hire. See website for more details.

Showtec Lighting & Sound
82 High Street, Shoreham-by-Sea, West Sussex, BN43 5DE
tel: 01273 464 999
fax: 01273 462 258
email: mark@showtec.co.uk
web: www.showtec.co.uk
contact: Mark Smith
info: Full production equipment available for hire for small PAs to large scale lighting staging audio-visual and more. Delivery service, sales and maintenance also available.

Sound by Design Ltd.
Unit 1D, The Lansbury Estate, Lower Guildford Road, Knaphill, Surrey, GU21 2EP
tel: 01483 797 242
fax: 01483 797 256
email: office@soundbydesign.net
web: www.soundbydesign.net
contact: Andy Callin
info: Audio equipment available for hire from small PAs to large outdoor events. Service and delivery also available.

Sound Foundation
Unit 23, Headley Park 10, Woodleigh, Reading, Berkshire, RG5 4SW
tel: 0118 969 0900
email: hire@soundfoundation.com
web: www.soundfoundation.com
info: PA and lighting equipment for hire. Dry hire and 24 hour backup available. Sound Foundation also cover the entire London area. Have a separate audio-visual department.

SoundBarrier Systems
4 Knowsley Cresent, Cosham, Portsmouth, PO6 2PJ
tel: 07709 815 242
web: www.soundbarriersystems.com
contact: Simon
info: Massive range of equipment available for hire. Small PAs to large outdoor arenas catered for. CD duplication amongst other services also offered.

Soundcheck Ltd.
70 Sydney Road, Watford, Hertfordshire, WD18 7PR
tel: 0870 728 5296
fax: 0870 728 5269
email: mail@soundcheckltd.co.uk
web: www.soundcheckltd.co.uk
contact: Graham Backhouse
info: Anything from small vocal PAs to large scale outdoor audio equipment. Delivery, engineer and repair service also available.

SRD Group Ltd. (Tonbridge)
27 Shipbourne Road, Tonbridge, Kent, TN10 3DN
tel: 01732 373 920
fax: 01732 373 921
email: info@srdgroup.co.uk
web: www.srdgroup.co.uk
contact: Stuart Roberts
info: Small vocal PAs to large outdoor equipment available for hire. Repairs offered. No delivery. Also branch based in London. See listing in Greater London region for details.

MUSIC SERVICES/RETAIL

Stage Services Ltd.
Unit C8, Ford Airfield Industrial Estate, Ford, Arundle, West Sussex, BN18 0HY
tel:	01903 716 333
email:	info@stage-services.co.uk
web:	www.stage-services.co.uk
contact:	Jon Collins
info:	Stockists of large scale production and audio equipment. Delivery and engineer also available.

Stage Two Ltd.
Unit J, Penfold Trading Estate, Imperial Way, Watford, WD24 4YY
tel:	01923 230 789
fax:	01923 255 048
email:	richard.ford@stage-two.co.uk
web:	www.stage-two.co.uk
contact:	Richard Ford
info:	Audio-visual equipment stockists. Backline available for hire.

Stagebeat Ltd.
Unit 3, Riverside Industrial Park, Dogflud Way, Farnham, Surrey, GU9 7UG
tel:	0871 550 0500
fax:	01252 718 656
email:	sales@stagebeat.com
web:	www.stagebeat.com
info:	Huge selection of instruments, equipment and accessories. Audio equipment available for hire with or without engineer. Call for more information.

Subfrantic Productions
Top Floor Suite, 90 Queen Anne Avnue, Bromley, BR2 0SD
tel:	01959 535 175
fax:	01959 535 176
email:	info@subfrantic.com
web:	www.subfrantic.com
contact:	Stephen Davies
info:	Live audio equipment from small PAs to large scale sound systems available for hire with delivery and engineer.

System Sound & Light
1 Liddall Way, West Drayton, Middlesex, UB7 8PG
tel:	01895 432 995
fax:	01895 432 976
email:	ralph@systemsound.com
web:	www.systemsound.co.uk
contact:	Ralph Biddulph
info:	Audio equipment available for hire from small vocal PAs to large outdoor systems. No dry hire.

Tiger Hire
Unit 3, Grove Farms, Milton Hill, Abingdon, Oxon, OX14 4DP
tel:	01235 834 000
fax:	0870 133 4707
email:	jim@tigerhire.com
web:	www.tigerhire.com
contact:	Jim Parsons
info:	Live audio equipment for hire from concert halls to village halls. Delivery sales and repair also available.

Tweeters 2 Studios
Unit C1, Business Park 7, Brook Way, Leatherhead, Surrey, KT22 7NA
tel:	01372 386 592
email:	info@tweeters2studios.co.uk
web:	www.tweeters2studios.co.uk
info:	Wide selection of instruments and equipment available for hire. Also provide recording and rehearsal facilities. See listiings in relevant sections for details.

Varnam Electroacoustic
3 Hazelmere Road, St. Albans, Hertfordshire, AL4 9RR
tel:	0870 066 0371
email:	info@varnam.biz
web:	www.varnam.biz
contact:	Chris Varnam
info:	Full range of professional live audio equipment available for hire. Support services also available including repairs, delivery, site management and additional lighting.

Wireless Mics & Ears
Unit 2, Heybridge Enterprise Centre, The Street, Heybridge, Maldon, CM9 4NN
tel:	01621 843 200
fax:	01621 843 201
email:	info@wirelessmics.co.uk
web:	www.wirelessmics.co.uk
info:	Wireless mics and in-ear monitor systems for hire.

SOUTHWEST

Announcement Audio Services
4 Oke Tor Close, Windmill Green, Paignton, Devon, TQ3 1TP
tel:	01803 527 811
fax:	01803 527 811
email:	an.norris@blueyonder.com
contact:	Steve Norris
info:	Sales and hire of pro audio equipment. No dry hire.

APR Audio
Lee House, Frobisher Way, Taunton, Somerset, TA2 6BB
tel:	01823 672 908
fax:	01823 282 598
email:	info@apraudio.com
web:	www.apraudio.com
contact:	Andy Reed
info:	Full range of audio equipment available for hire with or without engineer. Delivery service and sales also available.

Atlantic Audio Ltd.
50c Lynch Lane, Weymouth, Dorset, DT4 9DN
tel:	01305 781 010
fax:	01305 776 680
email:	office@atlanticaudio.co.uk
web:	www.atlanticaudio.co.uk
contact:	Phil Say
info:	Full range of live audio equipment available for hire with or without engineer. Sales and delivery also available.

Audioforum Ltd.
Unit 20, Dixon Business Centre, Dixon Road, Bristol, BS4 5QW
tel:	0870 240 6444
fax:	0117 972 3926
email:	hire@audioforum.co.uk
web:	www.audioforum.co.uk
contact:	Mike Reeves
info:	Full audio and visual rigs for nightclubs and gigs. Dry or with engineer. Delivery and pick up service available.

Bulrush Studios
Unit 5, Enterprise Park, Mart Road, Minehead, Somerset, TA24 5BJ
tel:	01643 707 277
email:	info@bulrushstudios.co.uk
web:	www.bulrushstudios.co.uk
info:	Hire service for PA and drum kits. Dry hire. Bulrush Studios also offer recording and rehearsal facilities, CD duplication and drum tuition services. See entries in relevant sections for details.

Concert Production Services Ltd.
Unit 47, Western Business Park, Aviation Park West, Bournemouth Airport, Christchurch, BH23 6NW
tel:	01202 572 000
fax:	01202 599 900
email:	enquiries@c-p-s.group.com
web:	www.c-p-s-group.com
contact:	Chris Caton
info:	Live sound equipment available for hire. Dry hire and nationwide delivery. Lighting and QV equipment also available.

Drum Bank Music Services
203 Gloucester Road, Bishopston, Bristol, BS7 8NN
tel:	0117 975 5366
email:	paul@drumbankmusic.co.uk
web:	www.drumbankmusic.co.uk
info:	Drum kits, vocal PAs, amps, as well as congas and bongos available for hire. Drum Bank also provide rehearsal facilities and music tuition services, plus run an instrument store. See relevant listings for details.

ESP Production
Unit 16, Lufton Heights Commerce Park, Boundry Way, Lufton, Somerset, BA22 8UY
tel:	01935 424 070
email:	info@espproduction.co.uk
web:	www.espproduction.co.uk
contact:	David Wynn
info:	Dry hire available for small vocal PAs. Large scale outdoor systems also available with engineer. Delivery service.

Glass Tone Productions Ltd.
Unit 3A, Riverside Business Park, Bath, Somerset, BA1 3DW
tel:	01225 487 700
email:	info@glasstone.co.uk
web:	www.glasstone.co.uk
contact:	Greg Brooker
info:	Sound equipment including speakers, amps, monitors and desk. Check website for hire rates and full technical specification. Glass Tone also offer recording and rehearsal studios, management, mastering and design services, as well as organising live events in Bath and Bristol. Refer to entries in appropriate sections.

WERE YOU BORN TO PERFORM TOO?

PA SERIES
Starting from just £399*

A Professional Mixer for the Real World

No other small format mixer makes it so simple to achieve a great audio performance every time.

With crystal clear sound, editable FX, full 100mm faders, digital output on SPDIF,
4 band EQ on inputs and outputs and a choice of 12 to 28 channel frame sizes, this mixer is a natural born player.

And in the powered versions, an amplifier delivering a massive 1000 watts of pure, unadulterated power – it's truly loud & clear.

Added to all these great features and like every other professional ALLEN&HEATH console, the PA Series is built to last – with individual circuit boards all firmly bolted to the panel, rugged faders and solid copper buss bar.

To find out how easy it is to get a great performance every time – check out the user guide at www.allen-heath.com

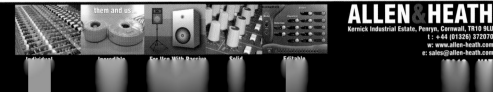

ALLEN&HEATH
Kernick Industrial Estate, Penryn, Cornwall, TR10 9LU
t : +44 (01326) 372070
w: www.allen-heath.com
e: sales@allen-heath.com

MUSIC SERVICES/RETAIL

Happy Daze Sound & Light
Unit 3, Dodnor Lane, Newport, PO30 5XA
tel: 01983 525 711
info: Sound, lighting, disco, audio-visual equipment. Plasma screens and projectors. Delivery and pick up. Dry hire, sales and repairs.

Hipposound PA Hire
Park Farm, Buckland Down, Buckland Dinham, Frome, Somerset, BA11 2RG
tel: 01373 813 590
fax: 01373 813 518
email: john.wirtz@hipposound.co.uk
contact: John Wirtz
info: Live audio equipment available for hire with engineer. Delivery service also available.

Nathan Williams Bmus (Hons)
21a Northload Road, Glastonbury, BA6 9JJ
tel: 01458 835 272
email: nathanvibration@yahoo.co.uk
info: PA hire for acoustic acts and sound engineering for live and studio work. Can produce demos for bands, and also teach basic sound engineering.

NUB Sound Ltd.
23-25 St. John's Road, Cattedown, Plymouth, PL4 0PA
tel: 01725 255 456
fax: 01725 252 227
email: clie@nubsound.co.uk
web: www.nubsound.co.uk
contact: Clive Barnes
info: Small vocal PAs to full production with staging and lighting. Dry hire or with engineer. Delivery service provided.

PMC Ltd.
21-24 St. John's Road, Cattedown, Plymouth, PL4 0PA
tel: 01752 201 275
fax: 01752 262 662
email: info@pmc.net
web: www.pmc.net
contact: Dave Summers
info: Live audio equipment hire.

Rock PA
5 Baydon Close, Eggbuckland, Plymouth, PL6 5QW
tel: 01752 774 904
fax: 01752 300 050
email: rockpauk@aol.com
web: www.rockpahire.co.uk
contact: Jeff Heape
info: Audio equipment available for hire from small vocal PAs to large scale events. Full service provided including engineer and delivery.

Sonix
Studio House, 5 Flowers Hill, Bristol, BS4 5JJ
tel: 0117 908 5558
email: hire@sonixaudio.com
web: www.sonixaudio.com
contact: Paul Gould
info: Range of live audio equipment available for hire with engineer. Delivery also offered.

Stage Electrics
Third Way, Avonmouth, Bristol, BS11 9YL
tel: 0117 938 4000
fax: 0117 938 4000
email: sales@stage-electrics.co.uk
web: www.stage-electrics.co.uk
contact: Adrian Searle
info: Live audio equipment available nationwide for hire with delivery and engineer.

Unique Sound Systems
Unit 40, Enterprise Way, Cheltenham Trade Park, Arle Road, Cheltenham, GL51 8LZ
tel: 01242 261 438
fax: 01242 254 942
email: info@uniquesoundsys.co.uk
web: www.uniquesoundsys.co.uk
info: Audio equipment available for hire with or without engineer. Sales, delivery and repairs also available.

YORKSHIRE

3D Productions
Wellington Mill, Wellington Grove, Bramley, Leeds, LS13 2TE
tel: 0113 236 3700
fax: 0113 257 9900
email: sales@3dproductions.co.uk
web: www.3dproductions.co.uk
contact: David Whittlestone
info: Wide range of live audio equipment available for hire. See website for more details.

Abbey Sound & Light
Unit A14, Whitemoore Business Park, Cliffe Common, Selby, North Yorkshire, YO8 6EG
tel: 01757 282 391
fax: 01757 282 392
email: abbeysound@aol.com
contact: Gary Mattison
info: Dry hire and engineer hire. Delivery and pick up service, as well as repairs and maintenance.

Audio Alchemy
177 Dalton Green Lane, Huddersfield, West Yorkshire, HD5 9TS
tel: 01484 538 905
email: audioalchemy@btinternet.com
contact: David Schofield
info: Full range of equipment to hire and purchase for live music events including PA systems and amps. Dry hire available, as well as delivery and collection service.

Big 3 Productions
Leeds
tel: 07843 556 730
email: info@big3.co.uk
web: www.big3.co.uk
contact: Mike Thrussell
info: 1kW PA available for hire, either dry or with engineer. Other equipment available. Contact Mike for details. Big 3 Productions also offer recording and mastering services. See listings in relevant sections for further information.

Bok
Stagworks, 84 John Street, Sheffield, S2 4QU
tel: 0114 279 5487
contact: Bert Rodgers
info: PA, studio equipment, mics, drum kit available for hire plus much more. Contact Bert Rodgers for more information. Bok also run rehearsal rooms and a recording studio. Refer to entries in relevant sections for further details.

Dave Cass Keyboard & PA Hire
135 Ring Road, Lower Wortley, Leeds, LS12 6LA
tel: 0113 263 9722
fax: 0113 263 5058
email: balloonparade@tinyworld.co.uk
contact: Dave Cass
info: Wide range of live audio equipment available for hire, including backline, keyboards and drum machines. Also provides backing tracks.

Dezign Audio (Sound & Light)
1 St. David's View, Airmyn, Goole, DN14 8JJ
tel: 01405 767 039/07768 996 255
fax: 01405 767 354
contact: Barry or June Newby
info: Full range of live and recording audio equipment for hire. Also offer crewing, trucking and tour management. Contact for more details.

Dilate Lighting
30 Stainburn Crescent, Moortown, Leeds, LS17 6NS
tel: 0113 269 4608/07890 577 680
email: dilatelighting@tiscali.co.uk
web: http://myweb.tiscali.co.uk/dilatelighting
contact: Sean Mason
info: Lighting rigs available for hire from £40 with engineer. Contact for more details.

Essentially Acoustic
16 Magna Cresent, Wickersley, Rotherham, S66 2HD
tel: 01709 546 555
email: pts@barrel.demon.co.uk
web: www.barrel.demon.co.uk
contact: Pete, Chris
info: Small vocal PAs to large outdoor equipment available for hire. See website for more information.

MUSIC SERVICES/RETAIL

Eurosound
42 High Street, Clayton West, Huddersfield, West Yorkshire, HD8 9NS
tel:	01484 861 507
email:	sales@eurosound.co.uk
web:	www.eurosound.co.uk
contact:	Paul Martin
info:	Eurosound specialises in the design of lighting rigs but also provides a full lighting and sound hire and sales service. Dry hire available if requested. Delivery and collection service.

Event Sound & Light
4 Brackenwood Close, Leeds, LS8 1RL
tel:	0113 266 1544
fax:	0113 266 1544
email:	callevent@aol.com
contact:	Keith Harper
info:	Sound equipment available for hire. Contact for more details.

Fairbank Harding Ltd.
38 Chapeltown, Pudsey, West Yorkshire, LS28 8BL
tel:	0113 257 0020
fax:	0113 257 0732
email:	sales@fairbankharding.com
web:	www.fairbankharding.com
contact:	Andrew Fairbank
info:	Audio-visual specialists. Dry hire, delivery and sales available.

Ghosttown Studio
Leeds
email:	info@ghosttownrec.co.uk
web:	www.ghosttownrec.co.uk
contact:	Simon
info:	Offer PA hire for £100 including engineer. Recording, mastering and duplication services are also available. See entries in relevant sections for further details.

HPSS Ltd.
Unit 5, Dairycoates Industrial Estate, Wiltshire Road, Hull, HU4 6PA
tel:	01482 221 810
fax:	01482 221 735
email:	hire@hpss.co.uk
web:	www.hpss.co.uk
contact:	Hugh Jones
info:	Full hire of live audio equipment. Delivery, repair and sales also available.

Jam Studios
Unit 4a, Roseville Trading Estate, Roseville Road, Leeds, LS8 5DT
tel:	0113 242 7700
email:	info@jamstudios.co.uk
web:	www.jamstudios.co.uk
info:	4.5kW Logic 1090 rig available for hire with engineer and transport from £250, or 2kW CM12 Logic rig from £165. No dry hire. 400W PA available for dry hire, £45 per day. Can also supply backline (full drum kits £35 per day, bass and guitar amps £20 per day). Cash deposit required for all rentals. Equipment can be collected from 6pm and must returned by 6pm the following day, although alternative times can be arranged. Range of lighting available to hire. Also offer rehearsal studio facilities. See listing in relevant section for further details.

JTB Audio
Leeds, LS17
tel:	0113 293 9800
email:	sales@jtbaudio.co.uk
web:	www.jtbaudio.co.uk
contact:	Jason Brooks
info:	Audio equipment hire with engineer. Delivery service, sales and repair also available.

Live Art Studios
1 Newton Street, Barnsley, South Yorkshire, S70 6DA
tel:	01226 244 889
email:	enquiries@liveartstudios.co.uk
web:	www.liveartstudios.co.uk
contact:	Phil Quinn
info:	Live audio equipment available for hire. PAs up to 1.5kW with engineer and delivery also available.

Onelouder Media Group
89 Romanby Road, Northallerton, North Yorkshire, DL7 8FH
tel:	01609 781 611
email:	richard@oneloudermedia.com
web:	www.oneloudermedia.com
contact:	Richard Doney
info:	Range of live audio equipment for hire from small vocal PAs to medium outdoor equipment. Delivery and engineer also offered.

PPA Sound Equipment
2 Westmoreland Mount, Leeds, West Yorkshire, LS13 2JG
tel:	0113 257 7076
email:	ppasound@ntlworld.com
contact:	Dave Bellwood
info:	Full PA hire service with the possibility of lighting hire through associated companies. Dry hire available, as well as delivery and collection services.

Pro Audio Systems Ltd.
153-155 Sunbridge Road, Bradford, West Yorkshire, BD1 2NU
tel:	01274 777 200
fax:	01274 777 100
email:	info@pasystems.co.uk
web:	www.proaudiosystems.co.uk
contact:	Andrew Brooks
info:	Small pub PAs to large scale festival equipment available for hire with or without engineer. Delivery service and repairs also provided.

Purple Pro Audio
Unit B, St. Catherine's Business Park, Broad Lane, Bramley, Leeds, LS13 2TD
tel:	0113 290 9161
email:	info@purpleproaudio.com
web:	www.purpleproaudio.com
contact:	Martin Robinson
info:	Purple Pro Audio supply individually tailored audio solutions at competitive rates. High quality audio equipment with professional and experienced crew. Can provide complete packages, from small vocal PAs to corporate presentations to outdoor festivals. Also offer rehearsal space and studio recording. See entries in relevant sections for details.

Rock-Tech Projects Ltd.
Murton Lane, York, YO19 5UF
tel:	01904 481 700
email:	info@rock-tech.co.uk
web:	www.rock-tech.co.uk
contact:	Phil Adlam
info:	Rock-Tech hire out sound and lighting equipment mainly as part of a full production package, but dry hire is available. All events can be catered for from 100 to 100,000 people!

Shadowland Audio Solutions
35 Wellington Terrace, Bramley, Leeds, LS13 2LH
tel:	0113 256 8663
contact:	Steve
info:	Range of audio equipment available for hire including desks, effects and DJ gear. Repairs delivery and installation also available. Contact for more details.

Snow Sound Projects
73 Royal Park Avenue, Leeds, LS6 1EZ
tel:	0113 274 0031
fax:	0113 228 0254
contact:	Om Smith
info:	Desks, effects and backline available for hire. Also offer tour management. See website for more details.

TMC
Hilam Road, Bradford, BD2 1QN
tel:	01274 370 966
fax:	01274 308 706
email:	sales@tmc.ltd.uk
web:	www.tmc.ltd.uk
info:	Sales hire and installation of live audio equipment.

Treble Clef Music Shop
23 Huddersfield Road, Brighouse, HD6 1LE
tel:	01484 715 417
email:	tclef@gotadsl.co.uk
info:	PA systems and amps for hire with or without engineers.

Viking Sound & Light Ltd.
Unit 9, Woodstock Close, Standard Way Industrial Estate, Northallerton, North Yorkshire, DL6 2NB
tel:	01609 780 190
fax:	01609 780 190
email:	steve@vikingsound.co.uk
web:	www.vikingsound.co.uk
contact:	Steve Williams
info:	Viking Sound specialise in larger scale live audio equipment available for hire. Delivery service provided for sales.

Yorkshire Audio
537 Dewsbury Road, Leeds, LS11 5LE
tel:	0113 277 0952/07836 769 136
fax:	0113 277 0952
contact:	Bob Collinson
info:	All industry standard outboard effects plus trucking and crewing. Usually do large scale events such as arena concerts. Contact for more details.

MUSIC SERVICES/RETAIL

Zig Zag Lighting
PO Box 62, Rawdon, Leeds, LS19 6XQ
tel:	0113 250 6980
fax:	0113 250 2980
contact:	Neil Hunt
info:	Lighting available from £40 with or without engineer.

Larger rigs available. Contact for details.

NORTHERN IRELAND

ACK Productions
Unit 2, Duncrue Industrial Estate, Duncrue Road, Belfast, BT3 9BP
tel:	028 9077 9999
fax:	028 9037 0687
email:	info@ackproductions.co.uk
web:	www.ackproductions.co.uk
contact:	Alastair Kerr
info:	Full range of audio-visual equipment available for hire

with or without engineer. Delivery and repairs also available.

All Round Productions
19 Haypark Avenue, Belfast, BT7 3FD
tel:	07855 037 657
email:	arproductions@bigfoot.com
contact:	Aidan Hughes
info:	Wide range of live audio equipment available for hire.

With or without engineer. Delivery also provided.

Ampec
3 Roseville Avenue, Bangor, County Down, BT19 1BZ
tel:	028 9127 0221
email:	ampec@btconnect.com
contact:	John McDowel
info:	Live audio equipment hire. Delivery and engineer

provided. No dry hire.

Art Lighting Services
49 Ballymena Road, Cullybackey, Antrim, BT42 1DT
tel:	028 2588 1007
fax:	028 2588 2055
email:	info@aptees.co.uk
web:	www.aptees.co.uk
contact:	Andrew Thompson
info:	Range of production equipment available for hire

including staging and backline.

Baird's Hire Service
208 York Street, Belfast, Antrim, BT15 1JJ
tel:	028 9074 3253
fax:	028 9074 1117
email:	info@bairdsoundsystem.com
contact:	Derren Baird
info:	Wide range of audio equipment available for hire

including backline and lighting rigs.

Production Services Ireland
Unit 15, Lowes Industrial Estate, Ballynahinch Road, Carryduff, Belfast, BT8 8EH
tel:	028 9081 4858
fax:	028 9081 4846
email:	info@productionireland.com
web:	www.productionireland.com
contact:	Brian Reilly
info:	Sound and lighting equipment hire. Sales service and

delivery available.

REA Sound NI Ltd.
57 Drum Road, Cookstown, County Tyrone, BT80 8QS
tel:	028 8676 4059
fax:	028 8676 4141
email:	sean@reasound.com
web:	www.reasound.com
contact:	Sean Gallagher
info:	Audio equipment available for hire with engineer and

delivery.

Zest Audio
Unit 412, Lisburn Enterprise Park, Ballinderry Road, Lisburn, BT28 2BP
tel:	028 9264 8898
email:	david@zestaudio.com
web:	www.zestaudio.com
contact:	David Honeyford
info:	Range of audio equipment available for hire.

SCOTLAND

A & R Martin Ltd.
Unit 20, 32 Dryden Road, Loanhead, Midlothian, EH20 9LZ
tel:	0131 448 2703
email:	mail@soundmartin.co.uk
web:	www.soundmartin.co.uk
info:	Full range of audio visual equipment available for hire,

either with or without engineer. Delivery, sales, service and repairs also available. See website for more details.

Acousta Sound Reinforcement Hire
51 Westfield Loan, Forfar, DD8 1JN
tel:	01307 467 754
web:	www.acousta.co.uk
contact:	Graham Irving
info:	Sound equipment available for hire. 1kW to 5kW

systems with engineer. Contact for more details.

ACR Productions
10c Canmore Street, Dunfermline, Fife, KY12 7NT
tel:	01383 741 500
email:	bal@acrproductions.co.uk
web:	www.acrproductions.co.uk
info:	PAs up to 2kW available for hire. ACR Productions also

provide recording and rehearsal facilities. See relevant sections for more details.

A-Line Audio Visual Services
Park Hill, Dyce, Aberdeen, AB21 7AT
tel:	01224 723 377
email:	info@a-line.co.uk
web:	www.a-line.co.uk
info:	Range of conference sized PAs available for hire with

some larger systems available. Contact for more details.

Ambient Sound Hire
44 Muirhead, Stonehouse, Larhall, ML9 3HQ
tel:	01698 794 848
info:	Live audio equipment available for hire and installation.

Small vocal PAs. Contact for more details.

Apex Acoustics Sound Services Ltd.
6 North Isla Street, Dundee, DD3 7JQ
tel:	01382 818 513
fax:	01382 423 252
email:	enquiries@apexacoustics.com
web:	www.apexacoustics.com
contact:	Paul Smith
info:	Full touring systems. Radio mic specialists. Simple

public address system to complex theatre productions, concerts and large scale events. Delivery and pick up service.

Banana Row
47 Eyre Place, Edinburgh, EH3 5EY
tel:	0131 557 5533
email:	music@bananarow.com
web:	www.bananarow.com
info:	Provide dry hire, collections, as well as lighting and

sales. Some repairs. Also provide rehearsal rooms and recording studios, as well as drums and percussion tuition.

BBG
51 Tower Street, Edinburgh, EH6 7BN
tel:	01875 823 320
contact:	Guss Boyd
info:	Hire of sound systems up to 8kW available with delivery

and engineer also offered. Contact for more details.

Blinding Light
40 Abbotswell Road, Aberdeen, Aberdeenshire, AB12 3AB
tel:	01224 877 800
email:	info@blindinglight.co.uk
web:	www.blindinglight.co.uk
info:	Range of live audio equipment available for hire as well

as lighting rigs. Contact or see website for more details.

Blue Audio
91 Coalburn Road, Lanark, Lanarkshire, ML11 0LS
tel:	01555 820 816
email:	info@blueaudio.co.uk
web:	www.blueaudio.co.uk
info:	Live audio equipment available for hire with or without

engineer. Delivery, sales, and repair also available. See website for more information.

Border Sound Services
33 Highcroft, Kelso, Roxburghshire, TD5 7NB
tel:	01573 223 341
email:	bdrsound@aol.com
contact:	Malcom McLaren
info:	Small vocal PAs and recording equipment available for

hire. Contact for more details.

the|unsigned|guide

System Hire
Theatre, Concert, Musical

Dry Hire
Radio Mics, PA, Backline

GB·AUDIO

Sales
Main Dealership for leading brands

System Design & Installation
Experienced professional team

www.gbaudio.co.uk   0131 661 0022

Carlton Studio
54 Carlton Place, Glasgow, G5 9TW
tel: 0141 429 5723
contact: James Mc Kechan
info: Guitar amp and cymbal hire. Also provide rehearsal and recording facilities. See relevant sections for more details.

DM Audio
22 Dudingston Road, Edinburgh, E15 1NE
tel: 0131 620 0456
fax: 0131 620 1423
email: info@dmaudio.co.uk
web: www.dmaudio.co.uk
info: Full range of live audio equipment including backline and DJ equipment available for hire. See website for prices.

Dyna-Mix
Craigend Place, Glasgow, Lanarkshire, G13 2UN
tel: 0141 950 2700
contact: Gerry Radford
info: From small vocal PAs to large scale concert equipment available for hire. Contact for more details.

EFX Audio
The Old Fire Station, 59-59a Muir Road, Bathgate, West Lothian, EH48 2QH
tel: 01506 633 356
fax: 01506 630 023
email: efxaudio@easynet.co.uk
web: www.efxaudio.org.uk
contact: John Ramsey
info: PA hire and installation. Engineer provided. Delivery and collection service. Will provide sound equipment for small scale gigs to festivals. Previous clients include T in the Park.

Equinox Events & Discos
214 Townhill Road, Dunfermline, Fife, KY12 0DW
tel: 0800 074 8365
email: info@equinoxdiscos.co.uk
web: www.equinoxdiscos.co.uk
contact: Ashley Duncan
info: Full production equipment available for hire, from small vocal PAs to 40kW outdoor rigs with staging and lighting. Delivery and installation offered.

Full Circle Training Ltd.
Arran House, Arran Road, Perth, PH1 3DZ
tel: 01738 459 260
info: AV equipment sales and hire. Contact for more details.

G.M.S (Recordings)
Kinneil House, Kirk Entry, Boness Road, Polmot, Falkirk, FK2 0QS
tel: 01324 711 011
email: info@gmsmusic.com
web: www.gmsmusic.com
info: Audio equipment available for hire from small vocal PAs to large outdoor events. Delivery and engineer also available. See website for more details.

GB Audio
Unit D, 51 Brunswick Road, Edinburgh, EH7 5PD
tel: 0131 661 0022
email: sales@gbaudio.co.uk
web: www.gbaudio.co.uk
contact: Graham Bodenham
info: Sales, installation, rentals and repair of live audio equipment.

Great Big Resources Ltd.
Unit 24-25, Mossedge Industrial Estate, 10 Moss Road, Linwood, PA3 3HR
tel: 0845 230 6160
email: info@greatbigresources.co.uk
web: www.greatbigresources.co.uk
info: Range of live audio and visual equipment available for hire and installation.

Hyper PA Hire
20 Waukglen Drive, Glasgow, G53 7UG
tel: 0141 620 0717
info: Small vocal PAs to large outdoor equipment available for hire. 24 hours a day with or without engineer.

Kirkby Sound
15 Craigs Park, Edinburgh, Midlothian, EH12 8UL
tel: 07859 832 112
email: enquiries@kirkbysound.co.uk
web: www.kirkbysound.co.uk
contact: Andrew Kirkby
info: Full range of audio equipment available for hire with delivery, sales, service and repair. See website for more details.

Knights Electronics
14 Stoneybank Road, Musselburgh, EH12 6HJ
tel: 0131 665 5169
email: sales@addabox.com
web: www.addabox.com
contact: Stuart Mind
info: Range of small vocal PAs available for hire 100W. Contact for more details.

Limelights
3 Connel Court, Ardconnel Street, Inverness, IV2 3EY
tel: 01463 714 019
email: info@limelights.co.uk
web: www.limelights.co.uk
info: Full range of live audio equipment available for hire with or without engineer. Delivery sales and repair also offered.

Live Systems
Unit 12, North Leith Sands, Leith, Edinburgh, EH6 4ER
tel: 0131 557 8752
fax: 0870 458 0615
email: info@livesystems.co.uk
web: www.livesystems.co.uk
info: Full range of audio and visual equipment available for hire. Engineer, delivery and sales also available.

MCL Edinburgh
Unit 12a, West Craigs Industrial Estate, Turnhouse Road, Edinburgh, EH12 8NR
tel: 0131 339 6202
email: elainep@mcl-scotland.com
web: www.mclav.com
contact: Elaine Pauline
info: Full range of audio visual equipment available for hire. Project management also offered. Contact for more details.

MCL Glasgow
Unit 13-14, Kinning Park Industrial Estate, 17-19 Maclellan Street, Glasgow, G41 1RR
tel: 0141 427 1326
web: www.mclav.com
info: Wide range of audio visual equipment available for hire. See website for more details.

Moray Firth Audio
Marchfield, Balnain, Drumnadrochit, Inverness, IV63 6TJ
tel: 01456 476 703
email: glen@morayfirthaudio.co.uk
web: www.morayfirthaudio.co.uk
contact: Glen Campbel
info: Full range of indoor/outdoor audio and lighting equipment. Sales delivery and service also available. See website for more details.

Musical Swap Shop
28 Nithsdale Road, Glasgow, Lanarkshire, G41 2AN
tel: 0141 423 1886
email: charles.markes@btconnect.com
info: Musical hire specialists. Guitar, drums, amp, PA equipment and pianos.

Pegasus Sound & Light
23-25 Canongate, Edinburgh, EH8 8BX
tel: 0131 556 1300
email: pegasussl@aol.com
web: www.pegasussl.co.uk
contact: David Hunter
info: Up to 2kW systems available for dry hire. Engineer provided. Contact for more details.

Powerhouse Sound & Light Hire
17 Pollock Road, Newton Mearns, Glasgow, G77 6DH
tel: 0141 639 4008
email: power.house@ntlworld.com
web: www.powerhousescotland.com
contact: David Curle
info: Sound and lighting systems available for hire. Short or long term, with or without engineer.

S.I. Sound & Light
3 Panmure Place, Edinburgh, Midlothian, EH3 9HP
tel: 0131 228 3636
email: hire@sisoundandlight.co.uk
web: www.sisoundandlight.co.uk
info: Full range of live audio equipment available for hire from small vocal PAs to large scale touring rigs. With or without engineer. Delivery and repair also available. See website for more details.

Sound Sense
Midforth Farm, 56 Manse Road, Forth, ML11 8AJ
tel: 01555 812 009
email: sales@soundsense.biz
fax: 01555 812 009
web: www.soundsense.biz
contact: John Weatherby
info: Range of PAs available for hire up to 8k. Delivery service and engineer also offered. Also provide recording services, see listing in relevant section for details.

Soundhire Scotland
Hillbarns, Dunkfeld Road, Blairgowrie, PH10 6SA
tel: 01250 873 988
email: ivor@soundhirescotland.fsnet.co.uk
contact: Ivor
info: Hire of live audio equipment available with engineer and transport. Also sales of anything from plectrums to PAs. Contact for more details.

Sounds Incorporated
17 Main Street, Strathkinness, St. Andrews, Fife, KY16 9RX
tel: 01334 850 588
fax: 01334 850 588
email: enquiries@soundsincscotland.co.uk
web: www.soundsincscotland.co.uk
contact: Gordon Sedgwick
info: Large range of live audio equipment available for hire from small PAs to large outdoor systems. Delivery and engineers also available.

TG Baker
173-175 Glasgow Road, Clydebank, Dunbartonshire, G81 1LQ
tel: 0141 941 3399
email: glasgow@tgbaker.com
web: www.tgbaker.com
contact: Ian Newport
info: Live audio equipment available for hire from small vocal PAs to large outdoor events, with or without engineer. Contact for more details.

W.S. Steele Ltd.
Unit 5-05, Oakbank Industrial Estate, Garscube Road, Glasgow, G20 7LU
tel: 0141 353 3393
email: sales@wssteele.com
web: www.wssteele.com
info: Up to 10kW rig available for hire with delivery and engineer. Also full range of audio equipment. See website for details.

The Warehouse (Edinburgh)
23 Water Street, Leith, Edinburgh, EH6 6SU
tel: 0131 555 6900
fax: 0131 555 6901
email: info@warehousesound.co.uk
web: www.warehousesound.co.uk
contact: Allan Brereton
info: Wide range of live audio equipment available for hire. Engineer, repair, lighting and delivery services also available.

The Warehouse (Glasgow)
40 Carmicheal Street, Glasgow, G51 2QU
tel: 0141 445 4466
fax: 0141 445 3636
email: glhires@warehousesound.co.uk
web: www.warehousesound.co.uk
contact: Ian Gibson
info: See Edinburgh listing.

Xcel PA
1094 Argyle Street, Glasgow, G3
tel: 0141 221 4659
web: www.xcelpa.co.uk
info: Sound and light equipment hire, sales and repairs. Dry hire or with engineer. Part of The Soundhaus which also comprises 350 capacity venue and rehearsal studio. See relevant sections for more details.

Zisys AVMN Ltd.
1 Alexander Place, Irvine, Ayrshire, KA12 0UR
tel: 01294 238 918
email: danny@zisysavmn.co.uk
web: www.zisysavmn.co.uk
contact: Danny Anderson
info: From small vocal PAs to large scale concert systems available for hire with or without engineer. Delivery, sales, repair and lighting also available.

WALES

24 Carrot Promotions
Dyffrynorion, Pentre-Cwrt, Llandysul, Dyfed, SA44 5DL
tel: 01559 362 957
email: info@24carrotpromotions.co.uk
web: www.24carrotpromotions.co.uk
info: Sound, lighting, DJ equipment and marquee hire. Also run online instrument and DJ equipment store (www.djandmusicshop.co.uk)

AB Acoustics
Unit 4, Ely Industrial Estate, Rhondda, Tonypandy, CF40 1RA
tel: 01443 440 404
email: hire@abacoustics.co.uk
web: www.abacoustics.co.uk
info: PA hire with engineer.

Aber Sound Productions Ltd.
Ystwyth Works, Llanfarian, Aberystwyth, Ceredigion, SY23 4NN
tel: 01970 615 079
web: www.abersoundproductions.ltd.uk
info: Front of house and monitor equipment available for hire. See website for full specifications and prices. Recording and rehearsal facilities also available.

Absolute Sound & Lighting Solutions
6-8 Greenfield Road, Colwyn Bay, LL29 8EL
tel: 01492 535 123
email: mail@cps-pa.fsnet.co.uk
web: www.cps-pa.co.uk
info: PA, lighting and crew hire. Event management. PA, lighting and guitar retail. Also an agency representing pub and club entertainers including a large number of covers.

Alteariamotive Sound System
South Wales
tel: 01656 871 305/07901 832 206 (text only)
email: ass@celticrockmusic.com
web: www.celticrockmusic.com
contact: Croc Dinearo
info: PA rigs for all events. Experienced engineers. Live mobile recording. Festival veterans. UV lighting, digital and analogue projection. Staging and tents available. For details of the company's recording studio see entry for Raging Imp Productions in the Recording Studios section. Also run a music retail website for independent, underground music from Wales, see website above.

Carlin Audio
3 Pen Y Parc, Berthddu, Rhosemor, Mold, Clwyd, CH7 6PR
tel: 01352 781 478
email: info@carlinaudio.co.uk
info: PA hire with or without engineer.

Carreg Ateb
Y Ganolfan Deledu, Cibyn, Caernarfon, Gwynedd, LL55 2BD
tel: 01286 677 134
email: post@carregateb.com
web: www.carregateb.com
contact: Louise Cliffe
info: PA hire service. Dry hire. Lighting and repairs also available. CD and DVD duplication service.

Depcult
The Coal Exchange, Mount Stuart Square, Cardiff Bay, Cardiff, CF10 5EH
tel: 02920 462 222
email: depcult@promo-cymru.org
web: www.promo-cymru.org
info: PA hire with or without engineer.

The DJ Warehouse
Unit 10, Neath Abbey Business Park, Neath Abbey, Neath, SA10 7DR
tel: 0870 055 5830
web: www.dj-warehouse.co.uk
info: PAs up to 1.5kW available to hire. Large range of PA, lighting and DJ equipment for sale. The DJ Warehouse also run an agency that books artists and entertainers in holiday parks and cruise ships.

Drake AV Video Ltd.
89 St. Fagan's Road, Fairwater, Cardiff, CF5 3AE
tel: 02920 560 333
email: helen@drakeav.com
web: www.drakeav.com
info: PA hire, dry or with engineer. Audio-visual equipment hire and installation. Video production.

Eight Ball
Penlan Mabws, Llanrhystud, SY23 5BD
tel: 01974 27 2295
fax: 01974 272 295
info: Full hire service available on systems up to 40kW. Delivery and engineer also offered. See website for more details.

Gwynedd PA & Celyn Sound Hire
Tyr Celyn, Clynnog Fawr, Caernarfon, Gwynedd, LL54 5NH
tel: 01286 660 231
email: huw@gpacss.fsbusiness.co.uk
info: PA hire.

Immtech
Unit C, Building 8, Curran Road, Butetown, Cardiff, CF10 5DF
tel: 02920 640 500
fax: 02920 640 600
email: immtech@immtech.co.uk
web: www.immtech.co.uk
info: PA hire available on request. Immtech specialise in training young people in music industry related subjects and multimedia technology. For details of courses provided by Immtech see listing in relevant section.

ITC Productions
Cefn Lea Park, Dolfor, Newtown, Powys, SY16 4AJ
tel: 01686 625 040
email: info@itcproductions.com
web: www.itcproductions.com
info: Sound and lighting equipment hire, sales, installation and production.

JimJam PA
Cardiff
tel: 02920 418 741
email: pa@jimjamsound.co.uk
web: www.jimjamsound.co.uk
info: PA hire for bands, parties, weddings, discos, DJs, dances, gigs and outdoor events. Up to 24 channels 2.4kW. All systems include setup and engineer. See Promoters section for details of JimJam open mic sessions.

JPL Sound & Communication
267 Holton Road, Barry, South Glamorgan, CF63 4HT
tel: 01446 722 711
email: info@jpl-sound.com
web: www.jpl-sound.com
info: PA hire with engineer for both indoor and outdoor events. For details of JPL Sound Communications' instrument shop see the relevant section.

KBMF Audio Ltd.
Llanvanches, Caldicot, Gwent, NP26 3AZ
tel: 01633 400 555
email: info@kbmfaudio.co.uk
web: www.kbmfaudio.co.uk
info: PA hire with or without engineer.

Live Sound Services
Ebenezer House, Cross Common Road, Hebron Hall, Dinas Powys, CF64 4YB
tel: 07915 085 334
email: enquiries@livesoundservices.co.uk
web: www.livesoundservices.co.uk
info: Staging, set, sound, lighting and video projection systems. Hire, sale and installations.

LTS Recording & PA Services
Llanon, SY23
tel: 01974 202 759
email: dfereday@ltsstudio.co.uk
web: www.ltsstudio.co.uk
contact: Dow Fereday
info: PA hire. Mastering is also available.

MAC PA Hire
21 St. David's Avenue, Llanilltud Fawr, Bro Morgannwg, CF61 1RR
tel: 01446 793 708/07703 460 260
email: info@macpahire.co.uk
web: www.macpahire.co.uk
info: PA hire with engineer. Some lighting available, but only when hired with sound equipment.

Magnum PA Ltd.
Head Office, Hafan Deg, Hodgeston, Pembroke, Dyfed, SA71 5JU
tel: 0800 169 2219
email: info@magnumpa.com
web: www.magnumpa.com
info: PA, lighting and audio-visual equipment hire. With or without engineer. Sales, repairs and installation.

MantraSound
Llanfyllin, Powys, SY22
tel: 01691 649 044
email: contact@mantradjs.co.uk
web: www.mantradjs.co.uk
info: PA hire with or without engineer covering the Shropshire and Powys area with scope for the Midlands. MantaSound can also supply disco equipment and DJs. See also The Beehouse (Recording Studios), Mantra CDs and Recording (Mastering and Duplication) and C'mon Records (Record Companies).

MUSIC SERVICES/RETAIL

Mountain Sound Hire System
Flint
tel: 07944 937 498
info: PA hire with or without engineer.

Paradox PA
Newport
tel: 07932 376 604
info: PA hire with engineer. Mackie active speakers.

The Picture Works Ltd.
Llwyndryssi Ty Mawr, Carmarthenshire, SA40 9RB
tel: 0845 310 8321
email: info@pictureworks.co.uk
web: www.pictureworks.co.uk
info: PA, lighting and staging hire. Engineers can be provided. Also produce promotional videos. See relevant section for details.

Pitch Perfect Audio
145 Moy Road, Roath, Cardiff, CF24 4TG
tel: 07729 450 890
email: madhousesounds@hotmail.com
info: PA hire with or without engineer. Up to 2kW.

Planet Earth Productions
8 Navigation Road, Risca, Newport, NP11 6FF
tel: 01633 601 933
info: PA hire. Dry or with full technical back up. Event production including lighting and staging.

Protech Sound & Light
Unit 1a, Sedbury Business Park, Grahamstown Road, Sedbury, Chepstow, NP16 7AD
tel: 01291 630 410
email: protechsoundandlight@tiscali.co.uk
info: PA hire, dry and with engineer. Sound and lighting equipment sales and services. Custom built flight cases for guitars and amps.

PSVS
12-14 Heol Nant Caiach, Millbrook, Treharris, CF46 5RZ
tel: 01443 412 300
email: wayne@psvs.co.uk
web: www.psvs.co.uk
info: PA sales, repair and hire. Audio-visual equipment sales and hire. Sound and lighting installations.

Red Flame Productions
The Regent Centre, Broad Street, Newtown, Powys, SY16 2NA
tel: 01686 624 923
fax: 01686 610 060
email: enquiries@redflame.co.uk
web: www.redflame.co.uk
info: Sound and lighting equipment hire, sales, installation and production. See website for price list.

Rees Sound Hire
Station Approach, Bridge Wharf, Carmarthen, SA31 1TF
tel: 01267 236 811
email: hire@reessound.com
web: www.reessound.com
info: PA hire, dry and with engineer. Lighting and audio-visual equipment hire including cameras and plasma screens. For a full catalogue see the website.

Richard Rayner
Bryn-y-Garreg, Bwlch-y-Frridd, Newton, Powys, SY16 3JW
tel: 07815 517 884
info: Production lighting design. Specialises in live concerts and events.

Rowland's Music
31 St. Helen's Road, Swansea, West Glamorgan, SA1 4AP
tel: 01792 600 269/01792 522 020
email: info@rowlandsmusic.co.uk
web: www.rowlandsmusic.co.uk
info: Instruments and PA equipment available for dry hire or with an engineer. Also run an instrument shop. For details see the relevant section.

SES
Willcroft, Mold Road, Gwersyllt, Wrexham, Clwyd, LL11 4AF
tel: 01978 720 183
email: tony@ses-audio.co.uk
info: PA and audio-visual equipment hire.

Snafu Sound Systems
Wernffrwd, Ponterwyd, Abersystwyth, SY23 3JY
tel: 01970 890 579
email: dave_snafu@hotmail.com
info: PA hire. Lighting, staging and marquees. Dry hire available within reasonable travelling distance. Contact for more details.

Stage Electrics
Unit B4, Westpoint Industrial Estate, Penarth Road, Cardiff, CF11 8JQ
tel: 02920 701 212
email: hires@stage-electrics.co.uk
web: www.stage-electrics.co.uk
info: Hire, sales and repair for sound, lighting and stage equipment. Any size of event can be catered for.

Stage Lighting Services
Unit 3, Field Way, Maes-y-Coed Road, Cardiff, CF14 4UY
tel: 02920 613 577
fax: 02920 523 443
email: phil.hurley@stagesoundservices.co.uk
web: www.stagesoundservices.co.uk
info: Sound, staging and lighting hire and sales suitable for bands, theatres and conferences.

Stav Sound Services
Cfen Coch, The Old Farmhouse, Aberhafesp, Newtown, Powys, SY16 3JG
tel: 01686 689 029
email: info@stavsound.com
web: www.stavsound.com
info: Sound equipment hire and sales. Engineers can be provided. Live music production for venues of all sizes. Lighting systems available for hire.

Sun Sound
4 Pennant Crescent, Cardiff, CF23 6LN
tel: 02920 415 210
email: pa@sunsound.co.uk
web: www.sunsound.co.uk
info: PA and other sound equipment hire, as well as lighting hire.

Sunshine Entertainment Productions Ltd.
106 Hereford Road, Monmouth, Gwent, NP25 3HH
tel: 01600 712 022
email: sunltd@aol.com
contact: Jeff Harris
info: PA, lights and disco hire. Can deliver and collect.

Superior Sound Services
5 Commercial Street, Risca, Newport, NP11 6AW
tel: 01633 612 362/07970 019 985
email: info@superiorsound.co.uk
web: www.superiorsound.co.uk
info: PA hire with or without engineer. Engineer also available for hire without equipment.

Total Sound Solutions
579 Trewyddfa Road, Morriston, Swansea, SA6 7QL
tel: 01792 428 181
email: chris@total-sound-solutions.com
web: www.total-sound-solutions.com
info: Sound, lighting and audio-visual equipment hire and installation.

Wat's On Lighting & Sound Ltd.
Lower Broadheath, Presteigne, Powys, LD8 2HG
tel: 01544 260 114
info: PA and lighting equipment manufacture and hire. Lighting and sound installations for club and live music venues.

Welsh Gigs
8 Fothergill Street, Treforest, Pontypridd, CF37 1SG
email: tom@welshgigs.com
web: www.welshgigs.com
contact: Tom Naylor
info: Equipment available from basic PA to full 10kW front of house system with foldback as well as digital video cameras, projectors and lighting systems. Hire with engineer. Welsh Gigs also run a website covering the Welsh music scene and also promote gigs. See listings in the relevant sections for details.

Winderton Sound & Studio
Winder Studio, Winderton Drive, New Hedges, Tenby, Pembrokeshire
tel: 01834 842 738
email: windertonstudio@hotmail.com
web: www.windertonstudio.co.uk
info: PA hire for all venues - 600W to 10kW systems available. Dry hire available on request. Also run a recording studio - see relevant section for details.

Wrexham Music & Disco Supplies
12 -14 Lord Street, Wrexham, LL11 1LG
tel: 01978 311 668
info: PA and DJ equipment sales and hire. Dry hire or with engineer. Club installations. Also run a record shop, Essential Records. See relevant section for details.

Zelma Sound & Lighting
Unit 10, Neath Abbey Business Park, Neath, SA10 7DR
tel: 01792 813 010
email: sales@zelma.co.uk
web: www.zelma.co.uk
info: Refer to listing for Blackwood branch of Zelma Sound & Lighting.

Zelma Sound & Lighting (Blackwood)
Unit D5 & D6, Britannia Enterprise Centre, Blackwood, Gwent, NP12 3SP
tel: 01443 822 422
email: sales@zelma.co.uk
web: www.zelma.co.uk
info: Lighting, PA and pyrotechnics hire. Dry hire or with engineer. Repair service. Also have branch at Unit 10, Neath Abbey Business Park, Neath, SA10 7DR, tel: 01792 813 010.

MUSIC SERVICES/RETAIL

3.5 INSTRUMENT SHOPS/REPAIR

EAST of ENGLAND 173 GREATER LONDON 175 MIDLANDS 184 NORTHEAST 192 NORTHWEST 194
SOUTHEAST 203 SOUTHWEST 206 YORKSHIRE 209 NORTHERN IRELAND 213 SCOTLAND 215 WALES 219

EAST of ENGLAND

SOUNDCONTROL
The UK's Number One Musical Instrument Retailer

Sound Control (Norwich)
2-4 Annes Walk, Norwich, NR3 1EB
tel: 01603 666 891
fax: 01603 765 239
email: norwich@soundcontrol.co.uk
web: www.soundcontrol.co.uk
contact: Greig Dunning
part exchange: Yes
info: As the largest music equipment retailer in Europe with 25 stores across the UK, Sound Control has the most extensive range of guitars, basses, backline, PA, hi-tech, recording and percussion equipment available at the lowest prices around. Coupled with over 25 years experience and unrivalled staff training, shopping at Sound Control is the easiest step you will make on the road to being signed. Visit the above website to locate your nearest store, or to buy online and have your purchase delivered direct to your door.

1066 Pianos
20-22 Pierce Lane, Fulbourn, Cambridge, CB1 5DL
tel: 01223 881 691
part exchange: No
info: Piano store specialising in top-end rebuilds and sales. Over 8,000 square feet of workshop and showroom space displaying over 80 grand pianos. Major repairs carried out.

Balaam's Music
103 Risbygate Street, Bury St. Edmunds, IP33 3AA
tel: 01284 766 933
email: info@balaamsmusic.co.uk
web: www.balaamsmusic.co.uk
part exchange: Yes
info: Classical instruments including brass, woodwind, digital pianos and keyboards, guitars, bass, drums and percussion. Repairs and notice board space available.

Cookes Band Instruments
34 St. Benedict's Street, Norwich, Norfolk, NR2 4AQ
tel: 01603 623 563
email: theteam@cookes.co.uk
web: www.cookes.co.uk
part exchange: Yes
info: Cookes sell and provide professional advice on guitars, drums, PA, sound and lighting. Notice board space for bands.

David West Music
Norwich Road, Norwich, NR11 7HA
tel: 01263 768 588
email: sales@davidwestmusic.co.uk
web: www.davidwestmusic.co.uk
part exchange: No
info: General music instrument store. Offer keyboard tuition.

Digital Village (Cambridge)
86 Mill Road, Cambridge, CB1 2AS
tel: 01223 316 091
fax: 01223 353 857
email: cambridge@digitalvillage.co.uk
web: www.digitalvillage.co.uk
part exchange: Yes
info: Wide range of recording equipment including computer hardware and software, equipment for DJ or live, MIDI instruments and monitoring. Digital Village has branches throughout London, as well as Birmingham, Southampton and Bristol. See listings in relevant sections for details.

East End Music
142 Felixstowe Road, Ipswich, IP3 8EF
tel: 01473 725 961
email: compassipswitch@btconnect.com
web: www.westendmusic.co.uk
part exchange: No
info: Guitars, amplification, percussion and PA equipment. New and used. Some vintage guitars. Repairs and notice board space available.

Elkin Music
31 Exchange Street, Norwich, NR2 1DP
tel: 01603 666 332
fax: 01603 666 332
part exchange: Yes
info: Sheet music specialists. Stock small range of guitars and basic flutes. Also run mail order service. All types of sheet music on catalogue. Notice board in-store, along with list of tutors.

Fenland Music
59 Market Street, Ely, CB7 4LP
tel: 01353 666 313
part exchange: Yes
info: General musical instrument shop stocking wide range of items. Repairs and tuition on most instruments. Band notice board space.

Gibson Music
5 St. John Maddermarket, Norwich, NR2 1DN
tel: 01603 663 262
email: sales@gibsonmusic.co.uk
web: www.gibsonmusic.co.uk
part exchange: No
info: Specialise in brass and woodwind instruments, sheet music and accessories, as well as offering a repair service, free valuations and local teachers lists. The shop also stocks a range of classical and Acoustic guitars.

The Guitar Shop
2 Soane Street, Ipswich, IP4 2BG
tel: 01473 219 071
email: sales@theguitarshop.co.uk
web: www.theguitarshop.co.uk
part exchange: No
info: New and used guitars. In-store tuition in guitar, sound engineering and PC recording. Notice board space available.

The Guyton Guitar
Unit 4, Park Farm, Harleston Road, Earsham, Bungay, NR35 2AQ
tel: 01986 896 689
web: www.guytonguitars.com
part exchange: Yes
info: The Guyton Guitar Company specialise in building high quality instruments to custom specifications. In the past the owner has done work for Brian May, Bryan Adams and Mark Chapman of 'A'.

Haven Keyboards
486 Felixstowe Road, Ipswich, IP3 8SU
tel: 01473 710 051
email: haven@eur-isp.com
web: www.havenkeyboards.co.uk
part exchange: No
info: New and used keyboards. Dealers of vintage Hammond organs. Repairs available.

Jack White Music
92 Fore Hamlet, Ipswich, IP3 8AF
tel: 01473 257 223
email: music@jackwhite.co.uk
web: www.jackwhite.co.uk
part exchange: No
info: General music store stocking pianos, guitars, keyboards and drums. Tuition in-store in piano, organ, guitar and trombone. Repairs and notice board space available.

John N. Bilham
4 Proctor Road, Sprowston, Norwich, Norfolk, NR6 7PE
tel: 01603 407 936
email: johnbilham@musicalinstrumentrental.co.uk
web: www.saxophonerental.co.uk
part exchange: No
info: Woodwind and brass sales and rentals. Repairs and tuition in clarinet, saxophone and flute.

The Live Music Shop
567-569 Lincoln Road, Peterborough, PE1 2PB
tel: 01733 555 505
email: theshop@thelivemusicshop.com
web: www.thelivemusicshop.com
part exchange: No
info: Guitars, drums and amps along with all other live music instruments. Tuition in guitar, bass and drums. Notice board space in-store.

Lynn Music
23 Norfolk Stret, Kings Lynn, PE30 1AN
tel: 01553 774 390
email: info@lynnmusic.freeserve.co.uk
web: www.lynnmusic.co.uk
part exchange: No
info: General music shop offering tuition in keyboards and guitar, and small repairs.

Mark's Music
Unit 4, Lion Lane, Needham Market, Suffolk, IP6 8NT
tel: 01449 722 733
email: shop@marksmusic.co.uk
web: www.marksmusic.co.uk
part exchange: No
info: Guitars new and used. Repairs offered.

Millers Music
Sussex Street, Cambridge, CB1 1PW
tel: 01223 354 452
email: info@millersmusic.co.uk
web: www.millersmusic.co.uk
part exchange: No
info: Largest music shop in East of England with all 16 staff musicians themselves. Stock everything from drums to triangles. New and second hand. Run rental and hire schemes. Offer discounts to students, interest free credit and money back on rental. Repairs and notice board space.

The Music Hut
16b Church Street, North Walsham, NR28 9DA
tel: 01692 409 716
email: info@music-hut.co.uk
web: www.music-hut.co.uk
part exchange: No
info: For your entire musical instrument needs stocking accessories, parts (i.e. hardware and valves), guitars, keyboards, string, brass and woodwind. Also stock wide range of affordable amplifiers, effects and recording equipment. Books, videos and clothing are available. Instrument and PA hire for all uses. Most types on tuition in-store. Notice board space on website.

Music World
16 Queen Street, Ipswich, IP1 1SS
tel: 01473 253 666
email: enquires@music-world-ipswich.co.uk
web: www.music-world-ipswich.co.uk
part exchange: No
info: General music store. Instruments include guitar, brass, woodwind, accessories and sheet music. Notice board space in-store.

Norwich Drum Acadamy
Unit 1 W2, Scott's Yard, Ber Street, Norwich, NR1 3HA
tel: 01603 443 313
email: info@norwichdrumacademy.com
web: www.norwichdrumacademy.com
part exchange: No
info: Drum store with a teaching studio facility. New and used kits. See website for details of drum master classes with famous Rock drummers such as Chad Smith from Chilli Peppers! Repairs offered.

Oundle Music
13 West Street, Oundle, Peterborough, PE8 4EJ
tel: 01832 273 669
part exchange: No
info: Across the board music store stocking brass, woodwind, strings, sheet music and accessories. In-store drummer offering tuition. Notice board space.

Panic Music Services
Unit D2, Button End Industrial Estate, Harston, Cambridge, CB2 5NX
tel: 01223 873 073
part exchange: Yes
info: Total electronic repair service for the music and recording industry.

Peterborough Music
4 Cattle Market Road, Peterborough, PE1 1TW
tel: 01733 345 385
email: sales@peterboroughmusic.com
web: www.peterboroughmusic.com
part exchange: No
info: Wide range of items including guitars, brass, woodwind, violins and small percussion instruments. Repairs and notice board space available.

Piano Portfolio
91 Heath Road, Norwich, NR3 1JW
tel: 01603 617 717
web: www.pianoportfolio.co.uk
part exchange: No
info: New and used pianos to sell and hire. Tuning, restoration and repairs available. Stock of around 50 pianos.

Procak Violins
15 Raynham Road, Hempton, Fakenham, NR21 7LN
tel: 01328 862 568
part exchange: No
info: Hand crafted violins made to order. Also work with violas and cellos. Works from home. Repairs on request.

Red Z Gig Bagz
4 Proctor Road, Sprowston, Norwich, Norfolk, NR6 7PE
tel: 01603 4079 36
email: sales@gigbagz.co.uk
web: www.gigbagz.co.uk
part exchange: Yes
info: Sell soft lightweight cases offering superb protection for instruments. Each bag incorporates individual design features for their respective instrument. See website for further information.

Rochfords
Old Stowmarket Road, Woolpit, Bury St. Edmunds, IP30 9QS
tel: 01359 245 287
part exchange: No
info: New and used piano sales and rentals, with option to buy. Repairs available.

RP Electronics
5 Websters Close, Glinton, Peterborough, PE6 7LQ
tel: 01733 253 022
email: r.paynter@btconnect.com
part exchange: Yes
info: Call out repairs (private and performance) to all types of electronic instruments for stage.

Savage's John
37 Norfolk Street, Kings Lynn, PE30 1AH
tel: 01553 774 026
email: johnsavages@hotmail.com
part exchange: No
info: Drum specialists. New, used and electronic. Range of accessories. Drum tuition and repairs in store. Notice board space available.

Simply MusicMusic
3-4 All Saints Passage, Huntingdon, PE29 3LE
tel: 01480 431 222
email: simplymusic@talk21.com
web: www.simplymusic-online.co.uk
part exchange: No
info: Stock guitars, bass, drums and accessories. Repairs and notice board space available.

Sounds
Nunns Way, Dereham, NR19 2AN
tel: 01362 696 995
email: info@soundsmusic.co.uk
web: www.soundsmusic.co.uk
part exchange: No
info: Most of store dedicated to guitars, although do sell other instruments as well. Repairs to guitars, brass, woodwind and amplifiers. Large stock of sheet music, CDs and DVDs.

Sounds Plus
8 Risbygate Street, Bury St. Edmunds, IP33 3AA
tel: 01284 703 366
email: sales@soundsplus.co.uk
web: www.soundsplus.co.uk
part exchange: No
info: Guitars, drums and bass. Repairs and notice board space available.

Thetford Music
2 Tanner Court, Tanner Street, Thetford, IP24 2BQ
tel: 01842 766 325
email: thetfordmusic@aol.com
part exchange: No
info: Sell instruments including guitars, drums, basses and accessories. Repairs and guitar tuition in-store. Notice board space available.

Top Joint Music
88 Waterloo Road, Norwich, NR3 1EF
tel: 01603 467 888
email: sales@topjoint.co.uk
web: www.topjoint.co.uk
part exchange: No
info: Brass and woodwind specialists with range of items catering for all your needs. Repairs available.

The Violin Workshop
70a Hartington Grove, Cambridge, CB1 7UB
tel: 01223 411 071
email: info@makeviolins.com
web: www.makeviolins.com
part exchange: No
info: Violin specialists. Make, sell and repair violins, both old and new. Also offer 1 week summer courses in violin making and bow making.

West End Music
27-29 Norwich Road, Ipswich, IP1 2ET
tel: 01473 214 331
email: via website
web: www.westendmusic.co.uk
part exchange: No
info: Guitars, amplification, percussion and PA equipment. New and used. Some vintage guitars. Repairs and notice board space available.

GREATER LONDON

SOUNDCONTROL
The UK's Number One Musical Instrument Retailer

Sound Control (London)
14-16 Oxford Street, London, W1D 1AR
tel: 020 7631 4200
fax: 020 7631 4050
email: london@soundcontrol.co.uk
web: www.soundcontrol.co.uk
contact: Mick Hughes
part exchange: Yes
info: As the largest music equipment retailer in Europe with 25 stores across the UK, Sound Control has the most extensive range of guitars, basses, backline, PA, hi-tech, recording and percussion equipment available at the lowest prices around. Coupled with over 25 years experience and unrivalled staff training, shopping at Sound Control is the easiest step you will make on the road to being signed. Visit the above website to locate your nearest store, or to buy online and have your purchase delivered direct to your door.

A.S.M. Music Rock Shop
318a Kennington Road, London, SE11 4LD
tel: 020 7735 1932
email: amamusic@btinternet.com
web: www.asmmusic.co.uk
part exchange: No
info: General music store offering repairs and noticeboard space for musicians.

ABC Music Ltd. (Eltham)
265 Eltham High Street, Eltham, London, SE9 1TY
tel: 020 8850 4422
fax: 020 8850 4422
web: www.abcmusic.co.uk
part exchange: No
info: Part of ABC music chain and franchise stores. See listing above for information.

ABC Music Ltd. (Hounslow)
433-437 Great West Road, Hounslow, TW5 0BY
tel: 020 8570 4444
fax: 020 8577 5818
web: www.abcmusic.co.uk
part exchange: No
info: Part of ABC music chain and franchise stores. See above listing for information.

ABC Music Ltd. (Kew Gardens)
9 Royal Parade, Station Approach, Kew Gardens, TW9 3QD
tel: 020 8940 1892
fax: 020 8948 2666
web: www.abcmusic.co.uk
part exchange: No
info: Part of ABC music chain and franchise stores. See listing above for information.

ABC Music Ltd. (Wimbledon)
20 Ridgway, Wimbledon Village, London, SW19 4QN
tel: 020 8739 0202
fax: 020 8947 2469
email: wimbledon@abcmusic.co.uk
web: www.abcmusic.co.uk
part exchange: No
info: Sell variety of instruments including brass, percussion, drums, woodwind, guitars, piano, keyboards, amps, sheet music and cases. Repair services available. Tuition in-house, and can recommend other external tutors. Instrument rental scheme on long term and short term basis. Space for musicians' notices and posters in-store. ABC Music also have branches in Greater London and South East regions. See listings in relevant sections for details. ABC Music run a management division for bands and acts. See entry in Management Companies section for further information.

All Flutes Plus
60-61 Warren Street, London, W1T 5NZ
tel: 020 7388 8438
fax: 020 7388 7438
email: enquiries@allflutesplus.co.uk
web: www.allflutesplus.co.uk
part exchange: Yes
info: New and second hand flutes, sheet music and related accessories. Repair service available. Small space for posters and notices.

Andy's Guitars
27 Denmark Street, London, WC2H 8NJ
tel: 020 7916 5080
email: aguitar@btinternet.com
web: www.andysguitarnet.com
part exchange: No
info: Huge selection of guitars and drums. Area on website to post details of local gig listings. Repair service. For guitar lessons, contact 020 7916 5954. Space for notices.

Angel Pianos
2 Albert Mansions, 359 Liverpool Road, London, N1 1NW
tel: 020 7697 0775
email: angelpianos@btinternet.com
part exchange: Yes
info: Piano tuning and repair. Also provide reconditioning and French polishing services.

Antenna Studios
Bowyers Yard, Near Bedwardine Road, Haynes Lane, Crystal Palace, London, SE19 3AN
tel: 020 8653 5285
email: info@antennastudios.co.uk
web: www.antennastudios.co.uk
contact: Jon Dickinson
part exchange: Yes
info: Custom build and repair guitars (electric, Acoustic, bass) and amps. Price list can be downloaded from website. Antenna also run recording and rehearsal studios, as well as offering variety of other services. Refer to entries in relevant sections for details. A skate shop will be opening

Fender®

THE SHAPE OF ROCK AND ROLL SINCE 1954

www.fender.com

Argiriadis Analogue Electronics
163 Alexandra Park Road, London, N22 7UL
tel: 020 8881 1623
web: www.argiriadis-electronics.co.uk
contact: Theo Argiriadis
part exchange: Yes
info: Amplification repairs. Also specialise in designing, building, customising and restoring high quality guitar amps, valve outboard and vintage units.

Audio Repair Shop
414 Uxbridge Road, Shepherds Bush, London, W12 0NR
tel: 020 8743 1400
part exchange: Yes
info: Audio equipment repairs for studio, DJ and hi-fi gear.

Bell Percussion
6 Greenock Road, Acton, London, W3 8DU
tel: 020 8896 1200
fax: 020 8896 0100
email: info@bellperc.com
web: www.bellperc.com
part exchange: Yes
info: Specialist percussion and percussion accessories retailer. Large range of percussion instruments also available for hire. For full equipment hire rates see the Bell Percussion website. Visitors to the website can submit details of second hand percussion instruments they wish to sell. This service is free of charge. Full repair service available. Small space for notices and posters in-store.

BEM Music (Brixton Exchange Mart)
395 Coldharbour Lane, Brixton, London, SW9 8LQ
tel: 020 7733 6821
web: www.bem-music.com
part exchange: No
info: Stock wide range of musical instruments, DJ equipment, and computer software and hardware. Area in-store to leave flyers only.

Blackheath Violin Workshop
26 Tranquil Vale, Blackheath, London, SE3 0AX
tel: 020 8318 0738
part exchange: Yes
info: Specialise in all services for violins. Make, restore and repair. Violins and bows bought and sold. Bow rehairing.

Blanks Music
271-273 Kilburn High Road, London, NW6 7JR
tel: 020 7624 7777
email: info@blanksmusic.co.uk
web: www.blanksmusic.co.uk
part exchange: No
info: Mainly specialise in guitars, although also stock drums, violins, mandolins, banjos, keyboards, woodwind and brass. Buy and sell. Repairs available for stringed instruments. Space for posters and notices.

Broadway Music Ltd.
310 Worple Road, Raynes Park, London, SW20 8QU
tel: 0845 456 1015/020 8739 0081
fax: 020 8739 0081
email: via website
web: www.thinkmusic.co.uk
part exchange: No
info: Stock a huge range of instruments including woodwind, brass, drums, percussion, keyboards, amps and a wide selection of guitars. Also sell printed music, spares and accessories. Repair service for guitars, woodwind and brass instruments. List of music tutors available. Space in-store for poster and flyer display.

C. Kypreos Pianos
5 Leopold Road, London, NW10 9LN
tel: 020 8453 0148
email: cgkypreos@hotmail.com
web: www.geocities.com/kypreospianos
part exchange: No
info: Wide range of pianos in stock. Repair and tuning services available.

Chandler Guitars
300-302 Sandycombe Road, Kew, Richmond, Surrey, TW9 3NG
tel: 020 8940 5874
fax: 020 8948 8203
email: sales@chandlerguitars.co.uk
web: www.chandlerguitars.co.uk
part exchange: No
info: Past clients include the Rolling Stones, The Who, Oasis, Blur, Ash and many more. Stock a range of guitars (Acoustic, electric and bass) including custom built instruments, as well as amps and accessories. Repair service for guitars and amps.

Chappell Of Bond Street
50 New Bond Street, London, W1S 1RD
tel: 020 7491 2777
fax: 020 7491 0133
email: enquiries_bs@chappell-bond-st.co.uk
web: www.chappellofbondstreet.co.uk
part exchange: Yes
info: Established in 1811, Chappell Of Bond Street is the oldest music shop in London. Stock range of instruments including electric and Acoustic pianos, synthesisers, guitars, brass, woodwind and stringed instruments, as well as amplification and software. Also have a massive selection of sheet music.

Chimes Music (Barbican)
Cromwell Tower, Silk Street, Barbican, EC2Y 8DD
tel: 020 7588 9242
email: barbican@chimesmusic.com
web: www.chimesmusic.com
part exchange: Yes
info: Stock some instruments such as recorders and harmonicas. Mainly sell printed music and accessories. Chimes Music has another branch located in Kensington. See listing for details.

Chimes Music (Kensington)
9 Harrington Road, South Kensington, London, SW7 3ES
tel: 020 7589 9054
fax: 020 7225 2662
email: kensington@chimesmusic.com
web: www.chimesmusic.com
part exchange: Yes
info: Mainly stock Classical instruments. Also sell Acoustic guitars, accessories and gifts. Wide selection of sheet music with order service. Repairs available on Acoustic instruments. Space for notices. Chimes Music has another branch located in London. See listing for details.

Chris Bryant Music Ltd.
16 Manette Street, London, W1D 4AP
tel: 020 7287 8823
part exchange: No
info: New and used goods. Stock guitars, amps and effects. Repair service available. Space for notices.

Cliff Owen Music
8-10 Cameron Road, Seven Kings, Ilford, Essex, IG3 8LA
tel: 020 8597 0813
part exchange: No
info: Stock guitars, keyboards, drums, electronic and acoustic pianos, amps and sheet music. Instrument and amp repair service. Space for musician's notices and posters.

Digital Village (Chadwell Heath)
10 High Road, Chadwell Heath, Essex, RM6 6PR
tel: 020 8510 1500
fax: 020 8407 8438
email: southlondon@digitalvillage.co.uk
web: www.digitalvillage.co.uk
part exchange: Yes
info: Part of Digital Village chain. See listing above for information. Digital Village have branches throughout London, as well as Brighton, Birmingham, Southampton and Cambridge. See listings in relevant sections for further details.

Digital Village (High Barnet)
141 High Street, High Barnet, Hertfordshire, EN5 5UZ
tel: 020 8440 3440
fax: 020 8275 3229
email: northlondon@digitalvillage.co.uk
web: www.digitalvillage.co.uk
part exchange: Yes
info: Wide range of recording equipment including computer hardware and software, equipment for DJ or live, MIDI instruments and monitoring. Branches throughout London, as well as Birmingham, Bristol, Southampton and Cambridge. See listings in relevant sections for details.

Digital Village (London)
14 The Broadway, Gunnersbury Lane, London, W3 8HR
tel: 020 8992 5592
fax: 020 8992 4550
email: westlondon@digitalvillage.co.uk
web: www.digitalvillage.co.uk
part exchange: Yes
info: Part of Digital Village chain of stores. See listing above for information. Digital Village have branches throughout London, as well as Bristol, Birmingham, Cambridge and Southampton. See listings in relevant sections for details.

MUSIC SERVICES/RETAIL

Digital Village (South Croydon)
562 Brighton Road, South Croydon, Surrey, CR2 6AW
tel: 020 8407 8444
fax: 020 8407 8438
email: southlondon@digitalvillage.co.uk
web: www.digitalvillage.co.uk
part exchange: Yes
info: Part of Digital Village chain. See listing above for information. Digital Village have stores throughout London, as well as Birmingham, Bristol, Southampton and Cambridge. See listings in relevant sections for details.

Doghouse Music
301-303 Broadway, Bexleyheath, Kent, DA6 8DT
tel: 020 8304 5331
email: sales@doghousemusic.net
web: www.doghousemusic.net
part exchange: No
info: Wide selection of musical instruments and equipment including guitars, keyboards, saxophones, trumpets, clarinets, flutes, violins, drums, amps, PA, microphones, DJ equipment, lighting, karaoke, books and accessories. Repair service for electrical items and instruments. Noticeboard in-store.

Dot's The Camden Music Shop
132 St. Pancras Way, Camden Town, London, NW1 9NB
tel: 020 7482 5424
fax: 020 7482 5434
email: dot@dotsonline.co.uk
web: www.dotsonline.co.uk
part exchange: Yes
info: Mainly stock instruments aimed at beginner level. Guitars (Acoustic, electric and classical), violins, clarinets, flutes, trumpets and sheet music. Repair service available. Can provide list of music tutors if required. Space for notices.

Dragon Servicing
32 Woodstock Road, Carshalton, Surrey, SM5 3DZ
tel: 020 8395 6774
fax: 020 8395 6774
web: http://home.clara.net/dragonser/dragon.htm
part exchange: Yes
info: Repairs on electronic musical equipment such as keyboards, guitar amps and mixing desks.

Drumshack
58 Lavender Hill, Battersea, SW11 5RQ
tel: 020 7228 1000
email: sales@drumshack.co.uk
web: www.drumshack.co.uk
part exchange: No
info: New, second hand and vintage drums and percussion including cymbals, snares, full kits and electronic kits. Also stock a range of guitars. Instruments bought for cash. Drum tuition available, as well as repair and recover service.

The Dulwich Music Shop
2 Croxted Road, Dulwich, SE21 8SW
tel: 020 8766 0202
part exchange: No
info: Mainly stock classical and orchestral instruments, but also some bass and electric guitars, as well as guitars strings, leads, amps, sheet music and accessories. Repair service for guitars. List of music teachers available, just ask in-store. Small space for posters and notices.

Ealing Strings
4 Station Parade, Uxbridge Road, Ealing, London, W5 3LD
tel: 020 8992 5222
fax: 020 8992 3993
email: mail@ealingstrings.info
web: www.ealingstrings.info
part exchange: No
info: Makers, dealers and restorers of violins, violas and cellos. Also stock cases, books, strings and accessories. Repair available. Can recommend good tutors in the area. Space for notices.

Electrohill
124-126 Green Lanes, London, N13 5UN
tel: 020 8886 9426
email: enquiries@electrohill.co.uk
web: www.electrohill.co.uk
part exchange: No
info: Stock guitars and all related equipment and accessories including amps, mixers, speakers, PAs, leads, strings, FX, microphones and recording equipment. Repair service available. Ask in-store for contact list of music teachers. Space to display posters and flyers.

Eric Lindsey Ltd.
20-22 Rushey Green, Catford, London, SE6 4AS
tel: 020 8690 8621
fax: 020 8690 7064
email: info@elmusic.co.uk
web: www.elmusic.co.uk
part exchange: No
info: Sell drums, guitars, keyboards, PA systems and DJ equipment. Repair service. Drum tuition available. Posters and flyers can be displayed in-store. Also try to support and advertise local bands and will accept demos and photos. Eric Lindsey has another branch in Reigate, Surrey. See listing in relevant section for details.

Feline Guitars
9 Coombe Road, Croydon, Surrey, CR0 1BD
tel: 020 8680 9131
email: info@felineguitars.com
web: www.felineguitars.com
part exchange: Yes
info: Feline Guitars have been building and repairing guitars for 15 years. Carry out repairs and upgrades ranging from basic set up and servicing to part replacements and full restorations. Also hand craft high end electric guitars (including left handed models) built to customer specifications.

Flying Pig Instrument Supply Co.
72-74 Uxbridge Road, Hanwell, London, W7 3SU
tel: 020 8567 0212/020 8567 1994
fax: 020 8567 6675
email: flyingpigmusic@btconnect.com
web: www.theflyingpiguk.com
part exchange: Yes
info: Stock all guitars, as well as drums, recording equipment, pedals, PA and amps. Repair service for guitars. Mail order service. Space for notices.

Footes Ltd.
10 Golden Square, London, W1F 9JA
tel: 020 7437 1811 (brass & wood)
                     020 7437 1822 (drums)
fax: 020 7734 3095
email: orchestral@footesmusic.com or
                     drums&percussion@footesmusic.com
web: www.footesmusic.com
part exchange: No
info: Stock wide variety of instruments including brass, woodwind, drums, percussion and string. Tuition available for drums. Area in-store to display posters and flyers.

The Gallery
142 Royal College Street, London, NW1 0TA
tel: 020 7267 5458
fax: 020 7267 5458
email: alex@thebassgallery.com
web: www.thebassgallery.com
part exchange: No
info: Specialise in bass guitars, amps and strings. Also repair and build basses. Space in-store for bands to display posters and flyers.

Garnett Woodwinds
3a Lacy Road, Putney, London, SW15 1NH
tel: 020 8785 9852
part exchange: Yes
info: Specialist in woodwind repairs, remakes and customisation.

Gigsounds Ltd.
86-88 Mitcham Lane, Streatham, London, SW16 6NR
tel: 0800 092 5681/020 8769 3206
fax: 020 8769 9530
email: gigsounds1@aol.com
web: www.gigsounds.co.uk
part exchange: No
info: Huge range of instruments including guitars, keyboards, drums, PA, recording equipment and a selection of accessories. Repair service in-store for guitars. Tuition available for percussion. Space to display posters and flyers.

Graham Noden
27 Denmark Street, London, WC2H 8NJ
tel: 020 7813 1142
part exchange: Yes
info: Specialise in repairs for stringed instruments ranging from guitars and basses to mandolins and ukuleles.

Guitar Classics
38 Webbs Road, London, SW11 6SF
tel: 020 7738 2974
email: info@guitar-classics.co.uk
web: www.guitar-classics.co.uk
part exchange: No
info: Specialists in top of the range vintage and contemporary guitars. Area in-store for bands to display posters and flyers.

The Guitar Tree Luthiery
3a Lacy Road, London, SW15 1NH
tel: 020 8780 1000/07834 346 058
email: thomas@anfield5424.fsnet.co.uk
part exchange: Yes
info: Make, repair and restore guitars. Sell Acoustic and electric guitars. Also service other stringed instruments. Space for notices and posters.

Hampstead Piano Service
131 Abbey Road, London, NW6 4SL
tel: 020 7624 0289
email: info@hampsteadpianos.co.uk
web: www.hampsteadpianos.co.uk
part exchange: No
info: Buy and sell Acoustic and digital pianos. Reconditioning service. Hire schemes available.

Hank's Guitar Shop
24 Denmark Street, London, WC2H 8NJ
tel: 020 7379 1139
email: hankslondon@aol.com
web: www.hanksguitarshop.com
part exchange: No
info: Acoustic specialists stocking guitars, banjos and mandolins plus accessories. Repair service available. Affiliated with other music shops Music Ground, Rockers and Tin Pan Alley Drum Co. See entries for further details.

Harrow Music Centre
52 Greenhill Way, Harrow, Middlesex, HA1 1LE
tel: 020 8427 2250
part exchange: Yes
info: General music store stocking a variety of instruments.

Herga Music
2a-4 High Street, Wealdstone, Harrow, Middlesex, HA3 7AA
tel: 020 8861 1590
fax: 020 8861 5501
email: retail@hergamusic.co.uk
web: www.hergamusic.co.uk
part exchange: Yes
info: Specialise in brass and woodwind beginners instruments. Also stock guitars, keyboards, digital and acoustic pianos, plus printed music, books, CDs and gifts.

Hobgoblin Music (London)
24 Rathbone Place, London, W1T 1JA
tel: 020 7323 9040
email: london@hobgoblin.co.uk
web: www.hobgoblin.com
part exchange: No
info: Folk specialists stocking Traditional, Celtic and Acoustic instruments from guitars to didgeridoos. Repair service on premises. Tuition available. Ask in-store to display posters and flyers. Hobgoblin has branches throughout UK. See other listings or website for details.

Holiday Music Ltd.
396-398 High Road, Leytonstone, London, E11 3HW
tel: 020 8558 2666
email: sales@holidaymusic.co.uk
web: www.holidaymusic.co.uk
part exchange: No
info: Guitar specialists for 30 years. Sell all types of guitar, as well as amplification. Stock the largest range of left-handed guitars in Europe. Repairs for guitars and amps.

Hooters Musical Instruments (London)
within Selfridges, Lower Ground Floor, 400 Oxford Street, London, W1A 1AB
tel: 020 7318 3731
part exchange: Yes
info: Guitars, amps, keyboards, pianos, brass, woodwind, as well as music books, accessories and a large selection of sheet music. Hooters also has branches in St. Albans, Windsor and Watford. See listings in relevant sections for details.

House Of Guitars/The Bass Centre/The Acoustic Centre
Brune Street, London, E1 7NH
tel: 020 7247 7847
email: deano@musicsports.ndo.co.uk
web: www.basscentre.com or www.acousticcentre.co.uk
part exchange: No
info: House of Guitars, The Bass Centre and The Acoustic Centre are all under one roof. In addition to guitars, they also stock amps and related accessories. Interest free credit available. Workshop on premises for repairs. Staff can recommend music tutors. Space in-store for posters and flyers.

Ian Lewington Musical Instruments
109 High Street, West Wickham, Kent, BR4 0LT
tel: 020 8776 2675
fax: 020 8776 1386
part exchange: No
info: Woodwind, brass, guitars, violins, cellos, sheet music and books. Spares including reeds and strings. New and second hand instruments. Repair service available for woodwind instruments.

Ian McLauchlan
46 South End, Croydon, Surrey, CR0 1DP
tel: 020 8662 8420
web: www.ianmclauchlan.co.uk
part exchange: Yes
info: Woodwind repairs. Specialist flute repairer and maker of flute and piccolo head joints.

Impact Percussion
7 Goose Green Trading Estate, 47 East Dulwich Road, London, SE22 9BN
tel: 020 8299 6700
fax: 020 8299 6704
email: sales@impactpercussion.com
web: www.impactpercussion.com
part exchange: Yes
info: Specialists in drums and percussion. Repair service available.

Ivor Mairant's Music Centre
56 Rathbone Place, London, W1T 1JT
tel: 020 7636 1481
fax: 020 7580 6272
email: info@ivormairants.co.uk
web: www.ivormairants.co.uk
part exchange: No
info: Guitar specialists stocking a wide selection including electric, classical, jazz, Acoustic, ovation and folk. Also stock percussion and related accessories. Repair service available for guitars. Will order violins and woodwind instruments if requested.

Jacques Samuel Pianos
142 Edgware Road, Marble Arch, London, W2 2DZ
tel: 020 7723 8818
fax: 020 7224 8692
part exchange: No
info: Piano specialists, mainly Acoustic but do stock some digital models. Rental scheme available. Repair, removal and tuning services. Tuition also provided. Practice room for Acoustic instruments.

John Coppen
Unit J, Room 302, Towerbridge Business Complex, Clements Road, London, SE16 4DG
tel: 020 7237 8989
email: johncoppen@btinternet.com
part exchange: Yes
info: Repairs for wide range of woodwind instruments including flutes, oboes, clarinets, bassoons and saxophones. Also sell reeds, and is main agent for Marca reeds.

John Procter Guitars
24 Kendrick Court, Woods Road, Peckham, London, SE15 2SS
tel: 020 7732 6844/07779 040 789
email: tsip2000@hotmail.com
web: www.johnprocterguitars.co.uk
part exchange: No
info: Maker and repairer of stringed instruments including Acoustic, electric and bass guitars, mandolins, lutes and violins. Price list available on website.

Len Stiles Music
268 Lewisham High Street, London, SE13 6JX
tel: 020 8690 7771/020 8690 2958
fax: 020 8690 7771
email: lenstilesmusic@aol.com
part exchange: No
info: General music shop stocking a wide range of instruments including drums, guitars, bass guitars, digital pianos, keyboards, Synths, brass, woodwind, violins and PAs. Repairs on brass, woodwind, guitars and bass guitars. Just ask staff to display posters and flyers in-store. Space for notices.

Les Aldwich Music Shop
98 Fortis Green Road, Muswell Hill, London, N10 3HN
tel: 020 8883 5631
fax: 020 8444 9805
email: info@muswellhillmusic.co.uk or music@muswellhillmusic.co.uk
web: www.lesaldrich.co.uk
part exchange: Yes
info: Stock guitars, violins, sheet music, accessories and CDs. Part exchange available on violins. Repairs on string instruments. List of music tutors in the region available on website. Area in-store for notices and poster and flyer display.

Lipkin & Algranati Guitars
68 High Street, Barnet, London, EN5 5SJ
tel: 020 8364 9726
email: websales@laguitars.com
web: www.laguitars.com
part exchange: Yes
info: Makers, repairers and customises of all stringed instruments. Can custom build instruments to any requirements. Specialise in set ups. Free return service on jobs over £60.

London Guitar Studio
62 Duke Street, London, W1K 6JT
tel: 020 7493 1157
fax: 020 7495 4610
email: info@londonguitarstudio.com or info@elmundoflamenco.com
web: www.londonguitarstudio.com
part exchange: No
info: Specialists in nylon stringed guitars for Classical or Flamenco. Also stock electro-acoustic guitars, cases, books, CDs, tuners and other accessories. Repair service available. Also run a music and dance tuition centre dedicated to Salsa and Flamenco called Latin Quarter. See entry in Music Tuition section for further details.

London Resonator Centre/Acoustic Heaven
21 Denmark Street, London, WC2H 8NA
tel: 020 7278 6332
email: sales@resocentre.com
web: www.resocentre.com
part exchange: No
info: Large range of resonator guitars including classic and vintage models. Repair services available. Also run tuition workshops. Acoustic Heaven is also located on-site stocking a huge selection of Acoustic guitars from top end, rare guitars to budget models. Private room to try out guitar in-store. Space for notices, posters and flyers.

Macari's
92-94 Charing Cross Road, London, WC2H 0BP
tel: 020 7836 2856
fax: 020 7379 8762
email: info@macaris.co.uk
web: www.macaris.co.uk
part exchange: No
info: Stock a range of instruments including electric and Acoustic guitars, FX pedals, woodwind, brass, violins, Ukuleles, mandolins, harmonicas, drums, amps and accessories. Small space for musicians' notices.

Make Music
109 Cockfosters Road, Cockfosters, Hertfordshire, EN4 0DA
tel: 020 8441 1050
email: cockfosters@makemusic.co.uk
web: www.makemusic.co.uk
part exchange: No
info: Stock huge selection of instruments including digital pianos, keyboards, guitars, brass, woodwind, drums, as well as amplification, microphones, home studio equipment, Synths, music books and accessories. Keyboard and singing lessons available. Ask in-store to display posters or flyers.

Mantilla Music
204 Chingford Mount Road, London, E4 8JR
tel: 020 8523 8050
email: barry@mantillamusic.fsbusiness.co.uk
part exchange: No
info: General music shop stocking all instruments including guitars, amps, brass, woodwind, keyboards and stringed instruments plus a good range of books and accessories. Repairs on guitars, brass and woodwind instruments. No tuition provided on-site but there are noticeboards advertising teachers and bands/musicians.

Markson Pianos
8 Chester Court, Albany Street, London, NW1 4BU
tel: 020 7935 8682/0800 0748 980
fax: 020 7224 0957
email: via website
web: www.marksonpianos.com
part exchange: No
info: Hundreds of Acoustic and digital pianos in stock. Main dealer for Yamaha and most other makes. Offer tuning and restoration services, and any advice required. Markson Pianos run tuition master classes and seminars, as well as a piano club from branch located at 49-51 Fortress Road, London, NW5 1AD (tel. 020 7485 2042).

Martin Block Woodwind Instrument Repairs
12 Elm Park, Stanmore, HA7 4BJ
tel: 020 8954 4347
part exchange: Yes
info: Specialises in saxophone and clarinet repairs.

Martin Phelps Music
9 South End, Croydon, Surrey, CR0 1BE
tel: 020 8256 6480
email: martin@mpmc.freeserve.co.uk
part exchange: No
info: Instruments in stock include keyboards, pianos, all types of guitars and amplification. Also sell accessories, printed music and books. Mail order service available. Guitar repair workshop on-site. Area in-store to display posters and flyers. Southend Music School is situated at the same address as Martin Phelps. See entry in relevant section for details.

Martin Piper
63 Ladbrooke Crescent, Sidcup, Kent, DA14 4RU
tel: 020 8300 2719/07812 693 889
email: martinpipermusic@hotmail.com
part exchange: Yes
info: Deal with most electrical repairs including digital pianos, keyboards, guitars and amplification. Can also carry out modifications to instruments.

Matthew Coltman
153 Acton Lane, London, W4 5HN
tel: 020 8742 7934
part exchange: No
info: Maker, dealer, repairer and restorer of bowed string instruments.

Matthew Wing Fine Violins
63 Orford Road, Walthamstow, London, E17 9NJ
tel: 020 8509 2726
web: www.mwingviolins.co.uk
part exchange: Yes
info: Maker, restorer and dealer of fine violins.

Michael White
11 Queens Parade, Queens Drive, London, W5 3HU
tel: 020 8997 4088
fax: 020 8566 9379
web: www.michaelwhitewind.co.uk
part exchange: Yes
info: Specialise in woodwind and brass instruments. In-house repair team. List of music tutors available. Space for posters, flyers and advertisements, just ask in shop.

Mike Edwardes Woodwind Repairs
60 Charlton Church Lane, London, SE7 7AB
tel: 020 8333 7130/07931 432 057
fax: 020 8333 7130
email: info@mike-edwardes-woodwind.co.uk
web: www.mike-edwardes-woodwind.co.uk
part exchange: Yes
info: Woodwind, brass, PA and stringed instruments repairs. Also sell new and second hand instruments including violins, guitars, woodwind, brass, pianos, drums, percussion, as well as sheet music, cases, spares and accessories. Space for noticeboards. Sheet music that is not in stock at the shop can be ordered directly from the distributors on the website.

Mill Hill Music Mart Ltd.
Unit 7, Bunns Lane Works, Bunns Lane, Mill Hill, London, NW7 2AJ
tel: 020 8906 9991
email: enquiries@millhillmusic.co.uk
web: www.millhillmusic.co.uk
part exchange: Yes
info: Sell variety of instruments and accessories. Dealers for several brands including Pearl and Fender. Repairs on guitars and drums available. Space in-store for posters and flyers. Mill Hill Music Complex also comprises recording facilities and rehearsal rooms. See entries in relevant sections for details.

Moore-Randall Electronics Ltd.
100 Tolworth Rise South, Surbiton, Surrey, KT5 9NL
tel: 020 8337 7577
part exchange: Yes
info: Field and on-site service for digital pianos and electronic organs.

Music Ground
25 Denmark Street, London, WC2H 8NJ
tel: 020 7836 5354
email: musicgnd@aol.com
web: www.musicground.com or www.londonpedal.com
contact: Scott
part exchange: No
info: Specialise in rare and vintage gear including guitars (electric, Acoustic and bass), amps, effects and accessories. Famous customers in the past have included Jimmy Page, Primal Scream, The Beatles, Oasis and Guns 'n' Roses. Repair service available. They also specialise in Boutique pedals with a wide selection, the separate website is above. Music Ground has several affiliate shops in London: Rockers, Hank's Guitar Shop and Tin Pan Alley Drum Co. See entries for further details.

Music Inc.
439 High Street North, London, E12 6TJ
tel: 020 8472 0004
email: kevin@musicinc.fsbusiness.co.uk
web: www.ebayshops.co.uk/musicincorporated
part exchange: No
info: General music store selling selection of instruments including drums, keyboards, flutes, guitars, mandolins, banjos, amps and music books. Repair service for guitars. Instruments can be bought online at the Ebay shop, see above web address. Area in-store to display posters and flyers.

Music Music Music
288 Kensington High Street, London, W14 8NZ
tel: 020 7603 1905
fax: 020 7602 3088
email: info@kensingtonpianos.com
web: www.musicmusicmusic.co.uk
part exchange: Yes
info: Store based within Piano World showroom. Store pianos, sheet music and related accessories.

MusicLand (Bromley)
422 Bromley Road, Downham, Bromley, Kent, BR1 4PL
tel: 020 8698 7300/0800 026 1055
email: info@musicland.co.uk
web: www.musicland.co.uk
part exchange: No
info: Buy and sell a wide range of instruments. Stock keyboards, digital pianos, organs, guitars, brass, woodwind and amps. There is a 'Boss R&B centre' separate room specialising in production. Repairs on most instruments. Tuition available for guitar and keyboard. Noticeboard in-store to display posters and ads. MusicLand also has branches in Romford, Southend-on-Sea and Canterbury. See listings in relevant sections for details.

Musicland East
52-54 Walton Road, East Molesey, Surrey, KT8 0DL
tel: 020 8979 9443
part exchange: Yes
info: Stock guitars, effects, keyboards, PAs, sheet music, books and accessories. Tuition available for guitar, bass, piano, drums and flute. Repair service primarily for guitars and stringed instruments. Will also carry out repairs on amps. Ask in-store to display posters.

Muswell Hill Pianos
104 Alexandra Park Road, London, N10 2AE
tel: 020 8444 9884
fax: 020 8444 9850
email: info@muswellhillpianos.freeserve.co.uk
web: www.muswellhillpianos.co.uk
part exchange: No
info: As well as stocking a range of Acoustic and digital pianos, Muswell Hill Pianos also sell a selection of other musical instruments. Interest free credit available. Rental scheme. Repair service for pianos. Staff can recommend local tutors. Noticeboard in-store.

New King Road Vintage Guitar Emporium
65a New King's Road, London, SW6 4SG
tel: 020 7371 0100
fax: 020 7371 0460
email: sales@newkingsroadguitars.co.uk
web: www.newkingsroadguitars.co.uk
part exchange: No
info: Stock vintage and new guitars, mainly American makes. Also sell bass guitars, amps and accessories. Backline rental service. Repair and tuition available. Space in-store for flyers.

Norman's Music
32 Well Hall Road, Eltham, London, SE9 6SF
tel: 020 8850 1263
email: info@normansmusic.co.uk
web: www.normansmusic.co.uk
part exchange: No
info: General music store with a selection of woodwind, brass and stringed instruments in stock. Also stock keyboards, drums, amps, printed music and books. Part exchange considered. Repair service for woodwind and brass, and minor repairs on guitars. Names of music tutors held at shop.

Northcote Music Shop
155c Northcote Road, London, SW11 6QB
tel: 020 7228 0074
part exchange: No
info: General music store stocking most instruments, equipment, sheet music and accessories. Repair service available. Small space on door to advertise gigs, and list of musicians available for tutoring.

Paxman Musical Instruments Ltd.
Unit B4, Linton House, 164-180 Union Street, London, SE1 0LH
tel: 020 7620 2077
email: info@paxman.co.uk
web: www.paxman.co.uk
part exchange: Yes
info: Specialise in French horns and related accessories. Repair service available.

Percussion Services
Skillion Commercial Centre, Lea Valley Trading Estate, Edmonton, N18 3SB
tel: 020 8803 3345
part exchange: No
info: Specialists in drums, percussion and related accessories. Also stock some other instruments such as guitars, violins and saxophones. Repair service available. Noticeboard in-store for poster and flyer display.

Peter Cook's Guitar World
69 Station Road, London, W7 3JD
tel: 020 8840 1244
email: petercooks@talk21.com
web: www.petercooks.co.uk
part exchange: Yes
info: Specialist in electric guitars and accessories. Stock a wide range of makes and models. Repair services available. Staff can recommend tutors in the area. Sister store, Unplugged, stocks Acoustic and classical guitars. See listing for further details.

Peter Salisbury Pianos Ltd.
Aladdin Business Centre, E5, 426 Long Drive, Greenford, Middlesex, UB6 8UH
tel: 020 8578 6741/020 8575 3300
email: info@petersalisburypianos.com
web: www.petersalisburypianos.com
part exchange: No
info: Specialist suppliers of Acoustic pianos with a comprehensive range in stock. Service centre offering full repair and tuning services. Piano tuition will be available in near future. Contact for further details.

Professional Percussion
205 Kentish Town Road, London, NW5 2JU
tel: 020 7485 4434
fax: 020 7485 9745
email: sales@propercussion.co.uk
web: www.propercussion.co.uk
contact: Eddie Chase
part exchange: No
info: Drum specialist stocking all leading brands. Drums, percussion, digital kits, books, spares and accessories. Small repairs service. In-store tuition. Contact Professional Percussion for further details. Space for notices.

Richmond Music Shop
16 Red Lion Street, Richmond, Surrey, TW9 1RW
tel: 020 8332 6220/020 8332 6477
fax: 020 8332 0552
email: vmarder@xin.co.uk
web: www.richmondmusic.co.uk
part exchange: No
info: Woodwind and violin specialists but also stock guitars, violins, brass, amps, sheet music and accessories. Repair service for all instruments. Hire scheme. 10% discount for Musicians' Union members.

Rock Around The Clock
11-13 Park Road, Crouch End, London, N8 8TE
tel: 020 8348 2311/020 8292 8484
fax: 020 8292 8485
email: info@rockaroundtheclockuk.com
web: www.rockaroundtheclockuk.com
part exchange: No
info: Mainly specialise in guitars and keyboards but also stock a range of other instruments. Repairs and noticeboard space available.

Rockbottom
68-70 London Road, West Croydon, Surrey, CR0 2TB
tel: 020 8680 1042
fax: 020 8681 0328
part exchange: No
info: Wide range of instruments in stock including keyboards, guitars, amps, drums, brass, woodwind, violins, cellos, PAs, digital pianos and mixers. Repair service available, and drum tuition in-store. Space for notices. Buy or part exchange. Rehearsal facilities available. See listing for Studio 69 in the relevant section for further information.

Rockers
5 Denmark Street, London, WC2H 8LU
tel: 020 7240 2610
email: rockersguitars@aol.com
part exchange: No
info: Stock a wide range of musical instruments and accessories. Affiliate store to Music Ground, Hank's Guitar Shop and Tin Pan Alley Drum Co. See entries for further details.

Rockstop Music Ltd.
128 Charing Cross Road, London, WC2H 0LA
tel: 020 7240 1542
part exchange: No
info: Stock variety of instruments ranging from guitars and FX units to recorders. Ask member of staff to display posters and flyers in-store.

The Sound Garden
36-38 High Street, Barnet, London, EN5 5RU
tel: 020 8441 8603
email: thesoundgarden@btclick.com
web: www.thesoundgarden.co.uk
part exchange: No
info: Guitars, keyboards, amps, brass, woodwind, percussion, stringed instruments, PAs, sheet music and accessories. In-house repairs on guitars. Repairs on most other instruments can be arranged through outside specialists. Rental scheme for brass, woodwind and string instruments. Space for notices.

Sounds Wicked
49 Craven Park Road, Harlesden, London, NW10 8SE
tel: 020 8961 3002
fax: 020 8961 6919
email: info@soundswicked.com
web: www.soundswicked.com
part exchange: No
info: Stock wide range of instruments, PA and sound equipment. Also sell used and ex-demo equipment. Repair service available. Space for musician's notices.

Spanish Guitar Centre
36 Cranbourn Street, London, WC2H 7AD
tel: 020 7240 0754/0800 371 339 (Freephone)
fax: 020 7240 0754
email: enquiries@spanishguitarcentre.com
web: www.spanishguitarcentre.com
part exchange: No
info: The oldest classical guitar centre in the world, comprising a shop and teaching institution. Sell a wide selection of classical guitars ranging in price. Also stock CDs, books and accessories. Repair service available. Space for notices. See entry in relevant section for details of teaching institution.

Stringbusters
A2 Kingsway Business Park, Oldfield Road, Hampton, Middlesex, TW12 2HD
tel: 020 8783 9090
email: buster@stringbusters.com
web: www.stringbusters.com
part exchange: Yes
info: Strings for guitar and bass, as well as picks, capos, slides, cables, straps and effects pedals. Online and mail order service.

Sutton Music
64 Haddon Road, Sutton, SM1 1RN
tel: 020 8642 2838
fax: 020 8643 2500
email: info@suttonandbansteadmusic.co.uk
web: www.suttonandbansteadmusic.co.uk
part exchange: No
info: Agents for most leading suppliers. Stock includes guitars, keyboards, drums, effects pedals and amplification. Also stock a selection of brass, woodwind and stringed instruments, as well as sheet music. Full repair service for all instruments and guitar set ups. List of music teachers available. Part exchange on guitars. Space for notices.

Synthesiser Service Centre
Unit 1, 30 Gorst Road, London, NW10 6LE
tel: 020 8961 7890
email: info@synthservice.com
web: www.synthservice.com
part exchange: Yes
info: Repairs for range of musical instruments and equipment including keyboards, synthesisers, samplers, FX units and mixers. Sell vintage and rare instruments. Also run recording and rehearsal facility, Soundstage Studio. Refer to entries in relevant sections for further details.

Talents Music
9 Brockley Rise, Forest Hill, London, SE23 1JG
tel: 020 8699 4216
fax: 020 8291 9799
email: info@talentsmusic.com
web: www.talentsmusic.com
part exchange: No
info: Instruments in stock include guitars, keyboards, violins, cellos, flutes, clarinets, saxophones, trumpets, drums, PA equipment and accessories. Repairs of woodwind instruments, as well as guitars, violins, cellos and keyboards. Space for notices. One to one tuition for all instruments on-site. See listing in relevant section for further details.

Tin Pan Alley Drum Co.
23 Denmark Street, London, WC2H 8NJ
tel: 020 7240 7307
email: tpadrumco@aol.com
web: www.tpadrumco.com
part exchange: No
info: Stock all major brand drum kits, as well as related accessories. Buy, sell and part exchange. Ask in-store for repair and tuition advice. Space to display posters and flyers. Affiliated with other music shops in London, Music Ground, Rockers and Hanks' Guitar Shop. See entries for further details.

Top Wind
2 Lower Marsh, London, SE1 7RJ
tel: 020 7401 8787
email: enquiries@topwind.com
web: www.topwind.com
part exchange: Yes
info: Specialist flute dealers. Also sell related accessories, CDs and sheet music. Repair service available. Will display posters and flyers and musician's notices for flautists.

Tune Inn
124-126 St. Mildred's Road, London, SE12 0RG
tel: 020 8698 4446
email: sales@tuneinn.co.uk
web: www.tuneinn.co.uk
part exchange: No
info: Stock a wide range of instruments and equipment including guitars, keyboards, brass, woodwind, DJ equipment, amps, PA systems and computer equipment. Hire scheme available. Repairs on most instruments. Staff can recommend good music tutors. Space for notices. Tune Inn also has a branch in London. See listing for details.

Tune Inn Guitars
409 Hither Green Lane, London, SE13 6TN
tel: 020 8698 8743
email: sales@tuneinn.co.uk
web: www.tuneinn.co.uk
part exchange: Yes
info: Guitar store. Tune Inn also has another branch in London, stocking a wide selection of instruments. See listing above for details.

Turnkey
114-116 Charing Cross Road, London, WC2H 0JR
tel: 020 7692 6618
email: via website
web: www.turnkey.co.uk
part exchange: Yes
info: Sell a large range of music studio equipment including computer hardware and software, mixing consoles, microphones, samplers, monitors, PA and amps. Also stock bass and electric guitars, keyboards and DJ equipment. Repair service for goods purchased at Turnkey. Good selection of B-stock (i.e. ex-display and demo equipment at cheap prices).

UK Pianos Ltd.
83 Southbury Road, Enfield Town, Middlesex, EN1 1PJ
tel: 020 8367 2080
email: via website
web: www.ukpianos.co.uk
part exchange: Yes
info: Guitars, violins, drums, flutes, as well as pianos. Repair and piano tuning service. Rental scheme. UK Pianos also run a music school. See entry in relevant section for details.

Unicorn Direct
324d Station Road, Harrow, HA1 2DX
tel: 020 8427 8445
email: info@unicorndirect.co.uk
web: www.unicorndirect.co.uk
part exchange: Yes
info: Carry out variety of repairs on guitars including customisation.

Unisound
171 Widmore Road, Bromley, Kent, BR1 3AX
tel: 020 8313 1161
fax: 020 8466 9676
email: info@unisound.co.uk
web: www.unisound.co.uk
part exchange: No
info: Stock all types of guitars, amps, drums, keyboards, pianos, digital pianos, brass, woodwind, sheet music, spares and accessories. Repair service for all instruments bought at Unisound. Space for notices.

Unplugged
118 Uxbridge Road, London, W7 3SU
tel: 020 8840 2715
part exchange: No
info: Specialise in Acoustic and classical guitars. Also sell Acoustic amps, strings and other related accessories. Repair service available. Staff can recommend local tutors. Store open from Tuesday to Saturday. Affiliated with Peter Cook's Guitar World. See listing for further details.

Vampire Music
20 Tanners Hill, Deptford, London, SE8 4PJ
tel: 020 8691 6666
fax: 020 8692 9999
email: info@vampiremusic.co.uk
web: www.vampiremusic.co.uk
part exchange: Yes
info: Sells range of accessories for most instruments and recording. Also stock second hand equipment. Vampire Music also incorporates recording studios, rehearsal rooms, equipment hire, duplication, as well as design and tuition services. See entries in relevant sections for details.

Vegas Sound House
Unit 39, Silicone Business Centre, 28 Wadsworth Road, Perivale, Middlesex, UB6 7JZ
tel: 020 8998 9122
fax: 020 8991 2661
email: loz@vegassoundhouse.com or matt@vegassoundhouse.com
web: www.lozvegasmusic.co.uk
part exchange: Yes
info: Stock amplification, PA, microphones and recording equipment. Space for notices. Vegas Sound House also run an equipment hire service under the same name, recording and rehearsal studios 'Loz Vegas Studios', promotions and booking agency 'Music Scene UK', 'Music Providers' management, 'Some Think Media' media design company, as well as running the Drum Academy. See entries in relevant section for further information.

Vintage & Rare Guitars (London)
6 Denmark Street, London, WC2H 8LX
tel: 020 7240 7500
email: enquiries@vintageandrareguitars.com
web: www.vintageandrareguitars.com
part exchange: Yes
info: Specialise in all guitars, and also stock amps and pedals. Buy, sell and part exchange. Space in-store for flyers only. Vintage & Rare Guitars have another branch in Bath. See listing in relevant section for details.

Walthamstow Music
2 Greenleaf Road, Walthamstow, London, E17 6QQ
tel: 020 8520 2163
fax: 020 8509 3005
email: info@walthamstowmusic.com
web: www.walthamstowmusic.com
part exchange: Yes
info: Wide variety of instruments in stock ranging from drum kits and guitars to recorders and Clavinovas. Repairs on brass, woodwind and stringed instruments. Tuition available for guitar, woodwind, keyboard, piano, violin and singing.

Wild Guitars
393 Archway Road, Highgate, London, N6 4ER
tel: 020 8340 7766
email: info@wildguitars.com
web: www.wildguitars.com
part exchange: No
info: Specialise in rare and vintage guitars. Also vintage pedals, as well as amps and valve amps. Repairs and customisation. Sell strings and accessories. Noticeboard for musicians and tutors.

Wing Music & Hire
442 Upper Elmers End Road, Beckenham, Kent, BR3 3HQ
tel: 020 8650 1118
fax: 020 8658 7989
email: info@wingmusic.co.uk
web: www.wingmusic.co.uk
part exchange: No
info: Guitars, drums, amps, PA and lighting. Instruments bought and sold. Repair service. DJ equipment, mics, PA systems and speakers are available for hire. Space for notices.

Woodwind Workshop
42 Whitgift Avenue, South Croydon, Surrey, CR2 6AY
tel: 020 8686 3530
email: woodwindworkshop@uk2.net
web: www.woodwindworkshop.co.uk
part exchange: No
info: Clarinets, flutes, saxophones, oboes and bassoons. Repair service. Hire scheme with option to purchase.

World Of Music
21 Denmark Street, London, WC2H 8NA
tel: 020 7240 7696
email: info@wom.co.uk
web: www.wom.co.uk
part exchange: Yes
info: World of Music incorporates the following stores under one roof: London PA Centre, London Bass Cellar, Rose Morris Specialist Guitars, World Of Pianos. Huge range of stock for bands. Orchestral instruments also available. Mail order service. Guitar technician on-site. World of Music also incorporates a publishing company, Orange Songs.

Wunjo Guitars Ltd.
55 St. Gile's High Street, London, WC2H 8LH
tel: 020 7379 0737
web: www.wunjoguitars.com
part exchange: No
info: Sell new and second hand guitars, and amps, FX pedals, cellos, basses and violins. Repairs on electric and Acoustic guitars, pedals and amps. Custom guitars made to order. Space on front counter for flyers. Noticeboard. The shop sells CDs by unsigned band without taking any commission.

X Electrical (Croydon)
43 Church Street, Croydon, CR0 1RH
tel: 020 8680 0007
fax: 020 8680 0008
email: croydon@xelectrical.com
web: www.xelectrical.com
part exchange: No
info: Stock all studio equipment, keyboards, samplers, effects, guitars, amps, DJ gear computers, hi-fi equipment and photographic equipment. New or second hand. Buy equipment for cash. Repairs on most music and hi-fi equipment. Notice board in-store to display posters and flyers. X Electrical also has branches in Kingston Upon Thames and Hammersmith. See listings for further details.

X Electrical (Hammersmith)
125 King Street, Hammersmith, London, W6 9JG
tel: 020 8563 7383
fax: 020 8563 7393
email: hammersmith@xelectrical.com
web: www.xelectrical.com
part exchange: No
info: Stock all studio equipment, keyboards, samplers, effects, guitars, amps, DJ gear computers, hi-fi equipment and photographic equipment. New or second hand. Buy equipment for cash. Repairs on most music and hi-fi equipment. Noticeboard in-store to display posters and flyers. X Electrical also has branches in Kingston Upon Thames and Croydon. See listings for further details.

X Electrical (Kingston Upon Thames)
4 Station Buildings, Fife Road, London, KT1 1SW
tel: 020 8546 1233
fax: 020 8549 1233
email: kingston@xelectrical.com
web: www.xelectrical.com
part exchange: No
info: Stock all studio equipment, keyboards, samplers, effects, guitars, amps, DJ gear computers, hi-fi equipment and photographic equipment. New or second hand. Buy equipment for cash. Repairs on most music and hi-fi equipment. Notice board in-store to display posters and flyers. X Electrical also has branches in Hammersmith and Croydon. See listings for further details.

MUSIC SERVICES/RETAIL

MIDLANDS

SOUNDCONTROL
The UK's Number One Musical Instrument Retailer

Sound Control (Birmingham)
89 Old Snow Hill, Birmingham, B4 6HW
tel: 0121 248 5868
fax: 0121 248 5854
email: birmingham@soundcontrol.co.uk
web: www.soundcontrol.co.uk
contact: Neil Crosier
part exchange: Yes
info: As the largest music equipment retailer in Europe with 25 stores across the UK, Sound Control has the most extensive range of guitars, basses, backline, PA, hi-tech, recording and percussion equipment available at the lowest prices around. Coupled with over 25 years experience and unrivalled staff training, shopping at Sound Control is the easiest step you will make on the road to being signed. Visit the above website to locate your nearest store, or to buy online and have your purchase delivered direct to your door.

SOUNDCONTROL
The UK's Number One Musical Instrument Retailer

Sound Control (Derby)
77-79 Osmaston Road, Derby, DE1 2JH
tel: 01332 348 156
fax: 01332 341 414
email: derby@soundcontrol.co.uk
web: www.soundcontrol.co.uk
contact: Roy Chudobskyi
part exchange: Yes
info: As the largest music equipment retailer in Europe with 25 stores across the UK, Sound Control has the most extensive range of guitars, basses, backline, PA, hi-tech, recording and percussion equipment available at the lowest prices around. Coupled with over 25 years experience and unrivalled staff training, shopping at Sound Control is the easiest step you will make on the road to being signed. Visit the above website to locate your nearest store, or to buy online and have your purchase delivered direct to your door.

SOUNDCONTROL
The UK's Number One Musical Instrument Retailer

Sound Control (Leicester)
22-32 Humberstone Road, Leicester, LE5 0AR
tel: 0116 262 4183
email: leicester@soundcontrol.co.uk
web: www.soundcontrol.co.uk
contact: Mick Whittemore
part exchange: Yes
info: As the largest music equipment retailer in Europe with 25 stores across the UK, Sound Control has the most extensive range of guitars, basses, backline, PA, hi-tech, recording and percussion equipment available at the lowest prices around. Coupled with over 25 years experience and unrivalled staff training, shopping at Sound Control is the easiest step you will make on the road to being signed. Visit the above website to locate your nearest store, or to buy online and have your purchase delivered direct to your door.

SOUNDCONTROL
The UK's Number One Musical Instrument Retailer

Sound Control (Nottingham)
11 Hockley, Nottingham, NG1 1FH
tel: 0115 958 1888
fax: 0115 958 0333
email: nottingham@soundcontrol.co.uk
web: www.soundcontrol.co.uk
contact: Phil Clair
part exchange: Yes
info: As the largest music equipment retailer in Europe with 25 stores across the UK, Sound Control has the most extensive range of guitars, basses, backline, PA, hi-tech, recording and percussion equipment available at the lowest prices around. Coupled with over 25 years experience and unrivalled staff training, shopping at Sound Control is the easiest step you will make on the road to being signed. Visit the above website to locate your nearest store, or to buy online and have your purchase delivered direct to your door.

SOUNDCONTROL
The UK's Number One Musical Instrument Retailer

Sound Control (Stoke On Trent)
16-22 Hillchurch Street, Stoke On Trent, ST1 2EX
tel: 01782 205 100
fax: 01782 206 002
email: stoke@soundcontrol.co.uk
web: www.soundcontrol.co.uk
contact: Mick Leadenham
part exchange: Yes
info: As the largest music equipment retailer in Europe with 25 stores across the UK, Sound Control has the most extensive range of guitars, basses, backline, PA, hi-tech, recording and percussion equipment available at the lowest prices around. Coupled with over 25 years experience and unrivalled staff training, shopping at Sound Control is the easiest step you will make on the road to being signed. Visit the above website to locate your nearest store, or to buy online and have your purchase delivered direct to your door.

A.J. Lucas
6 Macaulay Drive, Lincoln, LN2 4DY
tel: 01522 880 674
email: ajlucas@ntlworld.com
web: www.lucasguitars.co.uk
part exchange: Yes
info: Hand-made guitars built to order. See website or telephone for details.

Abbey Music Studios
114 Abbey Street, Nuneaton, CV11 5BX
tel: 02476 641 915
email: sale@abbeymusic.co.uk
web: www.abbeymusic.co.uk
part exchange: No
info: General music shop. Part exchange on keyboards only. Repairs and tuition for keyboard and pianos. Notice board for concert and gig flyers.

ABC Music Ltd. (Market Harborough)
7 St. Mary's Road, Market Harborough, Leicestershire, LE16 7DS
tel: 01858 463 144
email: mrhan@lineone.net
web: www.abcmusic.co.uk or www.mhmusic.co.uk
part exchange: No
info: Part of ABC music chain and franchise stores. Sell a variety of instruments and accessories. Also have online music store, see website above. ABC Music have several branches located in Greater London and South East regions, as well as one in Yorkshire. See listings in relevant sections for details.

Accordions Of Coventry
192 Binley Road, Coventry, CV3 1HG
tel: 02476 448 933
email: terrybirtley@tiscali.co.uk
web: www.accordionsofcoventry.co.uk
part exchange: No
info: Stock new and used accordions, harps and pianos. Also some melodeons, harps organs and concertinas. Buy and sell. Repairs offered.

Alexander Accessories
Beacon View Farm, Farley Way, Quorn, Loughborough, LE12 8RB
email: enquiries@alexanderaccessories.com
web: www.alexanderaccessories.com
part exchange: Yes
info: Produce chinrests and tailpieces for violins and violas by hand to individual order specification. As used by Vanessa Mae.

Arcade Music
49 Mill Street, Cannock, WS11 0DR
tel: 01543 503 460
email: arcade@aol.com
web: www.arcademusic.co.uk
part exchange: No
info: Stock range of instruments but mainly specialise in guitars. Offer repairs and notice board space in-store.

Bandwagon
5 Talisman Square, Kenilworth, CV8 1JB
tel: 01926 857 000
web: www.bandwagon.org
part exchange: Yes
info: Mainly stock guitars, drums and some woodwind instruments. All new items. Drum and guitar tuition in-store. Band notice board space available.

Be Musical
43 Abbey Street, Nuneaton, CV11 5BT
tel: 0800 970 1775
email: enquiries@be-musical.co.uk
web: www.be-musical.co.uk
part exchange: Yes
info: Sell all types of instruments.

Berrys Music
23 Bridge Place, Worksop, S80 1DT
tel: 01909 473 532
part exchange: Yes
info: General music shop stocking range of instruments and various sheet music. Repairs available. Notice board space in-store.

Birmingham Drum Percussion Centre
Unit 2, Hall Green, 11 Evelyn Street, Sparkhill, Birmingham, B11 3JJ
tel: 0121 778 3626
email: bhamdrum@aol.com
web: www.birminghamdrumcentre.co.uk
contact: Chris Payne (Manager)
part exchange: Yes
info: Large selection of new and used Drum kits. Also comprises King Midas Distribution wholesalers, including distribution for teachers and schools.

Boston Organs Centre
5 Pen Street, Boston, PE21 6TJ
tel: 01205 355 777
part exchange: No
info: Specialise in organs and electric pianos. Also stock wide range of music books, flutes and clarinets. Tuition in organ and piano.

Bridge Musical Instruments Ltd.
28 Boston Road, Sleaford, NG34 7ET
tel: 01529 415 372
email: info@bridgeinstruments.com
web: www.bridgeinstruments.com
part exchange: Yes
info: Designers and makers of professional electric violins, cellos and double basses. Workshop and showroom. Visit website for sales. Previous clients include Jon Sevink from The Levellers and Martin Bell from The Wonder Stuff.

Broken Winds
Wilvern, Dark Lane, North Wingfield, Chesterfield, S42 5NQ
tel: 01246 852 005
email: info@brokenwinds.co.uk
web: www.brokenwinds.co.uk
part exchange: Yes
info: Home based wind instrument repair.

Cadenza Music
113 Stimpson Avenue, Northampton, NN1 4JW
tel: 01604 630 485
web: www.cadenza-music.co.uk
part exchange: No
info: Provide on-site repairs and servicing for woodwind and brass instruments, and are saxophone, clarinet and flute specialists. Recent customers for repairs and servicing include John Dankworth, Soweto Kinch and Snake Davis.

Chas Foulds & Son
40 Iron Gate, Derby, DE1 3GA
tel: 01332 344 842
email: info@fouldsmusic.co.uk
web: www.fouldsmusic.co.uk
part exchange: No
info: Sell a little of everything. Offer in-store tuition in guitar and drums. Repairs also available. Space for band posters.

City Music
66 London Road, Leicester, LE2 0QD
tel: 0116 254 4441
part exchange: Yes
info: Sheet music specialists with wide range of classical music. Ordering and postal services available

City Music
Unit 14, Queensway Arches, 218 Livery Street, Birmingham, B3 1EU
tel: 0121 236 2229
email: info@citymusicbrum.co.uk
web: www.citymusicbrum.co.uk
part exchange: No
info: Sell guitars, amps, backline and PA equipment. Offer repairs. Notice board space available.

Clement Pianos
Lenton Boulevard, Nottingham, NG7 2BY
tel: 0115 970 1106
email: clementpianos@tiscali.co.uk
web: www.clementpianos.co.uk
part exchange: No
info: Sell new and used pianos. Family run business established in 1919. Repairs available.

Counterpoint
Newton House, 38 Grantham Street, Lincoln, LN2 1LW
tel: 01522 560 065
web: www.counterpointmusic.co.uk
part exchange: Yes
info: Sheet music store with wide ranging catalogue. Order service available.

Darkbrook Pianos
Buxton Road, Tideswell, Buxton, SK17 8PQ
tel: 01298 872 155
email: enquiries@darkbrookpianos.co.uk
web: www.darkbrookpianos.co.uk
part exchange: Yes
info: Acoustic piano specialist. Offer tuition and repairs.

Des Grey Music
Point Farm, St. Leonard's Drive, Chapel St. Leonards, PE24 5UX
tel: 01754 871 349
email: desgreymusic@yahoo.co.uk
web: www.desgreymusic.co.uk
part exchange: No
info: Vintage and budget guitars. PAs, speakers, lighting, mics, mixers, double CD players. Repairs and notice board space available.

Digital Village (Birmingham)
Dekota Buildings, 3-4 James Street, Birmingham, B3 1SD
tel: 0121 687 4777
email: birmingham@digitalvillage.co.uk
web: www.digitalvillage.co.uk
part exchange: Yes
info: Wide range of recording equipment including computer hardware and software, equipment for DJ or live, MIDI instruments and monitoring. Branches throughout London, as well as Bristol, Cambridge and Southampton. See listings in relevant sections for details.

DLC Protronics
The Chambers, 28 St. Edmund's Road, Northampton, NN1 5ET
tel: 01604 604 554
email: dondix@lineone.net
part exchange: No
info: Amps, mixers, speakers and other electronic equipment for hire and sale. Repairs also offered.

Doug's Cabin
21 Kirkby Folly Road, Sutton-in-Ashfield, NG17 5HP
tel: 01623 450 060
email: dougmilne@onetel.com
web: www.guitarwarehouse.co.uk
part exchange: No
info: Guitar store stocking new and second hand instruments. Repairs, tuition and notice board space all available.

Dream Guitar Services
6 Pleasant Row, Woodford, Kettering, NN14 4HP
tel: 01832 733 214
email: info@dreamguitarservices.co.uk
part exchange: Yes
info: Stringed instruments and guitars in particular are built to order, repaired and restored.

MUSIC SERVICES/RETAIL

The Drum Centre (Leicester)
The Drum Centre, 52a London Road, Leicester, LE2 0QD
tel: 0116 255 5501
email: leicester@thedrumcentre.co.uk
web: www.thedrumcentre.co.uk
part exchange: Yes
info: Store stocking over 150 kits and over 300 cymbals, with up to 50% off recommended retail prices. Brands include Premier, Mapex, Pearl, Yamaha, Sonor, Aria, Ludwig, Gretsch and Roland. See also listing for store based in Northampton.

The Drum Centre (Northampton)
75 Kettering Road, Northampton, NN1 4AW
tel: 01604 628 200
email: northampton@thedrumcentre.co.uk
web: www.thedrumcentre.co.uk
part exchange: No
info: Store stocking over 150 kits and over 300 cymbals, with up to 50% off recommended retail prices. Brands include Premier, Mapex, Pearl, Yamaha, Sonor, Aria, Ludwig, Gretsch and Roland. Also see listing for shop located in Leicester.

Drum Stop
179 Chatsworth Road, Chesterfield, Derbyshire, S40 2BA
tel: 07813 109 028
email: sales@drum-stop.co.uk
web: www.drum-stop.co.uk
part exchange: Yes
info: From starter kits and practice pads to electric and mid-range kits, right up to the top-end professional kits. Teaching studios and trial rooms available.

Fair Deal Music
81-83 Smallbrook Queensway, Birmingham, B5 4HX
tel: 0121 643 1685
email: info@fairdealmusic.com
web: www.fairdealmusic.com
part exchange: No
info: Stock all types of electric and Acoustic guitars, drums, brass, woodwind, digital pianos and keyboards. Along with a massive selection of amps, PAs, mics and studio gear.

Farnsworth Musical Supplies Ltd.
126 Nottingham Road, Nottingham, NG7 7AH
tel: 0115 960 8955
email: sales@farnsworth-musical.co.uk
web: www.farnsworth-musical.co.uk
part exchange: Yes
info: Sheet music specialists also stocking range of woodwind, brass and string instruments. Repairs available.

Flightcase Warehouse
Unit 2, Meltex House, Rear of Mitie Building, Lichfield Road Industrial Estate, Tamworth, Staffordshire, B79 7XE
tel: 01827 600 09
fax: 01827 313 877
email: info@flightcasewarehouse.co.uk
web: www.flightcasewarehouse.co.uk
part exchange: Yes
info: Wide range of discounted flight cases.

Fox's Music (Lincoln)
161-162 High Street, Lincoln, LN5 7AF
tel: 01522 537 141
email: enquires@foxmusic.co.uk
web: www.williams-music.co.uk
part exchange: No
info: Sell wide range of musical instruments, sheet music and music accessories. Tuition in organ, keyboard and piano. Notice board in-store. See also listings for stores located in Hull, Leeds, Sheffield and Nottingham.

Fox's Music (Nottingham)
6 Arnot Hill Road, Arnold, Nottingham, NG5 6LJ
tel: 0115 920 0070
web: www.williams-music.co.uk
part exchange: No
info: Part of the Williams music group. Stock range of instruments including electric guitars, keyboards and guitars. Offer minor repairs. Notice board in-store. See also listings for branches located in Leeds, Hull, Sheffield and Lincoln.

Freeman & Neale
40-42 Lawford Road, Rugby, CV21 2DY
tel: 01788 577 064
email: sales@freemanandneale.co.uk
web: www.freemanandneale.co.uk
part exchange: No
info: Sell guitars, keyboards, brass and woodwind instruments. Repairs and rental available. Notice board space in-store for adverts.

Gedling Piano Galleries
52 Main Road, Gedling, Nottingham, NG4 3HL
tel: 0115 961 3113
part exchange: Yes
info: Specialise in quality second hand and reconditioned small modern, antique and German over strung pianos. Occasionally have second hand grand pianos. Prices from £350 to £1,500. Repairs available.

Goddard's Music
45 High Street, Buxton, SK17 6HB
tel: 01298 225 67
part exchange: Yes
info: Mainly sell sheet music and CDs with some guitars and recorders.

Guitar & Son
147 Newport Road, Stafford, ST16 2EZ
tel: 01785 606 514
email: sales@guitarandson.co.uk
web: www.guitarandson.co.uk
part exchange: No
info: Stock drums, guitar, brass and woodwind instruments. Offer repairs and full service. Guitar and bass tuition in-store. Notice board space.

Guitar Base
24 Gordon Road, West Bridgford, Nottingham, NG2 5LN
tel: 0115 974 4864
email: shop@guitar-base.com
web: www.guitar-base.com
part exchange: No
info: Guitar and amplification store offering in-store tuition in guitars, bass, drums and keyboard. Repairs to amps and guitars. Notice board space.

The Guitar Doctor
The Rhythm House, 21-23 Hope Street, Hanley, Staffordshire
tel: 07708 897 651
email: theguitardoctor@blueyonder.co.uk
web: www.theguitardoctor.co.uk
part exchange: Yes
info: A comprehensive repair and maintenance service for all guitar players within all genres of music. The Guitar Doctor is also a supplier of strings, parts and accessories such as pick ups from Dimarzio, Schaller, Lawrence, Seymour Duncan, and many more.

Guitar Notes
44 Nottingham Road, Nottingham, NG7 7AE
tel: 0115 962 2709
email: sales@spanishguitar.com
web: www.spanishguitar.com
part exchange: Yes
info: Classical Spanish guitars for sale online and by appointment in-store. Stockists of Luis Romero and Amalio Burguet.

The Guitar Workshop
Suite 6, Project 57, High Street, Ibstock, Leicestershire, LE67 6LG
tel: 01530 267 324
email: sales@theguitarworkshop.co.uk
web: www.theguitarworkshop.co.uk
part exchange: No
info: Run by an active gigging band member. Sell anything from guitars, amps, leads, sound or lighting systems and all manner of spares. In-house tuition in a variety of styles. Quality repairs at competitive rates.

Guitars.co.uk
2 Regent Street, Leamington Spa, Warwickshire, CV32 5HW
tel: 01926 833 389
web: www.guitars.co.uk
part exchange: No
info: Store and online shop stocking large range of guitars. 2 floors dedicated to showrooms.

Hardcase International
Broombank Road, Chesterfield, S41 9QJ
tel: 01246 451 234
web: www.hardcase.com
part exchange: Yes
info: Manufacturers of cases for instruments including drums, percussion, amplifiers and guitars.

Hardy Smith Music
87 Outram Street, Sutton-in-Ashfield, NG17 4BG
tel: 01623 556 242
email: hardysmithmusic@aol.com
part exchange: No
info: General musical instrument store offering repairs on some items. Tuition available in guitar, piano and woodwind instruments.

Harmony Music
17-17a West Street, Boston, PE21 8QE
tel: 01205 355 366
email: sales@harmony-music.co.uk
web: www.harmony-music.co.uk
part exchange: No
info: Sells brass and woodwind instruments. Offers repairs, part exchange and tuition. Notice board space in-store.

Harvey Music
2 Bow Fell, Rugby, CV21 1JF
tel: 01788 332 877
part exchange: No
info: Sell new, second hand and vintage or collectable guitars. Tuition in-store. Repairs available.

Head Hands & Feet
5 Cattle Market, Hereford, HR4 9HX
tel: 01432 279 549
web: www.headhandsandfeet.com
part exchange: No
info: Music sales, hire and repair. PA and backline hire. Mainly stock guitar, drums and bass.

Heritage Music
Banbury Road, Brackley, NN13 6BA
tel: 01280 703 111
part exchange: No
info: Orchestral instruments such as brass, woodwind and string. Repairs and notice board in-store.

Hobgoblin Music (Birmingham)
1 Gibb Street, The Custard Factory, Digbeth, Birmingham, B9 4AA
tel: 0121 772 7780
email: hobgoblin.brum@turnerviolins.co.uk
web: www.hobgoblin.com
part exchange: No
info: Folk specialists stocking Traditional, Celtic and Acoustic instruments. Teach many instruments in-store at weekends. Repairs and noticeboard space available. Hobgoblin have branches throughout the UK. See other listings or the website for further details.

Hobgoblin Music (Nottingham)
76 Derby Road, Nottingham, NG1 5FD
tel: 0115 911 9440
web: www.hobgoblin.com
part exchange: No
info: Folk specialists stocking Traditional, Celtic and Acoustic instruments. Hobgoblin has branches throughout the UK. See other listings or website for details.

Horncastle Music Shop
9 North Street, Horncastle, LN9 5EB
tel: 01507 526 566
email: sheet.music@virgin.net
part exchange: No
info: Musical instruments, accessories, nostalgia CDs and vintage sheet music. Repairs and notice board space available.

Hot Rox (UK)
10 Avondale Road, Carlton, Nottingham, NG4 1AF
tel: 0115 987 3163
email: enquires@hotroxuk.com
web: www.hotroxuk.com
part exchange: Yes
info: Guitar accessories specialist. Huge range of effects pedals and discount strings. Range of hard to find speaker parts, pick ups and valves. Also stock some guitars and offer tuition in guitar and piano.

Intasound Music
70 Narborough Road, Leicester
tel: 0116 254 5456
email: intasound@ntlworld.com
web: www.intasound-music.co.uk
part exchange: No
info: Guitars, PA, amplification and karaoke equipment. Repairs, guitar tuition and notice board space.

Intersales Music
12-13 Silver Street, Kettering, NN16 0BN
tel: 01536 521 202
web: www.intersalesmusic.co.uk
part exchange: No
info: Sell a little of everything but mainly guitars, bass and drums. Repairs and tuition offered on all instruments. Small amount of poster space.

John Le Voi Gypsy Jazz Guitars
The Workshop, West Street, Alford, Lincolnshire, LN13 9EZ
tel: 01507 463 341
email: john@levoi.freeserve.co.uk
web: www.levoi.freeserve.co.uk
part exchange: Yes
info: John is a luthier based in the UK specialising in Gypsy Jazz guitars as played by Django Reinhardt. Established in 1970.

Josef's Pianos
5 Bridge Street, Rothwell, Kettering, NN14 6EW
tel: 01536 710 529
web: www.josefspianos.co.uk
part exchange: No
info: New and used Acoustic piano specialists. Offers repairs and tuning.

Just Music
42 Leicester Road, Loughborough, LE11 2AG
tel: 01509 234 881
email: justmusic_online@yahoo.co.uk
web: www.justmusic-online.co.uk
part exchange: No
info: Sell a little of everything from guitars to brass. Part exchange, repairs, and poster space all available.

Key Music
18 Dolphin Lane, Boston, PE21 6EU
tel: 01205 311 200
email: keymusicboston@hotmail.com
web: www.km-online.co.uk
part exchange: No
info: Sell a little of everything including brass, woodwind, guitars, keyboards, music CDs, DVDs and accessories. Specialise in Yamaha products. Repairs and notice board space available.

Keyboard Kavern
Silver Street, Wellingborough, NN8 4HX
tel: 01933 227 837
web: www.keykavern.com
part exchange: No
info: General music store specialising in keyboards. Tuition in keyboard and piano. Repairs and notice board space available. Online ordering service for music books.

Ladbrooke Pianos Ltd.
32 Bristol Street, Birmingham, B5 7AA
tel: 0121 622 4343
email: alan@ladbrookepianos.co.uk
web: www.ladbrookepianos.co.uk
part exchange: No
info: Piano specialist stock Grand, acoustic and uprights, new and reconditioned. Workshop on site along with practice rooms. Offer tuning, repairs, resting, polishing and full restoration. Pianos available to buy and hire.

Langstaffe J & B
41 High Street, Leominster, HR6 8LZ
tel: 01568 620 120
part exchange: No
info: Violin specialists offering part exchange on old instruments and repairs.

Lincoln Piano Centre
Unit 3, 39 Monks Way, Lincoln, LN2 5LN
tel: 01522 542 084
web: www.lincolnpianocentre.co.uk
part exchange: No
info: New and used piano sales, repairs, tuning and restoration.

Lovemore Music
The Old Chapel, Banbury Road, Brackley, NN13 6BA
tel: 01280 703 388
part exchange: No
info: Brass, woodwind and string specialists dealing in sales and repairs. Band flyer space.

Made of Music
Blaplex House, Bearwood Road, Bearwood, B66 4ED
tel: 07956 309 436
email: info@madeofmusic.com
web: www.madeofmusic.com
part exchange: No
info: Retailers of quality Indian instruments including dhal drums, tabla, sitar and algozay. Will modify and repair. Tuition available in Indian percussion and Bhangra dancing. Notice board space in-store.

MUSIC SERVICES/RETAIL

Make Music
50 Trafalgar Road, Kettering, NN16 8DD
tel: 01536 510 400
part exchange: No
info: Broad range on instruments. Offer tuition in guitar, bass and drum. Notice board space in-store.

MDM Music Store
30 The Square, Kenilworth, Warwickshire, CV8 1EB
tel: 01926 863 130
email: mickdolby@yahoo.co.uk
web: www.mdm-music.info
part exchange: No
info: Stock wide range of electric, acoustic, classical and bass guitars along with amplifiers and accessories. Buy and exchange. Repairs and set ups. Guitar tuition in-store. Band notice board space.

MH Music
7 St. Mary's Road, Market Harborough, Leicestershire, LE16 7DS
tel: 01858 463 144
email: mrhan@lineone.net
web: www.mhmusic.co.uk
part exchange: No
info: Full range of instruments including guitars, drums, pianos, keyboards, woodwind, brass, violins and cellos plus amplifiers, sheet music, PA systems and lighting. Services include on-site repairs and tuition, including a Casio music centre.

Millenium Music Software
172 Derby Road, Nottingham, NG1 2R
tel: 0115 955 2200
email: sales@millennium-music.biz
web: www.millennium-music.biz
part exchange: Yes
info: Specialists in music technology and computer based recording systems. Laptop recording systems available from £999.

The Music Inn
30-34 Alfreton Road, Nottingham, NG7 3NL
tel: 0115 978 4403
email: mail@themusicinn.co.uk
web: www.themusicinn.co.uk
part exchange: No
info: General music shop stocking new and used instruments. Top brand names. Discount for students. Repairs and notice board space.

Music Maker
6 Hotel Street, Coalville, LE67 3EP
tel: 01530 831 633
email: sales@musicmaker4music.co.uk
web: www.musicmaker4music.co.uk
part exchange: No
info: Stock a large range of instruments with main focus on keyboards. Repairs also available. Music school offering instrument tuition. See listing in relevant section for further details.

Music Makers
Gothic House, Melville Street, Lincoln, LN5 7HW
tel: 01522 871 921
part exchange: No
info: Sell electric guitars, bass and drums. Offer repairs, tuition and notice board space for bands.

The Music Makers
Bell House, Albert Road, Tamworth, B79 7JN
tel: 01827 696 99
email: sales@music-makers.co.uk
web: www.music-makers.co.uk
part exchange: No
info: Sheet music specialists with large catalogue. Also available for purchase online with free delivery. Also stock a few guitars and violins. Notice board space in-store.

Music Market
75 Kettering Road, Northampton, NN1 4AW
tel: 01604 628 419
email: musicmarket@btclick.com
web: www.guvnor.com/musicmarket
part exchange: No
info: Guitar specialist. Professional guitar tuition and repairs. Notice board space.

Music Plus
17a Watergate, Sleaford, NG34 7PG
tel: 01529 305 040
email: musicplus11@hotmail.com
web: www.musicplus-sleaford.org.uk
part exchange: Yes
info: General music shop offering repairs and tuition in piano, flute and guitar. Notice board space available.

Music Plus Ltd.
29a Union Street, Hereford, HR1 2BT
tel: 01432 356 194
web: www.musicplusltd.co.uk
part exchange: No
info: General music store boasting tuition in most instruments. Sheet music, repairs and band poster space available.

Music Room
246-247 Victoria Centre, Nottingham, NG1 3QQ
tel: 0115 948 2300
web: www.williams-music.co.uk
part exchange: No
info: Part of the Williams music group. Stock range of instruments including electric guitars, keyboards and guitars. Offer minor repairs. Notice board space in-store.

Music Scene (Mansfield) Ltd.
9a Albert Street, Mansfield, NG18 1EA
tel: 01623 631 174
web: www.music-scene.co.uk
part exchange: No
info: Stock guitars and keyboards. Tuition studios permanently offering guitar and keyboard lessons. Notice board space in-store.

The Music Shop
20 Barnbygate, Newark, NG24 1PZ
tel: 01636 610 588
email: robin@themusicshop.com
web: www.themusicshopuk.com
part exchange: No
info: General musical instrument store with wide variety of items including new and reconditioned pianos. Tuition for trumpet in-store. Repairs and notice board space available

The Music Shop
91 Dale Road, Matlock, DE4 3LU
tel: 01629 760 670
email: musicshop@aol.com
part exchange: No
info: Guitar specialists offering repairs, tuition and exchange.

Music World
91 Wycliffe Road, Northampton, NN1 5JQ
tel: 01604 637 444
web: www.hammondzone.com
part exchange: No
info: Hammond keyboard, organ and digital piano specialists. Keyboard, piano and organ tuition. LCM approved. New and used instruments.

Musical Electronic
89 Old Snow Hill, Birmingham, B4 6HW
tel: 0121 233 9390
email: hellorepairs@hotmail.com
part exchange: Yes
info: All musical related electronic repairs. PA equipment, amps, recording equipment, guitars and keyboards.

Musical World Ltd.
90 Far Gosford Street, Coventry, CV1 5EA
tel: 02476 555 585
email: enquries@musicalworld.co.uk
web: www.musicalworld.co.uk
part exchange: Yes
info: Basic music store selling beginners guitars and pianos. In-store tuition for guitar and piano.

Musicality
13 Queen Street, Louth, LN11 9AU
tel: 01507 602 901
email: musicalitycool@tiscali.co.uk
web: www.musicalitycool.co.uk
part exchange: No
info: Large friendly music store stocking guitars. Most makes of keyboards, drums, music books and accessories. Repairs and poster space in-store.

Musician Shop
Unit 75, The Shires, Leicester, LE1 4FQ
tel: 0845 226 0380
email: contact@musicianshop.com
web: www.musicianshop.com
part exchange: Yes
info: Stock guitars and drums and other traditional instruments. Have guitar tuition on-site. Very supportive of local unsigned bands and willing to display posters and sell unsigned CDs.

Neville Bros.
74 Babington Lane, Derby, DE1 1SX
tel: 01332 290 762
email: nevillebrothers@btinternet.com
web: www.nevillebros.com
part exchange: Yes
info: Sell and repair guitars, brass and woodwind instruments.

Norman's
Third Avenue, Centrum One Hundred, Burton on Trent, DE14 2WD
tel: 01283 535 333
email: sales@normans.co.uk
web: www.normans.co.uk
part exchange: No
info: Stock full range of musical instruments to rent or buy. Repairs available. Notice space in-store.

Northworthy Musical Instruments
Main Road, Hulland Ward, Ashbourne, DE6 3EA
tel: 01335 370 806
email: info@northworthy.com
web: www.northworthy.com
part exchange: Yes
info: Makers of fine, bespoke Acoustic guitars. Offer repairs and tuition in guitar making. Poster space in-store.

Nottingham Drum Centre
22-24 Southwell Road, Nottingham, NG1 1DL
tel: 0115 841 4148
email: info@nottinghamdrumcentre.com
web: www.nottinghamdrumcentre.com
part exchange: No
info: Drums and cymbals from the worlds leading brands. Also mail order next day delivery. Drum tuition available, along with repairs and poster space.

Nottingham Guitar Centre
22-24 Southwell Road, Nottingham, NG1 1DL
email: info@nottinghamguitarcentre.com
web: www.nottinghamguitarcentre.com
part exchange: No
info: Guitars, bass and amplification. Also stock hard to find bass amps. Guitar tuition, repairs and notice board space available in-store.

Palfreyman's Music Ltd.
171 Chatsworth Road, Chesterfield, S40 2AU
tel: 01246 271 737
part exchange: No
info: Music store selling mainly guitars and keyboards. Specialising in tuition for guitars, keyboards, singing and drums. Poster space available in-store.

Pandora's Music Box
1525-1527 Pershore Road, Stirchley, Birmingham, B30 2JH
tel: 0121 459 4464
part exchange: No
info: New and used instruments. Large range of guitars. Spares and repairs available.

Phoenix Soundworks
The Square, Earls Barton, Northampton, NN6 0NA
tel: 01604 466 499
email: sales@phoenixsoundworks.com
web: www.phoenixsoundworks.com
part exchange: No
info: Stock guitar and bass, PA,amplifiers and speakers, backline, home recording equipment, microphones and accessories.

Pianoforte
65 Birches Head Road, Stoke On Trent, ST1 6LH
tel: 01782 570 539
web: www.pianoforte.uk.net
part exchange: No
info: New and used upright and grand pianos to suit all budgets. Tuition available.

PMT Birmingham
136 Lawley Middleway, Birmingham, West Midlands, B4 7XX
tel: 0121 359 5056
email: birmingham@pmtonline.co.uk
web: www.pmtonline.co.uk
part exchange: No
info: Flag ship store for big music retailers. Huge store with café, acoustic department, drum department and sampler and software area. Drum, guitar and bass school. In-store technician. Notice space for band flyers at front of store.

Portass & Carter
26 Bridge Road, Sutton Bridge, Spalding, PE12 9UA
tel: 01406 350 407
part exchange: No
info: General instrument. New and used. Offer repairs and tuition on most instruments. Notice board space available.

Presto Classical
11 Park Street, Leamington Spa, CV32 4QN
tel: 01926 317 025
email: info@prestoclasical.co.uk
web: www.prestoclassical.co.uk
part exchange: Yes
info: Sell string, woodwind and brass instruments. Some string and woodwind repairs available. Notice board space.

Quad Studios
78 Friday Street, Leicester, LE1 3BW
tel: 0116 251 2516
web: www.quadstudios.co.uk
part exchange: Yes
info: Drum store selling mid to up-market kits. Offer repairs.

R.M. Electronic Services
15 Raeburn Drive, Beeston, Nottingham, NG9 6LF
tel: 0115 854 8077
part exchange: Yes
info: Services and repairs offered to electronic instruments, amps and PA equipment. Home based service.

Rattle & Drum (Derby)
137 London Road, Derby, DE1 1QH
tel: 01332 360 657
email: derby@rattleanddrum.com
web: www.rattleanddrum.com
part exchange: No
info: Drum and percussion store stocking new and used kits. Offer repairs and tuition on request. Band poster and notice space available. Also have stores located in Manchester and Stoke on Trent. See listings in relevant sections for details.

Rattle & Drum (Stoke On Trent)
16-22 Hillchurch Street, Stoke On Trent, ST1 2EX
tel: 01332 360 657
email: stoke@rattleanddrum.com
web: www.rattleanddrum.com
part exchange: No
info: Drum and percussion store stocking new and used kits. Offer repairs and in-house tuition on request. Band poster and notice space available. Also have stores located in Manchester and Derby. See listings in relevant sections for details.

Real Time Music Ltd.
5-9 Newbold Road, Chesterfield, S41 7PG
tel: 01246 277 702
email: info@realtimemusic.co.uk
web: www.realtimemusic.co.uk
part exchange: No
info: Sell guitars and drums. Also offer repairs, tuition and small notice board.

Regent Guitars & Tuition
2 Regent Street, Leamington Spa, CV32 5HW
tel: 01926 833 389
email: woz@regentguitars.co.uk
web: www.guitars.co.uk
part exchange: No
info: Guitar specialists stocking electric, Acoustic, classic and bass guitars plus some mandolins. Also stock left handed models. Repairs available. 3 tuition rooms for teaching guitar.

The Rhythm House
21-23 Hope Street, Stoke On Trent, ST1 5BT
tel: 01782 266 897
email: andy.holdcroft@btinternet.com
part exchange: No
info: Sell guitar, bass, drums and PA equipment. In-house repairs, and guitar, drum and bass tuition. Notice board for bands.

Roadhouse Music Store
94 Wide Bargate, Boston, PE21 6SE
tel: 01205 360 588
web: www.roadhousemusic.co.uk
part exchange: No
info: Mainly selling guitar orientated instruments including guitar, bass, amps, some drums, PA, lighting, recording and karaoke equipment. Specialise in Ibanez. Stock full range of Boss effects pedals. Free poster space.

Rock House
90 Narborough Road, Leicester, NG1 4HJ
tel: 0116 233 8333
part exchange: Yes
info: Guitars, bass, amps, PAs, spares and accessories. Mainly new, but some second hand instruments. Well stocked.

MUSIC SERVICES/RETAIL

Rock On Music
5 Forest Road East, Nottingham, NG1 4HJ
tel: 0115 958 5042
web: www.rockonmusic.co.uk
part exchange: No
info: Specialise in pre-loved and vintage guitars, amplifiers and effects. Offer repairs and notice board space.

Rocky Road Music
62-64 Rockingham Road, Corby, NN17 1AE
tel: 01536 203 810
email: rockyroadmusic@yahoo.co.uk
web: www.rockyroadmusic.co.uk
part exchange: No
info: Wide variety of instruments. Repairs and notice board space for band posters available.

The Rok Shop
35a Hills Lane, Shrewsbury, SY1 1QU
tel: 01743 232 356
part exchange: No
info: Mainly new, second hand and vintage guitars. Wide range of effects and amps. Repairs available and tuition. Poster space in-store.

Rushden Music
18 High Street, Rushden, Northamptonshire, NN10 0PR
tel: 01933 358 088
email: contact@rushdenmusic.co.uk
web: www.rushdenmusic.co.uk
part exchange: No
info: Stock guitars, bass, amps, accessories, drums, small range of woodwind and strings. Offer tuition in guitar and bass. Repairs and notice board space offered. Store is very supportive of unsigned local musicians and is willing to sell their CDs in-store.

S&J Music
13 Dam Street, Lichfield, WS13 6AE
web: www.sjmusicuk.co.uk
part exchange: No
info: Stock all instruments. Floor dedicated simply to guitars, and a floor dedicated to sheet music. Repairs to all instruments. Poster space in-store.

Salop Music (Shrewbury)
St. Michael's Street, Shrewsbury, SY1 2DE
tel: 01743 364 111
email: info@salopmusic.co.uk
web: www.salopmusic.co.uk
part exchange: No
info: Vast music store stocking all instruments. Large range of sheet music. Stage and platform hire on request. Repairs and tuition available.

Salop Music (Telford)
7 Bell Street, Wellington, Telford, TF1 1LS
tel: 01952 255 310
email: info@salopmusic.co.uk
web: www.salopmusic.co.uk
part exchange: No
info: Smaller sister store to shop in Shrewsbury focussing on guitars, PA equipment and amplification. Minor repairs in-store. Other repairs are sent out to Shrewsbury store. Notice board space available.

Sheehan's Music
50-52 London Road, Leicester, LE2 0QD
tel: 0116 255 7492
email: music@sheehans.com
web: www.sheehans.com
part exchange: No
info: Large music store with Acoustic, brass, woodwind, string and folk departments. Space for band posters.

Sheldon Music
2339 Coventry Road, Sheldon, Birmingham, B26 3PN
tel: 0121 743 1504
email: info@sheldonmusic.com
web: www.sheldonmuisc.com
part exchange: No
info: Guitar specialists stocking electric, acoustic and bass guitars, along with PA equipment and accessories. Offer repairs and full service. Guitar tuition in-store. Notice board space.

Soar Valley Music
3 Waldron Court, Loughborough, LE11 5GD
tel: 01509 269 629
web: www.soarmusic.demon.co.uk
part exchange: Yes
info: African and Brazilian instrument wholesaler.

Solo Music Superstore
137 Derby Road, Stapleford, Nottinghamshire, NG3 7AS
tel: 0115 917 1718
web: www.solomusicstore.co.uk
part exchange: Yes
info: Guitars, basses, amps, PA equipment, stage, lighting and effects, DJ gear and discs. Repairs and notice board space.

Sona Rupa Ltd.
103 Belgrave Road, Leicester, Leicestershire, LE4 6AS
tel: 0116 266 8181
email: music@sonarupa.co.uk
web: www.sonarupa.co.uk
part exchange: Yes
info: Indian instruments, as well as CD releases. Repairs offered.

Songstone Studios
44 Manchester Road, Buxton, SK17 6SY
tel: 01298 269 93
email: j_langley@btconnect.com
part exchange: Yes
info: Specialise in hand-made wind and Folk instruments.

Sounds
41 Church Street, Rugby, CV21 3PU
tel: 01788 535 020
email: soundsmusic@hotmail.com
part exchange: No
info: Guitar specialists. Repairs and guitar tuition. Band flyer space in-store.

Stamford Music Shop
11 St. Mary's Hill, Stamford, PE9 2DP
tel: 01780 751 275
email: stamfordmusicshop@hotmail.com
part exchange: No
info: General music store with large stock of guitars. Also sell Classical and Jazz CDs and sheet music. Will repair, exchange and hire.

The Stratford Music Shop
38 Rother Street, Stratford Upon Avon, CV37 6LP
tel: 01789 205 010
part exchange: No
info: General music store stocking brass, woodwind, drums, violins and guitars. Guitar repairs and tuition in-store. Poster space for bands on request.

Stringstore
Stringstore, c/o Sound Control, 89 Old Snow Hill, Birmingham, B4 6HW
tel: 0121 236 6066
email: sales@stringstore.co.uk
web: www.stringstore.co.uk
part exchange: Yes
info: Stringed instrument suppliers. Violins, violas, cellos and double bass. Cheaper prices than most high street shops.

Swain Electronic Services
Lime Tree Avenue, Darley Dale, Matlock, DE4 2FS
tel: 01629 735 520
email: info@swainelectronics.co.uk
web: www.swainelectronics.co.uk
part exchange: Yes
info: Electronic music specialists dealing in anything from simple service to complete re-builds. Supply parts for organs, keyboards and speakers.

Synth Repair Services
Unit 22, Shelton Enterprise Centre, Bedford Street, Stoke On Trent, ST1 4PZ
tel: 01782 262 611
email: info@synthrepairservices.com
web: www.synthrepairservices.com
part exchange: Yes
info: Restores and repairs vintage analogue musical equipment.

T.P. Music Ltd.
18 Victoria Road, Tamworth, B79 7HR
tel: 01827 62 00 69
part exchange: No
info: General musical instrument store stocking new and used items. Tuition available in guitar and keyboard.

Take 2 Music
116a Derby Road, Long Eaton, Nottingham, NG10 4LS
tel: 0115 973 5468
email: sales@take2music.com
web: www.take2music.com
part exchange: No
info: Guitar specialist also stocking amps, keyboards and Folk instruments. Tuition available in guitar, bass, fiddle, mandolin and keyboard. Repairs in-store plus notice board space.

the|unsigned|guide

The Unsigned Guide/UK/2006. Material published in this directory may not be reproduced (in any form) without written consent.

Telford Sound Division
1 Southwater Way, Town Centre, Telford, TF3 4NL
tel: 01952 210 186
part exchange: No
info: General music store with large range of new and used guitars . Repairs and notice board space available.

Toot Sweet
76 Derby Road, Nottingham, NG1 5FD
tel: 0115 959 8321
email: mactrane@aol.com
web: www.toot-sweet.co.uk
part exchange: No
info: Woodwind and brass specialists with on-site professional repairs. Saxophone tutor on premises. Notice board space available.

Total Music Co. Ltd.
196-204 Binley Road, Coventry, CV3 1HG
tel: 02476 635 766
email: info@totalmusiccompany.com
part exchange: No
info: Biggest music store in Coventry stocking guitars, drums, bass, keyboards, pianos and woodwind instruments. Band flyer space in-store.

TPM Music
98 Factory Road, Hinckley, LE10 0DS
tel: 01455 637 946
part exchange: No
info: Store selling guitars, drums and starter kits. Repairs and tuition for guitar available. Poster space in-store.

Trent Music Centre
1a Pelham Street, Newark, NG24 4XD
tel: 01636 677 626
part exchange: No
info: Wide variety of instruments with emphasis on guitars. Repairs to instruments and amps. Tuition for guitar. Notice board and flyer space in-store.

True Spirit Music
786 Bristol Road, Selly Oak, Birmingham, B29 6NA
tel: 0121 472 5106
email: truespiritmusic@fsmail.co.uk
part exchange: Yes
info: Sell acoustic and electric guitars, violins, saxophone, tom-tom drums, organs, keyboards and PA equipment along with accessories. Lessons in guitar, bass, piano, keyboard, piano, vocals, drums and more. Notice board space available.

Turner Violins Ltd. (Digbeth)
1 Gibb Street, The Custard Factory, Digbeth, B9 4AA
tel: 0121 772 7780
email: birmingham@turnerviolins.co.uk
web: www.turnerviolins.co.uk
part exchange: No
info: Large stringed instrument store specialising in fine old violins, violas, cellos and double bass. Tuition, valuation, exchange, restoration and rehearing all available in-store. See also listing for store in Nottingham.

Turner Violins Ltd. (Nottingham)
1-5 Lily Grove, Beeston, Nottingham, NG9 1QL
tel: 0115 943 0333
email: info@turnerviolins.co.uk
web: www.turnerviolins.co.uk
part exchange: No
info: Deal in new and old violin sales, repairs and tuition. See also listing for shop in Digbeth.

Wayne's Guitar Shack
376 Carlton Hill, Carlton, Nottingham, NG4 1HW
tel: 0115 961 6452
email: sales@waynesguitarshack.co.uk
web: www.waynesguitarshack.co.uk
part exchange: No
info: Guitar specialist also dealing in amps, effects and bass. Tuition in vocal, bass and guitar. Repairs and poster space available.

Wernick
2a Twycross Street, Leicester, LE2 0DU
tel: 0116 255 6225
email: will@wernick.net
web: www.wernick.net
part exchange: Yes
info: Rare and unusual electonic instruments such as the Xylosynth and Kiknote hand-made to order. Past customers have included UB40, William Orbit and Live8.

White & Sentance
The Temple, Eastgate, Sleaford, NG34 7DR
tel: 01529 302 037
email: enquiries@wspianos.co.uk
web: www.wspianos.co.uk
part exchange: No
info: Specialists in Acoustic pianos only. Offer repairs, tuning, restoration and hire.

White Room
93 Burton Road, Lincoln, LN1 3JZ
tel: 01522 822 282
web: www.white-room.co.uk
part exchange: No
info: Mainly stock guitars, bass and drums. Large emphasis on accessories. Offer repairs, tuition and band notice board space.

Wind & Brass
Unit 10, Berrows House, Bath Street, Hereford, HR1 2HE
tel: 01432 352 144
email: lawrence@musicrepairs.com
web: www.musicrepairs.com
part exchange: Yes
info: A comprehensive repair service dedicated to the repair and maintenance of all Classical musical instruments. Stock of spare parts and some second hand instruments for sale.

Wind World
1 Gibb Street, The Custard Factory, Digbeth, B9 4AA
tel: 0121 772 7780
email: info@wind-world.co.uk
web: www.wind-world.co.uk
part exchange: No
info: Woodwind and brass specialists catering for everyone from beginner to professional. Instruments by Jupiter, Yanagisawa, Pearl, Yamaha and Buffet. Variety of old saxophones, clarinets, early flutes and mouthpieces.

Windband
9 Greyfriars Road, Shrewsbury, SY3 7EN
tel: 01743 367 482
email: info@windband.co.uk
web: www.windband.co.uk
part exchange: No
info: Contemporary woodwind and brass instrument specialist. Offer repairs and notice board space in-store.

Windblowers
75-77 Derby Road, Nottingham, NG1 5BA
tel: 0115 941 0543
email: sales@windblowers.com
web: www.windblowers.com
part exchange: No
info: Brass and woodwind specialists. Stock wide range of sheet music. Repairs and notice board space for bands and musicians.

Zebra Muzik
336 Nottingham Road, Ilkeston, DE7 5BD
tel: 0115 930 8362
email: zebramuzik@ntlworld.com
web: www.zebramuzik.com
part exchange: No
info: Music shop selling electric and Acoustic guitars and bass. 4 teaching rooms upstairs for tuition. Repairs and noticeboard space available.

MUSIC SERVICES/RETAIL

NORTHEAST

SOUNDCONTROL
The UK's Number One Musical Instrument Retailer

Sound Control (Newcastle)
10 Mosley Street, Newcastle upon Tyne, NE1 1DE
tel: 0191 232 4175
fax: 0191 222 1837
email: newcastle@soundcontrol.co.uk
web: www.soundcontrol.co.uk
contact: Paul Hindmarsh
part exchange: Yes
info: As the largest music equipment retailer in Europe
with 25 stores across the UK, Sound Control has the most extensive
range of guitars, basses, backline, PA, hi-tech, recording and percussion
equipment available at the lowest prices around. Coupled with over 25
years experience and unrivalled staff training, shopping at Sound
Control is the easiest step you will make on the road to being signed.
Visit the above website to locate your nearest store, or to buy online
and have your purchase delivered direct to your door.

SOUNDCONTROL
The UK's Number One Musical Instrument Retailer

Sound Control (Stockton On Tees)
Unit 14, Portrack Lane, Ross Road, Stockton On Tees, TS18 2NH
tel: 01642 671 222
fax: 01642 267 5958
email: stockton@soundcontrol.co.uk
web: www.soundcontrol.co.uk
contact: Carl Jones
part exchange: Yes
info: As the largest music equipment retailer in Europe
with 25 stores across the UK, Sound Control has the most extensive
range of guitars, basses, backline, PA, hi-tech, recording and percussion
equipment available at the lowest prices around. Coupled with over 25
years experience and unrivalled staff training, shopping at Sound
Control is the easiest step you will make on the road to being signed.
Visit the above website to locate your nearest store, or to buy online
and have your purchase delivered direct to your door.

Air Guitars
344 Old Durham Road, Gateshead, Tyne & Wear, NE8 4BQ
tel: 0191 477 1990
web: www.airguitars.co.uk
part exchange: No
info: New and second hand guitars, as well as amps and
accessories. Repair service available.

Alenia's Musicart
314 High Street West, Sunderland, Tyne & Wear, SR1 3ET
tel: 0191 567 2004
email: aleniamusicart@yahoo.co.uk
part exchange: No
info: Shop stocking mixture of musical instruments and
artistic equipment. Mainly focus on Classical instruments.

Alt. Vinyl
61-62 Thornton Street, Newcastle upon Tyne, Tyne & Wear, NE1 4AW
tel: 0191 222 1213
email: info@altvinyl.com
web: www.altvinyl.com
part exchange: Yes
info: Notice board in shop. Sell new & used CDs, also
rare/collectibles. In-store gigs available, contact for details.

Andy Lee Woodwind
195 Osborne Road, Jesmond, Newcastle upon Tyne, Tyne & Wear,
NE2 3LH
tel: 0191 281 3585/07974 932 344
part exchange: No
info: Repair service available.

Bandland Music Store
Sedgefield Way, Portrack Interchange Business Park, Stockton-On-Tees,
TS18 2SG
tel: 01642 605 444
email: petebandland@btclick.com
web: www.bandland.co.uk
part exchange: Yes
info: Stock a range of musical instruments, amplification
and recording equipment.

Bass Place
First Floor, 3 Nun Street, Newcastle Upon Tyne, Tyne & Wear, NE1 5AG
tel: 0191 221 0948
part exchange: Yes
info: Specialise in bass at the moment, but will be
changing shortly to incorporate more guitars and amps.

Brotherton & Son (Bishop Auckland) Ltd.
205 Newgate Street, Bishop Auckland, DL14 7EL
tel: 01388 663 483
email: tim@broth4801.fsnet.co.uk
part exchange: No
info: Sell range of instruments, sheet music and PA
equipment. Repairs and limited guitar tuition available. Notice board
space for bands.

Buzz Music
159 High Street East, Wallsend, Tyne & Wear, NE28 7RL
tel: 0191 240 2597
part exchange: No
info: In-store tuition available.

Dennis Todd Music
86 Front Street, Bedlington, Northumberland, NE22 5AE
tel: 01670 822 085
fax: 01670 820 592
email: dtoddmusic@aol.com
web: www.dennistoddmusic.com
part exchange: No
info: Stock brass, woodwind, guitars and violins. Repair
service available. Tuition for piano, woodwind and keyboard. Space
in-store for posters and notices.

The Drum Shop
Heworth House, Kirkstone Road, Pelaw, Gateshead, NE10 0XQ
tel: 0191 495 0201
email: info@drumshop.co.uk
web: www.drumshop.co.uk
part exchange: No
info: New and used drum kits. Offer repairs and drum
tuition in-store.

EBGB Music
The Avenue, Durham, County Durham, DH1 4ED
tel: 0191 384 5613
email: ebgbmusic@btconnect.com
part exchange: No
info: Guitars and amplification. Sales and repairs
available. Tuition in-store in guitar, drum, bass and saxophone. Also
stock range of sheet music and accessories. Notice board space.

Greensleeves (Guisborough)
21 Chaloner Street, Guisborough, Cleveland, TS14 6QD
tel: 01287 636 028
part exchange: No
info: Stock range of instruments from brass, woodwind
and strings to ethnic percussion and sheet music. In-house repairs.
Notice board space available. Smaller sister store to Greensleeves based
in Northallerton, Yorkshire. See listing in relevant section for details.

Guitar Guitar Ltd. (Newcastle)
Unit 24, The Newgate Centre, Newgate Street, Newcastle Upon Tyne,
NE1 5RS
tel: 0191 261 1588
email: newcastle@guitarguitar.co.uk
web: www.guitarguitar.co.uk
part exchange: Yes
info: Guitar specialist. Offer repairs and notice board
space in-store. Also 2 branches located in Scotland. Refer to entries for
further details.

Guitar House 55
19 Castle Hill, Richmond, DL10 4QP
tel: 01748 850 919
email: mike@guitarhouse55.com
web: www.guitarhouse55.com
part exchange: No
info: New and used guitars, repairs and notice board
space available.

The Guitar Shop
3 Old George Yard, Rear of Cloth Market, Newcastle Upon Tyne, Tyne
& Wear, NE1 1EZ
tel: 0191 261 4056
part exchange: No
info: Repair service available. Notice board space.

J. Williams
16 Garden Walk, Metro Centre, Gateshead, Tyne & Wear, NE11 9XY
tel: 0191 493 2244
email: metro@williams-music.co.uk
web: www.williams-music.co.uk
part exchange: No
info: Sell wide selection of instruments and equipment.
Repairs and in-store tuition.

J.G. Windows Ltd.
1-7 Central Arcade, Newcastle Upon Tyne, Tyne & Wear, NE1 5BP
tel: 0191 232 1356
web: www.jgwindows.com
part exchange: No
info: Acoustic and electric guitars, amplification, drums, PA and accessories. Also stock CDs. Repair service available.

Jake Guitars Ltd.
Collingdon Building, Collingdon Road, High Spen, Rowlands Gill, Tyne & Wear, NE39 2EQ
tel: 01207 549 339
web: www.jakesguitars.com
part exchange: No
info: Dealers for Gibson, Epiphone, Fender, Takamine and Yamaha, amongst others. Repair service available.

John Ross Pianos
St. Helen's Street, Northumberland, NE45 5BE
tel: 01434 632 968
email: enquiries@johnrosspianos.com
web: www.johnrosspianos.com
part exchange: Yes
info: Piano sales, sheet music, musical instruments, tuning services and musical instrument repairs.

John Sylvester's Saxophone Emporium
95 Jesmond Park West, Newcastle Upon Tyne, Tyne & Wear, NE7 7BY
tel: 0191 281 8357
web: www.sax-emporium.co.uk
part exchange: No
info: Saxophone specialists. Also stock accessories. Repairs and tuition, as well as mail order service.

Live & Loud
55 High Street East, Wallsend, NE28 8PR
tel: 0191 262 5729
part exchange: No
info: Electric instrument store. Items including guitars, bass and keyboards. Instrument repairs and guitar tuition available. Notice board space in-store.

Making Music
67 Church Way, North Shields, NE29 0AE
tel: 0191 296 3049
email: musicshop@blueyonder.co.uk
web: www.making-music.net
part exchange: No
info: Guitar and drum shop. Buy, sell and repair. Also offer in-store guitar tuition. Notice board space for musicians.

McKay Sound & Music
100 Westgate Road, Newcastle upon Tyne, NE1 4AF
tel: 0191 232 4449
part exchange: No
info: Guitar and accessories store. Currently expanding stock. Willing to display adverts.

Middlesbrough Music Centre
15 Gilkes Street, Middlesbrough, TS1 5ET
tel: 01642 226 977
email: tony.carrington@ntlworld.com
web: www.middlesbroughmusic.co.uk
part exchange: No
info: General music store stocking guitars, bass, keyboards and amps. Guitars repairs available and notice board space for bands.

The Music Gallery
83b Marygate, Berwick-Upon-Tweed, Northumberland, TD15 1BA
tel: 01289 303 223
email: brian@themusicgallery.co.uk
web: www.themusicgallery.co.uk
part exchange: No
info: Repairs service. In-store tuition for guitar, bass and drums.

The Music Shop
7 Bridge Street, Berwick-upon-Tweed, TD15 1ES
tel: 01289 307 917
part exchange: Yes
info: Guitar and sheet music shop. All new items. Notice board space for adverts and flyers.

Newcastle Drum Centre Ltd.
10-12 Akenside Hill, Newcastle Upon Tyne, Tyne & Wear, NE1 3XP
tel: 0191 221 0301
email: team@newcastledrum.co.uk
web: www.newcastledrum.co.uk
part exchange: Yes
info: Stock everything drum related including electronic kits, as well as DVDs. In-store tuition available. See listing in relevant section for further information.

Newcastle Music
71 Westgate Road, Newcastle Upon Tyne, NE1 1SG
tel: 0191 221 0595
email: sales@newcastlemusic.co.uk
web: www.newcastlemusic.co.uk
part exchange: No
info: Specialise in Folk instruments including ukuleles, bagpipes, jaws harps and accordions. Also stock string, woodwind, brass and percussion, as well as accessories and sheet music. Repairs available.

Omega Music UK Ltd.
4 The Precinct, Wesley Court, Blaydon-on-Tyne, NE21 5BT
tel: 0191 414 7700
email: sales@omegamusic.co.uk
web: www.omegamusic.co.uk
part exchange: Yes
info: General musical instrument store selling everything and anything from guitars to pianos. Offer repairs to pianos and some repairs to other instruments. Northern Academy of Music is located upstairs. Sister store located in Brampton, Cumbria. See listings for further details.

The Pick Up Joint
The Land Of Green Ginger, 78 Front Street, Tynemouth, North Shields, Tyne & Wear, NE30 4BP
tel: 0191 257 8617
part exchange: No
info: Repairs available.

Piedog Ltd.
Unit F12, Morton Park, Darlington, County Durham, DL1 4PQ
tel: 0845 601 2078
web: www.piedog.com
part exchange: Yes
info: General musical instrument store catering for all your needs. From computer systems to music stands.

The Really Useful Music Co.
Chester Le Street, County Durham, DH3 1QT
tel: 0191 410 8080
email: admin@reallyusefulmusicco.co.uk
web: www.reallyusefulmusicco.co.uk
part exchange: Yes
info: Mail order company with large range of instruments.

Ron's Music
39 Blackwellgate, Darlington, DL1 5HW
tel: 01325 359 123
email: ron@ronsmusic.co.uk
web: www.ronsmusic.co.uk
part exchange: No
info: Stock guitars, amplification and percussion. Repairs and tuition available.

Seaton Music
3-4 The Front, Hartlepool, Cleveland, TS25 1BS
tel: 01429 867 300
part exchange: Yes
info: Specialise in pianos and guitars.

Sound World
29 Olive Street, Sunderland, SR1 3PE
tel: 0191 565 5606
part exchange: No
info: New and used guitar shop offering sales and repairs. Notice board space for musicians.

Sounds Live
27 Dean Street, Newcastle Upon Tyne, NE1 1PQ
tel: 0870 757 2360
email: sales@soundslive.co.uk
web: www.soundslive.co.uk
part exchange: No
info: Large store selling variety of instruments. Departments for keyboards, hi-tech and recording equipment, PAs and mics, as well as guitars and effects. Offer repairs for existing customers.

Staves Music
Dunning Road, Ferryhill, County Durham, DL17 8HN
tel: 01740 654 080
email: staves.music@virgin.net
part exchange: No
info: Mostly guitars and amplification. Notice board space for flyers.

MUSIC SERVICES/RETAIL

Sunderland Music
4-5 Tavistock Buildings, Borough Road, Sunderland, SR1 1PF
tel: 0191 564 1693
email: via website
web: www.sunderlandmusic.co.uk
part exchange: No
info: Drum and percussion specialists. New and second hand kits. Hire service and repairs available. Notice board space in-store.

Tim Gentle Music (Stockton)
PO Box 154, Stockton On Tees, TS20 1XJ
tel: 0870 740 6282
email: timgentle@fsnet.co.uk
web: www.timgentlemusic.co.uk
part exchange: No
info: Established 1976. Instruments for professional and semi-professional musicians. Repairs available. See also listing for branch in Southend on Sea.

Tyneside Piano Co.
34 Wellhead Terrace, Ashington, NE63 8PA
tel: 01670 815 313
email: via website
web: www.tyneside-piano.co.uk
part exchange: No
info: New and used pianos for sale. Also offer tuning, repairs and reconditioning.

The Violin Shop
27 Hencotes, Hexham, NE46 2EQ
tel: 01434 607 897
email: davehexviolins@aol.com
web: www.hexham-violins.co.uk
part exchange: No
info: Dealers, restorers and makers of fine new and reproduction instruments. Specialise in the sale, repair and restoration of violins, violas and cellos. Notice board in-store.

Williams Music Group
16 Garden Walk, Metro Centre, Gateshead, NE11 9XY
tel: 0191 493 2244
web: www.williams-music.co.uk
part exchange: No
info: General instrument store specialising in guitars and pianos. Repairs and tuition in-store for electric pianos and keyboard.

Words & Music
35 Fenkle Street, Alnwick, Northumberland, NE66 1HW
tel: 01665 510 345
email: wordsandmusic.alnwick@virgin.net
part exchange: Yes
info: General music shop. Offers repairs and tuition for woodwind. Willing to display flyers behind the counter.

NORTHWEST

SOUNDCONTROL
The UK's Number One Musical Instrument Retailer

Sound Control (Manchester)
1 New Wakefield Street, Manchester, M1 5WH
tel: 0161 236 0340
fax: 0161 236 7775
email: manchester.city@soundcontrol.co.uk
web: www.soundcontrol.co.uk
contact: Bob White
part exchange: Yes
info: As the largest music equipment retailer in Europe with 25 stores across the UK, Sound Control has the most extensive range of guitars, basses, backline, PA, hi-tech, recording and percussion equipment available at the lowest prices around. Coupled with over 25 years experience and unrivalled staff training, shopping at Sound Control is the easiest step you will make on the road to being signed. Visit the above website to locate your nearest store, or to buy online and have your purchase delivered direct to your door.

SOUNDCONTROL
The UK's Number One Musical Instrument Retailer

Sound Control (Preston)
7-11 Heatley Street, Preston, PR1 2XB
tel: 01772 204 567
fax: 01772 203 404
email: preston@soundcontrol.co.uk
web: www.soundcontrol.co.uk
contact: Steve Eaton
part exchange: Yes
info: As the largest music equipment retailer in Europe with 25 stores across the UK, Sound Control has the most extensive range of guitars, basses, backline, PA, hi-tech, recording and percussion equipment available at the lowest prices around. Coupled with over 25 years experience and unrivalled staff training, shopping at Sound Control is the easiest step you will make on the road to being signed. Visit the above website to locate your nearest store, or to buy online and have your purchase delivered direct to your door.

SOUNDCONTROL
The UK's Number One Musical Instrument Retailer

Sound Control (Salford)
Unit 5, Red Rose Retail Centre, Regent Road, Salford, Lancashire, M5 3GR
tel: 0161 877 6262
fax: 0161 877 6363
email: manchester.salford@soundcontrol.co.uk
web: www.soundcontrol.co.uk
contact: Colin Ford, Johnny Singh
part exchange: Yes
info: As the largest music equipment retailer in Europe with 25 stores across the UK, Sound Control has the most extensive range of guitars, basses, backline, PA, hi-tech, recording and percussion equipment available at the lowest prices around. Coupled with over 25 years experience and unrivalled staff training, shopping at Sound Control is the easiest step you will make on the road to being signed. Visit the above website to locate your nearest store, or to buy online and have your purchase delivered direct to your door.

1st Golborne Guitars
124 Church Street, Golborne, Warrington, WA3 3TW
tel: 01942 728 984
part exchange: No
info: Sell new and used guitars and a small range of brass items. Repairs available. Noticeboard space available after store is redecorated.

A&A Music
1 Mill Street, Congleton, Cheshire, CW12 1AB
tel: 01260 280 778
fax: 01260 298 311
email: mailorder@aamusic.co.uk
web: www.aamusic.co.uk
contact: Alan Farrah, Dave Wedgebury
part exchange: No
info: Stocks varied range of instruments. Musician's message board. A&A Music has another branch selling CDs. See listing in relevant section for details.

A&C Hamilton (Preston)
946 Blackpool Road, Lea, Preston, PR2 1XN
tel: 01772 722 468
email: info@achamilton.co.uk
web: www.achamilton.co.uk
part exchange: No
info: See listing above for Bolton branch for details of instruments stocked.

Aardvark Music
67 Bridge Street, Warrington, WA1 2HJ
tel: 01925 657 833
fax: 01925 471 487
email: info@aardvark-music.co.uk
web: www.aardvark-music.co.uk
part exchange: No
info: Sell guitars and accessories, including PA. Also stock Drum kits and a small amount of piano and vocal accessories. Guitar set up and repair service available. Also offer tuition services for most instruments including guitar, keyboard, piano, singing, Drums, flute, trumpet and saxophone. Speak to any employee with regards to displaying gig posters and flyers in-store. Message board in-store for musicians.

MUSIC SERVICES/RETAIL

Access All Areas Music
Unit 6, Logford Street, Warrington, WA2 7PG
tel: 01925 232 536
email: tuffgong@btconnect.com
web: www.tuffgong.co.uk
part exchange: No
info: Sells a wide range of new and second hand musical equipment including guitars, PAs, DJ equipment, lighting and much more.

Acoustic Instruments North West
41 Upper Aughton Road, Birkdale, Stockport, PR8 5ND
tel: 01704 564 036
email: sales@acousticinst.co.uk
web: www.acousticinst.co.uk
part exchange: Yes
info: New and used Acoustic instruments. Also do repairs. Space for posters in-store and for musicians to post notices. List of music tutors available.

ADC Drums & Percussion
19 Cheapside, Liverpool, L2 2DY
tel: 0151 227 3271
fax: 0151 707 7965
email: andy@adcdrums.co.uk
web: www.adcdrums.co.uk
part exchange: No
info: Drums, Drum accessories and guitar strings. Tuition, repairs and hire available. Buy/part exchange. Practice room with kit available at £4.99 per hour. Notice board in-store. Space for posters.

Alan Gregory Music & Musical Instruments
196-198 Moseley Road, Fallowfield, Manchester, M14 6PB
tel: 0161 224 8915
fax: 0161 224 6655
part exchange: No
info: Range of instruments including strings, brass, woodwind, classical guitars, sheet music and accessories. Repair services for strings, brass and woodwind. Notice board in-store.

Alligator Music
393 Manchester Road, Heaton Chapel, Stockport, SK4 5BY
tel: 0161 442 1980
fax: 0161 947 9787
email: customerservice@alligatormusic.com
web: www.alligatormusic.com
part exchange: No
info: Specialise in guitars. Repairs and tuition available. Noticeboard space in-store.

Arietta Music
51 Deardengate, Haslingden, Rossendale, BB4 5QN
tel: 01706 229 457
email: music@farmore.net
web: www.ariettamusic.co.uk
part exchange: Yes
info: Carries a range of instruments, mostly guitars and keyboards, but also didgeridoos. Can order instruments online . Repairs on stringed instruments. Also offer tuition services. Contact for details.

Ashton Instrument Repairs
13 Newmarket Road, Ashton Under Lyne, OL7 9LL
tel: 0161 330 7176
part exchange: Yes
info: Brass instrument repairs.

Ayres Violins
69-71 School Lane, Didsbury, Manchester, M20 6WN
tel: 0161 448 1860
fax: 0161 448 1860
email: info@ayresviolins.co.uk or sales@ayresviolins.co.uk
web: www.ayresviolins.co.uk
part exchange: No
info: Violins, cellos & bows bought, sold and repaired. Noticeboard in shop

MUSIC SERVICES/RETAIL

Back Alley Music
5 Chester Street, Mold, CH7 1EG
tel:	01352 758 619
email:	info@backalleymusic.co.uk
web:	www.backalleymusic.co.uk
part exchange:	No
info:	Over 1000 guitars in stock, mainly electric and

bass. Drums, brass, woodwind keyboards and general accessories. Instrument rental and in-store tuition. Also have branches in Chester, telephone 01244 322 229, and Warrington, telephone 01925 232 320. Opening online store in near future.

Barnby Music Service
14 Green Bank, Harwood, Bolton, BL2 3NG
tel:	01204 528 996
contact:	Peter Barnby
part exchange:	Yes
info:	Repairs for electronic instruments and equipment,

mainly organs, keyboards and amps.

Beats Ahead Music
10 Greenbank Lane, Northwich, CW8 1JG
tel:	01606 782 538
email:	colin@beatsaheadmusic.co.uk
web:	www.beatsaheadmusic.co.uk
contact:	Colin
part exchange:	No
info:	Stock drums, guitars, PA and lights. PA and

lighting hire available. Repair service for most instruments and equipment. Tuition available in drums and bass guitar. Space in-store for poster display and for musicians to post notices. Speak to Colin.

Big Discount Warehouse
404 Marine Road, Morecambe, LA4 5AR
tel:	01524 400 999
fax:	01524 410 802
email:	sales@bigdiscountwarehouse.co.uk
web:	www.bigdiscountwarehouse.co.uk
part exchange:	Yes
info:	Stock all types of instruments plus PAs, karaoke

and DJ equipment. There is a shop but is mainly a mail order service.

Billy Bowman Music
Unit 5, Lowther Went, Cockermouth, Cumbria, CA13 9RT
tel:	01900 826 708
fax:	01900 825 984
email:	info@billybowmanmusic.freeserve.co.uk
web:	www.billybowmanmusic.com
part exchange:	No
info:	Sell a wide variety of instruments and sheet music.

Part exchange and instrument rental scheme available. Enthusiastic, qualified musicians to help and advise. Will perform small keyboard and guitar repairs while you wait. List of music teachers available. Speak to any member of staff to display posters and flyers for gigs in-store. Musicians can post notices (not for the sale of equipment though).

Blackburn Guitar Studio
82 Queen Street, Great Harwood, Lancashire, BB6 7AL
tel:	01254 889 555
fax:	01254 889 555
email:	jackwilkinson@lineone.net
web:	www.guitarsclassical.net
contact:	Jack Wilkinson
part exchange:	No
info:	Stocks a range of classical, electric and Acoustic

guitars. Minor repairs and tuition available.

Bolton Guitar Studio
79 Mornington Road, Bolton, BL1 4EF
tel:	01204 845 784
email:	info@boltonguitar.co.uk
web:	www.boltonguitar.co.uk
part exchange:	Yes
info:	Guitars, amps, sheet music and accessories.

Tuition available. Space in-store for posters and notices.

Bonecat Music (Middleton)
77a Long Street, Middleton, Manchester, M24 6UN
tel:	0161 653 2323
fax:	0161 653 2323
email:	crispy@bonecat.co.uk
web:	www.bonecat.co.uk
contact:	Christine Banks
part exchange:	No
info:	Sell a range of instruments, predominantly guitars

and amps. Also do repairs. Buy and part exchange instruments. Space for posters, speak to Christine Banks. Good electrician/technician is available to repair most items. See also listing for shop located in Rochdale.

Bonecat Music (Rochdale)
79 Drake Street, Rochdale, OL16 1SD
tel:	01706 639 001
email:	crispy@bonecat.co.uk
web:	www.bonecat.co.uk
part exchange:	No
info:	See listing above for branch located in Middleton

for details of instruments stocked.

Booth's Music
17 Churchgate, Bolton, BL1 1HU
tel:	01204 522 908
fax:	01204 380 008
email:	info@boothsmusic.co.uk
web:	www.boothsmusic.co.uk
contact:	Tony Aspinall
part exchange:	No
info:	Stock everything except pianos and organs (though

do stock electric pianos). Also tens of thousands of music titles stocked. Repair service available for guitars, woodwind and brass instruments. Will display posters and flyers, speak to the manager. List of instrument tutors available in-store.

Brian Eastwood Guitars
408 Newchurch Road, Stacksteads, Bacup, Lancashire, OL13 0LD
tel:	01706 874 549
web:	www.brianeastwoodguitars.co.uk
part exchange:	Yes
info:	One of the UK's top guitar builders and repairers,

with over 30 years experience. Maker of the Bender Distortocaster model and many other one-off guitars. Price list can be found on website.

Buster Cases
Units 5-7, Peel Industrial Estate, Chamberhall Street, Bury, Lancashire, BL9 0LU
tel:	0161 761 2040
fax:	0161 761 6040
email:	mail@bustercases.co.uk
web:	www.bustercases.com
part exchange:	Yes
info:	Specialist manufacturers of flight cases. Custom

built to requirements. Will produce cases for anything related to the music industry at competitive prices.

Castle Music Ltd.
43 Shrewsberry Road, Oxton, Birkenhead, CH43 2JB
tel:	0151 652 1963
contact:	Peter Rainsford
part exchange:	Yes
info:	Selected range of instruments and sheet music.

Can get hold of anything which they do not have in stock.

Chas Hooper Drums
152 Belthorn Road, Belthorn, Blackburn, BB1 2NN
tel:	01254 672 354
fax:	01254 672 354
email:	chas@chashooperdrumshop.co.uk
web:	www.chashooperdrumshop.co.uk
contact:	Chas Hooper
part exchange:	No
info:	Large range of percussion instruments. Also do

repairs. Buy/part exchange. Space for posters and musicians' notices in-store, speak to Chas.

Chase
58 Oldham Street, Manchester, M4 1LE
tel:	0161 236 6794
part exchange:	No
info:	Sell and repair all types of musical instruments.

Notice board in-store for poster and flyer display.

Clitheroe Music
9 Moor Lane, Clitheroe, Lancashire, BB7 1BE
tel:	01200 429 942
fax:	01200 425 485
email:	mail@clitheroemusic.co.uk
web:	www.clitheroemusic.co.uk
part exchange:	Yes
info:	Range of instruments including classical and

Acoustic guitars, orchestral instruments and a large selection of harmonicas. Also sell sheet music, jazz and classical CDs. Repair and hire facilities. Notice board in-store (small fee for instrument sale adverts). Limited space available for posters.

Creighton & Tweedie
Poets Walk, Penrith, Cumbria, CA11 7HJ
tel:	01768 864 331
fax:	01768 899 778
web:	www.creighton-tweedie.com
part exchange:	No
info:	Digital pianos, keyboards and organs. Range of

Acoustic and electric guitars. Flute and clarinet rental. Part exchange and repairs available.

Cue Music
183 Duckworth Street, Darwen, Lancashire, BB3 1AU
tel: 01254 775 560
fax: 01254 775 560
email: djh@cuemusic.co.uk
web: www.cuemusic.co.uk
contact: Peter Holroyd
part exchange: No
info: Range of instruments and PAs. PA hire available.
Repairs. Buy/part exchange. Notice board in-store, space for posters.
Cue Music also run a recording studio. See listing in relevant section for
further details.

Curly Music
45 Ranlagh Street, Liverpool, L1 1JR
tel: 0151 709 8484
fax: 0151 709 4819
email: enquiry@curlymusic.co.uk
web: www.curlymusic.co.uk
part exchange: No
info: Guitars, Drums, PA, woodwind, brass. Also
stock sheet music. In addition to noticeboard in-store, there is also
noticeboard on the website for bands to advertise gigs and place
advertisements for band members. Offer tuition in flute, clarinet,
saxophone and Drums.

Custom Guitar Workshop
64 Mostyn Avenue, Old Roan, Liverpool, Merseyside, L10 2JQ
tel: 0151 476 2279
part exchange: Yes
info: Deal with repairs, refinishes and restoration of
stringed instruments. Custom build guitars to customer specifications.

D.E. Vernon Violins
898 Chester Road, Stretford, Manchester, M32 0PA
tel: 0161 865 7438/07973 904 789
fax: 0161 865 7650
email: sales@vernon-violins.co.uk
web: www.vernon-violins.co.uk
part exchange: Yes
info: Manufacturers, restorers and dealers in violins,
cellos, violas, strings, bows and accessories.

Dalmedo Custom Guitars
31 Deborah Avenue, Fulwood, Preston, Lancashire, PR2 9HU
tel: 01772 718 907/07989 168 597
email: tito@dalmedoguitars.co.uk
web: www.dalmedoguitars.co.uk
contact: Tito
part exchange: Yes
info: Custom guitars and basses made to order. Set ups,
customising and full range of repairs available. Guitar tuition available.

Dawson's Music (Altrincham)
52 Stamford New Road, Altrincham, WA14 1EJ
tel: 0161 928 3302
fax: 0161 926 9320
email: altrincham@dawsons.co.uk
web: www.dawsonsonline.com
part exchange: Yes
info: Stock large range of instruments, PA equipment,
amps, effects and accessories. Branches throughout the North West, as
well as across rest of UK. See listings for details.

Dawson's Music (Chester)
30 Pepper Street, Chester, CH1 1DF
tel: 01244 348 606
fax: 01244 321 967
email: chester@dawsons.co.uk
web: www.dawsonsonline.com
part exchange: Yes
info: Stock large range of instruments, PA equipment,
amps, effects and accessories. Branches throughout the North West, as
well as across rest of UK. See listings for details.

Dawson's Music (Liverpool)
37 Ranelagh Street, Liverpool, L1 1JP
tel: 0151 709 1455
fax: 0151 709 7446
email: liverpool@dawsons.co.uk
web: www.dawsonsonline.com
part exchange: Yes
info: Stock large range of instruments, PA equipment,
amps, effects and accessories. Branches throughout the North West, as
well as several across rest of UK. See listings for details.

Dawson's Music (Manchester)
30 Portland Street, Manchester, M1 4GS
tel: 0161 237 1770
fax: 0161 234 6757
email: manchester@dawsons.co.uk
web: www.dawsonsonline.com
part exchange: Yes
info: Stock large range of instruments, PA equipment,
amps, effects and accessories. Branches throughout the North West, as
well as across rest of the UK. See listings for details.

Dawson's Music (St. Helens)
30 Barrow Street, St. Helens, WA10 1RX
tel: 01744 730 424
fax: 01744 224 03
email: sthelens@dawsons.co.uk
web: www.dawsonsonline.com
part exchange: Yes
info: Stock large range of instruments, PA equipment,
amps, effects and accessories. Branches throughout the North West, as
well as across rest of UK. See listings for details.

Dawson's Music (Stockport)
5 High Bank Side, Off St. Petersgate, Stockport, SK1 1HG
tel: 0161 477 1210
fax: 0161 476 3221
email: stockport@dawsons.co.uk
web: www.dawsonsmusic.com
part exchange: Yes
info: Stock large range of instruments, PA equipment,
amps, effects and accessories. Branches throughout the North West, as
well as across rest of UK. See listings for details.

Dawson's Music (Warrington)
65 Sankey Street, Warrington, WA1 1SU
tel: 0870 442 4605
fax: 0870 442 4606
email: service@dawsons.co.uk
web: www.dawsonsonline.com
part exchange: Yes
info: Stock large range of instruments, PA equipment,
amps, effects and accessories. Branches throughout the North West, as
well as across rest of UK. See listings for details.

Dazamakiz Musical Instrument Shop
666 North Drive, Thornton Cleveleys, Lancashire, FY5 2QD
tel: 01253 822 215
email: daz@dazamakiz.co.uk
web: www.dazamakiz.co.uk
part exchange: No
info: Stock range of instruments and equipment for
Rock bands and schools including guitars, drums, amps, lighting, brass,
woodwind and accessories. Main dealers of ESP and Orange. Repairs on
amps and guitars. Tuition available for guitar, bass and banjo. Posters
can be displayed in-store.

Dolphin Music
Laxey House, Woodend Avenue, Speke, L24 9WX
tel: 0870 840 9060
email: info@dolphinmusic.co.uk
web: www.dolphinmusic.co.uk
contact: Jason
part exchange: Yes
info: Specialise in studio equipment, PAs, DJ equipment
and software. Offer installation and set up services.

Doug's Cabin
27 The Green, Houghton, Carlisle, CA3 0NF
tel: 01228 522 888
web: www.guitarwarehouse.co.uk
part exchange: No
info: Stock guitars and amps. Repair and tuition services
for guitars. Display posters and notices in-store, speak to a member of
staff.

Drum Centre
Bridgewater Mill, Legh Street, Eccles, Manchester, M30 0UT
tel: 0161 789 4415
fax: 0161 789 4415
email: info@manchesterdrum.com
web: www.manchesterdrum.com
part exchange: No
info: Largest Drum store in the North West. Also
provide mail order service, see website for further details. Noticeboard
in-store for musicians.

Electric Avenue
109 Whitegate Drive, Blackpool, Lancashire, FY3 9BY
tel: 01253 305 559
email: andy@theelectricavenue.com
web: www.theelectricavenue.com
part exchange: No
info: Guitars, drums, amps and related accessories.
Repair service for guitars. Space in-store for posters and notices, ask a
member of staff.

MUSIC SERVICES/RETAIL

Forsyth Bros. Ltd.
126 Deansgate, Manchester, M3 2GR
tel: 0161 834 3281
fax: 0161 834 0630
email: info@forsyths.co.uk
web: www.forsyths.co.uk
part exchange: No
info: Wide range of instruments including guitars, percussion, strings, brass, woodwind, keyboards and pianos. Also stock music books, scores and accessories. Repair services for most instruments and piano tuning. Run concert hire rental scheme. List of music tutors available. Noticeboard in-store for posters and flyers.

Frailers Vintage Guitars & Banjos
89a Church Street, Runcorn, Cheshire, WA7 1LG
tel: 01928 573 087
fax: 01928 591 623
email: frailers@btconnect.com
web: www.frailers.com
contact: Frank
part exchange: Yes
info: Vintage guitars and banjos. Over 500 guitars in stock, including American imports. Space for posters, notices and flyers.

Fred Rhodes Ltd.
The Doyen Centre, Vulcan Street, Oldham, OL1 4EP
tel: 0161 620 5899
fax: 0161 620 3199
email: fredrhodes@supanet.com
web: www.fredrhodes.com
part exchange: No
info: Specialise in brass, woodwind and percussion instruments and repair. Space in-store for poster and flyer display, speak to member of staff.

Frets Guitar Centre
33 Rossall Road, Cleveleys, Blackpool, Lancashire, FY5 1EE
tel: 01253 853 881
fax: 01253 853 881
email: info@fretsguitarcentre.co.uk
part exchange: No
info: Guitar specialists. Amplification equipment and accessories. Can carry out repairs. Buy good quality instruments and part exchange. Noticeboard in-store and space for posters.

Frets Old & New
294 Longmoor Lane, Fazakerly, Liverpool, L9 9BZ
tel: 0151 474 6343
fax: 0151 474 6343
part exchange: No
info: Guitars, banjos, mandolins, violins and woodwind. Large selection of printed music. Repair service available. Will display notices, gig posters and flyers, just ask member of staff.

The Full Octave
152 Market Street, Dalton-in-Furness, Cumbria, LA15 8RQ
tel: 01229 467 109
fax: 01229 467 109
email: info@thefulloctave.co.uk
web: www.thefulloctave.co.uk
part exchange: No
info: Specialise in pianos, woodwind, guitars and sheet music. Also carry a range of Folk instruments including melodeons, accordions and mandolins. Also stock accessories. Piano restoration and refinishing. Space in-store for notices, posters and flyers.

Hammersound (Birkenhead)
49-51 Grange Road West, Birkenhead, CH41 4BZ
tel: 0151 652 7454
email: denis@hammersound.co.uk
web: www.hammersound.co.uk
part exchange: No
info: Stock guitars, keyboards, Drums, PA, disco equipment and related accessories. Posters and flyers displayed in shop window, ask a member of staff. See also listing for shop based in Deeside.

Hammersound (Deeside)
304 High Street, Connahs Quay, Deeside, CH5 4DP
tel: 01244 811 447
email: denis@hammersound.co.uk
web: www.hammersound.co.uk
part exchange: No
info: Guitars, keyboards, drums and disco equipment. Repairs on guitars and amps. Notice board in-store. See also listing for shop in Birkenhead.

Harker & Howarth Music Instruments Ltd.
29-31 Goodwin Street, Folds Road, Bolton, BL1 1UN
tel: 01204 526 623
fax: 01204 366 710
web: www.harkerandhowarth.co.uk
contact: Hedley Jones
part exchange: No
info: Stock a wide range of instruments and accessories. Repair service available for electronic instruments, guitars, brass and woodwind. Also tuition services available in guitar, Drums, piano and keyboard. Musician's Noticeboard in shop.

Helen Whittaker
c/o Dawsons Music Ltd., 30 Pepper Street, Chester, CH1 1DF
tel: 01244 348 606
part exchange: Yes
info: Specialises in repairs on woodwind, brass and orchestral string instruments. No guitars!

Hobbs Music
105 Penny Street, Lancaster, LA1 1XN
tel: 01524 844 740
email: cbcmhobbs@aol.com
web: www.hobbsmusic.com
part exchange: No
info: Specialise in Acoustic guitars. Main brand Martin. Repairs available. Noticeboard in-store.

Hobgoblin Music (Manchester)
c/o Johnny Roadhouse Music, 123 Oxford Road, Manchester, M1 7DU
tel: 0161 273 1000
email: hobgoblin.manchester@johnnyroadhouse.co.uk
web: www.hobgoblin.co.uk
contact: Ken Thompson
part exchange: No
info: Folk specialists stocking Traditional, Celtic and Acoustic instruments from guitars to didgeridoos. Repair service available. Notice board in-store for posters. Hobgoblin has branches throughout the UK. See other listings or website for further details.

Howarths Music
13 Library Street, Wigan, WN1 1NN
tel: 01942 234 668/0800 093 2104
email: singsongsue1@hotmail.com
web: www.howarthsmusic.co.uk
part exchange: No
info: Range of orchestral and traditional instruments plus amps, PAs and sheet music. Teaching studios with tuition in brass and woodwind, guitars and Drums. Guitar repair service available.

HW Audio Ltd.
180-198 Georges Road, Bolton, BL1 2HP
tel: 0700 042 4848/01204 385 199
email: sales@hwaudio.co.uk
web: www.hwaudio.co.uk
part exchange: No
info: Large range of instruments, karaoke and DJ equipment, PAs, studio equipment, lighting, accessories, books and printed music. Talk to any member of staff to display posters or flyers for gigs.

Jalapeno Drums
2 Graham Street, Greave, Lancaster, LA1 4UE
tel: 01524 635 77
email: david@jalapenodrums.co.uk
web: www.jalapenodrums.co.uk
contact: David Nuttall
part exchange: Yes
info: Manufacture professional custom drum kits, snare drums and shells on order to customer specification. Mail order service. Repairs available.

John Forster
1 Lonsdale Gardens, Crosby Villas, Maryport, Cumbria, CA15 6TH
tel: 01900 814 113
email: forsterguitarist@aol.com
web: www.johnforsterguitars.co.uk
contact: John Forster
part exchange: No
info: Repairs on all guitars. Tuition in guitar and bass also available. Also craft Hawaiian guitars.

John Rose Drum Shop
115 Washway Road, Sale, Cheshire, M33 7TY
tel: 0161 976 6099
email: john@johnrosedrumshop.co.uk
web: www.johnrosedrumshop.co.uk
part exchange: No
info: The complete Drum specialist. New, used and part exchange. Also sells guitars and guitar accessories. Space for posters and flyers, send by post or bring in person. Repair service for Drums and guitars also available.

Johnny Roadhouse Music
123 Oxford Road, All Saints, Manchester, M1 7DU
tel: 0161 273 1111/0161 273 3069
fax: 0161 273 5749
email: johnny@johnnyroadhousemusic.fsnet.co.uk
web: www.johnnyroadhouse.co.uk
part exchange: No
info: New and used guitars and amps. Very large range of Drums, percussion, woodwind, brass, reeds, strings and separate Folk department. Buy and part exchange. Instrument and equipment hire. Noticeboard in-store.

Jones Music Store
32-36 Charlotte Street, Macclesfield, Cheshire, SK11 6JB
tel: 01625 422 677
email: info@jones-music.co.uk
web: www.jones-music.co.uk
part exchange: No
info: Stock guitars, amps, brass, woodwind and keyboards. Main Clavinova dealer in the area. Instrument repair and rental. PA and lighting sales and hire. Large sheet music department. Guitar tuition also available in-store.

JT Services
Unit 16, Generation Centre, Dane Street, Rochdale, OL12 6XB
tel: 01706 711 932
email: jtservices@btconnect.com
part exchange: Yes
info: Lighting and sound suppliers catering for all your bands needs. Offer repairs.

Keys
71-73 Henshaw Street, Oldham, Lancashire, OL1 2AA
tel: 0161 627 0614
fax: 0161 620 0614
email: peter@keysmusic.co.uk
web: www.keysmusic.co.uk
contact: Peter Braid
part exchange: No
info: Sells just about everything! Instruments bought for cash. Guitar set ups and electronic repair service. Tuition also available for guitar and keyboard. Space in shop for posters and notices, just ask a member of staff.

KGB Musical Instruments
Pacific Road Arts Centre, Birkenhead, Wirral, CH41 1LJ
tel: 0151 647 3268
email: keith@kgb-music.co.uk
web: www.kgb-music.co.uk
contact: Keith Bennion
part exchange: Yes
info: Custom made guitars and repairs on all fretted instruments. Large range of accessories and repairs. Noticeboard in-store. Limited space for posters.

Koby Drums
c/o BCP, 4-14 Oldham Street, Liverpool, L1 2SU
tel: 0151 709 8141
fax: 0151 709 8141
email: enquiry@koby.co.uk
web: www.koby.co.uk
contact: Colin Scholfield
part exchange: Yes
info: UK manufacturers of electronic drums. Can be used on stage, in the studio or integrated into a conventional Drum kit. For anyone and everyone, from professional to beginners.

Little Tinkler Music Works
210 Broadoak Road, Ashton-under-Lyne, Lancashire, OL6 8RP
tel: 0161 339 8410
part exchange: No
info: Sells range of instruments and equipment including guitars, keyboards, PAs, disco equipment and lighting. Repair service available on electrical equipment.

The Mad Monks Music Co.
Silver Yard, Orton, Cumbria, CA10 3RQ
tel: 01539 624 030
email: info@madmonksmusic.com
web: www.madmonksmusic.com
part exchange: Yes
info: Stock wide range of instruments and equipment including guitars, amps, PAs, drum kits, mandolins, electric violins and accessories. Repair service for guitars. Huge noticeboard in-store, speak to member of staff to display posters.

Margin Music
3 Market Place, Macclesfield, Cheshire, SK10 1EB
tel: 01625 619 013
fax: 01625 269 013
email: marginmusic@aol.com
web: www.marginmusic.co.uk
part exchange: No
info: Stock keyboards, brass, woodwind, guitars, Drums and PA. Repair service for most instruments. Tuition available for guitars, piano and keyboard. Also hire PA and lights. Space in-store to display notices and posters.

Market Music
A2 Henry Tate Aisle, Brikenhead Market, Grange Precinct, Birkenhead, CH41 2YJ
tel: 0151 650 1030
part exchange: No
info: Stock all kinds of musical instruments and amplification. Space in-store for posters and notices.

Marshall McGurk
Elm House Farm, Crosby, Maryport, CA15 6SH
tel: 01900 813 200
email: sdm@atmos.plus.com
web: www.marshallmcgurk.co.uk
part exchange: Yes
info: Specialise in brass and woodwind repairs. Occasionally stock some second hand instruments. Also offer tuition services for recorder and beginner guitar. Can print music and transposition.

Maryport Musical Instruments
51 Senhouse Street, Maryport, CA15 6BL
tel: 01900 813 088
part exchange: No
info: Violin specialists. Also offer repair services for violins and guitars. Violin tuition.

McQueen's Musical Instruments
Black Horse Workshop, 488 Bolton Road, Pendlebury, M27 8UR
tel: 0161 794 3543
fax: 0161 794 3543
email: info@mcqueens.com or sales@mcqueens.com
web: www.mcqueens.com
contact: Rick
part exchange: Yes
info: Manufacturers of bugles and cavalry trumpets. Repairs on any instrument.

Megasound UK
29 Standish Street, Burnley, Lancashire, BB11 1AP
tel: 01282 830 063
fax: 01282 830 110
email: info@megasoundkaraoke.co.uk
web: www.megasoundkaraoke.co.uk
part exchange: No
info: Guitars, brass, woodwind, violins, PAs, karaoke equipment and accessories. Megasound are dealers for manufacturers such as Fender, Washburn, Vintage, HK and Jackson, amongst others. Space to display posters and notices in-store.

Merben Music
128a Nantwich Road, Crewe, Cheshire, CW2 6AX
tel: 01270 582 728
part exchange: No
info: Stock pianos, keyboards, woodwind, brass and sheet music. Repair service for brass and woodwind. Tuition available for keyboards. Noticeboard for musicians.

Mersey Music Centre
6 Liscard Way, Liscard Precinct, Wallasey, Merseyside, CH44 5TP
tel: 0151 630 3009
contact: Tony Boce
part exchange: Yes
info: Guitars and organs, wide range of stock. Resident engineer for repairs. Speak to Tony about putting up posters and gig flyers in-store. Also buy instruments.

Micro Music
286-288 Smithdown Road, Wavertree, Liverpool, L15 5AJ
tel: 0151 733 1101
fax: 0151 734 3487
email: micromusic@btinternet.com
web: www.micromusic.co.uk
part exchange: No
info: Electric guitars, basses, Acoustic guitars and PA equipment. Part exchange available on certain items. Repair service available for guitars and PA equipment. To place posters in the shop, speak to the manager. Space for musician's notices in store.

Mike Kermode
60 Soutergate, Ulverston, Cumbria
tel: 01229 582 704
email: kmode@onetel.net.uk
part exchange: Yes
info: Specialises in repairs for brass and woodwind instruments.

Music & Mystic
5-7 Harrison Street, Barrow-in-Furness, Cumbria, LA14 1JF
tel: 01229 877 253
email: info@musicmystic.co.uk
web: www.musicmystic.co.uk
contact: Brian
part exchange: No
info: Range of instruments. Specialise in guitars, group amplification and lighting. Offer repair service for guitars. Noticeboard in-store and space for posters. Sell band merchandise such as t-shirts and hoodies. The shop also has group rehearsal rooms and a recording studio. Brian also organises monthly band nights. See entry for Music & Mystic in Promoters section.

Music 90
Wallgate, Wigan, WN3
tel: 01942 323 265
email: info@music90.net
web: www.music90.net
contact: Ian
part exchange: No
info: Stock guitars, Drums, keyboards, PA systems, accessories and sheet music. Tuition in guitar and Drums. Guitar repair available. Noticeboard in-store. Space available for posters. Speak to Ian in the shop.

Music Box
16 Whalley Road, Accrington, Lancashire, BB5 1AA
tel: 01254 383 571
email: beegee444@aol.com
part exchange: No
info: Stock a wide range of instruments including guitars (electric, Acoustic and classical), percussion, keyboards and woodwind. Accessories, amps, effects and recording equipment. Repairs for all instruments. Tuition available for guitar and violin. Speak to any member of staff about displaying posters and flyers in-store. Noticeboard in-store.

The Music Box
174 Market Street, Hyde, Cheshire, SK14 1EX
tel: 0161 366 5037
fax: 0161 366 9691
email: mus.box@talk21.com
web: www.musicandco.co.uk
part exchange: No
info: Sells a range of instruments and amps. Proprietor Bill Drain can repair most Acoustic or electric instruments. Tuition services for most instruments. Noticeboard in-store and space for posters.

The Music Cellar
12 Fox Street, Preston, PR1 2AB
tel: 01772 251 407
fax: 01772 251 412
email: sales@themusiccellar.co.uk
web: www.themusiccellar.co.uk
contact: Matt Wells
part exchange: No
info: Specialise in woodwind and brass instruments. Also stock guitars, pianos, instruments for education and sheet music. Repair service available. Space for notices and posters

The Music Corner
64 Market Hall, Market Street, Ashton Under Lyne, Lancashire, OL6 6BZ
tel: 0161 830 0880/0800 328 5294
fax: 0161 830 0880
email: sales@musiccorner.co.uk
web: www.musiccorner.co.uk
part exchange: Yes
info: Sells sheet music and a range of instruments. Online store on website.

Music Exchange (Manchester) Ltd.
12 St. Peter's Square, Manchester, M2 3DF
tel: 0161 236 1766
fax: 0161 946 1195
email: mail@music-exchange.co.uk
web: www.music-exchange.co.uk
part exchange: Yes
info: All types of printed music including classical, educational and Popular, from a wide range of publishers. Mail order service available. Some Acoustic instruments. To display posters and flyers in-store, talk to any member of staff. Noticeboard in-store. For main instrument stockists, contact the Stockport branch listed below.

Music Exchange (Stockport) Ltd.
9 St. Petersgate, Stockport, SK1 1EB
tel: 0161 474 7104
email: musicexchangestockport@ukonline.co.uk
web: www.music-exchange.co.uk
contact: Ian Dawes
part exchange: Yes
info: Sell a wide range of instruments, sheet music and accessories. Contact list available in-store for music tutors. Space for posters, just ask member of staff. Noticeboard in-store. See also listing for Music Exchange store located in Manchester.

The Music Man
Unit 3/4, The Mill, Back Gladstone Street, Oldham, OL4 1BB
tel: 0161 633 5407/07710 613 348
fax: 0161 633 5407
email: info@oldhammusicman.co.uk
web: www.oldhammusicman.co.uk
contact: Dave
part exchange: No
info: Stocks everything for the entertainment industries. Drums, guitars, bass, amps, speakers, lighting, DJ equipment, CD and minidisc players amongst other items. Repairs for amps and lighting. 24 hour turnaround. Tuition available for guitars and drums. Noticeboard in-store. The Music Man also organise weekly jam sessions every Tuesday in Oldham. Contact Dave on the above numbers to play.

Music Mania Guitar Centre
6 Swan Alley, Church Walks, Ormskirk, Lancashire, L39 2EQ
tel: 01695 570 023
contact: John S. Bennett
part exchange: No
info: Range of guitars plus amps, music books and accessories. Guitar repair service. Buy/part exchange. Posters and notices are displayed.

Music Notes
4 North John Street, Liverpool, L2 4SA
tel: 0151 227 9836
email: musicnotes@btopenworld.com
part exchange: Yes
info: Specialists in printed music. Mail order service available. Wide range of instruments such as guitars, flute, clarinet, drum kits and electronic pianos. Noticeboard in-store. List of instrument tutors available.

The Music Project
77 Mill Lane, Wallasey, Wirral, CH44 5UB
tel: 0151 639 0336
fax: 0151 630 3889
email: enquiries@musicproject.co.uk
web: www.musicproject.co.uk
part exchange: No
info: All types of instruments. Buy, sell and part exchange. Rental facilities. Space for posters and notices in-store, ask any member of staff.

The Music Room
28a Queen Street, Ulverston, Cumbria, LA12 7AF
tel: 01229 581 101
email: musicroomulverston@ukonline.co.uk
web: www.musicroomulverston.ukonline.co.uk
part exchange: Yes
info: Stock most instruments except pianos. Rental scheme available where customers can purchase instruments over 4 payments. Also stock sheet music, band t-shirts and a wide range of CDs. Happy to track down and import rare CDs, just ask Paul. Will display posters in window, speak to Paul.

Music To Your Ears
290 Middleton Road, Chadderton, Oldham, OL9 6JH
tel: 0161 287 1776
contact: Mrs Brown
part exchange: No
info: Buy, sell and part exchange most musical instruments. Area in-store for posters and flyers.

The New Raymond Wallbank Music Store & Studios
42 Woodlands Road, Lytham St. Annes, Lancashire, FY8 4BX
tel: 01253 736 462
fax: 01253 736 462
email: mailbox@music-stores.co.uk
web: www.music-stores.co.uk
part exchange: No
info: Large range of instruments (but no Drums) and accessories. Some small amps. Repairs on practically any instrument. Noticeboard in-store. Space for posters. Also run a music school with instruction in 24 different instruments and 5 styles of singing. 18 fully qualified teachers and 10 teaching studios. For further information speak to Graham Snellgrove.

North West Piano Centre
Unit 10, Imex Business Park, Hamilton Road, Longsight, Manchester,
M13 0PD
tel: 0161 225 4110
fax: 0161 225 4270
email: pianos@nwpc.co.uk
web: www.nwpc.co.uk
part exchange: No
info: Sell and hire all types of pianos and also piano
stools. New and refurbished pianos.

Northern Sounds
13 Oxford Street, Workington, Cumbria, CA14 2AL
tel: 01900 604 797
part exchange: No
info: Electric guitars, amps, Drums and PAs. Repair
service for most instruments. Space in-store for posters.

Northwich Music Centre
Unit 2, 41-43 London Road, Northwich, Cheshire, CW9 5HQ
tel: 01606 458 22
part exchange: No
info: Digital and Acoustic pianos, keyboards, guitars,
Drums, brass and woodwind. Books, videos and accessories. Tuning,
repairs and French polishing. Professional tuition for guitar, piano, flute
and keyboard.

Northwinds Music
54 Quarry Rigg, Bowness-on-Windermere, Cumbria, LA23 3DU
tel: 01539 488 426
fax: 01539 448 846
email: info@northwindsmusic.com
web: www.northwindsmusic.com
part exchange: No
info: Guitars, amps, brass, woodwind, drums,
percussion and sheet music. Repair service for guitars. Area in-store to
display posters and flyers.

Oakley Sound Systems
Oakley Barn, Gamblesly, Penrith, Cumbria, CA10 1HR
tel: 01768 881 934
email: tony@oakleysound.co.uk
web: www.oakleysound.com
contact: Tony Allgood
part exchange: Yes
info: Repairs on any electronic musical instruments and
equipment. Custom built synthesisers.

Omega Music UK Ltd.
Townfoot Estates, Brampton, Cumbria, CA8 1SW
tel: 01697 739 65
email: sales@omegamusic.co.uk
web: www.omegamusic.co.uk
part exchange: Yes
info: General musical instrument store selling
everything and anything from guitars to pianos. Offer repairs to pianos
and some repairs to other instruments. Sister store in Blaydon-on-Tyne.
See listing for further details.

The Overwater Bass Emporium
Atlas Works, Denton Holme, Carlisle, Cumbria, CA2 2ND
tel: 01228 590 591
fax: 01228 590 597
email: info@overwater.co.uk
web: www.overwaterbasses.com
part exchange: Yes
info: Specialist bass retailers and manufacturers. Also
sell bass amplification. Guitar repairs available. Noticeboard in-store.
Space for posters.

Peter Darwin Music
19-21 George Street, St. Helens, WA10 1DA
tel: 01744 757 812
part exchange: No
info: Acoustic and electric guitars, Drums and
percussion, amplification, brass and woodwind. Repair services
available for guitars and woodwind. List of music tutors available,
enquire in-store. Area to display notices and posters, ask a member of
staff.

Philip Porter Guitars
Unit 2e, Hallam House, Hallam Street, Stockport, Cheshire, SK2 6PT
tel: 0161 474 7999
email: philipporterguitars@ntlworld.com
web: www.philipporterguitars.co.uk
contact: James
part exchange: Yes
info: Full range of professional services for all your
guitar needs. Repair, restoration, customisation, resprays and bespoke
manufacture of all musical components including pick-up rewinds. Also
look out for Philip Porter Guitars own brand of futuristic hard bodied
guitars.

Pro Solo
101 Parliament Street, Burnley, Lancashire, BB11 3JY
tel: 01282 414 089
fax: 01282 414 089
email: pro.solo@btclick.com
web: www.prosolo.co.uk
part exchange: No
info: New and used sales and repair. Stock guitars,
amps, basses, sheet music and more. PA hire available. Main dealer for
Peavey and Marshall. Guitar tuition also available. Space for notices
and posters in-store.

Procom Professional Sound & Light
157 Stamford Street, Ashton-under-Lyne, Lancashire, OL6 6XW
tel: 0161 343 2782
email: sales@procommusic.co.uk
web: www.procommusic.co.uk
contact: Andy Elly
part exchange: No
info: Guitars, keyboards and PA systems. Large range of
audio-visual equipment. Accessories and consumables. Notice board
in-store.

Promenade Music
404 Marine Road East, Morecambe, Lancashire, LA4 5AR
tel: 01524 410 202
fax: 01524 410 802
email: sales@promenademusic.co.uk
web: www.promenademusic.co.uk
contact: David Wood
part exchange: No
info: Wide range of instruments including guitars,
Drum kits, keyboards and orchestral items. Also stock microphones,
DJ equipment, amps and PA systems, plus hi-fi and audio-visual
equipment. Repair services available for most instruments. Also offer
tuition services in keyboard, guitar, bass and vocal. Promenade's clients
have included Oasis, Blur and Take That. Promenade Music is also
linked with DMR Recordings who offer studio facilities and CD, cassette
and vinyl duplication. See entries in relevant sections for further
details.

R & B Music
193 Nantwich Road, Crewe, Cheshire, CW2 6DD
tel: 01270 584 333
part exchange: No
info: Mainly stock guitars including Acoustic, electric
and bass. Also stock banjos and drum kits. PA hire service available.
Also offer repair services for guitars and amps. Space in-store for
posters and notices, ask a member of staff.

R&T Music
8 Dalkeith Street, Barrown-in-Furness, Cumbria, LA14 1SP
tel: 01229 826 344
fax: 01229 826 344
contact: Vaughan Phelps
part exchange: No
info: Wide range of stock, including lights, PA,
woodwind and percussion. Mainly stock guitars with 400 in stock at
any one time. Repair and tuition services for most instruments.

Rainbow Music
3 Finkle Street, Carlisle, CA3 8UU
tel: 01228 537 469
web: www.rainbowmusic.co.uk
part exchange: No
info: Stock guitars, keyboards, amps, sheet music and
accessories. Guitar repairs available. Also tuition for keyboards, clarinet
and saxophone. Noticeboard in-store with space for posters.

Rattle & Drum (Manchester)
1 New Wakefield Street, Manchester, M1 5WH
tel: 0161 237 5720
email: manchester@rattleanddrum.com
web: www.rattleanddrum.com
part exchange: No
info: Stock drums, percussion and accessories.
Specialists in mail order. Repair and tuition services available. Band
book in-store which lists local musicians available or wanted. Display
posters and flyers, speak to member of staff. Also branches in Stoke on
Trent and Derby. See listings in relevant sections for details.

Read, Franklin & Heywood
11 Broad Street, Bury, Lancashire, BL9 0DA
tel: 0161 764 4624
fax: 0161 764 4624
email: info@musicshopuk.co.uk
web: www.musicshopuk.co.uk
contact: Andy Evenson, Phil Crampton
part exchange: No
info: Sell a range of instruments but specialise in
guitars, keyboards, PA systems and amps. Will repair any instrument.
Tuition service for keyboard. Noticeboard and space for posters in-store.
Speak to Andy or Phil about displaying flyers and posters.

Reidy's Home of Music
7-13 Penny Street, Blackburn, Lancashire, BB1 6HJ
tel: 0870 744 5065
fax: 0870 744 5102
email: sales@reidys.com or info@reidys.com
web: www.reidys.com
part exchange: No
info: Deal with almost all types of musical instruments including guitars, pianos and keyboards. Instrument valuations. Repair service available. Space for posters, flyers and musicians' notices. Do not offer music tuition on-site, but have list of local music tutors available.

Richard Behrend Brass Specialist
8 Greenbank Road, off Smithdown Road, Liverpool, L18 1HN
tel: 0151 733 2213
part exchange: No
info: Deal in brass, woodwind and orchestral string instruments. Also offer repair services. Small noticeboard space.

Rimmers Music (Blackburn)
53-55 Darwen Street, Blackburn, BB2 2BL
email: blackburn@rimmersmusic.co.uk
web: www.rimmersmusic.co.uk
part exchange: No
info: North West music chain selling wide range of instruments from guitars and drums to brass and woodwind. Tuition available in guitar, bass, drum, piano and keyboard. Repairs and notice board space in-store. See listings for details of other branches.

Rimmers Music (Blackpool)
62-64 Devonshire Road, Blackpool, FY3 8AA
tel: 01253 391459
email: blackpool@rimmersmusic.co.uk
web: www.rimmersmusic.co.uk
part exchange: No
info: North West music chain selling wide range of instruments from guitars and drums to brass and woodwind. Tuition available in guitar, bass, drum, piano and keyboard. Repairs and notice board space in-store. See listings for details of other branches.

Rimmers Music (Leyland)
20 Chapel Brow, Leyland, PR25 3NE
tel: 01772 433 281
email: leyland@rimmersmusic.co.uk
web: www.rimmersmusic.co.uk
part exchange: No
info: North West music chain selling wide range of instruments from guitars and drums to brass and woodwind. Tuition available in guitar, bass, drum, piano and keyboard. Repairs and notice board space in-store. See listings for details of other branches.

Rimmers Music (Southport)
173-175 Eastbank Street, Southport, PR8 6TH
tel: 01704 532 145
email: southport@rimmersmusic.co.uk
web: www.rimmersmusic.co.uk
part exchange: No
info: North West music chain selling wide range of instruments from guitars and Drums to brass and woodwind. Tuition available in guitar, bass, drum, piano and keyboard. Repairs and noticeboard space in-store. See listings for details of other branches.

Sound of Music
8 Library Road, Kendal, Cumbria, LA9 4QB
tel: 01539 721 009
contact: Pauline Whittaker
part exchange: No
info: Stocks guitars, mandolins, woodwind, strings, sheet music and accessories. Will display band posters and flyers in-store.

Sounds Great Music
180-182 Wilmslow Road, Heald Green, Cheshire, SK8 3BG
tel: 0161 436 4799
fax: 0161 498 6468
email: soundsgreat@btinternet.com
web: www.soundsgreatmusic.com
part exchange: No
info: Carry a range of instruments but specialise in guitars imported from America and rare and unusual effects pedals. Also stock amps and accessories. Repairs available. Buy and part exchange. Noticeboard in-store, plus space for posters.

Spectrum Music
144 Bury New Road, Whitefield, Manchester, M45 6AD
tel: 0161 796 0843
email: sales@spectrummusic.co.uk
web: www.spectrummusic.co.uk
part exchange: No
info: Guitars, basses, amps, Drums plus some digital recording equipment. Instrument repair and hire. Tuition available for guitars. Buy/part exchange. Noticeboard in-store and space for posters, speak to any member of staff.

Tafelmusik
43 Shrewsbury Road, Oxton, Birkenhead, CH43 2JB
tel: 0151 652 3440
fax: 0151 653 4817
email: admin@tafelmusik.co.uk
part exchange: No
info: Sell all types of instruments, but specialise in woodwind. Buy, sell and part exchange. Instrument hire available. Poster and notice space in-store. Associated with the Wirral School of Music. See listing in relevant section for further details.

Time & Tune
53 Preston New Road, Blackburn, Lancashire, BB2 6AY
tel: 01254 697 460
fax: 01254 696 570
email: timeandtune@btopenworld.com
web: www.timeandtunemusic.co.uk
part exchange: No
info: Stock woodwind, strings, piano, acoustic and classical guitar, but the main stock is sheet music. Part exchange available for purchase of new instruments. Repair service available for woodwind. Do allow posters in the shop, but only for classical concerts. There is also space for musician's notices.

Tomson Guitars
Eckersley Mill, Swan Meadow Road, Wigan, Lancashire, WN3 5BD
tel: 01942 820 532
part exchange: Yes
info: Guitar repairs, maintenance, restoration and custom building.

The Tower Music Shop
46-48 Topping Street, Central Promenade, Blackpool, Lancashire, FY1 3AQ
tel: 01253 627 359
part exchange: No
info: Sells all forms of musical instrument from guitar to brass and woodwind. Also stock karaoke equipment and sheet music. Repairs and noticeboard space in-store.

Uncle Neil's
93 Albert Road, Colne, Lancashire, BB8 0BS
tel: 01282 868 935
email: uncleneils@btconnect.com
part exchange: No
info: Guitar specialists. Repairs available. Also buy/part exchange. Noticeboard in-store with space for posters. Neil also puts on Blues bands as part of the Blues festival which is held every August over bank holiday weekend. Any Blues acts interested in playing can contact Neil at the above details.

V.S. Music Supplies
6 Cornbrook Close, Wardle, Rochdale, OL12 9NN
tel: 01706 378 973
email: vsmusic@fsmail.net
part exchange: Yes
info: Home delivery and mail order service for all types of sheet music and instrumental accessories such as clarinet reeds.

The Violin Shop
2nd Floor, The Royal Bank of Scotland Chambers, 9 Talbot Square, Blackpool, FY1 1LB
tel: 01253 622 451
email: kgeorge@violinshop.co.uk
web: www.violinshop.co.uk
contact: Kevin George
part exchange: No
info: Repair, restoration and dealing of violins. Practice room in-store to play instruments before buying. Help and advice available if needed. Mail order service available for accessories. Space for musician's notices and relevant posters.

Woodwind & Co.
208 Liverpool Road, Cadishead, Manchester, Lancashire, M44 5DB
tel: 0161 775 1842
part exchange: Yes
info: Specialise in the repair and maintenance of woodwind instruments.

Wright Greaves Ltd.
11 Goose Green, Altrincham, Cheshire, WA14 1DW
tel: 0161 929 6949
email: sales@printed-sheet-music.co.uk
web: www.printed-sheet-music.co.uk
part exchange: Yes
info: Stock sheet music, scores and music books. Mail order service available.

Wyre River Guitars
102 Bispham Road, Blackpool, FY2 0NN
tel: 01253 353 723
email: sales@wyreriverguitars.co.uk
web: www.wyreriverguitars.co.uk
contact: Steve Preston
part exchange: Yes
info: Custom made Acoustic and electric guitars. All repairs, resprays and customising.

Young's Music Stores
11-13 Stanley Road, Liverpool, L5 2PX
tel: 0151 207 0228
fax: 0151 207 0228
part exchange: No
info: Specialise in new and second hand instruments. Amps, woodwind, strings and percussion. Space for notices.

SOUTHEAST

SOUNDCONTROL
The UK's Number One Musical Instrument Retailer

Sound Control (Milton Keynes)
Unit 4, Xscape Centre, Milton Keynes, MK9 3XS
tel: 01908 240 840
email: miltonkeynes@soundcontrol.co.uk
web: www.soundcontrol.co.uk
contact: Ben Lashite
part exchange: Yes
info: As the largest music equipment retailer in Europe with 25 stores across the UK, Sound Control has the most extensive range of guitars, basses, backline, PA, hi-tech, recording and percussion equipment available at the lowest prices around. Coupled with over 25 years experience and unrivalled staff training, shopping at Sound Control is the easiest step you will make on the road to being signed. Visit the above website to locate your nearest store, or to buy online and have your purchase delivered direct to your door.

Abbey Music
48 Grosvenor Road, Tunbridge Wells, TN1 2AS
tel: 01892 511 611
web: www.abbeymusic.co.uk
part exchange: No
info: Stock range of musical instruments. Repairs available.

ABC Music Ltd. (Benfleet)
2 Roseberry Walk, Benfleet, Essex, SS7 4EW
tel: 01268 755 005
fax: 01268 569 236
web: www.abcmusic.co.uk
part exchange: No
info: Sell variety of instruments including brass, percussion, drums, woodwind, guitars, piano, keyboards, amps, sheet music and cases. Repair services available. Tuition in-house, and can recommend other external tutors. Instrument rental scheme on long term and short term basis. Space for musicians' notices and posters in-store. ABC Music also have branches in Greater London and South East regions, as well as one in the Midlands and one in Yorkshire. See listings in relevant sections for details. ABC Music run a management division for bands and acts. See entry in Management Companies section for further information.

ABC Music Ltd. Head Office (Esher)
85 High Street, Esher, Surrey, KT10 9QA
tel: 01372 466 191
fax: 01372 470 445
web: www.abcmusic.co.uk
part exchange: No
info: Part of ABC music chain and franchise stores. See listing above for information.

AC Drums
55a Princess Street, Luton, LU1 5AT
tel: 01582 877 300
part exchange: No
info: Specialise in drums and percussion. Open Monday, Tuesday and Thursday from 7pm to 9pm.

Alan's Music Centre
2 Station Parade, Ashford, TW15 2RX
tel: 01784 421 300
email: info@alansmusiccentre.co.uk
web: www.alansmusiccentre.co.uk
part exchange: No
info: Selection of guitars, basses, amplification, effects, keyboards, drums and PA. Also stock recording equipment, sheet music, software and accessories. Repairs available.

Amen Corner Music
Beehive Road, Binfield, Bracknell, RG12 8TR
tel: 01344 427 783
web: www.amencornermusic.co.uk
part exchange: Yes
info: Repairs available.

Andertons
58-59 Woodbridge Road, Guildford, Surrey, GU1 4RF
tel: 01483 456 733
email: sales@andertons.co.uk
web: www.andertonsonline.co.uk
part exchange: No
info: Great selection of guitars, drums, synthesizers, PA, studio and computer music products at very competitive prices. Repairs and notice board space available.

Apex Music
106 Loddon Bridge Road, Woodley, Reading, RG5 4AW
tel: 0118 969 8200
email: apexguitars@btconnect.com
web: www.apexguitars.com
part exchange: No
info: Guitars, keyboards and drums. Tuition and repairs offered.

Avalon Music Ltd.
44 Holly Bush Lane, Sevenoaks, TN13 3TJ
tel: 01732 453 183
email: jim@avalonmusic.co.uk
web: www.avalonmusic.co.uk
part exchange: Yes
info: Tuition and repairs offered. Specialise in guitars, drums and keyboards.

Beare & Son
Unit 18, Tavistock Place, Tavistock Street, Dunstaple, LU6 1NE
tel: 01582 477 130
email: beares1@btconnect.com
web: www.beare-tertisviola.com
part exchange: No
info: Specialise in string instruments. Repairs available.

Bedroom Acoustic Music
3-5 Kings Arms Yard, Church Street, Ampthill, Bedford, MK45 2PJ
tel: 01525 404 304
email: sales@bedroomacousticmusic.co.uk
web: www.bedroomacousticmusic.co.uk
part exchange: No
info: Selection of instruments including guitars, banjos, mandolins, bouzoukis, bodhrans, new and restored fiddles, whistles, recorders, and other Folk instruments. Repairs available.

Bird's Music
9 Sackville Road, Bexhill-on-Sea, TN39 3JB
tel: 01424 220 204
part exchange: No
info: Tuition and repairs available.

Brighton Guitar Centre
26 St. George's Road, Brighton, BN2 1ED
tel: 01273 819 222
email: bgc@gmx.co.uk
web: www.brightonguitarcentre.co.uk
part exchange: No
info: Guitars, amps and accessories. Repairs and tuition. Notice board.

Coda Music
7 Guildford Street, Luton, LU1 2NQ
tel: 01582 725 625
email: info@coda-music.com
web: www.coda-music.com
part exchange: No
info: Specialise in guitars. Notice board available.

Crazy Beat Records
87 Corbets Tey Road, Upminster, Essex, RM14 2AH
tel: 0170 822 8678
fax: 0170 864 0946
email: sales@crazybeat.co.uk
web: www.crazybeat.co.uk
part exchange: No
info: Poster/flyer space available. Ask in for details.

Dawkes Music Ltd.
Reform Road, Maidenhead, SL6 8BT
tel: 01628 630 800
email: info@dawkes.co.uk
web: www.dawkes.co.uk
part exchange: No
info: Woodwind and brass. Notice board available in the shop.

Dawson's Music (Abingdon)
7-9 High Street, Abingdon, OX14 5BB
tel: 01235 524 316
fax: 01235 524 330
email: abingdon@dawsons.co.uk
web: www.dawsonsonline.com
part exchange: Yes
info: Stock large range of instruments, PA equipment, amps, effects and accessories. Branches throughout the North West, as well as across rest of UK. See listings for details.

Dawson's Music (Basingstoke)
3-4 Chelsea House, Festival Place, Basingstoke, RG21 7JR
tel: 01256 464 663
fax: 01256 818 113
email: basingstoke@dawsons.co.uk
web: www.dawsonsonline.com
part exchange: Yes
info: Stock large range of instruments, PA equipment, amps, effects and accessories. Branches throughout the North West, as well as across rest of UK. See listings for details.

Dawson's Music (Reading)
65 Caversham Road, Reading, RG1 8AD
tel: 0118 958 1320
fax: 0118 959 7942
email: reading@dawsons.co.uk
web: www.dawsonsonline.com
part exchange: No
info: Stock large range of instruments, PA equipment, amps, effects and accessories. Branches throughout the North West, as well as across rest of UK. See listings for details.

Drumwright
Shop 4, Lodden Vale Centre, Woodley, Reading, RG5 4UL
tel: 0118 944 1418
email: enquiries@drumwright.co.uk
web: www.drumwright.co.uk
part exchange: No
info: Repairs available.

Eric Lindsey Ltd.
12 West Street, Reigate, Surrey, RH2 9BS
tel: 01737 221 481
email: info@elmusic.co.uk
web: www.elmusic.co.uk
part exchange: No
info: Sell drums, guitars, keyboards, PA systems and DJ equipment. Repair service. Drum tuition available. Posters and flyers can be displayed in-store. Eric Lindsey has another branch located in Catford, London. See listing in relevant section for details.

Fair Oak Bass Guitars
Moon River Pines Trading Park, Fir Tree Lane, Fair Oak, Eastleigh, Hampshire, SO50 7AH
tel: 02380 697 197
email: info@fairoak-bassguitars.com
web: www.fairoak-bassguitars.com
part exchange: No
info: Bass guitar specialists. Amps, effects, leads, straps, strings and tuition DVDs also available. Repairs, set up and tuition services.

GB Guitars
41 Prestonville Road, Brighton, BN1 3TJ
tel: 01273 220 055
email: gb@gbguitars.wanadoo.co.uk
web: www.gbguitars.co.uk
part exchange: Yes
info: Bass guitars and amps made to order. Repairs also available.

Guitar Centre
126 Meadfield Road, Slough, SL3 8JF
tel: 01753 542 720
part exchange: No
info: Repairs and tuition.

Guitar Heaven
42 St. Mary's Street, Wallingford, Oxfordshire, OX10 0EU
tel: 01491 824 488
email: nic@guitarheaven.biz
web: www.guitarheaven.biz
part exchange: No
info: Stock major brands such as Fender, Gibson, Marshall and Mesa Boogie and less well known brands such as AXL, Blade, Freshman, Norman, AER. Tuition and repair services.

Harmony Pianos
92 Audley Street, Reading, RG30 1BS
tel: 0118 950 0670
web: www.harmonypianos.co.uk
part exchange: No
info: Specialist repairer. Notice board available

Hickies Ltd.
153 Friar Street, Reading, RG1 1HE
tel: 0118 957 5771
web: www.hickies.co.uk
part exchange: No
info: Stock guitars, amps, woodwind, brass and keyboards. On-site repairs and tuition offered.

Hi-Tech Direct
57 Harpur Street, Bedford, MK40 2SR
tel: 01234 212 588
email: richard@hi-techdirect.co.uk
web: www.hi-techdirect.co.uk
part exchange: No
info: Specialise in digital pianos and workstations. Repairs available.

Hobgoblin Music (Crawley)
17 The Parade, Northgate, Crawley, West Sussex, RH10 8DT
tel: 01293 515 858
email: crawley@hobgoblin.co.uk
web: www.hobgoblin.com
part exchange: No
info: Folk specialists in Traditional, Celtic and Acoustic instruments. Hobgoblin have branches throughout the UK. See other listings or website for further details.

Hobgoblin Music (Newport Pagnell)
10 St. John's Street, Newport Pagnell, MK16 8HJ
tel: 01908 217 217
email: nphobgoblin@btconnect.com
web: www.hobgoblin.com
part exchange: Yes
info: Folk specialists stocking Traditional, Celtic and Acoustic instruments. Hobgoblin have branches throughout the UK. See other listings or website for details.

Hogan Music
40 Bartholomew Street, Newbury, RG15 5LL
tel: 01635 378 68
email: sales@hoganmusic.co.uk
web: www.hoganmusic.co.uk
part exchange: No
info: Guitars specialist stocking steel stringed guitars. Tuition, repairs and notice board.

Hollywood Music
The Old Fire Station, 201 Stratford Road, Wolverton, Milton Keynes, MK12 5RL
tel: 01908 225 888
email: info@hollywoodmusicmk.co.uk
web: www.hollywoodmusicmk.co.uk
part exchange: No
info: Guitars, drums and equipment for DJs. Repairs, hire and tuition.

Hooters Musical Instruments (St. Albans)
6 Chequer Street, St. Albans, Hertfordshire, AL1 3XZ
tel: 01727 860 301
part exchange: Yes
info: Guitars, amps, keyboards, pianos, brass, woodwind, as well as music books, accessories and a large selection of sheet music. Space for notices. Hooters also has branches in Windsor, London and Watford. See listings in relevant sections for details.

Hooters Musical Instruments (Watford)
13 Queens Road, Watford, Hertfordshire, WD17 2LH
tel: 01923 248 491
part exchange: Yes
info: Guitars, amps, keyboards, pianos, brass, woodwind, as well as music books, accessories and a large selection of sheet music. Space for notices. Hooters also has branches in London, St. Albans and Windsor. See listings in relevant sections for details.

Impact Music
14 Wokingham Road, Reading, RG6 1JG
tel: 0118 966 6333
web: www.impactpercussion.com
part exchange: No
info: Line 6 and Ashdown amps.

In Tune Music
410-412 Yorktown Road, College Town, Sandhurst, GU47 0PR
tel: 01276 348 00
part exchange: No
info: Repairs and tuition available. Notice board.

K2 Music Ltd.
Unit 70, Fresh Wharf Estate, Fresh Wharf Road, Barking, Essex, IG11 7BW
email: info@k2musicltd.co.uk
web: www.k2musicltd.co.uk
contact: Steve Gee
part exchange: Yes
info: Stock guitars, amps, drum kits, strings, guitar picks, drum sticks, as well as music videos and DVDs. K2 also provide rehearsal facilities, plus equipment hire and tuition services. See listings in relevant sections for further details.

Kingfisher Music Co.
909 London Road, Loudwater, High Wycombe, HP10 9TB
tel: 01494 520 837
email: kingfisherhw@btconnect.com
web: www.kingfishermusic.com
part exchange: No
info: Stock wide range of instruments such as guitars, basses, amps, drums, PA and effects pedals. Drum tuition and guitar technician. Notice board space.

Le Blond Ltd.
206 High Street North, Dunstable, LU6 1AU
tel: 01582 609 310
email: admin@leblond.co.uk
web: www.leblond.co.uk
part exchange: Yes
info: Sell and make percussion drum cases.

Manns Music Shop
123 High Street, Colchester, CO1 1SZ
tel: 01206 572 783
email: enquiries@mannsmusic.co.uk
web: www.mannsmusic.co.uk
part exchange: No
info: Wide range of musical instruments and accessories available. Repairs offered.

Martens Music
15 London Road, Bexhill-on-Sea, TN39 3JR
tel: 01424 222 560
part exchange: No
info: Repairs on pianos.

Mr Music Ltd.
The Bishop Centre, Bath Road, Taplow, Maidenhead, SL6 0NX
tel: 01628 661 155
email: sales@mrmusic.co.uk
web: www.mrmusic.co.uk
part exchange: No
info: Over 150 guitars and 50 digital pianos and keyboards in stock. Tuition available. Notice board space.

The Music Centre
35-37 Tavistock Street, Bedford, MK40 2RB
tel: 01234 346 206
email: info@musiccentre.co.uk
web: www.musiccentre.co.uk
part exchange: No
info: General music store. Repairs, tuition and notice board.

Music Land
54 North Street, Romford, RM1 1BH
tel: 01708 737 977
email: martin@musicland.co.uk
web: www.musicland.co.uk
part exchange: No
info: Stock most instruments. Keyboard lessons in the shop and private lessons via the staff. Repairs offered.

Music Network
6-8 Bridge Street, Leighton Buzzard, LU7 1AL
tel: 01525 376 622
email: enquiries@amusic.co.uk
web: www.amusic.co.uk
part exchange: No
info: Stock range of instruments, both new and second hand. Also stock sheet music.

The Music People
9 Greenend Close, Spencers Wood, Reading, RG7 1EH
tel: 0118 988 7444
email: sales@themusicpeople.co.uk
web: www.themusicpeople.co.uk
part exchange: No
info: Sell keyboards and related accessories. Also offer tuition for keyboard and organ.

The Music Shop
10 New Rents, Ashford, TN23 1JJ
tel: 01233 642 737
part exchange: No
info: Range of instruments available in-store.

The Music Trading Company
21 Lion Street, Rye, East Sussex, TN31 7LB
tel: 01797 222 966
email: info@musictradingcompany.com
web: www.musictradingcompany.com
part exchange: No
info: Specialists in guitars, amplifiers and effects. Buy second hand goods. Guitar set up service and amp repairs.

MusicLand (Canterbury)
22 Lower Bridge Street, Canterbury, Kent, CT1 2LG
tel: 01227 769 484
email: info@musicland.co.uk
web: www.musicland.co.uk
part exchange: Yes
info: Buy and sell a wide range of instruments. Stock keyboards, digital pianos, organs, guitars, brass, woodwind and amps. Repairs on most instruments. Tuition available for guitar and keyboard. Notice board in-store to display posters and ads. MusicLand also has branches in Romford, Southend On Sea and Bromley. See entries in relevant section for details.

MusicLand (Romford)
54 North Street, Romford, Essex, RM1 1BH
tel: 01708 737 977
email: info@musicland.co.uk
web: www.musicland.co.uk
part exchange: Yes
info: Buy and sell a wide range of instruments. Stock keyboards, digital pianos, organs, guitars, brass, woodwind and amps. Repairs on most instruments. Tuition available for guitar and keyboard. Notice board in-store to display posters and ads. MusicLand also has branches in Bromley, Southend-on-Sea and Canterbury. See entries in relevant section for details.

MusicLand (Southend On Sea)
98 Hamlet Court Road, Westcliff-On-Sea, Essex, SS0 7LP
tel: 01702 334 488
email: info@musicland.co.uk
web: www.musicland.co.uk
part exchange: Yes
info: Buy and sell a wide range of instruments. Stock keyboards, digital pianos, organs, guitars, brass, woodwind and amps. Repairs on most instruments. Tuition available for guitar and keyboard. Notice board in-store to display posters and ads. MusicLand also has branches in Romford, Bromley and Canterbury. See listings for further details.

Octave Ltd.
62 High Street North, Dunstable, LU6 1LE
tel: 01582 601 117
email: octave@uk2.net
web: www.octave-music.co.uk
part exchange: No
info: Variety of instruments including electric and Acoustic guitars, keyboards, electronic pianos, as well as studio and PA equipment.

Philip Brown
85a Northbrook Street, Newbury, RG14 1AE
tel: 01635 354 65
web: www.philipbrown-violins.co.uk
part exchange: No
info: Repairs and restoration for violins.

Pianoman
245 High Street, Arlesey, SG15 6TA
tel: 01462 733 733
web: www.pianomanpianos.co.uk
part exchange: No
info: Repairs and tuning. Tuition and notice board available.

Reid's Music Store
216 High Street, Bromley, BR1 1PW
tel: 020 8460 0165
part exchange: No
info: Repairs to pianos and keyboards.

MUSIC SERVICES/RETAIL

Sharon Music
12 High Street, Ashford, TN24 8TD
tel: 01233 625 005
part exchange: No
info: Tuition and repairs available.

Sheargold Pianos Ltd.
53 King Street, Maidenhead, SL6 1DU
tel: 01628 771 400
email: sales@sheargoldpianos.com
web: www.sheargoldpianos.com
part exchange: No
info: Offer repair and tuning services. Notice board space available. Also sell guitars.

Signetmusic.com
Crossroads Farm, Haversham, Milton Keynes, MK19 7DS
tel: 01908 321 794
web: www.signetmusic.com
part exchange: Yes
info: All types of instruments available. Mail order service provided.

Simply Instrumental
10 Holton Hill, Brighton, BN2 6RQ
tel: 01273 239 733
email: charles.kendall@ntlworld.com
web: www.simplyinstrumental.co.uk
part exchange: Yes
info: Woodwind and brass repairs.

Socodi Music Ltd.
49-50 Castle Street, Canterbury, CT1 2PY
tel: 01227 760 948
email: socodimusic@btclick.com
web: www.socodimusic.com
part exchange: Yes
info: Repairs offered. Guitars, drums, basses and DJ equipment stocked.

Stage One Music
121 Priory Street, Colchester, CO1 2PX
tel: 01206 578 975
email: sales@stageonemusic.fsbusiness.co.uk
part exchange: No
info: Guitars and drums available. Repair service.

Talkin Headz Drums & Percussion
6 Aspley Hill, Woburn Sands, Milton Keynes, MK17 8NJ
tel: 01908 282 898
email: info@talkinheadz.co.uk
web: www.talkinheadz.co.uk
part exchange: No
info: Drum and percussion specialists. Repairs and tuition offered.

Tema Music
34-36 High Street, Kempston, Bedford, MK42 7AL
tel: 01234 856 465
email: music@temamusic.co.uk
web: www.temamusic.co.uk
part exchange: No
info: Woodwind, brass and string instruments. Repairs available.

Tim Gentle Music (Southend on Sea)
39-45 Granger Road Industrial Estate, Southend on Sea, Essex, SS2 5DD
tel: 0870 740 6282
email: tingentle@fsnet.co.uk
web: www.timgentlemusic.co.uk
part exchange: No
info: Established 1976. Instruments for professional and semi-professional musicians. Repairs available. See also listing for branch in Stockton in Tees.

Unison Music
54 Unison Music, Wincheap, Canterbury, CT1 3RS
tel: 01227 764 580
email: enquires@unisonmusic.co.uk
web: www.unisonmusic.co.uk
part exchange: No
info: Specialists in woodwind and brass instruments, from the sale of new and refurbished brass and woodwind instruments, to the expert repair and renovation of instruments. Limited notice board space.

SOUNDCONTROL
The UK's Number One Musical Instrument Retailer

Sound Control (Bristol)
5 Rupert Street, Bristol, BS1 2PY
tel: 0117 934 9955
fax: 0117 934 9090
email: bristol@soundcontrol.co.uk
web: www.soundcontrol.co.uk
contact: Andy Smith
part exchange: Yes
info: As the largest music equipment retailer in Europe with 25 stores across the UK, Sound Control has the most extensive range of guitars, basses, backline, PA, hi-tech, recording and percussion equipment available at the lowest prices around. Coupled with over 25 years experience and unrivalled staff training, shopping at Sound Control is the easiest step you will make on the road to being signed. Visit the above website to locate your nearest store, or to buy online and have your purchase delivered direct to your door.

SOUNDCONTROL
The UK's Number One Musical Instrument Retailer

Sound Control (Southampton)
91-101 Queensway, Southampton, SO14 3HJ
tel: 02380 829 189
fax: 02380 829 176
email: southampton@soundcontrol.co.uk
web: www.soundcontrol.co.uk
contact: Richard Malpass
part exchange: Yes
info: As the largest music equipment retailer in Europe with 25 stores across the UK, Sound Control has the most extensive range of guitars, basses, backline, PA, hi-tech, recording and percussion equipment available at the lowest prices around. Coupled with over 25 years experience and unrivalled staff training, shopping at Sound Control is the easiest step you will make on the road to being signed. Visit the above website to locate your nearest store, or to buy online and have your purchase delivered direct to your door.

Allegro
359 Fishponds Road, Eastville, Bristol, BS5 6RD
tel: 0117 965 9191
email: roy@allegropianos.co.uk
web: www.allegropianos.co.uk
part exchange: No
info: New and used pianos from £200. Repairs available.

Barnstaple Music Centre
6 Cross Street, Barnstaple, EX31 1BA
tel: 01271 342 005
part exchange: Yes
info: General music shop selling all new instruments. Some repairs offered to brass and woodwind instruments. Notice board space available.

Bath Music Centre
20-22 Monmouth Place, Bath, BA1 2AY
tel: 01225 335 154
email: sales@bathmusiccentre.co.uk
web: www.bathmusiccentre.co.uk
part exchange: Yes
info: Specialise in brass, woodwind and drums but also carry guitars, sheet music and amplifiers. Repairs and notice board space available.

The Bristol Music Shop
30 College Green, Bristol, BS1 5TB
tel: 0117 929 0390
email: music@bristol-musicrm.demon.co.uk
web: www.musicroom.com
part exchange: Yes
info: Woodwind and brass specialists. Repairs available for these instruments only. Advert space outside shop, along with flyer space in-store.

The Bristol Violin Shop
12 Upper Maudlin Street, Bristol, BS2 8DJ
tel: 0117 925 9990
email: sales@bristol-violin-shop.co.uk
web: www.bristol-violin-shop.co.uk
part exchange: No
info: Stringed instrument specialists stocking new and used violins, violas, cellos and double bass. Part exchange on own instruments. Repairs available along with notice board space. 10% discount on accessories and sheet music for professional musicians, teachers and students. Hire service available.

Brook Guitars
Easterbrook, Hittisleigh, Exeter, EX6 6LR
tel: 01647 241 39
email: workshop@brookguitars.com
web: www.brookguitars.com
part exchange: Yes
info: Hand-made, custom designed steel stringed Acoustic guitars. Also do repairs and refinishing. View workshop by appointment only. Famous owners of these guitars include Jethro Tull, Portishead, Adrian Legg and Woody Man.

Cheltenham Soundhouse
295 High Street, Cheltenham, GL50 3HL
tel: 01242 525 967
email: soundhouse@yahoo.co.uk
web: www.soundhousedirect.com
part exchange: No
info: Mainly stock guitars and drum kits. Repairs to guitars.

Clevedon Music Shop
19 Alexandra Road, Clevedon, BS21 7QH
tel: 01275 342 090
email: info@clevedonmusic.co.uk
web: www.clevedonmusic.co.uk
part exchange: No
info: General musical instrument store stocking orchestral instruments and lots of guitars and sheet music. Guitar and drum tuition in-store. Repairs and notice board space available.

Craig's Guitars
28 Cross Street, Camborne, Cornwall, TR14 8EX
tel: 01209 715 800
part exchange: No
info: New and second hand electric, Acoustic and bass guitars. Sales and repairs. Willing to display notices.

Craig's Music
3 Bell Yard, Bell Lane, Bodmin, PL31 2JL
tel: 01208 777 44
email: nigel@craigsmusic.co.uk
web: www.craigsmusic.co.uk
part exchange: No
info: New and used guitars. Repairs offered to guitars and amps. Notice board space in-store.

Cremona House Violin Shop
7 Perry Road, Bristol, BS1 5BQ
tel: 0117 926 4617
email: contact@violinvaluations.com
web: www.violinvaluations.com
part exchange: No
info: New and used pianos. Repairs available. Limited advert space in-store.

Dance Of Delight
3 Northwick Terrace, Blockley, Moreton-in-Marsh, GL56 9BL
tel: 01386 700 496
web: www.danceofdelight.com
part exchange: Yes
info: Specialists in Folk violins. New and second hand. Also stockists of Tartina Rosin and the 'Incredabow'. View practice room by appointment.

Dave Ballard Musical Instruments
27 Albany Road, Newport, Isle of Wight, PO30 5JA
tel: 01983 529 903
email: info@daveballard.co.uk
web: www.daveballard.co.uk
part exchange: No
info: Brass and woodwind specialists. Repairs and overhauls, sales and rentals. Also sell reeds and mouthpieces.

Dawkes Music Ltd.
29 Winner Street, Paignton, TQ3 3BN
tel: 01803 664 891
email: southwest@dawkesmusic.co.uk
web: www.dawkesmusic.co.uk
part exchange: No
info: Woodwind and brass specialists. New and used items. Repairs available.

Digital Village (Bristol)
21 The Mall, Clifton Village, Bristol, BS8 4JG
tel: 0117 946 7700
email: bristol@digitalvillage.co.uk
web: www.digitalvillage.co.uk
part exchange: Yes
info: Stock digital recording equipment and PA equipment. Limited Apple tuition available. Digital Village also have branches throughout London, as well as Birmingham, Southampton and Cambridge. See listings in relevant sections for details.

Digital Village (Southampton)
Unit 3, Kingsgate Centre, St. Mary Street, Southampton, SO14 1NR
tel: 02380 233 444
fax: 02380 233 266
email: southampton@digitalvillage.co.uk
web: www.digitalvillage.co.uk
part exchange: Yes
info: Wide range of recording equipment including computer hardware and software, equipment for DJ or live, MIDI instruments and monitoring. Digital Village has branches throughout London, as well as Brighton, Birmingham and Cambridge. See listings in relevant sections for details.

Drum Bank Music Services
203 Gloucester Road, Bishopston, Bristol, BS7 8NN
tel: 0117 975 5366
email: paul@drumbankmusic.co.uk
web: www.drumbankmusic.co.uk
part exchange: No
info: Sell a wide range of musical equipment including guitars, amps, drums, cymbals, percussion, keyboards, PAs, effects and many other accessories. Drum Bank Music also offers tuition, rehearsal facilities, instrument repairs, hire of musical equipment and instrument tuning. Notice board space available.

The Drum Store
125 St. George's Road, Bristol, BS1 5UW
tel: 0117 929 8540
email: sales@bristoldrumstore.co.uk
web: www.bristoldrumstore.co.uk
part exchange: No
info: New and used drum and percussion shop. Repairs available. Open from Tuesday to Saturday.

EMIS
Cossham Street, Mangotsfield, Bristol, BS16 9EN
tel: 0117 956 1855
email: sales@emismusic.co.uk
web: www.emismusic.co.uk
part exchange: No
info: Synth and hi-tech music shop stocking synths, keyboards, range of recording equipment, electric drums, software, mics and sheet music. Stockists of German Doepfer synths. Repairs and limited notice board space available.

Ghana Goods
44 West Street, St. Philips, Bristol, BS2 0BH
tel: 0117 955 8668
email: ghanagoods@clara.co.uk
web: www.ghanagoods.co.uk
part exchange: Yes
info: West African instrument store. Stock wide range of percussion items including drums, xylophones, shakers, bells and flutes. Runs workshops and residential courses and offers one to one tuition. Repairs and re-skinning available.

The Glastonbury Music Shop
3 Benedict Street, Glastonbury, BA6 9NE
tel: 01458 835 212
email: glastonburymusic@aol.com
part exchange: Yes
info: Guitars, violins, Folk instruments. Repairs to most items. Teaching room in shop, along with notice board space.

Gloucester Sound House
49 Westgate Street, Gloucester, GL1 2NW
tel: 01452 417 429
web: www.soundhousedirect.com
part exchange: No
info: General shop. New and used items. Repairs and drum tuition offered.

Guernsey Pianos
7 The Grange, St. Peter Port, Guernsey, GY1 2PX
tel: 01481 700 408
email: guernseypianos@yahoo.co.uk
part exchange: No
info: New and used Acoustic pianos. Will part exchange on new pianos. Also offer tuning, repairs and reconditioning.

Guitar Inn
11 St. John's Road, Sandown, Isle of Wight, PO36 8ER
tel: 01983 400 008
web: www.guitarinn.co.uk
part exchange: No
info: Mostly new guitars with a few second hand available. Repairs and tuition for guitar in-store.

Harmony Music
The Forum Centre, Trinity Street, Dorchester, DT1 1TT
tel: 01305 260 360
email: sales@melodyworks.com
web: www.melodyworks.com
part exchange: No
info: General music shop stocking new and second hand items. Repairs and notice board space.

Hobgoblin Music (Bristol)
30 College Green, Bristol, BS1 5TB
tel: 0117 929 0902
email: bristol@hobgoblin.com
web: www.hobgoblin.com
part exchange: No
info: Folk specialists stocking Traditional, Celtic and Acoustic instruments. Repairs available. Hobgoblin have branches throughout the UK. See other listings or the website for further details.

Hobgoblin Music (Wadebridge)
1 Polmorla Walk, Wadebridge, PL27 7NS
tel: 01208 812 230
email: wadebridge@hobgoblin.co.uk
web: www.hobgoblin.com
part exchange: No
info: See above listing. Hobgoblin have branches throughout the UK. See other listings or website for further details.

Intersound
56 Parsonage Street, Dursley, GL11 4AA
tel: 01453 549 783
web: www.intersound.co.uk
part exchange: No
info: Mostly a guitar shop but also stock some keyboards and drums. Two guitar tutors in-store. Set ups, repairs for guitar and amps. Notice board space.

Kendall Guitars
30 Le Bordage, St. Peter Port, Guernsey, GY1 1DE
tel: 01481 726736
email: dominic@kendallguitars.co.uk
web: www.kendallguitars.co.uk
part exchange: No
info: New, used and handmade bespoke guitars. See website for hand-made styles. Create your ideal guitar! Repairs available. Notice board space for bands.

Lorelei Music
5 Great George Street, Weymouth, DT4 8NN
tel: 01305 788 766
email: sales@loreleimusic.co.uk
web: www.loreleimusic.co.uk
part exchange: No
info: General music shop stocking new and used instruments. Space on door for notices.

Manson's
39c New Bridge Street, Exeter, EX4 3AH
tel: 01392 496 379
email: sale@mansons.co.uk
web: www.mansons.co.uk
part exchange: No
info: Specialist guitar shop stocking new and second hand instruments. Professional repairs available. Notice board space. Linked with Academy of Music who offer tuition.

Modern Music
21 Kenwyn Street, Truro, TR1 3BU
tel: 01872 271 701
web: www.modernmusic.co.uk
part exchange: No
info: Guitar shop with nice range of vintage instruments. Repairs offered.

Mojo Guitars
6 The High Street, Falmouth, TR11 2AB
tel: 01326 312 895
part exchange: No
info: New and second hand electric, Acoustic and bass guitars, sales and repairs. Willing to display notices and flyers for local bands.

Mounts Bay Music
39 Causewayhead, Penzance, TR18 2ST
tel: 01736 333 500
email: malcolm@mountsbaymusic.freeserve.co.uk
part exchange: No
info: General music store mainly focussing on guitars and bass. Also stock range of woodwind and brass. Speak to Tracy Story in-store regarding guitar tuition. Will display notices in the window.

Music Central
18 Carisbrooke Road, Newport, PO30 1BL
tel: 01983 822 798
web: www.musiccentral.com
part exchange: No
info: Stock wide range of instruments. Offer repairs, tuition and notice board space in-store.

Music Is Life
779 Christchurch Road, Bournemouth, BH7 6AW
tel: 01202 430 820
email: shop@musicislife.co.uk
web: www.musicislife.co.uk
part exchange: Yes
info: All types of instruments from bagpipes to mouth organs, as well as large bank of sheet music. Notice board space.

Musical Instrument Megastore
Unit 19, Salisbury Road Business Park, Pewsey, Wiltshire, SN9 5PZ
tel: 01672 564 643
email: info@singingchicken.co.uk
web: www.singingchicken.co.uk
part exchange: Yes
info: General instrument store.

Nailsea Music Shop
79 High Street, Nailsea, Bristol, BS48 1AW
tel: 01275 855 021
email: sales@all-music.co.uk
web: www.all-music.co.uk
part exchange: No
info: General music store stocking orchestral instruments, electric guitars, drums, violins, double bass and flutes. Music school is run from shop. Repairs and notice board space available.

Palmgroves Guitars
24 The Lanes, Victoria Arcade, Union Street, Ryde, Isle of Wight, PO33 2LQ
tel: 01983 618 880
part exchange: No
info: Second hand guitars. Some repairs, set ups and restrings. Notice board space in-store.

Project Music
68 Bartholomew Street West, Exeter, EX4 3AJ
tel: 01392 425 125
email: info@projectmusic.net
web: www.projectmusic.net
part exchange: No
info: New and second hand guitars and drums. Guitar repairs and notice board space available.

The Providence Music Ltd.
1 St. George's Road, Bristol, BS1 5UL
tel: 0117 927 6536
email: sales@providencemusic.co.uk
web: www.providencemusic.co.uk
part exchange: Yes
info: Classical sheet music specialists.

Rikaxxe Music
12-16 Bond Street, Bristol, BS1 3LZ
tel: 0117 929 8481
part exchange: Yes
info: Guitar and amplifier stockists.

Rock House Music
11 St. John's Road, Sandown, PO36 8ER
tel: 01983 400 008
web: www.guitarinn.co.uk
part exchange: No
info: General instrument shop stocking new and used items. Repairs and guitar tuition in-store. Notice board space for flyers and posters.

Sounds International
5 Monmouth Place, Bath, BA1 2AT
tel: 01225 319 979
web: www.soundsinternational.co.uk
part exchange: No
info: Stock range of guitars, amps and keyboards. Limited repairs. Tuition available in guitar, keyboard and digital piano. Notice board space in-store and on website.

Strings Guitar Centre
106 Monkton Street, Ryde, Isle of Wight, PO33 1JN
tel: 01983 562 262
email: stringsgc@aol.com
web: www.stringsguitarcentre.co.uk
part exchange: No
info: New and used guitar shop offering repairs and notice board space for local bands.

Swift Music
63 Shirehampton Road, Bristol, BS9 2DW
tel: 0117 968 8427
email: nick@swiftmusic.co.uk
web: www.swiftmusic.co.uk
part exchange: No
info: New and second hand organ specialists. Also stock range of keyboards and pianos. Repairs and in-store tuition available.

Tottles Music Shop
30 Westgate Street, Launceston, PL15 7AE
tel: 01566 772 512
email: tottles.music@btconnect.com
part exchange: No
info: Across the board music shop stocking all types of instrument including pianos, drums, guitars and sheet music. Some repairs available.

Trevada Music
9 Chapel Street, Camborne, Cornwall, TR14 8EF
tel: 01209 714 353
fax: 01209 718 708
email: via website
web: www.trevadamusic.co.uk
part exchange: Yes
info: Range of brass, string, percussion and woodwind instruments. Pianos and keyboards. CDs, sheet music and accessories. Trial hire scheme available on selected instruments. Tuition and practice rooms. Shop online at the website above. See also listing for branch located in Carmarthenshire, Wales.

Vintage & Rare Guitars (Bath)
7-8 Saville Row, Bath, BA1 2QP
tel: 01225 330 888
email: enquiries@vintageandrareguitars.com
web: www.vintageandrareguitars.com
part exchange: No
info: Specialise in guitars and also stock amps and pedals. Buy, sell and part exchange. Also have another branch located in London. See listing in relevant section for details.

Westside Music Centre
51 Oxford Street, Weston Super Mare, BS23 1TN
tel: 01934 644 768
email: weston@westsidemusiccentre.co.uk
web: www.westsidemusiccentre.co.uk
part exchange: No
info: General music store offer repairs and in-store tuition in drums, guitar, bass, piano and keyboards. Notice board space available.

YORKSHIRE

SOUNDCONTROL
The UK's Number One Musical Instrument Retailer

Sound Control (Leeds City)
Unit 6 & 7, The Aireside Centre, Whitehall Road, Leeds, LS1 4AW
tel: 0113 242 6601
fax: 0113 242 6602
email: leeds@soundcontrol.co.uk
web: www.soundcontrol.co.uk
contact: Alison Lynch
part exchange: Yes
info: As the largest music equipment retailer in Europe with 25 stores across the UK, Sound Control has the most extensive range of guitars, basses, backline, PA, hi-tech, recording and percussion equipment available at the lowest prices around. Coupled with over 25 years experience and unrivalled staff training, shopping at Sound Control is the easiest step you will make on the road to being signed. Visit the above website to locate your nearest store, or to buy online and have your purchase delivered direct to your door.

SOUNDCONTROL
The UK's Number One Musical Instrument Retailer

Sound Control (Leeds East)
85 Roseville Road, Leeds, LS8 5DT
tel: 0113 245 6415
fax: 0113 245 6414
email: leeds.east@soundcontrol.co.uk
web: www.soundcontrol.co.uk
contact: Jon Green
part exchange: Yes
info: As the largest music equipment retailer in Europe with 25 stores across the UK, Sound Control has the most extensive range of guitars, basses, backline, PA, hi-tech, recording and percussion equipment available at the lowest prices around. Coupled with over 25 years experience and unrivalled staff training, shopping at Sound Control is the easiest step you will make on the road to being signed. Visit the above website to locate your nearest store, or to buy online and have your purchase delivered direct to your door.

SOUNDCONTROL
The UK's Number One Musical Instrument Retailer

Sound Control (Sheffield City)
The Workstation, 15 Paternoster Row, Sheffield, S1 2BX
tel: 0114 221 3007
fax: 0141 221 3008
email: sheffield@soundcontrol.co.uk
web: www.soundcontrol.co.uk
contact: John Stephenson
part exchange: Yes
info: As the largest music equipment retailer in Europe with 25 stores across the UK, Sound Control has the most extensive range of guitars, basses, backline, PA, hi-tech, recording and percussion equipment available at the lowest prices around. Coupled with over 25 years experience and unrivalled staff training, shopping at Sound Control is the easiest step you will make on the road to being signed. Visit the above website to locate your nearest store, or to buy online and have your purchase delivered direct to your door.

SOUNDCONTROL
The UK's Number One Musical Instrument Retailer

Sound Control (Sheffield East)
720 City Road, Sheffield, S2 1GJ
tel: 0114 264 0000
fax: 0114 264 6797
email: sheffield@soundcontrol.co.uk
web: www.soundcontrol.co.uk
contact: Paul Griffin
part exchange: Yes
info: As the largest music equipment retailer in Europe with 25 stores across the UK, Sound Control has the most extensive range of guitars, basses, backline, PA, hi-tech, recording and percussion equipment available at the lowest prices around. Coupled with over 25 years experience and unrivalled staff training, shopping at Sound Control is the easiest step you will make on the road to being signed. Visit the above website to locate your nearest store, or to buy online and have your purchase delivered direct to your door.

1st Floor Music
34 Bull Green, Halifax, HX1 5AB
tel: 01422 250 009
email: firstfloormusic@aol.com
part exchange: No
info: Guitar store. New and some used instruments. Repairs and notice board space available.

ABC Music Ltd.
192 Kings Road, Harrogate, North Yorkshire, HG1 5JG
tel: 01423 817 700
fax: 01423 565 006
web: www.abcmusic.co.uk
part exchange: No
info: Part of ABC music chain and franchise stores. Stock variety of instruments and accessories. ABC also have branches located in Greater London and South East regions, as well as one in the Midlands. See listings in relevant sections for details.

Accent On Music
103 Main Street, Garforth, Leeds, LS25 1AF
tel: 0113 287 4781
part exchange: Yes
info: Predominantly sheet music stockists but also sell
a small range of instruments and accessories. Repairs and notice board
space available.

Aire Guitars
266 Harrogate Road, Bradford, BD2 3RH
tel: 01274 632 000
email: aireguitars@msn.com
web: www.aireguitars.co.uk
part exchange: Yes
info: Guitar store with vast range of instruments,
amplifiers, effects pedals, accessories and clothing. Will display notices
in the window.

Alderson Woodwind & Brass
36 Cantley Manor Avenue, Doncaster, DN4 6TN
tel: 01302 371 587
email: aldwoodwind@supanet.com
web: www.aldersonwoodwind.co.uk
part exchange: Yes
info: High standard brass and woodwind repairs offered
by Mr. Alderson, who works from his workshop at home. Call or email
for details.

All Brass & Woodwind
Arch 70, 82 York Street, Leeds, LS9 8AA
tel: 0113 242 1332
email: abaw@btconnect.com
web: www.musicshops.tv
part exchange: No
info: Sell new and used brass and woodwind
instruments. Also stock percussion accessories, guitars and strings.
On-site repairs.

Andrews Violins
100 Duchy Road, Harrogate, HG1 2HA
tel: 01423 504 373
email: email@violinman.co.uk
web: www.violinman.co.uk
part exchange: Yes
info: Repairs for violins, cellos, violas and double bass.
Re-hairing for bows. Also buys, sells and rents violins.

Ant Music
28 Dunstall Street, Scunthorpe, DN15 6LD
tel: 01724 841 919
email: antmusic@btconnect.com
web: www.ant-music.co.uk
part exchange: No
info: Large stock of instruments such as guitars, bass,
drums and PA equipment, but also sell some Classical items. Small
repairs on request.

Band Supplies
Hunslet Road, Leeds, LS10 1JQ
tel: 0113 245 3097
email: leeds@bandsupplies.co.uk
web: www.bandsupplies.co.uk
part exchange: No
info: Specialise in brass and woodwind instruments but
also stock some violins and guitars. Offer repairs. In-store notice board
space.

Banks Music Ltd.
18 Lendal, York, YO1 8AU
tel: 01904 658 836
email: banksmusic@dial.pipex.com
web: www.banksmusic.co.uk
part exchange: Yes
info: Established in 1756. Banks is one of the largest
sheet music specialists in the UK. Also stock range of brass, woodwind
and string instruments.

Beverley Music Centre
14 Norwood, Beverley, HU17 9EZ
tel: 01482 881 584
part exchange: No
info: Quaint music store stocking guitars, woodwind
and brass instruments along with digital pianos. String repairs on-site.

Big Deal (Leeds)
6 Eastgate, Leeds, LS2 7JL
tel: 0113 244 3882
email: leeds@ukbigdeal.com
web: www.ukbigdeal.com
part exchange: No
info: Guitars, synths, pedals, amplifiers and PAs. Part
exchange and buy for cash. See also listing for store based in Sheffield.

Big Deal (Sheffield)
100 Pinstone Street, Sheffield, S12 HQ
tel: 0114 279 5416
web: www.ukbigdeal.com
part exchange: No
info: Selection of instruments such as guitars, synths,
pedals, amplifiers and PA equipment. Part exchange and buy for cash.
See also listing for store based in Leeds.

Big Rock
13-15 Savile Street, Hull, HU1 3EH
tel: 01482 322 107
email: andy@bigrock.caroo.co.uk
web: www.bigrock.co.uk
part exchange: No
info: Store selling guitars, amps, PA and hi-tech
computer programming and home recording systems. Guitar and bass
tuition located upstairs on premises. Repairs available. Band poster
space in-store.

Brewster Music
27 Huntriss Row, Scarborough, YO11 2ED
tel: 01723 374 610
web: www.brewstermusic.co.uk
part exchange: Yes
info: North Yorkshire's largest dealer of keyboards,
digital pianos and organs. Tuition available in both piano and keyboard.
Small poster space in-store.

Bridge Music
53 Holgate Road, York, YO24 4AA
tel: 01904 639 555
part exchange: No
info: Piano dealer stocking range of new and second
hand Acoustic pianos. Repairs and full restoration available along with
piano tuition.

Carcroft Organs & Keyboards
39a Skellow Road, Carcroft, Doncaster, DN6 8HQ
tel: 01302 338 445
email: ken@carcroftorgans.f9.co.uk
part exchange: No
info: Organ and keyboard specialists selling new and
second hand items. Also stock a small range of guitars. Offer repairs.

Crash Records
35 The Headrow, Leeds, LS1 6PU
tel: 0113 2436 743
email: rik@crashrecords.co.uk
part exchange: Yes

Deakin Musical Instruments
841 York Road, Leeds, LS14 6AA
tel: 0113 260 8008
email: bob@deakinguitars.wanadoo.co.uk
web: www.deakinguitars.co.uk
part exchange: No
info: New and used guitars, basses and amplifiers.
Repairs and notice board space available.

Diamond Music
48 Flowergate, Whitby, YO21 3BB
tel: 01947 601 564
part exchange: Yes
info: Across the board music store stocking brass,
woodwind, guitars, percussion, Folk instruments, music books and
CDs. Guitar re-stringing available. Notice board space in-store.

DK Electronics
Southview, Dunswell Road, Cottingham, HU16 4JB
tel: 01482 841 064
email: don@dkelect.caroo.co.uk
part exchange: Yes
info: Musical instrument repair and service shop. Deal
with amps, keyboards and organs.

Eagle Music
Springvale House, 198 Meltham Road, Huddersfield, HD4 7BG
tel: 01484 661 460
email: steve@eaglemusicshop.com
web: www.eaglemusicshop.com
part exchange: No
info: Traditional and Celtic musical instruments. Premier
dealer of Deering banjos. Other instruments include mandolin, guitar,
accordion, melodians and concertinas. Tuition books, DVDs, spares and
accessories.

Early Music Shop
38 Manningham Lane, Bradford, BD1 3EA
tel: 01274 393 753
email: sales@earlyms.deamon.co.uk
web: www.e-m-s.com
part exchange: Yes
info: Early Medieval and Renaissance musical instruments specialists with items ranging from lutes, recorders, harps, hurdy gurdys, harpsichords, percussion and Baroque violins.

Electro Music
82 Copley Road, Doncaster, DN1 2QW
tel: 01302 369 999
email: sales@electromusic.co.uk
web: www.electromusic.co.uk
part exchange: No
info: Sell electric, Acoustic and bass guitars, PA equipment, lighting, DJ and recording equipment and karaoke machines. Installation available. On-site tuition in guitar, bass and drums. Notice board space for bands, free for a month.

Fox's Music (Hull)
Haworth House, Clough Road, Hull, HU6 7PY
tel: 01482 441 515
web: www.williams-music.co.uk
part exchange: No
info: Stock guitars, bass, drums, amps and PA equipment. Tuition in guitar and keyboard. Repairs in-store. See also listings for other branches based in Sheffield, Leeds, Lincoln and Nottingham.

Fox's Music (Leeds)
97-99 Vicar Lane, Leeds, LS1 6PJ
tel: 0113 245 0350
web: www.williams-music.co.uk
part exchange: No
info: Stockists of digital pianos, orchestral instruments and catalogue of sheet music. Also see listings for stores located in Hull, Sheffield, Nottingham and Lincoln.

Fox's Music (Sheffield)
5 Furnival Gate, Sheffield, S14 1HW
tel: 01302 367 333
web: www.williams-music.co.uk
part exchange: No
info: Music store selling pianos, keyboards, guitars and more. Will display leaflets on the counter for local music events. Repairs offered. See also listings for branches located in Hull, Leeds, Lincoln and Nottingham.

Greensleeves (Northallerton)
8 Central Arcade, Northallerton, DL7 8PY
tel: 01609 780 253
part exchange: No
info: Stock all types of instruments from brass, woodwind, pianos, double bass to ethnic percussion and sheet music. In-house repairs. Notice board space available. Smaller sister store to Greensleeves based in Guisborough, Cleveland. See listing in relevant section for details.

GTR Guitars
14 Wood Street, Huddersfield, HD1 1DG
tel: 01484 530 794
email: gtrsupport@hotmail.co.uk
web: www.gtrguitars.co.uk
part exchange: No
info: Sell new and second hand guitars, bass and drums. Strong links with local unsigned musicians. All staff are full time giggers. Repairs available. Notice space available on door and over one wall.

Harland Music
36 Kirk Lane, Yeadon, Leeds, LS19 7ET
tel: 0113 250 5989
email: sharland@fsbdial.co.uk
part exchange: Yes
info: Sheet music and accessories store.

Hessle Music Centre
230 Hull Road, Hessle, HU13 9NH
tel: 01482 640 732
email: coolchords@hull24.com
web: www.coolchords.com
part exchange: No
info: Guitar specialists. Tuition available in guitar, keyboard and drums. Space for adverts and flyers in-store.

Hobgoblin Music (Leeds)
39 Call Lane, Leeds, LS1 7BT
tel: 0113 245 3311
email: leeds@hobgoblin.co.uk
web: www.hobgoblin.com
part exchange: No
info: Folk specialists stocking Traditional, Celtic and Acoustic instruments. Repairs and notice board space available. Hobgoblin has branches throughout the UK. See other listings or website for details.

Jarberry Music
Unit 20, Raglan Works, Methley Road, Castleford, WF10 1NX
tel: 01977 556 868
email: sales@jarberry-music.co.uk
web: www.jarberry-music.co.uk
part exchange: No
info: Professional recording equipment, keyboards, computers and mixing desks. Check out website for mail order sales. Repairs available.

Jax Music Centres
10 Pitt Street, Barnsley, S70 1AW
tel: 01226 206 326
email: jaxx1@tiscali.co.uk
web: www.jaxmusic.co.uk
part exchange: No
info: General music store stocking range of instruments. Repairs and notice board space in-store.

John Scheerer & Son
80/90 Merrion Centre, Leeds, LS2 8NG
tel: 0113 244 9592
email: sales@scheerers.com
web: www.scheerers.com
part exchange: No
info: A general music shop, Scheerers is divided into 2 levels. Downstairs are the orchestral instruments, upstairs is the more contemporary music section. Speak to the staff upstairs about displaying posters and flyers in-store.

Knight Music (Bridlington)
90 Hilderthorpe Road, Bridlington, YO15 3BQ
tel: 01262 606 969
part exchange: No
info: Sell most musical instruments with large stock of guitars. Repairs available. Band notice board space. See also listing for store based in Scarborough.

Knight Music (Scarborough)
3 Aberdeen Place, Scarborough, YO11 1XR
tel: 01262 606 969
part exchange: No
info: Across the board music store with large range of guitars and electrical equipment. Items bought for cash. Repairs in-store. Space for band notices. See also listing for shop located in Bridlington.

Knock On Wood
13 Eastgate, Leeds, LS2 7LY
tel: 0113 242 9146
email: sales@knockonwood.co.uk
web: www.knockonwood.co.uk
part exchange: Yes
info: World music specialists with big emphasis on percussion. Instruments include bongos, congas, timbales, steel pans, boomwhakers, xylophones, surdos, timbales, kalimbas and didgeridoos. Tuition in African and Latin drumming.

Maestro Music
25 Piece Hall, Halifax, HX1 1RE
tel: 01422 349 359
email: maestromusic@onetel.com
web: www.maestro-music.co.uk
part exchange: Yes
info: Guitar and accessories store. Also stock keyboards and drums. All new items. Tuition offered in guitar. Repairs and notice board space on request.

Mannings Musicals
75 Westgate, Bradford, BD1 2RD
tel: 01274 723 539
email: malcolm@manningsmusicals.co.uk
web: www.mannings-musicals.co.uk
part exchange: No
info: The place for all types of used instruments from ukuleles to banjos. Repairs to stringed instruments. Notice board space.

Milner & Hallows
28 The Green, Richmond, DL10 4RG
tel: 01748 822 284
email: alan.milner3@virgin.net
part exchange: No
info: Dealers and restorers of string and bowed instruments including violins, violas, cellos and double bass.

Moeck
38 Manningham Lane, Bradford, BD1 3EA
tel: 01274 721 646
part exchange: Yes
info: Retailers and suppliers of period Renaissance and Medieval instruments. Specialists in recorders.

MOR Music
52 Fossgate, York, YO1 9TF
tel: 01904 646 901
part exchange: No
info: Guitars and percussion. Repairs and notice board space in-store.

The Music Box
30-31 The Lane, Meadowhall Centre, Sheffield, S9 1EP
tel: 0114 256 9089
web: www.themusicbox.co.uk
part exchange: Yes
info: The Music Box sells new printed music, guitar tab, harmonicas, guitars, strings, brass, woodwind and musical accessories. Certain guitar repairs.

The Northern Guitar Centre
41 Call Lane, Leeds, LS1 7BT
tel: 0113 234 1976
part exchange: No
info: Dealers in second hand guitars, amplifiers and accessories. Notice board space in-store.

Octave Above
30 Town Road, Huddersfield, HD5 0HW
tel: 01484 431 725
email: octave@globalnet.co.uk
web: www.gig-bags.com
part exchange: No
info: Woodwind and brass specialists. New and second hand. Also sell gig bags (see above website). Limited notice space.

The Piano Shop
39 Holbeck Lane, Leeds, LS11 9UL
tel: 0113 244 3685
email: thepianoshop@freenet.co.uk
part exchange: No
info: Sell new and reconditioned pianos. Across the board prices from small acoustics to grands. Rentals, short term hire and rent to buy. French polishing and repairs available.

Piano Workshop
Unit 52, Asquith Bottom Mills, Asquith Bottom, Sowerby Bridge, HX6 3BT
tel: 01422 835 155
part exchange: No
info: Specialists in piano renovation and restoration.

PJS Music Services
57 High Street, Dodworth, Barnsley, S75 3RG
tel: 01226 200 102
email: info@pjsmusicservices.co.uk
web: www.pjsmusicservices.co.uk
part exchange: Yes
info: Vast range of instruments from most famous brands including brass, woodwind, strings and percussion. Guitar lessons available on-site along with repairs.

Pocklington Music
3 Pavement, Pocklington, York, YO42 2AU
tel: 01759 303 177
email: pockmusic@yahoo.co.uk
web: www.musicshops.uk.com
part exchange: No
info: Stock all types of musical instruments and accessories. Small stock of second hand items. Music school teaching most instruments from piano to banjo. Repairs and notice board space in-store. Currently expanding.

PSS (Music) Ltd.
43-45 Hainton Avenue, Grimsby, DN32 9AS
tel: 01472 343 211
email: info@pssmusic.co.uk
web: www.pssmusic.co.uk
part exchange: No
info: Biggest music store in the area. Stock wide range of most instruments including guitars by Fender and Ibanez. Repairs and notice board space available. 10% discount to students.

Redhouse Music
254 Tinshill Road, Leeds, LS16 7BT
tel: 0113 261 1414
email: info@redhousemusic.co.uk
web: www.redhousemusic.co.uk
part exchange: No
info: New and second hand guitars, amps and accessories along with selection of books. Big emphasis on friendly customer service and attention to detail. All guitars are 100% properly set up before leaving the store.

Repercussion Music Co.
Beverley Road, Hull, HU5 1BA
tel: 01482 348 649
email: repercussionsimon@yahoo.com
web: www.repercussionmusic.co.uk
part exchange: No
info: Percussion specialists stocking all types of drums and percussion instruments. Repair and refurbishment service. Also incorporates Repercussion Music Academy offering tuition services. See entry in relevant section for further information.

Rock Factory
Wheldon Road, Castleford, WF10 2SD
tel: 01977 513 643
email: guitars@rockfactory.co.uk
web: www.rockfactory.co.uk
part exchange: No
info: Large instrument store stretching over 3 floors. Guitar, drum and PA departments. Healthy stock of second hand items. Repairs and notice board space available.

Rock Steady Music
24 Regent Parade, Harrogate, HG1 5AZ
tel: 01423 529 000
email: info@rocksteadymusic.co.uk
web: www.rocksteadymusic.co.uk
part exchange: No
info: Deal in all types of musical instruments and accessories, from Acoustic and electric guitars to full PA systems. Repairs available. Staff are all gigging musicians and very friendly with local bands. Band notice board in-store.

Rockbox Group Gear
Central Arcade, Northallerton, DL7 8PY
tel: 01609 775 592
part exchange: No
info: Guitar, bass, drums, as well as electrical equipment such as samplers, PA equipment and amplification. Notice board space in-store. Linked with Greensleeves music store. See listing for further details.

Rockshack
164 Cardigan Road, Leeds, LS6 1LL
tel: 0113 230 6363
email: tony@rockshack.fsnet.co.uk
web: www.rockshack.fsnet.co.uk
part exchange: No
info: New and used guitars, basses and amplifiers offering sales and repairs. Notice board space available.

Saturn Music
The Old Vicarage, 24 Zetland Street, Wakefield, WF1 1QT
tel: 01924 299 214
email: sales@saturnmusic.net
web: www.saturnmusic.net
part exchange: No
info: Stock guitars, bass, drums, amplifiers, repairs, in-store guitar and drum tuition, as well as range of accessories and pedals. Large amount of poster and flyer space both in-store and outside.

SME Music Shop
55 Swadford Street, Skipton, BD23 1QY
tel: 01756 798 954
email: planetfender@aol.com
part exchange: No
info: Guitar specialists stocking range of Acoustics and electrics along with amplification. Repairs and tuition in guitar and bass.

Smedley E. & Son
19 Printing Office Street, Doncaster, DN1 1TJ
tel: 01302 323 248
part exchange: No
info: General music shop stocking brass, woodwind and stringed instruments. Repairs on some instruments available.

Street Life Music Retail
11-13 Guardian Centre, Rotherham, S65 1DD
tel: 01709 360 830
part exchange: No
info: General music instrument sales and repairs. Notice board space.

Stringstocks Ltd. (Barnsley)
50 Eldon Street North, Barnsley, S71 1LG
tel: 01226 292 792
email: sales@stringstocks.com
web: www.stringstocks.com
part exchange: No
info: Guitar store. Main dealers for Fender, Gibson, Ibanez, Aria, Carlsbro, ESP, Danelectro, Line 6, Orange, Vintage and Fender. Professionally trained guitar tutors on-site. Repairs and notice board space available. See also listing for shop located in Rotherham.

Stringstocks Ltd. (Rotherham)
173-175 Wellgate, Rotherham, S60 2NW
tel: 01709 835 004
email: sales@stringstocks.com
web: www.stringstocks.com
part exchange: No
info: Guitar store. Main dealers for Fender, Gibson, Ibanez, Aria, Carlsbro, ESP, Danelectro, Line 6, Orange, Vintage and Fender. Professionally trained guitar tutors on-site. Repairs and notice board space available. See also listing for store based in Barnsley.

Superbuy
25 Westmorland House, Westmorland Street, Wakefield, WF1 1QL
tel: 01924 386 479
part exchange: No
info: General music store with main emphasis on guitars and amplification.

Time & Tune
14-16 Victoria Street, Skipton, BD23 1JE
tel: 01756 798 515
part exchange: No
info: General music store stocking brass, woodwind and strings. Instrument rental scheme available. Notice board space in-store.

The Tone Zone
Rear Of 38 Alexandra Road, Grimsby, DN31 1RW
tel: 01472 362 041
email: anthony-watson@btconnect.com
web: www.the-tone-zone.co.uk
part exchange: No
info: Guitars, strings and amplification. Specialists in set ups and repairs. Wall space for band posters.

Treble Clef
23 Huddersfield Road, Brighouse, HD6 1LE
tel: 01484 715 417
email: tclef@gotadsl.co.uk
part exchange: No
info: Guitars, violins, keyboards, pianos, PAs and installations. Tuition in guitar and piano. Notice board space in-store.

Utopia Music
36B Shambles Street, Barnsley, S70 2SH
tel: 01226 771 675
email: utopiamusic@hotmail.com
part exchange: No
info: Guitar specialists stocking electric, Acoustic and classical guitars. Help with set up available. Staff teach guitar privately out of store. Band flyer space in-store.

Wavelength Music
165 London Road, Sheffield, S2 4LH
tel: 0114 258 0497
email: general@wavelengthmusic.co.uk
web: www.wavelengthmusic.co.uk
part exchange: No
info: Stockists of stringed instruments including guitars, mandolins and banjos. Repairs to all fretted instruments and in-store tuition. Notice board space.

Wharfe Valley Music
26 Leeds Road, Ilkley, LS29 8DS
tel: 01943 816 151
part exchange: No
info: Small music store with range of instruments such as guitars, melodians, harmonicas and various other strings.

Windstruments
1 Ryshworth Bridge, Bingley, BD16 2DX
tel: 01274 510 050
email: sales@windstruments.co.uk
web: www.windstruments.co.uk
part exchange: No
info: All types of wind instruments, guitars, pianos, amplifiers and much more. Repairs and tuition in all instruments. See website for master class details. Notice board space.

Wizard Guitars
50-52 Coply Road, Doncaster, DN1 2QW
tel: 01302 769 890
part exchange: No
info: Family owned store run by ex-professional guitarist. Stock of over 600 guitars, mainly second hand and vintage. Willing to part exchange anything music-related. Substantial discount offered for bands. Repair workshop. Will fix your instrument on the day, if not within the hour. Set ups, modifications and conversions also done in the day if booked in. Blues master classes taught by experts.

Woods Music Shop
20 Cross Street, Wakefield, WF1 3BW
tel: 01924 374 446
web: www.woods-music.co.uk
part exchange: No
info: Across the board music store. Specialists in pianos. Repairs and notice board space available.

NORTHERN IRELAND

2 Mac Music
Unit 6, Enville Court, Castlewellan Road, Banbridge, County Down, BT32 4AX
tel: 028 4066 0840
part exchange: Yes
info: Wide selection of instruments. Repairs available, as well as piano and guitar tuition.

AA Music
15 Leckey Road, Ballinderry Upper, Lisburn, County Antrim, BT28 2QA
tel: 028 9261 0634
web: www.aa-music.com
part exchange: Yes
info: Sales, hire, removals and reconditioning of pianos, digital pianos, keyboards and organs.

AC Electronics
10 Lower Captain Street, Coleraine, BT51 3DT
tel: 028 7035 4213
email: adrien@acelectronics.co.uk
web: www.acelectronics.co.uk
part exchange: No
info: Stock variety of instruments. Repairs and guitar tuition in-store. Small notice board space.

Accordion Fanatics
27 Spence Crescent, Cullybackey, Ballymena, County Antrim, BT42 1BR
tel: 028 2588 0099
part exchange: Yes
info: Accordion specialists.

Andante Percussion
97 Bannfield Road, Ballyroney, Banbridge, County Down, BT32 5JQ
tel: 028 4063 0932
email: sales@andantedrums.co.uk
web: www.andantedrums.co.uk
part exchange: Yes
info: Percussion specialists who also provide repair service.

Ards Music
33 South Street, Newtownards, BT23 4JT
tel: 028 9182 2990
part exchange: No
info: General music store. Majority of stock comprising digital pianos, keyboards and guitars, but also stock brass, woodwind, percussion, accessories and sheet music. Piano and guitar repairs.

Baird Sound Systems
208 York Street, Belfast, BT15 1JJ
tel: 028 9035 1358
email: info@bairdsoundsystems.com
web: www.bairdsoundsystems.com
part exchange: No
info: Catering for all your gigging needs. Large stock of guitars and basses, specialists in PA and recording equipment, lighting, stands and other computer equipment. Repairs available. Hire service for most electrical items. Separate department called 'Hire-An-Amp'. Band notice board space.

Beat Street
53 Station Road, Cullybackey, Ballymena, County Antrim, BT42 1BU
tel: 028 2588 0210
part exchange: No
info: Repairs and tuition available.

Bel Canto
36 Clifton Road, Bangor, BT20 5EP
tel: 028 9127 3073
email: bellcanto36@aol.com
web: www.bellcantomusic.co.uk
part exchange: Yes
info: Sheet music specialists with wide ranging catalogue. Ordering service available by telephone or via the website. Owner also offers tuition in vocals and brass.

Belfast Guitar Emporium Ltd.
20-22 Bradbury Place, Belfast, County Antrim, BT7 1RS
tel: 028 9024 2335
email: info@belfastguitaremporium.com
web: www.belfastguitaremporium.com
part exchange: No
info: As well as sales, also offer repairs and in-store tuition.

Belfast Music Supplies
283 Upper Newtownards Road, Belfast, BT4 3JH
tel: 028 9047 2555
email: linden@belfastmusicsupplies.freeserve.co.uk
web: www.belfastmusic.com
part exchange: Yes
info: Stock a range of instruments including flutes, saxophones, guitars, keyboards and pianos. Repairs available. Notice board space for bands and musicians. The owner, Mr Ronnie Mack, is a well known music composer, arranger and conductor, and is on hand at most times to give advice or customer support.

Danny Otterson
1a Fairhill, Maghera, BT46 5AX
tel: 028 7964 2651
email: danny@dannyotterson.com
web: www.dannyotterson.com
part exchange: No
info: Wide range of instruments available. Repair service.

Dawson's Music (Bangor)
12 Ballo Avenue, Bangor, County Down, BT19 7QT
tel: 028 9127 4886
fax: 028 9127 4412
email: bangor@dawsons.co.uk
web: www.dawsonsonline.com
part exchange: No
info: Stock large range of instruments, PA equipment, amps, effects and accessories. Branches across the UK. See listings for details.

Drum Sounds
96 Sandy Row, Belfast, BT12 5EX
tel: 028 9024 2684
email: thebandshop@btconnect.com
web: www.drum-sounds.co.uk
part exchange: Yes
info: Hand-made marching band drum specialists. New and used items. Noticeboard in-store for messages and posters.

Evan's Musical
53 Bridge Street, Lisburn, BT28 1XZ
tel: 028 9266 2011
part exchange: No
info: General musical instrument store. Items range from bagpipes to keyboards, guitars to disco equipment. Also cater for all your lighting and PA needs and offer installation. Repairs available. Willing to display posters on front door.

George Lowden Guitars
32-34 Down Business Centre, Down Business Park, 46 Belfast Road, Down Patrick, County Down, BT30 9UP
tel: 028 4461 9161
email: sarah@georgelowden.com
web: www.georgelowden.com
part exchange: Yes
info: Hand-crafted steel string guitars. Repair service available.

Instrumentals
Unit 1, Rawdon Court, Main Street, Moira, Craigavon, BT67 0LQ
tel: 028 9261 3322
part exchange: Yes
info: Repair and tuition services available.

James Henry Pianos
11 Charles Street, Ballymoney, County Antrim, BT53 6DX
tel: 028 2766 4637
part exchange: Yes
info: Quality new and second hand pianos. Also stock -music books and sheet music.

Kennedy's Music Mart
26 Upper Water Street, Newry, BT34 1DJ
tel: 028 3026 6715
part exchange: No
info: General instrument shop stocking new and used items. Some minor repairs offered.

Limavady Piano Services
21 Dowland Road, Limavady, BT49 0HP
tel: 028 7776 2979
email: sales@limavadypianos.com
web: www.limavadypianos.com
part exchange: No
info: Pianos to buy sell and hire, both new and used. From upright Acoustics to grands. Also offer tuning, repairs, reconditioning and rebuilding. Piano tuition in-store. Owner willing to display local band posters.

Mac's Music
Millennium Court, William Street, Portadown, Craigavon, County Armagh, BT62 3NX
tel: 028 3839 1212
email: macs.music@btconnect.com
web: www.macs-music.co.uk
part exchange: Yes
info: Stock wide range of instruments and accessories. Repair and tuition service available.

Marcus Musical Instruments Ltd.
125 Royal Avenue, Belfast, BT1 1FF
tel: 028 9032 2871
email: info@marcusmusicbelfast.com
part exchange: No
info: General instrument shop offering repairs and in-store tuition in guitar and drum. Notice board space for musicians.

Matchett's (Musical Instruments) Ltd.
6 Wellington Place, Belfast, BT1 6GE
tel: 028 9032 6695
email: info@matchettsmusic.com
web: www.matchettsmusic.com
part exchange: No
info: General music store. Instruments include brass, woodwind, guitars and pianos. Repairs and notice board space available.

McLeod Music
104 Queen Street, Lurgan, Craigavon, BT66 8BW
tel: 028 3832 1435
part exchange: No
info: Very wide ranging stock of instruments including guitars, keyboards, violins, clarinets, drums, PA equipment and sheet music. Repairs and notice board space in-store.

McMeekin's (Music) Ltd.
6 Abbey Street, Coleraine, BT52 1DS
tel: 028 7034 3045
part exchange: No
info: General musical instrument shop. Items include pianos, digital pianos, guitars and sheet music. Repairs available.

The Music Shop
Unit 20, Meadow Lane Shopping Centre, Moneymore Road, Magherafelt, County Londonderry, BT45 6PR
tel: 028 7963 2387
web: www.musicshopni.co.uk
part exchange: Yes
info: Range of musical instruments in stock.

The Pipers Cave
138 Dungannon Road, Cookstown, BT80 9BD
tel: 028 8676 3615
part exchange: Yes
info: Specialise in new and used bagpipes. Repairs available.

Reynolds
33 Castle Street, Omagh, BT78 1DD
tel: 028 8224 5767
part exchange: No
info: Quality musical instruments and service. Items include woodwind, brass, strings, folk instruments, keyboards and amplifiers. Repairs and notice board space available.

Richard Pianos
2 Oakleigh Park, Portadown, Craigavon, BT62 3QF
tel: 028 3835 0412/07802 358 095
part exchange: Yes
info: New, nearly new and used pianos bought and sold.

Spa Wells Piano Co.
120 Crossgar Road, Ballynahinch, BT24 8XT
tel: 028 9756 3838
email: info@spawellspianos.com
web: www.spawellspianos.com
part exchange: No
info: Deal in second hand pianos. View by appointment only as business is run from home. Repairs offered.

Spark's Music (Derry)
12 Little James Street, Derry, County Londonderry, BT48 7FB
tel: 028 7137 4354
email: info@sparksmusic.com
web: www.sparksmusic.com
part exchange: No
info: Guitars, basses, amplification, drums, effects and accessories. Repair service available. See also listings for other branch based in Strabane.

Spark's Music (Strabane)
24 Upper Main Street, Strabane, County Tyrone, BT82 8AS
tel: 028 7188 5858
email: info@sparksmusic.com
web: www.sparksmusic.com
part exchange: No
info: Guitars, basses, amplification, drums, effects and accessories. Repair service available. See also listings for other branches based in Derry.

T2 Music Enterprises
12 Lacker Park, Dumgiven, County Derry, BT47 4ND
tel: 028 7774 2463
email: info@t2me.com
web: www.t2me.com
part exchange: No
info: Professional sound, light and stage equipment needs. Also stock music equipment for DJs and bands.

Trevor Keys Music (Ballymena)
3 Wellington Street, Ballymena, BT43 6AB
tel: 028 2565 0057
email: trevor.keys7@btinternet.com
web: www.trevorkeysmusic.co.uk
part exchange: No
info: Selection of guitars, pianos and keyboards in stock. Repairs and in-store tuition available. See also listing for store in Derry.

Trevor Keys Music (Derry)
157 Spencer Road, Derry, County Londonderry, BT47 6AH
tel: 028 7134 6796
email: trevor.keys7@btinternet.com
web: www.trevorkeysmusic.co.uk
part exchange: No
info: Selection of guitars, pianos and keyboards in stock. Repairs and in-store tuition available. See also listing for store based in Ballymena.

Wilkinson Musical Instruments
101 Main Street, Cullybackey, Ballymena, BT42 1BW
tel: 028 2588 1065
email: musicalinstruments@hwilkinsons.wanadoo.co.uk
part exchange: Yes
info: Music shop specialising in accordions. Other instruments include marching drums and flutes. Repairs available along with in-store accordion tuition. Willing to display band posters, flyers and adverts.

SCOTLAND

SOUNDCONTROL
The UK's Number One Musical Instrument Retailer

Sound Control (Dundee)
29-31 Castle Street, Dundee, Angus, DD1 3AD
tel: 01382 225 619
fax: 01382 201 486
email: dundee@soundcontrol.co.uk
web: www.soundcontrol.co.uk
contact: Ralph Teviotdale
part exchange: Yes
info: As the largest music equipment retailer in Europe with 25 stores across the UK, Sound Control has the most extensive range of guitars, basses, backline, PA, hi-tech, recording and percussion equipment available at the lowest prices around. Coupled with over 25 years experience and unrivalled staff training, shopping at Sound Control is the easiest step you will make on the road to being signed. Visit the above website to locate your nearest store, or to buy online and have your purchase delivered direct to your door.

SOUNDCONTROL
The UK's Number One Musical Instrument Retailer

Sound Control (Dunfermline)
The Elgin Works, Elgin Street, Dunfermline, KY12 7SD
tel: 01383 733 353
fax: 01383 725 733
email: dunfermline@soundcontrol.co.uk
web: www.soundcontrol.co.uk
contact: David Hopkins
part exchange: Yes
info: As the largest music equipment retailer in Europe with 25 stores across the UK, Sound Control has the most extensive range of guitars, basses, backline, PA, hi-tech, recording and percussion equipment available at the lowest prices around. Coupled with over 25 years experience and unrivalled staff training, shopping at Sound Control is the easiest step you will make on the road to being signed. Visit the above website to locate your nearest store, or to buy online and have your purchase delivered direct to your door.

SOUNDCONTROL
The UK's Number One Musical Instrument Retailer

Sound Control (Edinburgh)
1 Grassmarket, Edinburgh, EH1 2HY
tel: 0131 229 8211
fax: 0131 221 9272
email: edinburgh@soundcontrol.co.uk
web: www.soundcontrol.co.uk
contact: David Tynan
part exchange: Yes
info: As the largest music equipment retailer in Europe with 25 stores across the UK, Sound Control has the most extensive range of guitars, basses, backline, PA, hi-tech, recording and percussion equipment available at the lowest prices around. Coupled with over 25 years experience and unrivalled staff training, shopping at Sound Control is the easiest step you will make on the road to being signed. Visit the above website to locate your nearest store, or to buy online and have your purchase delivered direct to your door.

SOUNDCONTROL
The UK's Number One Musical Instrument Retailer

Sound Control (Glasgow City)
61 Jamaica Street, Glasgow, Lanarkshire, G1 4NN
tel: 0141 204 0322
fax: 0141 204 0614
email: glasgow.city@soundcontrol.co.uk
web: www.soundcontrol.co.uk
contact: John Buchanan
part exchange: Yes
info: As the largest music equipment retailer in Europe with 25 stores across the UK, Sound Control has the most extensive range of guitars, basses, backline, PA, hi-tech, recording and percussion equipment available at the lowest prices around. Coupled with over 25 years experience and unrivalled staff training, shopping at Sound Control is the easiest step you will make on the road to being s

SOUNDCONTROL
The UK's Number One Musical Instrument Retailer

Sound Control (Glasgow West)
33 Otago Street, Kelvinbridge, Glasgow, G12 8JJ
tel: 0141 339 7766
fax: 0141 357 2703
email: glasgow.west@soundcontrol.co.uk
web: www.soundcontrol.co.uk
contact: Steve Caban
part exchange: Yes
info: As the largest music equipment retailer in Europe with 25 stores across the UK, Sound Control has the most extensive range of guitars, basses, backline, PA, hi-tech, recording and percussion equipment available at the lowest prices around. Coupled with over 25 years experience and unrivalled staff training, shopping at Sound Control is the easiest step you will make on the road to being signed. Visit the above website to locate your nearest store, or to buy online and have your purchase delivered direct to your door.

MUSIC SERVICES/RETAIL

SOUNDCONTROL
The UK's Number One Musical Instrument Retailer

Sound Control (Kirckcaldy)
63 Dunnikier Road, Kirckcaldy, Fife, KY1 2RL
tel:	01592 260 293
fax:	01592 642 251
email:	kirkcaldy@soundcontrol.co.uk
web:	www.soundcontrol.co.uk
contact:	John Bell
part exchange:	Yes
info:	As the largest music equipment retailer in Europe

with 25 stores across the UK, Sound Control has the most extensive range of guitars, basses, backline, PA, hi-tech, recording and percussion equipment available at the lowest prices around. Coupled with over 25 years experience and unrivalled staff training, shopping at Sound Control is the easiest step you will make on the road to being signed. Visit the above website to locate your nearest store, or to buy online and have your purchase delivered direct to your door.

Adamson Violins
77 Kingsknowe Road North, Edinburgh, Midlothian, EH14 2DE
tel:	0131 538 7098
part exchange:	Yes
info:	Violin maker and repairer.

Airdrie Music Center
45-49 South Bridge Street, Airdie, Lanarkshire, ML6 6JQ
tel:	01236 764 804
email:	scottsmate3@aol.com
web:	www.kandyman.co.uk
part exchange:	Yes
info:	Specialise in guitars and amplifiers. Flyer space

available in-store.

Andy Simpson Music Centre
38-40 The Arcade, Stirling, Stirlingshire, FK8 1AX
email:	sales@asmc.co.uk
web:	www.andysimpson.uk2k.com
part exchange:	Yes
info:	Mainly sell keyboards and digital pianos with the

full Yamaha, Yamaha Pro-Audio and Clavinova ranges.

The Band Room Ltd.
Unit W7, Rosemount Workplace, 141 Charles Street, Glasgow, G21 2QA
tel:	0141 552 7811
email:	brian.mccomish@bandroom.co.uk
web:	www.bandroom.co.uk
part exchange:	Yes
info:	Specialises in bagpipes and drums for pipe bands.

Items for sale and hire.

Band Supplies
13-15 Old Dumbarton Road, Glasgow, Lanarkshire, G3 8QY
tel:	0141 339 9400
email:	glasgow@bandsupplies.co.uk
web:	www.bandsupplies.co.uk
part exchange:	No
info:	Specialise in brass and woodwind instruments but

also stock some violins and guitars. Offer repairs. In-store notice board space.

Bandwagon Musical Supplies
9 St. Paul's Square, Perth, Perthshire, PH1 5QW
tel:	01738 637 714
web:	www.bandwagonperth.co.uk
part exchange:	No
info:	Acoustic and electric guitars, amps, effects,

accessories, books, videos, PA hire, tuition and repairs.

Biggars Music
273 Sauchiehall Street, Glasgow, G2 3HH
tel:	0141 332 8676
email:	info@biggars.co.uk
web:	www.biggars.co.uk
part exchange:	No
info:	Wide range of instruments with highly trained

staff. Tuition available for guitar, keyboard, vocal and woodwind. Orchestral repairs.

Brian Rattray
34a Spylaw Street, Edinburgh, Midlotian, EH13 0JT
tel:	0131 411 1098
part exchange:	Yes
info:	Violin dealer and maker. Top of the range violins

and guitars hand made. Repairs to all stringed instruments and bows, as well as bow re-haring.

Bruce Millers
363 Union Street, Aberdeen, AB11 6BN
tel:	01224 592 211
email:	ewan.blair@brucemillers.co.uk
web:	www.brucemillers.co.uk
part exchange:	No
info:	Stock all instruments including guitars, drums, PA

and amplification equipment, Folk instruments including mandolin and banjo. Two floors of music tutors for guitar, drum, piano, violin, fiddle and bass. Notice board for bands.

Caberfeidh Bagpipe Supplies
21 Market Hall, Academy Street, Inverness, IV1 1PJ
tel:	01463 239 869
email:	caberfeidhbagpipes@aol.com
part exchange:	Yes
info:	Bagpipes specialist. Sell and repair new and old

or antique bagpipes. Also stock accessories and Traditional music CDs. Tuition available.

Celtic Chords Traditional Music Shop
8 Barclay Street, Stonehaven, Kincardineshire, AB39 2BJ
tel:	01569 763 913
email:	info@celtic-chords.co.uk
web:	www.celtic-chords.co.uk
part exchange:	Yes
info:	Provide a wide range of traditional musical

instruments such as guitars and violins, CDs and associated products.

D. Smyth Musical Instrument Repairs
17 Considine Gardens, Edinburgh, Midlothian, EH8 7DZ
tel:	0131 652 2132
email:	david.smyth@smyth-clulow.co.uk
web:	www.smyth-clulow.co.uk
part exchange:	Yes
info:	Repairs to brass and woodwind instruments. Also

makes guitars on-site. Owner eager to teach customers how to properly care for their instruments.

Drum Central (Edinburgh)
61 South Clerk Street, Edinburgh, Midlothian, EH8 9PP
tel:	0131 667 3844
email:	edinburgh@drumcentral.co.uk
web:	www.drumcentral.co.uk
part exchange:	No
info:	Specialise in drums, cymbals and percussion.

Repairs available. In-store notice board for flyers and adverts. See also listing for store located in Glasgow.

Drum Central (Glasgow)
34 Gibson Street, Glasgow, Lanarkshire, G12 8NX
tel:	0141 334 7111
email:	glasgow@drumcentral.co.uk
web:	www.drumcentral.co.uk
part exchange:	No
info:	Specialise in drums, cymbals and percussion.

Repairs available. In-store noticeboard for flyers and adverts. See also listing for branch based in Edinburgh.

Drum Shop Glasgow
15 Blackie Street, Glasgow, Lanarkshire, G3 8TN
email:	info@drumshopglasgow.co.uk
web:	www.drumshopglasgow.co.uk
part exchange:	No
info:	Established 25 years. Specialise in selling and

hiring drums and percussion instruments. Tuition available. In-store flyer space.

Edinburgh Organ Studio
98 Cannongate, The Royal Mile, Edinburgh, Midlothian, EH8 8DD
tel:	0131 556 3005
web:	www.organstudio.co.uk
part exchange:	Yes
info:	Family run business specialising in high quality

electronic musical instruments including digital pianos, keyboards, organs and church organs. Offer hire and repairs.

Folk Revolution
22 Clarendon Place, Glasgow, G20 7PZ
tel:	0141 353 1285
email:	enquiries@folkrevolution.co.uk
web:	www.folkrevolution.co.uk
part exchange:	Yes
info:	Folk and Traditional music specialists selling

musical instrument including guitars, violins, mandolins and banjos. Also traditional CDs and accessories. Notice board space in-store.

Fonn Music Shop
19 Bayhead, Stornoway, Isle of Lewis, HS1 2DU
tel: 01851 704 632
part exchange: Yes
info: Suppliers of all musical instruments from various
manufacturers. Other services include CD and cassette sales (mainly
Traditional and Irish music) and PA hire from 300W up to 7kW. The
shop stocks music by local artists and welcomes contact from unsigned
acts wishing to distribute independently. The owner of the shop also
runs a recording studio and label, Croft Recordings. Call the above
number for details.

Frank Usher Guitars
The Glen Row, The Glen, Innerleithen, Scottish Borders
tel: 01896 830 040
email: frank@frankusherguitars.co.uk
web: www.frankusherguitars.co.uk
part exchange: Yes
info: Frank Usher makes electric 6 and 12 string guitars,
fretted and fretless basses, mandolins and lap steels. Each instrument is
hand made in the workshop by himself. Local timber from around his
home in the Scottish Borders, as well as more exotic species are used in
construction.

The Gig Bag
16-17 Olympia Arcade, High Street, Kirkcaldy, KY1 1QF
tel: 01592 200 001
email: info@gigbagmusic.co.uk
web: www.gigbagmusic.co.uk
part exchange: Yes
info: Sells and repairs most instruments. Also stocks
sheet music. Notice boards in-store.

Gillanders & McLeod Ltd.
25 Broughham Place, Edinburgh, Midlothian, EH3 9JU
tel: 0131 228 5535
email: mail@gandmbagpipes.co.uk
web: www.gandmbagpipes.co.uk
part exchange: Yes
info: Highland bagpipe and accessories specialist.

Goodacre Pipes
4 Elcho Street, Peebles, EH45 8LQ
web: www.goodbagpipes.co.uk
part exchange: Yes
info: High quality Scottish small pipes, English and
other bagpipes from one of Britain's most innovative makers. Waiting
list, please enquire.

Guitar Guitar Ltd. (Edinburgh)
283-287 St. John's Road, Edinburgh, Midlothian, EH12 7XF
tel: 0131 334 7100
email: edin@guitarguitar.co.uk
web: www.guitarguitar.co.uk
part exchange: No
info: Guitar specialist. Offer repairs and notice board
space in-store. Branches in Glasgow and Newcastle. See entries for
further details.

Guitar Guitar Ltd. (Glasgow)
36 Trongate, Glasgow, G15 ES
tel: 0141 552 9896
email: glasgow@guitarguitar.co.uk
web: www.guitarguitar.co.uk
part exchange: No
info: Guitar specialist. Offer repairs and notice board
space in-store. Branches in Edinburgh and Newcastle. See entries for
further details.

The Guitar Store
314 Argyle Street, Glasgow, G2 8LY
tel: 0141 572 0104
email: tom@guitarstore.co.uk
web: www.guitarstore.co.uk
part exchange: No
info: New and used guitars.

Haydock Music
55 Stockiemuir Avenue, Bearsden, Glasgow, Lanarkshire, G61 3JJ
tel: 01738 621 818
email: info@haydockmusic.co.uk
web: www.haydockmusic.co.uk
part exchange: No
info: Classical musical instrument specialists. Offer
repairs and flyer space in-store.

High Level Music
1 Gardie Court, Lerwick, Shetland, ZE1 0GG
tel: 01595 692 618
email: sales@shetlandmusic.co.uk
part exchange: Yes
info: Wide range of instruments including guitars, hand
made Shetland fiddles and accordians. Also stock local music CDs.
In-store noticeboard.

HSK Music
293 High Street, Kirkcaldy, KY1 1JH
tel: 01592 268 222
email: sales-hsk@btconnect.com
web: www.hskmusic.com
part exchange: No
info: General instrument store, friendly staff. Repairs
and notice board space.

Jimmy Clinkscale
81 High Street, Galashiels, Scottish Borders, TD1 1R2
tel: 01896 750 588
email: sales@clinkscale.co.uk
web: www.clinkscale.co.uk
part exchange: Yes
info: Wide selection of musical instruments catering for
beginners, bands, teachers and professionals.

Kelvin Delta Music
Unit 4, Kirky Arcade, Cowgate, Glasgow, G66 1HW
tel: 0141 578 0213
email: info@kelvindeltamusic.com
web: www.kelvindeltamusic.com
part exchange: Yes
info: Large selection of guitars, amplifiers and effects
pedals.

Live Music
12 Leven Street, Edinburgh, Midlothian, EH3 9LG
tel: 0131 229 2829
part exchange: Yes
info: Guitar specialists also stocking second hand
woodwind instruments. Repairs available. Buy and part exchange. Band
flyer space in-store.

Malcolm Smith Pianos Ltd.
35 Stenhouse Road, Edinburgh, EH11 3LJ
tel: 0800 435 653
web: www.mspianos.co.uk
part exchange: No
info: Piano tuning, repairs and sales. Call for
appointment.

McCormack's Music Ltd.
29-33 Bath Street, Glasgow, Lanarkshire, G2 1HT
tel: 0141 332 6644
email: info@mccormacks-music.com
web: www.mccormacks-music.com
part exchange: No
info: Sells a wide range of musical instruments and also
offers repairs. In-store notice board for band flyers and ads.

McNeil Music
7 Barclay Terrace, Edinburgh, Midlothian, EH10 4HP
tel: 0131 228 3666
email: sales@music-first.com
web: www.music-first.com
part exchange: Yes
info: Sheet music specialist.

Merchant City Music Ltd.
7 Garth Street, Glasgow, Lanarkshire, G1 1UT
tel: 0141 552 6290
email: sales@merchantcitymusic.co.uk
web: www.guitarstrings.co.uk
part exchange: Yes
info: Guitar and amplifier specialists. Selling cheapest
guitar strings in the UK. Mail order available online. Repairs in-store.

Mev Taylor's Music Shop
1 Grassmarket, Edinburgh, Midlothian, EH1 2HY
tel: 0131 229 7454
email: mevtaylors@ukonline.co.uk
web: www.mevtaylors.co.uk
part exchange: No
info: Established in 1946 selling a wide range of string,
woodwind and brass instruments. Full repair service and tuition
available. Rent to buy scheme.

The Music Centre
8 Wellmeadow Street, Paisley, PA1 2EF
tel: 0141 848 1033
email: paisleymusic@aol.com
web: www.paisleymusic.com
part exchange: No
info: Sell guitars, keyboards and amplifiers. Also sell
vouchers for tuition from local tutors. Large notice board in-store.

MUSIC SERVICES/RETAIL

Music for Granted
55 Stockiemuir Avenue, Bearsden, Glasgow, G61 3JJ
tel:	0141 942 6050
web:	www.musicforgranted.co.uk
part exchange:	Yes
info:	Specialist sheet music company. Music available

to buy in-store or online. Also stock music accessories. Notice board in-store.

Music in Print Ltd.
29 Castle Street, Dundee, Angus, DD1 3AD
tel:	01382 228 263
email:	sales@music-first.com
web:	www.music-first.com
part exchange:	Yes
info:	Music book specialists also selling music CDs and

DVDs. Notice board in-store for local advertisements.

The Music Shop
49 Chalmers Street, Dunfermline, Fife, KY12 8AT
tel:	01383 623 693
email:	davidbernthal@musicshop.freeserve.co.uk
part exchange:	No
info:	Guitar store offering repairs, tuition, accessories

and band flyer space.

The Music Shop
27 Church Street, Inverness, IV1 1DY
tel:	01463 233 374
email:	themusicshop@lineone.net
part exchange:	No
info:	General music shop selling guitars, amps, strings,

violins, pianos, drums and more.. Repairs and notice board space.

The Music Warehouse
46-48 Vicar Street, Falkirk, FK1 1JB
tel:	01324 670 391
email:	alexjohn@musicwarehouse.freeserve.co.uk
web:	www.themusicwarehouse.net
part exchange:	No
info:	All instruments sold in-store and online with

free next day delivery. Tuition available. Fully equipped custom built rehearsal studios for hire. Notice board in-store.

Pet Sounds
42 Woodmarket, Kelso, Roxburghshire, TD5 7AX
tel:	01573 225 097
email:	petsounds1@btconnect.com
part exchange:	Yes
info:	General instruments and accessories. Tuition,

repairs and poster space available in-store.

Peter Smith & Sons
60 Backsneddon Street, Paisley, PA3 2BY
tel:	0141 887 6160
web:	www.petersmithpianos.com
part exchange:	Yes
info:	New and used pianos. Stock famous names like

Steinway and Bechstein from Germany and Chappell from the UK.

Prosound Music Ltd.
96 Holburn Street, Aberdeen, AB10 6BY
tel:	01224 211 311
fax:	01224 211 311
part exchange:	No
info:	Stock drums, cymbals, percussion instruments,

guitars, mandolins, banjos and violins .

R.A. Music
72-74 Manor Street, Falkirk, Stirlingshire, FK1 1NU
tel:	01324 633 332
email:	info@ramusic.co.uk
web:	www.ramusic.co.uk
part exchange:	Yes
info:	Long standing music store selling wide selection

of instruments books and accessories. Large stock or sheet music. Ordering service available. Tuition and repairs in-store.

Rage Muzic
37 West Port, Arbroath, DD11 1RF
tel:	01241 431 666
email:	ragemuzic@hotmail.co.uk
web:	www.ragemuzic.com
part exchange:	No
info:	Specialise in guitars and other rock instruments.

Professional guitar tuition available. Promote bands and gigs, contact for details. Notice board in-store.

Rainbow Music
35 Cowgate, Dundee, Angus, DD1 2JF
tel:	01382 201 405
part exchange:	No
info:	Huge range of instruments available. Open 6 days.

RG Hardie
Unit W7, Rosemount Workspace, 141 Charles Street, Glasgow, G21 2QA
tel:	0141 552 7811
web:	www.rghardie.com
part exchange:	Yes
info:	Makers of high class bagpipes.

RGM Music
24 Nelson Street, Kilmarnock, Ayrshire, KA1 1BA
tel:	01563 537 711
email:	admin@rgmmusic.com
web:	www.rgmmusic.co.uk
part exchange:	No
info:	Sells everything from triangles to drums. Also

stock accessories and sheet music. Offer repairs.

Rock Electronics
113 Glasgow Road, Dumbarton, Dumbartonshire, G82 1RG
tel:	01389 732 588
part exchange:	Yes
info:	Electrical company with main line in guitars,

amplifiers, PA, lighting equipment and accessories. Space in window for band flyers.

Rolston Accordians
33 Clydesdale Street, Mossend, Bellshill, Lanarkshire, ML4 2RS
tel:	01698 733 787
email:	enquiries@accordion.co.uk
web:	www.accordion.co.uk
part exchange:	Yes
info:	Selling quality accordions for over 25 years. Stock

all brands. Repairs available.

RWJ Drumstore
56 Atholl Street, Perth, Perthshire, PH1 5NL
tel:	01738 445 100
part exchange:	Yes
info:	Tayside's largest dedicated drum store. Stock Pearl,

Mapex, Tama, Gretsch, Sabian, Meinl, Ufip, Gibraltor, Vic Firth, LP, Toca, Stagg, Istanbul and Roc N Soc. Drum and bass tuition available. Hire service provided.

Scayles Music
50 St.Patrick Square, Edinburgh, Midlothian, EH8 9EZ
tel:	0131 667 8241
email:	scayles@tiscali.co.uk
part exchange:	No
info:	Sells a little of everything. Large range of electric

guitars, percussion and amplifiers. Renowned for stocking most Traditional instruments. Also stock sheet music and DVDs. Repairs for instruments and amps available. Band flyer space.

Serenade for Strings
South Teavarran, Foxhole, Kiltarlity, Beauly, Inverness, IV4 7HT
tel:	01463 741 651
email:	serenade.strings@virgin.net
web:	www.serenadeforstrings.com
part exchange:	Yes
info:	Mail order only string music specialists based in

the Highlands.

Skyline Guitars
3 Murray Street, Annan, Dumfriesshire, DG12 6EG
tel:	01461 203 766
email:	craig@weild.freeserve.co.uk
web:	www.skylineguitars.co.uk
part exchange:	No
info:	Guitar specialists priced from £20-£2000. Also

stock some woodwind instruments. Repairs and guitar tuition in-store.

Sounds Instumental
25 High Street, Musselburgh, EH21 7AD
tel:	0131 653 0651
web:	www.soundsinstrumental.co.uk
part exchange:	No
info:	Sells most musical instruments and offers repairs.

Notice board space in-store.

Southside Music
599 Cathcart Road, Glasgow, Lanarkshire, G42 8AD
tel:	0141 423 5474
part exchange:	No
info:	Music store selling keyboards, string and

woodwind instruments. Offers repairs on instruments and amplifiers. Notice board space in-store.

Spence's Music Shop
4 Buccleuch Street, Hawick, Roxburghshire, TD9 0HW
tel:	01450 372 115
part exchange:	Yes
info:	Guitars and repairs.

Squeeze Box
3 East Lane, Paisley, Renfrewshire, PA1 1QA
tel: 0141 887 6565
part exchange: No
info: Accordion sales and repairs specialist. Also stock guitars and offer tuition in most instruments. Notice board space in-store.

St. Andrew's Music Shop
151 South Street, St. Andrews, Fife, Scotland, KY16 9UN
tel: 01334 478 625
part exchange: Yes
info: Sheet music, music accessories and gifts along with a few guitars.

Steve Burnett Pianos & Violins
Edinburgh, E11
tel: 0131 228 3638
email: steve@burnettviolins.co.uk
web: www.burnettviolins.co.uk
part exchange: Yes
info: Independent piano tuner. Makers old Italian style violins, violas and cellos.

Stringers of Edinburgh Ltd.
13 York Place, Edinburgh, Midlothian, EH1 3EB
tel: 0131 557 5432
fax: 0131 557 5432
email: info@stringersmusic.com
web: www.stringersmusic.com
part exchange: Yes
info: Special interest in providing string instruments for children and students. Large studio available for bookings for professional players to test out strings and bows.

Strung Out Guitars
9 Kings Court, King Street, Glasgow, G1 5RB
tel: 0141 552 4848
email: info@strungoutguitars.com
web: www.strungoutguitars.com
part exchange: No
info: Guitar specialists. Repairs and made to order guitars. Only store in Glasgow to stock range of vintage and second hand guitars.

Top Note
123 Crown Street, Aberdeen, AB11 6HN
tel: 01224 219 259
email: music@top-note.co.uk
web: www.top-note.co.uk
part exchange: Yes
info: Have catalogue of over 20,000 items of sheet music. Also stock small range of instruments including guitar and classical instruments. Notice board space available.

Varsity Music
8a-10a Nicolson Street, Edinburgh, Midlotian, EH8 9DH
tel: 0131 557 4310
web: www.varsitymusic.co.uk
part exchange: Yes
info: Over 30 years experience selling new and used pianos. Also stock string, brass and percussion instruments.

Village Music
29 Main Street, East Kilbride, Glasgow, Lanarkshire, G74 4JU
tel: 01355 244 562
email: enquiries@villagemusic.co.uk
web: www.villagemusic.co.uk
part exchange: No
info: Supply a large selection of musical instruments including guitars, keyboards, pianos and drums. Offer free service and set up on all products.

Vintage Strings
77 Perth Road, Dundee, Angus, DD1 4HY
tel: 01382 226 415
email: warddundee@hotmail.com
part exchange: Yes
info: Specialise in acoustic stringed instruments including violins, cellos and guitars. Also stock second hand violins and pianos and musical accessories. Repairs available.

The Violin Shop
Old Town House, High Street, Falkland, Cupar, Fife, KY15 7BU
tel: 01337 858 181
part exchange: No
info: Traditional violin shop which has been running for 30 years. Sells second hand violins. Repair service available.

The Violin Shop
7-11 Blackie Street, Glasgow, G3 8TN
tel: 0141 339 8078
email: rayandbill@theviolinshop-glasgow.co.uk
web: www.theviolinshop-glasgow.co.uk
part exchange: No
info: Stringed specialists. Repairs and accessories. Notice board in-store. High quality violins and violas made at on-site workshop.

The Wind Section Ltd.
7 York Place, Edinburgh, Midlothian, EH1 3EB
tel: 0131 557 6543
email: malcolm@thewindsection.com
web: www.thewindsection.com
part exchange: No
info: Specialise in woodwind and brass instruments. Repairs on site. Notice board space in-store.

WALES

1st Call Kits & Bits
1 Birchgrove Estate, Treharris, Mid Glamorgan, CF46 5NT
tel: 07855 429 090
email: kits.n.bits@btopenworld.com
part exchange: No
info: Drums and accessories. Repairs and tuition. Notice board in-store.

Absolute Sound & Lighting Solutions
6-8 Greenfield Road, Colwyn Bay, LL29 8EL
tel: 01492 535 123
email: mail@cps-pa.fsnet.co.uk
web: www.cps-pa.co.uk
part exchange: Yes
info: PA, lighting and crew available for hire. See Equipment Hire listings for more details. Also run an agency for pub and club entertainers, including many cover acts. Also run an instrument shop. See listing in relevant section for details.

Amplified Music
Shop Unit 1, Cross Hands Square, Pontarddulais, SA14 6NT
tel: 01269 833 808
web: www.amplifiedmusic.co.uk
part exchange: No
info: General store. Guitars, keyboards and drums all in stock. Tuition available in-store in drums, guitar, keyboard and singing.

Backtrax Music
26 Church Street, Abertillery, Gwent, NP13 1DA
tel: 01495 215 377
email: backtraxmusic@aol.com
part exchange: Yes
info: General musical instrument and record shop. Notice board in-store and space for flyers. Will stock demos on a sale or return basis.

Bowen's Organ & Keyboard Studio
1 Quay Street, Haverfordwest, Dyfed, SA61 1BG
tel: 01437 764 035
part exchange: No
info: Keyboards, pianos, organs and accessories. Main dealer for Yamaha and Hammond. Can source repairs. Tuition available.

Brecon Guitars
3 Castle Street, Brecon, Powys, LD3 9DD
tel: 01874 624 292
email: breconguitar@aol.com
part exchange: No
info: Guitars, amps, pedals, accessories and effects. Notice board in-store.

Bron-yr-aur
23 Holyhead Road, Bangor, LL57 2EU
tel: 01248 355 455
email: general@bron-yr-aur.co.uk
web: www.bron-yr-aur.co.uk
part exchange: No
info: Range of instruments and amps including Folk and Ethnic instruments. Repairs on all instruments. Notice board in-store and space for posters and flyers.

Cardiff Guitars
Unit 2, St. Clair Court 3-11, West Bute Street, Cardiff Bay, CF10 5EN
tel: 02920 461 234/07817 023 214
email: enquiries@cardiffguitars.co.uk
web: www.cardiffguitars.co.uk
part exchange: No
info: Electric, Acoustic and bass guitars. Bass and guitar amplification. Effects and accessories. Second hand department. Repairs and servicing.

Cardiff Violins
15-23 The Balcony Castle Arcade, Cardiff, CF10 1BY
tel: 02920 227 761
email: enquiries@cardiffviolins.co.uk
web: www.cardiffviolins.co.uk
part exchange: No
info: Violins and accessories. Repairs. Notice board in-store.

Cardigan Music
51 St. Mary's Street, Cardigan, Dyfed, SA43 1HA
tel: 01239 614 220
part exchange: No
info: General music instrument shop. Repairs available on all instruments. Tuition for most. Notice board in-store and space for posters and flyers. See Record Shop listings for more details.

Cerdd Gifts
26 Nine Mile Point Road, Cross Keys, Newport, NP11 7QP
tel: 01495 273 100
email: chris@cerddgifts.co.uk
web: www.cerddgifts.com
part exchange: Yes
info: Musical accessories and music related gifts including ties, pins, cards and posters.

Cerdd Ystwyth Music
7 Upper Portland Street, Aberystwyth, SY23 2DT
tel: 01970 623 382
fax: 01970 637 563
email: sales@cerddystwyth.co.uk
web: www.cerddystwyth.co.uk
part exchange: Yes
info: Range of instruments, sheet music, CDs and cassettes. Online Welsh sheet music database and shop at the website above.

Cranes Musical Instruments
5a High Street, Cardiff, CF10 1AW
tel: 02920 398 215
email: mikep@cranes.co.uk
web: www.cranes.co.uk
part exchange: No
info: General music shop with wide range of instruments including a large selection of guitars and amps. Sheet music. Noticeboard in-store. Guitar repairs. Cranes Musical Instruments was established in 1851.

Creative Electronics
21 Bridgend Square, Haverfordwest, Dyfed, SA61 2ND
tel: 01437 767 820
part exchange: No
info: Guitars, amps, PA equipment and accessories including a range of Boss FX pedals. Noticeboard in-store.

Crescendo Music
52 Pontypridd Road, Porth, Mid Glamorgan, CF39 9PG
tel: 01443 686 881
email: info@crescendomusic.com
web: www.crescendomusic.com
part exchange: Yes
info: Range of instruments, accessories and sheet music. Tuition available in guitar, bass, piano and woodwind. Musicians' message board. Will stock unsigned bands demos. Speak to Wayne in-store for more details.

Dale's Music Store
High Street, Tenby, SA70 7HD
tel: 01834 842 285
part exchange: Yes
info: Stock a range of guitars, harmonicas, Jewish harps and accessories. Other instruments can be ordered in upon request. Dale Music Store is also a record shop. See relevant section for more details.

Dragon Music Wales
66 Bethcar Street, Ebbw Vales, Gwent, NP23 6HG
tel: 01495 302 967
part exchange: No
info: General music instrument retail. Backing tracks for solo artists. Repairs on any instrument. Tuition in guitar and bass. Notice board in-store. Space for posters and flyers.

Drumbeat Ltd.
Portland Street, Pill, Newport, NP20 2BW
tel: 01633 221 381/07747 671 769
fax: 01633 253 429
web: www.drumbeatshop.com
part exchange: No
info: Drums and accessories. Repair and tuition available. Notice board in-store and space for posters and flyers. 3 rehearsal rooms available for hire. See relevant section for details.

Falcon Music
8 Park Street, Llanelli, Dyfed, SA15 3YE
tel: 01554 773 072
email: falconmusic@yahoo.co.uk
part exchange: Yes
info: General musical instrument retail. Repairs on guitars, keyboards and amps. Guitar and keyboard school. Notice board in-store and space for posters and flyers.

G.M. Music (Cardiff)
2 Wharton Street, Cardiff, CF10 1AG
tel: 02920 231 606
email: enquiry@gmmusic.co.uk
web: www.gmmusic.co.uk
part exchange: No
info: Huge selection of guitars. Also stock a wealth of orchestral and Folk instruments, accessories and books. See also listing for shop based in Newport.

G.M. Music (Newport)
14 Upper Dock Street, Newport, NP20 1DF
tel: 01633 840 606
email: enquiry@gmmusic.co.uk
web: www.gmmusic.co.uk
part exchange: No
info: General music shop stocking range of brass, woodwind and string instruments along with amplifiers, digital pianos and keyboards. Run an instrument rental scheme. See also listing for shop based in Cardiff.

Gamlin's Music Centre (Cardiff)
56 St. Mary Street, Cardiff, CF1 1FE
tel: 02920 220 828
email: info@gamlinsmusic.co.uk
web: www.gamlinsmusic.co.uk
part exchange: No
info: Guitars, keyboards and percussion instruments. Musicians' wanted noticeboard. Part exchange available on guitars and pianos only. See also listing for shop located in Newport.

Gamlin's Music Centre (Newport)
107 Commercial Street, Newport, NP20 1LU
tel: 01633 263 867
email: info@gamlinsmusic.co.uk
web: www.gamlinsmusic.co.uk
part exchange: Yes
info: Large selection of guitars and pianos. Offer tuition in keyboard and piano. Notice board space in-store. See also entry for store based in Cardiff.

Group-Eze
64 Port Talbot Road, Port Talbot, SA13 1LA
tel: 01639 894 464
part exchange: No
info: General instrument store. Tuition available for drums, piano, flute, clarinet, saxophone and guitar. Notice board in-store and space for posters and flyers.

Guitar-a-Rama
8 Yorke Street, Wrexham, Clwyd, LL13 8LW
tel: 01978 353 512
contact: Rick
part exchange: No
info: Specialise in guitars, basses and amps. Repairs, tuition and favourable part-exchange deals. Noticeboard in-store.

Hannah's Music (Abergavenny)
3 Brecon Road, Abergavenny, Monmouthshire, NP7 5UH
tel: 01873 857 721
email: sales@hannahsmusic.co.uk
web: www.hannahsmusic.co.uk
part exchange: Yes
info: Wide selection of instruments. Repair service available. Tuition offered at other branch of Hannah's Music based in Gwent. See listing for further details. For information about rehearsal facilities also available, see listing in relevant section.

Hannah's Music (Gwent)
6 Moor Street, Chepstow, Gwent, NP16 5DE
tel: 01291 627 122
email: sales@hannahsmusic.co.uk
web: www.hannahsmusic.co.uk
part exchange: No
info: General instrument retail. Repairs available on all instruments. Tuition in guitar, drums, saxophone, piano, keyboard, flute and clarinet available at Gwent branch. See also listing for store located in Abergavenny. For details of rehearsal facilities, see the relevant section.

Hardman Music
77 Talbot Road, Talbot Green, Pontycleon, CF72 8AE
tel: 01443 238 866
email: robert-hardman@btconnect.com
web: www.hardmanmusic.co.uk
part exchange: No
info: General music shop selling brass through to accessories. Guitar lessons on site. Repairs and notice board space.

Haydn James Music
3 Wesley Buildings, Newport Road, Caldicot, Gwent, NP26 4LY
tel: 01291 423 809
email: haydnmusic@btconnect.com
part exchange: No
info: General music shop. All stock discounted. Repairs available on most instruments. Tuition in a wide range of instruments. Notice board in-store and space for posters and flyers.

John Carpenter Musical Instruments
Llan Llyan, Foelgastell, Llanelli, Dyfed, SA14 7HA
tel: 01269 831 094
email: sales@cjcantiques.co.uk
web: www.cjcantiques.co.uk
part exchange: No
info: Violin, strings and Traditional instrument specialists. Used and vintage instruments. Repairs. Warehouse open to the public by appointment. Call or email to arrange a time.

John William's Music
1 Waterloo Street, Bangor, LL57 1DS
tel: 01248 355 622
part exchange: No
info: General music instrument store. Repairs available on guitars, keyboards, brass and woodwind. Notice board in-store. Space for posters and flyers.

JPL Sound & Communication
267 Holton Road, Barry, South Glamorgan, CF63 4HT
tel: 01446 722 711
email: info@jpl-sound.com
web: www.jpl-sound.com
part exchange: No
info: General music shop with large range of spares. Repairs on most equipment and guitar set-up. Can refer customers to relevant tutors if required. Notice board in-store. Also offer PA hire. See relevant section for details.

Laker Audio Systems
84 New Road, Skewen, Neath, SA10 6HE
tel: 01792 813 990
part exchange: No
info: Guitars, accessories, pedals, effects and PA systems. Electrical repairs. Notice board in-store. Space for posters and flyers.

The Leading Note
49 Eversley Road, Sketty, Swansea, West Glamorgan, SA2 9DE
tel: 01792 207 018
email: rj1lewis@aol.com
part exchange: No
info: Stock mainly stringed and woodwind instruments. No electronic instruments. Large range of sheet music and accessories. Repairs available on most instruments (except electronic). Music theory tuition. Notice board in-store. Space for posters and flyers. The Leading Note is closed on Sundays and Mondays.

Llandudno Music
6a Vaughn Street, Llandudno, Gwynedd, LL30 1AB
tel: 01492 876 649
email: sales@tk-music.co.uk
web: www.tkmusic.co.uk
part exchange: No
info: General music shop stocking a good range of Folk and Acoustic instruments. Repairs for all instruments. Noticeboard in-store. See also sister shop, TK Music.

Merthyr Music Centre
98 High Street, Merthyr Tydfil, Mid Glamorgan, CF47 8UH
tel: 01685 374 863
email: merthyrsound@aol.com
part exchange: No
info: Stock most instruments, except woodwind and brass. Repairs and in-store guitar tuition offered. Notice board.

Michael Morgan Musical Instruments
Trisant, Heol Las, Llantrisant, Glamorgan, CF72 8EG
tel: 01443 226 889
email: mikemorgan3@btopenworld.com
part exchange: Yes
info: Self-employed maker and restorer of violins and acoustic guitars. Works from full restoration workshop at home. Also has some recording facilities. Contact for orders or more details.

Mid Wales Music Centre
Linoworks Pool Road, Newtown, Powys, SY16 3AG
tel: 01686 622 161
email: phil.barnwell@midwalesmusic.co.uk
web: www.midwalesmusic.co.uk
part exchange: No
info: Guitars, keyboards, drums, sheet music, PA equipment. Repairs available. Drum, violin and guitar lessons in-store.

Mr Tuba
114 Springvale Industrial Estate, Cwmbran, Gwent, NP44 5BG
tel: 01633 871 506
email: mark@mrtuba.com
web: www.mrtuba.com
part exchange: No
info: Brass specialists selling used tubas. Also offer tuba repairs and instrument rental. Noticeboard in-store. See also listings for related stores, South Wales band Supplies and South Wales Piano Warehouse.

MSL Music
6 Church Road, Ton Pentre, Rhondda, CF40 1RY
tel: 01443 422 800
email: cerilewis@mslmusic.fsnet.co.uk
web: www.100megsfree2.com/msl
part exchange: Yes
info: General music instrument retail. Brass repairs. Tuition in guitar and piano. MSL Music is one the UK's leading brass band suppliers.

The Music Centre
4 Meyrick Street, Pembroke Dock, Dyfed, SA72 6UT
tel: 01646 682 811
part exchange: Yes
info: Range of instruments, printed music and accessories. Piano school. Notice board in-store and space for posters and flyers.

Music Direct
33 Tydfil Place, Roath Park, Cardiff, CF23 5HP
tel: 02920 496 080
part exchange: Yes
info: Wide range of printed music from all genres. Customer ordering service available.

Music Makers
12 Penrhyn Road, Colwyn Bay, Clwyd, LL29 8LG
tel: 01492 534 834
part exchange: Yes
info: Pianos, organs, keyboards, guitars, brass and strings. Tuition available, as well as tuning and repair services.

The Music Place
30 Brook Street, Wrexham, Clwyd, LL13 7LL
tel: 01978 265 308
part exchange: No
info: General music shop. Repairs on all instruments. Tuition for classical guitar and keyboard. Can refer customers to tutors for other instruments. Notice board in-store and space for flyers and posters.

The Music Station (Bridgend)
20a Dunraven Place, Bridgend, Mid Glamorgan, CF31 1JD
tel: 01656 767 801
email: musicstation@btconnect.com
web: www.music-station.com
part exchange: No
info: Range of instruments including guitars, drums, electric keyboards, amps and accessories. Notice board in-store. Limited space for posters and flyers. Also have a store in Swansea, see listing for further details.

The Music Station (Swansea)
Unit 1a, Lakeside Technology Park, Swansea Enterprise Park, Swansea, SA7 9FF
tel: 01792 775 751
web: www.music-station.co.uk
part exchange: No
info: Range of electronic instruments. Repairs available. Tuition in keyboard, piano and organ. Noticeboard in-store and space for posters and flyers. See also listing for branch located in Bridgend.

The Music Studio
2 Jackson Lane, Carmarthen, Dyfed, SA31 1QD
tel: 01267 223 108
email: fleecejames@hotmail.com
part exchange: No
info: All types of instruments including guitar, drum, brass, woodwind, pianos and keyboards. Repairs available. Ask in-store about tuition as all staff are teachers. Noticeboard space.

Musicland
148-154 North Road, Cardiff, CF14 3BH
tel: 02920 621 715
fax: 02920 621 285
email: enquiries@musicland-cardiff.co.uk
web: www.musicland-cardiff.co.uk
part exchange: No
info: Range of instruments, recording equipment, PAs and lighting. Repairs on all instruments. Notice board in-store.

Must Have Music
Unit 11-12, Emilys Indoor Shops, 152-154 High Street, Blackwood, Gwent, NP12 1AZ
tel: 01495 220 047
email: musthavemusicinfo@btopenworld.com
web: www.must-have-music.com
part exchange: No
info: General music shop. Repairs and notice board space in-store. Can refer customers to relevant tutors. Notice board in-store and space for flyers.

Neath Music
37 Water Street, Neath, West Glamorgan, SA11 3ET
tel: 01639 631 337
email: mail@neathmusic.co.uk
web: www.neathmusic.co.uk
part exchange: No
info: Stock all types of instruments with emphasis on sound recording equipment. Repairs and notice board space in-store. Staff are willing to help show customers how to properly use equipment.

Noble's Music
2 Old Church Road, Whitchurch, Cardiff, CF14 1AE
tel: 02920 613 867
email: noblesmusic@hotmail.com
web: www.noblesmusic.co.uk
part exchange: No
info: Stock a range of guitars, amps, PAs, drum kits, effects, Folk instruments, microphones, keyboards and lighting equipment. Repairs on guitars, amps, PA, lighting, keyboards and related items. Noticeboard in-store.

Pencerdd
4 Station Approach, Penarth, Vale Of Glamorgan, CF64 3EE
tel: 02920 709 982
fax: 02920 190 210
email: enquiries@pencerdd.com
web: www.pencerdd.com
part exchange: Yes
info: Sell a range of stringed instruments, specialising in harps. Accessories for all instruments. Large range of sheet music including Grade exam pieces. If you are travelling long distances to view harps it is recommended to call the shop in advance.

Percussion House
85 Whitchurch Road, Cardiff, CF14 3JP
tel: 02920 614 999
email: info@percussionhouse.com
web: www.percussionhouse.com
part exchange: No
info: Percussion specialists. Hire, repair and pre-owned instruments. Drum tuition for beginners to professionals. Range of accessories. Noticeboard in-store.

Pete's Music Trading Post
8 Quay Street, Haverfordwest, Dyfed, SA61 1BG
tel: 01437 760 725
part exchange: Yes
info: Guitars, ethnic instruments, drums, didgeridoos, violins and creative electronics.

Ray's Underground Music
4 York Street, Wrexham, Clwyd, LL13 8LW
tel: 01978 362 049
email: ray@rumguitars.co.uk
web: www.rumguitars.co.uk
contact: Ray Roberts
part exchange: No
info: Guitar specialists. PAs and amps, brass, percussion and woodwind. Expert advice. Repairs available. Space for gig flyers, notices and posters.

Rhyl Sound Centre
55 Wellington Road, Rhyl, LL18 1BD
tel: 01745 351 436
part exchange: Yes
info: Guitars, brass, woodwind, keyboards, drums, amps, PA equipment and lighting. Also stock music videos and DVDs. Repairs and noticeboard space available on request.

Rob Burnett Brass & Wind
161 Crwys Road, Cathays, CF24 4NH
tel: 02920 373 967
email: rob.burnett1@virgin.net
part exchange: No
info: Brass and woodwind specialists. Accessories and repairs. Notice board in-store.

Rowland's Music
31 St. Helen's Road, Swansea, SA1 4AP
tel: 01792 600 269/01792 522 020
email: info@rowlandsmusic.co.uk
web: www.rowlandsmusic.co.uk
part exchange: No
info: Electric, Acoustic and bass guitars. effects, pedals, accessories and recording equipment. Large selection of drums. Offer warranty repairs. Notice board in-store and space for gig posters. PA hire available. See relevant section for details.

Rowland's Music & Book Store
8-10 High Street Arcade, Cardiff, CF24 4NH
tel: 02920 221 199
part exchange: Yes
info: Sheet music and music related book titles. Share premises with Telynau Vining, a specialist harp retailer. Notice board in-store and space for poster and flyers.

Salvi Harps Ltd.
8 Cardiff Road, Taffs Well, Cardiff, CF15 7RE
tel: 02920 409 203
email: cardiff@salviharps.com
web: www.salviharps.com
part exchange: No
info: Harps and accessories. Repairs and tuition.

Sam's Guitars
141 High Street, Bangor, LL57 1NR
tel: 01248 372 525
email: sam@samsguitars.com
web: www.samsguitars.com
part exchange: No
info: Electric, Acoustic and bass guitars. Amplification, PA systems, percussion instruments, effects and accessories. Second hand stock available. Also provide repair service. Noticeboard in-store.

Soundwave Music Centre
Unit 46, Court Road Industrial Estate, Cwmbran, NP44 3AS
tel: 01633 482 501
part exchange: Yes
info: General music instrument retail. Repairs to guitars and amps. Notice board in-store.

South Wales Band Supplies
114 Springvale Industrial Estate, Cwmbran, NP44 5BG
tel: 01633 871 506
email: mark@mrtuba.com
web: www.mrtuba.com
part exchange: No
info: Brass and woodwind suppliers. Repair and tuition available. Notice board in-store. See also listings for related stores, South Wales Piano Warehouse and Mr Tuba.

South Wales Music Exchange
33-35 Broadway, Cardiff, CF24 1QE
tel: 02920 463 331
part exchange: No
info: Guitar and amp specialist. Range of vintage guitars always in stock. Repairs and tuition available. Notice board in-store. Space for posters and flyers.

South Wales Piano Warehouse
114 Springvale Industrial Estate, Cwmbran, NP44 5BG
tel: 01633 871 506
email: mark@mrtuba.com
web: www.mrtuba.com
part exchange: No
info: Piano sales, repairs, removals, tuning and restoration. Can refer customers to recommended tutors. Second hand and new pianos in stock. Removal and delivery nationwide. See also listings for related store, South Wales Band Supplies and Mr Tuba.

Speed Music (Cardiff)
7 Quay Street, Cardiff, CF10 1DZ
tel: 02920 342 211
email: cardiff@speedmusic.co.uk
web: www.speedmusic.co.uk
part exchange: No
info: Guitars, amps, effects, drums, keyboards, PAs and mics. Instrument and electrical repairs. Noticeboard in-store and space for posters and flyers. Can refer customers to suitable tutors. Instruments can also be purchased online at the website above. See also listings for branches in Newport and Swansea.

Speed Music (Newport)
177 Upper Dock Street, Newport, Gwent, NP20 1DY
tel:	01633 220 390
fax:	01633 266 636
email:	newport@speedmusic.co.uk
web:	www.speedmusic.co.uk
part exchange:	No
info:	Guitars, amps, effects, drums, keyboards, PAs

and mics. Instrument and electrical repairs. Notice board in-store and space for posters and flyers. Can refer customers to suitable tutors. Instruments can also be purchased online at the website above. See also listings for branches in Cardiff and Swansea.

Speed Music (Swansea)
391 The Kingsway, Swansea, SA1 5LQ
tel:	01792 455 456
fax:	01792 455 457
email:	swansea@speedmusic.co.uk
web:	www.speedmusic.co.uk
part exchange:	No
info:	Guitars, amps, effects, drums, keyboards, PAs

and mics. Instrument and electrical repairs. Notice board in-store and space for posters and flyers. Can refer customers to suitable tutors. Instruments can also be purchased online at the website above. See also listings for branches in Cardiff and Newport.

Spider Music Ltd.
109 High Street, Gorseinon, Swansea, SA4 4BP
tel:	01792 892 005
email:	sales@spidermusic.co.uk
web:	www.spidermusic.co.uk
part exchange:	No
info:	Guitar, bass, drums, amps and accessories. Guitar

repairs. Tuition in bass, guitar, drums and voice. Notice board in-store. The Spider Music website features a gig guide and local scene messageboard.

Swale's Music Centre
2-6 High Street, Haverfordwest, Pembrokeshire, SA61 2DJ
tel:	01437 762 059
email:	via website
web:	www.swalesmusic.co.uk
part exchange:	Yes
info:	Folk and Ethnic instruments, guitars and

percussion. Accessories for all instruments. Large range of printed music including a vast catalogue of music for choirs. Mail order available on selected products. Noticeboard in-store.

Telynau Vining
8-10 High Street Arcade, Cardiff, CF10 1BB
tel:	02920 221 199
fax:	02920 226 935
email:	telynauviningharps@boltblue.com
part exchange:	No
info:	Specialist harp retailers. Introductory lessons

available for customers new to the instrument. Repair service. Notice board in-store. Space for posters and flyers. Share premises with Rowlands Music & Book Store.

TK Music
121 Wellington Road, Rhyl, LL18 1LE
tel:	01745 330 220
email:	sales@tk-music.co.uk
web:	www.tkmusic.co.uk
part exchange:	No
info:	General music shop. Main dealers for all major

products. Repairs on all instruments. Noticeboard in-store. See also sister shop, Llandudno Music.

Trevada Music
Shoppers World, 18 Wind Street, Ammanford, Carmarthenshire, SA18 3DN
tel:	01269 596 607
fax:	01269 596 608
email:	via website
web:	www.trevadamusic.co.uk
part exchange:	Yes
info:	Range of brass, strings, percussion and woodwind

instruments, as well as pianos and keyboards. CDs, sheet music and accessories. Trial hire scheme available on selected instruments. Tuition and practice rooms. Shop online at the website above. Also see entry in relevant section for branch located in Camborne, Cornwall

MUSIC SERVICES/RETAIL

3.6 INSURANCE SERVICES

Albemarle Insurance Brokers
10b Printing House Yard, London, E2 7PR
tel: 020 7613 5919
email: ruth@albemarleinsurance.com
web: www.albmarleinsurance.com
contact: Ruth Sandler
info: Insurance brokers for the music industry since 1975, offering a whole range of bespoke policies. Albemarle actively encourage new bands, design insurance packages to suit your specific needs. Bolton office details: 7 Hodgkinson Farm, Boot Lane, Heaton, Bolton, BL1 5ST (Tel. 01204 840 444).

Allianz Cornhill Musical Insurance
6 Vale Avenue, Tunbridge Wells, Kent, TN1 1EH
tel: 0870 2400 303
email: via website
web: www.allianzcornhill.co.uk
info: Musical instrument insurance. Offer 2 plans - 'ClassicPlay' for stringed, woodwind, brass, orchestral percussion and Acoustic instruments, and 'PowerPlay' for electronic and digital instruments and equipment including drum kits and electric guitars.

Arthur Doodson (Brokers) Ltd.
219-225 Slade Lane, Levenshulme, Manchester, M19 2EX
tel: 0161 225 9060
fax: 0161 224 6150
email: info@arthurdoodson.co.uk
web: www.arthurdoodson.co.uk
contact: Richard Doodson
info: Over 40 years experience in the entertainment industry. Cover available includes show and event cancellation, public liability, equipment (including worldwide), travel, personal accident and vehicle. Proposal forms available to download from the website above. Call and speak to Richard Doodson or David Leech for more details.

Baxters Insurance
263 Cranbrook Road, Ilford, Essex, IG1 4TG
tel: 020 8554 5500
email: insurance@wbbaxter.co.uk
web: www.wbbaxter.co.uk
contact: Rita Aggarwal
info: Public liability, vehicle and equipment insurance.

Brass Band Insurance Services
312 High Street, Harlington, Hayes, Middlesex, UB3 5BT
tel: 020 8759 0825
email: brassband@bryanjames.co.uk
web: www.bryanjames.co.uk
contact: Janet Beeston
info: Offers policies that cover all types of musical instruments, whether they are owned by an individual or a band.

E&L Insurance Co. Ltd.
Thorpe Underwood, York, YO26 9SZ
tel: 0870 402 2800
email: info@eandl.co.uk
web: www.eandl.co.uk
contact: Tim O'mara
info: Offer insurance for instruments and equipment for both unsigned and professional musicians, as well as DJs. Covers most musical instruments for the UK, Europe and worldwide. Additional options such as unattended vehicle cover available.

Event Insurance Services Ltd.
Event House, 20a Headlands Business Park, Ringwood, Hampshire, BH24 3PB
tel: 01425 470 360
fax: 01425 474 905
email: info@events-insurance.co.uk
web: www.events-insurance.co.uk
contact: Justine Davies
info: Professional, original approach to the entire event spectrum. Offer public liability and cancellation cover, details of policies avaliable. For full details visit the website.

GM Imber Ltd.
Freepost SE5052, Grange House, Grange Walk, London, SE1 3DT
tel: 020 7231 5005
fax: 020 7252 3656
contact: Stuart Imber
info: All risk cover for equipment. Public liability. Record collections can be insured but it is advised to have contents valued by professionals. Motor insurance for musicians is not available.

HCF Partnership
Star House, 6 Garland Road, Stanmore, Middlesex, HA7 1NR
tel: 020 8731 5155
fax: 020 8731 5177
email: steve@hcf.co.uk
contact: Sheila Byers
info: Musical instrument insurance covering accidental loss or damage.

Heath Lambert Group - Entertainment Division
133 Houndsditch, London, EC3A 7AH
tel: 020 7234 4351
email: dlockwood@heathlambert.com
web: www.heathlambert.com
contact: Dave Lockwood
info: Media and TV insurance specialist.

Musicguard Insurance
Pavillion House, 15 Mercia Business Village, Westwood Business Park, Coventry, CV4 8HX
tel: 02476 851 000
fax: 02476 851 080
email: admin@musicguard.co.uk
web: www.musicguard.co.uk
info: All risk equipment cover (instruments, recording, stage lighting and sound equipment), public liability, personal accident cover, home insurance and vehicle cover including unattended vehicles. Any member of staff can provide a quote over the phone, or obtain your own quotes online.

Musicians Insurance Services
PO Box 12122, Cannon Gate House, Firs Parade, Matlock, Derbyshire, TE4 3RU
tel: 01629 760 101
fax: 0870 365 7529
email: enquiries@musiciansinsurance.co.uk
web: www.musiciansinsurance.co.uk
contact: Mark Prendergast
info: All equipment and liability cover. Travel and commercial premises cover, including recording studios and rehearsal rooms.

Musicians' Union
National Office, 60-62 Clapham Road, London, SW9 0JJ
tel: 020 7582 5566
fax: 020 7582 9805
email: webmaster@musiciansunion.org.uk
web: www.musiciansunion.org.uk
info: Members of Musicians Union are entitled to public liability insurance for working as a musician or teaching music. Cover is up to £10 million. Policies are administered through AON Ltd. and Hencilla Canworth Ltd. Check the website for further details of membership and regional office information.

Musicover Golden Valley Insurance
The Olde Shoppe, Ewyas Harold, Pontrilas, Herefordshire, HR2 0ES
tel: 01981 240 536
fax: 01981 240 451
email: gvinsurance@aol.com
web: www.goldenvalleyinsurance.co.uk
contact: Sharron L. O'Gorman
info: Equipment cover for all musical instruments, sound and audio equipment, computers and associated items, as well as legal expenses and personal accident cover. Eligible for no claims bonus after 1 year.

Robertson Taylor Insurance Brokers
33 Harbour Exchange Square, London, E14 9GG
tel: 020 7510 1234
fax: 020 7510 1134
email: enquiries@rtib.co.uk
web: www.robertson-taylor.co.uk
info: Specialist cover for musicians. Public liability policies payable per show - deposit required. Full risk equipment cover available, travel insurance, tour cash insurance and other insurances specific to the live entertainment and media industry.

Rollinson Smith & Co. Ltd.
2 Haygate Road, Wellington, Telford, Shropshire, TF1 1SG
tel: 01952 641 164
fax: 01952 641 600
email: sales@rollinsonsmith.co.uk
web: www.rollinsonsmith.co.uk
contact: Andy/Dave
info: Public liability, all risk equipment cover, vehicle and home cover. Insurance for recording studios.

Sound Insurance
6 Cherry Orchard Road, Croydon, CR9 5BB
tel: 020 8686 5050
fax: 020 8686 5559
email: mark.hopkinson@hencilla.co.uk
web: www.hencilla.co.uk
contact: Mark Hopkinson
info: All risk musical equipment policy, public and employers liability and entertainers' travel insurance.

Towergate Stafford Knight Co. Ltd.
55 Aldgate High Street, London, EC3N 1PD
tel: 020 7481 6200
fax: 020 7481 7638
email: info@towergate.co.uk
web: www.towergate.co.uk
contact: Tony Crawford
info: Recording equipment, instruments and hired items. Public liability. Cancellation insurance can be arranged on production of an itinerary.

Victor C. Knight Ltd.
Link House, 292-308 Southbury Road, Enfield, EN1 1TS
tel: 020 8351 2400
fax: 020 8351 2411
email: info@victorcknight.co.uk
web: www.victorcknight.co.uk
contact: Sandra O'Brien, Patrick McGee
info: Specialists in the field of music related insurance.
Negotiate discount rates exclusively for musicians. Policies available for
instruments and home, buildings, motor/cars and vans. Speak to
Sandra for instrument cover quotes and to Patrick for all other cover
quotes.

3.7 Lawyers/Legal Advice Foreword

Legal issues may well be the antithesis of the rock and roll ethos, lifestyle and philosophy. So you may find this subject mind-bendingly dull and it may even offend your artistic sensibilities. But legal contracts are a crucial part of the music industry and if your music and career are precious you need to protect them.

This section is designed to give you a short, sharp and relatively painless introduction to the types of legal contracts which may be put in front of you. It gives a brief introduction to contracts from the artist's point of view, bearing in mind that the more knowledge you have regarding agreements, the better position you are in to control your own music career. The information given is weighted in your favour, to ensure that you enter into any legal contract better informed than you might have been. It is not intended to be a definitive or exhaustive guide by any means, but it will increase your awareness of some of the basic issues involved.

It goes without saying that you will need good professional legal advice. This does not come cheap and as an unsigned band starting out it is unlikely that you will have this sort of cash at your disposal anyway. When looking for legal representation, you may want to contact several firms, find out their rates and get a feel for who you are dealing with and whether they understand your needs. Many of the established music law firms charge upwards of £200 per hour. Even if this is within your budget, it is no guarantee that you are getting a premium service. If you just need someone to advise you on a studio, demo or recording contract, or draft an inter-band or management contract and give you sound legal advice, it could be that a junior law person with good music industry knowledge is equally if not better qualified to do this.

Contrary to public belief, there are some creative, maverick lawyers out there who do have a more progressive and radical 'DIY' approach to the music business, without compromising on professionalism or quality of advice. In short, it is sometimes unnecessary to go to huge expense and you don't always get what you pay for. That said however, you do need someone who knows what they are doing and you should always go to someone who is legally qualified and specialises in music law. Good lawyers can open doors for you and you should utilise their contacts and experience to your best advantage.

> Contrary to public belief, there are some creative, maverick lawyers out there who do have a more progressive and radical 'DIY' approach to the music business.

Studio Deals

Depending on what stage you are at, one of the first types of agreements you may come across could be a studio deal. This works in the following way; if you don't have any money to make a demo, a studio may offer you time when it is not being hired out commercially. They may offer this to you cheaply or even free of charge, but the hidden catch is that you may be under onerous obligations when you get your first record deal. One of the conditions could be that you promise to sign away some of your royalties or that you will guarantee to use their facilities when you make your first album. If you are later subsequently signed to a record label, they may not like the fact that you have entered into one of these agreements, as they will want to exercise control over which studios and producers are used. So you need to make sure that the studio is not asking for too much or taking advantage. You may think that it is a good way to get into the studio, however you need to be aware of what the trade off is and whether you will forego too many of your rights in the future. Deals like this may seem like a good initially, but you may regret it later on.

The Demo Deal

In the event that you have A&R people showing an interest in you, a record company or publishing company may offer to pay for studio time to enable you to record material so that they can make a better decision about you. The advantage of this is that you will be given time in a professional recording studio. However you should be cautious that you do not sign away copyright ownership in your material. The company will want this, and here lies the tension. You should always seek legal advice before you give away any rights in a song. The company will however own the 'master' recording and you should ensure that they cannot do anything with this without your prior approval. They will also want you to remain 'exclusive' to them for a certain period of time. That means you cannot negotiate with another record company until they make a decision about whether or not to sign you. This period of 'exclusivity' to them should not be too long as it may prevent you from negotiating with other labels who are interested and you may miss your window of opportunity. You should also make sure that you are legally allowed to play the master to other companies in the event that the company do not offer you a deal.

Once you are at the stage that you have record company interest, you may be considering signing a deal. If you are dealing with a reputable label, most record companies have a standard form of contract. However, if the company really wants you, you have the added advantage of bargaining power. This opens up room for negotiating a better deal for you as some concessions could be made in your favour. Contracts can be long and unwieldy, encompassing many different permutations of highly sophisticated clauses. However, the following is a brief outline of some of the terms which will be in any recording contract.

Term: This determines how long you are committed to the contract. Very often this will be for the period of one album with an option by the record company to 'pick up' the option if they want to extend the contract. You may want to ensure that you are not tied exclusively to one company for a long period of time.

Territory: This states the geographical area that the deal will cover. Very often it is 'the world'. However if you are in a strong position, you may want to negotiate the deal to exclude certain territories.

Commitment: This is what the artist must deliver to the company and will depend on what kind of recording contract you sign. If it's a Development deal this could be four or five tracks, with the option to develop it into an album. Exclusive recording contracts are usually for one album with an option to extend if the company chooses to.

Advance: Although this is the amount of money you will receive upfront, you should bear in mind that this is the money you will be living off whilst recording the first single or album. It is better to think of it in terms of a loan because it will be recouped from royalties you will earn from sales. However, it is non-returnable if the record company doesn't sell enough records. Typically, the sum advanced will include recording and video costs, although these can be dealt with separately.

Royalties: The record company pays you a royalty on every record sold. An important factor is whether royalties are calculated on the retail or the dealer price of the record. It is common these days for it to be dealer price and this may be approximately 15 - 18 %. This sounds good until you consider that out of this they will deduct for example, packaging costs. Then from what is remaining you will probably pay your manager 20%. Realistically, this could leave very little left for you. For example, if you receive an 18% royalty on the dealer price, and the CD sold for £12.99, you would receive around 78 pence per CD. This is without your managers cut. (Bear in mind that this is an approximate sum as it depends on how much you negotiate for your packaging deduction in the contract, and other terms such as 'no reduction for CD's' etc.)

Release Commitment: This is your assurance that once you have delivered the single or album and the record company have accepted it, they will release it within a certain time period. This is usually 3-6 months.

Creative Control: This is a personal choice. Some artists will value creative control above all else and are willing to concede larger advances in order to maintain it. Other artists will relinquish a certain amount of control with the view that it may allow their record company to promote them in a way which will sell more records. Either way, it is an important issue and one which you should be clear about when entering into any contract.

You must always seek independent legal advice before you sign a contract. This ensures that you have the best deal possible in terms of money, rights, protection of your work, creative control and ultimately, career possibilities. A whole book could be written on this area alone and what is outlined here is only presented as a very brief introduction.

One last word of warning, any music lawyer worth his salt will advise you to walk away from contracts which are unduly onerous on you. Don't be tempted to enter into a contract which is unfair in an attempt to 'get things moving' or through seeing it as a stepping stone to other things. Once legally bound you could find yourself tied in to an agreement for a number of years and instead of having your options broadened, your rights and opportunities could be severely restricted. Approach the industry with your eyes wide open, get the best advice you can in terms of the direction you want to go in and be as fully informed as you can be. This should ensure you do yourself justice and give yourself the best possible chance of succeeding.

The above has been kindly written by Helen Worthington.

For more information please email helen@theunsignedguide.com

Financial Glossary

Income

Income can come in various forms and needs to be recorded and monitored. You will need a suitably qualified accountant to help you with recording your income and how you are to pay yourself in the most tax efficient way. You can offset all manner of expenses against your income and you should always keep invoices for any costs your have incurred.

How you receive income can be through a separate Limitedcompany or direct to you as a partnership or as a sole trader.

Limited Company

Limited Companies are used as a vehicle to process income and expenditure. You can then draw income from the company either as straightforward salary or as a dividend to the shareholders. It is advisable that you draw up a shareholders agreement if you wish to set up a Limited Company. This agreement basically outlines what the company can and can not do.

Accounts

Each year you will need to prepare a set of accounts declaring your income and expenses. These need to be filed with the Inland Revenue and also with Companies House if you trade as a Limited Company. It is essential that you maintain accurate books and records in order to prepare a set of accounts. Again your accountant will be able to advise you on this.

VAT & Payroll

If your vatable income is over the VAT limit (for 2004/05 £58,000) then you will need to be VAT registered and complete a VAT Return every 3 months. These need to be submitted to the Customs and Excise along with any VAT due. If you wish to take money out of the company as a salary you will need to setup a payroll scheme. The company can then pay you a salary to live on, from your music income. The company deducts tax and national insurance and pays this to the Inland Revenue each month.

Tax Returns

When you do start to receive income either directly through your Limited Company or as an individual then you will almost certainly need to complete a Self Assessment Tax Return. The Tax Return year runs from 6 April to the following 5 April and must be filed by the 31 January after eachal Advisor will help you with issues that may not seem important now but as your music career develops you will be glad that you took their advice in the first instance. Your current circumstances are likely to change dramatically over the coming years and good advice will help prepare you for these changes now!

Angel & Co.
1 Green Street, Mayfair, London, W1K 6RG
tel: 020 7495 0555
fax: 020 7495 7550
email: mail@legalangel-uk.com
contact: Nigel Angel
info: Experienced law firm offering advice on all aspects of the music industry.

Bright Partnership
Queen's Chambers, 5 John Dalton Street, Manchester, M2 6FT
tel: 0161 839 4656
email: info@thebrightgroup.co.uk
web: www.thebrightgroup.co.uk
contact: Mike Senior
info: Chartered Accountants offering clear, professional advice with a particular focus on ensuring you have the most appropriate business vehicle for your affairs whilst also ensuring your tax affairs are effectively organised, leaving you to concentrate on the music.

Carnson, Morrow & Graham Solicitors
20 May Street, Belfast, County Antrim, BT1 4JD
tel: 028 9023 4606
email: mail@cmgbelfastlaw.demon.co.uk
contact: Brien Spears
info: Provide advice on all aspects of music law.

Clintons
55 Drury Lane, London, WC2B 5RZ
tel: 020 7379 6080
fax: 020 7240 9310
email: info@clintons.co.uk
web: www.clintons.co.uk
contact: Peter Button
info: Clintons have a special interest in unsigned artists. Actively encourage and support new talent. All aspects of music law covered.

Coan & Co. Solicitors
3-9 North Place, Stockport, SK1 1HH
tel: 0161 477 5990/07968 775 050
fax: 0161 476 5434
email: enquiries@coan-solicitors.co.uk
contact: Sonia Coan
info: Music industry lawyers offering sound and quality legal advice on band & management agreements, media, PR, record deals and distribution contracts.

Cobbetts
1 Cornwall Sqare, Birmingham, B4 6AJ
tel: 0121 236 4477
fax: 0121 236 4710
email: frances.anderson@cobbetts.co.uk
web: www.cobbetts.co.uk
contact: Frances Anderson
info: Cobbetts offer comprehensive and expert advice in all areas of the music business including recording, publishing, management and live performance. Clients include both established and emerging solo artists and bands, together with recording companies, publishers, studios and promoters. Frances Anderson who heads the music law team is widely recognised as a leader in this field in the Midlands. Cobbetts also have offices in Leeds (0113 246 8123) and Manchester (0161 833 3333). For full addresses of the Leeds and Manchester offices, see the Cobbetts website.

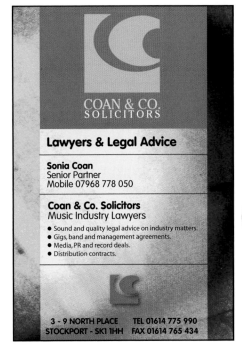

COAN & CO. SOLICITORS

Lawyers & Legal Advice

Sonia Coan
Senior Partner
Mobile 07968 778 050

Coan & Co. Solicitors
Music Industry Lawyers

- Sound and quality legal advice on industry matters.
- Gigs, band and management agreements.
- Media, PR and record deals.
- Distribution contracts.

3 - 9 NORTH PLACE TEL 01614 775 990
STOCKPORT - SK1 1HH FAX 01614 765 434

Collins Long Solicitors
24 Pepper Street, London, SE1 0EB
tel: 020 7401 9800
fax: 020 7401 9850
email: info@collinslong.com
web: www.collinslong.com
contact: Carol Rufener
info: Specialist music practice covering all aspects of the music industry. Offer a free first consultation and fixed fee billing.

Collyer Bristow Solicitors
4 Bedford Row, London, WC1R 4DF
tel: 020 7242 7363
fax: 020 7405 0555
email: nick.kamaar@collyerbristow.com
web: www.collyerbristow.com
contact: Nick Kamaar
info: The Collyer Bristow Music Media and Entertainment team have many years experience across the board in music, recording, music publishing, book publishing, artist agency and management, live performance and video, TV and film. For full details visit the website.

Davenport Lyons
1 Old Burlington Street, London, W1S 3NL
tel: 020 7468 2600
fax: 020 7437 8216
email: dl@davenportlyons.com
web: www.davenportlyons.com
contact: Rupert Sprawson
info: Dedicated music department. All contracts, inter-band agreements, tax advice, company formation and touring work. Contributed to the English Law section of "All You Need To Know About The Music Business" by Donald S. Passman. See Reading List for details.

Denton Wilde Sapte
1 Fleet Place, London, EC4M 7WF
tel: 020 7242 1212
fax: 020 7404 0087
web: www.dentonwildesapte.com
contact: Charles Law
info: Denton Wilde Sapte deal with all aspects of music law, and act for artists, labels and publishing companies. For more information see the website above. Denton Wilde Sapte have a strong relationship with the Association of Independent Musicians (AIM) and have written 'The AIM Guide To Survival And Success In The Music Business', a CD-Rom available from AIM on 020 8994 5599 .

DWF
5 Castle Street, Liverpool, L2 4XE
tel: 0151 907 3000
fax: 0151 907 3030
email: laurence.pritchard@dwf.co.uk
web: www.dwf.co.uk
contact: Laurence Pritchard
info: DWF can advise on contractual issues including management, recording contracts and copyright disputes. Offices in Manchester and Warrington.

Fullagar Brooks Solicitors
4 Cricklade Court, Cricklade Street, Swindon, SN1 3EY
tel: 01793 777 007
fax: 01793 777 006
email: enquiries@music-law.net
web: www.music-law.net
contact: David Brooks
info: English music copyright including recording and publishing contracts, performance rights, management and agency contracts, copyright infringement claims.

Gersten & Nixon
National House, 60-66 Wardour Street, London, W1F 0TA
tel: 020 7439 3961
fax: 020 7734 2479
email: law@gernix.co.uk
web: www.gernix.co.uk
info: Music and media experts. Provide advice on all aspects of music law.

Gray & Co.
Habib House, 3rd Floor, 9 Stevenson Square, Manchester, M1 1DB
tel: 0161 237 3360
fax: 0161 236 6717
email: rudi@grayand.co.uk
web: www.grayand.co.uk
contact: Rudi Kidd
info: Legal services to the entertainment industry. All aspects of the industry relevant to bands, artists, recording, publishing and management are covered.

Halliwells
St. James' Court, Briwn Street, Manchester, M2 2JF
tel: 0161 831 2932
fax: 0161 831 5005
email: jburns@halliwells.co.uk
web: www.halliwells.co.uk
contact: John Burns
info: Experienced in music law. Can advise on record, publishing, agency and commissioning contracts. Inter-band agreements. Assists with setting up of labels and publishing companies. All areas covered. Also have an office in Liverpool (0151 237 7777).

Harbottle & Lewis
Hanover House, 14 Hanover Square, London, W1S 1HP
tel: 020 7667 5000
fax: 020 7667 5100
web: www.harbottle.com
contact: Antony Bebawi
info: Well respected, experienced law firm offering advice on a range of issues in the music industry including contracts, copyright, inter-band agreements and sampling. Clients include PJ Harvey, Dave Clarke and Starsailor.

Hart Jackson Hall Smith
Watson House, Pilgrim Street, Newcastle Upon Tyne, Tyne & Wear, NE1 6QE
tel: 0191 261 5181
fax: 0191 222 1694
email: enquiries@hartjacksonhallsmith.com
web: www.hartjacksonhallsmith.com
contact: Peter Hall
info: Provide advice on any contract or agreement.

Howard Kennedy Solicitors
19 Cavendish Square, London, W1A 2AW
tel: 020 7636 1616
email: enquiries@howardkennedy.com
web: www.howardkennedy.com
info: Deal with all aspects of the media and entertainment industries and offers clients a team that is able to provide a cross-disciplinary service covering both the corporate and creative needs of the sector.

Howell-Jones Partnership
75 Surbiton Road, Leatherhead, Kingston Upon Thames, Surrey, KT1 2AF
tel: 020 8549 5186
fax: 020 8549 3383
email: kingston@hjplaw.co.uk
web: www.hjplaw.co.uk
contact: Peter Scott
info: Cover all aspects of music law. The first hour of your consultation is free.

Independent Label Scheme
c/o Dean Marsh & Co., 54 Kingsway Place, Sans Walk, London, EC1R 0LU
tel: 020 7553 4400
email: info@i-l-s-uk.com
web: www.i-l-s-uk.com
info: Industry endorsed initiative devised by music lawyers Dean Marsh & Co., with the goal of offering a range of value for money services to independent labels. Special start-up package also available to assist unsigned artists to set up their own label, by giving them legal and business advice, as well as setting up basic contracts for a fee of £500. See website or contact Marie Henley for further information.

James Joseph Music Management
85 Cicada Road, London, SW18 2PA
tel: 020 8874 8647
fax: 020 8877 1678
email: jj3@jamesjoseph.co.uk
web: www.jamesjoseph.co.uk
contact: James Joseph
info: As well as providing legal advice they also provide management services.

Lawdit Solicitors
Station House, 17 Saxon Road, Southampton, SO15 1JJ
tel: 02380 235 979
email: info@lawdit.co.uk
web: www.lawdit.co.uk
contact: Izaz Ali
info: Lawdit Solicitors is a niche intellectual property and media law Practice which has a growing international presence and reputation in this field. Lawdit offers a fast and efficient service tailored to suit the needs of its clients. Lawdit can assist you in securing the best deal when negotiating contractual terms.

Layton's Solicitors
22 St. John Street, Manchester, M3 4EB
tel: 0161 834 2100
fax: 0161 834 6862
email: music@laytons.com
web: www.laytons.com
contact: Eleanor Brody
info: Layton's aim to help those at the start of their career as well as those who are already established in the industry. Services available cover all aspects of music law including the drafting and negotiating contracts, setting up record labels, and advising on copyright issues. Please contact to receive a copy of the Sound Advice brochure.

Lea & Company
Bank Chambers, Market Place, Stockport, Cheshire, SK1 1UN
tel: 0161 480 6691
fax: 0161 480 0904
email: mail@lealaw.com
web: www.lealaw.com
contact: Claire Garside
info: Experienced law firm looking after the needs of independent record companies, artists and writers.

music law

merchandise & sponsorship

production & distribution

music art & design

recording contracts

band agreements

live performance

management

publishing

copyright

sampling

LAYTONS
SOLICITORS

For a copy of our Sound Advice brochure or to arrange an informal meeting, please contact Eleanor Brody. e: music@laytons.com t: 0161 834 2100 a: 22 St John Street, Manchester, M3 4EB

Leonard Lowy & Co.
500 Chiswick High Road, London, W4 5RG
tel: 020 89562 785
fax: 020 8956 2786
email: leonard@leonardlowy.co.uk
web: www.leonardlowy.co.uk
contact: Leonard Lowy
info: Works solely in the music industry covering all aspects from advising producers to musicians. The firm's website features free articles on different aspects of music law.

McBride & Co.
Kings Court, 36-40 Railway Street, Altrincham, Cheshire, WA14 2RD
tel: 0161 929 0229
fax: 0161 929 1982
email: jmmcbride@mcbridesolicitors.co.uk
web: www.mcbridesolicitors.co.uk
contact: Joe McBride
info: All aspects of music law covered.

Music Law Advice
14 Vane Close, Hampstead, London, NW3 5UN
tel: 07748 593 758
email: elliot@musiclawadvice.co.uk
web: www.musiclawadvice.co.uk
contact: Elliot Chalmers
info: The Music Law Advice website contains useful information about contracts, copyright and management deals. Any enquiries from record labels, artists and management companies amongst others can be directed to Elliot. Carry out a lot of contract analysis work for unsigned acts, and are also available to help with management and record company dealings.

Musicians' Union
National Office, 60-62 Clapham Road, London, SW9 0JJ
tel: 020 7582 5566
fax: 020 7582 9805
email: webmaster@musiciansunion.org.uk
web: www.musiciansunion.org.uk
info: Members of Musicians Union are entitled to public liability insurance for working as a musician or teaching music. Cover is up to £10 million. Policies are administered through AON Ltd. and Hencilla Canworth Ltd. Check the website above for details on how to join the Musicians' Union.

Pannone & Partners
123 Deansgate, Manchester, M3 2BU
tel: 0161 909 3000
email: charlotte.wigham@pannone.co.uk
web: www.pannone.com
contact: Charlotte Wigham
info: Full range of legal services including reviewing and negotiating contracts and agreements. Also provide artist management services. See listing in relevant section for further details.

Pinsent Masons
The Chancery, 58 Spring Gardens, Manchester, M2 1EW
tel: 0161 250 0100
fax: 0161 250 0142
email: via website
web: www.pinsentmasons.com
contact: Michael Robinson
info: Commercial licensing agreements, merchandising, distribution, piracy and counterfeiting. Specialise in copyright law, e-commerce and new media. Pinsent Masons also have offices in Leeds (0113 244 5000), Birmingham (0121 200 1050) and London (020 7418 7000).

Russells
Regency House, 1-4 Warwick Street, London, W1B 5LJ
tel: 020 7439 8692
fax: 020 7494 3582
email: media@russells.co.uk
info: Russells is a specialist music industry company that offers advice on all aspects of music law.

Seddons
5 Portman Square, London, W1H 6NT
tel: 020 7725 8000
fax: 020 7935 5049
email: enquiries@seddons.co.uk
web: www.seddons.co.uk
info: Seddons have extensive experience of music industry contracts and litigation.

Sheridans
14 Red Lion Square, London, WC1R 4QL
tel: 020 7775 9444
email: rroberts@sheridans.co.uk
web: www.sheridans.co.uk
contact: Russell Roberts, Tahir Basheer
info: Specialists in the music and entertainment industry for almost 50 years. Primarily act for artists and their management, but also act for independent record companies and music publishers. Currently Sheridans have a team of around 30 lawyers at the firm and offer a complete legal service including contractual work, general non-contentious issues, litigation, company commercial, employment, property, planning and probate work. They advise their clients not only on legal issues but also provide good business advice in order to help the client structure their affairs so that they develop and reach their full potential. Many of Sheridan's clients are household names, and have been with them from the start of their careers.

SJ Berwin
222 Grays Inn Road, London, WC1X 8XF
tel: 020 7533 2222
fax: 020 7533 2000
email: info@sjberwin.com
web: www.sjberwin.com
contact: Nigel Palmer
info: All aspects of music law covered.

Tax Watchdog Direct
Regent House, Heaton Lane, Stockport, SK4 1BS
tel: 0845 058 2222
web: www.taxbuddies.com
contact: Bernard Oster
info: Qualified accountants and ex-inland revenue staff offer low cost tax and accountancy package.

Turner Parkinson LLP
Hollins Chambers, 64a Bridge Street, Manchester, M3 3BA
tel: 0161 833 1212
fax: 0161 834 9098
email: andrew.booth@tp.co.uk
web: www.tp.co.uk
contact: Andrew Booth
info: Recording, publishing and management agreements. All contracts including inter-band agreements. Merchandising, piracy and counterfeiting. Experts in intellectual property rights (including band names and artwork). Relevant company commercial law.

Wake Smith
68 Clarkehouse Road, Sheffield, S10 4GF
tel: 0114 224 2028/07899 906 476
email: peter.rawlinson@wake-smith.com
web: www.wake-smith.com
contact: Peter Rawlinson

---

turnerparkinson LLP
solicitors

Creative lawyers
for **creative** people
in the North West.

Contact: **Andrew Booth,**
turner**p**arkinson LLP solicitors, Hollins Chambers,
64a Bridge Street, Manchester M3 3BA
Telephone: 0161 833 1212 Facsimile: 0161 834 9098
E-mail: andrew.booth@tp.co.uk

MUSIC SERVICES/RETAIL

3.8 MASTERING AND DUPLICATION

EAST of ENGLAND

A1 CDs
Oasis, 139 High Road, Islington, Kings Lynn, Norfolk, PE34 3BH
tel: 01553 617 546
fax: 01553 617 645
email: merv@a1cds.co.uk
web: www.a1cds.co.uk
contact: Mervyn Futter
design service: No
minimum run: 500
info: CD and DVD replication. Client normally
provides artwork, although A1 can assist with design if necessary. Full
packaging including on-body print and inlay.

A1 Duplications
East Anglia
tel: 01733 315 394
email: info@a1duplications.co.uk
web: www.a1duplications.co.uk
design service: No
minimum run: None
info: Short-run CD duplication service - up to 300
discs. Offer a finished CD package from supplied master media and
artwork files.

Amber Music Productions
PO Box 12, Cromer, Norfolk, NR27 9NL
tel: 01263 510 989
email: ambermuzik@aol.com
web: www.ambermusicproductions.co.uk
design service: Yes
info: Comprehensive mastering and post production
service.

Ashwood Studios
6a Craft Workshops, Toyle Road, Bowthorpe, Norwich, Norfolk,
NR5 9AA
tel: 01603 740 026
email: info@ashwoodstudios.com
web: www.ashwoodstudios.com
design service: Yes
info: Will duplicate onto CD, cassette and vinyl. Also
offer a vinyl cleaning and restoration service.

Chameleon Developments
Studio 2, Penn Farm, Haslingfield, Cambridge, CB3 7JZ
tel: 0845 009 3505
fax: 01223 873 050
email: office@chameleon-developments.co.uk
web: www.chameleon-developments.co.uk
contact: Tash
design service: Yes
minimum run: None
info: CD, DVD and VHS duplication. Full print,
packaging and design service. Mastering facilities available. No
minimum run.

Copytrax
4 Viking Way, Bar Hill, Cambridge, CB3 8EL
tel: 01954 782 929
fax: 01954 784 646
email: info@copytraxdirect.co.uk
web: www.copytrax.com
design service: Yes
info: Manufacturer of copying equipment, also
offering duplication services. In-house, "Fast Turnaround" CD and DVD
duplication, printing and packaging service.

See how CD's are made.
Visit our website for a virtual
tour of our pressing plant.

mediasourcing.com

INSTANT ONLINE LIVE QUOTES

Get Noticed!

Pressed CDs to the highest industry
quality at guaranteed lowest price

Why not let us design your artwork.
Our in-house design team can cater
for your every need.

web// www.mediasourcing.com
email// sales@mediasourcing.com
tel// 0845 686 0001

Digital Disc Duplication
25 Huntingfield Road, Bury St. Edmunds, Suffolk, IP33 2JA
tel: 01284 700 773
email: sales@digitaldiscduplication.com
web: www.digitaldiscduplication.com
design service: Yes
info: Audio CD, CD-ROM and DVD production.
Offer advice regarding overall product and creation of final master or
artwork.

M.J. Music Shop
139 High Road, Islington, Kings Lynn, Norfolk, PE34 3BH
tel: 01553 617 546
design service: Yes
info: CD and DVD duplicators. Regularly work with
small labels and unsigned bands.

MUSIC SERVICES/RETAIL

Meadowside Studios
Leverington Common, Wisbech, Cambridgeshire, PE13 5JH
tel: 0845 009 0154
email: enquiries@meadowsidestudios.co.uk
design service: Yes
info: CD duplication services. Meadowside also offer recording and rehearsal facilities. See listings in relevant sections for further details.

Media Direct
Audio House, Edison Road, St. Ives, Cambridgeshire, PE27 3LS
tel: 020 8446 3218
email: via website
web: www.mediadirect.co.uk
design service: Yes
minimum run: 500
info: CD-Rom, audio CD and DVD duplication. Print and packaging.

Myriad UK
330 Dereham Road, Norwich, NR2 4DL
tel: 0800 587 5967
email: sales@myriad-uk.net
web: www.myriad-uk.net
design service: No
minimum run: 100
info: CD duplication and on-body printing services. Can also supply high quality bespoke shaped CD duplication and printing services. All shaped CDs are produced using glass mastering process. Unique packaging options also available. Myriad also offer promotional merchandise. See listing in relevant section for details.

Noisebox
Windsor House, 74 Thorpe Road, Norwich, Norfolk, NR1 1BA
tel: 01603 767 726
email: info@noisebox.co.uk
web: www.noisebox.co.uk
contact: Pete Morgan
design service: Yes
minimum run: None
info: CD, DVD, cassette and vinyl duplication. All packaging print, including on-body. Scented scratch and sniff discs available. Low level mastering service available.

Sound Recording Technology Ltd.
Audio House, Edison Road Industrial Estate, St. Ives, Cambridgeshire, PE27 3LF
tel: 01480 461 880
fax : 01480 496 100
email: srt@btinternet.com
web: www.soundrecordingtechnology.co.uk
contact: S. Pownall, K. Kenney
design service: Yes
minimum run: 500
info: CD, DVD, cassette and VHS duplication. Art reproduction and design including on-body printing. Digital and analogue mastering offered.

Zoo Audio
1d Coles Road, Cambridge, Cambridgeshire, CB4 6BW
tel: 01223 519 296
email: info@zooaudio.co.uk
web: www.zooaudio.co.uk
contact: Andy Cross
design service: No
minimum run: None
info: Short run CD duplication up to 200 discs. On-body printing available. Mastering charges at studio hourly rate. Zoo Audio also provide recording facilities. See listing in relevant section for details.

GREATER LONDON

10th Planet
40 Newman Street, London, W1T 1QJ
tel: 020 7637 9500
email: studio@10thplanet.net
web: www.10pdm.com
contact: Richard
design service: Yes
info: CD-R, DVD-R and VHS duplication. DVD and CD manufacturing. DVD and CD-Rom authoring. CD mastering. Print and packaging.

24-7 DVD

24-7 DVD
1 Ravens Court Park, London, W6 0TZ
tel: 020 8748 2247
email: info@24-7dvd.co.uk
web: www.24-7dvd.co.uk
design service: Yes
minimum run: None
info: CD and DVD duplicators. Offer same day or next day service. Full print and packaging facilities.

A.L. Downloading Services
Chiswick Gate, 3rd Floor, 598-608 Chiswick High Road, Chiswick, London, W4 5RT
tel: 020 8742 0056
fax: 020 8994 4959
email: sales@aldownloading.co.uk
web: www.aldownloading.co.uk
contact: Rob Hopf
design service: Yes
minimum run: None
info: CD, DVD and video duplication. Design, printing and packaging services. Also provide DVD and multimedia authoring. Mastering facilities available.

Adaptatech
188-192 Sutton Court Road, London, W4 3HR
tel: 020 8987 6161
email: sales@adaptatech.co.uk
web: www.adaptatech.co.uk
contact: Geoff Gates
design service: Yes
minimum run: 20
info: CD, MD and DVD duplication and replication. DVD authoring. VHS and cassette duplication. On-body printing.

Alchemy Mastering
29th Floor, Centre Point, 103 New Oxford Street, London, WC1A 1DD
tel: 020 7420 8000
fax: 020 7420 8001
email: barry.grint@alchemysoho.com
web: www.alchemysoho.com
design service: Yes
info: Offers professional duplication and mastering.

Amstore CD Production Ltd.
Tower Bridge Business Complex, 100 Clements Road, London, SE16 4DG
tel: 020 7232 5820
email: james@amstore.co.uk
web: www.amstore.co.uk
contact: James Roth
design service: Yes
minimum run: None
info: CD and DVD duplication and artwork reproduction. DVD authoring. On-body printing. Audio mastering service.

Antenna Studios
Crystal Palace, London, SE19 3AN
tel: 020 8653 5200
email: info@antennastudios.co.uk
web: www.antennastudios.co.uk
design service: Yes
minimum run: 10
info: Small run CD duplication specialist. Colour printing on-body. Mastering available at £25 per hour. Also see Recording Studios section for studio details.

AudioPlexus
10 Manhattan, Fairfield Road, London, E3 2UJ
tel: 020 8980 8947
email: info@audioplexus.com
web: www.audioplexus.com
contact: Chris
design service: No
minimum run: None
info: High quality mastering facilities at £30 per hour. Check website for technical specifications. Can duplicate very small runs of CD-Rs.

MUSIC SERVICES/RETAIL

Blackfriars Entertainment
London
tel: 020 7928 4154
email: onestop@blackfriarsentertainment.com
web: www.blackfriarsentertainment.com
design service: No
minimum run: 1
info: 48 track digital recording, production and CD-R mastering. £20 an hour. Duplication from £1 per CD. Flyer, website and CD Design - phone for prices.

BonaFideStudio
Burbage House, 83 Curtain Road, London, EC2A 3BS
tel: 020 7684 5350/020 7684 5351
email: findus@bonafidestudio.co.uk
web: www.bonafidestudio.co.uk
contact: Brian
design service: Yes
minimum run: None
info: CD duplication and mastering facilities. See listing in Recording Studios section for studio specs. Package deals available for recording, mastering and duplication.

CD Press Ltd.
455 Green Lane, London, N13 4BS
tel: 020 8350 9677
email: info@cdpress.com
web: www.cdpress.com
contact: Sales
design service: Yes
minimum run: None
info: All formats. On-body printing. Contact for prices, but guide price is £100 for 100 CDs with cases.

CD Writer
49 Greenwich High Road, Greenwich, London, SE10 8JL
tel: 0870 760 5737
fax: 020 8694 6930
email: sales@cd-writer.com
web: www.cd-writer.com
design service: No
minimum run: None
info: Provider of CD duplication hardware now offering 1 to 499 CDR copying and printing from www.cd-writer.com. Larger quantities (500-5000) available including print on CD. 24 hrs turnaround available. Contact to request a quote or further info.

CDA Disc Ltd.
Abbey House, 450 Bath Road, West Rayton, UB7 0EB
tel: 020 8757 8968
fax: 020 8757 8972
web: www.cdadisc.com
contact: Ian Mackay
design service: No
minimum run: 500
info: London branch of large German pressing plant. Replicates CDs and DVDs from glass masters. Mastering facilities, printing facility, but no in-house design.

Century 23
3rd Floor, 54-55 Margaret Street, London, W1W 8SH
tel: 0871 700 0080
design service: Yes
info: Century 23 have been working in close association with the live music, clubbing, entertainment, and leisure industries across Britain for 7 years providing CD and vinyl duplication, as well as artwork design and printing. See Poster and Flyer Printing and Artwork and Design sections for details. Offices in Belfast and Edinburgh.

Clear Sound & Vision Ltd.
CSV House, Marlborough Road, London, E18 1AR
tel: 020 8989 8777
fax: 020 8989 9777
email: sales@c-s-v.co.uk
web: www.c-s-v.co.uk
design service: Yes
minimum run: 300 CDs
info: A complete one-stop manufacturing service for CD, DVD, vinyl, cassette and video, as well as offering design, authoring, printing and fulfilment solutions. CSV have fulfilled manufacturing requirements for The Strokes, The Libertines, The Delays, Simple Kid and Kate Rusby. For more information including print and label specification visit the website, or call for a free brochure. CSV will even feature your product in the unsigned section on their website!

CopyMaster International
8 Arundel Road, Uxbridge Trading Estate, Middlesex, UB8 2RR
tel: 01895 814 813
email: sales@copymaster.co.uk
web: www.copymaster.co.uk
contact: Rachelle Peterson
design service: Yes
minimum run: 50
info: CD, DVD, VHS and cassette duplication and replication. In-house graphic design centre. Fulfilment house. Deal with any quantities from 50 units to one million.

Curved Pressings Ltd.
Unit 1, 16a Kings Yard, Carpenters Road, Hackney Wick, London, E15 2HD
tel: 020 8533 8080
fax: 020 8533 8082
email: clare@curvedpressings.com
web: www.curvedpressings.com
contact: Clare Ireland
design service: No
minimum run: None
info: Vinyl pressing specialists. Visit the website for an automated quote.

The Cutting Suite
102c Elmbourne Road, London, SW17 8JH
tel: 020 8672 9951
email: info@thecuttingsuite.com
web: www.thecuttingsuite.com
contact: Carlos or Duncan
design service: Yes
info: London's premier mastering studio. Mainly deal with vinyl mastering and cutting, but also master CDs. Mastering charged at £65 per hour. Vinyl cutting starts from £120 for one sided 12 inch.

MUSIC SERVICES/RETAIL

CVB Duplication
179a Bilton Road, Perivale, Middlesex, UB6 7HQ
tel: 020 8991 2610
fax: 020 8997 0180
email: info@cvbduplication.co.uk
web: www.cvbduplication.co.uk
contact: Adrian Tubman
design service: Yes
minimum run: None
info: CD, DVD and VHS duplication. Full printing and packaging service. On-body printing.

Cybersound
Block C, Units C102 & C104, Faircharm Trading Estate, 8-12 Creekside, London, SE8 3DX
tel: 020 8694 9484
fax: 020 8694 9466
email: studio@cyber-sound.co.uk
web: www.cyber-sound.co.uk
design service: No
minimum run: None
info: Mastering and CD duplication with on-body printing. Printing available but no in-house design. Also have rehearsal and recording studios. See entries in the relevant sections for details.

The Data Business Ltd.
64 Turnmill Street, London, EC1M 5RR
tel: 020 7553 6047
email: damien.h@databiz.com
web: www.databiz.com
contact: Damien Hayden
design service: Yes
minimum run: None
info: CD, DVD, VHS, cassette, MD and DAT duplication. In-house artwork reproduction and design. Mastering facilities. DVD authoring and encoding. USB memory sticks, packaging and blank media from all tapes conversion to DVD. Graphic design facilities. Full professional edit suite.

Diverse Media
PO Box 3, South Croydon, Surrey, CR2 0YW
tel: 0870 765 4343/07956 233 332
fax: 0870 765 4344
email: sales@soundmastering.co.uk
web: www.soundmastering.co.uk
design service: Yes
info: Specialise in CD mastering and restoration.

Emasters
London
tel: 020 7565 3022
email: info@emasters.co.uk
web: www.emasters.co.uk
contact: Jane, Alex
design service: No
minimum run: None
info: Emasters is the online mastering service of The Soundmasters audio mastering service. Over 50 years experience including involvement with Paul McCartney, The Prodigy and Kasabian. Services offered include audio mastering, vinyl lacquer cutting, dubplate cutting, CD production masters. Also CD replication up to 10,000 units. Emasters also provides a free online music storage facility which is accessible worldwide. 10% discount available to readers of The Unsigned Guide. Quote promotional code TUG at online checkout.

Eurodisc Manufacturing Ltd.
1st Floor Howard House, The Runway, South Ruislip, Middlesex, HA4 6SE
tel: 020 8839 0060
fax: 020 8845 6679
email: lydie@euro-disc.co.uk
web: www.euro-disc.co.uk
design service: No
minimum run: 300 vinyl, 500 CD
info: Mainly vinyl duplication. Can also duplicate CD and DVD. On-body printing.

The Exchange
42 Bruges Place, Randolph Street, London, NW1 0TX
tel: 020 7485 0530
fax: 020 7482 4588
email: studio@exchangemastering.co.uk
web: www.exchangemastering.co.uk
design service: Yes
info: Recent and current projects include The Streets, Basement Jaxx, Depeche Mode, Goldfrapp, Lamb, Stereophonics, Peaches, So Solid Crew, Dizzee Rascal, Martina Topley-Bird, Sigur Ros and The Darkness.

Flying Ace Productions
Walders, Oldbury Lane, Ightham, Sevenoaks, TN15 9DD
tel: 01732 887 056
email: reiddick@netmatters.co.uk
contact: Will
design service: Yes
info: CD mastering and audio editing. No duplication facilities.

Gallus
6-8 Paxton Place, Gypsy Hill, London, SE27 9SS
tel: 020 8766 9050
email: sales@gallusmusic.co.uk
web: www.gallusmusic.co.uk
contact: Dylan
design service: No
minimum run: 500
info: CD and DVD duplication.

Golddust Studios
14 Cromwell Avenue, Bromley, Kent, BR2 9AQ
tel: 020 8466 7435
email: mark@golddust.co.uk
web: www.golddust.co.uk
contact: Mark Dawson
design service: Yes
minimum run: 10
info: CD duplication and mastering. Cassette copying. Full printing facilities for packaging, as well as free CD cases or wallets. See entry for Golddust recording studios in relevant section.

Grade A Media
11 Lanfrey Place, London, W14 9PY
tel: 0870 199 6112
fax: 07092 844 686
email: enquiries@gradeamedia.co.uk
web: www.gradeamedia.co.uk
design service: No
minimum run: 50
info: CD and DVD duplication and replication. On-body printing. Also sell blank media, see website for further details.

Heathmans Mastering
19 Heathmans Road, Parsons Green, Fulham, London, SW6 4TJ
tel: 020 7371 0978
fax: 020 7371 9360
email: heathmans@btclick.com
web: www.heathmans.co.uk
contact: Susana Martinez
design service: No
minimum run: 20
info: CD, DVD, DAT, Exabyte, vinyl and MD duplication. Digital watermarking available. High quality mastering at £100 per hour.

Hiltongrove Multimedia Ltd.
The Hiltongrove Business Centre, Hatherley Mews, London, E17 4QP
tel: 020 8521 2424
fax: 020 8521 4343
email: info@hiltongrove.com
web: www.hiltongrove.com
contact: Guy Davis, Dave Blackman
design service: Yes
minimum run: None
info: CD, DVD and vinyl mastering, duplication and design.

Hub 100
2b Swanfield Street, London, E2 7DS
tel: 020 7613 1813
email: oliver@hub100.com
web: www.hub100.com
contact: Oliver Dutton
design service: No
minimum run: None
info: CD duplication. No minimum run, but set up fee for runs under 50. Can print previously prepared artwork, but no in-house design service. Mastering service available.

Ideal Mastering
Ground Floor Shop, 696 Holloway Road, London, N19 3NL
tel: 020 7263 3346
fax: 020 7263 3396
email: work@idealmastering.co.uk
web: www.idealmastering.co.uk
contact: Mark Saunders
design service: Yes
info: CD duplication with on-body print. Artwork design and inlay printing. DVD and cassette duplication. No paper printing though.

Imagestor
Unit 1, Olympia Industrial Estate, Coburg Road, London, N22 6TZ
tel:	020 8881 0081
fax:	020 8881 0082
email:	info@imagestor.co.uk
web:	www.imagestor.co.uk
contact:	Maria Awad
design service:	No
minimum run:	None
info:	CD and DVD duplication in-house. Can

reproduce client's artwork. On-body printing. Also print inserts and booklets.

iMastering
The Power House, 70 Chiswick High Road, London, W4 1SY
tel:	020 8742 1111
fax:	020 8742 2626
email:	imaster@metropolis-group.co.uk
web:	www.metropolis-group.co.uk
contact:	Alex Sanders
design service:	Yes
info:	Part of Metropolis Group, who offer video

production services. See entry for M Productions in Video Promo Services section.

Impress Music Ltd.
Unit 5c, Northfields Industrial Estate, Beresford Avenue, Wembley, HA0 1NW
tel:	020 8795 0101
email:	alastair@impressmusic-uk.com
web:	www.impressmusic-uk.com
contact:	Alastair
design service:	No
minimum run:	50
info:	CD and DVD duplication and replication. Vinyl

pressing. On-body printing. Simple typesetting service.

Jet Star Phonographics
155 Acton Lane, Park Royal, London, NW10 7NJ
tel:	020 8961 5818
email:	production@jetstar.co.uk
web:	www.jetstar.co.uk
contact:	Philip, Vanessa
design service:	Yes
minimum run:	None
info:	CD, DVD, VHS, cassette and vinyl duplication.

Full reprographic facilities. On-body printing. Mastering suite and two recording studios available.

JTS Studio
73 Digby Road, London, E9 6HX
tel:	020 8985 3000
email:	sales@jtsstudio.co.uk
web:	www.jtsstudio.co.uk
contact:	Freddie
design service:	Yes
info:	Vinyl cutting and pressing specialists. Can print

labels and sleeves, but no in-house design service. See website for price list.

Key Production Ltd.
8 Jeffreys Place, London, NW1 9PP
tel:	020 7284 8800
fax:	020 7284 8844
email:	mail@keyproduction.co.uk
web:	www.keyproduction.co.uk
contact:	Melodie Greenwell
design service:	Yes
minimum run:	500
info:	Offer a complete manufacturing service for DVD,

CD, CD-R, vinyl, cassette and all associated print including specialist packaging. No mastering facilities.

KopyKings
A116 Faircham Trading Estate, 8-12 Creekside, Deptford, London, SE8 3DX
tel:	020 8469 9301/0870 760 7851
fax:	020 8469 2442
email:	mail@kopykings.com
web:	www.kopykings.com
contact:	Nicholas Beveney
design service:	Yes
minimum run:	None
info:	CD and DVD duplication. On-body printing. Also

offer mastering and DVD encoding services.

Kudos Records Ltd.
77 Fortess Road, Kentish Town, London, NW5 1AG
tel:	020 7482 4555
fax:	020 7482 4551
email:	info@kudosrecords.co.uk
web:	www.kudosrecords.co.uk
design service:	No
minimum run:	500
info:	Primarily a distributor, but they handle CD and

vinyl duplication. No printing or mastering facilities.

The Label That Never Sleeps
London
tel:	0871 250 0005
fax:	0870 112 3405
email:	info@sleeplesslabel.com
web:	www.sleeplesslabel.com
design service:	Yes
minimum run:	None
info:	CD, DVD and vinyl duplication and replication.

In-house design service and colour on-body printing. Only use top grade media. Although rates are not cheap, the service offered is high quality with a quick turnaround. Mastering facilities and recording studio available.

Liberty Hall Music
Battle House, 1 East Barnet Road, New Barnet, Hertfordshire, EN4 8RR
tel:	020 8440 0011/07961 447 589
email:	kristina@libertyhallmusic.com
web:	www.libertyhallmusic.com
contact:	Kristina
design service:	Yes
minimum run:	None
info:	Established in 1993, Liberty Hall Music offer

a wide range of services including studio recording, mastering and duplication services and various music training courses. See entries in relevant sections for more details.

Lighthouse Studios
15 Heathfield Park, London, NW2 5JE
tel:	07976 733 856
email:	dcathro@lighthouse-studio.co.uk
web:	www.lighthouse-studio.co.uk
contact:	David Cathro
design service:	Yes
info:	High quality mastering studio. Check website

for equipment list. 4 track demo will usually take around 4 hours to master. Charged at £50 per hour. Recommends using 24bit files at 44.1kHz sampling rate. No duplication facilities.

Liquid Mastering
6Q Atlas Business Centre, Oxgate Lane, London, NW2 7HU
tel:	020 8452 2255
fax:	020 8452 4242
email:	liquidmastering@aol.com
web:	www.liquidmastering.co.uk
contact:	Bob Kane
design service:	Yes
minimum run:	None
info:	Vinyl manufacture and mastering service. In-

house label design available.

The Little Bazaar
3/12 Wetherby Place, London, SW7 4ND
tel:	020 7370 7850
email:	info@littlebazaar.co.uk
web:	www.littlebazaar.co.uk
contact:	Paul, Matt
design service:	Yes
minimum run:	None
info:	Mastering and duplication studio with in-house

design assistance. Offers available include 100 CDs duplicated and printed for £69.

MAP Music
46 Grafton Road, London, NW5 3DU
tel:	020 7916 0544
fax:	020 7284 4232
email:	info@mapmusic.net
web:	www.mapmusic.net
design service:	Yes
minimum run:	None
info:	Short run CD duplication specialists. On-body

printing. Mastering facilities and recording studios available.

Masterpiece Media
Unit 14, The Talina Centre, Bagleys Lane, London, SW6 2BW
tel:	020 7731 5758
email:	leena.bhatti@masterpiecelondon.com
web:	www.masterpiecelondon.com
contact:	Leena Bhatti
design service:	Yes
minimum run:	None
info:	Mastering and reproduction for all formats.

The Masterroom
66 Paddenswick Road, London, W6 0UB
tel: 020 8743 8585
email: masterroom@btconnect.com
web: www.masterroom.co.uk
contact: Jeremy Cooper
design service: Yes
info: High end mastering facility willing to accommodate unsigned artists.

MediaDisc
Unit 4C, Farm Lane Trading Centre, 101 Farm Lane, London, SW6 1QJ
tel: 020 7385 2299
fax: 020 7385 4888
email: studio@mediadisc.co.uk
web: www.mediadisc.co.uk
contact: Ray
design service: No
minimum run: None
info: Duplication of DAT, CD, DVD, Exabyte, U-Matic (1630) and MD. On-body printing and artwork reproduction. Provide a digital watermarking facility. Mastering facilities available.

Method Productions
Global House, 92 DeBeauvoir Road, London, N1 4EN
tel: 020 7241 6880
email: team@method-productions.com
web: www.method-productions.com
design service: Yes
minimum run: None
info: CD, DVD and vinyl duplication. On-body printing and packaging. Mastering facilities available.

Metropolis Studios
The Power House, 70 Chiswick High Road, London, W4 1SY
tel: 020 8742 1111
fax: 020 8742 2626
email: mastering@metropolis-group.co.uk
web: www.metropolis-group.co.uk
contact: Michele Conroy
design service: Yes
info: High quality mastering studios. DVD 5.1 surround-sound, CD stereo and SACD mastering. Vinyl cutting and half-speed vinyl cutting for more high-end definition. Do not offer artwork reproduction or CD duplication facilities. For information on recording at Metropolis Studios, see the Recording Studios section.

Modo Productions
3rd Floor, 1a Adpar Street, London, W2 1DE
tel: 020 7535 6730
fax: 020 7563 7283
email: terry@modo.co.uk
web: www.modo.co.uk
contact: Tim Bezan, Henry Lavelle
design service: Yes
minimum run: 500
info: Creative packaging specialists. CD and vinyl duplication. Marketing and distribution services.

Modus Media Ltd.
18 Iliffe Yard, London, SE17 3QA
tel: 020 7740 6045
fax: 020 7708 4289
email: info@modus-media.com
web: www.modus-media.com
design service: Yes
minimum run: 500
info: CD, DVD, cassette, VHS and vinyl duplication. In-house design and artwork reproduction service, printing and web design.

Music Base
Mill House, Chapel Place, Rivingston Street, London, EC2A 3DW
tel: 020 7729 4446
email: ian@musicbase.uk.com
web: www.musicbase.uk.com
contact: Ian
design service: Yes
minimum run: None
info: CD and vinyl duplicators. Full artwork reproduction and design service. Also manufacture DVDs. Mastering facilities available.

Orlake Records
Sterling Industrial Estate, Rainham Road South, Dagenham, Essex, RM10 8HP
tel: 020 8592 0242
fax: 020 8595 8182
email: paula@orlakerecords.com
web: www.orlakerecords.com
contact: Paula Pearl
design service: Yes
info: Orlake Records, established in 1965 is the UK's oldest independent vinyl manufacturer. Products include 7", 10" and 12", also black, coloured vinyl, picture discs and shaped discs. Call for details of prices.

Portal Space Records
120 Blyth Road, Hayes, Middlesex, UB3 1SY
tel: 020 8756 0707
email: info@portalspacerecords.com
web: www.portalspacerecords.com
contact: Bob Bailey
design service: No
minimum run: None
info: Vinyl specialists. Printing available, but no in-house design.

Powermaster
30A Glenthorne Road, London, N11 3HJ
tel: 020 8368 3080
email: postduction@hotmail.com
web: www.cd-mastering.co.uk
contact: Dave Hewitt
design service: Yes
info: Post production and CD mastering studios.

Quick Press Production
Unit 23, Zennor Road Industrial Estate, Balham, London, SW12 0PS
tel: 020 8673 5333
email: info@quickpress.co.uk
web: www.quickpress.co.uk
contact: George Howard
design service: Yes
info: Vinyl pressing plant. Around £300 to press master copy, then 60p per pressing. Mastering facilities available.

Red:light
27 Lexington Street, London, W1F 9AQ
tel: 020 7287 7373/07796 958 115
fax: 020 7287 7602
email: craig@red-light.co.uk
web: www.red-light.co.uk
design service: Yes

Renegade CD Duplication
PO Box 38454, London, SE16 3WB
tel: 020 7237 8998
email: renegade.biz@btinternet.com
web: www.renegadecdcopy.biz
contact: Sabrina
design service: Yes
minimum run: None
info: On-body printing. Price example: £80 for 100 CD with on-body printing and wallets. Mastering available through associates Berry St. Studios.

Repeat Performance RPM
6 Grand Union Centre, West Row, London, W10 5AS
tel: 020 8960 7222
fax: 020 8968 1378
email: info@repeat-performance.co.uk
web: www.repeat-performance.co.uk
contact: Robin Springall
design service: Yes
minimum run: 10
info: CD, DVD and cassette duplication. Artwork reproduction and design services, on-body printing and packaging. High quality mastering studio charged at £65 + VAT per hour.

Revolution Digital
1st Floor, 34 Lexington Street, Soho, London, W1F 0LH
tel: 020 7439 3332
email: studio@rdigital.co.uk
web: www.rdigital.co.uk
design service: No
minimum run: None
info: Audio mastering service. Also offer DVD, ECD and Ecard authoring. Revolution Digital also has a branch in Manchester. See north west region listings.

RMS Studios
43-45 Clifton Road, London, SE25 6PX
tel: 020 8653 4965
email: rmsstudios@blueyonder.co.uk
web: www.rms-studios.co.uk
contact: Andy, Alan
design service: Yes
minimum run: None
info: CD duplication from any format. On-body printing and colour printing available. Cassette copying. Mastering service available, check website for price list. For details of RMS Studio's recording facilities, see the relevant section.

Slickdiscs
Unit 3, 25 Downham Road, London, N1 5AA
tel: 020 7241 0009
email: mail@slickdiscs.co.uk
web: www.slickdiscs.co.uk
contact: Leon Cox
design service: Yes
minimum run: None
info: Vinyl, CD, DVD, VHS to DVD replication and duplication. Mastering facilities. Artwork reproduction.

The Song Corporation Ltd.
Business Centre, 5 Blackhorse Lane, London, E17 6DS
tel: 020 8527 0447
email: info@songcorporation.com
web: www.songcorporation.com
contact: Delroy Murray
design service: Yes
minimum run: None
info: CD, DVD, MD and cassette duplication. On-body printing. Mastering facilities and recording studios. Contact for prices. The Song Corporation are musicians themselves and are sympathetic to you needs.

Sonic Arts
85 Barlby Road, London, W10 6BN
tel: 020 8962 3000
fax: 020 8962 6200
email: info@sonic-arts.com
web: www.sonic-arts.com
contact: Richard Simons
design service: No
minimum run: None
info: CD and DVD duplication. Watermarking and copy protection available. Mastering service, as well as e-CD and DVD authoring.

Sound Discs Ltd.
Unit 10, Linen House, 253 Kilburn Lane, London, W10 4BQ
tel: 0845 270 7080
fax: 0845 270 7082
email: master@sound-discs.co.uk
web: www.sound-discs.co.uk
contact: Peter Bullick
design service: Yes
minimum run: None
info: CD, DVD and MP3 mastering, duplication, design and manufacture.

Sound Performance
Unit 3, Greenwich Quay, Clarence Road, London, SE8 3EY
tel: 020 8691 2121
fax: 020 8691 3144
email: sales@soundperformance.co.uk
web: www.soundperformance.co.uk
design service: No
minimum run: Contact for details
info: Duplication services for CD, DVD, vinyl, VHS and cassette formats. Laser printing for booklets, plus on-body printing. Mastering studio on-site.

Sound Solution Mastering
201-203 Hackney Road, London, E2 8JL
tel: 020 7033 9639
email: soundsolutioncd@aol.com
web: www.soundsolutionmastering.com
contact: Byron Mitchell
design service: Yes
minimum run: None
info: CD replication and duplication. Vinyl and dub plate cutting (10" and 12"). Design and printing services also available.

Soundhouse Ltd.
Unit 11, Goldhawk Industrial Estate, 2a Brackenbury Road, London, W6 0BA
tel: 020 8743 2677
email: info@thesoundhousestudios.co.uk
web: www.thesoundhousestudios.co.uk
design service: Yes
info: Ideal for low-cost digital editing, mixing and mastering.

The Soundmasters
The New Boathouse, 136-142 Bramley Road, London, W10 6SR
tel: 020 7565 3020
email: jane@soundmasters.co.uk
web: www.soundmasters.co.uk
contact: Jane
design service: Yes
info: High-end mastering facility for CD, vinyl and 5.1 surround. Contact for prices.

Transition Studios
Kemble House, Kemble Road, London, SE23 2DJ
tel: 020 8699 7888
email: info@transition-studios.co.uk
web: www.transition-studios.co.uk
contact: Karen
design service: Yes
info: Vinyl mastering specialists. £175 for 12" vinyl. CD mastering charged at £60 per hour.

Tribal Manufacturing Ltd.
11 Hillgate Place, Balham Hill, London, SW12 9ER
tel: 020 8673 0610
email: sales@tribal.co.uk
web: www.tribal.co.uk
contact: Terry Woollner, Alison Wilson
design service: Yes
minimum run: 500
info: CD, DVD, vinyl and cassette duplication. Contact for prices.

Twentieth Century Video Ltd.
Wembley Commercial Centre, 80 East Lane, Wembley, Middlesex, HA9 7UU
tel: 020 8904 6271
fax: 020 8904 0172
email: sandra@tcvideo.co.uk
web: www.tcvideo.co.uk
contact: Clive Rumble
design service: Yes
minimum run: None
info: Duplication for CD, DVD and VHS. On-body printing.

MUSIC SERVICES/RETAIL

Vampire Music
20 Tanners Hill, Deptford, London, SE8 4JP
tel:	020 8691 6666
fax:	020 8692 9999
email:	info@vampiremusic.co.uk
web:	www.vampiremusic.co.uk
design service:	Yes
minimum run:	None
info:	Short run CD duplication. On-body printing and

packaging. Vampire Music also incorporates a music shop, recording and rehearsal studios, equipment hire, as well as design and tuition services. See listings in relevant sections.

Vanderson
PO Box 230, Ruislip, Middlesex, HA4 6DW
tel:	020 8426 4600
email:	enquiries@vanderson.co.uk
web:	www.vanderson.co.uk
design service:	Yes
info:	High quality media manufacturing services

for CD, DVD, ROM CARDS, VHS and audio cassette. From master to delivered product. Full range of packaging options available.

Vinyl Carvers
North London
tel:	020 7267 4071
email:	info@vinylcarvers.com
web:	www.vinylcarvers.com
contact:	Tina, Werner
design service:	No
minimum run:	None
info:	Specialists in one-off and short runs of vinyl

records. All formats, black and clear scratch proof vinyl, locked grooves. Mastering and manufacturing service. Vinyl Carvers also have recording facilities. See entry in relevant section for details.

Wolf Studios
83 Brixton Water Lane, London, SW2 1PH
tel:	020 7733 8088
fax:	020 7326 4016
email:	brethes@mac.com
web:	www.wolfstudios.co.uk
contact:	Dominique Brethes
design service:	Yes
info:	CD and vinyl mastering available at £35 per

hour. CD album mastering deal for £175 plus VAT. See Recording Studio section for more information on Wolf Studios.

MIDLANDS

Direct Duplication Services
Unit A3, 2 Bowyer Street, Digbeth, Birmingham, B10 0SA
tel:	0121 771 0220
fax:	0121 771 0440
email:	support@directduplication.com
web:	www.directduplication.com
design service:	Yes
minimum run:	None
info:	CD, DVD and tape cassette duplication. Printing

inlay cards, CD on-body printing, cases and wallets, cellophane wrapping, artwork design and next day delivery

Discus Group
PO Box 5613, Northampton, Northamptonshire, NN6 9ZN
tel:	0871 220 0199
web:	www.discusgroup.co.uk
design service:	No
minimum run:	100
info:	Discus Group offer duplication and/or replication

on CD and DVD.

Double Vision
The Studios, Halfkey Studios, Halfkey, Malvern, Worcestershire, WR14 1UP
tel:	01886 830 064
email:	sales@doublevisiongroup.com
web:	www.doublevisiongroup.com
contact:	John Griffiths
design service:	Yes
minimum run:	10
info:	CD, DVD and VHS duplication. On-body printing.

Also offer glass mastering service.

Downstream Ltd.
44 Marsh Lane, Nantwich, Cheshire, CW5 5LH
tel:	01270 625 125
fax:	0870 705 2846
email:	info@downstream.co.uk
web:	www.downstream.co.uk
contact:	Edward Leetham
design service:	No
minimum run:	None
info:	CD and DVD duplication. On-body printing, as

well as booklets and inserts. CD mastering service, and also master DVD from VHS.

Dupe.co.uk
Windsor Court, Trent Valley Road, Lichfield, Staffordshire, WS13 6EU
tel:	0800 092 1110
fax:	01543 416 914
email:	simon@dupe.co.uk
web:	www.dupe.co.uk
design service:	Yes
minimum run:	50
info:	CD and DVD duplication, replication and

printing. Linked with Studio Digital, who offer graphic design services. See listing in relevant section for information.

F1 Design
Kingsley Road, Lincoln Fields, Lincoln, LN6 3TA
tel:	01522 508 080
fax:	01522 508 085
email:	info@f1design.co.uk
web:	www.f1design.co.uk
design service:	Yes
info:	CD duplication, as well as graphic and web

design services. See listing in relevant section for further details.

Griffin Media Solutions
53 Regent Place, Hockley, Birmingham, B1 3NJ
tel:	0121 212 0044
email:	paul@askgriffin.co.uk
web:	www.askgriffin.co.uk
contact:	Paul Griffin
design service:	Yes
minimum run:	None
info:	Duplication services for CD, DVD, VHS, CD-Rom

and cassette. On-body printing. Print for packaging such as inserts, booklets and inlay is done externally, but can be arranged. Mastering service available.

Iceni
The Studio, Long Lane, Fradley, Lichfield, WS13 8NX
tel:	01283 792 990
fax:	01283 792 993
email:	info@iceni.tv
web:	www.iceni.tv
design service:	Yes
info:	Iceni works with the largest duplication houses

in the UK and can negotiate exceptionally low prices on your behalf. Provides a simple unit cost for copy protection, print, labelling, packaging and delivery.

Iris Production
The Hollymoor Centre, Manor Park Grove, Northfield, Birmingham, B31 5ER
tel:	07811 435 186
email:	info@iris-production.co.uk
web:	www.iris-production.co.uk
contact:	Scott Vale
design service:	Yes
info:	CD duplication. Iris Production also offers

graphic and web design services, as well as video production. See entries in relevant section for further details.

Katapult Ltd.
Vernon House, Vernon Street, Derby, DE1 1FR
tel:	01332 294 416
email:	info@katapult-studios.com
web:	www.katapult-studios.com
contact:	Dawn Lockett
design service:	Yes
info:	CD duplication, as well as graphic design and

printing services, music video production and motion graphics. See listings in relevant section for further details.

Media Hut
Kestrel Business Centre, Private Road No. 2, Colwick, Nottingham, NG4 2JR
tel:	0115 987 3777
fax:	0115 987 4181
email:	sales@mediahut.co.uk
web:	www.cdreplication.co.uk
contact:	Karl Dukes
design service:	Yes
minimum run:	250
info:	CD and DVD duplication. Please contact with

your specifications to discuss pricing.

MediaSourcing.com
5-6 Vennington, Westbury, Shrewsbury, SY5 9RG
tel:	0845 686 0001
fax:	07092 070 926
email:	sales@mediasourcing.com
web:	www.mediasourcing.com
design service:	Yes
minimum run:	500
info:	Specialise in providing volume CD manufacture

at competitive prices. Visit website for instant quotes for most specifications. All CDs are glass mastered and pressed to the highest industry standards. Guaranteed best volume discounts for labels, distributors and brokers.

Mooli
Beacon House, 10 Forest Road, Loughborough, Leicestershire, LE11 3NP
tel:	01509 240 040
email:	them@mooli.com
web:	www.mooli.com
design service:	Yes
info:	CD duplication. Mooli also provide web design

services and print production. See listing in relevant section for details.

Mothers Recording Studio
14 Rea Street, Birmingham
tel:	0121 622 7110/07753 147 756
email:	david.mccabe@btinternet.com
contact:	David McCabe
design service:	Yes
info:	CD duplication services. Recording and rehearsal

studios available. See listings in relevant sections for further details.

Mustard Mastering & Design
Nottingham, NG2 4AB
tel:	0115 910 0843
email:	daz@mustard-mg.com
web:	www.mustard-mg.com
design service:	Yes
minimum run:	50
info:	CD mastering and duplication. Also provides

design services for CD covers, website and posters.

Nexus Creative Ltd.
The Cider Mill & Stables, Court Farm, Church Lane, Norton, Worcester, WR5 2PS
tel:	01905 821 919
fax:	01905 821 313
email:	info@nexuscl.com
web:	www.nexuscl.com
design service:	Yes
info:	Duplication services. Can replicate up to 15,000

CDs or DVDs. Also provide graphic and web design. See entry in relevant section for details.

Noisegate
155 Tachbrook Road, Leamington Spa, Warwickshire, CV31 3EE
tel:	01926 330 135
email:	enquiries@noisegatestudios.com
web:	www.noisegatestudios.com
design service:	No
minimum run:	None
info:	CD duplication and mastering, including on-body

printing and a variety of packaging options. Noisegate also have a recording studio. See relevant section for details.

S2 Blue
Overton Bank House, Overton Bank, Leek, Staffordshire, ST13 5ES
tel: 01538 370 160
fax: 01538 372 595
email: info@s2blue.com
web: www.s2blue.com
contact: Simon
design service: No
minimum run: None
info: One copy of 74 minute CD costs £9.75, price can fall to £1.99 with increasing order quantities. Black and white inlay cards available, colour available on small runs. Printing onto body of disc. Delivery can be arranged. 24 hour turnaround on runs of up to 50.

Sabre Media Copying
28 Shrewsbury Road, Edgmond, Shropshire, TF10 8HU
tel: 01952 820 453
fax: 01952 811 438
email: info@mediacopy.co.uk
web: www.mediacopy.co.uk
design service: Yes
minimum run: None
info: CD and DVD duplication and printing. Also video, floppy disk and cassette copying along with a choice of printing, labelling and packaging options.

The Session Rooms
Waterworks Road, Worcester, Worcestershire, WR1 3EZ
tel: 07729 011 398/01965 338 972
email: info@thesessionrooms.com
web: www.thesessionrooms.com
design service: Yes
minimum run: None
info: CD reproduction and design, including on-body and inlay printing. Recording and rehearsal facilities also available - see relevant sections for more details.

Sky-com
Birmingham
tel: 0121 236 2594
email: info@sky-com.co.uk
web: www.sky-com.co.uk
contact: Margaret Blair
design service: No
minimum run: None
info: CD and DVD duplication. Full packaging and on-body printing.

Vision Associates
3 Drayton Road, Kings Heath, Birmingham, B14 7LP
tel: 0121 441 3300
fax: 0121 441 3311
email: visassocs@btinternet.com
web: www.visassoc.co.uk
design service: Yes
minimum run: None
info: Complete in-house facility for video and CD-R duplication. Packaging in plastic wallets or jewel cases. Also include CD business cards.

Xervia
139 Queens Road, Leicester, LE2 3FL
tel: 0845 045 0705
email: info@xervia.com
web: www.xervia.com
design service: Yes
info: CD duplication. Comprehensive design company with previous music experience. See listing in relevant section for further details.

NORTHEAST

Ace Copy Disc
Ouseburn Building, Albion Row, East Quayside, Newcastle Upon Tyne, NE6 1LL
tel: 0191 275 5034
email: info@acecopydisc.co.uk
web: www.acecopydisc.co.uk
design service: Yes
info: Full mastering and editing from any format at £35 per hour. Thermal on-body print. Jewel case or wallet. Contact production team to discuss requirements.

Axis Audio Ltd.
6 John Martin Street, Haydon Bridge, Northumberland, NE47 6AA
tel: 01434 684 547
email: ren@axisaudio.co.uk
web: www.axisaudio.co.uk
contact: Ren Hunter
design service: Yes
minimum run: 500 for CDs
info: CD and cassette duplication. Artwork reproduction and design. Can do simple design in-house. On-body printing for CDs and cassettes. No minimum run for CD-Rs. Masters using SADiE.

EPD Multimedia Ltd.
Unit E24, Innovator House, Wearfield, Sunderland, SR5 2TP
tel: 0191 516 6803
email: colin@e-p-d.co.uk
web: www.e-p-d-group.co.uk
contact: Colin
design service: Yes
info: CD-R design, production and replication.

Europa Magnetics Corporation Ltd.
Nelson Way, Nelson Park, Cramlington, Northumberland, NE23 1EB
tel: 01670 706 609
email: sales@emc-ltd.co.uk
web: www.emc-ltd.co.uk
design service: Yes
minimum run: 50
info: One-stop shop for all your manufacturing, duplication & replication needs.

High Fidelity Studios
37 Sutherland Grange, New Herrington, Houghton-le-Spring, Tyne & Wear, DH4 4UT
tel: 0191 584 2383
web: www.highfidelitymobile.co.uk
design service: Yes
info: High Fidelity can duplicate runs of up to 500 CD-R with on-body printing, in either single colour or 4-colour process. For quantities greater than 500, it is usually more cost effective to press, rather than duplicate, and High Fidelity will be happy to point you in the right direction.

Impact Studio
Sunderland, Tyne & Wear
tel: 0191 523 6418
email: info@impactstudio.biz
web: www.impactstudio.biz
design service: Yes
info: Artists can record their tracks at Impact Studio and have them mastered to CD, or have previously recorded tracks re-mastered at the studio. Impact can advise on type of CD printing, colour labels etc, and duplicate as many CDs as required. Please see the Recording Studios section for more details.

Octagon Advanced Media
A18 Stonehills, Shields Road, Gateshead, NE10 0HW
tel: 0191 495 2324
fax: 0191 495 2306
email: master@octagonadvancedmedia.com
web: www.octagonadvancedmedia.com
design service: Yes
minimum run: None
info: Octagon offer a full range of mastering, duplication and design services.

Quest Products Ltd.
Navigation House, Tyne Dock, South Shields, NE34 0AB
tel: 0191 454 4134
email: enquires@questproducts.co.uk
web: www.questproducts.co.uk
design service: Yes
info: Offer CD printing and duplication to musicians using top quality CD media and a 1400 dpi colour inkjet printer. Short-run CD duplication available.

Studio 64
90 Corporation Road, Middlesbrough, TS1 2RE
tel: 01642 860 006
web: www.studio64.org.uk
design service: No
minimum run: None
info: Prices start from £1.20 per disc, including on-body printing. Rehearsal, recording, PA hire and tuition services also available. See relevant sections for details.

T.S.M. Audio-Media
Broadcasting House, Newport Road, Middlesbrough, TS1 5JA
tel: 01642 225 460
email: sales@tsmaudio.co.uk
web: www.tsmaudio.co.uk
design service: Yes
minimum run: 50
info: Digital mastering and CD and DVD duplication. On-body digital thermal printing for a full colour scratch resistant and water proof surface. Fast turnaround in 2-5 working days.

T.V.V. Productions
Suite 310, Wingrove House, Ponteland Road, Newcastle Upon Tyne, NE5 3DP
tel: 0191 286 9800
email: studio@tvv.co.uk
web: www.tvv.co.uk
design service: No
minimum run: 10
info: Complete CD, DVD and VHS copying service with full printing and packaging service.

Travelled Music
The Tile Works, Paxton, Berwick Upon Tweed, TD15 1TJ
tel: 01289 386 737
email: info@travelledmusic.co.uk
web: www.travelledmusic.co.uk
contact: Alan Thompson
design service: No
minimum run: None
info: CD duplication service. Travelled Music also offer management, merchandise and equipment hire services, as well as promoting gigs. See listings in relevant sections for details.

White Wolf Recording Studio
Unit 11, Ever Ready Industrial Estate, Hanfield Lane, Stanley, County Durham, DH9 9QF
tel: 01207 282 555
email: ian@whitewolfrecording.co.uk
web: www.whitewolfrecording.co.uk
design service: Yes
minimum run: None
info: On-body printing, shrink wrapping and inlay print. Rehearsal and recording also available.
design service: Yes

NORTHWEST

A1 CD Duplication Ltd.
20 Upton Road, Moreton, Wirral, Merseyside, CH46 0PA
tel: 0151 678 5275
email: anything@a1cdduplication.co.uk
web: www.a1cdduplication.co.uk
contact: Billy, Sue
design service: Yes
minimum run: None
info: CD and DVD duplication. Can supply artwork, from text to full photograph screen print. Mastering service. Live 24 track recording.

ADL
The Old School House, 1 Green Lane, Ashton upon Mersey, Sale, Cheshire, M33 5PN
tel: 0161 905 1361
fax: 0161 282 1360
email: garry.adl@btinternet.com
contact: Garry Bowen
design service: Yes
minimum run: None
info: CD, cassette, video, MD and DVD duplication. CD-ROM production and duplication. Prices vary with requirements. Can reproduce artwork designed by client or by in-house graphic designer. Inlay cards and on-body printing. Mastering (including vinyl mastering) available. Transfer material from any format.

Airtight Productions
Unit 16, Albany Road Trading Estate, Albany Road, Chorlton, Manchester, M21 0AZ
tel: 0161 881 5157
email: info@airtightproductions.co.uk
web: www.airtightproductions.co.uk
contact: Anthony Davey
design service: Yes
info: Digital mastering service. Also operates recording studio under the same name.

Arc Sounds
Unit 9-14, Goodhope House, Ashton-Under-Lyne, Manchester, OL6 7SL
tel: 0161 330 5028
fax: 0161 343 7568
email: pod@arcmusic.freeserve.co.uk
web: www.arcsounds.com
contact: Pod
design service: No
minimum run: 20
info: Arc offer low cost, top quality professional CD duplication. Price list can be found on website. Also provide DVD and video copying service and large order cassette duplication. Arc also has rehearsal room facilities, refer to Rehearsal Studios section for details.

Audio Copying Corporation
Gorsey Mount Street, Waterloo Road, Stockport, Cheshire, SK1 3BU
tel: 0161 477 6531
email: tim@courtyardrecordingstudios.co.uk
web: www.courtyardrecordingstudios.co.uk
contact: Tim Woodward
design service: Yes
minimum run: None
info: CDs, DVDs, CD-ROMs, VHS and cassettes. Prices vary with quantity. Artwork design, delivery and wrapping all available. Pro-mastering at £45 per hour. Associated with Courtyard Studios.

Black Jack Recording Studio
129-131 Telegraph Road, Heswall, CH60 0AF
tel: 0151 342 6333
email: nes67@fsmail.net
contact: Mike Watson
design service: No
minimum run: None
info: CD, DAT and MD duplication. Artwork reproduction. On-body printing. Ideal for small runs. Mastering service also offered.

Blueprint
27-29 King Street West, Manchester, M3 2PN
tel: 0161 839 0661
fax: 0161 839 5267
email: print@blueprintrepro.co.uk
web: www.blueprint-copyshop.co.uk
contact: Jason Richards
design service: Yes
info: £9.99 for one CD. Unit price decreases as quantities increase. Can reproduce artwork onto inlay cards and back covers, or can design artwork in-house. Delivery available. Mastering service.

Blueroom Studio
Unit 75, Mount Heath Industrial Estate, Prestwich, Manchester, M25 9WB
tel: 0161 773 9615
email: phil@blueroomstudios.freeserve.co.uk
web: www.blueroomstudios.co.uk
contact: Phil Green
design service: Yes
minimum run: None
info: Digital mastering to CD and DVD. Mixing on Saw Pro. Call Phil for further details.

Bump Studios
8 Kremlin Drive, Liverpool, L13 7BY
tel: 0151 259 1676
email: info@bumpstudios.co.uk
web: www.bumpstudios.co.uk
contact: Kris Kristiansen
design service: Yes
minimum run: None
info: CD, audio and data duplication. Graphics and print can be provided by an in-house designer. On-body printing and sleeve design. Full audio mastering service. Get instant quotes online. Bump Studios also have a recording studio and are linked with Balboa Graphics, who provide web design and hosting services. Refer to entries in relevant sections for further details.

Cascade Duplication
61 Oaklands, Guilden Sutton, Chester, CH3 7HE
tel: 01244 303 330
email: cascade.duplication@virgin.net
web: www.cascadeduplication.com
design service: Yes
info: Duplication includes CD Extra, Open Session CD-Rs, both PC and MAC platforms.

Cavalier Studios Ltd.
280 Wellington Road South, Stockport, Cheshire, SK2 6ND
tel:	0161 480 6073
fax:	0161 429 8492
email:	info@cavalierstudios.co.uk
web:	www.cavalierstudios.co.uk
contact:	Debbie Cooper
design service:	Yes
minimum run:	None
info:	CD, DVD and CD-ROM duplication. CD-ROM

production. Inlay artwork and on-body printing (thermal, inkjet and screen printing).

CD Duplicator
33-45 Parr Street, Liverpool, L1 4JN
tel:	0151 709 7618
email:	info@cdduplicator.co.uk
web:	www.cdduplicator.co.uk
design service:	Yes
minimum run:	None
info:	Formats include CD, DVD, DAT and video

duplication. On-body printing. Contact CD Duplicator with any queries.

Clock Tower Creative
St. Martins Studios, Greenbank Road, Ashton on Mersey, Sale, M33 5PL
tel:	0161 969 7618
email:	studios@clocktowercreative.co.uk
web:	www.clocktowercreative.co.uk
contact:	Steve Halliwell
design service:	No
minimum run:	None
info:	CD and cassette duplication. Artwork

reproduction. On-body printing.

Colour Jay Ltd.
Power House, Dacre Street, Birkenhead, CH41 6LZ
tel:	0151 647 4861
fax:	0151 647 2540
email:	colourjay@aol.com
contact:	Mike Davis
design service:	Yes
minimum run:	None
info:	CD duplication and full artwork print facilities.

Constant C
16 Greencroft, Brampton, CA8 1AX
tel:	07867 525 125/01697 741 661
email:	jerry@constantc.org.uk
web:	www.constantc.org.uk
contact:	Jerry
design service:	Yes
minimum run:	None
info:	CD duplication. Transfers from vinyl, cassette

and DAT to CD. Artwork reproduction and design. On-body printing. Redbook mastering.

Copysoft Ltd.
Unit 9, The Embankment Business Park, Stockport, SK4 3GL
tel:	0161 442 1234
fax:	0161 442 5555
email:	sales@copysoft.co.uk
web:	www.copysoft.co.uk
contact:	Howard Sinclair
design service:	No
minimum run:	None
info:	CD, DVD and CD-ROM duplication. Prices vary

with size of order and print requirements. Can reproduce artwork onto inlay cards and back cover. On-body printing. Delivery available.

Cottage Recording
2 Gawsworth Road, Macclesfield, Cheshire, SK11 8UE
tel:	01625 420 163
email:	cmm@cottagegroup.co.uk
web:	www.cottagegroup.co.uk
contact:	Glenn Jones
design service:	Yes
minimum run:	None
info:	Prices vary with size of order and artwork.

Duplicate CDs, cassettes, DVDs and CD-ROMs. Range of cases available. Client artwork can be reproduced if in Quark format on PC or Mac. On-body printing on runs of less than 500.

Deluxe GMS Ltd.
Philips Road, Blackburn, Lancashire, BB1 5RZ
tel:	01254 505 401
fax:	01254 505 421
email:	sales@deluxemedia.com
web:	www.deluxemedia.com
contact:	Angela Kaye
design service:	Yes
minimum run:	None
info:	Offer complete in-house disc services for all pre-

recorded CD Audio, CD-ROM and DVD formats from pre-mastering to distribution. Also offer vinyl and audio cassette production, worldwide fulfilment, online e-commerce and order tracking services.

Discsmart Disc Services
Caxton House, Caxton Avenue, Blackpool, FY2 9AP
tel:	01253 508 670
email:	info@discsmart.co.uk
web:	www.discsmart.co.uk
contact:	Steve Sharples
design service:	Yes
minimum run:	None
info:	CD, DVD, cassette, VHS to CD/DVD and MD.

Artwork and design services. Full colour, on-body printing and sleeve artwork. Full mastering service offered. Upload your material on to website with photo and biog for £25 per year. In addition, also run Berlin Recording and Rehearsal facilities, see listings in relevant sections for further details.

the|unsigned|guide

The Unsigned Guide/UK/2006. Material published in this directory may not be reproduced (in any form) without written consent.

ESP Multimedia
33-45 Parr Street, Liverpool, L1 4JN
tel: 0151 708 5090
fax: 0151 708 6669
email: admin@espmultimedia.com
web: www.espmultimedia.com
design service: Yes
minimum run: None
info: ESP Multimedia offer a full CD and DVD duplicating service using in-house replication facilities. Also offer on-body print and packaging.

F.A.B.
Salford, Manchester
tel: 0161 792 0203
email: chris@fabstudios.co.uk
web: www.fabstudios.co.uk
contact: Chris Galbraith
design service: Yes
minimum run: 10
info: CD duplication service with on-body printing. F.A.B. also have recording studios, refer to listing in relevant section for further details.

Garage Studios
39 Longton Road, Burnley, BB12 0TF
tel: 01282 832 686
email: jcsteel@talk21.com
contact: Jason Steel
design service: Yes
minimum run: None
info: CD, MD and cassette duplication. Artwork reproduction can be provided in-house. On-body printing. Mastering service available.

Go Cre8
Mariners House, Queens Dock Business Centre, 67-83 Norfolk Street, Liverpool, L1 0BG
tel: 0845 226 3086
email: info@gocre8.co.uk
web: www.gocre8.co.uk
contact: Darryn
design service: Yes
minimum run: None
info: CD and DVD duplication. Full printing and packaging including on-body printing. Mastering service. Go Cre8 also provide web and graphic design services. See entry in relevant section for further details.

Lakeside Studios
Northwich, Cheshire
tel: 01606 863 642
email: jdelf@mac.com
contact: John Delf
design service: Yes
info: Digital mastering. Lakeside also have recording facilities. See entry in relevant section for further details.

Linden Studio
High Bankhill Farmhouse, Kirkoswald, Penrith, Cumbria, CA10 1EZ
tel: 01768 870 353
email: guy@lindenstudio.co.uk
web: www.lindenstudio.co.uk
contact: Guy Forrester
design service: Yes
info: CD mastering and duplication. Artwork reproduction. Linden Studio also has recording facilities. See entry in relevant section

Mad Dog Studio
Unit 57, Deeside Industrial Estate, Welsh Road, Deeside, CH5 2LR
tel: 01244 281 705
email: maddogstudios666@hotmail.com
web: www.maddogstudios.org
contact: Eddie
design service: No
info: Thermo printed discs. Maximum turnaround of 14 days, although usually completed in 7 days. Covers, inlays and plastic sleeves provided. Mad Dog also offer rehearsal facilities. See listing in relevant section for details.

The Media Magician
Unit 22, Lillyhall Business Centre, Jubilee Road, Workington, Cumbria, CA14 4HA
tel: 0845 060 2760
fax: 0845 060 2860
email: sales@media-magician.com
web: www.media-magician.com
design service: No
minimum run: None
info: CD and DVD duplication and replication. Can also duplicate vinyl and cassette formats through external contacts. Will reproduce client's artwork. Inlay and on-body printing. Mastering service available.

Mr Studio
PO Box 104, Liverpool, L12 0WW
tel: 07876 518 390
email: info@mrstudio.biz
web: www.mrstudio.biz
contact: Drew
design service: Yes
minimum run: None
info: CD duplication. Also mobile sound recording and production services.

The Music Factory
Unit 3a, Sycamore Trading Estate, Squires Gate Lane, Blackpool, FY4 3RL
tel: 0845 644 1627
email: info@themusicfactoryuk.co.uk
web: www.themusicfactoryuk.co.uk
contact: Andy
design service: Yes
minimum run: 100
info: CD and DVD duplication. Artwork reproduction and design. On-body printing. Mastering service available.

Music House Productions
8 Ley Drive, Hopwood, Heywood, OL10 2NA
tel: 01706 365 167
email: keith@music-house.freeserve.co.uk
contact: Keith Farrington
design service: Yes
minimum run: None
info: CD duplication. Artwork reproduction and in-house design. On-body printing. Mastering from virtually any format. Music editing service also available.

NPH Media Ltd.
10 York Avenue, Oldham, Lancashire, OL8 4BY
tel: 0161 678 6789
email: info@nphmedia.co.uk
web: www.nphmedia.co.uk
contact: Nigel Hobson
design service: Yes
minimum run: None
info: CD and DVD duplication. Can assist clients with design, or reproduce completed artwork. Thermal full colour on-body printing to a high standard. Fast, flexible service.

Phoenix Recording Services
Unit 3b, Townfoot Industrial Estate, Brampton, Cumbria, CA8 1SW
tel: 01697 741 773
email: alex@phoenixstudios.freeserve.co.uk
web: www.phoenixstudios.freeserve.co.uk
contact: Alex
design service: No
minimum run: 10
info: CD-R duplication. Specialise in small runs. 99p per disc including case. Disc with printed labels available (£1.20 matt, £1.50 gloss). Inlay card printing can be arranged. Cassette duplication also available, cost per unit depends on length. Phone Alex for further details.

Print Magic
Phoenix House, 16 Tanning Court, Howley, Warrington, WA1 2HF
tel: 01925 629 990
fax: 01925 444 438
email: info@print-magic.com
web: www.print-magic.com
contact: Paul, Karen
design service: Yes
minimum run: None
info: Duplication prices vary with quantity. Work from master supplied by client. Inlay and on-body printing. CDs available in a range of colours. Full design service and can also reproduce artwork supplied by client.

Promenade Music
404 Marine Road, East Morecambe, Lancashire, LA4 5AR
tel: 01524 410 202
fax: 01524 410 802
email: sales@promenademusic.co.uk
web: www.promenademusic.co.uk
contact: David Wood
design service: Yes
minimum run: None
info: Duplication services with on-body printing, inlay cards and booklets available. Can also duplicate cassettes and vinyl. Promenade Music will take care of all the Mechanical Copyright Protection Society (MCPS) requirements for your recording. Promenade Music also have recording studio facilities, and are a musical instrument retailer. See listings in relevant sections for further details.

Pure Music Manufacturing Ltd.
Bexley Chambers, 1-3 Bexley Square, Manchester, M3 6DB
tel:	0161 833 0099/0161 833 0089
fax:	0870 762 8215
email:	info@pure-music.co.uk
web:	www.pure-music.co.uk
contact:	Will Shaw
design service:	Yes
minimum run:	500
info:	Prices start at £475 for basic 500 CD run. CDs, vinyl, CD-ROMs, DVD, business card CD-ROMs. Crystal cases (album or slimline) or card wallet. Can provide wrapping and barcodes. Mastering service. Delivery service also available.

Red Cat Studios
Standish, Wigan
tel:	01257 421 357/07866 737 523
email:	redcatstudios@hotmail.com
web:	www.redcatstudios.co.uk
contact:	Alan
design service:	Yes
minimum run:	50
info:	CD and DVD duplication. Can reproduce client's artwork, or provide selection of designs. On-body printing. Mastering service available. Red Cat also run recording facilities. See entry in Recording Studios section for details.

Revolution Digital
5 Rolls Crescent, Manchester, M15 5JX
tel:	0161 232 9314
email:	studio@rdigital.co.uk
web:	www.rdigital.co.uk
design service:	No
minimum run:	None
info:	Audio mastering service. Also offer DVD, ECD and Ecard authoring. Up to 10,000 copies. Also have a branch in London. See relevant listings for more details.

Rich Video
351 Reddish Road, Reddish, Stockport, Cheshire, SK5 7EN
tel:	0161 480 3389
email:	sales@richvideo.co.uk
web:	www.richvideo.co.uk
contact:	Carolyn or David
design service:	No
minimum run:	None
info:	CD and DVD duplication. Inlay, on-body and label printing. CD-ROM business cards. Also offer video and multimedia CD-ROM production.

Ricta UK
Hyde Park House, Cartwright Street, Hyde, Cheshire, SK14 4EH
tel:	0161 351 0161
email:	rictauk@btclick.com
web:	www.rictauk.co.uk
contact:	Eric Taylor
design service:	Yes
minimum run:	None
info:	CD duplication, artwork print and design, on-body printing. Can also provide poster, flyer and t-shirt printing. See entries in relevant sections for details.

RTS One Stop
Unit M1, Albany Road, Prescot, Liverpool, L34 2UP
tel:	0151 430 9001
fax:	0151 430 7441
email:	sue@rtsonestop.co.uk
web:	www.rtsonestop.co.uk
contact:	Sue
design service:	Yes
minimum run:	None
info:	CD duplication prices vary with quantity. Inlay artwork available on runs over 500. Range of cases. Also duplicate cassettes, videos, CD-ROMs and CD business cards. Delivery and wrapping available. Mastering available, and sell a range of studio media formats. Distribution services.

Screentalk
The Orangery Estate, Chelford Road, Knutsford, Cheshire, WA16 8RD
tel:	01565 754 555
email:	info@screentalk.co.uk
contact:	Mark Ambrose
design service:	Yes

Shamrock Recording Studio
The Garth, Commons Lane, Balderstone, Blackburn, Lancashire, BB2 7LL
tel:	01254 812 131
email:	s.heffernan@btinternet.com
contact:	Seamus Heffernan
design service:	No
minimum run:	None
info:	Price varies with the number of units ordered (maximum 250), the length of audio, artwork requirements and cases. Artwork supplied by clients can be reproduced in full colour on inlay card and labels for CD body. Single and double jewel cases and plastic wallets available.

The Shed Recording Studio
Unit 46, Chadkirk Ind Estate, Vale Road, Romiley, Stockport, Cheshire, SK6 3NE
tel:	0161 427 6819
fax:	0161 427 6819
email:	shedstudio1@tiscali.co.uk
contact:	John Slater
design service:	No
minimum run:	None
info:	Maximum run 500. Price depends on size of order and printing requirements. Can reproduce colour artwork from any format for inlay cards. Also duplicate cassettes.

Shireshead Studio
Shireshead Old Church, Stony Lane, Forton, Preston, PR3 1BV
tel:	01524 792 020
email:	info@shiresheadstudio.com
web:	www.shiresheadstudio.com
contact:	Martin Hughes
design service:	No
minimum run:	None
info:	CD and cassette duplication. No minimum run. Artwork reproduction. Full colour or black on-body printing. Offer full mastering service.

Sound Production
8 Broomville Avenue, Sale, Cheshire, M33 3DD
tel:	0161 976 3733
fax:	0161 973 3936
email:	ian@sound-productions.co.uk
web:	www.sound-productions.co.uk
contact:	Ian Royle
design service:	No
minimum run:	100
info:	CD and cassette duplication. Price varies with requirements. Can reproduce artwork or provide design service. Inlay cards and on-body printing. Range of cases available.

Spirit Recording Studio
10 Tariff Street, Manchester, M1 2FF
tel:	0161 228 3072
fax:	0161 236 0078
email:	enquiries@s-s-r.com
web:	www.s-s-r.com
contact:	John Breakell
design service:	Yes
info:	Full mastering service available. Associated with the School of Sound Recording - see entry in Tuition/Training section for further details.

Splash Sound Productions
1 Mossley Hill Drive, Liverpool, L17 1AJ
tel:	0151 724 2100
fax:	0151 724 5813
email:	rick@splashsoundproductions.co.uk
web:	www.splashsoundproductions.co.uk
contact:	Rick Juckes
design service:	No
minimum run:	None
info:	CD, DVD, vinyl, cassette, VHS and DAT duplication. Digital mastering. Established for over 20 years.

Spool Multi Media (UK) Ltd.
Unit 30, Deeside Industrial Park, Deeside, Flintshire, CH5 2NU
tel:	01244 280 602
email:	admin@smmuk.co.uk
web:	www.smmuk.co.uk
contact:	Roy Varley
design service:	No
minimum run:	None
info:	CD, DVD and cassette duplication. Artwork reproduction. On-body printing. No minimum run on selected formats. Mastering service available.

Stonegate Studios
Unit 7, Pyes Mill, Bentham, Lancaster, LA2 7LJ
tel: 01524 263 433
email: info@stonegate-studios.co.uk
web: www.stonegate-studios.co.uk
contact: Sam Lawrence
design service: Yes
info: Mastering service. Will master individual tracks as sent in by bands.

Studio Studio Recording
Unit 4, Spodden Mill, Facit, Whitworth, Rochdale, OL12 8LJ
tel: 01706 853 518
email: zen39135@zen.co.uk
web: www.studio-studio.co.uk
contact: Pete
design service: Yes
info: Mastering from DAT or CD on Mac and PC to customers specifications.

Tailored Music
Unit 1a, Welch Hill Mill, Leigh, Lancashire, WN7 4DJ
tel: 01942 514 624
email: info@tailoredmusic.co.uk
web: www.tailoredmusic.co.uk
contact: Mark Gerard
design service: Yes
minimum run: None
info: CD, DAT and MD duplication. Artwork reproduction and in-house design. On-body printing. CD mastering service available. Recording studio facilities also available.

Tapeline Ltd.
72a Stockport Road East, Bredbury, Stockport, Cheshire, SK6 1AL
tel: 0161 406 8608
email: alan@tapeline.info
web: www.tapeline.info
contact: Alan or Louise
design service: No
minimum run: 100 (cassette). None for other formats
info: VHS, DVD, CD and cassette duplication. Prices vary. Contact for pricelist or quote.

Testa-Rossa Recording Studio
Unit 12, Longsight Industrial Estate, Manchester, M12 4EY
tel: 0161 273 2404
fax: 0161 273 2404
email: andy@testa-rossa.com
web: www.testa-rossa.com
contact: Andy Drelincourt
design service: Yes
minimum run: 50
info: On-body printing. Artwork by arrangement. Jewel and C-shell cases available. 100 CDs from £100, depending on printing and packaging requirements. Mastering facilities available.

West Coast Duplication
36 Trinity Gardens, Thornton-Cleveleys, Lancashire, FY5 2UA
tel: 01253 858 898
email: jim@westcoastduplication.com
web: www.westcoastduplication.com
design service: Yes
minimum run: 100
info: Minimum run usually 100 units, may do 50 by arrangement. 100 CDs including artwork and label costs £130. Can reproduce colour artwork supplied by band or in-house designer. On-body printing. Enhanced CD duplication. £10 for overnight delivery.

SOUTHEAST

Abandon Studios
44 1/2 The Mint, Rye, East Sussex, TN31 7EN
tel: 01797 222 498
email: abandonstudios@virgin.net
contact: Michael
design service: Yes
minimum run: None
info: Post production and mastering for CDs. CD duplication. Artwork provided by clients can be reproduced onto inlay cards.

AGR Manufacturing
The Stables, 44 Stortford Road, Great Dunmow, Essex, CM6 1DL
tel: 01371 859 393
fax: 01371 859 375
email: info@agrm.co.uk
web: www.agrm.co.uk
contact: Martin
design service: Yes
minimum run: None
info: CD, DVD, cassette and vinyl mastering and duplication. Full artwork reproduction and design service. Mastering facilities available.

Alpha Duplication
Unit A-D, The Brow Business Centre, Copyground Lane, High Wycombe, Buckinghamshire, HP12 3HE
tel: 01494 536 646
fax: 01494 536 651
email: info@alpha-duplication.com
web: www.alpha-duplication.com
contact: Chris
design service: Yes
info: CD, DVD, tape and disk duplication. CD and DVD packaging and printing. Fulfilment and distribution. Average lead times are 3 days for duplicated orders and 8 days for replicated orders. Screen print discs in-house.

Aquasonic
Caversham, Reading, Berkshire, RG4 6PP
tel: 07769 877 245
email: info@aquasonicstudio.co.uk
web: www.aquasonicstudio.co.uk
contact: Lawrence
design service: Yes
minimum run: 50
info: Aquasonic is a small but fully equipped studio based in the North Berkshire/South Oxfordshire borders. CD mastering and duplication available. See entry in relevant section for recording services.

BandBits
Prince Bros Site, Old Bath Road, Charvil, Berkshire, RG10 9QJ
tel: 0118 932 0032
fax: 0118 932 0016
email: nick@bandbits.com
web: www.bandbits.com
contact: Nick Lawson
design service: Yes
minimum run: None
info: CD duplication and video to DVD transfer and duplication. BandBits also offer studio recording and rehearsal space, see entries in relevant sections for details.

Bluecrest
Salamander Quays, Quay South Court, Park Lane, Harefield, Uxbridge, UB9 6NY
tel: 01895 822 020
email: info@bluecrest.com
web: www.bluecrest.com
contact: Nicky
design service: Yes
minimum run: 500
info: CD-Rom and audio CD replication and duplication. DVD duplication. On-body printing.

Brandedmedia Ltd.
Unit 4, Ringway Centre, Edison Road, Basingstoke, Hampshire, RG21 6YH
tel: 01256 355 533
email: sales@brandedmedia.net
web: www.brandedmedia.net
design service: Yes
minimum run: None
info: CD and DVD replication and duplication. Full artwork reproduction and design service. Have an innovative 'solar' range of CD and DVD packaging. Check the website for details.

C2 Productions Ltd.
Cromer House, Caxton Way, Stevenage, Hertfordshire, SG1 2DF
tel: 01438 317 333
fax: 01438 317 555
email: info@c2productions.co.uk
web: www.c2productions.co.uk
contact: Carlos Buhagiar
design service: Yes
minimum run: 10 (duplication only)
info: Small quantity CD and DVD duplication with high quality printing directly onto the disc. Large quantity CD & DVD manufacturing (1000 discs upwards). Design, print and packaging service. Friendly, helpful advice.

The CD Mule
27 Green Close, Didcot, Oxon, OX11 8TE
tel: 07748 337 625
email: mail@thecdmule.co.uk or
cd_mule@yahoo.co.uk
web: www.thecdmule.co.uk
contact: Andrew Hubbard
design service: Yes
minimum run: None
info: CD and DVD duplication. Barcoding and jewel
case options available. On-body printing, as well as inlays and booklets.

CD Team
Team House, 1 Fairview Estate, Reading Road, Henley on Thames,
Oxfordshire, RG9 1HE
tel: 01491 636 373
fax: 01491 636 374
email: info@cdteam.co.uk
web: www.cdteam.co.uk
design service: Yes
minimum run: None
info: Duplication for CD, DVD and blank media. Can
convert vinyl and cassette formats to CD. On-body printing, inserts and
booklets. Mastering service.

CD-R Print
Unit 3, Hurlands Business Centre, Farnham, Surrey, GU9 9JE
tel: 01252 722 201
fax: 01252 722 944
email: info@cdr-print.co.uk
web: www.cdr-print.co.uk
contact: Mr Steirs
design service: Yes
minimum run: None
info: CD and DVD duplication and replication.
Artwork reproduction and in-house design service. On-body printing.
No minimum run.

Central Recording Studio
Queen Mary's College, Cliddesden Road, Basingstoke, RG21 3HF
tel: 01256 417 511
email: nemazine@hotmail.com
web: www.centralstudio.co.uk
design service: No
minimum run: None
info: CD duplication, from small runs up to 1000. Also
have recording facilities. See entry in relevant section for further details.

Cine Wessex Ltd.
Westway House, St. Thomas Street, Winchester, Hampshire, SO23 9HJ
tel: 01962 865 454
fax: 01962 842 017
email: ema@cinewessex.co.uk
web: www.cinewessex.co.uk
contact: Ema Branton
design service: No
minimum run: None
info: CD and DVD duplication and replication. Basic
design available, but mainly prefer competed artwork to be submitted
by client. On-body printing. Also encoding and authoring services.

Complete Digital Solutions
1 Harthall Lane, Kings Langley, WD4 8JJ
tel: 01923 261 266
email: simon@designbytangerine.co.uk
web: www.designbytangerine.co.uk
contact: Rob Pickett
design service: Yes
info: DVD and CD production, mastering and
duplication. Also offers graphic design and packaging.

Connexion Studios
Hook, Nr Basingstoke, Hampshire
tel: 01256 769 415
email: info@connexionstudios.com
web: www.connexionstudios.com
design service: Yes
info: Connexion offer mastering services.

The Copyroom
85 Coleridge Street, Hove, East Sussex, BN3 5AA
tel: 07909 916 361
email: info@thecopyroom.co.uk
web: www.thecopyroom.co.uk
contact: Ross
design service: Yes
minimum run: None
info: The Copyroom is an independent music and
media services company. With over 15 years collective experience in
the professional recording and mastering industries, The Copyroom
provides affordable solutions for CD and DVD duplication, design and
packaging, manufacturing, recording, audio mastering, vinyl cutting,
and company branded blank CDs and DVDs.

Copysound Ltd.
West Street Studios, 3 West Street, Buckingham, MK18 1HL
tel: 01280 822 814
email: sales@copysound.co.uk
web: www.copysound.co.uk
contact: Nigel or Jamie
design service: Yes
minimum run: 100
info: CD and DVD duplication. On-body printing plus
booklets and inserts. Mastering service available. See also entry for
West Street Studios in Recording Studios section.

Cyclone Music Production
74 Riverside 3, Sir Thomas Longley Road, Rochester, Kent, ME2 4BH
tel: 01634 714 522
email: sales@cyclonemusic.co.uk
web: www.cyclonemusic.co.uk
contact: Graham Seamark
design service: Yes
minimum run: None
info: CD and cassette duplication. Artwork
reproduction and in-house design service. On-body printing. Mastering
facilities available at £40 per hour. Package deals available, check the
website for details.

Damont Audio
20 Blyth Road, Hayes, Middlesex, UB3 1BY
tel: 020 8573 5122
email: sales@damontaudio.com
web: www.damontaudio.com
contact: Chris Seymour
design service: Yes
minimum run: None
info: CD, vinyl and cassette duplication. On-body
printing.

Digital Media Duplication
PO Box 125, Brighton, BN2 3XR
tel: 01273 383 532/07817 649 660
email: david1103@yahoo.com
web: www.digitalmediaduplication.com
contact: David
design service: Yes
minimum run: 25
info: CD and DVD duplication. Can provide in-house
design service, or alternatively reproduce bands' artwork. Black on-
body thermal printing onto silver discs. Full colour resolution for
inlay and booklet printing. Mastering service available using fully
acoustically treated mastering room.

Direct CDs
Unit 8b, Swains Mill, Crane Mead, Ware, Hertfordshire, SG12 9PY
tel: 01920 465 023
fax: 01920 468 387
email: sales@directcds.co.uk
web: www.directcds.co.uk
contact: Martin Crowson
design service: Yes
minimum run: None
info: CD and DVD duplication. Full packaging service
including on-body print, booklets and inserts. Also offer brochure and
flyer printing service.

Discburner
8 Woodside Road, Chiddingfold, Surrey, GU8 4UH
tel: 01428 681 434
email: dave@discburner.co.uk
web: www.discburner.co.uk
design service: Yes
minimum run: 25
info: Family run business providing CD duplication.
Free artwork set-up and proof. Also runs a web design business. Also
offer internet streaming and design services.

Downsoft Ltd.
Downsway House, Woodview Close, off Epsom Road, Ashtead, Surrey,
KT21 1HA
tel: 01372 272 422
fax: 01372 276 122
email: work@downsoft.co.uk
web: www.downsoft.co.uk
design service: Yes
minimum run: None
info: CD, DVD and cassette duplication. Small runs are
their speciality. On-body printing and artwork reproduction available.

Duplidisk Ltd.
Thornham Cottage, 26 Oaks Road, Stanwell, Staines, Middlesex, TW19 7LG
tel: 01784 243 029
email: nick@duplidisk.co.uk
web: www.duplidisk.co.uk
contact: Nick Outteridge
design service: Yes
minimum run: None
info: Specialise in short run CD duplication. On-body printing and artwork reproduction. Limited in-house design service.

Effenel Studios
787 Southchurch Road, Southend On Sea, Essex, SS1 2PP
tel: 01702 614 857
email: info@effenel.com
web: www.effenel.com
design service: No
minimum run: 10
info: Effenel provides cost effective, low runs of full colour CD printing. Ideal for bands or groups who need small supplies of demos, but are not willing to compromise on quality. Prices start at £1 per CD. Specialise in small runs of 10 to 100 at a time.

E-Mart
Barn Studios, Peper Harow Park, Godalming, Surrey, GU8 6BB
tel: 0845 430 0345
fax: 01483 429 998
email: sales@e-mart.uk.com
web: www.e-mart.uk.com
design service: No
minimum run: 10
info: CD and DVD duplication. Digital on-body printing (Inkjet Print). Service available for quantities from 10 to 500. Turnaround is 3 to 5 working days.

Exemplar UK
Unit 4, Thornley Business Park, Thornely Lane North, Iver, SL0 9HF
tel: 0845 677 0033
email: emma@exemplar-uk.com
web: www.exemplar-uk.com
design service: Yes
info: All aspects of DVD and CD duplication for short-run or bulk projects, including a range of printing, packaging and delivery options.

Finesplice
1 Summerhouse Lane, Harmondsworth, West Drayton, Middlesex, UB7 0AT
tel: 020 8564 7839
fax: 020 8759 9629
email: info@finesplice.co.uk
web: www.finesplice.co.uk
design service: Yes
info: Every type of music mastered. Accept many different input formats. Surround-sound mastering available.

FocusMove Ltd.
15-16 Raynham Road Trading Estate, Bishops Stortford, Hertfordshire, CM23 5PD
tel: 0845 130 2200
email: sales@focusmove.com
web: www.focusmove.com
contact: Ben Bull
design service: No
minimum run: None
info: CD and DVD manufacture, mastering and duplication. From 1 copy to bulk orders. Call for further details.

Here and Now Distribution Ltd.
Unit 4d, Caxton Point, Caxton Way, Stevenage, Hertfordshire, SG1 2XU
tel: 01438 723 383
email: sales@hnprint.co.uk
web: www.hnprint.co.uk
contact: Adrian
design service: Yes
minimum run: None
info: CD and DVD printing and duplication. Print booklets, inlays and many other forms of packaging. Offer free samples using your own artwork.

John Bassett
Hastings, East Sussex
email: john@johnbassett.co.uk
web: www.johnbassett.co.uk
design service: Yes
info: Provide mixing, production and mastering for demo recordings. Mastering costs £12 per track for a CD single (4 tracks or less) or £7 per track for an album consisting of 5 tracks or more. Can also provide design for web and print. See relevant section for more details.

JRP Music Services
Empire House, Hereford Road, Southsea, Hampshire, PO5 2DH
tel: 02392 297 839/07776 006 107
email: james.perrett@noc.soton.ac.uk
web: www.jrpmusic.fsnet.co.uk
contact: James Perrett
design service: No
minimum run: None
info: Mastering and mixing service. Can transfer wide range of old formats (such as ADAT, 1/2 inch 16 track, 1/4 inch 8 track) to modern digital formats. Also offer small scale duplication of CDs and DVDs.

Keynote Audio Services
Smoke Tree House, Tilford Road, Rushmoor, Farnham, Surrey, GU10 2EN
tel: 01252 794 253
email: sales@keynoteaudio.co.uk
web: www.keynoteaudio.co.uk
design service: Yes
info: Audio mastering and sound restoration. CD-R and CD-ROM duplicating and copying. Factory-pressed CD packages and loop bin (high speed) cassette duplicating and printing. Mastering formats supported include DAT, CD, Minidisc, Cassette, and 1/4 inch open reel. Full print service available for CD and cassette.

Live Wire Duplication Services
Tamarind, Copthorne Common Road, Copthorne, West Sussex, RH10 3LF
tel: 01342 714 183
email: info@livewire-cds.com
web: www.livewire-cds.com
design service: No
minimum run: 10
info: CD, DVD, VHS and cassette duplication and replication. On-body print in either black thermal or full colour. Also print full colour insert cards and will reproduce artwork from client. Specialise in runs for unsigned bands and have large client portfolio. Will produce a free of charge approval copy so you to see exactly what you are getting before purchasing. Instant quote can be obtained online at above website.

The Liveroom
Horndean Campus, Barton Cross, Horndean, Hampshire, PO8 9PQ
tel: 02393 599 753
email: bookings@theliveroom.co.uk
web: www.theliveroom.co.uk
design service: Yes
info: Duplication services for CD, cassette, MD and DAT. The Liveroom also has recording and rehearsal facilities, as well as a design company, D-Code. See entries in relevant sections for further information.

Media Matters Technology
12-14 Somerset House, Hussar Court, Waterlooville, Hampshire, PO7 7SG
tel: 0870 870 1123
email: info@mediamatterstechnology.com
web: www.mediamatterstechnology.co.uk
design service: Yes
minimum run: None
info: CD and DVD duplication. Also offer replication service for larger quantities. Full packaging including on-body print, booklets and inlays. Mastering available.

MediaClone
Genestt House, 39 Bay Road, Bracknell, Berkshire, RG12 2NS
tel: 01344 868 885
fax: 0870 443 2677
email: info@media-clone.co.uk
web: http://mediaclone.virtualsite.co.uk/index.html
contact: Scott
design service: No
minimum run: None
info: Duplicating service for CD and DVD. Will produce all packaging. Can also create masters from files.

Multi Media Replication
Unit 4, Balksbury Estate, Upper Clatford, Andover, Hampshire, SP11 7LW
tel: 01264 336 330
fax: 01264 336 694
email: info@replication.com
web: www.replication.com
contact: Phillip Hall
design service: Yes
minimum run: None
info: CD, DVD and VHS replication. DVD authoring and encoding. Printing and packaging service.

Philia Studios
52 Gainsborough Hill, Henley-On-Thames, Oxfordshire, RG9 1SS
tel: 01491 575 516/01491 576 951
email: copromike@aol.com
web: www.philiastudios.com
contact: Mike
design service: Yes
minimum run: 500
info: Philia Studios is owned by Copro & Casket Records, who aim for something of a one-stop facility for young creative bands to fulfil their potential. See entry in relevant section for details of studio recording facilities.

Pogo Entertainment Ltd.
The Seedbed Business Centre, Vanguard Way, Shoeburyness, Essex, SS3 9QY
tel: 0870 766 2446
fax: 01702 384 043
email: info@pogoentertainment.com
web: www.pogoentertainment.com
contact: Shelley English, Terry Piper
design service: Yes
minimum run: None
info: CD-R and DVD duplication. On-body printing. Specialise in smaller runs. Barcoding available. Pogo Entertainment can also provide promotional merchandising, and run a website used as a platform for unsigned bands and musicians. See entries in relevant sections for details.

Pricedata
28 Danemead, Hoddesdon, Hertfordshire, EN11 9LU
tel: 01992 462 437
email: sales@pricedata.co.uk
web: www.pricedata.co.uk
contact: Trevor
design service: Yes
minimum run: None
info: CD and DVD duplication. Mastering service available.

RGM Media Ltd.
Unit 3, Balshaw Heath, Bullbeggars Lane, Berkhamsted, Hertfordshire, HP4 2RS
tel: 01442 877 311
fax: 01442 873 311
email: sales@rgmmedia.co.uk
web: www.rgmmedia.co.uk
contact: Kate, Nick
design service: Yes
minimum run: 500
info: CD, VHS, DVD, MD and cassette duplication. Print and design service. Mastering and barcodes available. Will provide help and guidance for unsigned artists, and can offer advice on distribution.

Rock Links
Gosport, Hampshire
email: cdduplication@rocklinks.co.uk
web: www.rocklinks.co.uk
contact: Craig Jones
design service: Yes
minimum run: None
info: CD duplication. Design service and can also reproduce client's artwork. On-body printing, as well as booklets and inlays. Also linked with New World Web Design. See entry in relevant section for further details.

Romulus
1 Dagnall Road, Edlesborough, Buckinghamshire, LU6 2EF
tel: 01525 222 900
email: info@romulus2000.co.uk
web: www.romulus2000.co.uk
contact: David Dean
design service: Yes
minimum run: None
info: CD duplication specialists. Artwork reproduction.

Selecta Sound
52 Rockingham Avenue, Hornchurch, Essex, RM11 1HH
tel: 01708 453 424/07779 140 311
fax: 01708 455 565
email: info@selecta-sound.co.uk
web: www.selecta-sound.co.uk
contact: John Smailes
design service: Yes
minimum run: None
info: CD, DVD, VHS and cassette duplication. Full reprographic facilities available and on-body printing.

SFH UK Ltd.
Unit 5, io Centre, Hatfield Business Park, Hearle Way, Hatfield, AL10 9EW
tel: 01707 274 444
fax: 01707 274 443
email: info@sfhuk.net
web: www.sfhuk.net
design service: Yes
minimum run: 500 for CDs, DVDs and cassettes, 300 for vinyl
info: CD, DVD, cassette and vinyl duplication. On-body printing. Mastering service available.

Silent Coup Studios
Hurst, Berkshire
tel: 0118 934 0934
email: admin@the-silent-coup.org
web: www.the-silent-coup.org
contact: Joe
design service: Yes
info: CD mastering services.

Silk Recordings
65 High Street, Kings Langley, Hertfordshire, WD4 9HU
tel: 01923 270 852/07812 602 535
email: info@silkrecordings.com
web: www.silkrecordings.com
contact: Bob Whitney
design service: Yes
minimum run: None
info: Mastering and CD duplication services. Silk Recordings also provide recording facilities. See entry in relevant section for further details.

Soundcheck CD Duplication
360 Havant Road, Farlington, Portsmouth, Hampshire, PO6 1NE
tel: 02392 642 919
email: enquirey@cd-duplicating.co.uk
web: www.cd-duplicating.co.uk
design service: Yes
minimum run: None
info: CD and DVD duplication. In-house digital printing and graphic design. Up to 5000 units.

Sounds Good Ltd.
12 Chiltern Enterprise Centre, Station Road, Theale, Berkshire, RG7 4AA
tel: 0118 930 1700
fax: 0118 930 1709
email: sales-info@sounds-good.co.uk
web: www.sounds-good.co.uk
design service: Yes
minimum run: None
info: CD, DVD, cassette and VHS replication. Three graphics studios providing a full artwork reproduction and design service. High quality mastering at £55 per hour.

Tangerine
Leewood Farm, Harthall lane, Kings Langley, Hertfordshire, WD4 8JJ
tel: 01923 261 266
fax: 01923 261 267
email: info@designbytangerine.co.uk
web: www.designbytangerine.co.uk
design service: Yes
minimum run: None
info: CD and DVD duplication. All artwork required can also be produced. On-body printing. General printing and graphic and web design available. See relevant sections for details.

Turan Audio Ltd.
Oxford, Oxfordshire
tel: 01865 716 466
email: ro@turanaudio.co.uk
web: www.turanaudio.co.uk
contact: Ro
design service: Yes
minimum run: None
info: CD mastering and duplication. On-body printing, as well as booklets and inserts.

UK Discs
33 Bath Street, Abingdon, Oxfordshire, OX14 3RH
tel: 01235 559 800
email: info@ukdiscs.com
web: www.ukdiscs.com
contact: Dale Olivier
design service: Yes
minimum run: 500
info: CD, DVD and vinyl replication and manufacturing from glass master. Professional packaging. Silk screen on-body printing, full colour booklets up to 12 pages, barcoding and shrink-wrapping. Linked with Matchbox Recordings, a label with internet broadcast facility. See entry in relevant section for further information.

W.E.B.S. Ltd.
The Old Clockshop, 19 Dorking Road, Bookham, Surrey, KT23 4PU
tel:	01372 750 563
email:	sales@cdrom-businesscard.co.uk
web:	www.cdrom-businesscard.co.uk
design service:	Yes
minimum run:	10
info:	Duplication and replication services for CD,

CD-R, DVD and DVD-R. Full printing and packaging service. Can also produce custom shaped and vinyl style discs. Audio mastering available.

Xpress Duplication
73 Birchwood Avenue, Hatfield, Hertfordshire, AL10 0PT
tel:	01707 260 790
fax:	01707 260 790
email:	info@xpressduplication.co.uk
web:	www.xpressduplication.co.uk
contact:	Andy Young
design service:	Yes
minimum run:	None
info:	CD and DVD duplication. Also mastering service.

Free audio mastering for 200 + units. On-body printing, booklets and inserts.

Xpress Ltd.
The Converted Barn, Widehurst Farm, Thorne Road, Marden, Tonbridge, Kent, TN12 9LN
tel:	01622 832 302
email:	info@xpresscds.co.uk
web:	www.xpresscds.co.uk
contact:	Danya Martin
design service:	Yes
info:	Replicate audio CDs, CD-Roms and DVDs using

glass masters. Offer on-body printing. Can reproduce client's artwork for booklets and inlays. Various packaging options for orders from 500 units. Mastering service. Inclusive packages available for unsigned bands and musicians to allow them to obtain a professional finished product at a reasonable price.
design service:	Yes

SOUTHWEST

APR Media
Lea House, Frobisher Way, Taunton, Somerset, TA2 6BB
tel:	0700 010 2030
email:	websales@aprmedia.com
web:	www.aprmedia.com
design service:	No
minimum run:	Contact for details
info:	CD, DVD and VHS duplication. Limited design

service. Will reproduce client's artwork. On-body printing plus booklets, inserts and inlay. Minimum run depends upon whether discs are duplicated by burning or pressing.

Audiomaster
273 Preston Road, Yeovil, Somerset, BA20 2EP
tel:	0870 446 0442
fax:	0870 137 1104
email:	info@audiomaster.co.uk
web:	www.audiomaster.co.uk
contact:	Steve Kitch
design service:	Yes
info:	Audiomaster provide professional CD mastering

at very low rates. Also offer mail order and online services. Unique system allowing clients to approve their mastered tracks before paying.

Autumn Studios
Poole, Dorset
tel:	01202 710 554
fax:	01202 723 609
email:	info@autumn-studios.co.uk
web:	www.autumn-studios.co.uk
design service:	Yes
info:	Offers a full range of CD duplication and

mastering services in-house. Prices start from £99 including VAT and include jewel cases.

Barber Thorne Creative
Black Moor Road, Ebblake Industrial Estate, Verwood, Dorset, BH31 6BB
tel:	01202 828 000
fax:	01202 826 222
email:	info@btcreative.co.uk
web:	www.btcreative.co.uk
design service:	Yes
minimum run:	None
info:	CD duplication up to 1000 units. Offer many

different creative services in addition to duplication. Mastering not available.

Bulrush Studios
Unit 5, Enterprise Park, Mart Road, Minehead, Somerset, TA24 5BJ
tel:	01643 707 277
email:	info@bulrushstudios.co.uk
web:	www.bulrushstudios.co.uk
design service:	No
minimum run:	None
info:	CD and cassette duplication. Bulrush Studios

also offer recording and rehearsal facilities, equipment hire and drum tuition services. See entries in relevant sections for further details.

The Bunker
72a Reedley Road, Bristol, BS9 3SU
tel:	0117 962 3155
email:	thebunker@bluyonder.co.uk
web:	www.bunkerstudios.co.uk
contact:	Bob Pierce
design service:	Yes
minimum run:	None
info:	On-body and inlay printing, all done in-house.

Recording facilities also available - see relevant section for more details.

CMG Audio
4A Blenheim Road, Weymouth, Dorset, DT3 5AZ
tel:	01305 771 607
email:	studio@cmgaudio.com
web:	www.cmgaudio.com
design service:	Yes
minimum run:	None
info:	CD duplication and audio transfer services. On-body printing. Also run studio and mobile recording facilities.

CPC
The Dairy, Pinkney Park, Malmesbury, Wiltshire, SN16 0NX
tel:	01666 841 148
fax:	01666 841 014
email:	sales@tcpc.co.uk
web:	www.tcpc.co.uk
design service:	Yes
minimum run:	500
info:	CD duplication services. Packaging option include wallets, jewel cases, slipcases and sierra boxes or more bespoke designs.

db Studios
36 Folly Lane, Stroud, Gloucestershire, GL5 1SD
tel:	01453 752 542
email:	dbstudios@enterprise.net
web:	www.dbstudios.co.uk
design service:	Yes
info:	CD mastering and duplication.

Deep Blue Studio
38 Looe Street, Plymouth, PL4 0EB
tel:	01752 601 462
email:	dbs@deepbluestudio.co.uk
web:	www.deepbluestudio.co.uk
design service:	Yes
info:	CD duplication and replication. Deep Blue also offer recording services. See listing in relevant section for details.

Dumb Yank Productions
40 Pembroke Road, Salisbury, Wiltshire, SP2 9DG
tel:	01722 326 017
email:	linda@dumbyank.co.uk
web:	www.dumbyank.co.uk
contact:	Linda
design service:	Yes
minimum run:	None
info:	CD and CD-Rom duplication. On-body printing plus inlays and booklets. Specialise in small runs. Mastering service provided. Dumb Yank also run a mobile recording facility and offer rehearsal space. See entries in relevant sections for further details.

DVD Quote
East Dene, 15 Waverley Road, Newton Abbot, TQ12 2ND
tel:	01626 201 330
email:	quote@dvdquote.co.uk
web:	www.dvdquote.co.uk
design service:	Yes
minimum run:	None
info:	CD, DVD and VHS duplication. Limited in-house design service. Can provide on-body print, as well as booklets and inserts.

Funkee Fish
Devon
tel:	07814 544 611
email:	studio@funkeefish.com
web:	www.funkeefish.com
design service:	Yes
minimum run:	None
info:	On-body printing. Refer to website for prices. Funkee Fish is also a record label and recording studio. See listings in relevant sections for details.

Glass Tone Productions Ltd.
Unit 3a, Riverside Business Park, Bath, BA2 3DW
tel:	01225 487 700/07973 730 161
email:	info@glasstone.co.uk
web:	www.glasstone.co.uk
contact:	Greg Brooker
design service:	Yes
info:	Mastering service charged at £20 per hour. Glass Tone also provide recording and rehearsal facilities, management, PA hire and design services, as well as organising live events in Bath and Bristol, and occasionally further afield. Refer to entries in appropriate sections for further information.

Heartland Productions
PO Box 444, St. Columb, Cornwall, TR9 6ZR
tel:	01726 862 816
email:	info@heartlandproductions.com
web:	www.heartlandproductions.com
contact:	Robert Allan
design service:	No
minimum run:	None
info:	CD and DVD duplication. Basic design service available, but mainly reproduce client's completed artwork. On-body print. Also offer video editing and production services. Contact for further details.

Hillside Studios
Hillside, Great Green, Mells, Somerset, BA11 3QE
tel:	01373 813 643
email:	pat@hillsidestudios.co.uk
web:	www.hillsidestudios.co.uk
design service:	Yes
info:	Mastering services to 48Hz DAT and redbook CD.

ISIS Duplicating Company Ltd.
Unit 11, Shaftesbury Industrial Centre, The Runnings, Cheltenham, Gloucestershire, GL51 9NH
tel:	01242 571 818
fax:	01242 571 315
email:	enquiries@isis-duplicating.com
web:	www.isis-duplicating.com
design service:	Yes
minimum run:	None
info:	Established for over 13 years. Offers a comprehensive range of services for cassette, CD, CD-R and DVD duplication. Conversion to CD from all formats. 4-colour on-body print. Enhanced CD mastering to bluebook standard.

Lemon Media Ltd.
Kings Castle Business Park, The Drove, Bridgwater, Somerset, TA6 4AG
tel:	01278 434 241
fax:	01278 434 243
email:	sales@lemonmedia.co.uk
web:	www.lemonmedia.co.uk
design service:	Yes
minimum run:	None
info:	Duplication for CD, DVD, vinyl and cassette formats. Full packaging print including on-body, booklets and inlays. Mastering service provided.

Loud Mastering
2-3 Windsor Place, Whitehall, Taunton, Somerset, TA1 1PG
tel:	01823 353 123
fax:	01823 353 055
email:	info@loudmastering.com
web:	www.loudmastering.com
design service:	Yes
info:	CD and vinyl mastering.

New Forest Post Production
Powells Farm, Salisbury Road, Plaitford, Romsey, Hampshire, SO51 6EE
tel:	01794 324 147
email:	info@nfpp.com
web:	www.nfpp.com
contact:	Nick Curtis
design service:	Yes
info:	DVD, VHS and CD duplication, complete with printing options.

Original Source
3 Brookside Road, Brislington, Bristol, BS4 4JS
tel:	0117 971 3947/07766 547 562
email:	info@originalsourcecds.co.uk
web:	www.originalsourcecds.co.uk
contact:	Mike
design service:	No
minimum run:	None
info:	CD and DVD duplication and replication. Inkjet on-body printing for small runs, and screen printing for larger runs.

PMC Studios Ltd.
21-24 St. John's Road, Plymouth, PL4 0PA
tel:	01752 201 275
email:	info@pmc.uk.net
web:	www.pmc.uk.net
contact:	Dave Summers
design service:	Yes
minimum run:	None
info:	CD and DVD duplication/replication. Full colour digital printing including on-body print. All associated packaging available. Can deal with everything from small to large scale runs. PMC Studios also run recording and rehearsal facilities. Contact or visit website for further details.

PVA Medialab
1 Kings Square, Bridport, Dorset, DT6 3QE
tel: 01308 459 071
email: stephen@pva.org.uk
web: www.pva.org.uk
design service: Yes
info: Mastering services available.

Rio Records
7 Tolver Place, Penzance, Cornwall, TR18 2AD
tel: 01736 330 004
email: rio_records@hotmail.com
web: www.pznow.co.uk/celtica.html
design service: No
minimum run: None
info: Specialise in short-run CD duplication. Mono-colour on-body printing and jewel cases included in price. Contact for a quote.

Riverside Media
Riverside, 13-14 Okehampton Street, Exeter, Devon, EX4 1DU
tel: 0845 430 9752
fax: 0845 430 9753
email: info@madborris.com
web: www.madborris.com
contact: Tim Jacques
design service: Yes
minimum run: 1000
info: Minimum run is less for bands recorded in the Mad Boris Studio. See entry in Southwest recording studios section for details.

Super Audio Mastering Ltd.
Monks Withecombe, Chagford, Newton Abbot, Devon, TQ13 8JY
tel: 01647 432 858
fax: 01647 432 308
email: info@superaudiomastering.com
web: www.superaudiomastering.com
design service: Yes
info: State of the art mastering facility housed in spacious stone roundhouse. Rural location on Dartmoor. Master projects in stereo and surround sound for CD, SACD and DVD.

Thamesdown SDC Ltd.
Frankland Road, Blagrove, Swindon, Wiltshire, SN5 8YG
tel: 01793 421 300
fax: 01793 511 125
email: sales@tsfltd.co.uk
web: www.tsfltd.co.uk
contact: Paula Baxter
design service: No
minimum run: None
info: CD and DVD duplication and replication. Artwork needs to be supplied by client. Packaging, in-house fulfilment and distribution service. Can offer in-house duplication for runs smaller than 1000. Mastering service available.

Yellow Shark
121 Promenade, Cheltenham, Gloucestershire, GL50 1NW
tel: 01242 515 160
fax: 01242 242 120
email: music@yellow-shark.co.uk
web: www.yellow-shark.co.uk
contact: Gareth Williams
design service: Yes
minimum run: None
info: Full duplication service available with artwork if required. Also offer analogue and digital studio recording. See entry in relevant section for details.

YORKSHIRE

Big 3 Productions
Leeds, West Yorkshire
tel: 07843 556 730
email: info@big3.co.uk
web: www.big3.co.uk
design service: Yes
info: Mastering and duplication services, as well as PA hire and recording. See listings in relevant sections for further details.

Circle CDs
Metro House, Pepper Road, Hunslet, Leeds, LS10 2RU
tel: 0870 765 1150
email: luke@circlecds.com
web: www.circlecds.com
contact: Luke Turner
design service: Yes
minimum run: None
info: CD and DVD duplication. On-body printing available.

Crystal Sound
Allerton Grange Vale, Leeds, LS17 6LS
tel: 0113 266 9189/07970 182 621
email: info@crystalsound.co.uk
web: www.crystalsound.co.uk
contact: Michael Cruise
design service: Yes
info: Mastering service. Can also offer assistance with producing demos. Contact for further details. Crystal Soundsis also a recording studio, and is linked with Cruise International Records. See entries in relevant sections for further details.

Datacatch Media
Unit 4d, Follifoot Ridge, Pannal Road, Harrogate, HG3 1DP
tel: 01423 810 555
fax: 01423 810 666
email: info@datacatch.co.uk
web: www.datacatch.co.uk
design service: Yes
minimum run: None
info: CD and DVD duplication. On-body printing. Also short run in-house screen printing available.

Fairview Duplication
Cavewood Grange Farm, Common Lane, North Cave, East Yorkshire, HU15 2PE
tel: 01430 425 546
fax: 01430 425 547
email: info@fairviewstudios.co.uk
web: www.fairviewstudios.co.uk
contact: Jackie
design service: Yes
minimum run: 50
info: CD, DVD, VHS and cassette duplication. DVD authoring and editing. On-body printing. Mastering service. Fairview also have recording facilities. Refer to entry in Recording Studios section for further details.

G2 Studios
Clifton Works, 72-74 John Street, Sheffield, South Yorkshire, S2 4QU
tel: 0114 270 6217/0114 279 5650
email: info@g2studios.co.uk
web: www.g2studios.co.uk
contact: John Sephton
design service: Yes
minimum run: None
info: Duplication of all products CD-R related. Specialise in fast turnaround for small orders (from 8 to 2000). On-body printing available as well as design assistance. G2 also have a recording studio. See relevant sections for further details.

Ghosttown Studios
Leeds, LS6
email: ghosttownrec@hotmail.com
web: www.ghosttownrec.co.uk
contact: Simon
design service: Yes
info: Duplication and mastering at £100 per 100 discs, with colour print. Mastering is flat rate of £30 pounds, or free with 100 CDs. Also offer PA hire and studio recording services. See entries in relevant sections for further details.

H.D.C. Associates
Bracken House, 53 Broad Lane, Bradford, West Yorkshire, BD4 8PA
tel: 01274 656 565
fax: 01274 656 575
email: sales@hdc.uk.com
web: www.hdc.uk.com
design service: Yes
minimum run: 100
info: CD and DVD duplication. Rapid turnaround time of 1-3 days. Full design service available.

Media Heaven
Unit 12, Castleton Close Industrial Estate, Off Armley Road, Leeds, LS12 2DS
tel: 0113 244 3550
fax: 0113 244 3994
email: info@mediaheaven.co.uk
web: www.mediaheaven.co.uk
contact: Paul Lines
design service: Yes
minimum run: 30
info: CD, DVD and mini CD duplication and replication. On-body printing, as well as inlays and booklets.

Supporting live music since 1987

The UK's No.1 choice
for the Unsigned Musician

PMC studios are guaranteed to be the only establishment you will consider for all your CD and DVD production. Excellent manufacturing capabilities and the technology to achieve a wide range of print solutions means you can be assured that your order will be handled in an environment that is friendly, professional and reliable. We have thousands of satisfied clients that continually return to us and we are confident our prices are the most competitive you will find in the UK.

• CD & DVD MANUFACTURING
Runs from 25 – 100,000+ discs

• GRAPHIC DESIGN & PRINT
Booklets / Inlays, Digipacks,
Card Wallets, Posters, Flyers, T-Shirts...

• 24 TRACK RECORDING STUDIOS
CD Mastering / DVD Authoring

• 6 REHEARSAL STUDIOS

In addition to CD and DVD manufacturing, PMC studios also offer the most competitive rates for Vinyl and Cassette production. Our in house graphic design team are able to create the professional image you require and our range of printed products include booklets/inlays, digipacks and card wallets right through to unique custom designed packaging. CD mastering is available within our onsite 24 track recording studio and our offices are open 7 days a week! Simply call or email us to discuss your requirements.

Call for an instant quotation and a free sample
pack to see the outstanding quality of our work

Tel: 01752 201275
info@pmc.uk.net   www.pmc.uk.net

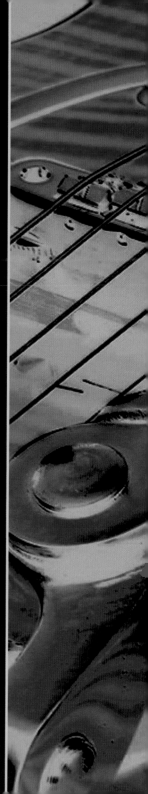

Multimedia Group

Armstrong House, 6 First Avenue, The Finningley Estate, Hayfield Lane, Doncaster, DN9 3GA
tel: 01302 623 050
fax: 01302 623 051
email: info@multimediagroup.co.uk
web: www.multimediagroup.co.uk
contact: Andrew Whittaker, Rick Hotchen
design service: Yes
minimum run: None
info: CD and DVD duplication and replication. Provide full packaging including on-body printing, inserts, booklets, sellowrap. Can also provide free barcoding. DVD authoring. Free delivery available.

One Louder Media

89 Romanby Road, Northallerton, North Yorkshire, DL7 8FH
tel: 01609 781 611
email: richard@oneloudermedia.com
web: www.oneloudermedia.com
design service: No
minimum run: 50
info: CD duplication with 50-200 unit runs. 4800dpi (photo quality) printers print directly on to CDs. Offer a basic mastering service from almost any source. Turnaround is 3 - 7 days from receiving master.

Press CDs

4 Buckingham Road, Doncaster, DN2 5DE
tel: 01302 321 122
email: sales@presscds.co.uk
web: www.presscds.co.uk
contact: Kevin
design service: Yes
minimum run: 10
info: CD and DVD duplication. All print for packaging, including on-body. Mastering service. Can also provide distribution through partner company Xtreme, see www.xtreme.cd

Sponge Studios

Cross Chancellor Street, Leeds, West Yorkshire, LS6 2TG
tel: 0113 234 0004
web: www.spongeonline.co.uk
design service: No
info: Sponge are primarily a rehearsal facility, although they offer studio recording and CD and DVD duplication.

Sunnybank Studios

2-6 Mill Fold, Ripponden, Selby Bridge, Halifax, HX6 4DJ
tel: 01422 823 361
email: sunnybankstudios@btconnect.com
web: www.sunnybankstudios.com
contact: Joss Worthington
design service: Yes
minimum run: None
info: CD duplication. Mastering service offered. Recording facilities available, see entry in relevant section.

Woodman Studio

Unit 2, Woodman Works, South Lane, Elland, Halifax, HX5 0PE
tel: 01422 372 800
email: info@woodmanstudio.co.uk
web: www.woodmanstudio.co.uk
contact: Jerry Barker
design service: Yes
minimum run: None
info: CD and cassette duplication. Artwork reproduction and design. On-body printing. Offers mastering service including glass mastering.

NORTHERN IRELAND

C&B Recordings

Glengormley & Carrickfergus, Belfast, BT36 7XR
tel: 07840 938 086
email: andy@cnbstudios.com
web: www.cnbstudios.com
design service: Yes
info: Offer in-house design, mastering and duplication. Please ring or see website for more information.

Century 23

2nd Floor, 111a Woodstock Road, Belfast, BT6 8AB
tel: 0871 700 0080
design service: Yes
info: Century 23 have been working in close association with the live music, clubbing, entertainment, and leisure industries across Britain for 7 years providing CD and vinyl duplication as well as artwork design and printing. See other relevant sections for details. Offices in Edinburgh and London.

Dupadisc Technologies

5 Clonium Road, Killeavy, County Down, BT35 8LB
tel: 028 3084 8844
email: sales@dupadisc.ie
web: www.dupadisc.ie
design service: No
minimum run: 100
info: CD and DVD duplication and replication. Can reproduce client's artwork. On-body printing. Also sell range of duplication equipment.

Duplitape

100 Duncairn Gardens, Belfast, BT15 2GN
tel: 028 9074 7411
fax: 028 9029 9001
email: duplitape@enterprise.net
web: www.duplitape.co.uk
design service: No
info: CD, DVD and VHS duplication. Transfer any format to CD and DVD.

Electric Studios

Westlink Enterprise Centre, Unit 2, 30-50 Distilery Street, Belfast, County Antrim, BT12 5BJ
tel: 07721 255 083
email: electric_studios@hotmail.com
web: www.sabp-web.co.uk/electricstudios
design service: Yes
info: On-body CD printing or full colour booklet CD printing. No quantity too big or small. Contact for details. Prices vary depending on quantity.

Hardlight Multimedia

37b Main Street, Markethill, County Armagh, BT60 1PH
tel: 0870 922 0043
fax: 028 3755 2559
email: info@hardlight.net
web: www.hardlight.net
contact: Greg Haire
design service: Yes
minimum run: None
info: CD and DVD duplication. On-body printing. Mastering service available. Also offer recording and photography services. See entry for Wild Goose Productions for further information.

Komodo

79 Magheraconluce Road, Hillsborough, Down, BT26 6PR
tel: 028 9268 8285
email: info@komodorecordings.com
web: www.komodorecordings.com
contact: William
design service: Yes
minimum run: 50
info: Can produce up to 1000 CDs per day. Minimum run is only 25 for artists recorded at the studio. Also offer studio recording, cover graphic design and printing and drum tuition. See entries in relevant sections for details.

MADD House Studios

Clotworthy Arts Centre, Randalstown Road, Antrim, County Antrim, BT41 4LH
tel: 028 9446 9669
fax: 028 9446 0360
email: info@maddhousestudios.co.uk
web: www.maddhousestudios.co.uk
design service: Yes
info: Mastering services available.

Mid Atlantic Digital

27a High Street, Enniskillen, County Fermanagh
tel: 028 6632 9437
fax: 028 6632 0420
email: robyn@enterprise.net
web: www.midatlanticdigital.com
design service: Yes
info: Mid Atlantic Digital is Ireland's only purpose built CD mastering facility with over 2000 sq. feet of studio space. On-premises accommodation for out of town clients.

Novatech Productions

122 Hyde Park Road, Newtownabbey, Antrim, BT36 4PZ
tel: 028 9083 8981
fax: 028 9084 4299
email: info@novatech-studios.com
web: www.novatech-studio.com
contact: Gary or Dale
design service: Yes
minimum run: None
info: One-stop CD and DVD recording, design and manufacturing service.

MUSIC SERVICES/RETAIL

P.I.C. Productions
18 Pine Grove Crescent, Ballymena, County Antrim, BT43 6TL
tel: 028 2564 9144
email: pic_music@hotmail.com
contact: Paul
design service: Yes
info: Digital mastering and CD duplication services. Also have recording studio. See listing in relevant section for further information.

Purity Studio
50 Silverstream Road, Bangor, BT20 3LT
tel: 028 9146 8776
email: info@puritystudios.com
web: www.puritystudios.com
contact: Spike
design service: Yes
minimum run: None
info: CD mastering and duplication. Professional in-house graphic design, internet and multimedia services are also available.

Wild Goose Productions
39 Lower Lisdrumchor Road, Glenanne, BT60 2HT
tel: 0870 922 0047
fax: 028 3750 7915
email: info@wildgoose.biz
web: www.wildgoose.biz
contact: Greg Haire
design service: Yes
minimum run: None
info: CD mastering and duplication. Wild Goose Productions also offer digital recording facilities for bands, song writers and composers. See entry in relevant section for details.

SCOTLAND

Alliance Multimedia
1 Lister Place, Hillington Park, Glasgow, G51 4HZ
tel: 0141 810 4664
fax: 0141 810 4774
email: info@alliancemultimedia.com
web: www.alliancemultimedia.com
contact: Iain Somerside
design service: Yes
minimum run: 30
info: CD and DVD duplication. On-body printing available.

Amarok Multimedia Ltd.
Coastal Technology Zone, 3 Anthony Court, Largs, Ayrshire, KA30 8TA
tel: 01475 689 096
email: mail@amarok.uk.com
web: www.amarok.uk.com
contact: Eric Letton
design service: Yes
minimum run: None
info: CD and DVD duplication and replication. Full packaging and printing services available, as well as mastering. Amarok can also offer web design. Contact for further details.

Beaufort Productions
Glencaple, Dumfries, DG1 4RD
tel: 01387 770 437
web: www.mdaudio.co.uk
contact: Malcolm Dunn
design service: No
minimum run: None
info: CD and DVD duplication. Artwork reproduction for sleeve art and on-body printing. Mastering services.

Birnam CD
Station Road, Birnam, Dunkeld, Perthshire, PH8 0DS
tel: 01350 727 158
fax: 01350 727 161
email: info@birnamcd.com
web: www.birnamcd.com
contact: Martin Hadden
design service: Yes
minimum run: None
info: CD and DVD replication. Video and audio cassette duplication. In-house duplication for short run CD and DVD. Full graphic design service. Booklet and inlay printing as well as posters, flyers and digital promo packs. Multimedia programming and authoring for DVD, CD Rom and enhanced CD.

Cameron Presentations
Burnfield Road, Giffnock, Glasgow, G46 7TH
tel: 0141 637 0368
fax: 0141 637 3559
email: dup@cameronpres.co.uk
web: www.cameronpres.co.uk
design service: Yes
info: CD and DVD duplication. Low volume CD duplication express service which includes full colour thermal printing. Minimum charge of £25 + VAT.

Century 23
17-19 Maritime Lane, Edinburgh, EH6 6RZ
tel: 0871 700 0080
email: andrew@century-23.com
web: www.century-23.com
contact: Andrew
design service: Yes
info: Century 23 have been working in close association with the live music, clubbing, entertainment and leisure industries across Britain for 7 years providing printed promotional products including flyers, posters and tickets. Artwork design. CD and vinyl duplication also available - see relevant section for details. Offices in Belfast and London.

Chow Productions
Unit 9, The Clyde Business Centre, 31 Clyde Street, Clydebank, G81 9PF
tel: 0141 952 3111
email: chowproductions@aol.com
design service: Yes
info: Offer CD, cassette, VHS and DVD duplication. Chow Productions also have recording facilities. See entry in relevant section for further details.

CME Duplication
14a Hunter Road, Duchess Trading Estate, Rutherglen, Glasgow, G73 1LB
tel: 0141 647 2810
fax: 0141 647 0194
email: mail@cmeduplication.co.uk
web: www.cmeduplication.co.uk
contact: Ronnie
design service: Yes
minimum run: 50
info: CD and DVD duplication. On-body and digital printing of booklets and inlays. Mastering and recording facilities. See entry in Recording Studios section for further details.

Gillies Audio
35 Dalgetty Court, Muirhead, DD2 5QJ
tel: 01382 580 746
email: info@gilliesaudio.com
web: www.gilliesaudio.com
design service: No
minimum run: None
info: Rapid turnaround. Next day delivery on all promotional copies, 3-5 day delivery on all singles, EPs and albums. Files are kept on record so that you can re-order more CDs as and when you need them. Colour or black and white on-body print.

GoGo Studios
6 Great George Street, Westend, Glasgow, G12 8PD
tel: 07811 438 468
email: info@gogostudios.com
web: www.gogostudios.com
design service: Yes
info: Mastering service. GoGo Studios also offers recording facilities. See entry in relevant section for details.

Headhunter Records
Stanley Street Lane, Killing Park, Glasgow, G41 1EZ
tel: 0141 429 7111
email: info@headhunterrecords.co.uk
web: www.headhunterrecords.co.uk
design service: Yes
info: CD duplication. Also offer recording and rehearsal facilities. See listings in relevant section for details.

Maybank Studios
654 Eglinton Street, Glasgow, G5 9RP
tel: 0141 429 8822
email: matt@maybankstudios.co.uk
web: www.maybankstudios.co.uk
design service: Yes
minimum run: None
info: Any quantity from 1 to 10,000 duplicated. Also a comprehensive recording studio.

McPherson's Document Solutions
102-122 Main Road, Elderslie, Glasgow, PA5 9AX
tel: 01505 331 534
fax: 01505 328 266
email: sales@trmcpherson.co.uk
web: www.trmcpherson.co.uk
design service: Yes
info: Specialise in CD duplication runs of between 100 and 1000 CDs, although happy to quote for large CD duplication runs.

Miller Reprographics Ltd.
21-22 Charing Cross Mansions, 30 St. George's Road, Glasgow, G3 6UJ
tel: 0141 331 5252
email: miller_repro@btconnect.com
design service: No
minimum run: None
info: CD duplication and printing.

Norwick Mastering
11 Hillhead Road, Wick, Caithness, KW1 4JE
tel: 01955 603 706/07786 046 838
fax: 01955 603 706
email: info@norwickmastering.com
web: www.norwickmastering.com
contact: David Shearer
design service: Yes
info: Professional and efficient mastering in Pro Tools-based high-resolution digital mastering studio. Over 12 years experience as a mastering engineer including all studio calibration. Contact to discuss your needs.

Orbis Digital
52e Sunnyside Road, Coatbridge, ML5 3DG
tel: 0845 607 6123
fax: 01355 813 346
email: info@orbisdigital.co.uk
web: www.orbisdigital.co.uk
design service: No
minimum run: None
info: CD and DVD duplication and packaging solution.

Red Barn Studios Ltd.
Monorgan Farm, Monorgan, Dundee, DD2 5HT
tel: 0870 742 0747
email: info@redbarn.co.uk
web: www.redbarn.co.uk
design service: Yes
info: CD mastering and duplication. Red Barn also has recording facilities. See entry in relevant section for further details.

Small Town Audio
Unit 1, Teriot Street, Ayr, Ayrshire, KA8 9JE
tel: 01292 619 365
email: simon@smalltownaudio.co.uk
web: www.smalltownaudio.co.uk
design service: Yes
info: CD replication. Also provide recording and equipment hire services. See entries in relevant sections for details.

Sound Doctor
54 George Street, Cellardyke, Fife, KY10 3AU
tel: 07867 763 582
email: info@sounddoctor.co.uk
web: www.sounddoctor.co.uk
contact: John Wills
design service: Yes
info: Sound Doctor is made up of a group of experienced musicians and staff are happy to advise unsigned acts on the presentation and quality of their recordings. Sound mastering service. Can accept music on CD, CDR, DAT, MD, WAV, MP3, cassette or vinyl. Also offer sound restoration and transfer services. Client is only billed when they are satisfied with their product. Sound Doctor also provides web design services. See entry in relevant section for further information.

The Sound Station
Unit 6, Napier Square, Houston Industrial Estate, Livingston, EH54 5DG
tel: 1506 440 505
email: thesoundstation@btinternet.com
design service: No
minimum run: 5
info: Mastering and duplication. Full colour on-body printing. Jewel case included in the price. Recording and rehearsal facilities also available. See relevant section for more details.

Timberwolf Media
Catchpell House, Carpet Lane, Bernard Street, Edinburgh, EH6 6SP
tel: 0131 553 2935
email: info@timberwolfmedia.com
web: www.timberwolfmedia.com
contact: Adam Foster
design service: Yes
minimum run: 100
info: DVD and CD-rom duplication only. Manage entire process from mastering to print, packaging and delivery including any licensing and copyright issues.

Zombie Works
1/1 The Angel Building, 12 Paisley Road West, Glasgow, G51 1LE
email: gareth@zombie-works.co.uk
web: www.zombie-works.co.uk
contact: Gillian or Gareth
design service: Yes
info: Reliable high quality CD duplication service, including full colour thermal printing.

WALES

Acoustic Record
South West Wales
tel: 07966 180 059
email: ingtons@clara.co.uk
web: www.acousticrecord.co.uk
design service: Yes
info: Mastering and re-mastering services. Also run recording studio. See relevant section for details.

Albany Studios
Units 3-4, Fairwater Workshops, Norbury Road, Cardiff, CF5 3BG
tel: 02920 555 515
fax: 02920 301 299
email: office@a-p-l.com
web: www.a-p-l.com
design service: No
minimum run: 15
info: CD and cassette duplication. CD duplication with jewel case or sleeve. On-body printed stickers, inlays and booklets. Silk screen print available on runs over 100. Also run a recording studio. See relevant section for details.

Black Sheep
103 Bute Street, Cardiff, CF10 5AD
tel: 02920 490 722
email: info@blacksheep.info
web: www.blacksheep.info
design service: Yes
info: CD duplication. Also provide graphic and web design services. See listing in relevant section for further details.

Burning Red
Suite 111, Wellfield Road, Cardiff, CF24 3DG
tel: 02920 912 459
email: enquiries@burningred.co.uk
web: www.burningred.co.uk
design service: Yes
info: Mastering and post-production. Also run design studio. See relevant section for more details.

David Liscombe Audio
67 Parkhill Terrace, Treboeth, Swansea, West Glamorgan, SA5 7DJ
tel: 01792 771 579
design service: No
minimum run: 10
info: CD and cassette duplication. Small run specialists. Can reproduce artwork provided by band.

Dischromatics Ltd.
Unit 20, Prince of Wales Industrial Estate, Abercarn, Newport, NP11 5AR
tel: 01495 243 222
fax: 01495 243 777
email: sales@dischro.co.uk
web: www.dischro.co.uk
design service: Yes
minimum run: Call for details
info: CD and DVD replication. On-body printing and various finishing effects available. Inlay cards, booklets and barcodes can be added. Range of packaging.

Dreamworld Studio
Priskilly Fawr, Hatscastle, Haverfordwest, Dyfed, SA62 5QF
tel:	01348 840 186
email:	info@dreamworldstudio.co.uk
web:	www.dreamworldstudio.co.uk
design service:	No
minimum run:	10
info:	Prices start from £10 for ten CDs. Labels and inserts available.

Drummers Hill
Nr Llanidloes, Powys
tel:	07764 189 379
email:	info@drummershill.co.uk
web:	www.drummershill.co.uk
design service:	Yes
info:	Mastering facilities with small duplication capacity.

Fairplay Replication
Derw Mill North, Pentre-Cwrt, Llandysul, Dyfed, SA44 5DB
tel:	01559 363 190
email:	fairplayreplication@btopenworld.com
design service:	No
minimum run:	300
info:	CD, CD-Rom and DVD replication. On-body printing, inlay cards and booklets. Can refer customers to businesses providing mastering, authoring and design. Fairplay Replication produce 1.5 million CDs per year.

Fideo Sain
Unit 4-5, Llanllyfni Road, Antur Nantle Estate, Caernarfon, Gwynedd, LL54 6LY
tel:	01286 880 977
web:	www.sainwales.com
design service:	Yes
minimum run:	None
info:	Short run specialists. CD, DVD, CD-Rom and VHS duplication. DVD authoring and encoding. Video enhancement to audio CDs. Printing for inlay cards and covers can be sourced. Can also supply promotional merchandise. See relevant section for details.

Frozen UK
Llanidloes, Powys
email:	sjp@frozenuk.com
web:	www.frozenuk.com
design service:	Yes
info:	Digital editing and mastering for CD, DAT, vinyl and cassette.

Gwynfryn Cymunedol Cyf
Snowdonia Park, Waunfawr, Caernarfon, Gwynedd, LL55 4AQ
tel:	01286 650 523
email:	gwynfryncymunedol@hotmail.com
web:	www.gwynfryncymunedol.co.uk
design service:	Yes
info:	CD recording, mastering and duplication. Thermal on-body printing and shrink wrapping also available.

KBMF
Hillside Studios, Newport, NP26 3AZ
tel:	01633 400 555
email:	info@kbmfaudio.co.uk
web:	www.kbmfaudio.co.uk
design service:	No
minimum run:	None
info:	DVD, VHS, cassette and CD-R duplication. DVD and CD printing.

KDG UK Ltd.
Unit 5, Triangle Business Park, Pentrebach, Merthyr Tydfil, Mid Glamorgan, CF48 4TQ
tel:	01685 354 700
fax:	01685 354 701
email:	sales@kdguk.com
web:	www.kdg-mt.com
design service:	Yes
minimum run:	500
info:	CD duplication. On-body printing, booklets and inlay cards. Range of cases available. Mastering service and DVD production.

Kissan Productions
Danycoed, Main Road, Gwaelodygarth, Cardiff, CF15 9HH
tel:	02920 811 730
fax:	02920 811 730
email:	info@kissanproductions.com
web:	www.kissanproductions.com
design service:	Yes
minimum run:	None
info:	Short-run duplication up to 100 units. Also a record label and publishing company. See relevant sections for details.

LTS Recording & PA Services
Llanon, SY23 5JZ
tel:	01974 202 759
email:	dfereday@ltsstudio.co.uk
web:	www.ltsstudio.co.uk
contact:	Dow Fereday
design service:	Yes
info:	Track laying, mastering and PA systems hire.

Make-Shift Recording Studio
The Post Office, London Road, Trelawnyd, LL18 6DN
tel:	01745 570 000
web:	www.makeshiftrecordingstudio.com
design service:	Yes
info:	CD and vinyl mastering.

Mantra CDs & Recording
Llanfyllin, Powys, SY22 5JG
tel:	01691 649 044
email:	contact@mantracds.com
web:	www.mantracds.com
design service:	No
minimum run:	50
info:	Digital mastering and duplication. Mastering £25 + VAT per hour. Duplication is short run or glass mastered depending on requirements. See also The Beehouse (Recording Studios), MantraSound (Equipment Hire) and C'mon Records (Record Companies).

Maxwell Publications
Unit 19, Pinfold Workshops, Pinfold Lane Industrial Estate, Buckley, Clwyd, CH7 3PL
tel:	01244 547 724
email:	maxwell.pub@btconnect.com
design service:	Yes
minimum run:	None
info:	CD duplication. On-body printing, inlay cards and booklets. Can also print posters and flyers. See relevant section for details.

Media Transcript Services
PO Box 208, Old St. Mellons, Cardiff, CF3 9WG
tel:	02920 363 311
fax:	02920 363 315
email:	via website
web:	www.m-t-s.co.uk
design service:	Yes
minimum run:	20
info:	CD duplication. On-body printing, booklets and inlays. DVD and VHS duplication. DVD authoring, which can include footage, audio tracks and stills.

Newid Studios
Antioch Centre, Copperworks Road, Llanelli, SA15 2NE
tel:	07971 422 024
email:	malowe@btinternet.com
web:	www.newidstudios.net
design service:	Yes
minimum run:	None
info:	Specialise in short run CD duplication for unsigned bands. Full colour glossy inlays. Rehearsal and recording facilities available. See relevant sections for details.

Proactive Video
Bridgend
tel:	01656 667 843/07974 000 857
email:	info@proactivevideo.co.uk
web:	www.proactivevideo.co.uk
design service:	Yes
minimum run:	None
info:	CD and DVD duplication and replication. Multimedia CD-Rom and DVD authoring. Booklets and inlays available. Web design and video production.

SBS Records
PO Box 37, Blackwood, NP12 2YQ
tel:	01495 201 116
fax:	01495 201 190
email:	enquiry@sbsrecords.co.uk
web:	www.sbsrecords.co.uk
design service:	No
minimum run:	20
info:	Specialise in short run CD duplication. On-body print and full colour booklet production.

Silverword Music Group
16 Limetrees Avenue, Llangattock, Crickhowell, Powys, NP8 1LB
tel: 01873 810 142
fax: 01873 811 557
email: silvergb@aol.com
web: www.silverword.co.uk
contact: Kevin King
design service: Yes
info: Unsigned package available consisting of 1000 CDs with cover and 4 page booklet (design included), bar-coding, shrink-wrapping, catalogue numbering and delivery. Speak to Kevin for details involving obligation free distribution.

South Wales Print Services Ltd.
Unit 9b, Enterprise Way, Newport, Gwent, NP20 2AQ
tel: 01633 216 060
email: enquiry@southwalesprint.co.uk
web: www.southwalesprint.co.uk
design service: Yes
minimum run: None
info: On-body printing and CD labels. Range of hard and soft cases. Poster and flyer printing also available. See relevant section for details.

Taffpop Records
1 The Kingsway, Swansea, SA1 5JQ
tel: 07963 372 818
email: artists@taffpop.com
web: www.taffpop.com
contact: Andy
design service: Yes
minimum run: None
info: CD duplication service. See Record Companies section for more information.

Video By Design
Wrexham, North Wales
tel: 01978 366 060
email: info@videobydesign.co.uk
web: www.videobydesign.co.uk
design service: No
minimum run: None
info: CD, DVD and VHS duplication. On-body print, booklets and inlays.

Wyastone
Wyastone Estate Ltd., Wyastone Leys, Monmouth, NP25 3SR
tel: 01600 890 007
fax: 01600 891 052
email: sales@wyastone.co.uk
web: www.wyastone.co.uk
design service: Yes
minimum run: None
info: Short run specialists up to 500 units. On-body printing, booklets and inlays. Can source DVD replication.

3.9 PHOTOGRAPHY SERVICES

Your music rocks, does your image?

www.rockphotography.co.uk

Live & Promotional photography (location or studio) by Al Pulford
email - info@rockphotography.co.uk   Call - (+44) 079708 37109

EAST of ENGLAND

Andrew Carruth
Cambridge
email: andrew@maximum-effort.com
web: www.acarruth.demon.co.uk
info: Undertakes a variety of commissions ranging from music photography to wildlife and commercial work.

Jemima Wilcox
Cambridge
tel: 01223 577 063
email: jem_abey@hotmail.com
prev. clients: Various unsigned bands
info: Photography and design for unsigned bands. Will work with client to achieve what they want. Digital, traditional, B&W, and any kind of effects welcome.

Marcus Kett
20 Ward Road, Salhouse, Norwich, Norfolk, NR13 6RG
tel: 01603 722 149
email: info@marcuskett.com
web: www.marcuskett.com
info: Photographer undertaking range of work. Marcus has been actively involved promoting unsigned bands all over the UK. Also offers web design services. Contact for further details.

Phil Scott Photography
Studio 10, Capitol House, 4-6 Heigham Street, Norwich, Norfolk, NR2 4TE
tel: 01603 667 854
info: Portrait shots, either B&W or colour. Digital enhancements available.

MUSIC SERVICES/RETAIL

Rock Photography
35 Hotblack Road, Norwich, NR2 4HG
tel: 07970 837 109
email: info@rockphotography.co.uk
web: www.rockphotography.co.uk
contact: Al Pulford
prev. clients: Terrorizer Magazine, Marshall Amplifiers, Celestian Guitars
info: Over 8 years music photography experience. Mainly live and location shoots, but can do studio sessions with smaller acts.

GREATER LONDON

Adam Lawrence
London
tel: 07973 672 007
fax: 07970 086 006
email: adam@adamlawrence.com
web: www.adamlawrence.com
prev. clients: Gorillaz, Goldie, Bez, Carl Cox

Alexandra Popoff
London
tel: 07967 755 674
email: bpopoff@hotmail.com
info: Keen to work with bands and artists of all types. Has experience in live and posed shots. Very amenable to different types of pictures to suit the needs of individual bands. B&W or colour, live or on location.

Alison Wonderland
45 Colworth Road, London, E11 1JA
tel: 020 8539 3604
fax: 020 8926 7774
email: alison@alisonwonderland.co.uk
web: www.alisonwonderland.co.uk
contact: Alison
prev. clients: Super Furry Animals, Cardigans, Holly Golighly, Gorky's Zygotic Mynci, Mogwai, Mojo, Q, Times, Guardian, NME, Time Out NY, Spin, Italian Vogue
info: Experience photographer.

Alistair Hughes Studio
21 Vyner Street, London, E2 9DG
tel: 020 8980 1224
email: alistair@alistairhughes.co.uk
web: www.alistairhughes.co.uk
info: See website above for examples of Alistair's work.

Amelia Dowsett
London
email: ameliadowsett@hotmail.com
web: www.ameliadowsett.co.uk
info: See website for examples of Amelia's work.

Ami Barwell
London
tel: 07787 188 452
email: ami@musicphotographer.co.uk
web: www.musicphotographer.co.uk
prev. clients: Cooper Temple Clause, The White Stripes, Radiohead
info: Highly experienced music photographer.

AML
London
email: amlevangie@yahoo.com
web: www.geocities.com/amlevangie/
prev. clients: Blink 182, Backstreet Boys, The Living End.

Anders Jacobsen
Greater London
email: via website
web: www.extrospection.com
prev. clients: The Swear, Revere, Farmers Market, Sambassadeur, Alys and others.
info: Live concert photographer. Interested in gigs in Central and South London areas. Reasonable rates.

Andrew Holt Photography
67 Connaught Gardens, London, N10 3LG
tel: 020 8444 1888/07050 264 264
email: contact@andrew-holt.com
web: www.andrew-holt.com
info: Andrew Holt is a creative photographer who works on location and in the studio.

Andrew Whittuck
12 Middleton Grove, London, N7 9LS
tel: 07860 104 400
email: andrew@andrewwhittuck.co.uk
web: www.andrewwhittuck.co.uk
prev. clients: Pink Floyd

Andrew Wiard
Floor 3, Chocolate Factory 2, Coburg Road, London, N22 6UJ
tel: 07973 219 201
email: andrew@reportphotos.com
web: www.reportphotos.com

Anthony Jones
London
tel: 07963 820 021
email: mail@ajphoto.info
web: www.ajphoto.info
contact: Anthony Jones
prev. clients: The Prince's Trust, Fuji
info: Published and exhibited London based portrait photographer accepting assignments throughout the city and beyond. Specialises in B&W photography.

ArenaPAL
London
tel: 020 7403 8542
email: enquiries@arenapal.com
web: www.arenapal.com
contact: Robert Piwko
info: Company representing several photographers who are experienced in the music world. See website for more details.

Barry Lategan Photographer
10 Bishops Terrace, London, SE11 4UE
tel: 020 7582 4992
email: barrylategan@hotmail.com
web: www.the-aop.org
prev. clients: The Doors, Wings, Yardbirds.
info: Barry has been working as a photographer since the early 60s, and took the first ever studio pictures of Twiggy.

Ben Rector
38 Longfield Road, Shotgate, Wickford, Essex, SS11 8PU
tel: 07770 467 791
email: ben@benrector.com
web: www.benrector.com
info: Professional photographer specialising in music and entertainment photography. Ben works with established and up and coming artists, both on and off stage. He has photographed some of the biggest stars in the world and believes in giving new talent the same level of service.

Bertrand Bosredon
tel: 07905 265 462
fax: 07092 301 146
email: photos@cafedumonde.net
web: www.cafedumonde.net
contact: Bertrand Bosredon
prev. clients: Bjork, Radiohead, Sonic Youth, Blur, James, Oasis.
info: Bertrand Bosredon is a French photographer based in London. Portraits in studio, colour or B&W. Digital photography.

Bob Glanville
49 Lichfield Grove, Church End, Finchley, London, N3 2JJ
tel: 020 8343 3296
email: info@bobglanville.com
web: www.bobglanville.com
info: Works with Rocksound and The Fly.

Bob Workman
Studio 103b, The Business Village, Broomhill Road, Wandsworth, SW18 4JQ
tel: 020 8874 0563
email: bob@robertworkman.demon.co.uk
web: www.robertworkman.demon.co.uk
info: Photographer specialising in portraits of actors and musicians.

Brian Glassborow
9 Montcalm Close, Bromley, BR2 7LZ
tel: 020 8462 6387
info: Brian works exclusively on location shoots.

Brian Leggett Photographer
15 Cairns Avenue, Woodford Green, London, IG8 8DH
tel: 020 8504 8578
email: brian@brianleggett.co.uk
web: www.brianleggett.co.uk
info: Carries out a variety of work. Contact Brian for details or to view his portfolio.

Brother Russia
London
tel: 07779 290 953
email: design@brotherrussia.co.uk
web: www.brotherrussia.co.uk
info: Live photography specialist. Can also provide artwork and design services. See relevant section for details.

Carl Fox @ Penny Rich Agency
27 Hoxton Street, London, N1 6NH
tel: 020 7613 3886
email: becky@pennyrich.co.uk
web: www.pennyrich.co.uk
info: Contact Carl via the agency for details of rates and equipment.

Carnegie & Conway Photography
Studio 1, 110 Petherton Road, London, N5 2RT
tel: 020 7354 3219
email: info@carnegieconway.com
web: www.carnegieconway.com
contact: James, Sean
prev. clients: The Zutons, Bloc Party, Dogs Die In Hot Cars
info: Colour and B&W, studio and location, as well as live work. Frequently work with unsigned acts.

Charlie Best Photography
1 Cumberland Gardens, London, WC1X 9AF
tel: 020 7837 3271
email: charlie@charlesbest.co.uk
web: www.charlesbest.co.uk
contact: Charlie Best
prev. clients: RAW, Thunder, Red Hot Chili Peppers, EMI, MCA Records, Bronze Records.

Chris McAndrew Photography
tel: 07740 424 810
email: chris@mcandrewphoto.co.uk
web: www.mcandrewphoto.co.uk
contact: Chris McAndrew
prev. clients: Groove Armada, Bjork, Madonna, Eminem, Joe Strummer
info: Experienced photographer specialising in music photography, people and portraits.

Colin Crisford
11a Greenwich South Street, London, SE10 8NJ
tel: 020 8858 5008/07956 142 077
email: studio@colincrisford.co.uk
web: www.colincrisford.co.uk
info: Digital photography, with all prints available on CD. Call Colin to discuss rates.

Dan Kenyon
London
tel: 07899 961 494
email: dan@dankenyon.com
web: www.dankenyon.com
info: Dan is a London based advertising photographer who is keen to work with bands. Very reasonable rates especially for those on a budget.

Danny Clifford Photography
tel: 07973 464 670
email: danny@dannyclifford.com
web: www.dannyclifford.com
prev. clients: NME
info: Live photography, home studio, prints to perfection.

David Williams Photography
16 Collingwood Road, London, N15 4LD
tel: 020 8809 0200
email: david@davidwilliamsphotography.co.uk
web: www.davidwilliamsphotography.co.uk
info: Digital and film.

Denis O'Reagan
36 Westwood Road, London, SW13 0LA
email: info@denis.co.uk
web: www.denis.co.uk
prev. clients: The Rolling Stones, Queen, Thin Lizzy, David Bowie
info: Denis has been photographing Rock musicians for the past 25 years. See his website for further examples of previous clients. Location and live, digital stills.

Department S
PO Box 727, Kenley, Surrey, CR8 5YF
tel: 020 8668 0493/07932 216 759
email: darkduke@yahoo.com
web: www.dept-s.freeserve.com/dept.html
contact: Jane M, Russ B
prev. clients: Sony, Future Legend Records, Pinnacle Distribution
info: Band shots and record sleeves packages include 6-8 shots indoors and outdoors, sometimes over 2 days, depending on what is required. All shots are available on CD and a dozen blow ups of the best shots are provided. Colour and B&W, digital and film.

Derek Brown
Greenwich, London, SE10 0DB
tel: 020 8305 2335/07956 365 167
email: unsigned@derekbrown.co.uk
web: www.derekbrown.co.uk
contact: Derek Brown
info: Live and location shoots a speciality. Colour or B&W, digital or film from 35mm to large format. Website design and construction also available in complete package.

Diana More-Riddle Photography
Hackney, London, N16 6NB
tel: 07960 290 832
email: dmrphotos@gmail.com
web: www.dmrphotos.com
contact: Diana More-Riddle
prev. clients: Terrorizer magazine, Vice magazine
info: Live and location shoots. Editorial work. B&W and colour photography.

Dinah Kenyon
18a Shrubland Road, London, E8 4NN
tel: 07939 245 739
email: dinahkenyon@yahoo.co.uk
prev. clients: NME, Mixmag
info: Colour and B&W, film and digital. Live gigs and location shoots.

D-Max Concert Photography
London
tel: 020 8524 2814
email: deanholt@tiscali.co.uk
web: http://web.ukonline.co.uk/deanholt/

Edward Lloyd
125a Ashley Gardens, Thirleby Road, London, SW1P 1HL
tel: 07956 685 077
info: Press photographer.

Edward Webb
1a Chance Street, London, E1 6JT
tel: 07774 236 272
email: edward@ewebb.co.uk
web: www.ewebb.co.uk
prev. clients: The Independent, The Times.

Elle Gould
London
tel: 07810 801 466
email: ellegould@fsmail.net
web: www.ellegould.com
prev. clients: The Thrills, Supergrass, Jet, The Delays, 22 20's
info: Elle Gould is a London based freelance photographer with high contrast style. Available for commissions and hire for live gig photography, location, studio, press releases and online publication. B&W and colour.

Emma Designs
London
tel: 020 8764 5887/07740 844 639
email: emma@emmadesigns.com
web: www.emmadesigns.com
contact: Emma Porter
prev. clients: NME, Daily Star, The Sun, Bang Mag. Official websites for The Strokes, Jewel, Stiff Little Fingers, Drowning Pool, Download Festival, Drowned in Sound
info: Specialises in live gig photography.

Excerpt
London
tel: 07976 453 580
email: tom@excerpt.org.uk
web: www.excerpt.org.uk
info: Experienced freelancers specialising in promos, photography and print design.

Fox Waterman Photography
24 Edward Road, Bromley, BR1 3NQ
tel: 020 8466 5330
email: johnwaterman@btconnect.com
info: Clients will be provided with 12 shots, either on transparency or in print.

Frank Grainger
Stafford Studios, 129a Stafford Road, Wallington, SM6 9AJ
tel: 020 8773 2161

Gary Taylor Photography
3 Scrutton Street, London, EC2A 4HF
tel: 020 7613 5881
email: cityimage@btinternet.com
info: Gary Taylor Photography employ several different photographers. Call to discuss your needs.

Gill Shaw
66 Westfield Road, Ealing, London, W13 9JA
tel: 020 8840 3155/07973 252 017
fax: 020 8566 3099
email: gill@gillshaw.co.uk
web: www.gillshaw.co.uk
info: Call or email Gill to discuss your needs. Digital and film.

Gina Phillips Represents
6 Leverton Palace, London, NW5 2PL
tel: 020 7284 2022
email: info@ginaphillips.co.uk
web: www.ginaphillips.co.uk
info: Represent several photographers whose work can be viewed on the website. Contact the agency to get in touch with individual photographers.

Grant Manuni-Triplow
London
tel: 07919 100 632
email: grant@gmtphotography.com
web: www.gmtphotography.com
contact: Grant Triplow
prev. clients: News of the World magazine, Daily Mail.
info: Photographs DJs and bands.

Gregory Nolan
London
email: greg@gregorynolan.com
web: www.gregorynolan.com
contact: Greg Nolan
prev. clients: 5 O'Clock Heroes, iForward Russia, Mando Diao
info: Excellent photographer who has worked with many bands, see the website for examples of his work.

Gry Garness Photography
tel: 07973 832 033
fax: 020 8983 9731
email: mail@grygarness.com
web: www.grygarness.com

Guy Holden
70 Strafford Gate, Potters Bar, London, EN6 1PR
tel: 07968 143 042
email: guyholden_photographer@hotmail.com
info: Guy is the former assistant of Rankin, and is keen to build up a portfolio including shots of musicians. Colour and B&W. Digital photography.

Hip Replacement
2 Newbury Muse, Chalk Farm, London, NW5 3HP
tel: 07980 663 246
email: leebaxter@hip-replacement.com
web: www.hip-replacement.com
contact: Lee Baxter
info: Live and location work using 35mm, digital, medium format. B&W and colour. Image manipulation. Rates negotiable.

Howard Kingsnorth
1a Chance Street, London, E1 6JT
tel: 020 7739 8655
email: info@howardkingsnorth.com
web: www.howardkingsnorth.com
info: Howard uses mainly digital photography.

Howard Sayer Photography
Greater London
tel: 07860 559 891
email: howard@howardsayer.com
web: www.howardsayer.com
info: Location and studio, colour and B&W. Digital photography.

Imagethirst
108 Great Portland Street, London, W1W 6PG
tel: 020 7323 5999
email: mail@imagethirst.co.uk
web: www.imagethirst.co.uk
prev. clients: Raging Speedhorn, Diesel, Sunday Mirror Magazine
info: Creative team of photographers and designers specialising in specific fields, including music.

Imago
67 Chatterton Road, Bromley, Kent, BR2 9QQ
tel: 0800 096 1991/020 8303 6003
email: studio@id2.co.uk
web: www.id2.co.uk

Inoya Photography
Apatment 23, Key House, Bowling Green Street, London, SE11 5TT
tel: 07888 723 197
email: admin@inoya.co.uk
web: www.inoya.co.uk
contact: Zen
prev. clients: Kerrang!, Rocksound, Future Publishing, Knowledge, IDJ, EMI, Virgin, Warners, Channel 4
info: Specialise in music and creative photography covering both live and press work.

James Davidson
25 Denmark Street, London, WC2H 8NJ
tel: 020 7240 1616
email: info@jamesdavidson.com
web: www.jamesdavidson.com
info: Digital photography.

Jenny Wicks Photography
1 Dalmore Road, London, SE21 8HD
tel: 07939 140 099
email: jenny@jenniferwicks.com
web: www.jenniferwicks.com
info: Specialises in portraits. Studio work, live gigs and location shoots. Colour and B&W, digital photography and image manipulation available.

Jeremy Larkin Photography
Flat 3, 68 Greencroft Gardens, London, NW6 3JQ
tel: 020 7372 4631/07715 174 708
email: jeremy@jeremylarkin.co.uk
web: www.jeremylarkin.co.uk
contact: Jeremy
info: Professional photographer.

JJ Lacey
London
tel: 07773 860 497
email: jasonjlacey@hotmail.com
contact: Jason Lacey
info: Offers music promotion services to artists and bands. 3 packages available including styling and photography, full video and video samples for promotional material, artwork and design services, as well as verification and adjustments of recordings. See listings in relevant sections for further details.

Jo Talbot & Sue Young
6M Hyde Park Mansions, Cabbell Street, London, NW1 5BJ
tel: 020 7262 0189
email: joandsue@btconnect.com
web: www.joandsue.com
info: Jo and Sue represent several photographers who may be willing to work with unsigned bands. Contact the agency for more details.

Joel Anderson Photography
56 Frith Street, London, W1 3JN
tel: 020 7439 0208/07973 384 033
email: joel@joelanderson.com
web: www.joelanderson.com
prev. clients: Flava Flav, Faithless, Jane's Addiction, The Cardigans
info: Joel shoots live gigs, portraits and album artwork. Previous work can be viewed on his website. Visitors to the site should select Level 4 for the music section.

John Bownas
The Little Barn, 7a Station Road, London, SE20 7BE
tel: 07876 390 650
email: john@virtualfestivals.com
info: Live video and post-production work also undertaken at £30 per hour plus expenses. Stage and tour management services also available at rate of £150 per day plus expenses.

John Butcher Photography
21 Hessel Street, London, E1 2LR
tel: 020 7702 0440
email: johnbutcher.photo@btconnect.com
web: www.johnbutcherphotography.co.uk
info: Digital photography.

John Carmichael Photography
2 Scotts Avenue, Bromley, BR2 0LQ
tel: 020 8464 5869
email: john@jc-photo.co.uk
web: www.jc-photo.co.uk
info: Portraiture specialists.

John Zammit Photography
121 The Manhattan Building, Bow Quarter, Fairfield Road, Bow, London, E3 2UG
tel: 07956 430 361
email: johnzammit@jzphotography.fsnet.co.uk
web: www.johnzammit.co.uk
info: John is willing to work to your budget. Studio and location shoots.

Johnny Greig Photography
46 Ramsden Road, Balham, London, SW12 8QY
tel: 020 8772 1259/07774 134 405
email: johnny@johnnygreig.com
web: www.johnnygreig.com
prev. clients: Robert Smith (The Cure)

Johnny Thompson Photography
Unit 5b, Rosemary Works, Branch Place, London, N1 5PH
tel: 020 7613 0136
info: Contact Johnny to discuss rates and equipment. Also has a photographic studio available for hire.

Jonathan Nunn
23 Hanger Lane, Ealing, London, W5 3HH
tel: 07788 427 843
email: info@jonathannunn.com
web: www.jonathannunn.com
contact: Jonathan Nunn
prev. clients: Mean Fiddler, UB1 Records
info: Freelance photographer specialising in music, fashion and film stills.

Jonathan Root
21 Ferdinand Street, Chalk Farm, London, NW1 8EU
tel: 020 7485 5522/07768 292 666
fax: 020 7485 5532
email: jonathan@jonathanroot.co.uk
web: www.jonathanroot.co.uk
info: Art-based, colour and B&W photography. Studio or location shoots.

Justin Grainge Photography
48 Arden Road, London, N3 3AE
tel: 020 8343 0629
email: photos@justingrainge.com
web: www.justingrainge.com
info: Digital photography.

Katie Carnage
London
email: info@katiecarnage.com
web: www.katiecarnage.com
prev. clients: Fugazi, Placebo

Katie Hammond
27 Eustace Road, London, SW6 1JB
tel: 020 7381 2727
email: k8hammond@hotmail.com
prev. clients: Mohair, Planet of Women
info: Katie is currently working as a photographer's assistant, and so has access to superior studio facilities. She is keen to work with unsigned bands. Location and studio, colour and B&W, digital and film.

Kelda Hole
Greater London
tel: 020 8694 1929
email: kelda@keldahole.com
web: www.keldahole.com
contact: Kelda Hole
prev. clients: Disorder, Kerrang!, Rock Sound, Big Cheese
info: Specialising in music and fashion photography. Location work, as well as based in the creative studio. Post production including retouching and enhancing. Own fully equipped studio.

Kenny McLeish
58 Lamb Court, Narrow Street, London, E14 8EJ
tel: 07879 428 165
email: kenny@kennymcleish.com
web: www.kennymcleish.com
prev. clients: Lostprophets, Sum 41, Alien Ant Farm
info: Kenny McLeish is a freelance photographer specialising in all aspects of youth culture. Contact for details of rates.

Kim Cunningham
London
tel: 07941 227 729
email: kim@kimcunningham.co.uk
web: www.kimcunningham.co.uk
contact: Kim Cunningham
prev. clients: Pete Doherty, Shane MacGowan
info: London based freelance photographer specialising in music people and documentary.

Kim Porritt Photoworks
10 Market Place, London, SE16 3UQ
tel: 020 7394 8615
email: contact@webphotoworx.com
web: www.webphotoworx.com
info: Undertakes a variety of photography assignments.

Klarke Caplin
London
email: klarke@freelance-photography.com
web: www.freelance-photography.com
prev. clients: David Bowie, Romeo, Big Bruvas, Ms Dynamite

Lancaster Studio
18 Forster Road, Beckenham, BR3 4LJ
tel: 020 8658 9975
email: design@lancasters.co.uk
web: www.lancasters.co.uk
info: Lancaster Studio use digital photography. They also offer a graphic and website design service. Contact for further details.

The Lemonade Factory
274-276 Queenstown Road, London, SW8 4LP
tel: 020 7498 8267
fax: 020 7720 8649
email: info@lemonadefactory.co.uk
web: www.lemonadefactory.co.uk
contact: Martin Griffin

Link Photography
33 Greyhound Road, London, W6 8NH
tel: 020 7381 2261
email: photogs@linkpicturelibrary.com
web: www.linkpicturelibrary.com
prev. clients: Capitol Radio
info: Link have been working in the industry for over 20 years, both nationally and abroad. Corporate, editorial, location and digital photography.

Lisa Gorman Agency
49 Neal Street, London, WC2H 9PZ
tel: 020 7240 8222
email: info@lisagormanagency.com
web: www.lisagormanagency.com
info: Lisa Gorman Agency represent several photographers and stylists. Call to discuss your needs.

M.J.P. Photography
9 Twinoaks, Cobham, Surrey, KT11 2QW
tel: 0845 061 6264
email: info@mjpphotography.co.uk
web: www.mjpphotography.co.uk
info: Variety of photographic work undertaken.

Manning Photographers
10 Windmill Row, London, SE11 5DW
tel: 020 7735 5896
email: manningphotographers@btclick.com
info: Colour and B&W photography.

Marc Broussely
72 Southerton Road, London, W6 0PH
tel: 07944 505 344
email: sonicmoo@gmail.com
web: www.loudpixels.co.uk
contact: Marc Broussely
prev. clients: 10,000 Things, Clor, Kaiser Chiefs, Soulwas, The Subways, Undertones
info: Photographer specialising in gig photography.

Mark C. O'Flaherty Photography
London
tel: 07956 970 197
email: mco@markcoflaherty.com
web: www.markcoflaherty.com
prev. clients: Scissor Sisters, Franz Ferdinand, Moby, Yoko Ono, Interpol, The Bravery & Girls Aloud
info: All images available on CD ready for web upload, as well as high resolution for print media.

Mark Okoh
London
tel: 020 8291 3978/07961 306 573
email: mark@okeycokey.com
web: www.okeycokey.com
contact: Mark Okoh
prev. clients: Alicia Keys, Terri Walker, Kelly Rowland
info: Mark specialises in portraiture and his previous work can be viewed on his website.

Mark Roe
London
tel: 020 7871 0892
web: www.markroe.co.uk
prev. clients: British Sea Power, Norma Jean, Nine Below Zero
info: See the above website for examples of Mark's work. Use the online form to contact Mark.

Mark Wragg
Gate Studios, Walkers Place, Putney, London, SW15 1PP
tel: 07836 238 225
email: mark@markwragg.co.uk
web: www.markwragg.co.uk
info: Mark has over 20 years experience working as a photographer. Call to discuss your needs. Location and studio shoots.

Martin Shallcross Photographer
26 Gracedale Road, London, SW16 6SW
tel: 07831 374 362
email: martfoto@mac.com
web: www.martfoto.net
info: Colour and B&W, digital and film photography.

Martin Worster
London
tel: 07764 198 474
email: martin@mikrogroove.com
web: www.martinworster.co.uk
prev. clients: Witness Festival, Glastonbury 2001
info: Specialises in digital photography.

Martyn Goddard
5 Jeffreys Place, London, NW1 9PP
tel: 020 7485 7568
email: photo.mg@virgin.net
web: www.martyngoddard.com
prev. clients: Queen, Blondie, Pete Townsend
info: Digital photography.

Matt Cooke
3 Derwent Road, Raynes Park, London, SW20 9NH
tel: 020 8330 4936/07831 570 289
email: info@mattcooke.co.uk
web: www.mattcooke.co.uk
prev. clients: Alex James (Blur), Murray Walker
info: Matt Cooke specialises in colour and B&W portraiture.

Michael R. Williams
13 Campbell Close, London, SW16 6NJ
tel: 07976 800 126
email: info@michaelwilliams.co.uk
web: www.michaelwilliams.co.uk
contact: Michael Williams
prev. clients: Blur, Interpol, The Distillers, The White Stripes
info: Specialises in portrait photography for editorial and promotional use. Special rates are available to unsigned bands for a set of 10x8 promo shots. Contact Michael for more details.

Michelle Sibthorp
53 Manston Way, Hornchurch, Essex, RM12 5PE
tel: 07951 206 989
email: michellesibthorp@aol.com
web: www.michellesibthorp.co.uk
contact: Michelle
prev. clients: EastLife Magazine, Beck, Starsailor
info: Michelle has also photographed various unsigned bands, as well as working on project 'A Year In The Life At Brixton Academy'.

Mike Ellis Photography
Box Studios, 15 Mandela Street, London, NW1 0DU
tel: 07860 275 287
email: mike@mikeellisphotography.com
web: www.mikeellisphotography.com
info: Contact Mike to discuss rates.

Mike Harding Photography
Unit 16, 11-17 Exmouth Place, London, E8 3RW
tel: 020 7254 5057
email: mike.harding40@virgin.net
info: Contact Mike to discuss rates in relation to your personal needs.

Mike McGoran Photography
Unit 6, Apollo Studios, Charlton Kings Road, London, NW5 2SB
tel: 020 7284 4875
email: mail@mikemcgoran.net
web: www.mikemcgoran.net
contact: Mike McGoran
prev. clients: Various bands and publications.
info: Specialist music photography.

www.sarahphotogirl.com
rock n roll photography live studio and session

Mike Prior
7 The Old Laundry, Alexander Studios, Haydon Way, London, SW11 1YF
tel: 07721 646 464/020 7207 1964
email: info@mikeprior.com
web: www.mikeprior.com
prev. clients: All Saints, Damage
info: Mike has his own studio, and is willing to offer lower rates to unsigned bands.

Miles Winter Photography
35 Anglesey Court Road, Carshalton, SM5 3HZ
tel: 020 8647 5805
email: miles@mileswinterphotography.co.uk
web: www.mileswinterphotography.co.uk
info: Digital or film. Colour and B&W.

Murray Lenton Photography
5 Brief Street, Camberwell, London, SE5 9RD
tel: 020 7733 6769/07941 427 458
email: murray@theatrephotography.co.uk
web: www.theatrephotography.co.uk
info: Murray specialises in live theatre photography, but will work with unsigned musicians. Colour and B&W, digital and film.

Nick Elliot
tel: 07881 650 883
email: nick@nicksgreatestflix.co.uk
web: www.nicksgreatestflix.co.uk
info: Creative music photographer working very closely with signed and unsigned artists, record labels and management agencies. Provides a unique and personal experience to create avant garde images for use in CD covers, promotional material, live gigs and tours.

Nik Milner Photography
Studio 202, Avro House, 7 Havelock Terrace, London, SW8 4AS
tel: 020 7720 8123
email: nik@nickmilner.com
web: www.nikmilner.com
prev. clients: Thin Lizzy

Old.Del.Passo
South London
email: derek_bremner@hotmail.com
web: www.olddelpasso.deviantart.com
contact: Derek Bremner
prev. clients: Big Cheese magazine, Suffrajets, Tsunami Bomb
info: Can carry out live work and promotional shots on location. B&W and colour photography.

Optum Photography
19 Effingham Road, Long Ditton, Surbiton, KT6 5JZ
tel: 020 8398 0934
email: dave@optumphotography.co.uk
web: www.optumphotography.co.uk
prev. clients: BBC, The Guardian, The Observer
info: Optum offer a fully equipped studio with on-site processing and digital shooting facilities.

Peter Ashworth
107 South Hill Park, London, NW3 2SP
tel: 020 7435 4142/07714 952 292
email: peter@ashworth-photos.com
web: www.ashworth-photos.com
prev. clients: Erasure, Space
info: Likes all kinds of shoots, the more adventurous the better. Peter Ashworth specialises in music photography, generally working generally for major record labels.

Peter Fordham Photographer
3b Marmora Road, East Dulwich, London, SE22 0RX
tel: 020 8693 4248
info: Peter Fordham took the photograph used for the John Lennon 'Imagine' posters.

Peter Hill
Trashed Management, Studio 471, 2 Old Brompton Road, London, SW7 3DQ
email: julia@trashedmanagement.com
web: www.trashedmanagement.com
contact: Julia Bevan
prev. clients: Variety of major record labels, advertising agencies, as well as unsigned bands

Peter John Hughes Photography
Enterprise House, 133 Blythe Road, Hayes, Middlesex, UB3
tel: 020 8813 5566
email: peter.hughes@2020studio.demon.co.uk
info: Studio and location shoots.

Phaedra
12 Fieldwick House, Retreat Place, London, E9 6RL
tel: 07800 828 529
email: ppblair@ukonline.co.uk
web: www.cpfarrell.freeserve.co.uk/phaedra
prev. clients: iD Magazine, The Guardian
info: Studio, live and location. Colour and B&W. Use digital, 35mm and medium formats. Most recently worked with London based band Jade.

Phil McCathy Photography
30 Magdalen Road, London, SW18 3NP
tel: 020 8874 8553
email: philphotography@hotmail.com
info: Digital studio photography.

Rainbow Consulting
London
tel: 07734 940 143
email: ben@rainbowconsulting.co.uk
web: www.rainbowconsulting.co.uk
info: Photography graduate with more than 10 years experience. Has worked with actors, models, musicians, business people and private individuals. Creates portraits with beautiful, sharp, fine art images.

Re-Think
London
tel: 020 8318 7762
email: kerry@rethinkmanagement.co.uk
web: www.rethinkphotography.com
contact: Kerry Morgen
prev. clients: Warner Records, Universal, Sony
info: Very experienced photographer in all formats. Will work to any situation.

Robert Aberman Photographer
64 Birnam Road, London, N4 3LQ
tel: 020 7263 7899/07970 185 838
email: robert@robertaberman.co.uk
web: www.robertaberman.co.uk
info: Robert Aberman has over 20 years experience as a photographer. Works with all camera formats. Competitive rates. As well as commissions, Roger is a keen social documentary photographer.

Robert Hall Photography
Gate Studios, Walters Place, Lacy Road, Putney, London, SW15 1PP
tel: 020 8789 6928
email: roberthallphoto@btconnect.com
web: www.roberthallphoto.co.uk
info: Digital and film, colour and B&W photography.

Russell's Photography
17 Elm Grove, Wimbledon, London, SW19 4HE
tel: 020 8947 6177
email: dave@russellsgroup.co.uk
web: www.russellsgroup.co.uk
prev. clients: Decca Records

Sara Bowery
The Little Barn, 7a Station Road, London, SE20 7BE
tel: 07973 856 644
email: sara@virtualfestivals.com
info: 5 years experience of live band photography with virtual festivals.com, as well as various studio and tour commissions.

Sarahphotogirl
London
tel: 07803 108 884
email: sarahphotogirl@hotmail.com
web: www.sarahphotogirl.com
prev. clients: The Darkness, Blur, The Libertines, NME
info: Live studio, press and backstage 'fly on the wall' photography. Colour and B&W, digital and film. See the website for examples of Sarah's work.

Scott Collier
49 Hertford Street, London, W1J 7SR
tel: 020 7495 1626
email: mail@scottcollier.co.uk
web: www.scottcollier.co.uk
info: Experienced photographer accepting a wide range of commissions. See website to view portfolio, as well as details of prices.

Showpix
Greater London
tel: 07830 108 467
email: office@showpix.co.uk
web: www.showpix.co.uk
contact: Mike Edwards
prev. clients: Suede, Deep Purple, Motorhead, Bob Geldof
info: Showpix specialise in live photography, indoor or outdoor. All images are taken using Digital SLR cameras and are available next day. It is best to contact Showpix via email.

Siab Studios
tel: 07773 535 170
email: info@siabstudios.co.uk
web: www.siabstudios.co.uk
contact: Colin Warhurst, Antony O'Hanlon
prev. clients: The Chase, Cohesion, The Circle, Groucho, SOC Records, The Palace Venue
info: Siab offer a number of services for unsigned bands including photography, logo design and CD cover and insert designs, as well as affordable music video production. Clients visiting the site have a choice of utilising the full resources of Siab Studios and/or allowing raw talent a chance to create work for them often at cheaper price, or even free of charge, in order for them to gain experience.

Simon Lewis Photography
PO Box 636, Richmond, Surrey, TW10 6XH
tel: 07860 235 544
email: mail@simonlewisphotography.com
web: www.simonlewisphotography.com
info: Musicians photographed for CD covers, booklets and promotional posters. Styles ranging from World music to Rock.

Slim Designs
91-95 Brick Lane, Old Truman Brewery, London, E2 6QL
tel: 020 7375 3995/07811 607 969
email: info@slimdesigns.com
web: www.slimdesigns.com
contact: Nick Slim
info: Photography and manipulation of images. Can also provide design and print services. See relevant sections for details.

Soma Photos
tel: 07766 753 300
email: hugh@somaphotos.com
web: www.somaphotos.com
info: Specialise in digital and colour photos.

Stefan Sieler
London
tel: 07816 416 022
email: sielerstefan@hotmail.com
prev. clients: Feeder
info: Mainly fashion photography. Works in all formats and styles. Work published regularly in Rant magazine.

Steve Gale
4 Ribblesdele Road, London, N8 7EP
tel: 020 8348 7724
email: sgale@dircon.co.uk
web: www.celticlandscapes.com
info: Colour and B&W photography.

Steve Gullick
London
tel: 07802 824 001 (Colin Brown-agent)
contact: Colin Brown
prev. clients: Several music publications and record companies
info: Steve is a highly experienced and respected photographer who is co-founder of the Loose Lip Sink Ships magazine. He may take photos for unsigned acts if he genuinely likes the music.

Stuart Nicholls
Trashed Management, Studio 471, 2 Old Brompton Road, London, SW7 3DQ
email: julia@trashedmanagement.com
web: www.trashedmanagement.com
contact: Julia Bevan
prev. clients: Major labels, advertising agencies and unsigned bands

Tara Darby @ East Photographic
8 Ironbridge House, 3 Bridge Approach, London, NW1 8DD
tel: 020 7729 9002
fax: 020 7729 9004
email: hq@eastphotographic.com
web: www.eastphotographic.com
prev. clients: Muse, Scissor Sisters, Kasabian, The Bees, Mylo
info: Tara Darby can be contacted via her agency. She does not frequently work with unsigned acts, but may consider doing so.

Theo Moye
London
tel: 07941 464 897
email: theo@theomoye.co.uk
web: www.theomoye.co.uk
info: Works on both digital and film formats and undertakes music and PR work. Theo strives to create original and eye-catching images.

Tim Spencer Photography UK
8 Coltman House, Welland Street, Greenwich, London, SE10 9DW
tel: 020 8858 1158
email: photos@timspencer.co.uk
web: www.timspencer.eclipse.co.uk
contact: Tim Spencer
info: Professional photography and digital imaging available for individuals and commercial companies. Website contains galleries of previous works including people, places, musicians and bands, which are also available for purchase.

Tina McClelland
Unit 11, Forest Business Park, South Access Road, London, E17 8BA
tel: 07855 715 202
email: info@photo2000.co.uk
web: www.photo2000.co.uk
contact: Tina McClelland
prev. clients: Elbow, Cooper Temple Clause, The Darkness
info: Specialises in concert work, press, alternative portraiture, CD artwork, reproduction and artwork licensing. Enthusiastic coverage of the unsigned scene. Email Tina with a brief history of your band and details of website. Very reasonable rates. London based, but commutes to Manchester regularly and is very keen to stay in touch with the unsigned scene in Manchester.

Tomas
London
email: info@tomas.info.uk
contact: Tom
info: Music photography. Also offer graphic design services. See entry in relevant section for details.

Trashed Management
Studio 471, 2 Old Brompton Road, London, SW7 3DQ
tel: 07932 703 810
email: info@trashedmanagement.com
web: www.trashedmanagement.com
contact: Julia Bevan
info: Company representing several music photographers. Will accept commissions from unsigned bands to major record labels and magazines.

Trevor Hurst
Unit 301, 203 Mare Street, London, E8 3QE
tel: 020 8533 5635
email: trevorh@dircon.co.uk
web: www.trevorhurstphotography.com
info: Contact Trevor to discuss rates.

Underexposed
London
email: enquiries@underexposed.org.uk
web: www.underexposed.org.uk
prev. clients: Uncut, Metal Hammer, Kerrang

Urban Image
London
tel: 020 7313 3326
email: richard@urbanimage.tv
web: www.urbanimage.tv
contact: Richard
prev. clients: See website
info: A picture archive containing excellent photos especially concerning youth culture and music. Top photographers can be contacted via the site, including Adrian Boot.

Virginia Fitzherbert
Greater London
tel: 07967 333 561
email: ginia@blueyonder.co.uk
web: www.virginiafitzherbert.co.uk
info: Spontaneous and creative live and location photography (35 mm colour and B&W, image manipulation). All rates reasonable and negotiable.

W6 Photo
359 Lillie Road, Fulham, London, SW6 7PA
tel: 020 7385 2272
fax: 020 7381 5252
email: info@w6studio.co.uk
web: www.w6studio.co.uk
info: Location and studio, colour and B&W photography.

Yves de Contade
Greater London
tel: 020 7386 8086/07957 246 845
email: studio@allaboutyves.com
web: www.allaboutyves.com
prev. clients: Maxim, Loaded
info: Yves de Contade works on both location and in his fully equipped digital studio. Colour and B&W.

MIDLANDS

3rd Eye Photography
Rugby
tel: 07731 313 163
email: musicpix@christianpayne.com
web: www.christianpayne.com or www.musicpix.co.uk
contact: Christian Payne
prev. clients: Damian Rice, Zutons, Cooper Temple Clause, Kings Of Leon
info: Experienced working photographer using Nikon digital equipment. Christian specialises in documentary photography but caters for all the needs of musicians and bands, whether signed or unsigned. A experienced musician himself, Christian offers reasonable rates for unsigned acts. Will undertake all kinds of work including CD artwork, promo shoots and gigs. Email or telephone for a free quote. Willing to travel.

Andrew Photographic
4 Robinson Road, Bedworth, Warwickshire, CV12 0EL
tel: 02476 364 235
fax: 02476 364 235
email: info@andrewphotographic.co.uk
web: www.andrewphotographic.co.uk
contact: Brian Leathley-Andrew
info: Will undertake a variety of work.

Andy Espin Photography
PO Box 7776, Leicester, LE3 5WT
tel: 07767 354 052
email: andy@andyespin.com
web: www.andyespin.com
info: Freelance music and fashion photographer. Andy uses Canon equipment. Live and portrait shots.

Anthony Fisher
12 George Street, Riddings, Alfreton, Derbyshire, DE55 4AU
tel: 01629 551 121
email: onty1@yahoo.com
web: www.tony-fisher.com
contact: Anthony Fisher
info: Professional photographer dealing with commissions of all kinds.

Brian Beddowes
Studio 7, 90 Litchfield Road, Sutton Coalfield, West Midlands, B74 2SY
tel: 07799 883 894
email: brianbeddowes@hotmail.com
web: www.brianbeddowes.co.uk
info: Live and studio work. Can also provide artwork and web design. See relevant section for more details.

Dan Barber
Leicester
web: www.danieljbarber.co.uk
info: Photographer available to work in both Leicester and Leeds. See the website for details of Dan's work.

David Baird
Nottingham
tel: 07976 072 867
email: davidbaird@pointandpress.co.uk
web: www.pointandpress.co.uk
contact: David Baird
prev. clients: Ash, Biffy Clyro, Graham Coxon, Felix Da Housecat
info: David uses all mediums including 35mm, medium and large formats, and digital, to create exciting images. Willing to travel.

The David Peters Photographic Studio
Unit 14, Fordhouse Road Industrial Estate, Steel Drive, Wolverhampton, WV10 9XB
tel: 01902 397 739
fax: 01902 397 001
email: dp@davidpeters.co.uk
web: www.davidpeters.co.uk
info: Studio is based in Wolverhampton, but work can be undertaken on location in London. Digital photography.

Elevator Productions Ltd.
The Smithy, Crawley Lane, Kings Bromley, Burton on Trent, D13 7JF
tel: 01543 472 473
fax: 01543 472 443
email: info@elevatorproductions.com
web: www.elevatorproductions.com
info: Wide range of services for the entertainment industry including photography and design. See also listing in Video Promo section.

G.I.P.P.A.
Office 6, The Balcony, The Cattle Market, Hereford, HR4 9HX
tel: 01432 270 752/07779 611 685
email: gippa@freedesignonlione.co.uk
web: www.gippa.co.uk
contact: Brendan Stephens
info: Photography service for the Performing Arts sector. Also offer illustration and design services. See listing in relevant section for details.

Get Your Band On
Leicester
email: via website
web: www.getyourbandon.com
info: Range of services for bands and artists to assist them in lifting their profile. Contact for further details. See also listings in Artwork & Design, and Video Promo sections for information.

GigJunkie
53 Collard Avenue, Newcastle Under Lyme, ST5 9TH
tel: 07811 826 527/07769 646 170
email: gigjunkie77@yahoo.com
web: www.gigjunkie.co.uk
contact: Sarah Thompson
prev. clients: Baby Shambles, The Killers, Razorlight, NME Tour
info: Professional gig photography. Live, location and studio work. Both B&W and colour shots. Image manipulation using Photoshop.

Groundfloor Observatory
tel: 07816 480 672
email: xen@groundfloorobservatory.com
web: www.groundfloorobservatory.com
contact: Xenia Randle
prev. clients: Biffy Clyro, Hell Is For Heroes, McLusky
info: Specialises in live, tour, press, art, CD inlay and promotion projects.

Hollis Photography
Devenshire House, Loughborough, Leicestershire, LE11 3DW
tel: 0800 032 0022
fax: 01509 238 234
email: info@hollisphotography.com
web: www.hollisphotography.com
contact: Hollis
prev. clients: Elvis Costello, The Bees, Patti Smith
info: Very experienced live band photographers, working with all the best and latest equipment.

Ian Woodcock
Flat 2, Princess Alley, Wolverhampton, WV1 1HB
tel: 07967 133 685
email: iwoodphoto@hotmail.com
web: www.meegie.com
contact: Ian Woodcock
prev. clients: Badly Drawn Boy, The Thrills, Twisted Nerve, Quest Management
info: Freelance photographer specialising in music photography. Portrait and live shots, as well as some design work.

Image Photo Studio
Wigston, Leicester
tel: 0116 257 1791/07961 945 936
email: sosbluesband@hotmail.com
contact: John
info: Live and location shoots. Contact John for further details.

James Akers
Leicester
email: info@jamesaker.com
web: www.jamesakers.com
prev. clients: Muse, Lamb, Super Furry Animals, Franz Ferdinand
info: James has worked with many unsigned bands from the local music scene.

Jennifer Tolly
Birmingham
tel: 07973 187 342
email: jennifertolley@blueyonder.co.uk
web: www.jhtphotography.co.uk
contact: Jenniffer Tolley
prev. clients: Kerrang!, Velvet Revolver
info: Band photographer. Both live and location shoots. High end digital and traditional prints. Willing to accept commissions from all around the country.

Leanne Marie Burgess Photographers
Staffordshire
email: anythingisart@hotmail.com
web: www.leanne-burgess.fotopic.net
contact: Leanne Burgess
prev. clients: The Wildhearts, Lite Audio, Girls Aloud, Bodyrockers, Mel C, Rooster
info: Live, location and studio work. Digital photography, both colour and B&W.

Mark Flowers Photography
39 Bury Road, Leamington Spa, Warwickshire, CV31 3JB
tel: 07759 710 912
email: markflowers@hotmail.com
web: www.markflowers.com
contact: Mark Flowers
prev. clients: Bon Jovi, Avril Lavigne, Counting Crows, Tangerine Dream, Hawkwind, Space Ritual.
info: Freelance photographer who regularly has work published in various books and magazines. Concerts, location and promotional work.

Mark Johnson Photography
Birmingham
tel: 07742 351 511
email: mark@mjohnsonphotography.com
web: www.mjohnsonphotography.com
contact: Mark Johnson
info: Specialises in studio photography for album covers, posters or press releases. B&W and colour. Has worked for several major music companies.

Rainstorm
Leek, Staffordshire
tel: 07793 008 037
email: shangri_la_gypsy@tiscali.co.uk
web: www.rainstormphotography.co.uk
contact: Becka
info: Photograph abstract and very artistic images suitable for CD covers and inlays.

River Studio
Studio 305, The Custard Factory, Gibb Street, Digbeth, Birmingham, B9 4AA
tel: 0121 624 4777/07860 824 101
email: info@riverstudio.co.uk
web: www.riverstudio.co.uk
contact: Richard Battye
prev. clients: Blur, Lemar, Tony Iommi of Black Sabbath
info: River Studio is heavily involved in photography for the music scene in Birmingham, working for BMN, The Arts Council, agents and managers as well as directly with local musicians. Everything from Classical, Brass, Metal, Gospel, Punk, Reggae and Alternative Country to tribute bands. All aspects of photography for the web, PR, and album covers are undertaken.

Rob Dunsford
Shropshire
tel: 01743 242 574/07968 204 469
email: info@robdunsford.com
web: www.robdunsford.com
info: Provides photography suitable for CD sleeves, websites and promotional campaigns. Rob has worked with many unsigned bands from the local scene.

Rock Photo
Birmingham
tel: 07977 446 362
email: stevegerrard@blueyonder.co.uk
web: www.rock-photo.co.uk
contact: Steve Gerrard
prev. clients: The Bravery, Moby, The Kills
info: Steve aims to capture the essence of the performer, whether it is an unsigned act or household name.

Sewell Photography
Leicester
tel: 07796 431 444
email: trevor@sewellphotography.co.uk
web: www.sewellphotography.co.uk
info: Digital band photography. Provide photo shoots for Pink Angel Promotions, who are a PR company. See listing in relevant section for details of their services.

NORTHEAST

Barney Britton
Newcastle
tel: 07812 509 740
email: occasionallybarney@yahoo.co.uk
web: www.barneybritton.com
info: Freelance photographer specialising in music, theatre and portraits. Barney is also in-house photographer for Newcastle Academy.

Bob Cooper
120 White Hall Road, Gateshead, Newcastle, NE8 4LE
tel: 07840 978 569
email: info@bobcooper.org.uk
web: www.bobcooper.org.uk
contact: Bob Cooper
info: Web designer for creative individuals.

cdfoto
Bensham, Gateshead, Tyne & Wear
tel: 07729 455 137
email: info@cdfoto.com
web: www.cdfoto.com
contact: Craig Donnelly
prev. clients: Manic Street Preachers, Doves, Velvet Revolver
info: Live and promotional shots of both signed and unsigned acts. Member of Grassroots exchange, profile can be viewed at www.grassrootsx.com/cdfoto.

JJR Photography
15 Satley Road, Billingham, TS23 3RU
tel: 01642 889 063
email: jjr.photography@ntlworld.com
web: www.jjrphotography.com
contact: Julian Richards
info: Provides photography and video services. Always interested in band photography.

NORTHWEST

A Comfortable Place
20 City South, 39 City Road East, Manchester, M15 4QA
tel: 07883 066 276
email: neemo@acomfortableplace.co.uk
web: www.acomfortableplace.co.uk
contact: Neemo
prev. clients: NY Sushi, Electric Chair, Homoelectric, Chips With Everything, Remedy, Art & Science, Rainy City
info: Neemo has been a freelance photographer for over eight years, and his work has featured in magazines such as The Face, Deluxe and various other music-related publications. Neemo uses a compact digital camera for location work, and a 35mm SLR camera and medium format camera for studio based work. Post production is a vital part of Neemo's work, for which he uses the Photoshop programme.

Adam J. Cooney
39 Priory Road, Sale, Cheshire, M33 2BU
tel: 07967 613 311
email: upstairs@acejoys.fslife.co.uk
web: www.acejoys.fslife.co.uk
contact: Adam Cooney
prev. clients: Gigwise
info: Specialising in live performance photography of bands or solo artists in the Manchester area. Portraits also available. Photographs in B&W or colour, on digital or film. Photographic manipulation also available.

Adam Peter Thorpe
53 Wennington Road, Southport, PR9 7ER
tel: 01704 213 786
email: info@adampeterthorpe.co.uk
web: www.adampeterthorpe.co.uk
info: Live gigs and promo shoots. B&W or colour. Digital photography. Also offers image manipulation. Adam is very keen to hear from new bands.

Adrian Cowin
Isle Of Man
web: www.adriancowin.com
info: If you would like Adrian to attend a gig, just contact him via the form on the website. Digital format.

Alien Eye
Manchester
tel: 07841 714 253
email: danwambam@yahoo.com
contact: Dan arge Sebastian
info: Expert live and location photographs. Old school B&W and colour prints. Dark room manipulation, and poster size enlargement capability. Based in Manchester, but also works in London.

Andrew Brooks
Manchester
tel: 07813 780 386
email: a_p_brooks@hotmail.com
web: www.andrewbrooksphotography.com
info: Promotional and live work. Specialises in colour and digital shots.

Anna Bates Photography
Withington, Manchester
tel: 07977 742 365
email: annabates@gmail.com
web: www.wiredmcr.co.uk
contact: Anna Bates
prev. clients: Wired Manchester, The Zeema Zees, Autokat, Behind Green Lights, The Harrisons, The Greats, Rotary Ten, TVH-3, Whiskycats
info: Resident photographer for Wired Manchester. See website above.

Anthony Tomlinson Studio
559 Old Chester Road, Birkenhead, CH42 4NQ
tel: 07974 966 968
email: mail@anthonytomlinson.co.uk
web: www.anthonytomlinson.co.uk
contact: Anthony Tomlinson
info: Promo shoots using film or digital photography. B&W or colour available. Image manipulation and additional text and graphics. Call Anthony for further details.

C Pictures
St. Thomas' Road, Preston, PR1 6AX
tel: 01772 517 262
email: sara@cpictures.co.uk
web: www.cpictures.co.uk
contact: Sara Cuff
info: Sara is a press and PR photographer. She has a great deal of experience in event photography and specialises in contemporary creative work. Digital or traditional film.

Castle Photography
4 Fisher Street, Carlisle, Cumbria, CA3 8RN
tel: 01228 591 248
email: lescasphoto@aol.com
contact: Les Brown
info: Studio and location work (within reasonable travelling distance). B&W or colour. Digital photography and image manipulation.

Charanjeet Birdie
Liverpool
email: c.birdie@gigwise.com.
contact: Charanjeet Birdie
info: Arts photography, specialising in music. Album covers, posters, festival and gig coverage. Digital work and manipulation of images. Has done work for a number of local bands in Liverpool.

Charles Griffin Photography
PO Box 36, Deeside, Cheshire, CH5 3WP
tel: 01244 535 252
fax: 01244 535 252
email: enq@charlesgriffinphotography.co.uk
web: www.charlesgriffinphotography.co.uk
contact: Charles Griffin
info: Registered with the British Film Commission. Specialises in performing arts photography. Make-up artists and stylists available at extra cost. Live, location and studio work in both the UK and overseas.

Charlotte Bird Studios
Eren Port House, 93 Seabank Road, Wallasey, CH45 7PB
tel: 0151 639 1747
email: enquiries@charlottebirdstudios.co.uk
web: www.charlottebirdstudios.co.uk
contact: Charlotte/Brian
info: Publicity shots, mainly location work in the local area. Offers digital printing and enhancement. Has worked with bands and musicians previously.

Charlotte Green
Manchester
email: charlotte1000@hotmail.com
prev. clients: Chikinki, The Libertines, The Paddingtons
info: Digital photography, either B&W and colour. Live and promotional shoots.

Chris Barber Photography
76 Railway Terrace, Great Harwood, BB6 7EH
tel: 01254 609 225
email: c.barberfreelancephoto@ntlworld.com
web: www.vantagephotography.co.uk
info: Chris Barber is a photographer and digital artist. His work is ideal for CD covers, flyers and promotional material. All his work is done digitally.

Chris Tofalos Photography
Bolton
tel: 01204 524 802
email: chris@ctp-photo.co.uk
web: www.ctp-photo.co.uk
contact: Chris Tofalos
info: Digital photo journalist. Additional graphics, text and manipulation can all be included in the service.

Clare Bailey
8 Kings Lynn Close, Didsbury, Manchester, M20 6WD
tel: 0161 434 0889/07749 709 976
email: clareb342@aol.com
contact: Claire Bailey
info: Specialises in fine art photography for live and location shoots, editorial and CD artwork.

Clive Barrow
37 Bourne Street, Wilmslow, SK9 5HA
tel: 01625 527 972
email: marriagesrme@yahoo.com
web: www.clivebarrow.co.uk
contact: Clive Barrow
info: Specialises in portraits. Clive has worked with various musicians previously. Location and studio work. Call Clive to discuss projects.

Cozz Photography
Trinity, Manchester
tel: 07976 001 343
email: cozz@cozzphotography.co.uk
web: www.cozzphotography.co.uk
prev. clients: The Mekkits
info: Band photographer with completive prices and extensive portfolio. Will photograph on location anywhere in the country. Open to all live gig photography.

CRD Photography
3 Heatherlea Road, Fence, Burnley, BB12 9EJ
tel: 01282 617 203
email: crdphotography@dsl.pipex.com
web: www.crdphotography.com
contact: Christopher Dxidek
info: B&W or colour photography. Location work and gigs. Digital photography and manipulation.

Creative Photography
Wallasey
tel: 0151 639 5338
fax: 0151 639 5338
email: creativephoto@btopenworld.com
contact: Robert Owen, Vince Clegg
info: Specialists in public relations and press photography. No live gig work, but all other locations considered.

David Burrows
North Manchester
tel: 0161 773 7791
email: dab1958@btopenworld.com
web: www.david-burrows.co.uk
contact: David Burrows
info: Has experience of live gigs, location and portraiture shoots, offering a full digital service with Photoshop editing and manipulation. Also offer conceptual work for album covers and flyers. Rates negotiable.

David Holt Photography
56 Dean Road, Handforth, Wilmslow, Cheshire, SK9 3AH
tel: 01625 549 599
email: davidholtphotography@btinternet.com
web: www.davidholtphotography.co.uk
info: Digital photography, B&W or colour. Image manipulation available. Gig and location shoots.

David Yates Studios
409 Hempshaw Lane, Stockport, Cheshire, SK1 4AQ
tel: 0161 476 0464
info: Live, studio and location shoots on either digital and traditional formats. Additional graphics and image manipulation in Photoshop. Call David to discuss your ideas.

Dean McDonald Photography
346 Station Road, Bamber Bridge, Preston, Lancashire, PR5 6EL
email: dean@deanmcdonald.com
web: www.deanmcdonald.com
info: Live, location and studio work. High end digital photography. As well as standard prints, can also publish to CD and DVD formats, and onto the web.

Digital Artwork
1st Floor, 21 Albion Street, New Brighton, Cheshire, CH45 9LE
tel: 0151 638 6755
email: pw@digitalartwork.demon.co.uk
contact: Peter Whitfield
info: Live and location work. B&W or colour using digital camera and Photoshop manipulation.

Electric Ink Photography
Accrington, Lancashire
email: macky@mackykills.co.uk
web: www.electricinkphoto.co.uk
prev. clients: Deftones, Beecher
info: Deals with many local unsigned bands in and around the Manchester and North West areas.

Emma Farrer
Manchester
tel: 0161 798 6517
email: firstthreesongsnoflash@yahoo.com
web: www.firstthreesongsnoflash.com or wwwemmtv.co.uk
contact: Emma Farrer
prev. clients: Queens Of The Stone Age, Henry Rollins, Deus, Soulwax, Jane's Addiction
info: Experienced band photographer. Specialises in live shows. See websites above to view archive of Emma's work.

Escape Photography
65 Craiglands, Rochdale, OL16 4RD
tel: 01706 861 372
email: enquiries@escapephotography.co.uk
web: www.escapephotography.co.uk
contact: Ian Edmondson
prev. clients: Wakestock
info: Live and location work. Specialise in event photography. Traditional film or digital formats. Additional graphic design for CD covers and flyers. Works in conjunction with FTL Images who are a graphic design company.

Figfilm
23 Beever Street, Old Trafford, Manchester, M16 9JR
email: mail@figfilm.co.uk
web: www.figfilm.co.uk
contact: Matthew Norman
prev. clients: Doves, Oceansize, Girls Aloud, Starsailor, The Distillers, Rebelski, Snow Patrol, Kaiser Chiefs
info: Matthew lives and works in Manchester, creating and projecting films and videos behind bands as they play live. He is also a film maker and has worked on videos and documentaries for Doves, Girls Aloud and Oceansize. His photographs have been used by various music and trade magazines.

Gary Roberts
Manchester
tel: 07974 085 706
fax: 0161 876 0379
email: enquiries@garyrobertsphotography.com
web: www.garyrobertsphotography.com
info: Freelance photographer. Gary's website contains a number of examples of his press work, including music and news pieces.

Gingersnapz
Manchester
tel: 0161 434 2820/07930 802 595
email: alyson@gingersnapz.co.uk
web: www.gingersnapz.co.uk
contact: Alyson Blanchard
prev. clients: Metal Hammer, Bang, BBC Online, NME
info: Any type of photography offered, flexibility and understanding in terms of what is wanting to be achieved. NME's photographer in the North West. Prices always negotiated depending on what you can afford.

HB Studios
21 Great Moor Street, Bolton, BL1 1NZ
tel: 01204 356 871
email: cat@ctimages.co.uk
web: www.ctimages.co.uk
contact: Cat Taylor
info: Studio or location shoots including gigs. B&W or colour. Manipulation of images. Welcomes client's ideas for the shoot. Previously worked as stylist and photographer for various tribute acts.

Helen Cathcart Photographer
Manchester
tel: 07890 560 315
email: cathcarthelen@hotmail.com
web: www.helencathcartphotography.co.uk
info: Various band and music photography. Artistic and reportage style photographs at very competitive rates.

Helen O'Sullivan
Liverpool
tel: 07866 673 174
email: mail@helenosullivan.co.uk
web: www.helenosullivan.co.uk
contact: Helen O'Sullivan
info: Experienced band photographer. Location work and live gigs. Colour and B&W prints, transparencies and cross processing. Examples of Helen's work can be seen at www.merseymusic.org and her own site. Covers Liverpool and Wirral areas.

Ian Simpson Imaging
62 Beach Way, Bebington, Wirral, CH63 3AZ
tel: 0151 334 0076
email: ian@simpsonimaging.clara.co.uk
web: www.simpsonimaging.clara.co.uk
info: Studio specialist. Live and location work also available. Shoots for album covers and promotional material. Shot on digital or film. Very reasonable rates. Call Ian to discuss your ideas.

Imago Photography
199 Green Lane, English Damside, Carlisle, Cumbria, CA2 7RA
tel: 01228 536 967
email: enquiries@imagophotography.co.uk
web: www.imagophotography.co.uk
contact: Paul Reid
info: Studio, location and gigs. Digital and film photography. Manipulation of images.

Inch Studio
Unit 22, 23 New Mount Street, Manchester, M4 4DE
tel: 0161 953 4232
email: keir@inchstudio.com
web: www.inchstudio.com
contact: Keir Stewart
info: Specialise in music photography. Live, location and studio shoots. Keir is open to experimentation with ideas and subject matter.

Industrio Productions
Blyth Lodge, 2 Somerville Road, Wigan, WN1 2RX
tel: 01942 242 750
email: andrewpaulayres@hotmail.com
contact: Andrew Paul Ayres
info: Photography and design for all promotional material including sleeve art, photoshoots, performance photography, posters and flyers.

Inventory
4 Links Way, Chadderton, Oldham, Manchester, OL9 6SW
tel: 07813 868 836
email: theorderingone@hotmail.com
web: www.inventory-photo.co.uk
contact: Gary Wolstenholme
info: Specialise in creative landscape and music photography. Can provide comprehensive photographic service covering promotional artwork or live action for bands and musicians.

IX Photography
Manchester
tel: 0161 732 4077/07977 201 032
email: matt@ixphotography.co.uk
web: www.ixphotography.co.uk
contact: Matt Hague
info: Casual images at concerts or pre-arranged photo shoots. Easy going style and friendly photographer. Specially set prices for those working to a budget. Portfolio available upon request.

James Lightbrown
Manchester
tel: 07970 643 580
email: james@flashimages.com
web: www.flashimages.com
info: Digital photography and manipulation. Experienced fashion photographer but is open to working with bands and musicians.

James Maddox Photography
15 Oldcroft, Springhead, Oldham, Lancashire, OL4 4RX
tel: 0161 626 1443
email: james@jamesmaddox.co.uk
web: www.jamesmaddox.co.uk
contact: James Maddox
info: Has done shoots for unsigned bands previously. Live shoots. Contact James for more details.

James Photography
The Studio, Lower Beechwood, Manchester, OL11 4LY
tel: 0870 444 5991
email: info@jamesphotography.co.uk
web: www.jamesphotography.co.uk
contact: James
info: Complete photographic service, from initial shoot to album artwork. Prints on CD, ready to be emailed or uploaded onto website. Also carry out design work for flyers, posters and websites. Contact for further details.

JC Photography
c/o 25 Brompton Avenue, Crosby, Liverpool, L23 3BA
tel: 0151 924 7576
email: jc@photoreal.co.uk
web: www.photoreal.co.uk
contact: John Callaghan
info: Internationally exhibited photographer. Qualified BA(Hons) and experienced in studio and location photography. Available for commissions covering gigs, events, rehearsals, festivals, performance and studio sessions. Creative cover imagery also produced. Colour, B&W and digital shots. Call with requirements or to discuss any ideas you may have.

Jim Hobbs
email: jim@thewonderwall.com
web: www.thewonderwall.com
contact: Jim Hobbs
prev. clients: The Duke Spirit, Nine Black Alps, Longcut, Akoustik Anarkhy, Friends Of Mine
info: Website designer and concert photographer, looking to work with unsigned and established acts. Please email for more details or visit the above site for examples of work.

Joel Fildes
Prestwich, Manchester, M25 1ES
tel: 0161 773 0070
email: joelcfildes@hotmail.com
contact: Joel Fildes
prev. clients: Manchester unsigned bands
info: Specialises in live and location shots. B&W or colour. Works mainly with digital photography and also uses image manipulation. Joel is a musician himself and has a genuine interest in new music.

Jon Super Photography Ltd.
Manchester
tel: 07974 356 333
email: jon.super@ntlworld.com
web: www.jonsuper.com
prev. clients: Rolling Stones, Slipknot, Eminem, Glastonbury Festival
info: Jon is a professional press and commercial photographer working out of Manchester since 1993. Covers live music, bands and festivals for newspapers, magazines and agencies.

Karen McBride
Manchester
tel: 07778 015 137
email: info@karenmcbride.com
web: www.karenmcbride.com
contact: Trashed Management
prev. clients: Doves, Haven, Bill Wyman
info: Dedicated to offering a quality photographic service at a reasonable price to unsigned bands and musicians. Digital, film, B&W and colour. Work includes live concerts, tour and studio documentary, album covers, media and promotions, as well as merchandise and portraits.

Layla Regan Photography
416a Wilbraham Road, Chorlton-cum-Hardy, Manchester, M21 0SD
tel: 07767 373 187
email: laylaphotography@yahoo.co.uk
web: www.acomfortableplace.co.uk/layla
contact: Layla
prev. clients: Gigwise
info: Specialises in live, location and studio work with a cutting edge look.

Mark McNulty
8 Sunnyside, Prince's Park, Liverpool, L3 3TD
tel: 07885 847 806
email: mark@mcnulty.co.uk
web: www.mcnulty.co.uk
contact: Mark McNulty
prev. clients: Travis, Ian McCulloch
info: Has worked on album covers and inlays for well known bands and artists. Studio and location work. Digital and traditional photography. Mark is also the in-house photographer for Carling Academy in Liverpool.

Martin Gardner
Hill Top, Bridge End Lane, Prestbury, Macclesfield, SK10 4DJ
tel: 07768 337 525
email: martin@shutterspeed.demon.co.uk
prev. clients: White Stripes, The Exports, Autokat, Loose Cannon
info: Martin has 20 years experience. Live and promotional shoots. Traditional and digital. Specialise in live and colour photography. Unsigned bands more than welcome.

Martin Sellars
19 Crosby Road North, Liverpool, L22 0LD
tel: 0151 920 7070
email: sellarsphoto@aol.com
web: www.martinsellarsphotography.com
contact: Martin Sellars
prev. clients: Beatles Tributes, Steve Ray
info: Offer studio facilities and location work including gigs. Packages available, enquire for details.

Matt Priestley Photography
Manchester
tel: 0161 881 2265
email: matthew@chorlton.com
web: www.mattpriestley.co.uk
contact: Matt Priestley
info: Worked with a variety of musicians. Location shoots including gigs. B&W or digital photography. Will also carry out Photoshop treatments.

Michael John Photography
11 Moreton Drive, Staining, Blackpool, FY3 0DR
tel: 01253 893 989
email: info@michaeljohnphotography.co.uk
web: www.michaeljohnphotography.co.uk
info: Live and location shoots. Film and digital formats. Image manipulation available. Has plenty of experience working with bands and offers a friendly, competitive service.

Michael Spencer Jones
Manchester
tel: 07768 128 161
email: msj.photo@virgin.net
web: www.michaelspencerjones.com
contact: Michael Spencer Jones
info: Specialises in band work. Album covers, band photographs and live work. Email Michael with details of your band and an idea of what you would like.

Miss Photography
Greater Manchester
tel: 01457 838 176/07763 736 058
email: emma@missphotography.com
web: www.missphotography.com
contact: Emma Jones
info: Emma is a creative, professional music photographer who specialises in gig and concert photography. Dedicated to photographing unsigned bands and helping them gain visual recognition. High quality digital images and artwork.

Dedicated to Photography

Tempted by Great Music...

Karen McBride
FREELANCE PHOTOGRAPHER

t 07778 015 137 www.karenmcbride.com

Negative Reality

Flat 2, 78 Underley Street, Liverpool, L7 4JX
tel:	07880 941 823
email:	negativereality@btopenworld.com
contact:	Sean Bickerton
info:	Gigs and promotional shoots, both studio and

location. Also work suitable for album covers. Shoots on film - any format. Images can be scanned and manipulated. Worked with lots of unsigned bands on the Liverpool scene.

Nick Robinson Photography

101a Anderton Street, Chorley, PR7 2AY
tel:	01257 275 506
email:	nickr0b@talk21.com
web:	www.nick-robinson-photography.co.uk
contact:	Nick Robinson
info:	Affordable session shoots in the studio,

on location or at gigs. B&W or colour. Digital facilities, image manipulation.

Paul Tsansos

Liverpool
tel:	07811 264 733
email:	paultsanos@hotmail.com
web:	www.paultsanos.co.uk
contact:	Paul Tsansos
prev. clients:	Catatonia, Stereophonics, The Melvins
info:	Experienced live band photographer. Special

rates for unsigned bands. Paul is a musician himself and is very keen to help out young talent.

Perfect Image Photography

139 Blackburn Road, Darwen, Lancashire, BB3 1ET
tel:	01254 278 4278
email:	perfectimagephoto@msn.net
web:	www.perfect-image-photos.co.uk
contact:	Jacqueline Gibson, Danielle Berry
info:	Studio, location and gig work. In-house make-up

artist and stylist available.

Photo Cover

108 Boundary Lane, Manchester, M15 6FD
tel:	0161 226 6535
email:	photocover@aol.com
contact:	Veronica Taylor
prev. clients:	Blue, Geri Halliwell, A1
info:	Studio and location work including gigs.

Photo Graphic Design

132 Bradford Street, Farnworth, Bolton, BL4 9JY
tel:	01204 707 725
email:	philip@photographicdesign.com
web:	www.photographicdesign.com
contact:	Philip Locker
info:	Live and location work. Digital photography and

digital video. Image manipulation. B&W and colour photography both available.

Photography By Alistair

109 Knoclaid Road, Clubmoor, Liverpool, L13 8DD
tel:	0151 220 5021
email:	www.abbeyphotography1@hotmail.com
web:	www.abbeyphotography.com
contact:	Alistair Adams
info:	Digital photography. Portfolio and stage publicity

shots. Manipulation and graphics can be added. Alistair is a musician himself and has a good understanding of the local scene.

Photos 2 U

Rose Dale, Fernyhalgh Lane, Fulwood, PR2 9NU
tel:	01772 652 222
email:	enquiries@photos2u.net
web:	www.photos2u.net
contact:	Alan Thrower
info:	Alan is an experienced theatrical photographer

who can accommodate the lighting scheme of any venue. See the website for further details.

Premier Photographics Ltd.

149 School Lane, Didsbury, Manchester, M20 6JP
tel:	07973 614 661
email:	premierphotographics@orange.net
web:	www.premierphotographics.net
contact:	Ed Johnson
info:	Live, location or studio work. Digital, 35mm and

medium formats. Shots can be manipulated or have text added - ideal for flyers and CD covers. Ed is very keen to work with musicians. Has recently worked with Manchester band Krank for an Amnesty gig.

Proud Fella

Unit 12, Vauxhall Industrial Estate, Reddish, Stockport, SK5 7BR
tel:	0161 431 5980
email:	rob@proudfella.co.uk
web:	www.proudfella.co.uk
contact:	Rob
info:	Award winning photographer. Studio and

location work, B&W or colour. See website for examples of Rob's work.

Ranch House Studios

The Ranch House, Bambers Lane, Blackpool, FY4 5LH
tel:	01253 760 101
email:	event-video@btclick.com
web:	www.andytorkington-photography.co.uk
contact:	Andy Torkington
info:	Live, location and studio work. B&W or colour.

Digital photography and manipulation available.

Ray Chan

4th Floor, 24 Lever Street, Manchester, M1 1DT
tel:	07890 632 454
email:	info@raychanphotography.com
web:	www.raychanphotography.com
contact:	Ray Chan
prev. clients:	Twisted Nerve Records, Parlophone, Polydor, XL,
	Virgin Records
info:	Highly experienced band photographer. Studio or

location shoots. Offer affordable rates.

Roger Savage Photography

Croft House, Berrier, Greystoke, Penrith, Cumbria, CA11 0XD
tel:	01768 483 859
email:	photography@rogersavage.co.uk
web:	www.rogersavage.co.uk
contact:	Roger Savage
info:	Studio and location work. Specialises in location

lighting. Will also cover gigs. Digital photography available.

Ross Ditchburn

102a Manchester Road, Nelson, BB9 7HD
tel:	01282 696 055/01282 843 120
contact:	Ross Ditchburn
info:	Experienced band photographer. Striking images

for posters and album covers. Location, studio and gig work with friendly, professional service.

Sakura Henderson

6 Harringay Avenue, Liverpool, Merseyside, L18 1JE
tel:	07989 947 423
email:	sakura@shuzoku.co.uk
web:	www.shuzoku.co.uk
prev. clients:	The Fly, Rock Sound, NME, Kerrang, Liverpool
	Live Magazine, Gigwise, Virtualfestivals,
	Europunk
info:	Freelance music photographer. Specialising in

live and studio band photography. Digital and film media. B&W, colour and slides available.

Sam Lighten

7 Beach Avenue, Marple, Stockport, SK6 6ER
tel:	07739 843 785
email:	sclighton@yahoo.co.uk
prev. clients:	Meanwhile in Tinseltown
info:	Live, location and studio shoots. Cover photos

and portfolios. Also willing to experiment with new styles and ideas. Medium format or digital photography covered. Photoshop image manipulation can be used.

Second Sight

4 Green Moss, Oakthwaite Road, Windermere, LA23 2BB
tel:	01539 444 939
email:	n-bell@telinco.co.uk
web:	www.normanbell.co.uk
contact:	Norman Bell
info:	Live and location shoots on digital format. B&W

or colour. Digital post production effects available.

Shirlaine Forrest Photography

8 Brunswick Road, Altrincham, Cheshire, WA14 1LR
tel:	07905 451 822
email:	jem@shirlainephotos.co.uk
web:	www.shirlainephotos.co.uk
prev. clients:	2 Many DJs, Arctic Monkeys, Beck,
	Chemical Brothers, The Futureheads, Green Day
info:	Freelance photographer specialising in music,

fashion and portrait photography. As well as working for a number of magazines and designers, with photographs published in Vogue and The New York Times, she has also directed music videos with a variety of acts including Neds' Atomic Dustbin and Back To The Planet.

Silver Horse Photography
102 Moorland Road, Poulton, FY6 7EU
tel: 01253 883 426
email: ron@silverhorse.co.uk
web: www.silverhorse.co.uk
contact: Ronald Hodgson
info: Theatrical studio with range of props and backgrounds. B&W or colour.

Smiles Portrait & Wedding Photography
7 Market Street, Hindley, Wigan, WN2 3AE
tel: 01942 256 217
email: brian@smilespwp.co.uk
web: www.smilespwp.co.uk
contact: Brian Moulton
info: Studio, location and gigs. Digital facilities. Full image manipulation available.

Star Photography
tel: 0161 861 8441/07901 876 518
email: imtiazphoto@aol.com
web: www.star-photography.co.uk
contact: Imtiaz Hussain
info: Live, location and studio work including fashion and PR shoots. Photos ideal for CD or flyers. Digital and traditional photography offered. Photos can be put onto CD if required.

Tim Hill Photography
Manchester
tel: 07766 700 809
email: rollinstonehill@hotmail.com
prev. clients: Loose Cannon, Pete Doherty, Bright Eyes
info: Traditional B&W and colour. Unsigned bands more than welcome.

Tony Smith
Manchester
tel: 07092 182 899
email: via website
web: www.hotpix.freeserve.co.uk
contact: Tony Smith
info: Specialises in band photography. Images in print or on CD. Stage, gig, studio or location shots. Website design also available. Visit www.hotpix.org.uk for examples of Tony's work. To get in contact, email via the Hotpix website above.

Velvet Skies Photography
Manchester
tel: 07799 125 502
email: markbristol@hotmail.co.uk
web: www.velvetskiesphotography.com
contact: Mark Bristol
prev. clients: Alterkicks, The Mekkits
info: Flyers, posters and CD covers. Live, promo and location photography. Works with digital, 35ml Film, Polaroid and can be as creative as you want. Competitive rates, for example a 2 hour session is £50 and will give you enough images to last you months.

Veronica Smith
286 Middleton Road, Heywood, Greater Manchester, OL10 2LG
tel: 07855 117 361
email: veronicafsm@yahoo.co.uk
contact: Veronica Smith
info: Mainly B&W shots. Promo shots, portraits and live gigs. Veronica has a genuine interest in new bands and the local music scene.

Xsync
66 Carnforth Road, Stockport, SK4 5LF
tel: 07799 853 554
email: dave@xsync.co.uk
web: www.xsync.co.uk
contact: Dave Brunton
info: Live, location and studio work. Digital photography and photo enhancement.

SOUTHEAST

Alex Flahive
Reading
tel: 0118 981 4117
email: unsigned@alexf.net
web: www.alexf.net
contact: Alex Flahive
prev. clients: 6 Music, BBC Online
info: Alex has worked with bands and musicians previously, both signed and unsigned.

Ray Chan

Photographer

m. 07890 632454
e. info@raychanphotography.com
www.raychanphotography.com

Andrew Future
The Old Firehouse, 19 Sandringham Gardens, Barkingside, Ilford, Essex, IG6 1NT
tel: 07968 124 545
email: andy@clubhedonistic.com
web: www.virtualfestivals.com
contact: Andrew Future
prev. clients: Kerrang, Q, NME, The Mirror, Guardian, Rolling Stone
info: Andrew shoots for an agency, as well as the Virtual Festivals website. Will offer cheaper rates for unsigned acts if he likes your music.

Andrew Spiers Photography
59 Ranelagh Crescent, North Ascot, Berkshire, SL5 8LQ
tel: 01344 886 224
email: contact@andrewspiers.co.uk
web: www.andrewspiers.co.uk
contact: Andrew Spiers
prev. clients: One Night Stand Acoustic, Lindbergh Babies
info: Music photographer specialising in live events. Will also undertake studio work.

Andrew Wood Photography
24 Buxton Road, Brighton, BN1 5DE
tel: 07789 547 098
email: anw@anwood.co.uk
web: www.anwood.co.uk
contact: Andrew Wood
prev. clients: British Council, Candoco Theatre, French Institute, TruThoughts Records.
info: Highly original and dynamic creative shots. Leftfield performance shots, alternative portraits, graphic and abstract illustration for publicity and promotional materials such as flyers and CD covers. All interesting projects considered.

Bip Mistry
Brighton & Hove
tel: 07956 870 991
email: info@bipinchandra.co.uk
web: www.bipinchandra.co.uk
contact: Bip Mistry
prev. clients: The Big Issue
info: Specialises in documentary photography. Also undertakes commercial work.

Brightside Photography
Oxford
tel: 07815 132 783
email: helen@brightside-photography.co.uk
web: www.brightside-photography.co.uk
contact: Helen
info: Exciting and fresh photography from a friendly professional photographer and music lover. Promotional photos at an hourly rate, prices from £40 per hour for digital. Live photos at flat rate of £50 plus travel expenses.

Chris Harris
92 London Road, Wokingham, RG14 1YF
tel: 07776 145 155
email: chrisharris_me@hotmail.com
web: www.chrisharrisphotography.co.uk
info: Studio, live or location shoots. Portraits, documentary and promotional work. Suitable for album or merchandise design. Also cover film and fashion commissions.

The Clicker
tel: 07862 284 529
email: clickersphoto@gmail.com or horswell@gmail.com
web: www.theclicker.co.uk or www.simplysi.com
contact: Simon Horswell
info: Simon is one half of photographic team, The Clicker. He specialises in music images. View galleries on either of the above websites.

Clive Woodley Photography
22 Andover Road, Orpington, Kent, BR6 8BP
tel: 01689 824 439/07885 379 479
email: info@clivewoodleyphotography.co.uk
web: www.clivewoodleyphotography.co.uk
info: Clive has been working in photography for 17 years, and is willing to work to your budget. Film and digital.

DarkDaze Photography
4a Devonshire Mansions, Devonshire Place, Brighton, BN2 1QH
tel: 07921 180 901
email: darkdaze_uk@yahoo.com
web: www.darkdaze.org
contact: Kevin Mason
prev. clients: Undercover, Graphotism, Blaze, Juice, Source, MTV2, Sony Playstation B-Boy Championship
info: Digital and 35mm formats. Live shows and gigs are a speciality, with strong portfolio of clients in this area. Kevin also shoots portraits on location and can provide a team of photographers and DV camera operators, depending on the needs of the client.

Gemma Shaw
36 Braybrooke Road, Hastings, East Sussex, TN34 1TA
tel: 07981 429 719
email: gemma.shaw@roomthirteen.com
contact: Gemma Shaw
prev. clients: www.room13.com, The Heaters, Dropkick Murphys
info: Freelance music photographer specialising in live gigs and promotional location shoots.

Greig Clifford Photography
Kings Meadow, West Lane, Lancing, West Sussex, BN15 9RS
tel: 07961 960 056
email: greigclifford@gc-enterprises.com
info: Greig holds an 'Unsigned Bands Day' once a month, when he offers special rates for unsigned artists. Contact Greig if you would like to be involved. Location and studio (either Brighton or London).

Helen Kitto
Kent
tel: 07712 222 192
prev. clients: Kooba Radio
info: Covers all sorts of photography, other than music, including commercial, events and activities.

Ian Dickson
31 Park Street, Brighton, East Sussex, BN2 0BS
tel: 01273 673 006
email: ian@late20thcenturyboy.com
web: www.late20thcenturyboy.com
info: Experienced Rock photographer working since 1972. Work published in Rolling Stone, Q, New Musical Express, Mojo, Sounds and Vox, amongst others.

IDPhoto
59 Shakespeare Street, Watford, Hertfordshire, WD24 5HE
tel: 07799 142 169
email: ian.davies@id-photo.co.uk
web: www.id-photo.co.uk
contact: Ian Davies
prev. clients: The Thrills, Thee Unstrung, Pink Grease
info: Enthusiastic, friendly photographer working with up and coming and more established artists. Live and promotional photography.

Image2Film
Studio 29-31 Stafford Road, Brighton, BN1 5PE
tel: 07958 272 333
email: info@image2film.com
web: ww.image2film.com
contact: David Fernandes
info: Experienced band photographer. Studio and location work. Also shoots and edits music promo videos. See relevant section for details.

Images Brighton
20b Robert Street, Brighton, BN1 4AH
tel: 07887 993 394
email: dg@imagesbrighton.com
web: www.imagesbrighton.com
contact: David Gray
info: See website above for selection of music related images in David's picture library.

Jay Myrdal
Old School House, High Street, Stanford-In-The-Vale, Oxfordshire, SN7 8LH
tel: 01367 710 168
email: jay@myrdal.com
web: www.myrdal.com
prev. clients: Kate Bush, Toyah
info: Jay is based in Oxfordshire, but is willing to commute to London for work.

Jim Gordon Photography
63 Stanmer Park Road, Brighton, BN1 7JL
tel: 01273 542 970
email: jim.gordon66@btopenworld.com
web: www.jimgordonphotography.co.uk
info: Renowned party and events photographer. Has previously photographed John Peel. Call Jim to discuss your needs.

Joe Bangay Photography
River House, Riverwoods, Marlow, Buckinghamshire, SL7 1QY
tel:	01628 486 193
fax:	01628 890 239
email:	joebangay@joebangay.com
web:	www.joebangay.com
contact:	Joe Bangay
prev. clients:	Eurythmics, U2, Madonna, Duran Duran, Sade, Iron Maiden, U2, Lionel Richie
info:	Studio publicity shots, album sleeves and live

concerts of all genres. Joe also manages bands and artists. See entry in Management Companies section for details. Joe is very approachable and keen to help new artists.

Keith Corcoran
Berkshire
tel:	07833 186 019
email:	keith_corcoran@hotmail.com
web:	www.keithcorcoran.co.uk
contact:	Keith Corcoran
prev. clients:	Sony BMG, Warners, IPC, JVC Japan, RCA Records.
info:	Specialist in promotional, live and reportage

photography. Will travel for shoots.

Keith Curtis
Powells Farm, Plaitford, Romsey, Hampshire, SO51 6EE
tel:	01794 323 366
email:	keith@keithcurtis.co.uk
web:	www.keithcurtis.co.uk
contact:	Keith Curtis
prev. clients:	The Stranglers, Wishbone Ash, The Rutles, The Zombies
info:	Highly experienced professional photographer.

Kenneth Bryant
6 Grays Road, Godalming, Surrey, GU7 3LT
tel:	01483 417 595
email:	kenbryant.photo@kennethmbryant.net
web:	www.kennethmbryant.net
contact:	Kenneth Bryant
info:	Experienced photographer, mainly promotional

work.

Lambton & Varsani Communications
21-22 The Old Steyne, Brighton, BN1 1EL
tel:	01273 648 373
email:	hash@lvcommunications.org
web:	www.lvcommunications.org
info:	Live and location work. Studios can also be hired

for any purpose. £150 for session lasting up to 3 hours, £450 for full day. See also listing for PR services offered by Lambton & Varsani in relevant section.

Landmark Art
PO Box 2901, Hove, BN3 1SS
tel:	01273 749 737
email:	info@landmarkart.co.uk
web:	www.landmarkart.co.uk
contact:	Carl O'Connell
info:	Will take on all kinds of photography

assignments.

Neil Lupin
18 Newmark Court, Goldsmith Way, St. Albans, Hertfordshire, AL3 5LN
tel:	07801 568 890
email:	neil@imagesworldwide.com
web:	www.imagesworldwide.com
prev. clients:	U2, Queen, Coldplay, Velvet Revolver, Paul Weller
info:	Live Rock and Pop photographer. Specialist in

vibrant, colourful, atmospheric live concert photographs. Previously published in Classic Rock Magazine, Amateur Photographer Magazine, local press and on the BBC Website.

NMG Design
20 Kingsbury Street, Brighton, BN1 4JW
tel:	07989 541 487
email:	nealgrundy@hotmail.com
web:	www.nmgdesign.co.uk
info:	Photography for promotional print, press and

CD artwork. Can undertake full design projects. See Artwork & Design listings for more details.

Paperwings
254 Green Way, Bromley, Kent, BR2 8EZ
tel:	07952 337 389
email:	melanie.winning@ntlworld.com
web:	www.paperwings-pro.com
contact:	Melanie Winning
info:	Digital photography. Once briefed on budget and

project, Paperwings can do the rest.

Paul Franks Photography
108 Windmill Road, Sunbury on Thames, Middlesex, TW16 7HB
tel:	01932 770 202
email:	info@paul-franks.com
web:	www.paul-franks.com
info:	Digital photography in studio only. In-house

printing available.

Paul Gregory Photography
10 Moor Copse Close, Earley, Reading, Berkshire, RG6 7NA
tel:	07899 984 310
email:	paul@paulgregoryphotography.co.uk
web:	www.paulgregoryphotography.co.uk
contact:	Paul Gregory
prev. clients:	Aubrey Lemmon, Afterglow, Summerland, GWR Group, Craig David, Louise Redknapp, Honeyz, Liberty X
info:	Specialising in innovative, colourful, fun and

attention grabbing images. Any commissions received will be treated with strict confidence and a high attention to detail.

Pro-Fotos - John Cotter (LBPPA)
110 Spelthorne Grove, Sunbury on Thames, Middlesex, TW16 7BY
tel:	01932 761 764/07946 425 460
email:	jcprofoto@hotmail.com
web:	www.pro-fotos.co.uk
contact:	John Cotter
info:	Serving South and West London and the Home

Counties. Mobile, location and studio. Digital or film formats. Creative, patient and friendly service. John is a musician and is sympathetic to the image requirements of artists.

Rob Thompson
692a Bath Road, Taplow, Maidenhead, Berkshire, SL6 0NZ
tel:	07970 204 619
email:	rob@photo-sight.co.uk
web:	www.photo-sight.co.uk
info:	Freelance photographer specialising in fantasy

and abstract imagery and unusual pictures, working in both colour and B&W. Image manipulation and scanning facilities are also available. Usually works by talking to the client about concepts for imagery and then arranging sessions. Visit website to view examples of portfolio.

Sal Jefferies Photography Ltd.
Brighton
tel:	01273 329 515/07801 254 098
email:	info@saljefferies.com
web:	www.saljefferies.com
contact:	Sal Jefferies
prev. clients:	Kasabian, The Von Bondies
info:	Music photography with a potent mix of

commercial skill and fresh creativity. From live events to cover shots and press images. Works with both signed and unsigned artists. See the above website for examples of Sal's work.

Troy Crause
High Wycombe
tel:	01494 870 247
email:	troykie@hotmail.com
contact:	Troy Crause
prev. clients:	Silent Scream, Speed Circus, King Adora, Not Katies
info:	Specialises in music photography. Live, location

and promotional work. Will travel to most locations.

Underachiever Photography
78 Crowstone Road, Westcliff On Sea, Essex, SS0 8BD
tel:	07732 437 300
email:	photography@underachiever.org.uk
web:	www.underachiever.org.uk
contact:	Penny Bennet
prev. clients:	The Ordinary Boys, Funeral For A Friend
info:	Freelance photographer specialising in band

photography. Available for live gigs, promotional shoots, studio sessions, tours and pretty much anything else.

Underwater Images
1st Floor, Gloucester House, 45 Gloucester Street, Brighton, East Sussex, BN1 4EW
tel:	07917 410 332
email:	sean@underwaterimage.co.uk
web:	www.underwaterimages.co.uk
contact:	Sean Clark
info:	Underwater Images provides live event

photography, from DJ based events to live band performances. Candid backstage portraits or abstract cover material. All images can be supplied using traditional or digital methods.

VisualChaos Studios Ltd.
Brighton
tel: 0870 161 1075/07764 883 636
fax: 0870 161 1071
email: info@visualchaos.co.uk
web: www.visualchaos.co.uk
contact: Sarah Fisher
info: Professional photographic studios offering flexible packages. Aiming for a fresh approach to all endeavours but ultimately and most importantly aim to please customer. Offer both traditional printed and digital output to all clients.

Zoe Moon
22 Clarence Square, Brighton, BN1 2ED
tel: 07782 133 114
email: zoemoonphotos@fastmail.fm
contact: Zoe
info: Freelance music photographer of live events especially Rock and Punk gigs in London and Brighton. Both backstage and onstage shots. Email to request portfolio.

SOUTHWEST

Andrew Powell Photography
10 Harrington Drive, Hatherley, Cheltenham, Gloucestershire, GL51 6ER
tel: 07879 466 843
email: aphotographix@hotmail.co.uk
web: www.aphotographix.com
info: Variety of photography work undertaken.

Anthony Mosley Photographer
16 Edgecombe Way, St. Ann's Chapel, Gunnislake, Cornwall, PL18 9HJ
tel: 01822 833 204
fax: 01822 833 204
email: info@anthonymosley-photographer.co.uk
web: www.anthonymosley-photographer.co.uk or www.acquireimagemedia.com
contact: Andrew Mosley
info: Anthony deals with all types of image. Gallery of his work can be viewed on either of above websites.

DJ Webb
Southampton
tel: 07968 242 508
email: dj@photography-of-rock.com
web: www.photography-of-rock.com or www.photography-of-rock.com
prev. clients: Dead! Dead! Dead!, Karalta, Idiot Pilot, Team Sleep
info: Based in Southampton but regularly travels around the South and to London for gigs. Keen to photograph live gigs, so contact via the above email address with any upcoming dates.

PhotoChromatics
19 Denmead Road, Bournemouth, Dorset, BH6 5QH
email: martin@photochromatics.org.uk or info@snub.co.uk
web: www.photochromatics.org.uk
contact: Martin
info: Highly experienced and very band friendly photographer.

BAND PHOTOGRAPHY

Renegade Photo
The Rowans, Chaxhill, Westbury on Severn, Gloucestershire, GL14 1QP
tel: 01452 760 147
email: studio@renegadephoto.net
web: www.renegadephoto.net
contact: Mark Terry
info: Experienced press and PR photographer. Gigs and events covered. Publicity material and album cover commissions accepted.

Sefton Park Photography
94 Sefton Park Road, St. Andrews, Bristol, BS7 9AL
tel: 07811 388 763
email: scott@seftonpark.com
web: www.seftonpark.com
contact: Scott Shackleford
info: Will undertake variety of work including photo journalism, landscape and photography of extreme sports. Has carried out work previously for local press, music listing magazines and websites. Contact for further details.

Skyla Graphics
Bournemouth
tel: 07977 915 889
email: skyla@skylagraphics.co.uk
web: www.skylagraphics.co.uk
info: Photography for bands and musicians of all genres. Offers full publicity and graphic support. See Artwork & Design listings for more details.

Spend Spend Spend
email: tom@spend-spend-spend.com
web: www.spend-spend-spend.com
contact: Tom Vinelott
info: Experience photographer, who will do both studio and live shoots. Colour and B&W photography. Also offers graphic and web design services. See listing in relevant section for details.

YORKSHIRE

123 Photographers
Leeds
tel: 0113 231 1233
email: enquiries@123photography.co.uk
web: www.123photography.co.uk
prev. clients: Sterophonics, Rage Against The Machine
info: Live photography only. B&W shots, specialising in digital format. Willing to travel.

Alex Coley
Leeds, West Yorkshire
tel: 07977 827 354
email: alexcoley@yahoo.com

AMI Music Photographer
Studio 7, 21 Cloughgarth, Hedon, Hull, HU12 8LS
tel: 07787 188 452
email: ami@musicphotographer.co.uk
web: www.musicphotographer.co.uk
contact: Ami Barwell
prev. clients: Radiohead, Blur, Beck, Interpol, Miss Black America, Kings Of Leon, The Libertines, Macy Gray, The White Stripes
info: Ami specialises in, live music photography, press shots, portraits, tour photography, album and single covers, TV stills, recording studio shots and B&W photography.

BGM
19 Osborne Place, Hebden Bridge, West Yorkshire, HX7 8BD
tel: 07989 419 240
email: benmcm@gmail.com
contact: Ben
prev. clients: Billy Cohen, Bare Naked Ladies, Ga-Ga's
info: Music photographer. Live and promotional shoots.

Bob Taylor
Leeds, West Yorkshire
email: slideshowbob30@yahoo.co.uk
web: www.bobtaylor-musicphotographer.co.uk
prev. clients: The Go! Team, The Cribs, The Paddingtons, Selfish C***

Carmel McNamara
Leeds, West Yorkshire
web: www.carmymac.com
info: Carmel does a lot of work on for the Leeds Music Scene website.

Chris Saunders
1 Murray Road, Sheffield, S11 7GF
tel: 07949 376 508
email: chrismsaunders@hotmail.com
web: www.chrismsaunders.com
contact: Chris Saunders
prev. clients: Dizzee Rascal, Flaming Lips, The Hives, The Kills

MUSIC SERVICES/RETAIL

Sefton Park Photography and Design Services
Bristol

Gigs
Festivals
Events
Outdoor Photoshoots

£150 per day plus expenses
All photos provided on C.D.
Printing Services Available.

✉ scott@seftonpark.com

☎ 07811 388763

Claire Morris Photography
Leeds
tel:	07821 757 761
email:	claire@clairemorrisphotography.co.uk
web:	www.clairemorrisphotography.co.uk
contact:	Claire Morris
prev. clients:	Yorkshire Post, Sony, Absolute Leeds Magazine,

The Leeds Guide, Music Weekly and many of Leeds' unsigned bands.
info: Music photographer who is based in Leeds but will travel for shoots.

Danny North
Leeds, West Yorkshire
tel:	07958 527 947
email:	photo@dannynorth.co.uk
web:	www.dannynorth.co.uk
prev. clients:	The Cribs, Kaiser Chiefs

David S. Brett – Photos Online
Bradford
tel:	07764 461 777
email:	me@dsbrett.co.uk
web:	www.photos-dsb.co.uk
contact:	David Brett
prev. clients:	Local unsigned bands

info: Part time freelance photographer willing to do promotional and live gig photography with new, up and coming bands based in West Yorkshire or surrounding areas.

Depix Music Photography
Leeds, West Yorkshire
tel:	07841 135 358
email:	info@depix.co.uk
web:	www.depix.co.uk
contact:	Ruth Stanley
prev. clients:	Therapy, Anti Product, Kaiser Chiefs, Electric Eel

Shock

EM Photography
Northgate House, 34 Northgate, Hessle, South Yorkshire, HU13 9AA
tel:	01482 627 634
email:	emphotouk@aol.com
contact:	Ian Wilis-Bentley
prev. clients:	Iron Maiden, Elton John

info: Experienced band photographer who will undertake all types of shoot.

Equilibrium Photography
Leeds, West Yorkshire
email:	maaknewtonphotography@yahoo.co.uk
web:	www.equilibriumphotography.cjb.net
contact:	Maak Newton
prev. clients:	Brendon Benson, Kaiser Chiefs, TV On The Radio

Geoff Allsop
15 Pagdin Drive, Styrrup, Doncaster, DN11 8LX
tel:	01302 744 082
email:	mr.geoff@ecossetel.com
web:	www.countrymusic.org.uk/geoff-allsop
prev. clients:	Music magazines including North Country,

Southern Country, Country Music Round Up and Linedancer
info: Music photographer specialising County&Western genre. Promo, live and shoots.

Lizzie Coombes
Leeds, West Yorkshire
tel:	0113 293 9904
info:	Previous experience has included extensive

theatre work, as well as commissions for Opera North, Bradford Festival and community arts work.

Mark Jordan Photography
Leeds
tel:	0113 228 8333
email:	info@markjordanphotography.co.uk
web:	www.markjordanphotography.co.uk
contact:	Mark Jordan
prev. clients:	Kaiser Chiefs, 10,000 Things
info:	Mark has photographed many unsigned acts

from the local scene.

Mark Pierce Photography
80 Market Street, Brass Castle Hill, Pocklington, York, YO42 2AB
tel:	01759 307 707/07811 204 566
email:	info@markpierce-photography.co.uk
web:	www.markpierce-photography.co.uk
info:	Experienced music photographer. Both live and

studio shoots. Can also provide artwork and web design. See listing for Revelator in relevant section.

Martin Roe Photography
5 Moorfield Avenue, Menston, Leeds, LS29 6HB
tel:	07843 830 557
email:	info@institutionaleyes.co.uk
web:	www.institutionaleyes.co.uk
prev. clients:	Alabama 3, The Music, The Duels

Monodigital Photography
Leeds, West Yorkshire
tel:	07709 706 146
email:	kirstress@ntworld.com
web:	homepage.ntlworld.com/kirstess
contact:	David Etherington
info:	Look at the above website for examples of

David's work.

Nick Fletcher
88 Langton Road, Norton, Malton, North Yorkshire, YO17 9AE
tel:	01653 694 802/07779 397 377
email:	nickfletcher@beeb.net
web:	www.nicholaslfletcher.com
contact:	Nick Fletcher
info:	Digital or film. Specialising in B&W high contrast

shots.

Paul Harness
41 Pondfields Drive, Kippax, Leeds, LS25 7HJ
tel:	0113 286 0909/07970 480 396
email:	musicphoto@freeuk.com
web:	www.musicphoto.freeuk.com
contact:	Paul Harness
info:	Undertakes photography ranging from music

and fashion to commercial. Check the above website to view Paul's portfolio.

Punk Shots
5 Glebe Avenue, Kirkstall, Leeds, LS5 3HN
tel:	07736 315 777
email:	bez@punkshots.co.uk
web:	www.punkshots.co.uk
contact:	Graham Berry
prev. clients:	Converge, Annihilation, Time-II, Red Stars Parade-Disko.
info:	Specialise in live photography. Colour and B&W.

Roberta Rayner
tel:	07966 706 581
email:	photo@robertarayner.com
web:	www.robertarayner.com
contact:	Robera Rayner
prev. clients:	The Cure, Willy Mason, Cylab, Kaiser Chiefs, Jesse Malin
info:	Professional, artistic photographer capable of
all kinds of photography including gigs, artwork, location and studio. Nationwide coverage.

Shari Denson
Yorkshire
tel:	07813 884 849
email:	sharidenson@yahoo.co.uk
web:	www.sharidenson.co.uk
contact:	Shari Denson, Shari Denson
prev. clients:	Interpol, Trap2, The Duke Spirit, Editors, I Am Kloot
info:	Works mainly in B&W and favours shadowy,
contrasted images. Occasionally works in colour. See the website for examples of work. Shari works mainly in the Yorkshire and North West areas, but will travel if appropriate.

Simon Ryder
North Yorkshire
tel:	07887 613 716
web:	www.simonryder.co.uk
prev. clients:	The Guardian, The Independent, The Times.
info:	Digital or traditional film based photography.
Editorial and PR. Simon has 7 years experience as a press and PR photographer and is very interested in music photography. Will do location, live and studio work.

Sphere Photography
Mill No. 6, Mabgate Mills, Leeds, LS9 7DZ
tel:	0113 245 9199

Tom Barnes
Sheffield
tel:	07966 018 055
email:	info@tombarnesphoto.com
web:	www.tombarnesphoto.com
info:	Traditional and digital, specialising in colour
photography. Will cover any event.

Tony Woolgar
32 Devonshire Gardens, Leeds, LS2 9BR
tel:	0113 216 8848
info:	Outside publicity plus live shots.

NORTHERN IRELAND

Alan Maguire
Belfast
email:	livemusicpics@gmail.com
web:	www.livemusicpics.com
contact:	Alan Maguire
info:	Freelance photographer based in Belfast.
Specialises in live music photography. Also available for promotional shoots and portraits.

Graham Smith
Belfast
email:	mail@grahamsmithphotography.com
web:	www.grahamsmithphotography.com
contact:	Graham Smith
prev. clients:	Razorlight, R.E.M., Velvet Revolver, Scissor Sisters, Beck, Franz Ferdinand, HIM, Jimmy Eat World, The Futureheads, The Mascara Story
info:	Both live and location shoots. B&W and colour.
Using digital format.

Harrison Photography
37-39 Great Northern Street, Belfast, BT9 7FJ
tel:	028 9066 3100
info:	Digital imaging. Studio facilities available.

Iona Bateman
Northern Ireland
tel:	07796 354 583
email:	ionabateman@gmail.com
web:	www.soulfluff.com
prev. clients:	Therapy?, Ash, Scissor Sisters, Green Day
info:	Rates vary depending on acts and usage. Iona
understands the budget restrictions of unsigned artists. Has undertaken commissions for most major record labels and magazines during her career. See the website for more details.

Michael Fish
Northern Ireland
email:	michael.fish@michaelfish.net
web:	www.itakebandphotos.co.uk or http://michael-fish.deviantart.com
info:	Travels between Dublin and Belfast to gigs. Work
can be viewed on website.

Sinead McGee
tel:	07834 971 126
email:	comeawaywithme@handbag.com
web:	www.sineadmcgee.co.uk
info:	Promotional and live based work. Willing to
travel but only within Ireland.

SCOTLAND

Andy Forman
57 Victoria Road, Lenzie, Glasgow, G66 5AP
tel:	0141 776 1327
email:	andyforman@bigfoot.com
info:	Portrait photography for press and PR.

Art Machine
44a King Harald Street, Lerwick, Shetland
tel:	01595 696 646
fax:	01595 692 313
email:	artmachine@zetnet.co.uk

The Buzz Group
32 Priory Place, Perth, PE2 0DT
tel:	01738 638 140
email:	info@thebuzzgroup.co.uk
web:	www.thebuzzgroup.co.uk
info:	Buzz offer a wide range of services including
photography, press, management and they run a label. Contact for further details.

The Camera Centre
72 Commercial Street, Lerwick, Shetland, ZE1 0DL
tel:	01595 694 345
fax:	01595 693 138

Colin Usher
Roslin
tel:	07092 003 130
email:	colin@juniorjetclub.net
web:	www.colinusher.tv
prev. clients:	Proclaimers, Little Buddha, Without Malice
info:	Accepts all kinds of work ranging from magazine
commissions, portraits, music and corporate photography.

Nick McGowan-Lowe
Unit 114, Kerse Road, Stirling, Stirlingshire, FK7 7SY
tel:	01786 474 448
email:	info@mmluk.com
info:	Specialises in digital, 35mm and medium
formats.

Resistance Photos
1 Lindsay Drive, Kelvindale, Glasgow, G12 0HB
tel:	0141 576 5832
fax:	0141 586 7369
email:	info@resistancephotos.com
web:	www.resistancephotos.com
contact:	Elaine Blakely
prev. clients:	System Of A Down, Disturbed, Dead Poetic, Fall Out Boy, Jimmy Eat World
info:	Photography company that provides cutting edge
imagery to clients within the music and entertainment industry since 1999. Provide discounted package deals for unsigned acts within the city.

MUSIC SERVICES/RETAIL

Zombie Works
1/1 The Angel Building, 12 Paisley Road West, Glasgow, G51 1LE
email: gareth@zombie-works.co.uk
web: www.zombie-works.co.uk
contact: Gillian, Gareth
info: Number of photographers available to capture your image on film. Location shots and studio shots. Zombie Works also offer other services to assist the promotion of bands and musicians, including video duplication, promo packs and web design.

Zone 5 Photography
11 Moss Road, Glasgow, G51 4JT
tel: 07971 665 553
email: info@zone5photography.co.uk
web: www.zone5picturelibrary.net or
www.zone5photography.co.uk
contact: Craig Dunbar
info: Freelance photographer working in a variety of styles.

WALES

Alfie Goodrich
tel: 01600 712 825
email: info@alfgoodrich.co.uk
web: www.alfgoodrich.co.uk
prev. clients: Glastonbury Festival, WOMAD
info: Experienced in working with unsigned bands and is the main photographer for an annual free music festival in Monmouth.

Canfod Photography
6 Monmouth Street, Cardiff, CF11 6SF
tel: 02920 377 423
email: waynejennings@mac.com
info: Specialise in location shots.

Chris Rees
St. Clears
tel: 01994 231 073
email: chrisrees@aol.com
web: www.chrisrees.net
info: Live photography specialist. Covers the South of Wales. Chris often has images published in the local press.

Erfyl Lloyd Davies Photography
Cefn Coed, Dolgellau, Gwynedd, LL40 2YP
email: erfyl@eldphotography.fsnet.co.uk
prev. clients: Sesiwn Fawr Dolgellau festival

Graham Harries (Gman)
Llanelli
tel: 07880 504 385
email: g.harries@tiscali.co.uk
web: www.void-music.net
prev. clients: Reef, The Damned, Har Mar Superstar, Saxon, Fishbone, Antiproduct, Hell Is For Heroes, The Gliteratti
info: Live photography a speciality. Graham is especially interested in Rock and Metal but is happy to photograph bands from any genre.

GW Paul
27 Llanmaes Street, Cardiff, CF11 7LQ
tel: 02920 228 686
info: Experienced photographer who has in the past photographed the likes of Tom Jones, Sophie Loren and Gregory Peck.

Heymisteritakepictures
Cardiff
tel: 07789 635 262
email: heymisteritakepictures@hotmail.com
web: www.heymisteritakepictures.com
contact: Chris McFall
info: Live, location or studio photography. Digital imaging, illustration and design.

Jeffrey F. Morgan
36 Barrack Hill, Newport, Gwent, NP20 5FR
tel: 01633 821 192
email: jeff@walespressphoto.com
web: www.walespressphoto.com
prev. clients: Brecon Jazz Festival
info: Digital photography. Live and location shots. Jeff has 20 years experience in the industry.

Jenny Potter © 2005
U2

Jenny Potter
Shirenewton
tel: 01291 673 221/07711 531 703
email: azteqmm@aol.com
web: www.photorebel.com or www.jennypotter.com
contact: Jenny Potter
prev. clients: Stereophonics, Green Day, Anthrax, Slayer, My Chemical Romance
info: Experienced in live and backstage photography, as well as PR and events such as CD and single launches, music award and festivals. Location and studio work. Willing to travel worldwide.

Koncept Photography
37 Hoel y Coed Rise, Brackla, Bridgend, CF31 2QD
tel: 01656 649 466
email: darren@konceptphotography.com
web: www.konceptphotography.com
info: Live music photography. See website for examples of Darren's work. Design service also available.

Mary Wycherley
6 Denton Road, Canton, Cardiff, CF5 1PE
tel: 07838 191 912
email: molejwych@yahoo.com
prev. clients: Super Furry Animals, Placebo, Doves, The Thrills, Gomez, Boo Radleys
info: Press and publicity shots. Studio, live or on location. Graphic design and artwork available. See relevant section for details.

Mei Lewis
27 Llantrisant, Cathays, Cardiff, CF24 4JD
tel: 07816 857 450
email: meirion.lewis@gmail.com
prev. clients: Big Issue, South Wales Argus, Plan B, Rock Sound, Hard Rock Café, BBC, BPI, AIM
info: Photography of gigs, DJs, as well as press release and promotional shots.

Nigel Hughes Photography
Stiwdio'r Gest, 120 High Street, Porthmadog, Gwynedd, LL49 9NW
tel: 01766 513 612
email: info@nigelhughesphoto.com
web: www.nigelhughesphoto.com
info: Press, PR, film and TV shots. Experience working with bands and musicians including shots used for album covers.

Rich Wood
15v Partridge Road, Roath, Cardiff, South Glamorgan, CF24 3QW
tel: 02920 902 208
email: richwoodphoto@ntlworld.com
info: Live, location and studio work. Rates are variable depending on what is required.

Swaddleprint
Aberystwyth
tel: 07984 115 362
email: dirtybottom@hotmail.com
contact: Brian Swaddling
prev. clients: The Mekkits
info: Live, location and studio work offered at very competitive rates. Brian works with traditional B&W photography, as well as being highly competent with digital medium.

Zero One Studios
71-73 Lower Dick Street, Newport, NP20 1EH
tel: 01633 253 589
email: info@zero-one-studios.co.uk
web: www.zero-one-studios.co.uk
info: Zero One Studios can help with the styling and concept of your shoot, including providing make-up artists. In-house studio or on location.

MUSIC SERVICES/RETAIL

3.10 PRINTING

EAST of ENGLAND 293 GREATER LONDON 295 MIDLANDS 301 NORTHEAST 303 NORTHWEST 306
SOUTHEAST 309 SOUTHWEST 312 YORKSHIRE 313 NORTHERN IRELAND 315 SCOTLAND 317 WALES 320

EAST of ENGLAND

Asgard Print & Design Services
12-14 Cooke Close, South Lowestoft Industrial Estate, Lowestoft, NR33 7NW
tel: 01502 501 028
design service: Yes
minimum run: None
info: All kinds of printing, both digital and conventional, including posters and flyers.

Austin Rose Printers Ltd.
6 Alfric Square, Peterborough, PE2 7JP
tel: 01733 230 883
fax: 01733 230 873
email: info@austinroseprinters.co.uk
web: www.austinroseprinters.co.uk
contact: Peter Drew
design service: Yes
minimum run: None
info: Posters, flyers, leaflets, stickers, postcards and rubber stamps.

BD & H Ltd.
37 Europa Way, Martineau Lane, Norwich, NR1 2EN
tel: 01603 620 780
fax: 01603 630 186
email: mail@bdandh.co.uk
web: www.bdandh.co.uk
design service: Yes
minimum run: None
info: Digital, litho, large format, vinyl and screen printing options. All sizes of posters available from A4 to 60" x 40", as well as billboards. Many other items including flyers, leaflets, banners, stickers and postcards.

Big Printing
Unit 8 Cirrus Court, Glebe Road, Huntingdon, PE29 7DL
tel: 01480 450 070
email: sales@bigprinting.co.uk
web: www.bigprinting.co.uk
design service: Yes
minimum run: None
info: Posters from A2 size and larger. Also supply banners.

Broadland Digital
Unit 1, Vulcan House, Vulcan Road North, Norwich, NR6 6AQ
tel: 01603 407 786
fax: 01603 407 787
email: info@broadlanddigital.co.uk
web: www.broadlanddigital.co.uk
design service: Yes
minimum run: None
info: Specialise in short run digital printing. Posters, flyers, leaflets, postcards and self adhesive labels.

The Business Printing Co.
Unit 6, Nene Road, Bicton Industrial Estate, Kimbolton, Huntingdon, PE28 0LF
tel: 01480 861 911
design service: Yes
minimum run: None
info: Posters up to A3, as well as leaflets and flyers.

Cambridge Printers
1 Mercers Row, Cambridge, CB5 8HY
tel: 01223 506 767
design service: Yes
minimum run: None
info: Poster and flyer printing service.

Cityprint (Peterborough) Ltd.
VP Square, Storys Bar Road, Fengate, Peterborough, PE1 5YS
tel: 01733 313 351
email: enquiries@cityprintltd.co.uk
web: www.cityprintltd.co.uk
design service: Yes
minimum run: None
info: Posters, flyers and leaflets all available. Screen, litho or digitally printed.

CLE Print
Media House, Burrell Road, St. Ives, PE27 3LE
tel: 01480 465 233
design service: Yes
minimum run: None
info: Design and print solutions. Mainly digital printing but with some litho capability.

Colour Print
6 Fletcher Way, Weston Road, Norwich, NR3 3ST
tel: 01603 488001
email: sales@col-print.co.uk
web: www.col-print.co.uk
design service: No
minimum run: 500
info: Can produce posters, flyers, CD covers, brochures and folders.

Crowes
50 Hurricane Way, Norwich, Norfolk, NR6 6JB
tel: 01603 403 349
fax: 01603 485 164
email: See contact list on website
web: www.crowes.co.uk
contact: Steven
design service: Yes
minimum run: None
info: Total print solutions. Litho and digital printing, posters up to A2.

Digital Imaging Centre Ltd.
58 Regent Street, Cambridge, CB2 1DP
tel: 01223 369 291
email: info@imagingcentre.co.uk
web: www.imagingcentre.co.uk
design service: Yes
minimum run: None
info: Posters, flyers, CD and DVD covers.

Elitian Ltd.
112 Mill Road, Cambridge, CB1 2BD
tel: 01223 358 011
design service: No
minimum run: None
info: Digital, litho and large format. Posters, flyers and tickets available.

Final Imaging
Unit 18, Brookside, Sawtry, Huntingdon, Cambridgeshire, PE28 5SB
tel: 0870 855 0304
fax: 0870 855 0305
email: sawtry@printing.com
web: www.printing.com
design service: Yes
minimum run: 250
info: Part of Printing.com franchise. Offer full range
of printing services and can produce most items at reasonable price
including stickers, leaflets and postcards. See website above for details
of offers available.

Giles Printing
Old Chapel, Langley Street, Langley, Loddon, Norwich, NR14 6DA
tel: 01508 528 606
design service: No
minimum run: None
info: Flyers and leaflets. Posters up to A3 can be
printed, B&W.

Gipping Press
Unit 2, Lion Barn Industrial Estate, Needham Market, Ipswich, IP6 8NZ
tel: 01449 721 599
email: enquiries@gipping-press.demon.co.uk
design service: Yes
minimum run: None
info: Print posters, flyers, programmes, CD covers and
tickets.

Halcyon Type & Design
Unit 7, Rutherford Centre, Dunlop Road, Hedleigh Road Industrial
Estate, Ipswich, IP2 0UG
tel: 01473 210 269
fax: 01473 231 560
email: graeme@htd-graphics.co.uk
web: www.htd-graphics.co.uk
contact: Graeme Everett
design service: Yes
minimum run: None
info: Can assist with large format work, banners,
backdrops and posters.

Hollinger Field
Unit 12, Burnet Road, Sweet Briar Road Industrial Estate, Norwich,
NR3 2BS
tel: 01603 309 000
design service: Yes
minimum run: None
info: Posters, flyers and leaflets. All litho printed.

Imprenta Ltd.
Unit 15, Meadow Drove, Earith, Huntingdon, PE28 3QF
tel: 01487 840 110
design service: No
minimum run: None
info: Lithographers. Can print large runs of posters,
flyers and leaflets. Some digital capabilities for smaller runs.

Ivory Graphics Ltd.
2 St. Margaret's Way, Stukeley Meadows Industrial Estate, Huntingdon,
Cambridgeshire, PE29 6DG
tel: 01480 417 511
web: www.ivorygraphics.co.uk
design service: Yes
minimum run: None
info: Poster, flyer and leaflet printing.

Just Digital Print
White Leather Barn, Woolley Road, Huntingdon, PE28 0UD
tel: 01480 896 677
fax: 01480 896 678
email: justask@justdigitalprint.co.uk
web: www.justdigitalprint.co.uk
design service: No
minimum run: None
info: Print posters, flyers, and postcards.

Labute
Cambridge Printing Park, Milton, Cambridge, CB4 6AZ
tel: 01223 423 000
fax: 01223 420 783
email: info@cambridgeprintingpark.com
web: www.cambridgeprintingpark.com
design service: Yes
minimum run: None
info: Massive range of printing options. Labute
consists of 2 companies working under 1 banner to provide total print
solutions. Posters up to 1500mm wide, any length. Digital and litho.

Leverpress
12-14 Goddard Road, Whitehouse Road Industrial Estate, Ipswich,
IP1 5NP
tel: 01473 461 464
fax: 01473 240 118
email: web@.leverpress.co.uk
web: www.leverpress.co.uk
design service: Yes
minimum run: None
info: Digital and litho printing.

Norwich Colour Print
Unit 2, Dunston Industrial Park, Taverham Road, Drayton, Norwich,
NR8 6RL
tel: 01603 868 862
design service: No
minimum run: 1000
info: Posters and flyers. Cost effective printing in
larger runs.

Oak Tree Press
Unit 14, Brome Industrial Estate, Eye, Suffolk, IP23 7HN
tel: 01379 873 057
fax: 01379 873 058
email: print@theoaktreepress.org.uk
web: www.theoaktreepress.co.uk
design service: Yes
minimum run: None
info: Can assist with print and design of labels,
leaflets, flyers, business cards, logos, artwork and websites.

PAR Printing Press
9 Garton Street, Peterborough, PE1 4EL
tel: 01733 562 666
design service: Yes
minimum run: None
info: Posters up to A3 size, as well as flyers and
leaflets. Digital and litho services.

Prestige Typographics
Units 3-4, Rougham Business Centre, Rougham, Bury St. Edmunds,
IP30 9ND
tel: 01359 271 321
fax: 01359 271 327
email: sales@prestige-typo.co.uk
web: www.prestige-typo.co.uk
design service: Yes
minimum run: None
info: Provide digital colour printing.

Print For Tomorrow
New Media House, 79a Broadway, Peterborough, PE1 4DA
tel: 01733 313 166
fax: 01733 310 007
email: mail@printfortomorrow.co.uk
web: www.printfortomorrow.co.uk
design service: Yes
minimum run: None
info: Specialise in short runs of posters and flyers.
Cost effective printing from 1 to 1000 copies.

Q Print
10 Warwick Court, Eaton Socon, St. Neots, Cambridgeshire, PE19 8HH
tel: 01480 352 991
email: qprint@bigfoot.com
web: www.qprint-litho.co.uk
design service: Yes
minimum run: None
info: Digital, spot colour and litho printing.
Promotional items available.

Rapide Design & Print
Threxton Road Industrial Estate, Watton, Thetford, IP25 6NG
tel: 01953 881 392
email: sale@rapideprint.co.uk
web: www.rapideprint.co.uk
contact: Peter Scott
design service: Yes
minimum run: None
info: Posters and flyers, plus stickers, postcards, labels
and CD covers.

Red Hot Media
The Old Post Office, Waterloo Road, Lowestoft, Suffolk, NR33 0AA
tel: 0870 855 0412
fax: 0870 855 0413
email: lowestoft@printing.com
web: www.printing.com
design service: Yes
minimum run: 250
info: Part of Printing.com franchise. Offer full range
of printing services and can produce most items at reasonable price
including stickers, leaflets and postcards. See website above for details
of offers available.

Red Ink
Unit 1, Holywells Close, Ipswich, IP3 0AW
tel: 01473 230 600
web: www.redink-print.co.uk
design service: Yes
minimum run: None
info: Flyers, posters and leaflets printed both digitally and lithographically.

Riverside Print Services
9 Leyton Avenue, Mildenhall, Bury St. Edmunds, IP28 7BL
tel: 01638 718 337
fax: 01638 712 525
email: info@riversideprintservices.co.uk
web: www.riversideprintservices.co.uk
design service: Yes
minimum run: None
info: Can print posters and flyers digitally.

RM Phoenix Ltd.
Unit 2, Riverside View, Wickham Market, Woodbridge, IP13 0TA
tel: 01728 747 138
email: rmphoenixprint@aol.com
design service: Yes
minimum run: None
info: Screen printing, digital and litho. Posters, flyers, banners and more.

St. Ives Quickprint
Unit 9, Bramley Road, St. Ives, Cambridgeshire, PE27 3WS
tel: 0870 855 0354
fax: 0870 855 0355
email: st.ives@printing.com
web: www.printing.com
design service: Yes
minimum run: 250
info: Part of Printing.com franchise. Offer full range of printing services and can produce most items at reasonable price including stickers, leaflets and postcards. See website above for details of offers available.

TSG Creative Solutions
105 Great North Road, Eaton Socon, St. Neots, PE19 8EL
tel: 01480 213 555
fax: 01480 218 887
email: info@tsgcs.co.uk
web: www.tsgcs.co.uk
design service: Yes
minimum run: None
info: Posters and flyers printed digitally and lithographically.

GREATER LONDON

1st Images
72 Chase Side, Enfield, EN2 6NX
tel: 020 8363 5667
fax: 020 8367 2673
email: mail@images-pdc.co.uk
web: www.images-pdc.co.uk
contact: Andrew Ridley
design service: Yes
minimum run: Varies
info: Laser and litho commercial printers. Posters, flyers, leaflets and CD inlays. Minimum run varies depending on product. Leaflets 500, B&W tickets 50, and full colour tickets 100.

24hrPrint.co.uk
Croydon House, Peal Road, Croydon, CR0 3EX
tel: 020 8286 6611
fax: 020 8286 6622
email: contact@24hrprint.co.uk
web: www.24hrprint.co.uk
contact: Phil Solomon
design service: Yes
minimum run: None
info: General commercial printers. Wide range of printing and promotional items available including flyers, tickets, lighters and keyrings.

ABC Printers
81-83 Norwood High Street, London, SE2 79JS
tel: 020 8761 7889
fax: 020 8761 4938
email: abcprinters@btconnect.com
web: www.abc-print.com
contact: Clive Hobbs
design service: Yes
info: Can provide any commercial printing including flyers, posters, tickets and CD inlays. Full colour printing. Free consultation available.

Absolute Print Ltd.
50 Junction Road, Archway, London, N19 5RD
tel: 0800 975 6571
fax: 020 7272 2228
email: sales@absoluteprint.com
web: www.absoluteprint.com
design service: Yes
minimum run: None
info: Digital printing of posters, CD inlays, flyers and promotional items. Can process small runs.

Absolute Proof
80 Long Acre, Covent Garden, London, WC2E 9NG
tel: 020 7828 8357
fax: 020 7828 7051
email: abproof@aol.com
web: www.absoluteproof.co.uk
contact: Steven Newman
design service: Yes
minimum run: None
info: Litho and digital commercial printers. Flyers, tickets, posters, CD inlays and newsletters. Promotional items such as keyrings are also available.

Aduo Colour Ltd.
Unit 5, Block 3, Woolwich Industrial Estate, Woolwich Church Street, London, SE18 5PQ
tel: 020 8317 1626
fax: 020 8316 4746
email: aduocolour@btconnect.com
contact: Terry Lynch
design service: No
minimum run: None
info: Commercial litho printers. Flyers, tickets, posters and CD inlays available.

AGI Media (London)
Berghem Mews, Blythe Road, London, W14 0HN
tel: 020 7605 1940
fax: 020 7605 1941
email: sales@uk.agimedia.com
web: www.agimedia.com
contact: Simon Turner
design service: Yes
minimum run: 1000
info: Posters, flyers, DVD packaging and CD covers.

AGM Printers Ltd.
17-18 Haywards Place, London, EC1R 0EQ
tel: 020 7490 5477
fax: 020 7608 0546
email: andrew@agmprint.co.uk
web: www.agmprint.co.uk
contact: Andrew
design service: Yes
minimum run: None
info: Commercial litho printing including flyers, tickets, posters and CD inlays.

Alexander Graphics
Enterprise House, 133 Blyth Road, Hayes, UB3 1DD
tel: 020 8797 1717
fax: 020 8797 9444
email: info@alexandergraphics.co.uk
web: www.alexandergraphics.co.uk
contact: Paul Turner
design service: Yes
minimum run: None
info: Large format digital printing including banners, displays, posters and backdrops. No minimum run, will do one-offs.

All Print & Design
Cherrywell House, Tamian Way, Hounslow, TW4 6BL
tel: 020 8569 6566
email: sales@allprint.co.uk
web: www.allprint.co.uk
contact: Janet Cheesman
design service: Yes
minimum run: Varies
info: Everything from business cards to full colour brochures. CD inlays, posters, flyers and promotional items. Minimum run will vary from product to product.

All Things Print
34 Lexington Street, London, W1F 0LH
tel: 020 7287 7000
fax: 020 7287 0303
email: allthingsprint@aol.com
web: www.allthingsprint.co.uk
contact: Steve Boyles
design service: Yes
minimum run: None
info: Litho, digital and web printing. Flyers, posters and tickets, as well as a range of promotional items such as keyrings. Short and long run printing.

ALP Print Services
7 Sundridge Parade, Plaistow Lane, Bromley, BR1 4DT
tel: 020 8466 6462/020 8466 7898
fax: 020 8466 7898
email: alpprintservices@btconnect.com
contact: Tony Wilkes
design service: Yes
minimum run: 250
info: Commercial litho printers. Tickets, posters, CD inlays and flyers.

Alpha Colour
127 Jamaica Road, London, SE16 4SH
tel: 020 7231 5454/020 7231 7373
fax: 020 7231 7373
email: print@alphacolourprint.co.uk
web: www.alphacolourprint.co.uk
contact: Henry
design service: Yes
info: Litho, graphic and digital printers. Flyers, tickets and posters. Large range of promotional items also available.

Andara Print Marketing
21 Creek Road, Hampton Court, Surrey, KT8 9BE
tel: 020 8224 4100
fax: 020 8224 4101
email: louisa@andara.co.uk
web: www.andara.co.uk
contact: Louisa
design service: Yes
minimum run: None
info: Flyers, tickets, posters (all sizes) and CD inlays. Can order in any promotional items. Digital printing. No minimum run but printing needs to be cost effective, call for further details. Also offer web design.

Aries Litho
78 Wavendon Avenue, London, W4 4NS
tel: 020 8742 2210
fax: 020 8742 2230
contact: Ian Kersey
design service: Yes
info: All commercial printing including flyers, posters, tickets and CD inlays. Can print promotional items. Offer digital printing.

The Beechgrove Press
2 Elmfield Avenue, Teddington, Middlesex, TW11 8BS
tel: 020 8977 3491
fax: 020 8977 6071
email: david@beechgrovepress.co.uk
web: www.beechgrovepress.co.uk
contact: Mr Nash
design service: Yes
minimum run: None
info: Digital and litho printers. Flyers, tickets and posters.

Belmont-Deal Print Ltd.
BDP House, Ironbridge Business Park, Ironbridge House, London, NW10 0UF
tel: 0870 833 8800
fax: 0870 833 8801
email: sales@bdp.uk.net
web: www.bdp.uk.net
contact: Steve or AJ
design service: Yes
minimum run: None
info: Flyers, posters, tickets and CD inlays. Range of promotional items such as t-shirts and lighters.

Bergamot Print Management
72 Lightermans Walk, Prospect Quay, Point Pleasant, London, SW18 1PS
tel: 020 8877 8810
fax: 020 8877 8818
email: info@bergamot.co.uk
web: www.bergamot.co.uk
contact: Seb Cole
design service: Yes
minimum run: 1000
info: Cost effective solutions for larger runs. Any kind of print job (excluding promotional items), from postcards to biog booklets, and from flyers to complete CD duplication and inlay/ packaging print such as digipacks and other bespoke packaging. Also offer coordinated multi-item campaigns and promo packs incorporating CD, booklet and any other printed items or devices you may need.

Berrico Ltd.
57-63 Churchfield Road, Acton, London, W3 6AU
tel: 020 8992 6454
fax: 020 8752 0670
email: berrico@berrico.co.uk
contact: Miles Hewitt
design service: Yes
minimum run: None
info: General commercial printing including flyers, posters, tickets and CD inlays.

Blackwing Press
69-85 Tabernacle Street, London, EC2A 4BD
tel: 020 7253 4106
fax: 020 7253 4108
email: mccann@blackwingpress.fsnet.uk
contact: John or Matthew
design service: No
minimum run: None
info: Litho printers and finishers. Print any paper or card products and promotional items.

Budget Printing
320 Croydon Road, Beckenham, Kent, BR3 4HR
tel: 020 8402 2777/020 8402 7272
fax: 020 8289 0088
email: abudgetprinting@aol.com
contact: Dennis Deverley
design service: Yes
minimum run: None
info: Flyers, tickets and posters (up to size A0) available. Promotional cards, stationery and CD inlays. Will print onto any material including t-shirts and caps.

Burford Printing
9 Ecclestone Street, London, SW1W 9LX
tel: 020 7730 8765
fax: 020 7730 8065
email: burfordprinting@btinternet.com
web: www.burford-printing.co.uk
contact: Hazel
design service: Yes
minimum run: None
info: Flyers, tickets, CD inlays and posters, in B&W or colour. Various promotional items including keyrings, t-shirts, pens and lighters. Fully equipped design studio including laser and full colour digital copiers. Free consultation available and band friendly service.

Capitol Printing
24 Wrights Place, London, NW10 OPY
tel: 020 8961 6160
email: capitolprint@btconnect.com
contact: Mr Partington
design service: Yes
minimum run: None
info: Commercial litho printers. Flyers, posters and tickets.

Cartier Graphics
Unit 4a, Worton Hall Industrial Estate, Worton Road, Isleworth, TW7 6ER
tel: 020 8560 3749
fax: 020 8560 0791
email: info@cartiergraphics.co.uk
web: www.cartiergraphics.co.uk
contact: Junior Karena
design service: Yes
minimum run: None
info: Any commercial printing including flyers, posters, tickets and CD inlays. Wide range of promotional items available including beer mats and lighters, call for more information.

Central Printers Ltd.
39-43 Brewer Street, London, W1F 9UD
tel: 020 7734 1588
fax: 020 7439 3242
email: central.printers@btconnect.com
contact: Bill Hill
design service: Yes
minimum run: None
info: Will print flyers, tickets and posters.

Century 23
3rd Floor, 54-55 Margaret Street, London, W1W 8SH
tel: 0871 700 0080
email: andrew@century-23.com
web: www.century-23.com
contact: Andrew
design service: Yes
info: Century 23 have been working in close
association with the live music, clubbing, entertainment, and leisure
industries across Britain for 7 years providing printed promotional
products including flyers, posters and tickets. Artwork can be submitted
online or through the post. Artwork design and CD/vinyl duplication
also available. See relevant section for details. Offices in Belfast and
Edinburgh.

City Printing Solutions
302 Ewell Road, Surbiton, Surrey, KT6 7AQ
tel: 020 8399 5399
email: citprintsol@aol.com
contact: Steve Budd
design service: Yes
minimum run: None
info: General commercial printing including flyers,
tickets, posters, books, magazines and CD inlays. Digital printing
available.

CMCS Group Plc
1 Kennet Road, Dartford, Kent, DA1 4QN
tel: 020 8308 5000
fax: 01322 553 741
email: sales@cmcs.co.uk
web: www.cmcs.co.uk
contact: John Chambers
design service: Yes
minimum run: 1000
info: Specialise in print for the music industry.
Previous clients include Arista, Gut Records, Sony BMG and V2.
Posters, leaflets, CD covers and flyers.

Colourstat Ltd.
68 Rochester Row, London, SW1P 1JU
tel: 020 7630 6364
fax: 020 7976 6723
email: info@colourstat.co.uk
web: www.colourstat.co.uk
contact: Damion
design service: Yes
minimum run: None
info: Posters, banners and flyers. CD and DVD
duplication service available for small runs only.

Compass Litho
Unit 3, 149 Roman Way, London, N7 8XH
tel: 020 7700 6660
fax: 020 7700 5006
email: unit3n7@aol.com
contact: John Offord
design service: No
minimum run: None
info: Litho and digital printers. Can print any
paper products including flyers, tickets and posters, and can order
promotional items on request.

The Copy Centre
70 Park Lane, London, N17 0JR
tel: 020 8808 7275
fax: 020 8365 1430
email: irwin@thecopycentre.com
web: www.thecopycentre.com
contact: Irwin Van Colle
design service: Yes
minimum run: None
info: Posters, flyers, leaflets and tickets. Largest print
size available is SRA0.

Copy Write
758 Finchley Road, London, NW11 7TH
tel: 020 8455 2922
fax: 020 8455 3128
email: info@copywriteprinters.co.uk
web: www.copywriteprinters.co.uk
contact: M. Harris
design service: Yes
minimum run: 100 (printing), None (photocopying)
info: Flyers, tickets and posters of any size. CD inlays
and booklets also available. Have worked with bands in the past.

Darwin Press
77a Blackheath Road, Greenwich, London, SE10 8PD
tel:	020 8691 1357
fax:	020 8691 6556
email:	sales@darwinpress.co.uk
web:	www.darwinpress.co.uk
contact:	Jane Wilson
design service:	Yes
minimum run:	500
info:	Commercial litho printers. Flyers, tickets, posters and CD inlays. Also print CD boxes.

Doyle Press Ltd.
32 Central Avenue, West Molesey, Surrey, KT8 2QZ
tel:	020 8224 9035
fax:	020 8873 9024
email:	doylebm@hotmail.com
contact:	Bruce Doyle
design service:	Yes
info:	Posters, flyers, tickets, CD and DVD inlays. No minimum run.

DP Graphics Ltd.
Unit 12c, Tower Workshops, Riley Road, London, SE1 3DG
tel:	020 7252 3700
fax:	020 7231 5288
email:	info@dpgraphics.co.uk
web:	www.dpgraphics.co.uk
design service:	No
minimum run:	None
info:	Short run digital printers. Can produce flyers, tickets and posters.

East Central One Media Ltd.
3-4 Bakers Yard, Bakers Row, London, EC1 R3DD
tel:	020 7837 0123
fax:	020 7278 3364
email:	info@eastcentral1.com
contact:	Mike Baxter
design service:	Yes
minimum run:	None
info:	Flyers, tickets, posters (up to A0) and CD inlays.

Elevator
117 Cleveland Street, London, W1T 6PX
tel:	020 7631 0628
fax:	020 7580 4456
email:	davidg@elevator.gb.com
contact:	David
design service:	No
minimum run:	None
info:	Digital and litho printing and internet consultants. Fast turnaround. Flyers, tickets and posters available.

ExpressCopy
9-11 Chipstead Valley Road, Coulsdon, Surrey, CR5 2RB
tel:	020 8668 9799
fax:	020 8668 6020
email:	order@expresscopy.co.uk
web:	www.expresscopy.co.uk
contact:	Anthony, Al
design service:	Yes
minimum run:	None
info:	Posters, flyers, signs, t-shirts and other promotional items. Have experience of working with bands.

Fairkey Design & Printing
Unit 2, 20b Spelman Street, London, E1 5LQ
tel:	020 7377 8905
fax:	020 7217 0141
email:	info@fairkey.com
contact:	Naz
design service:	Yes
minimum run:	None
info:	Commercial printing and design. Flyers, tickets, posters up to A1, plus banners.

Fernedge
18 Colville Road, London, W3 8BL
tel:	020 8992 4895
fax:	0845 456 8982
email:	info@atpfernedge.co.uk
web:	www.atpfernedge.co.uk
contact:	Pippa Redmond
design service:	Yes
minimum run:	None
info:	General commercial printing including flyers, posters, tickets and CD inlays. Print range of promotional items (including clothing).

First Stop Print
107 Clive Road, London, SE21 8DB
tel:	020 8761 7373
contact:	Dhaval
design service:	Yes
minimum run:	None
info:	Commercial and personal printing. Posters, tickets, CD inlays and flyers available.

The Flyer Printers
27 Old Gloucester Street, London, WC1N 3XX
tel:	0870 403 1990
email:	info@theflyerprinters.com
web:	www.theflyerprinters.com
contact:	Liam
design service:	Yes
minimum run:	Varies
info:	Print posters, flyers, business cards, CD inlays and covers, as well as promotional items including stickers, t-shirts, mugs and mousemats. Minimum runs vary - 50 for posters, 500 for flyers. Check website or contact for details of minimum run on other items.

Genie Print Ltd.
The Business Village, Broomhill Road, Wandsworth, London, SW18 4JQ
tel:	020 8871 5070
fax:	020 8877 3917
email:	info@genieprint.co.uk
web:	www.genieprint.co.uk
contact:	Mervyn Smith
design service:	Yes
minimum run:	None
info:	Digital and litho printing. Flyers, tickets, posters and CD inlays. Previous experience of working with bands.

Gilderson Print Ltd.
31-35 Pitfield Street, London, N1 6HB
tel:	020 7324 0180
fax:	020 7490 4333
email:	info@gildersons.co.uk
web:	www.gildersons.co.uk
contact:	Tom Brett
design service:	Yes
minimum run:	None
info:	Litho and digital printers. Flyers, tickets, posters and CD inlays available.

GM Printing Ltd.
138 Cherry Orchard Road, Croydon, Surrey, CR0 6BB
tel:	0800 216 620
fax:	020 8667 1682
email:	info@gmprinting.co.uk
web:	www.gmprinting.co.uk
design service:	Yes
minimum run:	1000
info:	As well as general printing, GM Printing provide services specifically for the music industry. CD booklets, feedback cards, LP sleeves, posters, flyers, stickers and many more items. Minimum run generally 1000.

Hensal Press Ltd.
Stonebridge House, 272 Abbeydale Road, Wembley, Middlesex, HA0 1QA
tel:	020 8998 9031
fax:	020 8991 0139
email:	sales@hensalpress.com
web:	www.hensalpress.com
contact:	Murray Sale
design service:	No
minimum run:	None
info:	Flyers, posters, tickets and range of promotional items available. No minimum run, but price per unit decreases as quantity increases.

Horseshoe Litho Ltd.
Unit 21, The Cremer Business Centre, 37 Cremer Street, London, E2 8HD
tel:	020 7739 8155
fax:	020 7739 8159
email:	production@hshoeprint4u.co.uk
contact:	Rob Avery
design service:	Yes
minimum run:	None
info:	Commercial litho printers. Flyers, tickets, posters and CD inlays.

Image 2 Image Printers
177 Somerset Road, Southall, Middlesex, UB1 2UQ
tel:	020 8575 8331
fax:	020 8578 6994
contact:	Mr M Bavishi
design service:	Yes
minimum run:	500
info:	Litho printers. Flyers, tickets and posters.

Impress Print Services Ltd.
10 Thornsett Road, London, SW18 4EN
tel:	020 8871 9950
fax:	020 8871 9908
email:	sales@impressprint.net
web:	www.impressprint.net
contact:	Helen
design service:	Yes
minimum run:	£50 minimum charge
info:	Produce all digital and litho printing. Competitive

prices on flyers, posters, CD inlays and pockets. Can offer discount package for flyers, tickets and posters.

Impressions the Printers Ltd.
121 Salisbury Road, Barnet, London, EN5 4JL
tel:	020 8441 2235
fax:	020 8441 2835
email:	josh@printguru.co.uk
contact:	Josh, Nicky
design service:	Yes
minimum run:	500 (business cards), 1000 (flyers)
info:	Flyers, tickets, posters and CD inlays. Range of

material products (including hats and t-shirts) and other promotional items (keyrings, lighters) available.

In Press Partnership
56 Beaulieu Avenue, Sydenham, London, SE26 6PP
tel:	020 8659 9449
fax:	020 8659 6556
email:	studio@in-press.net
contact:	Leo
design service:	Yes
info:	Litho and digital printers. Flyers, tickets, posters

and CD inlays. Promotional items including lighters and keyrings are also available.

Instant Print West One
4 New Burlington Street, London, W1S 2JG
tel:	020 7434 2813
fax:	020 7734 6207
email:	info@ipw1.com
web:	www.ipw1.com
contact:	Glen Robins
design service:	Yes
minimum run:	200
info:	Litho and digital output. Flyers, tickets and CD

inlays. Posters up to A0.

Jemprint Ltd.
St. Matthew's Works, St. Matthew's Row, London, E2 6ET
tel:	020 7739 0417
fax:	020 7729 2317
email:	jemprintltd@aol.com
contact:	Mr Robinson
design service:	Yes
minimum run:	None
info:	Litho printers, introducing digital printing soon.

Take work from disc, CD or Apple Mac. Posters, CD inlays, flyers and tickets.

JF Graphics
Litcombe, Catlins Lane, Pinner, HA5 2EX
tel:	020 8429 3387
fax:	020 8582 0733
email:	jfgraphics@blueyonder.co.uk
contact:	Flannery
design service:	Yes
minimum run:	None
info:	Special discount for musicians. Flyers, tickets,

posters (up to A1) and CD inlays. Range of promotional items including lighters, t-shirts and keyrings. Full studio facilities including in-house design and proofing.

Jubilee Printers
430 Edgware Road, London, W2 1EG
tel:	020 7724 1094
fax:	020 7706 0518
email:	info@jubileeprinters.co.uk
web:	www.jubileeprinters.co.uk
contact:	Kara
design service:	Yes
minimum run:	None
info:	Litho and digital quick print copy shop. Posters,

flyers and CD inlays. Range of promotional items available including keyrings, lighters and coasters. Also offer fax service.

Justasec Print Services Ltd.
Unit A5, Connaught Business Centre, Hyde Estate Road, Hendon, London, NW9 6JL
tel:	020 8200 4920/020 8200 4930
fax:	020 8905 9218
email:	christine@jpsprintgroup.demon.co.uk
design service:	Yes
minimum run:	None
info:	Flyers, tickets, posters and CD inlays. No

minimum run. In-house design available.

Kabir Design & Print
51 Fashion Street, London, E1 6PX
tel:	020 7375 1929
fax:	020 7247 2742
email:	kabir@ukprint.com
contact:	Mr Jay
design service:	Yes
minimum run:	None
info:	Litho and digital printers. Posters, tickets and

flyers, along with other paper and card products, are available.

Kallprint
Unit 9, Orion Business Centre, Surrey Canal Road, London, SE14 5RT
tel:	020 7231 5771
fax:	020 7231 5771
email:	juli@kallprint.freeserve.co.uk
contact:	Juli Carpenter
design service:	No
minimum run:	None
info:	Commercial printers offering flyer, poster and CD

inlay printing.

Keyprint Ltd.
Research House, Fraser Road, Greenford, Middlesex, UB6 7AQ
tel:	020 8566 7246
fax:	020 8566 7247
email:	info@keyprinters.co.uk
web:	www.keyprinters.co.uk
design service:	Yes
minimum run:	None
info:	Specialise in print for the music industry. Flyers,

posters and feedback slips used in CDs. Keyprint also offer web design services.

KTP Printers Ltd.
Unit G, 37 Princelet Street, London, E1 5LP
tel:	020 7247 0786
fax:	020 7377 6524
email:	ktpprinters@btconnect.com
web:	www.ktpprinters.com
contact:	Kevin, Gavin
design service:	Yes
minimum run:	None
info:	Digital and litho printers. Flyers, tickets, posters

and CD inlays. Offer special rates for charitable and benefit gigs. Have experience of working with musicians.

KWT Printing
80 Long Acre, London, WC2E 9NG
tel:	020 7240 2062
email:	mark@kwtprinting.co.uk
contact:	Mark
design service:	Yes
info:	Commercial digital and litho printers. Flyers,

posters and tickets. Previous experience of working with musicians.

LEA Printers
49 Leesons Hill, Orpington, Kent, BR5 2LF
tel:	0845 2322 322
email:	info@leaprinters.co.uk
web:	www.leaprinters.co.uk
contact:	Joe Ford
design service:	Yes
minimum run:	None
info:	Print flyers, posters and tickets, as well as CD

inlays.

Lynx Lithographics
Unit 9, Ropery Business Park, Anchor and Hope Lane, Charlton, London, SE7 7RX
tel:	020 8858 2210
fax:	020 8858 9936
email:	lynxlitho@lynxlitho.co.uk
contact:	Ray
design service:	Yes
minimum run:	None
info:	Commercial litho printers. Flyers, tickets, posters

and CD inlays available.

Metro Colour
Unit 2, The Huntingdon Estate, Bethnal Green Road, London, E1 6JU
tel:	020 7729 6192
fax:	020 7613 5194
email:	enquiries@metrocolour.co.uk
design service:	No
minimum run:	None
info:	Digitally print a wide range of paper products

including CD inlays, tickets, posters and flyers.

Metrostat Communications in Print Ltd.
577 Kingston Road, London, SW20 8SA
tel:	020 8540 9166
email:	sales@metrostat.co.uk
web:	www.metrostat.co.uk
design service:	Yes
minimum run:	None
info:	Digital and litho printers. Posters, flyers, tickets

and CD inlays.

Oasis Printing
40 Greyhound Road, London, W6 8NX
tel:	0800 018 5511
fax:	020 7610 2500
email:	info@oasisprinting.com
web:	www.oasisprinting.com
design service:	Yes
info:	Wide range of printing services. Colour

postcards, flyers, posters up to A0. Photocopying and design services
also available.

On Time Print &Design Ltd.
37 Redcross Way, London, SE1 1HG
tel:	020 7403 5752
fax:	020 7403 5765
design service:	Yes
minimum run:	None
info:	Litho printing including tickets, posters, flyers

and CD inlays.

Powerprint Partnership
254-258 Goswell Road, London, EC1 7EB
tel:	020 7250 1700
email:	joanne@powerprint.co.uk
web:	www.powerprint.co.uk
design service:	Yes
minimum run:	None
info:	Print specialists operating The Lambda, a 4

foot wide machine which can produce photographic quality images.
High resolution scanning, full print finishing and dry mount, hand
reproduced B&W prints, e6 film processing, graphic installations,
design and digital artwork.

Print For All
1-5 Clarkenwell Road, London, EC1M 5PA
tel:	020 7251 5153
fax:	020 7017 2719
email:	sales@print4u.co.uk
web:	www.print4u.co.uk
contact:	Graham Rice
design service:	No
minimum run:	None
info:	Off-set litho and digital printers. Print any paper

or card items. Courier service available.

Print Room Soho
112-114 Wardour Street, Soho, London, W1F 0TS
tel:	020 7287 2341
fax:	020 7287 2495
email:	jobs@copystop.co.uk
web:	www.copystop.co.uk
contact:	Martin Ringwood
design service:	No
minimum run:	None
info:	Digital printers. Any paper and card products

including flyers, tickets and posters. Range of promotional products
(such as t-shirts, caps and record bags) also available.

Printbusiness.org
The Chocolate Factory, Studio A08, Building A, Clarendon Road,
London, N22 6XJ
tel:	020 8365 8360
fax:	020 8365 8383
email:	pan2000@btclick.com
contact:	Alan Miller
design service:	Yes
minimum run:	None
info:	Specialise in poster printing, large format, flyers,

brochures, stationery, postcards and newsletters. Full colour printing.

Printset Ltd.
5-6 The Penarth Centre, Penarth Street, London, SE15 1TR
tel:	020 7277 6661
fax:	020 7277 7005
email:	printset@aol.com
design service:	Yes
minimum run:	None
info:	Leaflets, flyers, tickets and posters (up to A1).

Promotional items including lighters, pens and keyrings available.
Although Printset do not offer express service, they will print as fast as
possible for no extra charge. Call George on 07973 818 294, or Jenny on
07970 638 929 outside office hours.

Quickprint Services
324 Barking Road, London, E13 8HL
tel:	020 7511 6977
fax:	020 7511 6977
contact:	Subash
design service:	Yes
info:	Flyers, posters (up to A2), tickets, newsletters,

CD inlays and labels. Range of promotional items. Offer short-run
printing.

Senol Printing Ltd.
6 Sandiford Road, Kimpton Trading Estate, Sutton, Surrey, SM3 9RD
tel:	020 8641 3890
fax:	020 8641 3486
email:	info@senolprinting.co.uk
web:	www.senolprinting.co.uk
design service:	No
minimum run:	1000
info:	Printers to the music industry. Produce flyers,

posters, vinyl sleeves, CD booklets and inlays. Can print less than 1000
if necessary, but is often very costly.

Slim Designs
91-95 Brick Lane, Old Truman Brewery, London, E1 6QL
tel:	020 7375 3995/07811 607 969
email:	info@slimdesigns.co.uk
web:	www.slimdesigns.co.uk
contact:	Nick Slim
design service:	Yes
minimum run:	Contact for details
info:	Print posters, flyers and postcards. Can produce

5000 A6 postcards, full colour with back and front print on 350 gsm
paper for £150.

Splash Printing Ltd.
54 The Broadway, London, NW7 3LH
tel:	020 8906 4847
fax:	020 8959 3454
email:	jeremy@splashprinting.co.uk
web:	www.splashprinting.co.uk
contact:	Jeremy Harris
design service:	Yes
minimum run:	50
info:	Litho and digital commercial printing including

flyers, posters, CD inlays and tickets.

Supreme Printers
378 Kingsland Road, London, E8 4AA
tel:	020 7249 9211
fax:	020 7249 8199
email:	info@supremeprinters.com
web:	www.supremeprinters.com
design service:	Yes
minimum run:	500
info:	Print posters, flyers and promotional items such

as mugs, t-shirts, pens and keyrings. Minimum run varies depending on
product, but is usually 500.

T&C Printers
45 College Road, Bromley, BR1 3PU
tel:	020 8460 8416
fax:	020 8466 5981
email:	tandc@atlas.co.uk
contact:	David Spragg
design service:	Yes
minimum run:	500
info:	Posters, flyers and tickets. Full colour printing.

Fast turnover, and band friendly service.

MIDLANDS

Allen of Derby Ltd.
Clarion Works, 20 Webster Street, Derby, DE1 1PT
tel: 01332 349 788
fax: 01332 223 831
email: info@allenofderby.co.uk
web: www.allenofderby.co.uk
contact: Sharon Winfield
design service: Yes
minimum run: None
info: Digital and litho printing specialising in large print runs. Flyers and posters up to A2.

Artichoke Design
The Cemetery Lodge, Warstone Lane, Birmingham, B18 6NN
tel: 0870 855 0328
fax: 0870 855 0329
email: jewelleryquarter@printing.com
web: www.printing.com
design service: Yes
minimum run: 250
info: Part of Printing.com franchise. Offer full range of printing services and can produce most items at reasonable price including stickers, leaflets and postcards. See website above for details of offers available.

Artspec
Unit 2, Trafalgar Business Park, Baird Road, Willowbrook North Industrial Estate, Corby, NN17 5ZA
tel: 0870 750 4450
fax: 01536 201 495
email: info@art-spec.co.uk
web: www.art-spec.co.uk
design service: Yes
minimum run: None
info: Posters, flyers and CD printing on digital and litho.

Beaumanor Press
23 Bath Lane, Leicester, LE3 5BF
tel: 0116 233 1337
fax: 0116 233 5337
email: sales@beaumanor.co.uk
web: www.beaumanor.co.uk
contact: Peter Millrain
design service: Yes
minimum run: None
info: Mainly digital printing of posters, flyers, stickers and labels.

Big In Ink
9 Barford Close, Sutton Coldfield, B76 2UL
tel: 0800 085 1518
fax: 0121 378 1407
email: biginink@btconnect.com
web: www.biginink.com
contact: Tom Hollins
design service: Yes
info: Digital and litho. Large format up to A0. Minimum charge is £15.

Colour 2000 Printers Ltd.
Unit 3-4, Bennick Trading, Union Street, Bridgetown, Cannock, WS11 0BP
tel: 01543 570 338
fax: 01543 502 668
email: sales@colour2000.co.uk
web: www.colour2000.co.uk
contact: Mike Winston
design service: Yes
minimum run: None
info: Digital and litho printing services. 4 colour or B&W. Band friendly.

Colour Print Management
Unit 9, The Beaver Centre, Putney Road West, Leicester, LE2 7TD
tel: 0116 255 5572
fax: 0116 255 5247
email: r.tebbutt@colourprintmanagement.com
contact: R Tebbutt
design service: Yes
minimum run: None
info: Digital and litho printing. Can supply posters, flyers, badges, stickers.

Cre8ive Design
3 Millar Court, Station Road, Coventry, CV8 1JD
tel: 0870 855 0384
fax: 0870 855 0385
email: kenilworth@printing.com
web: www.printing.com
design service: Yes
minimum run: 250
info: Part of Printing.com franchise. Offer full range of printing services and can produce most items at reasonable price including stickers, leaflets and postcards. See website above for details of offers available.

custardcreative
14 Brookfield, Moulton Park, Northampton, NN3 6WL
tel: 0870 855 0344
fax: 0870 855 0345
email: northampton@printing.com
web: www.printing.com
design service: Yes
minimum run: 250
info: Part of Printing.com franchise. Offer full range of printing services and can produce most items at reasonable price including stickers, leaflets and postcards. See website above for details of offers available.

Dawn til Dusk Printers
Unit 1b, Perserverance Road, Hereford, HR4 9SN
tel: 01432 357 710
fax: 01432 357 232
email: enquiries@dawn-til-dusk.co.uk
web: www.dawn-til-dusk.co.uk
contact: David Bryner
design service: Yes
minimum run: None
info: Digital and litho services. Can provide posters, flyers, CD sleeves and CD labels.

Design Full Stop
The Byre, Pury Hill Business Park, Towcester, NN12 7LS
tel: 01327 810 100
fax: 01327 810 101
email: alan@designfullstop.com
web: www.designfullstop.com
contact: Alan Ingram
design service: Yes
minimum run: None
info: Large format printing with digital and litho. Posters, flyers, stickers, banners and drum skins. Band friendly service. Complete printing solutions, in-house and external contacts. Full online service and national delivery.

Express Print
98 Bromford Lane, Erdington, Birmingham, B24 8BY
tel: 0121 377 7888
email: express.print@dial.pipex.com
contact: Bal Gill
design service: Yes
minimum run: None
info: Specialise in digital and litho printing. Can produce flyers, posters and stickers.

First Image
86-88 Stonebury Avenue, Eastern Green, Coventry, CV5 7FW
tel: 0870 950 1534
fax: 0870 950 1535
email: easterngreen@printing.com
web: www.printing.com
design service: Yes
minimum run: 250
info: Part of Printing.com franchise. Offer full range of printing services and can produce most items at reasonable price including stickers, leaflets and postcards. See website above for details of offers available.

For Colour Ltd.
18 Friary Road, Newark, Nottinghamshire, NG24 1LE
tel: 0870 855 0288
fax: 0870 855 0289
email: newark@printing.com
web: www.printing.com
design service: Yes
minimum run: 250
info: Part of Printing.com franchise. Offer full range of printing services and can produce most items at reasonable price including stickers, leaflets and postcards. See website above for details of offers available.

Graphic Results
63-65 Bridge Street, Belper, Derbyshire, DE56 1AY
tel:	0870 855 0402
fax:	0870 855 0403
email:	belper@printing.com
web:	www.printing.com
design service:	Yes
minimum run:	250
info:	Part of Printing.com franchise. Offer full range
of printing services and can produce most items at reasonable price including stickers, leaflets and postcards. See website above for details of offers available.

Husselworks
Earls Way, Halesowen, West Midlands, B63 3HR
tel:	0870 855 0418
fax:	0870 855 0419
email:	halesowen@printing.com
web:	www.printing.com
design service:	Yes
minimum run:	250
info:	Part of Printing.com franchise. Offer full range
of printing services and can produce most items at reasonable price including stickers, leaflets and postcards. See website above for details of offers available.

The Ideas Room
206 Narborough Road, Leicester, LE3 0DL
tel:	0870 855 0382
fax:	0870 855 0383
email:	leicesterwest@printing.com
web:	www.printing.com
design service:	Yes
minimum run:	250
info:	Part of Printing.com franchise. Offer full range
of printing services and can produce most items at reasonable price including stickers, leaflets and postcards. See website above for details of offers available.

Ideas Taking Shape
17 Albert Street, Rugby, Warwickshire, CV21 2SD
tel:	0870 855 0426
fax:	0870 855 0427
email:	rugby@printing.com
web:	www.printing.com
design service:	Yes
minimum run:	250
info:	Part of Printing.com franchise. Offer full range
of printing services and can produce most items at reasonable price including stickers, leaflets and postcards. See website above for details of offers available.

Image Printing Co Ltd.
Lumsdale Mill, Lower Lumsdale, Matlock, DE4 5EX
tel:	01629 583 599
fax:	01629 580 761
email:	info@imageprinting.co.uk
web:	www.imageprinting.co.uk
contact:	Andrea Law
design service:	Yes
minimum run:	None
info:	Provide digital and litho printing services.
Posters, flyers, stickers, labels, CD sleeves and other promotional items such as keyrings.

Impression Direct Ltd.
Randall Park Way, Retford, DN22 7WF
tel:	0800 028 1962
fax:	0800 917 0128
email:	info@impressiondirect.com
web:	www.impressiondirect.com
contact:	Andrew Robinson
design service:	Yes
minimum run:	None
info:	Mainly litho and spot colour, but with some
digital capability. Posters, tickets, CD sleeves and digipacks. Free mainland UK delivery.

John E. Wright (Coventry)
52a Earlsdon Street, Coventry, CV5 6EJ
tel:	02476 674 775
fax:	02476 670 654
email:	coventrysales@johnwright.com
web:	www.johnwright.com
design service:	No
minimum run:	None
info:	Poster, flyers and leaflets printed digitally. Up
to A0 size. See also listings for John E.Wright branches located in Leicester, Derby, Nottingham, Oxford and Hull.

John E. Wright (Derby)
15-17 Brick Street, Derby, DE1 1DU
tel:	01332 344 743
fax:	01332 293 369
email:	derbysales@johnewright.com
web:	www.johnewright.com
design service:	No
minimum run:	None
info:	Posters, flyers and leaflets printed digitally. Up
to A0 size. See also listings for John E.Wright branches located in Leicester, Nottingham, Coventry, Oxford and Hull.

John E. Wright (Leicester)
9-11 Marble Street, Leicester, LE1 5XB
tel:	0116 255 6030
fax:	0116 247 1078
email:	leicestersales@johnewright.com
web:	www.johnewright.com
design service:	No
minimum run:	None
info:	Posters, flyers, leaflets printed digitally. Up to
A0. See also listings for John E.Wright branches located in Nottingham, Derby, Coventry, Oxford and Hull.

John E. Wright (Nottingham)
115 Huntingdon Street, Nottingham, NG1 3NF
tel:	0115 950 6633
fax:	0115 958 506
email:	nottinghamsales@johnewright.com
web:	www.johnewright.com
design service:	No
minimum run:	None
info:	Posters, flyers and leaflets printed digitally. Up
to A0. Another Nottingham branch located on Queens Drive Industrial Estate, tel. 0115 983 3200. See also listings for John E.Wright branches located in Leicester, Derby, Coventry, Oxford and Hull.

JWB Print & Design
Dixon Court, Dixon Street, Lincoln, LN6 7DA
tel:	01522 560 760
fax:	01522 567 272
email:	louise@jwbprint.co.uk
web:	www.jwbprint.co.uk
contact:	Jim Blyth
design service:	Yes
minimum run:	None
info:	Digital and litho printing. Posters, stickers and
flyers available.

K & S Print Ltd.
46 Steel Drive, Fordhouse Road Industrial Estate, Wolverhampton, West Midlands, WV10 9XF
tel:	01902 398 073
fax:	01902 398 074
email:	kandsprint@aol.com
web:	www.kandsprint.co.uk
contact:	David Bradburn
design service:	Yes
minimum run:	None
info:	All kind of posters, laminating, mounting. Digital
and litho.

Matlock Copy Centre
16 Bakewell Road, Matlock, DE4 3AU
tel:	01629 580 282
fax:	01629 580 282
email:	info@matlockcopycentre.co.uk
web:	www.matlockcopycentre.co.uk
contact:	Ken Ness
design service:	Yes
minimum run:	None
info:	Purely digital printing from A4 to A0 size. Ideal
for posters.

Ozmedia Print
15 Fennel Street, Loughborough, Leicestershire, LE11 1UQ
tel:	0870 855 0308
fax:	0870 855 0309
email:	loughborough@printing.com
web:	www.printing.com
design service:	Yes
minimum run:	250
info:	Part of Printing.com franchise. Offer full range
of printing services and can produce most items at reasonable price including stickers, leaflets and postcards. See website above for details of offers available.

Perfect Print Soloutions
7 Blackberry Close, Rugby, CV23 0UJ
tel: 01788 560 957
fax: 01788 550 436
email: ddaniels@dsl.pipex.com
contact: Dave Daniels
design service: Yes
minimum run: None
info: Digital and litho printing. Flyers, labels, leaflets and business cards.

Pewter Design
57 St. Mary's Road, Market Harborough, Leicestershire, LE16 7DS
tel: 0870 855 0348
fax: 0870 855 0349
email: marketharborough@printing.com
web: www.printing.com
design service: Yes
minimum run: 250
info: Part of Printing.com franchise. Offer full range of printing services and can produce most items at reasonable price including stickers, leaflets and postcards. See website above for details of offers available.

Peyton Company Printers Ltd.
67-69 Warstone Lane, Birmingham, B18 6NG
tel: 0121 236 3933
fax: 0121 236 3934
email: sales@peytonprinters.co.uk
contact: Matt Sherlock
design service: Yes
minimum run: None
info: Experienced printers. B&W and colour digital printing of posters and flyers.

Print & Design
Worcester City Digital, Britannia Road, Worcester, WR1 3BQ
tel: 01905 27642
fax: 01905 20276
email: prepress@worcesterdigital.co.uk
contact: Terry Clifford
design service: Yes
minimum run: None
info: Digital printing of flyers, posters, banners and programmes. Have carried out work for bands previously and specialise in short runs.

Printhouse
132 Littleover Lane, Littleover, Derby, DE23 6JL
tel: 01332 603 346
email: info@printhousederby.co.uk
web: www.printhousederby.co.uk
contact: Aki Caur
design service: Yes
minimum run: None
info: Digital and litho printing. Single to full colour.

printing.com (Coventry)
291-293 Walsgrave Road, Coventry, CV2 4BE
tel: 0870 950 7332
fax: 0870 950 7333
email: coventry@printing.com
web: www.printing.com
design service: Yes
minimum run: 250
info: Printing.com is a large chain with branches all over the UK. Offer full range of printing services and can produce most items at reasonable price including stickers, leaflets and postcards. For full list of stores see the above website.

printing.com @ Kaleidoscope
54 Willes Road, Leamington Spa, CV31 1BZ
tel: 01926 435 252
fax: 01926 881 800
email: paul@kscope.co.uk
web: www.printing.com
contact: Paul Cox
design service: Yes
minimum run: 250
info: Mainly litho printing. 1000 colour leaflets for £99. Also have a photography studio.

Progressive Print Services Ltd.
Midland Shires House, Firs Industrial Estate, Kidderminster, DY11 7QN
tel: 01562 747 356
fax: 01562 747 357
email: sales@progressive-print.co.uk
web: www.progressive-print.co.uk
contact: Steve Burrows
design service: Yes
minimum run: None
info: Digital and litho printing of posters, flyers, CD covers, CD packaging and large format items. Discount available for bands.

RCS Plc
Randall Park Way, Retford, Nottinghamshire, DN22 7WF
tel: 0800 328 5064
fax: 0800 328 5065
email: mail@rcs.plc.uk
web: www.rcs.plc.uk
design service: No
minimum run: None
info: Large format posters, A5 flyers and leaflets, CD and DVD covers, postcards, business cards, beer mats, boxes, badges and lots more print solutions. Full online service.

Sign It
108 Station Road, Beeston, Nottingham, NG9 2AY
tel: 0870 855 0368
fax: 0870 855 0369
email: beeston@printing.com
web: www.printing.com
design service: Yes
minimum run: 250
info: Part of Printing.com franchise. Offer full range of printing services and can produce most items at reasonable price including stickers, leaflets and postcards. See website above for details of offers available.

The Studio
79 Bridge Street, Walsall, WS1 1JQ
tel: 0870 855 0424
fax: 0870 855 0425
email: walsall@printing.com
web: www.printing.com
design service: Yes
minimum run: 250
info: Part of Printing.com franchise. Offer full range of printing services and can produce most items at reasonable price including stickers, leaflets and postcards. See website above for details of offers available.

Vision Print Marketing Ltd.
112 Sunbeam Studios, Sunbeam Street, Wolverhampton, WV2 4PF
tel: 01902 714 810
fax: 01902 425 747
email: simon@visionprint.info
web: www.visionprint.info
contact: Dan Cartwright
design service: Yes
minimum run: None
info: Digital and litho. Large format. Posters, flyers and leaflets. Also offer web design service.

Will-Print
Keys Hill, Baddesley Ensor, Atherstone, CV9 2DF
tel: 01827 712 933
fax: 01827 711 353
contact: Mark Garratt
design service: Yes
minimum run: None
info: Digital and litho. Posters, flyers, business cards, labels and stickers.

Words & Graphics
25 Church Lane, Anstey, Leicester, LE7 7AF
tel: 0116 234 0491
fax: 0116 234 0493
email: sales@wordsandgraphics.co.uk
web: www.wordsandgraphics.co.uk
contact: Sue Perkins
design service: Yes
minimum run: None
info: Digital and litho printing, specialising in short run digital print. Posters, flyers and postcards.

NORTHEAST

Aero Printing
Unit 54b, Aiden Court, Bede Industrial Estate, Jarrow, Tyne & Wear, NE32 3EF
tel: 0191 428 2428
fax: 0191 483 7266
email: sean@aeroprinting.co.uk
web: www.aeroprinting.co.uk
contact: Sean
design service: Yes
minimum run: None
info: Business cards, flyers, leaflets and posters. Mainly litho but have some digital capabilities.

Alison Jane Print
13 Grebe Close, Blyth, Northumberland, NE24 3QX
tel: 01670 351 805
contact: Alan James
design service: Yes
minimum run: None
info: Posters from A4 to A0 size. Also provide flyers and business cards. Digital and litho services.

Artisan Studio
Ouseburn Building, Albion Row, Newcastle, NE6 1LL
tel: 0191 265 4344
fax: 0191 265 5077
contact: Brian Ward
design service: Yes
minimum run: None
info: Digital and litho printing of posters and flyers.

Boddy Printers
210 Parliament Road, Middlesbrough, Cleveland, TS1 5PF
tel: 01642 224 800
fax: 01642 249 767
email: kevin.boddy@btconnect.com
contact: Kevin Boddy
design service: Yes
minimum run: None
info: Litho printing of posters, flyers and CD covers. Up to A3 size.

Capability's
13 Heaton Road, Byker, Newcastle Upon Tyne, NE6 1SA
tel: 0191 224 4022
fax: 0191 224 4022
contact: Gwen Carr
design service: Yes
minimum run: None
info: Digital printing service, Free price list available on request.

Chameleon Print and Design
Graphic House, Addison Industrial Estate, Blaydon-On-Tyne, NE21 4TE
tel: 0191 440 0440
email: info@newcastleprint.com
web: www.newcastleprint.com
contact: Shah Hussain
design service: Yes
minimum run: None
info: Litho printing, offering 5000 A5 full colour leaflets for £95.

City Printers Ltd.
Broadwood View, Chester Le Street, County Durham, DH3 3NJ
tel: 0191 388 3255
fax: 0191 389 5009
email: gary@cityprint.demon.co.uk
contact: Gary Henderson
design service: Yes
minimum run: None
info: Digital and litho printing. Call for a free quote.

CMDK
Unit 3b, IES Centre, Horndale Avenue, Aycliffe Industrial Park, Newton Aycliffe, County Durham, DL5 6DS
tel: 01325 311 166
fax: 01325 311 188
email: val@cmdk.co.uk
web: www.cmdk.co.uk
contact: Val Palmer
design service: Yes
minimum run: None
info: Posters, banners, CD covers and flyers. Digital printing.

Currie International
89 Derwent Street, Blackhill, Consett, County Durham, DH8 8LT
tel: 01207 505 191
contact: Des Currie
design service: Yes
minimum run: 1000
info: Specialise in business card printing. 10,000 cards for £81.

The Direct Print Group
Unit 7, Broadlanding, South Shields, NE33 1JL
tel: 0191 455 6027
email: info@thedirectprintgroup.com
web: www.thedirectprintgroup.com
contact: Steve Dixon
design service: Yes
minimum run: None
info: Posters, flyers and business card printing. Discounts available for unsigned bands.

The Docucentre
Gateshead College, Durham Road, Gateshead, Tyne & Wear, NE9 5BN
tel: 0191 490 2316
email: xerox@gateshead.ac.uk
contact: Barry Kimber
design service: No
minimum run: None
info: Digital colour copying, up to A3. Cheap rates. Flyers, leaflets and posters. Can only accept designs on PC format.

Express Printworks
Simcox Court, Riverside Park Industrial Estate, Middlesborough, TS2 1UX
tel: 01642 231 055
fax: 01642 231 788
email: epw@print.co.uk
contact: Stuart Stark
design service: Yes
minimum run: 1000
info: Range of printing services provided. Contact Express Printworks for a free quote.

J Snowball & Son
Park Avenue Press, Dundas Street, Spennymoor, DL16 6AR
tel: 01388 420 502
fax: 01388 420 503
email: spencer@jsnowballandson.fsnet.co.uk
design service: Yes
minimum run: None
info: Large format printing up to Double Crown 20" by 30" posters.

Jasprint Ltd.
12 Tower Road, Glover, Washington, NE37 2SH
tel: 0191 417 6766
fax: 0191 415 1351
email: info@jasprint.com
web: www.jasprint.com
contact: Sales Manager
design service: Yes
minimum run: None
info: Litho and digital printing. Large format posters available. Specialise in short print runs.

Linton's Printers
Unit 14B, Beechburn Industrial Estate, Crook, DL15 8RA
tel: 01388 762 197
fax: 01388 765 396
email: info@lintons-printers.co.uk
web: www.lintons-printers.co.uk
contact: Craig Dixon
design service: Yes
minimum run: None
info: Mostly litho printing, but with some digital capabilities. Competitive rates for unsigned bands.

Moments Print & Design
Unit 7, Premier Business Development Centre, Whitehouse Enterprise Centre, Whitehouse Road, Newcastle Upon Tyne, NE15 6EP
tel: 0870 757 7587
email: info@moments4solutions.com
web: www.moments4solutions.com
contact: Angela Carrington
design service: Yes
minimum run: None
info: Flyers, posters, banners and stickers. Band friendly service. Digital and litho printing.

MPC Ltd.
The Old Stables, Greys Yard, Morpeth, NE61 1QD
tel: 01670 504 646
fax: 01670 504 647
email: studio@morpethprint.com
web: www.morpethprint.com
design service: Yes
minimum run: None
info: Litho printing. Leaflets, flyers and posters. Negotiable rates, contact for details.

N.W. Printers
Dukesway, Team Valley Trading Estate, Gateshead, Tyne & Wear, NE11 0PZ
tel: 0191 487 6041
fax: 0191 491 5554
contact: Dorothy Edwards
design service: Yes
minimum run: None
info: Specialise in digital and litho printing.

Native Print
113 Chillingham Road, Heaton, Newcastle Upon Tyne, NE6 5XL
tel: 0191 224 5126
fax: 0191 224 5796
email: nativeprint@aol.com
contact: Kerry Milburn
design service: Yes
minimum run: None (posters), 100 (flyers)
info: Provide flyer and poster printing services.

The New Print House Ltd.
Unit 5, Prospect Terrace Industrial Estate, North Shields, NE30 1DX
tel: 0191 258 7027
fax: 0191 259 6738
email: info@newprinthouse.co.uk
contact: Nick Gray
design service: Yes
minimum run: None
info: Single to full colour printing available on leaflets, flyers and posters.

Ord's Group
Progress House, Usworth Road Industrial Estate, Hartlepool, TS25 1PD
tel: 01429 273 456
email: sales@ords.co.uk
web: www.ords.co.uk
contact: Angela Pearson
design service: Yes
minimum run: None
info: Ord's Group also have a branch situated on Tower Street, Hartlepool, which deals with short runs.

Photo-Line (City) Ltd.
4 St. Nicholas' Precinct, Cloth Market, Newcastle Upon Tyne, NE1 1EE
tel: 0191 232 5454
fax: 0191 261 0472
email: print@photoline.co.uk
web: www.photoline.co.uk
contact: Peter McGrady
design service: Yes
minimum run: None
info: Digital, large format, full colour print service. Also provide posters.

Printex Printers
1 Back Westfield Terrace, Gateshead, Tyne & Wear, NE8 4HX
tel: 0191 477 8726
fax: 0191 477 6430
email: paulprintex@hotmail.com
contact: Paul Walton
design service: Yes
minimum run: None
info: Posters, flyers and CD covers can be printed.

Printright Litho and Screen Printers
The Old School, Shincliffe, Durham, County Durham, DH1 2PD
tel: 0191 386 4555
email: printmaxx@aol.com
contact: Peter Wright
design service: Yes
minimum run: None
info: Posters, flyers, CD covers and box covers. Fully equipped with software including Photoshop, Illustrator and Word.

Red Press
14 Queen Street, Redcar, TS10 1AE
tel: 01642 515 966
fax: 01642 515 965
email: info@redpress.co.uk
web: www.redpress.co.uk
design service: Yes
minimum run: 500
info: Digital and litho. Posters, flyers, business cards and CD covers.

Smart Dezign
St. Mary's Business & Enterprise Centre, Oystershell Lane, Newcastle Upon Tyne, NE4 5QS
tel: 0191 261 0084
fax: 0191 261 0084
email: smartdezign@bluguru.co.uk
web: www.smartdezign.co.uk
contact: Tom Seymour
design service: Yes
minimum run: None
info: Free design service available. Will print posters and flyers.

Smith Bros (Hebburn & Jarrow) Ltd.
44 Glen Street, Hebburn, NE31 1NG
tel: 0191 483 2138
fax: 0191 483 2138
contact: Glenn
design service: Yes
minimum run: None
info: Digital and litho printing of posters and flyers.

Speed Office Supplies
Unit 32, Team Valley Business Centre, Earlsway, Team Valley Trading Estate, Gateshead, NE11 0QH
tel: 0191 491 1223
fax: 0191 491 0033
email: speedoffice@btconnect.co.uk
contact: Maureen Morrison
design service: No
minimum run: None
info: Printing on specialist paper using Inkjet media.

Spot On Displays Ltd.
42 Station Road, Stanley, DH9 0JL
tel: 01207 236 909
fax: 01207 284 636
email: sales@spotondisplays.com
web: www.spotondisplays.com
contact: Peter Redden
design service: Yes
minimum run: None
info: Litho and digital printing of posters and banners.

Stelro Print & Design
Unit 13, Nestfield Industrial Estate, Darlington, County Durham, DL1 2NW
tel: 01325 361 124
fax: 01325 358 181
email: stelro@aol.com
web: www.stelro.co.uk
contact: Ricky Milford
design service: Yes
minimum run: None
info: Digital up to A3 and litho up to A2.

Team Valley Printers
321h Mayoral Way, Team Valley Trading Estate, Gateshead, Tyne & Wear, NE11 0RT
tel: 0191 482 2994
fax: 0191 482 2994
email: teamvalley@printing2.totalserve.co.uk
contact: Janice Knight
design service: Yes
minimum run: 500
info: Digital and litho printing. Posters, flyers and CD covers.

Teesside Graphics Ltd.
The Grange Business Centre, Belasis Avenue, Billingham, TS23 1LG
tel: 01642 530 540
fax: 01642 530 460
email: teessidegraphics@teessidegraphics.co.uk
web: www.teessidegraphics.co.uk
contact: Brian or Kevin
design service: No
minimum run: None
info: Can produce flyers and large glossy posters. Band friendly. Call for a quote.

That's Bang On
42 Pink Lane, Newcastle, NE1 5DY
tel: 0191 261 1980
fax: 0191 261 1980
email: sales@thatsbangon.com
web: www.thatsbangon.com
contact: Simon Davidson
design service: Yes
minimum run: None
info: Flyers and up to extra large format posters. 10% discount for unsigned bands.

Vision Press
5-8 Redesdale Court, Riverside Park Industrial Estate, Middlesbrough, TS2 1RL
tel: 01642 222 005
fax: 01642 249 990
email: ian@visionpress.fsnet.co.uk
contact: Stevan Allgood
design service: No
minimum run: None
info: Litho printing of posters and flyers.

White's
Front Street, Ludworth, Durham, DH6 1NE
tel:	01429 820 487
fax:	01429 821 508
email:	whitesprint@aol.com
contact:	Paula White
design service:	Yes
minimum run:	None
info:	Digital and litho printing. Wide format posters. CD covers and labels.

NORTHWEST

A Touch Of Class
9 High Park Place, Southport, PR9 7QP
tel:	01704 225 563
fax:	01704 225 563
design service:	Yes
info:	Leaflets and flyers printed to your needs. Telephone for further details.

Abacus Media
41 Sherbourne Street, Manchester, M8 8NE
tel:	0845 130 4771
fax:	0161 834 6211
email:	sales@abacusmedia.tv
web:	www.abacusmedia.tv
contact:	Anthony
design service:	Yes
info:	Full colour print production, interactive CD and DVD production, graphics and web design. DVD authoring and video production.

Aden Tudor
Printwell House, 111 Eldon Street, Preston, PR1 7PL
tel:	01772 251 900
email:	sales@adentudor.co.uk
web:	www.adentudor.co.uk
design service:	Yes
info:	Stickers, posters, flyers and clothing to suit your bands needs. Small runs can be produced at low costs.

AW Perry Printers Ltd.
Units 1 & 2, Peel Industrial Estate, Chamber Halls Street, Bury, BL9 0LU
tel:	0161 764 2617
fax:	0161 762 9557
email:	print@awperryprinters.co.uk
contact:	Andrew Bucknall
design service:	Yes
info:	Flyers, posters (up to A2) and tickets available.

Badger Press Ltd.
Longlands, Bowness, Windermere, LA23 3AS
tel:	01539 445 399
fax:	01539 488 361
email:	designprint@badgerpress.co.uk
contact:	Ian Thompson
design service:	Yes
minimum run:	Contact for details
info:	Poster and flyers in single or full colour. Free consultation.

Bay Type
Manderley House, Heysham, LA3 1LN
tel:	07710 405 864
email:	r.cleet@btinternet.com
contact:	R. Cleet
design service:	Yes
minimum run:	None
info:	Flyers and posters up to A1 size. Band friendly.

Bebington Print
140 Bebington Road, New Ferry, Wirral, CH62 5BJ
tel:	0800 018 7592
fax:	0151 643 1777
email:	ian@bebprint.u-net.com
web:	www.bebprint.u-net.com
contact:	Ian
design service:	Yes
info:	Flyers and posters up to A3. Disk to print service for reproduction of your own designs.

BQ Printing Services Ltd.
PO Box 7, Unit 41, Gate 3, Offerton Industrial Estate, Hempshaw Lane, Stockport, SK2 6BE
tel:	0161 480 0055
fax:	0161 476 1840
email:	info@bqprinting.co.uk
web:	www.bqprinting.co.uk
contact:	Peter Clarke
design service:	Yes
minimum run:	None
info:	Will print posters, flyers and CD inlays.

Colour Copy Express
227 Stamford Street Central, Ashton-Under-Lyne, OL6 7QB
tel:	0161 343 4739
email:	martin@cybamall.com
contact:	Martin
design service:	Yes
minimum run:	None
info:	Total reprographic range from posters and flyers to t-shirts. CD cover art can be duplicated.

Colour Jay Ltd.
Power House, Dacre Street, Birkenhead, CH41 6LZ
tel:	0151 647 4861
fax:	0151 647 2550
email:	colourjay@aol.com
contact:	Mike Davis
design service:	No
info:	Flyer, CD inserts and posters up to B2. Full colour. Short and long runs available. CD duplication service also provided.

D.H. & P.I. Watson
Bridge House Stores, Sandy Lane, West Kirby, CH48 3JA
tel:	0151 625 5736
fax:	0151 625 6260
email:	dhwatson@btinternet.com
contact:	Dave Watson
design service:	Yes
info:	Flyers from £30 per 1000. Colour copying, enlarging, reducing and laminating.

Ditto Design
12a Crescent Road, Windermere, Cumbria, LA23 1EA
tel: 01539 444 456
email: sales@dittosolutions.co.uk
contact: Joan Lambert
design service: Yes
info: Colour and B&W photocopying. Small print runs available in leaflets, flyers and posters up to A3. Also offer t-shirt printing.

Flexipress
Unit 1, Windmill Avenue, Ormskirk, L39 4QB
tel: 0800 597 8427
fax: 01695 576 838
email: flexipress@aol.com
contact: Chris
design service: Yes
info: Flyers, posters up to A3, CD inlays and booklets.

Forsyth & Steele
161 Blackpool Old Road, Poulton, FY6 7RS
tel: 0800 073 3557
fax: 01253 883 700
email: ian@forsythandsteele.com or rob@forsythandsteele.com
web: www.forsythandsteele.com
design service: No
minimum run: None (Flyers)
info: Flyers and posters up to A3. Large format printing allows for posters up to 44" wide and any length. Laminating and encapsulating. Board mounting.

Grantham's
Corporation Street, Preston, PR1 2UQ
tel: 01772 250 207
email: jan.mulholland@granthams.co.uk
web: www.granthams.co.uk
contact: Jan Mulholland
design service: No
minimum run: None
info: Flyers, posters and CD covers. Posters up to 52 inches wide by any length. Can also print garments and a range of promotional items. For Blackpool branch call 01253 624 402.

Gtec Printers & Stationers
Systems House, Willow Street, Oldham, OL1 3QH
tel: 0161 620 0102
fax: 0161 620 4755
email: info@gtecprinters.net
web: www.gtecprinters.net
contact: John or Zoe
design service: No
minimum run: None
info: Flyers and posters up to A0 available.

Hobs Reprographics (Chester)
63 Watergate Row, Chester, CH1 2LB
tel: 01244 319 324/01244 319 325
fax: 01244 313 351
email: chester@hobsrepro.com
web: www.hobsrepro.com
design service: Yes
info: Full range of printing services provided including small and large format, copying, scanning, archiving abd finishing. Hobs Reprographics have branches throughout the UK. See website above for full list.

Image Design
44 Moor Street, Ormskirk, L39 YT
tel: 01695 578 811
email: studio44@btconnect.com
contact: Nick
design service: Yes
minimum run: None (Flyers)
info: Posters up to any size, flyers and CD inserts. Photographic facilities. Website design.

Imprint Offset
Unit 12a, Warrington Central Trading Estate, Bewsey Road, Warrington, WA2 7LP
tel: 01925 651 141
fax: 01925 651 335
email: sales@imprintoffset.co.uk
web: www.imprintoffset.co.uk
contact: Dave Hill
design service: Yes
minimum run: None
info: Specialists in multimedia printing for 15 years. Can print any packaging, posters, flyers, stickers or promotional items.

Ink Truck
Lorne Cresent, Carlisle, Cumbria, CA2 5XW
tel: 01228 818 980
email: print@inktruck.freeserve.co.uk
contact: John
design service: Yes
minimum run: None
info: Posters, flyers, and tickets available. Posters printed to A2 size. Also short runs of A3 prints, flyers and CD inlays. Full design service offered. Printing up to B2.

Jim Barlow
Park House, Manchester
tel: 0800 083 1202
email: print@jimbarlows.co.uk
web: www.jimbarlows.co.uk
design service: Yes
info: Posters, flyers and other promotional print. Price depends on size of run.

Kall Kwik
57 Watergate Street, Chester, CH1 2LB
tel: 01244 351 505
fax: 01244 320 961
email: digiprint@chester.kallkwik.co.uk
web: www.chester.kallkwik.co.uk
contact: Callum
design service: Yes
minimum run: 50
info: Posters, flyers, leaflets and almost any printing service you require. Turnaround of approximately 5 days. See website above for full list of Kall Kwik branches throughout the UK.

Kwik Communications Ltd.
12c Woodford Road, Bramhall, Stockport, SK7 1JJ
tel: 0161 440 9339
fax: 0161 439 8521
email: info@kwikcomms.com
web: www.kwikcomms.com
contact: Alan Lowe
design service: Yes
minimum run: None
info: Specialises in large print posters and large runs of leaflets and flyers. In-house designer is happy to work with band's ideas.

Logo Print
330 Slade Lane, Levenshulme, Manchester, M19 2BY
tel: 0161 248 0440
fax: 0161 248 0448
email: dave@logoprint.co.uk
web: www.logoprint.co.uk
contact: Dave Garson
design service: No
minimum run: None
info: Flyers, cassette and CD inserts, posters up to A3.

M Print
5 Jupitar Court, Jupitar Drive, Chester, CH1 4QS
tel: 01244 390 000
email: info@mprintchester.com
web: www.mprintchester.com
contact: Steve or Richard
design service: Yes
info: Paper and card printing including flyers, posters (up to A2) and tickets. Minimum run of 200 for flyers.

Michigan Reprographics
Link House, Warrick Road South, Old Trafford, Manchester, M16 0JT
tel: 0161 881 1114
email: info@michigan-design-print.co.uk
web: www.michigan-design-print.co.uk
contact: Peter Hill
design service: Yes
minimum run: None
info: Full design and print service from flyers and posters to CD inlays and stickers.

Microplan International Ltd.
Titchfield Street, Barrow-in-Furness, Cumbria, Barrow-in-Furness, LA14 5DA
tel: 01229 432 468
fax: 01229 432 467
email: info@microplan.co.uk
web: www.microplan.co.uk
contact: John Lucy
design service: Yes
info: CD covers, posters, flyers and tickets. Short and long runs available. Speak to John Lucy for further informations.

Minuteman Press (Bolton)
42 Bridge Street, Bolton, BL1 2EG
tel:	01204 397 434
fax:	01204 397 435
email:	info@minutemanbolton.co.uk
web:	www.minutemanbolton.co.uk
contact:	John King
design service:	Yes
minimum run:	None
info:	Posters, flyers and CD covers. Digital and offset

printing. Band friendly. Also starting a fanzine, and will be involved in putting gigs on around Bolton, please speak to Adam for further details.

The Mouse House Print Shop
The Barn, Bath Place, Hale, WA14 2XY
tel:	0161 929 5538
email:	info@mousehouseprintshop.co.uk
web:	www.mousehouseprintshop.co.uk
contact:	Dan
design service:	Yes
info:	Will print flyers and tickets.

Munro
4 Croft Court, Butts Close, Thornton Cleveleys, Lancashire, FY5 4JX
tel:	01253 863 388
fax:	01253 851 630
email:	sales@munroprint.co.uk
contact:	Simon Ashton
design service:	No
minimum run:	None
info:	Affordable ticket, poster and flyer printing.

MW Graphics
The Vulcan Works, Great Harwood, Glebe Street, Blackburn, BB6 7AA
tel:	01254 876 202
fax:	01254 876 204
email:	info@mwgraphics.co.uk
web:	www.mwgraphics.co.uk
contact:	Caroline
design service:	Yes
info:	Flyers, business cards and posters (maximum

60" wide, any length). Banners and vehicle graphics.

Nymphs of Bacchus
Manchester
tel:	07742 462 574
email:	enquiries@nymphsofbacchus.co.uk
web:	www.nymphsofbacchus.co.uk
contact:	Kelly
design service:	No
minimum run:	None
info:	Flyers, posters, business cards, CD and promo

covers. Small order specialists. Also offer full merchandising service. See entry in Promotional Merchandise section for further details.

Page Fast Ltd. Colour Printers
4-6 Lansil Way, Lancaster, LA1 3QY
tel:	01524 841 010
fax:	01524 841 578
email:	info@pagefast.co.uk
web:	www.pagefast.co.uk
contact:	Dawn
design service:	Yes
info:	Lithographic printers. Posters and flyers

available, along with other paper products such as business cards.

Parallel Printing Ltd.
Unit 16, Babbage Road, Engineer Park, Sandycroft, Deeside, CH5 2QD
tel:	01244 539 533
design service:	Yes
minimum run:	500
info:	Full colour flyer printing. Posters available on

request. Delivery service provided.

Photo Mechanical
1 Princes Street (off King Street), Blackburn, BB2 1LT
tel:	01254 569 981
fax:	01254 695 177
email:	sales@photo-mechanical.co.uk
web:	www.photo-mechanical.co.uk
design service:	Yes
info:	Posters and flyers, B&W or colour. 50 x A0

posters (black on white) for £59. 500 x A4 or 1000 x A5 flyers on heavy weight paper for £99. See website for full 20 page price list. Orders can be placed via email, you can also send over artwork stored on disk.

Planet Print
Unit 2, Sovereign Court, Wyerfields, Poulton Business Park, Lancashire, FY6 8JX
tel:	01253 899 008
email:	mike@planetprint.co.uk or
	nigel@planetprint.co.uk
web:	www.planetprint.co.uk
contact:	Nigel or Mike
design service:	Yes
minimum run:	None
info:	Flyers, posters, fanzines and CD covers. CD

duplication and glass mastering. Graphic and website design available in-house.

Premier Creative Print Ltd.
Unit 3, Burnden Industrial Estate, Manchester Road, Bolton, BL3 2NG
tel:	01204 388 299
fax:	01204 532 454
email:	info@premiercreative.co.uk
web:	www.premiercreative.co.uk
contact:	Dale
design service:	No
minimum run:	500 (Flyers)
info:	Flyers, posters and a range of promotional items.

Colour or B&W. Small runs of digitally printed A3 posters available. Posters of any size available.

Print Co-ordination Ltd.
Athey Street, Macclesfield, Cheshire, SK11 6QU
tel:	01625 616 111
email:	dford@printco.co.uk
web:	www.printco.co.uk
contact:	Derek Ford
design service:	Yes
info:	Flyers, posters and tickets. CD design,

duplication and artwork print available. Speak to Derek Ford for details.

Printworks
The Old Bakehouse, 54-56 Wallgate, Wigan, WN1 1BA
tel:	01942 703 703
email:	neil@printworks.demon.co.uk
contact:	Neil
design service:	No
minimum run:	Contact for details
info:	Flyers, posters and other paper products

including business cards and brochures. Minimum orders apply.

Prontaprint
65 Eastbank Street, Southport, PR8 1EJ
tel:	01704 543 010
fax:	01704 544 318
email:	sales@southport.prontaprint.com
web:	www.prontaprint.co.uk
contact:	Julia Gaudi
design service:	Yes
info:	Flyers and posters up to exhibition size. Range

or finishes available. CD covers, inlay cards and stickers. Prontaprint has branches throughout the UK. See above website to locate your local branch.

Publicity Print Marketing
415-415a Warrington Road, Culcheth, WA3 5SW
tel:	01925 765 995
fax:	01925 765 786
email:	steve.ppm@tiscali.co.uk
design service:	No
minimum run:	None
info:	Posters up to A3 and flyers.

The Purple Turtle
Trafalgar House, Trafalgar Straight, Burnley, Lancashire, BB11 1RA
tel:	01282 433 351
email:	david@thepurpleturtle.co.uk
web:	www.thepurpleturtle.co.uk
contact:	David
design service:	Yes
info:	Low runs of large and small format and digital

prints. Full colour backdrops printed onto material.

Ricta UK
Hyde Park House, Cartwright Street, Hyde, Cheshire, Hyde, SK14 4EH
tel:	0161 351 0161
email:	rictauk@btclick.com
web:	www.rictauk.co.uk
contact:	Eric Taylor
design service:	No
minimum run:	500
info:	Posters up to 1m wide, as well as flyers. Also

offer CD duplication, artwork design and t-shirt printing. See entries in relevant sections for details.

Riverside Press
Ford Quay, St. George's Quay, Lancaster, LA1 5QJ
tel: 01524 332 77
email: rivers@globalnet.co.uk
design service: Yes
info: Full design and print service. Posters, flyers, inlay cards and CD inserts. On-body printing and CD labels.

Servicepoint UK (Liverpool)
19 Brunswick Street, Liverpool, L2 0PJ
tel: 0151 236 0507
fax: 0151 231 1348
email: liverpool@servicepointuk.com
web: www.servicepointuk.com
contact: Sue Catterall-Molloy
design service: Yes
info: Services available include colour copying, high volume B&W printing and small format digital colour printing. Servicepoint has branches throughout the UK. See website above for full list of outlets.

S-Print
16 Halifax Street, Blackpool, FY3 9QQ
tel: 01253 316 875
email: art@s-print.co.uk
web: www.s-print.co.uk
contact: Trisha
design service: Yes
minimum run: 500
info: Promotional cards, leaflets and letterheads. Web design also available. Please call for a sample package.

Sturdy Print & Design Ltd.
15 Selby Place, Stanley Industrial Estate, Skelmersdale, WN8 8EF
tel: 01695 720 397
email: sales@sturdyprint.co.uk
web: www.sturdyprint.co.uk
contact: Chris Jones or Lisa Hardman
design service: Yes
info: Flyers and posters. Posters available up to any size. Can also print tickets and labels.

Uni Print & Design
Lancaster University, Lancaster, LA1 4YW
tel: 01524 592 069
email: s.thomas@lancaster.ac.uk
web: www.lancaster.ac.uk
contact: Steve Thomas
design service: Yes
info: Posters up to A3, flyers, garment prints plus a range of promotional items. Colour photocopying and binding facilities. For in-house design service, call 01524 592 075.

Uprint
Ground Floor, UMSU, North Campus, Manchester, M60 1QD
tel: 0161 200 3269
fax: 0161 200 3268
email: office@uprint.com
web: www.uprint.com
design service: Yes
minimum run: None
info: Posters up to A3, flyers and low run t-shirts. Smaller runs catered for. Matt finish. Also colour printing and channel binding available.

Vec Print
55-57 Garstang Road, Preston, Lancashire, PR1 1LB
tel: 01772 200 006
fax: 01772 200 008
email: info@vecprint.com
web: www.vecprint.com
contact: Emma Coulling
design service: No
minimum run: None
info: Will print leaflets and posters. Vec Print have worked in promoting club nights and other music events.

SOUTHEAST

4 Print & Design Ltd.
Unit A, Level 2, New England House, New England Street, Brighton, BN1 4GH
tel: 01273 606 244/07711 002 080
email: dave@4printanddesign.co.uk
web: www.4printanddesign.co.uk
contact: Dave Evans
design service: Yes
minimum run: None
info: Specialists in event flyers and posters.

Admark Design & Print Ltd.
Cameron House, Minoru Place, Binfield, Berkshire, RG42 4HS
tel: 0845 600 3447
fax: 0845 600 3295
contact: Paul Wakefield
design service: Yes
minimum run: None
info: Will meet all your printing requirements including flyers, posters, tickets and CD inlays. Also print onto any promotional items.

Audio Print
Wolseley Court, Woburn Road Industrial Estate, Kempston, Bedfordshire, MK42 7AY
tel: 01234 857 566
fax: 01234 841 700
email: peter@audioprint.com
web: www.audioprint.com
contact: Peter Hull
design service: Yes
minimum run: 1000
info: Print only self adhesives and stickers. Barcode and packaging printing. Overnight delivery available across the UK.

Bluehound Media Ltd.
Box 1, 51-52 Marine Parade, Brighton, East Sussex, BN2 1PH
tel: 0845 610 6484
email: hawken@bluehound.co.uk
web: www.bluehound.co.uk
design service: Yes
minimum run: None
info: Posters, flyers, CD covers. Digital and litho.

BN2 Ltd.
Unit 9, Coalbrook House, Freshfield Business Park, Stevenson Road, Brighton, East Sussex, BN2 0DF
tel: 01273 808 663
email: gary@bn2ltd.co.uk
web: www.bn2ltd.co.uk
design service: Yes
minimum run: None
info: Can produce posters, flyers and CD covers. Digital and litho.

Clifton Litho
29-31 Richmond Road, Staines, TW18 2AA
tel: 01784 458 127
fax: 01784 465 744
email: paul@canssen.fsnet.co.uk
contact: Ian Davidson
design service: Yes
minimum run: None
info: Will print flyers, posters, tickets and CD inlays.

Colprint Print & Design
186b Bushey Mill Lane, Watford, WD24 7TE
tel: 01923 247 458
email: ask@colprint.co.uk
web: www.colprint.co.uk
design service: Yes
minimum run: None
info: Colprint produce CD covers, posters, flyers, leaflet, as well as promotional items.

Constable Printing
57 Woodham Lane, New Haw, Addlestone, Surrey, KT15 3ND
tel: 01932 848 218
fax: 01932 821 572
email: constableprint@waitrose.com
contact: Alison Constable
design service: Yes
minimum run: None
info: Any commercial printing including flyers, posters, tickets and CD inlays. Range of promotional items available including lighters and keyrings. Use trade screen printers for any material printing.

Felix Ltd.
Unit 3, Phoenix Industrial Estate, Commissioners Road, Medway City Estate, Rochester, ME2 4HZ
tel: 0870 855 0296
fax: 0870 855 0297
email: rochester@printing.com
web: www.printing.com
design service: Yes
minimum run: 250
info: Part of Printing.com franchise. Offer full range of printing services and can produce most items at reasonable price including stickers, leaflets and postcards. See website above for details of offers available.

Flyer Boy
Top Floor Offices, 59-61 Lansdowne Place, Hove, East Sussex, BN3 1FL
tel:	0870 770 1994
fax:	0870 770 1995
email:	requests@facemediagroup.co.uk
web:	www.flyerboy.com
design service:	Yes
info:	Full colour double-sided flyers. Part of the Face
Media Group who also offer printing services for items such as posters, letterheads, business cards, leaflets and brochures. For further details see www.facemediagroup.co.uk.

Impression Print & Design
24 Carden Avenue, Patcham, Brighton, East Sussex, BN1 8NA
tel:	01273 501 431
fax:	01273 501396
email:	info@impressionprint.co.uk
web:	www.impressionprint.co.uk
design service:	Yes
minimum run:	None
info:	Posters up to size A1, plus flyers and CD covers.

Inprint
58a Head Street, Colchester, CO1 1PB
tel:	0870 855 0388
fax:	0870 855 0389
email:	colchester@printing.com
web:	www.printing.com
design service:	Yes
minimum run:	250
info:	Part of Printing.com franchise. Offer full range
of printing services and can produce most items at reasonable price including stickers, leaflets and postcards. See website above for details of offers available.

John E. Wright (Oxford)
3 Oxford Business Centre, Osney Lane, Oxford, OX1 1TB
tel:	01865 244 455
fax:	01865 793 921
email:	oxfordsales@johnewright.com
web:	www.johnewright.com
design service:	No
minimum run:	None
info:	Posters, flyers and leaflets printed digitally. Up
to A0 size. See also listings for John E.Wright branches located in Leicester, Nottingham, Coventry, Nottingham and Hull.

Kall Kwik
66 North Street, Brighton, East Sussex, BN1 1RH
tel:	01273 728 247
web:	www.kallkwik.co.uk
design service:	Yes
minimum run:	None
info:	Posters, flyers, CD covers. Digital and litho. See
website above for full list of Kall Kwik branches throughout the UK.

Medway Print
33 Skinner Street, Gillingham, Kent, ME7 IHD
tel:	01634 281 199
fax:	01634 281 718
email:	sales@medwayprint.com
web:	www.medwayprint.com
design service:	Yes
minimum run:	None
info:	Posters, flyers and CD covers. Bands based in
Medway bands, or outside bands playing in the area can download a flyer entitling them to a discount by visiting www.medwaymusic.net.

MMB
MMB House, Chelmsford Road Industrial Estate, Chelmsford Road, Dunmow, Essex, CM6 1HD
tel:	01371 875 319
fax:	01371 875 319
email:	sales@mbprint.co.uk
web:	www.mbprint.co.uk
contact:	Colette Edwards
design service:	Yes
minimum run:	None
info:	Can produce flyers, posters, leaflets, record
labels, picture discs and stickers.

Nexus Design & Print
99-102 Preston Road, Brighton, East Sussex, BN1 6AF
tel:	01273 702 525
email:	harley@nexusdp.co.uk
web:	www.nexusdp.co.uk
design service:	Yes
minimum run:	None
info:	Print, design and marketing services for clients
of all sizes. Can supply business cards, compliment slips, labels and large format posters.

PDC Copyprint
34 Queens Road, Brighton, BN1 3XB
tel:	01273 323 001
email:	print@pdc-brighton.co.uk
web:	www.pdc-brighton.co.uk
design service:	Yes
minimum run:	None
info:	Specialists in large format print, including A0
posters.

printing.com (Ashford)
Roff Media Ltd., 4 New Street, Park Mall Shopping Centre, Ashford, Kent, TN24 8UU
tel:	0870 855 0350
fax:	0870 855 0351
email:	ashford@printing.com
web:	www.printing.com
design service:	Yes
minimum run:	250
info:	Printing.com is a large chain with branches all
over the UK. Offer full range of printing services and can produce most items at reasonable price including stickers, leaflets and postcards. For full list of stores see the above website.

Propabanda
Cricket Corner, Lynch Hill Park, Whitchurch, Hampshire, RG28 7NF
email:	info@propabanda.co.uk
web:	www.propabanda.co.uk
contact:	Matt Payne
design service:	Yes
minimum run:	None
info:	Can print 5000 flyers for £125. Also provide
massive range of promotional material and products. See listing in Promotional Merchandise section for details.

Shepperton Digital Print & Copy Centre
19 Thurlestone Parade, High Street, Shepperton, TW17 9AR
tel:	01932 248 600
fax:	01932 245 730
contact:	Michael Watkins
design service:	Yes
minimum run:	None
info:	Flyers, posters, tickets and CD inlays.

Studio Direct
8 Lockside Industrial Estate, Navigation Road, Chelmsford, Essex, CM2 6HE
tel:	0870 855 0398
fax:	0870 855 0399
email:	chelmsford@printing.com
web:	www.printing.com
design service:	Yes
minimum run:	None
info:	Part of Printing.com franchise. Offer full range
of printing services and can produce most items at reasonable price including stickers, leaflets and postcards. See website above for details of offers available.

Tangerine
Leewood Farm, Harthall Lane, Kings Langley, Hertfordshire, WD4 8JJ
tel:	01923 261 266
fax:	01923 261 267
email:	info@designbytangerine.co.uk
web:	www.designbytangerine.co.uk
design service:	Yes
minimum run:	Varies
info:	Poster and flyers produced on different materials
including paper, board, vinyl and silk. Board mounting, encapsulation and lamination. Banners. Mastering and duplication and graphic design available. See relevant section for details.

Toppers
93 High Street, Stevenage, Hertfordshire, SG1 3HR
tel:	0870 950 7236
fax:	0870 950 7237
email:	stevenage@printing.com
web:	www.printing.com
design service:	Yes
minimum run:	250
info:	Part of Printing.com franchise. Offer full range
of printing services and can produce most items at reasonable price including stickers, leaflets and postcards. See website above for details of offers available.

UK Flyers
210 Victory Business Centre, Somers Road North, Portsmouth, Hants, PO1 1PJ
tel:	02392 293 050
fax:	02392 295 258
email:	sales@ukflyers.com
web:	www.ukflyers.com
design service:	Yes
info:	UK Flyers has been supplying printed products

since 1997. As well as their core products like flyers and posters, they also offer competitive rates on a variety of promotional printing such as badges, stickers, beer mats and much more.

SOUTHWEST

After Dark Media
Grosvenor House, Belgrave Lane, Plymouth, PL4 7DA
tel:	01752 294 130
fax:	01752 257 320
email:	info@afterdarkmedia.com
web:	www.afterdarkmedia.com
contact:	Nigel Muntz
design service:	Yes
minimum run:	None
info:	Posters, flyers, banners, stickers, CD booklets

and inlays. Also can produce tickets.

Anneset
5 The Mart, Locking Road, Weston-Super-Mare, BS23 3DE
tel:	0870 855 0352
fax:	0870 855 0353
email:	wsm@printing.com
web:	www.printing.com
design service:	Yes
minimum run:	250
info:	Part of Printing.com franchise. Offer full range

of printing services and can produce most items at reasonable price including stickers, leaflets and postcards. See website above for details of offers available.

Ashley Press
43 Balena Close, Creekmoor Trading Estate, Poole, BH17 7DY
tel:	01202 695 656
design service:	No
minimum run:	None
info:	Digital and litho printing for short and long runs.

Posters and flyers.

Askey Graphics & Design
Ashfeild Farm, Pilning Street, Tockington, Bristol, BS32 4LR
tel:	01454 616 120
web:	www.askeygraphics.co.uk
contact:	Simon
design service:	Yes
minimum run:	None
info:	Posters up to A1 size, plus flyers, stickers.

Bartlett Printing
Swan Yard, St. Thomas, Exeter, EX4 1HU
tel:	01392 254 086
design service:	Yes
minimum run:	None
info:	Docucolour and litho printing. Can print posters

and flyers.

C3 Imaging
Brewery Court, North Street, Ashton, Bristol, BS3 1JS
tel:	0117 963 7507
email:	sales@c3bristol.co.uk
web:	www.c3imaging.co.uk
contact:	Sara
design service:	Yes
minimum run:	None
info:	Digital and litho printing. Posters, flyers and

banners.

Chelprint
30 St. George's Place, Cheltenham, GL50 3JZ
tel:	01242 584 987
contact:	John Howland
design service:	No
minimum run:	None
info:	Posters up to A3 size, as well as flyers. Full

colour digital copying.

The Clarendon Press
Carlton House, Long Street, Wotton-Under-Edge, GL12 7EP
tel:	01453 843 571
email:	pete@clarendonpress.com
web:	www.clarendonpress.com
contact:	Pete
design service:	Yes
minimum run:	None
info:	Leaflets and flyers, posters up to large format.

Quotes can be given over email.

Coastline
784 Christchurch Road, Boscombe, Bournemouth, BH7 6DD
tel:	01202 302 378
design service:	Yes
minimum run:	None
info:	Posters up to A3. Digital and litho printing. Can

also do small and large runs of flyers.

Country Press (SW) Ltd.
1 Otter Court, Manaton Close, Exeter, EX2 8PF
tel:	01392 255 501
web:	ww.countrypressprint.co.uk
design service:	Yes
minimum run:	None
info:	Can produce posters and flyers. Large format

print machine, as well as digital facilities.

Distec Display Technology
Unit 1, Seavixen Industrial Estate, Wilverley Road, Christchurch, BH23 3RU
tel:	01202 470 196
design service:	Yes
minimum run:	None
info:	Digital and large format printing. Can meet all

your printing needs.

Excel The Office & Print Experts
24 Mannamead Road, Plymouth, PL4 7AA
tel:	01752 660 151
design service:	No
minimum run:	None
info:	Short run digital printing available.

First Impressions
18 Old Mill Road, Chelston, Torquay, TQ2 6AU
tel:	01803 605 394
design service:	Yes
minimum run:	None
info:	Digital and litho printing for leaflets and flyers.

GPDesign
2 Tekoa House, Alphinbrook Road East, Marsh Barton Trading Estate, Exeter, EX2 8QF
tel:	01392 255 501
email:	info@gpdesign.uk.com
web:	www.gpdesign.uk.com
design service:	Yes
minimum run:	100
info:	Posters and flyers can be printed digitally.

Green Ginger Studios
Unit 8a, The Old Dairy, Sancreed, Penzance, TR20 8QP
tel:	01736 811 118
email:	simon@blueiris.eclipse.co.uk
contact:	Simopn
design service:	Yes
minimum run:	10
info:	Design based print service. Can do short digital

runs of posters and flyers while it remains cost effective, switching to litho for larger runs.

Manor Printing Services (Wotton) Ltd.
Charfield Road, Kingswood, Wotton-Under-Edge, GL12 8RL
tel:	01453 843 891
fax:	01453 842 252
email:	enquiries@manorprinting.co.uk
web:	www.manorprinting.co.uk
contact:	Jim MacLeod
design service:	Yes
minimum run:	None
info:	Single to 5 colour printing. Posters and flyers.

Special print services. Band friendly.

Monkey Puzzle Repro Art
Unit 5, Mount Pleasant Eco Park, Chapel Hill, Porth Towen, TR4 8HL
tel:	01209 890 333
contact:	Eve Jemmett
design service:	Yes
minimum run:	10
info:	Design and print for posters up to A1.

Out Of Hand
Bristol
tel:	0117 907 1280
email:	info@outofhand.co.uk
web:	www.outofhand.co.uk
design service:	Yes
info:	Specialise in printing of promotional material

including banners, flyers, stickers and tickets. Short runs available. Hand-to-hand flyer distribution.Also offer design service. See relevant section for details.

Poole Instant Print
105-107 Commercial Road, Lower Parkstone, Poole, BH14 0JD
tel:	01202 740 321
email:	info@poole-instant-printing.com
design service:	Yes
minimum run:	None
info:	Posters up to A3 in-house, and up to A0

externally.

PP Printing
31a Bargates, Christchurch, Dorset, BH23 1QD
tel:	0870 855 0358
fax:	0870 855 0359
email:	christchurch@printing.com
web:	www.printing.com
design service:	Yes
minimum run:	250
info:	Part of Printing.com franchise. Offer full range

of printing services and can produce most items at reasonable price including stickers, leaflets and postcards. See website above for details of offers available.

Press To Print
Strathan House, Avon Street, Bath, BA1 1UN
tel:	01225 427 116
fax:	01225 445 715
email:	bath@presstoprint.co.uk
web:	www.presstoprint.co.uk
contact:	Vincent Cannella
design service:	Yes
minimum run:	None
info:	Happy to produce posters and flyers for bands

and musicians.

Print-Creative
7 Northumberland Buildings, Bath, BA1 2JB
tel:	0870 855 0386
fax:	0870 855 0387
email:	bath@printing.com
web:	www.printing.com
design service:	Yes
minimum run:	250
info:	Part of Printing.com franchise. Offer full range

of printing services and can produce most items at reasonable price including stickers, leaflets and postcards. See website above for details of offers available.

printing.com (Bournemouth)
288 Wallisdown Road, Bournemouth, BH11 8PN
tel:	0870 855 0366
fax:	0870 855 0367
email:	bournemouth@printing.com
web:	www.printing.com
design service:	Yes
minimum run:	250
info:	Printing.com is a large chain with branches all

over the UK. Offer full range of printing services and can produce most items at reasonable price including stickers, leaflets and postcards. For full list of stores see the above website.

Proprint 2K
Greenhayes, Elm Mill, Motcombe, Shaftesbury, SP7 9HL
tel:	01747 851 417
design service:	Yes
minimum run:	50
info:	Flyer printing, can be done digitally or

conventionally.

Severnprint Ltd.
Units 8-10, Ashville Road, Gloucester, GL2 5EU
tel:	01452 416 391
email:	info@severnprint.co.uk
web:	www.severnprint.co.uk
design service:	Yes
minimum run:	None
info:	Posters and flyers printed using both digital and

litho formats.

Sidford Print and Design Services
Post Office, School Street, Sidford, Sidmouth, EX10 9PF
tel:	01395 578 623
contact:	Tracey Aplin
design service:	Yes
info:	Posters up to A3, and flyers. Can do short runs

while it remains economical.

Sprint Signs & Graphics
18 Albany Road, Granby Industrial Estate, Weymouth, DT4 9TH
tel:	01305 761 027
design service:	Yes
minimum run:	Contact for details
info:	Digital and litho printing of posters and flyers.

Taylor Design & Print
106 Furnham Road, Chard, TA20 1BE
tel:	01460 679 58
fax:	01460 679 58
email:	malc@taylordesignandprint.co.uk
web:	www.taylordesignandprint.co.uk
contact:	Malcolm Taylor
design service:	Yes
minimum run:	None
info:	Posters, stickers and flyers. Large format printing,

digital and litho. Also provide wide range of promotional merchandise. Check relevant section for further information.

Top Coat Printers
84 Condor Close, Three Legged Cross, Wimborne, BH21 6SU
tel:	01202 820 959
design service:	Yes
minimum run:	None
info:	All types of printing including posters, flyers and

stickers.

WM Direct
24a East Reach, Taunton, Somerset, TA1 3EP
tel:	0870 855 0276
fax:	0870 855 0277
email:	taunton@printing.com
web:	www.printing.com
design service:	Yes
minimum run:	250
info:	Part of Printing.com franchise. Offer full range

of printing services and can produce most items at reasonable price including stickers, leaflets and postcards. See website above for details of offers available.

Zeralynx Print
Unit 11, Apple Business Centre, Off Bindon Road, Taunton, TA2 6BB
tel:	01823 251 888
email:	matt@zeralynx.co.uk
web:	www.zeralynx.co.uk
contact:	Matt
design service:	Yes
minimum run:	None
info:	Digital or litho printing for posters and flyers.

Zeta Printing Services
1 Reliance Works, Brigend, Stonehouse, GL10 2NG
tel:	01453 825 047
email:	sales@zetaprinting.co.uk
web:	www.zetaprinting.co.uk
design service:	Yes
minimum run:	None
info:	Conventional and digital printing. Can provide

posters, leaflets and flyers.

YORKSHIRE

A & R Tradeprint
515 Abbeydale Road, Sheffield, S7 1FU
tel:	0114 235 9900
fax:	0114 255 5236
email:	clive@arprintingservices.com
web:	www.arprintingservices.co.uk
contact:	Clive Jaques
design service:	Yes
minimum run:	None
info:	Digital and litho printing. Posters and flyers up to

A3 size.

Aceprint
Unit 1, Warneford Avenue, Ossett, WF12 7RD
tel:	01924 261 154
fax:	01924 280 310
design service:	Yes
minimum run:	None
info:	Aceprint specialise in printing posters, flyers and

CD inlays.

MUSIC SERVICES/RETAIL

Arundell Sinclair Ltd.
Wira House, West Park, Ring Road, Leeds, LS16 6EB
tel:	0113 275 7161
fax:	0113 275 9184
email:	arundellsinclair@aol.com
contact:	Ross Sinclair
design service:	Yes
minimum run:	250
info:	Will supply posters up to A1 size, and flyers

using digital and litho printing.

Colour It In
Unit 1, Hydro Business Park, Ripon Road, Harrogate, HG1 2BS
tel:	0800 542 0852
fax:	01423 858 801
email:	cii@harrogate.com
web:	www.colouritin.co.uk
contact:	Matthew Bourne
design service:	Yes
minimum run:	None
info:	Full colour digital specialists. Personal callers

welcome. Colour It In also offer full nationwide delivery.

Copy Shop (Chesterfield) Ltd.
23 Soresby Road, Chesterfield, S40 1JW
tel:	01246 273 044
fax:	01246 277 335
email:	kirsty@the-copy-shop.co.uk
web:	www.the-copy-shop.co.uk
contact:	Kirsty Barber
design service:	Yes
minimum run:	None
info:	Digital printing. Labels, stickers, posters, flyers

and tickets.

The Design & Print Project
2 The Courtyard, 27 The Village, Haxby, York, YO32 3HS
tel:	01904 768 899
fax:	01904 758 892
email:	info@thedpproject.com
web:	www.thedpproject.com
contact:	Helen Knutall
design service:	Yes
minimum run:	None
info:	Supply flyers and business cards. Also offer web

design services. Contact for further information.

The Display Link Ltd.
D2 Bradmarsh Way, Rotherham, S60 1BP
tel:	01709 836 123
fax:	01709 836 185
email:	studio@thedisplaylink.co.uk
web:	www.thedisplaylink.co.uk
contact:	Lorraine Crooks
design service:	No
minimum run:	None
info:	Digital and large format printing, ideal for

posters and banners.

DK Print Ltd.
Unit 8, Queens Square, Huddersfield Road, Honley, Holmfirth, HD9 6QZ
tel:	01484 304 304
email:	info@dkprint.co.uk
web:	www.dkprint.co.uk
contact:	Kathryn Wood
design service:	No
minimum run:	None
info:	Digital poster printing up to A3. Also print flyers

and business cards.

Docqwise
110a Albion Street, Leeds, LS2 8LA
tel:	0113 245 9585
fax:	0113 242 1299
email:	leeds@docqwise.co.uk
web:	www.docqwise.co.uk
contact:	Scott Thorgood
design service:	Yes
minimum run:	None
info:	Digital printing fior posters, flyers and stickers.

Large format.

Double Image
Burley Street, Elland, HX5 0AQ
tel:	01422 311 777
fax:	01422 311 888
email:	gary.pickles@doubleimageuk.com
web:	www.doubleimageuk.com
contact:	Gary Pickles
design service:	Yes
minimum run:	None
info:	Posters up to A0, digital laser printing up to A3.

Band friendly, call for a quote. Negotiable rates.

FedEx Kinko's
10 St. Paul's Street, Leeds, LS1 2LE
tel:	0113 236 4980
fax:	0113 236 4981
email:	leeds@fedexkinkos.co.uk
web:	www.fedexkinkos.co.uk
contact:	Andrew Overland
design service:	Yes
minimum run:	None
info:	Digital and litho printing. Posters, flyers,

business cards, signs and banners. Oversize printing (up to 60" wide).
Online printing. Free local delivery and full UK delivery.

G & L Services Ltd.
86 Harwood Street, Sheffield, S2 4SE
tel:	0114 275 4737
fax:	0114 272 9014
email:	glservices@tiscali.co.uk
contact:	Geoff Fearn
design service:	Yes
minimum run:	None
info:	Digital printing of posters. Up to 1500mm wide,

any length.

Hart & Clough Ltd.
Ezra House, Littlewood Drive, West 26 Business Park, Cleckheaton,
BD19 4TQ
tel:	01274 863 200
fax:	01274 863 201
email:	info@hartandclough.co.uk
web:	www.hartandclough.co.uk
design service:	Yes
minimum run:	None
info:	Litho printing for posters, CD covers, flyers and

leaflets.

Highlight Type Bureau Ltd.
Clifton House, 2 Clifton Villas, Bradford, BD8 7BY
tel:	01274 548 004
fax:	01274 543 005
email:	highlight.type@virgin.net
web:	www.highlight.co.uk
contact:	Angela Swaine
design service:	Yes
minimum run:	None
info:	Digital printing of posters, flyers and stickers.

J.W. Bullivant & Son
296 Bishopthorpe Road, York, YO23 1LG
tel:	01904 623 241
fax:	01904 621 670
email:	john@bwbullivant.fsnet.co.uk
web:	www.bullivantandson.co.uk
contact:	John Bullivant
design service:	Yes
minimum run:	None
info:	Litho printing. Will produce posters, flyers, CD

covers and tickets.

Jade Press
Unit 2, Eagle Industrial Estate, Torre Road, Leeds, LS9 7QL
tel:	0113 248 0939
fax:	0113 248 4609
email:	sales@jadepress.co.uk
web:	www.jadepress.co.uk
contact:	Glen Hauge
design service:	Yes
minimum run:	None
info:	Litho printing specialists.

John E. Wright (Hull)
6 Principal Trading Park, Scarborough Street, Hull, HU3 3EE
tel:	01482 308 621
fax:	01482 308 625
email:	hullsales@johnwright.com
web:	www.johnewright.com
design service:	No
minimum run:	None
info:	Posters, flyers and leaflets printed digitally. Up

to A0 size. See also listings for John E.Wright branches located in
Leicester, Nottingham, Coventry, Oxford and Derby.

John Siddall Printers Ltd.
Horncastle Street, Cleckheaton, BD19 3JL
tel:	01274 874 246
email:	jim@siddalls.co.uk
web:	www.siddalls.co.uk
contact:	Jim Frost
design service:	Yes
minimum run:	None
info:	Specialise in short run digital colour printing.

Economical service for quantities from 1 to 5000. Can cater for any size from A6 flyers, up to posters 1m wide by any length. Also produce CD labels, inlays and covers, as well as cassette inlays, VHS and DVD format labels and inlays, promotional flyers, plus artist photographs and postcards, all of which are ideally suited to the digital print process. Will also print self-adhesives for drum kits. For further details and pricing information contact Jim Frost.

K2 Digital Print
5 Louisa Street, Bradford, BD10 8NE
tel:	01274 410 333
fax:	01274 620 493
email:	info@k2digitalprint.com
web:	www.k2digitalprint.com
design service:	Yes
minimum run:	None
info:	Digital and litho printing. Posters, leaflets and flyers

Mercury Print & Packaging Ltd.
The Print Factory, Wood Lane, Leeds, LS12 6JY
tel:	0113 263 4463
fax:	0113 279 0310
email:	sales@mercury-print.co.uk
web:	www.mercury-print.co.uk
contact:	Roy Selby
design service:	Yes
minimum run:	None
info:	Provide range of printing services including digital and litho. Posters, flyers and packaging can be produced.

Moorprint
The Print Unit, Nile Road, Ilkley, LS29 8HJ
tel:	01943 609 760
fax:	01943 603 211
email:	info@moorprint.com
design service:	Yes
minimum run:	None
info:	Posters, flyers, leaflets, stickers. Digital or litho printing.

N.A. Screenprint Ltd.
Unit 4a, Portland Business Park, Richmond Park Road, Handsworth, Sheffield, S13 8HS
tel:	0114 242 1020
email:	nascreenprint@fsnet.co.uk
contact:	Neil Smith
design service:	Yes
minimum run:	None
info:	Digital printing for short runs, but specialists in screen printing. Ideal for banners, backdrops, stickers and posters.

Peter Turpin Associates
George Cayley Drive, Clifton Moor, York, YO30 4XE
tel:	01904 479 511
fax:	01904 690 248
email:	enquiry@pturpin-associates.co.uk
web:	www.pturpin-associates.co.uk
contact:	Simon Buckle
design service:	Yes
minimum run:	250
info:	High quality design and print suitable for posters, CD covers and flyers.

Platinum Print Ltd.
Park House, Hookstone Park, Harrogate, HG2 7DB
tel:	0800 652 2899
fax:	01423 886 072
email:	sales@platinumprint.com
web:	www.platinumprint.com
contact:	Mark Plummer
design service:	Yes
minimum run:	None
info:	Posters, flyers and CD covers. Digital and litho.

Print & Design Shop
279 Sharrow Vale Road, Sheffield, S11 8ZF
tel:	0114 267 9402
fax:	0114 267 9577
email:	a.lofthouse@btinternet.co.uk
web:	www.printanddesignshop.co.uk
contact:	Liz Mottram
design service:	Yes
minimum run:	None
info:	Digital and litho. Flyers, leaflets and banners, as well as posters up to A0 size. PC and Mac. Rates negotiable.

S.P.J. Marketing
Oak Lodge, 48 Wroot Road, Finningley, Doncaster, DN9 3DR
tel:	01302 772 288
fax:	01302 772 208
email:	simon@spjmarketing.co.uk
web:	www.spjmarketing.co.uk
contact:	Simon Judge
design service:	Yes
minimum run:	None
info:	SPJ will print posters, flyers, CD inlays and stickers.

Shipley Print Co.
Hirst Wood Works, Hirst Wood Road, Shipley, BD18 4BU
tel:	01274 530 041
fax:	01274 822 022
design service:	Yes
minimum run:	250
info:	Digital and litho printing specialists.

Xpress
Springhead Mills, Springfield Road, Leeds, LS20 9BP
tel:	01943 870 321
fax:	01943 876 027
email:	mail@xpressonline.co.uk
web:	www.xpressonline.co.uk
contact:	Lee Pearce
design service:	Yes
minimum run:	None
info:	Will produce posters, flyers, CD covers using digital and litho printing.

NORTHERN IRELAND

Action Press (NI) Ltd.
Unit 15-16, Down Business Park, 46 Belfast Road, Downpatrick, BT30 9UP
tel:	028 4483 9090
fax:	028 4483 8877
email:	info@actionpress.co.uk
web:	www.actionpress.co.uk
design service:	Yes
minimum run:	None
info:	Cost effective printing solutions including colour litho and digital services.

Anderson Print
32 Maynooth Road, Richhill, Armagh, County Armagh, BT61 9RG
tel:	028 3887 1560
design service:	No
minimum run:	None
info:	B&W print. Can provide flyers and leaflets.

B.E. Print
29a Charlemont Street, Moy, Dungannon, County Tyrone, BT71 7SL
tel:	028 8778 4822
web:	www.beprint.co.uk
design service:	No
minimum run:	250
info:	Will print A5 and A4 flyers, as well as CD covers.

B.J. McNally
33 Patrick Street, Newry, County Down, BT35 8EB
tel:	028 3026 7413
web:	www.bjmcnally.com
design service:	Yes
minimum run:	50
info:	Colour and commercial printing of variety of materials including CD covers, flyers and posters.

Bradbury Graphics
Bradbury Bureau, Equality House, 6-14 Donegall Pass, Belfast, BT7 1BS
tel:	028 9023 3535
fax:	028 9057 2057
email:	production@bradbury-graphics.co.uk
web:	www.bradbury-graphics.co.uk
design service:	Yes
minimum run:	None
info:	Bradbury Graphics incorporates art gallery and supply store, as well as digital printing services. Can cater for short runs of posters, flyers, CD covers and other promotional material.

Century 23
2nd Floor, 111A Woodstock Road, Belfast, BT6 8AB
tel: 0871 700 0080
email: andrew@century-23.com
web: www.century-23.com
contact: Andrew
design service: Yes
info: Century 23 have been working in close association with the live music, clubbing, entertainment, and leisure industries across Britain for 7 years providing printed promotional products including flyers, posters and tickets. Artwork can be submitted online or through the post. Artwork design and CD/vinyl duplication also available. See relevant sections for details. Offices in London and Edinburgh.

Clanrye Press Printers
Unit 18, Greenback Industrial Estate, Rampart Road, Newry, County Down, BT34 2QU
tel: 028 3026 2570
fax: 028 3026 0451
email: info@clanryepress.com
web: www.clanryepress.com
design service: Yes
minimum run: None
info: Single sheet litho and digital printers. Full range of stationery available.

Copyworld
6 Merville Garden Village, Shore Road, Newtownabbey, County Antrim, BT37 9TF
tel: 028 9080 0500
fax: 028 9087 9087
email: info@copyworld.co.uk
web: www.copyworld.co.uk
design service: No
minimum run: None
info: Provide conventional copying and large format printing. Other related services including photocopying, binding and lamination.

Dataplus Print & Design
13 Hill Street, Dunmurry, Belfast, BT17 0AD
tel: 028 9030 1717
design service: Yes
minimum run: None
info: Digital printing service.

DJ Print
29e Church Street, Maghera, County Londonderry, BT13 1GB
tel: 028 7964 4782
fax: 028 7964 4834
email: sales@djprint.com
web: www.djprint.com
design service: Yes
minimum run: None
info: Full range of printing services from A5 to A0 sizes. Commercial, large format and full colour digital printing. No minimum run on A3 posters.

Edenderry Print
Unit 6-8, Agnes Street Industrial Estate, Crumlin Road, Belfast, BT13 1GB
tel: 028 9074 4782
design service: Yes
minimum run: 50
info: Litho printing of posters, flyers and leaflets.

Glen Print
47 Cardinal O'Fiaich Square, Crossmalgen, Newry, County Down, BT35 9AA
tel: 028 3086 8004
design service: No
minimum run: None
info: Glen Print can produce posters, flyers and leaflets.

Good News Centre
7 Monaghan Street, Newry, County Down, BT35 6BB
tel: 028 3026 9555
email: jimneagle2@btconnect.com
web: www.goodnewscentre.co.uk
design service: Yes
minimum run: None
info: Specialise in one-off poster printing. Also print leaflets, flyers and business cards. Promotional items available. See listing in relevant section.

House of Print & Design
Unit 3, Greystone Road, Antrim, County Antrim, BT41 1JZ
tel: 028 9446 0072
design service: Yes
minimum run: None
info: Posters, flyers and CD covers available

J & D Printers
138-140 Ravenhill Road, Belfast, County Antrim, BT6 8ED
tel: 028 9073 1368
design service: No
minimum run: 2000
info: Will print flyers and leaflets for clients of all sizes.

J. D. Print
The Stables, 26 Bridge Street, Strabane, County Tyrone, BT82 9AE
tel: 028 7188 5585
design service: Yes
minimum run: None
info: J.D. Print can supply 100 posters, black on A3 day-glo paper priced at £40.

J.J. Gill
2 Dunree House, Thomas Street, Dungannon, County Tyrone, BT70 1HN
tel: 028 8772 5109
design service: Yes
minimum run: None
info: Will print flyers and posters up to A3 size.

JPP Printing
46 James Street, Cookstown, BT80 8LT
tel: 028 8676 6377
email: printroom@thetwopatricks.org
design service: No
minimum run: None
info: Posters, flyers, business cards and leaflets.

Komodo
79 Magheraconluce Road, Hillsborough, County Down, BT26 6PR
tel: 028 9268 8285
email: info@komodorecordings.com
web: www.komodorecordings.com
design service: Yes
minimum run: None
info: Komodo provide printing services for posters and flyers. Also design and produce promotional items. Other services offered include recording facilities, mastering and duplication services, drum tuition, graphic design, as well as organising gigs. See entries in relevant sections for further information.

Laganside Print & Heritage Ltd.
124 Grand Streets, Lisburn, County Antrim, BT27 4UE
tel: 028 9266 8316
email: lagansideprint@yahoo.co.uk
design service: No
minimum run: 1000
info: Flyer and CD cover printing. Posters up to A3 size. Next day turnaround. All digital print.

MC Print & Design
Unit 6, Boucher Business Centre, Apollo Road, Belfast, County Antrim, BT12 6HP
tel: 028 9068 3343
fax: 028 9068 3862
email: info@mc-print.co.uk
design service: Yes
minimum run: 500
info: Commercial printing of posters and flyers. Litho printing up to A3 size.

Mooney Media
Unit 45 Banbridge Enterprise Centre, Scarva Road Industrial Estate, Scarva Road, Banbridge, County Down, BT32 3QD
tel: 028 40660 390
fax: 028 4062 8392
email: banbridge@printing.com
web: www.printing.com
design service: Yes

M-Print
Unit 1, Kilkeel Business Park, 3 Moor Road, Kilkeel, Newry, County Down, BT34 4NG
tel: 028 4176 2000
design service: No
minimum run: None
info: 50 to 100 full colour posters for £1 each. Flyers and leaflets also available. Digital and litho formats.

New Century Printers
1 Sugarhouse Quay, Newry, County Down, BT35 6HZ
tel: 028 3026 7124
email: newcentury@digi-cube.com
design service: Yes
minimum run: None
info: Posters, flyers and CD covers. Digital and litho printing up to A3 size, fast turnaround.

One Stop Design & Display
Unit 9 McKibben House, Eastbank Road, Carryduff, Belfast, County Antrim, BT8 8BD
tel: 028 9081 2191
design service: Yes
minimum run: None
info: Digital printing, mainly large format posters but they can print flyers and CD covers. They also have a banner design service.

P & P Print
62 Trench Road, Newtownabbey, County Antrim, BT36 4TY
tel: 028 9084 9085
design service: No
minimum run: 1000
info: Lithographers specialising in large runs of printed items, such as posters.

Prestige Print & Design
Unit 6, ITEC Business Park, 52 Armagh Road, Newry, BT35 6HL
tel: 028 3026 6118
email: info@prestige-print.com
design service: Yes
minimum run: None
info: Posters, flyers, business cards, all full colour. Digital, litho and large format printing, can print any size required.

The Print Factory
Unit 1, Lackaghboy Industrial Estate, Temp Road, Enniskillen, County Fermanagh, BT74 4RL
tel: 028 6632 6960
fax: 028 6632 8389
email: info@theprintfactory.com
web: www.theprintfactory.com
design service: Yes
minimum run: None
info: Digital, litho and large format printing. CD covers, posters, flyers, business cards. Some items do have a minimum run, but always an affordable option. Ring for more information.

Print Library
Unit F3, Dundonald Enterprise Park, Carrowreagh Road, Dundonald, Belfast, BT16 1QT
tel: 028 9048 9800
design service: Yes
minimum run: None
info: Posters, flyers and leaflets.

Priory Press
31a Hibernia Street, Holywood, BT18 9JE
tel: 028 9042 2918
email: info@priorypress.net
web: www.priorypress.net
design service: Yes
minimum run: None
info: Short run colour print and commercial litho printing.

Proctor's
207 Castlereagh Road, Belfast, BT5 5FH
tel: 028 9045 6582
email: proctors@btclick.com
design service: Yes
minimum run: 250
info: Full colour digital printing. Proctor's can print most sizes. Posters, flyers and CD covers. Offer a student discount on art and craft supplies.

Quick Copy
28 Frances Street, Newtownards, County Down, BT23 7DN
tel: 028 9182 2355
design service: No
minimum run: 500
info: Digital and litho print. Posters, flyers and CD covers.

R Christie & Son
1 Meeting Street, Magherafelt, County Londonderry, BT42 6BN
tel: 028 7963 2407
design service: No
minimum run: 50
info: Lithographic printing, posters and flyers up to A3 size.

R.C.D. Digital & Lithographic Printers Ltd.
Resource Centre, Carnhill, Londonderry, County Londonderry, BT48 8BA
tel: 028 7135 6115
design service: Yes
minimum run: None
info: Posters, flyers and CD covers, printed digitally and lithographically.

Reid & Wright
62 Clifton Street, Belfast, County Antrim, BT13 1AB
tel: 028 9032 5524
design service: Yes
minimum run: None
info: Posters up to A3 size, as well as flyers, CD covers and leaflets.

Riverside Print
181 Ormeau Road, Belfast, BT7 1SQ
tel: 020 9043 7808
fax: 028 9043 7811
email: unapurdy@hotmail.com
web: www.riversideprint.co.uk
contact: Una Purdy
design service: No
minimum run: None
info: Digital and litho printing. Can do large and short runs on flyers.

Romac Press Ltd.
Unit 16, Bloomfield Commercial Centre, 5 Factory Street, Belfast, County Antrim, BT5 5AW
tel: 028 9045 4537
design service: Yes
minimum run: 500
info: Full colour printing service. Flyers and poster from A3 size.

Sam Hutchinson & Co.
265-269 Shore Road, Belfast, BT15 3PW
tel: 028 9077 4944
design service: Yes
minimum run: None
info: Posters and flyer printing using both digital and litho formats.

Trimprint Ltd.
36 Up English Street, Armagh, County Armagh, BT61 7BE
tel: 028 3752 2063
email: jeremy@trimprint.com
design service: Yes
minimum run: None
info: A2 and A3 posters, full colour. Digital and litho. Glossy CD covers.

Tyrone Printing Company Ltd.
58 Scotch Street, Dungannon, County Tyrone, BT70 1BD
tel: 028 8772 2274
design service: Yes
minimum run: 500
info: Full print service. Posters, flyers, leaflets and other items.

Ulster Services
B107 Portview Trade Centre, 310 Newtownards Road, Belfast, County Antrim, BT4 1HE
tel: 028 9073 8472
design service: No
minimum run: None
info: High speed laser print and lithography. Flyers and CD covers.

Xpress Printing
51 Mallusk Road, Newtownabbey, County Antrim, BT36 4PU
tel: 0870 855 0274
fax: 0870 855 0275
email: newtownabbey@printing.com
web: www.printing.com
design service: Yes

SCOTLAND

662C
86 Cadzow Street, Hamilton, South Lanarkshire, ML3 6DS
tel: 0870 950 1532
fax: 0870 950 1533
email: hamilton@printing.com
web: www.printing.com
design service: Yes
minimum run: 250
info: Part of Printing.com franchise. Offer full range of printing services and can produce most items at reasonable price including stickers, leaflets and postcards. See website above for details of offers available.

Academy Press
Unit 10, Abbotsford Rise, Dedridge, Livingston, West Lothian, EH54 6QD
tel: 0870 950 7767
email: westlothian@printing.com
web: www.printing.com
design service: Yes
minimum run: 250
info: Part of Printing.com franchise. Offer full range of printing services and can produce most items at reasonable price including stickers, leaflets and postcards. See website above for details of offers available.

Albert E. Parker
340-350 King Street, Aberdeen, Aberdeenshire, AB24 5BJ
tel: 01224 635 835
fax: 01224 647 952
email: sales@aeparker.co.uk
web: www.aeparker.co.uk
design service: Yes
minimum run: 500
info: Posters up to A3, flyers and business cards.

Alphagraphics
9c South Gyle Cresent, Edinburgh, EH12 9EB
tel: 0131 316 1800
email: edin010@alphagraphics.co.uk
web: www.alphagraphics.co.uk/uk010
contact: Lynsey Levy
design service: Yes
minimum run: None
info: One-stop print shop providing digital, litho, large format and high speed duplicating services.

Applecroft
76 Constitution Street, Edinburgh, Midlothian, EH6 6RP
tel: 0131 561 4444
fax: 0131 561 4447
email: post@applecroft.com
web: www.applecroft.com
design service: Yes
minimum run: 5000
info: Specialise is large print runs. Litho, screen, digital and web print.

Beaver Printing
Unit 3, 17 Avenue Street, Stewarton, Kilmarnock, Ayrshire, KA3 5AP
tel: 01560 485 412
design service: Yes
minimum run: None
info: Will print posters, flyers and leaflets, as well as CD inlays. Digital and offset printing available.

Big Byte Production
PO Box 23655, Edinburgh, EH6 5ZX
tel: 0131 554 6611
email: info@bigbyteproduction.com
web: www.bigbyteproduction.com
contact: Eddie MacNaughton
design service: Yes
minimum run: None
info: Big Byte can print posters, flyers and postcards. Digital or litho. Local delivery service included.

Birnam CD
Station Road, Birnam, Dunkeld, PH8 0DS
tel: 01350 727 158
fax: 01350 727 161
email: info@birnamcd.com
web: www.birnamcd.com
contact: Martin Hadden
design service: Yes
minimum run: None
info: Birnam will print 50 free posters if you use their CD duplication service. See listing in relevant section, and contact for further details.

Bridge Imaging Group Ltd.
65 Deveron Road, Troon, Ayrshire, KA10 7EG
tel: 01292 679 555
design service: No
minimum run: None
info: Large format digital printing of posters and banners.

Century 23
17-19 Maritime Lane, Edinburgh, EH6 6RZ
tel: 0871 700 0080
email: andrew@century-23.com
web: www.century-23.com
contact: Andrew
design service: Yes
minimum run: Varies
info: Century 23 have been working in close association with the live music, clubbing, entertainment, and leisure industries across Britain for 7 years providing printed promotional products including flyers, posters and tickets. Artwork can be submitted online or through the post. Artwork design and CD/vinyl duplication also available. See relevant section for details. Offices in Belfast and London.

Claremont Image & Print
17 Park Circus Place, Glasgow, Lanarkshire, G3 6AH
tel: 0141 332 8189
email: info@glasgowprinters.co.uk
design service: Yes
minimum run: None
info: Will produce flyers, posters and business cards.

The Color Co.
27 George Street, Edinburgh, EH2 2PA
tel: 0870 855 0252
fax: 0870 855 0253
email: georgestreet@printing.com
web: www.printing.com
design service: Yes
minimum run: 250
info: Part of Printing.com franchise. Offer full range of printing services and can produce most items at reasonable price including stickers, leaflets and postcards. See website above for details of offers available.

Compass Quick Print
Unit 1, Victoria House, St. Andrew Street, Greenock, PA15 1HD
tel: 01475 787 335
contact: Chris Bonnar
design service: Yes
minimum run: None
info: Litho printing. Posters, flyers, postcards plus more.

Copymade Ltd.
3 West Midland Street, Edinburgh, EH3 9DJ
tel: 0131 229 5431
fax: 0131 229 5431
email: copymade@btconnect.com
web: www.copymade.co.uk
contact: Grant McKeeman
design service: Yes
minimum run: None
info: Posters and flyers. If it can be printed on, Copymade can deal with it.

Creeds
9 Main Street, Golspie, KW10 6RA
tel: 01408 633 224
fax: 01408 633 225
contact: Jonathan Creed
design service: No
minimum run: None
info: A0 to A3 plan copying (B&W) and digital full colour printing.

Digital Typeline Publications Ltd.
Unit 2d, West Telferton Industrial Estate, Portobello, Edinburgh, Midlothian, EH7 6UL
tel: 0131 657 1001
design service: No
minimum run: None
info: Professional full colour digital printing. For short runs from 1 to 1000. Specialists in printing all types of short run orders from flyers to large format posters

Dual-Print
Unit 40b, Swanfield Industrial Estate, Edinburgh, EH6 5RX
tel: 0131 553 5973
fax: 0131 553 4824
email: info@dualprint.com
web: www.dualprint.com
contact: Dave Regan
design service: Yes
minimum run: None
info: Band friendly poster and flyer printers.

Exacta Print (Glasgow)
92 West Regent Street, Glasgow, Lanarkshire, G2 2RQ
tel:	0141 248 6802
email:	printsales@reid-print-group.co.uk
web:	www.jrreid.com
design service:	Yes
minimum run:	None
info:	Large format printing, digital and litho. Part of J.R. Reid print & Media Group.

Excel Images
193 Dumbarton Road, Clydebank, G81 4XJ
tel:	0141 951 4300
fax:	0141 951 8173
email:	excelimages@btclick.com
contact:	Bradley
design service:	Yes
minimum run:	None
info:	All digital full colour printing. Also offer t-shirt printing service. See entry in Promotional Merchandise section.

Gilmour Print
Irvinehill, Stewarton, Kilmarnock, Ayrshire, KA3 3EL
tel:	01294 850 217
fax:	01294 850 444
email:	enquiries_web1@ictus.co.uk
web:	www.gilmourprint.co.uk
design service:	Yes
minimum run:	100
info:	Digital and litho printing for flyers and posters.

Glasgowprint
Unit 3, Huntershill Business Centre, 25 Auchinairn Road, Bishopbriggs, Glasgow, G64 1RX
tel:	0870 855 0408
fax:	0870 855 0409
email:	bishopbriggs@printing.com
web:	www.printing.com
design service:	Yes
minimum run:	250
info:	Part of Printing.com franchise. Offer full range of printing services and can produce most items at reasonable price including stickers, leaflets and postcards. See website above for details of offers available.

Graphic Impressions Printers
Unit 27/2, Hardengreen Industrial Estate, Eskbank, Dalkeith, Midlothian, EH22 3NX
tel:	0131 654 0521
fax:	0131 454 0301
email:	enquiries@giprinting.co.uk
web:	www.giprinting.co.uk
design service:	Yes
minimum run:	500
info:	Design, typesetting, printing and finishing. Minimum cost is £240, which would get you 500 A3 posters.

Greenprint Ltd.
49-51 St. Leonard's Street, Edinburgh, EH8 9QN
tel:	0131 662 0302
fax:	0131 662 1900
email:	info@greenprint.co.uk
web:	www.greenprint.co.uk
design service:	Yes
minimum run:	250
info:	Specialise in full colour and spot colour printing. Can cater for large quantities, contact for a quote. Will produce posters and flyers.

HCV Design & Print
91 Alexander Street, Airdrie, ML6 0BD
tel:	01236 766 699
fax:	01236 766 644
contact:	Vicky O'Hare
design service:	Yes
minimum run:	None
info:	Litho and digital printing of flyers and posters.

Hot Off The Press
2 Turnbull Way, Livingston, West Lothian, EH54 8RB
tel:	01506 441 499
fax:	01506 442 072
email:	frazer@hotp.org.uk
web:	www.hotp.org.uk
design service:	Yes
minimum run:	None
info:	A5 flyers and business cards. Also produce other promotional material. See listing in Promotional Merchandise section for details.

JR Reid Print & Media Group Ltd.
79-109 Glasgow Road, Glasgow, Lanarkshire, G72 0LY
tel:	01698 826 000
fax:	01698 824 944
email:	printsales@reid-print-group.co.uk
web:	www.jrreid.com
design service:	Yes
minimum run:	None
info:	Large format printing, digital and litho.

Ken Duncan Print & Design
164 Blackness Road, Dundee, DD1 5PQ
tel:	01382 566 164
fax:	01382 566 164
email:	kendun2@btconnect.com
contact:	Ken
design service:	Yes
minimum run:	None
info:	Poster and flyer printing. Also offer many promotional items such as keyrings, balloons and magnets.

Miller Reprographics Ltd.
21-22 Charing Cross Mansions, 30 St. George's Road, Glasgow, G3 6UJ
tel:	0141 331 5252
email:	miller_repro@btconnect.com
design service:	No
minimum run:	None
info:	Digital printing and CD duplication services.

Minuteman Press
122 King Street, Aberdeen, AB24 5BB
tel:	01224 561 700
fax:	01224 643 080
email:	aberdeen@minutemanpress.com
web:	www.aberdeen.minutemanpress.com
contact:	Alex Keith
design service:	Yes
minimum run:	None
info:	Litho and digital printing. Posters, flyers, CD covers and CDs available.

Panache Print
129 Chalmers Street, Dunfermline, Fife, KY12 8DQ
tel:	01383 737 215
email:	jazreid@aol.com
design service:	No
minimum run:	500
info:	Panache offer litho printing for flyers, posters and business cards.

The Print & Stationery Office
66 Crossgate, Cupar, KY15 5HS
tel:	01334 655 776
fax:	01334 655 077
email:	thepandsoffice@aol.com
design service:	Yes
minimum run:	Varies
info:	Digital colour copying and print. Minimum run varies depending on item, 1000 for A6 size and 500 for A5 size.

Print Vision Ltd.
Unit 12, Castlebrae Business Centre, Peffer Place, Edinburgh, EH16 4BB
tel:	0131 661 8855
fax:	0131 661 2639
email:	print_vision@btconnect.com
contact:	Ross Davidson
design service:	Yes
minimum run:	None
info:	Posters, flyers and CD covers. Digital and offset printing. Band friendly.

printing.com (Edinburgh)
8 Home Street, Edinburgh, EH3 9LY
tel:	0870 855 0440
email:	edinburgh@printing.com
web:	www.printing.com
contact:	Sumon
design service:	Yes
minimum run:	250
info:	Special offers for unsigned bands, call for details. Printing.com is a large chain with branches all over the UK. Offer full range of printing services and can produce most items at reasonable price including stickers, leaflets and postcards. For full list of stores see the above website.

Printtec Online Ltd.
Scottish Media Village, 118 North Main Street, Carronshore, Falkirk, Stirlingshire, FK2 8HR
tel:	01324 552 102
email:	sales@printtec.co.uk
web:	www.printtec.co.uk
design service:	Yes
minimum run:	100
info:	Specialise in business cards. Can produce 250 for £29.

Radiant Design
35 Glebe Street, Hamilton, Lanarkshire, ML3 6PR
tel: 01698 303 624
design service: Yes
minimum run: None
info: Radiant Design can print posters up to A2 size, plus flyers and business cards. Specialists in short run digital printing.

Robert Parker Printers
Unit 5 & 6, Dunisnane Avenue, Dunsinane Industrial Estate, Dundee, DD2 3QN
tel: 01382 858 666
fax: 01382 833 995
email: enquiries@robertparker.co.uk
web: www.robertparker.co.uk
design service: Yes
minimum run: None
info: Litho printers and total image solutions.

Small Print
215 King Street, Castle Douglas, Kirkcudbrightshire, DG7 1DT
tel: 01556 503 718
fax: 01556 503 915
email: small.print@todnet.demon.co.uk
contact: Liz Stansfield
design service: Yes
minimum run: None
info: Small printing and photocopying facility.

Smart Design & Print Ltd.
Unit 11, West Gorgie Parks, Hutchinson Road, Edinburgh, EH14 1UT
tel: 0131 538 8020
fax: 0131 538 8050
email: sales@smartdesignandprint.com
web: www.smartdesignandprint.com
contact: Donna Smart
design service: Yes
minimum run: None
info: Design and print specialists. High quality spot-colour printing from one to full colour. Can cater for low runs with quick turnaround. Posters, flyers and CD covers available.

Square Peg Print Ltd.
62 Muirfield Road, Cumbernauld, Glasgow, G68 0EX
tel: 07766 833 615
fax: 01236 739 046
email: squarepegprint@aol.com
contact: Ken Rankin
design service: Yes
minimum run: None
info: Digital and litho printing from A4 to B1. Posters, flyers and CD covers available.

Tangerine
93-97 St. George's Street, Glasgow, G3 6JA
tel: 0141 946 2500
email: enquires@tangerine-ltd.co.uk
web: www.tangerine-ltd.co.uk
contact: James Harrop
design service: Yes
minimum run: None
info: Posters, flyers on both digital or litho formats. Can print up to A0 posters and offer a 10% discount for unsigned bands. Design and CD duplication services also available. See relevant listings for more information.

West Port Print & Design
14a Argyle Street, St. Andrews, Fife, KY16 9BP
tel: 01334 477 135
fax: 01334 472 072
email: info@westportprint.co.uk
web: www.westportprint.co.uk
design service: Yes
minimum run: None
info: Digital and litho printing for posters, flyers, labels and business cards, as well as any other promotional material.

Wishaw Printing
84 Stewarton Street, Wishaw, Lanarkshire, ML2 8AG
tel: 01698 357 223
email: printsales@reid-print-group.co.uk
web: www.jrreid.com
design service: Yes
minimum run: None
info: Large format printing on digital and litho. Part of J. Reid Printing Group.

Xpress Image Communication
61 Queen Street, Edinburgh, EH2 4NA
tel: 0131 226 2913
fax: 0131 226 7063
email: sales@xic.com
web: www.xic.com
contact: Pauline Haddow
design service: Yes
minimum run: None
info: Posters, flyers and CD covers. Digital and offset printing.

WALES

Beacon Printers Ltd.
Leyshons Buildings, Cornerswell Road, Penarth, CF64 2XS
tel: 02920 708 415
fax: 02920 703 754
email: sales@beaconprinters.co.uk
web: www.beaconprinters.co.uk
design service: Yes
minimum run: None
info: Litho and digital printers. Posters, flyers and CD inlays. Stickers, including vinyl and silk.

Beta Promotions
Unit 14, Lord Aurther Rank Centre, Trostre Road, Llanelli, SA14 9RA
tel: 01554 771 199
fax: 01554 778 333
email: enquiries@betapromotions.co.uk
web: www.betapromotions.co.uk
design service: Yes
minimum run: None
info: Will print flyers, as well as posters up to A3. Laminated business cards ideal for promoting products and events from £15 per 100.

Capper Print Ltd.
Lanelay Road Industrial Estate, Talbot Green, Pontyclun, Mid Glamorgan, CF72 8XX
tel: 01443 235 217
email: sales@capperprint.co.uk
web: www.capperprint.co.uk
design service: Yes
minimum run: None
info: Posters, flyers and CD inlays. Can source ticket printing.

Colwyn Business Services
12 Ffordd Bugail, Colwyn Bay, Clwyd, LL29 8TN
tel: 01492 513 758
design service: Yes
minimum run: None
info: Poster and flyer printing. Also provide photocopying service.

Craig-y-Don Printing Works Ltd.
23 Queens Road, Craig-y-Don, Llandudno, Gwynedd, LL30 1AZ
tel: 01492 877 119
design service: Yes
minimum run: 500
info: Posters, flyers and postcards.

CTA Print
1 New Road, Cockett, Swansea, SA2 0GA
tel: 01792 589 893
design service: Yes
minimum run: 1000
info: Posters (up to A3) and flyers (A5 and A6) in B&W or black on one colour. Full colour available on short runs. CD inlays.

Gemini Digital Colour Ltd.
North Road, Bridgend Industrial Estate, Bridgend, CF31 3TP
tel: 01656 652 447
fax: 01656 661 266
email: info@geminidigitalcolour.co.uk
web: www.geminidigitalcolour.co.uk
design service: No
minimum run: None
info: Short run specialists, maximum run of 1000. Poster, flyers and tickets. CD inlays and labels. Range of promotional items available.

beacon digital offers a wide range of new solutions for printing full colour, high quality, low volume runs at affordable prices

- cd design and print
- flyers
- vinyl labels
- programmes
- posters

Leyshons Buildings Cornerswell Road Penarth Vale of Glamorgan CF64 2XS
Telephone: +44 (0)29 2070 8415 Facsimile: +44 (0)29 2070 3754
ISDN: +44 (0)29 2071 0214 Email: sales@beacon-digital.com
www.beaconprinters.co.uk

Graphic Realm
35 Convent Street, Waun Wen, Swansea, SA1 2BX
tel: 01792 473 192
email: studio@graphic-realm.com
web: www.graphic-realm.com
design service: Yes
minimum run: None
info: Poster, flyers, postcards and business cards. CD inlays and tickets. Banners and backdrops. Range of promotional items including wallets, mugs and bags.

Graphics Service
The Arts & Social Studies Library, Corbett Road, Cardiff, CF10 3XT
tel: 02920 874 461
design service: No
minimum run: None
info: Photocopying, colour printing, scanning and large format (up to A0) copying. Can also print t-shirts. See relevant section for more details.

John Livsey Printers
Unit 6, Gabalfa Workshops, Clos Menter, Cardiff, CF14 3AY
tel: 02920 617 744
design service: Yes
minimum run: None
info: Posters, flyers and CD inlays. Litho-printing up to A2.

Kall Kwik
4 Derwen Road, Bridgend, Mid Glamorgan, CF31 1LH
tel: 01656 649 660
email: via website
web: www.kallkwik.co.uk
design service: Yes
minimum run: 10
info: Posters up to A3, plus flyers and CD inlays. See website above for full list of Kall Kwik branches throughout the UK.

Kingsbridge Print Ltd.
22-24 West Street, Gorseinon, Swansea, SA4 4AA
tel: 01792 897 321
design service: Yes
minimum run: Call for details
info: Poster, flyer and CD inlay print.

Lazer Type
Unit 6, Clwyd Court 2, Rhosddu Inustrial Estate, Rhosddu, Wrexham, LL11 4YL
tel: 01978 265 333
email: kevin@lazertype.freeserve.co.uk
design service: Yes
minimum run: None
info: Poster, flyers and postcards. Short runs available. Fast turnaround.

Maxwell Publications
Unit 19, Pinfold Workshops, Pinfold Lane Industrial Estate, Buckley, Clwyd, CH7 3PL
tel: 01244 547 724
email: maxwell.pub@btconnect.com
design service: Yes
minimum run: None
info: Flyers, posters and CD inlays. Range of promotional items including mugs, pens and mousemats. CD duplication also available. See relevant section for details.

Precision Print Ltd.
Rear of 1, Pentrepoeth Road, Morriston, Swansea, SA6 6AA
tel: 01792 414 040
fax: 01792 414 242
email: info@precisionprint.co.uk
web: www.precisionprint.co.uk
design service: Yes
info: Leaflets, flyers and posters, plus magazines and brochures. Also provide design services. See listing in relevant section for more information.

Print Shop
65 Robinson Street, Llanelli, Dyfed, SA15 1TT
tel: 01554 770 356
design service: Yes
minimum run: None
info: Poster and flyer printing, single to full colour.

Prism Print & Design Ltd.
Unit 14, Woodlands Workshops, Coed Cae Lane, Pontyclun, CF72 8DW
tel: 0808 197 0709
email: sales@prismprint.co.uk
web: www.prismprint.co.uk
design service: Yes
minimum run: 1000 (flyers)
info: Full colour poster and flyer printing. Can also
provide a range of promotional items including t-shirts and patches. See
relevant section for details.

South Wales Print Services Ltd.
Unit 9b, Enterprise Way, Newport, Gwent, NP20 2AQ
tel: 01633 216 060
email: enquiry@southwalesprint.co.uk
web: www.southwalesprint.co.uk
design service: Yes
minimum run: None
info: Poster and flyer print, CD inlays and labels.
CD on-body printing. Also offer CD duplication service. See relevant
section for details.

Zipprint
62 High Street, Bangor, Gwynedd, LL57 1NR
tel: 01248 355 500
email: mail@zipprint.co.uk
web: www.zipprint.co.uk
design service: Yes
minimum run: None
info: Posters (up to A0), flyers and postcards. CD
inlays and labels. Encapsulation, photocopying, both colour and B&W.

MUSIC SERVICES/RETAIL

3.11 PRESS/PR/PLUGGERS

EAST of ENGLAND 323 GREATER LONDON 323 MIDLANDS 328 NORTHEAST 328 NORTHWEST 329
SOUTHEAST 329 SOUTHWEST 331 YORKSHIRE 331 NORTHERN IRELAND 331 SCOTLAND 332 WALES 332

EAST of ENGLAND

Caragan Ltd.
5 The Meadows, Worlington, Suffolk, IP28 8SH
tel: 01638 717 390
fax: 0870 132 9753
email: info@caragan.com
web: www.caragan.co.uk
radio plugger: Yes
national coverage: Yes
info: Caragan charge £30 for promotion of a 3 track demo to industry professionals including labels, publishers, agents and promoters. See website for further details.

Frontier Promotions
The Grange, Cockley Cley Road, Hillborough, Thetford, Norfolk, IP26 5BT
tel: 01760 756 394
fax: 01760 756 398
email: sue@frontieruk.fsnet.co.uk
contact: Sue Williams
radio plugger: No
national coverage: No
info: Specialise in everything from Roots to Rock promotion, which sometimes crosses over into the mainstream. Cover all areas of promotion including press, TV, radio and specialised press.

Quite Great Publicity
Suite 1c, Langford Arch, London Road, Cambridge, CB2 4EG
tel: 01223 830 111
email: pete@quitegreat.co.uk
web: www.quitegreat.co.uk
contact: Pete Basset
radio plugger: Yes
national coverage: No
info: Press promotion including student press and fanzines plus arrange radio interviews and TV coverage. Promote on a national and regional basis in all areas of music. Currently working with unsigned bands and also established artists such as Chris Rea, Stevie Wonder, Van Morrison and Brian Eno.

GREATER LONDON

Alan James PR
60 Weston Street, London, SE1 3QJ
tel: 020 7403 9999
email: promo@ajpr.co.uk
web: www.ajpr.co.uk
contact: Alan James
radio plugger: No
national coverage: No
info: Mainly radio promotion on a national level. Specialise in Alternative music. Clients include The Flaming Lips, Ash, Mercury Rev, The Killers and Funeral For A Friend.

Anglo Plugging
Fulham Palace, Bishops Avenue, London, SW6 6EA
tel: 020 7384 7373
fax: 020 7371 9490
email: via website
web: www.angloplugging.co.uk
contact: Dylan White
radio plugger: No
national coverage: No
info: National and regional TV, radio and online promotion. Assess areas of exposure that can be realistically achieved for artists looking for first time radio play. All genres of music accepted. Clients include U2, Oasis and Radio 4.

Bad Moon Publicity
19B All Saints Road, London, W11 1HE
tel: 020 7221 0499
fax: 020 7792 0405
email: press@badmoon.co.uk
contact: Anton Brookes
radio plugger: Yes
national coverage: No
info: Deal in national press promotion including specialised music press and student press. Work with established as well as unsigned bands. Cover most music genres. Clients include My Morning Jacket, Ash, Beastie Boys, The Foo Fighters and Kaisers Chiefs.

Best PR
3rd Floor, Cowper Street, London, EC2A 4AT
tel: 020 7608 4590
fax: 020 7608 4599
email: beth@bestest.co.uk
contact: John Best
radio plugger: No
national coverage: No
info: National and regional press promotion. Deal with all genres of music.

Blazing Stations
Unit 16, Talima Centre, Baileys Lane, Chelsea, London, SW6 2BW
tel: 020 7384 3200
email: jodie@blazingstations.com
web: www.blazingstations.com
contact: Jodie
radio plugger: No
national coverage: Yes
info: Specialist radio promotions for Urban and Dance genres. Contact Jodie for further details.

Blue Cheer Media
13 Fairhazel Gardens, London, NW6 3QE
email: bluecheermedia@yahoo.co.uk
contact: Kim Shankar
radio plugger: No
national coverage: No
info: Specialist radio plugging and press promotion. Also work on tour booking. Ideally would like to deal with bands with interest from a label, rather than promoting demos. Contact through email.

Blurb PR
7 Tower Mansion, 136 West End Lane, London, NW6 1SB
tel: 020 7419 1221
email: hello@blurbpr.com
web: www.blurbpr.com
contact: Mike Plumley
radio plugger: No
national coverage: No
info: Mainly radio and press promotion, including student media.

MUSIC SERVICES/RETAIL

Chapple Davis
53 Great Portland Street, London, W1W 7LG
tel:	020 7299 7979
fax:	020 7299 7978
email:	james@chapdav.com
web:	www.chapdav.com
contact:	James C. Gill
radio plugger:	No
national coverage:	No
info:	Radio and TV promotion for any genre of

music. Clients include DJ Sammy, Ivor Novello Awards, Plump DJs and Van Morrison.

The Coalition PR
12 Barley Mow Passage, Chiswick, London, W4 4PH
tel:	020 8987 0123
fax:	020 8987 0345
email:	pr@coalitiongroup.co.uk
web:	www.coalitiongroup.co.uk
contact:	Tony Lincoln
radio plugger:	Yes
national coverage:	No
info:	National press including some student press.

Clients Bloc Party, The Strokes and Babyshambles. Also offer artist management services. See listing in relevant section.

Cool Badge
Office 604, Oxford House, 49a Oxford Road, Finsbury Park, London, N4 3EY
tel:	020 7272 8370
fax:	020 7272 8371
email:	music@coolbadge.com
web:	www.coolbadge.com
contact:	Russell Yates
radio plugger:	No
national coverage:	No
info:	National and regional TV and radio

promotion. All genres of music accepted. Clients include Ninja Tune and Sub Pop. Also involved in management, contact for further details.

Crunk! Promotions
Unit 11, Impress House, Mansell Road, London, W3 7QH
tel:	020 8932 3030
fax:	020 8932 3031
email:	duncan@crunk.co.uk
web:	www.power.co.uk/crunk
contact:	Duncan Stump
radio plugger:	Yes
national coverage:	No
info:	Club and radio promotion of Electronic and

Leftfield music. Clients receive weekly updates informing them of their track's progress and are given an end report, which analyses its overall performance.

Cypher Press & Promotion
Unit 2a, Queens Studios, 121 Salisbury Road, London, NW6 6RG
tel:	020 7372 4464
email:	info@cypherpress.uk.com
contact:	Tom Jenkins
radio plugger:	No
national coverage:	No
info:	National and regional TV, radio and press

promotion including specialist music press and online press. Cypher work with all music styles. Clients have included Sony (Classic Chillout Album), Channel 4 and Kelli Ali (ex Sneaker Pimps), as well as Virgin.

Darling Department
4th Floor, 19 Denmark Street, London, WC2H 8NA
tel:	020 7379 8787
fax:	020 7379 5737
email:	info@darlinguk.com
web:	www.darlingdepartment.com
contact:	Rachel Hendry
radio plugger:	No
national coverage:	No
info:	Deal with press on a national and regional

level, including specialist press and online services. Clients include Hope of the States, The Killers, The Duke Spirit, Fatboy Slim, Royksopp, The Bravery and Cut Copy.

Delta PR Consultancy
PO Box 25285, London, N12 0XD
tel:	020 8446 3762
email:	deltapr@delta-music.co.uk
web:	www.delta-music.co.uk
contact:	Mal Smith
radio plugger:	Yes
national coverage:	No
info:	Music PR consultants specialising in national

press, new artists, established artists and quality catalogue.

Diffusion PR
Unit 16, Talima Centre, Bajleys Lane, Chelsea, SW6 2BW
tel:	020 7384 3200
fax:	0871 277 3035
email:	jodie@diffusionpr.co.uk
web:	www.diffusionpr.co.uk
contact:	Jodie Stewart
radio plugger:	No
national coverage:	No
info:	Press, radio and club promotion on a regional

and national level. Also undertake marketing campaigns for music related ventures. Mainly work with House, Garage and Hip-Hop music, but are also branching out into Pop. Online DJ and radio services. See website for details.

DJ In The Mix
Unit 16, Talima Centre, Baileys Lane, Chelsea, London, SW6 2BW
tel:	020 7384 3200
email:	jodie@djinthemix.com
web:	www.djinthemix.com
contact:	Jodie
radio plugger:	Yes
national coverage:	Yes
info:	Online club promotion by sending tracks to

DJs in MP3 format, rather than CD or vinyl. Contact Jodie for further information.

Dog Day Press
Zeppelin Building, 59-61 Farringdon Road, London, EC1M 3JB
email:	via website
web:	www.dogdaypress.com
radio plugger:	Yes
national coverage:	No
info:	Current clients include Radio 4, Nada Surf

and Squarepusher. Use contact form via website for more details regarding services Dog Day Press offer.

Electric PR
24a Bartholomew Villas, London, NW5 2LL
tel:	020 7424 0405
email:	laurence@electricpr.co.uk
web:	www.electricpr.co.uk
contact:	Laurence
radio plugger:	No
national coverage:	No
info:	National and radio coverage. Specialise in

Drum&Bass and Urban culture. Clients include Ram Records and Full Circle.

Emms Publicity
100 The Aberdeen Centre, Highbury Grove, London, N5 2EA
tel:	020 7226 0990
fax:	020 7354 8600
email:	stephen@emmspublicity.com
web:	www.emmspublicity.com
contact:	Stephen Emms
radio plugger:	Yes
national coverage:	No
info:	Promote artists through the national press

including specialised music press. Can provide stylists, make-up artists and photographers. Clients include Carl Cox and Ministry Of Sound.

ePM
Unit 204, The Saga Centre, 326 Kensal Road, London, W10 5BZ
tel:	020 8964 4900
fax:	020 8962 9783
email:	jonas@electronicpm.co.uk
web:	www.electronicpm.co.uk
contact:	Jonas Stone
radio plugger:	No
national coverage:	No
info:	Specialising in Electronic music. Regional

and national press, club and radio coverage for labels such as Gigolo, Novamute, F Com and events such as Tribal Gathering and Encompass. Also have a DJ booking agency and have set up digital distribution company, ePM Online, handling distribution for Electronic labels.

Frukt
13-19 Vine Hill, London, EC1R 5DX
tel:	020 7837 1347
email:	see website
web:	www.fruktmusic.com
radio plugger:	Yes
national coverage:	No
info:	Work with a small number of clients at any

one time putting a great deal of focus and effort into fulfilling client's goals. Aim to build long term relationships with clients.

Future Studios International

PO Box 10, London, N1 3RJ

tel:	020 7241 2 83
fax:	020 7241 6233
email:	ladybelle888@blueyonder.co.uk
contact:	Michelle Goldberg
radio plugger:	Yes
national coverage:	No
info:	Deal only with African and World Music.

Unsolicited material is not accepted.

Hall Or Nothing

11 Poplar Mews, Uxbridge Road, London, W12 7JS

tel:	020 8740 6288
fax:	020 8749 5982
email:	emma@hallornothing.com
web:	www.hallornothing.com
contact:	Terri Hall
radio plugger:	Yes
national coverage:	No
info:	Represent bands to national, regional,

student and online press. Clients range from Oasis and Manic Street Preachers through to new bands such as Thirteen Senses, The Ordinary Boys and The Open. Also handle the press for Reading & Leeds Festivals.

Hard Zone

Gardiner House, Business Village, 3-9 Broomhill Road, London, SW18 4JQ

tel:	020 8870 8744
fax:	020 8874 1578
email:	info@hardzone.co.uk
web:	www.hardzone.co.uk
contact:	Sarah Hammad
radio plugger:	No
national coverage:	No
info:	Specialise in R&B and Hip-Hop, also moving

towards Rock. Contacts within student press. Club, radio and press promotion. Also use direct marketing such as posters and flyers. Past clients include Def Jam Records, Death Row Records, EMI and Sony BMG.

Hart Media

The Primrose Hill Business Centre, 110 Gloucester Avenue, London, NW1 8HX

tel:	020 7209 3760
email:	info@hartmedia.co.uk
web:	www.hartmedia.co.uk
contact:	Jo Hart
radio plugger:	No
national coverage:	Yes
info:	TV and radio coverage including specialist

and student radio. Unsigned bands need to have distribution and management factors in place before contacting Hart Media. Can also coordinate tours in all capacities whether it be a support tour, school tour, PA tour or headlining tour. Clients include Towers of London, The Subways and Jamie Cullum. See website for full list.

I-Inc.

63 Hanbury Street, London, E1 5JP

tel:	020 8981 4300
email:	info@illegalinc.com
web:	www.i-inc.co.uk
contact:	V.G. Biebuyck
radio plugger:	Yes
national coverage:	Yes
info:	Offer PR and promotion services for artists

and labels, as well as street and club promotions. See listing for video production in relevant section.

Impressive

9 Jeffreys Place, Camden, London, NW1 9PP

tel:	020 7284 3444
fax:	020 7284 1840
email:	mel@impressivepr.com
web:	www.impressivepr.com
contact:	Mel Brown
radio plugger:	Yes
national coverage:	No
info:	Press and internet promotion including

student press, specialist music press and fanzines. Accept any genre of music but mostly deal with Alternative and Rock music. Clients include Dogs Die In Hot Cars, People In Planes and Pure Reason Revolution.

Intermedia Regional

Byron House, 112a Shirland Road, London, W9 2EQ

tel:	020 7266 0777
fax:	020 7266 1293
email:	info@intermediaregional.com
web:	www.intermediaregional.com
contact:	Janice MacGregor
radio plugger:	No
national coverage:	Yes
info:	Regional radio promotions company. All

genres of music are accepted. Supporting unsigned bands is something they are looking to get more involved with in 2006. Clients include Embrace, Travis and Lost Prophets.

Ish-Media

2 Devonport Mews, Devonport Road, London, W12 8NG

tel:	020 8742 9191
fax:	020 8742 9102
email:	eden@ish-media.com
web:	www.ish-media.com
contact:	Eden Blackman
radio plugger:	No
national coverage:	No
info:	National radio only. Previous and present

campaigns include Mylo, Royksopp, Aaliyah, Black Rebel Motorcycle Club, So Solid Crew and Snoop Dogg.

The Jump Off

PO Box 697, Wembley, Middlesex, HA9 8WQ

tel:	020 7253 7766
fax:	020 7681 1007
web:	www.jumpoff.tv
contact:	Harold Antony
radio plugger:	No
national coverage:	No
info:	Specialise in Hip-Hop events and tours.

Organise battles aimed at unsigned talent, as well as launch parties for labels. See website for more information.

LoseControl Ltd.

London

tel:	020 8980 1253
email:	eef@losecontrol.com
web:	www.losecontrol.com
contact:	Bob Slayer
radio plugger:	No
national coverage:	No
info:	National and regional coverage including

student press and promotions. Specialise in Alternative and Rock.

Media Tours Management

2a Ferry Road, London, SW13 9RX

tel:	020 8834 7373
fax:	020 8834 7474
email:	info@airmtm.com
web:	www.airmtm.com
contact:	Sheila Bates
radio plugger:	No
national coverage:	No
info:	Specialise in Jazz music but would consider

working with other genres of music. Deals with TV, radio and press including specialist press and student press. Clients include Jamie Cullum.

Mercenary PR

Suite 210, Saga Centre, 326 Kensal Road, London, W10 5DZ

tel:	020 8354 4111
fax:	020 8354 4112
email:	kas@mercenarypr.co.uk
web:	www.mercenarypr.com
contact:	Kas Mercer
radio plugger:	Yes
national coverage:	No
info:	National press promotions only. Deal with all

genres of music. Clients include Def Leppard, Fightstar, Jamie Cullum, Juliette and The Licks, Lost Prophets and My Chemical Romance.

Mosquito Media

PO Box 33790, 18 Chelsea Manor Street, London, SW3 6WF

email:	mosquitomedia@aol.com
web:	www.mosquito-media.co.uk
radio plugger:	Yes
national coverage:	Yes
info:	Publicity and PR services designed to help

artists break into the industry. Also promote labels and live events. Provide video production services. See listing in relevant section for details.

Nobul Promotions

59 New River Crescent, London, N13 5RD
tel: 020 8882 3677
fax: 020 8882 3688
email: alex@nobul.prestel.co.uk
contact: Alex Alexandrou
radio plugger: No
national coverage: No
info: National and regional TV and radio promotion. Deal with all mainstream music. Clients include Eastwest Records, David Gray, Atlantic Records and Muse.

Piranha PR

Flat 51, The Gardens, London, SE22 9QQ
tel: 020 8299 1928/07956 460 372
email: rosie@piranha-pr.co.uk
web: www.piranha-pr.co.uk
contact: Rosie Wilby
radio plugger: Yes
national coverage: No
info: National and regional coverage in music press across the genres. Specialise in Singer-Songwriter music with contacts at Uncut, Mojo and Maverick magazines.

Press Counsel PR

5-7 Vernon Yard, London, W11 2DX
tel: 020 7792 9400
fax: 020 7243 2262
email: charlie@presscounsel.com
web: www.presscounsel.com
contact: Charlie Caplow
radio plugger: Yes
national coverage: No
info: National, regional and student online service. Clients include New Order, Hard-Fi and Million Dead.

Prohibition Ltd.

Fulham Palace, Bishops Avenue, London, SW6 6EA
tel: 020 7384 7372
fax: 020 7371 7940
email: caroline@theprogroup.co.uk
web: www.prohibitiondj.com
contact: Caroline Prothero
radio plugger: No
national coverage: Yes
info: Digital Dance promotion company introducing new music to DJs and specialist radio both nationally and regionally. Previous clients have included EMI, Universal, Island and Skint, amongst others.

Psi Pi

8 United House, Mayflower Court, London, SE16 4JL
tel: 07930 275 223
fax: 07092 275 223
email: info@psipi.com
web: www.psipi.com
contact: Simon Hedley
radio plugger: No
national coverage: No
info: Always happy to listen to demos, ideally supplied both in MP3 and CD format. Psi Pi can assist with creative input into tracks. Psi Thinking is the consultancy side of the company, which offers ideas for branding and marketing.

Rocket PR

St. Matthew's Church, Brixton Hill, London, SW2 1JF
tel: 020 7326 1234
email: radio@rocketpr.co.uk
web: www.rocketpr.co.uk
contact: Prudence Trapani
radio plugger: No
national coverage: No
info: Services include radio and TV promotion on a national and regional level. Also deal with student press. Interested in all specialist music genres, with exception of Mainstream Pop. Labels worked with include Domino, Epitaph, ArtRocker and Hydrogen Dukebox.

Sainted PR

Office 3, 9 Thorpe Close, London, W10 5XL
tel: 020 8962 5700
fax: 020 8962 5701
email: elim@saintedpr.com
web: www.saintedpr.com
contact: Elim Carlsson
radio plugger: Yes
national coverage: No
info: UK national press promotion, including all specialist music press. Work with all genres of music. Clients include Massive Attack, Air and Embrace.

Scruffy Bird

Floor 3, 205 Victoria Street, London, SW1E 5NE
tel: 020 7931 7990
email: info@scruffybird.com
web: www.scruffybird.com
contact: Duncan Ellis
radio plugger: No
national coverage: No
info: Press, TV and radio promotions on both national and regional levels. Clients include Bjork, Belarus and Human Television.

Serious Promotions

PO Box 13143, London, N6 5BG
tel: 020 8815 5550
fax: 020 8815 5559
email: sam@seriousworld.com
web: www.seriousworld.com
contact: Sam O'Riordan
radio plugger: No
national coverage: No
info: Mainly promote club nights and DJs. Also manage various DJs and bands, and promote them through radio and TV. Clients include Radio 1 DJs such as Judge Jules and Fat Boy Slim.

Shout About Media

NuGroove Productions, 91 Brick Lane, London, E1 6QL
tel: 020 7426 2006
fax: 020 8367 5091
email: unicornpr@hotmail.com
web: www.shoutaboutmedia.co.uk
contact: Samantha Galsworthy
radio plugger: No
national coverage: No
info: Press, PR and promotional support for any sector of the entertainment industry including live music, clubs, DJs and bands.

Silver PR

London
tel: 020 7503 3920
fax: 020 7503 3920
email: rachel.silver@silverpr.co.uk
web: www.silverpr.co.uk
radio plugger: Yes
national coverage: No
info: Eclectic roster specialising in Indie, Rock and Underground music.

Single Minded Promotions

Unit 11, Cambridge Court, 210 Shepherds Bush Road, London, W6 7NJ
tel: 0870 011 3748
fax: 0870 011 3749
email: tony@singleminded.com
web: www.singleminded.com
contact: Tony Byrne
radio plugger: No
national coverage: No
info: Mainstream coverage specialising in radio, television, press and student promotion with over 20 years experience.

Small Japanese Soldier

32-38 Saffron Hill, Farringdon, London, EC1N 8FH
tel: 020 7421 9400
fax: 020 7421 9334
email: andy@smalljapanesesoldier.com
web: www.smalljapanesesoldier.com
contact: Andy Hunns
radio plugger: No
national coverage: No
info: Small Japanese Soldier work with major and independent labels, and can execute the whole package from sleeve and logo design to TV and press adverts.

Societas Ltd.

Suite 2, 27 James Street, Mayfair, London, W1U 1DX
tel: 0870 910 4904
email: newbusiness@societas.ltd.uk
web: www.societas.ltd.uk
contact: Melissa Sterry
radio plugger: No
national coverage: No
info: Represent music producers specialising in both commercial music production of bands and artists. Clients include Fort Lauderdale, The Black Neon and Jazz FM.

Some Friendly
334 Old Street, London, EC1V 9DR
tel:	020 7684 4830
email:	sophie@somefriendly.co.uk
web:	www.somefriendly.co.uk
contact:	Sophie Williams
radio plugger:	Yes
national coverage:	No
info:	National and regional press promotion and

management including student and specialist music press and online services. Various genres of music accepted but mainly Guitar based and Electronic material. Clients include Badly Drawn Boy and The Warlocks.

Street Press PR
The Top Floor, The Outset Building, 2 Grange Road, London, E17 8AH
tel:	020 8509 6073
fax:	020 8509 6021
email:	heather@streetpress.co.uk
contact:	Heather
radio plugger:	No
national coverage:	No
info:	Specialist PR dealing mainly with Urban acts.

Tomkins PR
The Old Lamp Works, Rodney Place, London, SW19 2LQ
tel:	020 8540 8166
fax:	020 8540 6056
email:	susie@tomkinspr.com
web:	www.tomkinspr.com
contact:	Susie Tomkins
radio plugger:	No
national coverage:	No
info:	Handle all aspects of regional radio and

TV promotion needs. Promote singles and albums to all independent regional radio stations including FM, AM and BBC stations throughout the UK.

Triad Publicity
164 New Cavendish Street, London, W1W 6YT
tel:	020 7436 7600
email:	info@triadpublicity.co.uk
contact:	Vanessa Cotton
radio plugger:	Yes
national coverage:	No
info:	Deal in national and regional press

promotion including specialist music press. Accepts all genres of music. Clients include Primal Scream, Transcopic Records, Kasabian, The Others and Teenage Fan Club.

Up Shot
5th Floor, 2-12 Pentonville Road, London, N1 9PL
tel:	020 7923 5560
fax:	020 7923 5564
email:	info@upshotcom.com
web:	www.upshotcreek.com
contact:	Tom Roberts
radio plugger:	No
national coverage:	No
info:	Regional radio and press promotion,

including student media. Utilise clubs, colleges, bars, venues, street teams, local media, and even sports stadiums and retail outlets. Mainly work with Alternative music. Clients include Oasis, Dilated Peoples, Placebo, The Killers and Bloc Party.

Velocity Communications
4 Bourlet Close, London, W1W 7BJ
tel:	020 7323 1744
fax:	020 7436 4199
email:	info@velocitypr.co.uk
web:	www.velocitypr.co.uk
contact:	Scott Bartlett
radio plugger:	Yes
national coverage:	Yes
info:	Mainly deal with press promotion, including

contacts with student press and other specialist media. Will also handle radio promotion from time to time. Operate on a national and regional level. All genres of music accepted. Represent labels such as Telstar and EMI.

Vigilante
51 Westwick Gardens, London, W14 0BS
tel:	020 7371 6244
email:	rupert.withers@talk21.com
contact:	Rupert Withers
radio plugger:	No
national coverage:	No
info:	Work with national radio and any

mainstream music. Also deal with international rock press. Have represented bands such as Girlschool and Statetrooper.

Vision Promotions
22 Upper Grosvenor Street, London, W1K 7PE
tel:	020 7499 8024
fax:	020 7499 8032
email:	visionpromo@btconnect.com
web:	www.visionmusic.co.uk
contact:	Rob Dallison
radio plugger:	No
national coverage:	No
info:	Mainly deal with radio, press and DJ

promotion. Clients include Maxim and Unkle.

Vizarie Ltd.
TGEC, Town Hall Approach Road, London, N15 4RX
tel:	0845 130 6343
email:	michael@vizarie.com
web:	www.vizarie.com
contact:	Michael Lowe
radio plugger:	No
national coverage:	No
info:	Vizarie is an award winning marketing,

publicity and advertising firm.

White Disc
Devonshire House, 223 Upper Richmond Road, London, SW15 6SQ
tel:	0845 634 5369
fax:	0845 634 5368
email:	admin@whitedisc.com
web:	www.whitedisc.com
contact:	Rich Orchard
radio plugger:	Yes
national coverage:	Yes
info:	White Disc is established as crucial link

between record labels and DJs, providing a CD promotion service to professional DJs.

WhiteNoise Promotions
8 Southam Street, London, W10 5PH
tel:	020 7729 3320
fax:	020 8964 0021
email:	info@whitenoisepromo.com
web:	www.whitenoisepromo.com
contact:	Colin Hobbs, Jamie Charmers
radio plugger:	No
national coverage:	No
info:	Specialist radio and club promotion on a

national and sometimes international level. Specialist in Dance and Electronic related music. Clients include Goldfrapp, DJ Shadow and Scissor Sisters.

Wild
Unit 2b, Westpoint, 39-40 Warple Way, London, W3 0RG
tel:	020 8746 0666
fax:	020 8746 7676
email:	info@wild-uk.com
contact:	Dave Roberts
radio plugger:	No
national coverage:	Yes
info:	Regional press and radio promotion

specialising in student media. Organise club promotions. Special offers for unsigned bands. No specialised genre of music. Previous clients include 50 Cent, Metallica and Domino Records.

Work Hard PR
35 Farm Avenue, London, SW16 2UT
tel:	020 8677 8466
email:	enquires@workhardpr.com
web:	www.workhardpr.com
contact:	Roland Hyms
radio plugger:	No
national coverage:	No
info:	An independent company that deals with

national and regional TV, radio and press including fanzines and student press. Mainly deal with Rock and Pop, but have a diverse roster. Currently represent a variety of up and coming acts such as Breed 77. Established clients include Badly Drawn Boy, Black Sabbath, Terence Trent D'Arby and Motorhead.

Zen Media Management & Idea Generation PR
10 Greenland Street, London, NW1 0ND
tel:	020 7248 4948
email:	sacha@zenmedia.net
web:	www.zenmedia.net
contact:	Sacha Taylor-Cox
radio plugger:	Yes
national coverage:	No
info:	Idea Generation deal with national press

including specialist music press. Zen Media are now part of Idea Generation and handle band and artist development, as well as being management consultants. Interested in Indie, Rock and New Wave music. Previous clients have included Ludes, Metro Riots, BOA, Western Electric System, MC5, Bush, Ocean Colour Scene, Paul Oakenfold, Morcheeba, Moloko, Sound 5, Planet Funk, The Fades and Ciccone.

Zons PR
22 Stephenson Way, London, NW1 2HD
tel:	020 7813 1945
fax:	020 7813 1948
email:	nashira@zonspr.com
web:	www.zonspr.com
radio plugger:	No
national coverage:	No
info:	Music and entertainment agency. Current

clients include Shaggy, Rhian Benson and the MOBO Awards. Radio plugging, A&R scouting and consultancy. Also work alongside major and independent labels to groom potential talent. Connections with local and national BBC, commercial, digital, internet and community based radio networks, as well as DJs. Latest development 'Zons Streetz' delivers exposure for up and coming 'street' talent.

MIDLANDS

Firebird.com Ltd.
Kyrle House Studios, Edde Cross Street, Ross-Wye, Herefordshire, HR9 7BZ
tel:	01989 762 269
email:	info@firebird.com
web:	www.firebird.com
contact:	Joan Martin
radio plugger:	Yes
national coverage:	No
info:	Offer a complete creative package including

PR, styling and promotions. Deal with all genres of music on both national and regional levels.

FlatTop PR
46 Woodbridge Road, Moseley, Birmingham, B13 8EJ
tel:	0121 449 5394
email:	peter.black@flattop.co.uk
web:	www.flattop.co.uk
contact:	Peter Black
radio plugger:	Yes
national coverage:	No
info:	FlatTop is a small, enthusiastic and music-

obsessed company that has been operating for 5 years. Specialise in debut releases, small budgets and encompass all areas of music. Mail to all national and regional publications, and have solid contacts across the UK.

Gold Star
Po Box 130, Ross on Wye, HR9 6WY
tel:	01989 770 105
email:	nitagoldstar@btinternet.com
contact:	Nita
radio plugger:	Yes
national coverage:	No
info:	Deal with press mainly. Fanzines, student,

regional and national press. Do not usually deal with radio and TV coverage, but can do this on small scale if required. Everything from Punk, Folk, Country to Metal is accepted.

Holier Than Thou Promotions
46 Rother Street, Stratford on Avon, Warwickshire, CV37 6LT
tel:	01789 268 661
email:	httrecords@aol.com
web:	www.holierthanthourecords.com
contact:	David Begg
radio plugger:	Yes
national coverage:	Yes
info:	Holier Than Thou Promotions promote new

releases and demos to university radio stations and DJs associated with Rock and Alternative music. Send demos to the address above. Unfortunately, demos cannot be returned. For more information on the label and management services, see entries in the relevant sections.

MS&M International
103 Great Hampton Row, Hockley, Birmingham, B19 3AY
tel:	0121 241 0305
fax:	0121 241 2329
email:	marie.mills@ms8m-int.com
radio plugger:	No
national coverage:	No
info:	Music, media and entertainment company,

specialising in international marketing and promotion.

Phunk'd Promotions
83 Hamsterly Park, Southfields, Northampton, NN3 5DX
tel:	01604 491 805
email:	lesley1001@hotmail.com
contact:	Lesley Morrison
radio plugger:	No
national coverage:	No
info:	Promotional services for Pop, Indie, Rock

and Punk bands and artists. National press coverage. Will also assist with booking gigs. Send demo for consideration FAO Lesley Morrison to the above address. Also email Lesley to confirm your demo has been posted.

Pink Angel Promotion
Leicester Creative Business Depot, 31 Rutland Street, Leicester, LE1 1RE
tel:	0116 261 6838
email:	enquires@pinkangels.co.uk
web:	www.pinkangels.co.uk
contact:	Trevor Locke
radio plugger:	Yes
national coverage:	Yes
info:	Plan and implement promotional campaigns

for a variety of purposes such as launches, promotion of new products or publicity for DJs, singers or artists. Can assist with locating and booking venues and producing flyers and posters to help develop your fan bases. Also run a secondary website (www.getyourbandon. com) which specialises in promoting unsigned artists. In addition, they offer management services, design and maintenance of websites, photoshoots and video production within a regional area.

Resourse PR Ltd.
8 Lutterworth Road, Pailton, Warwickshire, CV23 OQE
tel:	01788 833 918
fax:	01788 833 832
email:	info@resource-pr.com
web:	www.resource-pr.com
contact:	Graham Brown
radio plugger:	Yes
national coverage:	No
info:	Specialist PR and marketing consultancy in

the events and entertainment sector.

Solar Creations
PO Box 9691, Birmingham, B27 7ED
tel:	0121 707 8504
email:	scott@solarcreations.net
web:	www.solarcreations.net
contact:	Scott Roe
radio plugger:	No
national coverage:	No
info:	Provide PR and plugging services. Also have

a record label, management company and promote gigs. See relevant sections for details.

Steve Osbourne Management
PO Box 69, Daventry, NN11 4SY
tel:	0870 741 5532
fax:	0871 277 2365
email:	steve@daventrynet.co.uk
contact:	Steve Osbourne
radio plugger:	No
national coverage:	No
info:	Includes specialist contacts such as stylists

and photographers. Offer various packages for bands. Reasonable rates. Contact Steve for details.

NORTHEAST

10xBetter
7 St. Nicholas' Church Yard, Newcastle Upon Tyne, NE1 1PS
tel:	0191 260 3377
email:	info@10xbetter.com
web:	www.10xbetter.com
contact:	Terry Hollingsworth
radio plugger:	No
national coverage:	No
info:	Regional coverage, as well as national and

student radio plugging. Terrestrial and digital TV promotion. Also have London based office (Tel. 020 7993 4593). 10xBetter also offer artist management services, and are affiliated with Subversive Records and Global Entertainment, who offer music industry courses. See listings in relevant sections for details.

Manilla PR
PO Box 82, Middlesbrough, TS6 6TD
tel:	01642 248 400
email:	info@manillapr.com
web:	www.manillapr.com
contact:	Tony McDonagh
radio plugger:	No
national coverage:	No
info:	Manilla PR provide regional coverage for

artists and bands, and also produce a monthly magazine distributed in the North East to help new and unsigned bands.

Tenacity
PO Box 166, Hartlepool, TS26 9JA
tel:	01429 424 603
email:	info@tenacitymusicpr.co.uk
web:	www.tenacitymusicpr.co.uk
radio plugger:	Yes
national coverage:	No
info:	Specialist, regional or national PR.

NORTHWEST

Aurora Borealis Music
Gostin Building, 32-36 Hanover Street, Liverpool, L1 4LN
tel:	0151 709 1299
email:	info@aurora-borealis.info
web:	www.aurora-borealis.info
contact:	Kaya Herstad
radio plugger:	Yes
national coverage:	Yes
info:	Artist development and promotion company

who can offer a promotional package solution to suit all budgets. Provide a wide range of consultancy services for the development and promotionof artists from entry-level upwards.

Blue Soap
PO Box 106, Manchester, M32 8RG
tel:	0161 611 8062
email:	blue.soap@virgin.net
contact:	Andy Woods
radio plugger:	No
national coverage:	No
info:	Primarily deal in specialist radio plugging at

both national regional levels. Artists worked with previously include My Morning Jacket, Tompaulin and Vinny Peculiar.

Fistral PR
114 The Royal, Wilton Place, Salford, M3 6FT
tel:	0161 835 4142/07905 448 607
email:	info@fistralpr.co.uk
web:	www.fistralpr.co.uk
contact:	Peggy Manning
radio plugger:	Yes
national coverage:	No
info:	Mainly deal with national and regional press

and promotion including student press. Very interested in representing new bands.

In House Press
4th Floor, 20 Dale Street, Manchester, M1 1EZ
tel:	0161 228 2070
fax:	0161 228 3070
email:	info@inhousepress.com
web:	www.inhousepress.com
contact:	David Cooper
radio plugger:	Yes
national coverage:	No
info:	National press promotion only. Have

represented artists such as Aim, The Coral, The Longcut, The Go! Team and The Earlies. Eclectic roster,

MsRepresentation PR
2 Olivia Grove, Birch, Manchester, M14 5JA
tel:	07980 878 824
email:	germaine@msrepresentation.com
web:	www.msrepresentation.com
contact:	Germaine Nichol
radio plugger:	Yes
national coverage:	No
info:	Specialise in creative industries. Coverage for

regional and national press, TV, web, student media and radio. Work with unsigned bands, as well as larger scale music and arts events.

Presswerk PR
22 Caledonia Street, Liverpool, L7 7DX
tel:	0151 707 9044
email:	presswerk@hotmail.com
contact:	Mat Tang
radio plugger:	Yes
national coverage:	No
info:	Marketing, press, publicity and event

management and production. Independent product, brand and event promotion. National and regional marketing campaign strategy development and implementation. Corporate event coordination, management and production. Regional press agent.

Sketchpad PR
11 Junction Works, Paradise Warf, 40 Ducie Street, Manchester, M1 2DF
tel:	0845 458 8662
fax:	0845 458 8663
email:	info@sketchpadpr.com
web:	www.sketchpadpr.com
contact:	Simon Morrison
radio plugger:	Yes
national coverage:	No
info:	Specialise in Dance music and promote DJs

and club nights. Clients include Sankeys Soap.

Terrie Doherty Promotions
40 Princess Street, Manchester, M1 6DE
tel:	0161 234 0044
email:	terriedoherty@zoo.co.uk
contact:	Terrie Doherty
radio plugger:	Yes
national coverage:	Yes
info:	Handle regional radio and TV promotion. No

specific genre of music.

SOUTHEAST

Assassination Music Promotions
Ardquoy, Pinstone Way, Gerrards Cross, Buckinghamshire, SL9 7BJ
tel:	01753 883 145
email:	richard@assassination.co.uk
web:	www.assassination.co.uk
contact:	Richard Daniels
radio plugger:	Yes
national coverage:	No
info:	Publicity for bands and artists. Contact for

further information.

Headhoncho PR
3 Tennyson Road, Thatcham, Berkshire, RG18 3FR
tel:	01635 868 385
email:	mark@headhonchopr.com
web:	www.headhonchopr.com
contact:	Owen Packard
radio plugger:	No
national coverage:	No
info:	Promote unsigned bands in the same

manner, and to the same standard as signed acts in the UK. They target A&R, journalists, press and online magazines, radio stations, agents, promoters and management companies with the main aims of increasing public awareness, building a profile and getting you noticed by the right people. Because Headhoncho can only work with a limited number of bands, you are asked to submit a demo to the address above, and to Headhoncho PR's other office at 38 Derwent Road, Harpenden, Hertfordshire, AL5 3NU.

Lambton & Varsani Communications
21-22 The Old Steyne, Brigton, BN1 1EL
tel:	01273 648 373
email:	hash@lvcommunications.org
web:	www.lvcommunications.org
radio plugger:	No
national coverage:	No
info:	Radio and press coverage on either national

or regional basis, depending on requirements of the client. Specialist contact with music journalists, radio presenters and copywriters. See also listing for photography services in relevant section.

Media Ink PR
Elvin House, Stadium Way, Wembley, Middlesex, HA9 0DW
tel:	07909 905 882
email:	mediainkpr@onetel.com
contact:	Anne Morgan
radio plugger:	Yes
national coverage:	No
info:	National press promotions including student

press. Specialises in Rock and Pop.

FISTRAL R

music press
www.fistralpr.co.uk
signed + unsigned

LEAD AMPLIFIER

FISTRAL R

Drive   Input   Gain   Tone   Volume   Head Phones   Power

0161 835 4142
info@fistralpr.co.uk

c/o 114 the royal
wilton place
salford
manchester
M3 6FT

FISTRAL R

Park Promotions

Po Box 651, Oxford, OX2 9RB

tel:	01865 241 717
fax:	01865 204 556
email:	info@parkrecords.com
web:	www.parkrecords.com
contact:	John Dagnell
radio plugger:	No
national coverage:	No
info:	Specialist in Folk, Rock and Acoustic music.

Clients include Steeleye Span and Radio 2. Also listed in Record Companies section.

Rush Release Ltd.

Cranhurst Lodge, 37-39 Curbitch, Surrey, KT6 4TS

tel:	020 8870 0011
fax:	020 8870 2101
email:	info@rushrelease.com
web:	www.rushrelease.com
contact:	Jo Underwood
radio plugger:	No
national coverage:	No
info:	National radio, TV and press promotion

including specialist radio. Club promotion in UK and Europe. All genres of music including UK Garage, R&B, Hip-Hop, Drum&Bass, House and Pop.

Singsong Entertainment Publicity

Market House, Market Square, Winslow, Buckinghamshire, MK18 3AF

tel:	01296 715 228
email:	peter@singsongpr.biz
web:	www.singsongpr.biz
contact:	Peter Muir
radio plugger:	No
national coverage:	No
info:	National and regional press and radio

coverage. Also provide fan club database management, web design and development, as well as event management. Covers Rock, Country, Jazz, Bhangra and Fusion, but specialises in music with Acoustic roots.

Caravan Music Promotions

PO Box 3674, Somerset, PA5 3ZR

tel:	07739 126 794
email:	caravanmusic@hotmail.com
web:	www.caravanmusicpromotions.com
contact:	JJ Kane
radio plugger:	No
national coverage:	No
info:	Currently working with platinum selling

artist and new as well as new artists. Accept all genres of music and have no age limits. Committed to promoting artist's music on radio or other media such as TV and film. Also see listing in Management Companies section.

DJ Chronicles

84 Atlantic Park View, West End, Southampton, SO18 3RQ

tel:	02380 471 935
email:	contact@djchronicles.co.uk
web:	www.djchronicles.co.uk
contact:	Lucy Carr
radio plugger:	No
national coverage:	No
info:	A great source for DJs and bands of all

genres. Feature profiles online. Also have a links page which enables artists to market themselves, and allows people to get in touch with them directly, therefore cutting out any agency or commission fees.

Mark Moore

22 Sir George's Road, Freemantle, Southampton, SO15 3AT

tel:	02380 329 573
fax:	02380 329 573
email:	markmoore@madasafish.com
contact:	Mark Moore
radio plugger:	Yes
national coverage:	No
info:	Specialise in Dance music and DJs. Clients

include Frankie Knuckles and Danny Ramping.

Ian Cheek PR

Suite 5, 51d New Briggate, Leeds, LS2 8JD

tel:	0113 246 9940
email:	iancheek@talk21.com
radio plugger:	Yes
national coverage:	Yes
info:	Regional press. Currently working with Bjork,

Muse, Ash, Goldie Lookin Chain, Maximo Park, JJ72, The Kills, Arctic Monkeys, The Cribs, Juliette & The Licks, Alabama 3, Funeral For A Friend and The Glitterati. All demos received will be responded to either by a phone call or email. Help and advice always offered.

Pomona

36 Bridgegate, Hebden Bridge, West Yorkshire, HX7 8EX

tel:	01422 846 900
email:	admin@pomonauk.co.uk
web:	www.pomonauk.co.uk
contact:	James Shewerd
radio plugger:	Yes
national coverage:	No
info:	Pomona deal with all regional press for most

of the major labels. They also accept demos from local unsigned bands whom they regularly help and advise.

Schism

Unit 8, Victoria House, Maghera, County Derry, BT46 5AF

tel:	028 796 45803
fax:	028 796 44487
email:	charlene@schism.ie
web:	www.schism.ie
contact:	Charlene
radio plugger:	Yes
national coverage:	No
info:	Deals with promotion on a regional and

national level. Work with both touring and unsigned bands.

Stephen Anderson Publicity

64 Donegal Street, Belfast, Antrim, BT1 2GT

tel:	028 9031 0949
fax:	028 9031 5905
email:	press@stephenandersonpublicity.com
web:	www.stephenandersonpublicity.com
contact:	Stephen Anderson
radio plugger:	No
national coverage:	No
info:	Specialist press and PR. Also deal with

student press and radio. Previous clients include Good Charlotte, Thursday and Drive Thru Records.

MUSIC SERVICES/RETAIL

SCOTLAND

Ordinary PR
Top Floor, 73 St. Vincent Crescent, Glasgow, G3 8NQ
tel: 0141 204 5974
fax: 0141 204 5974
email: hello@ordinarypr.co.uk
web: www.ordinarypr.co.uk
radio plugger: Yes
national coverage: Yes
info: Press and publicity services. Enquire for further details.

Page 6 Music
Culbokie, By Dingwall, IV7 8JY
tel: 01349 877 449
email: cara@page6music.com
web: www.page6music.com
contact: Cara Anderson
radio plugger: Yes
national coverage: Yes
info: Regional press coverage. Page 6 Music have many contacts within the Scottish music industry, and have also carried out agency work with UK venues. Send demo FAO Cara Anderson to the above address. Also manage signed and unsigned acts based in Scotland. See entry in Management Companies section for details.

WALES

Bare Entertainment PR
29 Pantbach Road, Birchgrove, Cardiff, CF14 1TW
tel: 02920 257 262
email: BareEntertainmentUK@hotmail.com
web: www.bareentertainmentwales.com
contact: Geraint Duddridge
radio plugger: No
national coverage: No
info: Newly established company providing promotion and marketing solutions for bands, DJs and solo artists at affordable prices. Offer discounted rates for students and under 25 year olds.

Plug Two
133 The Coal Exchange, Mount Stuart Square, Cardiff Bay, Cardiff, CF10 5ED
tel: 02920 190 151
email: john@plugtwo.com
web: www.plugtwo.com
contact: John Rostron
radio plugger: No
national coverage: No
info: National, regional plugging and press. Deals with all media including the internet and specialist music press. Specialise in Welsh promotion. Mainly deals with Electronica, Indie, Rock and Pop music. Clients have included Samo Hung, Kid Carpet, Culprit One and Camera.

Promo UK
16 Lime Trees, Llangattock, Crickhowell, Powys, NP8 1LB
tel: 01873 810 142
email: promoukgb@aol.com
contact: Kevin Holland King
radio plugger: No
national coverage: No
info: TV and radio promotion on a regional and national level including specialist music press. Handle broad spectrum of music from Classical to Pop, but mainly works with BBC Radio 2.

Shining Star UK Ltd.
Unit 10-11, Station Terrace, Cardiff, CF5 4AR
tel: 02920 560 200
email: info@shiningstargroup.com
web: www.shiningstargroup.com
contact: Angela Boffy
radio plugger: No
national coverage: No
info: Offer a starting package to unsigned bands and musicians. Specialise in launching new talent into the press, with full national and regional coverage.

MUSIC SERVICES/RETAIL

3.12 PROMOTIONAL MERCHANDISE

EAST of ENGLAND 333 GREATER LONDON 335 MIDLANDS 340 NORTHEAST 342 NORTHWEST 344
SOUTHEAST 348 SOUTHWEST 350 YORKSHIRE 353 NORTHERN IRELAND 355 SCOTLAND 356 WALES 358

EAST of ENGLAND

1st Incentives
Suite 13, The Grange, 20 Market Street, Swavesey, Cambridge, CB4 5QG
tel:	01480 497 785
email:	g.glenister@1st-incentives.co.uk
web:	www.1st-incentives.co.uk
contact:	Gordon
design service:	Yes
minimum run:	None
info:	Broad range of products available. Previously
supplied t-shirts to Roadrunner Records and MNCS Management. Can manufacture DJ slip mats and similar goods.

Ace Balloon Art
291 Woodbridge Road, Ipswich, Suffolk, IP4 4AS
tel:	01473 728 870
fax:	01473 727 585
email:	aceforballoons@aol.com
contact:	Mr S. Buckle
design service:	Yes
minimum run:	None
info:	Can print band logos onto balloons.

Adept
5 Raynham Street, Norwich, Norfolk, NR2 4LL
tel:	01603 631 277
email:	rtsrtops@creativityhouse.biz
design service:	Yes
info:	T-shirt printing with range of styles including
glow in the dark.

Admart Promotions
13 Industrial Centre, Gower Street, Ipswich, Suffolk, IP2 8EX
tel:	01473 602 152
email:	sales@admartpromotions.co.uk
web:	www.admartpromotions.co.uk
contact:	Graeme Kirk
design service:	No
minimum run:	25 (T-shirts)
info:	Deal with anything promotional. Specialise in
t-shirts, but offer range of products including mugs and pens. No in-house design service, but have good contacts for these purposes.

AKA Supplies
47 Lynn Road, Dersingham, Kings Lynn, Norfolk, PE31 6JY
tel:	01485 542 346
fax:	01485 544 770
email:	roger@akasupplies.co.uk
web:	www.akasupplies.co.uk
contact:	Roger
design service:	No
minimum run:	Depends on item
info:	Provide anything promotional such as mugs,
pens and badges. Also provide t-shirts and polo shirts. No in-house design service, but will work closely with another company who can meet most requirements. Contact for further information.

Baronjay Promotional Marketing
Trimilia, Tide Mill Yacht Harbour, Tide Mill Way, Woodbridge, IP12 1BP
tel:	01394 615 781
email:	sales@baronjay.co.uk
web:	www.baronjay.co.uk
design service:	Yes
info:	Variety of promotional merchandise available
such as stationery items, coasters, mousemats and badges.

Blue Salamander Promotions
30 Church Street, Wilingham, Cambridge, CB4 5HT
tel:	01954 260 718
design service:	No
minimum run:	6
info:	Printed t-shirts on request.

D & L Promotions Ltd.
5 Old Bank Chambers, Dartford Road, March, Cambridgeshire, PE15 8AQ
tel:	01354 656 300
email:	dlpromo@btconnect.com
web:	www.dlpromotions.co.uk
design service:	Yes
info:	Array of promotional items available.

Dandis
Ahtree Works, Mill Road, Barnham Broom, Norwich, Norfolk, NR9 4DE
tel:	01603 759 267
email:	dandis@freeuk.com
web:	www.dandis.co.uk
design service:	Yes
info:	T-shirt printing with up to 10 colours. Also
provide poster printing.

Doves Clothing Co.
6 The Business Centre, Earl Soham, Woodbridge, Suffolk, IP13 7SA
tel:	01728 685 774
email:	sales@doves-online.com
web:	www.doves-online.com
design service:	Yes
minimum run:	12
info:	Caps, bags and t-shirts available.

Dragonfly Screenprint
Unit 3, St. Margaret's Way, Stukeley Meadows Industrial Estate, Huntingdon, Cambridgeshire, PE29 6EB
tel:	01480 414 646
email:	sales@dragonflyhouse.co.uk
web:	www.dragonflyhouse.co.uk
design service:	Yes
minimum run:	20
info:	Screen printing onto t-shirts. Can also provide
stickers and other promotional goods.

Erban Garment Printing
40 Bridge Road, Lowestoft, Suffolk, NR32 3LR
tel:	0870 874 0047
design service:	Yes
info:	T-shirt printers.

Evolve Branding
23-26 Wulfric Square, Bretton, Peterborough, Cambridgeshire, PE3 8RF
tel:	01733 269 556
fax:	01733 265 679
email:	info@evolvebranding.com
web:	www.evolvebranding.com
design service:	Yes
minimum run:	6
info:	Evolve Branding offer massive range of
promotional goods that are suitable as gifts, or to promote your band.

Games & Giggles
5 The Walk, Ipswich, Suffolk, IP1 1EA
tel:	01473 212 171
design service:	No
info:	Put limited fonts and lettering onto t-shirts.

MUSIC SERVICES/RETAIL

Giftmark Enterprises Ltd.
1 Mowles Manor, Etling Green, Dereham, NR20 3EZ
tel: 01362 637 878
email: giftmarken@aol.com
design service: No
minimum run: None
info: Limited in-house design offered. All types of promotional material available including t-shirt printing.

Hadleigh Maid
Unit 13-14, Byford Court, Crockatt Road, Hadleigh, Ipswich, IP7 6RD
tel: 0845 330 6384
design service: Yes
info: Manufacture promotional chocolate and may be able to assist bands thinking of taking a unique approach to their marketing.

Identity Promotions Ltd.
Unit 3, Cloverfield Industrial Estate, Lopham Road, East Harling, Norwich, NR16 2LT
tel: 01953 718 534
fax: 01953 718 778
email: sales@waterfrontmanufacturing.co.uk
web: www.waterfrontmanufacturing.co.uk
contact: Alan
design service: Yes
minimum run: None
info: Specialise in clothing. Promotional gifts and incentives are also available.

Image 2 Screen
5 Fowell Close, Norwich, Norfolk, NR5 8NL
tel: 01603 453 600
email: chris.image2screen@ntlworld.com
design service: Yes
info: Printing onto t-shirts and polo shirts.

Impress Ipswich
235 Valley Road, Ipswich, IP4 3AH
tel: 01473 253 690
email: sales@impressipswich.co.uk
web: www.impressipswich.co.uk
contact: Graeme Peache
design service: Yes
minimum run: 6
info: Printed t-shirts and promotional clothing. Also provide badges, keyrings and sweets amongst other items.

Indigo Clothing
Downing House, Regent Street, Cambridge, Cambridgeshire, CB2 1DP
tel: 07771 864 807
email: info@indigoclothing.com
web: www.indigoclothing.com
design service: Yes
minimum run: 20
info: Promotional clothing including t-shirts and hoodies. Indigo have supplied many bands previously from the Cambridge and London areas.

Inkies.co.uk
Top Floor, 32 Marine Parade, Lowestoft, Suffolk, NR33 0QN
tel: 01502 514 196
email: info@inkies.co.uk
web: www.inkies.co.uk
design service: Yes
info: Caps, mats, t-shirts and mugs, plus host of other products available.

Just What You Want
54 West End, Langtoft, Peterborough, PE6 9LU
tel: 0845 351 0389
fax: 01778 342 008
email: sales@justwhatyouwant.co.uk
web: www.justwhatyouwant.co.uk
contact: John Morgan
design service: Yes
minimum run: None
info: Promotional gifts including keyrings and pens. Just What You Want also promote gigs. Enquire for further details.

Mr Bee Ltd.
22-24 Bridge Street, Downham Market, Norfolk, PE38 9DH
tel: 01366 382 323
email: mrbeeltd@aol.com
design service: Yes
info: Printing onto t-shirts and many other products.

Myriad UK
330 Dereham Road, Norwich, NR2 4DL
tel: 0800 587 5967
email: sales@myriad-uk.net
web: www.myriad-uk.net
design service: Yes
info: Provide range of promotional gifts. Specialise in unique CD packaging and duplication.

Phoenix Tees
Bentwaters Park, Anglia International Airpark, Rendlesham, Woodbridge, Suffolk, IP12 2TW
tel: 01394 461 361
email: phoenixtees@aol.com
contact: Mr Sibert
design service: Yes
info: T-shirt printing service.

The Print Shop
23 Ipswich Court, Bury St. Edmunds, Suffolk, IP33 1ST
tel: 01284 723 648
email: smatcarprinting@aol.com
design service: Yes
info: Stickers, graphics, flyers and t-shirts available.

Samuels of Norfolk
Units 2 & 3, Collers Way, Reepham, Norwich, Norfolk, NR10 4SW
tel: 01603 879 793
email: samuel.norfolk@vigin.net
web: www.schoolshirt.co.uk
design service: Yes
minimum run: 25
info: Can provide printing onto t-shirts and promotional clothing for unsigned bands.

Screen Works
Unit 2, Homefield Road, Haverhill, Suffolk, CB9 8QP
tel: 01440 212 171
email: sales@screenworks.co.uk
web: www.screenworks.co.uk
design service: Yes
minimum run: 20
info: Printing onto any textile products including t-shirts, bags and hats. Specialise in full colour products.

Silver Screen Studio
29 Bridge Street, Bungay, Suffolk, NR35 1HD
tel: 01986 894 499
email: info@silverscreenstudio.co.uk
web: www.silverscreenstudio.co.uk
design service: Yes
info: Printing onto shirts, hats, bags, bottles and stickers. Embroidery also available.

SSAF
Old Blacksmiths Workshop, Back Vane, Marthan, Great Yarmouth, Norfolk, NR29 4PE
tel: 01493 749 174
email: sales@ssafwindowfilms.com
contact: John
design service: Yes
info: T-shirt printing and signage.

The Sticker Factory
The Granary, Walnut Tree Lane, Sudbury, Suffolk, CO10 1BD
tel: 01787 370 950
fax: 01787 371 890
email: sticker.sales@btinternet.com
web: www.the-sticker-factory.co.uk
design service: No
minimum run: Contact for details
info: Customised stickers, badges and stamps.

Striptees UK
Hempsheaf House, Queen Street, Strabroke, Eye, Suffolk, IP21 5HH
tel: 01379 384 775
design service: No
minimum run: None
info: Screen and digital printing. Heat transfers onto t-shirts, hats, polo shirts, sweatshirts and banners.

Stuart Morris
Riverside Print House, Pound Lane, Hadleigh, Ipswich, Suffolk, IP7 5EQ
tel: 01473 824 212
email: info@stuartmorris.co.uk
web: www.stuartmorris.co.uk
design service: Yes
minimum run: Dependent on item
info: Leisurewear including t-shirts, caps and bags.

Suffolk Insignia 2000
Unit 11, Tomo Business Park, Creeting Road, Stowmarket, IP14 5AY
tel: 01449 770 120
email: embroideredmusic@talk21.com
design service: Yes
minimum run: 50
info: Printed or embroidered garments, as well as pens, pencils and stickers available.

Talking T's
Unit 2, 149b Histon Road, Cambridge, Cambridgeshire, CB4 3JD
tel: 01223 304 104
email: talkingts@t-shirts.co.uk
web: www.t-shirts.co.uk
design service: Yes
info: Custom print and embroidery onto t-shirts including fitted and children's t-shirts.

Technograph
4 Manor Drive, Baston, Peterborough, Cambridgeshire, PE6 9PQ
tel: 01778 560 548
fax: 01778 560 914
email: sales@technograph.co.uk
web: www.technograph.co.uk
contact: Graeme Kirk
design service: Yes
minimum run: None
info: A broad range of products available for personalisation including pens, balloons, caps, t-shirts and CDs.

Total Promotion
Unit 3, Woodston Industrial Estate, Welbeck Way, Peterborough, PE2 7WH
tel: 01733 394 758
email: sales@totalpromotions.co.uk
web: www.totalpromotions.co.uk
design service: Yes
minimum run: 18-20
info: Promotional t-shirts and polo shirts.

U Design
33a Whiffler Road, Norwich, Norfolk, NR3 2AW
tel: 01603 482 379
design service: No
minimum run: None
info: Embroidery, laser printing, screen printing and vinyl graphics onto promotional items.

West Suffolk Leisurewear
18 Merlin Park, Fred Dannatt Road, Mildenhall, Bury St. Edmunds, IP28 7RD
tel: 01638 717 172
email: sales@wsluk.com
web: www.wsluk.com
design service: Yes
minimum run: Varies
info: T-shirts, screen printing and embroidery. Minimum run of 25 on screen printed products. No minimum run for embroidered items.

Wild Raspberry
Thatch Cottage, Boot Drift, Ipswich, Suffolk, IP9 1EY
tel: 01473 787 213
email: beccabourne@yahoo.co.uk
contact: Becca Bourne
design service: Yes
info: Open studio available for transfer printing. Screen printing also available.

Windmill Prints
Unit 10, Forge Business Centre, Upper Rose Lane, Palgrave, Diss, IP22 1AP
tel: 01379 640 045
email: pauline@winprint.co.uk
web: www.winprint.co.uk
contact: Pauline
design service: Yes
minimum run: None
info: Can provide t-shirts, flyers, banners, CD inserts, pens, mugs and key fobs.

GREATER LONDON

1st C.S.
59 Borough Hill, Croydon, CR0 4LP
tel: 020 8686 2510
design service: No
minimum run: None
info: Offer a wide range of promotional items including clothing, mouse mats, mugs, baseball caps, badges and coasters. Digital printing onto banners.

1st Express T-Shirts
194 Kingston Road, New Malden, KT3 3RJ
tel: 020 8949 4099
design service: Yes
minimum run: 10
info: Fast, inexpensive screen printing and embroidery onto a range of garments.

3rd Level Garment Printing
64 Cedars Road, Surrey, KT1 4BE
tel: 020 8255 7954
email: garmentprinting@artoutthere.net
design service: Yes
minimum run: None
info: Offer a range of garments. Runs from 1 to 8,000.

A1 Club And Company
39 Passey Place, London, SE9 5DA
tel: 0800 018 0679
email: sales@mfa-uk.co.uk
web: www.mfa-uk.co.uk
design service: Yes
minimum run: 25
info: Over 1,000 promotional items available including t-shirts, keyrings and caps. Embroidery and screen printing. See website for an online catalogue.

Alexco
94 Guildford Road, Croydon, CR0 2HJ
tel: 020 8683 0546
fax: 020 8689 4749
email: alexco@btconnect.com
design service: No
info: Offer a range of promotional items including t-shirts, badges, caps and keyrings. Minimum run depends on the product.

APG T-Shirt Screen
Arch 140, Stamford Brook Archers, Hammersmith, London, W6 0TQ
tel: 020 8723 6456
web: www.abuzelondon.com
design service: Yes
minimum run: 20
info: Offer a wide range of screen-printed garments.

Apparelize Custom Streetwear
Studio 6, Unit B106, Faircharm Studios, 8-10 Creekside, London, SE8 3DX
tel: 020 8469 0707
fax: 020 8469 0179
email: simon@apparelize.com
web: www.apparelize.com
design service: Yes
minimum run: None
info: Offer customised clothing, brand identity and sample runs. This includes bespoke designs, custom footwear and artist sponsorship services, targeting the youth, music and fashion markets. Recent clients include UK Garage artists DJ EZ, Masterstepz, and EMI signed R&B artist Sean Emmanuel.

Arti Promotions
151 Trafalgar Road, Greenwich, London, SE10 9TX
tel: 020 8293 1280
fax: 020 8293 1283
email: info@artipromotions.com
web: www.artipromotions.com
design service: Yes
minimum run: None
info: Offer a range of garments. Embroidery and screen printing available.

Backstreet International Merchandise
1st Floor, Unit A, 16-24 Brewery Road, London, N7 9NH
tel: 020 7700 2662
fax: 020 7700 2882
email: andy@bsimerch.com
web: www.bsimerch.com
design service: Yes
minimum run: 100
info: Offer a range of promotional garments including t-shirts, vests and baseball shirts. Clients include The Libertines, Franz Ferdinand and The Cooper Temple Clause.

Badges For Bands
email: sales@badgesforbands.com
web: www.badgesforbands.com
design service: No
minimum run: 1
info: Custom pin badges. Typical price of £17.99 for 100 badges. Also run a scheme called Badges For Free and every time you tell someone about the Badges For Bands website who then goes onto make an order, you will be given 10 free badges.

Better Badges
Unit C, 9 Garman Road, London, N17 0UR
tel: 020 8365 1035
fax: 020 8365 1905
email: john@abetterbadge.com
web: www.abetterbadge.com
design service: No
minimum run: 100
info: Offer a range of button badges from 25mm to 55mm. Discounts available for bulk orders.

The Big Screen
5 Dace Road, London, E3 2NG
tel: 020 8986 3300
fax: 020 8986 3742
email: sales@thebigscreen.co.uk
web: www.thebigscreen.co.uk
design service: Yes
minimum run: None
info: Offer a variety of garments including t-shirts, bags, pens, mugs and jackets. Embroidery and screen printing. 24 hour service available in certain cases.

Blue Grape
c/o Roadrunner Records, Ealing Studios, Ealing Green, London, W5 5EP
tel: 0870 112 1284
fax: 020 8749 5897
email: emarlow@bluegrape.co.uk
web: www.bluegrape.co.uk
design service: No
minimum run: None
info: Offer a range of garments. Clients include The Strokes, The Charlatans and The Libertines.

Brand Inc.
2nd Floor, 54-56 Wharf Road, Islington, London, N1 7SF
tel: 020 7253 7110
fax: 0207 253 7112
email: london@brand-inc.net
web: www.brand-inc.net
design service: Yes
minimum run: 100
info: Offer a range of promotional items including t-shirts, caps and bags.

Bravado International Group Ltd.
12 Deer Park Road, London, SW19 3FB
tel: 020 8545 8100/020 8542 1807
email: ryan.norton@bravado.com
web: www.bravado.com
contact: Ryan Norton
design service: Yes
minimum run: Call for details
info: Bravado develops and markets licensed merchandise to a world-wide audience. Working closely with new and established entertainment clients, creating innovative products carefully tailored to each artist or brand and selling on live tours, via selected retail outlets, and through mobile downloads and web-based stores. Bravado International Group have offices in London, Los Angeles, New York, San Francisco and Stockholm with commercial partners in Japan, Australia and South America.

Bruce Elliott
2 Greaves Place, London, SW17 0NE
tel: 020 8682 3733
email: bruceelliot@blueyonder.co.uk
design service: Yes
minimum run: None
info: Range of garments including t-shirts and sweatshirts.

BTC Group
BTC House, 9 Millington Road, Hayes, Middlesex, UB3 4AZ
tel: 020 8569 2250
email: sales@btcgroup.co.uk
web: www.btcgroup.co.uk
design service: Yes
minimum run: None
info: Wide range of garments available for embroidery and screen printing.

Casual Tees
63 Vyner Street, London, E2 9DQ
tel: 0800 195 6956/020 8980 3497
fax: 020 8980 2591
email: info@casualtees.co.uk
web: www.casualtees.co.uk
design service: Yes
minimum run: None
info: Variety of garments available. Embroidery and screen printing.

Cat's Cream
266 Holloway Road, London, N7 6NE
tel: 020 7607 2961
email: catscream31@btconnect.com
web: www.catscream.co.uk
design service: Yes
minimum run: None
info: Offer a range of promotional items for screen printing including t-shirts, stickers and banners. No minimum run.

Charitees
37 Barnfield Avenue, Kingston Upon Thames, Surrey, KT2 5RD
tel: 020 8549 8653
email: info@charitees.co.uk
web: www.charitees.co.uk
design service: Yes
minimum run: 1
info: Offer a range of garments including t-shirts, baseball caps and all promotional clothing.

Colour Copy Centre
3 High Street, Purley, CR8 2AF
tel: 020 8763 9201
design service: Yes
minimum run: None
info: Can print any colour onto light coloured t-shirt.

Colour Screen
765-767 Harrow Road, London, NW10 5NY
tel: 020 8960 1613
fax: 020 8960 3603
email: info@colourscreen.co.uk
web: www.colourscreen.co.uk
design service: Yes
minimum run: None
info: Offer a variety of promotional materials including t-shirts, banners and stickers.

Crewe Issue
54a Holmdale Road, West Hampstead, London, NW6 1BL
tel: 020 7431 5548
fax: 020 7431 5547
email: info@crewe-issue.co.uk
web: www.crewe-issue.co.uk
design service: No
minimum run: Depends on the product
info: Offer a variety of promotional items. Crewe Issue frequently work with unsigned acts, and offer a full merchandising and licensing service. Clients include Duran Duran and Wheatus.

The Crow's Nest
38 Aragon Avenue, Thames Ditton, Surrey, KT7 0PX
tel: 020 8398 0077
fax: 020 8398 0077
email: sales@thecrowsnest.biz
web: www.thecrowsnest.biz
design service: Yes
minimum run: None
info: Range of garments available. Embroidery and screen printing.

Custom Print
2 Ashvale Road, Tooting, London, SW17 8PW
tel: 020 8682 4152
email: sales@customprint.co.uk
web: www.customprint.co.uk
design service: Yes
minimum run: One off.
info: Variety of promotional items including t-shirts, badges, mugs and keyrings. Full colour available.

Customskins
18 Iliffe Yard, Crampton Street, London, SE17 3QA
tel: 020 7708 4289
email: tim@customskins.co.uk
web: www.customskins.co.uk
contact: Tim
design service: Yes
info: Custom printed bass drumheads and back drops.

Dino Designs
72 Heston Avenue, Hounslow, Middlesex, TW5 9EX
tel: 020 8569 4602
email: sales@dinodesigns.co.uk
web: www.dinodesigns.co.uk
design service: Yes
minimum run: 12
info: Offer a range of garments including t-shirts and polo shirts. Embroidery and screen printing.

Dy-mensionscreen Printers Ltd.
5-6 Cooper's Yard, London, SE19 1TN
tel: 020 8670 3400
email: dy-mensionscreen@aol.com
design service: Yes
minimum run: None
info: Screen printing onto a variety of garments.

Ellenell
Promotion House, 1B Shrubbery Road, Edmonton, London, N9 0QQ
tel: 020 8887 0000
fax: 020 8887 0001
email: sales@ellenell.com
web: www.ellenell.com
design service: Yes
minimum run: 50
info: Offer a range of promotional items including t-shirts and bags. 7 day service available.

Embroidery by Design Ltd.
Unit 6, Imex House, 6 Wadsworth Road, Greenford, UB6 7JD
tel: 020 8998 1983
email: jasvirkaur@aol.com
web: www.embroidery-by-design.co.uk
design service: Yes
minimum run: Varies
info: Embroidery services onto selection of garments.

Event Merchandising Ltd.
Unit 11, The Edge, Humber Road, London, NW2 6EW
tel: 020 8208 1166
email: malcolm@eventmerchandising.com
web: www.eventmerchandising.com
contact: Malcolm Garnett
design service: Yes
minimum run: None
info: T-shirt printers.

FBM Ltd.
16 Greenways, Esher, KT10 0QD
tel: 020 8339 0334
fax: 020 8339 3461
email: fbmkt@aol.com
web: www.fbmpromotions.co.uk
design service: No
minimum run: None
info: A huge variety of products available with very friendly service.

Focus Merchandise
61 Barrowell Green, Winchmore Hill, London, N21 3AS
tel: 020 8245 9035
fax: 020 8245 6190
email: sales@focusmerchandise.co.uk
web: www.focusmerchandise.co.uk or www.wahwah.co.uk
design service: No
minimum run: 100
info: All promotional items including embroidery and printing services.

Green Island Promotions Ltd.
Unit 31, 56 Gloucester Road, Kensington, London, SW7 4UB
tel: 0870 789 3377
email: greenisland@btinternet.com
web: www.greenislandpromotions.com
design service: Yes
minimum run: None
info: Provide embroidery and screen printing onto a number of garments.

Imageopia
Unit 5, Village Arcade, 49-53 Station Road, Chingford, London, E4 7DA
tel: 020 8529 2085
email: enquiries@imageopia.co.uk
web: www.imageopia.co.uk
design service: Yes
minimum run: None
info: Offer a range of promotional items including t-shirts and keyrings. Can transfer onto almost any surface.

Inkerman Ltd.
2 Uxbridge Street, London, W8 7SY
tel: 020 7221 1012
email: sales@inkerman.co.uk
web: www.inkerman.co.uk
design service: Yes
minimum run: None
info: Bags and leather goods. No minimum run.

Iris
Unit 8a-10a, Southam Street, Kensington, London, W10 5PH
tel: 020 8969 4761
email: tim.bart@gmail.com
design service: Yes
minimum run: 20
info: Offer a range of garments. Embroidery and screen printing.

JeaP Clothing & Promotions
24 Higham Station Avenue, Chingford, London, E4 9AZ
tel: 020 8523 1617
email: debbie@jeap.makemymegastore.com
web: www.jeap.makemymegastore.com
design service: Yes
minimum run: None
info: T-shirts, caps, badges, bags and keyrings, as well as more promotional items. Embroidery and screen printing.

The Logo Centre
Unit 25, East Thamesmead Business Park, Kencot Way, Erith, Kent, DA18 4AB
tel: 020 8310 3030
email: info@thelogocentre.co.uk
web: www.thelogocentre.co.uk
design service: Yes
minimum run: None
info: Variety of garments available including t-shirts and sweatshirts. Embroidery and screen printing supplied.

Logoprint
17 Bowater Road, London, SE18 5TF
tel: 020 8854 1111
fax: 020 8854 7000
email: sales@logoprintuk.com
web: www.logoprintuk.com
design service: Yes
minimum run: None
info: Can print onto anything including range of garments.

Marks of Distinction
55 Central Avenue, West Molesey, KT8 2QZ
tel: 020 8941 5533
email: mod@chelsea.co.uk
web: www.marksofdistinction.net
design service: No
minimum run: varies
info: Supplier of promotional items, business gifts, as well as trophies and awards.

Microtees
31 Barnfield Avenue, Kingston Upon Thames, Surrey, KT2 5RD
tel: 020 8546 9606
fax: 020 8974 6001
email: saels@tshirt.co.uk
web: www.tshirt.co.uk
design service: Yes
minimum run: None
info: Offer a range of garments including t-shirts and baseball caps. Embroidery and screen printing.

Mirage Design & Print Ltd.
Unit 1, Hanover Trading Estate, 1-3 North Road, London, N7 9HD
tel: 020 7700 3336
email: info@miragetshirts.com
web: www.miragetshirts.com
design service: Yes
minimum run: 25
info: Screen printed promotional garments available.

Negs Photographic & Digital Imaging
45-47 Broadwick Street, London, W1F 9QP
tel: 020 7734 3577
fax: 020 8974 6001
email: info@negs.co.uk
web: www.negs.co.uk
design service: Yes
minimum run: None
info: Variety of services provided including digital printing onto garments in large formats, and professional photos.

Non Citizen
50a West Kensington Mansions, Beaumont Cresent, London, W14 9PF
tel: 07779 112 905
email: info@noncitizen.co.uk
web: www.noncitizen.co.uk
design service: Yes
info: Clients provide the design which can be printed or embroidered onto their choice of garment

Pacific Prints Ltd.
6a Well Street, Hackney, London, E9 7PX
tel: 020 8985 2525
email: emailus@pacificprints.co.uk
web: www.pacificprints.co.uk
design service: Yes
minimum run: 50
info: Offer a range of screen printed garments. Previous clients have included Supergrass and Stereophonics.

Paulro's
70 Sydenham Road, Sydenham, London, SE26 5QE
tel: 020 8778 5509
email: paulrosse26@aol.com
design service: No
minimum run: None
info: T-shirt printing.

Pier 32
Thames Ditton, Surrey, KT7 0SQ
tel: 020 8398 2847
fax: 020 8398 2687
email: gerry@pier32.co.uk
web: www.pier32.co.uk or www.tshirtprinters.uk.com
design service: Yes
minimum run: Contact for details
info: Range of garments available, printed or embroidered. Employ an 'Ethical Trade Policy', see website for details.

Print Inc.
43 Lower Addiscombe Road, Croydon, Surrey, CR0 6PQ
tel: 020 8681 8961
fax: 020 8668 6363
email: enquiries@printinc.sfbusiness.co.uk
design service: Yes
minimum run: None
info: Offer a range of garments including t-shirts, caps and jackets.

Pukka Promotions
PO Box 4430, London, SW19 1EW
tel: 020 8404 6211
email: info@pukkapromotions.co.uk
design service: Yes
minimum run: None
info: Provide a design service for promotional items.

Ram Promotions
Unit 3, 41-43 Roebuck Road, Hainault Industrial Estate, Ilford, IG6 3TU
tel: 020 8500 3333
fax: 020 8500 3030
email: info@ram-promotions.co.uk
web: www.ram-promotions.co.uk
design service: Yes
minimum run: None
info: Will print onto anything from t-shirts to mugs.

RGL Promotions
Unit 9, The Green Business Centre, The Causeway, Staines, Middlesex, TW18 3AL
tel: 0800 783 8517
email: sales@rglpromotions.com
web: www.rglpromotions.com
design service: Yes
minimum run: None
info: Supply screen printing and embroidery onto t-shirts and other garments.

Rocket Badge Co.
1 Torriano Mews, Torriano Avenue, Kentish Town, London, NW5 2RZ
tel: 0845 230 0112
fax: 0845 230 0114
email: sales@rocketbadge.co.uk
web: www.rocketbadge.co.uk
design service: Yes
minimum run: 300
info: Wide range of enamel and button badges.

Saint Phillip's
Unit 5, Horseshoe Close, Oxgate Lane, London, NW2 7JJ
tel: 020 8452 4266
design service: No
minimum run: None
info: Customised print runs and print effects specialists. Wll print onto t-shirts and other garments.

Shout Promotional Merchandise Ltd.
24 Sparkford Gardens, London, N11 3GT
tel: 020 8361 5222
design service: No
minimum run: None
info: Printed t-shirts, key rings, mugs and pens.

Spinnakers Ltd.
Unit 10, Park Works, Borough Road, Kingston, KT2 6BD
tel: 020 8974 9596
email: sales@spinnakersports.co.uk
web: www.spinnakersports.co.uk
design service: Yes
minimum run: None
info: Offer a range of promotional items including t-shirts, bags, caps and pens. Minimum costs apply.

Stop the Press
Unit 2, Burmarsh Workshops, 71 Marsden Street, London, NW5 3JA
tel: 020 7691 4242
email: studio@stop-the-press.co.uk
web: www.stop-the-press.co.uk
design service: Yes
minimum run: None
info: Offer a variety of promotional items, including t-shirts, banners, posters, flyers and stickers.

T.O.T. Shirts Ltd.
13a Bankshia Road, Eleys Estate, Angel Road, Edmonton, London, N18 3BH
tel: 020 8807 8083
fax: 020 8345 6095
email: sales@t-o-t-shirts.co.uk
web: www.t-o-t-shirts.co.uk
design service: Yes
minimum run: None
info: Offer a range of garments for screen printing.

Toxico
15d Winchester Buildings, Stonehill, Rivermead, Edmonton, London, N18 3QW
tel: 020 8803 3461
fax: 020 8803 3537
email: info@toxico.co.uk
web: www.toxico.co.uk
design service: Yes
minimum run: 40
info: Offer a variety of garments, including t-shirts, hooded tops and underwear. Toxico frequently work with bands and musicians.

T-shirt Crazy
Unit 3, Sutton Station, High Street, Sutton, Surrey, SM1 1JA
tel: 020 8661 7544
email: matt@tshirtcrazy.co.uk
web: www.tshirtcrazy.co.uk
design service: Yes
minimum run: None
info: Offer a range of garments, including t-shirts and sweatshirts.

The T-Shirtprinters.com
Stratford Workshops, Burford Road, Stratford, E15 2SP
tel: 020 8522 1133
email: sales@thetshirtprinters.com
web: www.thetshirtprinters.com
design service: Yes
minimum run: None
info: Variety of garments available including t-shirts, vests and baseball tops.

T-shirts 4 Less
12 Barnet Road, Barnet, Hertfordshire, EN5 3HB
tel: 020 8441 2244
email: tshirts4less@btconnect.com
design service: No
minimum run: 25
info: Screen printed or embroidered garments.

Upper & Lower Leisurewear
Leylands House, Molesey Road, Hersham, Walton-On-Thames, KT12 3PW
tel: 0800 096 2104
email: sales@upperandlower.co.uk
web: www.upperandlower.co.uk
design service: Yes
minimum run: 1
info: Offer a wide range of promotional items including stickers, banners and t-shirts. Embroidery and screen-printing.

White Horse Marketing Ltd.
Croydon House, Peall Road, Croydon, CR0 3EX
tel: 020 8665 5755
fax: 020 8665 5750
email: ian@whitehorsemarketing.co.uk
web: www.whitehorsemarketing.co.uk
design service: Yes
minimum run: None
info: Offer range of promotional items including mugs, mousemats and umbrellas. See the website for more details.

MUSIC SERVICES/RETAIL

Xen
11 Harrow Place, off Middlesex Street and Houndsditch, London, E1 7DB
tel: 020 7247 2634
email: mail@suits2boots.com
web: www.suits2boots.com
design service: Yes
minimum run: None
info: Offer a variety of garments including t-shirts and sweatshirts. Screen printing, embroidery and transfer. Specialists in short runs.

XS T-Shirts Ltd.
Unit 5, 61 Lorford Road, London, SE5 9HY
tel: 020 7978 8763
email: xs381@hotmail.com
design service: Yes
minimum run: None
info: Selection of garments available such as t-shirts and jackets.

MIDLANDS

A4 Apparel
Unit 97a, Blackpole Trading Estate, Blackpole, Worcester, WR3 8TJ
tel: 01905 755 595
web: www.a4apparel.co.uk
design service: Yes
minimum run: None
info: Screen printing and thermal transfers onto a range of clothing.

Ace Sports & Ladyline
49 Duke Street, Staveley, Chesterfield, S43 3PD
tel: 01246 280 473
email: malc@ace-sports.freeserve.co.uk
web: www.acesports.freeserve.co.uk
contact: Malcolm
design service: Yes
minimum run: None
info: T-shirt printers. Can also provide embroidery service.

Action Jacket Company
PO Box 1180, Stourbridge, West Midlands, DY9 02F
tel: 01562 887 096
email: info@actionjacket.co.uk
web: www.actionjacket.co.uk
contact: Brian
design service: Yes
info: Specialise in printing of corporate clothing. Also print variety of t-shirts and other garments.

Advance Printwear
26 Bordesley Trading Estate, Bordesley Green Road, Birmingham, West Midlands, B8 1BZ
tel: 0121 322 2111
design service: No
minimum run: None
info: Print or embroidery onto t-shirts, sweatshirts, caps and polo shirts.

Aim Promotions
72 Boston Road, Gorse Hill Industrial Estate, Leicester, LE4 1AW
tel: 0116 222 697
email: sales@aimpromotions.co.uk
web: www.aimpromotions.co.uk
contact: Dylan
design service: Yes
minimum run: 5
info: Will print banners and backdrops for bands. Can also provide t-shirts and range of promotional merchandise.

Alfabet Screen Print Ltd.
Unit 9, Sargeant Turner Trading Estate, Bromley Street, Lye, Stourbridge, DY9 8HZ
tel: 01384 897 355
web: www.alfabet.co.uk
contact: Janice
design service: Yes
minimum run: None
info: Can produce car stickers, t-shirts, pencil cases and other items.

ASAP Screen Printers & Embroidery
21 Station Terrace, Hucknall, Nottingham, Nottinghamshire, NG15 7TQ
tel: 0115 859 8626
design service: No
minimum run: 15
info: Shirts, caps and badges plus range of other promotional items and gifts. Screen printing and embroidery.

Bear & Booth
PO Box 3908, Burntwood, WS7 4ZE
tel: 07811 063 189
email: info@bearandbooth.com
web: www.bearandbooth.com
design service: Yes
info: 25mm button badges, t-shirts, stickers, hoodies, mesh tops and underwear. Other items also available, contact for details. Short run specialists with a minimum order of £5.

Compass Apparel
639 Harvey Road, Derby, Derbyshire, DE24 8GL
tel: 01332 752 003
email: control@compassapparel.co.uk
web: www.compassapparel.co.uk
design service: Yes
minimum run: None
info: Design your own badges. Also offer printing onto t-shirts and other garments. Accessories also available.

Creation Studios
Craigmore, Southpark Avenue, Darley Dale, Matlock, Derbyshire, DE4 2FY
tel: 01629 733 880
email: sales@creationstudios.biz
web: www.creationstudios.biz
design service: Yes
minimum run: None
info: Printing onto variety of garments and accessories.

D.G. Savage & Son Ltd.
Promotions House, 4 Casting Road, Derby, DE23 8YL
tel: 01332 349 010
design service: Yes
info: Printing onto t-shirts and promotional items available.

Demipa Incentives
8 Granby Business Park, Granby Avenue, Birmingham, B3 0TJ
tel: 0121 785 1118
fax: 0121 785 1119
email: sales@demipa.co.uk
web: www.adgifts.co.uk
design service: Yes
info: Range of promotional items. Turnaround of 5 working days. Request a free brochure of merchandise from the website.

Elite Screen Printers & Embroiderers
Elite House, 45 Sartoris Road, Rushden, NN10 9TL
tel: 01933 315 930
email: sales@eliteclothing.co.uk
web: www.eliteclothing.co.uk
design service: Yes
minimum run: None
info: T-shirt printers who have worked with a number of bands in the past.

Flame Red Graphics
10 Coronation Road, Nottingham, NG3 5JN
tel: 0115 955 2936
email: flameredgraphics@hotmail.com
web: www.flameredgraphics.co.uk
design service: Yes
minimum run: None
info: Print onto flags, signs, banners and t-shirts.

Flying Colours
16-18 Hockley, Nottingham, NG1 1FP
tel: 0115 950 8448
email: info@flyingcoloursprints.co.uk
web: www.flyingcoloursprints.co.uk
design service: Yes
minimum run: None
info: Colour t-shirt printers. Can also provide coasters, mousemats, keyrings and jigsaws.

Funky Concepts
Studio 5, Landsdowne Close, Coseley, Bilston, WV14 9TR
tel: 01902 651 239
fax: 01902 651 239
email: info@funkyconcepts.co.uk
web: www.funkyconcepts.co.uk
design service: Yes
info: Huge selection of promotional merchandise including pens, luggage, confectionery, drinks and umbrellas. See website for full catalogue.

GJ Merchandising Ltd.
Unit 3, Ground Floor, 4 Castle Boulevard, Nottingham, NG7 1FB
tel: 0115 947 6063
fax: 0115 979 9235
email: info@gjmerchandising.co.uk
web: www.gjmerchandising.co.uk
design service: Yes
minimum run: Dependent on item
info: Full range of merchandise. Coasters, pens, clothing and much more. See website for full catalogue.

Heated Graphics
90 Egypt Road, Nottingham, NG7 7GN
tel: 0115 942 4258
email: burnt_halo@tiscali.co.uk
contact: Jermaine
design service: Yes
minimum run: None
info: T-shirt printing service.

Images By Interprint
Ludlow Business Park, Lingen Road, Ludlow, Shropshire, SY8 1XD
tel: 01584 879 832
email: enquires@imagesbyinterprint.co.uk
web: www.imagesbyinterprint.co.uk
contact: Mandy Hughes
design service: Yes
minimum run: 12
info: T-shirt printing and embroidery services.

IMT Print
Unit 1, Talbot Street, Brierley Hill, DY5 3DL
tel: 01384 262 331
email: sales@imtprint.co.uk
web: www.imtprint.co.uk
design service: No
minimum run: 10
info: Print directly onto garments using ink. Suitable for single or multi-colour work. Embroidery also available.

JCP Print & Promotion
196-198 Dward Road, Birmingham, West Midlands, B12 9LX
tel: 0121 440 7919
email: admin@jcp.co.uk
web: www.jcp.org.uk/print
design service: Yes
minimum run: None
info: Design, printing and embroidery onto t-shirts, sweatshirts and polo shirts.

Julie's Fashion House
7 South Street, Chesterfield, S40 1QX
tel: 01246 559 309
email: juliesfashion@btconnect.com
web: www.juliesfashionhouse.co.uk
design service: Yes
minimum run: None
info: T-shirt printing. Specialise in one-off numbers and designs.

Leisure Print
165 High Street, Rowley Regis, B65 0DX
tel: 0121 561 4738
email: michael@leisureprint.fsnet.co.uk
contact: Mike
design service: Yes
minimum run: None
info: T-shirt and textile printers.

Maverick Promotions
4 Paddock Close, Ancaster, Grantham, Lincolnshire, NG32 3RP
tel: 01400 230 180
email: maverickprns@aol.com
contact: Andrew
design service: Yes
minimum run: 12
info: Offer t-shirt printing service.

Metro Merchandise Ltd.
4 Torridge Close, Telford Way Industrial Estate, Kettering, Northamptonshire, NN16 8PY
tel: 01536 415 005
fax: 01536 415 006
design service: No
minimum run: 50
info: Printing and embroidery onto all types of garments.

Monster Screenprints
Nottingham
tel: 07791 774 275/01623 799 351
email: monstertshirts@aol.com
web: www.monsterscreenprints.com
contact: Steve
design service: Yes
minimum run: 20
info: Screen printing onto t-shirts, hoodies and other garments. Next day delivery.

Motifs
24 Main Street, Kimberley, Nottingham, NG16 2LL
tel: 0845 130 6146
fax: 0115 945 9206
email: sales@motifs.co.uk
web: www.motifs.co.uk
design service: No
minimum run: None
info: Screen printing, t-shirt printers and embroiderers. Motifs are happy to supply small quantities from a single garment up.

Multiprint
1 Town End Street, Walsall, WS2 8LP
tel: 01922 625 651
fax: 01922 721 957
email: multiprintuk@btconnect.com
design service: Yes
info: Complete range of promotional merchandise available.

www.mustardmerchandise.co.uk

Mustard Merchandise
Studio A307, LCB Depot, 31 Rutland Street, Leicester, LE1 1RE
tel: 0116 261 6895
fax: 0116 261 6896
email: sales@mustardmerchandise.co.uk
web: www.mustardmerchandise.co.uk
design service: Yes
minimum run: None
info: Short run specialists. Graphic design team who have good links with the fashion industry. Previous clients include Ministry of Sound.

October T-shirt Printers
Unit C14, Hartley Workspace, Haydn Road, Sherwood, Nottingham, NG5 1DG
tel: 0115 962 6636
email: paul@october.co.uk
web: www.october.co.uk
contact: Paul Stephenson
design service: Yes
minimum run: None
info: Specialise in t-shirt printing, embroidery and screen printing services. Wide range of clothing and accessories available.

One Stop Promotions Ltd.
Unit 38, Hayhill Industrial Estate, Barrow-Upon-Soar, Loughborough, Leicestershire, LE12 8LD
tel: 01509 814 380
fax: 01509 814 929
email: sales@onestoppromotions.co.uk
web: www.onestoppromotions.co.uk
design service: Yes
minimum run: None
info: Turnaround time of between 2 and 4 weeks. Previous experience with the music industry.

The Promotional Mix Ltd.
28-29 Worcester Street, Kidderminster, Worcestershire, DY10 1ED
tel: 01562 864 515
fax: 01562 862 253
email: sales@promotional-mix.co.uk
web: www.promotional-mix.co.uk
design service: Yes
minimum run: Contact for details
info: Turnaround time of 10-15 working days. Wide selection of promotional merchandise available. Minimum run depends on item.

QuestARC
Unit 10, 4.2 Amber Trading Centre, Digby Industrial Estate, Artic Way, Giltbrook, Nottingham, NG16 2HS
tel: 0800 195 3625
email: info@questarc.com
web: www.questarc.com
contact: Jane
design service: Yes
minimum run: None
info: Banners and signs, plus range of promotional items available.

Recognition Express (Melton Mowbray)
Insignia House, North Street, Melton Mowbray, LE13 1NL
tel: 01664 568 108
fax: 01664 564 262
email: sales@em.recognition-express.com
web: www.re-eastmidlands.co.uk
design service: Yes
minimum run: 1
info: Variety of promotional items such as badges, mugs and pens. Turnaround time of 48 hours.

Revolution
The Factory, 43 North Avenue, Coalville, Leicestershire, LE67 3QX
tel: 0800 298 5086
web: www.revolutionshirts.co.uk
design service: No
minimum run: None
info: Digital printing service. Range of clothing such as t-shirts, sweatshirts, work wear and other promotional products.

Rock-It Promotions
Unit 1, 6 East Grove, Rushden, Northamptonshire, NN10 0AP
tel: 01933 311 179
email: sales@rockitpro.com
web: www.promoclothing.com
contact: Andy
design service: Yes
minimum run: None
info: Printing services onto a variety of garments such as t-shirts, fleeces and sweatshirts.

Shirty Something
PO Box 6519, Nottingham, NG3 5LU
tel: 0115 920 2645
email: mail@shirtysomething.com
web: www.shirtysomething.com
design service: Yes
minimum run: None
info: Hand printed t-shirts. Offer fast turnaround and reasonable rates. Willing to assist with design ideas.

Signature Promotional Leisure Wear
15-17 Stoney Street, The Lace Market, Nottingham, NG1 1LP
tel: 0115 941 9534
email: signatureleisure@aol.com
web: www.signatureleisurewear.co.uk
contact: Penny, Steve
design service: Yes
minimum run: None
info: Printing or embroidery onto a range of garments.

T.F.G. Copyprint
196b Saffron Lane, Leicester, Leicestershire, LE2 7NE
tel: 0116 283 7601
design service: No
minimum run: None
info: T-shirt printing service.

Terramerch
The Renewal Trust Business Centre, 3 Hawksworth Street, Nottingham, NG3 2EG
tel: 0115 948 2444
email: info@terramerch.co.uk
web: www.terramerch.co.uk
contact: Julia
design service: Yes
minimum run: None
info: Terramerch work with bands regularly. Promotional merchandise and t-shirts available. Complete online form for quote.

Trafford Print & Design
69 John Gray Road, Great Doddington, Wellingborough, NN29 7TX
tel: 01933 229 366
email: info@traffordprintdesignprinting.com
web: www.traffordprintdesignprinting.com
contact: Darrell
design service: Yes
minimum run: None
info: Print onto t-shirts, polo shirts and sweatshirts.

UK Banners & Signs
Unit 6, Spring Court Industrial Estate, Malvern, Worcestershire, G41 3JA
tel: 0845 644 1945
fax: 0845 644 4519
email: sales@ukbannersandsigns.co.uk
web: www.ukbannersandsigns.co.uk
design service: Yes
info: Banners and signage, as well as printed clothing and other promotional items.

Vision Marketing
256 Stourbridge Road, Bromsgrove, B61 9LQ
tel: 01527 875 348
fax: 01527 570 182
email: vision.marketing@ukgateway.net
web: www.visionmarketingonline.co.uk
design service: Yes
info: Short turnaround times. Wide variety of merchandise available including badges, pens, balloons and key rings.

WCM & A
Units 1-4, Woodend Business Park, Stoke Lacy, Herefordshire, HR7 4HQ
tel: 01885 490 500
fax: 01885 490 585
web: www.wcma.co.uk
design service: Yes
minimum run: 100
info: Design your own button and enamel badges.

NORTHEAST

Abstract Bottle Co. Ltd.
Unit 7-11, Morgan Business Centre, Camperdown Industrial Estate, Newcastle Upon Tyne, Tyne & Wear, NE12 5UJ
tel: 0191 216 0255
email: info@abstractbottles.com
web: www.abstractbottle.com
design service: Yes
info: Printed, colour coated wine and champagne bottles. Have dealt with bands before and advise them to design their own logos.

Agbula Designs
145 Tremiar Close, Plains Farm, Sunderland, SR3 1SY
tel: 0191 552 5336
email: info@agbula.com
web: www.agbula.com
contact: Phil
design service: Yes
minimum run: None
info: Print onto t-shirts, hooded tops and many other garments.

Apple Screen Print
Unit 7, Forth Goods Arches, Newcastle Upon Tyne, NE1 3PG
tel: 0191 261 7523
email: appletree@btclick.com
web: www.applescreenprint.co.uk
design service: No
minimum run: None
info: Print onto sweatshirts, polo shirts and t-shirts.

Aztec Printware & Promotions
c/o John Porter Ltd., North Hylton Road, Sunderland, Tyne & Wear, SR5 2SU
tel: 0191 561 0001
email: aztecpromo@promotee.wanadoo.co.uk
contact: Craig
design service: Yes
minimum run: None
info: T-shirt printing services. Will deal with any quantity.

Be Promotional
4 Hambleton Grove, Darlington, DL1 2FF
tel: 01325 364 349
email: johnwdol@btinternet.com
design service: Yes
info: Products include mousemats, pens, mugs, key rings and clothing.

Brilliant Source
13 Telford Court, Morpeth, Northumberland, NE61 2DB
tel: 01670 514 514
email: info@brilliantsource.com
web: www.brilliantsource.com
design service: Yes
info: Selection of products available. See website for full catalogue.

Compugift Ltd.
4 Lundy Court, Stockton On Tees, Cleveland, TS17 0YE
tel: 01642 763 800
email: sales@compugift.co.uk
web: www.compugift.co.uk
design service: Yes
minimum run: Contact for details
info: Large range of promotional gifts available such as badges, balloons, fridge magnets, clothing, wrist bands, bags, stationery and keyrings.

Dart Advertising
Richmond House, Starbeck Avenue, Sandyford, Newcastle Upon Tyne, NE2 1XG
tel: 0191 261 0456
email: dartadvertising@ukonline.co.uk
web: www.dartadvertising.co.uk
design service: Yes
info: Variety of products available from pens to confectionery. See website for full list.

Dimensions
20 Lorne Street, Middlesborough, Cleveland, TS1 5QY
tel: 01642 244 604
email: dimensions@webportel.co.uk
contact: Mark Williams
design service: Yes
minimum run: None
info: T-shirt printers. Use a range of textiles.

Eagle Graphics
The Mall, Morton Park Way, Darlington, County Durham, DL1 4PJ
tel: 01325 387 619
email: eagmike@aol.com
web: www.eagle-graphics.co.uk
contact: Pamela
design service: Yes
minimum run: None
info: T-shirt printers. Will print onto full colour and white shirts.

Festival Copy & Print Centre
32 High Street, Spennymoor, DL16 6DB
tel: 01388 810 855
fax: 01388 810 855
email: ronnie@festivalprint.co.uk
web: www.festivalprint.co.uk
contact: Ronnie McDonnell
design service: Yes
minimum run: None
info: Very band friendly. Can print anything needed. Can offer discounts to unsigned bands. Promotional items also available. Contact for further details.

The Gift House
32 High Street, Spennymoor, DL16 6DB
tel: 01388 810 855
fax: 01388 810 855
email: sales@thegifthouse.co.uk
web: www.thegifthouse.co.uk
contact: Ronnie McDonnell
design service: Yes
minimum run: None
info: Very band friendly. T-shirts, badges, banners and drum skins are just part of the range. Can even produce snow globes and teddy bears.

Jadnet Designs
E14 Innovator House, North East Business & Innovation Centre, Sunderland Enterprise Park (East), Sunderland, SR5 2TA
tel: 0800 043 2756
fax: 0191 516 6991
email: mail@jadnet.com
web: www.t-shirt-shop.co.uk
design service: No
minimum run: None
info: Print your own designs onto polo shirts, t-shirts and hoodies.

M.T.S. UK
10 Collyers Close, Hurworth, Darlington, DL2 2ES
tel: 0870 777 0630
design service: Yes
minimum run: 250
info: Personalised products including pens, mugs and clothing.

The Magic Touch
16 Blandford Square, Newcastle Upon Tyne, Tyne & Wear, NE1 4HZ
tel: 0191 230 3555
design service: Yes
minimum run: None
info: T-shirt printing services.

Mick Martin Promotions Ltd.
23 Woodpack Avenue, Wickham, Newcastle Upon Tyne, NE16 5YY
tel: 0191 488 5499
email: mickmartinis@hotmail.com
web: www.mickmartinpromotions.co.uk
design service: Yes
info: Clothing and promotional items.

Perfect Printwear
Unit 17, Team Valley Business Centre, Earlswa, Team Valley Trading Estate, Gateshead, NE11 0QH
tel: 0191 491 1832
design service: Yes
minimum run: 6
info: Printing onto t-shirts and other garments.

Piranha
115 New Bridge Street, Newcastle Upon Tyne, Tyne & Wear, NE1 2SW
tel: 0191 209 0902
email: sales@piranhaprint.com
web: www.piranhaprint.com
contact: Darrell Douglas
design service: Yes
minimum run: None
info: T-shirt print and embroidery.

Positive Image
Unit 4, St. Michael's Road, Newcastle Upon Tyne, NE6 1QU
tel: 0191 265 1265
design service: No
minimum run: 12
info: Screen printing and embroidery onto t-shirts.

Print & Promotional Services Ltd.
Old Billingham Business Centre, 1 Chapel Road, Billingham, TS23 1EN
tel: 01642 533 089
email: sales@pps-ltd.co.uk
web: www.pps-ltd.co.uk
design service: Yes
info: Variety of products available including pens, sweets, bags and mugs.

Spectrum Imaging
8 St. Mary's Place, Newcastle Upon Tyne, NE1 7PG
tel: 0191 261 1101
web: www.spectrumimaging.co.uk
design service: No
minimum run: None
info: Digital photo imaging, scanning and printing service onto t-shirts.

SRL Group
PO Box 74, Middlesborough, TS7 0WX
tel: 01642 318 926
email: sales@srleisure.freeserve.co.uk
web: www.srlgroup.co.uk
design service: Yes
minimum run: Contact for details
info: Over 10,000 promotional items available, plus range of garments.

Steel River Textiles
Unit 9-10, War Court, Wallis Road, Skippers Lane Industrial Estate, Middlesborough, TS6 6DU
tel: 01642 462 926
web: www.steelrivertextiles.co.uk
design service: No
minimum run: None
info: Embroidery and garment printing. Small and large orders welcome.

Surface Ink Ltd.
Unit 12, Delaval Trading Estate, Seaton Delaval, Whitley Bay, Tyne & Wear, NE25 0QT
tel: 0191 241 5707
email: sales@surfaceink.co.uk
web: www.surfaceink.co.uk
design service: No
minimum run: None
info: Made to order service available. Print and embroider onto large selection of garments. Efficient service.

Travelled Music
The Tile Works, Paxton, Berwick Upon Tweed, TD15 1TJ
tel: 01289 386 737
email: info@travelledmusic.co.uk
web: www.travelledmusic.co.uk
contact: Alan Thompson
design service: No
minimum run: None
info: Promotional items specifically for bands including t-shirts and badges. Travelled Music also provide management, equipment hire and duplication services, as well as promoting gigs. See entries in relevant sections for details.

MUSIC SERVICES/RETAIL

Washington Badge & Embroidery
Unit 7-8, Herthburn Estate, Hertburn, Washington, Tyne & Wear, NE37 2SF
tel:	0191 416 3558
web:	www.wbec.co.uk
design service:	Yes
minimum run:	None
info:	Screen and heat printing, as well as embroidery onto top quality garments.

NORTHWEST

123 Promo
72 The Rock, Bury, Lancashire, BL9 0PB
tel:	0870 121 1920
design service:	No
minimum run:	None
info:	Full colour printing onto t-shirts.

A&A Marketing
29 Hamilton Square, Birkenhead, Merseyside, CH41 6AZ
tel:	0151 650 1950
fax:	0151 650 1951
email:	sales@a-amarketing.com
web:	www.a-amarketing.com
contact:	Andrew
design service:	Yes
minimum run:	None
info:	A one-stop shop for all promotional, print and design needs.

A.B.C. Graphics
The Old Schoolhouse, Fletcher Street, Bolton, BL3 6NH
tel:	01204 395 888
fax:	01204 395 888
email:	sladen@abcgraphics.freeserve.co.uk
contact:	Marjorie Sladen
design service:	Yes
minimum run:	10
info:	Screen printing onto a range of garments.

A.P.P.S.
26 Thurman Street, Lancaster, LA1 1XU
tel:	01524 841 286
fax:	01524 842 330
email:	apps@promotional-goods.org.uk
web:	www.promotional-goods.org.uk
contact:	Steve Duckles
design service:	Yes
minimum run:	None
info:	Embroidery, screen printing or laser printing onto a range of promotional gifts including jigsaws, fridge magnets, mousemats and badges.

Abbey Promotions
Abbey Works, Back King Street, Whalley, Near Clitheroe, Lancashire, BB7 9SP
tel:	01254 823 014
email:	info@abbeypromotionsonline.co.uk
contact:	Patrick
design service:	Yes
minimum run:	None
info:	In-house screen printers and embroiderers. Also offer in-house design help if necessary.

Ad-Options
92 Langdale Road, Leyland, Lancashire, PR25 3AS
tel:	01772 435 010
fax:	01772 457 280
email:	info@ad-options.co.uk
web:	www.businessgift.uk.com
contact:	Steven Ward
design service:	Yes
minimum run:	None
info:	Screen and transfer print onto a range of garments. No minimum order for transferred garments. Also produce a range of promotional items including bottle openers, key rings and fridge magnets.

Artees
8 Lord Street, Southport, Merseyside, PR8 1QD
tel:	01704 500 114
email:	bobbiematthews@artees.freeserve.co.uk
web:	www.artees.co.uk
contact:	Bobbie Matthews
design service:	Yes
minimum run:	None
info:	Offer a more specialised service dealing with individually hand-painted garments. Mail order only.

Aztec Signs
10 Lound Road, Kendal, LA9 7DT
tel:	01539 724 897
fax:	01539 724 897
email:	info@aztecsigns.net
contact:	David Allenby
design service:	Yes
info:	Banners and vehicle graphics. Also undertake small printing runs of garments (one colour).

Bettaprint
Moss Industrial Estate, Unit 3H-3J, 3rd Floor, Woodbine Street East, Rochdale, OL16 5LB
tel:	01706 527 104
email:	sales@bettaprints.co.uk
web:	www.bettaprints.co.uk
contact:	Alan
design service:	No
minimum run:	None
info:	Garment printing and embroidery available. Hold 10,000 stock designs.

Blackburn's Printers
107-109 Oxton Road, Birkenhead, Merseyside, CH41 2TN
tel:	0151 652 0306
email:	rsb@blackburns-print.co.uk
web:	www.blackburns-print.co.uk
contact:	Stuart
design service:	No
minimum run:	None
info:	Laser printing onto a range of garments. Also supply a range of promotional items including jigsaws, mugs mousemats, posters and flyers. Also provide banners and vehicle graphics.

Blue Moon Promotions Ltd.
Unit 8A, Pool Street Industrial Estate, Pool Street, Macclesfield, Cheshire, SK11 7NX
tel:	01625 424 157
fax:	01625 429 981
email:	cm@bluemoon-promotions.com
web:	www.bluemoon-promotions.com
contact:	Graham Herbert
design service:	No
minimum run:	None
info:	Textile printing specialists.

Caractor Graphics
330 Moorhey Road, Maghull, Merseyside, L31 5LR
tel:	0151 520 0500
fax:	0151 520 2900
email:	caractorgraphics@yahoo.co.uk
contact:	Ian, Les
design service:	Yes
minimum run:	None
info:	T-shirts, sweatshirts, polo shirts. Also provide vehicle graphics, as well as umbrellas, cups, caps, calendars and more. Large format printers supplying posters up to 50" wide and unlimited length.

Compudos
124 Grovesnor Street, Manchester, M1 7HL
tel:	0161 274 4100
email:	sales@compudos.co.uk
web:	www.compudos.co.uk
contact:	Heidi
design service:	No
minimum run:	None
info:	T-shirt printing service. Student discount of up to 35% available. Can also produce mousemats.

Copy Stop
Oriel Chambers, 14a Water Street, Liverpool, L2 8TD
tel:	0151 236 1343
fax:	0151 255 0657
email:	sales@planprinting.co.uk
web:	www.planprinting.co.uk
contact:	Tony
design service:	Yes
minimum run:	None
info:	Garment printers and customised promotional items.

Copycats
18 Bryn Street, Ashton-in-Makerfield, Wigan, Lancashire, WN4 9AU
tel:	01942 714 944
fax:	01942 515 656
email:	copycat@tiscali.co.uk
contact:	Kevin Denaro
design service:	Yes
minimum run:	None
info:	Screen printing, laser printing and embroidery onto garments. Posters, flyers, business cards and banners. Also deal in vehicle graphics, key rings, pens, mugs and other promotional gifts.

Dee-sisions
4 Greenbank Road, Mossley Hill, Liverpool, L18 1HN
tel:	0151 733 1750
fax:	0151 733 1760
email:	sales@deesisionsgifts.co.uk
web:	www.deesisionsgifts.co.uk
contact:	Debra Boa
design service:	Yes
minimum run:	None
info:	Everything from t-shirts and record bags to
badges and CD cases.

D-Zyne
1a Longmeanygate, Leyland, Near Preston, Lancashire, PR26 7PA
tel:	01772 461 103
fax:	01772 491 654
email:	jackie@d-zyne.co.uk
web:	www.d-zyne.co.uk
contact:	Jackie
design service:	Yes
minimum run:	None
info:	Print and embroider garments. Can also
customise a range of promotional items including mugs, coasters, candles, bags, signs and banners.

Elm's Marketing
Unit 2, The Crown Centre, Bond Street, Macclesfield, Cheshire, SK11 6QS
tel:	01625 506 700
fax:	01625 506 707
email:	sales@elmsmarketing.co.uk
web:	www.elmsmarketing.co.uk
contact:	Carol, Janine
design service:	Yes
minimum run:	None
info:	Print onto garments including t-shirts,
sweatshirts and vests. Huge range of promotional items also available.

Embro-Print
38 Alexandra Road, St. Annes, FY8 3SL
tel:	0800 912 2126/01253 782 939
fax:	01253 782 939
email:	info@embroprint.co.uk
web:	www.embroprint.co.uk
contact:	Mark Gallagher
design service:	Yes
minimum run:	25
info:	Printing and embroidery onto textiles.

Epsom Incentives Ltd.
Stuweard House, Bury New Road, Salford, Manchester, M7 2YN
tel:	0800 652 9800
email:	sales@epsoms.com
web:	www.epsoms.com
design service:	Yes
info:	3-4 day turnaround.Full range of merchandise,
with over 10,000 products available.

Fastpicture Show T-Shirt Printers
Manchester
tel:	0161 766 2262
fax:	0161 959 0594
email:	enquiries@fastpictureshow.com
web:	www.fastpictureshow.com
contact:	Debra, Jackie
design service:	No
minimum run:	None
info:	T-shirts, sweatshirts, key rings and mousemats.
Fastpicture Show are a web-based company.

Fingerprints Ltd.
Unit 7-8, Rassbotton Industrial Estate, Stalybridge, Cheshire, SK15 1RH
tel:	0161 303 9677
fax:	0161 303 9688
email:	fingerprintsltd@aol.com
contact:	Russell Lear
design service:	No
minimum run:	None
info:	Print and embroider onto a range of clothing.

First Impressions
79a Twist Lane, Leigh, WN7 4DW
tel:	01942 671 680
fax:	01942 671 680
contact:	Emma Richardson
design service:	Yes
minimum run:	None
info:	Print onto garments and a range of other items
including mugs, keyrings, signs and banners.

Garlex Promtional Products
Castle Farm, Cholmondeley, Malpas, Cheshire, SY14 8AQ
tel:	01829 720 044
fax:	01829 770 027
email:	garlex@pulstar.co.uk
web:	www.garlex.co.uk
contact:	Philip Ellis
design service:	Yes
minimum run:	Contact for details
info:	Screen printing onto clothing. Range of
promotional gifts available. Minimum order varies depending on product.

Gatley Signs
1 Stonepall Road, Gatley, SK8 4EZ
tel:	0161 610 1302
fax:	0161 428 8470
email:	info@gatleysigns.co.uk
web:	www.gatleysigns.co.uk
contact:	Andy Johnson
design service:	Yes
info:	Print onto full range of clothing and promotional
items. Artwork from disk or in-house design.

Gelt Gifts Ltd.
Haytongate, Lanercost, Brampton, Cumbria, CA8 2HQ
tel:	01697 741 119
fax:	01697 742 229
email:	info@geltgifts.co.uk
web:	www.geltgifts.co.uk
contact:	Mike Nelson
design service:	No
minimum run:	6 garments
info:	Screen print onto a range of garments including
t-shirts, jackets and caps. Also supply other promotional items, such as mugs, keyrings, pens and badges.

Gineric
The Quiggins Centre, 12-16 School Lane, Liverpool, L1 3BT
tel:	0151 708 8699
web:	www.gineric.co.uk
design service:	Yes
info:	Print onto banners, dresses, hoodies, beanies,
baseball hats and t-shirts. Also print full colour vinyl stickers and badges.

Genuine Reproductions Ltd.
64 Liverpool Road, Crosby, Liverpool, L23 5SJ
tel:	0151 924 3362
email:	brian@genrepro.co.uk
web:	www.genrepro.co.uk
contact:	Brian
design service:	No
minimum run:	None
info:	Local based business offering t-shirt printing,
embroidery and copying.

Hand Prints
86 Westhead Road, Croston, Near Leyland, PR26 9RS
tel:	01772 601 309
email:	sandra@handprints.info
web:	www.handprints.info
contact:	Sandra
design service:	Yes
minimum run:	None
info:	Silk screen printing and embroidery onto any
garments including t-shirts and hoodies. Friendly service.

Impressions Screenprint & Embroidery
53 Boundary Lane, Liverpool, Merseyside, L6 5JG
tel:	0151 263 8313
fax:	0151 263 4222
email:	sales@easytees.co.uk
web:	www.easytees.co.uk
contact:	Steven, Dave
design service:	Yes
minimum run:	10
info:	Range of garments printed or embroidered. Full
artwork and design service. Other items can be printed including mugs, keyrings and bags.

Imprint Offset
Unit 12a, Warrington Central Trading Estate, Bewsey Road, Warrington, WA2 7LP
tel:	01925 651 141
fax:	01925 651 335
email:	sales@imprintoffset.co.uk
web:	www.imprintoffset.co.uk
contact:	Dave Hill
design service:	Yes
minimum run:	None
info:	Specialists in multimedia printing for 15 years.
Can print onto any promotional items including stickers, badges and t-shirts.

Indy Visuals
77-81 Seaforth Road, Liverpool, L21 3TY
tel: 0151 286 8277
web: www.rocknrollstuff.co.uk
contact: Steve Johnson
design service: Yes
minimum run: None
info: Primarily deal with t-shirts, sweatshirts or polo shirts customised with logo. Can print onto a range of other items such as mugs and magnets. Full promotions package available.

Jackson's Creative Solutions
Unit 15, Crown Business Centre, George Street, Failsworth, Manchester, M35 9BW
tel: 0161 688 9696
fax: 0161 688 9695
email: jacksonprint@btconnect.com
web: www.jacksonstheprintersltd.co.uk
contact: Nick Jackson
design service: Yes
minimum run: None
info: Posters, flyers, banners and business cards. Can also print vehicle graphics. Range of promotional gifts.

Kwik Communications Ltd.
12c Woodford Road, Bramhall, Stockport, Cheshire, SK7 1JJ
tel: 0161 440 9339
fax: 0161 439 8521
email: info@kwikcomms.co.uk
web: www.kwikcomms.co.uk
contact: Alan Lowe
design service: Yes
minimum run: None
info: Laser printing and embroidery onto a range of garments. Customised mousemats. Vehicle graphics, banners, posters and flyers.

Loomland (Mcr) Ltd.
Unit 4, Vaughan Industrial Estate, Vaughan Street, Gorton, Manchester, M12 5BT
tel: 0161 231 0492
fax: 0161 223 4950
email: nick@loomland.com
web: www.loomland.com
contact: Kelly, Nick
design service: Yes
minimum run: None
info: Will print any design onto any garment or material. Clients include Twisted Nerve Records and Rae & Christian. Very band friendly service.

Mega Shirts
18 Chatsworth Road, Manchester, Lancashire, M18 7AF
tel: 0161 230 7701
fax: 0161 220 7701
email: iain@megashirts.co.uk
web: www.megashirts.co.uk
contact: Iain Rae
design service: No
minimum run: None
info: Textile screen printers and embroidery. Can also print on selected pottery ware such as mugs and ashtrays. Although no minimum run, prefer larger orders of between 25 and 1000 units.

Musicstream Ltd.
Hesketh House, 3a School Road, Sale, Cheshire, M33 7XY
tel: 0161 973 9004
email: info@mustream.com
web: www.mustream.com
contact: Tom Carson
design service: Yes
info: Offer promotional merchandise and backdrop manufacturing services. Can also provide web design, as well as distribution. See listings in relevant sections for further information.

Nicholas Evans Designer & Screenprinter
3a Mary Street, Lancaster, LA1 1UW
tel: 01524 391 74
email: nedesignandprint@talk21.co.uk
web: www.nicholasevans-printers.co.uk
contact: Nicholas Evans
design service: Yes
minimum run: None
info: Garment printers and embroiderers. Badges, stickers, banners and car visors, as well as sports and kit bags.

Notorious T-shirts
Warmco Mill, Mossley, Lancashire
tel: 0161 205 4449/07733 204 127
fax: 0161 205 4449
email: notorious@notorious-online.co.uk
design service: Yes
minimum run: None
info: Screen printing and embroidery onto a range of garments.

Nymphs of Bacchus
Newton Street, Manchester, M1 1ER
tel: 0161 236 9359/07742 462 574
email: enquiries@nymphsofbacchus.co.uk
web: www.nymphsofbacchus.co.uk
contact: Kelly
design service: Yes
minimum run: None
info: Merchandisers for unsigned bands. Printers and embroiderers of various items including drum skins, t-shirts, hoodies, vests, badges, stickers, equipment bags and record bags. Also produce posters, flyers, promo and CD covers. See entry in Poster/Flyer Printing section for further details. Small order specialists. Professional and friendly, yet affordable service.

Print Magic
Phoenix House, 16 Tanning Court, Warrington, Cheshire, WA1 2HF
tel: 01925 629 990
fax: 01925 444 438
email: info@print-magic.com
web: www.print-magic.com
contact: Paul Wenlock
design service: Yes
minimum run: None
info: Full design service offered. Print onto garments, mugs, glasses and more. May offer discounts on larger orders.

Printability
57-59 Argyle Street South, Birkenhead, CH41 9DA
tel: 0151 647 4190
fax: 0151 647 4190
contact: Paul Brown
design service: Yes
minimum run: None
info: Textile printers. Vehicle signs, stickers and a full range of promotional gifts.

Promenade Shirts & Embroidery
Marathon Terrace, Queens Promenade, Douglas, Isle of Man, IM2 4NH
email: sales@ttshirts.com
web: www.ttshirts.com
design service: No
minimum run: Varies
info: Embroidered and printed clothing. Offer personalised and customised service.

Promotional Candy
Jackson House, Burton Road, Blackpool, Lancashire, FY4 4NW
tel: 01253 698 298
fax: 01253 698 600
email: info@promotionalcandy.com
web: www.promotionalcandy.com
contact: Sue Armstrong
design service: Yes
info: Specialise in placing any company, band or artist name on sweets and rock.

Razamataz
4 Derby Street, Colne, Lancashire, BB8 9AA
tel: 01282 861 099
fax: 01282 861 327
email: simon@razamataz.com
web: www.razamataz.com
contact: Simon Hartley
design service: Yes
minimum run: 25
info: Print and embroider onto a full range of garments including hoodies, skinny t-shirts and bandanas. Other promotional items such as patches, bottle openers and lighters are available.

Ricta UK
Hyde Park House, Cartwright Street, Hyde, Cheshire, SK14 4EH
tel: 0161 351 0161
email: rictauk@btclick.com
web: www.rictauk.com
contact: Eric Taylor
design service: Yes
minimum run: None
info: Print onto t-shirts, plus a range of promotional item including pens and mousemats. Also offer CD duplication, artwork design and poster and flyer printing. See entries in relevant sections for details.

Saycheese Instant Keyring Photographer
Liverpool
tel: 0151 288 9114
email: saycheesekeyrings@msn.com
contact: Stephen Kelly
design service: Yes
info: Photo of your band in a keyring. £2.50 per keyring. Discount available for bulk orders.

Screen & Design Ltd.
Unit 10a, Tardygate Mill, Lostock Hall, Preston, PR5 5JD
tel:	01772 626 712
fax:	01772 698 712
email:	nwsd@btconnect.com
web:	www.screenanddesign.co.uk
contact:	Andy, Craig
design service:	Yes
minimum run:	None
info:	Garment printing including t-shirts, sweatshirts

and caps. Stickers and vinyl graphics for vehicles. Also produce banners.

ScreenKing
14 Caxton Road, Rainhill, L35 6PN
tel:	0151 426 9373
email:	sales@screenking.co.uk
web:	www.screenking.co.uk
contact:	Stephen Edwards
design service:	Yes
minimum run:	10
info:	ScreenKing are an online business. Produce any

style of garments including t-shirts, fitted t-shirts (male and female), hooded sweatshirts, jackets and record bags.

Shepherd Printers
218 Oldham Road, Rochdale, OL11 2ER
tel:	01706 350 432
fax:	01706 654 314
email:	info@shepherdprinters.com
web:	www.shepherdprinters.com
contact:	Steven Shepherd, Gail Shepherd
design service:	Yes
minimum run:	None
info:	Print onto garments plus a range of other items

including keyrings, mousemats and coasters. Can also print flyers and posters up to A3.

Sports Print
Kendal Business Park, Appleby Road, Kendal, LA9 6ES
tel:	01539 729 579
fax:	01539 730 770
email:	sales@sportsprint.co.uk
web:	www.sportsprint.co.uk
contact:	Shaun
design service:	Yes
minimum run:	None
info:	Printing and embroidery onto textiles. Garments

can be supplied by clients or by Sports Print. No minimum order, although there may be a small charge for smaller orders. Turnaround of 7-10 days on most orders.

Subak Signs
9a Stocks Street, Manchester, M8 8GW
tel:	0161 835 9993
fax:	0161 835 9994
email:	info@subaksigns.co.uk
web:	www.subaksigns.co.uk
contact:	Mr Mohammad
design service:	Yes
minimum run:	None
info:	Print onto full range of garments and

promotional items. Banners also available.

Taurus Promotions Ltd.
Derby Mills, 13 Thomas Street, Bolton, BL3 6JU
tel:	0800 018 6555
fax:	01204 361 523
email:	sales@oimages.co.uk
web:	www.oimages.co.uk
contact:	Steve Birchall
design service:	Yes
minimum run:	None
info:	Garment printers. Full design and graphics

service.

Text Styles
76a Albert Road, Colne, Lancashire, BB8 0AG
tel:	01282 864 625
fax:	01282 869 776
email:	info@buythet-shirt.com
web:	www.buythet-shirt.com
contact:	Barry Jordan
design service:	Yes
minimum run:	None
info:	Print onto most garments. Full range of

promotional items including mugs, keyrings and pens.

Top Print
43-45 Winwick Street, Warrington, Cheshire, WA2 7TT
tel:	01925 413 299
fax:	01925 415 370
email:	info@topprintltd.com
web:	www.topprintltd.com
contact:	Mike
design service:	Yes
minimum run:	None
info:	B&W or colour print onto garments. Also do

backdrops, large posters and CD covers. Contact for details of full range available.

T-Shirt Xpress
93 Oldham Street, Manchester, M4 1LW
tel:	0161 839 5668
email:	printedtees@lycos.co.uk
design service:	Yes
minimum run:	None
info:	Embroidery, transfers and screen printing onto

garments. Also produce a range of gifts such as badges, mousemats and mugs. Discounts available for larger orders.

U.D.C.
21b Burscough Street, Ormskirk, L39 2EG
tel:	01695 576 800
fax:	01695 576 800
email:	uglyduckling@btconnect.com
contact:	Eugene O'Malley
design service:	Yes
minimum run:	None
info:	Print onto garments such as t-shirts, sweatshirts

and baseball caps. Banners, stickers and vehicle signs. Friendly service.

Union Leisurewear & Screen Print Co.
Unit 12, Cornbrook Park Road, Cornbrook, Manchester, Lancashire, M15 4EE
tel:	0161 877 7780
fax:	0161 877 1778
email:	sales@unionleisurewear.com
web:	www.unionleisurewear.com
contact:	Gordon
design service:	Yes
minimum run:	None
info:	Printing and embroidery on any garment. Can

also produce baseball caps, bags and stickers.

Westside Designs Ltd.
Westside House, Bute Street, Bolton, Lancashire, BL1 5JR
tel:	01204 847 292
fax:	01204 493 426
email:	t_shirts@westsidedesigns.fsnet.co.uk
contact:	John, Lyndsey
design service:	Yes
minimum run:	None
info:	Screen printing and embroidery onto a range of

textiles. Promotional gifts including pens and mugs also available.

Wild Thang
Unit 16, Sandon Industrial Estate, Sandon Way, Liverpool, L5 9YN
tel:	0151 207 6060
fax:	0151 207 5955
email:	sales@wildthang.co.uk
web:	www.wildthang.co.uk
contact:	Andrew Derryhouse
design service:	Yes
minimum run:	None
info:	Print onto clothing and textile. Large range of

promotional items including flashing bouncy balls, wristbands and water pistols.

Worlds Apart
Unit C, Aldow Enterprise Park, Ardwick, Manchester, M20 6AE
tel:	0161 274 3737
fax:	0161 274 3738
email:	email@t-shirtprinter.com
web:	www.t-shirtprinter.com
design service:	Yes
minimum run:	None
info:	Design, print and supply t-shirts to customers

from around the world.

Yomodo
18 Harewood Avenue, Simonstone, Burnley, BB12 7JB
tel:	01282 774 713
email:	info@yomodo.com
web:	www.yomodo.com
contact:	Carol
design service:	Yes
minimum run:	None
info:	Heat transfers onto garments. Full colour images

and logos onto any suitable clothing item.

SOUTHEAST

1st Stop Direct
Middleton Hall, Brentwood Road, West Hordon, Brentwood, Essex, CM13 3LX
tel:	01277 811 670
fax:	01277 811 185
email:	sales@1ststopdirect.com
web:	www.1ststopdirect.com
design service:	No
minimum run:	25
info:	Offer a range of promotional items including t-shirts, mugs and keyrings. Available from one colour to full colour, screen printed.

All About Image
25 West Hill, Dartford, Kent, DA1 2EL
tel:	01322 275 151
design service:	No
minimum run:	None
info:	Print and embroider onto any item including t-shirts, pens, bags, badges and banners.

Arrow Embroidery Services
Unit 7, Business Village, Wrexham Road, Slough, SL2 5HF
tel:	01753 533 503
email:	arrowrick@aol.com
web:	www.arrow-embroidery.co.uk
contact:	Rick
design service:	Yes
minimum run:	varies
info:	Sweatshirts, hats and t-shirts, as well as many other items.

BandBits
Prince Bros Site, Old Bath Road, Charvil, Berkshire, RG10 9QJ
tel:	0118 932 0032
fax:	0118 932 0016
email:	nick@bandbits.com
web:	www.bandbits.com
contact:	Nick Lawson
design service:	Yes
minimum run:	None
info:	Provide poster and bass drum printing. Bandbits also offer recording and rehearsal space, as well as CD mastering and duplication, see entries in relevant sections for full details.

Banners For All
Cottage In The Wood, Parsonage Lane, Farnham Common, Buckinghamshire, SL2 3PA
tel:	01753 646 557
email:	textile@bannersforall.co.uk
web:	www.bannersforall.co.uk
contact:	Ralph Ballhatchet
design service:	Yes
minimum run:	None
info:	Mainly deal with stage backdrops and banners. Also provide t-shirt printing.

BestBadges.co.uk
PO Box 7355, East Bergholt, Colchester, CO7 6YT
tel:	01206 299 370
fax:	01206 299 279
email:	info@bestbadges.co.uk
web:	www.bestbadges.co.uk
design service:	Yes
minimum run:	Dependant on product
info:	Offer a range of promotional badges, all shapes and sizes, as well as keyrings, bottle openers and t-shirts. 100x25mm pin badges for £25 with P&P included. Call for more details.

Cavalier's
118 Broad Street Mall, Reading, Berkshire, RG1 7QA
tel:	0118 957 2942
email:	cavaliers@btconnect.com
web:	www.cavalierst-shirts.com
contact:	Damien Issa
design service:	Yes
info:	Print onto t-shirts, polo shirts, sweatshirts and hooded sweatshirts. Cavalier's will print almost every colour.

Checkmate Corporate Gifts
The Granary, Pullens Farm, Lamberhurst Road, Horsmondon, Tonbridge, TN12 8ED
tel:	01892 724 474
fax:	01892 724 736
email:	checkmategifts@lineone.net
web:	www.checkmatecorporategifts.co.uk
design service:	Yes
info:	Short runs available for a variety of products. Contact for full catalogue.

Cultural Treachery
28 St. Michael's Lane, Leeds, LS4 2RX
email:	badges@culturaltreachery.com
web:	www.culturaltreachery.com
design service:	Yes
info:	Producers of keyrings, mirrors, magnets and badges.

Eclipse Embroidery & Print
Unit 3, Mole Business Park, Randalls Road, Leatherhead, KT22 7BA
tel:	01372 380 780
fax:	01372 380 781
email:	sales@eclipse-ep.co.uk
web:	www.eclipse-ep.co.uk
design service:	Yes
minimum run:	30
info:	Eclipse are able to produce less than 30 items, but a set up charge will apply. Mainly concerned with textiles.

Forge Trading UK Ltd.
Unit 1b, Deer Park Farm, Knowle Lane, Fair Oak, Eastleigh, Hampshire, SO50 7DZ
tel:	02380 696 961
design service:	No
minimum run:	None
info:	In-house embroidery onto a large range of garments.

Frontline Marketing
27 Long Ley, Harlow, CM20 3NJ
tel:	01279 323 583
email:	jason@frontlinemarketing.co.uk
web:	www.frontlinemarketing.co.uk
design service:	Yes
minimum run:	Varies
info:	Keyrings, mousemats, mugs, pens and t-shirts all available.

Global
4 Bowlers Croft, Basildon, Essex, SS14 3EG
tel:	01268 285 838
email:	sales@globalpsl.com
web:	www.globalpsl.com
design service:	Yes
minimum run:	None
info:	Offer a range of garments. Embroidery and screen printing.

GoldStar Textile Printer and Embroidery
Unit 6, Britannia Business Park, Mills Road, Quarry Wood Industrial Estate, Maidstone, ME20 7NT
tel:	01622 717 332
email:	goldstaruk@ukonline.co.uk
web:	www.goldstaruk.com
design service:	No
minimum run:	None
info:	Embroidery and printing onto a large amount of garments.

Indigo Clothing Ltd.
79 Lower Cookham Road, Maidenhead, Berkshire, SL6 8JY
tel:	0871 711 2151
design service:	No
minimum run:	None
info:	Printing and embroidery onto t-shirts and many other garments.

The Kit Room Company Ltd.
66 Crayford High Street, Dartford, Kent, DA1 4EF
tel:	01322 315 999
design service:	No
minimum run:	None
info:	T-shirt printing service.

Ktees Promotions
Unit 15-16, Northern Galleries, Fort Fareham Business Park, Fareham, Hampshire, PO14 1AH
tel:	01329 822 583
design service:	No
minimum run:	20
info:	T-shirt printing and embroidery. All promotional items supplied.

Mega Shirts
44 Southview, Downley, High Wycombe, Buckinghamshire, HB13 5UL
tel:	01494 533 660
email:	sales@e-ts.co.uk
web:	www.e-ts.co.uk
design service:	Yes
minimum run:	None
info:	Print t-shirts, polo shirts, baseball hats and fleece jackets. Embroidery and screen printing.

bestbadges.co.uk

PO BOX 7355
Colchester
C07 6YT
England

Amazing Prices...

100 25mm / 1" Badges for £25

FREE RECORDED DELIVERY

- NO EXTRAS

we also can print picks, stickers, drum sticks
please contact us for more details

BestBadges.Co.Uk
Badges With No Bullshit
Free Previews
Free Shipping.
Custom Picks
Sticks, Skins Stickers
and tones more
Made for Bands
By Bands Hands

Send a Cheque made out to
Best Badges

Post your Artwork & details

Or e-mail
info@bestbadges.co.uk

or online @
bestbadges.co.uk

Please contact for international orders
or any questions regaring our service
- fast turn around time so get in touch!

Merrison Ltd.
The Old Dairy Manor Farm, High Street, Tingrith, Milton Keynes, MK17 9EN
tel:	01525 872 122
email:	merrison@btconnect.com
web:	www.merrison.net
design service:	Yes
info:	All variety of promotional production including t-shirts and badges.

Panagraphics Ltd.
68b Sydney Road, Watford, Hertfordshire, WD18 7PX
tel:	01923 242 524
design service:	No
minimum run:	None
info:	Offer printing and embroidery onto t-shirts and polo shirts.

Paper Tigers
Woodland Mills, Woodland Road, Tonbridge, TN9 2NE
tel:	01762 771 731
email:	sales@papertigers.co.uk
web:	www.papertigers.co.uk
contact:	Bruce
design service:	Yes
minimum run:	Contact for details
info:	Can produce a range of promotional gifts, as well as diaries and calendars.

Pogo Entertainments
Vanguard Way, Shoeburyness, Essex, SS3 9QY
tel:	01702 384 030
email:	info@pogoentertainment.com
web:	www.pogoentertainment.com
contact:	Shelley English, Terry Piper
design service:	Yes
info:	In-house thermal printing for t-shirts. Screen printing also available. Colour laser printed posters up to A3 size, as well as leaflet print. Pogo can also offer CD duplication service, as well as promotional web resources. See entries in relevant sections for further details.

Premier Promotional Services
38 Bearton Road, Hitchin, Hertfordshire, SG5 1UE
tel:	01468 442 288
fax:	01462 458 883
email:	sales@premierpromotional.co.uk
web:	www.premierpromotional.co.uk
design service:	Yes
info:	Can provide short runs on all variety of products.

Printing & Embroidery
Hoo Lodge, Dahnal Road, Hemel Hempstead, HP1 3BP
tel:	01442 256 208
design service:	Yes
minimum run:	None
info:	Embroidery and printing oto all types of garment. Can be done while you wait.

Propabanda
Cricket Corner, Lynch Hill Park, Whitchurch, Hampshire, RG28 7NF
email:	info@propabanda.co.uk
web:	www.propabanda.co.uk
contact:	Matt Payne
design service:	Yes
minimum run:	Varies
info:	Supply vast range of products including stickers, badges, beer mats, t-shirts, plectrums, drum sticks, drum skins, keyrings, posters, bottle openers, lighters, guitar straps, banners, balloons, skater belts. Also print and design flyers and posters. See relevant section for details. Have worked with lots of bands, and are happy to hear from any band in the country. Open to any other suggestions for items. Propabanda pride themselves in trying to supply new innovative products branded with your band's logo, message or image. Everything from the latest wristband craze to plectrums and drum sticks.

Puffer Products
Oak Cottage, High Street, Leigh, Kent, TN11 8RW
tel:	01732 833 606
email:	sales@pufferproducts.com
web:	www.pufferproducts.com
design service:	Yes
minimum run:	None
info:	Puffer Products can supply mousemats, coasters, mugs, jigsaws and signs.

Rakemoor Ltd.
6 Parkstone Avenue, Hornchurch, Essex, RM11 3LU
tel:	01708 454 434/07775 677 772
email:	info@tshirtpromotions.co.uk
web:	www.tshirtpromotions.co.uk
design service:	Yes
minimum run:	None
info:	Embroidery and screen printing onto range of garments. No minimum run, ecept for embroidered garments.

Replika
Gray's Business Centre, 49 Lodge Lane, Grays, Essex, RM17 5RZ
tel:	01375 481 524
design service:	No
minimum run:	None
info:	Mono and colour copying available onto t-shirts, mugs and mousemats.

Springfield Promotions Ltd.
Unit 12, Eagle Centre Way, Luton, LU4 9US
tel:	01582 561 200
email:	sales@springfieldpromotions.com
web:	www.springfieldpromotions.com
design service:	Yes
minimum run:	Varies
info:	Specialise in personalisation of many items such as CD storage wallets, pens and balloons.

Teeone Ltd.
Unit B, Newman Court, Range Road, Witney, OX29 7LY
tel:	0800 027 8660
email:	peter@teeone.co.uk
web:	www.teeoneshop.co.uk
design service:	Yes
minimum run:	Varies
info:	Specialise in promotional printing. Clothing, novelty items and signage.

They Sound Good
1 Buckles Lane, South Ockendon, RM15 6RS
tel:	07830 184 177
email:	pbibb@theysoundgood.co.uk
web:	www.theysoundgood.co.uk
design service:	No
minimum run:	None
info:	Can cater for all merchandise requirements. T-shirts, skinny fit and football shirts available.

TJ's Sign Co.
Portland Business Park, Portland Road, Hove, East Sussex, BN3 5RY
tel:	01273 431 134
design service:	Yes
minimum run:	None
info:	Screen printing onto banners and flags.

Ultimate Incentive
The Dragonworks, Missenden Road, Great Kingshill, High Wycomb, Buckinghamshire, HP15 6ED
tel:	01494 711 155
fax:	01494 711 166
email:	sales@ultimateincentive.com
web:	www.ultimateincentive.com
design service:	Yes
minimum run:	None
info:	Anything promotional can be delivered. Turnover time depends on the product.

Unique Promotions
8 The Arcade, Bognor Regis, West Sussex, PO21 1LH
tel:	01243 826 123
design service:	No
minimum run:	None
info:	Print and embroidery for t-shirts for all occasions.

SOUTHWEST

Almega
Ramelsa, Chilsworthy, Gunnislake, PL18 9PB
tel:	01822 832 651
email:	almega@almegademon.co.uk
web:	www.almegaltd.co.uk
contact:	Sarah, Katherine
design service:	Yes
minimum run:	Varies
info:	Promotional items and clothing including balloons, badges, sweets and keyrings.

Avon Promotional Items
The Willows, Greyfield Road, High Littleton, Bristol, BS39 6XZ
tel: 01761 479 668
email: app-barry@bt.com
web: www.avonpp.co.uk
contact: Barry
design service: Yes
minimum run: Contact for details
info: Promotional mugs, pens, clothing and bags available.

Badge Boy
Exeter
email: spike@badgeboy.co.uk
web: www.badgeboy.co.uk
design service: Yes
minimum run: None
info: Previous clients include Hundred Reasons, Kids Near Water, Hell Is For Heroes and Goldblade.

Big Wight T-Shirt Co.
Daish Way, Dodnor Industrial Estate, Newport, Isle of Wight, PO30 5XB
tel: 01983 532 333
email: karen@bigwight.co.uk
web: www.bigwight.co.uk
design service: No
minimum run: None
info: Have worked with bands and musicians in the past. Price dependent on run. All designs must be provided. Can print onto all textiles.

Bolda
Unit 33, Scott Business Park, Beacon Park, Plymouth, PL2 2PQ
tel: 01752 690 060
email: sales@bolda.co.uk
web: www.bolda.co.uk
contact: James Abraham
design service: Yes
minimum run: 5
info: Promotional items specialist. Logos and branded items including confectionery, bags, lighters, pens and stickers.

Branded Image
SSI House, Marlborough Road, Pewsey, Wiltshire, SN9 5NU
tel: 01672 562 030
email: kevin@brandedimage.co.uk
web: www.brandedimage.co.uk
contact: Kevin
design service: Yes
minimum run: Varies
info: Promotional items including pens and mugs. Embroidery onto clothing.

Chris & Printers
23 Fircroft Road, Plymouth, Devon, PL2 3JU
tel: 01752 701 712
email: chrisand-printers@tiscali.co.uk
contact: Chris, Sandra
design service: Yes
minimum run: Varies
info: Range of promotional items available.

Complete Business Gifts Ltd.
88 Marshfield Road, Chippenham, Wiltshire, SN15 1JR
tel: 01249 650 869
email: cggltd@btconnect.com
web: www.cbgltd.co.uk
contact: Catherine Waleker
design service: Yes
minimum run: Varies
info: Range of promotional items. Full catalogue can be viewed online.

Couchebebe
Haze Lea, Hill Pound, Southampton, SO32 2UN
tel: 01489 893 784
web: www.couchebebe.com
design service: No
minimum run: None
info: T-shirt and polo shirt printers.

Designease Ltd.
Unit 7, Stonehouse Commercial Centre, Bristol Road, Stonehouse, GL10 3RD
tel: 01453 821 990
email: sales@designease.co.uk
web: www.designease.co.uk
design service: Yes
minimum run: Varies
info: Promotional folders and presentation folders available suitable for press packs.

FOOTPRINTS

- Printed t-shirts, polos, sweatshirts, tabards, etc, for fundraising events, mail order catalogues, sponsorships and band promotion
- Specialists in superb quality full/multi-colour prints
- Special high volume deals
- Garments sourced to meet your budget
- Efficient service and fast turnaround
- Storage/distribution facilities
- Also manufacturers of printed doormats

Watercombe Park · Yeovil · Somerset BA20 2HL
Telephone 01935 432400

Devon Tees Ltd.
Unit 5, Ermington Workshops, Ermington, Ivybridge, Devon, PL21 9NT
tel: 01548 830 948
design service: No
minimum run: None
info: Screen printing onto large selection of garments. Create your own design and send it online.

Falling Orb Productions
PO Box 145, Merrivale, Yelverton, Devon, PL20 6WJ
tel: 01822 890 669
email: info@fallingorb.com
web: www.fallingorb.com
contact: Nick
design service: Yes
minimum run: Contact for details
info: Falling Orb create a range of clothing aimed at skate, surf and sno markets. Also offer bespoke printing and embroidery service tailored to client's needs. Can design an individual garment, or work from client's artwork.

Footprints
Watercombe Park, Yeovil, Somerset, BA20 2HL
tel: 01935 432 400
fax: 01935 700 352
email: fp@spectrumformdesign.co.uk
contact: Tim Browning
design service: Yes
info: Print onto any textile item. Screen printing, embroidery and heat printing.

Fresh Prints
Marlands Shopping Centre, Civic Centre Road, Southampton, Hampshire, SO14 7SJ
tel: 02380 337 600
design service: No
minimum run: None
info: Print onto t-shirts, hoodies, bags, badges and caps. Discount for bulk orders.

Global Marketing Group
Unit 1a, 6 Blandford Heights, Shaftesbury Lane, Blandford Forum, DT11 7TE
tel: 01258 457 500
email: info@globalmarketinggroup.co.uk
web: www.globalmarketinggroup.co.uk
contact: Alex Murueta
design service: Yes
minimum run: Varies
info: Design and print services available for clothing items and products.

Impro Corporate Solutions
Unit 3, Halliday's Mill, London Road, Chalfords, Stroud, GL6 8NR
tel: 01453 885 506
email: sales@improsolutions.co.uk
web: www.improsolutions.co.uk
contact: Diane Phillips
design service: Yes
minimum run: Varies
info: Promotional items such as badges, pens and key fobs.

Leading Edge
11 Daneheath Business Park, Wentworth Road, Heathfield, Newton Abbot, Devon, TQ12 6TL
tel: 0845 230 3600
email: sales@leadingedgeuk.com
web: www.leadingedgeuk.com
contact: Leanne
design service: Yes
info: Promotional items including clothing, stickers and badges.

Let's Face It
28 New Road, Chippenham, Wiltshire, SN15 1HS
tel: 01249 656 635
design service: Yes
info: Printing onto t-shirts, polo shirts, sweatshirts and badges.

M & M Printing & Promotions
Woodland View, Far Stanley, Winchcombe, Cheltenham, GL54 5HF
tel: 01242 620 203
email: sales@mandmonline.com
web: www.mandmonline.com
contact: Chani
design service: Yes
minimum run: Varies
info: Promotional items available including keyrings, pens, umbrellas, chocolates and sweets.

MikkiMugs
Matravers Farm, Uploders, Bridport, DT6 4PH
tel: 01308 485 300
email: sales@mikkimugs.demon.co.uk
web: www.mikki-mugs.co.uk
contact: Sam Wood
design service: Yes
info: Specialise in printing logos and phrases onto mugs and tableware.

P.P.W.
Barclay House, Little Somerford, Chippenham, Wiltshire, SN15 5JT
tel: 01666 822 431
email: ppw@ppw.uk.com
contact: John
design service: Yes
info: Badges, pens and mugs available.

Pens Unlimited
Unit 1, Pottery Units, Forde Road, Brunel Industrial Estate, Newton Abbot, Devon, TQ12 6TZ
tel: 01626 334 520
email: frank@pensunlimited.co.uk
web: www.pensunlimited.co.uk
design service: Yes
minimum run: varies
info: Specialists in promotional pens. Capable of handling large orders.

Perennial Promotions Ltd.
31 Yeomead, Nailsea, Bristol, Avon, BS48 1JA
tel: 01275 852 864
email: gordon@perennialpromotions.co.uk
web: www.perennialpromotions.co.uk
contact: Gordon
design service: No
minimum run: Varies
info: Promotional items including mugs, clothing, key rings, pens and umbrellas.

Prostitch Ltd.
Unit 2, Magdalene Road, Torquay, Devon, TQ1 4AF
tel: 01803 296 699
email: info@prostitch.co.uk
web: www.prostitch.co.uk
design service: Yes
minimum run: Varies
info: A range of promotional items available. Screen printing and embroidery.

Purple Rhino Promotions
PO Box 15, Portishead, Bristol, Avon, BS20 6XS
tel: 01275 846 777
email: sales@purplerhino.co.uk
design service: Yes
info: Promotional items. Will print onto anything.

Recognition Express (Gloucester)
The Old Mill, Mill Lane, Avening, Tetbury, GL8 8PD
tel: 01453 834 440
email: sales@recognition-express.com
web: www.recognition-express.com
contact: Emma
design service: No
minimum run: Varies
info: Promotional items and products including clothing, name badges, signs, banners and vinyls.

Signature Merchandise
East Grafton, Marlborough, SN8 3DB
tel: 01672 811 911
email: sales@signature-merchandise.com
web: www.signature-merchandise.com
contact: Phillip Parkin
design service: Yes
minimum run: Varies
info: Promotional clothing and accessories. See online catalogue on the above website.

Taylor Design & Print
106 Furnham Road, Chard, TA20 1BE
tel: 01460 679 58
email: malc@taylordesignandprint.co.uk
web: www.taylordesignandprint.co.uk
contact: Malcolm Taylor
design service: Yes
minimum run: None
info: Wide range of in-house promotional merchandise available such as t-shirts, caps (embroidered or printed), banners and key rings. Other merchandise can be organised externally. Also provide printing service. See listing in relevant section.

Trius
PO Box 147, Paignton, Devon, TQ4 6YH
tel: 01803 844 101
email: sales@trius.co.uk
web: www.trius.co.uk
contact: Rosemary
design service: Yes
info: Range of promotional materials available.

T-shirt & Sons
11 Washington Road, West Wilts Trading Estate, West Bury, BA13 4JP
tel: 01373 301 645
email: andy@tshirtandsons.co.uk
web: www.tshirtandsons.co.uk
contact: Andy
design service: Yes
minimum run: 10
info: Specialise in t-shirt printing. Worked with bands previously including Keane and Radiohead.

Tshirt Studio
13 Horcott Industrial Estate, Gorcott Road, Fairford, Gloucestershire, GL7 4BX
tel: 0870 922 2838
fax: 0870 762 7185
email: contact@tshirtstudio.com
web: www.tshirtstudio.com
design service: No
minimum run: None
info: Quality custom t-shirts, mugs and mousemats. Design your own t-shirts, personalised gifts or promotional merchandise. 10% discount available on orders over £50.

Under the Sun
Unit 3, The Courtyard, Currendon Farm Buildings, Currendon Hill, Swanage, BH19 3BB
tel: 01929 450 090
email: phaedra@under-the-sun.co.uk
web: www.under-the-sun.co.uk
contact: Phaedra
design service: Yes
info: T-shirt printers and promotional items. Previously worked with TV and radio stations, as well as bands.

W.J. Nigh & Sons Ltd.
62 Landguard Road, Shanklin, Isle of Wight, PO37 7HX
tel:	01983 863 291
web:	www.wjnigh.co.uk
design service:	Yes
minimum run:	Varies
info:	Can place design onto wide variety of items

including badges, stickers and mugs. Have worked with bands previously.

www.personalisedstuff.net
6 Whittle Road, Ferndown Industrial Estate, Wimborne, Dorset, BH21 7RU
tel:	0870 0423 646
email:	info@personalisedstuff.net
web:	www.personalisedstuff.net
contact:	Jamie Davis
design service:	Yes
minimum run:	Varies
info:	Range of products available for customisation.

YORKSHIRE

1st Emblem Screenprint
63 Cross Green Lane, Halton, Leeds, West Yorkshire, LS15 7SA
tel:	0113 260 0555
contact:	Steve
design service:	Yes
minimum run:	None
info:	T-shirt printing service.

Ace Printers
18 Cairnborrow, York, North Yorkshire, YO24 2YY
tel:	01904 702 013
design service:	No
minimum run:	None
info:	Printing onto t-shirts.

Badge Planet
22 Broombank, Huddersfield, West Yorkshire, HD2 2DJ
tel:	07005 803 462
email:	support@badgeplanet.co.uk
web:	www.badgeplanet.co.uk
design service:	No
minimum run:	None
info:	Create and design your own badges. Choose

from a variety of sizes and shapes.

The Banner People
Multigraphics Ltd., 21 Commondale Way, Euroway Trading Estate, Bradford, BD4 6SF
tel:	0870 240 9983
email:	contact@thebannerpeople.com
web:	www.thebannerpeople.com
design service:	No
minimum run:	None
info:	Bold, bright and brilliant customised banners

made from high quality PVC for interior and exterior use.

Baskind Imaging
54 Otley Road, Leeds, West Yorshire, LS6 2AL
tel:	0113 275 1234
web:	www.baskind.com
design service:	No
minimum run:	None
info:	Print and embroidery service available for range

of garments. UK and offshore manufacturing.

Bridge Print Solutions Ltd.
3 Bridge Street, Tadcaster, North Yorkshire, LS24 9AW
tel:	01937 835 333
email:	bridge.print@btconnect.com
web:	www.bridgeprintsolutions.co.uk
contact:	Paul
design service:	Yes
minimum run:	None
info:	T-shirt and stationery printers.

Castle Pro Printing
15 St. John's Road, Scarborough, North Yorkshire, YO12 5ES
tel:	01723 377 723
email:	c.gibson3@btinternet.com
web:	www.castleproprinting.com
contact:	Chris, Michelle
design service:	No
minimum run:	None
info:	T-shirts, coasters, mugs and badges.

Chillaxx Print
Salisbury Hall, Park Road, Hull, HU3 1TD
tel:	01482 223 616
email:	info@chillaxx.co.uk
web:	www.chillaxx.co.uk
design service:	Yes
minimum run:	None
info:	Will print onto a range of clothing including

t-shirts.

Colourstyle
Unit 8, Electron House, 31-35 Moorfield Road, Leeds, LS12 3RN
tel:	0113 279 7971
email:	info@colourstyle.net
web:	www.colourstyle.net
contact:	Paul
design service:	Yes
minimum run:	None
info:	T-shirt print and embroidery. Free brochure

available on request.

Design Ink Printing Service
The Works, 307 Hough Lane, Wombwell, Barnsley, South Yorkshire, S73 0LR
tel:	01226 757 515
contact:	Keith
design service:	Yes
info:	T-shirt printing avaiable.

Everett Paul Print & Design
Unit M2 & M3, Enterprise Way, Bradford Road, Bradford, BD10 8EW
tel:	01274 612 998
email:	info@printanddesign.co.uk
web:	www.printanddesign.co.uk
contact:	paul
design service:	Yes
minimum run:	none
info:	Stationery and T-shirt printing service.

Fingerprints
126-128 Main Street, Bingley, BD16 2HL
tel:	01274 565 326
email:	design@fingerprintscoop.com
web:	www.fingerprintscoop.com
contact:	Rob Stanford
design service:	Yes
minimum run:	None
info:	Fair Trade and organic t-shirts. Also produce

stationery items and business cards.

Garment Transformations
Unit 8 Excelsior, 911 Bradford Road, Birstall, Batley, West Yorkshire, WF17 9JX
tel:	01924 422 231
email:	johnduffill@aol.com
contact:	John
design service:	Yes
minimum run:	None
info:	Provide t-shirts printing service.

Ibex Design
208 Whiteham, Broomhill, Sheffield, S10 2SS
tel:	0114 268 1923
email:	ifo@ibexdesign.uk.com
web:	www.ibexdesign.uk.com
contact:	Steven
design service:	Yes
minimum run:	None
info:	Unique and affordable t-shirt printing service.

IDD Enterprises
The Old Boat House, 66 London Road, Sheffield, S2 4LR
tel:	0114 273 9848
email:	sales@iddltd.co.uk
web:	www.iddltd.co.uk
contact:	Ian Bell
design service:	Yes
minimum run:	None
info:	Printing and embroidery. Full design and packing

service.

Image Printers & Suppliers
41 Park Avenue, Knaresborough, North Yorkshire, HG5 9ES
tel:	01423 869 533
contact:	Chris Clayton
design service:	Yes
minimum run:	6
info:	Print onto plain clothing, polo shirts, sweatshirts

and caps.

Im-Press Promotions
15 Hepworth Arcade, Silver Street, Hull, North Humberside, HU1 1JU
tel: 01484 216 606
email: gary@impressbeverley.co.uk
web: www.impressbeverley.co.uk
contact: Gary
design service: Yes
minimum run: None
info: Specialise in t-shirt print and high visibility garments. 250,000 promotional products available to print on. Enquire for furthe details.

Involution Ltd.
13 Holly Parks Mills, Woodhall Road, Calverley, Pudsey, LS28 5QS
tel: 0113 256 0217
email: mail@involution.co.uk
web: www.involution.co.uk
contact: Michael
design service: Yes
minimum run: 12
info: Can provide t-shirts, polos, baseball caps, fleeces, as well as pens and mugs.

Jetscreen Ltd.
Julia Avenue, Monks Cross, Huntington, York, YO32 9JR
tel: 01904 644 103
fax: 01904 623 227
email: studio@jetscreen.co.uk
web: www.jetscreen.co.uk
contact: Simon
design service: No
minimum run: None
info: T-shirt printers.

M.R.N. Screen Process Ltd.
Unit 10, Saxon Way, Priory Park, Hessle, HU13 9PB
tel: 01482 627 717
email: sales@mrnprint.com
design service: Yes
minimum run: None
info: T-shirts, stickers and signs available.

Mr Tee's
250a Manchester Road, Huddersfield, West Yorkshire, HD4 5AE
tel: 01484 308 030
email: mrtees90@hotmail.co.uk
contact: Julia, Vijan
design service: Yes
minimum run: None
info: T-shirt printing service.

P.F.M. Promotions
Unit 3 Valley Works, Grange Lane, Sheffield, S5 0DQ
tel: 0114 257 7385
contact: Mrs Fowler
design service: No
minimum run: None
info: Printing onto t-shirts.

Peco
Unit 10, Springfield Commercial Centre, Bagley Lane, Farsley, Pudsey, West Yorkshire, LS28 5LY
tel: 0113 236 3463
email: andi@sportsdirect-peco.co.uk
contact: Andi
design service: Yes
minimum run: None
info: Printing onto selection of garments.

Pickersgill Drake & Co.
Unit 26, Barkston House, Domestic Street, Leeds, West Yorkshire, LS11 9RT
tel: 0113 244 1521
email: pickersgill.drake@bt.com
contact: Mark, Rob
design service: Yes
minimum run: None
info: T-shirt printing service.

Pineapple Joes Ltd.
Unit 4b, Bessingby Industrial Estate, Bridlington, North Humberside, YO16 4SJ
tel: 01262 672 733
web: www.pineapplejoes.com
design service: No
minimum run: None
info: Screen printing and embroidery onto t-shirts and promotional wear.

Piranha Print Embroidery
Gymtec House, Commercial Yard, Whincup Avenue, Knaresborough, North Yorkshire, HG5 0JH
tel: 01423 866 972
web: www.piranhapromotions.co.uk
design service: No
minimum run: None
info: Printing and embroidery onto t-shirts and sweatshirts, as well as selection of novelty items.

The Print Factory
570 Beverly Road, Hull, North Humberside, HU6 7LG
tel: 01482 442 414
email: mail@theprint-factory.co.uk
web: www.theprint-factory.co.uk
contact: Alex
design service: Yes
minimum run: None
info: Print t-shirts, drum skins, banners and backdrops, flyers and giveaways.

The Promotion Company
Kingson House, Williamson Street, Hull, North Humberside, HU9 1EP
tel: 01482 222 227
email: info@thepromotioncompany.co.uk
web: www.thepromotioncompany.co.uk
contact: Richard Doroyd
design service: Yes
minimum run: 5
info: Range of promotional items available ranging from umbrellas to badges.

Quality Clothing Co. Ltd.
49-51 Church Lane, Adwick-le-Street, Doncaster, South Yorkshire, DN6 7AJ
tel: 01302 337 824
design service: Yes
minimum run: None
info: Quality Clothing have facilities to print onto a wide selection of garments.

Screen Machine
Valley Farm, Leeds, LS10 1SE
tel: 0113 276 0445
fax: 0113 277 0869
email: %20sales@printwear.co.uk
web: www.printwear.co.uk
contact: Tony
design service: Yes
minimum run: None
info: Personalised garments printed to order including hoodies, fleeces, caps and t-shirts. Happy to deal with both small and large orders. Worked with bands previously.

Select Embroidery
50 Broom Avenue, Rotherham, South Yorkshire, S60 3NQ
tel: 01709 375 812
email: elaineselect@aol.com
contact: Elaine
design service: Yes
minimum run: None
info: Print onto colour t-shirts and most other items.

Shirt Prints Direct
161-163 London Road, Sheffield, S2 4LH
tel: 0114 255 9000
email: info@shirtprintsdirect.com
web: www.shirtprintsdirect.com
contact: Dominic
design service: Yes
minimum run: None
info: Will print onto any garment. Also offer other promotional items such as mugs, mousemats and caps.

Snappies T-shirt Printing
1 New Street, Barnsley, South Yorkshire, S70 1RX
tel: 01226 207 107
email: info@snappies.com
web: www.snappies.com
design service: Yes
info: Have dealt with bands before and are comfortable with your needs.

Subedition
email: roar@subedition.co.uk
web: www.subedition.co.uk
design service: No
minimum run: None
info: Online T-shirt community. Submit designs and let others rate them. Highly rated designs will get printed. 10% profit goes to the designer. Will run special competitions for bands.

Toucan Screen Print Ltd.
Wakefield Commercial Park, Bridge Road, Horbury Bridge, Wakefield, West Yorkshire, WF4 5NW
tel: 01924 277 272
contact: Mark
design service: Yes
minimum run: None
info: T-shirt printing available, but only onto white shirts.

Tshirt Printers Ltd.
Alexandra Mill, Baker Street, Morley, Leeds, West Yorkshire, LS27 0QH
tel: 0113 238 1644
contact: Tony
design service: Yes
minimum run: 25
info: Will print onto all t-shirts.

Well Worn
Unit R7, Tenterfields Business Park, Luddenden Foot, Halifax, HX2 6EQ
tel: 01422 885 945
email: sales@wellworn.co.uk
web: www.wellworn.co.uk
design service: Yes
info: Embroidery and print onto various garments.

Witchprint Promotional Products
72 Mile End Avenue, Hatfield, Doncaster, South Yorkshire, DN7 6AS
tel: 01302 844 190
email: witchprint@aol.com
contact: Mike
design service: Yes
minimum run: None
info: Will print onto any item including clothing.

Zik Zak
15 Fossgate, York, North Yorkshire, Y01 9TA
tel: 01904 655 255
email: enquiries@zikzak.co.uk
web: www.zikzak.co.uk
contact: Christine
design service: Yes
minimum run: None
info: Print onto ceramic and glass items, as well as clothing.

NORTHERN IRELAND

Artistic Impressions Advertising
PO Box 93, Banbridge, County Down, BT32 4YF
tel: 028 4067 1100
email: info@artisticimpressions.ie
web: www.artisticimpressions.ie
design service: Yes
info: Designs printed onto pens, keyrings, mugs plus other items.

Bradbury Graphics
Equality House, 6-14 Donegall Path, Belfast, BT7 1BS
tel: 028 9023 3535
fax: 028 9057 2057
email: info@bradbury-graphics.co.uk
web: www.bradbury-graphics.co.uk
design service: Yes
minimum run: None
info: Turnaround time of around 24 hours. Full range of merchandise available.

C.A. Promotions
35 Ardenlee Avenue, Belfast, BT6 0AB
tel: 028 9045 6900
email: printedgifts@lineone.net
web: www.printedgifts.co.uk
design service: Yes
minimum run: Varies
info: Full range of printed promotional items available. Full catalogue can be requested.

Capall Promotions
2 Capall Court, Derry, BT48 8FJ
tel: 028 7135 0710
email: capall2@ntlworld.com
design service: Yes
info: Full range of promotional material.

Celebrations Oasis
11 North Street, Lurgan, Craigavon, BT67 9AG
tel: 028 3834 5599
email: paul@celebrationsoasis.com
web: www.celebrationsoasis.com
design service: Yes
info: Full garment printing and embroidery service. Also print onto other items such as mugs and jigsaws.

Good News Centre
7 Monaghan Street, Newry, County Down, BT35 6BB
tel: 028 3026 9555
email: jimneagle@btconnect.com
web: www.goodnewscentre.co.uk
design service: No
minimum run: None
info: Items include wallet sized cards, t-shirts, jigsaw puzzles, coasters, calendars, key rings and baseball caps. Also provide printing services. See listing in relevant section for more details.

JK Embroidery
102 Main Street, Maghera, BT46 5AF
tel: 028 7964 2215
email: jkembroidery@hotmail.com
design service: Yes
info: Specialise in embroidery service, but can also print t-shirts.

Kolormaster (Ireland)
Unit 23a, Kennedy Centre, Falls Road, Belfast, County Antrim, BT11 9AE
tel: 028 9061 6552
design service: Yes
minimum run: None
info: T-shirts, hats and other promotional items. T-shirts can only be printed on white.

Komodo
79 Magheraconluce Road, Hillsborough, County Down, BT26 6PR
tel: 028 9268 8285
email: info@komodorecordings.com
web: www.komodorecordings.com
design service: Yes
minimum run: None
info: Promotional items available include t-shirts, stickers and banners. Komodo also offer recording services, duplication facilities, printing and graphic design services, drum tuition, as well as organising gigs. See entries in relevant sections for further details.

Magic Moments
59 Market Street, Omagh, BT79 0AA
tel: 028 8225 2497
email: info@magikmoments.co.uk
web: www.magikmoments.co.uk
design service: Yes
info: Affordable personalised items. Printing onto t-shirts, records bags, coasters and mugs.

Prestige Enterprises
PO Box 1160, Netownabbey, County Antrim, BT36 5YP
tel: 0845 230 3818
email: info@prestigeenterprises.com
web: www.prestigeenterprises.com
design service: Yes
info: T-shirts, wristbands and stationery. See online catalogue to view full range.

PromoGift (NI)
20 Bay Road, Crumlin, County Antrim, BT29 4QP
tel: 028 9445 4278
email: info@promogiftni.co.uk
web: www.promogiftni.co.uk
design service: Yes
info: 3 or 4 weeks average turnaround time. Full range of promotional products available.

Tee-Shirt City
13 Egaltine Avenue, Belfast, BT9 6DW
tel: 028 9066 9613
web: www.teeshirtcity.co.uk
design service: Yes
info: Printing onto t-shirts, as well as many other garments.

Tri-Sport Trophies Ltd.
Unit 13, Alanbrooke Park Industrial Estate, Alanbrooke Road, Belfast, County Antrim, BT6 9HB
tel: 028 9079 2609
email: info@trisporttrophies.com
web: www.trisporttrophies.com
design service: Yes
info: Can provide printing onto many garments and also items including pens and mugs.

MUSIC SERVICES/RETAIL

T-Shirt City
23 Main Street, Portrush, County Antrim, BT56 8BL
tel: 028 7082 2088
email: tshirtcity@hotmail.com
design service: Yes
info: Thousands of transfers and colours available for t-shirt design.

SCOTLAND

50p Badges
23 Onslow Drive, Glasgow, G31 2LY
tel: 0141 554 2056
email: info@50pbadges.com
web: www.50pbadges.com
design service: No
minimum run: 4
info: Place your own message or design on a badge.

A Kind of Graphix
28 Gardenside Grove, Glasgow, Lanarkshire, G32 8EZ
tel: 0141 641 5464/07719 452 854
email: derek@akindofgraphix.co.uk
web: www.akindofgraphix.co.uk
contact: Derek MacFarlane
design service: Yes
minimum run: None
info: Print onto t-shirts, posters, leaflets and banners.

A1 Incentives Ltd.
45 Fotheringay Road, Glasgow, G41 4NN
tel: 0141 423 1668
email: a1incentives@btconnect.com
web: www.a1incentives.co.uk
design service: Yes
info: Badges, keyrings, pens, fridge magnets, umbrellas and mugs, amongst other products.

Abstitch Ltd.
Unit 2, Union Glen, Aberdeen, AB11 6ER
tel: 01224 586 060
email: abstitchemb@ukonline.co.uk
design service: No
info: Badge manufacturers. Can also embroider onto promotional wear.

Adline Personalised Products
Sterling House, 20 Renfield Street, Glasgow, G2 5AP
tel: 0141 221 1491
email: sales@adlinepersonalised.com
web: www.adlinepersonalised.com
design service: Yes
info: Personalised merchandise available. See online brochure for full listing.

Advance Signs & Design
The Trade Centre, Clackmannan Road, Alloa, Clackmannanshire, FK10 1RY
tel: 01259 218 216
fax: 01259 219 406
email: jim@advancesupplies.com
web: www.advancesupplies.com
contact: Jim McKenzie
design service: Yes
minimum run: None
info: T-shirts, hoodies, banners and signage.

Arrow Corporate Promotions
69 Rodger Avenue, Newton Mearns, Glasgow, Lanarkshire, G77 6JS
tel: 0141 639 4210
fax: 0141 639 0102
email: sales@arrowcorporate.co.uk
web: www.arrowcorporate.co.uk
contact: Angela Andrews
design service: No
minimum run: None
info: T-shirts, playing cards, banners and hoodies.

Bar One Ltd.
69-71 Lancefield Street, Glasgow, G3 8HZ
tel: 0141 226 4171
email: sales@barone.co.uk
web: www.barone.co.uk
contact: Gavin Roelston
design service: Yes
minimum run: 24
info: T-shirts, hoodies and wristbands. Printing and embroidery. Free brochures on request.

Blueprint Inverness
23 Seafield Road, Inverness, IV1 1SG
tel: 01463 241 623
fax: 01463 710 201
email: sales@acornsigns.co.uk
contact: Barry Geddes
design service: Yes
minimum run: None
info: Deal with t-shirts, caps, stickers, hoodies and banners. Contact for a price listing booklet.

Clear Keyrings
3 Bridge Street, Cowdenbeath, Fife, KY4 8LU
tel: 01383 513 592
email: sales@clearkeyrings.co.uk
web: www.clearkeyrings.co.uk
design service: Yes
minimum run: None
info: Print and include your own inserts to clear key rings, fridge magnets and coasters.

Concept Promotional Merchandise
39 Scott Street, Dundee, DD2 2AL
tel: 01382 660 523/07770 571 107
email: sales@conceptpm.com
web: www.conceptpm.com
design service: Yes
minimum run: None
info: Promotional items including pens, mousemats, coasters plus many more products.

Connect 2 Ltd.
Innova Campus, Rosythe Europarc, Rosythe, Fife, KY11 2UU
tel: 01383 428 008
email: central@connect2first.com
web: www.connect2first.com
design service: Yes
info: Items include umbrellas, baseball caps and pens.

Copymade
3 West Maitland Street, Edinburgh, EH12 5DS
tel: 0131 229 5432
fax: 0131 538 7109
email: copymade@btconnect.co.uk
web: www.copymade.co.uk
contact: Grant McKeeman
design service: Yes
minimum run: None
info: Deal with t-shirts, hoodies, banners, mugs and posters.

Craigdon Business Gifts
Advertsing House, Burghmuir, Blackhall Industrial Estate, Inverurie, AB51 4FS
tel: 01467 622 943
email: sales@craigdon.com
web: www.craigdon.com
design service: Yes
minimum run: 5
info: Embroidered promotional products including leisurewear.

Double T
21a Market Hall, Academy Street, Inverness, IV1 1PJ
tel: 01463 712 181
email: sales@doublet-tshirts.co.uk
web: www.doublet-tshirts.co.uk
contact: Dave
design service: No
minimum run: None
info: Printing onto t-shirts, mugs, mousemats and umbrellas.

Enterkin T-Shirt Co.
Barndennoch Schoolhouse, Auldgirth, Dumfries, Dumfriesshire, DG2 0TP
tel: 01387 740 488
design service: Yes
info: T-shirt printing.

Excel Images
193 Dumbarton Road, Clydebank, G81 4XJ
tel: 0141 951 4300
fax: 0141 951 8173
email: excelimages@btclick.com
web: www.excelimages.co.uk
design service: Yes
minimum run: None
info: Excel Images will print artwork or messages onto t-shirts and other garments. Also print posters and flyers. See entry in relevant section.

Florenta
17 Edison Street, Hillington Industrial Estate, Glasgow, G52 4JW
tel: 0141 810 2959
fax: 0141 810 2958
email: paul@florenta.co.uk
web: www.florenta.co.uk
contact: Paul Brown
design service: Yes
minimum run: 25
info: Deal with a huge range of products including t-shirts, pens, key rings, as well as less conventional products.

Freeze
116 Bruntsfield Place, Edinburgh, EH10 4ES
tel: 0131 228 2355
email: info@freeze-scotland.com
web: www.freeze-scotland.com
design service: Yes
info: Freeze are a ski and snowboard shop, but have designed clothing for customers in the past and are willing to work with bands. Please call for more details.

Groovy Chocolate Ltd.
Woodend Farm, Carnwath, Lanark, ML11 8LR
tel: 01555 840 405
email: info@groovychocolate.com
web: www.groovychocolate.com
design service: Yes
info: Customised chocolate designs.

GT Design & Marketing
35 Hawbank Road, East Kilbride, Glasgow, G74 5EG
tel: 01355 232 321
email: graeme@gtdesign.co.uk
web: www.gtdesign.co.uk
design service: Yes
info: Embroidery and printing onto garments. Range of promotional items available.

Hot Off The Press
2 Turnbull Way, Livingston, West Lothian, EH54 8RB
tel: 01506 441 499
fax: 01506 442 072
email: frazer@hotp.org.uk
web: www.hotp.org.uk
design service: Yes
minimum run: None
info: T-shirts and labels. Also do litho printing. See listing in relevant section.

Houston Designs
Skirling Mill Farm, Skirling, Biggar, Lanarkshire, ML12 6HB
tel: 01899 860 334
email: info@houstondesigns.com
web: www.houstondesigns.com
contact: Graeme Houston
design service: Yes
minimum run: None
info: T-shirts, sweatshirts, tracksuits, jackets, sunglasses, fleeces, caps and much more. Check website for full merchandise listing.

Ideal Publicity
26 Claremont Street, Aberdeen, AB10 6QS
tel: 01224 213 703
email: sales@idealpublicity.co.uk
web: www.idealpublicity.co.uk
design service: Yes
info: Mugs, baseball caps, pens and sweatshirts.

Im-Press Promotions Ayr Ltd.
3 Barclaugh Drive, Coylton, Ayr, Ayrshire, KA6 6HS
tel: 01292 570 495
email: im-pressayr@btconnect.com
web: www.im-press.co.uk
design service: Yes
info: Large variety of products available. See website for full catalogue.

Kelvin Promotions (Scotland) Ltd.
13 Sandyford Place, Glasgow, G3 7NB
tel: 0141 248 7758
email: enquiries@kelvinpromos.plus.com
web: www.kelvispromotions.co.uk
design service: Yes
info: Promotional products including badges, pens, bags, clothing and lighters.

Kidd Personalised Products
24-36 Dunedin Street, Edinburgh, EH7 4JG
tel: 0131 550 4848
email: sales@kidd-uk.com
web: www.kidd-uk.com
design service: Yes
info: Range of promotional products ranging from pens to umbrellas.

Mannik Promotions
Mannik House, 54 Sinclair Drive, Glasgow, G42 9PY
tel: 0141 632 1113
fax: 0141 632 1114
email: sales@mannik.co.uk
web: www.mannik.co.uk
design service: No
minimum run: Contact for details
info: Range of promotional items including key rings, clothing, balloons and stickers.

Marketing 2000
44 Glengarry Crescent, Falkirk, Stirlingshire, FK1 5UE
tel: 01324 623 015
email: info@01324.co.uk
web: www.01324.co.uk
design service: Yes
info: Marketing 2000 offer a selection of promotional and novelty items.

MPS Limited
120 Carstairs Street, Glasgow, Lanarkshire, G40 4JD
tel: 0141 556 4242
fax: 0141 556 2333
email: info@mpslimited.co.uk
web: www.mpslimited.co.uk
contact: Alan Adie
design service: Yes
minimum run: Flexible
info: Deal with wide range of products including t-shirts, baseball caps, key rings, pens and banners.

Non-Stop Stuff
12 South Bridge, Edinburgh, EH1 1DD
tel: 0131 556 6226
email: info@nonstopstuff.co.uk
web: www.nonstopstuff.co.uk
design service: Yes
minimum run: None
info: T-shirt printing plus banners and signage. Regularly work with unsigned bands.

Photo-Graphix
Unit 49-50, Clyde Shopping Hall, 36 Sylvania Way South, Clydebank, Dumbartonshire, G81 1EA
tel: 0141 952 4544
fax: 0141 952 4544
contact: Dave Thompson
design service: Yes
minimum run: None
info: T-shirt printing service.

Planet Boo
41 Braetongue, Tongue, By Lairg, Sutherland, IV27 4XN
tel: 01847 611 777
email: info@planetboo.com
web: www.planetboo.com
design service: No
minimum run: None
info: Create your own logo and send it to Planet Boo where it can be put onto t-shirts, key rings, stickers, badges, drum skins and record bags.

Prime Signs
The Golf House, Taymouth Terrace, Carnoustie, DD7 7JW
tel: 01241 858 400
fax: 01241 858 444
email: info@primesigns-scotland.co.uk
web: www.primesigns-scotland.co.uk
design service: Yes
minimum run: 10 (Printing), None (Embroidery)
info: Deal with printing a wide range of products including t-shirts, photographs and drum kits. Use both printing and embroidery.

Print One Ltd.
Unit 6a-6b, Old Ferry Road, North Ballachullish, Fort William, PH33 6RZ
tel:	01855 821 027
fax:	01855 821 035
email:	sales@printone.co.uk
web:	www.printone.co.uk
contact:	Tom Alexander
design service:	Yes
minimum run:	None
info:	Print your own design onto t-shirts, banners, caps and hoodies.

Promotion Matters Ltd.
45 Reres Road, Dundee, DD5 2QD
tel:	01382 477 118
email:	info@promotionmatters.com
web:	www.promotionmatters.com
design service:	Yes
info:	Wide range of promotional items including pens, bags and yo-yos.

Recognition Express (West Scotland)
19c Crown Street, Ayr, Ayrshire, KA8 8AG
tel:	01292 266 650
email:	sales@re-westscotland.co.uk
web:	www.re-westscotland.co.uk
design service:	Yes
info:	Promotional products for all purposes, as well as badges and signage.

Ross Promotional Products Ltd.
40 Crimea Street, Glasgow, G2 8PW
tel:	0141 221 1030
email:	enquiries@rosspromotional.co.uk
web:	www.rosspromotional.co.uk
design service:	No
minimum run:	Contact for details
info:	Variety of promotional products available. Check website for full catalogue.

Scotshirts Ltd.
24 West Telferton, Portobello, Edinburgh, EH7 6UL
tel:	0131 669 6964
fax:	0131 669 1238
email:	neil@scotshirts.com
web:	www.scotshirts.com
contact:	Neil Freednan
design service:	Yes
minimum run:	40
info:	Printing onto t-shirts, caps, hats and many more items.

Screen Printing Solutions
124 Crown Street, Aberdeen, Aberdeenshire, AB11 6HQ
tel:	01224 582 020
email:	screenprintingsolutions@hotmail.com
contact:	Robbie Phillips
design service:	No
minimum run:	None
info:	Will print onto most fabrics. Products include t-shirts, jackets and trousers. Contact for full catalogue.

Smart Promotions
31-35 Maclellan, Kinning Park, Glasgow, G41 1RR
tel:	0141 637 7071
email:	info@smart-promotions.co.uk
web:	www.smart-promotions.co.uk
design service:	Yes
info:	Print logos or messages onto range of products including coasters, mousemats and pens.

Sticker Monkey
75 Bread Street, Edinburgh, EH3 9AH
tel:	0131 229 8501
email:	info@stickermonkey.co.uk
web:	www.stickermonkey.co.uk
design service:	Yes
minimum run:	None
info:	Specialists in sticker printing. Design service available, or submit your own artwork. For price estimates, complete online quote form on website.

Sunrise Screenprint Workshop
Old School, Menmuir, Brechin, Angus, DD9 7RN
tel:	01356 660 430
email:	sunrise@gn.apc.org
web:	www.menmuir.org.uk/sunrise
contact:	Jennifer Tait
design service:	Yes
minimum run:	10
info:	T-shirt printing service.

Tay Shirt Co.
Meadow Mill, West Henderson's Wynd, Dundee, DD1 5BY
tel:	0800 970 0643
email:	bert@tay-shirt.com
web:	www.tay-shirt.com
design service:	Yes
minimum run:	None
info:	Embroidery or printing onto t-shirts and sweatshirts.

Trip
Unit 4, Kings Court, 105 King Street, Glasgow, Lanarkshire, G1 5RB
tel:	0141 553 1777
fax:	0141 553 2480
email:	info@teeshirtnation.com
web:	www.teeshirtnation.com
contact:	Pauline Leonard
design service:	No
minimum run:	None
info:	Deal with printing onto t-shirts, hoodies, drum skins, caps, pin badges and banners.

The T-Shirt Shack
46 Harrysmuir Gardens, Pumpherston, West Lothian, EH53 0PL
tel:	07803 942 791
email:	sales@t-shirtshack.net
web:	www.t-shirtshack.net
design service:	No
minimum run:	None
info:	Custom printers of t-shirts and other promotional wear. Printing and embroidery also available.

T-Shirtville
17 Newburgh Circle, Bridge of Don, Aberdeen, AB22 8QZ
tel:	01224 822 988
email:	tshirtville@aol.com
design service:	Yes
minimum run:	None
info:	Products available include t-shirts, sweatshirts, keyrings and mousemats.

Water Media Ltd.
Stirling Street, Blackford, Auchterarder, Perthshire, PH4 1QA
tel:	01764 682 828
email:	sales@watermedia.co.uk
web:	www.watermedia.co.uk
design service:	Yes
info:	Custom designed bottled media. Get your band logo on a bottle of water.

White Spark Promotions
Riverview Business Centre, Centurion Court, North Esglanard, Aberdeen, AB11 5QH
tel:	07966 364 804
email:	info@whitesparks.co.uk
web:	www.whitesparks.co.uk
design service:	Yes
minimum run:	Contact for details
info:	Upload your artwork and have it printed onto flyers, wristbands, beer mats, banners, CD covers and many other items.

Wright Impressions
7 Easter Currie Court, Currie, EH14 5PY
tel:	0131 538 7060
design service:	Yes
info:	Offer wide range of products including calendars and key rings.

Zombie Works
1/1 The Angel Building, 12 Paislay Road West, Glasgow, G51 1LE
email:	gareth@zombie-works.co.uk
web:	www.zombie-works.co.uk
contact:	Gareth, Gillian
design service:	Yes
minimum run:	None
info:	High quality promotional packs to get your recordings noticed. Also, posters and flyers to advertise gigs and events and press packs to gain media coverage. Also offer photography, video duplication and web design services. See listings in relevant sections for details.

WALES

100 Per Cent Uneek
Castleton Walk Arcade, Newton Road, Mumbles, Swansea, SA3 4AX
tel:	01792 367 677
design service:	Yes
info:	Short runs of embroidered and printed garments including t-shirts, sweatshirts and fleeces.

Argraff Screen Printers
Capel, Pen-y-Graig, Llangwnnadl, Pwllheli, Gwynedd, LL53 8NT
tel: 01758 770 468
email: argraff@llyn.net
design service: Yes
minimum run: None
info: Garment and textile printing. Can only work in the local area.

Brynwood Design & Print
Unit 13-15, Tir Llwyd Industrial Estate, St. Asaph Avenue, Kinmel Bay, Rhyl, LL18 5EF
tel: 01745 336 651
email: brynwood.graphics@btconnect.com
contact: Liz Bundy
design service: Yes
minimum run: None
info: Garment printers. Stickers, signs, banners and boards. Can refer clients to poster and flyer printers.

City Print & Promotions Ltd.
2a Leckwith Road, Canton, Cardiff, CF11 8HJ
tel: 02920 236 723
email: paul.sims1@ntlworld.com
web: www.cityprintandpromotions.com
design service: No
minimum run: None
info: T-shirts, back drops and signs, plus a range of other promotional items including mugs and pens.

Direct Source
75 Cardiff Road, Taffs Well, Cardiff, CF15 7RD
tel: 02920 810 094
design service: Yes
minimum run: Contact for details
info: Full range of promotional garments and items available including frisbees and radios. Minimum run varies depending on product.

Dynamite Design
7 Heath Mead, Heath, Cardiff, CF10 1DT
tel: 02920 754 518
email: dynamitedesign@btopenworld.com
web: www.dynamitetees.co.uk
design service: Yes
minimum run: None
info: T-shirt printing with other garments available on request. Band friendly.

Fideo Sain
Unit 4-5, Llanllyfni Road, Antur Nantelle Estate, Caernarfon, Gwynedd, LL54 6LY
tel: 01286 880 977
web: www.sainwales.com
design service: Yes
minimum run: Varies
info: Short run specialist. Range of promotional items available including t-shirts, mugs, coasters, badges and clock faces. Also offer CD duplication. See relevant section for details.

Genesis Screen Print & Embroidery
Tywyn, Gwynedd, LL36 9LW
tel: 01654 710 137
fax: 01654 712 461
email: info@genesis-uk.com
web: www.genesis-uk.com
design service: No
minimum run: None
info: Screen printing and embroidery for garments. Range of other promotional garments available.

Graphics Service
The Arts & Social Studies Library, Corbett Road, Cardiff, CF10 3XT
tel: 02920 874 461
design service: No
minimum run: None
info: T-shirt printing service based within Cardiff University campus. Can also provide printing and photocopying. See relevant section for more details.

Gwynedd T-Shirt Centre
Llanystumdwy, Criccieth, LL52 0SP
tel: 01766 522 733
design service: Yes
info: Short run specialists. Garment printing and embroidery. Products include t-shirts, sweatshirts, jackets, caps and hats.

Images
Sandringham House, The Square, Corwen, Clwyd, LL21 0DL
tel: 01490 413 338
email: lledingham@aol.com
design service: Yes
minimum run: None
info: Range of garments and promotional items including mouse mats, coasters and mugs. Vinyl signs for vehicles.

JLH Print & Promotions
Garth Works, Taffs Well, Cardiff, CF15 7YF
tel: 02920 814 195
design service: Yes
info: Garment printing. Runs smaller than 10 units can be catered for using transfers. Range of promotional items also available including pens, mugs, notepads and stickers.

Mike The Biz
1 Cawdor Terrace, Newcastle Emlyn, Dyfed, SA38 9AS
tel: 01239 711 797
email: info@mikethebiz.co.uk
web: www.mikethebiz.co.uk
design service: Yes
minimum run: 12
info: Garment printing and embroidery. Fast turnaround and friendly service.

Oner Signs & Leisure
4 Church Street, Cardiff, CF10 1BG
tel: 02920 396 989
email: info@onersigns.co.uk
web: www.onersigns.co.uk
design service: Yes
minimum run: None
info: T-shirts, stickers, badges, slip mats, record badges and other items available. Oner Signs & Leisure also stock a range of CDs in-store.

The Picquick Studio
4 Thompson Court, Romilly Court, Cardiff, CF5 1FL
tel: 02920 311 526
email: sales@picquickstudio.com
web: www.picquickstudio.com
design service: Yes
minimum run: None
info: Printing and embroidery. Range of products available including t-shirts, mousemats, fridge magnets, coasters, ties and caps.

Positive Images
Unit 7, Whittin Rosser Farm, Wakterston, Barry, CF62 3AS
tel: 01446 781 118
design service: No
minimum run: None
info: Silk screen printing and heat pressing for garments including t-shirts, polo shirts and caps. Banner printing.

Prism Print & Design
Unit 14, Woodlans Workshops, Coedcae Lane, Pontyclun, Mid Glamorgan, CF72 9DW
tel: 01443 237 231
email: sales@prismprint.co.uk
web: www.prismprint.co.uk
design service: Yes
minimum run: None
info: Garment print and embroidery. T-shirts, polo shirts, sweatshirts and patches. Range of promotional items including mugs and pens. Can also print posters and flyers. See relevant section for details.

Secret Spot Screen Printers
1 Newton Nottage Road, Porthcawl, Mid Glamorgan, CF36 5PF
tel: 01656 771 971
design service: Yes
minimum run: None
info: Screen printing for garments including t-shirts, polo shirts, sweatshirts, jackets and bags. Fast turnaround.

Tee's-R-Us
Rumbleway Filling Station, New Hedges, Tenby, SA70 8TN
tel: 01834 871 157
email: sales@teesrus.co.uk
web: www.teesrus.co.uk
design service: Yes
minimum run: None
info: Quality embroidery and printing services at a reasonable price.

T-Shirt Printing Shop
Unit 46-47, The Innshops, Newport, Gwent, NP20 1EX
tel: 01633 214 113
design service: No
minimum run: None
info: Screen printing service.

T-Shirt Rebel
PO Box 63, Pontypool, NP4 6WH
tel:	01495 758 781
web:	www.tshirtrebel.com or www.tshirtdoctor.com
design service:	Yes
minimum run:	None
info:	Short run specialists. T-shirts and other garments

available. Can print any portrait image. Range of promotional items including bags and keyrings. Website design also provided. Special rates for unsigned bands.

West Wales Print Co.
Unit 2 & 3, Lonlas Business Park, Skewen, Neath, SA10 6RP
tel:	01792 321 364
fax:	01792 321 364
email:	sales@westwalesprint.co.uk
web:	www.westwalesprint.co.uk
design service:	Yes
minimum run:	None
info:	Textile printing and embroidery. Vinyl boards

and signage ncluding signs for vehicles.

MUSIC SERVICES/RETAIL

3.13 RECORD SHOPS

EAST of ENGLAND 361 GREATER LONDON 363 MIDLANDS 373 NORTHEAST 379 NORTHWEST 382
SOUTHEAST 390 SOUTHWEST 396 YORKSHIRE 402 NORTHERN IRELAND 407 SCOTLAND 410 WALES 415

EAST of ENGLAND

Barney's
21a Cross Keys, Market Square, St. Neots, Cambridgeshire, PE19 2AR
tel:	01480 406 270
email:	keith.barnes2@btinternet.com
contact:	Keith
rack space:	No
flyer space:	Yes
poster space:	Yes
listening posts:	Yes
info:	Stock all types of music, although predominantly Rock.

baserecords.com
1-3 Eagle Street, Ipswich, Suffolk, IP4 1JA
tel:	01473 226 152
rack space:	No
flyer space:	No
poster space:	No
listening posts:	Yes
info:	CD, DVD, record and cassette retailers

specialising in Funky and US House. Also stock Breakbeat, Garage, Speed Garage. Business carried out mainly over the internet.

Better Leisure Ltd.
167a King Street, Great Yarmouth, Norfolk, NR30 2PA
tel:	01943 853 379
email:	malcomtims1@yahoo.co.uk
contact:	Malcom
rack space:	Yes
flyer space:	Yes
poster space:	Yes
listening posts:	Yes
info:	Stock all musical genres. Order system available

in-store. Lots of rack space is available for unsigned artists, as well as floor space for live performances.

Bounce Records
18 Bridewell Alley, Norwich, Norfolk, NR2 1AQ
tel:	01603 666 857
rack space:	Yes
flyer space:	Yes
poster space:	Yes
listening posts:	Yes
info:	Specialists in Drum&Bass and Dance music.

Circular Sounds
5 St. Benedict's Street, Norwich, Norfolk, NR2 49E
tel:	01603 630 130
fax:	01603 630 130
web:	www.circularsound.demon.co.uk
contact:	Maartin
rack space:	No
flyer space:	Yes
poster space:	Yes
listening posts:	Limited
info:	Deals in second hand vinyl only.

Compact Music
89 North Street, Sudbury, Suffolk, CO10 1RF
tel:	01787 881 160
email:	sales@compact-music.co.uk
web:	www.compact-music.co.uk
contact:	James Morgan
rack space:	Yes
flyer space:	Limited
poster space:	Limited
listening posts:	Yes
info:	Compact Music already stocks material for 3 local

bands and are quite happy to promote more up and coming unsigned artists. Stock all genres from Rock and Pop music to Classical and Jazz. Specialise in CDs, DVDs and vinyl. Mail order service available. Compact Music also sells instruments.

Disc-Chord
71 High Street, Lowestoft, Suffolk, NR32 1XN
tel:	01502 508 191
web:	www.discchord.gemm.com
rack space:	Yes
flyer space:	Limited
poster space:	Limited
listening posts:	No
info:	Mainly stock Rock music. Will sell material by

local artists.

Fine City Sounds
11 St. Gregory's Alley, Norwich, Norfolk, NR2 1ER
tel:	01603 630 727
rack space:	No
flyer space:	Yes
poster space:	Yes
listening posts:	Yes
info:	Second hand CD, DVD, record and cassettes. All

genres except Classical.

Fopp
37 Sydney Street, Cambridge, Cambridgeshire, CB2 3HX
tel:	01223 356 257
info:	Fopp are involved in 'The Unsigned Network'

- unsigned material is accepted centrally, distributed to stores and is placed in a specific 'Unsigned Section' which is promoted in-store. Material is only accepted in this way and you should refer to the 'Unsigned Network' link on the Fopp website to check whether they are accepting material at that time. Artists are paid a set amount on sales, on a sale-or-return basis. Applications for unsigned space is not on-going and Fopp will sell unsigned material on a sale/demand/space policy.

HMV
15-25 Lion Yard, Cambridge, Cambridgeshire, CB2 3NA
tel:	01223 319 090

HMV
20 Tavern Street, Ipswich, Suffolk, IP1 3AY
tel:	01473 213 127

HMV
87-88 High Street, King's Lynn, Norfolk, PE30 1BL
tel:	01553 765 900

HMV
21 Gentleman's Walk, Norwich, NR2 1NA
tel:	01603 622 329
web:	www.hmv.co.uk

HMV
4 Cathedral Square, Peterborough, PE1 1XH
tel:	01733 347 642
web:	www.hmv.co.uk

Lewks
3 Wales Court, Downham Market, Norfolk, PE38 9JZ
tel:	01366 383 762
rack space:	Limited
flyer space:	Limited
poster space:	Limited
listening posts:	No
info:	Stock all types of music. Happy to sell material by local unsigned acts.

Lucia Pop
4 Drozier House, 9-13 Market Place, Holt, Norfolk, NR25 6BE
tel:	01263 713 031
rack space:	Yes
flyer space:	Yes
poster space:	Yes
listening posts:	No
info:	CD, DVD, record and cassettes. Specialises in World music, Jazz and Folk. Luica Pop will stock unsigned material they like.

Malcolm's Media Mine
Provision Market, St. Peter's Street, Norwich, Norfolk, NR2 1ND
tel:	07771 857 682
rack space:	Limited
flyer space:	No
poster space:	No
listening posts:	Yes
info:	Malcolm's Media Mine stocks all genres of music and will accept material from any area.

Music Lovers
107 High Street, Gorleston On Sea, Great Yarmouth, Norfolk, NR31 6RF
tel:	01493 440 021
fax:	01493 440 021
contact:	Roger
rack space:	Yes
flyer space:	Yes
poster space:	Yes
listening posts:	No
info:	Music Lovers stock a wide variety of music. CDs, DVDs and vinyl. Ordering service available in-store.

MVC
Unit 4, St. Germain Walk, Huntingdon, Cambridgeshire, PE29 3FG
tel:	01480 456 964
web:	www.mvc.co.uk

MVC
4 Cornhill, Bury St. Edmunds, Suffolk, IP33 1BE
tel:	01284 749 534
web:	www.mvc.co.uk

MVC
Unit 22, Serpentine Green Shopping Centre, Hampton, Peterborough, PE7 8DE
tel:	01733 552 468
web:	www.mvc.co.uk

Out Of Time Records
46 Fore Street, Ipswich, Suffolk, IP4 1JY
tel:	01473 225 547
contact:	Chris
rack space:	No
flyer space:	Yes
poster space:	Yes
listening posts:	No
info:	Stock all types of music including Rock, Pop, Jazz, Blues, Punk and Indie. CDs, DVDs and Vinyl. Out Of Time Records also buy and sell music merchandise.

Ray's CDs
50 Magdalen Street, Norwich, Norfolk, NR3 1JE
tel:	01603 616 445
rack space:	Limited
flyer space:	Yes
poster space:	Yes
listening posts:	Yes
info:	Ray's CDs stocks a wide range of styles and is happy to sell material by local unsigned acts.

The Record Shop
10 St. James' Street, King's Lynn, Norfolk, PE30 5DA
tel:	01553 691 972
contact:	Tony
rack space:	Yes
flyer space:	Yes
poster space:	Limited
listening posts:	No
info:	Specialists in quality second hand and deleted CDs and DVDs. Section in-store dedicated to local bands. Turntables in-store. Only space to display posters under A4 size.

Recordman
70 Fulbridge Road, Peterborough, PE1 3LB
tel:	01733 890 482
email:	damianmca@aol.com
rack space:	No
flyer space:	Yes
poster space:	Yes
listening posts:	No
info:	Second hand vinyl. 50s,60s and 70s Rock, Soul, Beat, Jazz and Exotica. Unable to material from stock unsigned bands.

Red Pill Records
23 James Street, King's Lynn, Norfolk, PE30 5DA
tel:	01553 768 158
email:	sales@redpillrecords.com
web:	www.redpillrecords.com
contact:	Paul
rack space:	No
flyer space:	Yes
poster space:	Yes
listening posts:	Yes
info:	Specialise in Dance, Underground Hard House and Techno. Only stock vinyl.

Revolution Records
10 Mere Street, Diss, Norfolk, IP22 4AD
tel:	01379 652 711
rack space:	Yes
flyer space:	Yes
poster space:	Yes
listening posts:	Yes
info:	CD, DVD, record and cassette format available. Stocks all genres but specialises in Rock and Indie. Will stock unsigned CDs.

Sound Clash
28 St. Benedict's Street, Norwich, Norfolk, NR2 4AQ
tel:	01603 761 004
email:	soundclash@btinternet.com
rack space:	Yes
flyer space:	Yes
poster space:	Yes
listening posts:	Yes
info:	Sound Clash is an Alternative music store stocking Electronica, Dance, World music and Punk. Welcomes material from local unsigned bands.

Sounds Good Music
2a Nene Parade, March, Cambridgeshire, PE15 8TD
tel:	01354 661 850
rack space:	Limited
flyer space:	Limited
poster space:	Limited
listening posts:	No
info:	Stocks CDs, DVDs, videos and books of all genres. Rack space is available for unsigned artists.

Spindoctors
38 Magdalen Street, Norwich, Norfolk, NR3 1LQ
tel:	01603 633 800
email:	spindoctors.recordshop@virgin.net
contact:	Terry
rack space:	Yes
flyer space:	Yes
poster space:	Yes
listening posts:	Yes
info:	All genres stocked, including material from unsigned acts.

Streetwise Music
76 King Street, Cambridge, Cambridgeshire, CB1 1LN
tel:	01223 300 496
email:	staff@streetwisemusic.co.uk
web:	www.streetwisemusic.co.uk
contact:	Simon Ryan
rack space:	Yes
flyer space:	Yes
poster space:	No
listening posts:	Yes
info:	Specialise in Dance music. Mostly stock vinyl. Would consider selling records by local Dance acts.

Virgin Megastore
Unit 28a, Grafton Centre, Cambridge, Cambridgeshire, CB1 1PS
tel:	01223 360 333
web:	www.virginmegastores.co.uk

Virgin Megastore
15-19 Westgate Street, Ipswich, Suffolk, IP1 3DR
tel:	01473 233 880
web:	www.virginmegastores.co.uk

Virgin Megastore
Castle Mall, White Lion Gate, Norwich, NR1 3DD
tel: 01603 767 376
web: www.virginmegastores.co.uk

Virgin Megastore
Units 11-12, Queensgate Centre, Peterborough, PE1 1NH
tel: 01733 358 220
web: www.virginmegastores.co.uk

We Are The Music Men
12a Regent Road, Great Yarmouth, Norfolk, NR30 2AF
tel: 01493 842 400
contact: Graham
rack space: Yes
flyer space: No
poster space: No
listening posts: No
info: Specialises in Irish and Country music. Also stock DVDs.

wrapCD
158 High Street, Aldeburgh, Suffolk, IP15 5AQ
tel: 01728 454 525
email: admin@wrapcd.co.uk
web: www.wrapcd.co.uk
contact: Celia Allaby
rack space: Yes
flyer space: Yes
poster space: Limited
listening posts: Yes
info: Specialises in Classical music. Lots of rack space available for local unsigned artists. Also provide a listening corner where you can sample any CD in the shop.

Zone
11a West Street, Cromer, Norfolk, NR27 9HZ
tel: 01263 514 803
web: www.reload-zone.co.uk
rack space: Yes
flyer space: Yes
poster space: Yes
listening posts: Limited
info: Zone stocks mainly Rock and Chart music and will stock music by unsigned bands within these genres.#

GREATER LONDON

101 Records
11 Keeley Road, Croydon, Surrey, CR0 1TF
tel: 020 8681 8282
email: duncanathome@lineone.net
rack space: No
flyer space: Limited
poster space: Limited
listening posts: No
info: 101 is a second hand record store.

A&K Music
1 North Mall, London, N9 0EQ
tel: 020 8803 1773
rack space: Yes
flyer space: Yes
poster space: Yes
listening posts: No
info: A&K stock all genres of music, and will stock demos by local unsigned acts on a sale-or-return basis.

A.B.C. Music
7 The Broadway, Southall, Middlesex, UB1 1JR
tel: 020 8574 1319
email: abcmusicshop@aol.com
rack space: No
flyer space: Limited
poster space: Limited
listening posts: No
info: Specialise in Indian music.

Alan's Records
218 High Road, London, N2 9AY
tel: 020 8883 0234
rack space: Yes
flyer space: Yes
poster space: Yes
listening posts: Yes
info: Alan's Records stocks Reggae, Soul and Jazz amongst others, and will stock material by unsigned bands.

All Ages Record Shop
27a Pratt Street, Camden, London, NW1 0BG
tel: 020 7267 0303
rack space: Yes
flyer space: Yes
poster space: Yes
listening posts: No
info: All Ages is London's only specialist Punk Rock record shop. Happy to stock material from unsigned Punk acts.

ATS Digital.com
20-28 Hatton Wall, London, EC1N HAH
tel: 020 7404 1005
email: tony@abovethesky.com
web: www.atsdigital.com.
rack space: Yes
flyer space: No
poster space: No
listening posts: Yes
info: ATSDigital.com specialise in independent music downloads.

Banquet Records
52 Eden Street, Kingston Upon Thames, Surrey, KT1 1EE
tel: 020 8871 4538
email: shop@banquetrecords.com
web: www.banquetrecords.com
rack space: Yes
flyer space: Limited
poster space: Limited
listening posts: Yes
info: Banquet Records stock most genres of music, and may stock quality unsigned material in the shop.

Beano's
7 Middle Street, Croydon, CR10 1RE
tel: 020 8680 1202
fax: 020 8680 1203
email: shop@beanos.co.uk
web: www.beanos.co.uk
rack space: Limited
flyer space: Yes
poster space: Yes
listening posts: Yes
info: Beano's was included in the Top 20 record stores by Time Out Magazine. One of the largest second hand record stores in the world, covering four floors. Stock Hip-Hop, Rock, House and Soul. Also offer recording facilities, see listing for Moon Recording Studio in relevant section.

BGS Music
365 High Road, Ilford, IG1 IDF
tel: 020 8514 5650
rack space: No
flyer space: Yes
poster space: Yes
listening posts: No
info: BGS specialise in Asian music.

Black Dog Music
69 Berwick Street, Soho, London, W1F 8SZ
tel: 020 7287 6477
rack space: Yes
flyer space: Limited
poster space: Limited
listening posts: Yes
info: Black Dog stock all genres of music, and will stock material by unsigned acts on a sale-or-return basis.

Black Market
25 D'Arblay Street, London, W1F 8EJ
tel: 020 7439 2403
email: mailorder@blackmarket.co.uk
web: www.blackmarket.co.uk
rack space: Yes
flyer space: Yes
poster space: No
listening posts: Yes
info: Black Market specialise in House and Drum&Bass. Will consider stocking unsigned material by acts from these genres.

Blacker Dread Music Store
406 Coldharbour Lane, London, SW9 8LF
tel: 020 7274 5095
email: sendmirecords@aol.com
rack space: Limited
flyer space: Limited
poster space: Limited
listening posts: No
info: Specialists in Hip-Hop, R&B, Reggae and Soul. Blacker Dread have limited rack space for unsigned material. Please ask in-store if you would like your demo to be stocked.

MUSIC SERVICES/RETAIL

Body Music
261 High Road, London, N15 4RR
tel:	020 8802 0146
rack space:	Yes
flyer space:	Yes
poster space:	Yes
listening posts:	Yes
info:	Body Music stock all genres of music, and will

consider stocking material by unsigned acts.

Brick Lane Music House
74 Brick Lane, London, E1 6RL
tel:	020 7247 2547
rack space:	No
flyer space:	No
poster space:	Yes
listening posts:	No
info:	Brick Lane Music House specialise in Asian

music.

Bud's Country Music Store
184 High Street, Penge, London, SE20 7QB
tel:	020 8676 8801
fax:	020 8776 6535
email:	budscountry@ntlworld.com
rack space:	Limited
flyer space:	Limited
poster space:	Limited
listening posts:	No
info:	Bud's specialise in mail-order, and their

catalogue is distributed to around 4,000 customers. Send your demos to the address above. If Bud likes it, he will consider adding it to the catalogue.

Cage Records (Kingston Upon Thames)
2 Apple Market, Kingston Upon Thames, Surrey, KT1 1JE
tel:	020 8547 0113
email:	info@cagerecords.com
web:	www.cagerecords.com
rack space:	Yes
flyer space:	Yes
poster space:	Yes
listening posts:	Yes
info:	Cage Records specialise in Drum&Bass, House,

R&B, Garage and Hip-Hop. Already stock a wide range of unsigned material. Also stock DJ equipment including turntables. Also see listing for store based in West Ealing.

Cage Records (West Ealing)
8 Chignell Place, West Ealing, London, W13 0TJ
tel:	020 8567 1396
email:	info@cagerecords.com
web:	www.cagerecords.com
rack space:	Yes
flyer space:	Yes
poster space:	Yes
listening posts:	Yes
info:	Cage Records specialise in Drum&Bass, House,

R&B, Garage and Hip-Hop. Already stock a wide range of unsigned material.

Cavern Records
163-165 High Street, Walthamstow, London, E17 7BX
tel:	020 8503 7997
rack space:	Limited
flyer space:	Limited
poster space:	Limited
listening posts:	Yes
info:	Cavern stock all genres of music, and are willing

to stock music by local unsigned acts.

CD Joint
66 Kingsland High Street, London, E8 2JP
tel:	020 7923 4447
rack space:	Limited
flyer space:	Yes
poster space:	Yes
listening posts:	Yes
info:	CD Joint specialise in R&B, Gospel, Hip-Hop and

Jazz. They will consider stocking material by unsigned acts from these genres.

The CD Shop
206 Field End Road, Eastcote, Pinner, Middlesex, HA5 1RD
tel:	020 8866 0017
rack space:	No
flyer space:	No
poster space:	No
listening posts:	No
info:	The CD Shop sells all kinds of music.

CD Warehouse UK Ltd. (Ealing)
51 New Broadway, Ealing, London, W5 5AH
tel:	020 8567 2122
email:	cdwuk@btinternet.com
web:	www.cdwuk.com
rack space:	Yes
flyer space:	Yes
poster space:	Yes
listening posts:	Yes
info:	CD Warehouse stock both second hand and new

records, and will consider stocking material from local unsigned acts. See listings for stores in the South East and London.

CD Warehouse UK Ltd. (London)
46 The Broadway, London, SW19 1RQ
tel:	020 8543 2355
email:	cdwuk@btinternet.com
web:	www.cdwuk.com
rack space:	Yes
flyer space:	Limited
poster space:	Limited
listening posts:	Yes
info:	CD Warehouse stock both second hand and new

records, and will consider stocking material from local unsigned acts. See listings for stores in South East and London.

Cheapo Cheapo Records
53 Rupert Street, London, W1V 7HN
tel:	020 7437 8272
rack space:	Limited
flyer space:	No
poster space:	No
listening posts:	No
info:	Cheapo Cheapo Records stock all genres of music.

Choices Records
383b Green Street, London, E13 9AU
tel:	020 8472 4855
rack space:	Yes
flyer space:	Yes
poster space:	Yes
listening posts:	No
info:	Choices Records stock all genres of music on

vinyl and CD format.

City Sounds
5 Kirby Street, London, EC1N 8TS
tel:	020 7404 1800
email:	sales@city-sounds.co.uk
web:	www.city-sounds.co.uk
rack space:	Yes
flyer space:	Yes
poster space:	Yes
listening posts:	Yes
info:	City Sounds specialise in House and Garage

music. Will consider stocking material by unsigned acts from these genres.

Classical Music Exchange
36 Notting Hill Gate, London, W11 3HX
tel:	020 7229 3219
web:	www.mveshops.co.uk
rack space:	No
flyer space:	Limited
poster space:	Limited
listening posts:	No
info:	Part of Music & Video Exchange chain. Stock

second hand material. See website for details of other branches.

Collections
70 Lee High Road, Lewisham, London, SE13 5PT
tel:	020 8463 9388
rack space:	No
flyer space:	No
poster space:	No
listening posts:	No
info:	Collections specialise in second hand Soul and

Reggae vinyl. Do not stock unsigned material.

Compact Discounts
258-260 Lavender Hill, London, SW11 1LJ
tel:	020 7978 5560
rack space:	Yes
flyer space:	No
poster space:	Limited
listening posts:	Yes
info:	Compact Discounts stock all genres of music, and

may consider stocking material by local unsigned acts.

Cruisin' Records
134 Welling High Street, Welling, Kent, DA16 1TJ
tel:	020 8304 5853
fax:	020 8304 0429
email:	john@cruisin-records.fftnet.co.uk
rack space:	Limited
flyer space:	Yes
poster space:	Yes
listening posts:	No
info:	Cruisin' Records stock all genres of music.

Deal Real Records
3 Marlborough Court, London, W1F 7EF
tel:	020 7287 7245
fax:	020 7287 7246
email:	info@dealreal.co.uk
web:	www.dealreal.co.uk
contact:	Sef
rack space:	Yes
flyer space:	Yes
poster space:	Yes
listening posts:	No
info:	Hip Hop specialists. Willing to stock records by
unsigned acts. Open mic nights are held in-store on the first and third
Friday of the month. The third Friday is for female performers only.

Decksterity Records
115b Trafalger Road, Greenwich, London, SE10 9TX
tel:	020 8265 2000
email:	info@decksterityrecords.com
web:	www.decksterityrecords.com
rack space:	Yes
flyer space:	Yes
poster space:	Yes
listening posts:	Yes
info:	Decksterity specialise in Breakbeat and
Drum&Bass. Will stock unsigned acts of the above genres on a sale-or-
return basis.

Disque
11 Chapel Market, Islington, London, N1 9EZ
tel:	020 7833 1104
email:	sales@disque.org.uk
web:	www.disque.co.uk
rack space:	Yes
flyer space:	Yes
poster space:	Yes
listening posts:	Yes
info:	Disque specialise in Funk, Disco, Hip-Hop, Jazz,
Roots, Rock, Soul, House and Indie, and will consider stocking material
from local unsigned acts.

Dub Vendor Records
274 Lavender Hill, London, SW11 1LJ
tel:	020 7223 3757
email:	mailorder@dubvendor.co.uk
web:	www.dubvendor.co.uk
rack space:	Yes
flyer space:	Yes
poster space:	Yes
listening posts:	No
info:	Dub Vendor specialise in Reggae, R&B and Hip-
Hop. Will consider selling unsigned material of the above genres on a
sale-or-return basis.

Easy Vinyl
20 Denman Street, London, W1D 7HR
tel:	020 7734 7712
email:	sales@easyvinyl.com
web:	www.easyvinyl.com
rack space:	Yes
flyer space:	Yes
poster space:	Yes
listening posts:	Yes
info:	Easy Vinyl specialise in upbeat 'party' music, and
are willing to stock unsigned material if they think it will sell.

Essential Music
16 The Market, Greenwich, London, SE10 9HZ
tel:	020 8293 4982
rack space:	Limited
flyer space:	Limited
poster space:	Limited
listening posts:	Yes
info:	Essential stock an eclectic mix of music and will
consider stocking local unsigned bands' material.

Eukatech
49 Endell Street, Covent Garden, London, WC2H 9AJ
tel:	020 7240 8060
email:	shop@eukatechrecords.com
web:	www.eukatechrecords.com
contact:	Marcus Lenzi
rack space:	Yes
flyer space:	Yes
poster space:	Yes
listening posts:	Yes
info:	Eukatech specialise in House and Techno music,
and will consider stocking material by unsigned acts from these genres.
For more information on Eukatech's label, see the Record Company
listings.

Fab Music
55 The Broadway, Crouch End, London, N8 8DT
tel:	020 8347 6767
email:	fab@fabmusic.co.uk
web:	www.fabmusic.co.uk
rack space:	Yes
flyer space:	Yes
poster space:	No
listening posts:	Yes
info:	Fab Music will consider stocking material from
local unsigned acts.

Flashback
50 Essex Road, Islington, London, N1 8LR
tel:	020 7354 9356
email:	mark@flashback.co.uk
web:	www.flashback.co.uk
rack space:	Yes
flyer space:	Yes
poster space:	Yes
listening posts:	Yes
info:	Flashback stock a wide range of collectable vinyl,
CDs and videos. They will consider stocking high quality demos and
DVDs from local acts.

Fopp
1 Earlham Street, London, WC2H 9II
tel:	020 7379 0883
web:	www.fopp.co.uk
rack space:	Limited
flyer space:	No
poster space:	No
listening posts:	No
info:	Fopp are involved in 'The Unsigned Network'.
Unsigned material is accepted centrally, distributed to stores and is
placed in a specific 'Unsigned Section' which is promoted in-store.
Material is only accepted in this way and you should refer to the
'Unsigned Network' link on the Fopp website to check whether they are
accepting material at that time. Artists are paid a set amount on sales,
on a sale-or-return basis.

GJ's Music Centre
131 Ilford Lane, Ilford, IG1 2RJ
tel:	020 7511 8919
rack space:	No
flyer space:	No
poster space:	Yes
listening posts:	No
info:	GJ's stock all kinds of music.

Golden Grooves Records
193 Whitecross Street, London, EC1Y 8QP
tel:	020 7253 4550
email:	sales@goldengroovesrecords.com
web:	www.goldengroovesrecords.com
rack space:	Yes
flyer space:	Yes
poster space:	Yes
listening posts:	Limited
info:	Golden Grooves stock second hand material from
all genres. Will stock unsigned material in own rack space.

Haggle Vinyl
114-116 Essex Road, Islington, London, N1 8LX
tel:	020 7704 3101
email:	lyn@haggle.freeserve.co.uk
web:	www.hagglevinyl.com
contact:	Lynn
rack space:	No
flyer space:	Yes
poster space:	Yes
listening posts:	Yes
info:	Haggle Vinyl stock a wide range of vinyl from
every genre of music from 1960s onwards. Massive collection available,
and is by far and away the best shop in London.

MUSIC SERVICES/RETAIL

Hawkeye Record Store
2 Craven Park Road, London, NW10 4AB
tel: 020 8961 0866
rack space: Yes
flyer space: Yes
poster space: Yes
listening posts: Yes
info: Hawkeye specialise in Reggae and Soul music.
Stock demos by unsigned artists from these genres.

HMV
Unit 12, St. Ann's Centre, Harrow, HA1 1AT
tel: 020 8861 7970
web: www.hmv.co.uk
info: See Head Office listing.

HMV
Unit 49, Victoria Island, Victoria Station, London, SW1V 1JU
tel: 020 7963 8780
web: www.hmv.co.uk
info: See Head Office listing.

HMV
Trocadero, Coventry Street, London, W1V 7FD
tel: 020 7439 0447
web: www.hmv.co.uk
info: See Head Office listing.

HMV
150 Oxford Street, London, W1D 1DJ
tel: 020 7631 3423
web: www.hmv.co.uk
info: See Head Office listing.

HMV
360 Oxford Street, London, W1C 1AB
tel: 020 7514 3600
web: www.hmv.co.uk
info: See Head Office listing.

HMV
40-42 King Street, Covent Garden, London, WC2E 8LS
tel: 020 7379 8935
web: www.hmv.co.uk
info: See Head Office listing.

HMV
Unit G, Whiteleys Shopping Centre, London, W2 4YN
tel: 020 7313 8860
web: www.hmv.co.uk
info: See Head Office listing.

HMV
Unit MSU 3, Parkfield, Islington, London, N1 0PS
tel: 020 7704 7400
web: www.hmv.co.uk
info: See Head Office listing.

HMV
1 Whittington Avenue, Leadenhall, London, EC3V 1LE
tel: 020 7626 3246
web: www.hmv.co.uk
info: See Head Office listing.

HMV
167-169 High Street, Sutton, SM1 1JU
tel: 020 8661 5666
web: www.hmv.co.uk
info: See Head Office listing.

HMV
137 North End, Croydon, Surrey, CR0 1TN
tel: 020 8686 5557
web: www.hmv.co.uk
info: See Head Office listing.

HMV
23 The Broadway, Wimbledon, London, SW19 1RE
tel: 020 8947 6021
web: www.hmv.co.uk
info: See Head Office listing.

HMV
90-92 High Street, Bromley, Kent, BR1 1EY
tel: 020 8313 0727
web: www.hmv.co.uk
info: See Head Office listing.

HMV
81 The Mall, Broadway Shopping Centre, Bexleyheath, DA6 7JJ
tel: 020 8298 0876
web: www.hmv.co.uk
info: See Head Office listing.

HMV
28 Canada Place, Canary Wharf, London, E14 5AH
tel: 020 7512 9222
web: www.hmv.co.uk
info: See Head Office listing.

HMV
11-13 Church Street, Enfield, EN2 6AF
tel: 020 8363 0184
web: www.hmv.co.uk
info: See Head Office listing.

HMV
57-61 Heath Street, Hampstead, London, NW3 6UG
tel: 020 7435 6575
web: www.hmv.co.uk
info: See Head Office listing.

HMV
Unit 12, Shopping City, Wood Green, London, N22 6HE
tel: 020 8881 9239
web: www.hmv.co.uk
info: See Head Office listing.

HMV
Unit Y11a, Brent Cross Shopping Centre, Brent Cross, London, NW4 3FG
tel: 020 8201 5430
web: www.hmv.co.uk
info: See Head Office listing.

HMV
70 George Street, Richmond, Surrey, TW9 1HE
tel: 020 8940 9880
web: www.hmv.co.uk
info: See Head Office listing.

HMV
78-80 High Street, Putney, London, SW15 1RB
tel: 020 8780 2600
web: www.hmv.co.uk
info: See Head Office listing.

HMV
332-334 North End Road, Fulham, London, SW6 1NF
tel: 020 7386 5256
web: www.hmv.co.uk
info: See Head Office listing.

HMV
Unit 2b, Retail World, Parkgate, Hounslow, TW3 1BL
tel: 020 8577 5255
web: www.hmv.co.uk
info: See Head Office listing.

HMV
Units 11-12, 1st Floor, Bentalls Shopping Centre, Wood Street, Kingston Upon Thames, KT1 1TR
tel: 020 8974 8037
web: www.hmv.co.uk
info: See Head Office listing.

HMV
Unit 11, Selborne Walk Shopping Centre, Walthamstow, London, E17 7JR
tel: 020 8509 4340
web: www.hmv.co.uk

HMV
Unit C, Southside, Wandsworth Shopping Centre, London, SW18 4TF
tel: 020 8877 5990
web: www.hmv.co.uk

HMV
Selfridges, 400 Oxford Street, London, W1A 1AB
tel: 020 7495 3473
web: www.hmv.co.uk

HMV
Unit G, Whiteley's Shopping Centre, London, W2 4YN
tel: 020 7313 8860
web: www.hmv.co.uk

HMV
Unit 10, Gallions Reach, Beckton, London, E6 7FB
tel: 020 7540 9650
web: www.hmv.co.uk

HMV
2 Arcadia Centre, Ealing Broadway, Ealing, W5 2ND
tel: 020 8566 2590
web: www.hmv.co.uk

HMV
Unit 5, Greenwich Retail Park, Bugsby Way, Charlton, London, SE7 7SR
tel: 020 8312 8350
web: www.hmv.co.uk

HMV
Unit RU44, Airside, Terminal 4, Heathrow, TW6 3XA
tel: 020 8745 0692
web: www.hmv.co.uk

HMV
Unit SU3, Terminal 1, Heathrow Airport, Hounslow, Middlesex, TW6 3AF
tel: 020 8750 1440
web: www.hmv.co.uk

HMV
211-213 High Street, Hounslow, TW3 1BL
tel: 020 8577 5255
web: www.hmv.co.uk

HMV UK Ltd. (Head Office)
Film House, 142 Wardour Street, London, W1F 8LN
tel: 020 7432 2033
email: gennaro.castaldo@hmv.co.uk
web: www.hmv.co.uk
info: HMV do not generally stock unsigned material on a national basis. However individual stores have some leeway in stocking unsigned material from local acts. You are welcome to contact store management if you would like to be considered.

Honest Jon's Records
276-278 Portobello Road, London, W10 5TE
tel: 020 8969 9822
email: mail@honestjons.com
web: www.honestjons.com
rack space: Yes
flyer space: Limited
poster space: No
listening posts: No
info: Honest Jon's specialise in Jazz and Soul music, and will consider stocking material by unsigned acts from these genres.

HQ
88 Brixton Village, Coldharbour Lane, London, SW9 8PS
tel: 020 7274 4664
email: info@hqlondon.co.uk
web: www.hqlondon.co.uk
rack space: Yes
flyer space: Yes
poster space: Yes
listening posts: Yes
info: HQ specialise in UK Hip-Hop. Will consider stocking material by unsigned acts from these genres.

Independance
55 Lee High Road, Lewisham, London, SE13 5NS
tel: 020 8333 7777
email: info@independance-records.co.uk
web: www.independance-records.co.uk
rack space: Yes
flyer space: Limited
poster space: Limited
listening posts: Yes
info: Independance specialise in Funky House, Soulful House, UK Garage and R&B. Have previously stocked unsigned material by Wiley and Dizzee Rascal, and are always willing to stock material from quality unsigned acts of similar genres.

Intoxica
231 Portobello Road, London, W11 1LT
tel: 020 7229 8010
email: intoxica@intoxica.co.uk
web: www.intoxica.co.uk
rack space: Limited
flyer space: Yes
poster space: Yes
listening posts: No
info: Intoxica specialise in collectable Funk, Blues, Soul and Jazz vinyl. They may consider stocking material by unsigned artists, but only on vinyl format.

Jam & Wine Records
58 High Street, Acton, London, W3 6LE
tel: 020 8992 4054
rack space: No
flyer space: Yes
poster space: Yes
listening posts: Yes
info: Jam & Wine Records specialise in Calypso and Reggae music, featuring styles from all the Caribbean islands.

Jazz CDs
18 Linhope Street, London, NW1 6HT
tel: 020 7724 2389
email: info@jazzcds.co.uk
web: www.jazzcds.co.uk
rack space: Limited
flyer space: No
poster space: No
listening posts: Yes
info: Online Jazz music store. They will consider stocking unsigned material of professional quality, made available through their website.

JB's
36 Hanway Street, London, W1T 1UP
tel: 020 7436 4063
rack space: Yes
flyer space: Yes
poster space: Yes
listening posts: Yes
info: JB's specialise in Soul, Funk, Punk, R&B, Jazz and 60s and 70s Rock. They will consider stocking material from local unsigned acts.

JG's Music Centre
22 Rathbone Market, Canning Town, London, E16 1EH
tel: 020 7511 8919
rack space: Yes
flyer space: Yes
poster space: Yes
listening posts: No
info: JG's stock music from all genres, and will consider stocking material by unsigned acts.

Kinetec Records
15a Little Portland Street, Oxford Circus, London, W1W 8BW
tel: 020 7323 5303
email: info@kinetec.co.uk
web: www.kinetec.co.uk
rack space: Yes
flyer space: Yes
poster space: Yes
listening posts: Yes
info: Kinetec specialise in Dance music, and are keen to stock material by unsigned Dance acts. 12 listening posts in-store.

Klassique Records
22b Harrow Road, Wembley, HA9 6PG
tel: 020 8900 0160
email: daddyernie@hotmail.com
rack space: Limited
flyer space: Yes
poster space: Yes
listening posts: No
info: Klassique Records specialise in Reggae, R&B and Hip-Hop. Are willing to consider stocking material by unsigned acts from these genres.

Know How Records
3 Buck Street, Camden, London, NW1 8NJ
tel: 020 7267 1526
email: info@knowhowrecords.co.uk
web: www.knowhowrecords.co.uk
rack space: Yes
flyer space: Yes
poster space: Yes
listening posts: Yes
info: Know How Records specialise in Breakbeat, House, Techno, Electro and Drum&Bass. Stock material by unsigned acts from these genres.

Langley Records
466 Walton Road, West Molesey, Kent, KT8 2JG
tel: 020 8979 3648
rack space: Yes
flyer space: Yes
poster space: Yes
listening posts: No
info: Langley Records stock mainly vinyl, and will consider stocking material from local unsigned acts.

Leather Lane Music
67-69 Leather Lane, London, EC1N 7TJ
tel: 020 7405 1270
email: leatherlanemusic@hotmail.com
rack space: Yes
flyer space: Yes
poster space: Yes
listening posts: Yes
info: Leather Lane Music stock all genres of music. Will consider stocking unsigned material.

Lee Sound City
494 New Cross Road, Deptford, London, SE14 6TJ
tel: 020 8691 6765
rack space: Yes
flyer space: Yes
poster space: Yes
listening posts: Limited
info: Lee Sound City stock an eclectic mix of music, and they will consider stocking high-quality material from local unsigned acts. Listening facilities available but no posts as such.

Loppylugs Records
191 Station Road, Edgeware, Middlesex, HA8 7JX
tel: 020 8952 4343
rack space: No
flyer space: Yes
poster space: Limited
listening posts: Yes
info: Specialise in Soul and Dance. Prepared to stock material by local unsigned acts from these genres.

Maestro Records
161 Rye Lane, Peckham, London, SE15 4TL
tel: 020 7635 7299
rack space: No
flyer space: Yes
poster space: Yes
listening posts: No
info: Maestro stock a wide range of music.

The Mega Blast Music Centre
131 Ilford Lane, Ilford, Essex, IG1 2RN
tel: 020 8514 2666
email: megablast@hotmail.com
rack space: Yes
flyer space: Yes
poster space: Yes
listening posts: Yes
info: Mega Blast specialise in Asian music and consequently stock a wide range of unsigned artists from within this genre.

Memory Lane Records
55 Frith Road, Croydon, Surrey, CR0 1TB
tel: 020 8649 7220
rack space: No
flyer space: Limited
poster space: Limited
listening posts: No
info: Memory Lane stock rare 50s, 60s and early-70s vinyl.

Mira UK Ltd.
50 Brick Lane, London, E1 6RF
tel: 020 7377 6688
rack space: No
flyer space: No
poster space: No
listening posts: No
info: Mira UK specialise in Asian music.

Mister CD
80 Berwick Street, Soho, London, W1F 8TN
tel: 020 7439 1097
email: mrcd@btopenworld.co.uk
web: www.mrcd.co.uk
rack space: Yes
flyer space: Yes
poster space: Yes
listening posts: Yes
info: Stock all genres of music. Will be able to purchase music online soon via thier website. Will stock unsigned bands & artists on sale-or-return policy.

Mocking Bird Records
18 The Shopping Hall, Myrtle Road, East Ham, London, E6 1HY
tel: 020 8503 5263
email: chris@mockingbirdrecords.fsnet.co.uk
rack space: No
flyer space: No
poster space: No
listening posts: No
info: Mocking Bird specialise in 50s and 60s music, with particular emphasis on Soul and Reggae. Music DVDs also available.

Mole Jazz
2 Great Marlborough Street, London, W1F 7HQ
tel: 020 7437 8800
web: www.molejazz.co.uk
rack space: No
flyer space: Yes
poster space: Yes
listening posts: No
info: Mole Jazz does not accept unsigned music at the moment, but may do in the future.

Moments In Time
Unit 55, Seven Sisters Market, 231 High Road, London, N15 5BT
tel: 020 8802 6358
rack space: Yes
flyer space: Limited
poster space: Limited
listening posts: Yes
info: Moments In Time specialise in R&B and Hip-Hop, and will consider stocking demos by unsigned acts from these genres.

Morph Music
34 Lewisham Model Market, 196 Lewisham High Street, London, SE13 6LS
tel: 020 8297 1797
rack space: Yes
flyer space: Yes
poster space: Yes
listening posts: Yes
info: Morph stock everything but Classical music. Will consider stocking material from unsigned acts. Also see listing for store on New Cross Road.

Morph Music
275 New Cross Road, New Cross, London, SE14 6AS
tel: 020 8691 9977
rack space: Yes
flyer space: Yes
poster space: Yes
listening posts: Yes
info: Morph stock everything but Classical music. Will consider stocking material from unsigned acts. Also see listing for store on Lewisham High Street.

Mr CD
80 Berwick Street, London, W1F 8TN
tel: 020 7439 1097
email: mrcd@btopenworld.com
web: www.mrcd.co.uk
rack space: Limited
flyer space: Yes
poster space: Limited
listening posts: Yes
info: Selection of mostly Mainstream music at cheap prices.

Music & Video Exchange
95 Berwick Street, London, W1 3PP
tel: 020 7434 2939
web: www.mveshops.co.uk
rack space: No
flyer space: Limited
poster space: Limited
listening posts: No
info: Music & Video Exchange stock second hand material from all genres.

Music & Video Exchange
23 Greenwich Church Street, London, SE10 9BJ
tel: 020 8858 8898
web: www.mveshops.co.uk
rack space: No
flyer space: Limited
poster space: Limited
listening posts: No
info: Music & Video Exchange stock second hand material from all genres.

Music & Video Exchange
208 Camden High Street, London, NW1 8QR
tel: 020 7267 1898
web: www.mveshops.co.uk
rack space: No
flyer space: Limited
poster space: Limited
listening posts: No
info: Music & Video Exchange stock second hand material from all genres.

Music & Video Exchange
38-40 Notting Hill Gate, London, W2 4DS
tel: 020 7243 8573
web: www.mveshops.co.uk
rack space: No
flyer space: Limited
poster space: Limited
listening posts: No
info: Music & Video Exchange stock second hand material from all genres.

MVC
Unit 1, 131 Broadway, Bexleyheath, Kent, DA6 7HF
tel: 020 8303 8024
web: www.mvc.co.uk
rack space: No
flyer space: No
poster space: No
listening posts: Yes
info: MVC do not stock material by unsigned acts.

MVC
43 King William Street, London, EC4R 9AN
tel: 020 7623 6520
web: www.mvc.co.uk
rack space: No
flyer space: No
poster space: No
listening posts: Yes
info: MVC do not stock material by unsigned acts.

MVC
231-245 Chiswick High Road, Chiswick, London, W4 4PU
tel: 020 8987 0128
web: www.mvc.co.uk
rack space: No
flyer space: No
poster space: No
listening posts: Yes
info: MVC do not stock material by unsigned acts.

On The Beat Collectors Records
22 Hanway Street, London, W1T 1UQ
tel: 020 7637 8934
rack space: No
flyer space: Yes
poster space: Yes
listening posts: No
info: On The Beat specialise in collectable vinyl. Deal in every kind of music apart from Classical. No listening posts but can listen to music on the shop PA before you buy.

Out On The Floor Records
10 Inverness Street, Camden, London, NW1 7HJ
tel: 020 7485 9958
rack space: No
flyer space: Limited
poster space: Limited
listening posts: Yes
info: Out On The Floor stock Rock, Funk, Soul, Blues, Folk and Reggae on vinyl format. Music is mainly from the 70s.

Phonica
51 Poland Street, London, W1F 7NG
tel: 020 7025 6071
email: info@phonicarecords.co.uk
web: www.phonicarecords.co.uk
rack space: No
flyer space: Yes
poster space: Limited
listening posts: Yes
info: Specialises in all things Electronic, Reggae and Dub. Big name DJs are regular visitors to the shop.

Plastic Fantastic
35 Drury Lane, Covent Garden, London, WC2B 5RH
tel: 020 7240 8055
email: mailorder@plasticfantastic.co.uk
web: www.plasticfantastic.co.uk
rack space: No
flyer space: Yes
poster space: No
listening posts: Yes
info: Specialise in Funky, Tribal and Progressive Dance music. Plastic Fantastic also runs various record labels and is always looking for new talent. See relevant section for details.

Promo
47 Church Road, London, NW4 4EB
tel: 020 8203 8868
rack space: Limited
flyer space: No
poster space: No
listening posts: No
info: Promo is a record exchange shop. Will consider stocking material by local unsigned bands. It will be on a sale-or-return basis for limited quantities of music.

Psychedelic Dream Temple
Unit 22, The Stables Market, Chalk Farm Road, Camden, London, NW1 8AH
tel: 020 7267 8528
rack space: Yes
flyer space: Yes
poster space: Yes
listening posts: Yes
info: Psychedelic Dream Temple specialise in Trance, Chillout and Lounge. Will consider stocking material by unsigned acts from these genres. Also incorporates a vegan café, bookshop and clothes shop.

Pure Groove Records
679 Holloway Road, Archway, London, N19 5SE
tel: 020 7281 4877
email: info@puregroove.co.uk
web: www.puregroove.co.uk
rack space: Yes
flyer space: Limited
poster space: No
listening posts: Yes
info: Pure Groove specialise in House and Alternative Music. Will consider stocking material by acts from these genres.

Rat Records
348 Camberwell New Road, London, SE5 0RW SE5 SE5 0RW
tel: 020 7274 3222/020 8293 1368
rack space: Limited
flyer space: Limited
poster space: Limited
listening posts: Yes
info: Rat Records stock second hand material from every genre.

Ray's Jazz at Foyles
Within Foyles Bookshop, 113-119 Charing Cross Road, WC2H 0EB
tel: 020 7440 3205
email: rays@foyles.co.uk
web: www.foyles.co.uk
rack space: Yes
flyer space: Yes
poster space: Limited
listening posts: Yes
info: Ray's Jazz will consider stocking unsigned material by Jazz acts.

Reckless Records
92 Camden High Street, London, NW1 0LT
tel: 020 7387 1199
email: rarities@reckless.co.uk
web: www.reckless.co.uk
rack space: No
flyer space: Yes
poster space: Yes
listening posts: Yes
info: Sell second hand Rock, Indie, Soul, Dance and World music. Also see listing for branch located on Berwick Street.

Reckless Records
26-30 Berwick Street, London, W1F 8RH
tel: 020 7434 3362
email: rarities@reckless.co.uk
web: www.reckless.co.uk
rack space: No
flyer space: Yes
poster space: Yes
listening posts: Yes
info: Reckless Records sell second hand Rock, Indie, Soul, Dance and World music. Also see listing for branch located on Camden High Street.

Record Detective Agency
492 Green Lanes, London, N13 5XD
tel: 020 8882 6278
rack space: No
flyer space: Yes
poster space: Yes
listening posts: No
info: Specialise in 50s, 60s and 70s vinyl.

MUSIC SERVICES/RETAIL

Record Detector
3 & 4 Station Approach, Station Road, London, E4 6AL
tel:	020 8529 6361
email:	shirley@sorter.co.uk
web:	www.sorter.co.uk
rack space:	No
flyer space:	Yes
poster space:	Yes
listening posts:	No
info:	Record Detector stock second hand vinyl and CDs from the 50s to the present day.

Red Records
500 Brixton Road, Brixton, London, SW9 8EQ
tel:	020 7274 4476
rack space:	Limited
flyer space:	Yes
poster space:	Yes
listening posts:	Yes
info:	Specialists in Hip-Hop, R&B and Reggae and all kinds of Black Origin Music.

Regal Music Centre
92 Lower Clapton Road, London, E5 0QR
tel:	020 8986 5212
rack space:	Yes
flyer space:	Yes
poster space:	Yes
listening posts:	Yes
info:	Regal specialise in Reggae music, and will stock material by unsigned Reggae acts.

Remember When Records
9 The Arcade, Eltham High Street, London, SE9 1BE
tel:	020 8850 4393
rack space:	No
flyer space:	Yes
poster space:	Yes
listening posts:	No
info:	Specialise in 40s, 50s and 60s vinyl, and also stock CDs by artists from this period. They are willing to support local bands by displaying their flyers and posters in-store.

Resurrection
228 Camden High Street, London, NW1 8QS
tel:	020 7813 2917
email:	katrina@resurrectionmusic.com
web:	www.resurrectionmusic.com
rack space:	Yes
flyer space:	Yes
poster space:	No
listening posts:	No
info:	Resurrection specialise in Gothic, Punk and Metal, and will consider stocking material by unsigned acts from these genres. For detail of Resurrection's record label, see listing in relevant section.

Rhythm Division
391 Roman Road, London, E3 5QS
tel:	020 8981 2203
email:	mpmarkrd@aol.com
web:	www.rhythmdivision.co.uk
rack space:	Yes
flyer space:	Yes
poster space:	Yes
listening posts:	Yes
info:	Specialise in House, Garage and R&B music. Will consider stocking material by unsigned acts from these genres.

Rhythms
398 Cranbrook Road, Gants Hill, Ilford, IG2 6HW
tel:	020 8518 6070
email:	riddims@aol.com
rack space:	Yes
flyer space:	Yes
poster space:	Yes
listening posts:	Yes
info:	Rhythms specialise in Urban music, and are willing to stock material by unsigned artists from this genre.

Rough Trade
16 Neal's Yard, Covent Garden, London, WC2H 9DP
tel:	020 7240 0105
email:	shop@roughtrade.com
web:	www.roughtrade.com
rack space:	Yes
flyer space:	Yes
poster space:	Yes
listening posts:	Yes
info:	Rough Trade stock material from most genres, but specialise in Indie music. If you would like Rough Trade to consider stocking your demo, send an email introducing yourself and your music. For more information on live music events run by Rough Trade, including RoTa afternoon gigs, see the website above. See listing for store based on Talbot Road.

Rough Trade
130 Talbot Road, London, W11 1JA
tel:	020 7229 8541
email:	shop@roughtrade.com
web:	www.roughtrade.com
rack space:	Yes
flyer space:	Yes
poster space:	Yes
listening posts:	Yes
info:	See listing for Neal's Yard branch of Rough Trade.

Scenario Records
12 Ingestre Place, London, W1F 0JF
tel:	020 7439 0055
email:	info@scenariorecords.com
web:	www.scenariorecords.com
rack space:	Yes
flyer space:	Yes
poster space:	Yes
listening posts:	Yes
info:	Scenario Records specialise in Hip Hop, R&B, Funk and Soul, and are willing to stock material by unsigned acts from these genres.

Selectadisc
34-35 Berwick Street, Soho, London, W1F 8RP
tel:	020 7734 3297
email:	london@selectadisc.co.uk
web:	www.selectadisc.co.uk
rack space:	Limited
flyer space:	Limited
poster space:	Yes
listening posts:	No
info:	Select-a-disc stock music from all genres. May consider stocking quality material by unsigned acts.

Silverback Records
40 Bloomsbury Way, London, WC1A 2SA
tel:	020 7404 9456
email:	info@silverbackrecords.co.uk
web:	www.silverbackrecords.co.uk
rack space:	Yes
flyer space:	Yes
poster space:	Yes
listening posts:	Yes
info:	Silverback Records specialise in Dance music, and are willing to stock unsigned material by Dance acts. 4 listening posts avaliable in-store.

Sister Ray
94 Berwick Street, Soho, London, W1F 0QF
tel:	020 7287 8385
email:	sales@sisterray.co.uk
web:	www.sisterray.co.uk
rack space:	Yes
flyer space:	Yes
poster space:	Yes
listening posts:	Yes
info:	Sister Ray specialise in Indie, Punk, New Wave and Techno, and will consider stocking material by unsigned acts from these genres.

Smallfish Records
329 Old Street, London, EC1V 9LE
tel:	020 7739 2252
email:	justafish@smallfish.co.uk
web:	www.smallfish.co.uk
rack space:	Yes
flyer space:	Yes
poster space:	Yes
listening posts:	Yes
info:	Specialise in Electronica, Techno and House music. Will consider stocking quality material from unsigned acts.

Soul & Dance Exchange
42 Notting Hill Gate, London, W11 3HX
tel:	0845 644 1442
web:	www.mveshops.co.uk
rack space:	No
flyer space:	Limited
poster space:	Limited
listening posts:	No
info:	Part of Music & Video Exchange chain. Stock second hand material.

Soul Brother Records
1 Keswick Road, East Putney, London, SW15 2HL
tel:	020 8875 1018
rack space:	Yes
flyer space:	Limited
poster space:	Yes
listening posts:	Limited
info:	Soul Brother Records specialise in Soul, Funk and Jazz vinyl and CDs. Willing to stock quality unsigned material by acts from these genres.

Sound 323
323 Archway Road, Highgate, London, N6 5AA
tel: 020 8348 9595
email: info@sound323.com
web: www.sound323.com
rack space: No
flyer space: Yes
poster space: No
listening posts: No
info: Highly specialised music shop selling Avant Garde Jazz, Improvisation, Contemporary Classical, Post Rock and Electronica.

Sound Fusion Records
209 High Street, Bromley, Kent, BR1 1NY
tel: 020 8464 8123
email: martin@sfrecords.co.uk
web: www.sfrecords.co.uk
rack space: Yes
flyer space: Yes
poster space: Yes
listening posts: Yes
info: Sound Fusion specialise in Drum&Bass and Garage vinyl. They are willing to stock material by unsigned artists. Call into the shop with your vinyl demo, and speak to Martin.

Sounds
236 Portobello Road, London, W11 1LJ
tel: 020 7467 0708
rack space: Yes
flyer space: Yes
poster space: No
listening posts: Yes
info: Sounds stock all genres of music. Are willing to stock material by unsigned acts from these genres.

Sounds
3 Banks Buildings High Street, Harlesden, London, NW10 4SL
tel: 020 8963 1401
rack space: Yes
flyer space: Yes
poster space: Yes
listening posts: Yes
info: Sounds specialise in R&B, Reggae, Soul, Jazz, Pop and Rap. Will consider stocking material by unsigned acts from any of these genres.

The Sounds of the Universe
7 Broadwick Street, Soho, London, W1F 0DA
tel: 020 7494 2004
email: info@soundsoftheuniverse.com
web: www.souljazzrecords.co.uk
rack space: Limited
flyer space: Yes
poster space: Yes
listening posts: Yes
info: Sounds of the Universe specialise in Reggae, Hip-Hop, Jazz and Electronica, and may consider stocking material by unsigned acts from these genres. Call into the shop with your demo. For more information on the associated Soul Jazz label, see the relevant section.

Sounds Original
169 South Ealing Road, London, W5 4QP
tel: 020 8560 1155
email: mail@soundsoriginal.co.uk
web: www.soundsoriginal.co.uk
rack space: No
flyer space: Limited
poster space: Limited
listening posts: No
info: Sounds Original specialise in 50s and 60s second hand vinyl.

Sounds That Swing
46 Inverness Street, Camden, London, NW1 7HB
tel: 020 7267 4682
rack space: Yes
flyer space: Yes
poster space: Yes
listening posts: No
info: Mainly stock vinyl from the 50s, 60s and 70s. Will consider stocking demos on vinyl format.

Sounds To Go
130 Holloway Road, London, N7 8JE
tel: 020 7609 3851
rack space: Yes
flyer space: Yes
poster space: Yes
listening posts: No
info: Sounds To Go specialise in R&B, Hip-Hop, Soul, Jazz and House music, and will consider stocking material by unsigned acts from these genres.

Spin City Records
374 Edgeware Road, London, W2 1EB
tel: 020 7258 0300
email: spincitylondon@aol.com
rack space: Yes
flyer space: Yes
poster space: Yes
listening posts: Yes
info: Specialise in Jazz, R&B, Hip-Hop, House and Garage. Unsigned acts should bring their demos into the shop.

Spin It
13 High Road, Willesden Green, London, NW10 2TE
tel: 020 8459 0761
email: shop@spinitrecords.co.uk
web: www.spinitrecords.co.uk
rack space: Yes
flyer space: Yes
poster space: Yes
listening posts: Yes
info: Spin It stock all genres of music, and will consider stocking material by unsigned acts.

Stand Out Records
2 Blenheim Crescent, London, W11 1NN
tel: 020 7727 8406
rack space: No
flyer space: Limited
poster space: Limited
listening posts: No
info: Specialise in Rock music. Shop is mainly for collectors, but Stand Out do sell some new material.

Starlight Records
17 Craven Park Road, London, NW10 8SE
tel: 020 8965 5039
rack space: Yes
flyer space: Yes
poster space: Yes
listening posts: Yes
info: Starlight Records specialise in R&B, Hip-Hop, Reggae and Jazz. Will consider stocking material by unsigned acts from these genres.

Steve's Sounds
20a Newport Court, London, WC2H 7JS
tel: 020 7437 4638
rack space: No
flyer space: Limited
poster space: Limited
listening posts: No
info: Steve's Sounds stock all commercial music.

Street Vibes Records
Unit 3-4 Market Hall, Wood Green Shopping City, High Road, London, N22 6YE
tel: 020 8889 1832
rack space: Yes
flyer space: Yes
poster space: Yes
listening posts: Yes
info: Street Vibes specialise in R&B and Hip-Hop, and will consider stocking material by unsigned acts from these genres.

Supertone Records and CDs
110 Acre Lane, Brixton, London, SW2 5RA
tel: 020 7737 7761
email: wallyb@supertonerecords.co.uk
web: www.supertonerecords.co.uk
rack space: Limited
flyer space: Yes
poster space: Yes
listening posts: Yes
info: Supertone specialise in Reggae, Caribbean and Soul music.

Swag Records
42 Station Road, Croydon, Surrey, CR0 2RB
tel: 020 8681 7735
email: shop@swagrecords.com
web: www.swagrecords.com
rack space: Yes
flyer space: Yes
poster space: Yes
listening posts: Yes
info: Swag specialise in House, Techno and Drum&Bass. Will consider stocking material by unsigned acts from these genres.

Top Floor CDs
Unit 207, Elephant & Castle Shopping Centre, London, SE1 6TE
tel: 020 7252 6503
email: bunnyvio@btconnect.com
rack space: No
flyer space: Yes
poster space: Yes
listening posts: No
info: Top Floor stock all genres of music, but cannot carry unsigned material due to space restrictions.

Trax Records
55 Greek Street, London, W1D 5LR
tel: 020 7734 0795
email: shop@traxrecords.co.uk
web: www.traxrecords.co.uk
rack space: Yes
flyer space: Yes
poster space: Yes
listening posts: Yes
info: Specialise in House, Hard House and Trance. May consider stocking material by unsigned acts from these genres.

UDM Records
30 Southbury Road, Enfield, London, EN1 1SA
tel: 020 8366 5422
web: www.udm.co.uk
rack space: Yes
flyer space: Yes
poster space: Yes
listening posts: Yes
info: UDM specialise in House, UK Garage, Hip-Hop and R&B, and will consider stocking material by unsigned acts from these genres.

Ultimate Mixtape
Unit 76, 68-74 Church Street, Croydon, CR0 1RB
tel: 020 8686 5393
email: ultimatemixtape@aol.com
rack space: Yes
flyer space: Yes
poster space: Yes
listening posts: No
info: Ultimate Mixtape specialise in Hip Hop, R&B, Gospel, Dancehall and Reggae, and regularly stock material from unsigned bands.

Uptown Records
3 D'Arblay Street, Soho, London, W1F 8DH
tel: 020 7434 3639
email: ewen@uptownrecords.com
web: www.uptownrecords.com
rack space: Yes
flyer space: Yes
poster space: Limited
listening posts: Yes
info: Uptown specialise in Hip-Hop, R&B, Garage and Funky House. Will consider stocking unsigned material by acts from these genres.

Vinyl Addiction
6 Inverness Street, Camden, London, NW1 7HJ
tel: 020 7482 1114
email: info@vinyladdiction.co.uk
web: www.vinyladdiction.co.uk
rack space: Yes
flyer space: Yes
poster space: Yes
listening posts: Yes
info: Vinyl Addiction specialise in Breakbeat vinyl, and will consider stocking material by unsigned acts from this genre.

Vinyl Junkies
12 Berwick Street, Soho, London, W1F 0PJ
tel: 020 7439 2775
email: vjunkies@vinyl-junkies.co.uk
web: www.vinyl-junkies.co.uk
rack space: No
flyer space: Yes
poster space: Yes
listening posts: Limited
info: Vinyl Junkies stock all genres of Dance, Trance, Drum&Bass, and Techno music. To listen to music sold in the shop, visit the website listed above.

The Vinyl Resting Place
70 Shirley Road, Croydon, Surrey, CR0 7EP
tel: 020 8656 3350
email: sales@thevinylrestingplace.co.uk
web: www.thevinylrestingplace.co.uk
rack space: Limited
flyer space: Limited
poster space: Limited
listening posts: Yes
info: The Vinyl Resting Place stock all genres of music, but have a particularly extensive collection of Rock, Funk and Soul. They are willing to stock material by unsigned acts on a sale-or-return basis.

Vinyl Vault
5 Bradbury Street, London, N16 8JN
tel: 020 7923 0722
rack space: Yes
flyer space: Limited
poster space: No
listening posts: Limited
info: Vinyl Vault stock all genres of music, and may be willing to stock material from local unsigned acts.

Virgin Megastore
Retail Unit E2, Terminal 3 Airside, Heathrow Airport, London, TW6 1QG
tel: 020 8897 2516
web: www.virginmegastores.co.uk

Virgin Megastore
Unit 20, Airside Departure Lounge, Terminal 2, Heathrow Airport, London, TW6 1ER
tel: 020 8759 7226
web: www.virginmegastores.co.uk

Virgin Megastore
92-94 High Street, Sutton, SM1 1LT
tel: 020 8643 3619
web: www.virginmegastores.co.uk

Virgin Megastore
Unit 18-22, Centrale, 21 North End, Croydon, CR0 1TY
tel: 020 8686 8386
web: www.virginmegastores.co.uk

Virgin Megastore
152 Bishopsgate, London, EC2M 4LL
tel: 020 7247 2760
web: www.virginmegastores.co.uk

Virgin Megastore
213-219 Camden High Street, London, NW1 7BT
tel: 020 7482 5307
web: www.virginmegastores.co.uk

Virgin Megastore
Kings Walk Shopping Centre, Kings Road, Chelsea, London, SW3 4TR
tel: 020 7591 0957
web: www.virginmegastores.co.uk

Virgin Megastore
Unit 12, Fulham Broadway, Fulham, London, SW6 1BW
tel: 020 7385 9146
web: www.virginmegastores.co.uk

Virgin Megastore
62-64 Kensington High Street, Kensington, London, W8 4PE
tel: 020 7938 3511
web: www.virginmegastores.co.uk

Virgin Megastore
14-19 Oxford Street, London, W1D 1AR
tel: 020 7631 1234
web: www.virginmegastores.co.uk

Virgin Megastore
9 Kings Gate Parade, Victoria Street, London, SW1E 6SH
tel: 020 7828 0023
web: www.virginmegastores.co.uk

Virgin Megastore
Unit 200, The Glades Shopping Centre, High Street, Bromley, BR1 1DN
tel: 020 8290 1039
web: www.virginmegastores.co.uk

Virgin Megastore
Retail Unit E2, Heathrow Airport, Terminal 3 Airside, TW6 1QG
tel: 020 8897 2516
web: www.virginmegastores.co.uk

Virgin Megastore
1 Piccadilly Circus, London, W1J 0TR
tel: 020 7439 2500
web: www.virginmegastores.co.uk

Virgin Megastore (Head Office)
50 Brook Green, London, W6 7RR
tel: 020 8752 9000
web: www.virginmegastores.co.uk

Wanted: Music
415 Croydon Road, Beckenham, Kent, BR3 3PP
tel: 020 8658 7460
email: info@soundsoftheuniverse.com
rack space: No
flyer space: Yes
poster space: Yes
listening posts: Yes
info: Second hand record and CD shop, which stocks music from all genres.

Wax
12a Station Road, Croydon, Surrey, CR0 2RB
tel: 020 8680 9621
email: spamfree03@aol.com
rack space: Yes
flyer space: Yes
poster space: Yes
listening posts: Yes
info: Wax specialise in Hard House, Trance and Drum&Bass, and will consider stocking material by unsigned acts from these genres.

Webster's Record Shop
S61 Shepherd's Bush Market, Shepherd's Bush, London, W12 8DE
tel: 020 8740 4651
email: webstersrecords@aol.com
web: www.webstersrecordshop.co.uk
rack space: No
flyer space: Limited
poster space: Limited
listening posts: No
info: Specialise in Reggae and Caribbean music.

Wired For Sound
393 Mare Street, Hackney, London, E8 1HY
tel: 020 8985 7531
email: colin@wiredforsoundltd.freeserve.co.uk
rack space: Yes
flyer space: Yes
poster space: Yes
listening posts: Yes
info: Wired For Sound stock all genres of music, and will consider stocking material by unsigned acts.

Wyld Pytch
51 Lexington Street, Soho, London, W1F 9HL
tel: 020 7434 3472
email: digger@wyldpytch.co.uk
web: www.wyldpytch.com
rack space: Yes
flyer space: Yes
poster space: Yes
listening posts: Yes
info: Stockists of R&B, Hip-Hop and Broken Beats. Will consider stocking material from unsigned acts on a sale-or-return basis.

Zen Records
69 Broad Lane, London, N15 4DJ
tel: 020 8365 1145
rack space: Yes
flyer space: Yes
poster space: Yes
listening posts: No
info: Zen Records specialise in old vinyl and will consider stocking material by unsigned acts from related genres.

MIDLANDS

2 Funky
62 Belgrave Gate, Leicester, LE1 3GQ
tel: 0116 299 0700
email: shop@2-funky.co.uk
web: www.2-funky.co.uk
contact: V.J. Mystery
rack space: No
flyer space: Yes
poster space: Yes
listening posts: Limited
info: Strictly an Urban music specialist.

Andy Cash Music Ltd.
115 High Street, Harborne, Birmingham, West Midlands, B17 9NP
tel: 0121 427 8989
rack space: Limited
flyer space: Limited
poster space: Limited
listening posts: Yes
info: Andy Cash Music will stock good unsigned material after approval from manager.

Andy Cash Records & Tapes
596 Kingsbury Road, Birmingham, B24 9PJ
tel: 0121 384 1424
email: andy.cash@btconnect.com
contact: Andy
rack space: Limited
flyer space: Yes
poster space: Yes
listening posts: Limited
info: Stocks all genres and will help track down rare records. Will stock unsigned material.

Andy's Records
3-4 Carillion Court, Loughborough, Leicestershire, LE11 3XA
tel: 01509 216 626
rack space: No
flyer space: No
poster space: No
listening posts: No
info: Large catalogue of all genres of music ranging from Classical to Metal. Need to speak to the manager with regard to stocking unsigned material.

Audiowax
Topfloor, Subway Building, 13 Abington Square, Northampton, Northhamptonshire, NN1 4AE
tel: 07970 654 240
email: sales@audiowaxvinyl.com
web: www.audiowaxvinyl.com
rack space: Yes
flyer space: Yes
poster space: Yes
listening posts: Yes
info: Specialise in all genres of music. Please contact on the above number with reference to displaying unsigned material.

B.P.M. Records
3 Malcolm Arcade, Leicester, Leicestershire, LE1 5FT
tel: 0116 253 9988
web: www.bpm-records.co.uk
rack space: Yes
flyer space: Limited
poster space: Limited
listening posts: Yes
info: B.P.M. Records stock Dance, Americana, Indie, Rock, Pop, Classic Rock, Folk and Blues. Would be happy to stock material from unsigned bands within these areas.

B.R.A. Records UK
Unit T4, The Custard Factory, Gibb Street, Birmingham, B9 4AA
tel: 0121 766 5333
email: sales@brarecords.com
web: www.brarecords.com
contact: Tom
rack space: Yes
flyer space: Yes
poster space: Yes
listening posts: Yes
info: Specialise in Dance music. Also mail order specialists.

Becks Rock Box
75 Meadow Road, Clay Cross, Chesterfield, Derbyshire, S45 9NQ
tel: 01246 250 934
rack space: Yes
flyer space: Yes
poster space: Yes
listening posts: stereo
info: CD, cassette and vinyl retailers.

Bid Apple Second Hand Records
29 Heathcoat Street, Hockley, Nottingham, Nottinghamshire, NG1 3AG
tel: 0115 956 2722
rack space: Yes
flyer space: Yes
poster space: Yes
listening posts: No
info: Second hand CDs, cassettes and records.

MUSIC SERVICES/RETAIL

Classical CD
3-5 High Pavement, Nottingham, NG1 1HF
tel:	0115 948 3832
email:	classicalcd1685@aol.co,
web:	www.classicalcd.co.uk
contact:	Tom Barkes
rack space:	Limited
flyer space:	Yes
poster space:	Yes
listening posts:	Limited
info:	Strictly a Classical specialist. Would be willing to

stock records by local unsigned Classical musicians.

The Diskery
99-102 Bromsgrove Street, Birmingham, B5 6QB
tel:	0121 622 2219
contact:	Jimmy Shannon
rack space:	Yes
flyer space:	Yes
poster space:	Yes
listening posts:	Yes
info:	Jazz, Blues, Folk and Rock specialists. Mostly

deals in vinyl and has 2 listening decks in-store.

Double Four Records
6 Market Arcade, Glossop, Derbyshire, SK13 8AP
tel:	01457 860 085
rack space:	No
flyer space:	Yes
poster space:	Yes
listening posts:	No
info:	Stock most genres of music. Have space for

posters and flyers, but do not have room for unsigned material. See
listing for stores based in Stockport.

Farringdon Records
Symphony Hall, Broad Street, Birmingham, B1 2EA
tel:	0121 200 2382
email:	farringdon@hotmail.com
web:	www.farringdons.com
contact:	Martin Hare
rack space:	Limited
flyer space:	No
poster space:	No
listening posts:	No
info:	Classical music specialists. Willing to stock music

by local Classical musicians.

Fopp (Leamington Spa)
11 Lower Mall, Royal Priors Shopping Centre, Leamington Spa,
CV32 4XT
tel:	01926 428 127
web:	www.fopp.co.uk
info:	Fopp are involved in 'The Unsigned Network'

- unsigned material is accepted centrally, distributed to stores and is
placed in a specific 'Unsigned Section' which is promoted in-store.
Material is only accepted in this way and you should refer to the
'Unsigned Network' link on the Fopp website to check whether they
are accepting material at that time. Artists are paid a set amount on
sales, on a sale-or-return basis. Applications for unsigned space is not
on-going and Fopp will sell unsigned material on a sale/demand/space
policy.

Fopp (Nottingham)
The Frontage, Queen Street, Nottingham, NG1 2AR
tel:	0115 941 7602
web:	www.fopp.co.uk
info:	Fopp are involved in 'The Unsigned Network'

- unsigned material is accepted centrally, distributed to stores and is
placed in a specific 'Unsigned Section' which is promoted in-store.
Material is only accepted in this way and you should refer to the
'Unsigned Network' link on the Fopp website to check whether they
are accepting material at that time. Artists are paid a set amount on
sales, on a sale-or-return basis. Applications for unsigned space is not
on-going and Fopp will sell unsigned material on a sale/demand/space
policy.

Fopp (Solihull)
17 Mill Lane Arcade, Touchwood, Solihull, B91 3GS
tel:	0121 711 4011
web:	www.fopp.co.uk
info:	Fopp are involved in 'The Unsigned Network'

- unsigned material is accepted centrally, distributed to stores and is
placed in a specific 'Unsigned Section' which is promoted in-store.
Material is only accepted in this way and you should refer to the
'Unsigned Network' link on the Fopp website to check whether they
are accepting material at that time. Artists are paid a set amount on
sales, on a sale-or-return basis. Applications for unsigned space is not
on-going and fop will sell unsigned material on a sale/demand/space
policy.

Funkey Monkey
14 Goosegate, Nottingham, NG1 1FF
tel:	0115 956 1181
email:	info@funkeymonkey.co.uk
web:	www.funkeymonkey.co.uk
contact:	Phil Sanders
rack space:	Yes
flyer space:	Yes
poster space:	Yes
listening posts:	Yes
info:	Dance Music specialists. Wide and varied range

of all Dance styles. Rack space available for unsigned acts.

Global Groove Records
Global House, 13 Bucknall New Road, Hanley, Stoke On Trent, Stafford,
ST1 2BA
tel:	01782 215 554
email:	mail@globalgrove.co.uk
web:	www.globalgrove.co.uk
rack space:	No
flyer space:	Yes
poster space:	No
listening posts:	Yes
info:	Dance vinyl specialists. Mail order service

available.

Global Groove Records
Global House, 13 Bucknall New Road, Hanley, Stoke-On-Trent, ST1 2BA
tel:	01782 215 554
fax:	01782 201 698
email:	mail@globalgroove.co.uk
web:	www.globalgroove.co.uk
info:	Unsigned rack space for Dance acts, on Vinyl

format only. Space for flyers and posters. Posters no bigger than A3 as
they may be put into frames. Global Groove have worldwide mailing
list and mail order service. New items (including unsigned material) are
added to stock list, with attached 30 second audio file. Check website
for further information.

Good Vibrations
149 Mansfield Road, Nottingham, NG1 3FR
tel:	0115 941 1663
web:	gvrecords.gemm.com
contact:	Sharron Robinson
rack space:	No
flyer space:	Yes
poster space:	Yes
listening posts:	Limited
info:	Deals only in second hand records.

Henry's Records
117 Station Street, Burton-On-Trent, Staffordshire, DE14 1BX
tel:	01283 510 110
email:	henrysrecords@postmaster.co.uk
web:	www.henrysrecords.co.uk
contact:	John Bisbrowne
rack space:	Yes
flyer space:	Yes
poster space:	No
listening posts:	Limited
info:	Sells wide range of genres, both new and second

hand. Willing to stock music by local unsigned acts.

Herrick Watson Ltd.
8 High Street, Skegness, Lincolnshire, PE25 3NW
tel:	01754 763 481
email:	hwatsonltd@btconnect.com
rack space:	Yes
flyer space:	Yes
poster space:	Yes
listening posts:	No

Hi-Tech Music (UK)
89 Shireland Road, Smethwick, West Midlands, B66 4QJ
tel:	0121 558 5148
email:	info@hi-techmusic.com
web:	www.hi-techmusic.com
rack space:	Limited
flyer space:	Yes
poster space:	Yes
listening posts:	Yes
info:	Hi-Tech Music specialises in all Indian styles of

music, and will stock unsigned artists from within this field.

HMV
MSU2A, Bullring, Birmingham, B5 4BE
tel:	0121 654 9210
web:	www.hmv.co.uk

HMV
Unit 2, The Fort Shopping Park, 20 Fort Parkway, Bimringham, B24 9FP
tel:	0121 382 2388
web:	www.hmv.co.uk

HMV
38 High Street, Birmingham, B4 7SL
tel: 0121 643 2177
web: www.hmv.co.uk

HMV
Unit 3, The Pallasades Shopping Centre, Birmingham, B2 4XA
tel: 0121 633 7447
web: www.hmv.co.uk

HMV
9 Silver Street, Boston, Lincolnshire, PE21 6QU
tel: 01205 591 920
web: www.hmv.co.uk

HMV
Unit J, Freshney Place, Grimsby, Lincolnshire, DN31 1QL
tel: 01472 245 810
web: www.hmv.co.uk

HMV
Unit 9, 25-27 Vicar Lane Shopping Centre, Chesterfield, S40 1PY
tel: 01246 218 030
web: www.hmv.co.uk

HMV
32-35 Hertford Street, Coventry, CV1 1LF
tel: 02476 229 700
web: www.hmv.co.uk

HMV
39 Spring Lane, Swansgate Centre, Wellingborough, NN8 1EY
tel: 01933 277 034
web: www.hmv.co.uk

HMV
12-13 High Street, Stratford Upon Avon, CV37 6AU
tel: 01789 268 778
web: www.hmv.co.uk

HMV
8 The Gallery, Mander Square, Wolverhampton, WV1 3NJ
tel: 01902 429 978
web: www.hmv.co.uk

HMV
88-89 High Street, Worcester, WR1 2EX
tel: 01905 245 67
web: www.hmv.co.uk

HMV
Unit 4.5-4.6, 11 Walford Walk, Kingfisher Shopping Centre, Redditch, B97 4HJ
tel: 01527 594 960
web: www.hmv.co.uk

HMV
2-6 Princes Walk, Grosvenor Centre, Northampton, NN1 2EL
tel: 01604 232 662
web: www.hmv.co.uk

HMV
10-12 Mell Square, Solihull, B91 3AY
tel: 0121 709 0661
web: www.hmv.co.uk

HMV
2 Albions Street, Derby, DE1 2AL
tel: 01332 201 902
web: www.hmv.co.uk

HMV
38 Listergate, Nottingham, NG1 7EE
tel: 0115 950 2841
web: www.hmv.co.uk

HMV
Unit 28, The Victoria Centre, Nottingham, NG1 3QL
tel: 0115 983 8190
web: www.hmv.co.uk

HMV
32b Newlands Centre, Kettering, NN16 8JB
tel: 01536 521 760
web: www.hmv.co.uk

HMV
9-17 High Street, Leicester, LE1 4FP
tel: 0116 253 9638
web: www.hmv.co.uk

HMV
323 High Street, Lincoln, LN5 7DW
tel: 01522 539 349
web: www.hmv.co.uk

HMV
Unit 24, Four Seasons Shopping Centre, Mansfield, NG18 1FU
tel: 01623 420 666
web: www.hmv.co.uk

HMV
Unit 38-39, Merry Hill Shopping Centre, Brierley Hill, Dudley, DY5 1QX
tel: 01384 471 350
web: www.hmv.co.uk

HMV
10a Pride Hill Shopping Centre, Shrewsbury, Shropshire, SY1 1BU
tel: 01743 264 920
web: www.hmv.co.uk

HMV
31 Sherwood Street, Telford Centre, Telford, Shropshire, TF1 1LS
tel: 01952 200 506
web: www.hmv.co.uk

HMV
212 The Potteries Shopping Centre, Market Square, Hanley, Staffordshire, ST1 1PS
tel: 01782 283 232
web: www.hmv.co.uk

HMV
31-32 Ankerside Shopping Centre, Tamworth, Staffordshire, B79 7LQ
tel: 01872 300 880
web: www.hmv.co.uk

HMV
Unit 2, 21 Underhill Walk, Coopers Shopping Centre, Burton-On-Trent, Staffordshire, DE14 1DE
tel: 01283 527 050
web: www.hmv.co.uk

HMV
Unit 31-35, Guildhall Shopping Centre, Stafford, ST16 2BB
tel: 01785 283 320
web: www.hmv.co.uk

Infinity Music Megastores
113 Alum Road, Birmingham, West Midlands, B8 1ND
tel: 0121 328 0808
rack space: No
flyer space: Yes
poster space: Yes
listening posts: Yes
info: Infinity specialise in Bhangra and R&B music. They do not have enough rack space to stock CDs by unsigned musicians, but will consider displaying posters and flyers.

Jibbering Records
136 Alcester Road, Birmingham, B13 8EE
tel: 0121 449 4551
email: info@jibberingrecords.com
web: www.jibberingrecords.com
rack space: Yes
flyer space: Yes
poster space: Yes
listening posts: Yes
info: Specialise in World Music, Funk, Hip-Hop and Reggae. Plenty of rack space for local unsigned acts. Listening posts for both CD and vinyl.

Langland Records
2 Bell Street, Wellington, Telford, Shropshire, TF11LS
tel: 01952 244 845
contact: Ian
rack space: Yes
flyer space: Yes
poster space: Limited
listening posts: No
info: Will stock material from local unsigned artists on a sale or return basis - just contact Ian with your material. The shop stocks CD and vinyl, specialising in Rock, Metal, 60s Psychadelia and 70s Prog. Also stock T-shirts and DVDs.

The Left Legged Pineapple
24-25 Churchgate, Loughborough, Leicestershire, LE11 1UD
tel: 0150 923 6791
email: pineapple@left-legged.com
web: www.left-legged.com
contact: Jason White
rack space: Yes
flyer space: Yes
poster space: Yes
listening posts: Yes
info: Long established shop and online mail order facility. Deals in all genres and willing to stock records by local unsigned acts.

Main Street Music
11 Smithfield Centre, Leek, Staffordshire, ST13 5JW
tel: 01538 384 315
contact: David Hill
rack space: Yes
flyer space: Yes
poster space: Yes
listening posts: No
info: Rack space for local unsigned acts on a sale-or-return basis. Space for posters and flyers.

Massive Records
29-30 Stephenson Street, Birmingham, B2 4BH
tel: 0121 633 4477
fax: 0121 632 5933
email: help@massiverecords.com
web: www.massiverecords.com
contact: Dan Massive
rack space: Yes
flyer space: Yes
poster space: Yes
listening posts: Yes
info: Music Week Independent Retailer of the Year 2003. Rack space for local unsigned acts. House, Drum&Bass. Techno, Breakbeat, Urban, Hip-Hop, Jazz and Leftfield specialists.

MDT Classical
1 Grassy Court, Etwall Road, Mickleover, Derby, Derbyshire, DE3 0BX
tel: 01332 540 240
web: www.mdt.co.uk
info: Mail order record shop specialising in Classical music.

Mister Tee's Records
65 Blackwell Street, Kidderminster, Worcestershire, DY10 2EL
tel: 01562 515 291
rack space: No
flyer space: Yes
poster space: Limited
listening posts: No
info: Specialise in second hand music.

Muddys Records
5 King Street, Melton Mowbray, Leicestershire, LE13 1XA
tel: 01664 410 690
email: muddy@muddys.demon.co.uk
web: www.muddys-records.co.uk
rack space: No
flyer space: No
poster space: No
listening posts: No
info: Sells CDs, records and casettes of collectable music and rarieties of most genres.

Music & Video Exchange
8 Smallbrook, Queensway, Birmingham, B5 4EN
tel: 0121 632 6262
web: www.mveshops.co.uk
rack space: No
flyer space: Limited
poster space: Limited
listening posts: No
info: Music & Video Exchange stock second hand material from all genres.

Music Mania Midlands Ltd.
4-5 Piccadilly Arcade, Hanley, Stoke On Trent, Staffordshire, ST1 1DL
tel: 01782 206 000
email: sales@musicmaniauk.com
web: www.musicmaniauk.com
contact: Ian
rack space: Yes
flyer space: Yes
poster space: Yes
listening posts: No
info: Stocks most musical genres, although specialise in Punk, Indie and Metal. Also sell tickets for events at local venues. Section in-store dedicated to local bands.

Music Zone
Unit 217b, The Potteries Shopping Centre, Market Square, Hanley, Stoke-On-Trent, ST1 1PS
tel: 01782 289 273
web: www.musiczone.co.uk

Music Zone
Unit 26, Martineau Place, Bull Street, Birmingham, B2 4UB
tel: 0121 236 6865
web: www.musiczone.co.uk

Music Zone
Bullring Centre, High Street, Birmingham, B5 4BA
tel: 0121 643 0856
web: ww.musiczone.co.uk

Music Zone
Unit 15, Octagon SC, Burton-Upon-Trent, DE14 3TN
tel: 01283 563 777
web: www.musiczone.co.uk

Music Zone
Unit 15, Castle Walk, Newcastle-under-Lyme, Staffordshire, ST5 1AN
tel: 01782 799 111
web: www.musiczone.co.uk

Music Zone
27 Bradford Mall, Saddlers Centre, Walsall, WS1 1YT
tel: 01922 746 232
web: www.musiczone.co.uk

MVC
Unit 1, Crown Walk, Eagle Centre, Derby, DE1 2NP
tel: 01332 381 160
web: www.mvc.co.uk

MVC
7 Satchwell Court, Royal Priors Shopping Centre, Leamington Spa, CV32 4QE
tel: 01926 425 063
web: www.mvc.co.uk

MVC
23 Shelton Square, Coventry, West Midlands, CV1 1DG
tel: 02476 220 363
web: www.mvc.co.uk

MVC
156 Gracechurch Shopping Centre, Parade Mall, Sutton Coldfield, B72 1PH
tel: 0121 354 8967
web: www.mvc.co.uk

MVC
Unit 2, 3-5 The Bridge, Walsall, WS1 1LG
tel: 01922 635 982
web: www.mvc.co.uk

MVC
Unit 52-54, Mander Square, Mander Centre, Wolverhampton, WV1 3NN
tel: 01902 310 623
web: www.mvc.co.uk

MVC
No. 3 Kemble Square, Unis 10-12 & 14-16, Haymarket Centre, Leicester, LE1 3YD
tel: 0116 261 9239
web: www.mvc.co.uk

MVC
170 High Street, Lincoln, LN5 7AF
tel: 01522 589 008
web: www.mvc.co.uk

MVC
6 Mardol, Shrewsbury, Shropshire, SY1 1PY
tel: 01743 343 247
web: www.mvc.co.uk

Nervous Records
16 The Lawns, Hinckley, Leicestershire, LE10 1DY
tel: 01455 612 428
rack space: Limited
flyer space: Limited
poster space: Limited
listening posts: Yes
info: Nervous Records stock a wide range of Alternative genres including Rock and Indie.

Off The Beaten Tracks
29 Aswell Street, Louth, LN11 9BA
tel: 01507 607 677
email: www.beatentracks.co.uk
web: orders@beatentracks.co.uk
rack space: Yes
flyer space: Yes
poster space: Yes
listening posts: Yes
info: Buy, sell and exchange records and CDs across the board.

Ohmygosh
2 Hurts Yard, Nottingham, NG1 6JD
tel:	0115 924 3888
email:	ohmygosh@gmail.com
web:	www.ohmygosh.co.uk
contact:	Tom
rack space:	Yes
flyer space:	Yes
poster space:	Yes
listening posts:	Yes
info:	Underground music specialists with affiliated

label. Drum&Bass, Scratch, Beats and Breaks. Large amount of rack space in store dedicated to unsigned acts.

Oldies Unlimited
3 Worcester Street, Wolverhampton, WV2 4LD
tel:	01902 567 101
rack space:	No
flyer space:	Yes
poster space:	Yes
listening posts:	Yes
info:	Vinyl shop specialising in music from the 50s to

present day.

The Outback Classical Record Shop
19a Church Street, Hereford, Herefordshire, HR1 2LR
tel:	01432 275 063
rack space:	Limited
flyer space:	Yes
poster space:	Yes
listening posts:	No
info:	Mainly stock Classical and Jazz music. Call for

info on stocking unsigned material.

Pendulum Records
35 Market Place, Melton Mowbray, Leicestershire, LE13 1XD
tel:	01664 565 025
fax:	01664 560 310
email:	music@pendulum-direct.com
web:	www.pendulum-direct.com
rack space:	Limited
flyer space:	Limited
poster space:	Limited
listening posts:	Yes
info:	Pendulum will only stock unsigned material from

local bands. Listening posts are available, but only for specific material from record companies.

Pied Piper Records
293 Wellingborough Road, Northampton, Northamptonshire, NN1 4EW
tel:	01604 624 777
email:	piedmusic@aol.com
rack space:	Yes
flyer space:	Yes
poster space:	Yes
listening posts:	Yes
info:	Pied Piper Records stock all genres of music and

stock unsigned artists on a sale-or-return basis.

Polar Bear
10 York Road, Kings Heath, Birmingham, Midlands, B14 7RZ
tel:	0121 441 5202
email:	chris@polarbham.f2s.com
rack space:	No
flyer space:	Yes
poster space:	Yes
listening posts:	Yes
info:	Polar Bear stocks Rock, Pop, Jazz, Funk, Dance,

Blues and World music.

R&K Records
8 Clinton Arms Court, Newark, Nottinghamshire, NG24 1EB
tel:	01636 702 653
rack space:	Yes
flyer space:	Yes
poster space:	Yes
listening posts:	No
info:	CD, vinyl and cassette retailers.

The Record Centre
45-46 Loveday Street, Aston, Birmingham, B4 6NR
tel:	0121 359 7399
email:	ray@recordcentre.fsnet.co.uk
contact:	Ray Purslow
rack space:	No
flyer space:	Yes
poster space:	Yes
listening posts:	No
info:	Jazz, Swing and Nostalgia specialists.

The Record Village
The Old Post Office, Cole Street, Scunthorpe, North Lincolnshire, DN15 6RA
tel:	01724 851 048
email:	enquiries@recordvillage.co.uk
web:	www.recordvillage.co.uk
rack space:	No
flyer space:	Yes
poster space:	Yes
listening posts:	Yes
info:	Stock second hand and local unsigned music.

Listening posts are industry controlled.

Retro
5 Royal Arcade, Leicester, LE1 5YN
tel:	0116 242 5949
rack space:	Yes
flyer space:	Yes
poster space:	Yes
listening posts:	No
info:	CDs, records and casettes sold.

Reveal Records
63 St.Peter's Street, Derby, Derbyshire, DE1 2AB
tel:	01332 349 242
email:	sales@revealrecords.com
web:	www.reveal-records.com
contact:	Tom
info:	Stock Roots, Americana, Rock and Dance.

Section dedicated to local bands. Reveal Records was awarded Best Independent Record Shop 2005.

Rockaboom Records
4 St. Martin's Square, Leicester, LE1 5DF
tel:	0116 253 8293
rack space:	Yes
flyer space:	Yes
poster space:	Yes
listening posts:	Yes
info:	Rack space available for unsigned artists. Stock

all genres of music.

Ross' Books & Music
9 Church Street, Ludlow, SY8 1AP
tel:	01584 878 119
email:	rossbooksmusic@tiscali.co.uk
rack space:	Limited
flyer space:	Yes
poster space:	Yes
listening posts:	Yes
info:	Ross' Books and Music specialises in Classical,

Jazz, Folk and Country music. Will stock local unsigned bands from these genres.

Ruby Red Records
13b Cleveland Street, Wolverhampton, WV1 3HH
tel:	01902 771 186
email:	shop@rubyredrecords.net
web:	www.rubyredrecords.net
contact:	Maxx
rack space:	Yes
flyer space:	Yes
poster space:	Yes
listening posts:	Limited
info:	Soul, Reggae, Hip-Hop and Drum&Bass

specialists.

Seismic Records
1st Floor, 6 Bedford Street, Leamington Spa, Warwickshire, CV32 5DY
tel:	01926 831 333
email:	seismicrecords@btconnect.com
web:	www.seismicrecords.co.uk
rack space:	No
flyer space:	Yes
poster space:	Yes
listening posts:	Yes
info:	Sells a wide range of genres from Dance to Indie.

Will stock unsigned demos but may not have the room to display them on the racks. Also sells merchandise.

MUSIC SERVICES/RETAIL

Selectadisc
19-21 Market Street, Nottingham, NG1 6HX
tel: 0115 941 1663
web: www.selectadisc.co.uk
rack space: Yes
flyer space: Yes
poster space: Yes
listening posts: No
info: Unsigned rack space for artists from all genres.

Smokin' Vinyl
16 Coton Lane, Birmingham, B23 6TP
tel: 0121 373 7051
email: info@smokinvinyl.co.uk
web: www.smokinvinyl.co.uk
contact: Graham Leach
rack space: Yes
flyer space: Yes
poster space: Yes
listening posts: Yes
info: Dance specialists. Rack space available for unsigned acts.

Sonic Sounds
26 Guildhall Street, Lincoln, Nottinghamshire, LN1 1TR
tel: 01522 543 666
email: sales@sonic-sounds.net
web: www.sonic-sounds.net
rack space: Yes
flyer space: Yes
poster space: Yes
listening posts: Yes
info: Listening posts only for music from major labels. At present, only stock unsigned material by local acts, but open to demos from anywhere.

Spinadisc Records
21-22 Northway Clock Tower, Rugby, Warwickshire, CV21 2JR
tel: 01788 561 444
fax: 01788 561 777
rack space: Yes
flyer space: Yes
poster space: Yes
listening posts: Yes
info: Spinadisc already stock a fairly large selection of local unsigned acts, but will also consider materials from outside the area.

Spiral Archive Records
1st Floor Emporium, Abington Square, Northampton, Northhamptonshire, NN1 4AA
tel: 07974 885 450
email: alex@spiralarchive.com
web: www.spiralarchive.com
contact: alex
rack space: No
flyer space: Yes
poster space: Yes
listening posts: No
info: CD, record and casette retailers. Specialises in collector and second hand items.

Summit Records
184-188 Dudley Road, Birmingham, B2 5BG
tel: 0121 455 8844
contact: Winston Gordon
rack space: Yes
flyer space: Yes
poster space: Yes
listening posts: Yes
info: Reggae specialists. Willing to stock local unsigned acts.

Swordfish
14 Temple Street, Birmingham, B2 5BG
tel: 0121 633 4859
fax: 0121 643 9138
email: swordfishrecords@btconnect.com
contact: Mike
rack space: Yes
flyer space: Yes
poster space: Yes
listening posts: Yes
info: Will stock material from local, unsigned artists on a sale-or-return basis covering most genres. Space is available for posters and flyers and there are 3 listening posts. Wide variety of music is stocked from vintage Reggae to Japanese Experimental.

Tempest Records Ltd.
83 Bull Street, Birmingham, B4 6AB
tel: 0121 236 9170
email: info@tempestrecords.co.uk
web: www.temrec.com
contact: Richard or Nathan
rack space: Yes
flyer space: Yes
poster space: Yes
listening posts: No
info: Specialises in Rock and Indie. No listening posts but will play on in-store system.

Three Shades Records
16 Needless Alley, Birmingham, B2 5AE
tel: 0121 687 2772
email: info@threeshades.com
web: www.threeshades.com
contact: Martin Banks
rack space: Yes
flyer space: Yes
poster space: Yes
listening posts: Yes
info: Dance music specialists.

Tonys
Book in Hand Market, High Street, Mablethorpe, LN12 1AD
tel: 01507 477782
email: tony@countymusiccity.com
rack space: Limited
flyer space: Yes
poster space: Limited
listening posts: No
info: Country music and Elvis specialists. Buy and sell.

Tune In
109 Dale Road, Matlock, Derbyshire, DE4 3LU
tel: 01629 760 595
email: tuneinbuxton@btinternet.com
contact: Jill
rack space: Yes
flyer space: Limited
poster space: Limited
listening posts: Limited
info: Stock material from local, unsigned bands. Some space available for posters and flyers. Possible to listen to music on the in-store system, but no listening posts as such. Store also in Buxton.

Ultima Thule
1 Conduit Street, Leicester, Leicestershire, LE2 0JN
tel: 0116 285 4545
email: orders@ultimathulerecords.com
web: www.ultimathulerecords.com
rack space: No
flyer space: Yes
poster space: Yes
listening posts: No
info: Stock CDs, records and cassettes. Specialise in Progressive Rock and Psychedelic Rock.

Vacant Records
11 St.John's Street, Daventry, Northamptonshire, NN11 5YQ
tel: 01327 706 257
email: vacanttekno@hotmail.com
contact: Colin Salt or Carole Carrigan
rack space: Yes
flyer space: Yes
poster space: Yes
listening posts: Yes
info: Willing to stock records by unsigned acts on a sale-or-return basis. Offer a wide range of genres from Indie to Techno.

Vinyl Bank
64 Avon Street, Warwick, CV34 4PX
tel: 01926 400 472
email: queries@vinylbank.co.uk
web: www.vinylbank.co.uk
contact: Karen Johnson
info: Record and CD fair running 3 times a month across various venues in the South Midlands.

Vinyl Underground
80 Abington Street, Northampton, Northamptonshire, NN1 2BB
tel: 01604 634 433
email: aidy@vinylunderground.co.uk
web: www.vinylunderground.co.uk
rack space: No
flyer space: Yes
poster space: Yes
listening posts: Yes
info: Vinyl Underground specialises in Dance vinyl. Does not stock material by unsigned bands.

Virgin Megastore
3 Gormond Street, Maylords Orchards, Hereford, HR1 2DP
tel: 01432 358 458
web: www.virginmegastores.co.uk

Virgin Megastore
Unit 22, McArthurglen Designer Outlet, Mansfield Road, South Normanton, DE55 2JW
tel: 01773 545 112
web: www.virginmegastores.co.uk

Virgin Megastore
98 Corporation Street, Brimingham, B4 6SX
tel: 0121 236 2523
web: www.virginmegastores.co.uk

Virgin Megastore
Unit 41-43, The Pavilion Shopping Centre, 38 High Street, Birmingham, B4 7SL
tel: 0121 643 4189
web: www.virginmegastores.co.uk

Virgin Megastore
40-44 The Precinct, Coventry, CV1 1DE
tel: 02476 634 346
web: www.virginmegastores.co.uk

Virgin Megastore
28 The Gallowtree Gate, Leicester, LE1 1DA
tel: 0116 262 3010
web: www.virginmegastores.co.uk

Virgin Megastore
8 Churchgate, Leicester, LE1 4AJ
tel: 0116 242 5969
web: www.virginmegastores.co.uk

Virgin Megastore
The Rushes, Loughborough, LE11 5BE
tel: 01509 239 502
web: www.virginmegastores.co.uk

Virgin Megastore
28 Princess Walk, Grosvenor Centre, Northampton, NN1 2EL
tel: 01604 239 060
web: www.virginmegastores.co.uk

Virgin Megastore
6-8 Wheelgate, Nottingham, NG1 2NB
tel: 0115 947 6126
web: www.virginmegastores.co.uk

Virgin Megastore
16-18 Park Street, Walsall, WS1 1NG
tel: 01922 720 077
web: www.virginmegastores.co.uk

Virgin Megastore
46 Pride Hill, Shrewsbury, Shropshire, SY1 1DN
tel: 01743 344 488
web: www.virginmegastores.co.uk

Virgin Megastore
Units 151-153, New Street, Telford Shopping Centre, Telford, Shropshire, TF3 4BP
tel: 01952 201 079
web: www.virginmegastores.co.uk

Vision Records
Shop 2 Tyrone House, Church Street, Wellington, Telford, Shropshire, TF1 1DR
tel: 01952 255 456
email: jo@visionrecords.co.uk
contact: Jo
rack space: Limited
flyer space: Yes
poster space: Yes
listening posts: Yes
info: Specialises in Hard House, Trance, Drum&Bass and Funky House.

Your Price Music.com
280-282 Slade Road, Birmngham, West Midlands, B23 7LX
tel: 0121 382 6662
web: www.yourpricemusic.com
rack space: No
flyer space: No
poster space: No
listening posts: No
info: Stock CDs, vinyl and casettes, with a particular emphasis on Reggae music.

NORTHEAST

Air Records
8 High Bridge, Newcastle Upon Tyne, Tyne & Wear, NE1 1EN
tel: 0191 261 1923
email: neil@airrecords.co.uk
web: www.airrecords.co.uk
contact: Neil
rack space: No
flyer space: Yes
poster space: Yes
listening posts: Yes
info: Specialise in Dance music and related accessories. Also sell tickets in-store for local events.

Alt.Vinyl
61-62 Thornton Street, Newcastle Upon Tyne, Tyne & Wear, NE1 4AW
tel: 0191 222 1213
email: info@altvinyl.com
web: www.altvinyl.com
contact: Graham Thrower
rack space: Yes
flyer space: Yes
poster space: Yes
listening posts: Yes
info: Stock new and used music. Also stock a lot of material from unsigned bands based in the North East, as well as small label releases. Alt.vinyl also releases music under the label of the same name, and is linked with Downbeat Records. See entries in relevant section for details.

Concepts
57 North Road, Durham, County Durham, DH1 4SF
tel: 0191 383 0745
email: dave-murry@lineone.net
web: www.concepts-durham.co.uk
contact: Dave Murry
rack space: Yes
flyer space: Yes
poster space: Yes
listening posts: Yes
info: Concepts is a member of the 'Chain With No Name'. Also named Mojo Reccomended Retailer. Regularly stock material from up and coming local bands. Concepts stocks all music from Indie and Rock to Drum&Bass and Dance. Although Classical music is not stocked, it can be ordered in-store.

Factoria Sonora UK
101 Clayton Street, Newcastle Upon Tyne, Tyne & Wear, NE1 5PZ
tel: 0191 221 0040
email: info@factoriasonora.co.uk
web: www.factoriasonora.co.uk
rack space: Yes
flyer space: Yes
poster space: Yes
listening posts: Yes
info: Factoria specialises in European and Dance music. Regularly stocks CDs by unsigned and unknown dance DJs.

Fat Dog Records
90 Newport Road, Middlesbrough, Cleveland, TS1 5JD
tel: 01642 211 212
email: fatdogrecords@btinternet.com
web: www.fatdoguk.com
contact: Neil
rack space: No
flyer space: Yes
poster space: Yes
listening posts: Yes
info: Fat Dog Records is an independent vinyl specialist selling mainly House, Electro, Techno, Nu Jazz, Funk and Soul.

Flip Side
7a Laburnum Terrace, Ashington, Northumberland, NE63 0XX
tel: 01670 819 980
contact: Wendy Swinhow
rack space: No
flyer space: Yes
poster space: Yes
listening posts: No
info: Sell mostly Indie, Rock and Rap music. Also stock accessories, t-shirts and posters.

Gojo Records
5 Newman Way, Battle Hill, Hexham, Northumberland, NE46 1BB
tel: 01434 607 610
contact: Andrew Jackson
rack space: Yes
flyer space: Yes
poster space: Yes
listening posts: No
info: Specialise in Northumbrian, Irish, Scottish and Folk music.

new limited editions,
rarities & imports
on vinyl & cd,
collectable used vinyl,
reggae, electronic,
experimental, alt.country,
lo-fi, punk, indie...

stocking a wide
variety of DIY
releases from
local and national
unsigned bands
in-store gigs

downbeat records -
in-house label
demos welcomed!

0191 222 1213
info@altvinyl.com
www.altvinyl.com
61/62 thornton street
newcastle upon tyne
ne1 4aw

HMV
22 (68a) Cameron Walk, Metro Centre, Gateshead, Tyne & Wear,
NE11 9YR
tel: 0191 460 3883
web: www.hmv.co.uk

HMV
Unit 17, Wellington Square, Stockton On Tees, Cleveland, TS18 1NA
tel: 01642 525 010
web: www.hmv.co.uk

HMV
4-5 Cornmill Shopping Centre, Priestgate, Darlington, County Durham,
DL1 1LS
tel: 01325 483 183
web: www.hmv.co.uk

HMV
33 Centre Mall, Cleveland Centre, Middlesbrough, Cleveland, TS1 2NR
tel: 01642 242 322
web: www.hmv.co.uk

HMV
Unit Su02, The Bridges Centre, Sunderland, Tyne & Wear, SR1 3LB
tel: 0191 510 9307
web: www.hmv.co.uk

HMV
56 Northumberland Street, Newcastle, NE1 7DF
tel: 0191 230 0626
web: www.hmv.co.uk

Hot Rats
37 Stockton Road, Sunderland, Tyne & Wear, SR1 3NR
tel: 0191 567 2099
email: marty.hotratz@ntlworld.com
contact: Marty
rack space: Yes
flyer space: Yes
poster space: Yes
listening posts: Yes
info: Hot Rats specialises in Rock, Indie, Blues and
Jazz. Also sell vinyl, CDs, DVDs and t-shirts. Will stock material by
local unsigned and signed artists.

Lalas Video & Music
39b Hadrian Road, Fenham, Newcastle Upon Tyne, Tyne & Wear,
NE4 9HN
tel: 0191 272 3099
contact: Mr. Akrem
info: Specialises in Asian entertainment.

Mekina
Unit 16, Pennywell Business Centre, Portsmouth Road, Sunderland,
Tyne & Wear, SR4 9AS
tel: 0191 534 5500
email: mekinamusic@yahoo.co.uk
web: www.mekina.co.uk
contact: Scott
rack space: No
flyer space: No
poster space: No
listening posts: No
info: Internet based company, selling all types of
Dance music including Hardcore, Trance and House.

The Music Shop
7 Bridge Street, Berwick-Upon-Tweed, TD15 1ES
tel: 01289 307 917
rack space: Yes
flyer space: Yes
poster space: Yes
listening posts: No
info: Specialises in sheet music. Also have a large
selection of CDs, DVDs and t-shirts. Do stock unsigned demos on a
sale-or-return basis. No Pop music sold.

Music Zone
86 The Bridge, Sunderland, Tyne & Wear, SR1 3LB
tel: 0191 567 4700
web: www.musiczone.co.uk

Music Zone
Unit 9, Queen Street, Darlington, County Durham, DL3 6SH
tel: 01325 486 637
web: www.musiczone.co.uk

Music Zone
21 Market Place, Durham, DH1 3NJ
tel: 0191 383 9376
web: www.musiczone.co.uk

Music Zone
Unit 7b, 15 Newton Mall, Clevelend Centre, Middlesbrough, Cleveland, TS1 2NW
tel: 01642 231 888
web: www.musiczone.co.uk

Music Zone
6 Russell Way, Metro Centre, Gateshead, Tyne & Wear, NE11 9YZ
tel: 0191 460 8899
web: www.musiczone.co.uk

Music Zone
93b Middleton Grange Shopping Centre, Hartlepool, Cleveland, TS24 7RW
tel: 01429 264 727
web: www.musiczone.co.uk

Music Zone
Unit 1, Regent Walk Shopping Centre, Redcar, TS10 3FB
tel: 01642 478 593
web: www.musiczone.co.uk

Music Zone
135 High Street, Stockton On Tees, TS18 1LP
tel: 01642 611 397
web: www.musiczone.co.uk

Music Zone
Unit 82, The Galleries, Washington, NE38 7RT
tel: 0191 419 3388
web: www.musiczone.co.uk

Music Zone
10 Douglas Way, Eldon Square, Newcastle Upon Tyne, NE1 7XW
tel: 0191 222 0822
web: www.musiczone.co.uk

MVC
Unit A3, Millburngate Shopping Centre, Durham, County Durham, DH1 4SL
tel: 0191 375 7015
web: www.mvc.co.uk
contact: Simon Harris
rack space: No
flyer space: Yes
poster space: Yes
listening posts: Yes

Oldhitz Records
69 Grainger Street, Newcastle Upon Tyne, Tyne & Wear, NE1 5JE
tel: 0191 261 9563
email: sales@oldhitz.com
web: www.oldhitz.com
contact: Mr Hughes
rack space: No
flyer space: Yes
poster space: Yes
listening posts: No
info: Stock music dating from 1930 to 2000. Mainly vinyl with over 30,000 records to choose from. Oldhitz Records has the biggest stock of 7" singles in the North East.

The Other Record Shop
Errol Street, Hartlepool, TS24 8BG
email: sales@otherwebsite.freeserve.co.uk
web: www.otherrecordshop.co.uk
rack space: No
flyer space: Yes
poster space: Yes
listening posts: No
info: Will stock unsigned material for local bands. Also a major supplier of concert tickets.

Pet Sounds Records & Tapes
Bewick Street, Newcastle Upon Tyne, Tyne & Wear, NE1 5EF
tel: 0191 261 0749
email: info@petsounds.co.uk
web: www.petsounds.co.uk
rack space: No
flyer space: Yes
poster space: Yes
listening posts: No
info: Pet Sounds have an unsigned rack within the store. Also have a branch located on Old Eldon Square.

Pet Sounds Records, Tapes & CDs
Basement 6, Old Eldon Square, Newcastle Upon Tyne, Tyne & Wear, NE1 7GJ
tel: 0191 261 7364
email: info@petsounds.co.uk
web: www.petsounds.co.uk
rack space: Yes
flyer space: Yes
poster space: Yes
listening posts: No
info: Pet Sounds specialises in Rock and Indie music, but will accept demos from other genres. See listing for branch located on Bewick Street.

Plastik Trax
46, Dean Road, South Shields, Tyne & Wear, NE33 4DZ
tel: 0191 427 7701
email: plastiktrax@yahoo.com
web: www.plasiktrax.co.uk
contact: Chris
info: Sell Dance, Hard House, Techno, Hardcore and Spanish Makina vinyl.

Play
5 West Row, Darlington, County Durham, DL1 5PL
tel: 01325 460 464
contact: Richard Brooks
rack space: No
flyer space: No
poster space: Yes
listening posts: No
info: Stock chart releases and Rock music on CD format. Generally do not stock unsigned demos.

Reflex
23 Nun Street, Newcastle Upon Tyne, Tyne & Wear, NE1 5AG
tel: 0191 260 3246
email: andy@reflexcd.co.uk
web: www.reflexcd.co.uk
contact: Andy
rack space: Yes
flyer space: Yes
poster space: Yes
listening posts: Yes
info: Mail order service available. Also sell concert tickets in-store, as well as posters.

Roots Music
67b Wetgate Road, Newcastle Upon Tyne, Tyne & Wear, NE1 1SG
tel: 0191 230 2500
email: info@roots2music.com
web: www.roots2music.com
contact: Tony Raynolds
info: Stock all musical genres. Mail order service available.

RPM Music
25 High Bridge Street, Newcastle Upon Tyne, Tyne & Wear, NE1 1EW
tel: 0191 221 0201
email: info@rpm-music.co.uk
web: www.rpm-music.co.uk
rack space: Yes
flyer space: Yes
poster space: Yes
listening posts: Yes
info: RPM Music specialises in non-mainstream genres such as Indie, Hip-Hop, Electronica, Drum&Bass. Recently started hosting in-store gigs for local unsigned bands.

Sound It Out
15a Yarm Street, Stockton On Tees, Cleveland, TS18 3DR
tel: 01642 860 068
email: sounditout@yahoo.com
web: www.sounditoutrecords.co.uk
contact: Tom
rack space: Yes
flyer space: Yes
poster space: Yes
listening posts: No
info: Stock all styles of music, except Pop. Second hand stock available. No listening posts, but will play tracks over in-store system upon request. Turntables available. Will stock unsigned music.

Spin Compact Discs
8 High Bridge, Newcastle Upon Tyne, Tyne & Wear, NE1 1EN
tel: 0191 261 4741
email: spincds@btconnect.com
web: www.spincds.com
rack space: Yes
flyer space: Yes
poster space: Yes
listening posts: Yes
info: Specialise in Psychedelic and 70s Rock. Rack space for unsigned bands. Mail order service available.

MUSIC SERVICES/RETAIL

Spinning Disk
18, Olive Street, Sunderland, Tyne & Wear, SR1 3PE
tel:	0191 567 4292
contact:	David Mallan
rack space:	Limited
flyer space:	Limited
poster space:	Limited
listening posts:	No
info:	Specialists in Rave music. Rack space is available

for local, unsigned acts of this genre.

Steel Wheels
15-17 Vine Lane, Newcastle Upon Tyne, Tyne & Wear, NE1 7PW
tel:	0191 230 4886
email:	paul@steel-wheels.co.uk
web:	www.steel-wheels.co.uk
contact:	Paul
rack space:	Limited
flyer space:	Yes
poster space:	Yes
listening posts:	Yes
info:	Stock all music types.

Virgin Megastore
Monument Mall, 15-21 Northumberland Street, Newcastle Upon Tyne, Tyne & Wear, NE1 7AE
tel:	0191 230 5959
web:	www.virginmegastores.co.uk

Virgin Megastore
1 Captain Cook Square, Middlesborough, Cleveland, TS1 5UB
tel:	01642 221 811
web:	www.virginmegastores.co.uk
contact:	Helen Guy

Virgin Megastore
13 Ocean Road, South Shields, Tyne & Wear, NE33 2HT
tel:	0191 454 3604
web:	www.virginmegastores.co.uk

Virgin Megastore
28 Cameron Walk, Metro Centre, Gateshead, Tyne & Wear, NE11 9YE
tel:	0191 460 9310
web:	www.virginmegastores.co.uk

Virgin Megastore
Unit 16, The Royal Quays, Coble Dene, North Shields, NE29 6DW
tel:	0191 257 2726
web:	www.virginmegastores.co.uk

NORTHWEST

1st Call Music
PO Box 311, East Way, Chorley, Lancashire, PR6 8XN
tel:	01257 268 900
fax:	01257 268 900
email:	johnglowe@yahoo.co.uk
web:	www.1stcallmusic.com
contact:	Mr John G. Lowe
rack space:	No
flyer space:	No
poster space:	No
listening posts:	No
info:	Do not stock unsigned material. Online store,

specialising in vinyl from 1930s to the present day. Also stock CDs and music books.

3 Beat Records
5 Slater Street, Liverpool, L1 4BW
tel:	0151 709 3355
fax:	0151 707 0227
email:	sales@3beat.co.uk
web:	www.3beat.co.uk
contact:	Steve Parry
rack space:	Yes
flyer space:	Yes
poster space:	Yes
listening posts:	Yes
info:	Unsigned rack space available, call into the

shop and speak to Steve. Vinyl and CD Dance music specialists. Space available for posters and flyers.

A&A Discs & Tapes
15 Bridge Street, Congleton, CW12 1AS
tel:	01260 280 778
fax:	01260 298 311
contact:	Dave Wedgbury
rack space:	Yes
flyer space:	Yes
poster space:	Yes
listening posts:	Yes
info:	Unsigned rack space, avaliable on sale-or-return

basis. Room for posters and flyers. Listening facilities in store. Also have a store selling instruments. See listing in relevant section for details.

A.P.S. Records
13 Earle Street, Crewe, CW1 2BS
tel:	01270 215 496
fax:	01270 215 496
contact:	Tony Smith
rack space:	Yes
flyer space:	Yes
poster space:	Yes
listening posts:	No
info:	Unsigned rack space available for local acts.

Space available for posters and flyers.

Action Records
47a Church Street, Preston, PR1 3DH
tel:	01772 258 809
fax:	01772 252 255
email:	mail@action-records.co.uk
web:	www.action-records.co.uk
contact:	Gordon Gibson
rack space:	Yes
flyer space:	Yes
poster space:	Yes
listening posts:	Limited
info:	Unsigned rack space available on sale-or-return

basis. Space available for posters and flyers.

Action Replay Records & Video
24 Lake Road, Windermere, LA23 3AP
tel:	01539 445 089
fax:	01539 445 089
contact:	David Snaith
rack space:	Limited
flyer space:	Limited
poster space:	No
listening posts:	Yes
info:	Rack space available for Popular local acts on a

sale-or-return basis. No poster or flyer space.

Astonishing Sounds
3 Hall Street, Burnley, BB11 1QJ
tel:	01282 455 339
fax:	01282 455 339
email:	info@astonishingsounds.fsnet.co.uk
web:	www.astonishingsounds.fsnet.co.uk
contact:	Neil Kinder
rack space:	Yes
flyer space:	Yes
poster space:	Yes
listening posts:	Yes
info:	Unsigned rack space. Space available for posters

and flyers.

Bass Records
Ashburner Street Market, Ashburner Street, Bolton, BL1 1TQ
tel:	01204 361 894
fax:	01204 361 894
email:	bassrecordsbolton@hotmail.com
web:	www.bassrecords.net
contact:	Nelson
rack space:	Limited
flyer space:	Yes
poster space:	Yes
listening posts:	Limited
info:	Dance specialists. Will stock unsigned material

by Hard House, Trance, Happy House and Dance artists and DJs. Some space available for posters and flyers promoting Dance events.

Beatin' Rhythm
Unit G19, The Smithfield Buildings, 42 Tib Street, Manchester, M4 1LA
tel:	0161 834 7783
fax:	0161 834 9835
email:	music@beatinrhythm.com
web:	www.beatinrhythm.com
contact:	Tom or Derek
rack space:	Limited
flyer space:	Yes
poster space:	Yes
listening posts:	Limited
info:	Specialise in Northern Soul, Rare Funk and Soul

and Rock'n'Roll on vinyl and CD. Mail order service available.

Bevan's Sound Centre
67 The Strand, Longton, Stoke On Trent, ST3 2NS
tel:	01782 312 178
fax:	01782 312 178
contact:	John Oliver
rack space:	Yes
flyer space:	Yes
poster space:	Yes
listening posts:	No
info:	Unsigned rack space available on sale-or-return

basis. Poster and flyer space available on noticeboard. Stock all music types from Metal to Jazz, with the exception of Pop.

Blackburn CD, Video & Record Exchange
12 Higher Church Street, Blackburn, BB2 1JG
tel:	01254 671 932
email:	random_x@hotmail.com
web:	www.recordexchange.net
contact:	Alison Wrenn
rack space:	Yes
flyer space:	Yes
poster space:	Yes
listening posts:	Limited
info:	Will sell some unsigned music, at Alison's

discretion, on a sale-or-return basis.

Blue Vinyl
33 Tib Street, Manchester, M4 1LX
tel:	0161 834 6776
email:	sales@bluevinyluk.com
web:	www.bluevinyluk.com
contact:	Mark
rack space:	Yes
flyer space:	Limited
poster space:	Limited
listening posts:	Yes
info:	Dance music specialists. Stock some unsigned

material. Some space for posters and flyers. Three listening posts available.

Brown Sugar Records
Unit 14, The Arcade, 35 Oldham Street, Manchester, M1 1JG
tel:	0161 834 9595
email:	brownsugarrecords@btconnect.com
web:	www.brownsugarrecords.co.uk
contact:	Dave Golley
rack space:	Yes
flyer space:	Yes
poster space:	Yes
listening posts:	Yes
info:	Specialise in Reggae, Dub, Hip-Hop (UK and US),

Soul, Funk and Drum&Bass. Will stock unsigned music and have space for posters and flyers. There are facilities to listen to both CDs and vinyl in-store.

Bus Stop Records
22 Threeways, Northwich, CW8 2XJ
tel:	01606 881 884
email:	jon@busstop-records.co.uk
web:	www.busstop-records.co.uk
contact:	Jon Whaite
rack space:	Limited
flyer space:	No
poster space:	No
listening posts:	No
info:	Online record store selling mainly Hip-Hop,

Soul and Dance music genres. Do not generally stock material from unsigned artists, but may consider stocking some material on a sale-or-return basis. Mainly mail order.

Butterfly Music
117 Oldham Street, Manchester, M4 1LN
tel:	0161 834 6727
contact:	Mr Howard
rack space:	Yes
flyer space:	Yes
poster space:	Yes
listening posts:	Yes
info:	Long standing supporters of unsigned music

in Manchester. Unsigned rack space as well as space for flyers and posters.

Circa Records
Yard 39, Highgate, Kendall, Cumbria, LA9 4ED
tel:	01539 736 100
email:	circarecords@hotmail.com
rack space:	Yes
flyer space:	Yes
poster space:	Yes
listening posts:	No
info:	Rock, Pop and Indie specialists. Circa also stock

vinyl. Opening hours are 10am-5pm and half day closing on Thursday.

Clamp Down Records
9 Paton Street, Manchester, M1 2BA
tel:	0161 237 5932
email:	clampdownrecords@gmail.com
web:	www.clampdownrecords.com
rack space:	No
flyer space:	Yes
poster space:	Limited
listening posts:	No
info:	Space for flyers and possibly posters. No listening

posts as such, but can listen to music on the shop system.

Cobweb Music
Unit 23,, Teanlowe Centre, Poulton-le-Flyde, FY6 7DF
tel:	01253 886 022
fax:	01253 886 022
contact:	Dave or Geoff
rack space:	No
flyer space:	No
poster space:	No
listening posts:	Limited
info:	Sell Mainstream music. No space in-store for

flyers, posters or any unsigned material. EMI listening post available.

Custard Cube Music
6 The Market Hall, Peel Street, Accrington, Lancashire, BB5 1ER
tel:	01254 399 669
web:	www.custardcube.com
contact:	Jim Bows
rack space:	Yes
flyer space:	Yes
poster space:	Yes
listening posts:	Yes
info:	Rack space available for unsigned bands on a

sale-or-return basis. Space available for flyers and posters. Stock a wide selection of music from the 50s to present.

Disc Covery Records Ltd.
3 Kingsway, Huncoat, Accrington, BB5 6LA
tel:	01254 231 387
fax:	01254 237 806
email:	sales@disc-coveryrecords.com
web:	www.disc-coveryrecords.com
contact:	Andy Halstead
rack space:	Limited
flyer space:	No
poster space:	No
listening posts:	No
info:	Mainly mail-order service via telephone or the

website, specialising in Heavy Metal, Punk, Pop, Indie, BritPop, Rock and Dance music. Also take part in regular record fairs around the country.

Double Four Records
45 Lower Hillgate, Stockport, Cheshire, SK1 1JK
tel:	0161 477 1335
contact:	Robert
rack space:	No
flyer space:	Yes
poster space:	Yes
listening posts:	No
info:	Stock most genres of music. Have space for

posters and flyers, but do not have room for unsigned material. See listing for stores based in Stockport and Glossop.

Double Four Records
9 Derby Way Marple, Stockport, Cheshire, SK6 7AH
tel:	0161 477 1335
contact:	John
rack space:	No
flyer space:	No
poster space:	No
listening posts:	No
info:	Stock most genres of music. Have space for

posters and flyers, but do not have room for unsigned material. See listing for stores based in Stockport and Glossop.

DTM CD Exchange
8 Clarendon Street, Hyde, Cheshire, SK14 2EL
tel:	0161 366 6616
fax:	0161 366 6616
email:	dtmcd@btconnect.com
web:	www.dtmrecords.co.uk
contact:	Dennis Matthews
rack space:	Limited
flyer space:	Limited
poster space:	Limited
listening posts:	No
info:	Limited space available for flyers and posters.

Also run DTM Records, which specialises in Punk and Rock. Will accept demos in these genres.

Eastern Bloc Records
Unit 5-6, Central Buildings, Oldham Street, Manchester, M1 1JT
tel: 0161 228 6432
fax: 0161 228 6728
email: info@easternblocrecords.co.uk
web: www.easternblocrecords.co.uk
contact: John Berry
rack space: Yes
flyer space: Yes
poster space: Limited
listening posts: Yes
info: Call in and play your track (vinyl format only). If staff at Eastern Bloc like it, then rack space is available on a sale-or-return basis. Limited space on the poster wall, first come first served. Flyer rack available.

Electron Records
2 Hall Street, Burnley, BB11 1QJ
tel: 01282 428 118
contact: Les Baxter
rack space: Yes
flyer space: Limited
poster space: Limited
listening posts: Yes
info: Unsigned rack space, usually on a sale-or-return basis. Space available for posters and flyers.

Expansion MC
PO Box 6, Hayfield, Stockport, SK22 2FF
tel: 01663 742 211
email: expansion@expansion-mc.com
web: www.expansion-mc.com
contact: Dean Johnson
rack space: Yes
info: Mainly a mail-order service that specialises in Soul, Jazz, Funk, Blues and Reggae. Dean will accept demos in these genres and may stock material on a sale-or-return basis. There is also an associated record label.

Factory
53 Church Street, Manchester, M4 1PD
tel: 0161 834 8341
email: info@facoff.com
web: www.facoff.com
info: Web based service only. Stock genres from Underground, Indie and Dance to Hip-Hop. Email for more information.

Fat City Records
20 Oldham Street, Manchester, M1 1JN
tel: 0161 237 1181
fax: 0161 236 9304
email: shop@fatcity.co.uk
web: www.fatcity.co.uk
info: Limited rack space available for Hip Hop, Dance and Funk acts. Limited space for posters and flyers. Email for more information.

Flawless Records UK Retail
Units 1-3, Jaxons Court, Hallgate, Wigan, Lancashire, WN1 1LR
tel: 01942 237 999
email: andy@flawlessrecords.co.uk
web: www.flawlessrecords.co.uk
contact: Andy
rack space: Yes
flyer space: Yes
poster space: Yes
listening posts: Yes
info: Will stock unsigned material from local artists, contact Andy at the shop. Also run an independent Dance record label. The shop stocks a multitude of genres but specialises in Funk, Soul, Hip-Hop, R&B and Dance. Also sell DJ equipment.

Fopp
19 Brown Street, Manchester, M2 1DA
tel: 0161 827 1620
web: www.fopp.co.uk
info: Fopp are involved in 'The Unsigned Network' - unsigned material is accepted centrally, distributed to stores and is placed in a specific 'Unsigned Section' which is promoted in-store. Material is only accepted in this way and you should refer to the 'Unsigned Network' link on the Fopp website to check whether they are accepting material at that time. Artists are paid a set amount on sales, on a sale-or-return basis.

Global Grooves
65 Brook Street, Chester, CH1 3DZ
tel: 01244 343 781
fax: 01244 315 434
email: info@global-grooves.com
web: www.global-grooves.com
contact: Lee Ellis
rack space: No
flyer space: Yes
poster space: No
listening posts: Yes
info: Have associated label (Northern Records) that specialise in Underground House. Are always on the look out for new talent in any genre. Send demos to the shop. No unsigned rack space. Space for flyers, but not posters.

Gravy Train
61 Mill Lane, Liverpool, CH44 5UB
tel: 0151 639 0371
email: gravy@mersinet.co.uk
web: www.gravytrainonline.co.uk
rack space: No
flyer space: Yes
poster space: Yes
listening posts: Yes
info: Stockists of second hand vinyl and CD collectables, therefore there is no space available for unsigned material. However, space is available for posters and flyers.

Grey-N-Pink Collectors Records
57 Brook Street, Chester, CH1 3DZ
tel: 01244 311 921
contact: Paul Hickman
rack space: Yes
flyer space: Limited
poster space: Limited
listening posts: Yes
info: Will accept demos from unsigned artists. Paul will listen to material and if suitable, stock it on a sale-or-return basis. Limited space for flyers and posters.

Hairy Records
124 Bold Street, Liverpool, L1 4JA
tel: 0151 709 3121
contact: Mr Robert Johnsten
rack space: Limited
flyer space: Yes
poster space: Yes
listening posts: No
info: Very limited rack space for unsigned local bands, sale-or-return basis only. Predominantly second hand vinyl shop. Space for posters and flyers. Cover all genres except Classical.

HMV
Unit R6/R6a, The Coliseum Retail Park, Ellesmere Port, Cheshire Oaks, Chester, CH65 9HD
tel: 0151 355 4110
web: www.hmv.co.uk

HMV
25-27 Fishergate, Preston, PR1 3NN
tel: 01772 251 145
web: www.hmv.co.uk

HMV
Unit 12, The Lanes Shopping Centre, Carlisle, CA3 8NT
tel: 01228 404 700
web: www.hmv.co.uk

HMV
29 Town Square Shopping Centre, Oldham, Lancashire, OL1 1XE
tel: 0161 633 7332
web: www.hmv.co.uk

HMV
3-5 Exchange Street, Bolton, Lancashire, BL1 1RS
tel: 01204 524 641
web: www.hmv.co.uk

HMV
36-38 King William Street, Blackburn, BB1 7DP
tel: 01254 265 720
web: www.hmv.co.uk

HMV
90-100 Market Street, Manchester, M1 1PB
tel: 0161 834 8550
web: www.hmv.co.uk

HMV
21 Market Street, Manchester, M1 1WR
tel: 0161 834 9920
web: www.hmv.co.uk

HMV
Unit 1a, Gildabrook, West One Retail Park, Gildabrook Road, Salford, M5 2AR
tel: 0161 787 6170
web: www.hmv.co.uk

HMV
136 Peel Avenue, The Trafford Centre, Manchester, M17 8BH
tel: 0161 202 9415
web: www.hmv.co.uk

HMV
51-53 Merseyway, Stockport, Cheshire, SK1 1PW
tel: 0161 480 0548
web: www.hmv.co.uk

HMV
24-26 The Mall, Golden Square, Warrington, WA1 1QE
tel: 01925 629 768
web: www.hmv.co.uk

HMV
22-36 Church Street, Liverpool, L1 3AW
tel: 0151 709 1088
web: www.hmv.co.uk

HMV
48-50 Foregate Street, Chester, Cheshire, CH1 1HA
tel: 01244 310 307
web: www.hmv.co.uk

HMV
16-19 Marketgate, Lancaster, Lancashire, LA1 1JF
tel: 01524 382 792
web: www.hmv.co.uk

HMV
Unit 1, Tower Shopping Centre, Bank Hey Street, Blackpool, FY1 4RZ
tel: 01253 291 393
web: www.hmv.co.uk

HMV
New Mersey Retail Park, Speke, Liverpool, L24 8QB
tel: 0151 494 4110
web: www.hmv.co.uk

HMV
Unit 18, La Grange Shopping Arcade, St. Helens, Lancashire, WA10 1BN
tel: 01744 740 420
web: www.hmv.co.uk

HMV
Unit 6, Manchester Piccadilly Station, Manchester, M60 7RA
tel: 0161 200 5520
web: www.hmv.co.uk

HMV
23-27 Market Place, Rochdale Exchange Shopping Centre, Rochdale, OL16 1EB
tel: 01706 766 470
web: www.hmv.co.uk

HMV
Unit B/C, 1 Chapel Street, Southport, Merseyside, PR8 1AE
tel: 01704 511 020
web: www.hmv.co.uk

HMV
Unit 3, The Strand Shopping Centre, Douglas, Isle of Man, IM1 2ER
tel: 01624 616 450
web: www.hmv.co.uk

HMV
MSU4, Grange Road, Pyramids Shopping Centre, Birkenhead, CH41 2ZL
tel: 0151 649 1750
web: www.hmv.co.uk

Hottwaxx Records
Unit 6, Logford Street, Warrington, WA2 7PG
tel: 01925 232 536
email: hottwaxx@btconnect.com
web: www.hottwaxxrecords.co.uk
contact: Barry
info: Hottwaxx Records is part of the Tuff Gong complex, which incorporates recording studios, rehearsal rooms, a musical equipment shop 'Access All Areas Music' and a dance studio. Space for posters, flyers and CDs for unsigned acts who use the complex.

Hyde & Seek Records
Unit 61, Market Hall, Hyde, Cheshire, SK14 2QT
tel: 0161 368 0664
contact: Mrs Stubbs
info: Small stall in the market hall. Not really capable of holding any form of unsigned material.

Just Entertainments
Stall 100-103, New Market Hall, Wigan, WN1 1PX
tel: 01942 241 971
fax: 01942 706 682
info: Very small stall, sadly no room for unsigned CDs!

Kaleidoscope Records
30 Westfield Street, St. Helens, Merseyside, WA10 1QF
tel: 01744 454 190
fax: 01744 454 190
email: greg@krecords.com
web: www.krecords.com
contact: Greg Duggins
rack space: Yes
flyer space: Yes
poster space: Yes
listening posts: Yes
info: Rack space available for local bands, mainly rock or indie material. Space available for flyers and posters, and can listen to music on in-store system. New and second hand music with a large collection of vinyl.

Kingbee Records
519 Wilbraham Road, Chorlton, Manchester, M21 OUF
tel: 0161 860 4762
fax: 0161 860 4762
email: les@kingbee.fsnet.co.uk
contact: Neil or Les
info: Limited unsigned rack space is available for local bands on a sale-or-return basis. There is very limited space available for posters and flyers. Listen before you buy.

Malcolm's Musicland
Baptist Chapel, Chapel Street, Chorley, PR7 7BW
tel: 01257 264 362
email: sales@cdvideo.co.uk
web: www.cdvideo.co.uk
contact: Malcolm Allen
rack space: Yes
flyer space: Yes
poster space: No
listening posts: No
info: Rack space is available for local unsigned artists, speak to Malcolm. There is space for flyers, but not posters. Cater for most tastes, stocking a wide variety of genres.

The Music & Video Club Ltd.
12 Staveleigh Mall, Lady-smith Centre, Ashotn-Under-Lyne, OL6 7JQ
tel: 0161 343 6608
fax: 0161 343 2438
web: www.mvc.co.uk
rack space: Limited
flyer space: Limited
poster space: Limited
info: Space available for posters and flyers. Space for CDs, posters and flyers may be offered for a local acts.

Music Box
93 Botchergate, Carlisle, CA1 1RY
tel: 01228 595 696
fax: 01228 595 696
contact: Alan Thomson
info: Poster and flyer space available. Music from local acts considered for rack space.

Music Box
Unit 21-22, Admirals Market Place, Admiral Centre, Nelson, Lancashire, BB9 9SL
tel: 01282 614 963
contact: Kevin Wareing
rack space: Yes
flyer space: Yes
poster space: No
listening posts: No
info: Unsigned rack space, sale-or-return basis. Will happily display flyers but, unfortunately, no space for posters.

Music Zone
8 Church Street, St. Helens, Merseyside, WA10 1BD
tel: 01744 736 426
web: www.musiczone.co.uk

Music Zone
29-31 Princess Parade, Millgate Centre, Bury, Lancashire, BL9 0QL
tel: 0161 272 0202
web: www.musiczone.co.uk

Music Zone
St. Johns Pavement Grange Precinct, Birkenhead, Merseyside, CH41 2YB
tel: 0151 649 0649
web: www.musiczone.co.uk

Music Zone
Unit 8c, Ground Mall, Market Place, Bolton, BL1 2AL
tel: 01204 523 674
web: www.musiczone.co.uk

Music Zone
6 Strand Shopping Centre, Bootle, Merseyside, L20 4SN
tel: 0151 933 4363
web: www.musiczone.co.uk

Music Zone
16 Victoria Street, Blackpool, FY1 4RW
tel: 01253 299 591
web: www.musiczone.co.uk

Music Zone
64 Scotch Street, Carlisle, CA3 8PN
tel: 01228 539 227
web: www.musiczone.co.uk

Music Zone
12-16 Princes Street, Stockport, SK1 1SE
tel: 0161 480 8122
web: www.musiczone.co.uk

Music Zone
57-59 Yorkshire Street, Rochdale, OL16 1BZ
tel: 01706 630 351
web: www.musiczone.co.uk

Music Zone
14 Sankey Street, Golden Square, Warrington, WA1 1TD
tel: 01925 575 963
web: www.musiczone.co.uk

Music Zone
18a Mill Street, Macclesfield, Cheshire, SK11 6LY
tel: 01625 869 602
web: www.musiczone.co.uk

Music Zone
121 Peel Avenue, The Trafford Centre, Manchester, M17 8BN
tel: 0161 747 2422
web: www.musiczone.co.uk

Music Zone
37 Market Street, Manchester, M1 1WR
tel: 0161 839 6767
web: www.musiczone.co.uk

Music Zone
1st Floor, 49a Warrington Street, Ashton-under-Lyne, OL6 7JG
tel: 0161 830 0537
web: www.musiczone.co.uk

Music Zone
113 George Street, The Graftons, Altrincham, Cheshire, WA14 1RN
tel: 0161 928 5456
web: www.musiczone.co.uk

Music Zone
9 Frairgate, St. George's Shopping Centre, Preston, PR1 2TU
tel: 01772 200 220
web: www.musiczone.co.uk

Music Zone
2 Witton Walk, Northwich, Cheshire, CW9 5AT
tel: 01606 350 888
web: www.musiczone.co.uk

Music Zone
6 Williamson Square, St. John's Shopping Centre, Liverpool, L1 1EQ
tel: 0151 709 9010
web: www.musiczone.co.uk

Music Zone
Unit 39, The Galleries, Wigan, WN1 1EX
tel: 01942 820 247
web: www.musiczone.co.uk

Music Zone
Unit 26, Spinning Gate, Leigh, Lancashire, WN7 4PG
tel: 01942 262 250
web: www.musiczone.co.uk

Music Zone
43 St. James Street, Burnley, BB11 1QL
tel: 01282 457 840
web: www.musiczone.co.uk

Music Zone
Heapriding Business Park, Ford Street, Chestergate, Stockport, SK3 0BT
tel: 0161 477 5088
web: www.musiczone.co.uk

Music Zone
Unit 1, 16-18 Foregate Street, Chester, CH1 1HA
tel: 01244 311665
web: www.musiczone.co.uk

Music Zone
118-120 Dalton Road, Barrow-In-Furness, Cumbria, LA14 1JH
tel: 01229 829976
web: www.musiczone.co.uk

Music Zone
6-8 High Street, Oldham, Lancashire, OL1 1JA
tel: 0161 633 0575
web: www.musiczone.co.uk

Music Zone
6 Broadway, Market Square, Accrington, BB5 1EY
tel: 01254 230 700
web: www.musiczone.co.uk

Music Zone
13 Marketgate, Lancaster, LA1 1JF
tel: 01524 684 35
web: www.musiczone.co.uk

Music Zone
17 Queensway, Crewe, CW1 2HH
tel: 01270 505 799
web: www.musiczone.co.uk

Musical Box
457 West Derby Road, Liverpool, L6 4BL
tel: 0151 263 3845
contact: Tony Quinn
rack space: Yes
flyer space: Yes
poster space: Yes
listening posts: No
info: Will stock material from local unsigned
bands, speak to Tony. Work closely with Radio Merseyside and tend
to promote alongside them. Specialise in Rock, Pop, Country and
Nostalgia on vinyl and CD. Do not really stock much chart music.

MVC
Unit 13-15 Eastbank Street, Southport, PR8 1DL
tel: 01704 514 973
web: www.mvc.co.uk
contact: Andy Heeps

MVC
17-19 Curzon Street, Burnley, BB11 1BB
tel: 01282 413 971
web: www.mvc.co.uk

MVC
13-17 Borough Pavement, The Grange, Birkenhead, L41 2XX
tel: 0151 666 1983
web: www.mvc.co.uk

MVC
Unit 4a, 6 The Linkway, Middlebrook, Horwich, BL6 6JA
tel: 01204 691 090
web: www.mvc.co.uk

MVC
12 Staveleigh Mall, Ladysmith Centre, Ashton-Under-Lyne, Lancashire,
OL6 7JQ
tel: 0161 343 6608
web: www.mvc.co.uk

MVC
8 Elephant Yard, Kendal, Cumbria, LA9 4QQ
tel: 01539 737 668
web: www.mvc.co.uk

MVC
8 Elephant Yard, Kendal, Cumbria, LA9 4QQ
tel: 01539 737 668
web: www.mvc.co.uk

MVC
Unit 12, Broughton Retail Park, Chester Road, Broughton, Chester,
CH4 0PD
tel: 01244 538 632
web: www.mvc.co.uk

MVC
Unit 10-12, Paddock Row, Grosvenor Centre, Chester, CH1 1ED
tel: 01244 329 826
web: www.mvc.co.uk

Northern Record Supplies Ltd.
Starworks, Wham Street, Heywood, Lancashire, OL10 4QU
tel: 01706 367 412/01706 620 842
email: sales@northernrecords.co.uk
web: www.northernrecords.co.uk
contact: Simon Jones
rack space: Yes
flyer space: Yes
poster space: Yes
listening posts: Limited
info: Stock an extensive variety of music from Classical to Punk. Willing to stock unsigned music of all genres that are of local interest. The company also supplies local market traders. Space available for posters and flyers.

Paramount Book Exchange
25-27 Shudehill, Manchester, M4 2AF
tel: 0161 834 9509
info: Although not a music specialist, will perhaps buy unsigned music if they think it will sell. Space for posters and flyers from local acts. Speak to anybody in-store.

Pelican Neck Records
74-76 High Street, Manchester, M4 1ES
tel: 0161 834 2569
email: mailboy@boomkat.com
web: www.boomkat.com
contact: Conor, David or Mike
rack space: Limited
flyer space: Limited
poster space: Limited
listening posts: Yes
info: Stock Experimental, Electronica, Hip-Hop and Indie. Will consider stocking unsigned material. There is limited space available for flyers and posters. Best to contact Conor, David or Mike.

Pendlehawk Music
11 New Market Street, Colne, Lancashire, BB8 9BJ
tel: 01282 866 317
email: pendlehawkmusic@ntlworld.com
web: www.pendlehawkmusic.co.uk
contact: Adrian Melling
rack space: Yes
flyer space: Yes
poster space: Yes
listening posts: Yes
info: Large, long established record shop selling Jazz and Folk amongst other things. Also run a record label under the name Planet Records. Also run a 24 track recording studio under sister company Pendlehawk Music Studios. See relevant sections for details. Unsigned rack space as well as space for posters and flyers. Possible to listen to music before purchase.

Phase Records
Unit G17b, The Palace, Slater Street, Liverpool, L1 4BS
tel: 0151 709 9699
email: info@phaserecords.co.uk
web: www.phaserecords.co.uk
contact: Paul Nolan
rack space: No
flyer space: Yes
poster space: Yes
listening posts: Yes
info: Dance music specialists, particularly House and Drum&Bass. Generally only stock Dance white labels. Space in-store for suitable posters and flyers.

Piccadilly Records
Smithfield Buildings, 53 Oldham Street, Manchester, M1 1JR
tel: 0161 834 8789/0161 839 8008
fax: 0161 839 8008
email: enquiries@piccadillyrecords.com
web: www.piccadillyrecords.com
rack space: Yes
flyer space: Yes
poster space: Yes
info: Unsigned rack space on sale-or-return basis. Space also available for posters and flyers. New stock is included on the mailing list that is sent once a week via email.

Pop Art
9 Egerton Crescent, Withington, Manchester, M20 4PN
tel: 0161 448 8469
email: nick@popartrecords.co.uk
web: www.popartrecords.co.uk
contact: Nick
rack space: Yes
flyer space: Yes
poster space: Yes
listening posts: Yes
info: Unsigned rack space available for local bands on a sale-or-return basis. Space available for posters and flyers in the window. Listening posts available. Shop stocks second hand Rock, Pop, 60s Rock'n'Roll, Blues, Folk, Americana and Reggae on CD and vinyl.

Power Records
4 Crawford Street, Wigan, WN1 1NL
tel: 01942 518 552
email: recall.records@lycos.co.uk
contact: Mick
rack space: Yes
flyer space: Yes
poster space: Yes
listening posts: Yes
info: Will stock most genres of unsigned music to support the local scene. There are in-store listening facilities and space for posters and flyers.

Probe Records
9 Slater Street, Liverpool, L1 4BW
tel: 0151 708 8815
email: enquire@probe-records.com
web: www.probe-records.com
contact: Lee
rack space: Yes
flyer space: Yes
poster space: Limited
listening posts: No
info: Some rack space for unsigned music and for flyers but space for posters is limited.

Quantum Records
104 County Road, Walton, Merseyside, L4 3QW
tel: 0151 525 6192
fax: 0151 530 1026
email: sales@quantumrecords.co.uk
web: www.quantumrecords.co.uk
contact: Colin Taylor
rack space: Yes
flyer space: Yes
poster space: Yes
listening posts: No
info: Will stock material from unsigned local bands on a sale-or-return basis. Various genres. Space is available for flyers and posters.

Quirk's Records (Crosby)
40 Liverpool Road, Crosby, Merseyside, L23 5SF
tel: 0151 924 9481
fax: 0151 284 0710
email: quirks@quirkscrosby.fsnet.co.uk
web: www.quirks.co.uk
contact: Rob Quirk
rack space: Yes
flyer space: Yes
poster space: Yes
listening posts: No
info: See listing for store located in Ormskirk.

Quirk's Records (Ormskirk)
29 Church Street, Ormskirk, L39 3AG
tel: 01695 570 570
fax: 01695 570 519
email: quirks@email.com
web: www.quirks.co.uk
contact: Paul Quirk
rack space: Limited
flyer space: Yes
poster space: Yes
listening posts: No
info: Space available for flyers and posters. Some limited available rack space for local, unsigned bands at Paul's discretion. See listing for branch based in Crosby.

Real Records
118b Friargate, Preston, PR1 2EE
tel: 07952 609 018
contact: Terry Cahill
rack space: No
flyer space: Yes
poster space: Yes
listening posts: No
info: Stock most genres of music except Classical and Opera. Although there is no space for unsigned material, there is room for posters and flyers to be displayed.

Real Recordz
1a Finkle Street, Carlisle, Cumbria, CA3 8UU
tel: 01228 819 300
contact: Carol
rack space: No
flyer space: Yes
poster space: Yes
listening posts: Limited
info: Specialists in House music. Do not stock unsigned music but do have space for posters and flyers.

Records & Relics
7a-9b Caunce Street, Blackpool, FY1 3DN
tel: 01253 624 718
fax: 01253 624 718
contact: Mike Snowden
rack space: Yes
flyer space: Yes
poster space: Yes
listening posts: Yes
info: Sale-or-return unsigned rack space. Space available for flyers and posters. Shop stocks mainly 50s and 60s music to present day. No Pop or Dance. CD and vinyl listening facility.

Reflex
64 Oldham Street, Manchester, M4 1LE
tel: 0161 238 8727
fax: 0161 238 8728
email: reflex.info@fsmail.net
contact: Rupert Glover
rack space: Yes
flyer space: Yes
poster space: Yes
listening posts: Yes
info: Specalise in House and Breaks. Have rack space for unsigned Dance music. Posters and flyers can be displayed in-store.

Reidy's Home of Music
9-13 Penny Street, Blackburn, BB1 6HJ
tel: 01254 265 303
fax: 01254 693 768
email: sales@reidys.com
web: www.reidys.com
contact: Paul Nutall or Julie Farrer
rack space: Yes
flyer space: Yes
poster space: Yes
listening posts: No
info: Rack space dedicated to unsigned music. Space available for posters and flyers.

Replay
118 Fishergate Walk, St. George's Centre, Preston, PR1 2NR
tel: 01772 252 545
fax: 01772 252 545
email: replaypreston@btconnect.com
contact: Philip
rack space: Limited
flyer space: Limited
poster space: Limited
listening posts: Limited
info: Stock some unsigned local material, but the Wigan store tends to stock more. See listing for details. There is limited space for posters and flyers. Store has a listening facility via the main music system.

Replay
7 Leigh Arcade, The Galleries, Wigan, WN1 1XP
tel: 01942 821 744
email: replaywigan@btconnect.com
rack space: Yes
flyer space: Yes
poster space: Yes
listening posts: No
info: Will stock unsigned artists material, posters and flyers. Can listen to music via the stores main system.

Rocks Off
65 Drake Street, Rochdale, OL16 1SB
tel: 01706 521 818
contact: Mr Taylor
rack space: No
flyer space: Limited
poster space: Limited
listening posts: No
info: No unsigned rack space, but there is some display space for posters and flyers.

Rox Records
The Crescent, West Kirkby, Merseyside, CH48 4HL
tel: 0151 625 1750
contact: David Crosby
rack space: Yes
flyer space: No
poster space: Limited
listening posts: No
info: Rox Records can provide rack space for local unsigned bands, speak to David in-store. May also be able to display posters.

Save Records (Bury)
34 Market Hall, Bury, Lancashire, BL9 0BD
tel: 0161 797 5588/01706 367 412
info: Refer to listing for Rochdale branch.

Save Records (Oldham)
Unit 1-2, Tommyfield Market Hall, Albion Street, Oldham, OL1
tel: 0161 627 5267/01706 367 412
contact: Mr Jones
info: Refer to listing for Rochdale branch.

Save Records (Rochdale)
46 Market Hall, Hunters Lane, Rochdale, Lancashire, OL16 1XP
tel: 01706 358 522
contact: Maxine
rack space: No
flyer space: Limited
poster space: Limited
listening posts: No
info: Contact the stall on the above number and speak to the manager regarding stocking unsigned music.

Seeds Records
7 Oxton Road, Birkenhead, Merseyside, CH41 2QQ
tel: 0151 653 4224
fax: 0151 653 3223
email: orders@seedsrecords.co.uk
web: www.seedsrecords.co.uk
contact: Lee Hessler
rack space: Yes
flyer space: Yes
poster space: Yes
listening posts: Yes
info: Dance music specialists. Rack space for unsigned and independent Dance music. Also room available for posters and flyers.

Shoot The Moon Collectors Records
50 Hospital Street, Nantwich, CW5 5RP
tel: 01270 610 553
contact: Neil Davis
rack space: Yes
flyer space: Yes
poster space: Yes
listening posts: Limited
info: Unsigned rack space available for local artists and bands on a sale-or-return basis. Room for posters and flyers. Shop stocks all genres of music except Classical and Easy Listening.

Sifter's Records
117 Fog Lane, Didsbury, Manchester, M20 6FJ
tel: 0161 445 8697
contact: Peter Howard
rack space: No
flyer space: Limited
poster space: Limited
info: Limited space available for posters. No unsigned rack space.

Silica Discs
22 Finkle Street, Workington, CA4 2BB
tel: 01900 602 011
fax: 01900 602 011
email: grahamcaton@fsmail.net
contact: Graham Caton
rack space: Yes
flyer space: Yes
poster space: Yes
listening posts: Yes
info: Graham is happy to offer unsigned rack space on a sale-or-return basis. Most genres are accepted. Graham also advises to bring along a poster to display in the shop to advertise your CD. Space for posters and flyers are a flyer rack. 5 listening posts in-store.

Skeleton Records
1st Floor, 11 Oxton Road, Birkenhead, Merseyside, CH41 2QQ
tel: 0151 653 9003
fax: 0151 670 0079
email: johnskeleton@freeserve.co.uk
web: www.skeletonrecords.co.uk
contact: John Weaver
rack space: Yes
flyer space: Yes
poster space: Yes
listening posts: No
info: Stock unsigned music of varied styles on a sale-or-return basis. Also space for posters and flyers. No listening posts as such, but can use in-store system.

Sound Bytes
158 Bolton Road, Blackburn, BB2 4HL
tel: 01254 670 880
contact: Stuart Slater
rack space: No
flyer space: No
poster space: No
listening posts: No
info: Cannot provide space for unsigned CDs, posters or flyers.

Sounds Musical
72 Hospital Street, Nantwich, Cheshire, CW5 5RP
tel:	01270 625 579
email:	cds@soundsmusical.co.uk
web:	www.soundsmusical.co.uk
flyer space:	Yes
poster space:	Yes
info:	Do not accept material from unsigned artists.

Specialists in Jazz, World, Blues and Classical on CD. Also sell music related gifts.

Spin Inn
Unit G22, Smithfield Buildings, Tib Street, Manchester, M4 1LA
tel:	0161 839 7719
fax:	0161 839 7719
email:	sales@spininn.co.uk
web:	www.spininn.co.uk
contact:	Pete Seargent
rack space:	Yes
flyer space:	Yes
poster space:	Yes
listening posts:	Yes
info:	Underground Dance store. Available rack space

for Dance acts. Space available for flyers and posters.

Splash Records
7 Queens Square, Blackpool, Lancashire, FY1 1QU
tel:	01253 751 251
fax:	01253 751 251
email:	djdavito@splash-records.com
web:	www.splash-records.com
contact:	Daniel Vitellaro
rack space:	Yes
flyer space:	Yes
poster space:	Yes
listening posts:	Yes
info:	Will carry unsigned music on vinyl and CD. New

and second hand equipment also available. Space for posters and flyers. Possible to listen to material before purchase on the in-house system.

Townsend Records (Chorley)
117 Market Street, Chorley, PR7 2SQ
tel:	01257 264 727
fax:	01257 264 727
email:	sales@townsend-records.co.uk
web:	www.townsend-records.co.uk
contact:	Adrian
rack space:	Yes
flyer space:	Yes
poster space:	No
listening posts:	No
info:	Unsigned rack space is available at the shop's

discretion on a sale-or-return basis. Please call in or email to arrange having your demo stocked. See listings for brances based in Great Harwood, Clitheroe and Leyland.

Townsend Records (Clitheroe)
18 Moor Lane, Clitheroe, BB7 1BE
tel:	01200 443 092
fax:	01200 443 092
email:	sales@townsend-records.co.uk
web:	www.townsend-records.co.uk
contact:	Kevin Thompson
rack space:	Yes
flyer space:	Limited
poster space:	Limited
listening posts:	Limited
info:	Unsigned rack space, sale-or-return. Space

available in the window for posters up to A4. Very limited space available for flyers. Also branches based in Great Harwood, Leyland and Chorley. See listings for more details.

Townsend Records (Great Harwood)
30 Queen Street, Great Harwood, Lancashire, BB6 7QQ
tel:	01254 885 995
fax:	01254 887 835
email:	sales@townsend-records.co.uk
web:	www.townsend-records.co.uk
contact:	Steve Bamber
rack space:	Yes
flyer space:	Limited
poster space:	Limited
listening posts:	No
info:	Some rack space available for unsigned music,

at Steve's discretion. All on a sale-or-return basis. Limited poster and flyer space. See listings for branches based in Clitheroe, Leyland and Chorley.

Townsend Records (Leyland)
119 Towngate, Leyland, Lancashire, PR25 2LQ
tel:	01772 455 265
fax:	01772 455 265
email:	sales@townsend-records.co.uk
web:	www.townsend-records.co.uk
contact:	Glen
flyer space:	Limited
info:	No space available for posters, but can leave

flyers. Will sell unsigned music on a sale-or-return basis. See listings for branches in Great Harwood, Clitheroe and Chorley.

Tune In
82 Spring Gardens, Buxton, Derbyshire, SK17 6BZ
tel:	01298 77280
email:	tuneinbuxton@aol.com
contact:	Jill
rack space:	Yes
flyer space:	Limited
poster space:	Limited
listening posts:	Limited
info:	Stock material from local, unsigned bands and

there is some space available for posters and flyers. Possible to listen to music on the in-store system, but no listening posts as such.

Ultimate Sounds
8 Wright Street, Southport, PR9 OTL
tel:	01704 500 221
fax:	01704 510 668
email:	flawlessrecords000@hotmail.com
web:	www.dancemusiconline.co.uk
contact:	Lee Groves
rack space:	Yes
flyer space:	Yes
poster space:	Yes
listening posts:	Yes
info:	Dance music specialists who also sell DJ

equipment. Unsigned rack space for Dance acts on sale-or-return basis. Space for posters and flyers.

Vibes
3 Princess Parade, Bury, BL9 OQL
tel:	0161 764 3013
fax:	0161 764 3013
email:	vibesrecords@ukonline.co.uk
contact:	Joanne Truman
rack space:	Yes
flyer space:	Yes
poster space:	Yes
info:	Unsigned rack space for local bands. Space

available for posters and flyers.

Video & Music Exchange
Unit 11, Old Indoor Market, Eccles, Manchester, M30 0EW
tel:	0161 788 7550
contact:	James
rack space:	Limited
flyer space:	Yes
poster space:	Yes
listening posts:	No
info:	Willing to stock some unsigned material on

a sale-or-return basis depending on rack space available. Space for posters and flyers.

Vinyl Exchange
18 Oldham Street, Manchester, M1 1JN
tel:	0161 228 1122
fax:	0161 236 1613
email:	mailorder@vinylexchange.co.uk
web:	www.vinylexchange.co.uk
rack space:	No
flyer space:	Yes
poster space:	Limited
listening posts:	Yes
info:	Stock second hand material, hence do not

generally sell unsigned music. Flyer rack available. Also see listing for store on Bridge Street, Manchester.

Vinyl Exchange
67 Bridge Street, Manchester, M3 3BQ
tel:	0161 819 5440
fax:	0161 819 5455
email:	mailorder@vinylexchange.co.uk
web:	www.vinylexchange.co.uk
rack space:	Limited
flyer space:	Yes
poster space:	No
listening posts:	Yes
info:	Limited unsigned rack space on a sale-or-return

basis. Space available for flyers, but not posters. Stock a variety of music on CD format. See listing for store located on Oldham Street, Manchester.

Vinyl Revival
5 Hilton Street, Manchester, M4 1LP
tel:	0161 661 6393
email:	vinylrevival@btinternet.com
web:	www.vinylrevivalmcr.com
contact:	Colin White
rack space:	Yes
flyer space:	No
poster space:	No
info:	Specialise in Punk, Rock and Soul. Demos of

local bands are considered. A small amount of unsigned rack space is available on a sale-or-return basis.

Virgin Megastore
32-36 Foregate Street, Chester, CH1 1HA
tel:	01244 322 212
web:	www.virginmegastores.co.uk

Virgin Megastore
6-10 Grapes Lane, Lane Shopping Centre, Carlisle, CA3 8EF
tel:	01228 819 726
web:	www.virginmegastores.co.uk

Virgin Megastore
Unit 8-9, Tops Plaza, Clayton Square Shopping Centre, Liverpool, L1 1QR
tel:	0151 708 6708
web:	www.virginmegastores.co.uk

Virgin Megastore
35 King Street, Manchester, M2 7AT
tel:	0161 839 7659
web:	www.virginmegastores.co.uk

Virgin Megastore
64-67 Market Street, Crewe, CW1 2EY
tel:	01270 585 665
web:	www.virginmegastores.co.uk

Virgin Megastore
Unit 56, Cheshire Oaks Designer Outlet Village, Ellesmere Port, CH65 9JJ
tel:	0151 357 3849
web:	www.virginmegastores.co.uk

Virgin Megastore
Unit G11, Designer Outlet, The Lowry, Salford Quays, M50 3AG
tel:	0161 877 1292
web:	www.virginmegastores.co.uk

Virgin Megastore
Trafford Centre, 17-19 Regents Crescent, Manchester, M17 8AQ
tel:	0161 749 8650
web:	www.virginmegastores.co.uk

Void Records
16 Old Street, Ashton-Under-Lyne, Lancashire, OL6 6LB
tel:	0161 343 3766
fax:	0161 343 3766
web:	www.voidrecords.co.uk
contact:	Andy or Ryan
rack space:	Yes
flyer space:	Yes
poster space:	Yes
listening posts:	Yes
info:	Store specialises in Funky House but will stock

unsigned music from all genres. There is space for posters and flyers, and there are listening facilities available.

Vox Pop
Café Pop, 34-36 Oldham Street, Manchester, M1 1JN
tel:	0161 237 5767
email:	andy@voxpoprecords.com
web:	www.voxpoprecords.com
contact:	Andy or Dave
rack space:	Yes
flyer space:	Yes
poster space:	Yes
listening posts:	Yes
info:	Rack space available for unsigned bands. Space

available for flyers and posters.

X-Records
44 Bridge Street, Bolton, BL1 2EG
tel:	01204 524 018
fax:	01204 370 214
email:	xrecords@xrecords.co.uk
web:	www.xrecords.co.uk
contact:	Steve
rack space:	Yes
flyer space:	Yes
poster space:	Yes
listening posts:	Limited
info:	Unsigned rack space for local bands on a sale-or-

return basis. Speak to the manager, Steve. Limited space is available for posters and flyers.

Zero Records
47 Barlow Moor Road, Didsbury, Manchester, M20 6TW
tel:	0161 438 0211
contact:	Rob Lowder
rack space:	Limited
flyer space:	Yes
poster space:	Yes
listening posts:	No
info:	Sells new and second hand releases. Specialist

knowledge of 60s and 70s Progressive Indie and Psychedelia. No rack space for unsigned artists.

SOUTHEAST

Across the Tracks
110 Gloucester Road, Brighton, East Sussex, BN1 4AF
tel:	01273 677 906
contact:	Alan Childes
rack space:	No
flyer space:	Yes
poster space:	Yes
listening posts:	Limited
info:	Sells most genres but specialise in Soul, Jazz and

Funk. No rack space for unsigned acts.

Adrian's Records
36 High Street, Wickford, Essex, SS12 9AD
tel:	01268 733 318
fax:	01268 761 835
email:	sales@adrians.co.uk
web:	www.adrians.co.uk
contact:	Ray Leveridge
rack space:	No
flyer space:	Limited
poster space:	Limited
listening posts:	Yes
info:	Since 1969 Adrian's have been specialising in

new and old titles, rare and collectable items, and many different artists spanning over mainstream styles and specialist genres.

Ben's Collectors Records
5 Tunsgate, Guildford, GU1 3QT
tel:	01483 301 165
web:	www.bensrecords.co.uk
rack space:	Yes
flyer space:	Yes
poster space:	Yes
listening posts:	Limited
info:	Stocks all genres of music and regularly stocks

CDs by unsigned bands.

Big Shot Records
53a Harpur Street, Bedford, Bedfordshire, MK40 2SR
tel:	01234 355 542
email:	bigshot_records@hotmail.com
web:	www.bigshotrecords.com
contact:	Mario
rack space:	No
flyer space:	Yes
poster space:	Yes
listening posts:	Yes
info:	Specialise in Underground Dance music,

Drum&Bass and Hard House.

BPM Music Ltd.
4 Bartholomews, Brighton, East Sussex, BN1 1HG
tel:	01273 747 400
email:	bpmmusic@mistrial.co.uk
web:	www.bpm-music.co.uk
contact:	Ciaran
rack space:	No
flyer space:	Yes
poster space:	Yes
listening posts:	Yes
info:	Specialises in House Music. No rack space

available for unsigned acts.

Canterbury Rock
12 Whitstable Road, Canterbury, Kent, CT2 8DQ
tel:	01227 458 393
web:	www.canterburyrock.co.uk
rack space:	Limited
flyer space:	Yes
poster space:	Yes
listening posts:	Yes
info:	Canterbury Rock stocks a wide range of musical

styles and has a small amount of space for material from unsigned acts.

CD Warehouse UK Ltd. (Brighton)
163 Western Road, Brighton, East Sussex, BN1 2BB
tel:	01273 731 310
email:	cdwuk@btinternet.com
web:	www.cdwuk.com
rack space:	Yes
flyer space:	Limited
poster space:	Limited
listening posts:	Yes
info:	CD Warehouse stock both second hand and new

records, and will consider stocking material from local unsigned acts.
See listings for stores in South East and London.

CD Warehouse UK Ltd. (Uxbridge)
151 High Street, Uxbridge, Middlesex, UB8 1JY
tel:	01895 252 726
email:	cdwuk@btinternet.com
web:	www.cdwuk.com
rack space:	Yes
flyer space:	Yes
poster space:	Yes
listening posts:	Yes
info:	CD Warehouse stock both second hand and new

records, and will consider stocking material from local unsigned acts.
Please see listings for stores in the South East and London.

CD Warehouse UK Ltd. (Watford)
3, The Parade, Watford, Hertfordshire, WD17 1LQ
tel:	01923 252 300
email:	cdwuk@btinternet.com
web:	www.cdwuk.com
rack space:	Yes
flyer space:	Yes
poster space:	Yes
listening posts:	Yes
info:	CD Warehouse stock both second hand and new

records, and will consider stocking material from local unsigned acts.
Please see listings in London and South East for other stores.

Covert Records
39a Sydney Street, Brighton, East Sussex, BN1 4EP
tel:	01273 624 774
email:	contact@covert.uk.com
web:	www.covert.uk.com
contact:	Alex or Japhy
rack space:	Limited
flyer space:	Yes
poster space:	Limited
listening posts:	Yes
info:	Specialists in Techno, Electro, Breakbeat,

House, Acid House, Minimal House, Tech House, Deep House and
Underground styles. 4 listening posts. Rack space for unsigned acts on
sale-or-return basis.

Crazy Beat Records
87 Corbets Tey Road, Upminster, Essex, RM14 2AH
tel:	01708 228 678
email:	sales@crazybeat.co.uk
web:	www.crazybeat.co.uk
rack space:	Limited
flyer space:	Yes
poster space:	Yes
listening posts:	Yes
info:	Crazy Beat are keen to hear from any unsigned

acts producing Soul, Jazz, Funk, Hip-Hop, Rap or Reggae music. Please
contact shop for further details.

Dance 2 Records
129 Western Road, Brighton, West Sussex, BM1 2AD
tel:	01273 220 023
email:	sales@dance2.co.uk
rack space:	Yes
flyer space:	Yes
poster space:	Yes
listening posts:	Yes
info:	Specialise in Drum&Bass, Hip-Hop, Hardcore,

Breaks and House. Willing to stock unsigned acts on a sale-or-return
basis.

D'Vinyl Records
42 Market Street, Watford, Hertfordshire, WD1 7AY
tel:	01923 249 074
email:	jondvinyl@hotmail.com
contact:	Jon Manning
rack space:	Yes
flyer space:	Yes
poster space:	Yes
listening posts:	Yes
info:	Drum&Bass specialists. Rack space available for

unsigned acts.

Essential Music
15-16 Brighton Square, Brighton, East Sussex, BN1 1HD
tel:	01273 202 695
fax:	01273 202 695
email:	essmusicbrighter@yahoo.co.uk
contact:	Jake
rack space:	Yes
flyer space:	Limited
poster space:	Limited
listening posts:	Yes
info:	Specialise in back catalogues at low prices. CDs

only. Willing to stock music by unsigned acts.

The Excited Echelon
84 Pole Barn Lane, Frinton-on-Sea, Essex, CO13 9NH
email:	unsigned@the-excited-echelon.com
web:	www.the-excited-echelon.com
info:	Online music store, willing to sell unsigned

material. Contact by email.

Fives Records
103 Broadway, Leigh-On-Sea, Essex, SS9 1PG
tel:	01702 771629
email:	five103@btconnect.com
web:	www.fives-records.com
rack space:	Yes
flyer space:	Yes
poster space:	Yes
listening posts:	Yes
info:	Fives Records sells all types of music.

Focus Sounds
250 London Road, Waterlooville, PO7 7HG
tel:	02392 254 923
email:	focussounds@btinternet.com
web:	www.focussounds.co.uk
rack space:	Yes
flyer space:	Yes
poster space:	Yes
listening posts:	Yes
info:	Focus specialises in Rock, Metal, Punk and Indie

music and would be happy to stock serious material by unsigned
bands.

Fopp
19 West Street, Reading, RG1 1TZ
tel:	0118 939 1493
web:	www.fopp.co.uk
info:	Fopp are involved in 'The Unsigned Network'

- unsigned material is accepted centrally, distributed to stores and is
placed in a specific 'Unsigned Section' which is promoted in-store.
Material is only accepted in this way and you should refer to the
'Unsigned Network' link on the Fopp website to check whether they
are accepting material at that time. Artists are paid a set amount on
sales, on a sale-or-return basis. Applications for unsigned space is not
on-going and Fopp will sell unsigned material on a sale/demand/space
policy.

Forward Move Ltd.
1a The Broadway, Bedford, MK40 2TJ
tel:	01234 365 800
email:	enquiries@forwardmovereggae.com
web:	www.forwardmovereggae.com
info:	Specialise in Reggae, Hip-Hop, Dancehall, Gospel

and R&B. Contact the manager with regard to stocking unsigned
material, posters and flyers.

Golden Discs
2-4 Market Pavement, Basildon, SS14 1BH
tel:	01268 247 093
rack space:	Yes
flyer space:	Limited
poster space:	Limited
listening posts:	No
info:	Stocks music across all genres and will make

space for CDs from unsigned local acts.

Groovefinder Records
125 Albert Road, Southsea, Hampshire, PO5 2SQ
tel:	02392 732 940
email:	groovefinder@yahoo.com
web:	www.groovefinder.co.uk
contact:	Barry
rack space:	Limited
flyer space:	Yes
poster space:	Yes
listening posts:	Yes
info:	Willing to stock records by local unsigned acts

but would prefer vinyl pressings to CDs. Stocks a wide range of records from 70s to present.

Hedonizm Records
106 Trafalgar Street, Brigton, East Sussex, BN1 4ER
tel:	01273 700 061
fax:	01273 207 145
email:	mark@hedonizmrecords.com
web:	www.hedonizmrecords.com
contact:	Mark
rack space:	Yes
flyer space:	Yes
poster space:	Yes
listening posts:	Yes
info:	Dance music specialists. Willing to stock records

by unsigned acts.

HMV
16-17 Culver Walk, Colchester, Essex, CO1 1XJ
tel:　　　　　01206 714 450

HMV
Unit 32, County Square, Ashford, Kent, TN23 1YD
tel:	01233 739 010
web:	www.hmv.co.uk

HMV
Unit 6, 7 Friars Square, Aylesbury, Buckinghamshire, HP20 2SP
tel:	01296 399 290
web:	www.hmv.co.uk

HMV
Units 53-54, Castle Quay, Banbury, Oxfordshire, OX16 8UP
tel:	01295 265 005
web:	www.hmv.co.uk

HMV
19 Charles Square, Bracknell, RG12 1DF
tel:	01344 487 181
web:	www.hmv.co.uk

HMV
61-62 Western Road, Brighton, BN1 2HA
tel:	01273 747 221
web:	www.hmv.co.uk

HMV
12 St. Margaret's Street, Canterbury, CT1 2TP
tel:	01227 457 774
web:	www.hmv.co.uk

HMV
Unit 3-4, High Chelmer Shopping Centre, Chelmsford, Essex, CM1 1XL
tel:	01245 351 641
web:	www.hmv.co.uk

HMV
23 Eastgate Centre, Basildon, Essex, SS14 1AE
tel:	01268 271 477
web:	www.hmv.co.uk

HMV
Unit 28-29, Festival Place, Basingstoke, RG21 7BE
tel:	01256 338 500
web:	www.hmv.co.uk

HMV
75-79 The Friary Centre, Guildford, GU1 4YU
tel:	01483 565 650
web:	www.hmv.co.uk

HMV
Unit L4, Water Gardens, Harlow, CM20 1AR
tel:	01279 630 360
web:	www.hmv.co.uk

HMV
Unit 12 & 13, Comet Way, Hatfield, Hertfordshire, AL10 0XR
tel:	01707 280 580
web:	www.hmv.co.uk

HMV
Unit H, 19 The Martlets, Crawley, RH10 1ER
tel:	01293 523 204
web:	www.hmv.co.uk

HMV
7-8 East Street, Chichester, West Sussex, PO1 9HE
tel:	01243 756 980
web:	www.hmv.co.uk

HMV
29 The Ashley Centre, Epsom, Surrey, KT18 5DB
tel:	01372 840 920
web:	www.hmv.co.uk

HMV
Gatwick Airport, Unit S13, North Terminal Departure Lounge, Gatwick, West Sussex, RH6 0NP
tel:	01293 609 170
web:	www.hmv.co.uk

HMV
Unit 9a The Fort, Westwood Cross, Margaret Road, Broadstairs, Kent, CT10 2BF
tel:	01843 609 790
web:	www.hmv.co.uk

HMV
Unit 281, Lakeside Shopping Centre, West Thurrock Way, Grays, Essex, RM16 1WT
tel:	01708 860 110
web:	www.hmv.co.uk

HMV
111-112 Royal Victoria Place, Shopping Centre, Tunbridge Wells, Kent, TN1 2SR
tel:	01892 549 775
web:	www.hmv.co.uk

HMV
32 Peascod Street, Windsor, SL4 1EA
tel:	01753 838 440
web:	www.hmv.co.uk

HMV
Units 40-42, The Peacocks Shopping Centre, Woking, GU21 6GB
tel:	01483 228 000
web:	www.hmv.co.uk

HMV
Unit 33-34, Harlequin Centre, Watford, WD17 2TR
tel:	01923 294 190
web:	www.hmv.co.uk

HMV
25-27 St. Peter's Street, St. Albans, AL1 3DP
tel:	01727 860 406
web:	www.hmv.co.uk

HMV
Unit S5A, Two Rivers Retail Park, Staines, TW18 4WF
tel:	01784 495 610
web:	www.hmv.co.uk

HMV
Airside Departure Lounge, Terminal Building, Stansted Airport, Essex, CM24 1QW
tel:	01279 669 030
web:	www.hmv.co.uk

HMV
8-14 Queens Road, Southend, SS1 1LU
tel:	01702 435 158
web:	www.hmv.co.uk

HMV
Unit 50, 104-105 Curzon Mall, Queensmere Shopping Centre, Slough, SL1 1DQ
tel:	01753 511 176
web:	www.hmv.co.uk

HMV
7-9 Lockwood Walk, Romford, RM1 3RH
tel:	01708 734 643
web:	www.hmv.co.uk

HMV
13 Holy Brook Walk, The Oracle, Reading, RG1 2AQ
tel:	0118 951 2640
web:	www.hmv.co.uk

HMV
138-141 Friar Street, Reading, RG1 1EX
tel:	0118 957 6210
web:	www.hmv.co.uk

HMV
43-46 Cornmarket Street, Oxford, OX1 3HA
tel:	01865 728 190
web:	www.hmv.co.uk

HMV
78 Midsummer Arcade, Milton Keynes, MK9 3BB
tel: 01908 234 001
web: www.hmv.co.uk

HMV
79 Northbrook Street, Newbury, Berkshire, RG14 1AE
tel: 01635 573 630
web: www.hmv.co.uk

HMV
146 Arndale Centre, Luton, LU1 2TG
tel: 01582 401 414
web: www.hmv.co.uk

HMV
13a Upper Rose Gallery, Bluewater, Greenhithe, Kent, DA9 9SP
tel: 01322 624 600
web: www.hmv.co.uk
info: See Head Office listing.

HMV
Unit 110, The Chimes Shopping Centre, High Street, Uxbridge, UB8 1GA
tel: 01895 253 580
web: www.hmv.co.uk
info: See Head Office listing.

HMV
183-187 Commercial Road, Portsmouth, PO1 1EA
tel: 02392 829 678
web: www.hmv.co.uk

HMV
18-20 High Street, Winchester, SO23 9JX
tel: 01962 835 920
web: www.hmv.co.uk

HMV
Unit 24, Sirius Avenue, Gun Wharf Quay, Portsmouth, PO1 3TR
tel: 02392 778 640
web: www.hmv.co.uk

HMV
Unit 15, Fremlin Walk, Maidstone, ME14 1QG
tel: 01622 355 140
web: www.hmv.co.uk

HMV
48-50 Churchill Square Shopping Centre, Brighton, East Sussex, BN1 2RG
tel: 01273 749 919
web: www.hmv.co.uk

Infinite Records
111 Gloucester Road, Brighton, East Sussex, BN1 4AF
tel: 0127 368 9853
email: roocurrier@hotmail.com
web: www.infinite-records.com
contact: Roo
rack space: Yes
flyer space: Yes
poster space: Yes
listening posts: Yes
info: Specialises in Drum&Bass, New Jazz, Hip-Hop and Breakbeat. Willing to stock records by local unsigned acts.

Island Music
4 Kingsway, Barfield Road, West Mersea, Colchester, Essex, CO5 8TH
tel: 01206 383 900
contact: Robin
rack space: Yes
flyer space: Yes
poster space: Yes
listening posts: No
info: Stock all music types. Order service available. Island Music will stock material by local unsigned bands.

Jam (Brighton) Ltd.
39 Baker Street, Brighton, BN1 4JN
tel: 01273 620 321
email: jam_brighton@tiscali.co.uk
rack space: Yes
flyer space: Yes
poster space: Yes
listening posts: Yes
info: Jam sells all types of music and is happy to accept material from unsigned bands.

Let's Buy Some Music (Dover)
3 Worthington Street, Dover, CT17 9AF
tel: 01304 226 100
rack space: Limited
flyer space: Limited
poster space: Limited
listening posts: No
info: Due to the small size of this store, CDs will only be accepted from local artists of a high standard. Also see listing for store based in Hythe.

Let's Buy Some Music (Hythe)
123 High Street, Hythe, Kent, CT21 5JJ
tel: 01303 230 464
rack space: Limited
flyer space: Limited
poster space: Limited
listening posts: No
info: Due to the small size of this store, CDs will only be accepted from local unsigned acts of a high standard. See listing for store based in Dover.

Long Player
3 Grosvenor Road, Tunbridge Wells, Kent, TN1 2AH
tel: 01892 539 273
fax: 01892 516 770
email: shop@longplayer.fsnet.co.uk
web: www.longplayer.co.uk
rack space: Yes
flyer space: Yes
poster space: Yes
listening posts: Yes
info: Long Player specialise in Rock and Indie music but will accept unsigned material from other genres too.

Massive Records
95 Gloucester Green, Oxford, OX1 2BU
tel: 01865 792 770
fax: 01865 792 770
email: info@massiverecords.com
web: www.massiverecords.com
contact: Russell
rack space: Yes
flyer space: Yes
poster space: Yes
listening posts: Yes
info: Music Week Independent Retailer of the Year 2003. Rack space for local unsigned acts. House, Drum&Bass, Techno, Breakbeat, Urban, Hip-Hop, Jazz and Leftfield specialists.

Medway Record Centre
36 Canterbury Street, Gillingham, Kent, ME7 5TX
tel: 01634 281 750
rack space: No
flyer space: Limited
poster space: Limited
listening posts: No
info: Medway specialise in collectable vinyl from the 50s to the 80s, but also stock CDs, cassettes, videos and DVDs.

Music Mania
18 High Street, Clacton-On-Sea, CO15 1NR
tel: 01255 222 844
contact: Mr Stone
rack space: Yes
flyer space: Yes
poster space: Yes
listening posts: No
info: Stocks all genres of music, mainly on CD but some vinyl is available.

Music Search
109e Guildford Street, Chertsey, KT16 9AS
tel: 01932 569 901
email: musicsearch109e@msn.com
web: www.musicsearchuk.co.uk
rack space: Yes
flyer space: Yes
poster space: Yes
listening posts: Yes
info: Music Search is proud of its strong links with local venues, musicians and songwriters. Not only do they stock CDs by unsigned artists, can also help bands contact other useful companies and individuals.

The Music Trading Company
21 2Lion Street, Rye, East Sussex, TN31 7LB
tel: 01797 222 966
email: info@musictradingcompany.com
web: www.musictradingcompany.com
rack space: No
flyer space: No
poster space: No
listening posts: No
info: All genres covered but sadly no space at the moment for any unsigned bands music.

MVC
76-88 High Street, Staines, Middlesex, TW18 4DP
tel: 01784 465 738
web: www.mvc.co.uk
rack space: No
flyer space: No
poster space: No
listening posts: Yes
info: MVC do not stock material by unsigned acts.

MVC
Unit 4, Montague Centre, Worthing, West Sussex, BN11 1YJ
tel: 01903 236 693
web: www.mvc.co.uk

MVC
54/56 Park Street, Surrey, Camberley, GU15 3PT
tel: 01276 616 95
web: www.mvc.co.uk
rack space: No
flyer space: No
poster space: No
listening posts: Yes
info: MVC do not stock material by unsigned acts.

MVC
48-50 South Street, Essex, Romford, RM1 1RB
tel: 01708 747 937
web: www.mvc.co.uk
rack space: No
flyer space: No
poster space: No
listening posts: Yes
info: MVC do not stock material by unsigned acts.

MVC
34-38 Midland Road, Bedford, Bedfordshire, MK40 1PW
tel: 01234 211 488

MVC
51-53 High Street, Bracknell, Berkshire, RG12 1EA
tel: 01344 869 641
web: www.mvc.co.uk

MVC
103 The Broadway, Newbury, Berkshire, RG13 1AS
tel: 01635 521 078
web: www.mvc.co.uk

MVC
31-32 South Street, Chichester, West Sussex, PO19 1EL
tel: 01243 539 137
web: www.mvc.co.uk

MVC
8 Air Street, Brighton, East Sussex, BN1 3FB
tel: 01273 727 414
web: www.mvc.co.uk

MVC
25-29 Cornfield Road, Eastbourne, East Sussex, BN21 4QD
tel: 01323 720 931
web: www.mvc.co.uk

MVC
Unit 7-8, Queen's Road, Hastings, TN34 1QP
tel: 01424 439 290
web: www.mvc.co.uk

MVC
97 George Street, Hove, East Sussex, BN3 3YE
tel: 01273 730 748
web: www.mvc.co.uk

MVC
Unit 12, Westgate Park, Fodderwick, SS14 1AP
tel: 01268 523 621
web: www.mvc.co.uk

MVC
42-44 London Road, Southend, SS1 1NT
tel: 01702 431 130
web: www.mvc.co.uk

MVC
Unit 28c, The Chantry Centre, Andover, SP10 1RL
tel: 01264 333 401
web: www.mvc.co.uk

MVC
14-15 Westminster House, Festival Place, Basingstoke, RG21 7LS
tel: 01256 475 267
web: www.mvc.co.uk

MVC
Unit 29, Westbury Mall, Fareham Shopping Centre, Fareham, PO16 0PD
tel: 01329 284 535
web: www.mvc.co.uk

MVC
Unit 47, The Brooks, Winchester, SP23 8QY
tel: 01962 856 985
web: www.mvc.co.uk

MVC
Unit 43-44, Howard Centre, Welwyn Garden City, Hertfordshire, AL8 6HA
tel: 01707 375 925
web: www.mvc.co.uk

MVC
24-25 High Street, Maidstone, Kent, ME14 1JF
tel: 01622 683 747
web: www.mvc.co.uk

MVC
Unit 3, 2-12 High Street, Redhill, Surrey, RH1 1RH
tel: 01737 773 476
web: www.mvc.co.uk

Playback Music & Video
4 George Street, Hailsham, BN27 1AE
tel: 01323 849 763
rack space: Limited
flyer space: Yes
poster space: Yes
listening posts: No
info: Playback Music will stock material by unsigned bands across all genres.

Powerplay
Unit 8c, 55 Terminus Road, Eastbourne, West Sussex, BN21 3LX
tel: 01323 736 292
fax: 01323 431 151
email: eastbourneshop@powerplay.com
web: www.powerplaydirect.com
rack space: Yes
flyer space: Yes
poster space: Yes
listening posts: Yes
info: Powerplay stock all kinds of music and welcome unsigned acts from all genres.

Rapture Records
27-38 St. John's Street, Colchester, CO2 7AD
tel: 01206 542 541
email: john@rapturerecords.com
web: www.rapturerecords.com
contact: John
rack space: Yes
flyer space: Yes
poster space: Yes
listening posts: Yes
info: Specialises in Dance vinyl.

The Record Corner
Pound Lane, Godalming, GU7 1BX
tel: 01483 422 006
email: sales@therecordcorner.co.uk
web: www.therecordcorner.co.uk
rack space: Yes
flyer space: Yes
poster space: Yes
listening posts: Yes
info: The Record Corner is an old fashioned store stocking mainly Classical, Jazz, Rock and Folk music. May make space for material from local unsigned acts.

Replay Records
4 Bristol & West Arcade, Friar Street, Reading, Berkshire, RG1 1JL
tel: 0118 959 9959
email: martyn@replaymusic.co.uk
web: www.replaymusic.co.uk
contact: Martyn Mayger
rack space: Yes
flyer space: Yes
poster space: Yes
listening posts: Limited
info: Mostly a second hand dealer, however is willing to sell records by local acts, at owner's discretion.

Resident
28 Kensington Gardens, Brighton, East Sussex, BN1 4Al
tel: 01273 606 312
email: info@resident-music.com
web: www.resident-music.com
contact: Derry Watkins or Natasha Youngs
rack space: Yes
flyer space: Yes
poster space: Limited
listening posts: Limited
info: In depth back catalogue and new releases. Also a ticket agent. Willing to stock local unsigned music on a sale-or-return basis.

Revolutions
17 Crescent Road, Worthing, West Sussex, BN11 1RL
tel: 01903 209 553
email: info@revolutions33.co.uk
web: www.revolutions33.co.uk
contact: Darren
rack space: Limited
flyer space: No
poster space: No
listening posts: No
info: Classical music specialists. Mostly second hand stock. Would be willing to sell records by local Classical musicians.

Richards Records
48 St. Peter's Street, Canterbury, Kent, CT1 1MB
tel: 01227 452 268
rack space: Yes
flyer space: Limited
poster space: Limited
listening posts: Yes
info: Richards Records sells mainly Indie music but will consider stocking unsigned material from all genres.

Rik's Records
422 Portland Road, Hove, East Sussex, BN3 5SJ
tel: 01273 430 739
rack space: Yes
flyer space: Yes
poster space: Yes
listening posts: No
info: Deals in all most genres. Very willing to help out local bands. Would stock unsigned acts on a sale-or-return basis.

The Rock Box
151 London Road, Camberley, Surrey, GU15 3JY
tel: 01276 266 28
fax: 01276 678 776
email: ken.dudley@virgin.net
web: www.rockbox.co.uk
rack space: Yes
flyer space: Yes
poster space: Yes
listening posts: Yes
info: The Rock Box specialises in Rock and Indie music and is willing to stock local unsigned material from these genres.

Rounder Records of Brighton
19 Brighton Square, Brighton, East Sussex, BN1 1HD
tel: 01273 325 440
fax: 01273 776 991
email: philshop@btconect.com
rack space: Yes
flyer space: Yes
poster space: Yes
listening posts: Yes
info: Willing to sell tracks by unsigned acts.

Simply Music
80-82 Market Hall, The Luton Arndale Centre, Luton, Bedfordshire, LU7 0AP
tel: 01582 452 019
web: www.simplymusic2000.com
contact: Alan
rack space: No
flyer space: Yes
poster space: No
listening posts: No
info: Mainly stock R&B and Hip-Hop. Contact Alan on the above number for further information.

Slipped Discs
21a High Street, Billericay, Essex, CM12 9BA
tel: 01277 631 422
email: s.discs@btconnect.com
rack space: Limited
flyer space: Limited
poster space: Limited
listening posts: Yes
info: Stocks a wide variety of music genres.

Sounds Good
19 High Street, Stanford-Le-Hope, Essex, SS17 0HD
tel: 01375 677 843
rack space: Yes
flyer space: Limited
poster space: Limited
listening posts: No
info: Sounds Good stock most styles of music and sometimes stock material by unsigned artists.

Studio Records
Mill Hill Farm, Chalk Street, Rettendon Common, Chelmsford, CM3 8DE
tel: 01708 343 949
rack space: No
flyer space: Yes
poster space: Yes
listening posts: Yes
info: Due to limited demand Studio Records do not stock CDs by unsigned artists but are willing to display posters and flyers.

Total Recall Records
107-109 High Street, Orpington, Kent, BR6 0LG
tel: 01689 835 900
email: info@awards-uk.com
web: www.awards-uk.com
rack space: Limited
flyer space: Yes
poster space: Yes
listening posts: No
info: Total Recall specialise in back catalogue material from the 50s to the 80s.

Track Records
52 High Street, Chesham, Buckinghamshire, HP5 1EQ
tel: 01494 771 126
email: trackrecordschesham@hotmail.com
web: www.track-recordsuk.com
rack space: Yes
flyer space: Yes
poster space: Yes
listening posts: Yes
info: Track Records stock all genres of music including unsigned local acts.

Uni Star Records
Unit 5, 140 Queensway, Bletchley, Milton Keynes, Buckinghamshire, MK2 2RS
tel: 01908 369 115
email: unistarrecords@aol.com
rack space: Yes
flyer space: Yes
poster space: Yes
listening posts: Yes
info: Uni Star Records is an African music store and will stock material of this style by unsigned bands. May consider also stocking some European music from unsigned artists.

Virgin Megastore
Unit B, 18-20 Cornmarket Street, Oxford, OX1 3EY
tel: 01865 723 906
web: www.virginmegastores.co.uk

Virgin Megastore
Unit 11-12, The Peacocks Centre, Woking, GU21 6GB
tel: 01483 727 350
web: www.virginmegastores.co.uk

Virgin Megastore
Unit 3, The Forum, Stevenage, SG1 1ES
tel: 01438 747 470
web: www.virginmegastores.co.uk

Virgin Megastore
Unit 111, McArthur Glen Designer Outlet, Kimberley Way, Ashford, TN24 0SD
tel: 01233 645 772
web: www.virginmegastores.co.uk

Virgin Megastore
13,14 & 15 Paddington House, The Walks Shopping Centre, Basingstoke, RG21 7LG
tel: 01256 477 773
web: www.virginmegastores.co.uk

Virgin Megastore
9 George Yard Shopping Centre, Braintree, Essex, CM7 1RB
tel: 01376 552 959
web: www.virginmegastores.co.uk

Virgin Megastore
Unit D3, The Freeport Designer Outlet Centre, Charter Way, Chapel Hill, CM77 8YH
tel: 01376 554 679
web: www.virginmegastores.co.uk

Virgin Megastore
Unit MSU5, Churchill Square Shopping Centre, Brighton, BN1 2TB
tel: 01273 737 712
web: www.virginmegastores.co.uk

Virgin Megastore
Unit 15a, Whitefriars Shopping Centre, Gravel Walk, Canterbury, CT1 2TF
tel: 01227 452 123
web: www.virginmegastores.co.uk

Virgin Megastore
175-177 High Street, Chatham, ME4 4BA
tel: 01634 830 563
web: www.virginmegastores.co.uk

Virgin Megastore
Units 31, 32,81 & 82, County Mall, Crawley, RH10 1FF
tel: 01293 553 470
web: www.virginmegastores.co.uk

Virgin Megastore
Unit 3D, Level 3, Gatwick Airport, South Terminal Airside, RH6 0NP
tel: 01293 568 070
web: www.virginmegastores.co.uk

Virgin Megastore
Unit 1-2, 35 Broadwalk, Harlow, CM20 1JF
tel: 01279 442 173
web: www.virginmegastores.co.uk

Virgin Megastore
Unit TS4, Town Square, Priory Meadow, Hastings, TN34 1PH
tel: 01424 447 557
web: www.virginmegastores.co.uk

Virgin Megastore
Unit 40, The Gallerias, Hatfield, AL10 0XU
tel: 01707 251 566
web: www.virginmegastores.co.uk

Virgin Megastore
Unit 30, Hempstead Valley Shopping Centre, Gillingham, ME7 3PD
tel: 01634 377 023
web: www.virginmegastores.co.uk

Virgin Megastore
Unit D10, The Octagon Centre, High Wycombe, HP11 2HU
tel: 01494 461 200
web: www.virginmegastores.co.uk

Virgin Megastore
1-5 Grace Reynolds Walk, Camberley, Surrey, GU15 3SN
tel: 01276 686 006
web: www.virginmegastores.co.uk

Virgin Megastore
8 Midsummer Place, Milton Keynes, MK9 3GA
tel: 01908 395 705
web: www.virginmegastores.co.uk

Virgin Megastore
228-230 Commercial Road, Portsmouth, PO1 1HG
tel: 02392 838 833
web: www.virginmegastores.co.uk

Virgin Megastore
Unit 3B, Gunwharf Quays, Portsmouth, PO1 3TN
tel: 02392 838 618
web: www.virginmegastores.co.uk

Virgin Megastore
1-5 Oxford Road, Reading, RG1 7QG
tel: 0118 957 5222
web: www.virginmegastores.co.uk

Virgin Megastore
Unit N20/21, Laurie Walk, Romford, RM1 3RT
tel: 01708 730 831
web: www.virginmegastores.co.uk

Virgin Megastore
Unit 76, Queensmere Shopping Centre, Slough, SL1 1DG
tel: 01753 570 003
web: www.virginmegastores.co.uk

Virgin Megastore
27-30 Culer Square, Colchester, Essex, CO1 1WF
tel: 01206 547 733
web: www.virginmegastores.co.uk

Virgin Megastore
Units 103-109, Ketts Mall, The Harlequin Centre, Watford, WD17 2TH
tel: 01923 226 140
web: www.virginmegastores.co.uk

Virgin Megastore
Unit 7 The Orchards, Dartford, DA1 1DN
tel: 01322 271 741
web: www.virginmegastores.co.uk

Virgin Megastore
Units LO81/U082A, South Mall, Bluewater Park, DA9 9SL
tel: 01322 624 500
web: www.virginmegastores.co.uk

Virgin Megastore
184 High Street, G24 Victoria Plaza, Southend-On-Sea, Essex, SS1 1SJ
tel: 01702 616 348
web: www.virginmegastores.co.uk

Walton Rock
14 High Street, Walton On The Naze, Essex, CO14 8BH
tel: 01255 674 220
email: mikeandcaro@littlechambers.fsworld.co.uk
contact: Mike
rack space: Yes
flyer space: Yes
poster space: Yes
listening posts: No
info: Mainly stock Retro music on vinyl and CD. Also sells music memorabilia.

The Wax Factor
24 Trafalgar Street, Brighton, East Sussex, BN1 4EQ
tel: 01273 673 744
email: alwax@hotmail.com
rack space: Limited
flyer space: Yes
poster space: Yes
listening posts: No
info: General retail. Willing to stock some local unsigned acts.

White Label Music
2 Peacock Yard, Hockliffe Street, Leighton Buzzard, Bedfordshire, LU7 1HJ
tel: 01525 384 477
email: sales@uk-whitelabel.com
web: www.uk-whitelabel.com
rack space: Yes
flyer space: Yes
poster space: Yes
listening posts: Yes
info: Drum&Bass specialists, also expanding into Funky House and Garage. Will stock unsigned Drum&Bass acts.

wsrrecords.com
3 Mill Street, Bedford, MK40 3EU
tel: 01234 266 244
email: wsrrecords@aol.com
web: www.wsrecords.com
rack space: No
flyer space: Yes
poster space: Yes
listening posts: Yes
info: Specialises in Drum&Bass, Hard House, Hardcore and Techno. Mainly vinyl but some CDs available.

SOUTHWEST

Aardvark Music
9 Totnes Road, Paignton, Devon, TQ4 5JX
tel: 01803 664 481
rack space: Limited
flyer space: Yes
poster space: Yes
listening posts: No
info: Specialise in Metal and Hip-Hop, but do sell other genres. Speak to the manager with regard to stocking unsigned material.

Acorn Music
3 Glovers Walk, Yeovil, Somerset, BA20 1LH
tel: 01935 425 503
web: www.acornmusic.co.uk
rack space: Limited
flyer space: Limited
poster space: Limited
listening posts: Yes
info: Sells most genres of music. Please see website for details.

Badlands Records
11 St. George's Place, Cheltenham, Gloucestershire, GL50 1JS
tel: 01242 227 725
email: mailorder@badlands.co.uk
web: www.badlands.co.uk
contact: Kurtis
rack space: Yes
flyer space: Yes
poster space: Yes
listening posts: Yes
info: Caters for all musical tastes from Dance to Rock. Section dedicated to local bands. Extensive range of vinyl and DJ equipment available.

Bangbang
78 Colston Street, Bristol, Avon, BS1 5BB
tel: 0117 922 7377
email: shop@bangbangrecords.com
web: www.bangbangrecords.com
rack space: No
flyer space: No
poster space: No
listening posts: Yes
info: Specialists in Dance music. Sell music on vinyl format only. Please contact the manager with regard to stocking unsigned material.

Bath Compact Discs
11 Broad Street, Bath, BA1 5LJ
tel: 01225 464 766
fax: 01225 482 275
email: bathcds@btinternet.com
web: www.bathcds.btinternet.co.uk
contact: Steve or Sarah
rack space: No
flyer space: Limited
poster space: Limited
listening posts: Limited
info: Space available for flyers and posters. Stock Classical music only.

Bigga Records
15 Looe Street, Plymouth, Devon, PL4 0DY
tel: 01752 268 801
web: www.bigga-records.co.uk
rack space: Limited
flyer space: Yes
poster space: Yes
listening posts: Yes
info: Will stock local unsigned material on a sale-or-return basis. Alternatively, if Bigga Records like the music they will buy a certain number from the band upfront.

Blue River CDs & DVDs
13b North Street, Wareham, Dorset, BH20 4AB
tel: 01929 553 449
rack space: No
flyer space: No
poster space: No
listening posts: No

Bosstunes
10 Market Street, Swindon, Wiltshire, SN1 1RZ
tel: 01793 644 184
email: sales@bosstunes.co.uk
web: www.bosstunes.co.uk
rack space: Limited
flyer space: No
poster space: No
listening posts: Yes
info: Sell most genres of music on CD and Vinyl format. Also sells DVDs and merchandise. Specialists in DJ equipment. Please speak to the manager with reference to stocking unsigned material.

Bournemouth Classic Compact
110 Poole Road, Bournemouth, Dorset, BH4 9EF
tel: 01202 769 991
email: shop@bcc-classics.ndo.co.uk
web: www.bcc-classics.co.uk
rack space: No
flyer space: Yes
poster space: Yes
listening posts: No
info: Specialists in Jazz, Classical and Easy Listening. Will allow posters and flyers to advertise local events, however there is no space for unsigned material.

Bridport Record Centre
33a South Street, Bridport, Dorset, DT6 3NY
tel: 01308 425 707
rack space: Limited
flyer space: Yes
poster space: Yes
listening posts: Yes
info: Will stock material from local bands amoung other CDs in the store.

Cheap Thrills
Unit 8, Central Market, Scarrots Lane, Newport, Isle of Wight, PO30 1JD
tel: 01983 530 570
email: inquiries@cheap-thrills.co.uk
web: www.cheap-thrills.co.uk
rack space: Yes
flyer space: Yes
poster space: Yes
listening posts: Limited
info: Cheap Thrills stocks all types of Alternative music and sometimes sells material from unsigned bands from within these genres.

Chunes
9 Mitchell Street, Weymouth, Dorset, DT4 8BT
tel: 01305 788 880
web: www.chunes.net
rack space: Limited
flyer space: Yes
poster space: Yes
listening posts: Yes
info: Chunes are Dance specialists.

Cliffton Arcarde Music
Unit 15, Boyces Avenue, Bristol, Avon, BS8 4AA
tel: 0117 946 7016
rack space: No
flyer space: Yes
poster space: Yes
listening posts: No
info: Sell a wide range of genres from Metal to Classical.

Days Gone By
1 Bread Street, Penzance, Cornwall, TR18 2EQ
tel: 01736 330 544
email: simon@daysgoneby.fsnet.co.uk
rack space: Yes
flyer space: Yes
poster space: Yes
listening posts: No
info: Mainly stock 50s, 60s, 70s and 80s music. Will stock unsigned material on a sale-or-return basis.

Disc-n-Tape
17 Gloucester Road, Bishopstan, Bristol, BS7 8AA
tel: 0117 942 2227
email: graeme@disc-n-tape.co.uk
web: www.disc-n-tape.co.uk
rack space: Limited
flyer space: Yes
poster space: Yes
listening posts: Yes
info: Willing to stock records by local unsigned acts. Stocks a wide range of genres.

Dog House Music
27a Dreadnought Trading Estate, Bridport, Dorset, DT6 5BU
tel: 01308 420 403
rack space: Yes
flyer space: Yes
poster space: No
listening posts: No
info: Stock a wide range of genres. Will stock material by unsigned artists on a sale-or-return basis.

FM Music
3 Borough Parade, Chippenham, Wiltshire, SN15 3WL
tel: 01249 446 592
rack space: Limited
flyer space: Yes
poster space: Yes
listening posts: No

Fopp
8 The Corridor, Bath, BA1 5AP
tel: 01225 481 949
web: www.fopp.co.uk
info: Fopp are involved in 'The Unsigned Network'
- unsigned material is accepted centrally, distributed to stores and is
placed in a specific 'Unsigned Section' which is promoted in-store.
Material is only accepted in this way and you should refer to the
'Unsigned Network' link on the Fopp website to check whether they
are accepting material at that time. Artists are paid a set amount on
sales, on a sale-or-return basis. Applications for unsigned space is not
on-going and Fopp will sell unsigned material on a sale/demand/space
policy.

Fopp
43 Park Street, Bristol
tel: 0117 945 0685
web: www.fopp.co.uk
info: Fopp are involved in 'The Unsigned Network'
- unsigned material is accepted centrally, distributed to stores and is
placed in a specific 'Unsigned Section' which is promoted in-store.
Material is only accepted in this way and you should refer to the
'Unsigned Network' link on the Fopp website to check whether they
are accepting material at that time. Artists are paid a set amount on
sales, on a sale-or-return basis. Applications for unsigned space is not
on-going and Fopp will sell unsigned material on a sale/demand/space
policy.

HJ Knee
27 Fore Street, Trowbridge, Wiltshire, BA14 8EW
tel: 01225 754 161
email: info@kneesnet.co.uk
web: www.hjknee.co.uk
rack space: Limited
flyer space: Limited
poster space: Limited
listening posts: No
info: HJ Knee have limited space but will stock some
unsigned material from local bands.

HMV
c/o Voisins, 32 King Street, St. Helier, Jersey, Channel Islands, JE4 8NF
tel: 01534 639 272
web: www.hmv.co.uk

HMV
21-23 Broadmead, Bristol, BS1 3HF
tel: 0117 929 7467
web: www.hmv.co.uk

HMV
5-6 The Avenue, Commercial Road, Bournemouth, BH2 5RP
tel: 01202 556 297
web: www.hmv.co.uk

HMV
Unit 16, Vicarage Walk, The Quesdam Shopping Centre, Yeovil,
BA20 1EX
tel: 01935 381 790
web: www.hmv.co.uk

HMV
30-32 New George Street, Plymouth, PL1 1RW
tel: 01752 228 181
web: www.hmv.co.uk

HMV
111-113 High Street, Cheltenham, Gloucestershire, GL50 1DW
tel: 01242 230 930
web: www.hmv.co.uk

HMV
18-20 Kings Walk, Gloucester, Gloucestershire, GL1 1RW
tel: 01452 302 231
web: www.hmv.co.uk

HMV
Unit 114, The Mall, Cribbs Causeway, Bristol, Avon, BS34 5UP
tel: 0117 950 6581
web: www.hmv.co.uk

HMV
191 High Street, Exeter, Devon, EX4 3DU
tel: 01392 420 190
web: www.hmv.co.uk

HMV
Unit 73-75, Dolphin Centre, Poole, Dorset, BH15 1SY
tel: 01202 674 812
web: www.hmv.co.uk

HMV
16-17 Regent Street, Swindon, Wiltshire, SN1 1JQ
tel: 01793 420 963
web: www.hmv.co.uk

HMV
Unit C, Lemon Quay, Truro, Cornwall, TR1 2LW
tel: 01872 266 020
web: www.hmv.co.uk

HMV
13-15 Stall Street, Bath, Avon, BA1 1QE
tel: 01225 466 681
web: www.hmv.co.uk

HMV
62 High Street, Newport, Isle of Wight, PO30 1BA
tel: 01983 522 533
web: www.hmv.co.uk

HMV
56 -58 Above Bar Street, Southampton, SO14 7DS
tel: 02380 338 398
web: www.hmv.co.uk

In A Spin Records
Bridgwater Indoor Shopping Centre, 47-55 Eastover, Bridgwater,
Somerset, TA6 5AW
tel: 07952 248 501
rack space: Limited
flyer space: Limited
poster space: Limited
listening posts: Limited
info: Mainly second hand stock. Wide range of genres.
Will stock unsigned material on a sale-or-return basis.

John Oliver
33 Fore Street, Redruth, Cornwall, TR15 2AE
tel: 01209 216 494
rack space: No
flyer space: Yes
poster space: Yes
listening posts: No
info: John Elivers specialise in a wide range of Jazz
music.

Kane's Records
14 Kendrick Street, Stroud, Gloucestershire, GL5 1AA
tel: 01453 766886
email: sales@kanesrecords.com
web: www.kanesrecords.com
contact: Kane
rack space: Yes
flyer space: Yes
poster space: Yes
listening posts: Yes
info: Caters for all musical tastes from Folk to Indie.
Kane's Records are willing to support local bands.

Kays Discs & Tapes
7 High Street, Keysham, Bristol, Avon, BS31 1DP
tel: 0117 986 0996
rack space: Yes
flyer space: Yes
poster space: Yes
listening posts: No
info: Wide range of genres available. Will stock
unsigned material on a sale-or-return basis.

Knee's of Trowbridge
27 Fore Street, Trowbridge, Wiltshire, BA14 8BJ
tel: 01225 754 161
rack space: No
flyer space: Limited
poster space: Limited
listening posts: No
info: Sell a wide range of music.

Martain Records
222 High Street, Cheltenham, Gloucestershire, GK50 3HF
tel: 01242 518 840
contact: ian
rack space: Limited
flyer space: No
poster space: No
listening posts: No
info: Mainly stock Rock, Pop and Metal music. Some
second hand CDs available. Reasonable prices.

Millenium Music
16-18 The Arcade, Fore Street, Okehampton, Devon, EX20 1EX
tel: 01837 659 249
email: milleniummusic@btopenworld.com
web: www.millenium-music.net
rack space: Yes
flyer space: Limited
poster space: Limited
listening posts: No
info: Sell a wide range of genres and will stock
unsigned material.

Music & Video Exchange
139 Cornwall Street, Plymouth, PL1 1PA
tel: 01752 673 367
rack space: No
flyer space: Limited
poster space: Limited
listening posts: No
info: Music & Video Exchange stock second hand material from all genres.

Music & Video Exchange
11A La Motte St, St. Helier, Jersey, JE2 4SY
tel: 01534 736 606
rack space: Yes
flyer space: Yes
poster space: Yes
listening posts: Limited
info: General second hand musical paraphernalia store large range of records and CDs. Also a few instruments and some musical equipment. Very supportive of Jersey bands!

Music Box
7 Pemros Road, St. Budeaux, Plymouth, Devon, PL5 1LZ
tel: 01752 361 920
email: lerrynbry@aol.com
rack space: No
flyer space: Yes
poster space: Yes
listening posts: Yes
info: Sell a wide range of genres. Will order specialist CDs and Vinyl. Will stock unsigned material.

The Music Box
Unit 4, City Arcade, Fore Street, Exeter, Devon, EX4 3JE
tel: 01392 477 477
rack space: Yes
flyer space: Yes
poster space: Yes
listening posts: No
info: Specialise in Rock music but do stock other genres on CD and vinyl format. Also stock second hand vinyl, DVDs and Merchanise. Will stock unsigned material on a sale-or-return basis.

The Music Factory
115 High Street, Street, Somerset, BA16 0EY
tel: 01458 448 668
rack space: No
flyer space: Limited
poster space: Limited
listening posts: Limited
info: Stock a wide range of mainstream music.

Music Matters
11 Broad Street, Bath, Avon, BA1 5LJ
tel: 01225 427 494
web: www.musicmatters.btinternet.co.uk
rack space: Yes
flyer space: Yes
poster space: Yes
listening posts: No
info: Specialise in Jazz music. Will stock unsigned Jazz artists from the local area.

MVC
1 Seven Dials, 43 Monmouth Street, Bath, BA1 2AN
tel: 01225 311 206
web: www.mvc.co.uk

MVC
40-44 Kings Walk, Gloucester, Gloucestershire, GL1 1RX
tel: 01452 500 788
web: www.mvc.co.uk

MVC
Unit 2, Wharfside Shopping Centre, Market Jew Street, Penzance, Cornwall, TR18 2GB
tel: 01736 364 587
web: www.mvc.co.uk

MVC
1 Paris Street, Exeter, Devon, EX1 2JB
tel: 01392 425 208
web: www.mvc.co.uk

MVC
52-56 Royal Parade, Plymouth, Devon, PL1 1DZ
tel: 01752 251 576
web: www.mvc.co.uk

MVC
32 Kingland Crescent, Poole, Dorset, BH15 1TB
tel: 01202 687 358
web: www.mvc.co.uk

MVC
Unit 6, 1-12 New Bond Street, Weymouth, Dorset, DT4 8LY
tel: 01305 783 730
web: www.mvc.co.uk

MVC
Unit 12-13, Crosskey Centre, Salisbury, Wiltshire, SP1 1EY
tel: 01722 324 358
web: www.mvc.co.uk

MVC
15 East Street, Taunton, Somerset, TA1 3LP
tel: 01823 321 308
web: www.mvc.co.uk

Nasher's Music Store
72 Walcot Street, Bath, Avon, BA1 5BD
tel: 01225 332 298
email: nasher@nashers.demon.co.uk
web: www.nashers.demon.co.uk
rack space: Yes
flyer space: Yes
poster space: Yes
listening posts: Yes

Needle To The Groove
11 Frankfort Gate, Plymouth, Devon, PL1 1QA
tel: 01752 294 104
email: tunes@nttg.co.uk
web: www.needletothegroove.co.uk
rack space: Yes
flyer space: Yes
poster space: Yes
listening posts: Yes
info: Needle to the Groove specialise in House music.

Number Nineteen
19 The Pollett, Guernsey, Channel Islands, GY11 WH
tel: 01481 722 056
fax: 01481 722 056
email: info@numbernineteen.com
web: www.numbernineteen.com
rack space: Limited
flyer space: Limited
poster space: Limited
listening posts: No
info: Stockists of all types of music. Will sell material from local unsigned bands.

Number One Records
11 Old Bridge Street, Truro, Cornwall, TR1 2UX
tel: 01872 223 412
rack space: Yes
flyer space: Yes
poster space: Yes
listening posts: No
info: Vinyl specialists of most genres of music. Will stock unsigned material on a sale-or-return basis.

Onionheart
Unit 2, Staples Mews, Exeter Road, Exmouth, Devon, EX8 1PL
tel: 01395 223 435
email: michaelharvey100@hotmail.com
rack space: Yes
flyer space: Yes
poster space: Yes
listening posts: No
info: Onionheart are willing to sell unsigned material. The band or artist will receive the full amount of the price charged, and can therefore can select the price they want to sell the music at.

Opus
14a Guildhall Shopping Centre, Exeter, Devon, EX4 3HW
tel: 01392 214 044
email: enquiries@opus-classical.com
web: www.opus-classical.com
flyer space: Yes
poster space: Yes
listening posts: Limited
info: Opus is a Classical music shop but will put up posters and flyers of local music events.

R.P.M. Records
Unit 3a, Old Vicarage Place, St. Austell, Cornwall, PL25 5YY
tel: 01726 717 22
rack space: Yes
flyer space: Yes
poster space: Yes
listening posts: Yes
info: R.P.M. specialise in Rock, Punk and Metal but do stock all types of general releases.

MUSIC SERVICES/RETAIL

Raves From The Grave
2 Cheap Street, Frome, Somerset, BA11 1BN
tel: 01373 464 666
email: raves@tiscali.co.uk
web: www.ravesfromthegrave.co.uk
rack space: Yes
flyer space: Yes
poster space: Yes
listening posts: Yes
info: Stock most genres of music on CD, DVD, vinyl
and cassette. Speak to the manager about stocking unsigned material.

Refresh Records
Unit 9/10, Market Hall, Market Street, Swindon, Wiltshire, SN1 1RZ
tel: 01793 422 828
email: refresh@refresh.plus.com
web: www.refreshrecords.co.uk
rack space: Yes
flyer space: Yes
poster space: Yes
listening posts: Yes
info: Have a large selection of second hand CDs and
vinyl. Has space for posters and flyers in-store. Speak to the manager
with regard to stocking unsigned material.

Replay (Bath)
27 Broad Street, Bath, Avon, BA1 5LW
tel: 01225 404 060
fax: 01225 404 070
email: bath@replay.co.uk
web: www.replay.co.uk
contact: Ben
rack space: Yes
flyer space: Yes
poster space: Yes
listening posts: Yes
info: Willing to Stock records by Unsigned acts. Replay
is a small independent chain that stocks most genres. Also sells gig
tickets for the local area. See lstings for stores based in Bristol.

Replay (Bristol)
134 East Street, Bristol, BS3 4ET
tel: 0117 330 6393
fax: 0117 908 3410
email: eastst@replay.co.uk
web: www.replay.co.uk
contact: Hugo
rack space: Yes
flyer space: Yes
poster space: Yes
listening posts: Yes
info: Willing to stock records by unsigned acts. Replay
is a small independent chain. See listing for store based in Bath.

Replay (Bristol)
73 Park Street, Bristol, Avon, BS1 5PF
tel: 0117 904 1134
email: parkst@replay.co.uk
web: www.replay.co.uk
rack space: Yes
flyer space: Yes
poster space: Yes
listening posts: Yes
info: Will stock anything from local bands and artists
on a sale-or-return basis. Replay is a small independent chain of stores.
See listings for another store in Bristol and one for Bath.

Rhythms
538 Christchurch Road, Boscombe, Bournemouth, Dorset, BH1 4BE
tel: 01202 302 018
rack space: Limited
flyer space: No
poster space: No
listening posts: No
info: The shop is small and only deals in second hand
material.

RMD Coleford
17a St. John Street, Coleford, Gloucestershire, GL16 8AP
tel: 01594 837 433
email: meanprice@btinternet.com
web: www.meanprice.co.uk
rack space: Yes
flyer space: Limited
poster space: Limited
listening posts: No
info: Stock a wide range of musical genres on CD, DVD
and vinyl. Will stock unsigned material on a sale-or-return basis.

The Rock Shop
63-65 St. Nicholas' Market, Corn Street, Bristol, Avon, BS1 1LJ
tel: 0117 927 7300
rack space: Yes
flyer space: Yes
poster space: Yes
listening posts: Yes
info: The Rock Shop stock all types of Rock, Metal and
Indie music.

Rooster Records
42 East Street, Taunton, Somerset, TA1 3LS
tel: 01823 327 701
email: musicera@roosterrecords.wanadoo.co.uk
rack space: Limited
flyer space: Yes
poster space: Yes
listening posts: No
info: Have a wide range of material available in-store.
Will display unsigned demos on a sale-or-return basis. No listening
posts, but can listen to anything on the in-store system.

Rooted Records
9 Gloucester Road, Bristol, Avon, BS7 8AA
tel: 0117 907 4372
email: rootedrecords@aol.com
rack space: Yes
flyer space: Limited
poster space: Yes
listening posts: Yes
info: Stock mostly vinyl. Specialise in Reggae,
Drum&Bass, Hip-Hop, and Grime. 4 listening posts in-store. Will stock
unsigned material.

Roughneck Records
4 The Greebys, Paignton, Devon, TQ3 3DN
tel: 01803 529 457
rack space: Limited
flyer space: Limited
poster space: Limited
listening posts: No
info: Specialise in UK Hip-Hop, but do stock most
genres. Will stock local unsigned material on a sale-or-return basis.

Scene & Heard
49 Teign Street, Teignmouth, Devon, TQ14 8EA
tel: 01626 776 400
rack space: Limited
flyer space: Yes
poster space: Yes
listening posts: No
info: Mainly sell second hand stock of most genres.
Speak to the manager with regard to stocking unsigned material.

Seedee Jons
The Powerhouse, Queens Road, St. Helier, Jersey, JE2 3AP
tel: 01534 769 405
rack space: Yes
flyer space: Yes
poster space: Yes
listening posts: Yes
info: General music shop everything from Pop to
Rock. Big supporter of local bands and stock and sell lots of their CDs.
Official Apple retailer.

Snu-Peas
10 Ashley Road, Bournemouth, Dorset, BH1 4LQ
tel: 01202 303 309
email: snu.p@btinterbet.com
rack space: Yes
flyer space: Yes
poster space: Yes
listening posts: No
info: Mainly sell second hand stock of most genres of
music. Will stock unsigned material on a sale-or-return basis.

Solo Music Ltd. (Barnstaple)
61 High Street, Barnstaple, Devon, EX31 1JB
tel: 01271 325 274
email: barn@barn00.freeserve.co.uk
rack space: Yes
flyer space: Yes
poster space: Yes
listening posts: Yes
info: See lisiting for branch based in Truro. Also have
branch located in Exeter.

Solo Music Ltd. (Exeter)
22a Market Arcade, Guildhall Shopping Centre, Exeter, Devon, EX4 3HW
tel:	01392 496 564
rack space:	Yes
flyer space:	Yes
poster space:	Yes
listening posts:	Yes
info:	See listing for store based in Thuro. Also store located in Barnstaple.

Solo Music Ltd. (Truro)
21 Pydar Street, Truro, Cornwall, TR1 2AY
tel:	01872 223 327
rack space:	Yes
flyer space:	Yes
poster space:	Yes
listening posts:	Yes
info:	Stock all genres of music over two floors. Specialist floor for Jazz and Blues. Has four listening posts in-store. There is a section for local unsigned material and can also display posters and flyers. See listing for branches based in Barnstaple and Exeter.

Sound Travels
PO Box 800, Prestbury, Cheltenham, Gloucestershire, GL50 3NU
tel:	01242 571 659
email:	enquiries@soundtravels.co.uk
web:	www.soundtravels.co.uk
contact:	Jonothan Barnitt
rack space:	Limited
flyer space:	No
poster space:	No
listening posts:	No
info:	Specialises in relaxation and therapy music only.

Sounds Good
26 Clarence Street, Cheltenham, Gloucestershire, GL50 3NU
tel:	01242 234 604
email:	cds@soundsgoodonline.co.uk
web:	www.soundsgoodonline.co.uk
contact:	Mr John Ross
rack space:	Yes
flyer space:	Yes
poster space:	Yes
listening posts:	Yes
info:	Specialises in Classical, Folk and Jazz music.

Soundsville/Urban Solution
320 Gloucester Road, Horfield, Bristol, Avon, BS7 8TJ
tel:	0117 942 7791
rack space:	Yes
flyer space:	Yes
poster space:	Yes
listening posts:	No
info:	Urban music specialists. Will stock unsigned material on a sale-or-return basis.

Soundz
28 Fleet Street, Torquay, Devon, TQ1 1BB
tel:	01803 211 097
email:	gooeywong@yahoo.com
web:	www.soundz.co.uk
rack space:	Limited
flyer space:	Yes
poster space:	Yes
listening posts:	Yes
info:	Soundz specialise in Dance on vinyl.

Spin Central
43 Meadow Street, Weston-Super-Mare, North Somerset, BS23 1QH
tel:	01934 625 999
web:	www.spincentral.co.uk or www.q-bic.co.uk
rack space:	Yes
flyer space:	Yes
poster space:	Yes
listening posts:	Yes
info:	Spin Central specialise in Dance music. The Q Bic website is a Dance music events company run by Spin Central. 9 listening posts available in-store.

Teleskill Discs
Flat 3, Golden Lion, Market St, St. Peter Port, Guernsey, GY1 1HF
tel:	01481 736 363
rack space:	Yes
flyer space:	Yes
poster space:	Yes
listening posts:	No
info:	Sell most genres of music on CD and vinyl format. Will stock unsigned material on a sale-or-return basis.

Timelapse Records
102 Chelwood Drive, Bath, Avon, BA2 2PS
tel:	01225 835 888
email:	info@timelapse-records.co.uk
web:	www.timelapse-records.co.uk
rack space:	No
flyer space:	No
poster space:	No
listening posts:	No
info:	Mail order 'Progressive Rock' specialists.

Tor Records
2 Northload Street, Glastonbury, Somerset, BA6 9JJ
tel:	01458 834 836
rack space:	Yes
flyer space:	Yes
poster space:	Yes
listening posts:	Limited
info:	Deal in 2nd hand and new CDs, DVDs, videos and cassettes. Will stock unsigned material on a sale-or-return basis. Can listen to music on the in-store system.

Torre Records
240 Union Street, Torquay, Devon, TQ2 5QS
tel:	01803 291 506
email:	daveslocker2004@yahoo.co.uk
rack space:	Yes
flyer space:	Yes
poster space:	Yes
listening posts:	No

Trading Post
23 Nelson Street, Stroud, Gloucestershire, GL5 2HH
tel:	01453 759 116
rack space:	Yes
flyer space:	Yes
poster space:	Yes
listening posts:	Yes

Trading Post
23 Nelson Street, Stroud, Gloucestershire, GL5 2HH
tel:	01453 759 116
web:	www.the-tradingpost.co.uk
rack space:	Limited
flyer space:	Yes
poster space:	Yes
listening posts:	Yes
info:	Stocks all styles of music. Supports local unsigned artists. Trading Post also specialises in new and second hand vinyl.

True Reflections
25 High Street, Budleigh Salterton, Devon, EX9 6LD
tel:	01395 442 853
rack space:	No
flyer space:	No
poster space:	No
listening posts:	No
info:	True Reflections specialise in music for people with mature tastes.

Up Front Records
18 High Street, Barnstaple, Devon, EX31 1BG
tel:	01271 374 187
email:	info@upfront.eclipse.co.uk
rack space:	Yes
flyer space:	Yes
poster space:	Yes
listening posts:	Yes
info:	Deal mainly in CDs of most genres, but do a selection of vinyl. Also sell DVD and t-shirts. Have three listening posts in-store and will stock unsigned material.

Upbeat
Treveler, Belle Vue, Bude, Cornwall, EX23 8JL
tel:	01288 355 763
rack space:	Yes
flyer space:	Yes
poster space:	No
listening posts:	No
info:	Stock a wide range of genres from Metal to Jazz. Will display unsigned material on a sale-or-return basis.

Urban Solution
320 Gloucester Road, Horfield, Bristol, BS7 8TJ
tel:	0117 949 7758
email:	info@urbansolution.co.uk
web:	www.urbansolution.co.uk
rack space:	Yes
flyer space:	Yes
poster space:	Yes
listening posts:	Yes
info:	Specialise in Reggae, Hip-Hop, Soul and R&B. Also sell DVDs and clothing. Will stock unsigned material of a high standard. Please call the manager for more information.

Vinyl Vault
6 Cambray Place, Cheltenham, Gloucestershire, GL50 1JS
tel:	01242 227 454
email:	vinvault@aol.com
contact:	Phil Goode
rack space:	Limited
flyer space:	Limited
poster space:	Limited
listening posts:	No
info:	Mainly stock second hand vinyl, although some CDs available. Mostly 60s and 70s music. Vinyl Vault supports local musicians. Turntable in-store for people to use.

Virgin Megastore
174-186 High Street, Cheltenham, Gloucestershire, GL50 1EP
tel:	01242 222 123
web:	www.virginmegastores.co.uk

Virgin Megastore
Unit J, Castle Point, West Mall, Bournemouth, BH8 9UN
tel:	01202 547 696
web:	www.virginmegastores.co.uk

Virgin Megastore
28-30 Old George Mall, Salisbury, SP1 2AF
tel:	01722 415 452
web:	www.virginmegastores.co.uk

Virgin Megastore
Unit 7, Clarks Village, Farm Road, Street, BA16 0BB
tel:	01458 443 650
web:	www.virginmegastores.co.uk

Virgin Megastore
Unit 56, Great Western Outlet Centre, Swindon, SN2 2DZ
tel:	01793 644 110
web:	www.virginmegastores.co.uk

Virgin Megastore
Victoria House, 27a Fore Street, Taunton, TA1 1JQ
tel:	01823 365 726
web:	www.virginmegastores.co.uk

Virgin Megastore
88 Union Street, Torquay, TQ2 5PY
tel:	01803 211 765
web:	www.virginmegastores.co.uk

Virgin Megastore
Unit 7, Atlantic Village, Key Western Developments, Clovelly Road, Bideford, EX39 3QU
tel:	01237 479 436
web:	www.virginmegastores.co.uk

Virgin Megastore
The Galleries, Union Gallery, Broadmead, Bristol, BS1 3XD
tel:	0117 929 7798
web:	www.virginmegastores.co.uk

Virgin Megastore
Units LR 47-48, The Mall, Cribbs Causeway, Bristol, BS34 5GG
tel:	0117 950 9600
web:	www.virginmegastores.co.uk

Virgin Megastore
Unit 2, Odeon Development, 67b Above Bar, Southampton, SO14 7DZ
tel:	02380 330 380
web:	www.virginmegastores.co.uk

Virgin Megastore
7 Clarks Village, Street, Somerset, BA16 0BB
tel:	01458 443 650
web:	www.virginmegastores.com

Virgin Megastore
1-3 High Street, Exeter, Devon, EX4 3LF
tel:	01392 490 675
web:	www.virginmegastores.co.uk

Virgin Megastore
114-119 Brunel Centre, Swindon, Wiltshire, SN1 1LF
tel:	01793 526 762
web:	www.virginmegastores.co.uk

Virgin Megastore
140 Armada Way, Plymouth, Devon, PL1 1JB
tel:	01752 254 400
web:	www.virginmegastores.co.uk

West Quay Records
7 West Quay, Bridgewater, Somerset, TA6 3HL
tel:	01278 428 509
email:	adrianf@tvtopbox.net
rack space:	No
flyer space:	Yes
poster space:	Yes
listening posts:	No
info:	Second hand store dealing in CD, DVD, cassettes, videos and books. Can display posters and flyers, but no room for unsigned material.

White Label Records
4 Colomberie, St. Helier, Jersey, JE2 4QB
tel:	01534 725 256
email:	mal@whitelabelrecords.co.uk
web:	www.whitelabelrecords.co.uk
rack space:	Yes
flyer space:	Yes
poster space:	Yes
listening posts:	Yes
info:	Dance music specialists, supportive of local artists.

YORKSHIRE

Bernard Dean
10-12 S. Thomas Street, Scarborough, YO11 1DR
tel:	01723 372 573
email:	bernarddean@scarborough.co.uk
web:	www.musicatbernarddean.co.uk
rack space:	No
poster space:	Yes
info:	Would be willing to stock unsigned music.

Bradley's Records
42 Market Street, Halifax, West Yorkshire, HX1 1PB
tel:	01422 348 796
email:	danielgarside@hotmail.com
rack space:	Yes
flyer space:	Yes
poster space:	Yes
listening posts:	Yes
info:	Specialise in Rock, Metal and Punk music. Bradley's are prepared to stock unsigned demos, flyers and posters.

Calow Classics
721 Abbeydale Road, Sheffield, South Yorkshire, S7 2BE
tel:	0114 255 3440
email:	info@calowclassics.net
web:	www.calowclassics.net
rack space:	Limited
flyer space:	Yes
poster space:	Yes
listening posts:	No
info:	Predominantly stock Classical music and will stock unsigned demos of this genre.

Choonz Worldwide Records
100-102 Vicar Lane, Leeds, LS2 7NL
tel:	0113 244 9966
email:	sales@choonz.co.uk
web:	www.choonz.co.uk
contact:	Steve or Jim
rack space:	Yes
flyer space:	Yes
poster space:	Yes
listening posts:	Yes
info:	100% Dance music retailer. Stock unsigned material, mostly on a sale-or-return basis. Have space for posters and flyer.

Classical & Jazz
76 Micklegate, York, North Yorkshire, YO1 6LF
tel:	01904 625 482
web:	www.classicaljazz.net
rack space:	No
flyer space:	No
poster space:	No
listening posts:	Yes
info:	All stock is second hand material.

Coolwax Records
Unit 13, The Craft Centre, Orchard Square Shopping Centre, Sheffield, S1 2FB

tel:	0114 279 5878
fax:	0114 279 6144
email:	support@coolwax.co.uk
web:	www.coolwax.co.uk
contact:	Tom
rack space:	Yes
flyer space:	Yes
poster space:	Yes
listening posts:	No
info:	Specialises in Funky House, Trance, R&B and Drum&Bass. Willing to stock material from unsigned acts in these genres.

Crash Records
35 The Headrow, Leeds, LS1 6PU

tel:	0113 2436 743
email:	info@crashrecords.co.uk
web:	www.crashrecords.co.uk
contact:	Paul Hodgson
rack space:	Yes
flyer space:	Limited
poster space:	Limited
listening posts:	Yes
info:	Shop spans 2 floors covering genres from Indie, Punk and Hardcore to Hip-Hop, Drum&Bass and Jazz. Will stock unsigned music and offer support to local bands. Limited space for posters and flyers.

The Den
38 Cavendish Street, Keighley, West Yorkshire, BD21 3RG

tel:	01535 606 086
rack space:	No
flyer space:	No
poster space:	No
listening posts:	Yes
info:	The Den specialise in imported music.

Discovery Music Store
73 Westgate, Bradford, West Yorkshire, BD1 2RD

tel:	01274 304 207
rack space:	Yes
flyer space:	Yes
poster space:	Yes
listening posts:	No
info:	Stock all genres of music ranging from Metal to Classical. Will display unsigned demos of local artists on a sale-or-return basis.

Drum & Base Arena Records Store Ltd.
Unit 9, The Forum, 127-129 Devonshire Street, Sheffield, South Yorkshire, S3 7SB

tel:	0114 278 7776
email:	editorial@lists.breakbeat.co.uk
web:	www.breakbeat.co.uk
rack space:	No
flyer space:	Yes
poster space:	Yes
listening posts:	Yes
info:	Specialist Drum&Bass store. Can sell unsigned material via the website. Contact for more information.

Dyscworld Music
110 St. Thomas Street, Scarborough, North Yorkshire, YO11 1DU

tel:	01723 379 066
rack space:	No
flyer space:	Limited
poster space:	Limited
listening posts:	No
info:	Mainly stock second hand CDs and DVDs to suit most music tastes. Also sell related merchandise such as t-shirts and jewelery. Support local unsigned artists by stocking demos on a sale-or-return basis.

East Coast Music
12 Promemade, Bridlington, North Humberside, YO15 2PX

tel:	01262 409 437
contact:	Dylan
rack space:	Yes
flyer space:	Yes
poster space:	Yes
listening posts:	Yes
info:	Rack space for local unsigned acts. East Coast music sells a wide range of genres.

Ellison's
36 Bridlington Street, Hunmanby, Filey, North Yorkshire, YO14 0JR
tel: 01723 890 402
email: jonathan.ellison@btconnect.com
contact: Jonathan
flyer space: Yes
poster space: Yes
listening posts: No
info: Mainly stock mainstream chart music and DVDs. Will display demos for unsigned bands.

Ethix
4-6 Regent Arcade, Grimsby, DN31 1JP
tel: 01472 358300
rack space: Yes
flyer space: Yes
poster space: Yes
listening posts: Yes
info: Dance and Electronica vinyl store. Very open minded and supportive of unsigned artists.

Fascinating Rhythms
5 The Shambles, Malton, North Yorkshire, YO17 7LZ
tel: 01653 695 229
rack space: Yes
flyer space: Yes
poster space: Yes
listening posts: No
info: Stock second hand records of all genres. Prepared to stock unsigned music. Contact for details.

Fopp
40-44 Division Street, Sheffield, S1 4GF
tel: 0114 279 9708
fax: 0114 276 5327
web: www.fopp.co.uk
contact: Russell
rack space: Limited
flyer space: No
poster space: No
listening posts: Yes
info: Fopp are involved in 'The Unsigned Network'. Unsigned material is accepted centrally and distributed to the stores and is placed in a specific 'Unsigned Section' which is promoted in-store. Material is only accepted in this way and you should refer to the 'Unsigned Network' link at the Fopp website to check whether they are accepting material at that time. Artists are paid a set amount on sales, on a sale-or-return basis.

Forever Changes
6 Hickmocc Road, Sheffield, S11 8QF
tel: 0114 267 9787
email: chrismabbs@btconnect.com
web: www.foreverchanges.gemm.com
contact: Chris Mabbs
rack space: Limited
flyer space: Yes
poster space: Yes
listening posts: Limited
info: Limited unsigned rack space. Space is available for posters and flyers in-store.

Fox Records & Videos
42 Sharrow Lane, Sheffield, S11 8A
tel: 0114 258 1472
fax: 0114 258 1472
contact: Mr Fox
rack space: Yes
flyer space: No
poster space: No
listening posts: No
info: Space to stock material by unsigned Soul & Reggae acts, but unfortunately no space for posters or flyers.

Go Records & CDs
30 Cottingham Road, Hull, North Humberside, HU6 7RA
tel: 01482 446 160
email: john@gorecords.co.uk
web: www.gorecords.co.uk
rack space: No
flyer space: Limited
poster space: Limited
listening posts: Limited
info: Specialise in Soul, Funk, Jazz, 60s, Progressive Rock and Jazz. Please contact with reference to stocking an unsigned demo.

Hall's Music
21 Pasture Road, Goole, East Yorkshire, DN14 6BP
tel: 01405 764 191
email: hallsmusic@btconnect.com
rack space: Yes
flyer space: Yes
poster space: Yes
listening posts: Yes
info: Hall's Music has rack space dedicated to unsigned artists. Sell most mainstream music.

Hellraiser
97 Kirkgate, Leeds, West Yorkshire, LS2 7DJ
tel: 0113 247 0800
web: www.hellraiserrecords.co.uk
rack space: Yes
flyer space: Yes
poster space: Yes
listening posts: No
info: Hellraiser will support local unsigned acts by placing material in and amongst the rack space provided. Specialists in Punk and Metal Music.

HMV
Unit 2, 18 Broadway, Bradford, West Yorkshire, BD1 1EY
tel: 01274 394 900
web: www.hmv.co.uk

HMV
Unit 26 Kingsgate Centre, King Street, Huddersfield, West Yorkshire, HD1 2QB
tel: 01484 440 820
web: www.hmv.co.uk

HMV
34 High Street, Meadowhall Centre, Sheffield, South Yorkshire, S9 1EN
tel: 0114 256 8138
web: www.hmv.co.uk

HMV
2 Kirkgate, Wakefield, West Yorkshire, WF1 1SP
tel: 01924 291 281
web: www.hmv.co.uk

HMV
10 Frenchgate, Doncaster, South Yorkshire, DN1 1QQ
tel: 01302 340 484
web: www.hmv.co.uk

HMV
109 Westborough, Scarborough, North Yorkshire, YO11 1LD
tel: 01723 379 986
web: www.hmv.co.uk

HMV
51 Whitefriargate, Hull, North Humberside, HU1 2HT
tel: 01482 620 880
web: www.hmv.co.uk

HMV
5-7 Broadside, Barnsley, S70 1RQ
tel: 01226 323 640
web: www.hmv.co.uk

HMV
Unit 8, Birstall Retail Park, Holding Way, Batley, Leeds, WF17 9DT
tel: 01924 350 060
web: www.hmv.co.uk

HMV
10a Coney Street, York, YO1 1NA
tel: 01904 640 218
web: www.hmv.co.uk

HMV
Unit 1a, Monks Cross Shopping Park, York, YO32 9LF
tel: 01904 628 636
web: www.hmv.co.uk

HMV
1 Victoria Walk, Headrow Centre, Leeds, LS1 6DJ
tel: 0113 245 5548
web: www.hmv.co.uk

HMV
Unit SU015, White Rose Centre, Churwell Grange, Millshaw Road, Leeds, LS11 8EW
tel: 0113 277 7558
web: www.hmv.co.uk

HMV
14-18 High Street, Sheffield, S1 2GE
tel: 0114 263 4275
web: www.hmv.co.uk

HMV
Unit 2b, Retail World, Parkgate, Rotherham, S60 1TG
tel: 01709 780 068
web: www.hmv.co.uk

HMV
Unit LS U9 & U10, The Parishes, Jubilee Way, Scunthorpe, DN15 6RB
tel: 01724 747 640
web: www.hmv.co.uk

Jack's Records
Unit 1, Aberdeen Court, 95-97 Division Street, Sheffield, S1 4GE
tel: 0114 276 6356
email: sales@jacksrecords.idps.co.uk
web: www.jacksrecords.free-online.co.uk
rack space: Yes
flyer space: Yes
poster space: Yes
listening posts: No
info: Specialise in second hand music, mostly available on vinyl. Section dedicated to local bands, in-store. Everything available on sale-or-return basis. Jack's Records also acts as local ticket agent. No listening post, but will play tracks over in-store system upon request.

Jumbo Records
5-6 St. John's Centre, Leeds, LS2 8LQ
tel: 0113 245 5570
email: info@jumborecords.co.uk
web: www.jumborecords.co.uk
rack space: Yes
flyer space: Yes
poster space: Yes
listening posts: Yes
info: Specialises in Indie, Rock'n'Roll, Reggae, Jazz and Hip-Hop. Rack space available for unsigned acts.

Mix Music
22 Oxford Street, Harrogate, North Yorkshire, HG1 1PU
tel: 01423 528 900
fax: 01423 564 801
email: mmixmus@aol.com
contact: Mick Clayton
rack space: Yes
flyer space: Yes
poster space: Yes
listening posts: Yes
info: Wide range of stock covering most genres. Gladly support local and unsigned artists, space to publicise and stock unsigned stuff. No vinyl except 7". Space for posters and gig listings.

Movie Boulevard Ltd.
3 Cherry Tree Walk, Leeds, West Yorkshire, LS2 7EB
tel: 0113 242 2888
email: help@movieboulevard.co.uk
web: www.movieboulevard.co.uk
info: The shop specialises in movie soundtracks and music from films.

Mr Vinyl
16-18 Wharf Street, Sowerby Bridge, West Yorkshire, HX6 2AE
tel: 01422 835 919
rack space: Limited
flyer space: Yes
poster space: Yes
listening posts: Yes
info: Stock most genres of music on vinyl format. Would be prepared to display unsigned demos on CD format.

Music Zone
31 College Street, Rotherham, South Yorkshire, S65 1AG
tel: 01709 830 222
web: www.musiczone.co.uk

Music Zone
69 Briggate, Leeds, West Yorkshire, LS1 6LH
tel: 0113 245 4811
web: www.musiczone.co.uk

Music Zone
26-28 Baxtergate, Doncaster, DN1 1LD
tel: 01302 343 027
web: www.musiczone.co.uk

Music Zone
Unit 3, Nidderdale House, Cambridge Road, Harrogate, HG1 1NS
tel: 01423 564 895
web: www.musiczone.co.uk

Music Zone
Unit 36, Kingsgate Centre, Huddersfield, HD1 2QB
tel: 01484 425 537
web: www.musiczone.co.uk

Music Zone
19 Whitefriargate, Hull, HU1 2ER
tel: 01482 212 812
web: www.musiczone.co.uk

Music Zone
9 Cheapside, Barnsley, S70 1RQ
tel: 01226 786 141
web: www.musiczone.co.uk

Music Zone
72 The Moor, Sheffield, S1 4PA
tel: 0114 263 4410
web: www.musiczone.co.uk

MVC
8 Vicar Lane, Chesterfield, S40 1PY
tel: 01246 231 074
web: www.mvc.co.uk

MVC
19-20 Prospect Centre, Hull, North Humberside, HU2 8PN
tel: 01482 618 294
web: www.mvc.co.uk

MVC
Units 28-29, The Alhambra Shopping Centre, Barnsley, South Yorkshire, S70 1SB
tel: 01226 244 150
web: www.mvc.co.uk

MVC
43-44 Princess Alexandra Walk, The Piazza Centre, Huddersfield, West Yorkshire, HD1 2RS
tel: 01484 549 710
web: www.mvc.co.uk

NAS Music Centre
118 Abbydale Road, Sheffield, S7 1FF
tel: 0114 281 2976
fax: 0114 258 0950
contact: Mr Khan
rack space: No
flyer space: No
poster space: No
listening posts: No
info: Will only stock Indian music.

Out Of Step Records
100 Merrion Centre, Leeds, West Yorkshire, LS2 8PJ
tel: 0113 245 1730
email: shop@outofstep.co.uk
web: www.outofstep.co.uk
rack space: Yes
flyer space: Yes
poster space: Yes
listening posts: No
info: Specialist Punk Rock store. Stock CDs, DVDs and merchanise. Will display unsigned demos on a sale-or-return basis.

Play Music
Unit B7B, The Balcony, The Corn Exchange, Leeds, LS1 7BR
tel: 0113 243 2777
fax: 0113 242 6862
email: info@play-music.net
web: www.play-music.net
rack space: Yes
flyer space: Yes
poster space: Yes
listening posts: Yes
info: Stock a considerable amount of Dance white labels on a sale-or-return basis. Space for posters and flyers.12 listening posts available.

R.P.M.
2a Spark Street, Huddersfield, West Yorkshire, HD3 4XB
tel: 01484 643 392
web: www.rpm4music.com or www.rpm-promotions.com
rack space: No
flyer space: No
poster space: No
listening posts: No
info: RPM are a mail order company only. Orders can be made from either of the websites detailed above.

MUSIC SERVICES/RETAIL

Radar Records
20 Byram Arcade, Hudersfield, West Yorkshire, HD1 1ND
tel: 01484 426 767
email: p.sheeky@btopenworld.com
web: www.offtheradar.net
rack space: Yes
flyer space: Yes
poster space: Yes
listening posts: No
info: Mainly a second hand store that deals in most musical genres except mainstream Pop. Will stock demos from unsigned artists on a sale-or-return basis.

Rare & Racy
164-166 Devonshire Street, Sheffield, S3 7SG
tel: 0114 270 1916
fax: 0114 249 3324
email: shop@rareandracy.fsnet.co.uk
web: www.rareandracy.co.uk
contact: Joe
rack space: Yes
flyer space: Yes
poster space: Yes
listening posts: No
info: Will stock music from local unsigned bands and musicians. They have space for flyers and posters too.

Record Collector
233-235 Fulwood Road, Sheffield, S10 3BA
tel: 0114 266 8493
fax: 0114 267 1577
contact: Jeff
rack space: Yes
flyer space: Yes
poster space: Yes
listening posts: Yes
info: Rack space for unsigned music on a sale-or -return basis. Space for posters and flyers in-store.

Reflex Records
44 Union Street, Sheffield, S1 2JP
tel: 0114 275 9035
fax: 0114 273 1058
email: martin@reflex-records.co.uk
web: www.reflex-records.co.uk
contact: Martin
rack space: Yes
flyer space: Yes
poster space: Yes
listening posts: Yes
info: Unsigned rack space for Dance music genres. Space available for posters and flyers. Also stock DJ equipment.

Revo Records
26 Westgate, Halifax, West Yorkshire, HX1 1DJ
tel: 01422 345 789
rack space: No
flyer space: Yes
poster space: Yes
listening posts: No
info: Revo only stock second hand music. Some room available for flyers and posters.

Rhythm Nation
13 Copley Road, Doncaster, DN1 2PE
tel: 01302 326 752
rack space: Yes
flyer space: Yes
poster space: Yes
listening posts: Yes
info: Dance music specialist shop. Will stock unsigned artists.

Rhythm Nation Records
13 Copley Road, Doncaster, South Yorkshire, DN1 2PE
tel: 01302 326 752
fax: 01302 326 752
contact: Ian
rack space: Limited
flyer space: Yes
poster space: Yes
listening posts: Yes
info: Dance music specialists with rack space for unsigned material on vinyl only. Space available for posters and flyers. Facilities available to listen to music in-store before purchase.

Soul Alley
4-5 Grand Arcade, Leeds, West Yorkshire, LS1 6PG
tel: 0113 243 8231
email: sales@soulalley.co.uk
web: www.soulalley.co.uk
rack space: Yes
flyer space: Yes
poster space: Yes
listening posts: Yes
info: Broad ranging collection of music from Punk to Reggae through to Electronica.

Spin City Records
Unit 173, Lower Ground, Castle Market, Sheffield, S1 4GH
tel: 0114 276 2088
contact: Pauline Plaxton
rack space: Limited
flyer space: Yes
poster space: Yes
listening posts: No
info: Some unsigned rack space available. Can leave posters and flyers.

Studio Beatz
159 West Street, Sheffield, South Yorkshire, S1 4EW
tel: 0114 273 9107
email: info@studiobeatz.co.uk
web: www.studiobeatz.co.uk
rack space: Limited
flyer space: Yes
poster space: Yes
listening posts: Yes
info: Speed Garage and Funky House specialists.

That's Entertainment (Bradford)
203/4/5 John Street Market, Oastler Centre, Bradford, West Yorkshire, BD1 3ST
tel: 01274 731 237
rack space: No
flyer space: Yes
poster space: Yes
listening posts: No
info: See listing for store based in Huddersfield.

That's Entertainment (Huddersfield)
24 New Market Hall, Queensgate Market, Huddersfield, West Yorkshire, HD1 2UJ
tel: 01484 427 524
rack space: No
flyer space: Yes
poster space: Yes
listening posts: No
info: Sell a wide range of music on CD format. Also sell DVDs. Allow artists to display posters and flyers in-store. See listing for store based in Bradford.

Their Price
149-150 Castle Market, Sheffield, S1 2AJ
tel: 0114 272 1731
contact: Marie
rack space: No
flyer space: Yes
poster space: Yes
listening posts: No
info: Limited space available for posters and flyers. Thier Price stock a wide variety of genres.

Top Deck Tunes
Unit 45, Prince's Quay, Hull, HU1 2TD
tel: 014842 213146
email: topdecktunes@yahoo.com
web: www.topdecktunes.co.uk
rack space: Yes
flyer space: Yes
poster space: Yes
listening posts: Yes
info: Will stock demos. Specialist DJ equipment and a selection of vinyl available in-store.

Track Records (Doncaster)
23 Printing Office Street, Doncaster, DN1 1TJ
tel: 01302 344 494
fax: 01302 322 264
web: www.trackrecordsuk.com
contact: Steve Howe
rack space: Limited
flyer space: No
poster space: Yes
listening posts: Yes
info: Will consider stocking material from local unsigned artists, speak to Steve in-store. Stock most genres except Dance. Space for posters but not flyers. Also see listing for branch in York.

Track Records (York)
15 High Ousegate, York, North Yorkshire, YO1 8RZ
tel: 01904 629 022
fax: 01904 610 637
email: trackrecords@btinternet.com
web: www.trackrecordsuk.com
rack space: Yes
flyer space: Limited
poster space: Limited
listening posts: Yes
info: Will consider stocking material from local bands on a sale-or-return basis. Most music genres are covered. See listing for branch in Doncaster.

Tribe Records
7 Call Lane, Leeds, West Yorkshire, LS1 7DH
tel: 0113 242 0506
email: info@triberecords.co.uk
rack space: Yes
flyer space: Yes
poster space: Yes
listening posts: Limited
info: Dance music specialists, mainly on vinyl format. Speak to manager with regard to stocking unsigned material.

Virgin Megastore
15-17 Coney Street, York, North Yorkshire, YO1 9QL
tel: 01904 611 101
web: www.virginmegastores.co.uk

Virgin Megastore
Albion Arcade, Albion Street, Leeds, West Yorkshire, LS1 5ER
tel: 0113 243 8117
web: www.virginmegastores.co.uk

Virgin Megastore
61-63 New Street, Huddersfield, West Yorkshire, HD1 2BQ
tel: 01484 421 514
web: www.virginmegastores.co.uk

Virgin Megastore
Unit G7, Princess Quay, Kingston Upon Hull, Hull, Humberside, HU1 2PQ
tel: 01482 328 111
web: www.virginmegastores.co.uk

Virgin Megastore
Unit 172, Meadowhall Centre, Sheffield, S9 1EN
tel: 0114 256 8117
web: www.virginmegastores.co.uk
contact: Gayle, Rachel

Virgin Megastore
Unit 203, Yorkshire Designer Outlet, St. Nicholas' Avenue, Fulford, York, YO19 4TA
tel: 01904 633 010
web: www.virginmegastores.co.uk

Virgin Megastore
3 Orchard Square, Farate, S1 2FB
tel: 0114 273 1175
web: www.virginmegastores.co.uk

Virgin Megastore
1 Tyrrel Street, Bradford, BD1 1RU
tel: 01274 734 757
web: www.virginmegastores.co.uk

Virgin Megastore
Unit L10, Freeport Designer Outlet Centre, Carrwood Road, Glasshoughton, WF10 4SB
tel: 01977 551 533
web: www.virginmegastores.co.uk

Virgin Megastore
Unit R1, 35 Baxtergate Square, Freshney Place, Grimsby, DN31 1QL
tel: 01472 344 772
web: www.virginmegastores.co.uk

www.DVDhotbuys.com
91 Silcoates Lane, Wrenthorpe, Wakefield, West Yorkshire, WF2 0PA
tel: 07818 000 463
email: admin@dvdhotbuys.com
web: www.dvdhotbuys.com
info: DVD Hot Buys will soon be expanding into CD sales. If you would like you music listed on the website, please get in contact via the website or email address above.

NORTHERN IRELAND

Back Beat Records
121 Great Victoria Street, Belfast, County Antrim, BT2 7AH
tel: 028 9020 0397
fax: 028 9020 0398
email: info@backbeatrecords.co.uk
web: www.backbeatrecords.co.uk
rack space: Yes
flyer space: Yes
poster space: Yes
listening posts: Yes
info: Backbeat Records specialise in Hip-Hop, Funk and Soul. They have a large section for material from unsigned artists.

Bert McCormick
44 Main Street, Ballyclare, Antrim, BT39 9AA
tel: 02893 352 660
email: bert.mccormick@btconnect.com
contact: Bert McCormick
rack space: Limited
flyer space: No
poster space: No
listening posts: No
info: Specialises in American Country and Folk music. Limited rack space available for local acts only.

Caroline Music (Ballymena)
Unit 32, Tower Centre, Wellington Street, Ballymena, County Antrim, BT43 6AH
tel: 028 2564 6744
email: care@carolinemusic.com
web: www.carolinemusic.com
rack space: No
flyer space: No
poster space: No
listening posts: No
info: Stock a wide range of genres and will stock music by unsigned artists. Caroline Music has several branches throughout Northern Ireland. See listings for details.

Caroline Music (Belfast)
Unit 40, Park Centre, Donegall Road, Belfast, County Antrim, BT12 6HN
tel: 028 9043 8736
email: care@carolinemusic.com
web: www.carolinemusic.com
rack space: No
flyer space: No
poster space: No
listening posts: No
info: Stock a wide range of genres and will stock music by unsigned artists. Caroline Music has several branches throughout Northern Ireland. See listings for details.

Caroline Music (Enniskillen)
Unit 30, Erneside Shopping Centre, The Point, Enniskillen, County Fermanagh, BT74 6JQ
tel: 028 6632 3273
email: care@carolinemusic.com
web: www.carolinemusic.com
rack space: Limited
flyer space: Limited
poster space: Limited
listening posts: Limited
info: Stock a wide range of genres and will stock music by unsigned artists. Caroline Music has several branches throughout Northern Ireland. See listings for details.

Caroline Music (Lisburn)
6-10 Antrim Street, Lisburn, County Antrim, BT28 1AU
tel: 028 9266 4523
email: care@carolinemusic.com
web: www.carolinemusic.co.uk
rack space: No
flyer space: No
poster space: No
listening posts: No
info: Stock a wide range of genres and will stock music by unsigned artists. Caroline Music has several branches throughout Northern Ireland. See listings for details.

Caroline Music (Newry)

Unit 29 Buttercrane Shopping Centre, Buttercrane Quay, Newry, Couty Down, BT35 8HJ

tel:	028 3025 2986
email:	care@carolinemusic.com
web:	www.carolinemusic.com
rack space:	Yes
flyer space:	Yes
poster space:	Yes
listening posts:	No
info:	Stock a wide range of genres and will stock music by unsigned artists. Caroline Music has several branches throughout Northern Ireland. See listings for details.

CD Times

9a Francis Street, Newry, County Down, BT35 8BQ

tel:	028 3026 5591
rack space:	Yes
flyer space:	Yes
poster space:	Yes
listening posts:	Yes
info:	CD Times sells all kinds of music and will stock material from local unsigned bands.

Clublife Records

26 Rathfriland Street, Banbridge, County Down, BT32 3LA

tel:	028 4062 3223
rack space:	Yes
flyer space:	Yes
poster space:	Yes
listening posts:	Yes
info:	Clublife Records specialise in Dance music and often stocks CDs by relevant unsigned artists.

Discs

5 Woodhouse Street, Portadown, Craigavon, County Armagh, BT62 1JG

tel:	028 3839 1144
rack space:	Yes
flyer space:	Yes
poster space:	Yes
listening posts:	Yes

Energy 106 Store Ltd.

63 High Street, Belfast, County Antrim, BT1 2AB

tel:	028 9033 3122
email:	lj@energy106.com
rack space:	No
flyer space:	No
poster space:	No
listening posts:	No

Evans Musical

53 Bridge Street, Lisburn, Antrim, BT28 1XZ

tel:	028 9266 2011
rack space:	Yes
flyer space:	Yes
poster space:	Yes
listening posts:	Yes
info:	Evans Musical stocks all genres of music and also offers a hire facility for both instruments and disco equipment.

Final Junki

11 Magazine Street, Londonderry, County Londonderry, BT48 6HH

tel:	028 7130 9077
rack space:	No
flyer space:	Yes
poster space:	Yes
listening posts:	Yes

Gene Stuart

9 Irish Street, Dungannon, County Tyrone, BT70 1DB

tel:	028 8772 5286
email:	genestuart@btconnect.com
rack space:	Yes
flyer space:	Yes
poster space:	Yes
listening posts:	No
info:	Stock most mainstream genres. Will stock unsigned demos on a sale-or-return basis.

Graham's Record Shop

5 Circular Road, Coleraine, County Londonderry, BT52 1PS

tel:	028 7032 9761
rack space:	Yes
flyer space:	No
poster space:	No
listening posts:	Yes
info:	Sells most genres of music.

Gramophone Shop

16 Donegal Square North, Belfast, County Antrim, BT1 5GB

tel:	028 9043 8453
rack space:	No
flyer space:	No
poster space:	No
listening posts:	Yes
info:	Stock all genres of music. Cannot stock demos.

Hector's House

5 North Street, Belfast, Country Antrim, BT1 1NA

tel:	028 9023 4040
fax:	028 9023 4040
email:	hectorshouse@ntlworld.com
rack space:	Yes
flyer space:	Limited
poster space:	Limited
listening posts:	No
info:	Hector's House stocks all types of music. Also sell CDs by unsigned artists free of charge

HMV

Unit 40, Fairhill Shopping Centre, Bellymena, County Antrim, BT43 6UF

tel:	028 2563 8272
web:	www.hmv.co.uk

HMV

B31-B35, Bow Street Mall, Lisburn, County Antrim, BT28 1AW

tel:	028 9263 5360
web:	www.hmv.co.uk

HMV

Unit 35, The Quays Shopping Centre, Newry, County Down, BT35 8QS

tel:	028 3025 3690
web:	www.hmv.co.uk

HMV

Unit 6 Level 3, Richmond Shopping Centre, Derry, County Londonderry, BT48 6PE

tel:	028 7127 8960
web:	www.hmv.co.uk

HMV

Units 3-6, Donegall Arcade, Castle Place, Belfast, County Antrim, BT1 1PT

tel:	028 9023 8494
web:	www.hmv.co.uk

HMV

Unit J, Rushmere Shopping Centre, Central Way, Craigvon, County Armagh, BT64 1AA

tel:	028 3831 4910
web:	www.hmv.co.uk

HMV

25-27 Main Street, Bangor, County Down, BT20 6AU

tel:	028 9147 5700
web:	www.hmv.co.uk

HMV

Unit 22, The Diamond Centre, Coleraine, County Londonderry, BT52 1DT

tel:	028 7034 5950
web:	www.hmv.co.uk

HMV

Unit 11, Forestside Shopping Centre, Newtonbreda, Belfast, County Antrim, BT8 6FX

tel:	028 9064 4770
web:	www.hmv.co.uk

Island Discs

3 The Diamond, Enniskillen, County Fermanagh, BT74 7EQ

tel:	028 6632 4882
email:	info@islanddiscs.com
web:	www.islanddiscs.com
rack space:	Yes
flyer space:	Limited
poster space:	Limited
listening posts:	No
info:	Stock most genres of music. Will stock unsigned material on a sale-or-return basis.

Jingles

6 Market Street, Limavady, County Londonderry, BT49 0AA

tel:	028 7776 3973
rack space:	No
flyer space:	No
poster space:	No
listening posts:	No
info:	Sell most mainstream genres of music.

Kragtrak Records
1 West Street, Carrickfergus, County Antrim, BT38 7AR
tel:	028 9336 6377
fax:	028 9336 6377
rack space:	Yes
flyer space:	Yes
poster space:	Yes
listening posts:	No
info:	Stocks all genres of music.

Mega Music
323 Mountjoy Road, Stewartstown, Dungannon, County Armagh, BT71 5LJ
tel:	07749 677 855
email:	sales@megacountrymusic.com
web:	www.megacountrymusic.com
info:	Mega Music is a mail order company dealing in Country music.

Mixmaster Records
33 Queen Street, Belfast, County Antrim, BT1 6EA
tel:	028 9043 9159
web:	www.mixmasterecords.com
rack space:	No
flyer space:	Yes
poster space:	Yes
listening posts:	Yes
info:	The shop specialises in mostly Dance music.

Music & Video
6a Craigavon Shopping Centre, Craigavon, County Armagh, BT64 1AA
tel:	028 3834 5887
email:	music&video@btopenworld.com
rack space:	Yes
flyer space:	Yes
poster space:	Yes
listening posts:	Yes
info:	Music & Video stock a little bit of everything and are happy to accept material from local unsigned acts.

The Music Box
32 Church Street, Ballymoney, County Antrim, BT53 6DL
tel:	028 2766 2242
email:	musicbox@ballymoneyabelgratis.co.uk
rack space:	No
flyer space:	No
poster space:	No
listening posts:	No
info:	Stock all genres of music and are happy to stock unsigend material.

Music City
22 Lurgaboy Lane, Dungannon, County Tyrone, BT71 6JX
tel:	028 8775 0000
rack space:	No
flyer space:	Limited
poster space:	Limited
listening posts:	No
info:	Specialise in Irish and Country music. Would stock demos from local artists on a sale-or-return basis.

Music Master
4 Foundry Lane, Omagh, County Tyrone, BT34 2BN
tel:	028 8225 9225
rack space:	Yes
flyer space:	Yes
poster space:	Yes
listening posts:	No
info:	Music Master stock all genres of music.

The Music Shop
32 William Street, Cookstown, BT80 8NB
tel:	028 8676 2947
rack space:	No
flyer space:	Yes
poster space:	Yes
listening posts:	No
info:	General music shop with wide range of genres.

The Music Studio
30 North Street, Carrickfergus, Antrim, BT38 7AQ
tel:	028 9336 0827
rack space:	Yes
flyer space:	Yes
poster space:	Yes
listening posts:	No
info:	The Music Studio sells all genres of music and will stock local unsigned artists.

Music World
13 Frances Street, Newtownards, County Down, BT23 7DW
tel:	028 9182 8601
rack space:	No
flyer space:	Limited
poster space:	Limited
listening posts:	No
info:	Specialise in Rock and Country music. Cannot take demos due to space limitations.

Number One Records & Tapes
Unit 6, Murrayfield Shopping Centre, Larne, County Antrim, BT40 1HU
tel:	028 2826 0308
rack space:	No
flyer space:	Limited
poster space:	Limited
listening posts:	No
info:	Number One Records only stock chart material.

Premier Record Stores
3-5 Smithfield Square North, Belfast, County Antrim, BT1 1JE
tel:	028 9024 0896
web:	www.freeservepremier.co.uk
rack space:	Yes
flyer space:	Yes
poster space:	Yes
listening posts:	Yes
info:	Specialise in Irish music but stock most genres of music.

Sho'Nuff
40 Abbey Street, Bangor, County Down, BT20 4JA
tel:	028 9147 7926
email:	steve@shonuff.co.uk
web:	www.shonuff.co.uk
rack space:	Yes
flyer space:	Yes
poster space:	Yes
listening posts:	No
info:	Sho'Nuff specialises in Blues, Country, Folk, Jazz, Soul and Classic Rock, and has a large section dedicated to material by unsigned artists.

Smyth's Musique
4 Railway Street, Newcastle, Down, BT33 0AL
tel:	028 4372 2831
rack space:	No
flyer space:	Limited
poster space:	Limited
listening posts:	Yes
info:	Stock all genres of music. Buy, sell and exchange.

Sounds Good
4a Upper English Street, Armagh, BT61 7BH
tel:	028 3752 7031
rack space:	Limited
flyer space:	Yes
poster space:	Yes
listening posts:	No
info:	Sounds Good specialises in Country and Irish Folk music and occasionally stocks CDs for unsigned bands.

Sounds So Good
24 Upper Main Street, Strabane, Tyrone, BT82 8AS
tel:	028 7188 5858
fax:	028 7188 5858
rack space:	Yes
flyer space:	Yes
poster space:	Yes
listening posts:	Yes
info:	Sounds So Good also provides a hire service for instruments and equipment. Products from unsigned acts are sold but there is no specific rack section.

Still Sound
22A Waterloo Street, Londonderry, County Londonderry, BT48 6HE
tel:	028 7128 8890
rack space:	No
flyer space:	No
poster space:	No
listening posts:	No
info:	Stock most genres of music but specialise in Country and Traditional. Will take unsigned demos on a sale-or-return basis.

Top 40
1 Rainey Street, Magherafelt, County Londonderry, BT45 5DA
tel:	028 7963 3808
rack space:	No
flyer space:	No
poster space:	No
listening posts:	No
info:	Sell most genres of music. Need to speak to the manager with regard to stocking unsigned material.

MUSIC SERVICES/RETAIL

Trash
12 Waterloo Street, Londonderry, County Londonderry, BT48 6HE
tel: 028 7137 2124
email: trashderry@yahoo.com
rack space: No
flyer space: Limited
poster space: Limited
listening posts: No
info: Specialise in Rock and Classic music. Also sell DVDs, jewellery and merhandise. Speak to the manager with regard to stocking a demo.

Vinyl Nation
Unit 18b, Thomas Street, Ballymena, County Antrim, BT43 6AU
tel: 028 2563 2587
email: vinylshop@aol.com
rack space: Yes
flyer space: Yes
poster space: Yes
listening posts: Yes
info: Dance music specialists. Also sell t-shirts and record bags. Will stock unsigned material of this genre. No Trance please.

Virgin Megastore
Unit 2, Phase 5, Abbey Centre, Newton Abbey, BT37 9UH
tel: 028 9085 1936
web: www.virginmegastores.co.uk

Virgin Megastore
Unit M15, Foyleside Shopping Centre, 19 Orchard Street, Londonderry, County Londonderry, BT48 6XY
tel: 028 7137 1178
web: www.virginmegastores.co.uk

Virgin Megastore
Unit 1c, Castle Court, Royal Avenue, Belfast, County Antrim, BT1 1DD
tel: 028 9023 6623
web: www.virginmegastores.co.uk

Vital
9 Linehall Street, Banbridge, County Down, BT32 3EG
tel: 028 4066 9879
rack space: Limited
flyer space: Yes
poster space: Yes
listening posts: Limited
info: Vital is willing to stock some material from local unsigned artists, although limited space only.

SCOTLAND

1 Off Wax
PO Box 5139, Glasgow, G76 8WF
tel: 0141 585 7354
email: sales@1offwax.co.uk
web: www.1offwax.co.uk
info: Mail order only. See website for more details.

3rd Base
19-21 Chapel Street, Dunfermline, Fife, KY12 7AW
tel: 01383 722 554
rack space: No
flyer space: No
poster space: No
listening posts: No
info: Specialise in Rock and Metal music. Also stock DVDs and merchanise.

Avalanche
63 Cockburn Street, Edinburgh, Midlothian, EH1 1BS
tel: 0131 225 3939
rack space: Yes
flyer space: Limited
poster space: Limited
listening posts: No
info: Will stock unsigned material. Ask in-store for details.

Avalanche Records (Edinburgh)
17 West Nicolson Street, Edinburgh, Midlothian, EH8 9DA
tel: 0131 668 2374
web: www.avalancherecords.co.uk
rack space: Yes
flyer space: Yes
poster space: Yes
listening posts: No
info: Specialise in Indie, Punk and Metal. Will stock demos from unsigned local artists. See listing for store based in Glasgow.

Avalanche Records (Glasgow)
34 Dundas Street, Glasgow, G1 2AQ
tel: 0141 332 2099
web: www.avalancherecords.co.uk
rack space: Yes
flyer space: Yes
poster space: Yes
listening posts: Yes
info: Refer to listing for store based in Edinburgh. Will stock unsigned demos.

Backtrackmusic.co.uk
17 Brougham Street, Tollcross, Edinburgh, Midlothian, EH3 9JS
tel: 0131 228 4898
email: anything@backtrackmusic.co.uk
web: www.backtrackmusic.co.uk
rack space: No
flyer space: No
poster space: No
listening posts: Limited
info: Stock most genres of music. Generally do not stock unsigned demos but if there is something Backtrack really like, they will stock it.

Barnstorm
128 Queensberry Street, Dumfries, DG1 1BU
tel: 01387 267 894
rack space: Yes
flyer space: Yes
poster space: Yes
listening posts: Yes
info: Barnstorm stock all genres from Metal to Classical music. They often stock unsigned demos from local artists, on a sale-or-return basis.

Blue Note Music
24 Argyle Street, St. Andrews, Fife, KY16 9BU
tel: 01334 472 564
flyer space: Limited
poster space: No
listening posts: No

Bruce Millers
363 Union Street, Aberdeen, Aberdeenshire, AB11 6BN
tel: 01224 592 211
email: info@brucemillers.co.uk
web: www.brucemillers.co.uk
rack space: No
flyer space: Yes
poster space: Yes
listening posts: No
info: Stock a wide range of CDs, DVDs and Videos, as well a stocking Scottish related music. Generally do not stock unsigned demos.

C.D. Services
40-42 Brantwood Avenue, Dundee, Angus, DD3 6EW
tel: 01382 776 595
web: www.cd-services.com
rack space: No
flyer space: No
poster space: No
listening posts: No
info: CD Services are a mail order retailer. Do not to sell unsigned material.

Carbon Music
157 Buchanan Street, Glasgow, Lanarkshire, G1 2JX
tel: 0141 248 3737
email: info@carbonmusic.com
web: www.carbonmusic.com
rack space: Limited
flyer space: Limited
poster space: Limited
listening posts: Yes
info: Will stock material by local unsigned artists on a sale-or-return basis.

Cavern
13a Belmont Street, Aberdeen, Aberdeenshire, AB10 1JR
tel: 01224 625 005
email: cavern@btconnect.com
rack space: Limited
flyer space: Yes
poster space: Yes
listening posts: Yes
info: Cavern are vinyl specialists dealing in most genres. Will stock unsigned material.

CD Music
9 Whytescauseway, Kirkaldy, Fife, KY1 1XF
tel: 01592 266 651
rack space: Yes
flyer space: Yes
poster space: Yes
listening posts: No
info: Specialise in Rock and Hip-Hop music. Also sell merchandise and DVDs within the store. Will stock unsigned material from local artists.

Classics In The City
54 Dundas Street, Glasgow, G1 2AQ
tel: 0141 353 6915
web: www.classicsinthecity.co.uk
rack space: Limited
flyer space: Yes
poster space: Yes
listening posts: Yes
info: The shop mainly stocks Classical music but will do what it can to help promote local unsigned acts from any genre.

CODA Music
12 Bank Street, Edinburgh, EH1 2LN
tel: 0131 622 7246
fax: 0131 622 7245
email: via website
web: www.codamusic.co.uk
rack space: Yes
flyer space: Yes
poster space: Yes
listening posts: Yes
info: Specialise in Folk and World music.

The Concorde Music Shop
15 Scott Street, Perth, Perthshire, PH1 5EJ
tel: 01738 638 828
email: info@concordemusic.co.uk
web: www.concordemusic.com
rack space: Yes
flyer space: Limited
poster space: Limited
listening posts: Yes
info: Stock all genres of music. Will accept demos from unsigned artists on a sale-or-return basis.

Correction Records
13 Correction Wynd, Aberdeen, Aberdeenshire, AB10 1HP
tel: 01224 636 362
email: sales@45rpm.co.uk
web: www.45rpm.co.uk
rack space: Limited
flyer space: Yes
poster space: Yes
listening posts: No
info: Dance music specialists. Will accept demos on a sale-or-return basis.

Crossroads
The Paisley Centre, High Street, Paisley, Renfrewshire, PA1 2AW
tel: 0141 848 5250
rack space: No
flyer space: Limited
poster space: Limited
listening posts: Limited

Folk Revolution
22 Clarendon Place, Glasgow, G20 7PZ
tel: 0141 353 1285
web: www.folkrevolution.co.uk
rack space: Limited
flyer space: Limited
poster space: Limited
listening posts: No
info: Specialsie in Folk music. For a demo to be stocked, call for more information.

Foot Stompin' Celtic Music
17 Redford Drive, Edinburgh, EH13 0BL
tel: 0131 441 3135
email: info@footstompin.com
web: www.footstompin.com
info: Foot Stompin' is a mail order only company that specialises in Celtic music.

Fopp (Aberdeen)
136-138 Union Street, Aberdeen, Aberdeenshire, AB10 1JD
tel: 01224 636 777
web: www.fopp.co.uk
info: Fopp are involved in 'The Unsigned Network' - unsigned material is accepted centrally, distributed to stores and is placed in a specific 'Unsigned Section' which is promoted in-store. Material is only accepted in this way and you should refer to the 'Unsigned Network' link on the Fopp website to check whether they are accepting material at that time. Artists are paid a set amount on sales, on a sale-or-return basis. Applications for unsigned space is not on-going and Fopp will sell unsigned material on a sale/demand/space policy. Fopp has stores throughout the UK.

Fopp (Dundee)
L10 Overgate Centre, Dundee, DD1 1UE
tel: 01382 227 075
web: www.fopp.co.uk
info: Fopp are involved in 'The Unsigned Network' - unsigned material is accepted centrally, distributed to stores and is placed in a specific 'Unsigned Section' which is promoted in-store. Material is only accepted in this way and you should refer to the 'Unsigned Network' link on the Fopp website to check whether they are accepting material at that time. Artists are paid a set amount on sales, on a sale-or-return basis. Applications for unsigned space is not on-going and Fopp will sell unsigned material on a sale/demand/space policy. Fopp has branches throughout the UK.

Fopp (Edinburgh)
55 Cockburn Street, Edinburgh, Midlothian, EH1 1BS
tel: 0131 220 0133
web: www.fopp.co.uk
info: Fopp are involved in 'The Unsigned Network' - unsigned material is accepted centrally, distributed to stores and is placed in a specific 'Unsigned Section' which is promoted in-store. Material is only accepted in this way and you should refer to the 'Unsigned Network' link on the Fopp website to check whether they are accepting material at that time. Artists are paid a set amount on sales, on a sale-or-return basis. Applications for unsigned space is not on-going and Fopp will sell unsigned material on a sale/demand/space policy. Fopp has stores located throughout the UK.

Fopp (Edinburgh)
7-15 Rose Street, Edinburgh, Midlothian, EH7 2PR
tel: 0131 220 0310
web: www.fopp.co.uk
info: Fopp are involved in 'The Unsigned Network' - unsigned material is accepted centrally, distributed to stores and is placed in a specific 'Unsigned Section' which is promoted in-store. Material is only accepted in this way and you should refer to the 'Unsigned Network' link on the Fopp website to check whether they are accepting material at that time. Artists are paid a set amount on sales, on a sale-or-return basis. Applications for unsigned space is not on-going and Fopp will sell unsigned material on a sale/demand/space policy. Fopp has stores throughout the UK.

Fopp (Glasgow)
358 Byres Road, Glasgow, Lanarkshire, G12 8AW
tel: 0141 357 0774
web: www.fopp.co.uk
info: Fopp are involved in 'The Unsigned Network' - unsigned material is accepted centrally, distributed to stores and is placed in a specific 'Unsigned Section' which is promoted in-store. Material is only accepted in this way and you should refer to the 'Unsigned Network' link on the Fopp website to check whether they are accepting material at that time. Artists are paid a set amount on sales, on a sale-or-return basis. Applications for unsigned space is not on-going and Fopp will sell unsigned material on a sale/demand/space policy. Fopp has stores throughout the UK.

Fopp (Glasgow)
19 Union Street, Glasgow, G1 3RB
tel: 0141 222 2128
web: www.fopp.co.uk
info: Fopp are involved in 'The Unsigned Network' - unsigned material is accepted centrally, distributed to stores and is placed in a specific 'Unsigned Section' which is promoted in-store. Material is only accepted in this way and you should refer to the 'Unsigned Network' link on the Fopp website to check whether they are accepting material at that time. Artists are paid a set amount on sales, on a sale-or-return basis. Applications for unsigned space is not on-going and Fopp will sell unsigned material on a sale/demand/space policy. Fopp have brances throughout the UK.

Forge Music Exchange
Forge Shopping Centre, Gallowgate, Glasgow, G31 4EB
tel: 0141 554 0684
rack space: Limited
flyer space: Limited
poster space: Limited

MUSIC SERVICES/RETAIL

Gee CD's
5 Home Street, Edinburgh, Midlothian, EH3 9JR
tel:	0131 228 2022
email:	geecds@tiscali.co.uk
web:	www.gee-cds.co.uk
rack space:	Yes
flyer space:	Yes
poster space:	Yes
listening posts:	Yes
info:	Will stock unsigned material on a sale-or-return basis.

Goldrush Records
9 Kinnoull Street, Perth, Perthshire, PH1 5EN
tel:	01738 629 730
email:	sales@goldrushrecords.demon.co.uk
web:	www.goldrushrecords.co.uk
rack space:	Yes
flyer space:	No
poster space:	No
listening posts:	Yes
info:	Goldrush Records stocks a variety of music styles. Will also stock material from local unsigned acts.

Grooves
17 Albert Street, Kirkwall, Orkney, KW15 1HP
tel:	01856 872 239
fax:	01856 875 585
contact:	Neil Stevenson
rack space:	No
flyer space:	Yes
poster space:	Yes
listening posts:	No
info:	Stock all genres of music. Do not accept unsigned demos but have poster and flyer space available.

Groucho's
132 Nethergate, Dundee, Angus, DD1 4ED
tel:	01382 228 496
rack space:	Yes
flyer space:	Yes
poster space:	Yes
listening posts:	No
info:	Will stock unsigned material on a sale-or-return basis.

HMV
71-77 Murraygate, Dundee, Angus, DD1 2EA
tel:	01382 225 383
web:	www.hmv.co.uk

HMV
32-33 Eastgate Shopping Centre, Inverness, Inverness-Shire, IV2 3PP
tel:	01463 250 961
web:	www.hmv.co.uk

HMV
Unit 2, Almondvale Centre, Almondvale South, Livingston, West Lothian, EH54 6NB
tel:	01506 448 830
web:	www.hmv.co.uk

HMV
154-160 Sauchiehall Street, Glasgow, Lanarkshire, G12 8RE
tel:	0141 332 6631
web:	www.hmv.co.uk

HMV
Unit 6, Fort Retail Park, Lawhouse Toll, Edinburgh, Midlothian, EH15 3RH
tel:	0131 454 4860
web:	www.hmv.co.uk

HMV
11-12 Union Bridge, Aberdeen, Aberdeenshire, AB11 6BE
tel:	01224 593 535
web:	www.hmv.co.uk

HMV
48 Braehead Shopping Centre, Kings Inch Road, Glasgow, Lanarkshire, G51 4BP
tel:	0141 885 9005
web:	www.hmv.co.uk

HMV
Units Lr15a & Urs4, Centre West, East Kilbride, G74 1LL
tel:	0141 331 550
web:	www.hmv.co.uk

HMV
98/3 Ocean Terminal, Leith, Edinburgh, Midlothian, EH6 6JJ
tel:	0131 553 0210
web:	www.hmv.co.uk

HMV
83 Sylvania Way, Clydebank, Dunbartonshire, G81 2RR
tel:	0141 951 3370
web:	www.hmv.co.uk

HMV
Unit 5, Howgate Shopping Centre, High Street, Falkirk, Stirlingshire, FK1 1HG
tel:	01324 676 990
web:	www.hmv.co.uk

HMV
Unit 29-30, Thistle Centre, Stirling, FK8 2EE
tel:	01786 460 640
web:	www.hmv.co.uk

HMV
Unit 7, St John's Shopping Centre, Perth, PH1 5UB
tel:	01738 494 990
web:	www.hmv.co.uk

HMV
c/o Unit 5-6, Lewis's Building, Argyle Street, Glasgow, G2 8AD
tel:	0141 248 5396
web:	www.hmv.co.uk

HMV
129-130 Princes Street, Edinburgh, EH2 4AH
tel:	0131 225 7008
web:	www.hmv.co.uk

HMV
43-44 St. Jame's Centre, Edinburgh, EH1 3SL
tel:	0131 556 1236
web:	www.hmv.co.uk

Hog's Head
62 South Clerk Street, Edinburgh, Midlothian, EH8 9PS
tel:	0131 667 5274
email:	hogsheid@clara.co.uk
web:	www.hogs-head.com
flyer space:	Yes
poster space:	Yes
listening posts:	Yes
info:	Will stock unsigned material. Wil also advertise gigs and sell tickets at the shop for no extra charge.

Inverurie Music Centre
9 Market Place, Inverurie, Aberdeenshire, AB51 3PU
tel:	01467 624 415
rack space:	No
flyer space:	Yes
poster space:	Yes
listening posts:	Yes
info:	Specialise in all Scottish, Country and Irish music.

JMF Records
86 High Street, Invergordon, Ross-Shire, IV18 0DL
tel:	01349 853 369
contact:	James
rack space:	Yes
flyer space:	Yes
poster space:	Yes
listening posts:	No
info:	Stock all genres of music. Will stock demos from local, unsigned artists on a sale-or-return basis.

Kozmic Lounge
9a Bank Street, Galashiels, TD1 1EN
tel:	01896 758 249
email:	mail@kozmic-lounge.co.uk
rack space:	No
flyer space:	Yes
poster space:	Yes
listening posts:	No
info:	Stock most genres of music with the exception of Opera and Classical. Also stock second hand material.

Lost Chord
11 Park Road, Glasgow, G4 9JD
tel:	0141 334 5528
rack space:	No
flyer space:	Limited
poster space:	Limited
listening posts:	No
info:	Second hand dealership with thousands of records available. The shop also deal in film and DVD.

McAlister Matheson Music
1 Grindly Street, Edinburgh, Midlothian, EH3 9AT
tel: 0131 228 3827
email: sales@mmmusic.co.uk
web: www.mmmusic.co.uk
rack space: No
flyer space: Limited
poster space: Limited
listening posts: Yes
info: Specialise in Classical music.

Missing Records
48 Oswald Street, Glasgow, G1 4PL
tel: 0141 248 1661
flyer space: Limited
poster space: Limited
listening posts: No
info: Second hand store stocking all genres of music. Do not display unsigned demos, but will take posters and flyers.

Monorail
Kings Court 12, King Street, Glasgow, G1 5RB
tel: 0141 552 9458
email: dep@monorailmusic.com
web: www.monorailmusic.com
rack space: Yes
flyer space: Yes
poster space: Yes
listening posts: No
info: Have a section within the store dedicated to unsigned artists. Monorail is a specialist store, stocking independent music. 60% of their stock is on vinyl format, including 60s, electronic, jazz, soul-funk and world music genres.

The Music Box
1-2 Meadow Place, Blairgowrie, Perthshire, PH10 6NQ
tel: 01250 875 424
web: www.musicscotland.co.uk
rack space: No
flyer space: Yes
poster space: Yes
listening posts: No
info: Specialist store that deals in Scottish, Irish and Country music. However, they do stock other genres of music. Also stock DVDs and Videos. In order to have an unsigned demo displayed, speak to the owner on the above number.

The Music Shop Ltd.
54 High Street, Wick, Caithness, KW1 4BS
tel: 01955 603 553
email: mail@wickmusicshop.co.uk
web: www.wickmusicshop.co.uk
rack space: No
flyer space: Yes
poster space: Yes
listening posts: No
info: Sells all genres of music. Will display unsigned demos on a sale-or-return basis.

Music Zone
Unit 29a, Forge Shopping Centre, Gallowgate, Glasgow, Lanarkshire, G31 4EB
tel: 0141 554 6263
web: www.musiczone.co.uk

Music Zone
54 Sauciehall Street, Glasgow, Lanarkshire, G2 3AH
tel: 0141 353 6250
web: www.musiczone.co.uk

Music Zone
Unit 23, The Loreburn Shopping Centre, Dumfries, Dumfriesshire, DG1 2BD
tel: 01387 261 560
web: www.musiczone.co.uk

MVC
Unit 3a, Inverness Business & Retail Park, West Seafield, Inverness, IV2 7GD
tel: 01463 729 231
web: www.mvc.co.uk

MVC
43-45 Unicorn Way, The Kingdom Centre, Glenrothes, Fife, KY7 5NU
tel: 01592 619 680
web: www.mvc.co.uk

MVC
27 St. John's Centre, Perth, Perthshire, PH1 5UX
tel: 01738 451 714
web: www.mvc.co.uk

One Up Records
17 Belmont Street, Aberdeen, Aberdeenshire, AB10 1JR
tel: 01224 642 662
rack space: Yes
flyer space: Yes
poster space: Yes
listening posts: Yes
info: Funk, Rock, Metal and Dub music over 2 floors. Also stock a large array of vinyl.

Oxfam Charity Shop
171 Byres Road, Glasgow, Lanarkshire, G12 8TN
tel: 0131 667 7669
rack space: No
flyer space: Limited
poster space: No
listening posts: No
info: You can leave flyers on the counter.

Oxfam Music Shop
64 Raeburn Place, Edinburgh, Midlothian, EH4 1HJ
tel: 0131 332 7593
web: www.oxfam.org.uk
rack space: Yes
flyer space: Yes
poster space: No
listening posts: Limited
info: Specialist charity music shop. Will stock unsigned material but all proceeds will go to Oxfam.

Planet Of Sound (Scotland) Ltd.
236 High Street, Ayr, Ayrshire, KA7 1RN
tel: 01292 265 913
email: planet-of-sound@btconnect.com
rack space: Limited
flyer space: No
poster space: No
listening posts: No
info: Stock all genres of music. Will accept unsigned demos of a high standard, on a sale-or-return basis.

The Record Factory
48 Causeyside Steet, Paisley, Renfrewshire, PA1 1YH
tel: 0141 887 6293
email: ebay@therecordfactory.co.uk
web: www.recordfactory.co.uk
rack space: No
flyer space: No
poster space: No
listening posts: Yes
info: Stock all genres of music from Metal to Classical. Also sell DVDs and posters. The Record Factory has stores on Ebay and Amazon. Will accept unsigned demos, on a sale-or-return basis.

Record Fayre
13-15 Chisholm Street, Glasgow, Lanarkshire, G1 5HA
tel: 0141 552 5696
rack space: No
flyer space: Yes
poster space: Yes
listening posts: No
info: Second hand store selling all genres of music. Will not stock unsigned demos but will display flyers and posters.

Record Market
3 Broomlands Street, Paisley, Renfrewshire, PA1 2LS
tel: 0141 887 8888
email: george@madastoast.com
web: www.madastoast.com
rack space: Limited
flyer space: Yes
poster space: Yes
listening posts: Yes
info: Buy, sell and exchange Rock, Pop and Dance music. Will display unsigned demos on a sale-or-return basis.

The Record, Tape & Compact Disc Exchange
918 Pollokshaws Road, Glasgow, Lanarkshire, G41 2ET
tel: 0141 636 6686
rack space: No
flyer space: Limited
poster space: Limited
listening posts: No
info: Deal in second hand stock of all genres. Do not accept unsigned demos.

The Records Rendezvous
14a Church Street, Inverness, Invernessshire, IV1 1EA
tel: 01463 231 219
email: sales@recordrendezvous.co.uk
web: www.recordrendezvous.co.uk
info: Specialise in traditional Scottish and Irish music on CD and cassette. Speak to the manager with regard to stocking unsigned material and displaying posters and flyers.

MUSIC SERVICES/RETAIL

Rhythmic
2 Hamilton Gate, Greenock, Renfrewshire, PA15 1JW
tel:	01475 892 736
email:	andy@rhythmicnet.co.uk
rack space:	Yes
flyer space:	Yes
poster space:	Yes
listening posts:	No
info:	Stock all genres of music. Accept local artists

music on a sale-or-return basis.

Ripping Music & Tickets
91 South Bridge, Edinburgh, EH1 1HN
tel:	0131 226 7010
email:	john@rippingrecords.com
web:	www.rippingrecords.com
rack space:	No
flyer space:	Yes
poster space:	Yes
listening posts:	No
info:	Unable to stock unsigned music but can sell gig

tickets for you. Ask in-store for details.

Rub A Dub Records
35 Howard Street, Glasgow, Lanarkshire, G1 4BA
tel:	0141 221 9657
email:	info@rubadub.co.uk
web:	www.rubadub.co.uk
rack space:	Limited
flyer space:	Limited
poster space:	Limited
listening posts:	No
info:	Specialse in Dance music. Will accept unsigned

demos on a sale-or-return basis.

Rukmuzik Mania
290 Great Western Road, Glasgow, G4 9EJ
tel:	0141 332 5600
email:	jivadu@hotmail.com
flyer space:	Yes
poster space:	Yes
listening posts:	No
info:	Rukmuzik specialise in Asian music.

Salvation Sounds
Shawlands Arcade, Glasgow, G41 3NN
tel:	0141 636 6467
rack space:	No
flyer space:	Yes
poster space:	Yes
listening posts:	Yes
info:	Stock most genres of music from Metal to

Country.

Sound & Vision
14-18 South Street, Elgin, Morayshire, IV30 1LE
tel:	01343 543 778
web:	www.elginmusicshop.com
rack space:	Yes
flyer space:	Yes
poster space:	Yes
listening posts:	Yes
info:	Stock music of all genres. Will display unsigned

demos on a sale-or-return basis.

Underground Solution
9 Cockburn Street, Edinburgh, Midlothian, EH1 1BP
tel:	0131 226 2242
email:	simon@earcandy.co.uk
rack space:	Yes
flyer space:	Yes
poster space:	Yes
listening posts:	Yes
info:	Underground deal in Dance music, mainly on

vinyl format. Keen supporters of unsigned material.

Unknown Pleasures
78 South Street, St Andrews, Fife, Scotland, KY16 9QD
tel:	01334 479 090
email:	sales.enquiry@vinylnet.co.uk
web:	www.vinylnet.co.uk
rack space:	Limited
flyer space:	Yes
poster space:	Yes
listening posts:	Yes
info:	Rare and collectable vinyl and CDs. Space in

foyer to display posters and flyers.

Urbanology
27 Batchen Street, Elgin, Morayshire, IV30 1BH
tel:	01343 552 191
email:	www.elginboardshop.com
web:	urbanology@btconnect.com
rack space:	Yes
flyer space:	Limited
poster space:	Limited
listening posts:	No
info:	Stock most genres of music. Speak to the

manager with reference to stocking unsigned material.

Vinyl Villians
5 Elm Row, Edinburgh, Midlothian, EH7 4AA
tel:	0131 558 1170
rack space:	Yes
flyer space:	Limited
poster space:	Limited
listening posts:	No
info:	Will stock unsigned material on a sale-or-return

basis.

Virgin Megastore
Unit 25, Sterling Mills Village, Moss Road, Tillicoultry, Clackmannanshire, FK13 6HN
tel:	01259 753 311
web:	www.virginmegastores.com

Virgin Megastore
18 Cameron Toll Shopping Centre 6, Lady Road, Edinburgh, Midlothian, EH16 5PB
tel:	0131 666 1072
web:	www.virginmegastores.com

Virgin Megastore
83 Argyle Street, Glasgow, Lanarkshire, G2 8BJ
tel:	0141 221 2606
web:	www.virginmegastores.com

Virgin Megastore
41 Gyle Avenue, South Gyle Broadway, Edinburgh, Midlothian, EH12 9JT
tel:	0131 317 1419
web:	www.virginmegastores.com

Virgin Megastore
Unit 32, Kingsgate Centre, Dunfermline, Fife, KY12 7QU
tel:	01383 738 786
web:	www.virginmegastores.com

Virgin Megastore
187-195 High Street, Ayr, Ayrshire, KA7 1QT
tel:	01292 610 200
web:	www.virginmegastores.com

Virgin Megastore
Unit LSU1, The Thistle Marches, Stirling, Stirlingshire, FK8 2EA
tel:	01786 479 500
web:	www.virginmegastores.com

Virgin Megastore
Unit 9, Almondvale Avenue, Livingston, West Lothian, EH54 6QX
tel:	01506 419 903
web:	www.virginmegastores.com

Virgin Megastore
125 Princess Street, Edinburgh, Midlothian, EH2 4AD
tel:	0131 220 2230
web:	www.virginmegastores.com

Virgin Megastore
82-84 High Street, Perth, Perthshire, PH1 5TH
tel:	01738 441 117
web:	www.virginmegastore.com

Virgin Megastore
74-78 High Street, Falkirk, Stirlingshire, FK1 1DD
tel:	01324 639 300
web:	www.virginmegastores.com

Virgin Megastore
133 Union Street, Aberdeen, AB11 6BH
tel:	01224 213 050
web:	www.virginmegastores.com

Virgin Megastore
Unit 23, Bon Accord Centre, Aberdeen, AB25 1HZ
tel:	01224 625 716
web:	www.virginmegastores.com

Virgin Megastore
Block 3, Unit 11, Auchlinea Retail Park, Glasgow Fort, G33 5AL
tel:	0141 771 8401
web:	www.virginmegastores.com

Virgin Megastore
235 Buchanan Street, Glasgow, G1 2NG
tel: 0141 353 2993
web: www.virginmegastores.com

West End Records
74 Sylvania Way, Clydebank, Dunbartonshire, G81 2TL
tel: 0141 941 0101
email: andy@westendrecords.fsnet.co.uk
rack space: Yes
flyer space: Yes
poster space: Yes
listening posts: No
info: Willing to stock unsigned material on a sale-or-return basis.

Whirlie Records
14 Broughton Place, Edinburgh, EH1 3RX
tel: 0131 557 9099
email: info@whirlierecords.co.uk
web: www.whirlierecords.co.uk
info: Mail order only specialising in traditional Scottish music.

WALES

Abergavenny Music
23 Cross Street, Abergavenny, NP7 5EW
tel: 01873 853 394
fax: 01873 859 547
email: mail@abergavennymusic.com
web: www.abergavennymusic.com
contact: James Joseph
rack space: No
flyer space: No
poster space: No
listening posts: No
info: Do not stock material from unsigned artists. Specialise mainly in Classical, Jazz and World music. Also stock sheet music for exams.

Andy's Records
4 Northgate Street, Aberystwyth, S23 2JS
tel: 01970 624 581
email: andy@andys-records.co.uk
web: www.andys-records.co.uk
rack space: Yes
flyer space: Yes
poster space: Yes
listening posts: Yes
info: Stock many genres of music but no chart CDs. Good range of independent Welsh music. No listening facilities for vinyl.

AW Jazz
26 Market Street, Haverfordwest, Dyfed, SA61 1NH
tel: 01437 769 618
email: enquires@awjazz.co.uk
web: www.awjazz.co.uk
rack space: No
flyer space: Yes
poster space: Yes
listening posts: No
info: Jazz and Blues specialist record shop.

Backbeat Records
6 Alexandra Road, Aberystwyth, Dyfed, SY16 2LS
tel: 01970 610 009
email: sales@backbeatnet.co.uk
rack space: Yes
flyer space: Yes
poster space: Yes
listening posts: Yes
info: CDs and vinyl. Mail order Service.

Cardigan Music
51 St. Mary Street, Cardigan, SA43 1HA
tel: 01239 614 220
rack space: Yes
flyer space: Yes
poster space: Yes
listening posts: Limited
info: Cardigan Music also sell a range of instruments and sound equipment. See listing in relevant section for details.

Catapult
22 High Street Arcade, Cardiff, CF10 2BB
tel: 02920 228 990
email: enquiries@catapult.co.uk
web: www.catapult.co.uk
rack space: Yes
flyer space: Limited
poster space: Limited
listening posts: Yes
info: Dance music specialists. Stock CD and vinyl. Rack space for demos, ask in-store for details. DJ and sound equipment sales.

Cob Records (Bangor)
320 High Street, Bangor, LL57 1YA
tel: 01248 353 020
web: www.cobrecords.com
rack space: Yes
flyer space: Yes
poster space: No
listening posts: Yes
info: New and second hand CDs and vinyl. Dedicated local bands section, demos are stocked on a sale-or-return basis. See listing for branch in Porthmadog.

Cob Records (Porthmadog)
1-3 Britannia Terrace, Porthmadog, LL49 9NA
tel: 01766 512 170
email: cob@cobrecords.com
web: www.cobrecords.com
rack space: Yes
flyer space: No
poster space: Yes
listening posts: Limited
info: Rack space for Welsh bands' demos. Titles bought and part exchanged. See listing for branch based in Bangor.

D' Vinyl Records
4 Mckintosh Place, Cardiff, South Glamorgan, CF25 4RQ
tel: 02920 494 998
rack space: Yes
flyer space: Yes
poster space: Yes
listening posts: Yes
info: Collectable 50s music to present day. A wide range of music genres. Available on CD, vinyl and DVD.

Dale's Music Store
High Street, Tenby, SA70 7HD
tel: 01834 842 285
rack space: Yes
flyer space: Limited
poster space: Limited
listening posts: Yes
info: Predominantly stock non-chart titles. Customer ordering service available. Also sell a range of musical instruments. See entry in relevant section for more details.

Derrick's Music
221 Oxford Street, Swansea, SA1 3BQ
tel: 01792 654 226
web: www.derricksmusic.co.uk
rack space: No
flyer space: Yes
poster space: Yes
listening posts: Yes
info: Derrick's Music is a Ticketmaster outlet.

Diverse Music
10 Charles Street, Newport, NP20 1JU
tel: 01633 259 661
email: sales@diversevinyl.com
web: www.diversevinyl.com
rack space: Yes
flyer space: Limited
poster space: Limited
listening posts: Yes
info: Local band section in-store for unsigned demos. Diverse Music specialise in vinyl LPs and run a large online store. Mojo Recommended Retailer and Chain With No Name member (www.cwnn.org).

Essential Records
12-14 Lord Street, Wrexham, LL11 1LG
tel: 01978 311 668
email: info@essential-dj.com
web: www.essential-dj.com
rack space: Yes
flyer space: Yes
poster space: Yes
listening posts: Yes
info: Dance music specialists. DJ equipment and PA sales and hire . See listing for Wrexham Music & Disco Supplies in relevant section.

Fopp
89 Queen Street, Cardiff, CF10 2BG
tel: 029 2037 4090
web: www.fopp.co.uk
info: Fopp are involved in 'The Unsigned Network' - unsigned material is accepted centrally, distributed to stores and is placed in a specific 'Unsigned Section' which is promoted in-store. Material is only accepted in this way and you should refer to the 'Unsigned Network' link on the Fopp website to check whether they are accepting material at that time. Artists are paid a set amount on sales, on a sale-or-return basis. Applications for unsigned space is not on-going and Fopp will sell unsigned material on a sale/demand/space policy.

Hancock and Monks
15 Broad Street, Hay-on-Wye, Wales, HR3 5DB
tel: 01497 821 784
email: jerry@hancockandmonks.co.uk
web: www.hancockandmonks.co.uk
contact: Jerry Monks
rack space: No
flyer space: No
poster space: No
listening posts: No
info: Classical music specialists. No rack space for unsigned bands.

HMV
Unit 9-10, Island Green Retail Park, Wrexham, LL13 7LW
tel: 01978 316 780
web: www.hmv.co.uk

HMV
Unit 4, 53-57 Queen Street, Cardiff, CF10 2AS
tel: 029 2022 7147
web: www.hmv.co.uk

HMV
Unit 4, Westgate Buildings, Commercial Street, Newport, NP20 1LJ
tel: 01633 255 924
web: www.hmv.co.uk

HMV
74 Mostyn Street, Llandudno, LL30 2SB
tel: 01492 863 010
web: www.hmv.co.uk

HMV
Unit 1, 18-20 St Mary's Square, Swansea, SA1 5HR
tel: 01792 476 345
web: www.hmv.co.uk

The Jungle
3 Nolton Street, Bridgend, CF31 1BX
tel: 01656 645 111
email: monkey@jungle-cds.com
web: www.jungle-cds.com
rack space: Yes
flyer space: Yes
poster space: Yes
listening posts: Yes
info: Call in and speak to a member of staff regarding having your demo stocked.

Kavern Records
25 High Street, Rhyl, LL18 1ET
tel: 01492 879 262
rack space: Yes
flyer space: Limited
poster space: Limited
listening posts: Limited
info: Will stock demos by local bands. Carry a range of genres including Chart and Classical, specialise in Rock and Pop back catalogue. See listing for store based in Llandudno.

Kavern Records & Videos
108 Moston Street, Llandudno, LL30 2SW
tel: 01492 879 262
fax: 01492 874 715
contact: Kevin Kripps
rack space: Yes
flyer space: Limited
poster space: Limited
listening posts: Yes
info: Will stock local unsigned band CDs on a sale-or-return basis. Speak to the manager, Kevin. Very limited poster and flyer space available. Also has a store based in Rhyl.

Kelly's Records
222-226 The Balcony, Central Market, St. Mary Street, Cardiff, CF10 2AU
tel: 02920 377 355
fax: 02920 377 355
email: enquiries@kellysrecords.com
web: www.kellysrecords.com
rack space: No
flyer space: Yes
poster space: Yes
listening posts: Yes
info: Mainly second hand, buy and part exchange available. Can shop online at the website above.

Moonlight Records
27 Bridge Street, Wrexham, LL11 1HF
tel: 01978 264 940
rack space: Limited
flyer space: Yes
poster space: Yes
listening posts: No
info: Buy and part-exchange available on CDs and DVDs.

Moonlight Records
27 Bridge Street, Wrexham, LL13 7YP
tel: 01978 361 756
contact: Brian Davis
rack space: Limited
flyer space: Yes
poster space: Yes
listening posts: No
info: Rack space is available occasionally for local unsigned bands, speak to Brian. There is also space for flyers and posters. The shop specialises in Rock and Pop on both vinyl and CD format.

More Music
42 St. Helen's Road, Swansea, SA1 4AZ
tel: 01792 652 042
email: sales@moremusic.co.uk
web: www.moremusic.co.uk
rack space: Yes
flyer space: Yes
poster space: Yes
listening posts: Yes
info: Second hand record shop.

More Vinyl
221 Oxford Street, Swansea, West Glamorgan, SA1 3BQ
tel: 01792 472 555
email: morevinyl@hotmail.co.uk
web: www.morevinyl.co.uk
rack space: Yes
flyer space: Yes
poster space: Yes
listening posts: Yes
info: Specialise in Dance, Dub and Funk. Stock local unsigned artists.

Morning After Music
22 Penrallt Street, Machynlleth, Powys, SY20 8AJ
tel: 01654 703 767
rack space: Yes
flyer space: Yes
poster space: Yes
listening posts: Yes
info: Will stock unsigned material on a sale-or-return basis. Stock a range of musical genres, but specialise in Blues and Jazz.

Musiquarium
Unit 61, Swansea Market, Swansea, SA1 3PQ
tel: 01792 465 256
web: www.themusiquarium.com
rack space: Yes
flyer space: Yes
poster space: Yes
listening posts: Limited
info: Specialise in Blues, Metal, Punk and AOR. Import and rarities ordering service.

MVC
Unit 4-5, Kingsway Shopping Centre, Sovereign Arcade, Newport, NP20 1ED
tel: 01633 216 403
web: www.mvc.co.uk

MVC
11 Henblas Street, Wrexham, LL13 8AE
tel: 01978 314 478
web: www.mvc.co.uk

MVC
29-31 The Hayes, Cardiff, CF10 2DU
tel: 02920 934 650
web: www.mvc.co.uk

MVC
Unit 2, Greyfriars, Carmarthen, SA31 3BN
tel: 01267 220 964
web: www.mvc.co.uk

MVC
Unit 30-32, The Mall, Cwmbran, NP44 1PX
tel: 01633 870 824
web: www.mvc.co.uk

Oner Records & Paint
4 Church Street, Cardiff, CF10 1BG
tel: 02920 396 989
email: info@onersigns.co.uk
web: www.onersigns.co.uk
rack space: Yes
flyer space: Yes
poster space: Yes
listening posts: Yes
info: Oner Signs & Leisure can also produce promotional merchandise for you band. See relevant section for more details.

Penny Post Classics
102 Priory Road, Milford Haven, Dyfed, SA73 2ED
tel: 01646 692 752
email: pennypostclassic@aol.com
rack space: No
flyer space: No
poster space: No
listening posts: No
info: Budget Classical CDs available by mail order. Call or email for a catalogue.

Rainbow Records
30 Taff Vale Shopping Centre, Pontypridd, CF37 4TH
tel: 01443 407 261
rack space: No
flyer space: Yes
poster space: Yes
listening posts: Yes
info: Specialise in Dance vinyl but also carry a range of Rock and Pop titles.

Rainbow Records
1-2 Park Street, Newtown, SY16 1EE
tel: 01686 626 583
email: rainbownewtown@aol.com
rack space: Yes
flyer space: Yes
poster space: Yes
listening posts: Yes
info: Stock unsigned demos on a sale-or-return basis. Rainbow Records promote regular records fairs all over the UK. Call Mike at the number above for venue and date details.

Red House Music
9 The Market, Aberdare, Mid Glamorgan, CF44 7EB
tel: 01685 870 093
rack space: Yes
flyer space: Yes
poster space: Yes
listening posts: Limited
info: All revenue from demos sold in the shop goes back to the band, Red House Music do not take a cut.

Rockaway Records
3 Newport Provisions Market, Newport, NP20 1DD
tel: 01633 257 244
rack space: Yes
flyer space: Yes
poster space: Yes
listening posts: Yes
info: Regularly stock unsigned bands' demos and run live music night. See listing for Cheap Sweaty Fun Promotions for more details.

Shirilee Records
Unit 10, Market Hall, Sussex Street, Rhyl, LL18 1SE
tel: 01745 344 144
rack space: No
flyer space: Limited
poster space: Limited
listening posts: No
info: CD and videos. Golden oldies only.

Spillers
36 The Hayes, Cardiff, CF10 1AJ
tel: 02920 224 905
email: enquiries@spillersrecords.com
web: www.spillersrecords.com
rack space: Yes
flyer space: Yes
poster space: Yes
listening posts: Yes
info: Will stock local bands demos on a sale-or-return basis. Established in 1894, Spillers is the world's oldest record shop.

Sullivan's Record Centre
59 High Street, Gorseinon, Swansea, SA4 4BR
tel: 01792 893 602
rack space: Yes
flyer space: No
poster space: No
listening posts: Yes
info: Rock music specialists.

Tangled Parrot
15 Bridge Street, Carmarthen, SA31 3JS
tel: 01267 235 511
email: matt@tangledparrot.co.uk
web: www.tangledparrot.co.uk
rack space: Yes
flyer space: Yes
poster space: Yes
listening posts: Yes
info: Specialise in independent releases. Dedicated local band section. Tangled Parrot also run gigs at the Waterside in Carmarthen. See listings in Independent Promoters section for more details.

Vibes
42 Queen Street, Neath, SA11 1DL
tel: 01639 646 246
rack space: No
flyer space: Yes
poster space: Yes
listening posts: Yes
info: Specialise in back catalogue and hard to find titles.

Vinyl Express
210a High Street, Bangor, LL57 1NY
tel: 01248 354 535
fax: 07092 335 833
email: info@vinylexpress.co.uk
web: www.vinylexpress.co.uk
contact: Mike
rack space: Yes
flyer space: Yes
poster space: Yes
listening posts: No
info: Supports local Dance music producers and will stock material on a sale-or-return basis, or will buy outright depending on suitability. Space is available for posters and flyers on the noticeboard. Dance music only.

Virgin Megastore
Unit 91, Welsh Designed Village, Derwin, Bridgend, CF32 9SU
tel: 01656 649 922
web: www.virginmegastores.co.uk

Virgin Megastore
Units 7-9, Capitol Arcade, Queen Street, Cardiff, CF10 2HQ
tel: 02920 388 273
web: www.virginmegastores.co.uk

MUSIC SERVICES/RETAIL

3.14 RECORDING STUDIOS

EAST of ENGLAND 419 GREATER LONDON 421 MIDLANDS 438 NORTHEAST 445 NORTHWEST 447
SOUTHEAST 455 SOUTHWEST 462 YORKSHIRE 468 NORTHERN IRELAND 472 SCOTLAND 474 WALES 479

EAST of ENGLAND

AMS Music
85a Eastern Avenue, Peterborough, Cambridgeshire, PE1 4PL
tel: 01733 766 483
email: amsmusic@btconnect.com
web: www.amsmusic.co.uk
contact: Andy Nichols

Ashwood Recording Studios
6a Craft Workshops, Toyle Road, Bowthorpe, Norwich, Norfolk, NR5 9AA
tel: 01603 740 026
email: ashwoodstudios@btconnect.com
web: www.ashwoodstudios.com
desk: Soundtrax Quartz
rates: £160 for 8 hour day
info: Also offer vinyl to CD transfer service. Contact for further details.

B & H Sound Services
The Old School Studio, Crowland Road, Eye, Peterborough, PE6 7TN
tel: 01733 223 535
email: sound@bhsound.co.uk
web: www.bhsound.co.uk
desk: Audient ASP8024
monitors: Genelec 1032A/Yamaha NS10M
info: Recording studio as well as location recording including editing, mastering and mixing services.

The Blue Room Sound Studio
Darrow Wood Farm, Shelfanger Road, Diss, Norfolk, IP22 4XY
tel: 01379 641 679
email: info@blueroomstudio.net
web: www.blueroomstudio.net
contact: Graham Hart
desk: Panasonic Ramsa
info: Studios are run by musicians and are very band friendly. There is a wide range of state of the art equipment and baby grand piano available. The studios are in the peaceful setting of a farm which makes it easy to unload and park. Competitive rates and specialise in demo deals.

Diametrics Recording Studio
36 Station Road, Reedham, Norwich, Norfolk, NR13 3TB
tel: 01493 700 790
email: info@diametrics.net
web: www.diametrics.net
contact: Stephen Povey
desk: DDA 16 track
monitors: Harbeth
rates: Negotiable
info: Small professional set up catering for Singer-Songwriters and small acts. Studio has good facilities with comfortable accommodation available. Equipped with selection of computer software combined with good quality mics. Call for more information.

G2 Studios
Woodbridge Road East, Ipswich, Suffolk
tel: 07961 123 881
desk: DVA
monitors: Uri
rates: £30 per hour
info: Linked with Gemini Studios. See listing for details.

Gemini Recording Studios
Gemini House, Levington Road, Ipswich, Suffolk, IP3 0NJ
tel: 01473 272 756
desk: Trident
monitors: Quested
rates: £45 per hour
info: Mastering service available. Also linked with G2 Studios. See listing for details.

Jigsaw Studios
65 Frognall, Deeping St. James, Peterborough, Cambridgeshire, PE6 8RR
tel: 01778 343 598
email: info@jigsawstudio.co.uk
web: www.jigsawstudio.co.uk
desk: Allen & Heath
monitors: Genelec
rates: £25 per hour

Kite Recording Studio
38 James Street, Cambridge, Cambridgeshire, CB1 1HX
tel: 01223 511 651
email: info@kitestudio.co.uk
web: www.kitestudio.co.uk
contact: Roger Chatterton
desk: Pro Tools
monitors: Tannoy/Genelec
rates: From £25 per hour
info: Various types of recording from music to spoken word projects. Acoustic and Singer-Songwriters. Small studio with separate voice booth.

Meadowside Studio
406 Leverington Common, Wisbech, Cambridgeshire, PE13 5JH
tel: 01945 410 608
email: enquiries@meadowsidestudio.co.uk
web: www.meadowsidestudio.co.uk
rates: £25 per hour (inc. engineer)
info: Also offer rehearsal and CD duplication facilities. See listings in relevant sections for further details.

Mikesound Studio
21 St. Peter's Close, Henley, Ipswich, Suffolk, IP6 0RH
tel: 01473 831 465
email: info@mikesound.co.uk
web: www.mikesound.co.uk
contact: Mike Briggs
desk: Tascan M3700
monitors: Alesis monitor two
rates: From £20 per hour (+ VAT)
info: Friendly creative Suffolk studio. Location and studio recording. Please refer to website for more information.

The Mill
Mill House, Mill Road, Winfarthing, Diss, IP22 2DZ
tel: 01379 652 535
email: info@themillstudio.co.uk
web: www.themillstudio.co.uk
contact: Jonny Cole
desk: Mackie 32/8 analogue
monitors: Genelec
rates: Contact for details
info: Focusrite and TL Audio mic pre amps. Shared control/live room with Pro Tools. Chillout area with kitchen facilities. On-site parking. Quality demos to full production available. Previous clients include EMI, Rough Trade Records and Dreamworks.

Orchard Cottage Studio
Orchard Cottage, 60 High Street, Willingham, Cambridge, CB4 5ES
tel: 01954 202 350
email: info@orchardcottagestudio.co.uk
web: www.orchardcottagestudio.co.uk
contact: Mick Venning
desk: Soundtracs
monitors: JBL
rates: £25 per hour
info: The live room is fully isolated and acoustically treated, and is spacious enough to comfortably accommodate large projects. Kitchenette, bathroom and secure private parking are available on-site. Package deals available, contact for details.

Peter Kiely Productions
15 Purfleet Street, King's Lynn, Norfolk, PE30 1ER
tel: 01553 774 874
email: peterkielyprods@hotmail.com
info: Peter mainly deals with radio commercials, computer game soundtracks and voiceovers, but will work with bands he likes and feels he can do a good job for.

Plug Studios
Units 9-13, The Old Fishmarket, Mountergate, Norwich, NR1 1PZ
tel: 01603 219 337/07946 649 859
email: plugstudios@aol.com
web: www.plugstudios.co.uk
contact: Errol Watson
rates: Call for details
info: Plug Studios are part of E.L.K. Promotions. There is also rehearsal space available, see relevant entry for details.

Purple Studios
Old Parish Hall, The Street, Trouse, Norwich, Norfolk, NR14 8SX
tel: 01603 622 550
email: info@purplestudios.co.uk
web: www.purplestudios.co.uk
contact: Andrew Gunn
desk: Harrison MR3
monitors: HHB
rates: £180 per 10 hour day, £150 per 8 hourr day, £20 per extra hour, Mastering £25 per hour
info: Offers gig recording. Accommodation, chillout rooms, large live room. Purple Studios has been established for 19 years. Recording available to broadcasting standard. Embrace a wide variety of music, especially Indie and Rock.

Real Deal Studios
near Cambridge
tel: 07909 542 121
email: tom@realdealproductions.co.uk
web: www.realdealproductions.co.uk
contact: Tom
desk: Soundcraft Spirit LX7
monitors: Tannoy
rates: Call for details
info: Offer studio and on-location gig recording. Complete packages available comprising recording, mixing and mastering. Can also offer assistance with graphic design and CD artwork. Enquire for further details.

The Rehearsal Room Studios
4 St. Andrew's Street South, Bury St. Edmunds, Suffolk, IP33 3PH
tel: 01284 700 353
email: neil@therehearsalrooms.co.uk
web: www.therehearsalrooms.co.uk
contact: Neil Attridge
desk: Berringer 32 track
monitors: Tannoy Reveals
rates: £15 per hour
info: Ideal for demo recordings. Also has rehearsal space, see relevant section for details.

Rock Lobster Studio
Unit 3, Southwold Business Centre, St. Edmund's Road, Southwold, Suffolk, IP18 6LB
tel: 01502 724 722
email: rocklobsterstudio@tiscali.co.uk
web: www.rocklobsterstudio.co.uk
contact: Kev or Tim
desk: Berringer Eurorack
monitors: Fostex Nearfield
rates: £20 per hour
info: Live room and control room with 2 Peavey PAs. Yamaha AW4416 16 track digital hard disc recorder. Guitar amps available for use, as well as Yamaha drum kit and Paiste cymbals. Also fully equipped with condenser and dynamic microphones. See also listing in Rehearsal Studios section.

Sickroom Studios
Meadway, Narborough Road, Pentney, Kings Lynn, Norfolk, PE32 1JD
tel: 01760 337 248
email: owen@thesickroom.co.uk
web: www.thesickroom.co.uk
monitors: NS10
rates: Call for details
info: Running Cubase SX.

Simply Studios
23 Roman Way, Small Business Park, London Road, Godmanchester, Cambridgeshire, PE26 2QQ
tel: 01480 456 000
email: info@simply-studios.com
web: www.simply-studios.com
contact: Charley
desk: Behringher
monitors: Mackie
rates: Call for details
info: Also have a rehearsal room, see relevant entry for details.

Sonic Zone
Pipers Oak, East Harling, Norwich, Norfolk, NR16 2PX
tel: 01953 718 404
email: enquiries@soniczone.co.uk
web: www.soniczone.co.uk
contact: Clive
desk: Soundcraft
monitors: BNW
rates: £22 per hour

The Soundhouse
Unit 6, Capital Trading Estate, Whapload Road, Lowestoft, Suffolk, NR32 1UL
tel: 01502 513 050
email: the_soundhouse@btconnect.com
contact: John, Marty
desk: Soundcraft Ghost
monitors: Alesis
rates: £150 per day
info: 24 track digital recording. Offer a complete service for recording, production and mastering. Rehearsal rooms available. Also provide equipment hire services. See listings in relevant sections for details.

Springvale Studios
Chantery Park Road, Sproughton, Ipswich, IP8 3AS
tel: 01473 288 388
email: springvalestudios@btinternet.com
web: www.springvalestudios.com
contact: Mark Hartwood
desk: Pro Tools
info: Pro Tools recording, editing and mixing.

Steelsound Recording & Entertainment
Mill Lane, Walpole Highway, Wisbech, Cambridgeshire, PE14 7QF
tel: 01945 880 097
contact: Duncan Partington
rates: Contact for details
info: 16 track digital studio. Also incorporates an entertainment agency. Contact Duncan for further details.

Zig Zag Music Productions
Croeso, Church Lane, Hilton, Cambridgeshire, PE28 9NH
tel: 01480 830 073
email: info@zigzagmusic.com
web: www.zigzagmusic.com
monitors: Tannoy
rates: Contact for details
info: 32 track studio. Also offer location recording services. Various pricing packages available, contact for further information.

Zoo Audio
1d Coles Road, Cambridge, Cambridgeshire, CB4 6BW
tel: 01223 519 296
email: info@zooaudio.co.uk
web: www.zooaudio.co.uk
contact: Andy Cross
desk: Studiomaster
monitors: Mackie/Yamaha
rates: £25 per hour, £180 per 10 hour day
info: Also offer location recording for live gigs. Gibson, Fender and Takamine guitars and basses are available, as well as Fender and Marshall amps, and a Pearl drum kit. CD duplication services are offered, see entry in relevant section for details.

GREATER LONDON

2 KHz Studios
Castgoal Ltd., 97a Scrubs Lane, London, NW10 6QU
tel: 020 8960 1331
email: info@2khzstudios.co.uk
web: www.2khzstudios.co.uk
contact: Mike Nelson
desk: Trident 80B
monitors: Boxer/Yamaha NS10/B&W DM1200/acoustic research/ Dynaudio/Alesis M1
rates: Call for details
info: Fully equipped professional standard studio. Includes Pro Tools 24bit 32 track recording. Selection of effects units, microphones and kit available. Previous clients include The Darkness, Doves, Nick Cave, Unkle and Franz Ferdinand.

2002 Studios
123a Kenton Road, Harrow, Middlesex, HA3 0AZ
tel: 020 8907 8634
web: www.2002studios.com
desk: Pro Tools
rates: £45 per hour (inc. engineer)
info: Studio suitable for vocal and instrumental tracking, demo production and Urban music production, as well as voice overs. 2002 Studios is a music production company which offers a variety of different services. See website for further details.

3Sixty Studios
Unit 2, Marric House, Bishops Road, London, SW6 7AD
tel: 020 7386 3960
email: info@3sixtystudios.com
web: www.3sixtystudios.com
contact: Tom
desk: Mackie
monitors: Mackie/Bose
rates: Call for details
info: Comprehensive studio, with Pro Tools HD2 system, 56 channel Mackie desk. Lots of outboard, microphones and other equipment available.

Abbey Music Studios
Lodge Hill, Abbeywood, London, SE2 0AY
tel: 020 8312 4916
email: info@abbeymusicstudios.co.uk
web: www.abbeymusicstudios.co.uk
info: 24 track studio. Separate drum and vocal booths. Large live room. Smaller rooms suitable for specialist acoustics. Specialise in live music. DJ projects also undertaken with use of digital editing suite. Also have rehearsal rooms and equipment hire service. See listings in relevant sections.

ACM Records & Production Company
The Apollo Unit 3, 18 All Saints Road, London, W11 1HH
tel: 020 7221 2275
email: mike@acm-records.co.uk
web: www.acm-records.co.uk
contact: Mike Allison
desk: Soundtracs
monitors: Tannoy/Yamaha NS10
rates: Call for details
info: ACM Records & Production are a music production company comprising its own in-house recording studio, production team, label (ACM Records). See listing in relevant section for details.

Air-Edel Recording Studios
18 Rodmarton Street, London, England, W1U 8BJ
tel: 020 7486 6466
email: trevorbest@air-edel.co.uk
web: www.air-edel.co.uk
contact: Trevor Best
desk: Cadac
monitors: Dynaudio
rates: Call for details
info: Studio 1 accommodates up to 30 musicians and is equipped with a Steinway 'B' grand piano. It also offers full Dolby 5.1 surround mixing. Studio 2 is ideal for smaller line-ups and voice-over recordings. Studio 3 offers digital editing facilities and is also often used for dubbing sound effects. Pro Tools HD 24 input & 40 output.

Alaska Studios
127-129 Alaska Street, London, SE1 8XE
tel: 020 7928 7440
fax: 020 7928 8070
email: alaska01@btclick.co.uk
web: www.alaskastudio.co.uk
contact: Beverley Lodge
desk: MCI JH 6000
monitors: Yamaha NS10/Quested
rates: Call for details
info: Established in 1977, Alaska is a fully equipped, acoustically designed studio with comprehensive backline available and drum room. 24 track recording on to an MCI desk. 96 track hard disk recording on GL1 using Macs with Logic Audio. Alaska uses in-house and freelance producers and engineers to help nurture your sound. Chillout area with complimentary refreshments and cooking facilities. The studio has a comprehensive selection of processors, effects units, compressors and some vintage gear. As well as recording facilities, there are 3 fully equipped rehearsal rooms. Refer to entry in relevant section for details.

Albert Studios
Unit 29, Cygnus Business Centre, Delmeyr Road, London, NW10 2XA
tel: 020 7704 8888
email: info@albertmusic.co.uk
web: www.albertmusic.co.uk
desk: Neve VR60 flying fader/Yamaha OTR
monitors: Yamaha NS10/Genelec 1031A/ATC SCM 20A/SCM 300A
rates: Call for details
info: Studio complex houses recording and mixing facilities, plus 2 programming rooms with state of the art equipment. 60 channel Neve desk, full Pro Tools digital hard disk recording system and expansive recording areas.

Alleycat Studios
212 Kilburn High Road, London, NW6 4JH
tel: 020 7624 6448
contact: John Cooper
desk: Allen & Heath
monitors: Tannoy
rates: Call for details
info: Rehearsal room also available. See entry for Airwave Studios in the relevant section.

Antenna Studios
Bowyers Yard, Bedwardine Road, London, SE19 3AY
tel: 020 8653 5200
email: info@antennastudios.co.uk
web: www.antennastudios.co.uk
contact: Jakob Kaye
desk: Tascam DM24
monitors: Tannoy
rates: £180 per day (+ VAT)
info: Large studio incorporating a number of multimedia services, including web and graphic design and video production. See relevant sections for more information. The recording studio features a selection of compressors and effects, NTC Works, Focusrite pre-amps with PCs running Cubase SX. All digital recording, with the option of putting final mix through a Behringer tube compressor. The studio also has a resident guitar maker for repairs and commissions. Also offers rehearsal facilities. See relevant entry for details.

Arc Sound Studio
Lower Ground Floor, 443 New Cross Road, London, SE14 6TA
tel: 020 8691 8161
fax: 020 8691 8161
email: info@arcsound.co.uk
web: www.arcsound.co.uk
contact: James Dougill
desk: Yamaha 02R/Cadac
monitors: Dynaudio Acoustic/Yamaha MSPO'5
rates: Call for details
info: Main system is an Atari Radar 2. The studio specialises in live recording (including location recording). Multi-track and live performance engineering. Fully fitted control room, main live room and voice over booth. Lounge area with kitchen. Arc Sound also run rehearsal facilities. See entries in relevant sections for details.

Arclite Productions
c/o Grove Studios, Unit 10, Latimer Road Industrial Estate, Latimer Road, London, W10 6RQ
tel: 020 8964 9047
email: alan@arcliteproductions.com
web: www.arcliteproductions.com
contact: Alan Bleay
info: Arclite Productions are also involved in professional music production for TV, film and commercials.

MUSIC SERVICES/RETAIL

Ariwa Sounds Ltd.
34 Whitehorse Lane, London, SE25 6RE
tel: 020 8653 7744
fax: 020 8771 1911
email: info@ariwa.com
web: www.ariwa.com
contact: Joseph Fraser
desk: Soundcraft
monitors: Tannoy
info: A well equipped air-conditioned control room especially designed for mixing. Located on the ground floor, it is ideal for loading. Connected by lines to a live room and a custom designed vocal booth. See website for full equipment list.

Ascape Studios
Unit E, The Clan Works, 1a Howard Road, Bromley, Kent, BR1 3QJ
tel: 020 8460 0048
email: info@ascapestudios.com
web: www.ascapestudios.com
contact: Nick
desk: Pro Tools
monitors: Genelec
rates: Call for details
info: Large studio with a mix of analogue and digital technology. Lots of outboard, effects and processors, see the website for full equipment list.

Atomic Studios
Building B, 2nd & 3rd Floors, Tower Bridge Business Complex, 100 Clements Road, London, SE16 4DG
tel: 020 7237 2233
email: robinrawlinson@yahoo.co.uk
web: www.atomicstudios.co.uk
contact: Rob Rawlinson
rates: Call for details
info: Atomic Studios have 27 studio spaces that are ready for rehearsal, recording and programming use. You provide the equipment. Flexible, long or short term lets from £120 per week. Linked with The Animal Farm record label, see listing in relevant section for details.

Audio Underground
12 Northwold Road,, London, N16 7HR
tel: 020 7241 1818
email: admin@audiounderground.co.uk
web: www.audiounderground.co.uk
rates: £25 per hour, £150-£250 per day
info: Weekly rates are negotiable. Also provides rehearsal facilities, check relevant section for details.

Autograph Sound Recording Ltd.
2 Spring Place, London, NW5 3BA
tel: 020 7485 4515
email: studio@autograph.co.uk
web: www.autograph.co.uk
contact: Clare Hazeldine
desk: Yamaha DM2000
monitors: Genelec
rates: Call for details
info: Autograph Sound Recording, together with their sister company Autograph Sales, make up the Autograph Group of companies. The group concentrate on delivering professional audio services, which include equipment hire, equipment sales, live sound design, sound effects, composing and permanent installation consultancy. The studio has a high specification and is suitable for recording any material.

Bark Studio
1a Blenheim Road, London, E17 6HS
tel: 020 8523 0110
email: brian@barkstudio.co.uk
web: www.barkstudio.co.uk
contact: Brian
desk: MCI 600
monitors: Auratone/Yamaha NS10/UREI 811
rates: Call for details
info: Bark Studio offers a mix of old and new recording technology with a good selection of vintage amplifiers available. Rates are negotiable. Brian will try to cater for most budgets.

Battenburg Studios
Unit 35, DRCA Business Centre, Strasburg Road, Battersea, London, SW11 5JE
tel: 07931 531 851
email: contact@breakfaststudios.co.uk
web: www.breakfaststudios.co.uk
desk: Mackie 1604VLZ-Pro & 1202
monitors: Event 20/20 studio monitors
rates: £15 per hour (inc. engineer)
info: Offer complete recording, mixing and mastering capabilities. Also provide rehearsal facilities, Breakfast Studios. See listing in appropriate section for details.

Berry Street Recording Studios
1 Berry Street, London, EC1V 0AA
tel: 020 7253 5885
fax: 020 7635 8293
email: info@berrystreetstudio.com
web: www.berrystreetstudio.com
contact: Kevin Poree
desk: DAB/Trident/Neve
monitors: Dynaudio 6A/Yamaha NS10
rates: Call for details
info: Very large live room incorporating an isolation booth, control room and further isolation area. Clients have included Billy Bragg, Freddie Mercury, Afrika Bambaataa, Radiohead, Barry White and The Mekons.

BFD Studios
West Heath Works, 174 Mill Lane, London, NW6 1TB
email: info@bigfuckingdigital.com
web: www.bigfuckingdigital.com
contact: Jamie Maher
desk: Apogee AD/DA
monitors: Genelic 1030 1A
rates: Call for details
info: Studio equipped with Logic and Pro Tools, using valve pre-amps through 24 tracks. There are a wide variety of Synth modules and keyboards including Korg Triton, E-Synth and Novation.

Big Box Studios
31 Penrose Street, London, SE17 3DW
tel: 020 7703 7293
email: jeremy@bigboxstudios.com
web: www.bigboxstudios.com
contact: Jeremy
desk: Chiltern QM3
monitors: Tannoy/Yamaha NS10
rates: Call for details
info: Location and studio recording. Big Box also have 11 studio spaces available to hire, as well as offering music production courses.

BonaFideStudio
Burbage House, 83 Curtain Road, London, EC2A 3BS
tel: 020 7684 5350/020 7684 5351/020 7729 7935
email: info@bonafidestudio.co.uk
web: www.bonafidestudio.co.uk
contact: Deanna Gardner
desk: Mackie 32A
monitors: Yamaha NS10/Alesis 2
rates: £20 per hour (up to 5 hours), £16.50 per hour (5-9 hours), £12.50 per hour (10 hours or more)
info: Fully equipped studio with TLA 50/51 and dual 50/21. Lexicon MPS1 reverb, Alesis quadraverb. Roland JV1080 and Planet Phat modules amongst others. Also run one-to-one tutorials in sound engineering. Contact BonaFide for more information. Rehearsal facilities available. See listing in relevant section for details.

Boomtown Studio
Valetta Road, London, W3 7TG
tel: 020 8723 9548
email: info@boomtownstudio.co.uk
web: www.boomtownstudio.co.uk
contact: Simon Wilkinson
desk: Panasonic DA7
monitors: Genelic
rates: From £25 per hour
info: Pro Tools studio with Logic Audio. The studio has a collection of retro amps and specialises in vintage keyboard. There is a variety of classics available to use, including the Mini Moog. Studio is well suited to recording Electronic music. Also offer CD duplication, enquire for further details.

Born To Dance Studios
DRCA Centre, Unit 34, Charlotte Despard Avenue, Battersea, London, SW11 5JE
tel: 01273 301 555/07787 155 014
email: studio@borntodance.com
web: www.borntodance.com
contact: Gavin McCall
desk: Mackie D8B
monitors: Genelec/Yamaha NS10
rates: Introductory offer of £15 per hour
info: Equipped with 2 live rooms, a vocal booth and a Mackie D8B 56 input/72 channel digital console. Studio offers fully integrated hard disk editing/mastering system. For more information on the Born To Dance label, see the relevant section.

the|unsigned|guide

The Unsigned Guide/UK/2006. Material published in this directory may not be reproduced (in any form) without written consent.

Brain Dead Studios
PO Box 3775, London, SE18 3QR
tel: 020 8316 4690
fax: 020 8316 4690
email: marc@wufog.freeserve.co.uk
contact: Marc Bell
desk: Mackie 24/8
monitors: Alesis Monitor 2/JBL
rates: Call for details
info: Friendly, long established studio with a range of kit, including vintage equipment. The studio specialises in live recording using a fully loaded Mackie HDR 24 recorder in conjunction with PCs. The studio was rebuilt in 2000 and is fully acoustically treated. There is a large live area and separate machine room. Also facilities available for CD duplication. The studio can be booked at cheaper rates on Mondays and Tuesdays.

Britannia Row Studios
3 Bridge Studios, 318 - 326 Wandsworth Bridge Road, London, SW6 2TZ
tel: 020 7371 5872
fax: 020 7371 8641
email: bookings@britanniarowstudios.co.uk
web: www.britanniarowstudios.co.uk
contact: Jamie, Kate Koumi
desk: Neve 51/Pro Tools HD3 Accel & Mix 3
monitors: Boxer T3s/HR8-24
rates: Call for details
info: Britannia Row comprises 3 studios, each fully equipped with Pro Tools. Studios 2 and 3 recently reconfigured acoustically and re-equipped. Previous clients include Snow Patrol.

The Brothel
32 Berrick Street, Soho, London, W1F 8RL
tel: 020 7437 3202
email: peter@coresoho.co.uk
web: www.coresoho.co.uk
contact: Peter Morris
desk: O2R
monitors: Genelec 10-31s
rates: Call for details
info: Logic Audio 6 HD system, live room, recording, mixing and mastering.

Bush Studios
151 MacFarlane Road Arches, Shepherds Bush, London, W12 7LA
tel: 020 8740 1740
email: recording@bushstudios.co.uk
web: www.bushstudios.co.uk
contact: Malcolm Ford
desk: Mackie
monitors: KRK/custom
rates: From £25 per hour
info: Live and MIDI recording, all projects considered. Previous clients include Macy Gray, Toploader, The Waterboys and One Giant Leap. Also provide rehearsal facilities. See listing in relevant section.

Café Music
18 Ordell Road, Bow, London, E3 2DS
tel: 07931 310 945/07958 004 953
fax: 020 8981 2588
email: info@cafestudio.co.uk
web: www.cafestudio.co.uk
contact: Mark Sutherland, Dan Franklin
desk: Mackie D8B Digital/Amek Analogue
monitors: Tannoy/Quested/Mackie/Scanspeak
rates: Call for details
info: Hard disk recording, Logic Audio, Cubase VST, large live room. Full backline and PA plus various instruments including drums, guitars, bass and synths. Experienced in-house producers, engineers and musicians. Also run Studio Experience courses for singers, contact for further details.

The Centre
Gosforth Lane, Watford, WD19 7AX
tel: 020 8499 8012
email: paul.herwin@threerivers.gov.uk
web: www.threerivers.gov.uk/default.aspx/web/music
desk: Mackie
info: 32 track recording studio comprising of a control room and live/practice room. Studio can be booked for demo recording, CD burning or to learn about production packages and techniques. Also run DJ and scratching workshops.

Church Path Studios
78 Church Path, Chiswick, London, W4 5BJ
tel: 020 8994 3142
email: kris.gray@btinternet.com
contact: Kris Grey
desk: Amek
monitors: JBL
rates: Call for details
info: 24 track Pro Tools studios with live room.

Conversion 2 Productions
13 Dallyell Road, London, SW9 9SD
tel: 020 7274 4668
email: info@conversion2.co.uk
web: www.conversion2.co.uk
desk: Audioent
monitors: Genelec Surround Sound

Core Soho
Basement, 32 Berwick Street, London, W1F 8RL
tel: 020 7437 3202
email: peter@coresoho.co.uk
web: www.coresoho.co.uk
contact: Peter
desk: OTR
monitors: Genelec 10-31a
rates: Call for details
info: Logic Audio HD recording.

The Cowshed
Myddleton Road, London, N22 8NG
tel: 020 8881 2288
email: info@cowshedstudio.com
web: www.cowshedstudio.com
contact: Biba Leach
desk: Amek Angela
monitors: Dynaudio Acoustic/Yamaha NS10
rates: Call for details
info: Ideal live music recording faculties. 90 input analogue desk, 20 vintage Neve mic pre-amps. 2" 24 track analogue tape recording, as well as HD recording using Apple Mac G4. Wide range of equipment and instruments to use including Fender Rhodes organ, Hammond Porta B, Hammond HX-100 organs and a Yamaha piano. Engineer Joe Leach has 17 years of experience.

Cromwell Sound
email: cromwellsound@yahoo.co.uk
web: www.cromwellsound.tk
contact: Daniel Cromwell
info: Mobile studio with professional recording quality. Operates around Greater London and South East areas. Contact Daniel for further information.

Cybersound Studios
Unit C104, Faircharm Trading Estate, 8-12 Creekside, London, SE8 3DX
tel: 020 8694 9484
fax: 020 8694 9466
email: studio@cyber-sound.co.uk
web: www.cyber-sound.co.uk
desk: Allen & Heath GS3V 24-8-2
monitors: Yamaha NS10/JBL 4311/Event 20-20
rates: £33 per hour, £275 per day
info: 48 track studio with 2 live rooms and vocal booth. Rates include sound engineer. Cybersound also run rehearsal rooms. See entry in relevant section for details.

The Dairy Ltd.
43-45 Tunstall Road, London, SW9 8BZ
tel: 020 7738 7777
fax: 020 7738 7007
email: info@thedairy.co.uk
web: www.thedairy.co.uk
contact: Emily Taylor
desk: Neve VRL60 Legend/DDA AMR 24/AMEK 2500
monitors: ATC 200/Genelic 10-31A/Yamaha NS10
rates: Call for details
info: Fully equipped with 3 studios. Wide range of outboard gear and microphones available to use. All studios use Logic Audio 6 and Pro Tools.

Dave Hunt Sound Studios
30 Stronsa Road, London, W12 9LB
tel: 020 8743 3055
email: davehuntaudio@btinternet.com
contact: Dave Hunt
desk: Mackie D8B
monitors: Dynaudio/JBL
rates: Call for details
info: Pro Tools, surround sound monitoring. Dave also does a great deal of picture soundtracking.

Deep Recording Studio
187 Freston Road, London, W10 6TH
tel: 020 8964 8256
email: deep.studios@virgin.net
web: www.deeprecordingstudios.com
contact: Mark Rose
desk: NAS P8024
monitors: Quested/Yamaha NS10
rates: Call for details
info: Equipped with 3 24 track machines, full MIDI Apple G5 kit running Logic Audio 6 Pro. Wide range of outboard including valve gear. In-house instruments available for bands to use. A production company is run from the studio by a group of producers, engineers, artists and remixers who help and develop new artists and bands. Artists or producers should send demo CDs or MDs to Deep, PO Box 38134, London, W1O 6XL.

Deep See Studios
15 Stoke Newington Road, London, N16 8BH
tel: 07739 384 688
email: deepsee@ilove.screaming
contact: Milan
desk: Pro Tools
monitors: Tannoy
rates: £15 per hour (inc. engineer)
info: 32 track digital studio using Pro Tools for Mac. Live room, sound-proofed vocal booth, Chillout room with internet access. Also offer rehearsal facilities. See listing in Rehearsal Studios section for further information.

The Depot
29-31 Brewery Road, London, N7 9QH
tel: 020 7609 1366
fax: 020 7609 6844
email: info@thedepotstudios.com
web: www.thedepotstudios.com
contact: Jeff Hilton
desk: Yamaha 02R/Soundtrac
monitors: Dynaudio BM50
rates: Call for details
info: Large rooms. In-house engineer available. Café and chillout bar.

DNA Studios
302-304 Barrington Road, Brixton, London, SW9 7JJ
tel: 020 7274 5983
contact: Steve
desk: Mackie
monitors: Tannoy
rates: Call for details
info: ADAT and Fostex recording. Lots of outboard available.

The Dolls House Studio
Bell Lane, Hendon, London, NW4 2AD
tel: 020 8732 8511/07976 371 944
email: bongojoe50@hotmail.com
web: www.dollshousestudio.co.uk
contact: Joe, Graham
desk: Allen & Heath
monitors: Genelec
rates: £20 per hour (inc. engineer)
info: Friendly, air conditioned studio with reasonable prices. Session musician available. Also have rehearsal space and offer tuition, see relevant entries for details.

DSL Productions
tel: 07731 407 406
email: info@dslproductions.co.uk
web: www.dslproductions.co.uk
monitors: Kef Pro
rates: £15 per hour
info: Studio suitable for Dance and Electronic music, also equipped with decks. DSL are songwriters themselves and involved in artist development, sound design, music composition for film.

Earthchild Studios
244-254 Cambridge Heath Road, Bethnal Green, London, E2 9DA
tel: 020 8983 4755
email: info@earthchildmusic.com
web: www.earthchildmusic.com
contact: Princeton
desk: Mackie
monitors: Adams/Genelec/Dynaudio
rates: Call for details
info: Well equipped studio suitable for recording any type of material. For details of Earthchild Studio's other services, please see website above.

Earthworks Studio
62 (The rear of) Barnet High Street, Barnet, Hertfordshire, EN5 5SJ
tel: 020 8449 2258
email: info@earthworksstudio.co.uk
web: www.earthworksstudio.co.uk
contact: Leigh Darlow
desk: TLA Audio (valve)
monitors: Yamaha NS10/Alesis/Quested
rates: From £25 per hour
info: Facilities to record any type of music. 2 rehearsal rooms also available. The owner runs a production company called Swing System Productions, call for more details.

Eastcote Studios
249 Kensal Road, London, W10 5DB
tel: 020 8969 3739
fax: 020 8960 1836
email: info@eastcotestudios.co.uk
web: www.eastcotestudios.co.uk
contact: Philip Bagenar
desk: MCI JH542C/Mackie
monitors: Yamaha NS10/Urei/Auratone
rates: From £350 for 12 hours
info: Contains 2 recording studios, one with a classic American 1970s console. Pro Tools and Macs as well as a wide variety of synths and compressors. Studio 2 has large control room with natural light. Space for up to 6 musicians. Previous clients include Futureheads, Depeche Mode, Death From Above 1979, Neneh Cherry and Maximo Park.

Ebony & Ivory Studios
11 Varley Parade, Edgware Road, London, W4 5AP
tel: 020 8200 7090
email: apbaudio@aol.com
contact: Alan Bradshaw
desk: Focus Rite Pro Tools HD
monitors: Genelec 22-20's/Yamaha NS10
rates: Call for details
info: Fully digital Mac-based Pro Tools studio. Plug-ins and outboard available.

Eden Studios
20-24 Beaumont Road, Chiswick, London, W4 5AP
tel: 020 8995 5432
fax: 020 8747 1931
email: natalie@edenstudios.com
web: www.edenstudios.com
contact: Natalie Horton
desk: SSL 6000
monitors: Quested/KRK
rates: Call for details
info: Professional studio with 35 years of recording experience. Massive client list including Coldplay, Dido and Feeder. 2 SSL studios as well as pre and post-production studios, some available for long term hire. See the website for more detailed technical information.

Edsongs
17a The Burroughs, Hendon, London, NW4 4AR
tel: 020 8202 3763
email: edsongs@mac.com
contact: Eddie Adamberry
desk: Pro Tools
monitors: Studiophiles/Century 500
rates: £40 per day
info: Pro Tools 34 mix plus studio using Logic Audio 7 with total automation. Special rates available, contact for more details.

Eight Barr Productions
Cross House, Hornsey, London, N8 7SA
tel: 020 8347 8008/07951 466 005
email: eight_barr_productions@hotmail.com
web: www.eightbarrproductions.co.uk
contact: Paul
monitors: Alesis
info: The studio has a fully sound-proofed control room and live room. Chillout area with TV and Playstation. Friendly environment.

EQ Studios
28c Kilburn Lane, London, W10 4AH
tel: 020 8968 3322
email: eq.studios@virgin.net
web: www.eqstudios.co.uk
contact: John Hamilton
desk: Mackie D8B
monitors: AE 1s
rates: Call for details
info: Comprehensive studio with a good range of synths and outboard with Logic Audio Pro 6. EQ Studios have been providing services dedicated to the needs of writers, producers and re-mixers for the past 12 years, and offer songwriting assistance for lyricists.

Escapade Studio
13b Greenwich South Street, London, SE10 8NW
tel: 020 8858 8546
email: gary@pearlsforswine.co.uk
web: www.pearlsforswine.co.uk
contact: Gary
desk: Soundcraft Ghost
monitors: Tannoy SR12x/Yamaha NS10
rates: Call for details
info: Large live room where a whole band can play together.

Evelyn Studio
198 Hainault Road, Leytonstone, London, E11 1EP
tel: 020 8539 2704
fax: 020 8558 6659
email: csbl98@tiscali.co.uk
contact: Chan
desk: Soundtrac IL48
monitors: Yamaha NS10/Studio
rates: Call for details
info: Full studio with digital recording suite. Grand and upright pianos available. Lots of synths and outboard. Logic Audio, Cubase and Pro Tools. Also offer CD mastering service.

Evolution Media
2nd Floor, 22 Great Windmill Street, Soho, London, W1D 7LD
tel: 020 7734 5395
fax: 020 7734 5395
email: info@evolutionmediauk.com
web: www.evolutionmediauk.com
contact: Corin Giles
desk: Yamaha
monitors: Beyer Dynamic
rates: Call for details
info: Evolution Media is a company totally dedicated to new and unsigned bands, or anyone without the money for a full studio recording. Also have a fully equipped digital post-production and mastering studio in the heart of Soho.

Fabquirin
Lyncroft House, Lyncroft Gardens, London, NW6 1LB
tel: 07865 052 464
email: fabquirin67@hotmail.com
web: www.fabquirin.com
contact: Fabrice
desk: Pro Tools
rates: £30 per hour
info: Studio with large live room. Kitchen facilities. Contact Fabrice to agree on rate for full day.

The Famous Yard Recording Studios
133-137 Kilburn Lane, London, W10 4AN
tel: 020 8354 7702/07765 270 035
email: chx@thefamousyard.com
web: www.thefamousyard.com
contact: Charles Reeves
desk: Pro Tools
monitors: Mackie
rates: Call for details
info: Large selection of vintage guitar amps available. Also have use of Rhodes piano and lots of synths.

Faraday Studios
Unit 61b, Westminster Industrial Estate, Faraday Way, London, SE18 5TR
tel: 020 8855 6333
email: info@faradaystudios.co.uk
web: www.faradaystudios.co.uk
desk: Sony DMXR-100
monitors: Quested
rates: Call for details
info: State of the art recording suites with live rooms. Rehearsal facilities also available. See listing in relevant section for details. Also have in-house production and record label. Contact Faraday Studios for information.

Fast Forward Recording Studio
63 Clinton Road, Bow, London, E3 4QY
tel: 020 8983 4442
email: jazzyjohn@foward.fsbusiness.co.uk
web: www.fastforward-studios.co.uk
contact: John
desk: Yamaha OTR
monitors: Genelec 1029a
rates: £15 per hour
info: Offer a wide range of recording facilities for bands and solo artists producing albums, EPs and single tracks. Live room and control room. The studio has been used in voice-over audition tapes for television, film scores, Classical pieces for large orchestras, right through to backing tapes for art and dance exhibitions. John also offers guitar tuition.

Fat Fox Studios
24a Radley Mews, Kensington, London, W8 6JP
tel: 020 7376 9555
email: info@fatfoxstudios.co.uk
web: www.fatfoxstudios.co.uk
desk: Pro Tools HD3
monitors: Genelic/Yamaha
rates: Call for details
info: Studio has a large live room with isolation booth.

Fluid Studios
24 Store Street, Off Tottenham Court Road, London, W1
tel: 020 7691 2446
email: fluidstudios@london.com
contact: Mark Thomas
desk: Soundcraft
monitors: Absolute
rates: £20 per hour (inc. engineer)
info: Valve outboard, Macs, classic Electronica instruments including a Minimoog. Combination of digital and analogue equipment. Live room. Drum kit available.

Fluke Productions
89a Kingsland High Street, London, E8 2PB
tel: 020 7254 9019
email: luke@flukeproductions.com
web: www.flukeproductions.com
contact: Luke Henderson
desk: Mackie
monitors: Tannoy
rates: £20 per hour, £140 for 8 hours
info: Fluke run a production company and studio. Producers are on hand to aid song composition. Introductory offers available, contact for details.

Fortress Studios
34-38 Provost Street, London, N1 7NG
tel: 020 7251 6200
fax: 020 7251 5892
email: fortessstudios@compuserve.com
web: www.fortressstudios.co.uk
contact: Shaun Harvey
desk: Neve VI 48 track
monitors: Quested/Genelic/Yamaha NS10
rates: Call for details
info: Large studio with digital and analogue recording (Pro Tools HD24 and 24 track tape). Wide selection of microphones and instruments (including 2 pianos and Hammond organ), plenty of outboard, amplifiers and large live room. The studio is well suited to live recording and many bands use the studio to record their sessions for university radio. Fortress also have writing suites available to let from £500 per month including VAT, and 2 new rehearsal rooms on-site. See entry in relevant section for details.

Gadget Studios
73 Leonard Street, London, EC2H QS4
tel: 07973 788 118
email: info@gadgetstudios.co.uk
web: www.gadgetstudios.co.uk
contact: Denis Gajetic
desk: Mackie
monitors: Dynaudio
rates: Call for details
info: Studio specialises in recording Singer-Songwriters. The owner is a multi-instrumentalist and will be able to assist on the recording if required. Samples of Gadget's work are available on the website.

The Gaff Recording Studio
346 North End Road, Fulham, London, SW6 1NB
tel: 020 7385 1816
email: thegaff@tiscali.co.uk
web: www.thegaffrecordingstudio.com
contact: Lee Hirons
desk: Soundcraft Sapphire
monitors: Mackie
rates: Call for details
info: Full studio with Macs running Cubase. 64 track recording and 48 track recording onto Radar. The studio's engineer has industry experience with U2 and REM. Located near a station, bars and shops.

Gateway Studios
Kingston Hill Centre, Kingston Upon Thames, Surrey, KT2 7LB
tel: 020 8549 0014
email: studio@gsr.org.uk
web: www.gsr.org.uk
contact: Gurjit Dhansa
desk: Soundcraft DC2020
monitors: PMC/Monroe/Yamaha NS10
rates: £35-£60 per hour
info: Associated with the Gateway School of Recording at Kingston University. Large range of equipment and facilities suitable for recording any kind of music.

GB Studio
Barnet Business Centre, Alston Road, High Barnet, EN5 4EL
tel:	07977 556 701
email:	studio@gb-sound.co.uk
web:	www.gb-sound.co.uk
contact:	Gavin
desk:	Pro Tools
monitors:	Dynaudio
rates:	From £25 per hour
info:	Large live room capable of housing up to 10 people.

Genesis Recording Studio
29a Mayville Road, London, IG1 2HU
tel:	020 8514 5379
email:	bucky12001@yahoo.co.uk
web:	www.genesisrecordingstudio.co.uk
contact:	Bucky
desk:	Studio Master Series II
monitors:	Tannoy/Alesis
rates:	Call for details
info:	Studio has 2 live rooms, and isolation booth for vocals. Pro Tools and tape recording. Full studio drum kit, bass and electric guitars for hire. Lots of outboard and effects units.

Gizzard Recording
Unit 1, 2-4 Crown Close, London, E3 2JQ
tel:	020 8981 7848
email:	soundsfat@hotmail.com
web:	www.gizzardrecording.zoomshare.com
contact:	Ed
desk:	Alice AM series (ex BBC)
monitors:	BBC LS' 5
info:	Spacious acoustically designed live room. Suitable for recording live. Kitchen facilities. Parking area.

Gold Seal Music
Unigate House, Depot Road, Wood Lane, London, W12 7RP
tel:	020 8743 0009
email:	info@goldsealrecordings.com
web:	www.goldsealrecordings.com
contact:	Davide
desk:	Mackie
monitors:	Alesis
rates:	£20 per hour
info:	Specialising in Urban, Hip-Hop, Garage and House Music, Gold Seal Music believe that music and musical facilities should be available to all, regardless of financial situation or ethnic background. Provide workshops, seminars and affordable studio time to individuals interested in the music industry. Discounts available for block bookings.

Golddust Studios
14 Cromwell Avenue, Bromley, Kent, BR2 9AQ
tel:	020 8466 7435
email:	mark@golddust.co.uk
web:	www.golddust.co.uk
contact:	Mark Dawson
desk:	Mackie D8b digital
monitors:	Dynaudio BM15s, Yamaha XS350 and aurotones Dynaudio BM15/Yamaha XS350
rates:	Contact for details
info:	Established since 1979. 24 track studio. 3 recording rooms with daylight. Main recording studio with Mackie HDR recorder and 2" analogue multitrack. Separate chillout area. Also offer duplication services. See entry in Mastering and Duplication section for details.

Gravity Shack
Unit 3, Rear of 328 Balham High Road, London, SW17 7AA
tel:	020 8672 5969
contact:	Pat Collier
desk:	Soundcraft
monitors:	Quested
rates:	£250 per 9 hour day
info:	Work exclusively with Indie and Rock based bands.

Green Studio
11 Hungerford Road, London, N7 9LA
tel:	07990 972 184/07903 188 743
email:	info@greenstudio.co.uk
web:	www.greenstudio.co.uk
contact:	Dave, Felix
rates:	£30 per hour, £220 for 8 hour session
info:	Acoustically designed live room and spacious control room. Fully air-conditioned.

Groove Yard Productions
79 Larkswood Road, Chingford, London, E4 9DU
tel:	020 8523 8083
email:	info@groove-yard-productions.com
web:	www.groove-yard-productions.com
contact:	Paul
desk:	Digital
monitors:	Alesis Monitor 1
rates:	Call for details
info:	Fully automated digital mixing, with 64 track recording and Apple Mac sequencing. MIDI sound modules, digital and analogue effects, dynamic processing as well as valve, vocal and instrument processing. Multi format output to CD or DAT. All media requirements can be produced. Separate vocal booth featuring Neumann mics.

Henry Wood Hall
Trinity Church Square, London, SE1 4HU
tel:	020 7403 0118
fax:	020 7378 8294
email:	bookings@hwh.co.uk
web:	www.hwh.co.uk
rates:	£540 for 3 hours, £1300 per day
info:	Elegant and large recording and rehearsal space. Bands will need to provide recording equipment. Often used to record orchestras, but this is not a policy.

Heron
Heron House, Hale Wharf, Ferry Lane, London, N17 9NF
tel:	020 8442 3509
email:	jgeddef@staff.coneo.ac.uk
contact:	Douglas
desk:	Otari Status 18R
monitors:	Genelic
rates:	Call for details
info:	Heron have 2 fully equipped recording studios, including a separate mastering booth. Wide range of outboard, synths and plug-ins. Pro Tools and Logic Audio Pro. Heron also have facilities for video editing and multimedia requirements (including 3 digital editing suites).

Hi-Grade Music Productions Ltd.
97-130 Fonthill Road, London, N4 3JH
tel:	020 8986 5527
email:	highgrademusic46@aol.com
web:	www.hi-grademusic.co.uk
contact:	Dayne Macho
desk:	02R (24 track)
monitors:	Tannoy/Yamaha NS10
rates:	Negotiable
info:	Studio is fully equipped to cater for all recording needs, good for live work. Musicians available. Excellent variety of outboard and plug-ins, plus vocal booth and good drum area. Also cater for video production.

Hoo-Hah Recording Studios
Building B, Unit 7, Tower Bridge Business Complex, 100 Clements Road, London, SE16 4DG
tel:	07941 342 797
email:	hoohahrecording.studios@virgin.net
web:	www.hoohahrecordingstudios.co.uk
contact:	Jonathan Wood
info:	Audio recording and editting capabilities suitable for bands, songwriters and composers.

The Hutch
31-35 Pitfield Street, London, N1 6HB
tel:	07891 677 447
email:	griff@griffproducer.com
web:	www.griffproducer.com
contact:	Griff
monitors:	Mackie HR624
rates:	Contact for details
info:	Griff is a producer with his own studio. Full technical specification can be found on the website.

Iguana Studio
Unit 1, 88a Acre Lane, London, SW2 5QN
tel:	020 7924 0496
web:	www.iguanastudio.co.uk
desk:	Mackie
monitors:	Mackie
rates:	From £25 per hour
info:	Iguana has 2 highly developed studios with good selection of equipment.

Inigo Recordings
642 Wandsworth Road, London, SW8 3JW
tel: 020 7622 8686/07949 555 802
email: info@inigorecordings.com
web: www.inigorecordings.com
contact: Alex
desk: Mackie 16 04 VLZ Pro
monitors: JBL LSR 25P
rates: Call for details
info: The studio is suited to recording live bands, as well as Dance music. Large live room and a variety of instruments and amplifiers available. The studio own a lot of high-end. Hard disk recording using a specially built audio PC system. Inigo also run a record label, as well as bar featuring live music. See listings in relevant sections for further information.

The Instrument
429 Harrow Road, London, W10 4RE
tel: 020 8964 2001
fax: 020 8960 6441
email: the-instrument@mutehq.co.uk
web: www.the-instrument.com
contact: MJ, Dave, Ann
desk: Amek Hendrix/Amek Einstein
monitors: ATC 200/Dynaudio BM15/Yamaha NS10M
rates: From £250 for 10 hours (Studio 1), From £150 for 10 hours (Studio 2)
info: Range of vintage synths and large outboard. Audio post-production studio also available with Logic and Pro Tools.

Intimate Recording Studios
The Smokehouse, 120 Pennington Street, London, E1 9BB
tel: 020 7702 0789
email: p.madden47@ntlworld.com
web: www.intimatestudios.com
contact: Paul Madden
desk: Harrison
monitors: Dynaudio M4
rates: Call for details
info: Classic 70s Harrison console. All formats include Pro Tools, IZ Radar 24, 2" and 1/2" analogue. Large live area with Yamaha Grand and Hammond. Recent clients include The White Stripes, Jah Wobble and The Divine Comedy. Bed and breakfast available from £25 per night.

Jamestown Studio
20 Damien Street, London, E1 2HX
tel: 020 7790 3578
fax: 020 7790 3578
email: georgina@jamestown.co.uk
web: www.jamestown.co.uk
contact: Georgina Morris
rates: £90-£170 per week
info: Not a conventional recording studio, but a scheme where you pay for the space and supply the recording equipment. The studios are designed for recording. All are sound-proofed and have vocal booths. There are 23 studios available ranging in size.

Joe Public Studios
79 Vernon Crescent, East Barnet, Hertfordshire, EN4 8QQ
tel: 07958 283 009
email: mail@joepublicstudios.com
web: www.joepublicstudios.com
contact: Joe Lonsdale
desk: Logic Audio
monitors: Alesis
rates: £15 per hour
info: Fully virtual studio using Logic Audio. Ideal for pre-production and songwriting.

Kay Produtions
128 White Hart Lane, Tottenham, N17 8HS
tel: 020 8801 4963/07947 685 523
email: kennethsamuels52@yahoo.co.uk
contact: Kenneth
desk: Pro Tools
rates: Call for details

Konk Studios
84-86 Tottenham Lane, London, N8 7EE
tel: 020 8340 7873
fax: 020 8348 3952
email: linda@konkstudios.com
contact: Sarah Lockwood, Linda
desk: Neve Custom made/SSL
monitors: Yamaha NS10/Quested
rates: Call for details
info: Comprehensive studio with Pro Tools. Large variety of synths and outboard. Large live room, overdub booth and piano. Catering facilities also available.

"Probably the last affordable recording room in London"

The best of classic analoge combined with the latest in digital Pro Tools & Radar 24 etc...
NOW WITH B & B ACCOMADATION FROM £25 NIGHT
Website: www.intimatestudios.com
Phone: 07860 109 612

Lab 24
346 Ground Floor, Kingsland Road, London, E8 4DA
tel: 07970 309 470
contact: Hamish
desk: Studiomaster 24 Track
monitors: Yamaha NS10/Absolute Zeros
rates: Call for details
info: Specialises in producing House and Garage music.

Lab Studios
Unit 2G, Clapham North Arts Centre, 26-32 Voltaire Road, London, SW4 6DH
tel: 020 7622 3332
email: drewhorley@hotmail.com
contact: Drew Horley
desk: Allen & Heath
monitors: Spirit Absolute 2
rates: Call for details
info: Specialise in recording using analogue equipment. Large live room with drum kit. Fender Rhodes keyboard and Moog synthesizer. Logic Audio also available. Lab Studios is equipped for the recording and production of any style of music, although the studio is used predominately by Urban acts. Drew produced Ty's Mercury Music prize nominated album 'Upwards'.

Lansdowne Recording Studio
Lansdowne House, Lansdowne Road, London, W11 3LP
tel: 020 7727 0041
email: info@cts-lansdowne.co.uk
web: www.cts-lansdowne.co.uk
contact: Sharon Rose
desk: AMS-Neve VXS/Pro Tools HD2/Yamaha O2R
monitors: ATC 5.1
rates: Call for details
info: Surround sound monitoring. Great deal of analogue kit available including vintage valve microphones and signal processors. Large range of outboard. Lounge with cable TV and kitchen.

Leisure Lounge Studios

Floor 3, Chocolate Factory 2, 4 Coburg Road, Wood Green, London, N22 6UJ

tel:	020 8829 8981/07971 413 107
email:	info@leisureloungestudios.co.uk
web:	www.leisureloungestudios.co.uk
contact:	Stuart Maxwell
desk:	Soundcraft 6000 24:16
monitors:	Dynaudio BM5 Nearfield
rates:	£150 per day
info:	2 separate live rooms. Competitive hourly rates, contact for details. Also offer rehearsal studios. See listing in relevant section for details.

Liberty Hall Music

Battle House, 1 East Barnet Road,, Barnet, Hertfordshire, EN4 8RR

tel:	020 8440 0011/07961 447 589
email:	kristina@libertyhallmusic.com
web:	www.libertyhallmusic.com
contact:	Kristina
desk:	Soundcraft Spirit
monitors:	Tannoy/Genelec
rates:	£25 per hour
info:	Established in 1993, Liberty Hall Music offer a wide range of services including studio recording, mastering and duplication services and various music training courses. See entries in relevant sections for more details. Discount available on block bookings, contact for further information.

Library Productions

41b Emdymion Road, London, N4 1EQ

tel:	07956 412 209
email:	info@librarystudio.com
web:	www.librarystudio.com
contact:	Julian Standen
desk:	Digi Design ProControl
monitors:	Adam S4A
rates:	Call for details
info:	Library Productions specialise in producing unsigned acts and are very enthusiastic about meeting new bands. Julian Standen produced 'Mrs. Robinson' for The Lemonheads.

Livingstone Recording Studio

The Church Hall, Brook Road, Off Mayes Road, London, N22 6TR

tel:	020 8889 6558
email:	mail@livingstonstudios.co.uk
web:	www.livingstonstudios.co.uk
contact:	Lisa, Verity
desk:	SSL/Amek Rembrandt
monitors:	Genelec/Yamaha NS10/Eastlake TM3
rates:	Call for details
info:	Well equipped, friendly studio with an extensive array of equipment. Studio 1 has a mic suite with 24 high-end microphones, live room and piano room, as well as 2 separate booths laid out so there is good visual contact between each area. Pro Tools HD, 2" analogue tape or Radar II. Previous clients include Placebo, Muse, Ry Cooder, The Smiths, Ash, John Leckie, Coldcut and Ruben Gonzales.

The Lost Studio

25 Heathman's Road, London, SW6 4TJ

tel:	020 7371 5756
email:	studio@pureuk.com
web:	www.pureuk.com
contact:	Tom Belton
desk:	Pro Tools
monitors:	Genelec/KRK
rates:	£200 per day (inc. engineer)
info:	Mainly pre-production, programming and Dance music production. Control room and live room. Good selection of analogue synths. Studio uses 2GHz duel processor G5 Apple Macs with Logic Audio. Lots of software and plug-ins. Also run a label and publishing company, enquire for further details.

Loz Vegas Studios

Unit 39, Silicone Business Centre, 28 Wadsworth Road, Perivale, Middlesex, UB6 7JZ

tel:	020 8998 9122
fax:	020 8991 2661
email:	loz@vegassoundhouse.com or matt@vegassoundhouse.com
web:	www.lozvegasmusic.co.uk
desk:	Allen & Heath
monitors:	Samsung Resolve
rates:	Call for details
info:	Specialises in recording bands, the studio has a large live room. Instruments available. Logic Audio. Loz Vegas also run rehearsal rooms under the same name, equipment hire service and music shop 'Vegas Sound House', promotions and booking agency 'Music Scene UK', 'Music Providers' management, 'Some Think Media' media design company, as well as running the Drum Academy. See entries in relevant sections for further information.

Luxybus Mobile Recordings

London

tel:	07932 884 832/07976 399 848
email:	sirstevelewis@yahoo.co.uk
contact:	Steve Lewis
desk:	Soundtrac
monitors:	Yamaha NS10/Mackie
rates:	Call for details
info:	The Luxybus is a converted 40ft coach with all the usual tour bus facilities, such as shower, bunks and dining areas, as well as lots of storage and control room. Any job considered, call for details.

Manor Recording Studio

Breaks Manor, Links Drive, Hatfield, Hertfordshire, AL10 8TP

tel:	07810 410 892
email:	manorstudio@hotmail.co.uk
web:	www.manorstudio.co.uk
contact:	Tom Chaney
desk:	Mackie
monitors:	Genelec
rates:	£20 for first hour, £17.50 (2-4 hours), £15 (5-10 hours)
info:	Studio offering analogue and digital recording. Will deal with all genres. Fully treated live room, analogue mixer, digital recording and an unlimited virtual track count. Non-musical and audio work is also welcome.

MAP Music

46 Grafton Road, London, NW5 3DU

tel:	020 7916 0544/020 7916 0545
fax:	020 7284 4232
email:	info@mapmusic.net
web:	www.mapmusic.net/studios.htm
contact:	Taylor
desk:	Amek
monitors:	KRK V8
rates:	Call For details
info:	3 studios offering recording and pre-production. Live room/vocal booth, Pro Tools, Macs. CD duplication also available. See listing in relevant section for details.

Mark Angelo Studios

Unit 13, Impress House, Mansell Road, London, W3 7QH

tel:	020 8735 0040
email:	mimi@markangelo.co.uk
web:	www.markangelo.co.uk
contact:	Mimi Kerns
desk:	Neve VX60
monitors:	Quested/Yamaha NS10/Tannoy
rates:	Call for details
info:	Large live room, drum booth and Steinway piano. Pro Tools and Radar II available.

Maximum Music

Bow Business Centre, Unit B4B, 153-159 Bow Road, London, E3 2SE

tel:	07958 141 439
email:	maxmusic@virgin.net
contact:	Mr A. Simons
rates:	Flat rate of £70 per track
info:	2 studios with live rooms. Music technology suite with 5 computers available. Maximum Music also has rehearsal facilities. See entry in relevant section for further details.

The Mayfair Studios

Mayfair Farm, Churt, Farnham, Surrey, GU22 0PP

tel:	01428 712 750
email:	info@themayfairstudio.com
web:	www.themayfairstudio.com
contact:	Rupert
desk:	Cubase SX2/Sony Sound Forge/Soundtrax/Drawmer
monitors:	Soundcraft/Tannoy
rates:	Call for details
info:	Located on a farm in Surrey with leisure facilities. Lounge room with refreshment making facilities, TV, Sky and DVD player. Discounts available for students, enquire for details. Also have rehearsal facilities, see entry in relevant section. For more information on equipment, please visit website.

MD Produxions

PO Box 38478, London, SE16 2WS

tel:	0845 644 2869
fax:	0871 433 4522
email:	contact@mdproduxions.com
web:	www.mdproduxions.com
contact:	Master Dodge
desk:	Mackie Analogue
monitors:	Genelec
info:	Recording studio for vocal sessions, voice overs, pre-production and final mixdowns for computer based production projects and demos, remixes and backing tracks. Specialise in Urban and Underground Dance but also cater for Pop and Mainstream. Can undertake project management for unsigned acts which includes CD artwork, internet presence, music video production and networking in the London area. Contact for further information.

Melodic Productions Ltd.

Wembley Commercial Centre, 115 East Lane, Wembley, HA9 7UR

tel:	020 8908 0090
rates:	Call for details.
info:	24 track digital recording studio. Live room, control room and chill out room with kitchen.

Metropolis Studios

The Powerhouse, 70 Chiswick High Road, London, W4 1SY

tel:	020 8742 1111
fax:	020 8742 2626
email:	reception@metropolis-group.co.uk
web:	www.metropolis-group.co.uk
contact:	Alison Hussey
desk:	SSL (G, J, K series)/Neve VR/Digidesign ICON
monitors:	Genelic/PMC
rates:	Call for details
info:	Metropolis houses 5 studios in total. Fully equipped with Pro Tools, lots of outboard, synths. For more information of Metropolis Studios' mastering facilities, see the Mastering and Duplication section.

The Mews Recording Studios

27B Belfast Road, Stoke Newington, London, N16 6UN

tel:	020 8806 6663/07790 002 472
email:	info@themews.co.uk
web:	www.themewsrecordingstudios.com
contact:	David Clarke
desk:	Analogue 56 channel 8 Buss Mackie (32:8:2 and 24E) & Meterbridge
monitors:	Quested VS2108/Yamaha NS10M/Beyerdynamic Blueprint A150 amp
rates:	Call for details
info:	The Mews is a competitively priced production, recording and mixing facility. Control room is acoustically designed with natural daylight. Extensive mics, keyboards, soundmodules, plugins and backline available. Includes live area, kitchen, bathroom and lounge. Host to Grammy nominated Prodigy album 'Always Outnumbered Never Outgunned'.

Mill Hill Recording Company

Mill Hill Music Complex, Bunns Lane Works, Bunns Lane, Mill Hill, London, NW7 2AJ

tel:	020 8906 9991
email:	recording@millhillmusic.co.uk
web:	www.millhillmusic.co.uk
contact:	Darren
desk:	2x24 track Soundtrax Analogue
monitors:	Fostex/Tannoy/JBL/HHB
rates:	£25 per hour
info:	Large live room that has been sonically tuned to optimise instrument and vocal sound. Wide selection of instruments for hire, as well as mics, effects and reverb units, compressors and samplers. It is also possible to hire an engineer. Mill Hill Music Complex also comprises rehearsal rooms and an instrument shop. See entries in relevant sections for more information.

Milo Music (Miloco Studios)
36 Leroy Street, London, SE1 4SP
tel:	020 7232 0008
email:	jess@miloco.co.uk
web:	www.miloco.co.uk
contact:	Jess Gerry
desk:	Neve VR60 & V3/DDA QMR48/Amek 2520
monitors:	Munro M4/ATC SCM 200/Yamaha NS10/Genelic/ Eastlake/Urei
rates:	Call for details
info:	4 high spec studios, as well as 'dry' studio suitable for bands and artists with their own equipment looking for long term hire. Prices vary depending on your needs, see website for details. Clients have included Ocean Colour Scene, The Chemical Brothers, Richard X, Roots Manuva, Blak Twang, British Sea Power, Bloc Party and Ash.

Mind Loop UK
13 Swanyard, Highbury, Islington, London, N1 1SD
tel:	020 7704 0888/07791 630 128
email:	info@mindloopuk.com
web:	www.mindloopuk.com
contact:	Steve Davidson, Nick Caffrey
desk:	SSL G+/Yamaha 02R
monitors:	Boxer/Dynaudio
rates:	Call for details
info:	Full Pro Tools HD3 and Logic Audio Pro. Large amount of software and plug-ins available.

Modernfidelity
The Decam Building, Taggs Boatyard, 44 Summer Road, Thames Ditton, KT7 0QQ
tel:	07817 049 583
email:	info@modernfidelity.co.uk
web:	www.modernfidelity.co.uk
contact:	Mark Rushton
desk:	Mackie
monitors:	Alesis
rates:	Call for details
info:	Recently moved into new premises, Modernfidelity also offer rehearsal space. See entry in relevant section for details.

Moon Recording Studio
Middle Street, Croydon, London, CR0 1RE
tel:	020 8680 1202
email:	shop@beanos.co.uk
web:	www.beanos.co.uk
desk:	Allen & Heath
monitors:	Tannoy
rates:	Call for details
info:	Part of Beano's music shops in Croydon. See listing in Record Shops section for details.

Motion Studio
Forest Hill, Lewisham, London
tel:	07748 778 830
email:	info@motionstudio.co.uk
web:	www.motionstudio.co.uk
contact:	Alan
desk:	Spirit 328
monitors:	Yamaha NS10/Genelic
rates:	Call for details
info:	From pre-production to the final CD master, Motion Studio caters for the needs of artists at all levels. The studio is well equipped with some of the latest digital technology. Engineer, producer and session drummer available. The studio also have a good database of session musicians. Please feel free to give Alan a call with any queries.

Music Room
116-118 New Cross Road, London, SE14 5BA
tel:	020 7252 8271
fax:	020 7252 8252
email:	sales@musicroomsolutions.com
web:	www.musicroomsolutions.com
contact:	Dean
desk:	Mackie
monitors:	KRK
rates:	Call for details
info:	Music Room primarily provide rehearsal space, but can cater for recording. Also offer equipment hire service. See listings in relevant sections for details.

New Age Studios
3 Partridge Close, Arkley Gate, Barnett, Hertfordshire, EN5 2DT
tel:	07903 482 181
email:	alanzipper@aol.com
contact:	Alan Zipper
desk:	Soundcraft
monitors:	Tannoy
rates:	Call for details
info:	Specialises in Mac based Logic and Cubase MIDI sequencing.

New Music Production
Hoxton, London, EC1Y
tel:	020 7250 1054
email:	reception@newmusicproduction.com
web:	www.newmusicproduction.com
contact:	Steve Honest
desk:	Pro Tools
monitors:	DynaudioBM 15a active monitors
rates:	Call for details
info:	Motu Pro Tools system with Focusrite outboard, using Logic Audio software. Aurlex Acoustic treatment in both rooms. There are a variety of guitars available including a pedal steel guitar and a custom built guitar rig through which to play them. Studio is built next to a roof terrace which boasts panoramic views of the city. For full details on recording equipment and rates, visit the website.

Niburu Recordings
Unit 24, Enfield Enterprise Centre, 26-28 Queensway, Enfield, Middlesex, EN3 7DX
tel:	020 8804 0829
email:	niburu_7@hotmail.com
desk:	Behringer
rates:	Call for details
info:	Digital and analogue recording available.

NuCool Studios
34 Beaumont Road, London, W4 5AP
tel:	020 8248 2157
email:	r.niles@richardniles.com
web:	www.richardniles.com
contact:	Richard Niles
desk:	Mackie D8B
monitors:	PMC
rates:	Call for details
info:	24 track digital studio comprising Mackie D8B digital console, Pro Tools 24 Mix+, MOTU Digital Performer, Opcode Studio Vision Pro, Emagic Logic Audio. Piano and drum kit with an excellent set of cymbals. Nucool is available for hire at reasonable rates with an engineer. Richard's production services are available at additional but reasonable rates. Previous clients have included Paul McCartney, Ray Charles, Kylie Minogue, James Brown, Tina Turner, Cher and Westlife.

Ocean Studios
58 Lavander Hill, Battersey, London, SW11 5RQ
tel:	020 7228 5050
email:	thebestsmallstudio@yahoo.com
web:	www.ocean-studios.co.uk
contact:	Mark Bhalla
desk:	Mackie
monitors:	Tannoy
rates:	Call for details
info:	Studio has Pro Tools TDM 64, live room and vocal booth.

Odessa Wharf Sound Studios Ltd.
38 Upper Clapton Road, London, E5 8BQ
tel:	020 8806 6319
contact:	Bartrum
desk:	Amek with Neve EQ
monitors:	Urei/HHB Nearfill/Genelec/Yamaha NS10
rates:	Call for details
info:	Odessa Wharf comprises 2 studios. Studio 1 has a large Eastlake-designed oak-lined live room, which can hold 20 musicians, an Amek Angela desk, and UREI 815 monitoring. Studio 2 has a Yamaha 02R desk. Clients range from big bands, Hip-Hop artists, Reggae to Heavy Metal, Indie and Acoustic music.

Oilville Studio
Holloway Road, London
tel:	07977 003034
email:	tomaitkenhead@hotmail.com
contact:	Tom
desk:	Pro Tools
monitors:	Absolute 4P
rates:	£190 for 8 hours
info:	Specialists in recording bands, 32 tracks, good mics, mastering services available. Large (22 x 16 ft) live room. Amps, drums and piano available. Located several minutes from Holloway tube station.

One Life Productions
2 Warwick Road, London, SE20 7YL
tel:	020 8659 5381
email:	info@onelife-productions.co.uk
web:	www.onelife-productions.co.uk
contact:	Simon
desk:	Digidesign/Pro Tools
monitors:	Mackie HR824
rates:	£120 per 8 hour day (inc. VAT, engineer, producer)
info:	New large live area. Video production services are also available. See website for more information. Discounts available for students, unemployed and under 18s.

Online Studios
Unit 18-19, Croydon House, 1 Peall Road, Croydon, Surrey, CR0 3EX
tel: 020 8287 8585
email: info@onlinestudios.co.uk
web: www.onlinestudios.co.uk
contact: Rob Pearson
desk: Allen & Heath G3000/Behringer MX8000
monitors: Spirit Absolute/Cerwin Vega
rates: Call for details
info: Specialise in producing Dance and Urban music. 2 studios available equipped for writing, recording and production. Also offer CD mastering services, as well as music production and DJ training courses.

Opaz Studio
293-295 Mare Street, Hackney, London, E8 1EJ
tel: 020 8533 9533
email: rayopaz@aol.com
web: www.rayhayden.com
contact: Ade, Celeste
desk: Seck
monitors: Yamaha NS10
rates: Call for details
info: Small production based studio specialising in Hip-Hop and Urban genres. Also offer production courses. Produce their own music and mix-tapes, and are looking to promote and release unsigned artists.

Orient Recording Studios
PO Box 33973, London, NW9 0WJ
tel: 0208 930 1930
email: orientrecordings@aol.com
web: www.orientrecordings.com
contact: Luis Paris
desk: Mackie
monitors: Dynaudio
rates: Call for details
info: Specialise in House music. Also offer mastering services.

OTR Studios Ltd.
The Basement, 143 Mare Street, Hackney, London, E8 3RH
tel: 020 8985 9880
fax: 020 8986 9575
email: info@otrstudios.wanadoo.co.uk
web: www.otrstudios.co.uk
rates: £250 per 10 hour day
info: 24 track digital recording studio. Contact for full technical specification. Music spares are available for purchase on-site. OTR also run rehearsal rooms. See entry in relevant section for details.

Ovni Audio
33-37 Hatherley Mews, Walthamstow, London, E17 4QP
tel: 020 8534 0101/07967 615 647
email: flavio.uk@ukonline.co.uk
contact: Flavio Curras
desk: Soundcraft Ghost
monitors: JBL 6208 5.1
rates: Call for details
info: Live room with a variety of classic keyboards available. Full Pro Tools rig with AV and sound to picture facilities. Live recording mixing and 5.1 surround for DVD a speciality. Timecoded DAT and ADAT in-house.

Oz Productions
30 Cullesden Road, Kenley, London, CR8 5LR
tel: 020 8668 4833
email: ozprods@hotmail.com
web: www.ozprods.co.uk
contact: Ozwin
desk: Soundcraft
monitors: Tannoy
rates: From £25 per hour
info: Specialise in production for songwriters. Special offers available, see website or call for details.

Papa Joe's Sound Studios
Unit 30, Merrick Road, Southall, Middlesex, UB2 4AU
tel: 020 8571 2707
email: info@papajoesstudios.com
web: www.papajoesstudios.com
desk: Mackie DB8
monitors: Genelec 1031
rates: Contact for details
info: See also listing for rehearsal facilities in relevant section.

Parafanalia
Unit 5 b201, Tower Bridge Business Complex, 100 Clements Road, SE16 4DG
tel:	020 7740 1008
email:	info@parafanalia-studio.com
web:	www.parafanalia-studio.com
desk:	Yamaha
monitors:	Alesis/Skytec
rates:	£20 per hour, £200 per 10 hour day
info:	Recording for music of all genres. Also offer rehearsal

facilities. See listing in relevant section for details.

The Pierce Rooms
Pierce House, London Apollo Complex, Queen Caroline Street, London, W6 9QU
tel:	020 8563 1234
email:	meredith@pierce-entertainment.com
web:	www.pierce-entertainment.com
contact:	Meredith
desk:	Neve VR-72-60
monitors:	Dynaudio M4/Yamaha NS10/Genelec/Auratone
rates:	Call for details
info:	High spec professional studio situated at the famous

London Apollo complex.

Playtime Productions
29 Kneller Road, Brockley, London, SE4 2AR
tel:	020 8694 9768
email:	info@playtime.org.uk
web:	www.playtime.org.uk
contact:	Hugh Griffith, Marina Fusella
desk:	Harrison
monitors:	Urei
rates:	Call for details
info:	Specialise in live band recording. Producers, engineers

and programmers available. Engineering credits include Placebo, Suede, Robert Plant, Desiree, BMG and Virgin.

The Premises
201-209 Hackney Road, London, E2 8JL
tel:	020 7729 7593
fax:	020 7739 5600
email:	premisesstudios@btconnect.com
web:	www.premises.demon.co.uk
contact:	Viv Broughton
desk:	Amek Einstein
monitors:	Mackie/Genelec/Yamaha NS10
rates:	Call for details
info:	Wide range of backline available to hire, as well as a

grand piano. Logic 6 Platinum, valve pre-amps, separate vocal booth. Also offer rehearsal studios. See listing in relevant section for more information.

Q Sound
Queen's Studios, 117-121 Salusbury Road, London, NW6 6RG
tel:	020 7625 5359
email:	queries@qsound.uk.com
web:	www.qsound.uk.com
contact:	Adam Helal
desk:	Focusrite Control 24
monitors:	Genelec
rates:	Call for details
info:	2 studios available for hire. Recent clients include The

Rakes. Pro Tools tuition and mastering services available.

Quince Recording Studios
62a Balcombe Street, Marylebone, London, NW1 6NE
tel:	07810 752 765
fax:	020 7723 1010
email:	info@quincestudios.co.uk
web:	www.quincestudios.co.uk
contact:	Matt Walters
desk:	Yamaha O2R
monitors:	Yamaha NS10/Phillips
rates:	Call for details
info:	Nuendo, Cubase, Logic Audio and Reason. Large client

list, see website for details.

Quit Dreaming
Hampton, Middlesex, TW12 1BG
tel:	020 8979 2624/07834 548 815
email:	studio@quitdreaming.com
web:	www.quitdreaming.com
contact:	Phil Eve
desk:	Akai
monitors:	Tannoy/Alesis
rates:	£21 per hour
info:	Quit Dreaming Studio comprises a fully equipped control

room and sound-proofed studio room large enough to accommodate a full-sized drum kit.

Quo-Vadis Recording Studio
Unit 1, Morrison Yard, 551a High Road, London, N17 6SB
tel:	020 8365 1999
email:	quo_vadis2002@yahoo.co.uk
web:	www.quovadisstudios.com
contact:	Don Mackenzie
desk:	Allen & Heath
monitors:	JBL/Yamaha NS10
rates:	From £25 per hour
info:	Pro Tools and many instruments, as well as backline

available. 2 live rooms. Quo-Vadis also run rehearsal studios. See entry in relevant section for details.

Raezor Studio
25 Frogmore, Wandsworth, London, SW18 1JA
tel:	020 8870 4036
fax:	020 8874 4133
email:	raezor.studio@virgin.net
web:	www.raezor.co.uk
contact:	Ian Wilkinson
desk:	SSL 4048e
monitors:	Yamaha NS10/JBL/KRK V6 active
rates:	Call for details
info:	Studio has vintage pre-amps. Digidesign Pro Tools Mix

32. Range of effects and processors. Baby grand piano available. Recent clients include Razorlight and Tom McRae.

RAK Recording Studios
42-48 Charlbert Street, London, NW8 7BU
tel:	020 7586 2012
fax:	020 7722 5823
email:	trisha@rakstudios.co.uk
web:	www.rakstudios.co.uk
contact:	Trisha Wegg
desk:	API/Neve 51
monitors:	Tannoy/PMC/Dynaudio
rates:	Call for details
info:	RAK houses 3 studios. Accommodation, parking and

catering available.

Raya Recording Studios
Unit 13, 326 The Sage Centre, Kensal Road, London, W10 5BZ
tel:	07973 673 724
email:	rrs@plasticfantastic.co.uk
web:	www.rayarecordingstudios.co.uk
contact:	Luis Paris
desk:	Mackie
monitors:	Dynaudio
rates:	Call for details
info:	Specialising in Dance music, services on offer include

music production and mastering, CD duplication and mastering, and DJ mixing and recording. Associated with Plastic Fantastic and Orient recordings.

Redchurch Sudios
Unit 2, 51 Tudor Road, London, E9 7SN
tel:	020 8986 1663
email:	fredbags@btconnect.com
web:	www.redchurchrecordingslondon.co.uk
contact:	Fred
desk:	Soundtracs CM4400 analogue
monitors:	Tannoy/KEF/Mordant/Teac
rates:	From £140 per day
info:	Large studio complex housing 3 studios. Grand

piano and other instruments available. Fred has 21 years of industry experience and has worked with Robert Palmer and Peter Gabriel. Good range of outboard.

Redroom Productions
Bromley
tel:	020 8776 0193
email:	redroom_studio@postmaster.co.uk
web:	www.redroomproductions.co.uk
desk:	Soundtracs analogue
rates:	Call for details
info:	Range of outboard and plug ins available. For full

technical specification see the website above.

Resident Studios
57a Windsor Road, Willesden, London, NW2 5DT
tel:	020 8830 4321
email:	info@residentstudios.com
web:	www.residentstudios.com
contact:	Bruno Newman
desk:	Soundcraft Ghost 24/Yamaha 01V
monitors:	Mackie
rates:	See website for details
info:	Large studio complex housing a live room and 2 studios.

Guitars, synths, samplers and percussion available to use. Apple Mac G4 running Logic Audio and Cubase SX. Mastering and rehearsal also available, see relevant sections for more information.

RK Productions
Unit 42, The Truman Brewery, 91 Brick Lane, London, E1 6QL
tel: 020 7375 2297
email: lena@dreadrecordingsuk.com
web: www.dreadrecordingsuk.com
contact: Lena
desk: Tascam
rates: Call for details
info: Drum&Bass specialists, associated with Ray Keith's UFO, Penny Black and Dread Recordings. Comprehensive studio with Apple Mac, Akai and Emu samplers, lots of outboard.

RMS Studios
43-45 Clifton Road, London, SE25 6PX
tel: 020 8653 4965
fax: 020 8653 4965
email: rmsstudios@blueyonder.co.uk
web: www.rms-studios.co.uk
contact: Alan Jones
desk: Soundcraft 1600/Soundtracs
monitors: JBL/Tannoy/Yamaha
rates: Call for details
info: Fully equipped studio with grand piano and Hammond C3 available. Also offer mastering and CD duplication services.

Rogue Studios
Railway Arch 4, Bermondsey Trading Estate, Rotherhithe New Road, London, SE16 3LL
tel: 020 7231 3257
fax: 020 7231 7358
email: info@roguestudios.co.uk
web: www.roguestudios.co.uk
contact: Dave Folwer
desk: Soundtracs Megas
monitors: Alesis Monitor 1 and 2
rates: £12.50-£22.50 per hour
info: Mix of analogue and digital technologies to ensure a warm sound. Fully experienced engineer who has worked with Muse and Phil Collins. Rehearsal facilities also available. See listing in relevant section.

Roll Over Studios
29 Beethoven Street, London, W10 4LJ
tel: 020 8969 0299
fax: 020 8968 1047
email: bookings@rollover.co.uk
web: www.rollover.co.uk
contact: Phil Jacobs
desk: Soundtracs Jade/Mackie 32 channel
monitors: Yamaha NS10/Custom made
rates: Call for details
info: Record onto tape or via Pro Tools. Logic Audio available. Well located in West London, with a pleasant and friendly working environment. Caters to all budgets.

Roll Your Own Productions
16 Farren Road, London, SE23 2EA
tel: 020 8699 2212/07956 856 298
email: info@rollyourownproductions.co.uk
web: www.rollyourownproductions.co.uk
contact: Spy
desk: Allen & Heath
monitors: Event 20/20
rates: Call for details
info: Specialise in production of Urban music, although music from all other genres is welcome.

Rooster Studios
117 Sinclair Road, London, W14 0NP
tel: 020 7602 2881
email: info@roosterstudios.com
web: www.roosterstudios.com
contact: Nick Sykes
desk: Otari Status
monitors: Quested/M&K
rates: Call for details
info: Recording using Radar 24 and Nuendo. Large selection of outboard.

Scorpio Productions
152 Katherine Road, East Ham, London, E61 ER
tel: 07931 874 232
email: scorpioproductions@hotmail.com
web: www.scorpioproductions.co.uk
contact: Desire
desk: Eurodesk
monitors: Genelec 80-30
rates: Call for details
info: 48 channel desk put through 128 tracks via hard disk. Lots of software including Logic Audio, Cubase, Fruitloops and Acid. Scorpio can also provide a video production service (see relevant section for more details) and DJ hire.

ROGUE STUDIOS

Rehearsals
Recording
Music Videos
Backline &
PA Hire

Experts In Analogue & Digital Recording.

CD & DVD Mastering.

Experienced Producers & Engineers

South London's Premier Music & Dance Studio

3 Rehearsal Rooms

16 Channel 2.5K P.A. In Each Room

2 Mirrored Rooms (Ideal For Dance)

(020) 7231 3257
www.roguestudios.co.uk
RA4 Bermondsey Trading Estate, Rotherhithe New Road, SE16 3LL

Scream Studios
20c South End, Croydon, Surrey, CR0 1DN
tel: 020 8686 5788
email: croydon@screamstudios.co.uk
web: www.screamstudios.co.uk
desk: Mac-based Digital Performer
monitors: Alesis/Genelec
rates: £150 per day (weekdays), £200 per day (weekends)
info: Scream Studios also have 17 rehearsal rooms. See entry in relevant section for details.

Secret Sound
64 1/2 Englefield Road, London, N1 3LG
tel: 020 7354 8843
email: kieron.hunter@btconnect.com
contact: Kieron
desk: Studiomaster
monitors: Tannoy
rates: Call for details
info: Studio comprises both analogue and digital equipment. Separate control and live room. Instruments and amplification available for hire. Contact Kieron on the above number for details of rates.

Sensible Studios
90-96 Brewery Road, London, N7 9NT
tel: 020 7700 9900
email: studio@sensible-music.co.uk
web: www.sensible-music.co.uk
contact: Pat Tate
desk: Euphonix
monitors: PMC/Yamaha NS10/KRK/Mackie/AE1/Auratones
rates: Call for details
info: Largest Euphonix console in Europe with 96 faders. Production suites and showcase room. Sensible also run a mobile recording suite, equipment rental and PA system hire, see listing for details.

Seven Studios
49-51 Leswin Road, London, N16 7NX
tel:	020 7923 9533
email:	seventhmusic@hotmail.com.uk
web:	www.seventhmusic.co.uk
contact:	Dan Chudley
desk:	Mackie
monitors:	JBL
rates:	Call for details
info:	Mac G5 with Logic Audio. Pro Tools and 2" tape
recording. Seven also provide rehearsal space and run music courses, see relevant sections for details.

Shiftworks
7 Overbury Road, London, N15 6RH
tel:	020 8880 1022/07973 294 204
email:	info@shiftworks.net
web:	www.shiftworks.net
contact:	Ellis
desk:	Soundcraft
monitors:	Mackie
rates:	Call for details
info:	Specialising in electronic analogue recording, the studio
has lots of vintage synthesizers, Moog's, Korg's and modules. Pro Tools set up recently installed. Live engineers also available to hire. Rehearsal space also provided, see the relevant section for more information.

Slap Studio
Unit M1, 245a Coldharbour Lane, London, SW9 8RR
tel:	020 7274 0139
email:	slapstudio@freenetname.co.uk
web:	www.slapstudios.co.uk
contact:	Simon
desk:	Mackie
monitors:	Mackie
rates:	Call for details
info:	Specialise in band recording.

Soho Recording Studio
The Heals Building, 22-24 Torrington Place, London, WC1E 7HJ
tel:	020 7419 2444
email:	dominic@sohostudios.co.uk
web:	www.sohostudios.co.uk
contact:	Dominic
desk:	SSL 4000 G+/Yamaha O2R
monitors:	Yamaha NS10/Genelec 1034A/1031/Auratone
rates:	Call for details
info:	Professional standard studio with Apple G4, Pro Tools
and Logic Platinum 5. Wide range of outboard including Joe Meek compressors and Trident. Chillout area with table football and X-Box. Previous clients include The Neptunes, Cinematic Orchestra, Roni Size and Matt Black.

Soleil
Unit 10, Buspace Studios, Conlan Street, London, W10 5AP
tel:	020 8968 8222
fax:	020 7460 3164
email:	soleil@therecordingworkshop.co.uk
web:	www.therecordingworkshop.co.uk
contact:	Mr. Gross
desk:	Studiomaster Series 24-16
monitors:	Tannoy
rates:	£32 per hour
info:	Lots of kit available including Gretsch drum kit, Fender
twin reverb, various valve amps. Pro Tools and tape recording. 'The Recording Workshop' is located in the same premises, and offers a wide range of music technology, production and engineering courses.

The Song Corporation Ltd.
Business Centre, 5 Blackhorse Lane, London, E17 6DS
tel:	020 8527 0447
fax:	020 8527 5592
email:	recording@songcorporation.com or
	info@songcorporation.com
web:	www.songcorporation.com
desk:	Pro Tools/Eurodesk
monitors:	Yamaha
rates:	Call for details
info:	For more details of mastering and duplication services
provided by The Song Corporation, see the relevant section.

The Sonic Bunker
243B Victoria Park Road, Hackney, London, E9 7HD
tel:	020 8986 0740/07930 30436
email:	info@sonicbunker.com
web:	www.sonicbunker.com
contact:	Rob
desk:	Trident series 65
monitors:	JBL
rates:	Call for details
info:	30 channel in-line mixing desk. 24bit hard disk
recording (Mac + PC). 4 way main monitors, AR 18 Nearfield. Good selection of mics including valve and ribbon. Outboard includes Valve compressors and EQ. The studio has a control room with natural light and live room with separate vocal booth. 10 years experience of recording bands and solo artists of all genres, undertaking projects ranging from quick demos to mastered albums. Contact Rob for more information and details of rates.

Sonica Music
Welmar Mews, 154 Clapham Park Road, London, SW4 7DD
tel:	020 7498 2990
email:	info@sonicamusic.co.uk
web:	www.sonicamusic.co.uk
contact:	Matt
desk:	Soundtracs Jade
monitors:	Genelec 80-50
rates:	Call for details
info:	Specialise in all aspects of audio recording and post-
production. Suitable for music, film, animation and multimedia.

The Sound Joint
10 Parade Mews, Tules Hill, London, SE27 9AX
tel:	020 8678 1404
email:	chris@soundjoint.fsnet.co.uk
web:	www.soundjoint.fsnet.co.uk
contact:	Barnaby Smith
desk:	Soundcraft
monitors:	Dynaudio
rates:	Call for details
info:	The studio is owned by freelance producers who often
record unsigned bands, and have in the past offered publishing deals to those they like.

The Sound Suite
92 Camden Mews, London, NW1 9AG
tel:	020 7485 4881
email:	peter@thesoundsuite.co.uk
web:	www.thesoundsuite.co.uk
contact:	Peter
desk:	Amek Hendrix
monitors:	Quested
rates:	From £250
info:	Pro Tools HD3, digital recording. Instruments available.

Soundstage Studio
Unit 1, 30 Gorst Road, London, NW10 6LE
tel:	020 8961 7890
email:	info@synthservice.com
web:	www.synthservice.com/studio.html
contact:	Dave
desk:	Mackie/Studiomaster
monitors:	JBL/SRM 450
rates:	Call for details
info:	Well equipped studio with spacious, custom designed
live room and control room. Vintage instruments available for hire including Hammond organs and Fender Rhodes pianos. Rehearsal space also available, and run repair centre, Synthesiser Service Centre. See listings in relevant sections for details.

Soup Studio
108b Myddleton Road, London, N22
tel:	07779 280 222
email:	simon@soup-studio.co.uk
contact:	Simon
info:	16 track 1/2" tape and 24 track Pro Tools. Vintage gear
provided.

Southern Studio
10 Myddleton Road, London, N22 8NS
tel:	020 8888 8949
email:	studio@southern.com
web:	www.southern.com/studio
contact:	Harvey Birrell
desk:	Raindirk
monitors:	Yamaha NS10/Tannoy Gold
rates:	Call for details
info:	Part of Southern Records, the studio has a 32 input
Mackie desk in addition to the Raindirk. Stereo valve compressors, Focus rite and Drawmer valve mic pre amps. Lots of microphones, reverb, delay and effects units. Live room with space for full backline and drum kit. Programming facilities include Apple Mac G4, Pro Tools and Logic Audio.

Spirit Productions
1 Audley Close, Lavander Hill, London, SW11 5RG
tel: 07973 253 186
email: contact@spiritproductions.com
web: www.spiritproductions.com
contact: Studio Manager
desk: Soundcraft
monitors: PMC IB1/Genelec
rates: Call for details
info: Analogue and digital studio equipped with Pro Tools.

Spotlight Studios
58c Knightshill, West Norwood, London, SE27 0JD
tel: 020 8761 8324
email: graham.spotlightstudios@virgin.net
contact: Graham
desk: Yamaha
monitors: Dynaudio
rates: Call for details
info: 64 track Pro Tools studio with live recording areas.
Location recording and mastering services also available.

Stakeout Studios
Unit 503, Platts Eyot, Lower Sunbury Road, Hampton, Middlesex,
TW12 2HF
tel: 020 8783 1110/07881 625 399
email: sam@stakeoutstudios.com
web: www.stakeoutstudios.com
contact: Sam Burden
info: Range of state of the art equipment and great facilities.

Stakeout Studios
Unit 503, Platts Eyot Lower Sunbury Road, Hampton, Middlesex,
TW12 2HF
tel: 020 8783 1110
email: sam@stakeoutstudios.com
web: www.stakeoutstudios.com
contact: Sam
info: A whole range of state-of-the-art equipment and great
facilities

Strip Studios Ltd.
100 Wellington Road, London, E6 6EA
tel: 020 8586 9743
email: studio@strip.fm
web: www.strip.fm
contact: Ray, Shane
desk: Soundcraft Ghost
monitors: Absolute 2
rates: Call for details
info: Urban music specialist. Tuned vocal booth built to
broadcast standard. Lots of synths and FX. Extensive sample collection
(including entire live sampled orchestra). Can mix in stereo 5.1. Also
provide video production facilities, from shooting to editing using Final
Cut Pro.

Strongroom Ltd.
120-124 Curtain Road, London, EC2A 3SQ
tel: 020 7426 5100
fax: 020 7426 5102
email: mix@strongroom.com
web: www.strongroom.com
contact: Nina Mistry
desk: Neve VR60/SSL 4056 G + /Mackie 32-8-2
monitors: Boxer/Genelic/Yamaha
rates: Call for details
info: Established for over 15 years, Strongroom houses 4
studios and 8 programming rooms. Well equipped with a mix of the
latest Pro Tools technology and traditional equipment. Previous clients
include Underworld, The Thrills, Sophie Ellis-Bextor and David Gray.
See website for more information. Complex also incorporates The
Strongroom Bar which plays host to live music events. See listing in
relevant section for details.

Studio 53
Brockley, London
tel: 020 8692 4869
email: info@thestudio53.co.uk
web: www.thestudio53.co.uk
contact: Dave
desk: Behringer MX3242X
monitors: Tannoy
rates: Contact for details
info: Studio 53 also have rehearsal facilities. See listing in
relevant section for further details.

Studio 54 Recording
54 Bradfield Drive, Barking, Essex, IG11 8RA
tel: 020 8252 8688
email: info@studio-54.co.uk
web: www.studio54.co.uk
desk: Roland
rates: £20 per hour
info: CD duplication and artwork services also available.
Enquire for details.

Studio 7k
Rear of 8 Cameron Road, Seven Kings, Ilford, Essex, IG3 8LA
tel: 020 8599 0103
email: info@studio7k.com
web: www.studio7k.com
contact: Dee
desk: Soundcraft
monitors: Alesis
rates: Call for details
info: Very professional recording studio designed to cater for
all acts. Rehearsal space also available, see entry in relevant section for
details. Also offer tuition, as well as artist development, management
and CD duplication.

Studio 99
99 Herbert Road, London, SE18 3QH
tel: 020 8854 0860
fax: 020 8854 0860
email: mike@studio99.net
contact: Mike
desk: TAC Scorpian
monitors: Yamaha NS10/Absolute/Tannoy
rates: Call for details
info: Otari 24 track analogue recording available. Various
guitars, amplifiers and synthesizers available to use.

Studio Sonic
Enterprise Studios, 1-6 Denmark Place, London, WC2H 8NL
tel: 020 7379 1155
email: andy@studio-sonic.co.uk
web: www.studio-sonic.co.uk
contact: Andy, Nik
desk: Alesis X2/Roland
monitors: Quested VS3208
rates: Call for details
info: Analogue or digital recording, plus Pro Tools, Cubase
and Reason. Instrument hire available. The Enterprise Rehearsal
Studios are located in-house.

Sultan Sound
51 Loveridge Road, London, NW6 2DU
tel: 020 7624 1816
fax: 020 7624 1816
email: enquiries@sultansound.com
web: www.sultansound.com
contact: Dave Yowell
desk: Tascam M3500
monitors: Genelic/Yamaha NS10/Tannoy
rates: £25 per hour
info: Specialists in World Dance fusion. Dave has worked
with a diverse range of artists including Leftfield, Transglobal
Underground and Judge Jules.

Supernova Studio
tel: 07808 524 697
email: keith@supernovastudio.com
web: www.supernovastudio.com
contact: Keith
desk: Pro Tools
monitors: Adam S3A
rates: £250/day or £600/3 days
info: Band friendly studio. Will help with any project from a 3
track demo to a finished album. Studio is naturally lit and has Pro Tools
6.1 running on Apple Mac G4 with Pro Tools HD2 128 track recording.
Various MIDI synths and keyboards, as well as a variety of microphones
and effects plug-ins. Prices include VAT and engineer. Deals available
for longer projects. Production services also available.

Sweet Georgia Brown's
Unit 12, 407 Hornsey Road, London, N19 4DX
tel: 020 7263 1219
email: info@sweetgeorgiabrowns.co.uk
web: www.sweetgeorgiabrowns.co.uk
contact: Mick
desk: Trident
monitors: JBL 44-35
rates: £35 per hour
info: Large live room. Analogue and digital technologies and
lots of kit available. See website for more details. Clients have included
Alabama 3, Arthur Baker, Jocelyn Brown, Felix The Housecat and New
Order. Off road parking facilities.

MUSIC SERVICES/RETAIL

Sync City Studios
16-18 Millmead Business Centre, Millmead Road, Tottenham Hale, London, N17 9QU
tel:	020 8808 0472
fax:	020 8808 0719
email:	sales@synccity.co.uk
web:	www.synccity.co.uk
contact:	Ron Niblett
desk:	Allen & Heath
rates:	Call for details
info:	Sync City have 2 studios, one live based and one for programming. Suitable for all types of musicians. There are a number of other services available including tuition, web design and promotion, duplication and backing tracks. See the website for more details. Linked with Bally Studios offering rehearsal facilities. See listing in relevant section for details.

Theorem Music Complex
385 Willesden High Road, London, NW10 2JR
tel:	020 8451 4545
email:	expo@theoremmusic.co.uk
contact:	Curtis, TJ
desk:	Raindirk
monitors:	Custom built/Yamaha NS10/Dynaudio
rates:	Call for details
info:	Studio is ideal for bands. Live room. Also have rehearsal space available. See listing in relevant section.

Thompsound Music
50 Chestnut Avenue, London, N8 8NY
tel:	07720 707 744
email:	info@thompsoundmusic.co.uk
web:	www.thompsoundmusic.co.uk
contact:	Billy Thompson
info:	Since receiving Prince's Trust funding in 1999, Thompsound Music has been producing music for various artists and the media. On-site violinist available.

TIN PAN ALLEY
STUDIO WC2

WWW.TINPANALLEYSTUDIO.COM

Tin Pan Alley Studio
22 Denmark Street, London, WC2H 8NG
tel:	020 7240 0816
email:	info@tinpanalleystudio.com
web:	www.tinpanalleystudio.com
contact:	Alexandra Fry
desk:	Sony DMX R100
monitors:	Genelec/Tannoy
rates:	Call for details
info:	Tin Pan Alley Studio has been in existence since the 1950s, located in London's famous Denmark Street music district. The studio combines state of the art digital technology with classic valve equipment. The studio has an EMT stereo valve plate reverb unit from Abbey Road Studios (as used by The Beatles). See the website for comprehensive technical information.

Toerag Studios
166a Glyn Road, London, E5 0JE
tel:	020 8985 8862
email:	toeragstudios1@hotmail.com
contact:	Liam Watson
desk:	EMI Redd 17/Calrec M series
monitors:	Tannoy
rates:	Call for details
info:	Analogue based recording studio.

Tony Lowe Productions
32 Monson Road, London, NW10 5UP
tel:	020 8965 8147/07974 759 768
email:	info@tonylowe.com
web:	www.tonylowe.com
info:	Music producer who has worked with many well known artists in the past.

The Town House
150 Goldhawk Road, London, W12 8HH
tel:	020 8932 3200
fax:	020 8932 3207
email:	recording@sanctuarygroup.co.uk
web:	www.sanctuarystudios.co.uk
contact:	Nikki Affleck
desk:	SSL 4000G/SSL 8072G
monitors:	Genelec 1035a/Yamaha NS1O
rates:	Call for details
info:	Part of the Sanctuary Group, which also owns Sanctuary Westside studios and a dedicated Pro Tools studio in a separate location. 3 studios, acoustically designed by Sam Toyoshima of JVC Japan. See website for more detailed technical specification. Studio 1 can house up to 27 musicians. Previous clients include Oasis, Placebo, The Music, Def Leppard, Alpinestars, Bryan Ferry, Busted and Robbie Williams.

Treacle Sound Solutions
Basement 71, Leonard Street, Shoreditch, London, EC2A 4QS
tel:	020 7739 2626
email:	treaclestudio@btconnect.com
monitors:	Harbeth
rates:	£25 per hour
info:	Cubase studio with Tascam FireWire interface. Splitter bus available for band and gear transport. Rehearsal spaces for rent. See relevant section for more details.

Treasure Hunte Productions
Suite 6, Cross House, Cross Lane, London, N8 7SA
tel:	07774 265 211
email:	od@odhunte.com
web:	www.odhunte.com
contact:	Od Hunte
info:	Producer, writer and remixer for Hip-Hop, R&B and Soul genres. Previously worked with labels including Sony BMG, V2 and Urbanstar Records.

Tribal Tree Studios
66 Chalk Farm Road, London, NW1 8AN
tel:	020 7482 6945
email:	enquiries@tribaltreemusic.co.uk
web:	www.tribaltreemusic.co.uk
contact:	Louise, Nikki
desk:	Mackie
monitors:	Yamaha NS10/Dynaudio
rates:	Call for details
info:	Tribal Tree provide access to professional standard music and music technology courses for disadvantaged young people aged between 11 and 25 years. They pride themselves on offering knowledge sharing and consultation to various organisations involved with music technology set up, education and training. 3 studios with separate vocal areas and a live room for Acoustic recording. All are equipped with air conditioning, adjustable lighting, sofas and have access to a kitchen. See the website for more information.

Unit 21
21 London Lane, London Fields, London, E8 3PR
tel:	020 8525 1101
fax:	0870 1617619
email:	info@unit21recording.com
web:	www.unit21recording.com
contact:	Mike, Fiona
desk:	Euphonics CS3000
monitors:	PMC M32
rates:	Call for details
info:	High spec studio equipped with Pro Tools and good selection of outboard. Plenty of effects/reverb.

The Uptown Studios
Unit 19, Cygnus Business Centre, Dalmayer Road, London, NW10 2XA
tel:	07951 712 480
email:	info@uptownstudios.co.uk
web:	www.uptownstudios.co.uk
contact:	Anthony Galatis
desk:	Digi 002
monitors:	Genelic
rates:	£25 per hour
info:	Pro Tools studio which specialises in producing high quality demos for aspiring artists and songwriters. The in-house producer is an accomplished musician who can assist in many areas, from drum programming to melody writing. Rates are fully inclusive.

Vampire Music
20 Tanners Hill, Deptford, London, SE8 4JP
tel: 020 8691 6666
fax: 020 8692 9999
email: info@vampiremusic.co.uk
web: www.vampiremusic.co.uk
contact: Miles Bradley
desk: Soundcraft Sapphire
monitors: JBL LSR 28P
rates: £30 per hour, £199 per 8 hour day (both inc. VAT and engineer)
info: Fully air conditioned studios. Apple Macs running Cubase. Vampire Music also incorporate rehearsal studios, equipment hire service, music shop, equipment hire, CD duplication, as well as design and tuition services. See entries in relevant sections for details.

Vinyl Carvers
North London
tel: 020 7267 4071
email: info@vinylcarvers.com
web: www.vinylcarvers.com
contact: Tina, Werner
desk: SSL 4000B
monitors: Dynaudio M3
rates: Contact for details
info: Affordable residential studio set in the heart of the countryside. Large selection of valve and analogue outboard gear. Experienced producers, engineers, arrangers and musicians available. Also offer vinyl duplication services. See listing in relevant section for further details.

WALstudio
81 Marlborough Road, London, N19 4PA
tel: 07971 457 663
email: wmcintyre@blueyonder.co.uk
web: www.walstudio.com
contact: Wayne Mcintyre
desk: Pro Tools
monitors: PMC
rates: Call for details
info: Mobile and studio based Pro Tools HD recording.

Warm Fuzz Productions
London, W9
tel: 020 8962 9413
email: ian@warmfuzz.com
web: www.warmfuzz.com
contact: Ian
desk: Pro Tools with Neve
monitors: Tannoy
rates: Call for details
info: Studio is run by experienced band producer. Has a good mix of equipment including valve equipment.

Waveffect Ltd.
34 Salisbury Street, London, NW8 8QE
tel: 020 7402 9111
fax: 020 7402 9111
email: eliot@amimedia.co.uk
web: www.amimedia.co.uk
contact: Eliot Cohen, Anthony Fisher
desk: SSL 6053E/MCI JH 524B
monitors: Quested
rates: Call for details
info: Formerley Redbus Studios, established in 1978, much of the analogue equipment has been maintained and is operational. Studio is well stocked with Pro Tools and instruments available include a Steinway baby grand piano. Studio 1 has live and dead ends, and can hold up to 30 musicians. See the website for more details.

Westpoint
Unit GA, 39-40 Westpoint, Warple Way, London, W3 0RG
tel: 020 8740 1616
fax: 020 8740 4488
email: respect@mailbox.co.uk
contact: Ian
desk: Euphonic CS3000
monitors: ATC/Yamaha NS10
rates: Call for details
info: Pro Tools, MTR 90 (24-track analogue recording). Lots of classic instruments, analogue synths and amps available to use.

Westside Studios
10 Olaf Street, London, W11 4BE
tel: 020 7221 9494
fax: 020 7727 0008
email: westsidestudios@btconnect.com
contact: Olly Henshall
desk: Neve/SSL/EMI
monitors: Yamaha NS10
rates: Call for details

Whitfield Street Studios
31-37 Whitfield Street, London, W1T 2SF
tel: 020 7636 3434
fax: 020 7580 2219
email: info@whitfield-street.com
web: www.whitfield-street.com
contact: David Anderson
desk: Neve URP/SSL J series
monitors: Yamaha NS10/Genelec 1032a/Nautilus BMW/Neil Grant Boxer 5
rates: Call for details
info: Large, long established studio complex housing 4 studios. Studio 1 has an exceptionally large live area with space to cater for up to 90 musicians. Studio 2 is a Pro Tools suite that combines old and new technologies, utilising the studios selection of classic outboard. See the website for detailed kit lists. The studio also has facilities for mastering, re-mastering, editing and duplication. In addition, studios are available for event hire.

Wolf Studios
83 Brixton Water Lane, London, SW2 1PH
tel: 020 7733 8088
fax: 020 7274 4016
email: brethes@mac.com
web: www.wolfstudios.co.uk
contact: Dominique
desk: Amek Angela
monitors: Yamaha NS10/JBL
rates: Call for details
info: 2 studios available, both equipped with Pro Tools.

Word Sound & Power Recording Studio
Unit 4, Hanovia House, 28 Eastman Road, London, W3 7YG
tel: 020 8743 4529
email: info@wordsoundpower.co.uk
web: www.wordsoundpower.co.uk
contact: Robert
desk: Soundcraft
monitors: Alesis/Yamaha
rates: Call for details
info: Well equipped studio with facilities for dub plate cutting and engineering training.

The Works Studio Ltd.
1 Greenwich Quay, Clarence Road, London, SE8 3EY
tel: 020 7375 0510
email: james4real@btinternet.com
web: www.the-works-studios.co.uk
contact: James, Tim
desk: Mackie D8B
monitors: Genelec/Yamaha NS10
rates: Call for details
info: Professional digital recording at affordable prices. Separate DJ room.

Worlds End Sound
44 Worlds End Lane, Orpington, BR6 6AQ
tel: 07813 357 774
email: info@worldsendsound.com
web: www.worldsendsound.com
contact: Martin Kingston
desk: Mackie
monitors: Genelec 1032A/Yamaha NS10
rates: From £17 per hour
info: Professional Pro Tools HD3 set up with a mix of cutting edge digital and vintage analogue gear. Spacious live room, chillout lounge and garden on-site. Microphones by Neumann/Earthworks. The live room is equipped with a state of the art drum booth, ideal for live recordings.

York Street Music
43 York Street, London, W1H 1PW
tel: 020 7487 3767
email: info@yorkstreetmusic.com
web: www.yorkstreetmusic.com
contact: Dan
desk: Yamaha (analogue)
monitors: Mackie
rates: Call for details
info: A fully-equipped, modern studio, based around a 32-track Yamaha desk and the latest DSP cards, top of the range recording channels & FX from Focusrite, TFPro and Lexicon, plus wide selection of quality mics (Neumann, AKG, Rode) for any purpose.

Zed One Studios
225a Camden Road, Camden, London, NW1 98A
tel: 020 7482 3500
email: recording@zed-one-studios.co.uk
web: www.zed-one-studios.co.uk
contact: Pete Lyons
desk: Soundcraft DC2000
monitors: Genelec/Tannoy
rates: £195 per day
info: Caters for a wide range of clients from record companies and management agencies to unsigned bands and solo artists. Specialists in recording live sound, the studio has a 32-track Pro Tools system and a 32 channel Mackie providing 76 available inputs at mixdown. A constantly updated range of industry standard microphones and outboard is also available to use. Discounts and package deals available, contact for details. Rehearsal rooms also available, see separate entry for further information.

MIDLANDS

7th Wave
Unit 8, Sherriff Street, Worcester, WR14 9AB
tel: 01905 617 177
email: 7thwave@amserve.com
desk: 24 channel Mackie
info: Live recording with full separation on everything except for drums. Also offer rehearsal space and tuition. See relevant sections for more details.

Abbey Lane Studios
Unit 3a, Darley Abbey Mills, Off Haslams Lane, Derby, DE22 1DZ
tel: 0845 686 8742
email: info@abbey-lane.co.uk
web: www.abbey-lane.co.uk
desk: Mackie HDR24
monitors: Mackie HR-624
rates: £50 for one live session, £120 per day
info: Rehearsal facilities also available. See relevant section for more details.

Access To Music Recording Studios
3rd Floor, Silvergate House, 32 Clasketgate, Lincoln, Lincolnshire, LN2 1JS
tel: 01522 589 684
email: atm.lincoln@access-to-music.co.uk
web: www.accesstomusic.co.uk
contact: Pete Mackie
desk: Mackie/Behringer
monitors: Top spec monitors
rates: Call for rates as they may vary.
info: Access To Music is a Leicester based organisation providing popular music, education and consultancy. Courses run from the studio located in Lincoln, but it is also available to hire at any time. Rehearsal space, meeting rooms and seminar space. Shower facilities. Engineers and producers available.

AGP Studio
58 King Street, Broseley, Shrophsrire, TF12 5NA
tel: 01952 882 909/07973 866 198
email: alistair@agpstudio.co.uk
web: www.agpstudio.co.uk
contact: Alistair Gilles
desk: Yamaha O2R
monitors: MackieHR24
rates: Call for details
info: Intimate and comfortable studio which specialises in Acoustic, Jazz and Folk. A full range of microphones including the Neumann U87A and AKG.

Arch Recording Studios
6 Grain Warehouse Yard, Derby Street, Burton-On-Trent, Staffordshire, DE14 2JJ
tel: 01283 510 026
contact: Paul Gibson
desk: Studio Masters 2
monitors: Yamaha NS10/JBL/Sub Speakers
rates: £100 per day
info: Demo suite, ideal for recording a 3 track demo in 1 day. Live room and control room. Rehearsal space also available, contact for further details.

Aroia Music UK
4 St. George's Court, George Street, Newark, Nottinghamshire, NG24 1NW
tel: 01636 679 577/07903 743 581
email: aroiamusicuk04@hotmail.com
web: www.freewebs.com/aroiamusicuk04
contact: Mat, Gareth
desk: Yamaha 01V
rates: Call for details
info: Small pre-production studio offering highly competitive prices. 5, 8 and 12 hour packages are also available, call for details.

AR-One
Lillie House, 1a Conduit Street, Leicester, LE2 0JN
tel: 0116 223 0303
email: sales@stayfree.co.uk
web: www.stayfreemusic.co.uk
contact: Rich Henderson
rates: Contact for details
info: Ideal for Dance music recording. Digital mixing and backing track production. Cubase SX and Reason v2.5. Games room and chillout area. Part of Stayfree Music, which houses 2 other recording studios, see listings for Cordelia Studio and Memphis Studio. Rehearsal facilities also available. Refer to listing for Stayfree Music in relevant section.

Artisan Audio
46a Woodbridge Road, Moseley, Birmingham, West Midlands, B13 8EJ
tel: 0121 249 0598
email: info@artisanaudio.com
web: www.artisanaudio.com
contact: Jon Cotton
desk: Pro Tools
monitors: ATC
rates: £25 per hour (+ VAT)
info: Birmingham's leading music production studio offering recording, music production, audio mastering, editing and restoration. Selection of vintage keyboards available including acoustic piano, Wurlitzer, Hammond, Prophet-5 and JX8P.

Audio XL Location Recording
1 Riders Lea, Shrewsbury, Shropshire, SY3 6AA
tel: 01743 366 542
email: info@audioxl.co.uk
web: www.audioxl.co.uk
contact: John Cubbin
rates: £30 per hour
info: Location recording ideal for practices and gig recording.

Aura Studios
Union Building, Ashby Road, Loughborough, Leicestershire, LE11 3TT
tel: 01509 635 045
email: media@lborosu.org.uk
web: www.lufbra.net
contact: Anna Bowen
desk: Spirit 328
monitors: Tannoy
rates: £24 per hour (commercial), £13 per hour (students)
info: Part of Loughborough Students' Union, Aura is a professional audio recording facility, complete with practice rooms. Engineers provided. Facilities available to student members and non members of Loughborough Students' Union.

Bandwagon Studio
Westfield Lane, Mansfield, Nottinghamshire, NG13 1TL
tel: 01623 422 962
fax: 01623 633 449
email: info@bandwagonstudios.co.uk
web: www.bandwagonstudios.co.uk
desk: Megas
info: Digital recording studio with 2 live rooms and 3 booths.

Blue Lizard Studio
31 Gayton Road, Cleethorpes, Lincolnshire, DN35 0HN
tel: 07941 688 918
email: info@bluelizardstudio.com
web: www.bluelizardstudio.com
contact: Richard Davidson
desk: Yamaha 01V
monitors: Mackie
rates: Call for details
info: Also offer location recording for live studio and gig recording.

Blue Whale Studios
Unit 414, Custard Factory, Gibb Street, Digbeth, Birmingham, B9 4AA
tel: 0121 245 6035
email: ben@bluewhale-studios.com
web: www.bluewhale-studios.com
contact: Ben
desk: Allen & Heath
monitors: Mackie
rates: Call for details
info: Capable of recording 24 channels simultaneously. Specialises in working with unsigned bands and helping them along in the industry.

Bluewater Studios
Grice's Yard, Station Road, Ollerton, Newark, Nottinghamshire, NG22 9BN
tel: 01623 823 236
fax: 01623 825 101
email: info@bluewaterstudios.co.uk
web: www.bluewaterstudios.co.uk
contact: Ian Wall
desk: Digi Design Pro Tools
monitors: Genelec 1031 A
rates: Contact for details
info: Offer mastering and mixing, as well as artwork design services. Located on ground floor with easy access to car park.

BMP
The Red House, Aswardby, Spilsby, Lincolnshire, PE23 4JU
tel: 01790 754 400
fax: 01790 754 400
email: info@bmp-recording.co.uk
web: www.bmp-recording.co.uk
contact: Ken Blair
desk: Tascam Digital
monitors: ATC
rates: From £500 per day
info: Specialising in location sound recording, audio editing, mastering and music video production. See Video Promo section for further information.

Bob Lamb's Recording Studio
11a Highbury Road, King's Heath, Birmingham, B14 7QO
tel: 0121 443 2186
email: boblamb@recklessltd.freeserve.co.uk
contact: Bob Lamb
desk: Tascam
monitors: JBL
rates: Call for details
info: Analogue recording studio. 2 rehearsal rooms are available, see entry in relevant section for details.

Born In A Barn
Studio 01, Mobbs Wood Farm, Nettle Hill, Ansty, Coventry, CV7 9JN
tel: 02476 210 094
email: enquiries@borninabarnstudio.co.uk
web: www.borninabarnstudio.co.uk
contact: Roger
desk: Pro Tools
monitors: Mackie HR8
rates: Call for details
info: Pro Tools studio with dedicated chillout area that can comfortably accommodate 6 people, overnight if necessary. Discounts available on block bookings, call for details.

BPM Studios
42 Higham Road, Rushden, Northamptonshire, NN10 4DD
tel: 01933 395 631
email: john.hynes@ntlworld.com
web: www.bpmstudios.co.uk
contact: John Hynes
desk: Mackie
monitors: Tannoy
rates: Contact for details
info: Chill out room, TV, internet and kitchen. Relaxed and friendly working environment. Check website for audio restoration information and details of other services provided.

Brick Hit House
172 Middleton Hall Road, Kings Norton, Birmingham, B30 1DP
tel: 0121 608 2238/07778 332 488
email: john@brickhithouse.com
web: www.brickhithouse.com
contact: John Purser
desk: Yamaha 01V
monitors: Event 20/20
rates: Call for details
info: Good project studio for songwriters. John has worked with many artists throughout the years, from the likes of Matt Monroe in the 80s through to cutting edge R&B and Dance acts of today.

Broad Oak Studio
Pump Row, Broad Oak, Hereford, Herefordshire, HR2 8QU
tel: 01981 580 132
email: broadoakstudio@aol.com
contact: D.W. Wood
desk: TLA VTC 32 channel valve console
monitors: ATC/NS10
rates: £25 per hour (+ VAT)
info: Relaxed recording environment. Combine analogue and digital technology.

The Building
37 Rowley Street, Stafford, ST16 2RH
tel: 01785 245 649/07866 718 010
email: info@thebuilding.co.uk
web: www.thebuilding.co.uk
contact: Tim Simmons
desk: Sountrac Solitaire
monitors: Genelec/Bluesky
rates: Call for details
info: Analogue or digital recording. At the heart of the studio is an Apple G5 running Logic Pro and Cubase SX. 32 channel Soundtracs Solitaire console adds some analogue character to the digital recordings.

Cabin Studio
84 London Road, Coventry, West Midlands, CV1 2JT
tel: 02476 220 749/07969 453 010
email: office@sonar-records.demon.net
web: www.cabinstudio.co.uk
contact: Jon
desk: Soundcraft 2400
monitors: Yamaha N S10
rates: £20 per hour
info: Full recording studio for live bands. Cubase SX with equipment to hire including Vox AC30s and drum kits. Full selection of microphones and outboard gear. Mastering to all formats. TV room with free tea and coffee. Package deals available, contact for details. Also run a record label who in the pat have released music from artists recorded at Cabin Studio. See listing for Sonar Records in relevant section.

The Cellar
Dovedale House, Wilson Street, Derby, Derbyshire, DE1 1PL
tel: 01332 206 902
email: ian@tnts.co.uk
web: www.tnts.co.uk
contact: Ian Tompkins
desk: Mackie
monitors: 17" TFT
rates: Call for details
info: Reception area, office with Playstation. In the centre of Derby. 16 track studio equipped with Pro Logic 7.0. Rehearsal studio available, see relevant section for details.

Chapel Studios
Bryants Corner, South Thoresby, Alford, Lincolnshire, LN13 OAS
tel: 01507 480 305
email: andydransfield@btconnect.com
web: www.chapelstudios.com
desk: Amek/Neoteck
monitors: ATC/Dyn audio
rates: £1000 per day
info: 3 residential studios available. Discounts available for unsigned acts, contact Chapel Studios to discuss.

Clock House Studios
The Clock House, Keele, Newcastle, Staffordshire, ST5 5BG
tel: 01782 583 301
fax: 01782 583 301
email: c.bradbury@mus.keele.ac.uk
web: www.keele.ac.uk/depts/mu
contact: Cliff Bradbury
desk: Soundcraft/Mackie
monitors: ATC
rates: Call for details
info: Part of Keele University campus, the studios are mainly for student use, however are worth contacting for details of availability.

Cordelia Studios
Lillie House, 1a Conduit Street, Leicester, LE2 0JN
tel: 0116 223 0303
email: sales@stayfree.co.uk
web: www.stayfreemusic.co.uk
contact: Alan Jenkins
desk: Soundcraft Spirit
monitors: Soundcraft Spirit Absolute
rates: £14 per hour (Mon-Fr)i, £16 per hour (Sat & Sun)
info: Games room and chillout area. 24 track digital recording studio. Part of Stayfree Music, which houses 2 other recording studios, see listings for AR-One Studio and Memphis Studio. Rehearsal facilities also available. Refer to listing for Stayfree Music in relevant section.

Cornerstudios
Unit 71, Imex Business Park, Upper Villiers Street, Wolverhampton, WV2 4NU
tel: 01902 354 882
email: info@cornerstudios.co.uk
web: www.cornerstudios.co.uk
contact: Lee Philips
desk: Soundcraft Spirit
monitors: Spirit Absolute
rates: £20 per hour
info: Analogue and digital recording studio. Special weekend offers available, £275 for 16 hours over 2 days. Live room doubles as a rehearsal space in the evenings, see relevant entry or call for details.

Crush Music
Unit 417, The Custard Factory, Gibb Street, Digbeth, Birmingham, B9 4AA
tel: 0121 772 7169
email: info@crushmusic.com
web: www.crushmusic.com
contact: Jez Collins
info: Community based studio which also deals with film and television scores. Crush also manage a couple of local young bands.

Deadline studios
693 Aylestone Road, Leicester, LE2 8TG
tel: 0116 224 8303
email: info@deadlinestudios.co.uk
web: www.deadlinestudios.co.uk
contact: Adam Ellis
desk: Control 24
monitors: Yamaha NS10
rates: Call for details
info: Pro Tools based studio. Able to record any type of music.

Dehavilland Studios
17a Lichfield Street, Ramworth, Staffordshire, B79 7QD
tel: 01827 646 00/07956 494 884
email: mark@dehavilland-studios.co.uk
web: www.dehavilland-studios.co.uk
contact: Mark
desk: Yamaha 01V
monitors: Tannoy/Wharfedale
rates: Call for details

Dep International
1 Andover Street, Digbeth, Birmingham, B5 5RG
tel: 0121 633 4742
email: enquiries@ub40.co.uk
contact: Paul
desk: SSR/DDA
monitors: Yamaha NS10
rates: £450 per 12 hour day (Studio 1), £350 per day (Studio 2)
info: Dep International has 2 studios. Wide range of outboard equipment in both rooms. Can use Pro Tools, Logic and 2" analogue. Recreation area with toilets, Sky TV, shower and kitchen facilities.

Die Hard Studios
The Music Village, 55 Great Hampton Street, Birmingham, B18 6EL
tel: 07947 405 393
email: diehardproduction@blueyonder.co.uk
contact: Ken White, Joel Farrell
desk: Pro Tools
monitors: Alesis/Tannoy
rates: Call for details
info: Also offer vocal tuition, see entry in relevant section or call for further information.

Digital Image Recording Studios
144 Park Road, Chesterfield, Derbyshire, S40 2LG
tel: 01246 208 659
email: digital@imageco.freeserve.co.uk
contact: Glenn
desk: Yamaha
monitors: Mackie 8R824
rates: £15-£20 per hour
info: Studios located 5 minutes from the M1.

Digitallunarsea
Great Barr, Birmingham, West Midlands
tel: 07765 708 899
email: matt@digitallunarsea.co.uk
web: www.digitallunarsea.co.uk
contact: Matt Fisher
desk: Tascam
monitors: Genelec
rates: £25 per hour
info: Digitallunarsea is a Electronic music and audio production studio offering a wide range of audio based services including stereo and 5.1 production and mixing, online 24 hour turnaround mastering, jingle and sound effect creation. Also offer studio tuition, call Matt for more information.

Direct Recording Services Ltd.
37 Beacon Hill Drive, Hucknall, Nottinghamshire, NG15 6QG
tel: 0845 226 8591
email: enquiries@directrecordings.co.uk
web: www.directrecordings.co.uk
contact: Ben Marshall
desk: Yamaha Digital Consoles: 02R96/01v96
rates: Packages from £129
info: Specialist location recording company offering a range of services including PA Hire, 24 track digital recording (mobile and studio), mixing and editing, mastering, demo production and web design. Available throughout the UK, Direct Recordings operate 3 mobile recording/editing studios which can be booked to record a whole session at a location of your choice. Alesis HD24/RME Hammerfall DS P recording. AKG, Audio Technica, Sennheiser, Shure microphones. Pro Tools, Logic Audio and Peak VST software.

Dreamstage
12 Lambrook Drive, East Hunsbury, Northampton, Northamptonshire, NN4 0WA
tel: 01604 708 546
email: studio@dream-stage.co.uk
web: www.dream-stage.co.uk
contact: Mark Smith
desk: 32 Channel Allen & Heath Analogue
monitors: Tannoy Reveal/Mission
rates: £80 per half day, £150 per 9 hour day
info: Production studio working with local singer-songwriters and artists.

Earth Productions
163 Gerrard Street, Lozells, Birmingham, B19 2AH
tel: 0121 554 7424
email: info@earthproductions.co.uk
web: www.earthproductions.co.uk
desk: Soundtracs/Mackie
monitors: Tannoy/Dynaudio
rates: £15 per hour
info: Eart Productions comprises 2 studios, 2 lecture rooms and a fully equipped media suite. Also offer training in all aspects of sound recording.

Electric Mayhem Studios
6-10 Convent Street, Nottingham, NG1 3LL
tel: 0115 859 9807
email: jonlord@electricmayhem.co.uk
web: www.electricmayhem.co.uk
contact: Jon Lord
desk: Neve VR60
monitors: ATC
rates: £360 per day
info: Part of the Confetti Institute of Creativ Technologies comprising 24 studios. Analogue or digital Pro Tools recording.

Energy Music
PO Box 9600, Birmingham, B24 8RF
tel: 0121 682 0702/07802 410 834
fax: 0121 377 7731
email: info@energymusic.co.uk
web: www.energymusic.co.uk
contact: Sarah Bowen
desk: Yamaha
monitors: Genelec 22-20s
rates: £60 per hour
info: Studio which also offers vocal coaching services. Contact for further information.

ERS Studios
Neilston Street, Leamington Spa, Warwickshire, CV31 2AZ
tel: 01926 889 153
email: info@ersstudios.co.uk
web: www.ersstudios.co.uk
contact: Andy Hardwick
desk: Soundcraft Ghost
monitors: KRK/Tannoy
rates: £25 per hour
info: Dedicated recording studio with the ability to record bands as live. Quality analogue desk and outboard.

Fame Factory Studios
Unit 4c, Old Knows Factory, St. Ann's Hill Road, Nottingham, Nottinghamshire, NG3 4GP
tel: 0115 950 9888
email: events@thefamefactory.tv
web: www.thefamefactory.tv
contact: Mark
desk: Mackie
monitors: Dynaudio
rates: Call for details
info: Chillout room, bar café and on-site photography studio. Located in the city centre with free parking facilities.

Far Heath Recording Studios
Far Heath, Coton, Northampton, Northamptonshire, NN6 8RH
tel: 01604 740 739
email: info@farheath.com
web: www.farheath.com
contact: Angus Wallace
desk: Mackie 32 Input Analogue Console
monitors: Dynaudio Acoustic M2s/Yamaha NS10s
rates: £19 per hour (weekdays), £25 per hour (weekends)
info: Set in beautiful surroundings. Specialise in recording live music. Very experienced engineer on hand. Previous clients include The Prodigy, Spiritualized and The Fall.

Fatback Studios
28 Stratford Street North, Camphill, Birmingham, B11 1BY
tel: 0121 248 2525
email: info@fatbackstudios.co.uk
web: www.fatbackstudios.co.uk
desk: Mackie
monitors: JBL
rates: £30 for first hour, £20 per hour thereafter
info: Studio is part of Fatback Rehearsal Studios which has 16 rehearsal rooms, see entry in relevant section for details.

Fidget Studios
Unit B10, Little Heath Industrial Estate, Old Church Road, Coventry, CV6 7NB
tel: 024 7658 1133
email: enquiries@fidget-studios.com
web: www.fidget-studios.com
desk: Beringher
monitors: Mackie
rates: £150 per day (inc. engineer)
info: Dance music production and live band recording. Several tracks produced at Fidget Studios have appeared on the Euphoria series of compilations. Rehearsal space available. See listing in relevant section for details.

Fitdog Recoring Studio
12 Milton Road, Gayton, Northampton, Northamptonshire, NN7 3HE
tel: 01604 878 979
email: chris@fit-dog.com
web: www.fit-dog.com
contact: Chris
desk: Digi 02
monitors: Mackie
rates: £18 per hour
info: Pro Tools specialists. Full backline including piano and drum kit. Recreational area available for bands that make block booking.

Flux Studios
Unit F1, Brookstreet Business Centre, Brookstreet, Tipton, West Midlands, DY4 9DD
tel: 0121 557 5777
email: fluxstudios@btinternet.com
web: www.fluxstudios.co.uk
contact: Mike Rowley
desk: Yamaha AW4416
monitors: Tannoy Reveal
rates: £20 per hour
info: Flux Studios is run by qualified experienced sound engineers who take a keen interest in Alternative styles of music and production methods including Punk, Emo, Hardcore, Metal, Grunge, Indie, New Wave, Lo-fi, Rap, Hip-Hop and R&B.

The Forge Recording Studio
The Old Smithy, Church Street, Owestry, Shropshire, SY11 2SP
tel: 01691 658 550
fax: 01691 658 549
email: phil@forgestudio.com
web: www.forgestudio.com
contact: Phil Beaumont
desk: Amek Rembrandt
monitors: Dynaudio/Yamaha NS10
rates: Contact for details
info: 32 track digital studio housed in an 18th century building, staffed by friendly professionals. Previous clients include James, Suede and Ian Brown, who recorded his solo debut Unfinished Monkey Business at the studio. For full specification see website. Special rates available for unsigned bands.

Framework Studios
226-234 Barr Street, Hockley, Birmingham, B19 3AG
tel: 07790 158 210
email: simon@frameworkstudios.co.uk
web: www.frameworkstudios.co.uk
contact: Simon
desk: Allen & Heath
monitors: Genelec
rates: £150 per day
info: Framework offer a happy and relaxed atmosphere for bands working in virtually lock-out conditions. Also offer a selection of instruments for band use including drum kit.

Frantic
394 Ladypool Road, Birmingham, West Midlands, B5 5RG
tel: 0121 449 0606
contact: Singh
desk: Soundcraft 6000
rates: Contact for details
info: Full studio. Apple Mac based recording with Logic and Cubase. A-DAT also available. Specialise in Asian music, but has also recorded Pop and Chart acts. Facilities included a good size live room, chillout area and pool room.

Gamesound Ltd.
13 Oswald Road, Oswestry, Shropshire, SY11 1RB
tel: 01691 670 440
email: info@gamesound.co.uk
web: www.gamesound.co.uk
desk: Yamaha
rates: Contact for details
info: 24 bit 96Khz 7.1 surround sound recording studio with large purposr built live drum room.

Gighouse Recording Studio
Harbury Lane, Leamington Spa, Warwickshire, CV33 9SA
tel: 01926 888 502
email: info@gighouse.co.uk
web: www.gighouse.co.uk
contact: John Black, Andy Thompson
desk: Soundcraft Ghost
monitors: Genelec
rates: Call for details
info: Analogue recording studio with 3 live areas. Facilities include kitchen area and quiet room.

Glasshouse Productions Ltd.
Upper York Street, Coventry, West Midlands, CV1 3GQ
tel: 02476 223 892
email: sharon@glasshouseproductions.co.uk
web: www.glasshouseproductions.co.uk or www.a2tel.co.uk
contact: Sharon Jones
desk: Jade
rates: Call for details
info: Located just outside city centre. Plenty of free parking. Glasshouse also provide training in sound engineering, music production, DJ courses which are National Open College Network graded. For further information see www.a2tel.org.uk.

Greg's Music Room
Leicester
tel: 07808 793 136
email: info@gregsmusicroom.co.uk
web: www.gregsmusicroom.co.uk
contact: greg
desk: Akai DPS 24
monitors: Behringer Truth
rates: Call for details
info: Sepcialise in recording duos and solo Acoustic artists.

Hellfire Productions
158 Crankhill Lane, Wednesbury, Birmingham, WS10 0EB
tel: 0121 556 2559/07870 657 747
email: ajeet@hellfireproductions.com
web: www.hellfireproductions.com
contact: Ajeet Gill
desk: Yamaha 02R
monitors: Genelec
rates: Call for details
info: Hellfire offer a professional service. Although they specialise in Heavy Metal and Hip-Hop subgenres, any type of music is welcome. Also provide a wide range of services, including tuition and rehearsal space. See listings in relevant sections for details.

Hijack Music
5b The Basement, Millsborough House, Ipsley Street, Redditch, B98 78L
tel: 07855 271 834
email: info@hijackmusic.co.uk
web: www.hijackmusic.co.uk
contact: Nigel Clark
desk: Tascam
monitors: Tannoy/Yamaha NS10
rates: Call for details
info: Nigel is a songwriter himself and can offer help with song arrangement throughout the recording process. Also offer instrument and studio tuition, see entry in relevant section for details.

Hive Recording Studio Ltd.
44a Agard Street, Derby, Derbyshire, DE1 1DZ
tel: 01332 362 966
contact: Rob Newman
desk: Souncraft
monitors: PMC
rates: Call for details
info: Pro Tools 64 track recording with 2 spacious live rooms.

Hush Recording Studio
Unit B3, Little Heath Industrial Estate, Old Church Road, Coventry, West Midlands, CV6 7ND
tel:	0870 930 2263/07715 559 271
email:	info@hushstudio.co.uk
web:	www.hushstudio.co.uk
contact:	Daz Wood
desk:	Mackie D8B
monitors:	Yamaha NS10/Spirit
rates:	Call for details
info:	Daz has over 15 years experience in music projects, ranging from Folk, Bhangra, Rap, Rock and Indie.

Junction Studio
Great Barr, Birmingham
tel:	0121 682 2354
email:	info@junctionstudio.co.uk
web:	www.junctionstudio.co.uk
contact:	Dennis Matthews
desk:	Mackie
monitors:	Mackie
rates:	From £15 per hour
info:	Mackie recording system with Mac G4 running Logic. Mainly for guitar based bands. 20 years of recording experience.

Live Sound Recording
7 Barley Fileds, Audley, Stoke-On-Trent, ST7 8ED
tel:	01782 723 860
email:	info@livesoundrecording.co.uk
web:	www.livesoundrecording.co.uk
contact:	Jeff Cooke
desk:	Roland
monitors:	Neovo
rates:	Contact for details
info:	Offer state of the art, computer based digital recording, up to 24 bit, 96khz sampling rate.

Location Recording
Unit 4-5, Kinglsey Street, Kirkby-In-Ashfield, Nottinghamshire, NG17 7BA
tel:	07944 850 575
email:	bookings@locationstudios.co.uk
web:	www.locationstudios.co.uk
contact:	Lee Sewkes
desk:	Allen & Heath GS300 24 Track
monitors:	Alesis
rates:	£80 per 8 hour day
info:	Full midi set up. Affordable rates. Chillout room and games system available.

The Lodge Recording Studio
23 Abington Square, Northampton, NN1 4AE
tel:	01604 475 399
email:	info@lodgerecording.co.uk
web:	www.lodgerecording.co.uk
contact:	Robert Godfrey
desk:	Cadac Console
monitors:	Tannoys
rates:	See website
info:	Experienced studio that offers cut priced deals for unsigned bands. Specialises in live music from Indie to Punk Rock.

Mad Hat's Studio
The Upper Hattons Media Centre, Pendeford Hall Lane, Coven, Wolverhampton, WV9 5BD
tel:	01902 840 440/07968 758 780
fax:	01902 840 448
email:	studio@madhat.co.uk
web:	www.madhat.co.uk
contact:	Mark
desk:	Amec
monitors:	Yamaha/Genelec/Tannoy
rates:	Call for details
info:	Digital and analogue recording, digital mastering and editing. Also provide video recording services. Enquire for further information.

Madhouse Rehearsals
41 Hampton Street, Hockley, Birmingham, B19 3LS
tel:	0121 233 1109
fax:	0121 233 1286
email:	committed@madhouserehearsals.com
web:	www.madhouserehearsals.com
desk:	Tascam
monitors:	Genelec
rates:	From £15 per hour
info:	Logic 6 running on a G5 Mac. Previous clients include Robert Plant and Ocean Colour Scene. Licensed bar on-site. Rehearsal facilities available. See listing in relevant section for more details.

Magic Garden
Unit 17, Showell Road Industrial Estate, Wolverhampton, WV10 9LU
tel:	01902 429 148
email:	gavinmonaghan@gmail.com
contact:	Gavin Monaghan
monitors:	ATC/Zen
rates:	Call for details
info:	Pro Tools studio also incorporating plenty of analogue equipment. Tend to work with bands based on recommendations and word of mouth. Feel free to ring and discuss.

Memphis Studio
Lillie House, 1a Conduit Street, Leicester, LE2 0JN
tel:	0116 223 0303
email:	sales@stayfree.co.uk
web:	www.stayfreemusic.co.uk
contact:	Kev Reverb
rates:	£9 per hour (inc. engineer)
info:	16 track analogue studio, also offering digital facilities. Games room and chillout area. Previous clients include Reef, The Stranglers and 3 Colours Red. Part of Stayfree Music, which houses 2 other recording studios, see listings for Cordelia Studio and Memphis Studio. Rehearsal facilities also available. Refer to listing for Stayfree Music in relevant section.

Middle C Recording Studio
Wolverhampton
tel:	01902 568 835
contact:	Byron
rates:	Call for details
info:	Keen to record Gospel, Soul, Hip-Hop, Jazz, Pop and R&B genres, but no Heavy Rock bands. Contact Byron for further information.

Morrell Recording Studio
61 Abbey Road, Enderby, Leicester, Leicestershire, LE19 2DB
tel:	0116 286 2565
email:	leighton.morrell@btinternet.com
web:	www.morrellstudio.tripod.com
contact:	Leighton Morrell
desk:	Soundcraft
monitors:	Logic
rates:	£40 per afternoon session
info:	Morrell Studios are vocal specialsts that use Cubase SX. Please call for more information.

MPM Records
Units 3, 5 & 6, Talisman House, 47-49 Bath Street, Walsall, WS1 3BX
tel:	01922 642 123
email:	record@mpmrecords.com
web:	www.mpmrecords.com
contact:	Mark
desk:	Mackie
monitors:	Genelec
rates:	£30 per hour, £250 per 10 hour session
info:	Studio suitable for both live bands and solo artists.

The Music Shed
Unit 6, Derby Small Business Centre, Canal Street, Derby, DE1 2RJ
tel:	07736 777 130
email:	info@musicshed.co.uk
web:	www.musicshed.co.uk
desk:	Allen & Heath
rates:	£16 per hour
info:	24 track digital recording. Studio is air conditioned with ground floor access. Refreshments and accessories for sale on-site. Engineer has over 20 years experience. Rehearsal space also available, see relevant section for more details.

Muther's Studio
14 Rea Street South, Digbeth, Birmingham, B5 6LB
tel:	0121 622 7110/07815 323 871
email:	info@muthersstudio.com
web:	www.muthersstudio.com
contact:	Adam Dufrane
desk:	24 track
rates:	£10 per hour
info:	Pool table and reception area. The studio is situated in the heart of Birmingham. See also listing for rehearsal studios.

Neosonix
13-17 Oswald Road, Oswestry, Shropshire, SY11 1RB
tel: 01691 670 440
email: info@neosonix.co.uk
web: www.neosonix.co.uk
desk: Yamaha DM2000
monitors: Genelec/Yamaha
rates: Call for details
info: A high quality, fully comprehensive studio catering for all recording needs. 96 channel, 24-bit, 96Khz digital mixing console. Tascam MX24 24 track digital multitrack x2. Akai MPC 3000, 3000LE and 4000. Emu emulator 4. Excellent range of rack units. Live rooms and drum booths, as well as equipment hire. Studio has chillout room with fridge, microwave, sofa beds, Xbox, PS2 and DVD. Home cooked food is available from 11am to midnight everyday. Neosonix also range of services including artist management, video promo service and online music shop. Contact for further details.

Noisegate Recording Studio
155 Tachbrook Road, Leamington Spa, Warwickshire, CV31 3EE
tel: 01926 330 135
email: enquiries@noisegatestudios.com
web: www.noisegatestudios.com
contact: Matt
desk: Mackie 8 Bus 32 Channel
monitors: Tannoy/Adam
rates: £25 per hour (+ VAT), £180 per day (+ VAT)
info: Bands benefit from the ability to simultaneously record up to 24 tracks and overdub up to 128 tracks. Recreation area and chillout rooms.

Oasis
Unit 6A, Brockhill Works, Windsor Road, Redditch, B97 6DJ
tel: 01527 592 800
email: info@oasis-studios.co.uk
web: www.oasis-studios.co.uk
contact: Alan
desk: Mackie
monitors: HHP
rates: Contact for details
info: Oasis have a fully equipped 24 track recording studio with a range of quality equipment. Also run rehearsal rooms. See entry in relevant section for further details.

Old Smithy Studios
Post Office Lane, Kempsey, Worcestershire, WR5 3NS
tel: 01905 820 659
fax: 01905 820 015
email: joe@oldsmithy.com
web: www.oldsmithy.com
contact: Muff Murfin
desk: Pro Tools
monitors: Quested
rates: £45 per hour, £350 per day

Orchard Recording Studios
Orchard Road, Finedon, Northamptonshire, NN9 5JG
tel: 01933 398 038
email: orchardroadstudios@hotmail.com
web: www.orchardroadstudios.com
contact: Matt Hendry
desk: Pro Tools
monitors: Focal/Dynaudio
rates: Contact for details
info: Established studio providing high quality recording.

Orchard Studios
Alsager
tel: 01270 877 208
email: info@orchardstudios.co.uk
web: www.orchardstudios.co.uk
contact: John Newbould
desk: Various
monitors: JBL/BSS/Tannoy/Yamaha NS10
rates: Negotiable
info: Purpose built studio with 4 live rooms, digital and analogue recording Pro Logic. A wide variety of outboard modules. 2 control rooms plus video editing suite.

The Oxygen Rooms
122 Barr Street, Hockley, Birmingham, B19 3DE
tel: 0121 551 7001
email: via website
web: www.theoxygenrooms.com
contact: Nick Rendall
rates: Call for details
info: Complex also houses 5 rehearsal rooms. DJ, vocal and instrument tuition is available, see relevant entries for details.

Pals ID Studio
Unit 315, Jubilee Trades Centre, 130 Pershore Street, Digbeth, Birmingham, B5 6ND
tel: 0121 622 2539
fax: 0121 622 2539
email: contact@dubtransmissions.net
web: www.dubtransmissions.net
contact: Fay George
desk: Mac-based Logic Audio
monitors: Event
rates: £15 per hour
info: Studio is linked with Pals Arts & Media, a community arts organisation.

Paper Stone
Unit 6, OPM House, Haydn Road, Sherwood, Nottingham, NG5 2LB
tel: 0115 985 8444
email: studio@paper-stone.co.uk
web: www.paper-stone.co.uk
contact: Huw Jones
desk: Spirit 3201
monitors: Haffler
rates: £20 per hour, £150 per 8 hour day

Paperdoll Media
West Bromwich
tel: 07786 706 454
email: gpatel@paperdollmedia.co.uk
web: www.paperdollmedia.co.uk
rates: Call for details
info: Ideal demo studio. Instruments can be provided if required. Artwork and design services, including web design also available. See relevant section for details.

Parlour Studio
The Parlour, Glendon Lodge Farm, Kettering, Northants, NN14 1QF
tel: 01536 517 377
email: neil@parloursound.co.uk
web: www.parloursound.co.uk
contact: Neil Haynes
desk: Tascam
monitors: Dynaudio
rates: Call for details
info: Good selection of digital and vintage analogue equipment. Excellent acoustics in the studios.

Platinum Recording Studio
39 Chesterwood Road, Acres Wood, Stoke-On-Trent, Staffordshire, ST6 7EL
tel: 01782 417 471
email: ukplatinum@ntlworld.com
web: www.platinum-recording-studio.co.uk
contact: Alan Cartlidge
rates: Call for details
info: Studio has recently been refurbished. Contact for details of equipment and rates.

Pride Rock Studio
Deppers Bridge Farm, Deppers Bridge, Southam, Warwickshire, CV47 2SZ
tel: 01926 614 640/07782 172 101
email: dutch@bighelpmusic.com
web: www.bighelp.biz
contact: Dutch
desk: Allen & Heath Valve
monitors: Genelec 22-20/Yamaha NS10/Tannoy
rates: Call for details
info: Pro Tools and Logic Audio. Large live room.

Priory Recording Studios
3 The Priory, London Road, Canwell, Sutton Coldfield, B75 5SH
tel: 0121 323 3332
fax: 0121 308 8815
email: greg@prioryrecordingstudios.co.uk
web: www.prioryrecordingstudios.co.uk
contact: Greg Chandler
desk: Yamaha 02R
monitors: Dynaudio
rates: £30 per hour
info: Broadcast quality 64 track digital professional recording and post production studio. Welcome music from a range of genres including Metal, Rock and Indie.

Psyrex Soundlab
397 Hucknall Road, Nottingham, NG5 1FW
tel: 0115 841 3184
email: mark@psyrex.net
web: www.psyrex.net
desk: Soundcraft Spirit
monitors: Yamaha MSP10s
rates: £130 per 8 hour day
info: Internal desk from Creamware soundcard. Up to 35% discounts available for students and the unemployed. Rehearsal space also available, see relevant section for more details.

Quad Studios
78 Friday Street, Leicester, Leicestershire, LE1 3BW
tel: 0116 251 2516
email: info@quadstudios.co.uk
web: www.quadstudios.co.uk
contact: Bob Bryars
desk: Mackie/Soundcraft/Allen & Heath/Yamaha 01V, 02R, DM200
monitors: Mackie Powered SM450/1530
rates: From £30 per hour
info: Analogue and digital recording. Bands and singer-songwriters welcome. Quad is predominantly a rehearsal facility, see listing in relevant section for details.

Rainbow Sound & Vision Productions
Conkers, Rawdon Road, Moira, Derbyshire, DE12 6GA
tel: 01283 551 555/07986 236 913
email: info@rsvpshows.com
web: www.rsvpshows.com
contact: Paul Jarvis
desk: Allen & Heath
monitors: Vega
rates: Call for rates
info: Fully staffed studio with technicians on hand. Can cater for live recordings. Chillout room, rehearsal area, parking, tea and coffee making facilities. 1k rig is available for hire.

Rich Bitch Studios
505 Bristol Road, Selly Oak, Birmingham, B29 6AU
tel: 0121 471 1339
email: richbitchstudios@aol.com
web: www.richbitchstudios.com
contact: Robert Bruce
desk: Soundcraft Solitaire
monitors: Genelec 22-20s
rates: £25 per hour
info: Complex also houses 13 rehearsal rooms, see relevant entry for details.

Roar Studios
Unit 7, The Old Dairy, 47 North Street, Melton, Mowbray, Leicestershire, LE13 1NL
tel: 01664 410 900
email: roarstudios@hotmail.com
contact: Jo De Bie
desk: Soundcraft Ghost
monitors: NP1
rates: Contact for details
info: Recording facility mainly for live bands, but also cater for voice over work. Rates are variable so contact for further information.

Robannas Studios
Robanna House, Cleveland Street, Birmingham, B19 3SN
tel: 0121 333 3201
fax: 0121 359 3647
email: robannas.studios@btinternet.com
web: www.robannas-studios.co.uk
contact: Robert Hoffman
desk: Soundcraft
monitors: Dynaudio
rates: Call for details
info: Bands recorded at Robannas receive the opportunity to represent themselves in the Birmingham music scene through the gigs they promote. Contact for further information. Client list includes Lostprophets, Hundred Reasons and Ocean Colour Scene.

Rooksmere Studios
130 Sywell Road, Overstone, Northamptonshire, NN6 0AG
tel: 01604 495 310
email: info@rooksmerestudios.com
web: www.rooksmerestudios.com
contact: Mark Hutchinson
desk: Audient 8024 Console
monitors: Yamaha NS10
rates: Call for details
info: Studio set in a rural location. Combines both analogue and digital recording. Special rates for unsigned bands. Will record music of any genre.

S & P Studios
Ewefields Farm, Chesterton, Leamington Spa, Warwickshire, CV33 9LQ
tel: 0870 744 3054
email: nick@sandpproductions.co.uk
web: www.sandpstudios.co.uk
contact: Nick Myerscough
desk: Tascam/Trident
monitors: Dynaudio/BMC
rates: Call for details
info: Studio has 3 live rooms, one of which can be used for rehearsal. See relevant entry for details.

Sable Rose
91 Middleborough Road, Coventry, CV1 1GG
tel: 02476 520 643
contact: Andy Faulkner
desk: Soundtracs Jade
monitors: Tannoy/JBL
rates: Call for details
info: Residential studio, particularly keen on demo recording for unsigned guitar bands.

Scorpion Studios
Peregrine Mews, Dowding Road, Lincoln, Lincolnshire, LN3 4PH
tel: 01522 524 888
email: gameala@gameala.wanadoo.co.uk
web: www.scorpionstudios.tk
rates: £150 per 8 hour day, £190 per 10 hour day, £20 per hour (+ room rental)
info: 2 Yamaha 01Vs and Mackie hard disk recorder. Mixing charged at £350 per song. Pre-production. Rehearsal space also available, see relevant section for more details.

The Session Rooms
Waterworks Road, Worcester, Worcestershire, WR1 3EZ
tel: 07729 011 398/01905 338 972
email: info@thesessionrooms.com
web: www.thesessionrooms.com or www.bandpractice.co.uk
desk: Yamaha 02R
monitors: Bose 208
info: Rehearsal space also available. All post-production work including CD duplication undertaken. See relevant sections for more details.

Shadowless
Unit 33, 65-66 Caroline Street, Hockley, B3 1UG
tel: 07958 281 379
email: tomo@shadowless.com
web: www.shadowless.com
contact: Tomo
desk: Mackie
monitors: PM2 Fostex
rates: Contact for details
info: Live booth available. Shadowless also run a record label. See entry in relevant section for details.

Sherborne Sound
15 Bingham Road, Radcliffe-On-Trent, Nottingham, NG12 2FY
tel: 0115 933 2111
email: sherbornesound@dial.pipex.co.uk
web: www.sherbornesound.co.uk
contact: Sandy Beevers
desk: Spirit
monitors: HHB Cirlce 5
rates: £25 per hour
info: Range of studio services and packages. The room has superb acoustics, and is ideal for small groups or solo Folk and Jazz artists. Parking on-site.

Silver Studios
2b Church Road, Moorgreen, Nottingham, Nottinghamshire, NG16 2AB
tel: 01773 715 289
email: jordan@silver-studios.net
web: www.silver-studios.net
contact: Jordan
desk: Studio Master
monitors: Yamaha NS10
rates: Contact for details
info: Production and recording services. Focused on creative process. No Rock bands as studios are not equipped with live drum recording facilities. Excellent vocal recording suite.

Slicktone Studios
Welford, Leicester
tel: 0116 257 1559
email: janwilson2@hotmail.com
web: www.slicktonesstudio.com
contact: Jan Wilson
desk: Behringer MX9000
monitors: Yamaha NS10
rates: £12 per hour
info: Gear for hire during sessions includes Hammond organ, Rhodes piano, a selection of guitars, bass, drums and percussion. Affordable rates for unsigned artists

Sonic Arts Services
23 Anderson Drive, Kettering, Northamptonshire, NN15 5DG
tel: 01536 515 159
email: jonny@sonicartsservices.co.uk
web: www.sonicartsservices.co.uk
contact: Jonny
rates: Call for details
info: Digital mobile recording available.

Soundcraft Productions
1 Tennyson Street, Leicester, Leicestershire, LE2 1HS
tel: 0116 255 8440
email: ds.roberts@ntlworld.com
contact: Derek Roberts
desk: Yamaha 02R
monitors: Dynaudio
rates: £25 per hour
info: Hard disc recording, outboards include TLA valve pre-amps and compressors, TC electronic gold channel, high-end TC electronic M6000 all in the home studio recording set up. Full facilities in-house.

StarVocals.Com
Worcestershire
tel: 01562 822 222
email: info@starvocals.com
web: www.starvocals.com
contact: Colin Day
desk: Mackie
rates: Package deals available
info: The studio is designed for singers. Backing tracks available.

Sub Sound Studio
54 Oxford Street, Penkhull, Stoke-On-Trent, Staffordshire, ST4 7EE
tel: 01782 416 306
email: studio@sub-sound.co.uk
web: www.sub-sound.co.uk
contact: Gordon Lee
desk: Soundcraft
monitors: Yamaha NS10
rates: £20 per hour
info: Kitchen with tea and coffee making facilities. Located 5 minutes from the motorway.

Suburban Suite Studio
124 Yelverton Road,, Coventry, CV6 4AH
tel: 02476 638 086/07891 694 368
email: info@suburbansuitestudio.co.uk
web: www.suburbansuitestudio.co.uk
contact: Stuart Proud
desk: Behringer Eurodesk
monitors: Yamaha NS10
rates: Call for details
info: Studio for Dance and Urban music. Good rates for unsigned artists.

Subway Studios
Alferton Rd, Nottingham, Nottinghamshire, NG7 3JL
tel: 0115 978 2002
email: madhatter1@ntlworld.com
web: www.subwaystudios.co.uk
contact: Vaughn
desk: Soundcraft
monitors: Tannoy
rates: £15-£25 per hour
info: Subway Studios also has rehearsal facilities, see relevant section for details. Chillout room available.

Subzone
Chesterfield, Derbyshire, S41 7YQ
tel: 07890 412 043
email: sidworm@supanet.com
contact: Danny Clarke
desk: Mackie
monitors: Event
rates: £5-£7 per hour (inc. engineer)
info: PC based. Up to 96 tracks in digital. Free use of Marshall Valvestate guitar amp and Trace Elliot bass amp. Free accommodation is offered to travelling bands.

Ultim8 Studio
54 Millholm Road, Desborough, Kettering, Northamptonshire, NN14 2NE
tel: 01536 762 305
email: chris@ultim8studio.com
web: www.ultim8studio.com
desk: Digidesign
monitors: Genelec/Tannoy/JBL
info: Fully equipped home studio with Pro Tools TDM.

Underground Recording Studios
Roden House, Roden Street, Nottingham, Nottinghamshire, NG3 1JH
tel: 07966 462 138
contact: John
desk: Mackie/Behringer
rates: £200 per day
info: Lounge, kitchen and 2 rehearsal spaces. Contact for further information.

Urthworks Audio Recording
Aldridge, West Midlands
tel: 01922 453 192
email: enquiries@urthworksaudio.co.uk
web: www.urthworksaudio.co.uk
contact: Simon Ash
desk: Tascam M2600 (32inp, inline)
monitors: KRK/PMC
rates: Flat rate of £20 per hour
info: Urthworks is a purpose built project studio. Services include tracking, location recording, restoration, mastering/audio editing, schools work and studio based tuition. Mics by AKG, Rode, Neuman, Shure and SE, Focusrite blue series pre-amps, Carillon PC(SX) or multitrack HDR.

V Studios
Hammerwich, Lichfield, Staffordshire
tel: 07766 094 360
email: philipbharper@ntlworld.com
web: www.v-studios.co.uk
desk: 40 channel Studio Master
monitors: NS10s
rates: £120 per day (8 hours)
info: Also offer rehearsal facilities, see relevant section for more details.

White House Sound Ltd.
24a Brookfield Street, Syston, Leicester, Leicestershire, LE7 2AD
tel: 0116 260 9401
email: mikemiller.whs@btopenworld.com
contact: Mike Hester
rates: Call for details
info: Facilities include kitchen, 2 reception areas and free parking.

Whitelight Studios
28 Victoria Terrace, Stafford, Staffordshire, ST16 3HA
tel: 01785 227 751
email: whitelight.studios@virgin.net
web: www.whitelight-studios.com
contact: Tim Wardle
desk: Allen & Heath 24 track
rates: £150 per day
info: Previous clients include Blueboy, Quireboys and Paul Young Band. Chillout area and kitchen available.

Woodbine Street Recording Studios
1 St. Mary's Crescent, Leamington Spa, Warwickshire, CV31 1JL
tel: 01926 338 971
email: via website
web: www.woodbinestreet.com
contact: John Rivers
desk: Audioent/Pro Tools HD3
monitors: Mission/K&H 0300s
rates: Call for details
info: Catering facilities available, as well as accommodation. The studio is situated 5 minutes from the M40.

Zoo Recording Studio
89 Plough Hill Road, Nuneaton, Warwickshire, CV10 9NY
tel: 02476 395 210/07796 038 323
email: guapo@scud89.fsnet.co.uk
web: www.zoorecording.co.uk
contact: Carl Harris
desk: Yamaha RM800
monitors: Acoustic
rates: £15 per hour
info: Live room. Also provide CD duplication services.

NORTHEAST

AG's Guitars Practice & Studio
Richard Street, Hetton-Le-Hole, Houghton Le Spring, Tyne & Wear, DH5 9HN
tel: 0191 526 5741
email: anthsguitars@hotmail.com
desk: Soundcraft
rates: £12.50 per hour
info: AG's also run a practice room and guitar shop. Contact for further information.

The Audio Loft
28 Bourn Lea, Houghton Le Spring, Tyne & Wear, DH4 4PG
tel: 0191 385 5351
email: info@audioloft.co.uk
web: www.audioloft.co.uk
contact: Ron Angus
rates: £25 per hour, £160 per day
info: Full studio facilities for recording, restoration and mastering. Transfer to CD. Previous clients include Fairport Convention.

MUSIC SERVICES/RETAIL

Base HQ
Kings House, Fourth Banks, Newcastle, NE1 3PA
tel:	0191 261 1030
email:	basehq@btconnect.com
web:	www.basehq.com
desk:	Yamaha O2R
monitors:	Dynaudio
rates:	Call for details
info:	Prices are flexible depending on the length of your

session. Call or visit website for full list of services. Also have rehearsal facilities. See entry in relevant section for details.

Bright Blue Studios
The Ellers, Ulverston, Cumbria, LA12 0AB
tel:	01229 585 242
email:	info@brightbluestudios.co.uk
web:	www.brightbluestudios.co.uk
contact:	Charley Darbishire, charley Darbishire
rates:	£20 per hour, £120 per day
info:	Fully sound-proofed live room, and has substantial

acoustic treatment including bass traps, diffusers and mid-high frequency absorbers. Mobile recording also available.

Bunker
29 Stockton Road, Sunderland, Tyne & Wear, SR2 7AQ
tel:	0191 567 1777
email:	info@bunkeruk.com
web:	www.bunkeruk.com
contact:	Kenny Sanger
rates:	From £10 per hour
info:	Bunker offer recording and rehearsal facilities, as well as

putting on gigs in the area. See listings in relevant sections for details.

Cluny Studios
36 Lime Street, Newcastle upon Tyne, NE1 2PQ
tel:	0191 232 3934
email:	mail@clunystudios.co.uk
web:	www.clunystudios.co.uk
desk:	Mackie D8B
monitors:	Mackie HR824
rates:	Call for details
info:	Logic system integrated into recording. Top-end pre-

amps and mics available.

Dave Maughan
Wingrove Road, Newcastle Upon Tyne, Tyne & Wear, NE4 9DB
tel:	0191 273 4443
email:	info@davemaughan.co.uk
web:	www.davemaughan.co.uk
info:	Freelance producer with own studio, but will usually

work wherever the band want to record. Has worked in the past with professional acts and will want to hear the material first before taking on any project.

First Avenue Studios
32 First Avenue, Heaton, Newcastle Upon Tyne, NE6 5YE
tel:	0191 265 3879
fax:	0191 276 7882
email:	info@firstave.co.uk
web:	www.firstave.co.uk
desk:	Allen & Heath GS3000
monitors:	Mackie
rates:	£200 per day
info:	Fully equipped digital studio, see website for details.

Also have 3 rehearsal spaces, see entry in relevant section for details.

The Forum Music Centre
Borough Road, Darlington, County Durham, DL1 1SG
tel:	01325 363 135
email:	info@theforumonline.co.uk
web:	www.theforumonline.co.uk
contact:	Chris Davidson
desk:	Mackie
monitors:	Mackie
rates:	£14 per hour (members)
info:	Studio 1 sound room can comfortably accommodate

several musicians at any one time. Incorporates separate isolation booth with full visibility ideal for drummers and other acoustic separation requirements.

Greenhouse Music
Unit 2, Pennywell Business Centre, Portsmouth Road, Sunderland, SR4 9AR
tel:	0191 534 1112
email:	greenhousemusic@tiscali.co.uk
web:	www.greenhousemusic.co.uk
desk:	Roland VS2000
monitors:	Mackie
rates:	£15 per hour, £70 per day
info:	Also run a rehearsal space. See listing in relevant section

for more information.

Handshake
68-70 High North Gate, Darlington, County Durham, DL1 1UW
tel:	01325 250 903
email:	info@handshake-uk.com
web:	www.handshake-uk.com
desk:	O1X with PreSonus Pre Amps
monitors:	JBL/Control 12s
rates:	£160 per day
info:	Mobile recording studio available if required.

Hangtime Studios
10 Wharfedale Gardens, Blyth, Northumberland, NE24 5LY
tel:	07849 400 881
email:	flatlandrideruk@aol.com
web:	www.hangtime.uni.cc
contact:	Graham Davis
desk:	Outboard
monitors:	Alesis Active Mk 1
rates:	£8 per hour
info:	Mobile studio. Bands can also come to Wharfdale

Gardens address to record.

High Fidelity Studios
37 Sutherland Grange, New Herrington, Houghton-le-Spring, Tyne and Wear, DH4 4UT
tel:	07768 410 511
email:	info@highfidelitymobile.co.uk
web:	www.highfidelitymobile.co.uk
contact:	David Dorn
desk:	Allen & Heath
rates:	£175 oer 4 hour session
info:	Mobile recording studio.

Impact Studio
Sunderland, Tyne & Wear
email:	info@impactstudio.biz
web:	www.impactstudio.biz
desk:	Yamaha 44/16
monitors:	Spirit
rates:	Contact for details
info:	Studio ideal for vocalists. Main control room and

acoustically treated vocal booth available. Cubase system. For full technical specification see the website. Impact also provide CD duplication services. Please see relevant section for details.

Lorne Street Studios
19 Lorne Street, Middlesborough, TS1 5QY
tel:	01642 246 090
email:	stesmith44@yahoo.co.uk
desk:	Yamaha 02R
monitors:	Circle 5
rates:	£20 per hour
info:	Rehearsal space and equipment hire available. See

relevant sections for more details.

Mill Studios
7-9 Dispensary Street, Alnwick, Northumberland, NE66 1LS
tel:	01665 604 195
email:	ally@millstudios.co.uk
web:	www.millstudios.co.uk
contact:	Ally
desk:	Soundtracks Quartz - 32/24
monitors:	Tannoy Stratford
rates:	£10 per hour
info:	Rehearsal facilities also available at £5 per hour. Contact

for more information. Free parking on-site.

My Big Bedroom
Unit 21, Grassmere Way, Kitty Brewster Industrial Estate, Blyth, Northumberland, NE24
tel:	07708 587 648
email:	mark@mybigbedroom.co.uk
web:	www.mybigbedroom.co.uk
rates:	£17.50 per hour
info:	Live demo recording specialists. The My Big Bedroom

website features a jukebox hosting tracks by bands and artists that used the facilities. Rehearsal rooms also available, see relevant section for more details.

Oldwell Recording Studio
1 Oldwell Avenue, Winlaton, Blaydon-on-Tyne, NE21 5RA
tel:	0191 440 2467/07764 932 975
email:	oldwellstudio@blueyonder.co.uk
web:	www.oldwellstudio.pwp.blueyonder.co.uk/index.html
desk:	Soundcraft M12
monitors:	Fostex/Tannoy
rates:	£12.50 per hour
info:	Offer complete recording facilities for bands, solo

artists or any other type of projects. There are facilities for pre and post-production, including programming (Nuendo, Cubase SX, Logic, Cakewalk, Soundforge, Acid etc) on PC and final mastering onto CD. The Studio offers 24 input/output hard disk recording, 16 tracks of digital audio (ADAT) and 1/4 inch (8-track) reel-to-reel recorder.

PFL Audio
Tweedmouth Industrial Estate, Berwick-Upon-Tweed, TD15 1XF
tel:	01289 308 036
email:	neil@pflaudio.co.uk
web:	www.pflaudio.co.uk
contact:	Neil Forrest
desk:	Allen & Heath
monitors:	Alesis/Tannoy
rates:	Call for details
info:	Facilities include 2 live rooms, video suite, 2 private
tuition rooms, and café.

Polestar
Uptin House, Stepney Road, Shieldfield, Newcastle upon Tyne, NE2 1EZ
tel:	0191 230 1831
email:	info@polestarstudios.co.uk
web:	www.polestarstudios.co.uk
desk:	Focusrite Octopre
monitors:	Twin monitor Apple G5 computer
rates:	£160 per 10 hour day
info:	The studio control room is equipped with a twin
monitor Apple G5 computer running a Digi 002 FireWire-based Pro
Tools LE music production system accompanied by an 8 channel
Focusrite Octopre processor with 24-bit, 96kHz A/D converters.
Capable of recording live bands or electronic based midi projects. Live
room also available. Also has rehearsal rooms available, see relevant
section for details.

Sanity Studio
Castlegate Quay, Quayside Road, Riverside, Stockton, TS18 1BZ
tel:	01642 602 292
email:	info@sanitymultimedia.com
web:	www.sanitymultimedia.com
desk:	Soundcraft
monitors:	Genelec/Fostex
rates:	Contact for details
info:	Comprises 2 recording studios. Full technical
specifications for studios can be found on the above website. Also
provide rehearsal space. See relevant listing for details.

Sean Clarke
Wylam
tel:	01661 881 048
email:	sean@v7web.com
info:	Producer and engineer with 10 years experience and
32 + track digital/analogue studio. Flexible, efficient and creative set
up. Contact Sean for further details.

The Soundroom
Redheugh Studios, Cuthbert Street, Gateshead, Tyne & Wear, NE8 1AF
tel:	0191 477 1116
email:	thesoundroom@hotmail.com
web:	www.thesoundroom.org.uk
desk:	32 channel Mackie 8 Bus
monitors:	Soundcraft Spirit
rates:	£10 per hour
info:	Good mastering software. The Soundroom is a
community music project that also offers rehearsal space. See relevant
section for more details.

The Studio
Tower Street, Hartlepool, Cleveland, TS24 7HQ
tel:	01429 424 440
email:	studiohartlepool@btconnect.com
web:	www.studiohartlepool.com
desk:	Amek Big By Langley/Mackie
monitors:	Quested/Tannoy
rates:	From £10 per hour
info:	Comprises 3 fully equipped, high quality recording
studios which are acoustically designed and air-conditioned, all with
good disabled access. The Studio complex also houses a live music
venue and rehearsal facilities. See listings in relevant sections for
further information.

Studio 64
90 Corporation Road, Middlesborough, Teeside, TS1 2RE
tel:	01642 860 006
email:	info@studio64.org.uk
web:	www.studio64.org.uk
desk:	Soundcraft 500
monitors:	Tannoy
rates:	£20 per hour
info:	Studio 64 record onto Soundcraft series 500 2" analogue
tape recorder. Also provide rehearsal space, CD duplication, equipment
hire and tuition services. See listings in relevant sections for details.

Trinity Heights
428-430 Denton Road, Newcastle Upon Tyne, NE15 7HB
tel:	0191 274 2190
email:	trinityheightsuk@aol.com
web:	www.trinityheights.co.uk
contact:	Fred Purser
desk:	Tweed
monitors:	Quested/Meyer Sound HD1/Yamaha NS10
rates:	£220 per day (+ VAT)
info:	Chillout room, kitchen, shower and ample free car
parking.

White Wolf Recording Studios
Unit 11, Ever Ready Industrial Estate, Hanfield Lane, Stanley, County
Durham, DH9 9QF
tel:	01207 282 555
email:	ian@whitewolfrecording.co.uk
web:	www.whitewolfrecording.co.uk
desk:	32 channel Soundtrac
rates:	£150/8 hour day
info:	Digital and analogue recording. CD duplication and
rehearsal space available, see relevant sections for more details.

NORTHWEST

2dB Music Productions
17 Stoney Lane, Wilmslow, Cheshire, SK9 6LG
tel:	01625 548 879
email:	2db@2dbmusic.com
contact:	Doug/Dave
desk:	Soundcraft Ghost
monitors:	Adam
rates:	From £30 per hour
info:	Project studio with extensive range of midi gear, ideal
for singer-songwriters. Cubase SX, 128 track recording, 72 channel
desk. Separate live room, Focusrite ISA & Green outboard. Production
and mastering available.

Acid Studios
Unit 4/1a, Meadowmill, Water Street, Stockport, SK1 2BY
tel:	0161 477 8668
contact:	Mark Hallard
rates:	£15 per hour
info:	Pro Tools. Professional live room and isolation booth.
Contact Mark for further information.

Airtight Productions Ltd.
Unit 16, Albany Road Trading Estate, Albany Road, Chorlton,
Manchester, M21 0AZ
tel:	0161 881 5157
email:	info@airtightproductions.co.uk
web:	www.airtightproductions.co.uk
contact:	Anthony Davey
desk:	Pro Tools Control 24
monitors:	Genelec
rates:	Call for details
info:	Digital 128 track Pro Tools recording studio with large
live room and piano. Dedicated midi suite. Digital mastering. Lounge
and kitchen facilities. Video, DVD and CD-Rom production.

Alive Recording
312 Preston Road, Clayton le Woods, Chorley, Lancashire, PR6 7HZ
tel:	01257 249 113/07796 495 142
email:	mike@aliverecording.co.uk
web:	www.aliverecording.co.uk
contact:	Mike
desk:	Behringher
monitors:	Alesis
rates:	£12 per hour
info:	On location recording service that specialises in
recording band demos. Being a mobile studio means Alive can record in
a convenient location for the band. Ideal for a band wanting to capture
that live 'feel', but with a studio-quality sound. Also offer gig recording.

Altered States
37 Brighton Grove, Fallowfield, Manchester, M14 5JG
tel:	0161 248 4604
email:	alteredstates@post.com
web:	www.alteredstates.co.uk
contact:	Robert Groves
desk:	Tascam US2400
monitors:	Mackie 824
rates:	Negotiable
info:	Mac and PC based with digital performer, Cubase SX
and Sonar. Valve outboard units for the analogue purist. Guitars,
basses, saxophone, piano all available free of charge. Session musicians
also available. Graphic design provided for sleeve art, flyers and press
packs. Tuition offered for every musical need. Enquire for further
information.

airtight productions

Digital Recording Studio

Pro Tools Recording Studio
Large Purpose-Built Live Room
MIDI Studio & Production Suite
Video & DVD Production
Great Rates & Free Parking!

Chorlton, Manchester
Tel: 0161 881 5157
www.airtightproductions.co.uk
info@airtightproductions.co.uk

Ameritz Music Productions
479a Smithdown Road, Wavertree, Liverpool, L15 5AE
tel:	0151 734 0645
email:	talk2us@ameritz.co.uk
web:	www.ameritz.co.uk
info:	Ameritz only deal in backing tracks.

Amplisound Studios
4 Old Garden Street, Stockport, SK1 3WJ
tel:	0800 996 1061
email:	info@amplisound.com
web:	www.amplisound.com
contact:	Robin Housman
rates:	Variable
info:	Equipment list includes Pro Tools system. Competitive rates quoted by the project.

Analogue Catalogue
PO Box 4095, Manchester, M60 12Q
tel:	0161 283 3063
email:	info@analoguecat.co.uk
web:	www.analoguecat.co.uk
contact:	Julie
desk:	Trident Series 80B
monitors:	Quested & BBC Reference Monitors
rates:	Call for details
info:	Well equipped studio with lots of vintage, analogue gear. 4 live rooms with lots of instruments (grand piano, Fender Rhodes keyboard, Accordion and many more). Desk is vintage, 2", analogue, 24 track.

Assembly Line Recording Studio
Unit A50, Red Scar Business Park, Longridge Road, Lancashire, Preston, PR2 5NB
tel:	01772 794 433
fax:	01772 794 433
email:	peter@assemblyline.freeserve.co.uk
web:	www.assemblyline.freeserve.co.uk
contact:	Peter Knight
desk:	Studiomaster
monitors:	Yamaha NS10
rates:	£18 per hour (inc. engineer), £25 per hour (inc. producer)
info:	Discounts for bookings over 12 hours. Package including studio, producer, photo shoot and inclusion of your MP3 on Assembly Line website available. Your MP3 will be sent to record companies by Assembly Line. 16 track analog, 32 track digital. Audio restoration, digital editing and mastering. CD and cassette duplication. 4k PA hire (with engineer) available. Also offer rehearsal rooms. See listing in relevant section.

The Bassment
16 Bentinck Street, Ashton-Under-Lyne, OL6 7SS
tel:	0161 330 7335
email:	ste@peopleinthebassment.com
contact:	Steve
desk:	Roland VS2480
rates:	£14 per hour, £100 per day
info:	24 track digital studio. In-house drum kit, bass amp, guitar amp, Hammond Organ, Congas and various other instruments. Session musicians available. Friendly and helpful approach to recording your music. All styles welcomed.

Berlin Recording & Rehearsal Studio
Caxton House, Caxton Avenue, Bispham, Blackpool, Lancashire, FY2 9AP
tel:	01253 591 169
fax:	01253 500 488
email:	berlin.studios@virgin.net
web:	www.berlinstudios.co.uk
contact:	Steve Sharples
desk:	Mackie/Soundtracs Quartz
monitors:	Urei 913A
rates:	From £20 per hour
info:	32 track Adat, 24 track 2", Pro Tools. Mackie hard disk recorder. Lounge, tea and coffee making facilities. Indoor heated swimming pool available for residential clients. Rehearsal facilities also available. See listing in relevant section for further details.

Black Jack Recording Studio
129-131 Telegraph Road, Heswall, Wirral, CH60 0AF
tel:	0151 342 6333
contact:	Andy Miles
desk:	Studiomaster
rates:	£140 per day
info:	Digital 48 track studio. Large live recording area. Ideal for bands. Songwriters and session musicians available for solo artists. 24 track desk. 4 band EQ.

Blenn Music Productions
PO Box 80, Liverpool, L36 7WZ
tel:	0151 489 1823
email:	info@blennproductions.co.uk
web:	www.blennproductions.co.uk
contact:	Paul Blenn
desk:	Mackie
monitors:	Genelec
rates:	From £25 per hour
info:	High spec studio. Neve pre-amps, Nuendo 3 software. 200 track recording, 192kHz frequency response. Suitable for singer-songwriters, small ensembles, string quartets and Pop production.

Blue Room Studios
Unit 75, Mountheath Industrial Park, Ardent Way, Prestwich, M25 9WB
tel:	0161 773 9615
email:	phil@blueroomstudios.freeserve.co.uk
web:	www.bluerooomstudios.co.uk
contact:	Phil Green
desk:	Behringer MX8000
monitors:	Soundcraft
rates:	£25 per hour
info:	72 track fully automated digital recording studio. Artwork and website design services available.

Blueprint Studios
Elizabeth House, 39 Queen Street, Manchester, M3 7DQ
tel:	0870 011 2760
fax:	0870 011 2780
email:	info@blueprint-studios.com
web:	www.blueprint-studios.com
contact:	Tim Thomas, Tim Thomas, Ian Stewart
desk:	Neve VR Legend
monitors:	Genelec
rates:	Call for details
info:	Large live room and control room. Private lounge for artists using the studio. Production, arrangement and writing services. The Blueprint complex also houses 6 sound-proofed, heated and air conditioned rehearsal rooms. See relevant section for further details.

Boxroom Studios
82 Englefield Avenue, Connah's Quay, Deeside, CH5 4SY
tel:	01244 815 641
email:	via website
web:	www.boxroom-studios.co.uk
rates:	Call for details
info:	Mobile recording facilities. Can play back 32 tracks of uncompressed digital audio and effects via Pro Tools. Digidesign 001. Tracks can be recorded on location, 8 at a time, then digitally transferred into Pro Tools, building up to 32 tracks of audio. The tracks can then be edited, mastered and burnt to CD or MD.

Cassette
53 Hudson Gardens, 136 Duke Street, Liverpool, L1 5BB
tel: 07765 267 116
email: info@cassettemusic.net
web: www.cassettemusic.net
contact: Tim Jones
desk: Yamaha 01V
monitors: Genelec/Tannoy
rates: 2 songs for £50, 4 for £100
info: Cassette Music provide an affordable professional recording service. Sessions are sold as packages.

Catalyst Studios
Units 7-17, Catapult Too, Charles Street, St. Helens, Merseyside, WA10 1LX
tel: 01744 733 222
email: info@catalyst-studios.co.uk
web: www.catalyst-studios.co.uk
contact: Andy Bowes
desk: Allen & Heath GS3000
rates: See website
info: Professional acoustically designed recording facility. Rates vary depending on whether an engineer is required or not. Chillout area, on-site parking, disabled access. Catalyst also provide rehearsal studios. See listing in relevant section for details.

Cheshire Sound Productions
Unit 2, Hadfield Street, Northwich, CW9 5LU
tel: 01606 350 022
email: info@cheshiresound.com
web: www.cheshiresound.co.uk
desk: Behringer/Korg DX 32 XD
monitors: Event/Tannoy
rates: Call for details
info: 32 track digital and 48 track analogue recording. Offer a complete one stop recording studio facility including composition and music production, sequencing and audio editing, re-mixing and mastering.

Chill Recording Studio
Hempshaw Business Park, 351 Hempshaw Lane, Stockport, Cheshire, SK1 4NB
tel: 0161 480 1997
email: al@chillstudios.co.uk
web: www.chillstudios.co.uk
contact: Alan Wrench
desk: Otari Status 18r
monitors: FAR DVW80/Tannoys
rates: £25 per hour
info: 24 track Adat, Cubase VST on Mac. Pro Tools 96 channel analogue mixing desk. 2 live rooms, one for drums, larger one for band. Large control room. Chillout area available. Band friendly service. Discounts available on longer bookings.

Clouds Music Production
Braytop House, Whitehill Road, Blackpool, FY4 5LA
tel: 01253 767 007
fax: 01253 792 970
email: mail@cloudscars.co.uk
contact: Kelvin Futers
info: Ideal for singer-songwriters and duos. Maximum of 3 performers in booth.

Coach House Studio
Ford Park, Ulverston, Cumbria, LA12 7JP
tel: 01229 581 711
email: colin@lakesounds.co.uk
contact: Colin
desk: Allen & Heath
monitors: Tannoy Eclipse and DC200
rates: £120 per day
info: Digital and analogue multitrack recording studio. Superb views of the Pennines and Morecambe Bay from the live room. 8 track digital mobile recording unit available. Involved with the Ulverston Contemporary Project.

coiled
Manchester
email: greg@coiled.com
web: www.coiled.com
contact: Greg Hutchison
info: Well connected, freelance producer. Music production services, as well as writing and mixing. Very reasonable rates for unsigned artists. Can offer production deals or artist development for exceptional talent.

Cottage Studios
2 Gawsworth Road, Macclesfield, Cheshire, SK11 8UE
tel: 01625 420 163
email: info@cottagegroup.co.uk
web: www.cottagegroup.co.uk
contact: Glenn Jones
desk: Soundcraft/Tascam digital
monitors: JBL/Tannoy
info: Well equipped digital and analogue studio. Prices individually negotiated. The Cottage Group are also involved in music publishing and artist management. Contact Glenn at the studio for more details.

Courtyard Recording Studios
Gorsey Mount Street, Off Waterloo Road, Stockport, Cheshire, SK1 3BU
tel: 0161 477 6531
email: tim@courtyardrecordingstudios.co.uk
web: www.courtyardrecordingstudios.co.uk
contact: Tim Woodward
desk: A&H Saber
monitors: F.A.R.
rates: £20-£40 per hour
info: A&H Saber, Tascam MSR 24s + Motu. 5 recording areas, very large live room. Backline and engineer provided.

Cue Music
183 Duckworth Street, Darwen, BB3 1AU
tel: 01254 775 560
fax: 01254 775 560
email: djh@cuemusic.com
web: www.cuemusic.com
contact: Peter Holroyd
desk: Studiomaster P7
monitors: Samsung/Tannoy
rates: £15 per hour (+VAT)
info: Studiomaster P7 desk, 16 track Tascam digital. PA, backline and guitars included. Session musicians available. Digital mastering onto CD. Opening hours by arrangement with Peter. Also have an instrument shop. See listing in relevant section for details.

The Cutting Rooms
Abraham Moss Centre, Crescent Road, Crumpsall, Manchester, M8 5UF
tel: 0161 740 9438
fax: 0161 908 8315
email: cuttingrooms@hotmail.com
web: www.citycol.com/cuttingrooms
contact: Alan Oatey
desk: Raindirk Symphony/Behringer 24
monitors: Dynaudio M3
rates: £25 per hour
info: Saturn 2" 24 track studio with Raindirk Symphony 56 input analogue desk. Extensive outboard including classic valve compressors and EQ, BSS compressors/limiters, Joe Meek VC1 voice channel and Lexicon 300. Mac G4, Cubase VST and Logic Audio. Over 30 mics in total. Grand piano. Large, air conditioned live room and control room. The Cutting Rooms also house a digital editing suite and 8 track studio with Behringer 32 input desk.

D.C.M. Recording Studios Ltd.
Dovetales Christian Centre, Gospel Mission, Maygate, Westwood, OL9 6TR
tel: 0161 628 3838
fax: 0161 628 3838
email: admin@dcmstudios.co.uk
web: www.dcmstudios.co.uk
contact: Marcus Heap
info: Full Pro Tools digital studio. 4 recording spaces including large hall, stage (ideal for live recording), live room and vocal booth.

DMR Recordings
404 Marine Road, East Morecambe, Lancashire, LA4 5AR
tel: 01524 410 202
fax: 01524 410 802
email: dmr@promenademusic.co.uk
web: www.promenademusic.co.uk
contact: David Wood
desk: Soundtracs
info: Mobile and studio recordings. Pro Tools and Cubase. CD, cassette and vinyl duplication also available. DMR Recordings is also part of Promenade Music, musical instrument retailers. See entries in relevant section for further details.

Edge Lane

95 Edge Lane, Stretford, Manchester, M32 8PU
tel: 0161 864 4604
email: graham@stables-studio.demon.co.uk
web: www.stables-studio.demon.co.uk
desk: Soundtracs
monitors: Genelec
info: Edge Lane Studio is a state of the art music production and post production studio set in a large Victorian house at the edge of Manchester city. Located in Stretford, there is very easy access to the M60, M62, Manchester public transport, regional and main line rail links, and Manchester International Airport.

Elevator Recording Studios

23-27 Cheapside, Liverpool, L2 2DY
tel: 0151 255 0195
email: info@elevatorstudios.com
web: www.elevatorstudios.com
desk: Amek Mozart RN24
monitors: Yamaha NS10/Westlake BBSM12
rates: Call fot details
info: Established recording studio. Full selection of microphones and outboard gear. Large live room with natural light. Have previously recorded bands like The Coral, The Zutons and Echo and the Bunnymen. Also offer rehearsal facilities. Refer to listing in relevant section for details.

F.A.B. Recording Studios

Salford, Manchester
tel: 0161 792 0203
email: chris@fabstudios.co.uk
web: www.fabstudios.co.uk
contact: Chris Galbraith
desk: 64 track Tascam
monitors: JBL/Sony
rates: Call for details
info: 16 track analogue tape. Lots of outboard, valve microphones. Digital desk. CD duplication also available, see entry in Mastering and Duplication section for further details.

Firehouse Studios

Rear of the Market Hall, Market Square, Millom, Cumbria, LA18 4HZ
tel: 07732 927 603
email: info@firehousestudios.co.uk
web: www.firehousestudios.co.uk
contact: Barry
desk: Pro Tools
info: 2 recording rooms available. Contact Barry for details of rates. Firehouse also run rehearsal studios and PA hire service. Refer to entries in relevant sections for further details.

Frog Studios

Unit 2B, Bank Quay Trading Estate, Slutchers Lane, Warrington, Cheshire, WA1 1PJ
tel: 01925 445 742
fax: 01925 445 742
email: info@frogstudios.co.uk
web: www.frogstudios.co.uk
contact: Steve Oates, Steve Millington
desk: Soundtracs Jade
monitors: UREI
rates: Contact for details
info: 48 channel desk with automation, 24 track 2 inch analogue tape. Equipped with Pro Tools software. Engineer provided. Mastering to tape. Kitchen and lounge area. Frog Studios are also part of Sound Image Management and Publishing Companies. See entries in relevant sections for further details.

The Fuzzbox Ltd.

8 Clayton Street, Wigan, Lancashire, WN3 4DA
tel: 01942 230 888
email: admin@thefuzzbox.com
contact: Jamie Cavanagh
rates: Call for details
info: Newly built recording studio, call for details on equipment and rates. 5 rehearsal rooms also available, see relevant entry for details.

Fynk

284a Poulton Road, Wallasey, CH44 4DB
tel: 0151 639 0200
email: info@fynk.co.uk
web: www.fynk.co.uk
contact: Paul Robotham
desk: Spirit
monitors: Linear Phase
rates: £15 per hour, £250 per track
info: The typical fee is £250 per song, giving the customer unlimited time and the opportunity to work in a relaxed and creative environment, until they are totally satisfied with the result. Customers are offered as much help as they need throughout the process including arrangement, playing of instruments, programming, production and mastering onto CD. Typically a song will be completed over a period of 1 month, or an album will take 3 to 6 months. An hourly rate of £15 can alternatively be applied. This is more suited to artists who want to put together a quick demo in a single session. More detailed information, equipment specification, and MP3 samples of Fynk productions can be found at the above website.

Glass Studios

Unit 22, Price Street Business Centre, Price Street, Birkenhead, Wirral, CH41 4JQ
tel: 0151 651 1666
email: info@glasstudios.com
web: www.glasstudios.com
contact: Alan Lewis
desk: Studiomaster
monitors: Custom built
rates: £16 per hour
info: Analogue and digital multitrack recording including post production. Phone studio for further details. Conversions from virtually any format to CD. Glass Studios also has rehearsal space, as well as video editing services. See listings in relevant sections for more information.

Gorse Hill Studios

Gorse Hill Arts Centre, Cavendish Road, Stretford, Manchester, M32 0PS
tel: 0161 864 1745
fax: 0161 912 5251
email: ottilia.ordog@trafford.gov.uk
web: www.gorsehillstudios.com
contact: Ben Roberts
rates: Free
info: 10 free hours studio time to people aged 11-25 years who live in the Trafford area.

Gracieland

382 Edenfield Road, Rochdale, OL12 7NH
tel: 01706 648 829
email: rhodes@gracieland.co.uk
web: www.gracieland.co.uk
contact: Martin Rhodes
desk: Amek/Rupert Neve 9098
monitors: Dynaudio M3s/Tannoy System 12s/Genelec 1031As/ Yamaha NS10
rates: Call for details
info: Analogue and digital recording. Amek/Rupert Neve console with full automation and supertrue recall. Extensive range of outboard, mics, vintage equipment and instruments. Special demo rates apply, call or email for details.

HQ Studio

Unit 32, Commerce House, Sherborne Street, Manchester, M8 8HF
tel: 0161 832 5868
contact: Mike Vindice
desk: Behringer DDX 3216
monitors: Tannoy
rates: Call for details
info: Fully digital recording and mixing, analogue if required.

IC Studios

2 Cop Lane, Penwortham, PR1 0SR
tel: 01772 465 082
fax: 01772 465 082
email: colinpotter@another.com
web: www.icrdistribution.com
contact: Colin Potter
desk: Soundcraft Ghost 24 track
monitors: Tannoy
rates: Negotiable
info: Extremely well equipped digital 16 track studio. Location recording also available. Sound effects, production and sound engineering. Mastering and duplication.

the Jaraf House studio

Well equipped studio with a friendly, creative atmosphere
Specialising in recording bands and acoustic artists. From high
quality demo's to commercial releases (Universal, Twisted
Nerve-see website for recent client list)

- Pro-tools HD system
- Quested Monitoring
- Good range of outboard and mics
- Selection of interesting guitar equipment
- Experienced engineer/producer
- Full production packages
- In-house session musicians available
- Great live drum room
- 3 Performance spaces
- Day-lit control room
- Affordable rates
- Just off junction 25 of the M6 near Wigan

**CONTACT: JOHN KETTLE
01942 273393 OR 07760162182
EMAIL: JOHNKETTLE@SUPALIFE.COM**

Imperial Recording Studio (at Crash)
Imperial Warehouse, 11 Davies Street, Liverpool, L1 6HB
tel: 0151 236 1880
email: andyb@imperial-recording-studio.co.uk
contact: Andy Bowes
desk: Allen & Heath GS3000
monitors: Yamaha NS10
rates: £20 per hour, £125 per day
info: 24 track digital recording studio. Mastering backing
tracks, production and composition. Call Andy for details and to
discuss rates further, as weekday and weekend prices vary.

Inch
23 New Mount Street, Manchester, M4 4DE
tel: 0161 953 4232
fax: 0161 953 4001
email: keir@inchstudio.com
web: www.inchstudio.com
contact: Keir Stewart
desk: 70's Vintage Chiltern QN1
monitors: Quested H208
rates: Call for details
info: High spec studio with Pro Tools, live room and control
room acoustically designed by Andrew Parry. Extensive outboard
and a range of instruments available. Also provide video, DVD and
CD-Rom production, professional photography. Professional lighting
also available. Studio has excellent acoustics and can be booked for
mastering purposes. Also takes commissions for soundtracks (TV ads,
promos etc). Rehearsal rooms also available, see entry in relevant
section for further details.

Insect Orange
98 Oxford Road, Macclesfield, SK11 8JG
tel: 01625 500 178
email: scott@boygenius.demon.co.uk
contact: Scott Darlington
desk: Mackie
monitors: Tannoy
rates: £12 per hour (bands), £10 per hour (solo musicians)
info: 48 track digital studio. Mackie mixing desk, Akai
sampler, Apple Mac G4. Vocal harmonisers, outboard. Range of
instruments including drum kit available at no extra cost. CD mastering
and artwork available. Video production. Also run music software
training courses.

The Jaraf House
Nr. Wigan
tel: 01942 273393
email: johnkettle@supalife.com
contact: John Kettle
desk: Tascam TMD 8000/Pro Tools HD
monitors: Quested
rates: Call for details

Jelly Jam Studios
Unit 3, Expressway Industrial Estate, Pimlico Road, Runcorn, WA7 4US
tel: 01928 577 944
email: info@jellyjam.co.uk
web: www.jellyjam.co.uk
contact: Graham Woodcock
desk: Yamaha DN2000
monitors: Genelec 10-37B
rates: Call for details
info: Very high spec studio with Nuendo 2, Lexicon 960 and
TCM 6000.

Keylink Studios
Roughwood Drive, Kirby, Merseyside, L33 8XF
tel: 0151 549 2499
fax: 0151 549 0745
email: sound@keylinkstudios.org.net
web: www.keylinkstudios.org.uk
contact: Allan Crookes
info: Keylink Studios is a community media charity that
delivers a range of projects and services. Fully equipped studio
available for hire including 24 track, 24 bit digital sound which can
cater for all recording needs. Pearl drum kit and pre-installed amps
provided. Contact for details of rates. Engineer is included in price.

The Kif
23 Parr Street, Liverpool, L1 4JN
tel: 0151 706 0008
web: www.livingbrain.co.uk
contact: James or Dominic Pagella or Lewington
desk: Korg 16 Track
monitors: Acoustic Technology
rates: Negotiable
info: 16 track digital desk, valve pre-amps, Tascam Desk.
Wide selection of instruments and vintage gear.

KJI Studios (Mobile Recording)
PO Box 163, Wallasey, CH44 2G
tel: 0871 871 6628
fax: 0871 871 6629
email: info@kjistudios.co.uk
web: www.kjistudios.co.uk
contact: Kevin Irvine
desk: Behringer
rates: £35 per hour
info: Mobile recording studio. Up to 15 track recording.

L.P. Studios
Unit 4/2, Meadowmill, Water Street, Stockport, SK1 2BY
tel: 0161 477 7676/07929 448 928
email: lpstudios@hotmail.com
web: www.lpstudios.co.uk
contact: Leigh Eaton
desk: Roland MVC 7200
monitors: Mackie 624
rates: £15 per hour, £120 per day
info: 24 track Pro Tools studio with digital mixing. Full details
can be found on the website, along with information about offers on
rates.

Lakeside Studios
Lakeside View, Winsford, Cheshire, CW9 8RR
tel: 01606 863 642
email: jdelf@mac.com
contact: John Delf,
monitors: Dynaudio
rates: Call for details
info: Hard disk digital recorder and Cubase SX. Dynaudio
monitoring. Behringer mixer CD mastering. Clients include The
Chameleons, The Delgados and Arab Strap.

Lancaster Music Co-Op
1 Lodge Street, Lancaster, LA1 1QW
tel: 01524 388 544
email: musiccoop@musiccoop.co.uk
web: www.musiccoop.co.uk
contact: Dave Blackwell, Ian Dickon
desk: Soundcraft
monitors: Tannoy
rates: From £12.50 per hour
info: 2 systems; 8 track analogue and 32 track digital
Logic Audio. See website for full technical specification. Live room.
Equipment available for hire. Also sell a range of accessories. See also
listing in Rehearsal Studios and Regional Organisations section for
details of facilities available.

Level One
Unit 12, The Progress Centre, Ardwick Green, Manchester, M12 6HS
tel:	0161 272 6260
fax:	0161 274 3655
email:	petewilliams@levelonestudios.co.uk
web:	www.levelonestudios.co.uk
contact:	Pete Williams
desk:	O2R
monitors:	Spirit 4/Mackie
rates:	Call for details
info:	The studio is run by musicians who are very willing to support unsigned acts. Equipment includes O2R desk, Mac computers and PCs, 16 track hard disk, Logic Audio. Engineers and production help included.

Linden Studio
High Bankhill Farm, Kirkoswald, Cumbria, CA10 1EZ
tel:	01768 870 353
email:	guy@lindenstudio.co.uk
web:	www.lindenstudio.co.uk
contact:	Guy Forrester
desk:	Soundcraft 2400
monitors:	Tannoy LRM
rates:	From £20 per hour
info:	Comprehensive and professional studio with a good mix of vintage and contemporary technologies. 2" 16 track recorder, Neve mixer (excellent for vocals), 450W power amp, 1200w monitoring, custom built twin reflex cabinets excellent for sub-bass work. Cubase VST 24 SX, Delta 1010 audio hardware. Variety of microphones available inc. AKCG 414. Studio is based in a farm house in a superb rural setting and the owner has lots of industry experience and contacts. Can assist with productionr, composition and arranging. CD mastering and duplication services also available, see entry in relevant section for details.

Lolipop Studios
7 Kestral Close, Whitefield, Manchester, M45 6SB
tel:	0161 798 0120
fax:	0161 798 0120
contact:	Lol Harris
desk:	Mackie D8b
monitors:	Soundcraft
rates:	£30 per hour
info:	Ideal for singer-songwriters, duos and trios. Demos, multitracks, arranging and backing tracks. Mastering service.

Loose Recording Studio
Runcorn
tel:	01928 566 261
email:	jaki.florek@virgin.net
contact:	Bill Leach
rates:	£75 per day
info:	Small, good quality studio run by Loose Music Collective. Excellent, experienced sound engineer. Demos, albums and experimental projects. All music considered from Acoustic artists to Punk bands. For full information about services provided by the collective, see listing in Useful Regional Organisations section.

Low Fold Audio
Shires Head Studio, Old Church, Stony Lane, Forton, Preston, PR3 1DE
tel:	01524 792 020
fax:	01524 792 305
email:	sales@lowfold.com
web:	www.lowfold.com
contact:	Martin Hughes
desk:	Yamaha O2R
monitors:	Dyaudio Acoustics
info:	Pro Tools. Air conditioned studio, large live room.

Mac Musica
8b High Sand Lane, Cockermouth, Cumbria, CA13 9NA
tel:	01900 828 194
email:	mac-musica@freeseve.co.uk
contact:	Paul Mackay
desk:	Samson
monitors:	JBL
rates:	£26 per hour
info:	Recording, digital editing, production and mastering. Mobile service, mainly for use at live venues. CD duplication. Paul also offers tuition services. See listing for Paul Mackay in relevant section for details.

Machete Records & Productions
18b Greenheys Lane, Hulme, Manchester, M15 6NQ
tel:	07976 230 365
email:	jamesjonah007@orange.net
web:	www.macheterecords.com
contact:	James Jones
desk:	Mackie
monitors:	Event/Project Studio
rates:	Call for details
info:	Lots of outboard including Akai sampler, Triton racks and synth modules. Access to rehearsal space is available, call for details. Also operate a record label.

The Madhouse Studio
Unit 1, Henry Street, Crewe, Cheshire, CW1 4BH
tel:	01270 251 014
email:	themadhouse@cd2.com
info:	16 track professional digital studio with live Drum room. Lots of outboard gear. Dormatory available for overnight stays. Discounts available for block bookings. 2 practice rooms. Also provide video production at affordable rates, as well as website design and management.

Manchester Midi School
23 New Mount Street, Manchester, M4 4DE
tel:	0161 953 4072
fax:	0161 839 3030
email:	info@midischool.com
web:	www.midischool.com
contact:	Patrick
desk:	Mackie D8b
monitors:	Quested
rates:	£15 per hour

MJM Recording Studio
27 Dudley Avenue, Oswaldtwistle, Lancashire, BB5 4NU
tel:	01254 237 565
fax:	www.mjmrecording.com
email:	mjmrecording@aol.com
contact:	Mark Jones
desk:	Soundcraft
monitors:	Dynaudio BN15A/Yamaha NS10
rates:	Call for details
info:	Large range of outboard, Pro Tools 72 track digital recording. 48k system.

Moolah Rouge
4a Hallam Mill, Hallam Street, Stockport, SK2 6PT
tel:	0161 429 0986
email:	info@moolahrouge.com
web:	www.moolahrouge.com
desk:	Pro Tools HD3
rates:	£25 per hour (Studio 1), £15 per hour (Studio 2)
info:	Digital and analogue recording available in Studio 1, with 2 live rooms available. Experienced engineers available. Also provide space for rehearsals. Refer to listing in relevant section for further details.

MR Studio - Mobile Recording
PO Box 104, Liverpool, L12 0WW
tel:	07876 518 390
email:	info@mrstudio.biz
web:	www.mrstudio.biz
contact:	Drew Hamilton
desk:	Alesis HD24 digital multi-track
monitors:	Behringer Truth B2031 active
rates:	Contact for details
info:	An excellent, high spec, mobile recording studio. Can offer a complete service from conception to finished product. The studio can be used anywhere to record practically anything from bands to choirs, either at home or in a venue of your choice. Studio has Behringer gates and compressors, Roland U220, Behringer MX1804 and MX3242 mixers. Sony PCM 300 DAT recorder. The studio offers discounts to schools and charities who wish to produce CDs to raise funds (eventually they want this to be a free service), and offers discounts to the unemployed. It is recommended that you check the comprehensive website for even more information.

The Music Factory
Unit 3a, Sycamore Trading Estate, Squire's Gate, Blackpool, FY4 3RL
tel:	01253 348 037
fax:	01253 348 055
email:	info@themusicfactoryuk.co.uk
web:	www.themusicfactoryuk.co.uk
contact:	Andy Mudd
desk:	Mackie D8B
monitors:	Mackie
rates:	£25 per hour (+ VAT)
info:	Cubase SX2. Mastering onto CD, cassette, DAT or MD.

The Music Farm
Grange Brow Farm, Grange, Egremont, CA22 2PG
tel:	01946 822 449
email:	tom@themusicfarm.co.uk
web:	www.themusicfarm.co.uk
contact:	Tom Tyson
desk:	Soundtracks
monitors:	JBL
rates:	Negotiable
info:	24 track digital. Soundtracks MRX with a total of 52 inputs, 6 aux sends. Cubase 5.1 VST plus many modules. Outboard (Lexicon, Drawmer, Yamaha, Behringer). Amps, keyboards, guitars, bass and drum kit are all available. Spacious playing area, 400 square feet of performance space and is based on the live end/dead end approach for maximum flexibility. Microphones are Neumann U87i.

Noise Box
New Islington Mill, Oldfield Road, Salford, Manchester, M5 4DE
tel: 0161 798 5677
fax: 0161 798 5677
email: steve.noise@btclick.com
web: www.noiseboxsound.co.uk
contact: Steve Lloyd
desk: Amek Recall
monitors: Tannoy
rates: From £12 per hour
info: 2" 24 track analogue, 48 track digital to hard disk or 56 channel Amek. Mastering to DAT or CD.

Northern Underground Ltd.
The Cluster of Nuts, Burnley Road, Altham, Accrington, BB5 5UA
tel: 01282 777 323
email: mark@northernunderground.com
web: www.northernunderground.com
contact: Mark Gregson
desk: Mackie 24 8 bus
info: Recording into Logic Audio on Mac. Post production, mastering, acoustical design. Sound reinforcement.

Parr Street Studios
33-45 Parr Street, Liverpool, Merseyside, L1 4JN
tel: 0151 707 1050
fax: 0151 707 1813
email: info@parrstreet.co.uk
web: www.parrstreet.co.uk
contact: Paul Lewis
desk: SSO/Neve/Yamaha
monitors: Quested
rates: Vary
info: Residential studio complex based around 3 studios and located in Liverpool's City Centre. Offer tracking and mixing facilities to suit all budgets. Large air-conditioned rooms with daylight and private kitchen and office. Professional assistants and 2 full time in-house maintenance engineers. The complex also features a licensed bar and restaurant with private parking. See website for more details.

Pendlehawk Studios
11 New Market Street, Colne, Lancashire, BB8 9BJ
tel: 01282 866 317
email: pendlehawkmusic@ntlworld.com
contact: Adrian Melling
desk: Soundcraft
monitors: Tannoy
rates: £14 per hour
info: A nice friendly atmosphere, free accommodation if needed. 5 in-house producers, lots of backline, outboard and effects and is only 20 yards from the nearest pub. Parking and there is ample loading space.

Polygon Studios
8 The Polygon, Eccles, M30 0DS
tel: 0161 789 7620
email: theoddness@lykos.co.uk
contact: Colin Crichton
desk: Behringer
monitors: Monitor 1's Alesis
rates: Call for details
info: Pro Tools studio. Wide range of equipment available.

Press-X
4 Huntsman Wood, West Derby, Liverpool, L12 0HY
tel: 0151 283 8161
fax: 0151 283 8161
email: steve@press-x.co.uk
web: www.press-x.co.uk
contact: Steve Erickson
desk: Yamaha 01V
monitors: Absolute Zero
rates: £20 per hour
info: 24 track digital recording studio, Cubase SX, good quality microphones. Master onto CD or MD. Also run production and publishing company. Enquire for further details.

Prostar Studios
72 Tresham Drive, Grappenhall, Warrington, Cheshire, WA4 3DU
tel: 01925 600 709
email: info@prostarstudio.co.uk
web: www.prostarstudios.co.uk
contact: Dean Edwards
desk: Mackie
monitors: Fostex PM2
rates: £15.50 per hour, £140 per day
info: Digital based studio. Fully equipped and designed for vocalists and boy/girl groups.

Red Cat Recording Studios
Standish, Wigan
tel: 01257 421 357
email: redcatstudios@hotmail.com
web: www.redcatstudios.co.uk
contact: Allan Murrell
desk: Mackie
monitors: Alesis RA300/Genelec 8040/JBL/Benchmark/Mackie
rates: Call for details
info: Live room, fully acoustically treated vocal booth, drum room and Pro Audio control room. For full studio specification see above website. CD duplication also available, with on-body CD thermal printing. See listing in Mastering & Duplication section for details.

Redbridge Studios
Brieghtmet Fold Lane, Bolton, Lancashire, BL2 5PH
tel: 01204 525 579
fax: 01204 811 373
email: info@redbridgestudios.com
web: www.redbridgestudios.com
contact: Andy Wyatt
rates: From £15 per hour
info: Pro Tools recording studio, large studio, fully soundproofed. Control room and live room. Refer to website for full technical specifications. Rehearsal space also available, see entry in Rehearsal Rooms section for further details.

Reload Studios
The Stables, Hollin Grove Street, Darwen, Lancashire, BB3 1HG
tel: 01254 701 603
email: info@reloadstudios.com
web: www.reloadstudios.com
desk: Mackie 32.4
monitors: Spirit
rates: £15 per hour, £100 per day
info: Studio equipped with Yamaha O1V, M-Audio digital soundcards, Lexicon effects, Behringer dynamics processing, Yamaha and Emu tone modules, Yamaha Roland synths, Marshall guitar amplification, POD guitar amp modelling, AKG and Shure microphones. Rehearsal studios also available. See listing for further information.

Revolution Studios
11 Church Road, Cheadle Hulme, Cheshire, SK8 7JD
tel: 0161 485 8942
fax: 0161 485 8942
email: revolution@wahtup.com
contact: Andy McPherson
desk: Amek 2500
monitors: JBL
rates: Call for details
info: Desk: Amek 2500. Recorders: Otari MTR90. Main Monitors: JBL 24 track 2" analogue, Sony 24 track DASH digital recording. Akai DR16 24 bit 48 track system. 1 Pro Tools HD3, 1 Pro Tools HD2 and control 24. 1/2" mastering (Pro Tools HD system). Large live area, vocal booth, top quality instruments and amps. Kitchen facilities on-site.

Satellite Studio
Victoria Mill Anex, Worrall Street, Congleton, Cheshire, CW12 1DT
tel: 01260 281 185
email: satellite_studio@btconnect.com
web: www.theorchestrater.co.uk
contact: Paul Marshall
desk: Tascam
monitors: JBL
rates: £25 per hour
info: Studio for vocalist, instrumentalist and backing tracks only. Digital recording, 32 channel Tascam mixing desk. Paul also works with songwriters on arrangements.

Semi-Precious Studios
13b Northenden Road, Sale, Manchester, M33 2DH
tel: 0161 374 1258
fax: 0161 969 5972
email: info@semiprecious.co.uk
web: www.semiprecious.co.uk
contact: Jonathon Dunn
desk: Mackie 32.8
monitors: Alesis/Dynaudio
rates: Contact for details
info: Price includes engineer but not production. 16 channel ADAT, 64 channel hard disc recording. Extensive live room. Full MIDI set up. Associated Dance music label (Semi Precious Records) and computer game soundtrack composition.

Shamrock Recording Studio
The Garth, Commons Lane, Balderstone, Lancashire, BB2 7LL
tel: 01254 812 131
email: s.heffernan@btinternet.com
contact: Seamus Heffernan
desk: Customised Studiomaster
monitors: Kef
rates: £20 per hour
info: Tascam multitrack recorders sync'd to Steinberg digital
multitrack system, digital mastering and editing. Free drum set up and
soundcheck time for bookings of 2 days or more.

The Shed Recording Studio
Unit 35, Chadkirk Industrial Estate, Otterspoll Road, Romiley, Stockport,
Cheshire, SK6 3NE
tel: 0161 427 6819
fax: 0161 427 6819
email: shedstudio1@tiscali.co.uk
contact: John Slater
rates: £20 per hour
info: 24 track digital or analogue studio. Digital editing. CD
mastering and location recording available.

Shireshead Recording Studio
Stony Lane, Forton, Preston, PR3 1BV
tel: 01524 792 020
email: info@shiresheadstudio.com
web: www.shiresheadstudio.com
contact: Martin Hughes
desk: Yamaha O2R
monitors: Dynaudio
rates: £325 per day (+ VAT)
info: Air-conditioned control Room with Digidesign Pro Tools,
Tascam MX 24/24, Yamaha 02/R, TL Audio Valve pre-amps, ISDN
and Dynaudio monitors. Vast range of analogue keyboards and Akai
samplers. Live room, isolation booth, choir room and vocal booth. In
house CD production and duplication. Recording time only booked in
half day or full day slots.

The Sound House Studios
25-27 Sefton Street, Liverpool, L21 7PD
tel: 0151 928 1400
contact: Sean Hunt
desk: SSL
monitors: JBL
rates: £200 per day (+ VAT)
info: 40 track digital desk. Extensive outboard. Live room and
drum booth. Bar and rest room on-site.

Sound of the Loud Minority
188 Ayres Road, Manchester, M16 9QB
tel: 0161 877 8096
email: aniff@aniff.freeserve.co.uk
contact: Aniff Akinola
rates: Call for details
info: Home studio for mainly his own use, but will accept
smaller acoustic or computer based projects.

Splash Sound Productions
1 Mossley Hill Drive, Liverpool, Merseyside, L17 1AJ
tel: 0151 724 2100
fax: 0151 724 5813
email: rick@splashsoundproductions.co.uk
web: www.splashsoundproductions.co.uk
contact: Rick Jockes
desk: Yamaha 02R
monitors: Soundcraft
rates: Negotiable
info: Computer based (Mac and digital audio) midi studio.
Logic Audio and Pro Tools. Ideal for vocalist, solo performers and
computer based music. Not suitable for full bands.

Stonegate Studio
Pyes Mill, Bentham, Lancaster, LA2 7LJ
tel: 01524 263 433
rates: £20 per hour
info: Please ring for details regarding special deals and
equipment

Strangeway Studios Ltd.
Unit 3, Victoria Mills, Dickinson Street, Salford, M3 7LW
tel: 0161 834 3233
email: info@strangewaystudios.co.uk
web: www.strangewaystudios.co.uk
desk: Beringher
monitors: Whardale Pro Diamond Active
rates: £18 per hour, £150 per 10 hour day
info: Large rehearsal room also available, see relevant section
for more details.

Studio Nyne
31 Roe Street, Macclesfield, Cheshire, SK11 6UT
tel: 07939 216 031
email: gareth@studio-nyne.co.uk
web: www.studio-nyne.co.uk
contact: Gareth Metcalf
desk: Yamaha 01B
monitors: Mackie HR824
rates: Negotiable
info: Mobile recording facilities, ideal for recording live gigs
and from rehearsal rooms. 24 track mobile recording, PC running Logic
Audio 5.5 for midi and audio editing and sequencing. Recent clients
include Babyshambles and Nick Harper. Mastering and web design also
available.

Studio Studio Recording
Unit 4, Spodden Mill, Whitworth, Lancashire, OL12 8LJ
tel: 01706 853 518
email: zen39135@zen.co.uk
web: www.studio-studio.co.uk
contact: Peter
monitors: Yamaha NS10
rates: Call for details
info: 32, 24, 16 and 8 track digital recording facilities. DDA
AMR 36 into 48 with optifile automation.

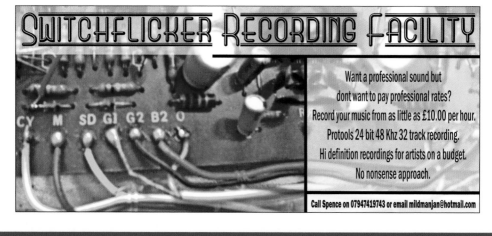

Switchflicker Audio Engineering
Chorlton, Manchester
tel: 07947 419 743
email: mildmanjan@hotmail.com
contact: Spencer
rates: Call for details
info: Pro Tools 24 bit recording with analogue outboard. Specialise in producing high quality recordings for musicians on a budget.

Tailored Music
Unit 1a, Welch Hill Mill, Leigh, Lancashire, WN7 4DJ
tel: 01942 514 624
email: info@tailoredmusic.co.uk
web: www.tailoredmusic.co.uk
contact: Mark Gerrad
desk: Neve/Mackie
monitors: Mackie HR 824
rates: Negotiable
info: 32 digital/32 track analogue. Loads of effects/processors. Live room, control room and vocal/drum booths. Library of over 3000 backing tracks available. Midi suite.

Testa-Rossa Recording Studios
21 Beechfield Drive, Bury, Lancashire, BL9 9QT
email: andy@testa-rossa.com
web: www.testa-rossa.com
contact: Andy Drelincourt
desk: Digidesign
monitors: Genelec
rates: From £400 per day (inc. Pro Tools operator and producer)
info: Digidesign Pro Tools HD3 running on Mac G5, with all plug ins available, Digidesign 192 interface, Focusrite pre amps and Neumann mics. Deal with label signed clients only. CD duplication also available.

Tonewood Productions
Bridleway, Aintree, Liverpool, L30 4UA
tel: 0151 933 7788
email: markreader@tonewood.co.uk
web: www.tonewood.co.uk
contact: Mark Reader
desk: Command 8
monitors: Genelec 1030 1A
rates: £200 per day
info: 24 track desk, 16 track analogue. Digital recording direct to hard disk. Pro Tools for Mac G5, M-Audio 1010 on PC. Lots of outboard. Can transfer from most formats. Also have video production and AVID editing facilities.

Tuff Gong Studioplex
Unit 6, Logford Street, Warrington, WA2 7PG
tel: 01925 232 536
email: tuffgong@btconnect.com
web: www.tuffgong.co.uk
contact: Lee Parker
desk: DDA DM12/Yamaha O2R
monitors: Yamaha NS10
rates: From £17 per hour
info: Studio 1 is equipped with Pro Tools software. Spacious live room. Studio 2 has a vocal booth, and is ideal for DJs, Electronic music and overdubs. Equipment and instrument hire available. Can also provide session musicians. The Tuff Gong complex also houses rehearsal rooms, a record shop 'Hottwaxx', musical equipment shop 'Access All Areas Music', Foundry dance studios, the Brown Sugar Bar café and music school. See relevant sections for further details.

Ward & Warn
210 Broadoak Road, Ashton Under Lyne, Lancashire, OL 8RP
tel: 01706 343 176
contact: Harold
rates: £15 per track
info: 24 track digital recording studio. Also run instrument shop, contact for further details.

West Coast Recording Studios
4 South King Street, Blackpool, Lancashire, FY1 4LS
tel: 01253 752 220
email: simon@westcoaststudios.co.uk
web: www.westcoaststudios.co.uk
contact: Simon Morgan
desk: Behringer
monitors: Yamaha NS10
rates: Contact for details
info: West Coast Recording Studio is a fully digital based studio with 2 live rooms, a spacious control room and a rehearsal room. The studio can cater for any recording project. Includes backline and engineer. 24 channel digital recording on to hard disk. Mastering facilities. Rates are charged per track, rather than on an hourly basis.

West Orange
Unit 1, 16B Pechell Sreet, Ashton, Preston, Lancashire, PR2 2RN
tel: 01772 722 626
fax: 01772 722 626
email: westorange@btclick.com
contact: Alan Gregson
desk: Pro Tools
monitors: Tannoy
rates: Call for details

Whitby Studios
32 Whitby Road, Ellesmere Port, Merseyside, CH65 8AE
tel: 0151 356 0641
email: whitbystudios@hotmail.com
web: www.whitbystudios.co.uk
desk: Audient 8024
monitors: Tannoy
rates: Call for details
info: 24 track analogue/digital recording. Large sound room. Full MIDI and keyboard programming available. Mastering services also available.

White's Farm Studios
122 Mosley Common Road, Worsley, Manchester, M28 1AN
tel: 0161 790 4830
fax: 0161 703 8521
email: whitesfarmstudios@aol.com
web: www.whitesfarmstudios.com
contact: Gary Hastings
desk: Amek Einstein
monitors: Yamaha NS10/Genelec/Dynaudio
rates: Call for details
info: 48 track, 24 track, 2 inch analogue. 24 track digital. Live Room. Tape machines: Tascam, Alesis, Pro Tools and Fostex. Outboard and effects including Lexicons, AMS, Neve, SSL, Korg, Eventide, Alesis, Yamaha and Roland. Synths including Akai, Korg, Moog, Arp, Emu and Yamaha. Apple Mac and PC. Well connected with major record company A&R.

Zig Zag (Recording Services)
Winter Hill Cottage, Darwen, Lancashire, BB3 0LB
tel: 01254 774 945
contact: Steven Lindley
rates: £25 per hour
info: Digital recording and production studio. 16 track digital audio plus MIDI onto DAT and CDR. Association of Professional Recording Services (APRS) registered.

SOUTHEAST

23 Degrees Ltd.
The Ford, Arundel, Sussex, BN18 0DE
tel: 01243 552 338
email: info@fordlane.com
web: www.fordlane.com
contact: Nicki Morey
desk: Amek Einstein/Allen & Heath Sabre 36
monitors: Genelec1037B/DynaudioM1/Dynaudio BM5/Yamaha NS10
rates: Contact for details
info: 2 fully equipped control rooms, each with their own glass partitioned vocal booths. 2 further live rooms, video linked and acoustically treated to create a variety of different sound environments. Rehearsal space available. See relevant listing for details.

24/7 Studios
6 Hertford Street, Cowley, Oxford, OX4 3AJ
tel: 01865 435 981/07768 410 080
email: robin@247studios.co.uk
web: www.247studios.co.uk
contact: Robin Leggett
desk: TAC Scorpion 50
monitors: Dynaudio BM6/Alesis RA-100
rates: £27.50 per hour
info: Recording for bands or solo artists suitable for demo or release standard. For package deal prices, refer to website. Also provide voiceover recording and mastering services. Full technical specifications can be found on the website. 24/7 also offer rehearsal and equipment hire services. See listings in relevant sections for details.

3rd Room Productions
Studio 8, The Mayford Centre, Mayford, Woking, Surrey, GU22 0PP
tel: 07941 355 929
email: brian@3rdroom.co.uk
web: www.3rdroom.co.uk
contact: Brian Wilkinson
info: The studio uses Reason, Pulsar and Logic software.

A & J Recording Studio
Old Woking, Surrey, GU22 9ET
tel: 01483 839 837
email: info@ajrecordings.co.uk
web: www.ajrecordings.co.uk
contact: Alex or Joanna
monitors: Genelec 8050a/Event 20-20/M-Audio BX8
rates: £18 per hour (inc. engineer)
info: For full technical specification see the website.

A.L.T. Records
7 Old Shoreham Road, Brighton, East Sussex, BN1 5DQ
tel: 01273 711 749
email: info@alt-hire.co.uk
contact: Alex
desk: Allen & Heath
monitors: Alesis
rates: From £25 per hour, From £125 per day
info: Professional studio that deals with recording demos for bands. Also deal with work for TV such as voiceovers.

Absolute Recording Studios
Little Palmstead Cottage, Bosingham Lane, Stelling Minnis, Canterbury, Kent, CT4 6AG
tel: 01303 812 715
email: office@absolute-studios.co.uk
web: www.absolute-studios.co.uk
desk: Soundtracs
monitors: Meyer/Absolute 2/Yamaha NS10
rates: £35 per hour, £210 per 8 hour day
info: Professional 48 track digital/analogue studios. Pre and post-production services. Minimum booking is 3 hour slot.

Adam Whittaker
6 The Waterhouse, 7-9 Gosbrook Road, Caversham, Reading, Berkshire, RG4 8BT
tel: 07767 692 950
email: adam_w@zen.co.uk
web: www.adamwhittaker.net
contact: Adam Whittaker
info: Adam is a freelance producer who has recently worked with Dogs Die In Hot Cars, The Rakes and New Rhoads.

Adventure Studios
5 Stables Lane, Eastbourne, East Sussex, BN21 4RE
tel: 01323 720 784
email: doug@serecords.freeserve.co.uk
contact: Doug
desk: Calrec/Pro Tools
monitors: Yamaha NS10/KRK
rates: Call for details
info: Centrally based studio with recording and rehearsal facilities. There is a wide range of professional equipment and the studios are very band friendly. For details regarding rehearsal space, see listing in relevant section.

Airtight Studios
1 Shopwhyke Industrial Center, Shopwhyke Road, Chichester, West Sussex, PO20 2GD
tel: 01243 839 565
email: info@airtightstudios.com
web: www.airtightstudios.com
desk: Allen & Heath
monitors: Various
rates: Call for details
info: Airtight are a recording and rehearsal facility, see entry in relevant section for details of rehearsals. Parking and refreshments available.

Aktivator Studios
Basement Offices, 45a Trafalgar Street, Brighton, BN1 4EN
tel: 01273 686 877
fax: 01273 686 877
email: info@aktivator.co.uk
web: www.aktivator.co.uk
contact: Max
desk: Soundtracs
monitors: Bluesky
rates: Call for details
info: Offer a high grade production facility, and an experienced friendly engineer, professionally trained in music production, studio design and sound engineering. Also offer studio training, call for details.

Appletree Studios
Glebe Farm, Piddington Road, Lugershall, Aylesbury, Buckinghamshire, HP18 9PL
tel: 01844 237 916
email: info@appletreestudio.co.uk
web: www.appletreestudios.com
desk: Tascam 8000/Studiocraft
monitors: Tannoy Gold/Tannoy Reveal/JBL Custom 1/Viscount David
rates: Contact for details
info: 64 track digital & 24 track analogue. All the latest editing equipment available. Also run CD duplication and mastering services. Enquire for details.

Aquasonic Studio
Caversham, Reading, Berkshire, RG4 6PP
tel: 07769 877 245
email: info@aquasonicstudio.co.uk
web: www.aquasonicstudio.co.uk
contact: Lawrence
desk: Yamaha 02R
monitors: Yamaha NS10
rates: From £15 per hour
info: Aquasonic Studio is a small but fully equipped studio based in the North Berkshire/South Oxfordshire borders. In-house engineer/producer who regularly writes music for a record label. Studio comprises control room, live room and chillout area. Specialise in Electronic and Dance music production.

Arvo Studios
Avro Close, Regents Park, Southampton, Hampshire, SO15 4AE
tel: 02380 777 446
email: clivek@dsl.pipex.com
web: www.clivek.dsl.pipex.com
contact: Clive Knightley
desk: DAW Computer
monitors: Circle S
rates: £15 per hour

Audio Sorcery
Little Wold, Station Road, Groombridge, Kent, TN3 9NE
tel: 01892 862 489
email: info@tgas.co.uk
web: www.tgas.co.uk
contact: Paul Midcalf
desk: Mackie D8B
monitors: Mackie HR824
rates: Call for details
info: Specialise in band recording & production, songwriter music production, TV & radio commercial jingles, spoken word and voiceovers. Gift vouchers available.

Backline Rehearsal & Recording Studio
1-2 The Archways, Guildford Park Road, Guildford, Surrey, GU2 7NP
tel: 01483 533 876
email: mail@backlinestudios.co.uk
web: www.backlinestudios.co.uk
contact: Dave Neale
desk: Mackie
rates: Contact for details
info: Professional set up for recording and rehearsing. See entry in rehearsal section. Also specialise in gift packages such as singing to a backing track.

BandBits
Prince Bros Site, Old Bath Road, Charvil, Reading, Berkshire, RG10 9QJ
tel: 0118 932 0032
fax: 0118 932 0016
email: nick@bandbits.com
web: www.bandbits.com
contact: Nick Lawson
desk: Roland
monitors: Alesis
rates: £30 per hour
info: BandBits also offer rehearsal space and CD mastering and duplication, see relevant entries for details.

The Barn Studio
Maidenhead, Berkshire
tel: 07976 717 352
email: millarmsb@ntlworld.com
web: www.readingrocks.co.uk
info: Demo studio with a rehearsal space available. Contact for further information. For details regarding rehearsal facilities, see relevant section for details.

The Base
91 Third Street, New Greenham Park, Newbury, West Berkshire, RG19 6HN
tel: 01635 521 515/07795 217 818
email: baserehearsals@btconnect.com
web: www.thebase.org.uk
contact: Moon
desk: Studiomaster
monitors: Alesis
rates: £35 per hour (inc. engineer)
info: Also offer rehearsal space, see entry in relevant section for details. Can also provide on location DVD gig recording, as well as road crews for tours nationwide and beyond.

Black Dog Recording Studios
Unit 5, Winters Farm, Spring Lane, Burwash, East Sussex, TN19 7ER
tel: 07977 477 776
email: blackdogmanagement@hotmail.co.uk
contact: Tom
desk: Behringer
rates: £30 per hour
info: Studios runs latest Pro Logic 7. Has a good range of mics and in-house Ludwig drum kit. Latest plug ins and many digital effects available.

Black Man Jack Productions
1st Floor, Office Suite, 122 Montague Street, Worthing, West Sussex, BN14 0BJ
tel: 01903 606 513/07861 232 006
email: blackmanjackproductions@gmail.com
contact: Owen Smith
desk: Sound Craft Midi PC series 16/32 track analogue
monitors: Acoustic Reference 100W/Cermin-Vega 1000W
rates: £200 per 8 hour day
info: Cubase FX 2.2. Flexible studio times. Can operate 24 hours, 7 days a week if necessary.

Central Recording Studio
Queen Mary's College, Cliddesden Road, Basingstoke, RG21 3HF
tel: 01256 417 511
email: phil.pennington@qmc.ac.uk
web: www.centralstudio.co.uk
contact: Phil Pennington
desk: Digidesign Control 24
monitors: Genelec 8040a/Tannoy System 800
rates: Contact for details
info: For full technical specification see the website above. 2 live rooms available, 1 standard sized room suitable for bands, as well as a larger room including baby grand piano. Contact for details about rates, can offer cheaper prices for student bands. Central also has a 150 seater venue available for hire. Live recordings can be made from venue. Also offer CD duplication services, see entry in relevant section for details.

C-field Studios
St. Albans
tel: 01707 333 463
email: recording@c-fieldstudios.co.uk
web: www.c-fieldstudios.co.uk
contact: Paul
desk: Soundcraft Ghost
monitors: Spirit Absolute
rates: Call for details

Church Road Studios
197-201 Church Road, Hove, BN3 2AH
tel: 01273 327 889
email: info@churchroad.net
web: www.churchroad.co.uk
desk: Soundtracs Quartz
monitors: Gelelec
rates: £250 per day
info: 24 track digital and analogue recording facilities. Specialise in recording guitar based bands. Kitchen area is available for use. Also have rehearsal facilities, see section for details.

City Studios
Unit 5, Woodfield Road, Welwyn Garden City, Hertfordshire, AL7 1JQ
tel: 07976 775 537
email: rob@citystudios.net
web: www.citystudios.net
contact: rob
rates: £19.95 per hour
info: 24 track digital recording suite. Linked with Farm Factory Studios, who provide rehearsal facilities. See listing in relevant section for details.

The Cold Room Studios
Gees Farm, Denmans Lane, Cumnor, Oxford, OX2 9PF
tel: 07947 710 740
email: rick@coldroomstudios.co.uk
web: www.coldroomstudios.co.uk
contact: Rich
desk: Soundtracs
monitors: Spirit Absolute/Tannoy
rates: £20-25 per hour
info: Established studio also offering rehearsal space, see entry in relevant section for details

Connexion Studios
Basingstoke, Hampshire
tel: 01256 769 415
email: info@connexionstudios.com
web: www.connexionstudios.com
desk: Soundtracs
monitors: Mackie/Tannoy/Yamaha/Celestion
rates: Call for details
info: Duplication and mastering also available.

The Cream Room
Home Farm, Munden Road, Dane End, Hertfordshire, SG12 0LL
tel: 01920 438 926
email: info@creamroom.co.uk
web: www.creamroom.co.uk
contact: Lindsay Weight, Rob Clydesdale, Mike Coombs
desk: Yamaha 02R
monitors: Westlake/Tannoy Gold
rates: Call for details
info: The studio is situated in a picturesque rural location and has a spacious live and control room. Suitable for all kinds of recording.

d2j Studios
Unit 4, Templefields Enterprise Centre, South Road, Harlow, Essex, CM20 2AR
tel: 01279 431 161
email: d2jstudios@hotmail.com
contact: James Donoghue, Mick Donoghue
monitors: Yamaha NS-10
rates: £20 per horr
info: Control/production room and vocal booth. Free pick up service in Harlow area to eliminate worry of carrying equipment around. Service also available for surrounding areas for small petrol fee. Enquire for further details. D2j Studios also offer rehearsal facilities and artwork design services. See listings in relevant sections for information.

Delta Recording Studio
Unit 1, Deanery Farm, Bolts Hill, Chartan, Kent, CT4 7LD
tel: 01227 732 140
email: deltastudios@btconnect.com
web: www.deltastudios.co.uk
contact: Julian Whitfield
desk: Pro Tools HD
monitors: Mackie/Tannoy
rates: £29 per hour (inc. engineer)
info: Large live room with 2 booths.

The Dugout
Unit 1, Fort Fareham Business Park, Newgate Lane, Fareham, Hampshire, PO14 1AH
tel: 01329 829 809
email: info@dugoutstudio.com
web: www.dugoutstudio.com
desk: Soundcraft Ghost
monitors: Genelec
rates: Call for details
info: Pro Tools recording and editing. 2 large studios equipped to deal with both solo artists and bands.

Dungeon Studios
Cumnor, Oxfordshire
tel: 07790 193 260
contact: Rich Haines
info: Contact Dungeon directly for information regarding equipment and rates.

Earth Terminal Studios
The Hop Kiln, Hillside, Odiham, Hampshire, RG29 1HX
tel: 01256 704 043
email: studio@earthterminal.co.uk
web: www.earthterminal.co.uk
contact: Alison
desk: DDA DMR12
monitors: Yamaha NS10
rates: Contact for details
info: Earth Studios is a unique and inspiring recording location, situated deep in the Hampshire countryside whilst retaining excellent communication links. Studios are based approximately 40 minutes from London.

Eastwood Studios
Unit 2, The Courtyard, Bullington End, Manor Farm, Hanslope, MK19 7BQ
tel: 07811 134 164
email: info@eastwoodstudios.co.uk
web: www.eastwoodstudios.co.uk
contact: Darren
desk: Pro Tools
rates: Call for details
info: Milton Keynes based, premier recording and rehearsal rooms. Wide range of professional equipment and sound treated studio. Can provide PA and full backline. Please call Darren for more information. Details of rehearsal facilities can be found in relevant section.

Effenel Studios
787 Southchurch Road, Southend-On-Sea, Essex, SS1 2PP
tel: 01702 614 857
email: info@effenel.com
info: Effenel can provide high quality recordings at a low cost from demos to a whole album. Also provide rehearsal facilities, see listing for further information.

Escape Recording Studios
Colchester, Essex
tel: 07876 083 786
email: info@escaperecordings.co.uk
web: www.escaperecordings.co.uk
desk: Behringer DDX3216
rates: £15 per hour
info: Mobile recording studio equipped with Cubase SL 3.0.

The Esselle Beat Company
South Lodge, 196 Dyke Road, Brighton, East Sussex, BN1 5AA
tel: 01273 561 900
email: info@essellebeat.com
web: www.essellebeat.com
desk: Soundtracs
monitors: Dynaudio M3/Yamaha NS10/AKG Reference
rates: £45 per hour
info: Recently refurbished studio featuring mixing room and 3 vocal/instrument booths. Ideal for mixing and post-production, as well as being capable of recording full live band set ups.

Fairbridge Recording Studios
The Historic Dockyard, Chatham, ME4 4TW
tel: 01634 848 653
email: kent.studio@fairbridge.org.uk
web: www.fairbridge.org
contact: Calvin Beedle
desk: Roland
monitors: Tannoy
rates: From £10 per hour
info: Part of a youth development centre which runs courses and workshops for the local young community.

The Farm Studios
Gerpins Lane, Upminster, RM14 2XR
tel: 01708 640 128
desk: Mackie
monitors: Mackie
rates: £20 per hour
info: 24 channel recording. Rehearsal space also available, see relevant section for more details.

Faversham Youth & Community Centre
South House, 46 South Road, Faversham, Kent, ME13 7LR
tel: 01795 532 238
email: mick.cahill@kent.gov.uk
contact: Mick Cahill
rates: Contact for details
info: 24 track recording studio. Drum kit and piano. Mastering service.

Gallery Record Production Ltd.
PO Box 175, Hove, BN3 3UQ
email: info@gallerystudios.co.uk
web: www.gallerystudios.co.uk
desk: Euphonix CS2000M
monitors: Miller & Kreisel 2510P & 2810P
rates: Contact for details
info: Services include record production, mixing, mastering and songwriting .

Garden Studios
The Shooting Lodge, Woking Road, Guidford, Surrey, GU4 7PZ
tel: 01483 236 434
email: nev@gardenstudios.net
web: www.gardenstudios.net
rates: From £200 per day
info: 3 professional recording facilities; main, live and project studios. Also have rehearsal space on-site. See listing in relevant section for more information.

GCMP
Unit 5, Knight Properties, Brewery Road, Hoddesdon, EN11 8HF
tel: 01992 461 089
email: geoff.cooper@btinternet.com
web: www.gcmp.co.uk
contact: Geoff Cooper
desk: Soundtrac
monitors: Urei/Westlake
rates: Call for details
info: Pro Tools studio with lots of outboard available. Also offer drum tuition. See listing in relevant section for details.

Gorse Road Studios
2 Long Lane, Staines, Middlesex, TW19 7AA
tel: 01784 255 629
email: cliff@telco4u.net
contact: Cliff
desk: Mackie 32
monitors: Dynaudio
rates: Call for details
info: Studio has been used for remix and production work on a number of acts including D-Side, Sean Paul, Run DMC, Aaliyah and Ashanti.

Ground Zero Studio
43 Coombe Terrace, Brighton, East Sussex, BN2 4AD
tel: 01273 819 617
email: studio@g-zero.co.uk
web: www.g-zero.co.uk
desk: Sony DMXR100
monitors: Dynaudio
rates: Call for details
info: Ground Zero is a studio complex with 4 recording studios and 8 residential rehearsal rooms, see entry in relevant section for further info. Quality analogue recording equipment and large live room with natural daylight and acoustic dampening.

Hatch Farm Recording Studio
Unit 16, Chertsey Road, Addlestone, Surrey, KT15 2EH
tel: 01932 828 715
email: info@hatchfarmstudios.co.uk
web: www.hatchfarmstudios.co.uk
desk: SSL 4040 G Plus/Yamaha O2R
monitors: ATC 100A/Yamaha NS10/Genelec 1030
rates: Call for details
info: Comprehensive studio with a range of equipment, suitable for recording any material. 3 room suite with Pro Tools, Cubase and Logic on both Mac and PC. Also offer CD mastering and video editing services.

Hats Off Studios
Church Street, Stonesfield, Witney, Oxfordshire, OX29 8PS
tel: 01993 898 620
email: hatsoff@netmatters.co.uk
web: www.hatsoffstudios.co.uk
contact: Michael Taylor
desk: Roland VM 7200
monitors: MC LB1/Yamaha NS10/Tannoy HPD12/Kef Concerto Custom
rates: £50 per hour (inc. engineer)
info: Recording, editing and mastering.

HS Recording
87a High Street, Codicote, Hitchin, Hertfordshire, SG4 8XE
tel: 01438 820 246
fax: 01438 829 225
email: info@hsrecording.co.uk
web: www.hsrecording.co.uk
contact: Del
desk: Pro Tools
monitors: Mackie
rates: Call for details
info: All aspects of recording are catered for, including location recording. The studio is based in rural Hertfordshire between Welwyn Garden City and Stevenage, see website for directions. A free pick up service from the train or nearest bus station is available if required.

Ivories
28 Lindford Chase, Lindford, Bordon, Hampshire, GU35 0TB
tel: 01420 478 063
email: binopot@aol.com
contact: Tim Dyke - Smith
desk: Cubase
monitors: M Audio
rates: From £20 per hour
info: Studio mainly deals with solo artists and singer-songwriters. Ivories also offer piano and keyboard tuition.

Ivy Arch Studios

Unit 5b, Ivy Arch Road, Worthing, BN14 8BX
tel: 01903 536 106
email: info@ivyarchstudios.co.uk
web: www.ivyarchstudios.co.uk
desk: Roland VS 2480
rates: From £250 per 8 hour day
info: Rehearsal spaces also available, see relevant section for more details.

Jelly Studios

Mountfield, Tunbridge Wells, East Sussex, TN32 5JN
tel: 07957 478 318
email: ray@jellorecords.com
web: www.jellorecords.com
contact: Ray
desk: Behringer MX8000
rates: Call for details
info: Jelly Studios have been recording Rock and Punk bands since the mid 70s, having recorded such artists as Siouxsie and the Banshees, Girls School and The Slits. Lots of analogue equipment, including some very hard to find original equipment.

Jeremy Knox

Holybourne, East Sussex
tel: 07754 624 918
contact: Jeremy Knox
desk: Soundcraft Spirit
monitors: Bang & Olufsen
rates: Call for details
info: Freelance studio engineer specialising in Electronic and Dance music. Studio or location recording.

Kool World

PO BOX 884, Luton, LU2 7ZX
tel: 0845 644 1445
email: info@koolworld.co.uk
web: www.koolworld.co.uk
contact: Dave
desk: Soundtracs Jade/Soundtracs Solitaire
monitors: Dynaudio/Yamaha/Genelec
rates: £30 per hour
info: 2 recording studios available. Full technical specifications can be found on above website. Lounge area, tea and coffee making facilities.

Lightbug Recording Studio

Aintree Close, Horton Heath, Eastleigh, Hampshire, SO50 7PU
tel: 02380 696 034/07050 089 165
email: mail@lightbug.co.uk
web: www.lightbug.co.uk
desk: Mackie
rates: Call for details
info: Lightbug will also master your CD free of charge.

Little London Studios

Manor Road, Hastings, East Sussex, TN34 3LL
tel: 01424 422 898
email: enquiries@littlelondonstudios.com
web: www.littlelondonstudios.com
rates: Contact for details
info: Can record demos and albums for all types of artist. Live room can cope with bands and also has separate vocal booth for solo singers. Use a wide range of professional equipment. Little London also have rehearsal space, management team and record label. Call for more information.

The Liveroom

Horndean Campus, Barton Cross, Horndean, Hampshire, PO8 9PQ
tel: 02393 599 753
email: bookings@theliveroom.co.uk
web: www.theliveroom.co.uk
contact: Will Yates
desk: Pro Control
monitors: Quested VS2205 Active
rates: Contact for details
info: Pro Tools 24 mix and 888/24 interface. Spacious live room. Also run rehearsal rooms and can provide duplication services. Linked with D-Code design company. See entries in relevant sections for details.

Lost Boys Studio

Hillgreen Farm, Bourne End, Cranfield, Bedfordshire, MK43 0AX
tel: 01234 750 730
email: lostboystudio@onetel.net
web: www.lostboysstudio.com
contact: Ru Cook
desk: Mackie D8B
monitors: JBL
rates: Call for details
info: Multiple live areas with separate TV, kitchen and dining facilities.

Lo-Tek

Friars Gate Farm, Mardens Hill, Crowborough, East Sussex, TN6 1XH
tel: 01892 610 010
email: studio@lo-tek.co.uk
web: www.lo-tek.co.uk
contact: Andy, Guy
desk: 3G Cygnet
monitors: Yamaha NS10
rates: £30 per hour
info: Rural location in the Ashdown Forest. Medium sized studio ideal for singer-songwriters and bands alike. Demo and day packages are available, call for details.

Lumen Studio

103 Islingwood Road, Brighton, BN2 9SG
tel: 01273 690 149
email: info@lumenstudio.co.uk
web: www.lumenstudio.co.uk
desk: Yamaha O2R
monitors: B&W Blueroom House Pod/Yamaha NS10
rates: Call for details
info: Pro Tools HD3, Yamaha digital consoles, full racks of valve outboard and a good range of mics. Full technical specification can be viewed at the above website.

MA Music Studios

PO Box 106, Potton, Sandy, Bedfordshire, SG19 2ZS
tel: 01767 262 040
email: info@mamusicstudios.co.uk
web: www.mamusicstudios.co.uk
contact: Nole Rafferty
desk: Mackie D8B
monitors: Yamaha NS10
rates: Contact for details
info: MA Studios deals with all aspects for recording artists. The studio has a spacious live recording area, hard disk recording and editing facilities, fully programmable mixing and full mastering service with a top class engineer. Studio is also available for acoustic rehearsals.

Metway Studios

55 Canning Street, Brighton, BN2 0EF
tel: 01273 698 171
fax: 01273 624 884
email: lois@levellers.co.uk
web: www.metwaystudios.co.uk
contact: Lois
desk: Pro Tools
monitors: Yamaha/Dynaudio
rates: Call for details
info: Studio has a great vibe, natural daylight and visual contact with large control room. Clients include The Levellers, Orbital, Electric Soft Parade and Asian Dub Foundation.

Model Music

Newbury, Berkshire
tel: 0870 808 0100/07747 848 896
fax: 0870 808 0098
email: info@modelmusic.co.uk
web: www.modelmusic.co.uk
desk: Roland
monitors: Genelec
rates: Call for details
info: Work closely with Pan Artist who help raise the profile of unsigned acts. Also offer PA, lighting and backline hire, see entry in relevant section for details.

Mr Gig Studios

15 Tavistock Street, Bletchley, Buckinghamshire, MK2 2PF
tel: 01908 376 500
desk: Studiomaster
monitors: Tannoy
rates: £15 per hour, £150 per 8 hour day
info: 24 track Pro Tools studio. Rehearsal facilities also available, see relevant section for more details.

Multitrak Studios

Hermitage, Newbury
tel: 07766 526 061
email: ali.moore@multitrakmusic.com
web: www.multitrakmusic.com
contact: Ali Moore
desk: Pro Tools
monitors: Behringer
info: Lots of professional quality gear including Alesis 3630 compressors, Shure mics and various plug ins.

No Machine Studios
Unit 4, 127a Reading Road, Wokingham, Berkshire, RG41 1HD
tel:	0118 979 3921
email:	enquiries@nomachine.co.uk
web:	www.nomachine.co.uk
contact:	Neil Sadler
desk:	56 channel Mackie
monitors:	Tannoy
rates:	£30 per hour
info:	G5 Mac based running Audio Logic, unlimited tracks.

Large live room (6m x 6m). Specialise in live band recording. Rehearsal facilities also provided, see relevant section for more details.

Nutbrown Recording Studio
Riding Lane, Holtspur, Beaconsfield, Buckinghamshire, HP9 1BT
tel:	01494 680 436
email:	contact@nutbrownstudios.co.uk
web:	www.nutbrownstudios.co.uk
contact:	Rod, Kris
desk:	Soundtracs
monitors:	Tannoy/Dynaudio
rates:	Demos from £250
info:	Nutbrown Studios are recording and rehearsal studios

situated just outside High Wycombe, Buckinghamshire. Providing both residential and non-residential services for musicians, freelance producers and independent record labels. See listing in relevant section for details of rehearsal facilities.

Outhouse
PO Box 19, Virginia Water, Surrey, GU25 4YE
tel:	0118 967 4326/07989 047 259
email:	john_christianmitchell@ntlworld.com or
	info@outhousestudios.co.uk
web:	www.outhousestudios.co.uk
contact:	John
desk:	Soundtracs
monitors:	Tannoy/Yamaha
rates:	£180 per 8 hour day
info:	The Outhouse Studios is a professional recording studio

with a large spacious control room, a sound-proofed vocal booth and a floating sound-proofed drum booth which is also used for cab micing.

Philia Studios
PO Box 4429, Henley on Thames, Oxfordshire, RG9 1GH
tel:	01491 575 516/01491 576 951
email:	copromike@aol.com
web:	www.philiastudios.com
contact:	Mike
desk:	Control 24
monitors:	Yamaha NS10/Genelec
rates:	From £250 per day
info:	Pro Tools studio specialising in Rock and Metal

recording. High quality mastering and duplication available, see entry in relevant section for details. Philia studio is owned by Copro & Casket Records, who aim for something of a one-stop facility for young creative bands to fulfil their potential.

Pie Factory Music
67a Chapel Road, Ramsgate, Kent, CT11 0BS
tel:	01843 596 777
email:	info@piefactorymusic.com
web:	www.piefactorymusic.com
contact:	Matt Smyth
rates:	Contact for details
info:	Professional 193 track studio using Pro Tools HD3

ACCEL system. The studio uses state of the art outboard equipment and fully complimented plug ins. There are professional and experienced engineers with 2 live recording areas available to use. Competitive rates, contact Matt to discuss.

Plastic Jam
Unit 2, Middlebrook Farm, Hoe Lane, Nazeing, Waltham Abbey, EN9 2RJ
tel:	01992 890 066
email:	plasticjam@ntlworld.com
contact:	Sue Bowden
rates:	£25 per hour
info:	Full professional studio with wide range of equipment.

Also have 2 fully equipped rehearsal rooms available from £10 per hour. Contact for further information.

Playback Systems
Unit 1b South, New England House, Brighton, BN1 4GH
tel:	01273 671 297
email:	info@playbacksystems.com
web:	www.playbacksystems.com
contact:	James Porch
desk:	Soundtrac
monitors:	B&W Silver Signature
rates:	Call for details
info:	Small studio mainly for demo recording and pre-

production. Large client list including Electrelane, Orbital, Eighties Matchbox B-Line Disaster and The Kooks. Also rehearsal facilities, as well as equipment hire services. See listings in relevant sections for further details.

Plug n Play Studios
33-35 Milford Road, Reading, Berkshire, RG1 8LG
tel:	0118 958 1447
email:	info@plugnplay.tv
web:	www.plugnplay.tv
desk:	Yamaha O2R
monitors:	Yamaha NS10/Genelec
rates:	£25 per hour
info:	In-house producers and engineers on hand. Free

refreshments, relaxation area, changing room, licensed bar, showcase space. Small orchestras accommodated. Also offer rehearsal space, see entry in relevant section for details.

POD Music
Phuture Tower, Barker Chambers, Barker Road, Maidstone, Kent, ME16 8SF
tel:	0870 200 0763
email:	info@podmusic.co.uk
web:	www.podmusic.co.uk
info:	Vocal recording to a backing track. Large library of

tracks to choose from. POD Music have studio locations across the country, full list on website. Vocal coaching and rehearsal space available, see relevant sections for more details.

R & R Studios
13 Nutberry Avenue, Grays, Essex, RM16 2TL
tel:	01375 382 291
email:	robertagass1@aol.com
contact:	Robert Agass
desk:	Rowan 2000 CD
rates:	Call for details
info:	Mobile recording unit. Will record anywhere anytime.

Range of top spec mics and keyboards available, amongst other items.

Red Rebel Studios
29 Totland Road, Brighton, BN2 3EP
tel:	01273 702 250
email:	info@redrebelrecords.co.uk
web:	www.redrebelrecords.co.uk
contact:	Ben
desk:	Fostex 454 4:8:2
monitors:	Pageant
rates:	From £30 per session
info:	Red Rebel have experienced staff with the expertise to

put you in contact with an extended network of producers, composers and musicians to assemble the best team to work on your project. See website for more details.

Red Room Studios
Central Units 1 & 3, Level 8, New England House, New England Street, Brighton, BN1 4GH
tel:	01273 697 126/07941 615 561
email:	info@redroom-studio.com
web:	www.redroom-studio.com
contact:	Studio manager
desk:	See website
monitors:	Yamaha NS10
rates:	From £20 per hour
info:	Red Room is a friendly and professional studio that can

cater for all budgets. Use range of analogue and digital production techniques. Red Room have produced many releases that have been played on various BBC Radio 1 shows. See website for more information.

Rotator Studios
74-77 Magdalen Road, Oxford, OX4 1RE
tel:	01865 205 600
fax:	01865 205 700
email:	translate@rotator.co.uk
web:	www.rotator.co.uk
info:	A full Pro Tools equipped recording studio in the centre

of Oxford with highly experience engineers.

Running Frog Music
127 St. Leonard's Road, Windsor, Berkshire, SL4 3DW
tel:	01753 620 857
email:	studio@runningfrog.com
web:	www.runningfrog.com
contact:	Phil Ray
desk:	Amek/Yamaha/Mackie
monitors:	Quested/Yamaha/Genelec
rates:	Call for details
info:	Offer all types of recording facilities including CD and DAT mastering, full band recordings, solo sessions, programming, re-mixing, production, demos, soundtracks. Rehearsal space is available, see entry in relevant section for details.

The Shack Studio
Old Church Road, East Hanningfield Road, Chelmsford, Essex, CM3 8BH
tel:	01245 403 074
email:	via website
web:	www.shackstudio.co.uk
contact:	Pual Richardson
desk:	Studiomaster
monitors:	Tannoy
rates:	From £220 per session
info:	Studio is owned and run by 4 musicians who have had years of experience in performing, composing and producing various styles of music from Dance and Breakbeat to 1940s Swing and R&B. Rehearsal space also available, see listing for information.

The Shonk Studios
74-77 Madgalen Road, Oxford, OX4 1RE
tel:	01865 203 922
email:	info@theshonk.com
web:	www.theshonk.com
desk:	Mackie
monitors:	Mackie HR824/Soundcraft Absolute
rates:	Contact for details
info:	Control room, live room and a separate vocal/guitar booth. Good quality gear available for hire including drums and amps.

The Silent Coup
Unit 3, Grange Farm Units, Nelsons Lane, Hurst, Berkshire, RG10 0RR
tel:	07900 687 558/01189 340 934
email:	admin@the-silent-coup.org
web:	www.the-silent-coup.org
desk:	Behringer Eurodesk mx 3282A
monitors:	Spirit Absolute/Linear Phase 8812
rates:	£150 per day
info:	Range of recording and sequencing equipment and outboard. DJ facilities. Design, rehearsal and tuition services. See relevant sections for details.

Silk Recordings
65 High Street, Kings Langley, Hertfordshire, WD4 9HU
tel:	01923 270 852/07812 602 535
email:	info@silkrecordings.com
web:	www.silkrecordings.com
contact:	Bob
desk:	Pro Tools
rates:	Contact for details
info:	Studio suitable for recordings, as well as live concerts. Package deals available from recording sessions to finished CDs. Silk Recordings also provide mastering and duplication services. See entry in relevant section for further details.

Sniff 'n' Break
Hillside Lane, Farnham, Surrey, GU9 0LB
tel:	01252 319 496
email:	ali@sniffnbreak.co.uk
web:	www.sniffnbreak.co.uk
desk:	Studiomaster
rates:	Contact for details
info:	Studio comprises separate control room. Offer mastering to CD and large sample library.

Sound Rules
Croydon House, 1 Peall Road, Thornton Heath, Surrey, CR0 3EU
tel:	07985 733 177
email:	reachmike@hotmail.com
web:	www.soundrules.com
contact:	Mike Sogga
desk:	Mackie 24 Track
monitors:	Mackie
rates:	£15-£22 per hour
info:	Logic 7 sequencer, Diamond plug ins, Ivory compressors, Focus rite compressors.

SoundArc
Unit 3b, St. Francis' Way, Shefford, Bedfordshire, SG17 5DZ
tel:	07931 985 801
email:	music_at_soundarc@hotmail.com
web:	www.soundarc.com
contact:	John
desk:	Soundcraft Series 1600
monitors:	Dual monitor set up
rates:	Contact for details
info:	Friendly, professional recording studio run by musicians, for musicians. Packages available for all customers ranging from novice karaoke singer to full recording sessions for DJs, solo musicians and bands. Also provide rehearsal facilities. See listing in relevant section for details.

SoundArt
Unit E1, St. George's Business Park, Sittingbourne, ME10 3TB
tel:	07961 177 013
email:	viv_soundart@hotmail.com
web:	www.soundart.co.uk
contact:	Viv
desk:	Mackie 1604 VLZ Pro
monitors:	Mackie HR 626/Alesis M1
rates:	From £30 per hour
info:	Air-conditioned fully digital studio. Full technical specifications and list of rates can be viewed on website. Kitchen facilities. Offer 'All In' demo package. Contact Viv for details. Also provide rehearsal facilities, see listing in relevant section.

Soundcheck UK
360 Havant Road, Farlington, Portsmouth, Hampshire, PO6 1NE
tel:	02392 642 919
fax:	02392 783 010
email:	bob@soundcheckuk.com
web:	www.soundcheckuk.com
contact:	Andy
desk:	Allen & Heath
monitors:	JBL Nearfield
rates:	Call for details
info:	72 track digital recording on award winning software. Also offer CD duplication and digital printing. Run special offers on studio time, contact for further details.

Sounds Amazing
7 School Lane, Castlethorpe, Milton Keynes, Buckinghamshire, MK19 7EN
tel:	01908 510 698
email:	soundsamazing@castlethorpe.co.uk
info:	Location recording ideal for recording gigs and rehearsals.

Sour Apple Studios
34 Boundary Road, Newbury, Berkshire, RG14 5RR
tel:	01635 582 266
email:	sourapplestudios@hotmail.com
web:	www.sourapplestudios.tk
contact:	Paul
desk:	Fostex
monitors:	Collins
rates:	£13-£17 per hour
info:	Sour Apple are primarily a rehearsal studio, although 8 track recording is available.

Stag Studios
Unit 3, The Surridge Centre, Stepfield, Witham, Essex, CM8 3TH
tel:	01376 502 209/07740 478 578
email:	info@stagstudios.com
web:	www.stagstudios.com
rates:	£28 per hour, £75 per half day, £140 per day
info:	56 channel recording. See the website for a full list of equipment. Also offer rehearsal space, see relevant section for more details.

Stanbridge Studios
Brighton Road, Handcross, Haywards Heath, West Sussex, RH17 6BB
tel:	01444 400 432
web:	www.stanbridgestudio.demon.co.uk
contact:	Mr Berthrite
desk:	32 track Platinum
monitors:	Yamaha NS10/Tannoy
rates:	Call for details
info:	Visit the website for a full technical specifications.

Sticky Studios
Great Oaks Granary, Kennel Lane, Windlesham, Surrey, GU20 6AA
tel:	01276 479 255
email:	admin@stickycompany.com
web:	www.stickycompany.com
contact:	Jake Gosling
desk:	Yamaha O2R
monitors:	Yamaha NS10/JBL
rates:	Call for details
info:	Studio is equipped with Pro Tools and has a good selection of vintage analogue synths available to use.

Studio 24
Benedict Close, Romsey, Hampshire, SO51 8PN
tel: 01794 501 774
email: info@s24.uk.net
web: www.audio-production.co.uk
contact: Alan Cotty
desk: 48 channel Mackie
monitors: Adam S3A
rates: Call for details
info: Studio 24 offers audio recording and production. Specialise in spoken word, radio commercials and voiceovers. Also offer mixing and post production services.

Studio 284
284 Madeira Drive, Brighton, East Sussex, BN2 1EN
tel: 01273 572 277/07790 609 966
email: studio284@btconnect.com
web: www.studio284.com
contact: Austin
rates: £100 per day
info: Recording and rehearsal studio, see entry in relevant section for details of rehearsal rooms. 24 track digital recording.

Studio 93
16 Queens Park Terrace, Brighton, East Sussex, BN2 9YA
tel: 07939 037 442
email: info@studio93.co.uk
web: www.studio93.co.uk
rates: £10 per hour.
info: We are an acoustic recording studio in Brighton. Our clients are predominantly unsigned acoustic acts and voiceover projects. Digital studio running Cubase SX3.

Studio Adelaide
Langford Bridge Farm, Kelveden Hatch, Brentwood, CM15 0LB
tel: 01277 366 432
web: www.studioadelaide.co.uk
contact: Grant Matthews
desk: Soundcraft 2400
monitors: Tannoy
rates: Call for details

Tweeters 2 Studios
Unit C1, Business Park 7, Brook Way, Leatherhead, Surrey, KT22 7NA
tel: 01372 386 592
email: info@tweeters2studios.co.uk
web: www.tweeters2studios.co.uk
desk: Tascam 3700
rates: Call for details
info: Fully equipped 24 track studio. Lounge/TV area and parking. Also provide extensive rehearsal space and equipment hire. See entry in relevant sections for details.

Virtual Beatz
Unit 4, Military Road, Colchester, Essex, CO1 2AA
tel: 01206 540 140
email: studio@virtualbeatz.co.uk
web: www.virtualbeatz.co.uk
desk: Mackie SR40·8
monitors: Mackie HR624
rates: £35 per hour (first 2 hours), £25 per hour thereafter
info: Studio specialising in recording for DJs and Dance projects. Sound-proofed control room, vocal booth and experienced engineers on hand.

Wanna Be Management
Essex
tel: 01708 688 088
info: Call for details of recording and rehearsal facilities.

Warehouse Studios
Unit 60, Sandford Lane, Kennington, Oxford, OX1 5RW
tel: 01865 736 411
email: info@warehousestudios.com
web: www.warehousestudios.com
desk: DDA AMR24
monitors: Court Acoustics/Yamaha NS10
rates: Call for details
info: Fully air-conditioned 300sq. ft computer designed control room. 2 live rooms and separate over-dub suite. Also offer rehearsal space, see entry in relevant section for details.

Warner Music Studios
New England House, New England Street, Brighton, BN1 4GH
tel: 01273 605 550
email: warnermusicstudios@yahoo.co.uk
web: www.warnermusicstudios.co.uk
monitors: EV
rates: £20 per hour
info: Pro Tools. Digital and analogue studio. Range of classic amps and instruments. Central Brighton location. Rehearsal space available, see relevant section for more details.

Water Rat Music Studio
Unit 2, Monument Way East, Woking, Surrey, GU2 5LY
tel: 01483 764 444
email: jayne@waterrat.co.uk
web: www.waterrat.co.uk
contact: Jayne Wallis
desk: Behringer MX8000
rates: Contact for details

West Street Studios
3 West Street, Buckingham, Buckinghamshire, MK18 1HL
tel: 01280 822 814/822 564
email: jamie@weststreetstudios.co.uk
web: www.weststreetstudios.co.uk
contact: Jamie
desk: DDA AMR analogue
monitors: Quested 2108/Yahama NS10/JBL Control 10
rates: £75 per hour, £400 per 8 hour day
info: Refer to website for full technical specification. Live room with grand piano. West Street Studios are part of Copysound, who offer duplication services. See entry in Mastering and Duplication section for details.

West Way Beats
15 Meadow Walk, Maidstone, Kent, ME15 7RY
tel: 01622 201 758/07704 201 133
email: bigleedogg23@hotmail.com
web: www.westwaybeats.com
info: Production services for Hip-Hop, R&B and Rap music. Have range of contacts throughout UK, as well as in the US.

Wired Studios Ltd.
26-30 Silver Street, Reading, Berkshire, RG1 2ST
tel: 0118 986 0973
email: info@wiredstudios.co.uk
web: www.wiredstudios.co.uk
contact: Chris Britton
desk: Pro Tools
monitors: Westlake/Dynaudio/Yamaha
rates: Call for details

SOUTHWEST

Aardvark Mecotech
Heathlands, Sourton, Okehampton, EX20 4HN
tel: 01837 861 415
email: vauxhalljeff@aol.com
web: www.aardvarkrecording.co.uk
contact: Jeff
rates: Contact for details
info: Small, family run studios with a professional set up. Can cater for amateurs and semi-professionals with facilities to record a 6 piece band. 24 track digital recording with drum/vocal booth large enough to accommodate 5 piece band. Range of effects and equipment available.

Amplifeye Studio
Churchtown, St. Agnes, Cornwall, TR5 0QW
tel: 07974 518 056
email: rich@amplifeye.co.uk
web: www.amplifeyestudio.com
contact: Richard Searby-Bates, Dan Mitchell
desk: Studiomaster
monitors: Tannoy
rates: £15 per hour
info: Studio is owned by the Amplifeye music community. Concessions for students and the unemployed are available, as well as a 15% discount for people who sign up to the website.

Ariel Music Centre
Mullacott Cross, Ilfracombe, Devon, EX34 8ND
tel: 01271 862 701
email: info@ariel.org.uk
web: www.ariel.org.uk
contact: Leigh Crossman
desk: Behringer
monitors: Yamaha
rates: £15 per hour
info: The Ariel Recording Studio is a state of the art facility for solo artists, choirs and small or large bands who wish to create professional recordings in a cost effective, relaxed and comfortable environment. The studio facility consists of 2 live rooms and a control room, and backing tracks or musicians are available. Rehearsal rooms are available, see entry in relevant section for details.

Attic Attack
25 Portland Square, Bristol, BS2 8NN
tel: 0117 924 4411
fax: 0117 924 4411
email: info@attic-attack.com
web: www.attic-attack.com
contact: Pete Rowley
desk: Yamaha 02R
monitors: Genelec
rates: From £20 per hour
info: Also offer cassette and CD duplication service. Contact for further information.

Autumn Studios
Poole, Dorset
tel: 01202 710 554
fax: 01202 723 609
email: info@autumn-studios.co.uk
web: www.autumn-studios.co.uk
info: Offering complete in-house production of all audio projects and cater for all styles from solo Acoustic artists to full Rock bands. With a large live room and comfortable control room, Autumn Studios is the perfect place to work on any recording project.

Blue In Green Studios
Thurleco, Haytor, Newton Abbot, Devon, TQ13 9XT
tel: 01364 661 420
email: info@joyaa.com
web: www.blueingreenstudios.co.uk
desk: Yamaha DM2000
monitors: Dynaudio
rates: Call for details
info: Also offer in-house graphical design services. See entry for 'Joyaa' in Artwork & Design section.

Bulrush Studios
Unit 5, Enteprise Park, Mart Road, Minehead, Somerset, TA24 5BJ
tel: 01643 707 277
email: info@bulrushstudios.co.uk
web: www.bulrushstudios.co.uk
desk: Soundtracs MRX
monitors: Urie 809/Yamaha NS10
rates: £15 per hour
info: 24 track. Live room and vocal booth. Bulrush Studios also offer rehearsal facilities, CD duplication, equipment hire and drum tuition services. See entries in relevant sections for further details.

The Bunker
72a Reedley Road, Bristol, BS9 3SU
tel: 01978 263 295
email: thebunker@blueyonder.co.uk
web: www.thebunkerstudios.co.uk
contact: Bob Pierce
desk: Pro Tools Control 24
monitors: Spendor
rates: £30 per hour, £200 per 8 hour day
info: Vocal and drum booths. Live recordings available. Recordings may be mixed elsewhere if required. CD duplication services, see relevant section for more details.

Candyland Studios
Stapleton Farm, Langtree, Torrington, Devon, EX39 8NP
tel: 01237 421 944/07971 667 241
desk: Midas Pro 4
monitors: Alesis
rates: £20 per hour

CMG Audio Mobile & Recording Studio
4a Blenheim Road, Weymouth, Dorset, DT3 5AZ
tel: 01305 771 607
email: studio@cmgaudio.com
web: www.cmgaudio.com
desk: Yamaha 01V
monitors: Yamaha MP5
info: Run by a small family team, catering for choirs, singers and voice overs.

Conversion Studios
Milton On Stour, Gillingham, Dorset, SP8 5PX
tel: 01747 824 729
email: info@conversionstudios.co.uk
web: www.conversionstudios.co.uk
contact: Owen
desk: Audio Console
monitors: Dynaudio BM6A Nearfield
rates: £35 per hour, £300 per day.
info: Residential studios. Rate includes experienced engineer and assistant, 2 live rooms, drinks machine, pool table, tabel tennis, chillout area and rural surroundings. See website for a list of previous clients.

Coombeshead Studios
Coombeshead College, Coombeshead Road, Newton Abbot, TQ12 1PT
tel: 01626 201 838
email: coombeshead_studios@hotmail.com
contact: Niel George
monitors: Various
rates: Contact for details
info: Offer recording services for bands and singers. Offer CD duplication services and re-mastering of old recordings.

Corn Mill Studio
Old Mill Lane, Roseworthy, Camborne, Cornwall, TR14 0DX
tel: 01209 719 481
email: cornmillstudio@aol.com
web: www.cornmillstudio.com
contact: Steve Nunn
desk: Behringer MX8000
rates: £15 per hour
info: Cubase SX and Wavelab 4. Vocal booth. Negotiable rates for block bookings.

Crazy Cat
Unit 1, Cowley Bridge Road, Exeter, EX4 4NX
tel: 01392 434 007
email: info@crazycatsound.co.uk
web: www.crazycatsound.co.uk
contact: Rick Walker
desk: Pro Tools (with valve front end)
monitors: Rogers
rates: Call for details
info: With over 20 years experience in the industry Crazy Cat Sound offers professional music production, whether you are a solo artist, band or orchestra. Studio is based around Mac based Pro Tools, both analogue and digital equipment, featuring a valve desk and equalisers, as well as solid state mic preamps. Also offer mobile sound recording, as well as rehearsal space and video and media services. Refer to entry in relevant section for information regarding on rehearsal rooms.

db Studios
36 Folly Lane, Stroud, Glocestershire, GL5 1SD
tel: 01453 752 542
email: dbstudios@enterprise.net
web: www.dbstudios.co.uk
desk: Audient
info: Well equipped studio with full backline and comprehensive outboard and recording facilities.

Deep Blue Recording Studio
38 Looe Street, Plymouth, PL4 0EB
tel: 01752 601 462
email: dbs@deepbluesound.co.uk
web: www.deepbluestudio.co.uk
contact: Matt Bernard
desk: Neve 51
monitors: Quested VS3208
rates: Call for details
info: Based on the South West coast with major transport links throughout the UK and Europe. Range of engineers, producers and programmers to suit all styles and budgets. Recording packages including accommodation and CD duplication are available. See listing in relevant section for details.

Dormdust Productions
Cotswold, High Street, Kempsford, Fairford, GL7 4EY
tel: 01285 810 461
email: ian@dormdust.co.uk
web: www.dormdust.co.uk or www.cutademo.co.uk
contact: Ian Housley
desk: Roland VS 2480 24 track digital
monitors: HBB Circle 5
rates: Call for details
info: The studio has a professional set up with a wide range of equipment . Variety of packages available. Range of software available depending on the project.

Dumb Yank
40 Pembroke Road, Salisbury, Wiltshire, SP2 9DG
tel: 01722 326 017
email: steven@dumbyank.co.uk
web: www.dumbyank.co.uk
contact: Steven
info: Dumb Yank also provide CD mastering and duplication service, as well as rehearsal space. Refer to relevant section for further details.

Farmyard Studios
Blue Close Bungalow, Great Rissington, Cheltenham, GL54 2LL
tel: 01451 821 256
email: info@farmyardstudios.co.uk
web: www.farmyardstudios.co.uk
contact: Simon Plater
desk: Soundcraft
monitors: Tannoy
rates: £150 per day
info: Fully equipped studio which can record any genre of live music. Records onto hard disk with Pro Tools. Wide selection of gear is for hire including drum kit, bass and guitar amps.

Ffg
Bredon Fields, Ekington Road, Bredon, Tewksbury, GL20 7HE
tel: 01684 772 664
email: david@ffg.org.uk
web: www.ffg.org.uk
contact: David Pick
desk: Apple Mac Nuendo
monitors: ATC/Focusrite pre amps
rates: Contact for details
info: Very professional studio set up with 2 live rooms. Expert production assistant for unsigned artists and very band friendly. Competitive rates.

Funkee Fish Studio
Little Cob, Cockington, TQ2 6XA
tel: 07814 544 611
email: studio@funkeefish.com
web: www.funkeefish.com
contact: Katie
rates: £15 per hour
info: CD duplication and design also available. Funkee Fish also run a record label. See entries in relevant sections for further details.

Glass Tone Productions Ltd.
Unit 3a, Riverside Business Par, Bath, BA2 3DU
tel: 01225 487 700/07973 730 161
email: studio@glasstone.co.uk
web: www.glasstone.co.uk
contact: Greg Brooker
desk: Mackie DB 72 channel
info: Pro Tools recording system and acoustically designed live room. Glass Tone also provide rehearsal, management, PA hire, mastering and design services, as well as organising live events in Bath and Bristol. Refer to entries in appropriate sections for more details.

Hillside Studios
Hillside, Great Green, Mells, Somerset, BA11 3QE
tel: 01373 813 643
email: pat@hillsidestudios.co.uk
web: www.hillsidestudios.co.uk
contact: Patrick O'Brian
desk: 48 channel analogue Euro Desk
monitors: Yamaha NS10/NS40
rates: From £200 per day
info: Hillside Studios provide 24 track digital hard disk recording. Mastering to 48Hz DAT masters and redbook CD master disks. Using Samplitude producer software, Cubase SX is also available. Hillside have very fast duplication service for CDs and can also provide artwork.

HL Studios
65 Salisbury Road, Totton, Southampton, SO40 3HY
tel: 02380 487 669
email: info@hlstudios.co.uk
web: www.hlstudio.co.uk
desk: Mackie D8B
monitors: Mackie HR824s
rates: £250 per 10 hour day
info: Studio comprises 2 live rooms, kitchen and bathroom facilities. All projects, from vocals over tracks to full band production, are undertaken.

Hollow Altar Recordings
Ash Grove Farm, Balcarras Road, Charlton Kings, Cheltenham, GL53 8QQ
tel: 01242 520 411
email: info@hollow-altar.co.uk
web: www.hollow-altar.co.uk
contact: Del Campbell
desk: Soundtracs PC MIDI
monitors: Miller & Kriesel
rates: £120 per 10 hour day
info: 1 large live room which can be partitioned as band requires. A vast experience in recording is offered. Del is a musician and offers quality service at an affordable price. Some amps and instruments available.

The House of Light
107 Savage Road, Plymouth, Devon, PL5 1BS
tel: 01752 299 176
email: roo@houseoflight.co.uk
web: www.houseoflight.co.uk
contact: Andy McKellar
desk: PC based
rates: £10 per hour
info: Music production company who offer remixing, mastering and production services. Ideal for demo recording. House based recording suite with full home facilities.

J & J Studios
Easton, Bristol, BS5 6JF
tel: 0117 951 9909
email: mr.jabears@btinternet.com
web: www.theguitarcircle.com
contact: Jim Barr
desk: Vintage Soundcraft
monitors: ATC
rates: Contact for details
info: Large, comfortable control room and live room with natural light. Professionally designed acoustics. Vintage instruments and amps available for use. Selection of valve and condenser mics. Kitchen facilities on-site. Follow studios link on the above website for further details.

Jaba
Weeke Barton, North Tawton, Devon, EX20 2AB
tel: 01837 822 94
email: info@jaba.co.uk
web: www.jaba.co.uk
contact: Ben Roberts
desk: Mackie
monitors: Yamaha NS10
rates: Rates vary
info: Jaba Studios offers recording, mixing, production and post-production/mastering facilities. Full technical specification can be viewed on the website.

Jonathan Recordings
St. George, Bristol, BS5 8ER
tel: 0117 935 0474
email: jonathan@recordings.demon.co.uk
contact: Jonathan Lane
desk: 24 channel Mackie
monitors: ATC/Quad
rates: From £20 per hour
info: Large equipment pool available to suit any job including good quality mics such as Royer, AKG and Beyer. Location recording, studio post production and high-end mastering is available.

Jon's Place
11 Salcombe Gardens, Weston Super Mare, Avon, BS22 6NJ
tel: 01934 518 831
email: thesleeptalkers@hotmail.com
contact: Jon
desk: Digital Performer 4/Motu Audio Interface
rates: Call for details
info: Small digital based project studio. Home based, all house facilities available to bands.

Kewsound
Kew Gardens, Crookes Lane, Kewstoke, Weston Super Mare, BS22 9XL
tel: 01934 415 645/07932 570 869
email: steve@kewsound.co.uk
web: www.kewsound.co.uk
contact: Steve Allan
desk: Pro Tools
monitors: Tannoy
rates: From £15 per hour
info: The studio is based around 32 track hard disk recording process. Top quality microphones and excellent acoustics ensure a professional result. Hygiene and access facilities are provided for individuals with special needs. Secure on-site parking is available at no extra cost. Range of refreshments available on site. See also listing for rehearsal facilities.

Laughing Cat Studio
Hyacinth Cottage, Cubert, Newquay, Cornwall, TR8 5EZ
tel: 01637 831 199
email: mike@laughingcat-studio.co.uk
web: www.laughingcat-studio.co.uk
contact: Mike Norfolk
rates: Contact for details
info: Small studio that is primarily digital but can cater for live bands. Rates vary depending on project.

Livewire Recording Studios
Brooke Close, Saltash, Cornwall
tel: 01752 290 650
email: info@kristiansharpe.com
rates: £16 per hour
info: 24 track digital. Equipped with Pro Tools and Mac using Logic. 5 live rooms.

Lyme Green
Pinhay Lodge, Lyme Regis, Dorset, DT7 3RQ
tel: 01297 444 314
email: jonathangear@excite.com
contact: Johnthan Gear
rates: Call for details
info: Small studio ideal for singer-songwriters. If a band would like to record then ideal locations can be found. Please call for more details.

Mad Borris Records
Riverside Centre, 13-14 Okehampton Street, Exeter, Devon, EX4 1DU
tel: 0845 430 9752
fax: 0845 430 9753
email: info@madborris.com
web: www.madborris.com
contact: Tim Jacques
desk: Mackie/Pro Tools
monitors: Roland
rates: £17.50 per hour
info: Mad Borris is recording label, based in Exeter offering the latest in analogue and digital recording techniques. High quality equipment available. Can also provide mobile recording at concerts and gigs. CD mastering and duplication services available, see listing for Riverside Media in relevant section for details.

Metier Productions
127 Stanford Cottages, Semley, Shaftsbury, Dorset, SP7 9AT
tel: 01747 830 979
email: info@metierproductions.co.uk
web: www.metierproductions.co.uk
contact: David Lefeber
rates: Call for details
info: Mobile Acoustic music production. CD mastering and DVD authoring. Demo packages available. Full digital recording facility with location recording.

Mojo Sound Studios
The Old Coach House, St. Luke's Road, Torquay, TQ2 5NX
tel: 01803 290 074
email: info@mojostudios.co.uk
web: www.mojostudios.co.uk
contact: Leo Brown
desk: Sony MXP-3036
monitors: ATC
rates: Call for details
info: Large live room geared for live band recording. Nearby accommodation can be arranged, call for details.

The Moles Studio
14 George Street, Bath, Avon, BA1 2EN
tel: 01225 404 445
fax: 01225 404 447
email: paul@moles.co.uk
web: www.moles.co.uk/studio
contact: Paul
desk: Otari MTR 90
monitors: Yamaha NS10
rates: Call for details
info: Part of the Moles live music venue. See listing in relevant section for further details.

Mr Pand
Plymouth
email: mr_pand@hotmail.com or mrpand@gmail.com
web: www.mrpandrecords.tk
contact: Anthony Pand
info: 16 track recording studio with MIDI and programmable drum machine capabilities. Also run a record label. See listing in relevant section for details.

NAM Recording
4-7 Forewoods Common, Holt, Wiltshire, BA14 6JP
tel: 01225 782 281
fax: 01225 782 281
email: namanage@aol.com
web: www.namrecording.com
contact: Mick Allen
desk: MTA
monitors: NS10s, Mackie
rates: £29/hour including VAT and engineer
info: Rural residential recording studio with swimming pool for summer use and private garden. Air conditioned. Off road parking. When recording facilities are not in use the studio is available as a rehearsal space, see relevant section for more details.

New Sound Studios
20 Station Road, Blockley, Moreton-In-Marsh, Gloucestershire, GL56 9ED
tel: 01386 700 640
email: newsoundstudios@aol.com
contact: Mark Newton
info: Digital recording studio. Up to 94 tracks of audio. Spacious live room and drum room. Kitchen and chill outroom available. Rural setting in the heart of the Cotswolds.

Paramor Productions Studio

Tinkers Cottage, Burcombe Lane, Burcombe, Salisbury, Wiltshire, SP2 0EN
tel: 01722 744 196
email: susan@tinkers10.wanadoo.co.uk
contact: Sue
desk: Mackie
rates: £20-£22 per hour
info: Specialise in teaching vocalisation with microphone techniques. Sue has 25 years of experience and now deals in recording solo artists and duos.

Pipeline Studios

Bristol
tel: 0117 904 0626
email: sales@inthepipeline.net
web: www.inthepipeline.net
contact: Ian Baguley
desk: AMEK/TAC Scorpion
rates: Call for details
info: Pipeline Studios offer the best in combined digital and analogue recording and production. Studios use leading industry standard software as well as vintage equipment to offer a unique sound and flexibility. Specialise in helping with project work. See website for more information.

Press House Studios

Hooperhayne, Colyton, Devon, EX24 6SH
tel: 07876 596 606
email: presshouse@zetnet.co.uk
contact: Mark Tucker
monitors: Genelec/Yamaha/ATC
rates: £350 per 10 hour day
info: Fully residential studio. Genelec, Otari 2" digital systems. Very well equipped with fantastic rates. Studio has chillout area, parking and kitchen facilities.

Prism

Park View Farm, Braydon, Swindon, SN5 0AQ
tel: 08700 424 121/0845 257 1324
email: recording@dsl.pipex.com
web: www.prism-mobile.biz
contact: Peter Zak
desk: Soundtrac Solitaire/Mackie
monitors: Genelec 1031
rates: Call for details
info: Mobile recording studio available for production services across the UK and Europe.

The Propagation House Studios

East Lodge Obeare, North Tamerton, Holsworthy, Devon, EX22 6SE
tel: 01409 271 111
email: info@propagationhouse.com
web: www.propagationhouse.com
desk: Amek Einstein Super E
monitors: Quested H 208
rates: From £200 per day
info: Residential studio with 5 bedrooms. 3 live rooms, one with stage and lighting system including 7K PA. Full technical specifications can be found on above website.

Purple Squares Studio

St. James' Road, Southampton, Hampshire, SO15 5XX
tel: 07742 963 603
email: bookings@purplesquaresstudios.co.uk
web: www.purplesquaresstudios.co.uk
contact: Chris Taylor
desk: Mackie
monitors: Alesis
rates: Free
info: Community church run studios. Students working part time to help young bands. Tea and coffee facilities, kitchen and table football. Can cater for full scale albums and mixing, as well as location and Classical recording. Well worth calling Chris, no matter where you are based.

RNT Studios

Pine Tree Farm, Cranborne, Wimbone, Dorset, BH2 5RR
tel: 01725 517 204
email: info@rntstudios.com
web: www.rntstudios.com
contact: Rick
desk: Digidesign/Focusrite
monitors: Yamaha NS10/Mackie HR824
rates: £30 per hour (all inclusive)
info: Full Pro Tools TDM setup. See website above for full technical specification.

RS Studios

St Phillips, Bristol, BS2 0SE
tel: 0117 9711 495
email: rsstudios@hotmail.com
web: www.rs-studios.co.uk
contact: Rich Weaver
rates: £15 per hour
info: Mainly a rehearsal studios but does offer recording facilities. See relevant section for more details.

S.T.A.R. Services

61 RL Stevenson Avenue, Bournemouth, Dorset, BH4 8ED
tel: 01202 768 084
email: claudette@worldofbusby.com
web: www.worldofbusby.com
contact: Claudette
desk: Spirit FX
monitors: Tannoy
rates: £20 per hour
info: Modern music tuition studio specialising in teaching home recording . Also have a record label, 'World of Busby'.

Shockerwick Studios

Bathford, Bath
tel: 01225 859 290
email: info@shockerwickstudios.co.uk
web: www.shockerwickstudios.co.uk
contact: James Shepard
desk: Mackie 48 track
monitors: Event
rates: From £200 per day
info: Professional studio specialising in live bands and DJ acts. Studio has a live room with a large selection of equipment.

SOA Recordings

Unit 4, Lawnwood Industrial Estate, Lawnwood Road, Easton, Bristol, BS5 0EF
tel: 0117 955 4008
fax: 0117 954 1075
email: stuart@soastudios.net
web: www.soastudios.net
contact: Stuart Matthews
desk: DDA MR24
monitors: ATC SCM100A/Yamaha NS10
rates: Call for details
info: Spacious recording areas within a very professional studio set up. Studio has isolation rooms with a range of equipment. Daily and hourly rates available.

Sound Conception

82-84 York Road, Bedminster, Bristol, BS3 4AL
tel: 0117 966 2932
fax: 0117 963 5059
email: soundconception@btconnect.com
contact: Ken Wheeler
desk: 52 Channel Soundcraft
monitors: Tannoy/Auratone
rates: Contact for details
info: Studios have been established since 1976. Very professional set up with a large range of equipment. Use high quality mics. Large control room and also live room with a grand piano. Pro Tools, Logic and Performer. Loads of experience with very reasonable rates.

Sound On Sound

148 Rownhams Lane, North Baddesley, Southampton, Hampshire, SO52 9LT
tel: 02380 733 903
email: mkgddn@aol.com
web: www.soundonsoundinternational.co.uk
contact: Mike Godden
desk: Neve
monitors: Mackie
rates: £20 per hour
info: Studios offer digital and analogue recording. Also offer mastering and restoration, as well as DVD and CD duplication with on-body printing.

Soundkitz

Bramley Cottage, The Green, Compton Dando, BS39 4LE
tel: 01761 492 540/07787 921 557
email: biz@soundskitz.biz
web: www.soundskitz.biz
contact: Will Alleyne
desk: Mackie
monitors: Various
rates: Call for details
info: Will is an arranger, mixer and producer that works in conjunction with Glasstone. Professional set up with a wide range of equipment. Offer discounts for unsigned bands. Work with signed artists also.

MUSIC SERVICES/RETAIL

South Star Music
PO Box 1350, Southampton, SO15 5WX
tel: 07789 882 368
email: admin@southstarmusic.co.uk
web: www.southstarmusic.co.uk
contact: Stewart Dugdale
desk: Mackie
monitors: Tannoy
rates: £125 per day
info: Small studio, attached to a house.

Sprint Music Ltd.
High Jarmany Farm, Jarmany Hill, Barton St. David, Somerton, Somerset, TA11 6DA
tel: 01458 851 010
email: info@sprintmusic.co.uk
web: www.sprintmusic.co.uk
contact: John Ratcliff
desk: Mackie d8b with Logic Control
monitors: Mackie 824/624/HRS 120/Yamaha NS10
rates: Call for details
info: Sprint Music have more than 30 years experience of the entertainment industry. The studio is equipped with state of the art technology and designed for all types of recording including 5.1 surround sound. Spacious and friendly environment. Sprint can cater for songwriters and bands, as well as jingles, TV and film soundtracks and have a fine selection of session musicians if required. In-house production is also available.

Stonebench Studios
Lydbrook House, Lower Lydbrook, Lydbrook, GL17 9NN
tel: 01594 861 267
email: stonebenchstudio@ukonline.co.uk
contact: Kozmo Hayes
desk: Behringer DDX3216
monitors: Fostex PM1 Studio Reveal
rates: Contact for details
info: State of the art digital recording facilities with professional results and excellent rates. Record for bands, solo artists and DJs. Can also cater for radio ads and voice overs. 2 very well equipped rooms with rehearsal space available. Guitar and music technology lessons available.

Studio Tan
6 Clifton Road, Exeter, Devon, EX1 2BR
tel: 01392 437 861
email: tan@spendspendspend.com
web: www.spendspendspend.com
contact: Tom Bainelott
rates: £22 per hour (all inclusive)
info: 20 years recording experience. Deal with all styles of music and can cater for unsigned bands. Fully qualified and experienced engineers and producers. Also deal in voice overs, graphics and design.

Thinking Productions
30b Downleaze, Bristol, BS9 1LY
tel: 0117 968 2865
email: info@thinkingproductions.co.uk
web: www.thinkingproductions.co.uk
contact: James
desk: Mackie
monitors: Mackie active
rates: £40 per hour (all inclusive)
info: Top quality mics, compression and pre-amps. Do not have facilities to record drum kits, large bands or orchestras at the in-house studio, although can arrange for such recordings to be made at an associated studio, at a discounted rate.

Toybox Studios
25 Portland Square, Bristol, BS2 8NN
tel: 0117 989 2642
email: info@toyboxstudios.co.uk
web: www.toyboxstudios.co.uk
contact: Ali Chant
desk: Trident
monitors: Mackie/Yamaha/Westlake
rates: Contact for details
info: Professional studio with large format analogue console. Use Pro Tools mix plus and have a 24 track 2 inch tape machine. Studio has 4 different rooms. Isolation booth available. Competitive prices. Previous clients include Universal Music, Beggars Banquet, One Little Indian and Warp Records.

Troubador Studios
Pearce's Mill, Falmouth Wharf, North Parade, Falmouth, Cornwall, TR11 2TF
tel: 01326 212 022
email: chris@troubadour.net
web: www.troubadour.net
contact: Chris Gray
desk: Protools Digital/Soundcraft Ghost Analogue
monitors: Event
rates: £22 per hour, £180 per 9 hour day
info: Equipped with both digital and analogue gear.

V.I.P. Lounge
Parade Chambers, 10 Parade street, Penzance, Cornwall, TR18 4BU
tel: 01736 332 592
email: dare.manson@virgin.net
web: www.viplounge.org.uk
contact: Dare Mason
desk: Mackie
monitors: Yamaha NS10
rates: £30 per hour
info: Combines classic analogue with up to date digital gear. Apple Mac G4 with Cubase VST recording that specialises in guitar bands.

Western Star Recording Studio
PO Box 1441, Bristol, BS39 7ZN
tel: 01761 411 747
email: info@westernstar-studio.co.uk
web: www.westernstar-studio.co.uk
desk: Mackie
monitors: Tannoy
rates: Call for details
info: The studio is very popular and is usually booked up 6 months in advance. Excellent rates and great sound.

MUSIC SERVICES/RETAIL

The White House
98 Kewstoke Road, Kewstoke, Weston Super Mare, BS22 9YH
tel: 01934 633 773
email: info@whstudio.co.uk
web: www.whstudio.co.uk
contact: Martin Nichols
desk: Hill 32 channel concept
monitors: Various
rates: £15 per hour
info: Established in 1987. Provide friendly, reliable service. Helpful engineer with over 20 years experience in all aspects of production, from drum tuning and microphone techniques to mixing and mastering. Live room and isolation booths. 24 tracks on 2 inch analogue or hard-drive digital. Set in relaxed, rural location.

Yellow Shark
121 Promenade, Cheltenham, Gloucestershire, GL50 1NW
tel: 01242 515 160
fax: 01242 242 120
email: music@yellow-shark.co.uk
web: www.yellow-shark.co.uk
contact: Gareth Williams
desk: Soundtracs Jade
monitors: ATC/Yamaha
rates: Call for details
info: Based in the centre of Cheltenham, Yellow Shark Studios offer every type of recording format. Lots of outboard available, as well as a large selection of instruments, including pianos, keyboards, guitars, drums and samplers. Also offer mastering and duplication services, see entry in relevant sections for details.

YORKSHIRE

2 Fly Studios
84 John Street, Sheffield, South Yorkshire, S2 4QU
tel: 0114 249 1176
contact: Alan Smyth
desk: Soundcraft Ghost
monitors: Mackie
rates: Call for details
info: Digital Pro Tools studio with analogue Soundcraft desk. Alan has worked with many Sheffield bands including The Arctic Monkeys.

2DF Studio
Halifax, West Yorkshire
tel: 07814 826 486
email: mail@2degreefield.co.uk
web: www.2degreefield.co.uk
contact: Matt
desk: 32 channel
rates: £80 for 10 hours
info: 2DF pride themselves on offering professional sounding recordings at a reasonable cost. The studio is suitable for all types of musical recordings from Jazz, through to Extreme Metal.

A Side Recording Studio
Newton Lodge, 489 Leeds Road, Wakefield, WF1 2ND
tel: 01924 825 165
fax: 01924 825 165
email: lee@asidestudio.co.uk
web: www.asidestudio.co.uk
contact: Lee
desk: VM7 2000
monitors: Tannoy
rates: Call for details
info: Fully digital recording studio. Many samplers, sound modules and keyboards available.

Adrenalin Recording Studios
111 Matilda Street, Sheffield, S1 4QF
tel: 0114 278 7767
email: info@adrenalinstudios.co.uk
web: www.adrenalinstudios.co.uk
contact: Mark
desk: Studer
monitors: Tannoy/JBL/Yamaha
rates: Call for details
info: Adrenalin is a quality, spacious, digital and analogue studio, running digital Pro Tools and analogue 'Studer 2' professional. The studio has a highly flexible design which enables full live band recording, right through to programming for a single artist.

Avelone
2 Milton Street, Trafalgar Court, Sheffield, S1 4JU
tel: 01142 768 282
contact: Kevin Simons
desk: Yamaha 02R
monitors: JBL/Yamaha NS10
rates: Call for details
info: 48 track digital studio and equipment hire.

Axis Recording Studios
Doncaster
tel: 01302 769 676/07961 423 397
email: info@axisproductions.co.uk
web: www.axisproductions.co.uk
contact: Matt Elliss
desk: Amek
monitors: Tannoy/Yamaha
rates: Call for details
info: State of the art facility offering Pro Tools, Radar or 2" analogue recording options. The studio features an acoustically designed air-conditioned control room, spacious live room, custom designed vocal booth, as well as recreational areas to relax and recharge. Mark has produced artists such as Louise, Grand Theft Audio, Number 1 Sun, Kinesis and Laika Dog.

Big 3 Productions
tel: 07843 556 730
email: mike@big3.co.uk
web: www.big3.co.uk
contact: Mike Thrussel
info: Contact Mike on the above telephone number or via website. Big 3 Productions also provide mastering and duplication, as well as PA hire services. See relevant listings for further details.

Blank Tape Studios
4 Folds Crescent, Beauchief, South Yorkshire, S8 0EQ
tel: 0114 236 6699
email: blanktape@blueyonder.co.uk
web: www.blanktape.co.uk
contact: Tom Chester
desk: Spirit 48 channel
monitors: Quad/Dynaudio
rates: Call for details
info: Small studio, suits Acoustic outfits or singers with backing tracks. No bands please.

Bok
Stagworks, 84 John Street, Sheffield, S2 4QU
tel: 0114 279 5487
contact: Bert Rodgers
rates: £175 per day
info: 64 track Pro Tools recording studio available at rate of £175 per day but packages are available. Bok also run rehearsal rooms, as well as an equipment hire service. Refer to entries in relevant sections for further details.

Cadman Lane Studio
Snaith, East Yorkshire, DN14 9JR
tel: 01405 869 700
email: studio@cadmanlane.co.uk
web: www.cadmanlane.co.uk
contact: Nev Barker
desk: Soundcraft
monitors: JVL
rates: Call for details
info: Full studio with live, acoustic and drum rooms. Up to date equipment that records onto the Mackie HDR24/96 that is compatible with Pro Tools, Cubase, Logic and Sonar. Can record any type of music, Studio has chillout area and free accommodation for longer sessions.

Calder Recordings
Unit 9D, Top Land Country Business Park, Cragg Vale, Mytholmroyd, Nr. Hebden Bridge, HX7 5RU
tel: 01422 881 815/07817 986 527
email: studio@calder-recordings.co.uk
web: www.calder-recordings.co.uk
contact: Steve Fenton
desk: 72 channel Mackie
monitors: Genelec/Kef/DB Technologies/Yamaha/Gale/Behringer
rates: Call For Details
info: Professional recording and rehearsal facilities in a relaxing countryside location with ample parking and easy access. Large main room, 2 control rooms, secure storage. Chillout area with full kitchen, TV, video games and sofa. Classic and state of the art equipment including Pro Tools and HDR24/96kHz multitrack. Wide selection of mics including Shure, Rodes, AKG, Beyer and Audio Technica. Previous clients include Supertramp, Crème Anglais, Crowded House, Clive Russel, Operator Six, Mabel Blue and more. Friendly and experienced staff make for a good creative atmosphere. Calder also run a record label, Cone Records. See listing in relevant section for more information.

The Collective
17-21 Charter Square, Left Message, Sheffield, S1 4HS
tel: 07941 701 255
email: karen@pandemoniumpromotions.com
web: www.pandemoniumpromotions.com
contact: Karen
rates: £15 for 3 hours (daytime), £18 (evening)
info: Affordable studio time for young bands. Has catering facilities. Rehearsal facilities available. Also put on gigs in the area. See listings in relevant sections for details.

Crystal Sound Studio
35 Allerton Grange Vale, Leeds, LS17 6LS
tel: 0113 266 9189
fax: 0113 266 9189
email: info@crystalsound.co.uk
web: www.crystalsound.co.uk
contact: Michael Cruise
desk: Spirit 24/48ch
monitors: Tannoy/NS10/Genelic 1030A
info: 32 track studio. Offer assistance to unsigned bands and artists with producing demos. Contact for further information, as well as details of rates. Crystal Sound also offer a mastering service, and have a record label, Cruise International Records. Refer to entries in relevant sections.

Cube Media
The Melbourne Centre, Eskrick Street, York, YO10 4EW
tel: 01904 626 695
email: rose@cubemedia.biz
web: www.cubemedia.biz
desk: Soundcraft DC2020
monitors: Genelec 1032A/KEF CODA 7/Tannoy Stratford
info: Cube Media (formerly the Old Dairy Studios) is a progressive multimedia centre with over 20 years of experience in all aspects of media production. They have a 56 track digital (simultaneous) recording studio with full MIDI integration and a wealth of sound modules, dedicated synths and sample library. See website above for full technical specification.

Diamond Studios
Suite A, Moor Park Business Centre, Thornes Moor Road, Wakefield, West Yorkshire, WF2 8NZ
tel: 01924 201 169
email: info@diamondstudios.co.uk
web: www.diamondstudios.co.uk
contact: Joe
desk: Beringher
monitors: Mackie
rates: 16 per hour
info: Modern and friendly environment. Mostly guitar based bands.

Drawingboard Production
Leeds
tel: 07748 800 661
email: info@drawingboardproductions.co.uk
web: www.drawingboardproductions.co.uk
rates: Call for details
info: Professional sound engineer who can work in a studio or in live venues. Will help locate suitable venues for recording if required. Also provide artwork and design services. See listing in relevant section for details.

Epic Head
56 Garden Street, Sheffield, South Yorkshie, S1 4BJ
tel: 0114 273 1398
email: oknort@hotmail.com
contact: Nort
desk: Allen & Heath
monitors: Rogers
rates: Call for details
info: Live room and drum booth.

Fairview Recording Studio
Cavewood Grange Farm, Common Lane, North Cave, East Yorkshire, HU15 2PE
tel: 01430 425 546
fax: 01430 425 547
email: andy@fairviewstudios.co.uk
web: www.fairviewstudios.co.uk
contact: Andy Newlove
desk: Soundcraft 2400
monitors: JBL 4350
rates: Contact for details
info: Decent floor space and lots of gear. Set close to public amenities and in proximity to rural countryside. Easy access and ample parking. Fairview also offer mastering and duplication services. See entry in relevant section for further information.

G2 Studios
72 John Street, Sheffield, South Yorkshire, S2 4QU
tel: 0114 279 5650/0114 270 6217
email: info@g2studios.co.uk
web: www.g2studios.co.uk
contact: Paul, John
desk: Mackie/Yamaha 02R
monitors: Bluesky
rates: £25 per hour, £200 per track
info: G2 is a spacious studio designed by Acoustic Architecture using industry standard digital and analogue recording systems. Pro Tools and analogue 16 track. Spacious studio. Details of rates and packages can be found on website. G2 also offer a CD duplication service, refer to relevant section for further details. Rehearsal space available. Please ring for any additional information regarding rates.

G2 Studios
Clifton Works, 74 John Street, Sheffield, S2 4QU
tel: 0114 270 6217
fax: 0114 279 5650
email: info@g2studios.co.uk
web: www.g2studios.co.uk
contact: Paul/John
info: Pro Tools and Analogue 16 track. Spacious studio. Details of rates and packages can be found on website. G2 also offer a CD duplication service, refer to relevant section for further details. Rehearsal space available. Please ring for any additional information regarding rates.

Ghosttown Recording Studio
Leeds
email: info@ghosttownrec.co.uk
web: www.ghosttownrec.co.uk
contact: Simon
rates: £30 per track
info: Also offer PA hire and CD mastering and duplication services, see entries in relevant sections for details.

HD1 Studio
St. Peter's Chambers, St. Peter's House, Huddersfield, West Yorkshire, HD1 1RA
tel:	01484 452 013
email:	samroberts@hd1studios.co.uk
web:	www.hd1studios.co.uk
contact:	Sam Roberts
desk:	Amek Rembrant
monitors:	Genelec 1025C
rates:	Call for details
info:	Yorkshire's premier recording studio. Past clients include

Terrorvision, Shed Seven, Embrace and the Kaiser Chiefs. Purpose built with separate vocal, drum and live areas and can cater for all types of recordings, from first demos to major recording artists. Can also offer small scale CD production and mastering for acts recorded in the studio.

Higher Rhythm Recording Studio
1st Floor, 13 Copley Road, Doncaster, South Yorkshire, DN1 2PE
tel:	01302 327 769
email:	mail@higherrhythm.co.uk
web:	www.higherrhythm.co.uk
contact:	Steve Mundin
desk:	Mackie 24-8
monitors:	Genelec 10-30
rates:	Call for details
info:	Combination of professional analogue outboard

equipment, including several classic synths, and industry level software and hardware packages (including Pro Tools, Cubase SX3 and Nuendo).

House of Mook
Authorpe Works, Authorpe Road, Leeds, West Yorkshire, LS6 4JB
tel:	0113 230 4008
email:	mail@mookhouse.ndo.co.uk
web:	www.mookhouse.ndo.co.uk
contact:	Phil Mayne
desk:	Soundtracs
monitors:	JBL
rates:	Call for details
info:	Situated only a couple of minutes' drive from the centre

of Headingley, House of Mook offer analogue recording at competitive rates. Rehearsal and equipment storage space with an in-house record label, Mook Records. See entries in relevant sections for further details.

Imp Hut
9 Melrose Yard, Walmgate, York, YO1 9XF
email:	jan@imp-hut.co.uk
web:	www.imp-hut.co.uk
rates:	£25 per hour
info:	36 channel recording. Lots of outboard. Recording is

part of the Imp Hut facility that also comprises 3 rehearsal rooms. The control room is linked to each rehearsal room, allowing live recording. Discounts available for block bookings. Video link and talk-back between control room and rehearsal spaces. Accessories shop on-site. For more details on the rehearsal facilities, see the relevant section.

Interstellar Sandwich Studios
c/o Melody House,, Manchester Road, Deepcar, Sheffield, S36 2QY
tel:	0114 278 9572/07903 437 063
email:	interstellar_sandwich@hotmail.com
contact:	Robyn
rates:	Call for rates
info:	House based studios. Kitchen facilities available. Contact

Robyn for further information.

Jam Factory
106 Eldon Street, York, YO31 7NH
tel:	01904 339 879
email:	jamfactorychris@hotmail.com
desk:	Industry Standard
monitors:	Apple Mac G5
rates:	£18 per hour
info:	Also has 4 Rehearsal rooms and offers Access to Music

course, see relevant section for details.

Jump Studios
Unit 2, Briar Rhydding, Baildon, West Yorkshire, BD17 7JW
tel:	01274 596 547/07976 201 847
email:	banksy@jumprecords.com
web:	www.jumprecords.com
contact:	Les
rates:	From £15 per hour
info:	Studio is part of the Jump Records label, also offering

rehearsal space, see entries in relevant sections for details.

Kenwood Studios
23 Kenwood Park Rd, Sheffield, S7 1NE
tel:	0114 249 9333
email:	adam@kenwoodstudios.co.uk
web:	www.kenwoodstudios.co.uk
contact:	Adam
desk:	Yamaha O2R
monitors:	Yamaha NS10
rates:	Call for details
info:	Has a history with established artists, as well as wanting

to encourage and promote new talent. Has recorded Jazzy Jeff, DJ Format and Dizzee Rascal in the past.

Mosaic Studio
Portland Street, Sheffield, South Yorkshire, S6 3DN
tel:	0114 266 6145
email:	info@mosaicstudio.co.uk
web:	www.mosaicstudio.co.uk
desk:	56 channel Mackie
rates:	£20 per hour (inc. engineer)
info:	See website for full kit list. In-house production

company (Lacuna). Mosaic Studio can also provide an 8 to 24 track mobile digital recording system. Demos deals available, call for details. Also offer rehearsal facilities. See listing in relevant section.

Park Head Studio
10 Park Head, Birdsedge, Huddersfield, HD8 8XW
tel:	01484 606 401/01484 606 230
email:	brian@brian-bedford.com
web:	www.parkheadstudio.com
contact:	Brian Bedford
info:	A small, friendly digital recording studio, specialising

in recording Acoustic music, both vocal and instrumental, Park Head Studio is set in a rural village location, high up in the West Yorkshire Pennines.

Pravda
48 Cottage Road, Leeds, LS6 4DD
tel:	0113 293 0101
email:	matt@pravdauk.com
web:	www.pravdauk.com
contact:	Matt Peel
desk:	Mackie D8B
monitors:	Genelec/Yamaha/HHB/Mackie
rates:	£22 per hour
info:	Pravda Studio is well suited to both tracking and mixing.

The extensive backline and high quality guitar/line/speaker cabling between control and live rooms make it very usable for guitar bands. Introductory packages are available, call for details.

Pro Two Woodlands
Unit 20, Raglan Works, Methley Road, Castleford, West Yorkshire, WF10 1NX
tel:	01977 552 141
email:	info@protwostudio.co.uk
web:	www.protwostudio.co.uk
contact:	Paul
desk:	DDA 56 Frame Analogue/Pro Tools
monitors:	Genelec
rates:	Call for details
info:	Pro Two Woodlands attracts high profile bands and

musicians, but remains committed to providing affordable recording and mastering sessions for local, unsigned bands. 50% discount on studio rates available for unsigned artists, see website or call for details.

Purple Pro Audio
Unit B, St. Catherine's Business Park, Broad Lane, Bramley, Leeds, LS13 2TD
tel:	0113 290 9161
email:	info@purpleproaudio.com
web:	www.purpleproaudio.com
contact:	Martin Robinson
desk:	Soundcraft Spirit
monitors:	Tannoy Reveal
rates:	Call for details
info:	Purple Recording is a 24 track digital studio set in a

creative and acoustically engineered space. Mac G5 based Logic and Cubase and large live room. Also offer PA hire and rehearsal space. See relevant sections for details.

The Radar Rooms
Perseverance Works, Morrison Street, Castleford, West Yorkshire, WF10 4BE
tel:	01977 517 672
email:	ryan@uk2.net
web:	www.theradarrooms.moonfruit.com
contact:	Ryan
desk:	SSL
monitors:	Genelec/Yamaha
rates:	Call for details

The Recording Company
23 Bank Parade, Otley, West Yorkshire, LS21 3DY
tel: 07941 179 415
email: info@recordingcompany.co.uk
web: www.recordingcompany.co.uk
contact: Lee Bloomfield
desk: Pro Tools
monitors: Alesis
rates: Call for details
info: Offer location recording for rehearsals and live performances.

Red Shift Studios
The Barn House, Morrison Street, Castleford, West Yorkshire, WF10 4BE
tel: 01977 603 996/07771 605 502
email: info@redshiftstudios.com
web: www.redshiftstudios.com
rates: Call for details
info: Contact for details on equipment and rates.

Ric Rac Studios
12 Kirkdale Avenue, Leeds, LS12 6AP
tel: 0113 231 0715
email: info@ricrac.co.uk
web: www.ricrac.co.uk
contact: Wendy Reynolds
desk: Soundcraft
monitors: Tannoy
rates: £25 per hour, £185 per 8 hour day (+ VAT)
info: Studio equipped with Pro Tools. Games room and kitchen. Located several minutes from the M1.

Riverside Studios
Four Horse Shoes Yard, Milnsbridge, Huddersfield, HD3 4NE
tel: 01484 642 131/07810 838 346
web: www.riversidestudios.info
contact: Marcus
desk: Mackie D8B/Tascam
monitors: ATC/Spirit
rates: £24 per hour
info: Large studio also offering rehearsal space, see entry in relevant section for details. Recording discounts are available for rehearsing bands.

Sponge Studios
Cross Chancellor Srreet, Leeds, West Yorkshire, LS6 2TG
tel: 0113 234 0004
web: www.spongeonline.co.uk
rates: Call for detail
info: Sponge are primarily a rehearsal facility, although they offer studio recording and CD and /DVD duplication services.

Stag Works
84 John Street, Sheffield, South Yorkshire, S2 4QU
tel: 0114 249 6557
email: info@electroworks.org
web: www.electroworks.org
info: Network of 12 studios. Call for details.

Steelworks Studios
3 Brown Street, Sheffield, S1 2BS
tel: 0114 272 0300
fax: 0114 272 0303
email: steelworksmu@aol.com
web: www.steelworks-studios.com
contact: Tim Lever
desk: Neve
monitors: Genelec
rates: £250 per day (Studio 1), £150 per day (Studio 2)
info: Both studios are fully equipped with Cubase and Nuendo recording systems, plus large range of softsynths and plug ins.

Strange Reality Music Productions
Goole
tel: 01405 869 929
email: c_miley@hotmail.com
contact: Chris Miley
rates: Call for details
info: Specialise in the production of high quality singles, albums and demos for artists who aspire to the very best. Fully equipped production studio with live room and our mobile Pro Tools studio Also have state-of-the-art recording studio with live area and high-end audio kit. Can cater for almost any project and any budget. Strange Reality pride themselves on attention to detail towards recording and mixing your music, coupled with our philosophy of a relaxed, friendly and productive working environment. Also offer artist management services, and are always on the lookout for talented and dedicated artists to promote. Please call or email to discuss your project.

Sunnybank Studios
2-6 Mill Fold, Ripponden, Halifax, HX6 4DJ
tel: 01422 823 961
email: sunnybankstudios@btconnect.com
web: www.sunnybankstudios.com
contact: Joss Worthington
desk: Soundtracs Solitaire
monitors: Tannoy
rates: £20-£25 per hour
info: 24 track digital as well as 2" analogue tape recording. Can cater for up to 40 microphones. Pro Tools, Cubase SX, host of outboard including Lexicon. Have produced many CDs for all kinds of groups from Classical through Choral and Folk, to Rock and Jazz. Also CD duplication service, see entry in relevant section.

Sunnybank Studios
2-6 Mill Fold, Ripponden, Halifax, HX6 4DJ
tel: 01422 823 361
email: sunnybankstudios@btconnect.com
web: www.sunnybankstudios.com
contact: Joss Worthington
desk: Soundtracs Solitaire
monitors: Dynaudio/Tannoy Big Red
rates: Call for details
info: Have produced many CDs for all kinds of groups from classical through choral and folk, to rock and jazz. See entry in relevant section for information on CD duplication services.

Touchwood Audio Productions
6 Hyde Park Terrace, Leeds, LS6 1BJ
tel: 0113 278 7180
email: info@touchwoodaudio.com
web: www.touchwoodaudio.com
contact: Bruce Wood
desk: Tascam M3500
monitors: Tannoy/JBL/NS10/Yamaha
rates: Call for details
info: Mastering services available. Kitchen, chillout area and 2 live rooms. Situated 5 minutes from the city centre.

Uppercut Productions
96 Robin Lane, Beighton, Sheffield, S20 1BD
tel: 07790 458 893
email: claire.bland1@btopenworld.com
contact: Claire Bland
desk: Sonar
rates: Call for details
info: Claire would like to deal with Folk, Acoustic based musicians or bands, singer-songwriters, storytellers or vocalists. For further information, please contact Claire Bland at Uppercut Productions. Home based studio.

Voltage Studios
St. Stephen's Mill, Ripley Street, Bradford, West Yorkshire, BD5 7JW
tel: 01274 393 998/07789 121 360
email: info@voltagestudios.com
web: www.voltagestudios.com
contact: Tim Walker
desk: Soundcraft Ghost
monitors: Tannoy/Yamaha
rates: £19 per hour
info: The studio offers a choice of analogue and digital multitrack recording, with various PC based programs for simultaneous input recording, MIDI sequencing and mastering. Package deals available. The complex also houses 6 rehearsal rooms, see entry in relevant section for details.

Woodman Recording Studios
Unit 2, Woodman Works, South Lane, Elland, Halifax, HX5 0PE
tel: 01422 372 800
email: info@woodmanstudio.co.uk
web: www.woodmanstudio.co.uk
contact: Jerry Barker
desk: Amek Angela
monitors: Tannoys
rates: £25 per hour
info: Large live room, grand piano, 24 Track recording.

Yellow Arch
30-36 Burton Road, Sheffield, South Yorkshire, S3 8BX
tel: 0114 273 0800
email: mail@yellowarch.com
web: www.yellowarch.com
desk: AMEK Angela
monitors: Absolute 2/Martin
rates: £30 per hour, £15 per hour (Programming room)
info: Programming room available, ideal for Hip-Hop and Dance artists. Can also provide rehearsal space, see relevant section for details.

NORTHERN IRELAND

Belfast Central Recording Studios
2 Gloucester Street, Belfast, BT1 4LS
tel: 028 9024 6006
email: info@francismcpeake.com
web: www.francismcpeake.com
contact: Sara Gunn, Francis Mpeake
desk: Soundtrac
monitors: Alesis
rates: £40 per hour, £250 per 8 hour day
info: High spec studio based on the premises of the Francis McPeake School of Music. Can cater for any genre of music, although quality Acoustic music will be especially welcome. 2 live rooms and spacious control room. Lounge area with TV and gaming facilities and a kitchenette. Also offer rehearsal space, see entry in relevant section for details.

Best Cellars
Ballybeen Activity Centre, Dundonald, County Down, BT16 2QE
tel: 028 9048 6290
fax: 028 9048 6290
email: dean@thecellars.org.uk
web: www.thecellars.org.uk
contact: Dean
desk: Pro Tools
rates: £25 per hour
info: Part of the Best Cellars music collective. Studios with large live and control rooms. For details of rehearsal facilities available, see listing in relevant section.

Big Space Studios
43 University Street, Belfast, Antrim, BT7 1FR
tel: 07984 578 726
email: info@bigspacestudios.co.uk
web: www.bigspacestudios.co.uk
contact: Declan Legge
monitors: Mackie HR824/Samson
info: Studio ideal for Singer-Songwriters, Acoustic artists, DJs and small bands.

Blast Furnace Recording Studio
Unit 11, Rath Mor Business Park, Derry, BT48 0LZ
tel: 028 7137 7870
fax: 028 7137 7870
email: rory@blast-furnace.com
web: www.blast-furnace.com
contact: Rory Donaghy
desk: DDA DMR12
monitors: Genelec/Dynaudio/Yamaha
rates: From £15 per hour, £150 per day
info: Non profit business which has been established for 10 years. Will work to any budget. 2 control rooms, both with Pro Tools. Live room with drums, piano and amps. Musicians, engineers and producers on call.

C & B Studio
Glengormely & Carrickfergus
tel: 07754 053 173
email: graham@cnbstudios.com
web: www.cnbstudios.com
desk: Soundcraft Ghost
monitors: Tannoy
info: See website for full technical specification.

CPR Studios
3a Bingham Lane, Bangor, BT20 5DR
tel: 028 9146 7631
fax: 028 9146 7631
rates: £25 per hour
info: Contact for details of equipment.

Doghouse
81 Knutsford Drive, Belfast, Antrim, BT14 6NA
tel: 028 9075 5039/07718 897 225
email: info@epkmusic.co.uk
web: www.epkmusic.co.uk
contact: Eammonn Keyes
desk: Behringer Eurodesk
monitors: Alesis/Yamaha/Mackie
rates: Call for details
info: 24 track digital hard disc and PC based project studio (up to 60 audio tracks) with emphasis on helping less experienced musicians to obtain a high quality final product.

Earthmusic
39 Lough Road, Lisburn, Antrim, BT27 6TS
tel: 028 9263 8483
email: earthmusicni@yahoo.co.uk
contact: Vic
desk: Soundcraft Spirit
monitors: Alesis
rates: £10 per hour
info: Competitively priced analogue recording studio. Also offers rehearsal room. See entry in relevant section for details.

Einstein Studios
133 Abbeyview, Muckamore, Antrim, BT41 4QA
tel: 028 9446 2701
email: frankie@einsteinstudios.co.uk
web: www.einsteinstudios.co.uk
desk: Allen & Heath Saber Plus
monitors: yamaha NS10/Tannoy
info: Fully equipped 32 track analogue and digital hard disk music recording facility. Einstein has always kept up to date with the latest recording technology.

Electric Studios
Westlink Enterprise Centre, Unit 2, 30-50 Distilery Street, Belfast, County Antrim, BT12 5BJ
tel: 07921 255 083
email: electric_studios@hotmail.com
web: www.sabp-web.co.uk/electricstudios
desk: Soundcraft Spirit SX
info: Acoustic recording suite. Rehearsal room, design, photography and CD duplication services.

EMS Audio
12 Balloo Avenue, Bangor, County Down, BT19 QT
tel: 028 9127 4411
email: ems@musicshop.to
web: www.musicshop.to
desk: Mackie
monitors: Yamaha NS10
rates: £35.25 per hour, £300 per 10 hour day

Glen's Music
86 Knocknacarry Road, Cushenden, County Antrim, BT44 0NS
email: sales@glensmusic.com
web: www.glensmusic.com
contact: Sean Quinn
monitors: Goodmans
rates: £15 per hour
info: Yamaha AW16G hard disk recorder with built-in mixing desk. Kitchen and chillout area. Parking available.

Homestead Recording Studio
57a Main Street, Randalstown, County Antrim, BT41 3BB
tel: 028 9447 3592
fax: 028 9447 3707
email: mudd@muddwallace.com
web: www.muddwallace.com
desk: Amek Gallileo
info: Production, mastering and location recording. In-house accommodation.

Komodo Recording Studios
79 Magheraconluce Road, Hillsborough, Down, BT26 6PR
tel: 028 9268 8285
email: info@komodorecordings.com
web: www.komodorecordings.com
contact: William
desk: Mackie
monitors: Mackie/Behringer/Spendor
rates: £20 per hour
info: Offer studio recording, cover graphic design and printing, duplication services and drum tuition. See entries in relevant sections for details.

Mach 2
412 Beersbridge Road, Belfast, Antrim, BT5 5EB
tel: 028 9065 4450
email: michael@machtwo.co.uk
web: www.machtwo.co.uk
contact: Michael
desk: Tascam
monitors: Genelec
rates: Call for details
info: Specialise in on location recording for live acts. Record all genres of music from Rock and Pop acts to Jazz and Irish Folk music. Previous clients include U2, David Holmes and John Martyn. See also listing for affiliated record label, Red Records in relevant section.

MADD House Studios
Clotworthy Arts Centre, Antrim Castle Gardens, Randalstown Road, Antrim, BT41 4LH
tel: 028 9446 9669
email: info@maddhousestudios.co.uk
web: www.maddhousestudios.co.uk
contact: Darren Porter, Catherine Pollitt
desk: Tascam
monitors: Genelec
rates: £20 per hour
info: Also offer a practice and rehearsal room. See entry in relevant section for details.

Mid Atlantic Digital
41 The Limes, Drumlyon, Enniskillen, County Fermanagh, BT74 5NQ
tel: 028 6632 0420
email: robyn1225@btconnect.com
contact: Robyn Robins
desk: Pro Tools HD3
monitors: Genelec
rates: Call for details
info: Large complex offering many audio and video services. Visit website or call for further information. Studios equipped with full Dolby Surround Sound. Previous clients include U2, The Corrs and The Cranberries.

Natural Sound Studio
17 Windmill Drive, Ballynahinch, County Down, BT24 8WD
tel: 028 9756 0881/07875 020 290
email: mail@naturalsound.force9.co.uk
contact: Simon Monaghan
info: Project studio which caters for Rock bands to Chamber ensembles and choirs. See website for technical specification.

Novatech Productions
122 Hyde Park Road, Newtownabbey, Antrim, BT36 4PZ
tel: 028 9083 8981
fax: 028 9084 4299
email: info@novatechstudios.com
web: www.novatechstudios.com
contact: Gary, Dale
desk: Pro Tools
monitors: Mackie
rates: £230 per day
info: Deliver creative solutions from web design to recording facilities through to final project delivery.

Numbnut Sounds
11 Barleywood Mill, Lisburn, Antrim, BT28 3RZ
tel: 07752 207 553
email: numbnutsounds@gmail.com
contact: Stephen Hill
desk: Soundcraft/Allen & Heath
monitors: Peavey
rates: Call for details
info: Although studio is mainly used for rehearsals, recording services also available. For full details of rehearsal facilities, see relevant section.

P.I.C. Productions
18 Pine Grove Crescent, Ballymena, County Antrim, BT43 6TL
tel: 028 2564 9144
email: pic_music@hotmail.com
contact: Paul
desk: Behringer Digital
rates: £20 per hour
info: Pro Tools system. Also offer digital mastering and CD duplication services.

Press Record
tel: 028 9147 1678/07871 591 717
email: info@pressrecord.co.uk
web: www.pressrecord.co.uk
info: 96kHz 24 bit multitrack recording using MOTU hardware and Digital Performer 4.5.

Purity Studios
50 Silverstream Road, Bangor, BT20 3LT
tel: 028 9146 8776
email: info@puritystudios.com
web: www.puritystudios.com
contact: Spike
desk: Mackie
monitors: Mackie
rates: Call for details
info: In-house professional graphic design, internet and multimedia services are also available. Also offer CD mastering and duplication. See listings in relevant sections for details.

Railway Studios
15 Wardborough Estate, Lisburn, County Antrim, BT28 1XF
tel: 07779 223 668
email: ross@railwaystudios.com
web: www.railwaystudios.com
contact: Ross
desk: Mackie
monitors: Event
rates: £20 per hour, £160 per 10 hour day
info: Chillout room, pool table, kitchen and coffee facilities. Also has rehearsal rooms available. See listing in appropriate section for details.

Red Lagoon Music
37 Drumbeggan Road, Monea, Enniskillen, Fermanagh, BT74 8EU
tel: 028 6864 1558
email: gerry@redlagoonmusic.com or ian@redlagoonmusic.com
web: www.redlagoonmusic.com
contact: Gerry, Ian
desk: Tascam/Mackie
monitors: Quested
rates: £35 per hour
info: Block bookings welcome. Contact for details. There is also access to a rehearsal room within the building.

Soundhouse Studio
12c Turmore Road, Newry, BT34 1PJ
tel: 028 3026 5352
email: p.mccaul1@btinternet.com
contact: Patrick McCaul
desk: SSL
monitors: Genelec
rates: Call for details

The Stables Studio
14 Circular Road, Coleraine, BT52 1PS
tel: 028 7034 4207
desk: Soundcraft
monitors: Beringher Truth
rates: £20 per hour
info: Pro Tools studio. Also offer rehearsal space. See entry in relevant section for details.

Stronge Studios
13 Carnesure Park, Comber, Down, BT23 5LT
tel: 028 9187 0465
email: mark@strongestudios.com
web: www.strongestudios.com
contact: Mark Stronge
desk: Behringer
info: Top quality recording equipment and processors. Mainly work with Christian and Gospel artists.

Studio 1 Digital Productions
17 Tudor Brae, Donaghcloney, Craigavon, County Antrim, BT66 7LF
tel: 028 3888 2783
email: malcolm@studio1music.com
web: www.studio1music.com
info: Studio 1 mainly deal with Christian acts but have an open mind to all aspects of music. Please call or email for further details.

Studio 2
69A Whiteside Hill, Portadown, Armagh, BT62 3RJ
tel: 028 3884 1335/07791 949 199
contact: James
desk: Studiomaster
monitors: Dynaudio
rates: £20 per hour
info: Mainyl deal with Rock, Country and Folk-based artists. Also offer rehearsal space See entry in relevant section for details. CD printing can be arranged. Contact James for further information.

Studio Ferox
Belfast
email: studio@studioferox.co.uk
web: www.studioferox.co.uk
desk: Behringer
monitors: Tannoy Reveal/Pioneer A400/Sennheiser HD530 II/Beyer DT100
rates: £10 per hour or £60 per song
info: See website for full list of equipment and email for more details. Special inclusive price deal, setting a fee per song for musicians working to a budget.

Triangle Studios
49 Tartaraghan Road, Portadown, Craigavon, County Armagh, BT62 1RH
tel: 028 3885 2045
email: marty@rowland49.wanadoo.co.uk
web: www.trianglestudios.net
contact: Marty
rates: Contact for details
info: Studio designed for live recording. 40 track digital recording with analogue and digital mixers. Large control room with high spec mics and outboard processors. Cubase facilities and midi sync. All musical styles and genres catered for.

Wild Goose Productions
39 Lower Lisdrumchor Road, Glenanne, BT60 2HT
tel: 0870 922 0047
fax: 028 3750 7915
email: info@wildgoose.biz
web: www.wildgoose.biz
contact: Greg Haire
desk: Studiomaster
monitors: Tannoy
rates: £25 per hour
info: Wild Goose Productions offers digital recording facilities for bands, songwriters and composers. Also offer CD mastering and duplication. See entry in relevant sections for details.

SCOTLAND

4th Street Studios
11 Forth Street, Pollokshields, Glasgow, G41 2SP
tel: 0141 420 6175
email: mail@4thstreet.co.uk
web: www.4thstreet.co.uk
contact: Iain, Aiden, Gal
desk: Tascam DM24
monitors: Dynaudio BM5
rates: Call for details
info: Studio also contains Roland digital piano and Moog synthesiser. 2 well equipped rehearsal studios also available. See relevant section for more details.

ACR Productions
10c Canmore Street, Dunfirmline, Fife, KY12 7NT
tel: 01383 741 500
email: info@acrproductions.co.uk
web: www.acrproductions.co.uk
contact: Val, Jill
desk: Mackie D8B
monitors: Yamaha NS10/Mackie
rates: Call for details
info: Part of Sonic Lizard production company (www.soniclizard.com) which provides a full audio visual package. Rehearsal space is also available.

Alpha Dynamic Audio
7 Gleneagles Court, Whitburn, EH47 8PG
tel: 01501 740 781
email: alphadynamic@yahoo.co.uk
contact: Ben
desk: Mackie

ARC Recording Studio
Aden Country Park, Mintlaw, Aberdeenshire, AB42 5FQ
tel: 01771 623 938
email: arc@enterprise.net
contact: Gavin Sutherland
desk: Soundcraft
monitors: Tannoy
rates: Call for details
info: Small studio ideal for singer-songwriters. Out of city setting, ideal for songwriting.

Attic Recordings
PO Box 23695, Edinburgh, EH7 4XQ
tel: 0131 554 3473/07961 990 232
email: info@alextronicrecords.co.uk
web: www.alextronicrecords.co.uk
desk: Behringer/Mackie
info: Part of the Alex Tronic Record Company who specialise in Chillout Electronica music. Lots of synths available for use.

Audixion
Glen Street, Toll Cross, Edinburgh, EH3 9JE
tel: 07870 567 139
email: b_mcgrail@yahoo.com
contact: Brian McGrail
desk: Akai
monitors: Blueroom
rates: £45 for 4 hours
info: Small studio for singer-songwriters only. Fully digital MIDI and sampler based studio with full orchestration and arrangement on PC based Logic software.

Banana Row
47 Eyre Place, Edinburgh, EH3 5EY
tel: 0131 557 2088
fax: 0131 5589848
email: music@bananarow.com
web: www.bananarow.com
desk: Pro Tools
monitors: Yamaha NS10
rates: From £25 her hour
info: Digital and analogue recording. Digital studio with Pro Tools, Cubase, Logic and Reason. Rehearsal facilities are also available. See listing in relevant section for details.

The Beat Factory
tel: 01324 610 741
email: scott@beatfactory.co.uk
web: www.beatfactory.co.uk
info: Fully mobile service within Scotland. Can cater for variety of budgets and projects. Use high quality 16 track digital recording equipment.

Beatcave Productions
3/2, 568 Paisley Road West, Glasgow, G51 1RF
tel: 0141 419 9558
email: studio@beatcave.co.uk
web: www.beatcave.co.uk
contact: Greg Debleck
desk: PC based
monitors: Alesis
rates: Call for details
info: A company run according to Christian ethics and standards of service, but open to work from Christian and non-Christian artists and labels alike.

Beaufort Productions
Glencaple, Dumfries, DG1 4RD
tel: 01387 770 437
email: md@beaufort.dabsol.co.uk
web: www.mdaudio.co.uk
contact: Malcolm Dunn
desk: Soundcraft
monitors: Tannoy Gold
rates: Call for details
info: Mostly broadcast recording. Willing to record singer-songwriters. Live gig recording also offered.

BeLive Records
12 Millcroft Road, Shawfield Industrial Estate, Rutherglen, G73 1EN
tel: 07796 646 324
email: beliverecords@ntlworld.com
contact: Craig Hosie
desk: Behringer
rates: 4 track demo for £400
info: Specialise in solo artists but can record bands. Can be picked up by arrangement.

Big Byte Sound Solutions
Edinburgh
tel: 0131 226 3180
email: info@bigbytesound.co.uk
web: www.bigbytesound.co.uk
desk: Mackie D8B
monitors: Yamaha NS10
rates: Call for details
info: 72 track recording studio.

Blue Cat Studios
45 Back Sneddon Street, Paisley, PA3 2BB
tel: 0141 583 4282
email: simonbluecat@hotmail.co.uk
desk: Yamaha O2R
monitors: Yamaha
rates: £150 per 8 hour day
info: Nuendo program used on PC and desks are used for routing purposes only.

Blue Cloud Productions
16 Argyle House, 1103 Argyle Street, Glasgow, G3 8ND
tel: 0141 204 3568
email: info@bluecloud-productions.co.uk
web: www.bluecloud-productions.co.uk
info: Well designed sound room. Recording onto 24 track Mac based Pro Tools. Range of effects including, Alesis, Joemeek, Digidesign and Focusrite.

Blue Productions
24 Gairbraid Avenue, Maryhill, Glasgow, G20 8YE
tel: 0141 946 3366
email: info@blueproductions.co.uk
web: www.blueproductions.co.uk
desk: Soundcraft Ghost 32
monitors: Tannoy
rates: From £175 per day

Brever Studios
60A Craigour Drive, Edinburgh, EH17 7NT
tel: 0131 664 1096
email: info@breverstudios.com
web: www.breverstudios.com
contact: Colin Myers
info: 16 track digital recording, mastering and multimedia services. See Artwork, Creative & Design and Recording Services listings.

Bulbous Sound
30 New Holygate, Borxburn, West Lothian, EH52 5RN
tel: 07840 072 272
email: bulbous_sound@hotmail.com
contact: Kenny McCabe
desk: Ysmshs BW16G
monitors: Tannoy
rates: Call for details
info: 16 track digital mobile recording studio. Will record any style of music. Based in West Lothian but willing to travel anywhere in Scotland.

The Byre
16 - 22 Culburnie, Kiltarlity, IV4 7JJ
tel: 01463 741 829
email: mail@the-byre.com
web: www.the-byre.com
desk: Amek Media 51
monitors: Genelec 1029/Yamaha NS10
rates: £350 per day
info: Residential facilities available within walking distance. Provide in-house video facilities, from producing a few clips to be included in a future video or documentary, through to the creation of complete television programmes or DVD.

Captain Tom Music
11-15 Ann Street, Aberdeen, AB25 3LH
tel: 01224 647 500
email: info@captaintommusic.co.uk
web: www.captaintommusic.co.uk
desk: Mackie
monitors: Spirit Absolute
rates: £22 per hour
info: Package deals available. Large complex housing rehearsal rooms, also offer equipment hire and instrument tuition, see relevant sections for details.

Carlton Studio
54 Calton Place, Glasgow, G5 9TW
tel: 0141 429 5723
contact: James Mc Kechen
desk: Amek
monitors: Tannoy
rates: £120 per 8 hour day
info: 3 rehearsal rooms and amp hire also available. See relevant sections for more details.

Castlesound Studios Ltd.
The Old School, Main Street, Pencaitland, Tranent, East Lothian, EH34 5DW
tel: 0131 666 1024
web: www.castlesound.co.uk
contact: Freeland Barbour
desk: Pro Tools HD3
monitors: MNK/Tannoy

Cava
30 Bentinck Street, Glasgow, G3 7TT
tel: 0141 334 5099
email: byoung3752@aol.com
web: www.cavastudios.co.uk
desk: Neve CR Legend
monitors: Genelec/Yamaha 1032
info: 2 studios in operation, one equipped with broadcast facilities using Pro Tools.

Central Sound Studio
61 Berkely Street, Glasgow, G3 7DX
tel: 0141 248 8665/07792 748 912
email: info@centralsound.co.uk
web: www.centralsound.co.uk
contact: Kevin Burley, Dave
desk: Amek
monitors: ATC
rates: Call for detaills
info: Pro Tools HD3 based. No obligation tour available, call for details.

Chamber Recording Studio
120a West Granton Road, Edinburgh, EH5 1PF
tel: 0131 551 6632
email: stephen@chamberstudio.co.uk
web: www.chamberstudio.co.uk
info: Linked with Human Condition Records. See listing in Record Companies section for further information.

Chem 19 Studios
Unit 5c, Peacock Cross Industrial Estate, Burnbank Road, Hamilton, ML3 9AY
tel: 01698 286 882
email: email@chem19studios.co.uk
web: www.chem19studios.co.uk
contact: Shaun
desk: Amek Einstein
rates: Call for details
info: Also offer CD mastering. Large client list including Sons and Daughters, Mogwai, The Delgados, Arab Strap and Teenage Fanclub. 2 rehearsal rooms available. See listing in relevant section for details.

Chow Productions
Unit 9, The Clyde Business Centre, 31 Clyde Street, Clydebank, G81 9PF
tel: 0141 952 3111
email: chowproductions@aol.com
contact: Derek Chalmers
desk: TAC 24
monitors: Genelec 1037
rates: Call for details
info: Massive room with space for up to 50 musicians. Studio doubles as video sound stage. Also offer CD, cassette, VHS and DVD duplication. See listing in Mastering & Duplication section for details.

Clark Sorley
49 Titchfield Street, Kilmarnock, Ayrshire, KA1 1QS
tel: 01563 550 950
email: mail@clarksorley.com
contact: Clark Sorley
desk: Mac-based Pro Tools
monitors: Bluesky
rates: Call for details
info: Very broad selection of music, specialises in Rock and Pop.

Clearwater Studio
Shore Road, Perth, PH2 8BE
tel: 01738 443 217
email: enquiries@clearwaterstudios.co.uk
web: www.clearwaterstudios.co.uk
desk: Tascam
monitors: Genelec/Yamaha NS10/Tannoy
rates: Call for details

CME Studio
14a Hunter Road, Dutchess Trading Estate, Rutherglen, Glasgow, G73 1LB
tel: 0141 647 2810
email: mail@cmeduplication.co.uk
web: www.cmeduplication.co.uk
contact: Ronnie
desk: Soundcraft
monitors: KRK
rates: Contact for details
info: Mastering and post-production services offered. Studio has a 195 sq ft live room. Lots of instruments and synths available. Also offer mastering and duplication services. Refer to entry in relevant section for information.

Colorsound Audio
68 Fountain Bridge, Edinburgh, EH3 9PY
tel: 0131 229 3588
contact: Bob Heatlie
desk: Yamaha 02R
monitors: Genelec/Yamaha
rates: Call for details
info: Rehearsal rooms also available. See listing in relevant section for furthe information.

Conrad Productions
21 Meadowbank Crescent, Edinburgh, EH8 7AJ
tel: 0131 661 8659
fax: 07092 177 472
email: info@conradproductions.co.uk
web: www.conradproductions.co.uk
contact: Mick McGarr
info: Conrad Productions is a music production facility offering custom written music arrangements and backing tracks for songwriters, composers and independent musicians. See website for rates.

Core Studios
7 Osbourn Street, Glasgow, G1 5QN
tel: 0141 552 6677
fax: 0141 552 1354
email: mail@corestudios.co.uk
web: www.corestudios.co.uk
contact: Martin
desk: Spirit Ghost/Pro Tools HD
rates: From £175 per 9 hour day (inc. engineer and VAT)
info: Situated in the city centre. 2 recording studios with Pro Tools HD and LE. Rehearsal rooms also available. See relevant section for more details.

Duo-Record
Haddington, Edinburgh
tel: 07910 371 912
email: graham.small@btopenworld.com
contact: Steven Small
desk: Fostex VF80/Yamaha NG12/4
rates: Free
info: Steven is currently looking for studio experience and will travel anywhere within 20 miles of Edinburgh to record and master free of charge. Shure drum and vocal microphones, and Ibanez guitar with Line 6 amplifier are available. A demo CD of previous recordings can be requested, call for details.

Evolution Studios
Broomhill, Glasgow, G11 7AE
tel: 0141 337 2358
email: johnsweeney7@hotmail.co.uk
contact: John Sweeney
desk: Spirit 24
monitors: Alesis
rates: Call for details
info: Production specifically for singer-songwriters. In-house producer and arranger, session musicians available.

The Exile Studio
7 Weigh-house Square, Aberdeen
tel: 01224 593 855
email: xilestudio@aol.com
web: www.exilestudio.co.uk
contact: Mark Nicol
desk: Allen & Heath Spectrum
monitors: Yamaha NS10
rates: £15 per hour, 4 track demo from £75
info: Lots of outboard available. Also offer rehearsal space, see relevant entry for details.

Foyer Music
Aberdeen Foyer, Marywell Street, Aberdeen, AB11 6JF
tel: 01224 252 894
fax: 01224 252 899
email: music@aberdeenfoyer.com
web: www.foyerlive.com
contact: Dave Stewart
desk: Mackie
monitors: Alesis
rates: £14 per hour (inc. engineer)
info: Foyer Music is the music department of a charity based in the North East of Scotland who provide supported accommodation, education and training to people under 25 years of age. 24 channel recording, DJ room. Also provide rehearsal facilities. See relevant section for more details. They also promote music and are involved with the Go North (www.goevents.info) festival.

GoGoStudios
6 Great George Street, Westend, Glasgow, G12 8PD
tel: 07811 438 468
email: info@gogostudios.com
web: www.gogostudios.com
contact: Phil Howie
info: Recording, mixing and production, both singles and albums. Also offer mastering, composition, studio tuition, crew hire, vinyl transfer and dubbing. See website for details.

Groove Tunnel
Eldin Cottage, Eldin Industrial Estate, Edgefield Road, Loanhead, EH20 9QX
tel: 0131 448 2170
email: rodspark@groovetunnel.com
web: www.groovetunnel.com
contact: Rod
desk: Tascam
monitors: Absolute
rates: Call for details
info: Free parking and refreshment lounge available. Also have mastering and remixing services, and offer help with TV soundtracks and arrangements. 4 rehearsal rooms available, see relevant entry for details

Headhunter Records (UK) Ltd.
Unit 4, Stanley Street Lane, Glasgow, Lanarkshire, G41 1EZ
tel: 0141 429 7111
email: info@headhunterrecords.co.uk
web: www.headhunterrecords.co.uk
contact: Andrew Lowry
desk: Mackie D8B
monitors: Mackie HR8/Behringer
rates: £15 per hour
info: Independent record company based in Glasgow, who cover all aspects of music and video recording, production, duplication and distribution. Also offer 24 hour rehearsal facilities. See further details of rehearsal facilities and record label, see listings in relevant sections.

Heartbeat Recording Studio
Guildie Howse Farm, North Middleton, Gorebridge, Midlothian, EH21 7UL
tel: 01875 821 102
email: heartbeat_studios@hotmail.com
contact: David Valentine
desk: Tascam
monitors: Tannoy
rates: Call for details
info: Analogue and digital equipment available. Rehearsal space with drum kit and PA. David has lots of old equipment and will help with most projects.

Hell-Planet Productions
Flat 1, 5, Bothwell Street, Hamilton, Lanarkshire, ML3 0BS
tel: 07960 415 457
email: info@hell-planetproductions.com
web: www.hell-planetproductions.com
contact: Craig Struthers
monitors: Tannoy Reveal
rates: Call for details
info: Specialises in recording unsigned acts. Small vocal booth especially good for singer songwriters. Drums can be recorded on location.

Homegrown Productions
Todhill Farm, Larbert, Stirlingshire, FK5 4SH
tel: 01324 562 897
email: info@homegrown-productions.co.uk
web: www.homegrown-productions.co.uk
contact: James Taylor
desk: Soundtrack
monitors: Yamaha NS10
rates: Call for details
info: Rural location. MP3 samples are available for download, see website above for details.

JMB Recording Studio
9 Fyrish Crescent, Evanton, Dingwall, IV16 9YS
tel: 01349 830 540
email: johnny.bremner@virgin.net
contact: Johnny Bremner
desk: Mackie
monitors: Midiman
rates: Call for details
info: Specialises in Country music.

Kontakt Productions
44b Whifflet Street, Coatbridge, Lanarkshire, ML5 4EL
tel: 01236 434 083
email: info@kontaktproductions.com
web: www.kontaktproductions.com
contact: Sean, Scott
desk: Yamaha 0V1
monitors: Tannoy/Behringer Truth
info: Cater for all types of band. Also offer music and DJ workshops for young people.

Leapfrog Audio Visual
1 Currievale Farm Cottages, Currie, Midlothian, EH14 4AA
tel: 0131 449 5808
email: cloudeharper@supanet.com
desk: Bell
monitors: Tannoy

Lighthouse Studios
20-22 West Harbour Road, Granton, Edinburgh, EH5 1PN
tel: 0131 551 5788
email: via website
web: www.lighthousestudios.org
contact: Amy
desk: Yamaha 02R
monitors: Yamaha NS10
rates: Call for details
info: Film production area available. Also provide rehearsal studios and drum tuition. See relevant sections for more details.

Lightsand Productions
103 Abercorn Industrial Estate, Abercorn Street, Paisley, Renfrewshire, PA3 4AT
tel: 0141 848 0777
email: info@lightsand.co.uk
web: www.lightsand.co.uk
contact: Steven Galert
desk: Behringer/Soundcraft Spirit
monitors: Yamaha NS10/Quested/Alesis
rates: Call for details
info: Analogue and digital recording studio with Pro Tools. Will also master and duplicate.

Machine Room Studios
19 Lovers Walk, Dumfries, DG1 1LR
tel: 01387 264 103
email: themachineroom@hotmail.com
contact: Grant Henverson
desk: Mackie
monitors: Mackie
rates: Call for details
info: Equally at home recording bands or Dance acts. Lots of synths and samples available.

Mark Freegard
Glasgow
tel: 0141 533 1837
email: mark.freegard@ntlworld.com
contact: Mark Freegard
desk: Nuendo
monitors: Genelec
rates: Call for details
info: Previously transportable studio based in Glasgow, now with a permanent room. Mark's credits included Del Amitri, Manic Street Preachers and The Breeders.

Maybank Studios
652-654 Eglinton Street, Glasgow, Lanarkshire, G5 9RP
tel: 0141 429 8822
email: matt@maybankstudios.co.uk
web: www.maybankstudios.co.uk
contact: Matt Harvey
desk: Allen & Heath
monitors: Tannoy Reveal
rates: £120 per day
info: Also offer 26 track mobile recording for live gigs.

Mix Records
North Lodge, Auchineden, Glasgow, G63 9AX
email: mick@mixrecords.com
web: www.mixrecords.com
contact: Mick
info: 24 bit Pro Tools TDM Mix and Logic systems for the recording, editing, mixing, sequencing and mastering. Location and studio recording available. Cater for all musical genres, both bands and solo artists, as well as other projects including soundtracks and TV work. Also run a recrd label, contact for further details.

More Human Recordings
6/2 Mentone Avenue, Edinburgh, EH15 1HZ
tel: 07932 525 768
email: more.human@virgin.net
contact: Graeme
monitors: Yamaha NS10
info: G4 Mac with Pro Tools. Any type of recording considered from solo acoustic through to live band recording. Demo CD of previous work is available on request.

NuSound
18 Viewforth, Edinburgh, EH10 4JT
tel: 07989 929 844
email: nusound@edinburghdj.com
contact: David
info: Small studio specialising in Electronic music only, particularly House and Hip-Hop.

Nutshell Music
Mcleud Units, Lochevullin Industrial Estate, Oban, Arglye, PA34 4ED
tel: 01631 570 782
email: finlaywells@btopenworld.com
web: www.theshoesmusic.co.uk
desk: Soundcraft Ghost
monitors: Soundcraft Spirit

Ocean View Recording Studio
Coach House Cottage, St. Germains, Longniddry, East Lothian, EH32 0PQ
tel: 01875 852 491
email: oceanviewrecordingstudio@fsnet.co.uk
web: www.oceanviewrecordingstudio.co.uk
desk: Digidesign Control 24
monitors: Genelec 1031A/Tannoy 1000
rates: Call for details
info: Aim to produce well crafted Contemporary songs including R&B, Acoustic and Rock genres. Production/writing collaborations always welcome. Also looking for good vocalists for own projects, contact for details.

OSL Sound
Tranent
tel: 01875 616 050
email: info@oslsound.com
web: www.oslsound.com
desk: Allen & Heath GS3000
monitors: Mackie HR824/Tannoy Reveal/Quad 306
rates: Contact for details
info: Equipped with both digital and analogue 24 track stand alone machines. Computer based audio and Midi options on either Apple Mac or PC platforms. Professionally designed control room.

Paul's Halls Studios
11 Glencryan Road, South Carbrain, Cumbernauld, G67 2UH
tel: 01236 722 228
email: practice@paulshalls.com
web: www.paulshalls.com
contact: Paul
desk: DM24 32 channel
monitors: Tannoy Elipses
rates: From £25 per hour
info: Equipped with Logic 7 on G5 Mac. Also offer rehearsal facilities and tuition. See relevant sections for more details.

The Practice Pad
Unit B1, Glasgow Media Park, Maryhill, Glasgow, G20 9BT
tel: 0141 946 7656
email: info@thepracticepad.com
web: www.thepracticepad.com
desk: Genelec 1030A
monitors: Alesis
rates: From £23.50 per hour
info: 24 digital recording. Can accommodate up to 30 players. Large showcase room with stage and stereo PA. Secure storage available from £20 per month. For full studio spec see website. Pool table, seating area, hot and cold food available. Rehearsal facilities available. See relevant section for more details.

Primrose Hill Studio
Glasgow
tel: 0141 440 0909
web: www.primrosehill.freeserve.co.uk
contact: Dave
desk: Roland VS 1680
monitors: Tannoy Reveals
rates: Contact for details
info: All recordings are recorded onto hard disk. Mainly deal with acoustic artists and singer-songwriters.

QPQ Productions
The Lighthouse, Dunnet Head, Dunnet, Thurso, KW14 8XS
tel: 01847 851 692
email: info@qpqproductions.com
web: www.qpqproductions.com
contact: Isaac Sutherland
desk: Control 24
monitors: Tannoy/JBL
rates: Call for details
info: The most Northerly based recording studio in the British Isles, offering musicians a chance to isolate themselves with their music. A rehearsal room is also available, see relevant entry for details.

Random Rhythms Music Workshop
Bridgehaugh Road, Stirling, FK9 5AP
tel: 01786 479 082
web: www.randomrhythms.net
contact: Guy
desk: Mackie DB8/Soundcraft Ghost
monitors: Mackie
rates: Call for details
info: Random Rhythms is a registered charity offering recording and rehearsal rooms at reduced rates for students, OAPs, unemployed, special needs and community groups.

Red Barn Studios Ltd.
Monorgan Farm, Monorgan, Dundee, DD2 5HT
tel: 0870 742 0747
email: info@redbarn.co.uk
web: www.redbarn.co.uk
contact: Stuart Duncan
desk: Pro Tools
rates: £25 per hour
info: Also offer CD mastering and duplication. See listing in relevant section for further details.

Red Eye Recording Studio
11 Hume Street, Clydebank, G81 1XL
tel: 0141 951 1554
email: reillymusic@yahoo.co.uk
contact: John Nairn
desk: Pro Tools Focus Right
monitors: Mackie
rates: £150 per 8 hour day
info: Red Eye Studio supply top end basses and amplifiers available upon request. 2 fully qualified engineers on hand. Rehearsal rooms also available. See relevant section for more details.

Reeltime Music
High Street, Newarthill, ML1 5JU
tel: 01698 862 860
fax: 01698 861 170
email: info@reeltimemusic.net
web: www.reeltimemusic.net
desk: Mackie 32 track
monitors: Mackie HR824
rates: £11 per hour
info: Rehearsal facilities also available. See relevant section for more details. Recording and rehearsal packages, mixing and mastering. Discounts available for those aged under 25 years, unemployed or students.

Rise2Red
40 Balnakyle Road, Lochardil, Inverness, IV2 4BS
tel: 01463 225 222
fax: 01463 798 042
email: info@rise2red.com
web: www.rise2red.com
contact: Graham Gillanders
desk: Soundcraft Spirit
monitors: Yamaha NS10/Mackie
rates: Call for details
info: Rise2Red also runs music production courses for all levels of students. Both group and private training are available. More details of courses being run are available on the website.

Riverside Studios Ltd.
7 Lowermill Road, Clarkston, G76 8BJ
tel: 0141 644 5572/0141 644 4333
email: info@riversidestudios.net
web: www.riversidestudios.net
desk: Amek Mozart
monitors: Westlake Audio/Yamaha NS10
rates: Call for details

Ruglen Digital Studio
Bridgestone Farmhouse, Glenlochar, Castle Douglas, DG7 2LU
tel: 01556 670 001
email: ianbruce3@aol.com
web: www.ianbruce.org
contact: Ian Bruce
desk: Tascam DM24
monitors: Genelec 1031
rates: Call for details
info: Specially catered for Acoustic music and singe-songwriters. Also offer mastering services.

Seagate Recording Studios
97 Seagate, Dundee, DD1 2ER
tel: 01382 200 725
email: mike.seagate@virgin.net
desk: Amek
monitors: Dynaudio, Yamaha NS10
rates: £30 per hour
info: Hard disk recording. Industry standard equipment.

Seven-A
7a Clarkston Road, Glasgow, G44 4EF
tel: 0141 637 5403
email: info@seven-a.net
web: www.seven-a.net
desk: Sony DMX R-100
monitors: Yamaha NS10
rates: Call for details

Small Town Audio
Unit 1, Teviot Street, Ayr, Ayrshire, KA8 9JE
tel: 01292 619 365
email: simon@smalltownaudio.fsnet.co.uk
web: www.smalltownaudio.com
contact: Simon
desk: Crest
monitors: Yamaha NS10
rates: Call for details
info: Also offer CD duplication, as well as PA and lighting hire.

Sound Café
3 Walston Steading, Nine Mile Burn, EH26 9LS
tel: 01968 674 913
email: soundcafe@btinternet.com
web: www.sound-cafe.co.uk
contact: David Gray
desk: Mackie
monitors: Bluesky
rates: Call for details
info: Fully digital studio catering for all styles. Live room and drum booth.

Sound Sense Recordings
Mid Forth Farm, Manse Road, Forth, South Lanarkshire, ML11 8AJ
tel: 01555 812 009
email: john@soundsense.biz
web: www.soundsense.biz
contact: John
desk: Mackie
monitors: Genelec
rates: Call for details
info: Mobile studio specialising in Acoustic music. PA hire service also available, refer to listing in relevant section for details.

Sound Space Ltd.
Park House, 2 Well Road, Moffatt, Dumfiresshire, DG10 9AS
tel: 01683 222 862/07734 504 562
email: mail@soundspace.org.uk
web: www.soundspace.org.uk
rates: From £150 per day
info: Music production, sound installation and acoustic engineering. Mobile studios.

The Sound Station
Unit 6, Napier Square, Houston Industrial Estate, Livingston, EH54 5DG
tel: 01506 440 505
email: thesoundstation@btinternet.com
rates: £20 per hour
info: Digital 18 track recording and mastering. Vocal booth and drum booth. Live recording, except vocal which is laid over the top of the track. CD duplication services and rehearsal space available. See relevant section for more details.

Sound Station Recording Studio
42 High Street, Galashiels, TD1 1SE
tel: 01896 750 190
email: dave@soundstation.co.uk
web: www.soundstation.co.uk
contact: Dave
desk: Yamaha 02R
monitors: JBL
rates: Call for details
info: Fully digital studio with ADAT and Apple Mac hard disk recording. Extensive outboard and software.

The Soundplace
Craigshill Campus, Maree Walk, Craigshill South, Livingston, West Lothian, EH54 5BP
tel: 01506 777 690/01506 777 691
fax: 01506 777 596
contact: John Hoey
desk: Mac G5 based Pro Tools 5.1
monitors: Tannoy
rates: Call for details
info: Part of the Craigsfarm multimedia complex, also offering a live stage and DVD recording facilities with a view to producing a DVD of the act performing live. Bar and canteen available on campus.

Splash Productions Complex
20 Thorn Brae, Johnstone, PA5 8HE
tel: 01505 323 888/07768 374 730
fax: 01505 326 888
email: info@splashproductionscomplex.com
web: www.splashproductionscomplex.com
contact: Marc Andrew
desk: Control 24
rates: Call for details
info: Pro Tools enhanced 64 track digital recording studio. Also offer rehearsal space, see relevant entry for details.

Split Level
3 East Mains, Ingilston, Newbridge, EH28 8NQ
tel: 0131 333 5024
email: neil@split-level.freeserve.co.uk
contact: Neil
desk: Mackie
monitors: Mackie/Yamaha NS10
rates: Call for details
info: Hybrid digital/analogue studio. Rehearsal space is available. See relevant section for details. Also offer mastering.

Spook Music
34 King Street, Lossiemouth, Morayshire, IV31 6AE
tel: 01343 814 749
email: stu@spookmusic.co.uk
web: www.spookmusic.co.uk
contact: Stu
desk: Yamaha
monitors: Mackie
rates: £15 per hour
info: Particularly interested in unsigned solo artists. Will also master and duplicate the CD.

Stealth Recording Studio
Strathclyde Business Centre, 120 Carstairs Street, Glasgow, G40 4JD
tel: 0141 554 9244
email: eddiemacarthur@yahoo.com
web: www.stealthrecordingstudio.com
contact: Eddie MacArthur
rates: Call for details
info: Stealth offer digital recording, editing and mixing. The studio is suitable for bands, solo performers and corporate clients. Full production service offered, from initial recording to a mastered CD, complete with on-body CD printed graphics if required. Custom artwork service is available too. A free audio sample CD is available on request, and there are MP3 samples to download from the website.

Studiograff
Lamigo, Sibminster Road, Murkle, Thurso, Caithness, KW14 8SP
tel: 01847 821 845
email: admin@studiograff.co.uk
web: www.studiograff.co.uk
contact: Duncan McLachlan
desk: Allen & Heath GS3000
monitors: Yamaha NS10/Mackie HR824
rates: £20 per hour
info: Self-contained, custom built facility for small group recording, specialising in acoustic instrument and computer based audio. Full production packages available including artwork, photography, design and duplication. Package deals available, contact for details.

Unity Recording Studio
Blackhills, Auldearn, Nairn, IV12 5JZ
tel: 01309 641 547
email: alan@wgm.demon.co.uk
web: www.unityrecordingstudio.co.uk
contact: Alan
desk: Soundcraft/Mackie
monitors: Dynaudio
rates: Call for details
info: Purpose built air-conditioned studio with large live room and separate vocal booth. Mac G5 based Pro Tools, Digital Performer and Cubase. Situated near Inverness airport, accommodation can be arranged. Contact for further information.

Urban Studios
279 Abercrombie Street, Glasgow, G40 2DD
tel: 0141 551 0202
email: info@urbanstudios.co.uk
web: www.urbanstudios.co.uk
contact: Davie Roddie
desk: Mackie
monitors: Mackie/JBL
rates: Call for details
info: Urban Studios also comprises 5 fully equipped rehearsal rooms available, see entry in relevant section for details.

Verden Studios
Fishwives Causeway, Edinburgh, EH15 1DT
tel: 0131 538 0555
email: info@verdenstudios.co.uk
web: www.verdenstudios.co.uk
desk: Mackie 1604-VLZ Pro
monitors: Tannoy Reveal/Yamaha MSP5
rates: Call for details
info: 64 track digital studio with 16 track monitoring desk, 12 pre amps and a wide selection of microphones. Rehearsal facilities also available, see listing in appropriate section for details.

Vital Spark Music
1 Waterloo, Isle of Skye, IV42 8QE
tel: 01471 822 484
fax: 01471 822 952
email: chris@vitalsparkmusic.demon.co.uk
contact: Chris Harley, Allan Cuthbertson
desk: Sony DMXR100
monitors: Quested HQ210/Yamaha NS10
rates: £350 per day (inc. engineer)
info: Also restore old tape master recordings and transfer to digital medium. Prefer solo artists. Accommodation can be arranged nearby.

Voodoo Sound Recording & Production
47 King Street, Hamilton, Lanarkshire, ML3 9JH
tel: 01698 335 209
email: david@red-toad.com
contact: David
desk: Behringer
monitors: Spirit Absolute
rates: Call for details
info: Voodoo is also a production company, who will record unsigned acts that are on their books.

Watercolour Music
Home Farm, Ardgour, Fort William, PH33 7AB
tel: 01397 701 352
email: watercolourmusic@aol.com
web: www.watercolourmusic.com
contact: Nick Turner
desk: Yamaha 02R
monitors: Tannoy SRMB10
rates: Call for details
info: Idyllic residential 40 track recording studio in Scottish Highlands.

Windmill Sound
23 Victoria Road, Newton Grange, Dalkeith, Midlothian, EH22 4NN
tel: 07891 539 792
email: daniel@windmillsound.fsnet.co.uk
contact: Daniel
desk: Mackie
monitors: Genelec 1030a
rates: Call for details
info: Small project studio. Particularly keen to work with singer-songwriters, although more than happy to record bands as well.

WALES

3rd Ear
Tredomen, Esgerdware, Llandeilo, Dyfed, SA19 7SF
tel: 01558 650 499
email: meic@3rdear.co.uk
contact: Meic Bromwell
info: Mobile recording and CD mastering. 3rd Ear can visit your rehearsal room (along with other locations) and record your session.

48v
Newport
tel: 01633 840 849
email: info@48v.co.uk
web: www.48v.co.uk
contact: Nick Salt
desk: Soundtracs Topaz
monitors: BBC LS 5/8 and 3/5 8
rates: £20 per hour, £150 per 12 hour day
info: 2 live rooms. 48v is listed in the Guinness Book Of World Records for hosting the fastest full album recording ever (23 hours from start to finish).

Aber Sound Productions Ltd.
Ystwyth Works, Llanfarian, Aberystwyth, Ceredigion, SY23 4NN
tel: 01970 615 079
web: www.abersoundproductions.ltd.uk
rates: £20 per hour (+ VAT)
info: 40 track recording with rehearsing, recording, post-production and mastering facilities. Sound-proofed live room which comfortably holds a drum kit and 4-5 people. Separate isolation booth and control room. Plenty of storage space and a lounge/kitchen with cooking facilities. Mobile 24 track recording. See also listing for rehearsal studios.

Aberystwyth Arts Centre
The University of Wales, Aberystwyth, Penglais Campus, Aberystwyth, SY23 3DE
tel: 01970 622 882
fax: 01970 622 883
email: wnj@aber.ac.uk
web: www.aber.ac.uk/artscentre
desk: Spirit Ghost
rates: Call for details
info: The Aberystwyth Arts Centre also houses a theatre, exhibition space, cinema and live music venue. See website for full technical specifications.

Acoustic Record
South West Wales
tel: 07966 180 059
web: www.acousticrecord.co.uk
desk: Mackie Onyx 1640
monitors: PMC LB1
rates: £180 per 10 hour day
info: Specialise in Acoustic recording. Also offer mobile 16 channel recording facilities (to hard drive). Mastering and re-mastering.

Albany Productions
Unit 3-4, Fairwater Workshops, Norbury Road, Cardiff, CF5 3BG
tel: 02920 555 515
fax: 02920 301 299
email: office@a-p-l.com
web: www.a-p-l.com
desk: Mackie
monitors: Genelec, Yamaha NS40Ms/AR
info: Soundscape, 32 track 24 bit recorder/editor, compatible with Pro Tools. Range of microphones. For full specification see the website. Also offer CD and cassette duplication, see relevant section for details.

Amelia Music
Unit 8, The Ethel Huggard Workshops, Amelia Trust Farm, Five Mile Lane, Walterston, Barry, CF62 3AS
tel: 01446 781 391
email: chrisk@ameliatrust.org.uk
contact: Chris Kelly
rates: £22.50 per hour
info: Large live room, 32 track mixing desk, Soundscape software. Ideal demo studio. Rehearsal space also available, refer to listing in relevant section for details.

The Apartment Studios
Unit 12, The Douglas Building, Royal Stuart Lane, Butetown, Cardiff, CF10 5EL
tel: 01446 408 054
email: lyniseuk@yahoo.com
desk: Soundtracs MIDI PC, 24 into 16 into 8
monitors: JBL 440/Tannoy Active/Yamaha NS10
rates: From £15 per hour
info: MIDI based studio (Cubase), some vintage equipment. Restoration from vinyl and tape. Mastering service.

Autumn Road Studios
54 Beechley Road, Hightown, Wrexham, LL13 7BA
tel: 01978 352 243
email: nino_errico@lineone.net
web: www.autumnroad.com
contact: Nino Errico
monitors: Dynaudio M15
rates: Call for details
info: Alesis HD24, Pro Tools, outboard gear. Live room and amp room. Local accommodation can be organised, contact for details.

Backyard Recording Studio
West Pen-y-llan, Churchstoke, Powys, SY15 6HT
tel: 01588 620 129
email: those.very.nice.people@backyardstudios.co.uk
web: www.backyardstudios.co.uk
desk: MTA Series 980
rates: Contact for details
info: 3 isolated recording areas available. See website above for full studio tour. Chillout area.

Battery Park
Albany Road, Cardiff, CF24 3RQ
tel: 02920 460 757
email: richard@battery-park.co.uk
contact: Richard Adlam
desk: Soundcraft Ghost
monitors: Event/Korg MS10
info: Battery Park is a Pro Tools studio specialising in pop productions.

The Beehouse
Craignant, Llanfihangel, Llanfyllin, Powys, SY22 5JG
tel: 01691 649 044
email: contact@beehouse.co.uk
web: www.beehouse.co.uk
desk: Yamaha O2R
monitors: Mackie
rates: £25 per hour (+ VAT)
info: Digital recording. Classic and original professional sounds, music production, advanced technical recording spec. Engineer inclusive in rates. Also linked with record label (C'mon Records), equipment hire company (MantraSound), and mastering and duplication services (Mantra CD & Recording). See listings in relevant sections.

Black Sun Mobile Recording
10 Heol Gwrangfryn, Rhigos, Aberdare, CF44 9EF
tel: 01685 812 306
email: blacksunrecording@hotmail.com
contact: Chris
desk: Soundcraft 1682
monitors: Wharfedale
rates: £90 per session (recording), £80 per session (mix down)
info: Mobile recording facility. Call for details of rehearsal space.

Blossom Studio
Station Road, Blaina, Gwent, NP13 3BW
tel: 01495 290 960/07932 377 109
email: noel101082@lycos.co.uk
web: www.blossomstudio.co.uk
contact: Noel Watson
rates: £20/hour, £350/2days
info: Pro Tools HD2 digital recording. Recording and pre-production. 2 day session is usually sufficient to complete a 4 track EP. Previous clients include Goldie Lookin Chain.

Bryn Derwen Studio
Coed-y-Parc, LL56 4YW
tel: 01248 600 234
email: laurie@brynderwen.fsbusiness.co.uk
web: www.brynderwen.co.uk
desk: Soundcraft760 2" 24 Track
monitors: Mackie HR 824/Dynaudio BM15/Yamaha NS10/Urei 809
rates: From £200 per day (non residential)
info: The studio is located in the Snowdonia Mountains. Accommodation available, full board or self catering. See website for a full specification list.

BTM Sound Services
The Band Hall, Newport Road, Bedwas, Caerphilly, Mid Glamorgan, CF83 8BJ
tel: 02920 868 042/07865 062 274
email: btmband@hotmail.com
web: www.btmband.com
contact: Mark Hutcherson
rates: £20 per hour
info: 24 channel Allen & Heath desk, DR16 channel hard disk recorder. The studio is run by musicians.

Cadillac Ranch Recording Studios
Cwmbach, Whitland, SA34 0DT
tel: 01994 484 466
email: cadillacranch@telco4u.net
web: www.nikturner.com
info: Also run 2 record labels (Riddle Records and Nikt Records), publishing company (Hello Qtie), Money Talks Management, Money Talks Agency, and Riddle Hallucinations Video Productions. See entries in relevant sections for further details.

Cardiff Sound Scene
36 Cathays Terrace, Cathays, Cardiff, CF24 4HX
tel: 02920 373 144
email: studio@soundsceneuk.com
web: www.soundsceneuk.com
desk: Seck 1882
monitors: Alesis
rates: £15 per hour
info: See website for full studio spec. Experienced in-house recording, mixing and mastering engineer. Chillout area. Acoustically treated live room. Digital and analogue recording. Cardiff Sound Scene also incorporates rehearsal room and music workshops for young people, see relevant sections for more details. The rehearsal rooms are located within Cathays Community Centre, which once a month holds a live music night featuring 3 or 4 bands - send a demo to the address above.

Dreamworld Studio
Priskilly Fawr, Hayscastle, Haverfordwest, Dyfed, SA62 5QF
tel: 01348 840 186
email: info@dreamworldstudio.co.uk
web: www.dreamworldstudio.co.uk
desk: VTC Audio 24 channel console
monitors: Link
rates: £200 per 8 hourday (+ VAT)
info: Large live room suitable for choirs and orchestras. Accommodation and catering available. Discounts available for block boolings. For details of CD duplication services at Dreamworld Studio see the relevant section.

Faded Lamentable
87 Heathway, Heath, Cardiff, CF14 4JS
tel: 01903 813 171/07731 932 459
email: flbrighton@tiscali.co.uk
rates: £150 per recording, £250 per recording + mastering
info: Mobile recording facilities covering the South Wales and Sussex regions. Can record live gigs and rehearsals. Prices include CD artwork design.

Fflach
Llys-y-Coed, Tenby Road, Cardigan, Dyfed, SA43 3AH
tel: 01239 614 691
email: info@fflach.co.uk
web: www.fflach.co.uk
desk: Yamaha O2R
rates: £200 per day (+ VAT)
info: Full technical specification can be viewed on above website.

Foel Studio
Foel Studio, Llanfair, Caerenoin, Powys, SY21 0DS
tel: 01938 810 758
fax: 01938 810 758
email: foel.studio@dial.pipex.com
web: www.foelstudio.co.uk
contact: Dave Anderson
desk: Trident 80B
monitors: JBL/Yamaha NS10/Genelac
rates: Call for details
info: Please get in touch to discuss rates. 48 track radar digital. Pro Tools HD3 system and Genelic 5.1 surround sound. Self contained accommodation. Fully equipped studio in rural surrounds. Also linked with Demi Monde recording and publishing companies. See listings in relevant sections for further information.

Fried Egg Studios
6 Blandy Terrace, Nantymoel, Bridgend, CF32 7NR
tel: 07970 277 035/01656 841 885
email: chris@friedeggstudios.com
web: www.friedeggstudios.com
contact: Chris Williams
rates: Call for details
info: Digital recording and mastering studio. Fried Egg Studios provide songwriting services for artists across a range of genres. For details of the studio's management company see the relevant section.

Frozen UK
Llanidoles, Powys
email: sjp@frozenuk.com
web: www.frozenuk.com
rates: Call for details
info: Digital editing and mastering, remix service, track arrangement and layout, CD/DAT mastering and vinyl and cassette digital re-mastering. PC music tuition and hardware advice also available. Website design and construction.

Giant Wafer Recording Studios
Tyllwyd, Llanbadarn Fynydd, Llandrindod Wells, Powys, LD1 6YH
tel: 01597 840 287/07712 449 300
email: admin@giantwafer.com
web: www.giantwafer.com
desk: 2 Mackie Digital 8-Busses
monitors: Tannoy DTM 15 Mk II
rates: £20 per hour, £150 per 8 hour day
info: Giant Wafer are undergoing expansion to make the studio residential. Check the website or call for details.

Gold Disc Productions
39 Blaen-Y-Cwm Terrace, Treorci, CF42 5ND
tel: 01443 774 246
email: jon@goldcd.co.uk
web: www.goldcd.co.uk
contact: Jonathan Gregory
desk: Cubase SX
rates: Call for details
info: Set in a village in the mountains of South Wales. Suitable for singer-songwriters. Producers will give input on song development and can provide vocal coaching.

Grassroots
58 Charles Street, Cardiff, CF10 4EG
tel: 02920 255 608/02920 231 700
desk: Pro Tools
rates: £3-£8 per hour
info: Prices vary according to the number of people and instruments being recorded. Ideal demo studio. Grassroots is a community run project for the under 25 year olds. Rehearsal facilities and training courses are also available. See relevant sections for details.

Hot Town Music
Oakfield, 21 Lucas Road, Glais, Swansea, SA7 9EU
tel: 01792 535 256
email: peter@hottownmusic.co.uk
web: www.hottownmsic.co.uk
desk: Soundcraft
monitors: Tannoy
info: Analogue and valve studio specialists. Digital recording also available.

Hunter Music
6 Mansel Street, Swansea, SA1 5SF
tel: 01792 412 762
email: whizzy@whizzysguitaremporium.com
web: www.whizzysguitaremporium.com
desk: Eurodesk MX8000 24/8/2
rates: Negotiable
info: 24 track recording. Rehearsal facilities also available, see relevant section for details.

Immtech
Unit C, Building 8, Curran Road, Butetown, Cardiff, CF10 5DF
tel: 02920 640 500
fax: 02920 640 600
email: immtech@immtech.co.uk
web: www.immtech.co.uk
contact: Paul Bowen
rates: Call for rates
info: Bang in the heart of Cardiff, busy studios fully staffed with engineers.

In Company Multimedia Productions
tel: 01633 881 356
email: info@incompany.co.uk
web: www.incompany.co.uk
contact: Adam Courquin
info: In Company Multimedia Productions write and produce for a wide range of Welsh acts including DV8, Steve Strange, ex-Pop Idol Nikitah, Newport singer-songwriter Kevin Dyer and girl group Dragonheart. They also support new talent by offering a limited number of free Studio sessions, call for details.

John Evans
5 Glanmor Terrace, Penclawdd, Swansea, West Glamorgan, SA4 3YL
tel: 01792 851 738
info: Mobile recording studio and CD duplication.

Kissan Productions
Danycoed, Main Road, Gwaelodygarth, Cardiff, CF15 9HH
tel: 0290 811 730
email: info@kissanproductions.com
web: www.kissanproductions.com
info: Studio consists of 2 rooms, a control room and sound-proof live room. Established customers include Sony Music, Karl Jenkins Music and BBC Radio sessions. Contact for more information.

Le Mons Recording Studio
Unit 18, Albany Trading Estate, Albany Street, Newport, NP20 5NQ
tel: 01633 857 878
email: chris@le-mons.co.uk
web: www.le-mons.co.uk
desk: Allen & Heath GS3V
monitors: Yamaha NS10
rates: £25 per hour, £200 per 10 hour day
info: Run Pro Tools on G5. Established Punk, Rock, Metal and Indie studio.

Livewire Recording
c/o Paul Terry, 3 Llys Emlyn, Towyn, Conwy, LL22 9NX
tel: 07771 924 051
email: livewire_studios@hotmail.com
desk: Studiomaster Classic 8
monitors: JBLs
rates: From £25 per hour
info: 32 track studio on digital format. 2 large recording areas ideal for full live sessions as well as ensemble recordings.

LTS Recording & PA Services
West Wales
tel: 01974 202 759
email: dfereday@ltsstudio.co.uk
web: www.ltsstudio.co.uk
desk: Soundtracs MR Series
monitors: Auratone/Wharfedale/Tannoy
rates: Contact for details

MUSIC SERVICES/RETAIL

Make-Shift Recording Studio
The Post Office, London Road, Trelawnyd, LL18 6DN
tel:	01745 570 000
email:	scottkemix@aol.com
web:	www.makeshiftrecordingstudio.com
contact:	Scott Patterson
desk:	Mackie 24x8x2, 8 bus mixing desk
monitors:	Fostex PM 1s
rates:	£20 per hour, £140 per day
info:	Recording, production and mastering. DJ workshops

(male and female instruction) and music production tuition.

MASE (Music & Sound Experience)
The Old Church Hall, Min y Don Park, Old Colwyn, Conway, LL29 9SD
tel:	01492 517 788/07979 794 782
email:	charles.hildrew@mase.org.uk
web:	www.mase.org.uk
contact:	Charles Hildrew
desk:	Beringer
monitors:	Alesis
rates:	£15 per hour, £100 per 8 hour day (inc. engineer)
info:	Cakewalk, Cubase, T-Rex mastering software and Sony

Sound Forge. Good range of mics. MASE is a Youth Music project
(www.youthmusic.org.uk), however is open to musicians of all ages.
For details of rehearsal facilities at MASE, see the relevant section.

Matrix Studios AV
1 Gerrdi Margaret, The Waterfront, Barry, CF62 5AP
tel:	07817 087 424
email:	info@matrixstudios.com
web:	www.matrixstudios.com
contact:	Steve
monitors:	Mackie HR824
rates:	From £180 per day
info:	In-house engineers, producers and session musicians.

Range of equipment available for hire. Shure and Neumann mics. See
the website above for a full equipment list.

Mighty Atom
1st Floor, Dylan Thomas House, 32 Alexandra Road, Swansea, SA1 5DT
tel:	01792 476 567
email:	studio@mightyatom.co.uk
web:	www.mightyatom.co.uk
desk:	Soundscape Red 24 track/Otari MTR90 2" 24 track
monitors:	ATC 100/Active One/Yamaha NS10
rates:	£300 per day
info:	Extensive range of outboard including Easy Rider

Gemini reverb unit. Backline. For a full equipment list see the website.
Mighty Atom also run a record label, see relevant section for details.

Mirage
105 Springvale Industrial Estate, Cwmbran, Gwent, NP44 5BG
tel:	01633 869 877
email:	mirage4real2004@hotmail.com
contact:	Charlie
desk:	Mackie 1604
monitors:	Yamaha NS10
rates:	£15 per hour
info:	Mirage also comprises a rehearsal room, see relevant

section for details.

Monnow Valley Studio
Old Mill House, Rockfield Road, Monmouth, NP25 5QE
tel:	01600 712 761/07770 988 503
fax:	01600 715 039
email:	enquiries@monnowvalleystudio.com
web:	www.monnowvalleystudio.com
contact:	Jo Hunt
rates:	Call for details
info:	High spec residential studio. Previous clients include

The Coral, Biffy Clyro, Black Sabbath, Portishead and Cradle Of Filth.

musicalsex
Heath, Cardiff, CF14 4LU
email:	ben@musicalsex.com
web:	www.musicalsex.com
contact:	Ben Kolb
rates:	From £50 per demo track
info:	Provide music and audio services including multitrack

acoustic recording, electronic programming, mastering, audio
restoration and audio-post for video and sound design. Personalised pro
demo with multiple track discount, pay for the end product not by the
hour. Contact for further information or quotes.

Newid Studios
Antioch Centre, Copperworks Road, Llanelli, SA15 2NE
tel:	07971 422 024
email:	malowe@btinternet.com
web:	www.newidstudios.net
rates:	£15 per hour
info:	Pro Tools digital studio. Rehearsal facilities and CD

duplication services also available - see the relevant sections for details.

Pathway Studio
59 Canon Lane, Caerwent, Caldicot, Gwent, NP26 4QQ
tel:	01291 425 613
contact:	Mike Scott
desk:	Mackie
monitors:	Yamaha NS10/Vegas
rates:	£25 per hour
info:	Friendly Christian recording studio, although will or

course deal with secular musicians.

Pinewood Audio
4 Pine Gardens, Tranch, Pontypool, NP4 6BS
tel:	01495 752 700
email:	pinewoodaudio@ukonline.co.uk
desk:	Tascam
monitors:	Yamaha NS40
rates:	Call for details
info:	Project studio suited to solo artists and instrumentalists.

Mainly digital. Pinewood Audio also produce backing tracks.

The Pop Factory
Welsh Hills Works, Jenkin Street, Porth, Rhondda, CF39 9PP
tel:	01443 688 500
email:	via website
web:	www.thepopfactory.com
rates:	Call for details
info:	Sound recording and production. The Pop Factory

comprises a number of studio spaces, sound recording facilities, venue,
record label and video production facilities. See relevant sections for
more details.

Promo
Coal Exchange, Mount Stuart Square, Cardiff, CF10 5EB
tel:	02920 462 222
fax:	02920 450 475
email:	info@promo-cymru.org
web:	www.promo-cymru.org
contact:	Marco Gil-Cervantes
info:	For full details on rates and equipment contact Promo

direct as they offer a range of packages for clients. Also provide
training, advice and funding for young people involved in the creative
industries. See listing in Regional Organisations section for details.

Raging Imp Productions
Pontycymer
tel:	01656 871 305/07901 832 206 (text only)
email:	rip@celticrockmusic.com
web:	www.celticrockmusic.com
contact:	Croc Dinearo
rates:	Call for details
info:	Digital and analogue recording, mixing and mastering.

Live Mobile 24 Bit 24 track recording. Session musicians available.
Long history of experiments in strange places. For details of the
company's PA hire and sound production services see the entry for
Alteariamotive Sound System in the Equipment Hire section. Also run a
music retail website for independent, underground music from Wales.
See www.celticrockmusic.com.

Redrock
Unit D3, Britannia Centre For Enterprise, Pengam Road, Pengam,
Blackwood, Gwent, NP12 3SP
tel:	01443 879 222
email:	info@redrockstudios.co.uk
web:	www.redrockstudios.co.uk
desk:	Roland VS2480
monitors:	Alesis
rates:	£120 per day for bands, £100 per day for solo artists
info:	Half days are available at half rates (days run from 10am

to 6pm). For details of rehearsal facilities provided by RedRock, see the
relevant section.

Rockliffe Recording Studio
Bryncliffe Lodge, Bryn y Bia Road, Llandudno, Gwynedd, LL30 3AS
tel:	01492 860 107
contact:	Simon
desk:	32 channel Tascam
monitors:	JBL
rates:	From £12 per hour
info:	Studio runs Cubase VST. Specialise in songwriting and

production.

Sain (Recordiau) Cyf
Canolfan Sain, Llandwrog, Caernarfon, Gwynedd, LL54 5TG
tel:	01286 831 111
fax:	01286 831 497
email:	ellen@sainwales.com
web:	www.sainwales.com
desk:	56 channel AMEK Rembrandt
monitors:	ATC SCM 100A/Genelec 1029/Auratone/Yamaha NS10
info:	Wide range of microphones and instruments.

Recording packages including duplication, cover design and printing
and copyright clearing available, see website for full details. If your
compositions are performed on TV or radio you can register them with
Sain and they will collect and any payments due on your behalf.

Shabbey Road Studios
Caerfilly Business Park, Van Road, Caerphilly, CF83 3ED
tel: 02920 862 164
email: enquiry@shabbeyroad.com
web: www.shabbeyroad.com
desk: Soundcraft Delta
monitors: Tannoy/Yamaha/Behringer Truth
rates: £30 per hour
info: Shabbey Road has 2 separate studio spaces, both with large recording rooms. 96 track digital recording (Logic Platinum and Pro Tools 001). Mastering to all digital formats.

Simply Sound Promotions Ltd.
64 Idwal, Acrefair, Wrexham, LL14 3HA
tel: 01978 810 549
email: ssp@promotions9908.freeserve.co.uk
web: www.simplysound.co.uk
rates: From £35-£50 per recorded track
info: Digital recording studio. Prices are charged per recorded track rather than per hour. Simple Sound Promotions also produce MIDI files and backing tracks, see the above website for details.

Sonic-One Studio
The Pop Works, Maes Road, Llangennech, SA14 8UG
tel: 01554 890 834
email: tim@sonic-one.co.uk
web: www.sonic-one.co.uk
contact: Tim
desk: SSL
monitors: Tannoy/Quested
rates: £300 per day
info: Big live room. Chill out room which doubles as a kitchen, TV with games console and PC with internet for bands to use. Situated close to J48 of the M4.

Soundworks
1-2 Mount Stuart Square, Cardiff, CF10 5EE
tel: 02920 331 010
email: mail@soundworks.co.uk
web: www.soundworks.co.uk
info: Soundworks comprises 5 studios. See website for individual technical specs. Specialist high-end sound design, recording and post production.

Steer Multimedia Studio
Tairgwaith, Ammanford, Dyfed, SA18 1UP
tel: 01269 823 815
email: info@steerstudios.net
web: www.steerstudios.net
desk: Soundtracs
monitors: Mackie/Yamaha
rates: £20 per hour
info: Steer Studios run a 32 channel Sountracs desk into a Mackie hard disc recorder and a Pro Tools system. Sound engineering tuition available. For details of the studio's rehearsal facilities see the relevant section.

Stir Studio
6 Williams Court, Cardiff, CF10 5DQ
tel: 02920 231 026
email: info@stir-recording.com
web: www.stir-recording.com
contact: Paul
desk: Trident TSM 40/Otari MTR 90
monitors: Westlake
rates: From £20 per hour
info: The vintage Trident mixing console in Stir Studio has been used to record albums by Oasis, Queen, The Charlatans and the Stone Roses, amongst others.

Stiwdio Aran
PO Box 83, Caernarfon, LL54 7ZS
tel: 01286 831 346
email: post@emyrrhys.com
web: www.emyrrhys.com
contact: Emyr Rhys
desk: Tascam DM24
monitors: HHB Circle A
rates: Call for details
info: Live room, kitchen, free parking. Village based recording studios. Happy to record all genres of music.

Stiwdio Eglwys
48 Brynffynnon Road, Y-Felinheli, LL56 4SJ
tel: 01248 671 663
email: george@stiwdioeglwys.fsnet.co.uk
web: www.stiwdioeglwys.co.uk
rates: Call for details
info: Stiwdio Eglwys is a production studio. Production to CD or DAT master. Artwork and packaging. Audio and video production training. Also run 2 record labels (Recordiau Menai Records and JUDmusic Records) and a publishing company (JUDmusic publishing), see relevant sections for more details.

Stiwdio Pandy
Pandy Mill, Penraeth, Ynts Mons, LL75 8BJ
tel: 01248 450 007
email: stiwdiopandy@btopenworld.com
monitors: Tannoy/ADI
rates: Call for details
info: 40 channel desk, Digital Performer, small live room. Also run a publishing company (Cyhoeddiadau Pandy Publishing) and a record label (Recordiau Awen Records), see relevant sections for details.

Street Level
Cardiff
tel: 07814 584 260
desk: Full Pro Tools System
rates: £140 per day
info: Mobile phone message indicates rates and equipment, if interested leave a message.

Street Youth Project
The Wellfare Hall, Wind Street, Ammanford, Cardiff, SA18 3DN
tel: 01269 596 956
email: street.project@btinternet.com
web: www.streetyouthproject.co.uk
contact: Barry Roberts
info: Contact Barry for full details. Also see listing in Training and Tuition section.

Strongbox
87 Glebe Street, Penarth, CF64 1EF
tel: 02920 650 690
email: studio@strongbox.uk.com
web: www.strongbox.uk.com
contact: Nick
rates: £240 per day (+ VAT)
info: Hard disk recording with plenty outboard. Large collection of classic mics. Refreshments available. Contact for further information regarding rates for block bookings.

Studio Blaen-y Cae
Blaen Y Cae, Dolbenmaen, Garndolbenmaen, Gwynedd, LL51 9UJ
tel: 01766 530 629
email: blaencae@yahoo.com
desk: Yamaha 02R
monitors: Yamaha NS10/Alessi
rates: varialble

Studio Juno
57 Hollybush Road, Cardiff, CF23 6TZ
tel: 07709 338 033
contact: Zand
desk: Roland VS2480
rates: From £79 per demo
info: The studio's large live room is available as a rehearsal space when the recording facilities are not in use.

Sunshine Studios
Llantrisant, Mid Glamorgan, Cardiff
tel: 07876 340 172
email: sunshine_studio@hotmail.com
web: www.freewebs.com/sunshinestudio
contact: Harry Grey
desk: Behringer Eurodesk MX8000A 48 input analogue console
monitors: 'Classic' Goodmans Havant SL/Soundcraft Spirit Absolute 2
rates: Call for details
info: Recording and production studio. Wide range of professional microphones from companies such as Shure, Rhode and Sennheiser, variety of outboard and effects. See website for full spec. Video production also available, see relevant section for details.

Sylem
Coed- y-Celyn, Betws-y Coed, Conwy, LL24 0SH
tel: 01690 710 652
email: info@sylem.com
web: www.sylem.com
contact: Paul or Andrea
desk: Behringer MX 8000
monitors: Spirit Absolute 2
rates: £140 per 8 hour day
info: See the website above for full equipment list. Mastering facilities also available. Previous clients include Super Furry Animals and Grandaddy.

Transpose Music Rooms
Albany Trading Estate, Newport, NP20 5NQ
tel: 01633 854 100
email: d.mccalden@ntlworld.com
info: Digital recording studio. Tranpose Music Rooms can also provide rehearsal facilities, see relevant section for more details.

Twin Peaks Music
Ty Neuadd, Torpantua, Methyr Tydfil, CF48 2UT
email: twinpeaksstudio@aol.com
web: www.twinpeaksstudio.com
contact: Adele
desk: Roland VM7200s/VC7200
monitors: Mackie 824/Urei 813/Yamaha NS10/Genelec
rates: Negotiable
info: Roland 7200 and Soundscape Red System. Twin Peaks Studio is the highest fully residential studio in the British Isles (located at an altitude of 2,500 feet).

Warwick Hall of Sound
Warwick Hall, Banastre Avenue, Cardiff, CF14 3NR
tel: 02920 694 455
email: whos@ffvinyl.com
web: www.warwickhall.co.uk
info: Pro Tools studio run with G5 Mac. 24 channel mixing desk. Good range of mics. Large live room (6m x 10m) and separate vocal booth. The live room is available for hire as a showcase venue. For details of the Warwick Hall of Sound rehearsal facilities and associated record label, FFVinyl, see the relevant sections.

Welsh Media Music
Gorwelion, Llanfynydd, Carmarthen
tel: 01558 668 525
info: Project studio. Call for more details.

Winderton Studio & Sound
Winderton Drive, New Hedges, Tenby, Pembrokeshire
tel: 01834 842 738
email: windertonstudio@hotmail.com
web: www.windertonstudio.com
contact: Bruce Campbell
desk: 32 channel Mackie
monitors: KRK
rates: £20 per hour
info: Use 24 track A-DAT for live recording. Logic Audio. Can also provide PA hire and rehearsal, see equipment hire and rehearsal studio listings for more information.

MUSIC SERVICES/RETAIL

3.15 REHEARSAL ROOMS

EAST of ENGLAND 485 GREATER LONDON 486 MIDLANDS 495 NORTHEAST 499 NORTHWEST 500
SOUTHEAST 505 SOUTHWEST 510 YORKSHIRE 511 NORTHERN IRELAND 514 SCOTLAND 515 WALES 518

EAST of ENGLAND

Band Practice Rooms
Station Yard, Wilbraham Road, Fulbourn, Cambridge, CB1 5ET
tel:	01223 882 207
email:	info@warehousetv.tv
web:	www.warehousetv.tv
contact:	Paul
rates:	Call for info
rooms:	2
hours:	Day, evening and weekends
secure storage:	No
equipment:	PA
info:	Large, warm rooms that provide a good sound.

Earth
9 Caston Industrial Estate, Salhouse Road, Norwich, NR7 9AQ
tel:	07759 331 506
web:	www.earthstudios.co.uk
rates:	From £15 for 3 hours
rooms:	6
hours:	11am-Midnight
secure storage:	No
equipment:	Drum kit, PA, backline incuded
info:	Acoustically designed and expertly sound-proofed. All rooms are ventilated and open 7 days a week.

Flightpath Studios
2 Quy Water Cottages, Newmarket Road, Teversham, Cambridge, Cambridgeshire, CB1 5AT
tel:	01223 295 213
contact:	Bruce
rates:	£6 per hour
rooms:	1
hours:	6 pm-10:30pm and weekends
secure storage:	Yes
equipment:	PA and 2 microphones.

The Garage
14 Chapel Field North, Norwich, Norfolk, NR2 1NY
tel:	01603 283 382
email:	info@thegarage.org.uk
web:	www.thegarage.org.uk
rates:	Please call for details
rooms:	2
hours:	8:30am-10pm
secure storage:	Yes
equip. for hire:	Digital piano.
info:	Rehersal space available as well as a fully equipped, high spec theatre space.

The Lock Up
Cave Industrial Estate, Fen Road, Cambridge, CB4 1UN
tel:	01223 420 244
email:	help@thelockup.org or booking@thelockup.org
web:	www.thelockup.org
contact:	Matt James
rates:	£4.50-£6.50 per hour
rooms:	4
hours:	6pm-12am (Mon-Thurs), 6pm-10pm (Fri), 6pm-10pm (Sat & Sun)
secure storage:	Yes
equipment:	PA, mics, bass and guitar amps
equip. for hire:	PA, mics, guitar and bass amps, drum kit
info:	Can also provide in-house drum tuition, CD duplication and offer outside equipment hire for gigs. Contact for further details.

Meadowside Studios
Leverington Common, Wisbech, Cambridgeshire, PE13 5JH
tel:	0845 090 0154
email:	enquiries@meadowsidestudios.co.uk
web:	www.meadowsidestudios.co.uk
rates:	£10 per hour
secure storage:	Yes
info:	Rehearsal space available. Meadowside also have recording and CD duplication facilities. See listings in relevant sections for further details.

Plug Studios
Units 9-13, The Old Fishmarket, Mountergate, Norwich, NR1 1PZ
tel:	01603 219 337/07946 649 859
email:	plugstudios@aol.com
web:	www.plugstudios.co.uk
contact:	Errol Watson
rates:	£10 for 3 hours
rooms:	5
secure storage:	No
equipment:	PA, bass amp
equip. for hire:	Guitar amps, drum kit
info:	Plug Studios are part of E.L.K. Promotions. The rehearsal room offers secure and insured storage for instruments. There is also a recording studio. See relevant entry for details.

The Rehearsal Rooms
4 St. Andrew's Street South, Bury St. Edmunds, Suffolk, IP33 3PH
tel:	01284 700 353
email:	neil@therehearsalrooms.co.uk
web:	www.therehearsalrooms.co.uk
contact:	Neil Attridge
rates:	£5 per hour
rooms:	2
hours:	10am-11pm, 7 days per week
secure storage:	No
equipment:	PA, mics, stands
equip. for hire:	Drum kit, bass and guitar amps
info:	Includes lounge and chillout room. Also provides recording studio. See relevant section for details.

Simply Studios
23 Roman Way, Small Business Park, London Road, Godmanchester, Cambridgeshire, PE26 2QQ
tel:	01480 456 000
email:	info@simply-studios.com
web:	www.simply-studios.com
contact:	Charley
rates:	£10 per hour
rooms:	1
hours:	6pm-12am
secure storage:	No
equipment:	Drums, PA
info:	Also have a recording studio. See relevant entry for details.

The Soundhouse
Unit 6, Capital Trading Estate, Whapload Road, Lowestoft, NR32 1TY
tel:	01502 513 050
rates:	£5 per hour
rooms:	3
hours:	Flexible
secure storage:	No
equipment:	PA, mics
equip. for hire:	Drum kit, amps, other items available
info:	Equipment is available to hire at £5 per session, regardless of the length of that session. Recording facilities available. See relevant section for more details.

Studio Rooms

28 Upland Industrial Estate, Sawtry Way, Wyton, Huntingdon, Cambridgeshire, PE28 2DY

tel:	01480 450 355
email:	info@studio-rooms.com
web:	www.studio-rooms.com
rates:	From £20 for 4 hours
rooms:	3
secure storage:	No
equipment:	PA, mics, mic stands, basic drum kit
info:	Also run a band agency. Ask at the studio for details.

GREATER LONDON

Abbey Music Studios

Lodge Hill, Abbeywood, London, SE2 0AY

tel:	020 8312 4916
email:	info@abbeymusicstudios.co.uk
web:	www.abbeymusicstudios.co.uk
rates:	£28-£40 depending on room size
rooms:	3
hours:	Contact for details
secure storage:	Yes
equipment:	PA, mics, stands
equip. for hire:	Full backline for £8
info:	Spacious rooms with quality equipment

available. Largest room contains sizeable PA system and stage. Bookings made in 4 hour slots. Refreshments available. Free on-site parking. Recording facilities and equipment hire service available. See listings in relevant sections for details.

Airwave Studios

212 Kilburn High Road, London, NW6 4JH

tel:	020 7624 6448
contact:	John Cooper
rates:	Call for details
rooms:	1
hours:	Call for details
secure storage:	Yes
equipment:	Full backline
equip. for hire:	Additional instruments on request

Alaska Street Studios

127-129 Alaska Street, Waterloo, London, SW9 9SL

tel:	020 7928 7440
email:	alaska01@btclick.co.uk
web:	www.alaskastudio.co.uk
contact:	Bev Lodge
rates:	From £6 per hour
rooms:	3
hours:	10am to 11pm, 7 days a week
secure storage:	No
equipment:	Marshall and H&H guitar amps, bass amps, SM58 mics
equip. for hire:	Drumkit
info:	Alaska Street Studios, opened in 1977, comprises

3 rehearsal rooms and a recording studio. For more details see website and Recording Studio section.

Alienistic Studios

Arch 11, Gales Gardens, Bethnal Green, London, E2 0EJ

tel:	07931 834 547
email:	vanderhorne@yahoo.co.uk
rates:	£40 for 4 hours
rooms:	3
hours:	12pm-12pm, 7 days a week
secure storage:	No
equipment:	Backline, mics
info:	Rock rehearsal studios. Lounge area and bar.

Antenna Studios

Bowyers Yard, Haynes Lane, Crystal Palace, London, SE19 3AN

tel:	020 8653 5200
fax:	020 8653 5327
email:	info@antennastudios.co.uk
web:	www.antennastudios.co.uk
rates:	£10 (10am-7pm weekdays), £12 (evenings and weekends)
rooms:	1
hours:	24 hours, 7 days a week
secure storage:	No
equipment:	Full backline, PA
info:	Indoor and outdoor chillout areas. Antenna also

have recording facilities, dance studio, guitar workshop, graphics studio for merchandise design, printing services and CD duplication. See entries in relevant sections for further information. Dance studio also available, useful for acoustic rehearsals.

Arc Sound Studio

Lower Ground Floor, 443 New Cross Road, London, SE14 6TA

tel:	020 8691 8161
email:	info@arcsound.co.uk
web:	www.arcsound.co.uk
rates:	Contact for details
rooms:	1
hours:	10am - 11pm
secure storage:	Yes
equipment:	Basic 5 piece drum kit, guitar amp, bass amp
equip. for hire:	Selection of amps, drumkits, cymbals, keyboards, guitars and basses
info:	Opening times can be flexible. Rate vary

depending on the length of session. See website or enquire for details. Arc Sound also run a recording studio and equipment hire service. Refer to relevant sections for further details.

Atomic Studios

Block B, Towerbridge Business Complex, 100 Clements Road, London, SE16 4DG

tel:	020 7237 2233
email:	atomic-rob@cwcom.net
web:	www.atomicstudios.co.uk
rates:	Contact Rob for details
rooms:	27
hours:	24 hours
secure storage:	No
info:	Atomic Studios offers soundproof units for let.

Rooms suitable for rehearsals, programming suites, recording studios and general workspace. Flexible, long or short term lets from £120 per week. Previous clients have included Dizzee Rascal, Moloko, The Cure and Will Young. Contact Rob for further details.

Audio Underground

12 Northwold Road, London, N16 7HR

tel:	020 7241 1818
web:	www.audiounderground.co.uk
rates:	£6-£15 per hour
rooms:	4
hours:	Flexible
secure storage:	No
equipment:	Range of equipment and instruments
equip. for hire:	Range of equipment and instruments
info:	Equipment and instruments are available either

on a hire basis, or included in rates. Also sell musical accessories on-site. Room available for bands to arrange private showcases with industry contacts. Chillout area. Audio Underground also has recording facilities, see relevant section for details. Also provides digital video facilities.

Backstreet Studios

313 Holloway Road, Islington, London, N7 9SU
tel:	020 7609 1313
fax:	020 7609 5229
email:	info@backstreet.co.uk
web:	www.backstreet.co.uk
rates:	See website for details
rooms:	8
hours:	10am-11pm (weekdays & Sun), 10am-6:30pm (Sat)
secure storage:	No
equipment:	PA, mics, leads
equip. for hire:	Drumkit, bass amps, guitar amps, keyboards and guitars
info:	Lounge area with pool table and snack bar.

Backstreet also has a music shop (products available online as well), and car parking facilities.

Bally Studios

16-18 Millmead Business Centre, Millmead Road, Tottenham Hale, London, N17 9QU
tel:	020 8808 0472
email:	info@ballystudios.co.uk
web:	www.ballystudios.co.uk
contact:	Fran Agati
rates:	£40-£45 for 4 hours
rooms:	3
hours:	24 hours a day, 7 days a week
secure storage:	No
equipment:	PA, mics, drum kits, amps
equip. for hire:	Amps, drum kits
info:	Tea, coffee and snacks available on-site. Also

provide tuition in guitar, bass guitar, keyboards, sight reading and audio engineering. See website for details. Linked with Sync City, who run a recording studio. See relevant section for further information.

The Barns

101 Walm Lane, London, NW2 4QG
tel:	020 8208 1709
email:	collaborart@mac.com
web:	www.collaborart.co.uk
contact:	Juliet Hughes-Rees
rates:	Contact for details
rooms:	4
secure storage:	Yes
info:	Main space (Hedley's Hay) including Bluthner

Grand piano. This barn also has a kitchen and bathroom, plus sleeping for 2 people. Excellent acoustics and perfect for recording, although bands would have to bring their own equipment. The second barn, The Cowshed, has accommodation for 6 people with 2 bathrooms and kitchens plus 2-3 further rehearsal spaces. Accommodation is all self-catering. Prices vary depending on requirements, enquire for details. The Barns have been created to provide for people wishing to run courses, record and rehearse. It is also available as a showcase venue. Good transport links with the city.

BonaFideStudio

Burbage House, 83-85 Curtain Road, London, EC2A 3BS
tel:	020 7684 5350/020 7684 5351
email:	home@bonafidestudio.com
web:	www.bonafidestudio.co.uk
rates:	From £5 per hour
rooms:	3
hours:	24 hours, 7 days a week
secure storage:	No
equipment:	Full backline
equip. for hire:	Guitars, keyboards, amps and additional equipment
info:	Piano room also available for hire. Kitchen

facilities with free tea and coffee. BonaFideStudio also run recording studio. Refer to relevant section for further details.

Breakfast Studios

Arches 20 & 21, Grant Road, Clapham Junction, London, SW11 2NU
tel:	07931 531 851
email:	contact@breakfaststudios.co.uk
web:	www.breakfaststudios.co.uk
rates:	From £10 per hour
rooms:	2
hours:	Flexible
secure storage:	No
equipment:	Full backline
equip. for hire:	PA for use out of studio
info:	One rehearsal room is equipped with a piano

which is included in the rate. Parking facilities. Breakfast Studios also have recording and equipment hire services. See entries in relevant sections for further details.

Bush Studios

151 MacFarlane Road Arches, Shepherds Bush, London, W12 7LA
tel:	020 8740 1740
fax:	020 8740 1740
email:	bushstudios@btconnect.com
web:	www.bushstudios.co.uk
rates:	From £8 per hour or £220 per day
rooms:	5
hours:	10am-12am, 7 days a week
secure storage:	No
equipment:	Guitar amps, bass amps, PA, mics
equip. for hire:	Drum kits available at £2 per hour. Enquire about other instruments.
info:	All studios are air-conditioned. Hot drinks

available. Free parking. Bush Studios also run recording facility. See entry in relevant section for further details.

Cybersound Studios

Block C, Units C102, Faircharm Trading Estate, 8-12 Creekside, London, SE8 3DX
tel:	020 8694 9484
fax:	020 8694 9466
email:	studio@cyber-sound.co.uk
web:	www.cyber-sound.co.uk
rates:	Call for details
rooms:	5
hours:	10am-11pm, 7 days a week
secure storage:	No
equipment:	Mics
equip. for hire:	Amps, backline
info:	Rates vary depending on room size and any

offers running. Cybersound also have a recording studio. See entry in Recording Studios section for details.

D Suite

18 French Place, Whitechapel, London
tel:	020 7729 2916
secure storage:	Yes
info:	D Suite can only accommodate unplugged

musicians.

Deep See Studios

Dalston, E8
tel:	07739 384 688
email:	deepsee@ilove.screaming.net
web:	www.plummusic.com
contact:	Milan
rates:	£30 for 4 hours
rooms:	1
hours:	7pm-11pm Mon - Fri, also open weekends
secure storage:	Yes
equipment:	Full backline, PA
info:	Chillout area with internet access and tea and

coffee making facilities. Deep See Studios also have recording service for demos.

The Dolls House Studio

24 Bell Lane, Hendon, London, NW4 2AD
tel:	020 8732 8511/07976 371 944
email:	bongojoe50@hotmail.com
web:	www.dollshousestudio.co.uk
contact:	Joe, Graham
rates:	Call for details
rooms:	1
hours:	24 hours, 7 days a week
secure storage:	Yes
equipment:	PA, mics, guitar and bass amps, drum kit
info:	Dollshouse Studio also have recording facilities

and offer tuition. See entries in relevant sections for information.

Faraday Studios

Unit 61B, Westminster Industrial Estate, Faraday Way, London, SE18 5TR
tel:	020 8855 6333
email:	info@faradaystudios.co.uk
web:	www.faradaystudios.co.uk
contact:	Paul Castle
rates:	£10 per hour
rooms:	3
hours:	24 hours, 7 days a week
secure storage:	No
equipment:	Full backline
info:	Recording facilities available. See listing in

relevant sections for further details. Also have in-house production and record label. Contact Paul for information.

Farm Factory Studios
Unit 5, Woodfield Road, Welwyn Garden City, Hertfordshire, AL7 1JQ

tel:	01707 392 030
email:	info@farmfactorystudios.com
web:	www.farmfactorystudios.com
rooms:	6
hours:	7 days a week
secure storage:	Yes
equipment:	Powered vocal mixer PA, 2 cabs and stands, mic stands, Shure mics
equip. for hire:	Drum kits, guitar combos, guitar heads and cabs, Ampeg bass rigs
info:	Small locked storage area, left at the owner's

risk. Drinks and snacks available. Equipment shop selling guitars, equipment and accessories. Front door load in with no stairs or awkward obstacles. For details of recording facilities, see entry for City Studios in relevant section.

Fortress Studios
34-38 Provost Street, London, N1 7NG

tel:	020 7251 6200
email:	info@fortressstudios.co.uk
web:	www.fortressstudios.co.uk
rates:	Contact for details
rooms:	2
hours:	10am-11pm, 7 days a week
secure storage:	No
info:	Newly constructed rehearsal rooms. Contact for

information about rates and equipment available. Fortress also have recording facilities and 12 writing suites available for long term let from £500 per month including VAT. Secure storage is accessible 24 hours a day.

Gracelands Rehearsal Studio
East Acton Lane, East Acton, London, W3 7HD

tel:	020 8740 8922
fax:	020 8740 8922
email:	paul@gracelandsstudios.co.uk
web:	www.gracelandsstudios.co.uk
rates:	£5-£8 per hour (depending on studio)
rooms:	3
hours:	11am-11pm Monday-Friday, 11am-6pm Saturday, 12pm-11pm Sunday
secure storage:	Yes
equipment:	Backline
info:	Comfortable rehearsal rooms. Any additional

equipment provided is free of charge. Kitchen facilities with free tea and coffee.

The Grove Music Studios
10 Latimer Industrial Estate, Latimer Road, London, W10 6RQ

tel:	020 8960 9601
email:	info@musicspace.co.uk
web:	www.musicspace.co.uk
rates:	Call for details
rooms:	3
hours:	10am-12pm
secure storage:	No
equip. for hire:	Backline, PA

Henry Wood Hall
Trinity Church Square, London, SE1 4HU

tel:	020 7403 0118
fax:	020 7378 8294
email:	bookings@hwh.co.uk
web:	www.hwh.co.uk
contact:	Andrew Stevens, Charles Strickland
rates:	£540 for 3 hours or £1300 per day
rooms:	1
hours:	9am-11pm
secure storage:	No
equipment:	Steinway D grand piano
info:	Elegant and large space suitable for rehearsal and

recording. Bands will need to supply the recording equipment. Often used to record orchestras, but this is not a policy.

Husky Music Services
29a Amelia Street, London, SE17 3PY

tel:	020 7701 8003
fax:	020 7701 8003
email:	husky.studios@virgin.net
web:	www.huskystudios.com
rates:	£8-£16 per hour
rooms:	7
hours:	10am-11pm Monday-Friday, 10am-7pm Saturday, 10am-9pm Sunday
secure storage:	No
equipment:	All rooms contain good quality PA
equip. for hire:	Full backline
info:	Dance and music rehearsal studios. 6 large

rooms with pine floors, mirrors and air conditioning. Smaller drum/vocal studio also available. Chillout area with food served.

IMT Space
Unit 2, 210 Cambridge Heath Road, London, E2 9NQ

tel:	020 8980 5475
email:	space@imagemusictext.com
web:	www.imagemusictext.com
contact:	Gemma Wilks
secure storage:	Yes
info:	Space available suitable for rehearsals or

photographic shoots. Contact Gemma for further details.

Islington Arts Factory
2 Parkhurst Road, Holloway, London, N7 0SF

tel:	020 7607 0561
fax:	020 7700 7229
email:	iaf@islingtonartsfactory.fsnet.co.uk
web:	www.islingtonartsfactory.org.uk
rates:	From £4.50 per hour
rooms:	2
hours:	10am-9:30pm (Mon-Fri), 10am-7pm (Fri), 2pm-5:30pm (Sat), 11am-5:30pm (Sun)
secure storage:	Yes
equipment:	Bass and guitar amps, mics, PA, drum kit, piano
equip. for hire:	Cymbals, additional mics, keyboard. Extra equipment costs £5 per item per session
info:	One of the rooms accommodates up to 4 people,

the other up to 6.

Jam Space Studio Ltd.
Creekmouth Industrial Estate, 57 River Road, Barking, Essex, IG11 0DA

tel:	020 8507 2226
rates:	£35 for 4 hours
rooms:	3
hours:	Evenings and weekends only
secure storage:	Yes
equipment:	PA, drums, backline

John Henry's
16-24 Brewery Road, London, N7 9NH

tel:	020 7609 9181
fax:	020 7700 7040
email:	andrew@johnhenrys.com
web:	www.johnhenrys.com
contact:	Andrea Westwood
rates:	Contact for details
rooms:	6
hours:	10am-10pm, 7 days a week
secure storage:	No
equipment:	Full backline
info:	Full audio equipment and backline hire also

available. See listing in relevant section for details.

The Joint
1-6 Field Street, London, WC1X 9DG

tel:	020 7833 3375
email:	info@thejoint.org.uk
web:	www.thejoint.org.uk
rates:	£10-£16 per hour
rooms:	5
hours:	10am-11pm (Sun-Fri), 10am-8pm (Sat)
secure storage:	No
equipment:	PA, mics
equip. for hire:	Backline
info:	Acoustically designed rooms with both monitor

mix and front of house. All rooms are air-conditioned and have natural daylight. Full wheelchair access. Tuck shop on-site.

Karma Studios Ltd.
7a Bouverie Mews, London, N16 0AE

tel:	020 8809 4200
web:	www.karman16.co.uk
rates:	£10 per hour
rooms:	2
hours:	12pm-12:30am, 7 days a week
secure storage:	No
equipment:	Backline, PA, mics
equip. for hire:	Cymbals and extra amps available at £1 each per hour
info:	Both rooms air conditioned. Sessions run from

12pm-3pm, 3pm-6pm, 6.30pm-9.30pm, and 9.30pm-12:30am. Chillout area with free tea and coffee.

Leisure Lounge Studios
Studio 2, 3rd Floor, Chocolate Factory 2, 4 Coburg Road, Wood Green, London, N22 6UJ

tel:	020 8829 8981/07929 519 910
email:	info@leisureloungestudios.co.uk
web:	www.leisureloungestudios.co.uk
contact:	Stuart Maxwell
rates:	£10 per hour, £30 for 4 hours
rooms:	2
hours:	24 hours, 7 days a week
secure storage:	No
equipment:	PA, mics
equip. for hire:	Guitars, keyboards, bass, percussion, Hammond organ, guitar and bass amps, drums, speaker cabs
info:	Maximum booking slot of 20 hours per day.

Large lounge area with tea and coffee making facilities, as well as microwave, fridge, television, Playstation, access to broadband internet and a piano. Leisure Lounge also have a recording studio. Refer to entry in relevant section for details.

Live Wire
386 Streatham High Road, London, SW16 6HT

tel:	020 8835 9913
rates:	From £25 for 4 hours
rooms:	3
secure storage:	Yes
equipment:	Backline, PA, drum kit
equip. for hire:	Cymbals, cymbal stands and extra mics
info:	Sessions are cheapest earlier in the day, getting

more expensive as the afternoon and evening progresses.

Loz Vegas Studios
Unit 39, Silicone Business Centre, 28 Wadsworth Road, Perivale, Middlesex, UB6 7JZ

tel:	020 8998 9122
fax:	020 8991 2661
email:	loz@vegassoundhouse.com or matt@vegasvegasmusic.co.uk
web:	www.lozvegasmusic.co.uk
contact:	Matt
rates:	Monday - Friday, 11am - 6pm, £30 for a 7 hour session. Weekends and evenings £8-£9/hour
rooms:	3
hours:	11am-12:15am (Sun-Fri), 11am-9pm (Sat)
secure storage:	No
equipment:	Full backline, PA
info:	Free tea and coffee. Loz Vegas also run recording

studio under the same name, equipment hire service and music shop 'Vegas Sound House', promotions and booking agency 'Music Scene UK', 'Music Providers' management, 'Some Think Media' media design company, as well as running the Drum Academy. See entries in relevant sections for further information.

Maximum Music
Bow Business Centre, Unit B4B, 153-159 Bow Road, London, E3 2SE

tel:	07958 141 439
email:	maxmusic@virgin.net
contact:	Mr A. Simons
rates:	£15 per hour
rooms:	2
hours:	24 hours, 7 days a week
secure storage:	Yes
equipment:	PA, 2 mics, drum kit
equip. for hire:	Backline
info:	Maximum Music also has recording facilities. See

entry in relevant section for further details.

Middle Eight Rehearsal Studios
Unit 17, The IO Centre, 59-71 River Road, Barking, Essex, IG11 0DR

tel:	020 8507 3488
email:	info@middleeightstudios.co.uk
web:	www.middleeightstudios.co.uk
contact:	Elliot Brown
rates:	£30 for 4 hours
rooms:	8
hours:	11am-11pm, 7 days a week
secure storage:	Yes
equipment:	PA, mics
equip. for hire:	See website for equipment list and rates
info:	All rooms are air-conditioned and heated.

Instrument shop on-site.

Mill Hill Music Complex
Bunns Lane Works, Bunns Lane, Mill Hill, London, NW7 2AJ

tel:	020 8906 9991
email:	enquiries@millhillmusic.co.uk
web:	www.millhillmusic.co.uk
rates:	From £3.50 per hour
rooms:	12
hours:	11am-11pm (Sun-Fri), 11am-6pm (Sat)
secure storage:	No
equipment:	All rooms fully equipped
equip. for hire:	Additional instruments and amps
info:	Mill Hill Music Complex also has recording

facilities and an instrument shop. See entries in relevant sections for details.

The Moat
13 Gainsborough Road, London, W4 1NJ

tel:	020 7978 8480
email:	info@themoat.demon.co.uk
web:	www.themoat.demon.co.uk
rates:	£35 for 4 hours
hours:	12pm-6pm (Mon-Fri)
secure storage:	Yes
info:	Powerful, ceiling-suspended PA systems

delivering clean sound are included in the rates. Drum kits and backline are available at very reasonable rates.

Modernfidelity
The Decam Building, Taggs Boatyard, 44 Summer Road, Thames Ditton, KT7 0QQ

tel:	07817 049 583
email:	info@modernfidelity.co.uk
web:	www.modernfidelity.co.uk
contact:	Mark Rushton
rates:	Call for details
rooms:	2
hours:	24 hours, 7 days a week
secure storage:	Yes
equipment:	Drumkit, PA
info:	Recently moved to new premises. Modernfidelity

also offer recording services. See entry in relevant section for details.

The Music Room
116-118 New Cross Road, London, SE14 5BA

tel:	020 7252 8271
fax:	020 7252 8252
email:	sales@musicroomsolutions.com
web:	www.musicroomsolutions.com
rates:	Refer to website or contact for details
rooms:	5
hours:	10am-11pm (Mon-Fri), 10am-6pm (Sat & Sun)
secure storage:	Yes
equipment:	PA, mics
equip. for hire:	Drum kit available at £10 per session. Backline at £5 per item
info:	Large rooms with lots of natural light. Rates

vary depending on size of room and time of session. Chillout area with free tea and coffee. Garden area. The Music Room also offer sound equipment hire. See relevant section for details.

The Music Studios
29 Marylebone Lane, London, W1U 2NQ

tel:	020 7486 0025
fax:	020 7935 8454
rates:	From £9.50 per hour
rooms:	7
hours:	12pm-8.30pm (Mon), 10am-8.30pm (Tues-Fri), 10am-5.30pm (Sat)
secure storage:	Yes
equipment:	Grand piano
info:	Strictly acoustic rehearsal studios. Closed

Sundays and bank holidays. Advance booking advised as sessions are filled quickly.

OTR Studios Ltd.
The Basement, 143 Mare Street, Hackney, London, E8 3RH

tel:	020 8985 9880
fax:	020 8986 9575
web:	www.otrstudios.co.uk
rates:	£27-£47 for 4 hours
rooms:	4
hours:	12pm-12am (Mon-Fri), 12pm-8.30pm (Sat), 10am-11pm (Sun)
secure storage:	Yes
equipment:	PA
equip. for hire:	Backline
info:	Can be flexible with opening hours.

Refreshments available. OTR Studios also run a 24 track digital recording studio and PA hire. See entry in relevant section for details.

Panic Rehearsal Studios
Unit 14, Trading Estate Road, London, NW10 7LU
tel:	020 8961 9540/020 8965 1122
fax:	020 8838 2194
email:	mroberts.drums@virgin.net
web:	www.panic-music.co.uk
rates:	From £6.75 per hour
rooms:	6
hours:	10am-12:30am, 7 days a week
secure storage:	No
equipment:	PA and backline
equip. for hire:	Cymbals
info:	5 rehearsal rooms and 1 room dedicated to drum

practice. Air conditioned rooms. Lounge area with drink machines.
Also sell spares on-site.

Papa Joe's Sound Studios
Unit 30, Merrick Road, Southall, Middlesex, UB2 4AU
tel:	020 8571 2707
email:	info@papajoesstudios.com
web:	www.papajoesstudios.com
rates:	Contact for details
rooms:	3
hours:	Contact for details
equipment:	Full backline, Peavey RQ 2318 powered mixer
info:	Air-conditioned rooms. Internet access available.

See also listing for Papa Joe's recording facilities in relevant section.

Parafanalia
100 Clements Road, London, SE16 4DG
tel:	020 7740 1008
email:	info@parafanalia-studio.com
web:	www.parafanalia-studio.com
rates:	From £30 per slot
rooms:	1
secure storage:	Yes
equipment:	Backline
info:	3 slots available throughout the day of 4 hours

each: 10am-2pm, 2.30pm-6.30pm, and 7pm-11pm. Studio is also
available for nightshift from 12 midnight until 9am. Also have recording
services. See listing in relevant section for details.

The Peel
160 Cambridge Road, Kingston, KT1 3HH
tel:	020 8546 3516
fax:	020 8255 8104
email:	info@peelmuzik.com
web:	www.peelmuzik.com
rates:	See website
rooms:	3
secure storage:	Yes
equipment:	Backline, PA
info:	The Peel is a live music venue with rehearsal

studios. See entry in Venues section for further details. Rates are
dependant on size of room and time of day booked. Chillout area with
free tea and coffee available.

Pipe Dream Studios
2nd Floor, Chocolate Factory 2, Coburg Road, London, N22 6UJ
tel:	020 8889 9048/07970 792 865
email:	info@pipedreamstudios.co.uk
web:	www.pipedreamstudios.co.uk
rooms:	1
secure storage:	Yes
equipment:	Full backline, PA, drum kit
equip. for hire:	See website for equipment listing
info:	Room comes equipped with a remote controlled

air-conditioning unit.

The Premises
201-209 Hackney Road, London, E2 8AL
tel:	020 7729 7593
fax:	020 7739 5600
email:	premisesstudios@btconnect.com
web:	www.premises.demon.co.uk
contact:	Viv
rates:	£7-£11 per hour
rooms:	7
hours:	10am-11pm, 7 days a week
secure storage:	No
equipment:	PA, mics
equip. for hire:	Guitar and bass amps, pianos, drum kits
info:	Rooms have natural light and are air-conditioned.

Previous clients at The Premises have included David Gray, Carleen
Anderson and Badly Drawn Boy.

Pulse Studios
Unit K, Blackhorse Mews, Blackhorse Lane, London, E17 6SL
tel:	020 8527 0440
email:	practice@pulsestudiose17.co.uk
web:	www.artsense.co.uk/pulsestudios
rates:	£36 for 4 hours (Daytime), £30 for 3 hours
	(Evening/Weekend)
rooms:	3
hours:	10am-11pm, 7 days a week
secure storage:	Yes
equipment:	Backline, amps, mics
info:	Drum practice room also available at an hourly

rate of £6. Pulse also have digital recording facilities. Contact for further
details.

Quo-Vadis Recording & Rehearsals
Unit 1, Morrison's Yard, 551a High Road, Tottenham, London, N17 6SB
tel:	020 8365 1999
email:	quovadis_2002@yahoo.co.uk
web:	www.quovadisstudios.com
rates:	£36 for 4 hours, £30 for 3 hours
rooms:	2
hours:	10am-12am
secure storage:	Yes
equipment:	2 guitar amps, 1 bass amp, full PA, drum kit
equip. for hire:	Guitar, bass
info:	Quo-Vadis also have a recording studio. See

relevant entry for details.

Razorback Studios
293 Crown Street, Crown Street, Camberwell, London, SE5 0UR
tel:	07866 258 382
email:	theashman007@hotmail.com
contact:	Ashley
rates:	From £260 per month
rooms:	2
hours:	Contact for details
secure storage:	No
equipment:	PA
info:	Razorback have 2 very large rehearsal rooms.

Hire is on a monthly basis and rates apply to 9 separate 5 hour
sessions. Price includes secure storage. Call for more details.

Red Onion Productions
Suite 100, Hilton Grove Business Centre, 25 Hatherley Mews, London,
E17 4QP
tel:	020 8520 3975
fax:	020 8521 6646
email:	info@redonion.uk.com
web:	www.redonion.uk.com
rates:	From £13.50 + VAT per hour
rooms:	1
hours:	9am-10pm (Mon-Fri), 10am-10pm (Sat & Sun)
secure storage:	No
equipment:	PA, mics
equip. for hire:	Video equipment
info:	Space can be used for music rehearsals, or there

are wooden sprung floors and full length mirror for dance rehearsals.
Café on-site.

Resident Studios
57a Windsor Road, Willesden, London, NW2 5DT
tel:	020 8830 4321
email:	info@residentstudios.com
web:	www.residentstudios.com
rates:	£8-£12 per hour (peak times), £5-£10 per hour
	(off-peak times)
rooms:	3
hours:	10am-12am, 7 days a week
secure storage:	No
equip. for hire:	Backline
info:	Free tea and coffee available. Resident Studios

also have recording facilities. Refer to entry in Recording Studios
section for details.

Riot Club
Unit 4, 27a Spring Grove Road, Hounslow, Middlesex, TW3 4BE
tel:	020 8572 8809
email:	riot@riotclub.co.uk
web:	www.riotclub.co.uk
rates:	From £5 per hour
rooms:	5
secure storage:	Yes
equipment:	Backline except drum kit
info:	Riot Club also run a record label and

management company. See entries in relevant sections for further
details.

MUSIC SERVICES/RETAIL

Station Studios
MUSIC REHEARSAL STUDIOS

RATES
Evenings and Weekend Rates from £7.50 p/h
Daytimes Monday–Friday (before 6pm) £5.00 p/h

BACKLINE & HIRE
Amps: Marshall, Fender, Trace Elliott, Laney...etc £1.50p/h
Drums: Mapex, Pearl, Premier £1.50p/h
Full Kit with Cymbals £2.50p/h

P.A. HIRE – REPAIRS
GROUND FLOOR ACCESS – PARKING
STORAGE – ESTABLISHED 1990

CLIENTS
Coldplay, Seafood, Wurzell, Motorhead, Nico(Iron Maiden)
Fierce Panda Records, EMI, Keith Airey(Tom Jones Band), Canola.... etc

info@stationstudios.co.uk – 020 8361 8114 – New Southgate, North London, N11.

Ritz Rehearsal Studios
110 Disraeli Road, Putney, London, SW15 2DX

tel:	020 8870 1335
fax:	020 8877 1036
email:	lee@ritzstudios.com
web:	www.ritzstudios.com
rooms:	4
secure storage:	Yes
equipment:	PA, desk, lighting
info:	Full specifications for rooms can be viewed on website.

Rogue Studios
Unit RA4, Bermondsey Trading Estate, Rotherhithe New Road, London, SE16 3LL

tel:	020 7231 3257
email:	rehearsals@roguestudios.co.uk
web:	www.roguestudios.co.uk
rates:	Check website for details
rooms:	3
hours:	12pm -11pm, 7 days a week
secure storage:	No
equipment:	2K PA rig, mics
equip. for hire:	Backline at £5 per item
info:	Rates vary according to room size and time of day. Check website for further details. Rogue also has a recording studio. See relevant section for information.

Rooz Studios
2a Corsham Street, London, N1 6DP

tel:	020 7490 1919
rates:	See below
rooms:	14
hours:	11am-11pm, 7 days a week
secure storage:	No
equipment:	Backline including 5 piece Pearl Export drum kits and brand new Orange amps
info:	8 rooms available for £200 per week full lock-out. Remaining 6 studios range between £50-£60 for 4 hours, or during the week £7.50 per hour. 7 storage cages suitable for 4 piece band available for £20 per week. Refreshments available and chillout area on-site. Rooz also have equipment hire services, as well as tour bus hire. See relevant sections for further details.

Scar Studios
20 Castlehaven Road, Camden, London, NW1 8RA

tel:	020 7813 3662
rates:	From £10 per hour
rooms:	3
hours:	Flexible
secure storage:	No
equipment:	Full backline
equip. for hire:	Guitars, keyboards, piano
info:	Chillout area and kitchen facilities. Drum school 'Planet Drum' also runs from the same premises. See entry in relevant section for details. Scar Studios offer a 1/2 price rate for individual musicians booking at late notice.

Scream Studios
20c South End, Croydon, Surrey, CR0 1DN

tel:	020 8686 5788
email:	croydon@screamstudios.co.uk
web:	www.screamstudios.co.uk
rates:	£18 for 4 hours Monday-Friday before 7pm, £33 for 4 hours Monday-Friday after 7pm and weekends
rooms:	17
hours:	11am-12am, 7 days a week
secure storage:	No
equipment:	PA, mics
equip. for hire:	Guitar and bass amps, drum kits, cymbals. Available at £2 per item
info:	Clean, bright rooms. Chillout area with pool tables and table tennis. Café on-site. Scream also has recording studio, see entries in relevant section for details.

Seven Studios
49-51 Leswin Road, Stoke Newington, London, N16 7NX

tel:	020 7923 9533
email:	lsdchudley@hotmail.com
contact:	Dan
rates:	£8 per hour daytime, £10 per hour evenings
rooms:	2
hours:	12pm-12:30am, 7 days a week
secure storage:	No
equipment:	Full backline, PA
equip. for hire:	Extra amps, cymbals
info:	Evening and weekend sessions are booked in 3 hour slots. Lounge area with Sky TV and refreshments available.

Shiftworks
7 Overbury Road, London, N15 6RH
tel:	020 8880 1022/07973 294 204
email:	info@shiftworks.net
web:	www.shiftworks.net
contact:	Ellis
rates:	From £5 per hour (off-peak times), £30 for 4 hours (Evenings)
rooms:	1
hours:	24 hours, 7 days a week
secure storage:	No
equipment:	Backline
equip. for hire:	Specialist analogue synthesizers
info:	Friendly service. Just ring to see if there is space

available. Recording facilities available, see relevant section.

Soundstage Studio
Unit 1, 30 Gorst Road, London, NW10 6LE
tel:	020 8961 7890
email:	info@synthservice.com
web:	www.synthservice.com/studio.html
rooms:	1
secure storage:	No
equip. for hire:	Vintage instruments such as Hammond organs, Wurlitzers and Fender Rhodes pianos.
info:	Soundstage Studio comprises rehearsal space

and a recording studio. Synthesiser Service Centre, a repairs centre, is part of same firm. Also offer recording facilities and run repair centre, Synthesiser Service Centre. See entries in the relevant sections for details.

Station Studios
New Southgate BR, 91 Station Road, London, N11 1QH
tel:	020 8361 8114
email:	info@stationstudios.co.uk
web:	www.stationstudios.co.uk
rates:	From £5 per hour
rooms:	3
hours:	Flexible
secure storage:	No
equipment:	Full backline
equip. for hire:	Backline available at £1.50 per hour
info:	Station Studios opening hours are flexible,

varying with the requirements of bands. PA hire and repair. Parking facilities. Ground floor access. Previous clients include Coldplay, Motorhead, Fierce Panda Records and The Honeycombs.

Studio 53
Brockley, London
tel:	020 8692 4869
email:	info@thestudio53.co.uk
web:	www.thestudio53.co.uk
contact:	Dave
rates:	Contact for details
rooms:	1
secure storage:	Yes
equipment:	Drum kit, bass amp, 2 guitar amps, keyboard amp, 1kW PA, 5 mics
info:	Studio 53 also provide recording facilities. See

listing in relevant section for further details.

Studio 69
68-70 London Road, Croydon, Surrey, CR0 2TB
tel:	020 8680 1042
rates:	Varies, but typically £35 for 4 hours at peak time
rooms:	5
hours:	Flexible
secure storage:	Yes
equipment:	Guitar amps, bass amp, Pearl Export drumkit, PA, mics and leads, cymbals
info:	Situated below Rockbottom instrument shop. See

entry in relevant section for details.

Studio 7k
Cameron Road, Seven Kings, Ilford, IG3 8LA
tel:	020 8599 0103
email:	studio7k@aol.com
web:	www.studio7k.com
rates:	Contact for details
rooms:	2
secure storage:	Yes
equipment:	PA, backline, drum kit
info:	Very large rehearsal rooms. 2 recording studios

are available. See the relevant section for more details. Full range of music tuition also available. Contact or see website for details.

Survival Studios
Acton Business Centre, School Road, London, NW10 6TD
tel:	020 8961 1977
fax:	020 8961 1977
rates:	£5-£8 per hour
rooms:	14
hours:	11am-1am
secure storage:	Yes
equipment:	Full backline, mics, PA
info:	All rooms are fully air conditioned.

The Telegraph
228 Brixton Hill, Brixton, London, SW2 1HE
tel:	020 8678 0777
email:	alex@thebrixtontelegraph.co.uk
web:	www.thebrixtontelegraph.co.uk
contact:	Alex
rates:	£10 per hour
rooms:	1
secure storage:	Yes
equipment:	PA with desk and effects, drum kit, amps, mics
info:	Spacious rehearsal room.

Terminal Studios
4-10 Lamb Walk, London Bridge, London, SE1 3TT
tel:	020 7403 3050
fax:	020 7407 6123
email:	info@terminal.co.uk
web:	www.terminal.co.uk
rates:	Contact for details.
rooms:	5
hours:	10am-11pm, 7 days a week
secure storage:	No
equip. for hire:	Backline, PA
info:	Complex also contains shop, café and repairs

workshop. Full specifications for each studio can be found on the website. Previous clients have included Brian Wilson, David Bowie, The Streets, Basement Jaxx, Foo Fighters, Placebo and many more.

Theorem Music Complex
385 Willesden High Road, London, NW10 2JR
tel:	020 8451 4545
fax:	020 8451 4546
email:	expo@theoremmusic.co.uk
rates:	From £24 for 4 hours
rooms:	4
hours:	10am-late (Weekdays), 12pm-8pm (Weekends)
secure storage:	No
equip. for hire:	Backline, keyboards
info:	Rates vary depending on size of room. Also run

full 24 track recording studios.

Treacle Sound Solutions
Basement 71, Leonard Street, Shoreditch, London, EC2A 4QS
tel:	020 7739 2626
email:	treaclestudio@btconnect.com
contact:	Paul Burnley
rates:	From £10 per hour
rooms:	2
secure storage:	No
equipment:	Drum kit, PA, backline
info:	Rates vary depending on size of the room.

Splitter van available for hire. Treacle Sound also offer recording facilities. See relevant section for more details.

Unit 9 Rehearsal Studio
Unit 9, Zenner Road Industrial Estate, Weir Road, Balham, London, SW12 0PS
tel:	020 8675 9666
rates:	£6-£8 per hour (Daytime), £8-£14 per hour (Evenings & Weekends)
rooms:	8
hours:	11am- 12am, 7 days a week
secure storage:	Yes
equipment:	Full backline, PA, mics
equip. for hire:	Cymbals
info:	Air conditioning in every room. Rates dependant

on room size. Parking facilities. Refreshments available.

Urban Studios
279 Abercrombie Business Centre, Suite 306, Glasgow, G40 2BB
tel:	0141 551 0202
email:	info@urbanstudios.co.uk
web:	www.urbanstudios.co.uk
contact:	David
rates:	£10.50 for 3hours (Daytime), £21-£25 for 3 hours (Evening)
rooms:	5
hours:	12pm-12am, 7 days a week
secure storage:	No
equipment:	Full PA, drum kit
equip. for hire:	Full backline and a range of equipment including Hammond Organs
info:	Urban Studios have 5 large rooms lit by natural daylight. Other facilities include refreshments, a games rooms and parking available on-site.

Vampire Music
20 Tanners Hill, Deptford, London, SE8 4JP
tel:	020 8691 6666
fax:	020 8692 9999
email:	info@vampiremusic.co.uk
web:	www.vampiremusic.co.uk
rates:	£6-£11.50 per hour
rooms:	5
hours:	24 hours, 7 days a week
secure storage:	No
equipment:	PA, mics
equip. for hire:	Backline, amps. See website for full list and prices
info:	Vampire Music also incorporates recording studios, equipment hire, CD duplication, music shop, as well as design and tuition services. See entries in relevant sections for details.

Vatican Studios
Railway Arch 190, Bancroft Road, London, E1 4ET
tel:	020 7790 7026
email:	oscar@thevatican.free-online.co.uk
web:	www.thevatican.free-online.co.uk
contact:	Oscar
rates:	Contact for details
rooms:	5
hours:	24 hours, 7 days a week
secure storage:	No
equip. for hire:	Most equipment and instruments available
info:	Lounge area with bar. Dance studio available. Parking facilities.

Waterloo Sunset Studios
Building D, Tower Bridge Business Complex, 100 Clements Road, London, SE16 4DG
tel:	020 7252 0001
fax:	020 7231 3002
email:	julie@musicbank.org
web:	www.musicbank.org/Studios/studios.htm
contact:	Julie
rates:	From £175 per day
rooms:	4
hours:	10am-10pm, 7 days a week
secure storage:	No
equipment:	Monitors
equip. for hire:	Backline
info:	Waterloo Sunset Studios has 2 large rehearsal rooms, and 2 smaller sized rooms which are available at different rates. Full specifications of the studios can be found on the website. All rooms with natural daylight. In-house catering. Past clients have included George Michael, Pulp, Madonna, The Cure and Oasis. Waterloo Sunset is part of the Music Bank company, which also offers equipment and instrument rental and tour bus hire (Direct Tour Hire). See relevant sections for details.

Westbourne Rehearsals
The Rear Basement, 92-98 Bourne Terrace, Little Venice, London, W2 5TH
tel:	020 7289 8145
rates:	£4-£12 per hour
rooms:	4
hours:	10am-11pm, 7 days a week
secure storage:	No
equipment:	PA, guitar and bass amps
equip. for hire:	Drum kit
info:	All rooms are sound proofed, air-conditioned and mirrored. Shop on-site and kitchen facilities available, as well as limited free parking.

Zed One Studios
225a Camden Road, London, NW1 9AA
tel:	020 7482 3500
email:	rehearsals@zed-one-studios.co.uk
web:	www.zed-one-studios.co.uk
rates:	From £6 per hour
rooms:	4
hours:	12pm-12am, 7 days a week
secure storage:	No
equip. for hire:	Backline, amps, cymbals
info:	Zed One Studios also have a recording studio. See relevant section for details.

7th Wave
Unit 8, Sherriff Street, Worcester, WR14 9AB
tel:	01905 617 177
email:	7thwave@amserve.com
rates:	From £7 per hour
rooms:	4
secure storage:	Yes
equipment:	PA, drumkit, bass and guitar amps
equip. for hire:	PA, bass and guitar amps
info:	Limited storage. Recording and tuition also available. See relevant section for more details.

Abbey Lane Studios
Unit 3a, Darley Abbey Mills, Off Haslams Lane, Derby, DE22 1DZ
tel:	0845 686 8742
email:	info@abbey-lane.co.uk
web:	www.abbey-lane.co.uk
rates:	£8 per hours
rooms:	4
hours:	6pm-12am
secure storage:	No
equipment:	PA, drum kit
equip. for hire:	Amps, guitars
info:	Discount available for block bookings. One of the rehearsal rooms is hired out on a residential basis. Recording facilities also available. See relevant section for more details.

Arch Studios
6 Grain Warehouse Yard, Derby Street, Burton-On-Trent, Staffordshire, DE14 2JJ
tel:	01283 510 026
secure storage:	Yes
info:	Arch Studios also offer recording facilities. See relevant section for details.

Backbeat Rehearsal Rooms
Unit 7, Gosford Industrial Estate, Coventry, CV1 5ED
tel:	02476 220 059
rates:	£7 per hour (Daytime), £9 per hour (Evenings & Weekends)
rooms:	3
hours:	12pm-12am, 7 days a week
secure storage:	No
equipment:	Guitar and bass amps, drum kit, PA, keyboard amps, cabs
equip. for hire:	Range of instruments, cymbals and snares.
info:	Full air conditioned. Refreshments available. Free parking.

Beat Foundry
15 Princess Alley, Wolverhampton, WV1 1HB
tel:	01902 421 991
web:	www.beatfoundry.co.uk
contact:	Jackie, Nicki
rates:	£8 per hour
rooms:	4
hours:	Contact for details
secure storage:	Yes
equipment:	Drum kit (minus snare, cymbals and kickdrum pedal), PA, guitar and bass amps, mics
equip. for hire:	Snare, cymbals, kickdrum pedal

Big Noise
12 Gregory Street, Northampton, Northamptonshire, NN1 1TA
tel:	01604 634 455
email:	kim.gordelier@btinternet.com
rates:	£6 per hour
rooms:	4
hours:	Flexible
secure storage:	Yes
equipment:	PA, mics
equip. for hire:	Backline
info:	Fully sound-proofed rooms. Special rates for students. Opening hours can be flexible, call for more information.

Big Wheel
Yeoman Street, Leicester, LE1 1UT
tel:	0116 242 2200
email:	rocky@bigwheelentertainments.co.uk
web:	www.bigwheelentertainments.co.uk
contact:	Rocky
rates:	from £5 per hour
rooms:	14
secure storage:	No
equipment:	Backline, PA, drum kit
equip. for hire:	Backline, vocal PA
info:	Rates vary depending on size of the room.

Accessories shop, chillout area and cafe with pool table. Once a year Big Wheel hosts a showcase event to which they invite industry professionals. Contact Rocky for details of how to play at event.

Bob Lamb's Studios
122a Highbury Road, Kings Heath, Birmingham, B14 7QO
tel:	0121 443 2186
email:	boblamb@recklessltd.freeserve.co.uk
contact:	Bob Lamb
rates:	Call for details
rooms:	2
hours:	Negotiable
secure storage:	Yes
equipment:	Backline, PA
info:	Also offer analogue recording. See entry in

relevant section for details

The Cellar
Dovedale House, Wilson Street, Derby, Derbyshire, DE1 1PL
tel:	01332 206 902
email:	ian@tnts.co.uk
web:	www.tnts.co.uk
contact:	Ian Tompkins
rates:	£7.50 per hour
rooms:	2
hours:	6pm-11pm (Weekdays), 12pm-11pm (Sat), 12pm-10pm (Sun)
secure storage:	Yes
equipment:	Drumkit, PA
equip. for hire:	Cymbals, Guitar and Bass Amps
info:	Also has recording studio. See relevant section

for details.

Chiltern Studios
Unit A, Cross Road Commercial Centre, Cross Road, Lemmington Spa, Warwickshire, CV32 5PB
tel:	01494 449 800
email:	completesound@btconnect.com
web:	www.completesoundrehearsalstudio.com
contact:	Adam or Mike
rates:	£9 per hour
rooms:	1
hours:	9am-11pm, 7 days a week
secure storage:	Yes
equipment:	Full PA, drum kit, guitar, bass and keyboard amps, mics
equip. for hire:	Range of equipment including guitars, mics, cymbals, snares
info:	Chiltern also offer 24 track recording facilities.

Refreshments such as tea, coffee and food are available. Parking facilities.

Complete Sound Rehearsal Studio
Unit A, Crossroad Commercial Centre, Rear of 4-5 Cross Road, Leamington Spa, Warwickshire, CV32 5PB
tel:	01926 833 455
email:	completesound@btconnect.com
web:	www.completesoundrehearsalstudio.com
rates:	£9 per hour
rooms:	1
hours:	Contact for details
secure storage:	Yes
equipment:	Full PA, mics, drum kit, amps, leads
equip. for hire:	Sabian Pro Sonix crash and ride available at £5 per session
info:	Complete Sound have a large, comfortable and

fully equipped room. Tea and coffee provided free of charge, as well as range of refreshments for sale.

Cornerstudios
Unit 71, Imex Business Park, Upper Villiers Street, Wolverhampton, WV2 4NU
tel:	01902 354 882
email:	info@cornerstudios.co.uk
web:	www.cornerstudios.co.uk
contact:	Lee Phillips
rates:	Call for details
rooms:	1
secure storage:	Yes
equipment:	Backline
info:	Cornerstudios is predominantly a recording

studio, although the live room is available for rehearsal in the evenings.

Fatback Rehearsal Studios
28 Stratford Street North, Camphill, Birmingham, B11 1BY
tel:	0121 248 2525
email:	info@fatbackstudios.co.uk
web:	www.fatbackstudios.co.uk
rates:	£6 per hour (Daytime), £8 per hour (Evenings)
rooms:	16
hours:	12pm-12am
secure storage:	Yes
equipment:	PA, drumkit, amps
info:	Advisable to book in advance as studio is not

open if no one is booked in. Fatback also offer recording services. See entry in relevant section for details.

Fidget Studios
Unit B10, Little Heath Industrial Estate, Old Church Road, Coventry, CV6 7NB
tel:	024 7658 1133
email:	enquiries@fidget-studios.com
web:	www.fidget-studios.com
rates:	£10 per hour
rooms:	1
hours:	24 hours, 7 days a week
secure storage:	Yes
equipment:	PA, backline, drums
info:	Air-conditioned. Also offer live band recording

and a Dance music production studio. See relevant section for more details.

Hellfire Productions
158 Crankhall Lane, Friar Park, Wednesbury, Birmingham, WS10 OEB
tel:	0121 556 2559
email:	enquires@hellfireproductions.com
web:	www.hellfireproductions.com
rates:	from £6 per hour
rooms:	1
hours:	Contact for details
secure storage:	Yes
info:	DIY recording which can also be used as a

rehearsal space. Also provide professional recording studio and tuition services. See relevant section for more details.

JJM Studios
20 Pool Street, Walsall, WS1 2EN
tel:	01922 629 700
email:	info@jjmstudios.co.uk
web:	www.jjmstudios.co.uk
rates:	from £6 per hour
rooms:	8
hours:	11am-Late, 7 days a week
secure storage:	No
equipment:	PA, backline, drum kit
info:	Each room has a raised stage. JJM Studios has a

Pearl and Peavey endorsement deal.

Madhouse Rehearsals
41 Hampton Street, Hockley, Birmingham, B19 3LS
tel:	0121 233 1109
fax:	0121 233 1286
email:	committed@madhouserehearsals.com
web:	www.madhouserehearsals.com
rates:	From £9 per hour
rooms:	11
hours:	12pm-11pm (Mon-Fri), 12pm-6pm (Sat), 11am-10pm (Sun)
secure storage:	Yes
equipment:	Backline, PA, drum kit
equip. for hire:	Cymbals, guitar, bass, keyboards
info:	Licensed bar on-site. Recording facilities also

available. See relevant section for more details.

Magnet Studios
Unit 2, Davisella House, Newark Street, Sneinton, Nottingham, NG2 4PP
tel:	0115 924 3324
email:	rob@magnetstudios.co.uk
web:	www.magnetstudios.co.uk
contact:	Rob Reid
rates:	£7 per hour
rooms:	4
hours:	5pm-12am (Mon-Fri), 10am-6pm (Sat), 10am-10pm (Sun)
secure storage:	No
equipment:	PA, mics, mic stands, leads
equip. for hire:	Guitar and bass amps, speaker cabinets, drums, keyboards
info:	Chillout area Shop also situated within the studio

selling strings, leads and refreshments. Also offer backline hire service and splitter van rental. See listings in relevant sections for further details.

Metheringham Music Factory
Barff Farm Fenside, Fen Lanr, Metheringham, Lincoln, Lincolnshire, LN4 3AQ

tel:	01526 323 319
email:	geanius@musicandleisure.fsnet.co.uk
web:	www.metheringhammusicfactory.co.uk
rates:	Contact for details
rooms:	2
hours:	9am-12am
secure storage:	No
equipment:	Premier drum kits, PA, mics
info:	Overnight hospitality. Car parking and camp site.

MPM Records
Units 3, 5 & 6, Talisman House, 47-49 Bath Street, Walsall, WS1 3BX

tel:	01922 642 123
email:	record@mpmrecords.com
web:	www.mpmrecords.com
secure storage:	Yes
info:	A studio with practice space and a full backline.

The Music Shed
Unit 6, Derby Small Business Centre, Canal Street, Derby, DE1 2RJ

tel:	07736 777 130
email:	info@musicshed.co.uk
web:	www.musicshed.co.uk
contact:	Gez
rates:	from £7 per hour
rooms:	4
hours:	24 hours, 7 days a week
secure storage:	No
equipment:	PA
equip. for hire:	Drum kits, bass and guitar amps
info:	Ground floor access. All rooms are air conditioned. Ample parking space. Refreshment and accessories for sale on-site. Recording facilities also provided. See relevant section for more details

Muther's Studios
14 Rea Street South, Digbeth, Birmingham, B5 6LB

tel:	0121 622 7110
email:	info@muthersstudio.com
web:	www.muthersstudio.com
contact:	Adam Dufrane
rates:	From £6 per hour
rooms:	20
hours:	Monday-Friday: 12noon-11pm, Saturday: 12noon-6pm, Sunday: 12noon-10pm
secure storage:	Yes
equipment:	Yamaha PA, backline, Marshall guitar amps, Peavy Bass amps, Pearl drum kit
info:	Currently 20 rooms available, with a further 10 being built. Chillout room, pool table and refreshments all available. Also run 24 track recording studio, as well as Birmingham Drum Academy providing tuition. Refer to relevant sections for further details.

Oasis
Unit 6A, Brockhill Works, Windsor Road, Redditch, B97 6DJ

tel:	01527 592 800
email:	info@oasis-studios.co.uk
web:	www.oasis-studios.co.uk
contact:	Alan
rates:	£12.50 per hour
rooms:	3
hours:	Contact for details
secure storage:	Yes
equipment:	PA, drum kit, 2 guitar valve amps, bass amp
equip. for hire:	Full range of backline including bass combos, 3K engineered PA
info:	Large rehearsal rooms with high quality equipment in each. Also have showcase room and recording studio. Offer discount for members. Contact for details.

The Oxygen Rooms
122 Barr Street, Hockley, Birmingham, B19 3DE

tel:	0121 551 7001
web:	www.theoxygenrooms.com
contact:	Nick Rendall
rates:	£8 per hour
rooms:	5
hours:	12pm-11pm
secure storage:	No
equipment:	Drums, PA, amps
info:	3 rooms available for bands and 2 for DJs. Also offer the opportunity to record sessions onto CD. Instrument, DJ and vocal tuition is available. See relevant entry for details.

Pick n Styx
2 Napier Street, Coventry, CV1 5PR

tel:	02476 55 00 76
email:	info@picknstyx.co.uk
web:	www.picknstyx.co.uk
contact:	Mike
rates:	From £10 per hour
rooms:	8
hours:	7 days a week
secure storage:	Yes
equipment:	PA, drum kit, amps
equip. for hire:	Drum hardware, guitars
info:	Located on ground floor for easy access. All music types welcome. Lounge area and ample parking available.

Premier Studios
Occupation Road, Corby, Northants, NN17 1EH

tel:	01536 407 770
email:	iain@premierstudios.co.uk
web:	www.premierstudios.co.uk
rates:	£16-£20 per session
rooms:	3
hours:	10am-10pm
secure storage:	Yes
equipment:	Vocal PA, Shure mic, stand
equip. for hire:	Range of equipment
info:	Rates vary depending on room used.

Psyrex
397 Hucknall Road, Sherwood, Nottingham, NG5 1FW

tel:	0115 841 3184
email:	mark@psyrex.net
web:	www.psyrex.net
contact:	Mark Parkins
rates:	£7 per hour
rooms:	1
hours:	24 hours, 7 days a week
secure storage:	Yes
equipment:	Backline
equip. for hire:	Drum kit
info:	The rehearsal room doubles as a live room for Psyrex recording studio. See relevant entry for details.

Quad Studios
78 Friday Street, Leicester, LE1 3BW

tel:	0116 251 2516
email:	info@quadstudios.co.uk
web:	www.quadstudios.co.uk
rates:	From £12 per hour
rooms:	8
secure storage:	No
equip. for hire:	Drum kit, mics, PA, amps
info:	Range of different sized rooms available, including one that can accommodate an orchestra. The price of room depends on the equipment included. Closed mic recording to CD available.

Rich Bitch Studios
505 Bristol Road, Selly Oak, Birmingham, B29 6AU

tel:	0121 683 1339
contact:	Robert Bruce
rates:	From £8 per hour
rooms:	13
hours:	Call for details
secure storage:	Yes
equipment:	PA, backline
equip. for hire:	Guitar, bass
info:	Some of the studios offer the opportunity to record the session onto MD. There is also a dedicated recording studio, see entry in relevant section for details.

Ricochet Music Rooms
Unit A, 117 Stafford Street, Walsall, WS2 5DX

tel:	01922 613 063
rates:	£8.50-£9.50 per hour
rooms:	6
hours:	12pm-Late (Mon-Fri), 10am-Late (Sat & Sun)
secure storage:	No
equipment:	PA, drum kit, cymbals, 2 Marshall stacks, Laney bass cabs
info:	Rates vary depending on size of room. External PA hire available. See relevant section for more details.

Robannas Studios

Robanna House, Cleveland Street, Birmingham, B19 3SN
tel:	0121 333 3201
fax:	0121 359 3647
email:	robanna.studios@btinternet.com
web:	www.robannas-studios.co.uk
contact:	Robert Hoffman
rates:	From £5 per hour
rooms:	34
secure storage:	No
equipment:	PA, drums, guitar and bass amps
equip. for hire:	Guitars, electric piano
info:	Bands using the studios should also enquire

about the local gigs promoted by Robannas. Client list including
Lostprophets, Hundred Reasons and Ocean Colour Scene.

S & P Studios

Ewefields Farm, Chesterton, Leamington Spa, Warwickshire, CV33 9LQ
tel:	0870 744 3054
email:	nick@sandpproductions.co.uk
web:	www.sandpstudios.co.uk
contact:	Nick Myerscough
rates:	£8 per hour
rooms:	1
hours:	Until 10pm, 7 days a week
secure storage:	Yes
equipment:	Drum kit, PA
info:	Also offer studio recording. See relevant entry for

details.

Scorpion Studios

Peregrine Mews, Dowding Road, Lincoln, Lincolnshire, LN3 4PH
tel:	01522 524 888
email:	gameala@gameala.wanadoo.co.uk
web:	www.scorpionstudios.tk
rates:	From £20 for 3 hours
rooms:	2
hours:	10am-10pm
secure storage:	Yes
equipment:	PA, drum kit
equip. for hire:	Backline at £5 per session
info:	Recording facilities also available. See relevant

section for more details.

The Session Rooms

Waterworks Road, Worcester, Worcestershire, WR1 3EZ
tel:	01905 338 972/07729 011 398
email:	info@thesessionrooms.com
web:	www.thesessionrooms.com or
	www.bandpractice.co.uk
rates:	£10-£12 per hour
rooms:	4
secure storage:	Yes
equipment:	2 rooms are equipped with PA. Remaining 2 have

PA, backline and drum kit
info:	Also offer recording and CD duplication services.

See relevant sections for more details.

The Sound Bunker

Unit 12, Victoria Business Centre, Neilston Street, Leamington Spa,
Warwickshire, CV31 2AZ
tel:	01926 832 929
email:	thesoundbunker@btconnect.com
rates:	£9 per hour
rooms:	2
hours:	24 hour access
secure storage:	No
equipment:	PA, backline, drums
equip. for hire:	Guitars, cymbals, guitar and bass amps, PA
info:	Drum booth also available. Accessories shop on-

site. PA and amps available to hire for external use. See Equipment Hire
section for more details.

Startrak Studios

27 Liverpool Road, Stoke-on-Trent, Staffordshire, ST4 1AW
tel:	01782 416 312
contact:	Keith
rates:	15 for 3 hours
rooms:	2
secure storage:	Yes
equipment:	Full backline
info:	Sessions available 10am-5pm for students and

the unemplyed at rate of £15. Other sessions during the week are
5-8pm at £10, and 8-11pm at £15. 3 hour sessions at weekends are also
£15. Also provide small PA hire services. Contact for further details.

Stayfree Studios

Lillie House, 1a Conduit Street, Leicester, LE2 0JN
tel:	0116 223 0303
email:	music@stayfree.co.uk
web:	www.stayfreemusic.co.uk
rates:	£5-£8 per hour
rooms:	7
secure storage:	No
equipment:	2 guitar amps, 1 bass amp, drum kit, PA, mics,
	leads
equip. for hire:	Contact for details
info:	The rooms are large, bright and air conditioned

with interesting colour schemes. Games room and vending machines
on-site. Also provide band web space. See listing in relevant section for
details.

Subway Studios

Alferton Road, Nottingham, Nottinghamshire, NG7 3JL
tel:	0115 978 2002
email:	madhatter@ntlworld.com
web:	www.subwaystudios.co.uk
contact:	Vaughn
rates:	£5-£7 per hour
rooms:	7
hours:	10am-12am
secure storage:	No
equipment:	PA
equip. for hire:	Backline
info:	Also run recording studio. See relevant section

for details. Chillout space available.

The Session

Waterworks Road, Worcester, Worcestershire, WR1 3EZ
tel:	01905 338971
email:	info@thesessionrooms.com
web:	www.thesessionrooms.com
rates:	£10-12 per hour
rooms:	4
hours:	11am-11pm all week
secure storage:	Yes
equipment:	All backline plus PA and mics available. Provide

drum kits, guitar and bass tabs in some rooms.

Toilets Rehearsal Studios

4 Hill Street, Stoke On Trent, ST4 1NL
tel:	07973 253 542
web:	www.toiletsrehearsalstudios.com
rates:	£20 for 3 hours
rooms:	2
hours:	10:30am-10:30pm, 7 days a week
secure storage:	No
equipment:	PA
equip. for hire:	Drums, amps
info:	Both rooms have a stage. Refreshments available,

tea and coffee making facilities. Ground floor access for easy loading.

Tracks Rehearsal Studios

Old Hathern Railway Station, Normanton on Soar, Loughborough,
Leicestershire, LE12 5EH
tel:	01509 842 560
email:	mick@tracks-studios.co.uk
web:	www.tracks-studios.co.uk
contact:	Mick Peacock
rates:	£6 per hour
rooms:	2
hours:	24 hours, 7 days a week
secure storage:	No
equipment:	PA, drum kit, bass amp
info:	Rehearsal rooms are spacious, fully equipped

and sound-proofed. Hours are flexible. Live recording available. Contact
for Mick for details.

Tremelo Studio

Unit 6, Crown House, Oldmill Street, Stoke On Trent, ST4 2RP
tel:	01782 749 989
contact:	Andy Gower
rates:	£6 per hour
rooms:	6
hours:	11am-11pm (Mon-Thurs), 11am-9pm (Fri), 11am-
	6pm (Sat), 11am-11pm (Sun)
secure storage:	No
equipment:	PA, mics, bass amp
equip. for hire:	Drum kit
info:	Accessories and refreshments shop.

Turn Up Plug In
The Studio, Lower Works, Horsehay Estate, Telford, TS4 3PY

tel:	07909 664 986
email:	turnup_plugin@yahoo.com
rates:	From £8 per hour
rooms:	3
hours:	6pm-11pm (Weekdays), 12pm-5pm (Weekends)
secure storage:	Yes
equipment:	PA, backline
equip. for hire:	Drums and amps available for rehersal use.

V Studios
Hammerwich, Litchfield, Staffordshire

tel:	07766 094 360
email:	philipbharper@ntlworld.com
web:	www.v-studios.co.uk
rates:	£10 per hour
rooms:	1
hours:	24 hours, 7 days a week
secure storage:	No
equipment:	PA, drumkit and amp
info:	Recording facilities also available. See relevant section for details.

Wild Sounds
Longacre Farm, Coventry Road, Bickenhill, Solihull, B92 OEH

tel:	01675 443 099/07813 168 684
email:	thewildroses69@hotmail.com
web:	www.24hourrehearsal.co.uk
contact:	Russell
rates:	From £6 per hour
rooms:	1
hours:	24 hours, 7 days a week
secure storage:	Yes
equipment:	Drum kit, PA, Marshall guitar amps, Trace Elliot bass amps

NORTHEAST

Axe Victims
324-330 High Street, Gateshead, Tyne and Wear, NE8 1EN

tel:	07939 070 405
rates:	£6 per hour
rooms:	3
hours:	Please call for details
secure storage:	No
equipment:	PA
equip. for hire:	Full backline available

Base HQ
Kings House, Fourth Banks, Newcastle, NE1 3PA

tel:	0191 261 1030
email:	basehq@btconnect.com
web:	www.basehq.com
rates:	£6 per hour (before 5pm), £8 per hour (after 5pm & weekends)
rooms:	3
hours:	10am-12am
secure storage:	Yes
equipment:	PA, mics
equip. for hire:	Drum kits, amps available from £2 per item.
info:	3 large rehearsal spaces on the ground floor. Refreshments and chill out area with pool table available. Also run recording studio. See relevant listing for details.

Bunker
29 Stockten Road, Sunderland, SR2 7AQ

tel:	0191 567 1777
email:	info@bunkeruk.com
web:	www.bunkeruk.com
contact:	Kenny Sanger
rates:	From £4 per hour
rooms:	17
hours:	9am-10pm, 7 days a week
secure storage:	Yes
equipment:	Drum kit, PA
equip. for hire:	Variety of amps
info:	Offers available on block bookings. Bunker also have a recording studio and promotions company.

Church Road Studios
197-201 Church Rd, Hove, BN3 2AH

tel:	01273 327 889
email:	info@churchroad.net
web:	www.churchroad.net
rates:	£8.50 per hour
rooms:	1
hours:	10am-Midnight
secure storage:	Yes
equipment:	400 Watt PA and full backline.
info:	Also run a recording studio. See listing for details.

First Avenue Rehearsal Studios
32 First Avenue, Heaton, Newcastle Upon Tyne, NE6 5YE

tel:	0191 265 3879
fax:	0191 276 7882
email:	info@firstave.co.uk
web:	www.firstave.co.uk
rates:	£5 per hour (Daytime), £6.50 per hour (Evenings)
rooms:	3
hours:	Contact for details
secure storage:	No
equipment:	PA
equip. for hire:	Drum kit, amps
info:	Spacious rooms with quality equipment. Minimum booking is 2 hour slot. Also have recording facilities. See entry in relevant sections for details.

Forest Rehearsal
Archway House, Edwinstowe, Nottinghamshire, NG21 9HF

tel:	01623 824 016
fax:	01623 824 016
rates:	Please call
rooms:	1
hours:	Please call
secure storage:	No
equipment:	Full PA and backilne available.
info:	Based in the heart of Sherwood Forest.

Greenhouse Music
Unit 2, Pennywell Business Centre, Portsmouth Road, Sunderland, SR4 9AR

tel:	0191 534 1112
email:	greenhousemusic@tiscali.com
web:	www.greenhousemusic.co.uk
rates:	£5 per hourrooms: 1
hours:	Contact for details
equipment:	PA
info:	Greenhouse Music provide recording facilities. Refer to listing in relevant section for further information.

Lorne Street Studio
19 Lorne Street, Middlesbrough, TS1 5QY

tel:	01642 246 090
email:	stesmith44@yahoo.co.uk
rates:	£5 per hour, £6 per hour (with drum kit)
rooms:	4
hours:	10
secure storage:	Yes
equipment:	PA
info:	Recording facilities and PA hire also available. See relevant sections for more details.

My Big Bedroom
Unit 21, Grassmere Way, Kitty Brewster Industrial Estate, Blyth, Northumberland, NE24 4RR

tel:	07708 587 648
email:	mark@mybigbedroom.co.uk
web:	www.mybigbedroom.co.uk
contact:	Mark
rates:	£5 per hour (Weekdays), £9 per hour (Evenings & Weekends)
rooms:	2
secure storage:	Yes
equipment:	PA, drum kit
equip. for hire:	Backline
info:	Website above features a jukebox with tracks from bands and artists that use the rooms. Recording facilities also available. See relevant section for more details.

PFL Audio
Tweedmouth Industrial Estate, Berwick-Upon-Tweed, TD15 1XF

tel:	01289 308 030
email:	neil@pflaudio.co.uk
web:	www.pflaudio.co.uk
rates:	£7.50 hour all inclusive
rooms:	2
hours:	Call for details
secure storage:	No
equipment:	Full backline provided.
info:	Also run a recording studio. See website for details.

Polestar
Uptin House, Stepney Road,, Shieldfield, Newcastle upon Tyne, NE2 1TZ
tel:	0191 230 1831
email:	info@polestarstudios.co.uk
web:	www.polestarstudios.co.uk
rates:	£5.50-£6.50 per hour
rooms:	3
hours:	10am-11pm (Sun-Fri), 10am-6pm (Sat)
secure storage:	No
equipment:	PA, mics, stands
equip. for hire:	Drum kit, bass and guitar amps, PA, mics
info:	Facilities include on-site shop and parking. Also

houses its Recording Studio, see relevant section for details.

Sanity Multimedia
9-11 Castlegate Mill, Castlegate Quay, Quayside Road, Stockton-On-Tees, TS18 1BZ
tel:	01642 602 292
email:	info@sanitymultimedia.com
web:	www.sanitymultimedia.com
rooms:	3
secure storage:	Yes
equipment:	Vocal PA. mics
info:	Fully sound-proofed rooms suitable for dance,

theatre and music rehearsals. Bar and restaurant on-site. Disabled access. Parking facilities. Also have recording studios. See listing for further details.

The Soundroom
Redheugh Studios, Cuthbert Street, Gateshead, NE8 1AF
tel:	0191 477 1116
email:	thesoundhouse@hotmail.com
web:	www.thesoundroom.org.uk
rates:	£5 per hour
rooms:	2
secure storage:	Yes
equipment:	PA, backline, drum kit, decks
info:	The Sound room is a community music project

that also offers recording facilities. See relevant section for more details.

The Studio
Tower Street, Hartlepool, TS24 7HQ
tel:	01429 424 440
email:	studiohartlepool@btconnect.com
web:	www.studiohartlepool.com
rates:	Contact for details
rooms:	2
hours:	Contact for details
secure storage:	Yes
equipment:	PA, amps
equip. for hire:	Drum kit
info:	The Studio complex also houses a live music

venue, as well as recording studios. See listings in relevant sections for further information.

Studio 46
46 English Street, Hull, HU3 2DT
tel:	01482 589 605
rates:	From £22 for 4 hours
rooms:	4
hours:	7pm-11pm (Mon-Fri), all day Sun
secure storage:	No
equip. for hire:	PA, amps
info:	Rates vary depending on size of the room.

Studios are available by arrangement beyond opening times listed.

Studio 64
90 Corporation Road, Middlesborough, TS1 2RE
tel:	01642 860 006
email:	info@studio64.org.uk
web:	www.studio64.org.uk
rates:	£5 per hour
rooms:	3
hours:	10am-10pm (Mon-Fri), 3pm-10pm (Weekends)
secure storage:	Yes
equipment:	PA, mics
equip. for hire:	Drum kit at £5 per session, amps at £3 per session.
info:	Studio 64 also offer recording facilities, CD

duplication, equipment hire and tuition services. See listings in relevant sections for further details.

White Wolf Recording Studio
Unit 11, Everyready Industrial Estate, Hanfield Lane, Stanley, Co. Durham, DH9 9QF
tel:	01207 282 555
email:	ian@whitewolfrecording.co.uk
web:	www.whitewolfrecording.co.uk
rates:	£8 for 1 hour, £15 for 2 hours, £20 for 3 hours
rooms:	2
hours:	24 hour, 7 days a week
secure storage:	No
equipment:	PA, drum kit
info:	Recording and CD duplication also available. See

relevant sections for more details.

NORTHWEST

Achieve Fitness Studios
Rehearsal Rooms, New Islington Mill, Regent Trading Estate, Manchester, M5 4RF
tel:	0161 832 9310
fax:	0161 832 9310
email:	glenn.ashton@btinternet.com
contact:	Glenn Ashton
rates:	From £35 per week
rooms:	16
hours:	24 hours, 7 days a week
info:	All rooms fully sound-proofed. Equipment can be

left in situ, very secure premises. Rates vary depending on the size of the room.

AL Music Services
1 South View, Bentham, Lancaster, LA2 7LJ
tel:	07715 323 748
email:	adrian.leigh3@virgin.net
contact:	Adrian Leigh
rates:	Contact for details
rooms:	1
hours:	Flexible
secure storage:	Yes
equipment:	Drum kit, PA

Apocalypse Studios
The Office Block, Bealy Industrial Estate, Manchester, M26 9QE
tel:	0161 724 0006
contact:	Dave
rates:	£30 per week
rooms:	9
hours:	7pm-11pm
secure storage:	No

Arc Studios
Unit 9-14, Goodhope House, Bentinck Street, Ashton-under-Lyne, Manchester, OL6 7SL
tel:	0161 330 5028
fax:	0161 343 7568
email:	pod@arcmusic.freeserve.co.uk
web:	www.arcsounds.com
contact:	Pod
rooms:	18
hours:	11am-11pm, 7 days a week
secure storage:	No
equipment:	PA
equip. for hire:	Backline from £4
info:	Rehearsal room rental price includes storage

space for equipment. Arc also provide a CD duplication service, refer to relevant section for details.

Assembly Line Studio
Unit A50, Redscar Business Park, Longridge Road, Preston, PR2 5NB
tel:	01772 794 433
fax:	01772 794 433
email:	peter@assemblyline.freeserve.co.uk
web:	www.assemblyline.freeserve.co.uk
contact:	Mr Knight
rates:	£15 for 3 hours
rooms:	1
hours:	Evening only
secure storage:	Yes
equipment:	Amp, PA
info:	Recording facilities also available. See relevant

section for more details.

BLUEPRINT STUDIOS

ELIZABETH HOUSE
39 QUEEN STREET
MANCHESTER
M3 7DQ
+44 (0)8700 11 2760
www.blueprint-studios.com

Attic Studios
1st Floor, Unit 2, Longford Street, Warrington, Cheshire, WA2 7PG
tel:	07876 521 555
contact:	Andy Hill, Liam
rates:	£15 for 2 hours, £20 for 3 hours
rooms:	1
hours:	Flexible
secure storage:	Yes
equipment:	Full PA, backline
info:	Contact Andy or Liam to arrange bookings. PC
based recording studio using Logic Audio also available. Attic Studios
also provide Drum, guitar and keyboard tuition. Contact the above
number for details.

Berlin Rehearsal Studios
Caxton House, Caxton Avenue, Blackpool, FY2 9AP
tel:	01253 508 670/01253 591 169
fax:	01253 508 670
email:	promidibfp@aol.com
web:	http://members.aol.com/promidibfp
contact:	Ron Sharples
rooms:	1
secure storage:	Yes
equipment:	PA, amps, bass rig, rising drum stand
info:	Free tea, coffee and chocolate. Recording studio
with lounge and shower room is also available.

The Big Fish Corporation
Beehive Mill, Jersey Street, Manchester, M4 6JG
tel:	0161 228 0357
fax:	0161 228 0357
email:	wayne@bigfish21.fsnet.co.uk
contact:	Wayne Chappell
rates:	From £15 per session
rooms:	12
hours:	11am-11pm
secure storage:	Yes
equipment:	Vocal PA
equip. for hire:	Backline
info:	Backline equipment is available for hire - £4
for bass amp, £3.50 for guitar amp, £7 for drum kit with cymbals (£4
without). Sessions are between 11am and 5.30pm, and 6pm and 11pm.
2 showcase rooms with stages. Equipment hire service also provided.
See listing in relevant section for further details.

Blueprint Studios
Elizabeth House, 39 Queen Street, Manchester, M3 7DQ
tel:	0870 011 2760
fax:	0870 011 2780
email:	info@blueprint-studios.com
web:	www.blueprint-studios.com
contact:	Frederik
rates:	From £6per hour (Daytime), From £8 (Evenings
	& Weekends)
rooms:	6
hours:	11am-11pm (Sun-Fri), 11am-6:30pm (Sat)
info:	6 sound-proofed, fully air conditioned and
heated practice rooms. Special rates may be arranged for block
bookings. PAs, SM58s and sound engineers on hand. Chillout area
with pool table and refreshments. The Blueprint complex also houses a
recording studio. See relevant section for further details.

Catalyst Studios
Units 7-17, Catapult Too, Charles Street, St. Helens, Merseyside,
WA10 1LX
tel:	01744 733 222
email:	info@catalyst-studios.co.uk
web:	www.catalyst-studios.co.uk
contact:	Andy Bowes
rates:	See website
rooms:	3
secure storage:	No
equip. for hire:	1K rig, drums, guitar and bass amps
info:	Discounts available for block bookings. Rehearsal
time is broken down into the following slots: 11am-3pm, 3pm-7pm, and
7pm-11pm. On-site parking, chillout area and disabled lift. Recording
facilities also available. See listing in relevant section for further details.

Crash Rehearsal Studios
Imperial Warehouse, 11 Davies Street, Liverpool, L1 6HB
tel:	0151 236 0989
fax:	0151 236 0989
contact:	John White, Mark Davies, Andy Fernihough
rates:	From £16 per 4 hour session
rooms:	14
hours:	11am-11pm (Sun-Fri), 11am-7pm (Sat)
equip. for hire:	Backline (Marshall, Trace Elliot, Ashdown), PA
info:	Fully licensed bar and accessories shop. Storage
from £7 per week.

DOA Rehearsal Studios
Unit F, Wordsworth Trading Estate, Halliwell, Bolton, BL1 3ND
tel:	01204 844 333
email:	info@doastudios.com
web:	www.doastudios.com
rates:	Contact for details
rooms:	6
hours:	Flexible
secure storage:	No
equipment:	PA. Additional mics and leads if required.
equip. for hire:	Drum kit, bass and guitar amps

Elevator Recording Studios
23-27 Cheapside, Liverpool, L2 2DY
tel:	0151 255 0195
fax:	0151 255 0195
email:	tim@elevatorstudios.com
web:	www.elevatorstudios.com
contact:	Tim, Paul
rates:	£60-£100 per week
rooms:	35
hours:	24 hours, 7 days a week
secure storage:	No
equip. for hire:	PA, backline
info:	All rehearsal rooms have natural light.R ecording
facilities also available. See relevant section for more details.

Firehouse Studios
Rear of the Market Hall, Market Square, Millom, Cumbria, LA18 4HZ
tel:	07732 927 603
email:	firehouse@firehousestudios.com
web:	www.firehousestudios.com
contact:	Barry
rates:	£5 per hour
rooms:	2
hours:	Flexible
secure storage:	Yes
equipment:	Backline, 200W vocal PA
equip. for hire:	Range of equipment available
info:	Opening hours are flexible, but generally
between 9am and midnight. Firehouse also run a recording studio and
PA hire service. Refer to entries in relevant sections for further details.

The Fuzzbox Ltd.
8 Clayton Street, Wigan, Lancashire, WN3 4DA
tel:	01942 230 888
email:	admin@thefuzzbox.com
web:	www.thefuzzbox.com
contact:	Jamie Cavanagh
rates:	Contact for details
rooms:	5
secure storage:	Yes
equip. for hire:	PA, drum kits
info:	Rates variable depending on time of day, as well
as introductory offers. Relaxation areas available including DVD player
and pool table.

G2
1st Floor, Wellington House, Pollard Street East, Manchester, M40 7FS
tel:	0161 275 9211
email:	nbh@easynet.co.uk
contact:	Mark Powell
rates:	From £22 for 4 hours
rooms:	17
hours:	11am-11pm (Sun-Fri), 11am-6pm (Sat)
secure storage:	No
equip. for hire:	Drum kits, mics, PAs, amps
info:	Rooms with 24 hour access are available.

Glass Studios
Unit 22, Price Street Business Centre, Price Street, Birkenhead, Wirral,
CH41 4JQ
tel:	0151 651 1666
fax:	0151 651 1888
email:	info@glassstudios.com
web:	www.glassstudios.com
contact:	Alan Lewis
rates:	£6 per hour
rooms:	5
hours:	24 hours, 7 days a week
secure storage:	Yes
equipment:	PA
info:	Glass Studios also has audio and video recording
facilities. See relevant section for further details.

The Greenhouse
Unit 16, Brighton Road Industrial Estate, Heaton Norris, Stockport, SK4 2BE

tel:	0161 431 4127
contact:	Mark Powell
rates:	From £22 for 4 hours
rooms:	7
hours:	10am-11pm 7 days a week (except Sat evening)
secure storage:	Yes
equip. for hire:	PA, amps, drum kit

Inch
Unit 22, 23 New Mount Street, Manchester, M4 4DE

tel:	0161 953 4232
email:	keir@inchstudio.com
web:	www.inchstudio.com
contact:	Keir Stewart
rates:	From £10 per hour
rooms:	2
hours:	Flexible
secure storage:	No
equipment:	PA
equip. for hire:	Amps, drum kit, range of instruments
info:	Also offer recording facilities. See entry in relevant section for further details.

Lancaster Music Co-op
1 Lodge Street, Lancaster, LA1 1QW

tel:	01524 388 544
fax:	01524 388 544
email:	musiccoop@musiccoop.co.uk
web:	www.musiccoop.co.uk
contact:	Dave Blackwell, Ian Dickon, Tom Myall
rates:	From £2.50 per hour
rooms:	4
hours:	1pm-10pm (Sun-Fri), 1pm-8pm (Sat)
secure storage:	Yes
equip. for hire:	Guitar and bass amps, mics
info:	Range of accessories for sale. Also run a recording studio. Refer to entry in relevant section for further details.

LP Studios
Unit 4/2, Meadowmill, Water Street, Stockport, SK1 2BY

tel:	0161 477 7676/07979 767 778/07929 448 928
email:	lpstudios@lpstudios.co.uk
web:	www.lpstudios.co.uk
contact:	Leigh Eaton
rates:	£25 for 4 hours
rooms:	2
hours:	10am-11pm, 7 days a week
secure storage:	No
equipment:	PA, 2 mics
equip. for hire:	Additional mics, drum kit
info:	2 practice rooms, as well as a live room and recording booth. Lock-out available from £400 per month. Recording facilities also available. See relevant section for more details.

Mad Dog Studio
Unit 57, Deeside Industrial Estate, Welsh Road, Deeside, CH5 2LR

tel:	01244 281 705
email:	maddogstudios666@hotmail.com
web:	www.maddogstudios.org
contact:	Eddie Dog
rates:	From £3 per hour
rooms:	3
secure storage:	Yes
equipment:	Backline
info:	Specialise in live recordings. The studios also provide a number of other services, including CD duplication and mastering. See listing in relevant section for details.

The Madhouse Studio
Unit 1, Henry Street, Crewe, Cheshire, CW1 4BH

tel:	01270 251 014
email:	themadhouse@cd2.com
contact:	Steve
rooms:	2
secure storage:	Yes
equipment:	PA
info:	Also run 16 track recording studio. Video production and website design and hosting available. See relevant sections for more information.

Moolah Rouge

Unit 4, Hallam Mill, Hallam Street, Stockport, SK2 6PT

tel:	0161 429 0986
email:	moolahrouge@virgin.net
web:	www.moolahrouge.com
contact:	Colin McLeod
rates:	From £28.50 for 4 hours
rooms:	6
hours:	10am-11pm
secure storage:	Yes
equipment:	PA, mics
equip. for hire:	Backline, drum kits
info:	6 spacious rooms, including a very large showcase room with baby grand piano. Easy access, lifts, secure parking, chill out area. Creative environment for musicians. See also Recording Studio listings.

The Music Factory

Unit 3a, Sycamore Trading Estate, off Squires Gate Lane, Blackpool, FY4 3RL

tel:	01253 348 037
fax:	01253 348 055
email:	info@themusicfactoryuk.co.uk
web:	www.themusicfactoryuk.co.uk
contact:	Andy Mudd
rates:	£30 for 4 hour session
rooms:	1
hours:	6pm-10pm (Mon-Fri)
secure storage:	Yes
equipment:	Backline, PA

Pacific Rehearsal Rooms

4 Birchall Street, Sandhills, Liverpool, L20 8PD

tel:	0151 933 0505
contact:	Lee Radcliffe
rates:	£3 per hour
rooms:	16
hours:	12pm-12am, 7 days a week
secure storage:	No
equip. for hire:	Range of equipment including PA and backline

Redbridge Studios

Breightmet Fold Lane, Bolton, BL2 5PH

tel:	01204 525 579
email:	info@redbridgestudios.com
web:	www.redbridgestudios.com
contact:	Andy Wyatt
rates:	From £21 per session
rooms:	6
hours:	24 hours, 7 days a week
secure storage:	No
equipment:	PA, mics, mic stands
equip. for hire:	Marshall half stacks, drum kits, Trace Elliot bass cabs, minidisc players
info:	Fully sound insulated with fridge and sofa in every room. The Redbridge complex also comprises a chillout area and shop selling musical equipment. Also have a recording studio on-site. See listing in relevant section for details.

The Rhythm Section

Oyston Mill, Strand Road, Preston, Lancashire

tel:	07786 521 815
email:	lynz2121@hotmail.com
contact:	Lindsey
rates:	£6 per hour
rooms:	3
hours:	10am-2pm, 7 days a week
secure storage:	Yes
equipment:	Full PA, backline
equip. for hire:	Guitar and bass amps, drum kits, PA, mixers, mics
info:	Snack shop on-site.

The Shed Recording Studios

Unit 35, Chadkirk Industrial Estate, Vale Road, Romiley, Stockport, SK6 3NE

tel:	0161 427 6819
fax:	0161 427 6819
email:	shedstudio1@tiscali.co.uk
contact:	John Slater
rates:	From £18 for 4 hours
rooms:	3
hours:	12pm-12am, 7 days a week
secure storage:	No
equipment:	PA, mics
info:	Rates vary depending on size of the room.

Soundhouse

Warflex House, Wood Street, Darwen, Lancashire, BB3

tel:	01254 701 603
email:	info@soundhouse-web.co.uk
web:	www.soundhouse-web.co.uk
contact:	Patrick Dixon
rates:	From £5 per hour
rooms:	2
hours:	10am-2pm, 6pm-11pm (Mon-Fri), 10am-6pm (Sat), 12pm-11pm (Sun)
secure storage:	Yes
equipment:	Vocal PA with mic
equip. for hire:	Basic drum kit and amps
info:	2 rehearsal rooms available, 1 large room sized 28 x 14ft, and smaller room sized 12 x 12ft. Rates vary depending on room used. Bands can rent storage space from £5 per week. Also refer to entry in Recording Studios section.

Strangeways Studios

Dickinson Street, Salford, M3 7LW

tel:	0161 834 3233/07865 220 428
email:	info@strangewaystudios.co.uk
web:	www.strangewaystudios.co.uk
contact:	Martin
rates:	£6 per hour
rooms:	1
hours:	Flexible
secure storage:	No
equipment:	PA, mics
equip. for hire:	Drum kit, backline
info:	One very large room also suitable for use as a showcase venue. Free refreshments. Recording facilities available - see relevant section for more details.

Tuff Gong

Unit 6, Longford Street, Warrington, WA2 7PG

tel:	01925 232 536
email:	tuffgong@btconnect.com
web:	www.tuffgong.co.uk
contact:	Lee
rates:	£7 per hour
rooms:	8
hours:	10am-5pm, 7pm-12am (Mon-Fri), 9am-6pm (Sat), 12pm-12am (Sun)
secure storage:	No
equipment:	PA
equip. for hire:	Range of equipment and instruments
info:	The Tuff Gong complex also includes a recording studio, a record shop called Hottwaxx, dance studio, café, music school and musical equipment shop called Access All Areas Music. See relevant sections for further details.

Urban Sound Rehearsal Rooms

Suite 16, Kirkless House, Kirkless Industrial Estate, Aspull, Wigan, WN2 1HF

tel:	01942 244 007
email:	info@urbansoundstudios.co.uk
web:	www.urbansoundstudios.co.uk
contact:	Stuart Hurst, Alex Hurst
rates:	£6 per hour
rooms:	6
hours:	11am-11pm all week, except Saturdays
secure storage:	No
equipment:	Full PA, mics and mic stands

Vulcan Studios

68 Waterloo Road, Liverpool, L3 7BE

tel:	0151 236 2724
email:	info@vulcanstudios.co.uk
web:	www.vulcanstudios.co.uk
contact:	Barry Jenkins
rates:	From £3 per hour
rooms:	14
hours:	11am-11pm, 7 days a week
secure storage:	No
equip. for hire:	PA, backline, drum kit, recording equipment
info:	Refreshments available. Recording facilities also offered, 16 track and 8 track at around £10 per hour. Contact for further details.

SOUTHEAST

23 Degrees Ltd.
The Ford, Arundel, Sussex, BN18 ODF
tel:	01243 552 338
fax:	01243 552 380
email:	info@fordlane.com
web:	www.fordlane.com
contact:	Nicky Moray
rates:	£28 for 4 hours
rooms:	2
hours:	7 days a week
secure storage:	No
equipment:	PA, mics, leads
info:	Parking facilities available. Tea and coffee. 23 Degrees also run recording studio. See entry in relevant section for details.

24/7 Studios
6 Hertford Street, Cowley, Oxford, OX4 3AJ
tel:	01865 435 981/07768 410 080
email:	robin@247studios.co.uk
web:	www.247studios.co.uk
contact:	Robin Leggett
rates:	See website
rooms:	1
secure storage:	Yes
equipment:	Vocal PA, backline, upright piano, drum kit, mics
equip. for hire:	Cymbals
info:	Also offer recording facilities, and equipment hire for gigs. See listings in relevant sections for further information.

Adventure Studios
5 Stables Lane, Eastbourne, East Sussex, BN21 4RE
tel:	01323 720 784/07889 160 147
email:	doug.sturrock@btconnect.com
web:	www.adventurestudios.co.uk
contact:	Doug
rates:	£80 per month
rooms:	2
secure storage:	No
equipment:	PA, bass amp
info:	Bands can hire a room on monthly basis, allowing them access to once a week for the month, for up to 6 hours at a time. Also provide recording facilities. See relevant section for more details.

Air Tight Studios
1 Shopwhyke Industrial Centre, Shopwhyke Road, Chichester, West Sussex, PO20 2GD
tel:	01243 839 565
email:	info@airtightstudios.com
web:	www.airtightstudios.com
rates:	£30 for 3 hours
rooms:	1
hours:	11am -11pm
secure storage:	No
equipment:	PA, mics
info:	Air Tight have 1 large rehearsal room and 3 recording studios. See entry in relevant section for details. Parking and refreshments available.

Amber Sound & Light Ltd.
Unit 12, Robjohn's House, Navigation Road, Chelmsford, Essex, CN2 6ND
tel:	01245 261 065
email:	via website
web:	www.ambersoundandlight.co.uk
rates:	Contact for details
rooms:	4
hours:	10am-12am
secure storage:	Yes
equipment:	PA, mics
equip. for hire:	PA, drum kit

Backline Rehearsal Studio Ltd.
1-2 The Archways, Guildford Park Road, Guildford, Surrey, GU2 7NP
tel:	01483 533 876
email:	mail@backlinestudios.co.uk
web:	www.backlinestudios.co.uk
contact:	Dave Neale, Brian Tuitt
rates:	Contact for details
rooms:	4
hours:	10am-11pm (weekdays) 10am-10pm (weekends)
secure storage:	No
equipment:	Full PA, drum kits, guitar and bass amps
equip. for hire:	Electric and acoustic guitars, bass, drum equipment
info:	Backline have 4 spacious air conditioned rooms. Prices vary depending on size of room. Lounge area and refreshments available. Parking facilities. Also 24 track recording studio, see recording studios section. Contact for further details.

Bandbits
Prince Bros Site, Old Bath Road, Charvil, Reading, RG10 9QJ
tel:	0118 932 0032
fax:	0118 932 0016
email:	nick@bandbits.com
web:	www.bandbits.com
contact:	Nick Lawson
rates:	From £11 per hour
rooms:	2
hours:	24 hours, 7 days a week
secure storage:	No
equipment:	PA, mics
equip. for hire:	Drum kit
info:	Bandbits also offer studio recording and CD mastering and duplication. See relevant entries for details.

The Barn Studio
Hawthorn Hill, Maidenhead, Berkshire
tel:	07976 717 352
email:	millarmsb@ntlworld.com
secure storage:	Yes
info:	Contact via the above email address or telephone number and give details of your band. Spaces at the studio are rare, but every now and again places do come up.

The Base
91 Third Street, New Greenham Park, Newbury, West Berkshire, RG19 6HN
tel:	01635 521 515/07795 217 818
email:	baserehearsals@btconnect.com
web:	www.thebase.org.uk
contact:	Moon
rates:	From £12 per hour
rooms:	4
hours:	Flexible
secure storage:	Yes
equipment:	PA, drums, mics
equip. for hire:	Guitar and bass amps
info:	Membership is available at £15 per head, this gives 10% off rates for a year. Also offer studio and location recording, see entry in relevant section for details. Can also provide DVD gig recording, as well as road crews for tours nationwide and beyond.

Burst Studios
Unit 8, Bilting Farm Business Centre, Canterbury Road, Bilting, Ashford, Kent, TN25 4HF
tel:	01233 663 148/07760 491 877
email:	info@burststudios.com
web:	www.burststudios.com
rates:	£10 per hour
rooms:	2
hours:	Call for availability
secure storage:	Yes
equipment:	PA, mics, backline, drum kit
info:	Reception and kitchen area.

Casemates
Music Rehearsal Centre, Bastion 4, Scott Rd, Hilsea, Portsmouth, PO3 5JH
tel:	02392 669 000
email:	derek@casemates.co.uk
contact:	Derek
rates:	From £16 for 3 hours
rooms:	4
hours:	Flexible
secure storage:	No
equipment:	PA
equip. for hire:	Backline
info:	Ample parking facilities.

Castmates Bastion
4 Scott Road, Hilsea, Portsmouth
tel:	02392 669 000
rooms:	4
secure storage:	No
equipment:	PA in 3 rooms, PA and backline in 1 larger room
info:	Situated close to the M27.

Cats Eye Studios
1B Lowesden Works, Lambourn Woodlands, Hungerford, Berkshire, RG17 7RU
tel:	01488 670 228
email:	info@catseyestudios.com
web:	www.catseyestudios.com
rates:	From £9 per hour
rooms:	4
hours:	11am-11pm (Mon-Fri), 11am-7pm (Sat & Sun)
secure storage:	Yes
equipment:	Yamaha PAs, mics, stands, cables
equip. for hire:	Pearl 5 piece drum kit, Marshall guitar combo, Ashdown bass combo
info:	Cats Eye have a chillout room with Sky TV. Hot and cold drinks and snacks available. Unlimited free parking.

The Cold Room Studios
Gees Farm, Denmans Lane, Cumnor, Oxford, OX2 9PF
tel:	07947 710 740
email:	rich@coldroomstudios.co.uk
web:	www.coldroomstudios.co.uk
contact:	Rich
rates:	£9 per hour
rooms:	4
hours:	10am-12am, 7 days a week
secure storage:	No
equipment:	PA, drum kit (without cymbals), bass and guitar amps
info:	Established studio also offering analogue and digital recording. See entry in relevant section for details.

Creative Rehearsal Studio
Unit 2a, Middleton Hall, Brentwood Rd, Brentwood, Essex, CM13 3OX
tel:	01277 811 886/07717 503 797
email:	info@creativestudios2000.com
web:	www.creativestudios2000.com
rates:	£12-£16 per hour
rooms:	3
hours:	Contact for details
secure storage:	Yes
equipment:	PA, backline
info:	Creative can offer live recording of your session. All 3 studios are fully equipped, sound-proofed and acoustically treated. Hot and cold drinks and snacks available. Also run a music academy teaching a wide range of instruments. See entry in relevant section for details.

d2j Studios
Unit 4, Templefields Enterprise Centre, South Road, Harlow, Essex, CM20 2AR
tel:	01279 431 161
email:	d2jstudios@hotmail.com
contact:	James Donoghue, Mick Donoghue
rates:	£10 per hour
rooms:	1
secure storage:	Yes
equipment:	Drums, keyboard, mics
info:	Rehearsal rooms for bands, as well as DJ practice space. Also offer recording facilities and artwork design services. See listings in relevant sections for further details.

Denmark Studios
Unit 3a, Denmark Street, Maidenhead, Berkshire, SL6 7BN
tel:	01628 771 710/07899 777 577
email:	denmarkstudios@denmarkstudios.net
web:	www.denmarkstudios.net
contact:	Heather
rates:	£14 per hour
rooms:	4
hours:	24 hours, 7 days a week
secure storage:	Yes
equipment:	PA, drums, amps
info:	Packages available, £40 for 8 hours (before 6pm weekdays) and £40 for 4 hours (Saturdays). Call for further details.

Eastwood Studios
Unit 2, The Courtyard, Bullington End, Manor Farm, Hanslope, Milton Keynes, MK19 7BQ
tel:	07811 134 164
email:	info@eastwoodstudios.co.uk
web:	www.eastwoodstudios.co.uk
rates:	£30 for 4 hours
rooms:	2
hours:	9am-11pm, 7 days a week
secure storage:	Yes
equipment:	PA, mics, stands
equip. for hire:	Backline
info:	Eastwood Studio also have recording facilities. See relevant section for more details.

Effenel Studios
787 Southchurch Road, Southend On Sea, Essex, SS1 2PP
tel:	01702 614 857
email:	info@effenel.com
web:	www.effenel.com
rates:	From £5 per hour
rooms:	8
secure storage:	Yes
equipment:	Amps, PA, drum kit, mics, stands, leads
info:	Also provide recording facilities. See entry in Recording Studios section for more information.

The Farm Studios
Gerpins Lane, Upminster, RM14 2XR
tel:	01708 640 128
rates:	From £32 for 4 hours
rooms:	3
hours:	Evenings
secure storage:	Yes
equipment:	PA, mics
equip. for hire:	Guitar amps, drum kit
info:	Rates vary depending on size of room used. Recording facilities also available. See relevant section for more details.

Faversham Youth and Community Centre
46 South Road, Faversham, Kent, ME13 7LR
tel:	01795 532 238
fax:	01795 532 238
email:	mick.cahill@kent.gov.uk
rates:	ask for details
rooms:	1
hours:	negotiable
secure storage:	Yes
equipment:	Drum kit and PA
info:	Also have a 24 track recording studio.

Garden Studios
The Shooting Lodge, Woking Road, Guildford, Surrey, GU4 7PZ
tel:	01483 236 434
fax:	01483 237 004
email:	nev@gardenstudios.net
web:	www.gardenstudios.net
contact:	Neville Dean
rates:	From £35 for 4 hours
rooms:	2
hours:	24hr, 7 days
secure storage:	No
equipment:	All included, PA, drums, mics.
info:	Also a recording studios as well as providing guitar and drum tuition. See listings for more information.

Garden Studios
61 Dugard Avenue, Colchester, Essex, CO3 9EL
tel:	01206 562 155
rates:	£20 for 3 hours
rooms:	1
secure storage:	Yes
equipment:	PA, drum kit, backline

Ground Zero Studio
43 Coombe Terrace, Brighton, East Sussex, BN2 4AD
tel:	01273 819 617
email:	studio@g-zero.co.uk
web:	www.g-zero.co.uk
contact:	James Stringfellow
rates:	Call for details
rooms:	8
hours:	Call for details
secure storage:	Yes
info:	Ground Zero is a studio complex with 4 recording studios and 8 residential rehearsal rooms. See entry in relevant section for info of recording services.

Impact Studios
14 Wokingham Road, Reading, Berkshire, RG6 1JG
tel:	0118 935 1479
email:	mail@impactstudios.co.uk
web:	www.impactstudios.co.uk
rates:	From £4.50 per hour
rooms:	6
hours:	12pm-12am (Mon-Fri), 10am-8pm (Sat), 10am-12am (Sun)
secure storage:	Yes
equipment:	PA, drum kit, bass and guitar amps
equip. for hire:	Snare drum, cymbals
info:	Impact run 6 air conditioned rooms across 2 sites. Rates depend on size of room. Also offer support services such as PA and lighting hire, short run CD duplication and even an on-site music shop which is open late, 7 days a week. Contact for further information.

Ivy Arch Studios
5B Ivy Arch Road, Worthing, BN14 8BX
tel:	01903 536 106
email:	info@ivyarchstudio.co.uk
web:	www.ivyarchstudios.co.uk
rates:	£11 per hour
rooms:	2
secure storage:	No
equipment:	Drum kit (without cymbals), PA, 2 guitar amps, bass amps, mics, stands
equip. for hire:	Keyboard
info:	Acoustic amp available if required. Stage available for rehearsal at £15 per hour. Sessions can be filmed to DVD. Recording facilities also available, see relevant section for details.

K2 Music Ltd.
Unit 70, Fresh Wharf Estate, Fresh Wharf Road, Barking, Essex, IG11 7BW
email: info@k2musicltd.co.uk
web: www.k2musicltd.co.uk
contact: Steve Gee
rates: Contact for details
rooms: 4
hours: Contact for details
secure storage: Yes
equip. for hire: Full backline
info: Rates vary depending on size of rehearsal room booked. Free parking. K2 also offer equipment hire and repair services, tuition and a music shop. See listings in relevant sections for details.

The Liveroom
Horndean Campus, Barton Cross, Horndean, Hampshire, PO8 9PQ
tel: 02393 599 753
email: bookings@theliveroom.co.uk
web: www.theliveroom.co.uk
contact: Will Yates
rates: Contact for details
rooms: 3
secure storage: No
info: Large live room, as well as additional tuition rooms which can also be booked for rehearsals. Recording studio and duplication services also provided. Linked with D-Code design company. See entries in relevant sections for further information.

MachineHead Studios
72a North Street, Portslade, Brighton, East Sussex, BN41 1DG
tel: 0845 345 8099/07712 132 855
email: steve@fcscassettes.co.uk
web: www.machineheadstudios.co.uk
contact: Steve Priest
rates: Contact for details
rooms: 6
hours: Contact for details
secure storage: Yes
equipment: Drum kit, guitar, bass, mics

Madcap Arts Centre
Creed Street, Wolverton, Milton Keynes, MK12 5LY
tel: 01908 320 179
email: info@madcap.org.uk
web: www.madcap.org.uk
secure storage: Yes
info: Also offer rehearsal facilities. See relevant section for details.

Maple Studios
Unit 39-45, Grainger Road Industrial Estate, Southend On Sea, SS2 5DD
tel: 01702 613 066
fax: 01702 603 559
rates: Contact for details
rooms: 5
secure storage: Yes
equipment: Vocal PA, mics
equip. for hire: Amps

The Mayfair Studio
Mayfair Farm, Churt Road, Churt, Farnham, Surrey, GU10 2QS
tel: 01428 712 750/07831 333 502
email: rupert@themayfairstudio.com
web: www.themayfairstudio.com
contact: Rupert
rates: Call for details
rooms: 1
hours: Flexible
secure storage: No
equipment: PA, drums, guitar and bass amps, Hammond organ, Roland pianos
info: Secure storage is available for bands using the studio. Also offer studio and location recording, as well as drum and guitar tuition. See entries in relevant sections for details.

The Mick Jagger Centre
Shepherds Lane, Dartford, Kent, DA1 2JZ
tel: 01322 291 101)/01322 291 100
email: mail@themickjaggercentre.com
web: www.themickjaggercentre.com
rates: See below
rooms: 8, of varying sizes
hours: Evening and weekends during termtime, daytime, evenings and weekends during holidays
secure storage: Yes
equipment: Piano (grand and upright) available on request.
info: Rehearsal facilities comprise of 4 smaller rooms, 2 medium sized rooms and 2 large performance spaces (suitable for showcases). Small rooms cost £10 per hour for first hour, then drop to £8 per hour and £6 per hour for second and third hours booked. Medium sized rooms have a similar cost structure, with first hour charged at £15, then falling to £13 and £12. See website for details of cost of using large performance spaces. The centre is part of Dartford Grammar School and also houses a live venue.

The Mill Arts Centre
Spiceball Park, Banbury, Oxon, OX16 5QE
tel: 01295 252 050
email: info@oxfordshire.gov.uk
web: www.millartscentre.org.uk
contact: Liz Reed
rates: £5 per hour, £30 per day
rooms: 1
hours: 9am-11pm
secure storage: Yes
info: Situated in an excellent arts venue. Bar facilities on-site.

Monster Studios
Unit 25, Hove Enterprise Centre, Basin Road North, Portslade, BN41 1UY
tel: 01273 416 699
email: aaron@monsterstudios.co.uk
web: www.monsterstudios.co.uk
contact: Aaron Miller
rates: Contact for details
rooms: 3
hours: Contact for details
secure storage: Yes
equipment: PA, drum kit, amps, mics, leads, stands
info: Refreshments are available. Ample free parking.

Mr Gig Studios
15 - 26 Tavistock Street, Bletchley, Buckinghamshire, MK2 2PF
tel: 01908 376 500
rates: £25 for 4 hours
rooms: 2
hours: 11am-11pm
secure storage: Yes
equipment: PA, backline
equip. for hire: Drum kit
info: Rooms are sound-proofed and air-conditioned. Free tea and coffee. Also offer recording facilities. See relevant section for more details.

Mushroom Rehearsal Studio
Lubards Farm, Hullbridge Road, Rayleigh, Essex, SS6 9QG
tel: 01268 784 599
email: mushroomstudio@aol.com
web: www.mushroomrehearsalstudios.com
rates: £28-£40 for 4 hours
rooms: 7
hours: 7pm-11pm (Mon-Fri), 10am-6.30pm (Sat), 10am-11pm (Sun)
secure storage: No
equipment: PA, mics
equip. for hire: Drums,bass and guitar combos, extra monitoring
info: Situated in rural Essex, Mushroom offers easy loading and parking for over 40 vehicles. Daytime sessions and lock-outs by arrangement. Small lounge. Hot and cold snacks are also available.

No Machine Studio
Unit 4, 127a Reading Road, Wokingham, Berkshire, RG41 1HD
tel: 0118 979 3921
email: enquiries@nomachine.co.uk
web: www.nomachine.co.uk
rates: £16 per hour
rooms: 4
hours: 7pm-11pm (Mon-Fri), 10am-6pm (Sat), 10am-10pm (Sun)
secure storage: Yes
equipment: PA, mics
equip. for hire: Backline
info: All rooms 6m x 4m. Also offer recording facilities. See relevant section for details.

Nutbrown Studio
Riding Lane, Holtpsur, Beaconsfield, Buckinghamshire, HP9 1BT
tel:	01494 680 436
email:	contact@nutbrownstudios.co.uk
web:	www.nutbrownstudios.co.uk
contact:	Rod, Kris
rates:	From £15 per hour
rooms:	2
hours:	24 hours, 7 days a week
secure storage:	No
equipment:	PA, drums, backline
info:	Recording and rehearsal studios situated just

outside High Wycombe. Providing both residential and non-residential services for musicians, freelance producers and independent record labels.

Playback Systems
Unit 1b South, New England House, Brighton, BN1 4GH
tel:	01273 671 297
email:	info@playbacksystems.com
web:	www.playbacksystems.com
contact:	James Porch
rates:	£12 per hour
rooms:	1
hours:	24 hours, 7 days a week
secure storage:	Yes
equipment:	PA, guitar and bass amps
info:	Large client list including Orbital, Electrelane,

Eighties Matchbox B-Line Disaster and The Kooks. Also offer a pre-production and demo recording service, as well as equipment hire. See entries in relevant sections for details.

Plug n Play Rehearsal Studio
33-35 Milford Road, Reading, Berkshire, RG1 8LG
tel:	0118 958 1446
email:	info@plugnplay.tv
web:	www.plugnplay.tv
rates:	£12 per hour (off peak times), £16-£20 (peak times)
rooms:	4
hours:	10am-12am
secure storage:	Yes
equipment:	PA, mics, leads, drum kit, amps
info:	Free tea and coffee and licensed bar on-site. Fully

ventilated studios with high standard of sound design. Photographic studio and showcase facilities also available. Close to M4 and Reading train station.

POD Music
Phuture Tower, Barker Chambers, Barker Road, Maidstone, Kent, ME16 8SF
tel:	0870 2000 763
email:	info@podmusic.co.uk
web:	www.podmusic.co.uk
rates:	Contact for details
rooms:	1
secure storage:	Yes
equipment:	PA, drum kit
info:	Hourly rate decreases as number of hours

booked increases. Also offer vocal coaching and recording services. See relevant sections for more details.

React Studios
3 Fleece Yard, Market Hill, Buckingham, MK18 1JX
tel:	01280 821 840
fax:	01280 821 840
email:	info@reactstudios.co.uk
web:	www.reactstudios.co.uk
rates:	From £30 per session
rooms:	3
secure storage:	No
equipment:	PA, mics
equip. for hire:	Range of equipment including monitors and backline
info:	Sessions run 7pm-11pm, and 1pm-6pm. Other

hours by arrangement.

Running Frog Music
127 St. Leonard's Road, Windsor, Berkshire, SL4 3DW
tel:	01753 620 857
email:	studio@runningfrog.com
web:	www.runningfrog.com
contact:	Phil Ray
rates:	Call for details
rooms:	4
hours:	24 hours, 7 days a week
secure storage:	Yes
equipment:	PA, drums, amps
info:	Air-conditioned rehearsal studios. During all

sessions in-house engineers will help with set up or any technical problems. Also offer studio recording, see entry in relevant section for further details.

Scream Studios
Module A1, Enterprise Point, Melbourne Street, Brighton, East Sussex, BN2 3LH
tel:	01273 671 086
email:	brighton@screamstudios.co.uk
web:	www.screamstudios.co.uk
rates:	Call for details
rooms:	12
hours:	Call for details
secure storage:	Yes
equipment:	PA
equip. for hire:	Drums, guitar and bass amps
info:	150 capacity showcase room available for A&R

showcases. Call for more information.

The Shack Studio
Old Church Road, East Hanningfield Road, Chelmsford, Essex, CM3 8BH
tel:	01245 403 074
web:	www.shackstudio.co.uk
rates:	From £30 per session
secure storage:	Yes
equip. for hire:	Drum kit, bass and guitar amps
info:	Recording studios with rehearsal space available.

Can also provide equipment for external hire. See listing in Recording Studios section for further information.

Shut Up Fool Studios
Unit 4, Allshots Enterprises, Woodhouse Lane, Kelvedon, Essex, CO5 9DF
tel:	07990 772 273
rates:	£9 per hour
rooms:	3
hours:	Flexible
secure storage:	Yes
equipment:	PA, mics, stands
info:	Chillout area with TV, games and CD player. Free

tea and coffee. Minimum booking of 3 hour slot applies.

The Silent Coup
Unit 6a, Grange Farm Units, Nelsons Lane, Hurst, Berkshire, RG10 0RR
tel:	0118 934 0934/07094 601 059/07976 242 725
email:	admin@the-silent-coup.org
web:	www.the-silent-coup.org
rates:	£7 per hour
rooms:	4
hours:	12pm-Late, 7 days a week
secure storage:	No
equipment:	Full backline, PA, drum kit
info:	2 practice isolation booths available. Also

provide recording, design and tuition services. See relevant section for details.

Silent Hill Studio
Unit B, Perram Works, Merrow Lane, Guildford, GU4 7BN
tel:	01483 304 956/07771 752 475
email:	info@silenthillstudio.com
web:	www.silenthillstudio.com
contact:	Julian Hoddy
rates:	From £10 per hour
rooms:	4
hours:	10am-12am, 7 days a week
secure storage:	No
equipment:	PA, mics
equip. for hire:	Backline
info:	All rooms are fully mirrored. Live recording

available, suitable for demos. PA hire service. Contact for details.

SoundArc
Unit 3b, St. Francis' Way, Shefford, Bedfordshire, SG17 5DZ
tel:	07931 985 801
email:	music_at_soundarc@hotmail.com
web:	www.soundarc.co.uk
contact:	John
rates:	From £5 per hour
rooms:	2
hours:	Contact for details
secure storage:	Yes
info:	Full technical specifications for rooms can be

viewed on website above. Facility to record your session for extra cost of £10 for 80 minutes. Also run a recording studio. See listing for more information.

SoundArt
Unit E1, St. George's Business Park, Sittingbourne, ME10 3TB
tel:	07961 177 013
email:	viv_soundart@hotmail.com
web:	www.soundart.co.uk
contact:	Viv
rates:	See website
rooms:	2
secure storage:	Yes
equipment:	PA, guitar amp, bass rig, drum kit
info:	Discount available for block bookings. Also offer recording facilities. See entry in relevant section for details.

Sour Apple Studios
34 Boundary Road, Newbury, Berkshire, RG14 5RR
tel:	01635 582 266
email:	sourapplestudios@hotmail.com
web:	www.sourapplestudios.tk
contact:	Paul
rates:	£8-£12 per hour
rooms:	5
hours:	10am-11pm
secure storage:	No
equipment:	PA, drums, guitar and bass amps
info:	Also offer 8 track session recording, see relevant entry for details.

Stag Studios
Unit 3, The Surridge Centre, Stepfield, Witham, Essex, CM8 3TH
tel:	01376 502 209/07740 478 578
email:	info@stagstudios.com
web:	www.stagstudios.com
rates:	soundbase#
rooms:	5
secure storage:	Yes
equipment:	PA
equip. for hire:	Backline
info:	All rooms have been acoustically designed. Can also provide recording facilities. See relevant section for more details.

Strummers
1 Roedean Road, Brighton, East Sussex, BN2 5RU
tel:	01273 695 814
email:	ken@strummers.com
web:	www.strummers.com
contact:	Ken Stagles
rates:	£7 per hour
secure storage:	Yes
equipment:	Pearl drum kit, Marshall amps, Korg Keyboard, Shure mics
info:	Cater for bands and musicians of all styles. Facility to record rehearsal session.

Studio 284
284 Madeira Drive, Brighton
tel:	01273 572 277/07790 609 966
email:	studio284@btconnect.com
rates:	From £5 per hour (Daytime), From £7 per hour (Evenings)
rooms:	2
hours:	Flexible
secure storage:	Yes
equipment:	Full backline, PA, drum kit, piano, keyboard. Hammond organ available on request.
info:	Recording facilities also available. See relevant section for more details.

The Music Centre
35-37 Tavistock Street, Bedford, MK40 2RB
tel:	01234 346 206
email:	info@musicentre.co.uk
web:	www.musicentre.co.uk
rates:	£30 for 4 hours
rooms:	1
hours:	10am-6pm Monday - Saturday
secure storage:	No
equipment:	PA
equip. for hire:	Drum kit, backline and amps.
info:	Also a music retailer. Storage is £10 per week.

Tweeters 2 Studios
Unit C1, Business Park 7, Brook Way, Leatherhead, Surrey, KT22 7NA
tel:	01372 386 592
email:	info@tweeters2studios.co.uk
web:	www.tweeters2studios.co.uk
rates:	From £24 for 4 hours
rooms:	6
hours:	10am-11pm
secure storage:	No
equipment:	PA
equip. for hire:	Contact for details
info:	Tweeters have 6 rehearsal rooms available, size and equipment varies from room to room. Contact for details. Also have outside equipment hire and recording facilities. See entry in relevant section for details.

Voodoo Rooms
Unit 75c, South Street, Bishops Stortford, Hertfordshire, CM23 3AL
tel:	01279 460 222
email:	info@voodoorooms.com
web:	www.voodoorooms.com
contact:	Richard
rates:	£6/hour, daytime and Saturday; £8/evenings and Sunday
rooms:	2
secure storage:	No
equipment:	PA
equip. for hire:	Drumkit and backline.
info:	Large rooms. Free storage facilities. Block booking deals available.

Wanna Management Studio Hire
Essex
tel:	01708 688 088
secure storage:	Yes
info:	Call for details of recording and rehearsal facilities.

Warehouse Rehearsal Studio
60 Sandford Lane, Kennington, Oxford, OX1 5RW
tel:	01865 736 411
email:	info@warehousestudios.com
web:	www.warehousestudios.com
contact:	Mr Smith
rates:	£10 per hour
rooms:	2
hours:	11am-11pm
secure storage:	No
equipment:	Full PA, vocal mics
info:	Rates vary depending on length of session, call for details. Refreshments, games room and TVs on site. Parking available. Warehouse also have a recording studio, see entry in relevant section for details.

Warner Music Studios
New England House, New England Street, Brighton, BN1 4GH
tel:	01273 605 550
email:	warnermusicstudios@yahoo.co.uk
web:	www.warnermusicstudios.co.uk
rates:	£8 per hour
rooms:	3
hours:	10am-12am
secure storage:	Yes
equipment:	Drumkit, PA, backline
equip. for hire:	Guitars, percussion, organ, keyboards, piano, CD players, MD recorders
info:	Central Brighton location. Warner Music Studios also provides the 'Amp Taxi' service, where your equipment can be collected from venues and returned to its original destination. Recording services also available. See relevant section for more details.

Wyngray Studio
St. Marys Lane, Upminster, Essex, RM14 3NX
tel:	01708 228 972
rates:	£35 for 4 hours
rooms:	2
hours:	7pm-11pm, 7 deys a week
secure storage:	No
equipment:	PA
info:	Rehearsal slots other than the times stated can be arranged. Large car park.

SOUTHWEST

Ariel Music Centre
Mullacott Cross, Ilfracombe, Devon, EX34 8ND
tel:	01271 862 701
email:	info@ariel.org.uk
web:	www.ariel.org.uk
contact:	Leigh Crossman
rates:	£4 per hour
rooms:	6
hours:	Contact for details
secure storage:	No
equipment:	PA
equip. for hire:	Drums, amps
info:	A state-of-the-art complex in rural Devon with

stunning coastal views. Also offer studio recording. See entry in relevant sections for details.

ATM Studios
Unit 309, Central Park, Petherton Road, Hengrove, Avon, BS14 9BZ
tel:	01275 891 847/01275 547 428
web:	www.access-2-music.co.uk
rates:	from £26 for 4 hours
rooms:	6
hours:	7pm-11pm (Mon-Fri), 11am-3pm (Sat), 3pm-11pm (Sun)
secure storage:	Yes
equipment:	PA
equip. for hire:	Drums, guitar and bass amps
info:	PA ranging between 300W to 1kW, depending on the room.

Bulrush Studios
Unit 5, Enterprise Park, Mart Road, Minehead, Somerset, TA24 5BJ
tel:	01643 707 277
email:	info@bulrushstudios.co.uk
web:	www.bulrushstudios.co.uk
rates:	£7 per hour
rooms:	2
hours:	Flexible
secure storage:	Yes
equipment:	PA, drum kit
equip. for hire:	Guitar and bass amps
info:	Bulrush Studios also offer recording facilities, CD

duplication, equipment hire and drum tuition services. See entries in relevant sections for further details.

Carncrees Rehearsal Studio
Cornwall, TR3 7AW
tel:	01209 860 345
email:	studio@cancressstudio.fsnet.co.uk
web:	www.carncreesstudio.fsnet.co.uk
contact:	David Stafford
rates:	Contact for details
rooms:	1
hours:	10am-10pm
secure storage:	Yes
equipment:	Backline, PA

Crazy Cat
Unit 1, Cowley Bridge Road, Exeter, EX4 4NX
tel:	01392 434 007
email:	info@crazycatsound.co.uk
web:	www.crazycatsound.co.uk
contact:	Rick Walker
rates:	Call for details
rooms:	10
hours:	24 hours, 7 days a week
secure storage:	No
equip. for hire:	Call for details
info:	Over 20 years experience in the. Crazy Cat Sound

offer professional music production services. Unique rates available. Rehearsal units available for bands to hire for up to a month at a time. Crazy Cat also offer a studio recording, see entry in relevant section for details.

Cruisin Rehearsal
Charlton Farm, Wiltshire, BA3 5XS
tel:	01373 834 161
fax:	01373 834 164
email:	al@cruisin.co.uk
web:	www.cruisin.co.uk
contact:	Al Hale
rates:	Contact for details
rooms:	1
hours:	10am-10pm
secure storage:	No
equipment:	PA

Drum Bank Music Services
203 Gloucester Road, Bishopston, Bristol, BS7 8NN
tel:	0117 975 5366
email:	paul@drumbankmusic.co.uk
web:	www.drumbankmusic.co.uk
rooms:	2
hours:	11am-11pm, Monday to Saturday
secure storage:	Yes
equipment:	Vocal PA, Drum kit, amps
info:	Drum Bank also provide music tuition and

instrument hire services, as well as running an instrument shop. See relevant listings for further information.

Dumb Yank
40 Pembroke Road, Salisbury, Wiltshire, SP2 9DG
tel:	01722 326 017
email:	info@dumbyank.co.uk
web:	www.dumbyank.co.uk
rates:	£10 per hour
rooms:	1
secure storage:	Yes
equipment:	PA, drum kit, mics
info:	Dumb Yank can provide (on a limited basis) an

equipped rehearsal space or showcase room, strictly by appointment only. Dumb Yank is primarily a recording studio where the live room is used a rehearsal space when not in use. Also offer mastering and duplication services. See listings for further information.

Factory Studios
Strachan & Henshaw Building, Foundry Lane, Bristol, BS5 7UZ
tel:	0117 952 5655
email:	sol@factory-studios.co.uk
web:	www.factory-studios.co.uk
rates:	£7 per hour
rooms:	6
secure storage:	No
equipment:	PA
equip. for hire:	Bass rigs, guitar amps, drum kit
info:	Also provide facilities for basic demo recordings.

Contact Factory for further information.

Glass Tone Productions Ltd.
Unit 3a, Riverside Business Park, Bath, BA2 3DW
tel:	01225 487 700/07973 730 161
email:	studio@glasstone.co.uk
web:	www.glasstone.co.uk
contact:	Greg Brooker
rooms:	1
secure storage:	Yes
equipment:	Drum kit, bass and guitar amps
info:	Acoustically designed room. 8 channel PA. Glass

Tone also provide recording facilities, management, PA hire, mastering and design services, as well as organising live events in Bath and Bristol. Refer to entries in appropriate sections for further information.

Kewsound
Kew Gardens, Crookes Lane, Kewstoke, Weston Super Mare, BS22 9XL
tel:	01934 415 645/07932 570 869
email:	steve@kewsound.co.uk
web:	www.kewsound.co.uk
contact:	Steve Allan
rates:	£6 per hour
rooms:	2
secure storage:	Yes
equipment:	PA, mics
info:	Secure parking and kitchen facilities. Kewsound

also provide recording services. See listing in relevant section for further details.

NAM Recording
4-7 Forewoods Common, Holt, Wiltshire, BA14 6JP
tel:	01225 782 281
fax:	01225 782 281
email:	namanage@aol.com
web:	www.namrecording.com
contact:	Mick Allen
rates:	£4.50 per hour
rooms:	1
hours:	9am-11pm, 7 days a week
secure storage:	Yes
equipment:	PA, mics, leads
info:	Rehearsal space is available when recording

facilities are not in use. Limited storage. Off road parking. Air conditioned. For more information on the residential recording studio, see the relevant section.

Planet Sounds
The Arches, 40 Terminus Terrace, Southampton, SO31 5FR
tel:	02380 334 040
email:	planet-sounds@btconnect.com
web:	www.planet-sounds.com
contact:	Tim Betts
rates:	From £20 for 4 hours
rooms:	5
hours:	10am-11pm
secure storage:	No
equipment:	PA, drum kit
equip. for hire:	Backline
info:	Planet Sounds have 5 large air conditioned

rehearsal rooms all on one level. Parking facilities. Refreshments available, as well as a range of music consumables for sale.

RS Studios
St. Phillips, Bristol, BS2 0SE
tel:	0117 9711 495
email:	rsstudios@hotmail.com
web:	www.rs-studios.co.uk
contact:	Rich Weaver
rates:	£7 per hour
rooms:	7
secure storage:	No
info:	All equipment provided at studios. Also has

a simple recording set up that bands can use to record an affordable demo. See relevant section for more details.

The Spice Works
Moravian Road, Kingswood, Bristol, BS15
tel:	07720 470 508
email:	alienaxeman04@yahoo.com
contact:	Dave
rates:	£25 for 4 hours
rooms:	1
hours:	Call Dave for info
secure storage:	No
equipment:	400W PA, Shure mics, backline
equip. for hire:	Backline
info:	Large rehearsal room available, owned by band

Alien Stash Tin. Looking for a trustworthy band in the area to share the studio regularly, to help cover costs.

Stonebench Studios
Lydbrook House, Lower Lydbrook, Lydbrook, GL17 9NN
tel:	01594 861 267
email:	stonebenchstudio@ukonline.com
secure storage:	Yes
info:	Rehearsal space available. Contact for more

information. Also run a recording studio. See relevant section for details.

Uncle Pablo's Music Workshop
Unit 23, Cahlwyn Industrial Estate, Clements Road, Poole, Dorset, BH12 4PE
tel:	01202 718 712
email:	unclepablos@hotmail.com
web:	www.unclepablo.co.uk
rates:	From £8 per hour
rooms:	3
hours:	6pm-11pm (Mon-Fri), 11am-6pm (Sat), 11am-11pm (Sun)
secure storage:	Yes
equipment:	PA, mic, stands, drum kit, backline
info:	Rooms with sound panelling for better sound

performance. Rates vary depending on size of room.

YORKSHIRE

Audio Zone Studios
Back Garden Street, Wakefield, WF1 1DX
tel:	01924 298 591
fax:	07715 167 212
email:	clink@audiozone.org
web:	www.audiozone.org
contact:	Neil Clarkson
rates:	£7 per hour
rooms:	2
hours:	24 hours, 7 days a week
secure storage:	No
equipment:	Drum kit, vocal PA, bass amps
equip. for hire:	Guitar amps
info:	Large rehearsal rooms. Student and other

discounts available. Contact for details.

Avalon
2 Milton Street, Unit 7, Trafalgar Court, Sheffield, S1 4JU
tel:	0114 276 8282
fax:	0114 241 4131
email:	avalonstudios2003@yahoo.co.uk
web:	www.avalon-studios.co.uk
contact:	Kevin Simons
rates:	£5 per hour
rooms:	4
hours:	11am til midnight
secure storage:	No
equip. for hire:	Drumkits and amps.
info:	Of the 4 rehearsal rooms available, 3 have PA

only. The other is equipped with full backline. Storage available at £35 per month.

Backfeed Rehearsal Studios Ltd.
Black Dyke Mills, Brighouse Road, Queensbury, Bradford, BD13 1QA
tel:	01274 817 817/07769 972 537
email:	backfeed@backfeed.co.uk
web:	www.backfeed.co.uk
rates:	£30 for 4 hours
rooms:	8
hours:	7pm-11pm (Mon-Fri), 12pm-8pm (Sat & Sun)
secure storage:	No
equipment:	PA available in 1 room

The Bassments
Vulcan House, Foundry Street, Brighouse, West Yorkshire, HD6 1LT
tel:	01484 401 010/07966 256 740
email:	info@thebassments.co.uk
web:	www.thebassments.co.uk
contact:	Mervyn
rates:	£6 per hour
rooms:	4
hours:	10am-11pm
secure storage:	No
equipment:	Drums, PA, amps
info:	Premises are alarmed and secure. For bands that

use The Basements regularly, equipment can be hired out for that all important gig. Also option of a large PA available with sound engineer.

Blink Studios
44 Canal Road, Armley, Leeds, LS12 2PL
tel:	0113 231 9326
email:	info@blinkstudios.co.uk
web:	www.blinkstudios.co.uk
contact:	Paul Westerman
rates:	Contact for details
rooms:	3
hours:	9am-10pm Mon-Sat, 10am-6pm Sun
secure storage:	No
equipment:	Varies depending on room
info:	Friendly rehearsal studio which offers spacious

rehearsal rooms. 30% discount on first session. NUS offers also available. Technical specifications for each room can be viewed on the website above. Storage space available at competitive prices.

Bok
Stagworks, 84 John Street, Sheffield, S2 4QU
tel:	0114 279 5487
web:	www.bokstudios.co.uk
contact:	Bert Rodgers
rates:	£15 for 2 hours, £20 for 3 hours
rooms:	4
hours:	11am-11pm
secure storage:	Yes
equipment:	Full backline, mixing desks, amps, mics
equip. for hire:	PA, backline, mics, drum kits
info:	Bok also have a recording studio available, as

well as providing an equipment hire service. Refer to entries in the relevant sections for further details.

The Boom Rooms
Unit 6a, Albion Works, Saville Street, Millsbridge, Huddersfield, HD3 4PG
tel:	01484 644 455
email:	boomooms@btinternet.com
rates:	Contact for details
rooms:	3
hours:	7 days a week
secure storage:	No
info:	Reasonable rates. Also provides digital recording

services. Facilities include refreshments and secure floodlit parking.

Soundmill Rehearsal Rooms

Edenderry Industrial Estate
356 Crumlin Road
Belfast
BT14 7EE
07720 051 264

Please contact for rates

PA, FULL BACKLINE, REFRESHMENTS AND RELEXATION AREA.

Calder Recordings
Unit 9D, Top Land Country Business Park, Cragg Road, Mytholmroyd, Hebden Bridge, HX7 5RU

tel:	01422 881 815
email:	studio@calder-recordings.co.uk
web:	www.calder-recordings.co.uk
contact:	Steve Fenton
rates:	Contact for details
rooms:	1
hours:	Flexible
secure storage:	No
equipment:	Drums, PA, amps, mics
info:	Also offer recording services. See relevant entry for details.

The Collective
31 Regent's Terrace, Sheffield, S3 7QA

tel:	0114 276 6082/07941 701 255
email:	karen@pandemoniumpromotions.com
web:	www.pandemoniumpromotions.com
rates:	£15/3 hours before 6pm midweek; £18/3 hours at all other times
rooms:	3
hours:	7 days a week
secure storage:	Yes
equipment:	Full backline, drums, PA
equip. for hire:	Breakables for the kit including kick pedal, snare, hats, cymbals, leads
info:	Secure storage charged at £20 per month. The Collective is run by Pandemonium Promotions. For information on gigs see the Independent Promoters section.

Diamond Studios
Suite A, Moor Park Business Centre, Thornes Moor Road, Wakefield, West Yorkshire

tel:	01924 201 169
email:	enquiries@diamondstudios.co.uk
web:	www.diamondstudios.co.uk
contact:	Joe
rates:	£8 per hour
rooms:	3
hours:	Contact for details
secure storage:	No
equipment:	PA, mics, stands
equip. for hire:	Drum kit, guitar and bass amps, mics
info:	Refreshments available. Also offer recording facilities. See relevant section for details.

Epic Head
66 Garden Street, Sheffield, S1 4JB

tel:	0114 273 1398
email:	oknort@hotmail.com
web:	www.yonni.co.uk
rates:	Contact for details
rooms:	3
hours:	12pm-11pm
secure storage:	No
equipment:	PA, backline, drum kit

G2 Studios
72 John Street, Sheffield, South Yorkshire, S2 4QU

tel:	0114 270 6217/0114 279 5650
email:	info@g2studios.co.uk
web:	www.g2studios.co.uk
contact:	Paul, John
rates:	£8 per hour
rooms:	1
hours:	Contact for details
secure storage:	Yes
equipment:	PA, drums, guitar and bass amps
info:	G2 is a spacious studio designed by Acoustic Architecture using industry standard digital and analogue recording systems. Also provide CD duplication and mastering services. See entries in relevant sections for details.

Hall Place Studios
4 Hall Place, Leeds, LS9 8JD

tel:	0113 248 1508
fax:	0113 248 1508
email:	julianwellington@mac.com
contact:	Julian Wellington
rates:	£10 per hour
rooms:	1
hours:	10am-10pm
secure storage:	No
equipment:	Full backline and 5kW PA

House of Mook
Authorpe Works, Authorpe Road, Leeds, West Yorkshire, LS6 4JB

tel:	0113 230 4008
email:	mail@mookhouse.ndo.co.uk
web:	www.mookhouse.ndo.co.uk
contact:	Phil Mayne
rates:	From £4 per hour
rooms:	3
hours:	11am-11pm
secure storage:	No
equipment:	PA, mics
equip. for hire:	Drums, amps
info:	Situated only several minutes' drive from centre of Headingley. House of Mook offer rehearsal and equipment storage space. Analogue recording is also available, as well as an in-house record label, Mook Records. See entries in relevant sections for further details.

Imp Hut
9 Melroses Yard, Walmgate, YO1 9XF

tel:	01904 642 828
email:	jan@imp-hut.co.uk
web:	www.imp-hut.co.uk
rates:	£25 for 4 hours
rooms:	3
hours:	9am-10pm
secure storage:	Yes
equipment:	4kW PA, mics, stands
info:	Accessories shop. Free tea and coffee. 36 channel recording facilities linked to each room. See Recording Services section for more details.

The Jam Factory
106 Eldon Street, York, YO31 7NH
tel: 01904 339 879
email: jamfactorychris@hotmail.com
rates: £6 per hour
rooms: 4
hours: 10am-10pm (Mon-Sat)
secure storage: No
equipment: Vocal PA
equip. for hire: Drum kit, amps
info: Also has a recording studio and offers Access to
Music Course. See relevant sections for details.

Jam Rehearsal Studios
Unit 4a Roseville Trading Estate, Roseville Road, Leeds, LS8 5DT
tel: 0113 242 7700
email: info@jamstudios.co.uk
web: www.jamstudios.co.uk
contact: Steve
rates: From £7.50 per hour
rooms: 10
secure storage: No
equipment: PA, mics
equip. for hire: Backline, drums
info: Rates depend on the size of the room. In-house
repair centre, as well as PA and equipment sales. All situated on ground
floor for easy access. Large car park with CCTV. External PA hire
available. See relevant section for more details.

Jump Studios
Unit 2, Briar Rhydding, Baildon, West Yorkshire, BD17 7JW
tel: 01274 596 547
email: banksy@jumprecords.com
web: www.jumprecords.com
contact: Les
rates: £10 per hour
secure storage: Yes
equipment: PA, drum kits, Digital pianos, amps
info: Studio is owned by the Jump Records label, who
also offer studio recording. See entries in relevant sections for details.

Jump Studios
43-45 Bailey Street, Sheffield, South Yorkshire, S1 4EH
tel: 0114 275 4914
email: tomojump@totalise.co.uk
contact: Paul Thompson
rooms: 7
hours: 24 hours, 7 days a week
secure storage: No
info: Rooms are hired on a monthly basis, access is
unlimited and available 24 hours a day. Bands organise rotas between
themselves. See also listings for record label and recording studios.

Live Art Rehearsal Studios
1 Newton Street, Barnsley, S70 6DA
tel: 01226 244 889/07782 115 962
email: enquiries@liveartstudios.co.uk
web: www.liveartstudios.co.uk
contact: Tom, Dave, Phil
rates: £6 per hour
rooms: 5
hours: 10am-10pm
secure storage: No
equipment: PA, drum kit, mics
equip. for hire: Range of amps and mics
info: Live Art have 5 spacious, ground floor rehearsal
facilities with equipment for live recording available. Chillout area.
Parking available.

Mosaic Studio
Portland Street, Sheffield, South Yorkshire, S6 3DN
tel: 0114 266 6145
email: info@mosaicstudio.co.uk
web: www.mosaicstudio.co.uk
contact: Brian Gray
rates: £6 per hour or £7.50 per hour (with drumkit)
rooms: 1
hours: Weekday evenings
secure storage: No
equipment: PA and backline
equip. for hire: Drumkit
info: Mosaic Studios is primarily a recording studio,
the rehearsal space available is the live room. Opening hours can be
flexible. See the Recording Services listings for more details.

Old Chapel Studios
1 Crossland Court, Czar Street, Holbeck, Leeds, LS11 9PR

tel:	0113 246 5173
email:	oldchapel@hotmail.com
contact:	Mark Hubbard
rates:	£6-£8 per hour
rooms:	5
hours:	12pm-11pm (Mon-Thurs), 12pm-6pm (Fri-Sun)
secure storage:	No
equipment:	PA, mics
equip. for hire:	Drum kits, guitar and bass amps
info:	Old Chapel have 5 spacious rooms. Car parking and refreshments available.

Purple Pro Audio
Unit B, St. Catherine's Business Park, Broad Lane, Bramley, Leeds, LS13 2TD

tel:	0113 290 9161
email:	info@purpleproaudio.com
web:	www.purpleproaudio.com
contact:	Martin Robinson
rates:	Call for details
rooms:	3
hours:	6pm-12am (Mon-Fri), 12pm-12am (Sat & Sun)
secure storage:	Yes
equipment:	PA
info:	Purple Rehearsals offer unique monthly rates.

For example, £140 guarantees a room for 6 hours a week for a month. Also offer PA hire and studio recording. See entries on relevant sections for details.

Riverside Studios
Four Horse Shoes Yard, Milnsbridge, Huddersfield, West Yorkshire, HD3 4NE

tel:	01924 280 242/07810 838 346
web:	www.riversidestudios.info
contact:	Marcus
rates:	From £6 per hour
rooms:	3
hours:	10am-Late
secure storage:	No
equipment:	PA
equip. for hire:	Backline
info:	Also offer recording facilities, with discounts available for bands who use the rehearsal studios. See entry in relevant section for details

Sponge Studio
Cross Chancellor Street, Leeds, West Yorkshire, LS6 2TG

tel:	0113 234 0004
web:	www.spongeonline.co.uk
rates:	Call for details
rooms:	6
hours:	Call for details
secure storage:	Yes
equipment:	Drums, PA, bass amp
info:	Sponge are primarily a rehearsal facility, although they offer studio recording and CD and DVD duplication services.

Voltage Studios
St. Stephen's Mill, Ripley Street, Bradford, West Yorkshire, BD5 7JW

tel:	01274 393 998/07789 121 360
email:	info@voltagestudios.com
web:	www.voltagestudios.com
contact:	Tim Walker
rates:	£15 for 4 hours
rooms:	6
hours:	24 hours, 7 days a week
secure storage:	No
equip. for hire:	PA
info:	PA can be hired from £5 per session. The PA is also available for venue hire, call for details. Studio also offers a choice of analogue and/or digital multitrack recording. See entry in relevant section for details.

Yellow Arch
30-36 Burton Road, Neepsend, Sheffield, S3 8BX

tel:	0114 273 0800/0114 275 7295
fax:	0114 281 3540
email:	mail@yellowarch.com
web:	www.yellowarch.com
contact:	Waq
rates:	£6.50 per hour (Daytime), £7.50 per hour (Evening & Weekends)
rooms:	4
hours:	11am-11pm, 7 days a week
secure storage:	No
equipment:	Full backline
info:	Recording studios also available, refer to entry in relevant section for further details. Programming room available ideal for Hip-Hop and Dance artists.

NORTHERN IRELAND

Belfast Central Studios
2 Gloucester Street, Belfast, BT1 4LS

tel:	028 9024 6006
email:	info@francismcpeake.com
web:	www.francismcpeake.com
contact:	Francis Mpeake
rates:	£25 per hour
rooms:	2
hours:	Flexible
secure storage:	Yes
equip. for hire:	PA
info:	High spec studio based on the premises of the Francis McPeake School of Music. Can cater for any genre of music, although quality acoustic especially welcome. Access to lounge area with television and gaming facilities and a kitchenette. Also offer studio recording, see entry in relevant section for details.

Best Cellars
Ballybeen Activity Centre, Dundonald, County Down, BT16 2QE

tel:	028 9048 6290
fax:	028 9048 6290
email:	bestcellars@ukgateway.net
web:	www.thecellars.org.uk
rates:	£7.50 per hour
rooms:	1
secure storage:	Yes
equipment:	Backline

Earthmusic
39 Lough Road, Boardmills, Lisburn, BT27 6TS

tel:	028 9263 8483
email:	earthmusicni@yahoo.co.uk
web:	www.earthmusicni.com
contact:	Vic
rates:	£5 per hour
rooms:	1
hours:	11am-11pm, 7 days a week
secure storage:	Yes
equipment:	PA, drums, backline
info:	Also offer analogue studio recording, see relevant entry for details.

MADD House Studios
Clotworthy Arts Centre, Antrim Castle Gardens, Randalstown Road, BT41 4LH

tel:	028 9446 9669
email:	info@maddhousestudios.co.uk
web:	www.maddhousestudios.co.uk
contact:	Darren Porter, Catherine Pollitt
rates:	£5 per hour
rooms:	1
hours:	10am-10pm (Mon-Fri), 10am-5pm (Sat)
secure storage:	Yes
equipment:	Vocal PA, guitar amps, drum kit
info:	Also offer studio recording, see entry in relevant section for details.

Nerve Centre
7-8 Magazine Street, Derry, BT48 6HJ

tel:	028 7126 0562
fax:	028 7137 1738
email:	s.mcneilly@nerve-centre.org.uk
web:	www.nerve-centre.org.uk
contact:	Tony Doherty
rates:	Contact for details
rooms:	3
hours:	Contact for details
secure storage:	Yes
equipment:	PA, mics, drumkit, amps
info:	Live music venue offering range of facilities. Contact for details of rehearsal space, editting suites, duplication services and venue hire.

Numbnut Sounds
11 Barleywood Mill, Lisburn, Antrim, BT28 3RZ

tel:	07752 207 553
email:	numbnutsounds@gmail.com
contact:	Stephen Hill
rates:	Ciontact for details
rooms:	1
hours:	Flexible
secure storage:	No
equipment:	PA, guitar and bass amps, drums, mics
info:	Block bookings welcome. Also offer digital recording, see entry in relevant section for details.

Railway Studios
15 Wardborough Road, Lisburn, County Antrim, BT28 1XF
tel: 07779 223 668 07779223668
email: ross@railwaystudios.com
web: www.railwaystudios.com
contact: Ross
rates: £10 per hour, £8 per hour if rehearsing twice a week or more, minimum session of 3 hours
rooms: 1
hours: 9am-12am
secure storage: No
equipment: PA, mics, full backline, drum kit
info: Also offer recording facilities. See appropriate section for details.

Soundmill Rehearsal
Edenderry Industrial Estate, 326 Crumlin Road, Belfast, BT14 7EE
tel: 07720 051 264
email: soundmill@come.to
web: www.come.to/soundmill
contact: Philip Andrews
rates: Contact for details
rooms: 1
hours: Contact for details
secure storage: No
equipment: PA, 800W Ashdown bass stack, Remo drum kit, Peavy/Marshall guitar amps and stacks, Shure SM58 mics
info: Relaxation area with refreshments available.

The Stables Studio
14 Circular Road, Coleraine, BT52 1PS
tel: 028 7034 4207
email: thestablestudios@hotmail.com
rates: £7.50 per hour
rooms: 1
hours: 10am-10pm
secure storage: Yes
equipment: PA, backline, drum kit
info: Town centre location. Also offer studio recording, see entry in relevant section for more information.

Studio 2
69A Whiteside Hill, Portadown, Armagh, BT62 3RJ
tel: 028 3884 1335/07791 949 199
contact: James Wilson
rates: £20 for 3 hours
rooms: 2
hours: Contact for details
secure storage: No
equipment: PA, drums, amps
info: Studio recording facilities also provided. See relevant listing for further information.

SCOTLAND

4th Street Studios
11 Forth Street, Pollokshields, Glasgow, G41 2SP
tel: 0141 420 6175
email: mail@4thstreet.co.uk
web: www.4thstreet.co.uk
rates: £24 for 3 hours (Evenings & Weekends), £15 for 3 hours (Weekdays)
rooms: 2
hours: 24 hours, 7 days a week
secure storage: No
equipment: PA, backline
info: Also offer recording facilities. See relevant section for more details.

ACR Productions
10c Canmore Street, Dunfermline, Fife, KY12 7NT
tel: 01383 741 500
email: booking@acrproductions.co.uk
web: www.acrproductions.co.uk
rates: From £5 per hour
rooms: 2
hours: 12pm-10pm
secure storage: No
equipment: PA, mics, stands
equip. for hire: Drum kits, backline
info: Secure storage from £5 per week. Recording facilities and PA hire also provided. See relevant sections for details.

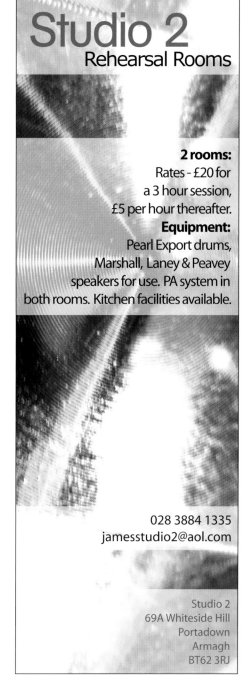

Studio 2
Rehearsal Rooms

2 rooms:
Rates - £20 for a 3 hour session, £5 per hour thereafter.
Equipment:
Pearl Export drums, Marshall, Laney & Peavey speakers for use. PA system in both rooms. Kitchen facilities available.

028 3884 1335
jamesstudio2@aol.com

Studio 2
69A Whiteside Hill
Portadown
Armagh
BT62 3RJ

MUSIC SERVICES/RETAIL

Arc Studios
61 Commerce Street, Glasgow, G5 8AD
tel: 0141 418 0818
contact: Gary
rates: Call for details
rooms: 7
hours: 12am-12pm
secure storage: Yes
equipment: All equipment is included in the price of the room.

Banana Row Music Services
47 Eyre Place, Edinburgh, EH3 5EY
tel: 0131 557 2088
email: info@bananarow.com
web: www.bananarow.com
rates: £6/hour for soloists; £8/hour daytime and £11 evening and weekends for bands
rooms: 5
secure storage: Yes
equipment: PA, backline
equip. for hire: Range of equipment and instruments
info: 2 rooms dedicated to soloists and duos and 1 dedicated to solo drummers. Pro-shop on-site. Large drum hire business and tuition services. See relevant sections for more details.

Barrowland Studios
244 Gallowgate, Glasgow, G4 0TT
tel: 0141 553 2515
email: barrastudios@netscape.net
rates: £7 per hour
rooms: 3
hours: 12pm-12am
secure storage: No
equipment: Drums, bass gear, Marshall Stereo Chorus combos, full PA, mics
equip. for hire: Range of equipment
info: Barrowland Studios consists of 3 good sized air-conditioned rooms. Lounge and TV area, plus pool room on-site. Free street parking. Contact for special rates. Hours can be flexible.

Berkley 2
54 Washington Street, Glasgow, G3 8AZ
tel: 0141 248 7290
rates: £28 for /3 hours
rooms: 11
hours: 10am-12am
secure storage: Yes
equipment: Drum kit, guitar and bass amps, PA
equip. for hire: Keyboard
info: Limited overnight storage.

The Bongo Club
37 Holyrood Road, Edinburgh, EH8 8BA
tel: 0131 558 7604
email: ally@thebongoclub.co.uk
web: www.thebongoclub.co.uk
rates: £15/hour with engineer
rooms: 1
hours: Contact for details
secure storage: Yes
equip. for hire: PA
info: Rehearsal space available in The Bongo Club live music venue, when bookings allow. Cafe and exhibition space upstairs.

Captain Tom Music
11-15 Ann Street, Aberdeen, AB25 3LH
tel: 01224 647 500
email: info@captaintommusic.co.uk
web: www.captaintommusic.co.uk
rates: £14 per hour
rooms: 4
secure storage: Yes
equipment: Drums, PA, amps
equip. for hire: Guitars
info: Part of a large complex also housing recording studios. Also offer instrument tuition.

Carlton Studio
54 Carlton Place, Glasgow, G5 9TW
tel: 0141 429 5723
contact: James Mc Kechan
rates: from £7.50 for 3 hours
rooms: 3
hours: 9am-12am
secure storage: Yes
equipment: Full PA, backline
equip. for hire: Cymbals, amps (including off site hire)
info: Recording facilities also available. See relevant section for more details.

Chem19 Studios
Unit 5c, Peacock Cross Industrial Estate, Burnbank Road, Hamilton, ML3 9AY
tel: 01698 286 882
email: email@chem19studios.co.uk
web: www.chem19studios.co.uk
rates: From £18 for 3 hours
rooms: 2
hours: 12pm-12am
secure storage: Yes
info: Also has recording studio, see appropriate section for details.

Colorsound
68 Fountainbridge, Edinburgh, EH3 9PY
tel: 0131 229 3588
rates: from £7 - £10/hour, depending on room size
rooms: 5
hours: 12pm-12am
secure storage: No
equipment: PA, backline, drum kit
info: Recording facilities also available. See relevant section for more details.

Core Studios
7 Osborne Street, Glasgow, G1 5QN
tel: 0141 552 6677
email: crstudios@aol.com
web: 0141 552 1354
rates: Bands from £22/3 hours; soloists from £6/3 hours
rooms: 4
hours: 9am-12am
secure storage: Yes
equipment: Drum kit, bass and guitar amps, PA, desk
info: Occasional special offers and regular discounted rates for students and the unemployed - call for details. Recording facilities also available. See relevant section for more details.

Exile Studio
Weigh-house Square, Aberdeen, AB11 5AF
tel: 01224 593 855
email: xilestudio@aol.com
web: www.exilestudio.co.uk
contact: Mark Nicol
rates: £10 per hour
secure storage: Yes
equipment: Drums, PA, mics
info: Also offer demo recording, see relevant entry for details.

Floyd's Rehearsal Rooms
81 Portland Street, Edinburgh, EH6 4AY
tel: 0131 553 0021
email: floyd.lindsay@btinternet.com
rates: £10 per hour
rooms: 2
hours: 10am-10pm, 7 days a week
secure storage: Yes
equipment: PA, backline, drum kit with cymbals
info: Newly refurbished rehearsal rooms. Minimum booking is 2 hour slot.

Foyer Music
Aberdeen Foyer, Marywell Street, Aberdeen, AB11 6JF
tel: 01224 252 894
email: dave@foyerlive.com
web: www.foyerlive.com
rates: £8 per hour
rooms: 1
secure storage: Yes
equipment: Backline, PA
info: Foyer Music is the music department of a charity based in the North East of Scotland who provide supported accommodation, education and training to people under the age of 25. Also comprises a recording studio and DJ room. See relevant section for more details. Foyer Music regularly put gigs on around Scotland and Europe, and are involved in the Go North (www.goevents.info) festival.

The Gallery Studios
15 Edison Street, Hillington Industrial Estae, Glasgow, G52 4JW
tel: 07792 804 874
rates: £20 for 3 hours
rooms: 3
hours: 9am-Midnight
secure storage: No
equipment: Full PA, mics, backline
equip. for hire: Cymbals
info: Lounge area with TV and Playstation etc on-site. Ample free parking in the area. Contact for further details.

Groove Tunnel
Eldin Cottage, Eldin Industrial Estate, Edgefield Road, Loanhead, EH20 9QX

tel:	0131 448 2170
email:	rodspark@groovetunnel.com
web:	www.groovetunnel.com
contact:	Rod
rates:	Call for details
rooms:	4
hours:	24 hours, 7 days a week
secure storage:	No
equipment:	Full backline, PA, drums, Marshall and Trace Elliot amps.
info:	Free parking and refreshment lounge available.

Complex also houses digital recording studio, as well as offering mastering and remixing services. See listing in Recording Studios section for details.cks and arrangements.

Headhunter Records
Stanley Road Lane, Kinning Park, Glasgow, G41 1EZ

tel:	0141 429 7111
email:	info@headhunterrecords.co.uk
web:	www.headhunterrecords.co.uk
contact:	Andrew
rates:	From £20 for 3 hours
rooms:	2
secure storage:	No
info:	Special rates for block bookings. Free equipment

storage for bands who make block bokings of 4 weeks or more. Free tea and coffee. Headhunter also run a studio and label. See relevant sections for details.

Jam Jar Rehearsals
27 Hill Street, Alloa, FK10 2BG

tel:	01259 724 848
rates:	£22 for 4 hours, £140 per month (lock-out)
rooms:	7
hours:	Flexible
secure storage:	No
equipment:	PA, mixing desk
info:	Daytime opening times are flexible. Usually open

from 7pm-11pm during evenings.

Jinx Audio
1 Dixon Place, East Kilbride, G74 5JF

tel:	07966 194 396/01355 229 449
rates:	From £17.50 for 3 hours
rooms:	2
hours:	9am-12am
secure storage:	No
equipment:	PA, backline, drumkit
info:	Chill out area with pool table and TV.

Lighthouse Studios
20-22 West Harbour Road, Edinburgh, EH5 1PN

tel:	0131 551 5788
fax:	0131 551 5787
email:	via website
web:	www.lighthousestudios.org
rates:	Contact for details
rooms:	6
hours:	10am-11pm (Mon-Thurs), 10am-9pm (Fri), 10am-6pm (Sat), 12pm-11pm (Sun)
secure storage:	Yes
equipment:	PA, backline, drum kit
info:	Rate vary depending on time and day of booking.

Instrument accessory shop on-site. Recording facilities and drum tuition available. See relevant sections for details.

Loch Lomond Studios
Unit 20, Block 1, Vale Of Leven Industrial Estate, Dumbarton, G82 3PD

tel:	07812 746 985
email:	llstudiosphil@yahoo.com
contact:	Phil
rates:	£20 for 3 hours
rooms:	2
hours:	Flexible
secure storage:	Yes
equipment:	Drums, PA, amps
info:	With a full backline of DJ equipment, the studio

can also be hired out on Friday and Saturday nights for DJ practice. Concessions available, particularly for those aged under 17 years. Sessions can also be recorded. A Prince's Trust affiliated organisation also offering music tuition in various disciplines. Studio also offers PA hire packages for approximately £60/night.

Lofi Rehearsals
20 Anchor Lane, George Square, Glasgow, G1 2AB

tel:	0141 248 5050
email:	info@lofi.co.uk
web:	www.lofi.co.uk
rates:	From £15 per 3 hours
rooms:	6
hours:	9am-3am, 7 days a week
secure storage:	No
equipment:	PA. backline, Marshall and Line 6 guitar stacks
equip. for hire:	Storage, cymbals, bass, guitars, keyboards
info:	Facilities include lounge, TV room, internet

access, snack machine and shop selling accessories. Pubs, shops, hotels, bus, rail and subway links all close by. Live recording facilities.

Paul's Halls
11 Glencryan Road, South Carbrain, Cumbernauld, G67 2UH

tel:	01236 722 228
email:	practice@paulshalls.com
web:	www.paulshalls.com
rates:	From £28 for 3 hours
rooms:	4
hours:	6pm-12am (Weekdays), 12pm-12am (Weekends)
secure storage:	Yes
equipment:	PA, backline, drum kit
equip. for hire:	Cymbals, keyboards
info:	Rates vary depending on room. CD recording

available in all rooms. Recording studio and tuition also available. See relevant sections for details.

The Practice Pad
Unit B1, Glasgow Media Park, Maryhill, Glasgow, G20 9BT

tel:	0141 946 7656
email:	info@thepracticepad.com
web:	www.thepracticepad.com
rates:	from £18 for 3 hours
rooms:	5
secure storage:	No
info:	5 rooms available, one specifically for soloist and

duos. Secure storage from £20 per month. Pool table, seating area, hot and cold food available. 24 track digital recording. See relevant section for details.

QPQ Productions
The Lighthouse, Dunnet Head, Dunnet, Thurso, KW14 8XS

tel:	01847 851 692
email:	info@qpqproductions.com
web:	www.qpqproductions.com
contact:	Isaac Sutherland
rates:	Call for details
rooms:	1
secure storage:	Yes
info:	The most Northerly based rehearsal room in the

British Isles, offering musicians a chance to isolate themselves with their music. Recording studio also available. See relevant entry for details.

Random Rhythms Music Workshop
Bridgehaugh Road, Stirling, FK9 5AP

tel:	01786 479 082
web:	www.randomrhythms.net
contact:	Guy
rates:	Call for details
rooms:	3
secure storage:	Yes
equipment:	PA, drums, guitar and bass amps
info:	Random Rhythms is a registered charity

offering recording and rehearsal rooms at reduced rates for students, unemployed, special needs and community groups.

Red Eye Studios
11 Hulme Street, Clydebank, G81 1XL

tel:	0141 951 1554
email:	reillymusic@yahoo.couk
rates:	£25 for 3 hour
rooms:	3
hours:	12pm-12am, 7 days
secure storage:	No
equipment:	PA, drumkit, guitar and bass amps, keyboard amp
equip. for hire:	Cymbals
info:	All rooms are air conditioned. Recording facilities

also available. See relevant section for more details.

MUSIC SERVICES/RETAIL

Reeltime Music
High Street, Newarthill, ML1 5JU
tel:	01698 862 860
fax:	01698 861 170
email:	info@reeltimemusic.net
web:	www.reeltimemusic.net
rates:	£6 per hour
rooms:	1
hours:	10am-10pm (Mon-Fri)
secure storage:	No
equipment:	Full backline, PA, drum kit
equip. for hire:	Range of equipment and accessories
info:	Discounts available for young people (under 25 years), students and the unemployed. Recording facilities available. See relevant section for more details. Recording and rehearsal packages.

Riptide Music
34-40 Blinshall Street, Dundee, DD1 5DF
tel:	01382 220 234
email:	eddielynch@riptidemusicstudios.co.uk
web:	www.riptidemusicstudios.co.uk
contact:	Eddie Lynch
rates:	£8.50 per hour
rooms:	2
hours:	5pm-11pm
secure storage:	No
equipment:	Fully equipped
info:	Also rooms available for keyboard and drum tuition. Chill out areas with pool table and internet access.

The Sound Station
Unit 6, Napier Square, Houstoun Industrial Estate, Livingston, EH54 5DG
tel:	01506 440 505
email:	thesoundstation@btinternet.com
rates:	£10 per hour
rooms:	3
hours:	4pm-12am (Mon-Fri), 12pm-12am (Weekend)
secure storage:	No
equipment:	PA, backline, drum kit
info:	On-site cafe with recreation area. Recording, mastering and CD duplication available. See relevant sections for more details.

The Soundhaus
47 Hydepark Street, Anderston, Glasgow, G3 8BW
tel:	0141 221 4659
email:	info@soundhaus.co.uk
web:	www.soundhuas.co.uk
rates:	£15 for 3 hours (Daytime), From £22 for 3 hours (Evenings)
rooms:	2
hours:	12 noon - 12 midnight, can open earlier by arrangement
secure storage:	Yes
equipment:	PA and backline
equip. for hire:	Selection of amps. Mics and stands.
info:	Rates vary depending on room. Larger mirrored room available with 2kW PA, the other is equipped with 1kW PA. The Soundhaus also incorporates a 350 capacity venue and PA hire company (Xcel PA). See relevant sections for more details.

Splash Productions Complex
20 Thorn Brae, Johnstone, PA5 8HE
tel:	01505 323 888
email:	info@splashproductionscomplex.com
web:	www.splashproductionscomplex.com
contact:	Kirsty Young
rates:	£7.50 per hour, £21 for 3 hours
rooms:	1
hours:	10am-10pm
secure storage:	No
equipment:	Full PA, drum kit, guitar and bass amps
equip. for hire:	Drum hardware
info:	Splash is located in very stylish surroundings. Lounge area and games room on-site. Private parking available. Room fully air conditioned. Also run a recording studio. See listing for further details.

Split Level
3 East Mains, Ingliston, Newbridge, EH28 8NQ
tel:	0131 333 5024
email:	neil@split-level.freeserve.co.uk
rates:	£8 per hour, £150 per month
rooms:	3
hours:	24 hours, 7 days a week
secure storage:	Yes
equipment:	PA, backline, drum kit
info:	Recording facilities also available. See relevant section for details.

Stage 2000
Taybridge Station, Riverside Drive, Tayside, Dundee, DD1 4DB
tel:	01382 223 332
email:	info@stage2000.co.uk
web:	www.stage2000.co.uk
rates:	from £8 per hour (discounts for students and under 18s)
rooms:	5
hours:	Monday - Friday, Noon-Midnight; Saturday 10am-10pm; Sunday
secure storage:	Yes
equipment:	PA, backline, drum kit
equip. for hire:	Bass and guitar amps, PA
info:	Half price rates for under 18 year olds on Saturday afternoons. Students receive £1 off each hour at any time. Also offer instrument tuition services. See relevant section for more details.

Urban Central
St. Enoch Square, Glasgow, G40 2DD
tel:	0141 551 0202
email:	info@urbanstudios.co.uk
web:	www.urbanstudios.co.uk
contact:	David
rates:	£10.50 for 3 hours (Daytime), From £21 for 3 hours (Evenings)
rooms:	5
hours:	12pm-12am, 7 days a week
secure storage:	No
info:	New luxury rehearsal complex in Glasgow city centre. Opening hours can be flexible.

Verden Studios
Fishwives Causeway, Edinburgh, EH15 1DF
tel:	0131 538 0555
email:	info@verdenstudios.co.uk
web:	www.verdenstudios.co.uk
rates:	£10 per hour
secure storage:	Yes
info:	Facilities include smoking lounge, free tea and coffee, plus use of freezer and microwave. Equipment and snack shops on-site.

Wandering Fish Rehearsal Rooms
1 Jane Street, Edinburgh, EH6 5HE
tel:	07720 708 256
email:	wanderingfishuk@yahoo.co.uk
contact:	Jonathan Tait
rates:	£20 for 3 hours
rooms:	1
hours:	6pm-12am (Mon-Fri), 12pm-12am (Sun)
secure storage:	No
equipment:	Backline, PA, drum kit, mics

Westway Studios
Westway Business Park, Porterfield Road, Westway Business Park, Renfrew, PA4 8DJ
tel:	0141 886 1100
email:	info@westway-studios.org
web:	www.westway-studios.org
contact:	Ivan Nichol
rates:	Contact for details
rooms:	5
hours:	9am-12am
secure storage:	No
equipment:	PA, 2 Marshall amps, bass amp, Fender Hotrod Deluxe, Yamaha drum kit
info:	Opening hours can be flexible. Westway also have facilities for bands to record their sessions. Refreshments are available as well as free parking. 24 hour security on-site.

WALES

Aber Sound Productions Ltd.
Ystwyth Works, Llanfarian, Aberystwyth, Ceredigion, SY23 4NN
tel:	01970 615 079
web:	www.abersoundproductions.ltd.uk
rates:	From £5 per hour
secure storage:	Yes
equip. for hire:	Drum kit, bass and guitar amps, mics, stands, DI boxes
info:	Prices vary depending on equipment required. Also run a recording studio and offer PA hire service. See relevant sections for more details.

Afan Valley Recording & Workshop
Old Telephone Exchange, Depot Road, Cwmavon

tel:	01639 871 871
email:	billval.haddon@tesco.net
contact:	Bill Haddon
rates:	£5 per hour
rooms:	1
hours:	24 hours a day, 7 days a week (except Sunday morning)
secure storage:	Yes
equip. for hire:	PA
info:	Minimum booking is 3 hours. Equipment may be stored at the owner's risk. Chillout area. Analogue recording available, contact for further details.

Amelia Music
Unit 8, The Ethel Huggard Workshops, Amelia Trust Farm, Five Mile Lane, Walterston, Barry, CF62 3AS

tel:	01446 781 391
email:	chrisk@ameliatrust.org.uk
contact:	Chris Kelly
rates:	£7.50 per hour
rooms:	1
hours:	5pm-9pm (Mon-Fri), 9am-10pm (Sat & Sun)
secure storage:	Yes
equipment:	Drum kit, PA, mics
equip. for hire:	Bass, guitar, guitar and bass amps
info:	Amelia Music also comprises a recording studio ideal for demos. See relevant section for more details.

Cardiff Sound Scene
36 Cathays Terrace, Cathays, Cardiff, CF24 4HX

tel:	02920 373 144
email:	studio@soundsceneuk.com
web:	www.soundsceneuk.com
contact:	Matthew Thorne
rates:	£15 for 3 hours
rooms:	2
hours:	12pm-9:30pm
secure storage:	Yes
equipment:	Bass and guitar amps, PA, 2 mic stands, basic drum kit
info:	Cardiff Sound Scene also incorporates a recording studio and music workshops for young people. See the relevant sections for more details. The rehearsal rooms are located within Cathays Community Centre, which once a month holds a live music night featuring 3 or 4 bands. Send a demo to the address above.

The Clock Tower
Coast Road, Mostyn, North Wales

tel:	01745 560 011
email:	info@theclocktower.org.uk
web:	www.theclocktower.org.uk
secure storage:	Yes
info:	The Clocktower is a multipurpose campus, providing facilities for a wide range of services for dance, theatre and music communities. Rehearsal rooms available. Contact for further details.

Cockle Doodle Doo
Pontglas, Llanbody, Whitland, Dyfed, SA34 0EX

tel:	01994 448 357
rates:	£25 per night
secure storage:	Yes
equipment:	Drum riser, PA
info:	Cockle Doodle Doo is a converted farmhouse, hired per night as a rehearsal space. Self catering. 5 beds plus extra sleeping space on futons.

Drumbeat Ltd.
Portland Street, Pill, Newport, NP20 2BW

tel:	01633 221 381
web:	www.drumbeatshop.com
rates:	Call for details
rooms:	3
hours:	9am-12am
secure storage:	Yes
equipment:	Drum kit, amps, speakers, mics
info:	Also run a drum shop. See entry in relevant section for further information.

Dulais Valley Music Centre
5 Brynbedd Terrace, Severn Sisters, Neath, SA10 7DG

tel:	01639 701 339
rates:	£10 per session
rooms:	1
hours:	Contact for details
secure storage:	Yes
equipment:	Keyboard, drums, PA, mics
equip. for hire:	Guitars, double bass, large selection of brass instruments
info:	Room hire is charged per rehearsal rather than per hour, so there is no time limit on the length of each session.

Grassroots
58 Charles Street, Cardiff, CF10 4EG

tel:	029 2025 5608/029 2023 1700
contact:	Suke Driver
rates:	£4 per hour
rooms:	1
hours:	1.30pm-5.30pm
secure storage:	Yes
equipment:	PA, mics, drum kits, 3 guitar amps, 2 bass amps, Technics 1210 decks
info:	Grassroots is a community run project for the under 25 year olds. Recording facilities and training courses are also available. See entries in relevant sections for details.

Hannah's Music
6-8 Moor Street 6-8 Moor Street, Chepstow, NP16 5DE

tel:	01291 627 122
email:	sales@hannahsmusic.co.uk
web:	www.hannahsmusic.co.uk
rates:	£5 per hour
rooms:	1
hours:	9am-11pm
secure storage:	Yes
equipment:	PA, mics, drum kit
info:	Equipment left at owner's risk. Also run a music instrument retail business with branches in Gwent and Abergavenny. See relevant section for details.

Hunter Music
6 Mansel Street, Swansea, West Glamorgan, SA1 5SF

tel:	01792 412 762
email:	whizzy@whizzysguitaremporium.com
web:	www.whizzysguitaremporium.com
rates:	From £16 per hour
rooms:	1
hours:	24 hours, 7 days a week
secure storage:	Yes
equipment:	PA, drums, backline
equip. for hire:	Upgraded equipment is available for hire
info:	Storage is available, but any equipment is left at the owner's risk. For more information on Hunter Music's recording facilities see the relevant section.

The Jam Shop Rehearsal Studios
60 Cartlett, Haverfordwest, Dyfed, SA61 2LH

tel:	01437 766 100
rates:	£8-£10/hour or £20-£25/3 hours
rooms:	2
hours:	10.30am-10.30pm, 7 days a week
secure storage:	Yes
equipment:	PA, drum kit, bass amp
info:	Sound-proofed rehearsal rooms, one larger than the other. Prices vary between rooms. Live recording available in the larger room. Tuition room and computer room with 3 PCs for internet access. Drums and drum accessories available to buy.

Lisburn Arts Centre
Lagan Valley Island, Island Civic Centre, Lisburn, County Antrim, BT27 4RL

tel:	028 9250 9250
fax:	028 9250 9288
email:	enquiries@lisburn.gov.uk
web:	www.lisburncity.gov.uk
rates:	£10 per hour
rooms:	1
hours:	Flexible
secure storage:	Yes
equipment:	Contact for details

Marrs
Building 7, Unit N, Cardiff, Curran Industrial Estate, Curran Road, Cardiff, CF10 5DF

tel:	07973 671 710
contact:	Rob Clark
rates:	£20 for 3 hours
rooms:	3
hours:	24 hours, 7 days a week
secure storage:	No
equipment:	1K vocal PA, 12 channel mixing desk, Alesis Midi Verb effects unit, mics, stands, cables
equip. for hire:	Backline
info:	All rooms are fully sound-proofed.

MASE (Music And Sound Experience)
The Old Church Hall, Min y Don Park, Old Colwyn, Conway, LL29 9SD
tel:	01492 517 788/07979 794 782
email:	charles.hildrew@mase.org.uk
contact:	Charles Hildrew
rates:	£5 per hour
rooms:	2
hours:	9am-9pm (Mon-Thurs)
	9am-10pm (Fri & Sat)
secure storage:	Yes
equipment:	2 guitar amps, bass amp, 2 mics, PA
info:	MASE is a youth music project (see www.

youthmusic.org.uk). Open to musicians of all ages. For details of recording facilities at MASE see the relevant section.

Mirage
105 Springvale Industrial Estate, Cwmbran, Gwent, NP44 5BG
tel:	01633 869 877
email:	mirage4real2004@hotmail.com
contact:	Charlie
rates:	£6.50 per hour
rooms:	1
hours:	24 hours, 7 days a week
secure storage:	Yes
equipment:	100W stereo PA, basic drum kit
info:	Storage is available but equipment is left at the

owner's risk. Recording facilities available. See the relevant section for details.

Music Box Studios
40 Daisy Street, Canton, Cardiff, CF5 1EP
tel:	02920 373 707
email:	musicbox@btconnect.com
web:	www.musicboxstudios.co.uk
rates:	£8 per hour
rooms:	3
hours:	10am-10pm, 7 days a week
secure storage:	No
equipment:	Vocal PA
equip. for hire:	Basic backline

Newid Studios
Antioch Centre, Copperworks Road, Llanelli, SA15 2NE
tel:	07971 422 024
email:	malowe@btinternet.com
web:	www.newidstudios.net
rates:	£5 per hour
rooms:	1
hours:	6pm-12am
secure storage:	Yes
equipment:	PA
info:	Recording facilities and CD duplication services

also available. See relevant sections for details.

The Practice Pad Ltd.
Unit 5a, St. Margaret's Park, Pengam Road, Aberbargoed, CF81 9FW
tel:	01443 838 484
email:	mail@thepracticepad.co.uk
web:	www.thepracticepad.co.uk
rates:	£8 per hour
rooms:	4
hours:	10:30am-10pm (Mon-Sat)
secure storage:	Yes
equipment:	PA, 3 mics, 2 guitar amps, bass amp, drum kit
	(with cymbals)
info:	Music instrument shop on-site. Tuition available

for bass and lead guitar, drums, piano and keyboard. Also provide PA hire services. See relevant section for details.

Redrock
Unit D3, Britannia Centre For Enterprise, Pengam Road, Pengam, Blackwood, Gwent, NP12 3SP
tel:	01443 879 222
email:	info@redrockstudios.co.uk
web:	www.redrockstudios.co.uk
rates:	£7 per hour
rooms:	2
hours:	10am-10pm
secure storage:	Yes
equipment:	PA, drum kit, guitar and bass amps
info:	Recording facilities also available. See relevant

section for details.

Splinter Studio
207 Oxford Street, Swansea, SA1 3HT
tel:	07811 371 267
email:	splintysound@aol.com
rates:	From £25 per session
rooms:	2
hours:	24 hours, 7 days a week
secure storage:	Yes
equipment:	Small PA
equip. for hire:	Drum kit, guitar and bass amps, mics
info:	Splinter studios do not apply hourly rates.

Rehearsals are available only in sessions.

Steer Multimedia Studios
Tairgwaith, Ammanford, Dyfed, SA18 1UP
tel:	01269 823 815
email:	info@steerstudios.net
web:	www.steerstudios.net
rates:	£5 per hour
rooms:	1
hours:	Flexible
secure storage:	No
equipment:	PA
info:	Sound engineering tuition available. For details

of the studio's recording facilities, see the relevant section.

Transpose Music Rooms
Albany Trading Estate, Newport, NP20 5NQ
tel:	01633 854 100
email:	d.mccalden@ntlworld.com
rates:	£5-£7 per hour
rooms:	5
secure storage:	No
equipment:	PA
equip. for hire:	Drum kit, bass and guitar amps
info:	Rates vary depending on size of room. Recording

facilities also available. See relevant section for more details.

Warwick Hall of Sound
Warwick Hall, Banastre Avenue, Cardiff, CF14 3NR
tel:	02920 694 455
email:	whos@ffvinyl.com
web:	www.warwickhall.co.uk
rates:	From £4 per hour
rooms:	2
hours:	11am-12am (Mon-Fri)
	11am-11pm (Sat & Sun)
secure storage:	Yes
equipment:	PA, mics
equip. for hire:	Backline, drum kit
info:	Bands to have rehearsed in Warwick Hall of

Sound include Stereophonics, Manic Street Preachers, Super Furry Animals and Franz Ferdinand. For details of recording facilities and the associated FFVinyl label, see the relevant sections.

Winderton Studio
Rowston Drive, New Hedges, Tenby, Pembrokeshire, SA70 8TL
tel:	01834 842 738
email:	windertonstudio@hotmail.com
web:	www.windertonstudio.com
rates:	from £7 per hour
rooms:	2
hours:	9am-5pm
secure storage:	No
info:	Recording facilities and PA hire available. See

relevant sections for more details.

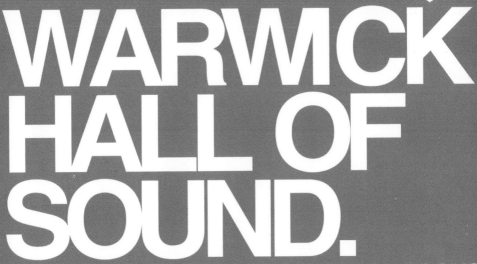

MUSIC SERVICES/RETAIL

MUSIC SERVICES/RETAIL

3.16 VEHICLE HIRE

EAST of ENGLAND 523 GREATER LONDON 524 MIDLANDS 528 NORTHEAST 530 NORTHWEST 531
SOUTHEAST 535 SOUTHWEST 538 YORKSHIRE 540 NORTHERN IRELAND 542 SCOTLAND 543 WALES 544

EAST of ENGLAND

1van1.com
1 William Frost Way, Longwater Business Park, Costessey, Norwich, NR5 2ET
tel: 0113 387 5559
email: sales@1van1.com
web: www.1van1.com
info: Self drive minibus, car, van and MVP. Other branches in East Anglia include Peterborough and Cambridge. All contactable on the above number. Also branches across rest of the UK. See listings in other regions.

Access Motor Rentals
Thetford Road, Ingham, Bury St. Edmunds, IP31 1NR
tel: 01284 729 053
web: www.access-rentals.co.uk
contact: Shaun Metson
info: Wide range of vans. Must be at least 21 years to rent. Self drive.

Added Value Auto Rentals
31a Clifton Road Industrial Estate, Cherry Hinton Road, Cambridge, CB1 7EB
tel: 01223 412 655
email: info@ava.com
web: www.value-autorentals.co.uk
contact: Paul Smith
info: Massive range of vans, people carriers and minibuses. Most vehicles are available to hire out to people aged 21 years and over, but some may only to hired out to those aged 25 years and above.

Advance Vehicle Rental
Global Park, Spitfire Road, Norwich, NR6 6EB
tel: 01603 410 510
web: www.advancevehiclerental.com
contact: Wayne Rogers
info: Brand new range of VW Transporters vans and LT35s. Must be 21 years and over to rent. All self drive.

Anglian Self Drive Ltd. (Huntingdon)
Stukeley Meadows Industrial Estate, Blackstone Road, Huntingdon, PE1 1QL
tel: 0870 112 087
email: hiredesk.aim@anglianselfdrive.co.uk
web: www.anglianselfdrive.co.uk
info: Massive range of vans available to suit all needs. Must be aged 21 years and over and have been driving for over 2 years. Anglian Self Drive has several outlets in East Anglia.

Anglian Self Drive Ltd. (Ipswich)
Europa Way, Eastway Business Park, Ipswich, IP1 5DL
tel: 01473 240 321
fax: 01473 747 888
email: hiredesk@anglianselfdrive.co.uk
web: www.anglianselfdrive.co.uk
info: See listing above for Huntingdon branch. Anglian Self Drive has several outlets in East Anglia.

Anglian Self Drive Ltd. (Norwich)
16 Burnet Road, Sweet Briar Industrial Estate, Norwich, NR3 2BS
tel: 0870 112 087
email: norwich@anglianselfdrive.co.uk
web: www.anglianselfdrive.co.uk
info: See listing above for Huntingdon branch. Anglian Self Drive has several outlets in East Anglia.

Anglian Self Drive Ltd. (Peterborough)
Oxney Road, Peterborough, PE1 5YW
tel: 01733 558 358
email: peterborough@anglianselfdrive.co.uk
web: www.anglianselfdrive.co.uk
contact: Ian Fairchild
info: See listing above for Huntingdon branch. Anglian Self Drive has several outlets in East Anglia.

Applegate Van Hire
7 Spencer Court, Howard Road, Eaton Socon, St. Neots, PE19 8ET
tel: 01480 403 403
contact: Neil Evans
info: Daily, weekly and long term hire. All types of vans. Must be 25 years or over. All insurance coverage, subject to status.

Arriva Vehicle Rental
Eastern Way Industrial Estate, Bury St. Edmunds, Suffolk, IP32 7AD
tel: 01284 762 888
email: centralres@arriva.co.uk
web: www.arrivarental.co.uk
info: Wide range of vans from Astra to Luton. All self drive. Arriva have branches throughout England. See website for details of all locations.

Avis Rent A Car
Midland Road, Peterborough, PE3 6DD
tel: 0870 608 6356
web: www.avis.co.uk
info: Renault vans available on self drive basis. Hire available to those aged 23 years and above, but those under 25 years may face a higher insurance premium. Avis has outlets throughout the UK. See website for locations.

Barford Hire
Watton Road, Barford, Norwich, NR 9 4GB
tel: 01603 758 181
email: barfordrequests@barfordhire.co.uk
web: www.barfordhire.co.uk
info: Transits available. Must be aged 25 years or over.

Budget
East Anglia
tel: 0870 153 9170
fax: 0870 010 2391
email: via website
web: www.budget.co.uk
info: Budget operates around 80 locations across the UK. Check location for details. Each location has a range of vehicles available including people carriers, minibuses of varying sizes, trucks and vans, and cars. All locations offer self drive rentals. Rentals can be made for any length of time. Bookings can be made online or through the call centre number above.

Charringtons Ltd.
Charringtons Yard, Station Road East, Stowmarket, IP14 1EQ
tel: 01473 231 230
contact: John Eaves
info: Whole range of vans available for self drive. Insurance subject to status.

CR Motors
Unit 4, Hereford Way, Hardwick Narrows Estate, King's Lynn, PE30 4JD
tel: 01553 660 022
info: Must be 21 years or over to rent vans, however there is an insurance premium on those aged under 25.

Deeping St. James Car Hire
115 Spalding Road, Deeping St. James, Peterborough, Cambridgeshire, PE6 8SD
tel: 01778 347 827
contact: Mike
info: Caddy vans, Kangoo models, short and long wheel based. All self drive. Must be 23 years or over and have held a licence for over 2 years.

Eastern Rent-A-Van & Cars
Lynn Road, Wisbech, PE14 7AL
tel: 01945 582 458
email: easternvans@aol.com
contact: Keith Burlingham
info: Full range of vans available for self drive hire to those aged 21 years and over. Minibuses available to those aged 25 and over.

Enterprise Rent-A-Van
North Street, King's Lynn, Norfolk, PE30 1QW
tel: 01553 661 200
web: www.enterprise.com
info: Self drive. Range of cars (including estates), 7 seater MPVs and Transit vans available. Enterprise also has other branches in East Anglia, as well as throughout the UK. See website for locations.

Eurodrive Van Rental
East Anglia
tel: 0870 160 9060
email: mail@eurodrive.com
web: www.eurodrive.com
info: Range of vehicles available include cars, vans and MPVs. Self drive. Vehicle hire for the UK and worldwide. Eurodrive have several branches located across East Anglia, check website for details.

Europcar
East Anglia
tel: 0870 607 5000
web: www.europcar.co.uk
info: Extensive car hire service. Obtain a quote either online or by contacting the above number. Europcar have branches throughout the UK and worldwide. See website for full list of locations.

First Self Drive
7 Paddock Street, Norwich, NR2 4TW
tel: 01603 624 275
email: info@firstselfdrive.co.uk
web: www.firstselfdrive.co.uk
contact: Jonathan Howes
info: Wide range of vans. Minimum age of 21 years for self drive hire and must have licence for at least 2 years.

Global Self Drive (Cambridge)
Unit A, Swanns Road, Cambridge, CB5 8JZ
tel: 01223 565 500
web: www.driveglobal.com
contact: David, Paul
info: Massive range of vans. Must be aged 25 years or over. Self drive. Global also have outlets in Ipswich, Colchester, Grantham, Peterborough and Stamford. See listings in relevant sections for details.

Global Self Drive (Ipswich)
Global House, Europa Way, Eastways Business Park, Ipswich, Suffolk, IP1 5DL
tel: 01473 744 446
web: www.driveglobal.co.uk
info: Massive range of vans. Must be aged 25 years or over. Self drive. Global also have outlets in Cambridge, Colchester, Grantham, Peterborough and Stamford. See listings in relevant sections for details.

Global Self Drive (Peterborough)
Global Business Park, Saville Road, Westwood, Peterborough, PE3 7PR
tel: 01733 771 177
web: www.driveglobal.com
info: Massive range of vans. Must be aged 25 years or over. Self drive. Global also have outlets in Ipswich, Colchester, Grantham, Cambridge and Stamford. See listings in relevant sections for details.

Hammond's Commercial Centre
Broadway Drive, Norwich Road, Halesworth, IP19 8BU
tel: 01986 834 090
web: www.hammondgroup.co.uk
contact: Stuart Richardson
info: Full range of short and long wheel based Transit vans. Must be 25 years or over.

Harber Hire (Autos) Ltd.
4 Concorde Road, Norwich, NR6 6BW
tel: 01603 483 522
email: sales@harberhire.co.uk
web: www.harberhire.co.uk
contact: Marie Owen
info: Wide range of vans from small combo vans to Lutons. Insurance restrictions are subject to status.

Hertz
Europa Way, Eastways, Ipswich, Suffolk, IP1 5DL
tel: 01473 240 822
web: www.hertz.co.uk
info: Self drive car and van hire available. Hertz is a worldwide chain with branches throughout East Anglia, and the rest of the UK. See website above to locate your nearest branch.

Pertwee & Back
134 Lowestoft Road, Gorleston, Great Yarmouth, NR31 6JA
tel: 01493 442 775
email: fordrental@pertwee-and-back.co.uk
web: www.pertwee-and-back.co.uk
contact: John Burton
info: All rentals are subject to individual status, terms and conditions. Must be 23 years or over to hire. Self drive. Transit vans available.

Practical Van & Car Rental
115 Spalding Road, Deeping St. James, Peterborough, Cambridgeshire, PE6 8SD
tel: 01778 344 493
email: enquiry@practical.co.uk
web: www.practical.co.uk
info: Whole fleet of vehicles available for hire. Cars, vans, people carriers and minibuses. All self drive. Practical has several branches in East Anglia, as well as branches all over the UK. See website for details.

Thrifty Can & Van Rental
East Anglia
tel: 01494 751 600
fax: 01494 751 601
email: thrifty@thrifty.co.uk
web: www.thrifty.co.uk
contact: Julie Barnes
info: Self drive vehicles. Must be at least 23 years old to hire a van and have held a licence for 1 year. Vans available include Mercedes Sprinters, Transits, VW Transporters and other long and short wheel based vans. Thrifty has branches throughout the UK. See website for details.

Tilson Autos Ltd.
35 Infields Road, Glatton, Huntingdon, PE1 5UT
tel: 01487 832 415
fax: 01487 832 394
contact: Kirsty Roberts
info: Transit, long wheel based vans and minibuses. Must be aged at least 25 years. All self drive.

Tim Brinton Cars
Alington Road, Little Barford, St. Neots, PE19 6YH
tel: 01480 217 776
email: rental.stneots@marshallmotorgroup.co.uk
web: www.marshallrental.co.uk
contact: Corrine Sellens
info: All drivers must be over 21 years. Those aged between 21 and 24 years must have held a licence for 2 years, 25 years and over for 1 year. Full range of vans, people carriers and minibuses.

United Rental Group
East Anglia
tel: 01246 506 100
fax: 01246 506 256
email: enquiries@urg.co.uk
web: www.unitedrentalsystem.co.uk
info: Extensive range of cars and vans for self drive hire. United Rental Group have branches located throughout the UK. See the website for further details.

W. W. Rent-A-Van
35 Yaxham Road, Dereham, NR19 1HB
tel: 01362 692 580
email: enquiries@wwrentavan.com
web: www.wwrentavan.com
contact: Tim Warner
info: Full range of self drive vehicles, vans, people carriers and minibuses.

GREATER LONDON

1st Ace Van Hire
663-665 Watford Way, London, NW7 3JR
tel: 020 8201 1077/020 8201 1078
info: Full range of cars and vans for hire. People carriers and 15 seater minibuses also available. Self drive only.

1st Call Transit Centre
Wickford Street, Bethnal Green, London, E1 5QN
tel: 020 8981 2345
info: Vans and transits of all sizes available, as well as 12 and 15 seater minibuses. Provided either with driver or on self drive basis.

1st City Van Hire
348-349 Bocking Street, Hackney, London, E8 3RU
tel: 020 7275 0101
fax: 020 7275 0168
web: www.1stcityvanhire.com
info: Vehicles available include Transits, 15 and 17 seater minibuses, as well as a range of cars, including people carriers. Self drive or driver can be provided. 1st City Van Hire also have a branch at 128 Chigwell Road, Woodford E18 1NN (tel. 020 8989 3300).

1st Easy Van Hire
161a The Garage, Malden Way, New Malden, Surrey, KT3 5QX
tel: 020 8241 3669
contact: Mr B. Khan
info: Transit and Luton vans available. All areas of South London covered. Self drive. Free delivery and collection.

1st Hattons Van Rental
45-53 Beckton Road, London, E16 4EA
tel: 020 7476 1914
fax: 020 7474 4740
email: markhattonvans@aol.com
contact: Mark
info: Self drive hire. Vans and 8 to 15 passenger minibuses.

1st London Car Rentals
158 Marlebourne Road, London, NW1 5PN
tel: 020 8903 7777
email: info@lcr.co.uk
web: www.lcr.co.uk
info: Self drive vehicles including cars, transits, Mercedes Sprinter vans, minibuses and people carriers. Bookings can be made on the above number or via the website.

1st Mint Minicoaches
3 Coventry Close, London, NW6 4DA
tel: 020 7624 6796
fax: 020 7624 6814
email: info@minttravel.com
web: www.minttravel.com
info: 16 passenger minicoaches available for hire with driver. Also larger 29 and 39 seater coaches.

1st On The Road
Waring House, Waring Street, London, SE27 9LH
tel: 0800 980 0482
fax: 0870 770 2474
email: tony@otrtravel.com
web: www.otrtravel.com
info: Chauffeur driven vehicles to seat between 7 and 16 people, as well as 22, 29 and 33 + passenger minicoaches. Cars also available for hire.

1st Stage Coach European
32 Bredinghurst, Overhill Road, Dulwich, London, SE22 0PJ
tel: 020 8693 6387
contact: Barry
info: Chauffeur driven 16 seater executive minicoaches with large boots for storage.

1van1.com
Greater London
tel: 020 8897 9899
email: sales@1van1.com
web: www.1van1.com
info: Self drive minibus, car, van and MVP. Branches in Greater London include King's Cross, Stansted, Heathrow, Tower Bridge, Gatwick, Heston, Leytonstone, Tottenham and Shepherd's Bush. Also branches across rest of the UK. See listings in other regions.

ADC Minibus Services
25a Windsor Road, Forestgate, London, E7 0QX
tel: 020 8555 2494/07971 685 727
email: adc.minibus@virgin.net
web: www.adcminibus.com
contact: David, Linda
info: 14 seater minibuses with driver available for hire.

A Star Mini Buses
55 Middleton Gardens, Ilford, Essex, IG2 6DX
tel: 020 8554 2987/07947 751 482
info: 14 seater minibuses with driver available for hire.

A2B Budget Van Rental
59 Cobham Road, Kingston Upon Thames, Surrey, KT1 3AE
tel: 020 8296 9206
info: Range of cars and vans available for hire. Self drive.

A2B Self Drive Van Hire
Riverside House, Leaside Road, Upper Clapton, London, E5 9LU
tel: 020 8806 3155
email: a2bselfdrive@aol.com
web: www.a2bselfdrive.co.uk
info: Vehicles for hire ranging in size from courier vans to Transits and Lutons. Self drive.

Acorn Van Hire
561 High Road, Ilford, Essex, IG1 1PZ
tel: 020 8597 6565
info: Specialise in van hire. Transits and Lutons. Self drive only.

Active Travel
33 Park Way, West Molesey, KT8 1PF
tel: 020 8979 7212
info: 8 to 53 seater chauffeur driven minibuses available for hire.

Adlib Coach Hire
3 Houlder Crescent, Croydon, CR0 4EL
tel: 020 8686 0879
contact: Peter
info: 49 seater executive coaches with driver.

Alfred Premier Luxury Mini Coaches
15 Laxfield Court, Hackney, London, E8 4PU
tel: 020 7923 1812
info: 16 seater minibuses available with driver.

Arriva Vehicle Rental
The Old Dairy, Meadowstile (off High Street), Croydon, Surrey, CR0 1NH
tel: 020 8681 3181
fax: 020 8681 3775
email: centralres@arriva.co.uk
web: www.arrivarental.co.uk
info: Wide range of vans from Astra to Luton. All self drive. Arriva have branches throughout England. See website for details of all locations.

Autodrome Van Hire
137 Hatton Road, Feltham, Middlesex, TW14 8LR
tel: 020 8384 2299
info: Vans available including Transits, hi-tops and Lutons. Self drive only.

Avis Rent A Car
8 Balderton Street, Mayfair, London, W1K 6TF
tel: 0870 153 9104
web: www.avis.co.uk
info: Renault vans available on self drive basis. Hire available to those aged 23 years and above, but those under 25 years may face a higher insurance premium. Avis has outlets throughout the UK. See website for locations.

B&B Hire & Sales Ltd.
312 High Street, Stratford, London, E15 1AJ
tel: 020 8519 7848/020 8985 1414
fax: 020 8519 6277
email: bandbhireandsales@aol.com
web: www.bandbhireandsales.com
contact: Barry
info: Vehicles ranging from Escort vans to Transits and Lutons. Self drive.

Bliss Travel Ltd.
3 Ecclestone Place, Victoria, London, SW1 9NF
tel: 020 7730 8867
fax: 020 7730 6492
info: 8 to 29 seater vehicles available for rental with driver included.

Blue Moon Limo Services
27 Clewer Crescent, Harrow Weald, Middlesex, HA3 5QA
tel: 020 8537 6891/07903 813 666
email: sales@bluemoonlimos.com
web: www.bluemoonlimos.com
info: Fleet of chauffeur driven luxury vehicles including a pink limousine. Blue Moon will also be adding a stretched Hummer H2 to their fleet.

Bristol Street Motors
Greater London
tel: 0870 444 0506
email: enquiries@bristolstreet.co.uk
web: www.bristolstreet.co.uk
info: Self drive hire. Vans and people carriers available through a variety of dealers. Bristol Street have several branches in England. See website above for locations.

Budget
Greater London
tel: 0870 153 9170
fax: 0870 010 2391
email: via website
web: www.budget.co.uk
info: Budget operates around 80 locations across the UK. Check website for details. Each location has a range of vehicles available including people carriers, minibuses of varying sizes, trucks and vans, and cars. All locations offer self drive rentals. Rentals can be made for any length of time. Bookings can be made online or through the call centre number above.

MUSIC SERVICES/RETAIL

CCS Rent A Van Ltd.
Former Goods Yard, 45 Hornsey Road, London, N7 7DD
tel: 020 7700 0707
fax: 020 7700 0300
email: sales@ccsrentavan.co.uk
web: www.ccsrentavan.co.uk
info: Transits, hi-tops and Lutons available for hire. Self drive only.

Chadwell Heath Coaches
30 Reynolds Avenue, Chadwell Heath, Romford, Essex, RM6 4NT
tel: 020 8590 7505
fax: 020 8597 8883
email: c.h.coaches@btconnect.com
info: Coaches to seat 35, 49 and 53 passengers. Driver supplied.

Chivers Coaches
13a Ross Parade, Wallington, Surrey, SM6 8QG
tel: 020 8647 6648
fax: 020 8647 6649
info: 25, 46 and 53 passenger coaches with driver. Some vehicles with executive facilities.

The Civilised Car Hire Company
50 Parsons Green Lane, Parsons Green, London, SW6 4HU
tel: 020 7384 1133
fax: 020 7384 3366
email: mail@londoncarhire.com
web: www.londoncarhire.com
info: Splitter vans for up to 11 people with air conditioning and CD and DVD players. Range of cars also available for hire, as well as limousines, MPVs and people carriers. Provide tour buses through sister company Silvergray. See relevant entry in South East region for details.

Cole Hire
Westar House, 690 Great West Road, Osterley, Middlesex, TW7 4PU
tel: 020 8568 0733
email: arles@colehire.co.uk
web: www.colehire.co.uk
info: Vehicles available to hire include cars, transits, 8 or 15 seater minibuses and people carriers. Self drive only.

Crest Coach Company
1 Dalys Road, Rochford, Essex, SS4 1RA
tel: 020 8471 3287
email: enquiries@crestcoaches.com
web: www.crestcoaches.com
contact: Donna
info: Chauffeur driven vehicles to seat between 14 and 43 people.

Crossbow Tours
Heathrow
tel: 020 8841 3487
email: info@crossbowtours.co.uk
web: www.crossbowtours.co.uk or www.splitterbus.com
contact: Mick, Gillian
info: Luxury Mercedes 410D splitter bus available for hire with driver only. 8 passenger seats. DVD, video and CD players on board. UK and European destinations. Contact Mick or Gillian on above number for bookings.

Croydon Coaches
151 Whytecliffe Road North, Purley, Surrey, CR8 2AQ
tel: 020 8763 0077
info: Single deck coaches available to seat up to 57 people. Driver provided.

CVS (Commercial Vehicle Sales)
72 White Hart Lane, Tottenham, London, N17 8HP
tel: 020 8808 7236
fax: 020 8808 5730
email: commveh.sales@virgin.net
web: www.commercialvehicle-sales.co.uk
info: Fleet of vehicles available including 15 seater minibuses and transit vans of varying sizes. Self drive only.

Dan's Luxury Travel
Royal Forest Coach House, 109 Marybank Road, London, E18 1EJ
tel: 020 8505 8833
fax: 020 8559 1937
email: coaches@minibushire.fsnet.co.uk
info: From 16 seater minibuses to 51 seater coaches with toilet, video and air conditioning. Driver included.

Dimple Self Drive Hire Ltd.
16-19 Varley Parade, Edgware Road, London, NW9 6RR
tel: 020 8205 1200/7898
fax: 020 8200 7426
email: info@dimpleselfdrive.com
web: www.dimpleselfdrive.com
contact: Mrs Joshi
info: Fleet of cars and vans. Also supply 8, 12, 15 and 17 seater minibuses. Self drive.

Direct Tour Hire
Building D, Tower Bridge Business Complex, 100 Clements Road, London, SE16 4DG
tel: 020 7394 8111
fax: 020 7394 8555
email: chrisr@musicbank.org
web: www.musicbank.org
contact: Chris
info: Mercedes 9-13 seater Sprinter splitter vans. Dimensions of vehicles can be found on website. Self drive only. Can also organise travel for Europe. Linked with Music Bank equipment hire services, and Waterloo Sunset Studios rehearsal facilities. See listings in relevant sections for details.

Dulwich Van Hire
38 Barry Road, East Dulwich, London, SE22 0HU
tel: 020 8299 2745
info: Fleet of Ford Transits of varying sizes available for self drive hire.

Enterprise Rent-A-Van
145b Bow Road, London, E3 2AN
tel: 020 8980 5600
fax: 020 8980 3436
web: www.enterprise.com
info: Self drive. Range of cars (including estates), 7 seater MPVs and Transit vans available. Enterprise also has other branches in Greater London, as well as throughout the UK. See website for locations.

Eurodrive Van Rental

London
tel: 0870 160 9060
email: mail@eurodrive.com
web: www.eurodrive.com
info: Range of vehicles available include cars, vans and MPVs. Self drive. Vehicle hire for the UK and worldwide. Eurodrive have several branches located across London, check website for details.

Europcar

Greater London
tel: 0870 607 5000
web: www.europcar.co.uk
info: Extensive car hire service. Obtain a quote either online or by contacting the above number. Europcar have branches throughout the UK and worldwide. See website for full list of locations.

GBN Van Hire

BMS House, Oxlow Lane, Dagenham, RM10 8PS
tel: 020 8593 8282
email: storeatgbndag@btinternet.com
info: Fleet of Transit Lutons available. Self drive only. GBN also have self storage units which are suitable for bands to store equipment.

Goldenstand Southern Ltd.

13 Waxlow Road, Park Royal, London, NW10 7NY
tel: 020 8961 9974/020 8961 9975
fax: 020 8961 9949
email: info@goldenstand.co.uk
web: www.goldenstand.co.uk
info: Minibuses seating between 8 and 16 passengers, as well as coaches for 42 to 53 people. Vehicles only available with driver.

Hertz

Central Way, North Feltham Trading Estate, Feltham, Middlesex, TW14 0RX
tel: 020 8831 4450
web: www.hertz.co.uk
info: Self drive car and van hire available. Hertz is a worldwide chain with branches throughout Greater London, and the rest of the UK. See website above to locate your nearest branch.

Hounslow Mini Coaches

2 Vineyard Road, Feltham, Middlesex, TW13 4HQ
tel: 020 8890 8429
fax: 020 8893 1736
email: hounslowminicoaches@btconnect.com
web: www.hounslowminicoaches.co.uk
info: Mercedes air conditioned mini coaches for 8, 12, 16 and 22 passengers. Driver provided.

Impact

1 Leighton Road, West Ealing, Middlesex, W13 9EL
tel: 020 8579 9922
email: info@impactgroup.co.uk
web: www.impactgroup.co.uk
info: Chauffeur driven coaches available to seat 16, 24, 35 or 49 passengers.

Imperial Self Drive

Norflex House, Anchor Business Park, 102 Beddington Lane, Croydon, CR0 4YX
tel: 020 8686 8088
email: hiredesk@imperialselfdrive.co.uk
web: www.imperialselfdrive.co.uk
info: Supply cars, transits and people carriers for self drive hire.

International Coaches

19 Nursery Road, Thornton Heath, Croydon, Surrey, CR7 8RE
tel: 020 8684 8308
fax: 020 8689 3483
email: enquiries@internationalcoaches.co.uk
web: www.internationalcoaches.co.uk
contact: Ronnie, Sue, Kelly
info: 16 seater minibuses, 49 to 74 passenger coaches including traditional red double decker London buses. All provided with drivers.

Isleworth Coaches

Unit 14-15, Phoenix Distribution Park, Phoenix Way, Heston, Middlesex, TW5 9NB
tel: 020 8754 0800
fax: 020 8759 8080
email: sales@isleworthcoaches.co.uk
web: www.isleworthcoaches.co.uk
info: Smaller vehicles available to seat between 18 and 29 people, as well as larger coaches for 49 to 53 passengers. All vehicles provided with driver.

Kendall Car Hire Ltd. (Wimbledon)

11 Lombard Road, Wimbledon, London, SW19 3TZ
tel: 020 8542 0403
web: www.kendallcars.com
info: Escort vans, short wheelbase Transits are available for self drive hire to those aged 21 years and over. Long wheelbase Transits and Lutons are available to those 25 years and over. Kendall Car Hire have several branches based in the South East of England. Refer to relevant listings.

Kensington Coaches

45c Philbeach Gardens, London, SW5 9EB
tel: 020 7370 2507
fax: 020 7244 0898
email: rachel@kensingtoncoaches.com
web: www.kensingtoncoaches.com
contact: Rachel
info: Coaches to seat between 7 and 53 people. Driver provided.

Lea Bridge Van Hire

83 Lea Bridge Road, Leyton, London, E10 7QL
tel: 020 8556 8888
contact: George
info: Escort vans, Transits and Lutons available with driver or for self drive hire.

LP Hire

Unit 3E, Dentons Wharf, Mulberry Way, Belvedere, Kent, DA17 6AN
tel: 020 8317 2595/07949 572 898
email: lphire2002@yahoo.co.uk
web: www.lphire.co.uk
info: Vans and minibuses of all sizes available. Self drive.

The Luxy Bus

London
tel: 07932 884 832
email: stevelewis@yahoo.co.uk
web: www.upallnightmusic.com/resource.cfm
contact: Steve Lewis
info: The Luxy Bus is a very spacious vehicle suitable for touring, and has a full recording studio on board. Seats 8 and sleeps 6. Driver provided. Contact Steve for further details and bookings.

Mayday Travel of London

Unit 8, Mill Lane House, Mill Lane Trading Estate, Mill Lane, Croydon, CR0 4AA
tel: 020 8680 5111
fax: 020 8680 8624
email: info@coachhirelondon.co.uk
web: www.coachhirelondon.co.uk
info: Range of coaches available for rent, with driver. To seat 16, 21, 25 or 49 people.

Minibus Shuttle Services Ltd.

68 Lupus Street, London, SW1V 3EH
tel: 020 7821 1157
fax: 020 7834 6748
email: mbsreserve@aol.com
web: www.minibusshuttle.com
info: Chauffeur driven luxury Mercedes vehicles to seat 8, 12 and 16 passengers. Air conditioned. Rates and vehicles can be viewed online at the above address.

Moving Space

93b Scrubs Lane, London, NW10 6QU
tel: 020 8968 7798
fax: 020 8968 3377
email: tourbuses@btinternet.com
web: www.movingspaceuk.co.uk
contact: Nick Yateman
info: Mercedes 9 seater splitter bus with CD, DVD and Playstation on board. Drivers can be provided or self drive (drivers must be 25 years or over with full clean driving licence). Fully insured. Covers UK and Europe. Also run tour production company called Grand Tours which provide tour managers, backline technicians, crew and session musicians. For further information contact John Dawkins on 07967 729 097.

North London Van & Truck Hire Ltd.

BP Garage, 1320 Mollison Avenue, Brimsdown, Enfield, London, EN3 7NJ
tel: 020 8805 0011
info: Transit vans. Self drive only.

Parker Minibus Service

6 Park Road, Teddington, Middlesex, TW11 6AA
tel: 0800 064 6422
info: Cars and 8 seater Mercedes minibuses available for hire. Driver provided.

Portobello Mini Hire Ltd.
Arch 44, Lockton Street, Bramley Road, London, W10 6HR
tel: 020 8741 4458
email: info@portobello-vans.co.uk
web: www.portobello-vans.co.uk
info: Cars and Ford Transits available for hire. Self drive only.

Practical Car & Van Rental
4a East Street, Brentford, Middlesex, TW8 8LR
tel: 020 8560 5522
email: enquiry@practical.co.uk
web: www.practical.co.uk
info: Whole fleet of vehicles available for hire. Cars, vans, people carriers and minibuses. All self drive. Practical has several branches in Greater London, as well as branches all over the UK. See website for details.

Rooz Studios
2a Corsham Street, London, N1 6DP
tel: 020 7490 1919
contact: Graham Clark
info: Provide self drive splitter vans from £50. Some vehicles available with beds, DVD players and other facilities on board. Smaller and cheaper Transits available too. Rooz also run a rehearsal studio complex and equipment hire service. See entries in relevant sections for details.

Sigma Self Drive Ltd.
Longreach Road, River Industrial Estate, Barking, Essex, IG11 0JN
tel: 020 8507 8900
email: hiredesk@sigmaselfdrive.co.uk
web: www.sigmaselfdrive.co.uk
info: Mercedes Sprinter splitter vans available for hire. Also provide cars and Transits. Self drive.

Smart Rental
116 Maidstone Road, Sidcup, Kent, DA14 5HS
tel: 020 8300 8610
fax: 020 8300 9676
email: smart.hire@btconnect.com
web: www.smarthire.co.uk
info: Cars and vans for hire, including Transits and minibuses seating up to 15 people. Self drive.

South Ruislip Self Drive
Runway House, The Runway, South Ruislip, Middlesex, HA4 6SE
tel: 0800 032 33 63/020 8841 1901
email: via website
web: www.interent.co.uk
info: Self drive. Cars, Transits and 9, 15 and 17 seater minibuses for hire.

Speedicars
15 Coulgate Street, London, SE4 2RW
tel: 020 8694 2244/020 8692 6555
fax: 020 8694 2229
email: speedicars@aol.com
web: www.speedicars.co.uk
contact: Paul Buckley
info: Vehicles including cars, executive minibuses and minicoaches available for hire. Seat 12, 16, 24 and 35 passengers. Driver provided.

Star Events
Unit 4, Brentway Trading Estate, Brentway, Brentford, TW8 8ES
tel: 020 8847 1616
email: grandunion1@btconnect.com
contact: Ron
info: Music industry specialists. 3.5 and 7.5 tonne vehicles. Driver provided. Storage facilities available. Star Events also run rehearsal rooms. See entry in relevant section for details.

T & C Hire
Unit 2, Mill Farm, Whalebone Lane North, Mill Farm, Marks Gate, Romford, RM6 5QX
tel: 020 8599 9000
web: www.tandchire.co.uk
info: Box Vans, Lutons, small vans, tail lift vehicles and Transits all available for self drive hire.

Thrifty Car & Van Rental
Greater London
tel: 01494 751 600
fax: 01494 751 601
email: thrifty@thrifty.co.uk
web: www.thrifty.co.uk
info: Self drive vehicles. Must be at least 23 years old to hire a van and have held a licence for 1 year. Vans available include Mercedes Sprinters, Transits, VW Transporters and other long and short wheel based vans. Thrifty has branches throughout the UK. See website for details.

Tigertours Ltd.
81-83 Wembley Hill Road, Wembley, Middlesex, HA9 8BU
tel: 020 8902 1006/07831 837 367
email: info@tigertours.co.uk
web: www.tigertours.co.uk
contact: Kieran Barry
info: Splitter bus hire. Must be 25 years and hold full clean driving licence for at least 2 years.

Town & City Coach Ltd.
18 Parry Road, South Norwood, London, SE25 6RJ
tel: 020 8239 0831
fax: 020 8239 0831
email: towncitycoach@hotmail.com
web: www.towncitycoach.com
info: Cars and coaches to seat between 1 and 16 passengers available. Driver provided.

United Rental Group
Greater London
tel: 01246 506 100
fax: 01246 506 256
email: enquiries@urg.co.uk
web: www.unitedrentalsystem.co.uk
info: Extensive range of cars and vans for self drive hire. United Rental Group have branches located throughout the UK. See the website for further details.

Westway
7a Rainbow Industrial Estate, Station Approach, Raynes Park, London, SW20 0JY
tel: 020 8944 1277
fax: 020 8947 5339
email: david@westway-coaches.co.uk
web: www.westway-coaches.co.uk
info: 8 to 15 berth sleeper coaches. 16 and 71 seater coaches also available. Driver provided. Fleet of vehicles can be viewed online at the address above.

MIDLANDS

1van1.com
23 Kenyon Street, Birmingham, B18 6AR
tel: 0113 387 5559
email: sales@1van1.com
web: www.1van1.com
info: Self drive minibus, car, van and MVP. Other branches in the Midlands include Nottingham, Northampton, Stoke, Redditch, Leicester, Wolverhampton and Coventry. All contactable on the above number. Also branches across rest of the UK. See listings in other regions.

Afford Rent A Car
560 Hartshill Road, Hartshill, Stoke On Trent, ST4 7NH
tel: 01782 622 888
contact: Peter Williamson
info: Transit vans available for self drive hire, subject to status.

Allen Ford
Bedford Road, Northampton, NN1 5NX
tel: 01604 625 000
contact: Sue Dunkley
info: Long and short wheel based vans including Transit vans. Must be 25 years or over. Insurance can be provided, subject to status.

Arriva Vehicle Rental
Bridge Street, Oldbury, West Midlands, B69 4BT
tel: 0121 541 4141
email: centralres@arriva.co.uk
web: www.arrivarental.co.uk
info: Wide range of vans from Astra to Luton. All self drive. Arriva have branches throughout England. See website for details of all locations.

Avis Rent A Car
Tower Street, Coventry, West Midlands, CV1 1JN
tel: 0870 608 6332
web: www.avis.co.uk
info: Renault vans available on self drive basis. Hire available to those aged 23 years and above, but those under 25 may face a higher insurance premium. Avis has outlets throughout the UK. See website for locations.

Bristol Street Motors
Midlands
tel: 0870 444 0506
email: enquiries@bristolstreet.co.uk
web: www.bristolstreet.co.uk
info: Self drive hire. Vans and people carriers available through a variety of dealers. Bristol Street have several branches in England. See website above for locations.

Budget
Midlands
tel: 0870 153 9170
fax: 0870 010 2391
email: via website
web: www.budget.co.uk
info: Budget operates around 80 locations across the UK.
Check website for details. Each location has a range of vehicles
available including people carriers, minibuses of varying sizes, trucks
and vans, and cars. All locations offer self drive rentals. Rentals can be
made for any length of time. Bookings can be made online or through
the call centre number above.

East Midlands Vehicle Hire Ltd. (Derby)
Chester Park, Alfreton Road, Derby, DE21 4AS
tel: 01332 292 727
fax: 01332 295 816
email: derby@eastmidlandsvehiclehire.co.uk
web: www.eastmidlandsvehiclehire.co.uk
contact: Marie Horner
info: Small Astra vans to 7.5 tonnes and long wheel bases
and box vans. Must be 20 years or over. See also listing for branch in
Leicester.

East Midlands Vehicle Hire Ltd. (Leicester)
50 St. Ives Road, Leicester, LE4 9FN
tel: 0116 246 0212
email: leicester@eastmidlandsvehiclehire.co.uk
web: www.eastmidlandsvehiclehire.co.uk
info: Full range of vans available for hire. Minimum age is
21 years, with at least 2 years driving experience. See also listing for
branch in Derby.

Enterprise Rent-A-Van
248 Loughborough Road, Leicester, LE4 5LH
tel: 0116 268 2111
web: www.enterprise.com
info: Self drive. Range of cars (including estates), 7 seater
MPVs and Transit vans available. Enterprise also has other branches in
the Midlands, as well as throughout the UK. See website for locations.

Eurodrive Van Rental
Midlands
tel: 0870 160 9060
email: mail@eurodrive.com
web: www.eurodrive.com
info: Range of vehicles available include cars, vans and
MPVs. Self drive. Vehicle hire for the UK and worldwide. Eurodrive
have several branches located across the Midlands, check website for
details.

Europcar
Midlands
tel: 0870 607 5000
web: www.europcar.co.uk
info: Extensive car hire service. Obtain a quote either online
or by contacting the above number. Europcar have branches throughout
the UK and worldwide. See website for full list of locations.

Foley Self Drive Ltd.
Stourport Road, Kidderminster, DY11 7QL
tel: 01562 862 626
web: www.foleyvehiclerentals.co.uk
info: All sorts of vans available. Self drive. Musicians must
provide their own insurance, and therefore can be any age.

GK Group (Alfreton)
Nottingham Road, Somercotes, Alfreton, Derbyshire, DE55 4GR
tel: 01773 833 622
email: rental@gkford.co.uk
web: www.gkford.co.uk
info: Ford dealership. Available for self drive hire are Transits,
minibuses and Tourneos. Must be 23 years or over to hire vans,
although for a higher insurance premium 21 year olds and over may
hire them. Must be 27 years or over to hire minibuses. In all cases
anyone wanting to hire a vehicle must have been driving for at least 2
years and have no more that 6 points on their license. The GK Group
cannot insure any professional musicians. Also branches in Yorkshire,
Scotland and Cumbria. See listings in relevant sections for details.

GK Group (Chesterfield)
Chatsworth Road, Chesterfield, Derbyshire, S40 2BJ
tel: 01246 209 999
email: rental@gkford.co.uk
web: www.gkford.co.uk
info: Refer to listing above for information. Also branches in
Yorkshire, Scotland and Cumbria. See listings in relevant sections for
details.

GK Group (Derby)
Locomotive Way, Pride Park, Derby, DE24 8PU
tel: 01332 399 000
email: rental@gkford.co.uk
web: www.gkford.co.uk
info: See listing above for Alfreton branch for information.
Also branches in Yorkshire, Scotland and Cumbria. See listings in
relevant sections for details.

GK Group (Mansfield)
Chesterfield Road South, Mansfield, Nottinghamshire, NG19 7BA
tel: 01623 622 522
email: rental@gkford.co.uk
web: www.gkford.co.uk
info: Refer to Alfreton branch listing for information. Also
branches in Yorkshire, Scotland and Cumbria. See listings in relevant
sections for details.

GK Group (Retford)
London Road, Retford, Nottinghamshire, DN22 6AZ
tel: 01777 702 266
email: rental@gkford.co.uk
web: www.gkford.co.uk
info: See listing above for Alfreton branch for further
information. Also branches in Yorkshire, Scotland and Cumbria. See
listings in relevant sections for details.

GK Group (Staveley)
Duke Street, Staveley, Derbyshire, S43 3PD
tel: 01246 471 188
email: rental@gkford.co.uk
web: www.gkford.co.uk
info: Refer to listing for Alfreton branch for details. Also
branches in Yorkshire, Scotland and Cumbria. See listings in relevant
sections for details.

GK Group (Worksop)
Turner Road, Worksop, S81 7AE
tel: 01909 476 821
email: rental@gkford.co.uk
web: www.gkford.co.uk
info: Refer to Alorton branch listing for information. Also
branches in Yorkshire, Scotland and Cumbria. See listings in relevant
sections for details.

Global Self Drive (Grantham)
Global Business Park, Londonthorpe Road, Alma Park, Grantham,
NG31 9SN
tel: 01476 577 701
web: www.driveglobal.com
info: Massive range of vans. Must be aged 25 years or over.
Self drive. Global also have outlets in Ipswich, Colchester, Cambridge,
Peterborough and Stamford. See listings in relevant sections for details.

Global Self Drive (Stamford)
Van & Truck World, A1 Southbound, Wittering, Nr. Stamford, PE8 6HJ
tel: 01780 781 496
web: ww.driveglobal.com
info: Massive range of vans. Must be aged 25 years or over.
Self drive. Global also have outlets in Ipswich, Colchester, Grantham,
Peterborough and Cambridge. See listings in relevant sections for
details.

Hertz
Unit 2b, Everoak Industrial Estate, Bromyard Road, Worcester,
WR2 5HP
tel: 01905 748 260
web: www.hertz.co.uk
info: Self drive car and van hire available. Hertz is a
worldwide chain with branches throughout Worcester, and the rest of
the UK. See website above to locate your nearest branch.

Listers Van Centre
347-367 Bedworth Road, Longford, Coventry, CV6 6BN
tel: 02476 644 747
email: vwcomm.coventry@listersgroup.co.uk
web: www.listers-volkswagen.co.uk
contact: Andy Hunt
info: Full range of VW vans, minibuses and people carriers.
Must be 25 years or over. Insurance can be provided, subject to status.

Long Marsh Ltd. (Corby)
Sondes Road, Willowbrook East Industrial Estate, Corby, NN17 5XL
tel: 01536 402 302
fax: 01536 402 304
email: longmarshcorby@btconnect.com
contact: Simon Coleman
info: Wide range of vans. Must be aged between 25 and 70
years and have held a driving licence for over 1 year. No more than
6 points on licence in 5 years. See also listing for outlets located in
Bedford and Wellingborough.

Long Marsh Ltd. (Wellingborough)
Heron House, The Embankment, Wellingborough, Northamptonshire, NN8 1LD
tel: 01933 222 872
web: www.longmarshltd.co.uk
info: Wide range of vans. Must be aged between 25 and 70 years and have held a driving licence for over 1 year. No more than 6 points on licence in 5 years. See also listing for outlets located in Bedford and Corby.

Magnet Vehicle Hire
Unit 2, Davisella House, Newark Street, Sneinton, Nottingham, NG2 4PP
tel: 0115 924 3324/07879 452 976
email: rob@magnetstudios.co.uk
web: www.magnetstudios.co.uk
contact: Rob Reid
info: Splitter van hire. Contact Rob for details of prices. Magnet also run rehearsal rooms and an equipment hire service. See listings in relevant sections for further information.

Practical Car & Van Rental
65-69 Rixon Road, Finedon Road Industrial Estate, Wellingborough, Northamptonshire, NN8 4BA
tel: 01933 272 465
email: enquiry@practical.co.uk
web: www.practical.co.uk
info: Whole fleet of vehicles available for hire. Cars, vans, people carriers and minibuses. All self drive. Practical has several branches in the Midlands, as well as branches all over the UK. See website for details.

Senior Self Drive Hire
Riverside Industrial Estate, Rockingham Road, Market Harborough, LE16 7PT
tel: 01858 464 466
info: Full range of small and large vans. Self drive. Must be at least 25 years with no more than 6 points on your licence in the previous 5 years.

Six Rent A Car
Durrant House, 47 Hollywell Street, Chesterfield, Derby, S41 7SJ
tel: 01246 220 111
contact: Melanie Molton
info: 3.5 tonne Luton vans, high roof long wheel vans, Transits, Ford connects, Astral vans and drop side vans. 9 seater and 15-17 seater minibuses available.

Thrifty Car & Van Rental
Midlands
tel: 01494 751 600
fax: 01494 751 601
email: thrifty@thrifty.co.uk
web: www.thrifty.co.uk
info: Self drive vehicles. Must be at least 23 years old to hire a van and have held a licence for 1 year. Vans available include Mercedes Sprinters, Transits, VW Transporters and other long and short wheel based vans. Thrifty has branches throughout the UK. See website for details.

United Rental Group
Midlands
tel: 01246 506 100
fax: 01246 506 256
email: enquiries@urg.co.uk
web: www.unitedrentalsystem.co.uk
info: Extensive range of cars and vans for self drive hire. United Rental Group have branches located throughout the UK. See website for further details.

Willoughby Garages (Nottingham) Ltd.
375 Mansfield Road, Nottingham, NG5 2DA
tel: 0115 961 6467
email: liam.mitchel@peugeotmail.co.uk
web: www.peugeot-cars.co.uk
contact: Liam Mitchel
info: Full range of vans available. Self drive. Insurance is subject to status. Contact for more details.

NORTHEAST

1van1.com
Copthorne Hotel, The Close, Quayside, Newcastle, NE1 3RT
tel: 0113 387 5559
web: www.1van1.com
info: Self drive minibus, car, van and MVP. Also branches across rest of the UK. See listings in other regions.

Academy Hire Ltd.
16 Pierson Street, Redcar, TS10 1SW
tel: 01642 487 997
fax: 01642 490 699
email: academyhire@btconnect.com
contact: Mark Hordforth
info: Wide range of vans available for self drive hire. Also hire minibuses.

Arriva Vehicle Rental
Transport Solutions House, Riverbank Road, Sunderland, Tyne & Wear, SR5 3JJ
tel: 0191 516 3000
email: centralres@arriva.co.uk
web: www.arrivarental.co.uk
info: Wide range of vans from Astra to Luton. All self drive. Arriva have branches throughout England. See website for details of all locations.

Atlas Garage
Longbenton Service Station, Whitley Road, Longbenton, Newcastle Upon Tyne, NE12 9SR
tel: 0191 266 6593
fax: 0191 266 7199
web: www.atlasgarages.co.uk
contact: Ross
info: Vans and people carriers available for self drive.

Avis Rent A Car
7 George Street, Newcastle Upon Tyne, Tyne & Wear, NE4 7JL
tel: 0870 608 6350
web: www.avis.co.uk
info: Renault vans available on self drive basis. Hire available to those aged 23 years and above, but those under 25 years may face a higher insurance premium. Avis has outlets throughout the UK. See website for locations.

Bishop Auckland Van & Car Hire
Etherley Moor Garage, Etherley Moor, Bishop Auckland, County Durham, DL14 0JU
tel: 01388 450 683
info: Transit and Luton vans available. Self drive.

Bristol Street Motors
North East
tel: 0870 444 0506
email: enquiries@bristolstreet.co.uk
web: www.bristolstreet.co.uk
contact: David Holland
info: Self drive hire. Vans and people carriers available through a variety of dealers. Bristol Street have several branches in England. See website above for locations.

Budget
North East
tel: 0870 153 9170
fax: 0870 010 2391
email: via website
web: www.budget.co.uk
info: Budget operates around 80 locations across the UK. Check website for details. Each location has a range of vehicles available including people carriers, minibuses of varying sizes, trucks and vans, and cars. All locations offer self drive rentals. Rentals can be made for any length of time. Bookings can be made online or through the call centre number above.

Capital Car Hire
Unit G Portberry, Portberry Street, South Shields, NE33 1QX
tel: 0191 454 2676
contact: Steve Bent
info: Vans including Ford Transit vans, and minibuses available for hire. Self drive. 24 hour hire starting from £45.

Charter Self Drive Ltd.
Charter House, Forge Way, Cleveland Street, Darlington, DL1 2PJ
tel: 01325 481 814
email: sales@charterselfdrive.co.uk
web: www.charterselfdrive.co.uk
contact: Richard Harmer
info: Full range of Transit vans, people carriers and minibuses. To drive the bigger vans you must be over 25 years but the smaller Transit vans may be rented to those over 21 years with 2 years driving experience.

City Motors Peugeot
Bensham Bank, Gateshead, NE8 4YJ
tel: 0191 493 3500
info: No problem providing insurance cover for musicians. Self drive hire for a large range of vans and minibuses. Must be 21 years to hire.

Eden Park Self Drive Hire
Seaton Lane, Seaton Carew, Hartlepool, Cleveland, TS25 1JG
tel: 01429 268 546
fax: 01429 268 546
contact: Keith Hair
info: Full range of vans available. All self drive.

Enterprise Rent-A-Van
16-18 North Bridge Street, Sunderland, SR5 1AB
tel: 0191 567 9200
fax: 0191 514 1111
web: www.enterprise.com
contact: Dan Martin
info: Self drive. Range of cars (including estates), 7 seater MPVs and Transit vans available. Enterprise also has other branches in the North East, as well as throughout the UK. See website for locations.

Eurodrive Van Rental
North East
tel: 0870 160 9060
email: mail@eurodrive.com
web: www.eurodrive.com
info: Range of vehicles available include cars, vans and MPVs. Self drive. Vehicle hire for the UK and worldwide. Eurodrive have several branches located across the North East, check website for details.

Europcar
North East
tel: 0870 607 5000
web: www.europcar.co.uk
info: Extensive car hire service. Obtain a quote either online or by contacting the above number. Europcar have branches throughout the UK and worldwide. See website for full list of locations.

Fifty-Fifty Car & Van Rental
Halifax Place, Dunston, Gateshead, NE11 9JZ
tel: 0191 461 1914
info: Large Luton vans and smaller Kangoo vans, along with 7 seat cars are all available for self drive hire.

Fleetserve Rental Ltd.
Unit 3-4, Canute Street, Preston, PR1 1PL
tel: 01772 563 939
contact: Adam
info: Offer self drive MPVs and vans.

Hall & Hall Vehicle Hire
Gratthorp Industrial Estate, Graythorp, Hartlepool, TS25 2DF
tel: 01429 234 141
info: Self drive Transit van hire.

Hertz
2 Forth Banks, Newcastle Upon Tyne, Tyne & Wear, NE1 3PA
tel: 0191 232 5313
web: www.hertz.co.uk
info: Self drive car and van hire available. Hertz is a worldwide chain with branches throughout the North East, and the rest of the UK. See website above to locate your nearest branch.

Lisles Auto Hire Services Ltd.
31a Front Street, Monkseaton, Whitley Bay, Tyne & Wear, NE25 8AQ
tel: 0191 252 1895
email: jeff@lislesautohire.co.uk
web: www.lislesautohire.co.uk
info: Range of vans includes Transits, both long and short wheel base, as well as Lutons. Ask for details of half day rates.

Maxwell Motors Ltd.
Unit 7, North Road Industrial Estate, Berwick Upon Tweed, TD15 1UN
tel: 01289 306 000
fax: 01289 306 555
email: enquiries@maxwellmotorsford.co.uk
web: www.maxwellmotorsford.co.uk
contact: Sandra Collum
info: Self drive hire, mainly Ford Transit vans.

Noble Self Drive Ltd.
23 Allington Way, Yarm Road Business Park, Darlington, DL1 4QB
tel: 01325 461 125
fax: 01325 356 530
email: hiredesk@nobleselfdrive.co.uk
web: www.nobleselfdrive.co.uk
contact: Angela Walton
info: Transits, Sprinters and smaller vans available for self drive. 12-15 seat minibuses.

Patterson Ford
Forth Street, Newcastle Upon Tyne, Tyne & Wear, NE1 3PF
tel: 0191 261 0722
fax: 0191 239 4949
email: dave.robertson@pattersonford.co.uk
web: www.pattersonford.co.uk
contact: Steve Atkinson
info: Mid range transit vans, short and long wheel based. 23 year olds can hire self drive. Higher insurance premiums for those aged under 23 years.

Peugeot Car & Van Rental
79 Benton Road, Newcastle Upon Tyne, NE7 7DT
tel: 0191 266 6361
fax: 0191 270 0660
contact: Angela MacIntyre
info: No problem providing insurance cover for musicians. Self drive hire for a large range of vans and minibuses. Must be 21 years or over to hire.

Practical Car & Van Rental
Vulcan Place Garage, Vulcan Place, Bedlington, NE22 5DL
tel: 01670 824 287
email: enquiry@practical.co.uk
web: www.practical.co.uk
contact: Linda Cuthbert
info: Whole fleet of vehicles available for hire. Cars, vans, people carriers and minibuses. All self drive. Practical has several branches in the North East, as well as branches all over the UK. See website for details.

R.S. Johnson (Blyth)
Tower Garage, Regent Street, Blyth, NE24 1LL
tel: 01670 354 812
email: info@rsjohnson.co.uk
web: www.rsjohnson.co.uk
contact: Paul Dixon
info: Band friendly. Can rent cars, small vans and people carriers. See also listing for branch in Morpeth.

R.S. Johnson (Morpeth)
Unit 18, Coopies Hough, Morpeth, NE61 6JT
tel: 01670 519 970
email: info@rsjohnson.co.uk
web: www.rsjohnson.co.uk
contact: Paul Dixon
info: Band friendly. Can rent cars, small vans and people carriers. Self drive. See also listing for branch in Blyth.

S.H.B. Hire Ltd.
Station Lane, Birtley, Chester Le Street, County Durham, DH3 1DB
tel: 0191 492 2223
fax: 0191 492 2221
contact: Susan Hislop
info: Smaller vans and minibuses available for self drive hire. Customers must provide their own fully comprehensive insurance.

Thrifty Car & Van Rental
North East
tel: 01494 751 600
fax: 01494 751 601
email: thrifty@thrifty.co.uk
web: www.thrifty.co.uk
info: Self drive vehicles. Must be at least 23 years old to hire a van and have held a licence for 1 year. Vans available include Mercedes Sprinters, Transits, VW Transporters and other long and short wheel based vans. Thrifty has branches throughout the UK. See website for details.

United Rental Group
North East
tel: 01246 506 100
fax: 01246 506 256
email: enquiries@urg.co.uk
web: www.unitedrentalsystem.co.uk
info: Extensive range of cars and vans for self drive hire. United Rental Group have branches located throughout the UK. See the website for further details.

NORTHWEST

1van1.com
Unit 25, Owen Drive, Speke, Liverpool, L24 1YL
tel: 0113 387 5559
email: sales@1van1.com
web: www.1van1.com
info: Self drive minibus, car, van and MVP. Other branches in the North West include Manchester, Carlisle, Warrington, Manchester Airport and Chester. All contactable on the above number. Also branches across rest of the UK. See listings in other regions.

MUSIC SERVICES/RETAIL

A1 Minibuses & Coaches
Units 4&5 Hall Street, Blackburn, Lancashire, BB2 3RH
tel: 01254 265 151
fax: 01254 665 777
contact: Sean Casey
info: 12-33 seater coaches. Hire only available with driver supplied.

ABC Car & Van Hire
Viola Street, (off Blackburn Road), Bolton, BL1 8NG
tel: 01204 300 075
fax: 01204 593 014
contact: Peter, Phil
info: Self drive cars and vans for hire. Range of vans available, up to 3.5 tonnes. Drivers must be over 25 years.

All Over Minibuses
18 Tarbet Road, Duckinfield, SK16 4BE
tel: 0161 304 8430
fax: 0161 304 8460
contact: Mr. S Robertson
info: 8, 11, 14, 16, 25 and 33 seater minibuses. Only available with driver supplied.

APT
378 Manchester Road West, Little Hulton, Manchester, M38 9XU
tel: 0161 790 4455
contact: Mr Pawson
info: 8 seater minibuses available with driver.

Archway Travel
Unit H, Cocker Avenue, Poulton Industrial Estate, Poulton le Fylde, FY6 8JU
tel: 01253 896 208
email: archwaytravel@hotmail.com
web: www.archwaytravel.com
contact: Dawn
info: 49, 51 and 71 seater coaches for hire. Driver provided.

Arriva Vehicle Rental
Cross Street, Wigan, WN3 4ET
tel: 01942 231 104
email: centralres@arriva.co.uk
web: www.arrivarental.co.uk
info: Wide range of vans from Astra to Luton. All self drive. Arriva have branches throughout England. See website for details of all locations.

Atlantis Minibuses
6 Crossland Street, Accrington, BB5 0RY
tel: 01254 879 000
contact: Jul Zaman
info: Private hire for all occasions. Offering 12, 14 and 16 seater minibuses with driver.

Avis Rent A Car
Back Caton Road, Lancaster, LA1 1DG
tel: 01524 841 700
web: www.avis.co.uk
info: Renault vans available on self drive basis. Hire available to those aged 23 years and above, but those under 25 years may face a higher insurance premium. Avis has outlets throughout the UK. See website for locations.

Banner Self Drive
Birch Garage, Manchester Road, Birch, Heywood, OL10 2QD
tel: 0800 146 974
contact: Louise
info: Self drive. Minibuses, cars and vans. For car and van hire, must be over 21 years old. Minibus hire, over 25 years old. 2 years experience with full licence essential.

Bristol Street Motors
North West
tel: 0870 444 0506
email: enquiries@bristolstreet.co.uk
web: www.bristolstreet.co.uk
info: Self drive hire. Vans and people carriers available through a variety of dealers. Bristol Street have several branches in England. See website above for locations.

Budget
North West
tel: 0870 153 9170
fax: 0870 010 2391
email: via website
web: www.budget.co.uk
info: Budget operates around 80 locations across the UK. Check website for details. Each location has a range of vehicles available including people carriers, minibuses of varying sizes, trucks and vans, and cars. All locations offer self drive rentals. Rentals can be made for any length of time. Bookings can be made online or through the call centre number above.

C.I.R. Transport
1 Wharton Bridge, Winsford, Cheshire, CW7 3BA
tel: 01606 860 111
fax: 01606 860 222
email: info@cirgold.com
web: www.cirgold.com
contact: Gilbert, Dave, Chris
info: Offer predominantly splitter buses, also MPV rental exclusively to bands, musicians and equipment touring the UK and Europe. 20 years experience in the music industry. Complete service with high quality vehicles holding up to 12 passengers. Also offer tour production. Clients have included Elbow, Cradle of Filth and The Pixies. No self drive.

Caremore Travel
Units 8 & 9, Thatto Heath, Brindley Road, St. Helens, WA9 4HY
tel: 01744 818 516
web: www.caremorecars.co.uk
contact: Mr Richards
info: 8-16 seater mini-buses and American stretch limousines.

Cass of Wirral
22 Tarran Way West, Moreton, Wirral, CH46 4TP
tel: 0151 677 1684
fax: 0151 677 5549
contact: Steve
info: 45-76 seater coaches for hire.

CME Ltd.
12 Thompson Lane, Chadderton, OL9 8LT
tel: 0161 620 2000
fax: 0161 620 2200
contact: Mary
info: Self drive. Range of cars and vans available for hire.

County Minibus Hire
St. Mary's Way, Stockport, SK1 4AP
tel: 0161 474 1515
email: enquiries@county-rental.co.uk
web: www.county-rental.co.uk
contact: Karen Berridge
info: Range of self-drive vehicles from cars, 8-17 seater minibuses to transit vehicles.

Easi-Rent
40-46 Queen Street, Wigan, WN3 4HX
tel: 01942 821 077
email: head-office@easirent.com
web: www.easirent.com
contact: Paul Hanley
info: Self drive. Car, van, truck, motor home and limousine hire. Vans available in a range of sizes, including splitters. Easi-Rent's clients include Starsailor. Also have a branches in Liverpool, Preston, Rochdale and Leeds. See website for details.

Economy Car & Van Rental/Carefree Contracts
Factory Lane Trading Estate, Penwortham, Preston, PR1 9TD
tel: 01772 750 110/01772 750 202
fax: 01772 743 020
email: carefreecontract@aol.com
web: www.carefreecontracts.com
contact: Geoff Kellet
info: Extensive range of cars, vans and 7 seaters for self drive hire.

Enterprise Rent-A-Van
Vantage Vauxhall, Accrington Road, Burnley, BB11 5EX
tel: 01282 410 280
web: www.enterprise.com
info: Self drive. Range of cars (including estates), 7 seater MPVs and vans available. Self drive. Range of cars (including estates), 7 seater MPVs and Transit vans available. Enterprise also has other branches in the North West, as well as throughout the UK. See website for locations.

Eurodrive Van Rental
North West
tel: 0870 160 9060
email: mail@eurodrive.com
web: www.eurodrive.com
info: Range of vehicles available include cars, vans and MPVs. Self drive. Vehicle hire for the UK and worldwide. Eurodrive have several branches located across the North West, check website for details.

Europcar
North West
tel: 0870 607 5000
web: www.europcar.co.uk
info: Extensive car hire service. Obtain a quote either online or by contacting the above number. Europcar have branches throughout the UK and worldwide. See website for full list of locations.

Excel Chauffeur Services Ltd.
Unit 8, Warrington Business Park, Long Lane, Warrington, WA2 8XP
tel: 0871 288 1433
fax: 0871 288 1433
email: bookings@xl-cars.co.uk
web: www.xl-cars.co.uk
info: Chauffeur driven executive people carrier suitable for touring. Seats 8 passengers. Air conditioned with fridge, drinks machine, DVD player and 2 monitors. Other vehicles available including minibuses and coaches, to seat between 8 and 73 people.

Fawlty Tours
Harrison Street, Horwitch, Bolton, BL6 7AH
tel: 07850 030 663
info: 8-35 seater minibus and coach hire.

Formby Coaches
97a Altcar Road, Formby, Merseyside, L37 8DL
tel: 01704 875 858
fax: 01704 833 383
contact: Angela, John
info: 24-51 seater coaches.

Freebird
Revers Street Garage Tottington, Woodhill, Bury, BL8 1AQ
tel: 01204 887 344
fax: 0871 277 3124
email: info@freebirdcoaches.co.uk
web: www.freebirdcoaches.co.uk
contact: Paul/Rob/Gary
info: 16, 29 and 51 mini-coach and coach hire with driver. Ample boot space.

GK Group (Carlisle)
Wakefield Road, Kingstown Industrial Estate, Carlisle, Cumbria, CA3 0HE
tel: 01228 517 200
email: rental@gkford.co.uk
web: www.gkford.co.uk
info: Ford dealership. Available for self drive hire are Transits, minibuses and Tourneos. Must be 23 years or over to hire them, although for a higher insurance premium 21 year olds and over may hire them. Must be 27 years or over to hire minibuses. In all cases anyone wanting to hire a vehicle must have been driving for at least 2 years and have no more that 6 points on their license. The GK Group cannot insure any professional musicians. Also branches in Midlands, Scotland and Yorkshire. See listings in relevant sections for details.

GK Group (Penrith)
Old London Road, Penrith, Cumbria, CA11 8JJ
tel: 01768 861 500
email: rental@gkford.co.uk
web: www.gkford.co.uk
info: See listing above for information. Also branches in Midlands, Scotland and Yorkshire. See listings in relevant sections for details.

GK Group (Workington)
Blackwood Road, Lillyhall Industrial Estate, Lillyhall, Workington, CA14 4JW
tel: 01900 811 000
email: rental@gkford.co.uk
web: www.gkford.co.uk
info: Refer to Carlisle listing above for information. Also branches in Midlands, Scotland and Yorkshire. See listings in relevant sections for details.

Glossop Car & Van Hire
Unit 14, Dinting Vale Business Park, Glossop, SK13 9LG
tel: 01457 864 480
email: pgglossopmotors@aol.com
web: www.glossopcars.co.uk
info: Self drive. Full range of cars, vans, lorries, MPVs, estates, minibuses, pick-ups and Lutons. Drivers must have 2 years experience and be at least 21 years of age to hire vehicles up to 1500cc, 25 years for multi-seated vehicles.

Go Goodwins Coaches
Lyntown Trading Estate, Old Wellington Road, Eccles, Manchester, Lancashire, M30 9QG
tel: 0161 789 4545
fax: 0161 789 0939
email: gogoodwins@aol.com
web: www.gogoodwins.co.uk
contact: Suzanne Goodwin
info: 24-49 seater coaches and minicoaches. Clients include Justin Timberlake touring party.

Grayway Coaches
237 Manchester Road, Ince, Wigan, WN2 2EA
tel: 01942 235 586
fax: 01942 824 807
contact: Mr & Mrs Gray
info: 18-55 seater coaches and minicoaches.

H&K Travel
The Mount, Mount Pleasant, Tebay, CA10 3TH
tel: 01539 624 001
contact: Helen Hall
info: 8-14 seater coaches with driver.

Hall Brow Services
Gate House, Hallwood Road, Lillyhall, Workington, Cumbria, CA14 4JR
tel: 01900 680 30
fax: 01900 680 33
web: www.hallbrowservices.co.uk
contact: Mr Alderson
info: Self drive. Cars, 7 seater MPVs and vans up to 7.5 tonnes for hire.

Happy Al's Coach Hire
400 Cleveland Street, Birkinhead, Merseyside, CH41 8EQ
tel: 0151 653 0053
fax: 0151 670 0509
info: 49-71 seater coaches, executive coaches and double-decker buses.

Hattons Travel
Unit 15, AC Complex, Shaw Street, St.Helens, WA10 1DQ
tel: 01744 454 188
fax: 01744 616 668
contact: David Hatton
info: 21-52 seater coaches.

Haytons Executive Travel Ltd.
Unit 3, Belos House, Foxmere Street, Gorton, M18 8EF
tel: 0161 223 3103
fax: 0161 223 9528
email: enquiries@haytonstravel.co.uk
web: www.haytonstravel.co.uk
contact: Kerry, Dave
info: 12 seater minibuses to 53 seater executive coaches, with driver.

Healings International
251 Higginshaw Lane, Royton, Oldham, OL2 6HW
tel: 0161 624 8975
info: 20-53 seater mini-coaches and coaches with driver. Britain and the continent. No self drive.

Hertz
Mona Place, Croft Street, The Old Brewery Trading Estate, Preston, Lancashire, PR1 8XA
tel: 01772 563 600
web: www.hertz.co.uk
info: Self drive car and van hire available. Hertz is a worldwide chain with branches throughout the North West, and the rest of the UK. See website above to locate your nearest branch.

Home James Travel
STC House, Speke Hall Road, Liverpool, L24 9HD
tel: 0151 486 5111
email: am1land@supernet.com
info: Coaches and mini-coaches, 30-53 seater. 24 hour back-up and roadside assistance. Pan-European hire.

Huyton Minicoaches
93 Lawton Road, Huyton, Liverpool, L36 4HN
tel: 0151 489 4116
fax: 0151 480 4919
email: pamturner@copperstream.co.uk
contact: Mrs Turner
info: 8-35 seater mini-coaches with driver. Large boots. Run active airport service.

James Lewis Travel
47 Further Field, Rochdale, OL11 5PJ
tel: 01706 713 343
contact: Beverly Taylor
info: 16 seater mini-coaches with driver. Seats can be removed to create larger storage space for equipment.

John Hoban
22 King Street, Workington, Cumbria, CA14 4DJ
tel: 01900 603 579
fax: 01900 603 579
email: johnahoban@aol.com
contact: Mr Hoban
info: 24-33 seater minicoaches and 16 seater minibuses. With driver only.

Kent Estuary Travel
2a Beetham Road, Milnthorpe, Cumbria, LA7 7QR
tel: 01539 562 917
contact: Joe
info: Minibuses up to 16 seats with driver. Vehicles with wheelchair access available.

Kingfisher Self Drive
Sandwich Close, Rainford Industrial Estate, St. Helens, Merseyside, WA11 8LY
tel: 01744 886 555
contact: Dean
info: Range of cars, MPVs, vans and 7-17 seater minibuses. Some vehicles fitted with tow bar. Trailers available by prior arrangement. Green cards available for continental travel. Call Kingfisher with your requirements.

Kirkby Lonsdale Coach Hire
Twenty Acres, Moor End, Hutton Roof, Carnforth, LA6 2PF
tel: 01524 272 239
fax: 01524 272 239
info: 16, 24, 33 and 51 seater coaches.

Lakeland Coaches
Cricket Field Ground, Shap Road, Kendal, Cumbria, LA9 6BZ
tel: 01539 741 388
fax: 01539 734 234
email: airport-services@btconnect.com
contact: David Birkett
info: 16 seater minibuses. No self drive.

M Travel Minibuses
25 Cornbrook Park Road, Manchester, M15 4EH
tel: 0161 877 0019
fax: 0161 877 1700
email: mtravelminibuses@aol.com
contact: Mr Butt
info: 5-16 seater minibuses available with driver. Local and long distance areas covered.

Man With Van
Chorlton, Manchester
tel: 07974 236 541
web: www.manwithvan.biz
info: Offers specialist services for bands that are gigging around Manchester or nationally. He can deliver equipment to venues in Manchester and pick up after the gig. If the whole band, kit and musicians need to get to the gig, he can also hire a Mercedes minibus. With driver only.

Messengers Coaches
Station Road Garage, Asparia, Carlisle, CA7 2AJ
tel: 01697 320 244
fax: 01697 323 900
info: 21-57 seater coaches, including executive options with TV, video and toilet. UK and continental work.

Mostonian 2000
23 Kenyon Lane, Manchester, M40 9JG
tel: 0161 681 0297
fax: 0161 681 4119
email: mostonian2000@btconnect.com
web: www.mostonian2000.co.uk
info: 48 and 72 seater coaches. Family run business with over 40 years experience.

Nationwide Vehicle Bank
91 Eastham Village Road, Wirral, CH62 0AN
tel: 0151 327 8883
info: Self drive. Cars, vans, minibuses, 4-wheel drives and MPVs available for hire.

Orion Travel
Newbank Street, Manchester, Lancashire, M12 4TN
tel: 0161 273 3895
fax: 0161 225 9560
email: bookings@oriontravel.co.uk
web: www.oriontravel.co.uk
info: 7-29 seater minicoaches. Wheelchair accessible vehicles available. No self drive.

P & S Self Drive
P&S Buildings, Station Road, Rainhill, Merseyside, L35 0LL
tel: 0151 430 8464
info: Self drive. Cars, MPVs, minibuses and vans (range of vehicle available below 7.5 tonnes).

Pentagon Oldham Car & Van Rental
Park Road, Oldham, OL4 1SR
tel: 0161 622 0300
email: shelly.turner@pentagon-vauxhall.co.uk
web: www.pentagon-vauxhall.co.uk
contact: Shelly, Christine
info: Self drive. Range of cars and vans including combo vans, transit size vans and estate cars. Customers must be over 25 years old and have held a full driver's licence for at least 12 months.

Polar Motors (Runcorn)
Victoria Road, Runcorn, Cheshire, WA7 5SP
tel: 0870 085 3166
email: via website
web: www.polar-motor.co.uk
info: Full range of long and short wheel vans. Must be 23 years old and held driving licence for at least 2 years. To hire the 17 seat minibus must be 25 years or over and held licence for 6 years. Polar have several branches throughout Yorkshire and North West. See listings in relevant regions for details.

Polar Motors (St. Helens)
City Road, St. Helens, Merseyside, WA10 6NZ
tel: 0870 085 3169
email: via website
web: www.polar-motor.co.uk
info: Full range of long and short wheel vans. Must be 23 years old and held driving licence for at least 2 years. To hire the 17 seat minibus must be 25 years or over and held licence for 6 years. Polar have several branches throughout Yorkshire and North West. See listings in relevant regions for details.

Polar Motors (Warrington)
Winwick Road, Warrington, WA2 7NY
tel: 0870 085 3183
email: via website
web: www.polar-motor.co.uk
info: Full range of long and short wheel vans. Must be 23 years old and held driving licence for at least 2 years. To hire the 17 seat minibus must be 25 years or over and held licence for 6 years. Polar have several branches throughout Yorkshire and North West. See listings in relevant regions for details.

Practical Car & Van Rental
Bridge Street, Accrington, Lancashire, BB5 4HU
tel: 01254 392 929
email: enquiry@practical.co.uk
web: www.practical.co.uk
info: Whole fleet of vehicles available for hire. Cars, vans, people carriers and minibuses. All self drive. Practical has several branches in the North West, as well as branches all over the UK. See website for details.

Robinson's Coaches
Station Road Garage, Appleby, Cumbria, CA16 6TX
tel: 01768 351 424
info: 16-53 seater coaches with driver.

S & D Executive Hire
Freshfields, 601 Hindley Road, Hindley, WN2 4EX
tel: 01942 256677
fax: 01942 259667
email: info@sandd.fsnet.co.uk
web: www.sandd.fsnet.co.uk
contact: Mrs White
info: Large up to date fleet of 14-29 seater chauffeur driven minibuses. Limousines also available.

Salford Van Hire
Sherborne Street, Manchester, M3 1EJ
tel: 0161 833 0771
email: info@salfordvanhire.com
web: www.salfordvanhire.com
info: Range of vans and transits for hire, plus MPVs (7 to 12 seater). Telephone bookings taken with credit cards. Self drive.

Speedy Self Drive (Accrington)
Spring Garden, Grange Lane, Accrington, BB5 2BT
tel: 01254 386 000
web: www.speedyselfdrive.co.uk
info: Self drive. Range of cars and vans available. See also listings for Bury and Oldham branches.

Speedy Self Drive (Bury)
61-65 Bell Lane, Bury, BL9 6BB
tel: 0161 763 4144
web: www.speedyselfdrive.co.uk
info: Self drive. Range of cars and vans. See also listings for branches in Oldham and Accrington.

Speedy Self Drive (Oldham)
Beal Lane, Shaw, Oldham, OL2 8PF
tel: 01706 291 136
email: headoffice@speedyselfdrive1.freeserve.co.uk
web: www.speedyselfdrive.co.uk
info: Self drive. Range of cars and vans including Escorts and Transits. Also have branches in Bury and Accrington. See listings for further details.

Taurus Self Drive Ltd.
55 Wyverne Road, Chorlton, Manchester, M21 0ZW
tel: 0161 434 9823
fax: 0161 434 9823
email: sean.taurus.t21@btinternet.com
web: www.taurus-splitters.co.uk
contact: Sean
info: 9 seater Sprinter splitters for hire. Self drive only. Damage deposit required. Credit cards bookings accepted.

Thrifty Car & Van Rental
North West
tel: 01494 751 600
fax: 01494 751 601
email: thrifty@thrifty.co.uk
web: www.thrifty.co.uk
info: Self drive vehicles. Must be at least 23 years old to hire a van and have held a licence for 1 year. Vans available include Mercedes Sprinters, Transits, VW Transporters and other long and short wheel based vans. Thrifty has branches throughout the UK. See website for details.

Tilly Hire
8 Boundary Street, Great Howard Street, Liverpool, L5 9UF
tel: 0151 2071441
email: hire@tillyhire.co.uk
web: www.tillyhire.co.uk
contact: John Boyce
info: Self drive van hire. Range of sizes available.

TJS Self Drive
135-137 Higher Bridge Street, Bolton, Bl1 2HN
tel: 01204 394 803
email: paul.carter@tjsselfdrive.co.uk
web: www.tjsselfdrive.co.uk
contact: Paul Carter
info: Full range of light commercials for self drive hire. Bands and musicians must have full insurance cover, as not included in service.

United Rental Group
North West
tel: 01246 506 100
fax: 01246 506 256
email: enquiries@urg.co.uk
web: www.unitedrentalsystem.co.uk
info: Extensive range of cars and vans for self drive hire. United Rental Group have branches located throughout the UK. See the website for further details.

Wright Bros Coaches Ltd.
Central Garage, Nenthead, Nr. Alston, Cumbria, CA9 3NP
tel: 01434 381 200
fax: 01434 382 089
email: info@wrightbros.co.uk
web: www.wrightbros.co.uk
contact: Ian Wright, Gary Wright
info: 31-49 seater coaches with driver. Air conditioned day buses and 14 berth sleepers with CD player, TV and fridge also available. UK and Pan-European.

Wrigley's Coaches Ltd.
4 Fiddlers Lane, Irlam, Manchester, Lancashire, M44 6QE
tel: 0161 775 2414
fax: 0161 775 1558
email: sales@wrigleyscoaches.com
web: www.wrigleyscoaches.com
contact: Alan, Louise
info: From 16 seater minicoaches with tables to 71 seater executive coaches. Can also provide business class limousines.

SOUTHEAST

1van1.com
11 Broomfield Road, Chelmsford, Essex, CM1 1SY
tel: 0113 387 5559
email: sales@1van1.com
web: www.1van1.com
info: Self drive minibus, car, van and MVP. Other branches in the South East include Milton Keynes, Maidstone, Colchester, Croydon, Luton, Reading, Slough, Tunbridge Wells, Watford and Barking. All contactable on the above number. Also branches across rest of the UK. See listings in other regions.

Alley Cat Car & Van Rental
Unit 7a, Italstyle Buildings, Cambridge Road, Harlow, CM20 2HE
tel: 01279 436 236
info: Short and long wheel based vans for self drive hire. Must be aged 25 years or above, and have been driving for over 1 year. Can insure those aged 23 and 24 years, and who held a clean licence for at least 2 years, but at a higher premium.

Arrival Vehicle Rental
2b Buckingham Avenue, Slough, Sl1 4NB
tel: 01753 694 497
email: centralres@arriva.co.uk
web: www.arrivarental.co.uk
info: Wide range of vans from Astra to Luton. All self drive. Arriva have branches throughout England. See website for details of all locations.

Avis Rent A Car
The Causeway, Staines, Middlesex, TW18 3AL
tel: 0870 608 6418
web: www.avis.co.uk
info: Renault vans available on self drive basis. Hire available to those aged 23 years and above, but those under 25 years may face a higher insurance premium. Avis has outlets throughout the UK. See website for locations.

Axe Hire
Unit 3, Rivermead Industrial Estate, Bishop Hall Lane, Chelmsford, CM1 1PD
tel: 01245 347 370
email: via website
web: www.axehire.co.uk
info: Berlingo, Transit and high top vans available for self drive hire. Must be 21 years with 1 year driving experience.

Bristol Street Motors
South East
tel: 0870 444 0506
email: enquiries@bristolstreet.co.uk
web: www.bristolstreet.co.uk
info: Self drive hire. Vans and people carriers available through a variety of dealers. Bristol Street have several branches in England. See website above for locations.

Budget
South East
tel: 0870 153 9170
fax: 0870 010 2391
email: via website
web: www.budget.co.uk
info: Budget operates around 80 locations across the UK. Check website for details. Each location has a range of vehicles available including people carriers, minibuses of varying sizes, trucks and vans, and cars. All locations offer self drive rentals. Rentals can be made for any length of time. Bookings can be made online or through the call centre number above.

CC Hire
67 Layer Road, Colchester, CO2 7JP
tel: 01206 761 011
info: Escorts and Transits. Must be 25 years and have been driving for 2 years.

Choice Vehicle Rentals Ltd.
Auction House, Arkwright Road, Lottbridge Drove, Eastbourne, BN23 6QL
tel: 01323 520 353
info: Transit vans available for self drive hire. Must be over 21 years with 2 years driving experience.

Drive & Go
41 Progress Road, Leigh On Sea, Essex, SS9 5PR
tel: 01702 527 272
web: www.drive-go.com
info: Short and long wheel based vans, Transits, Combos and Couriers. Must be 21 years and have a clean driving licence with over 2 years driving experience.

Eurodrive Van Rental
South East
tel: 0870 160 9060
email: mail@eurodrive.com
web: www.eurodrive.com
info: Range of vehicles available include cars, vans and MPVs. Self drive. Vehicle hire for the UK and worldwide. Eurodrive have several branches located across the South East, check website for details.

Europcar
South East
tel: 0870 607 5000
web: www.europcar.co.uk
info: Extensive car hire service. Obtain a quote either online or by contacting the above number. Europcar have branches throughout the UK and worldwide. See website for full list of locations.

Fargo Vehicle Hire
Unit 67, Victoria Road, Chelmsford, Essex, CM1 1PA
tel: 01245 345 222
web: www.fargoselfdrive.co.uk
contact: Vince
info: Vans and 9, 12 and 17 seater minibuses. Lutons and Transits. Must be 25 years, hold a clean licence and have at least 2 years driving experience.

Fastrack Car & Van Rental
Unit 5 Swan Vale Industrial Estate, Colchester Road, Witham, CM8 3DH
tel: 01376 515 575
web: www.fastrackservices.co.uk
info: Short and long wheel based vehicles. Must be 21 years and have held a clean licence for 2 years.

Global Self Drive (Colchester)
8 The Westside Centre, London Road, Colchester, Essex, CO3 5PD
tel: 01206 210 022
web: www.driveglobal.com
info: Massive range of vans. Must be aged 25 years or over. Self drive. Global also have outlets in Ipswich, Cambridge, Grantham, Peterborough and Stamford. See listings in relevant sections for details.

Handy Hire
Wards Yard, Springfield Park Road, Chelmsford, CM2 6EE
tel: 01245 353 555
fax: 01245 267 075
email: handyhire@btconnect.com
web: www.handyhireltd.co.uk
info: Short wheel based and some long wheel Luton Transits. Must be 23 years and have been driving for 3 years.

Haynes Brothers
23 Ashford Rd, Maidstone, Kent, ME14 5DQ
tel: 01622 756 781
web: www.haynesford.co.uk
info: All Ford vehicles, large range of Transits. Must be 21 years to hire, although there are extra insurance premiums for those aged under 25.

Hendy Hire (Chichester)
Terminus Road, Chichester, West Sussex, PO19 2TX
tel: 01243 536 100
fax: 01243 523 401
email: chich.hire@hendy-group.com
web: www.hendy-hire.com
info: Must be at least 23 years old and have been driving for 2 years or more to hire any of the wide range of vans. All self drive. Hendy have several branches throughout the South East and South West. See listings for details.

Hendy Hire (Eastbourne)
Unit 2, Birch Close, Eastbourne, East Sussex, BN23 6PE
tel: 01323 431 794
fax: 01323 725 521
web: www.hendy-hire.com
info: Must be at least 23 years old and have been driving for 2 years or more to hire any of the wide range of vans. All self drive. Hendy have several branches throughout the South East and South West. See listings for details.

Hendy Hire (Eastleigh)
37-43 Bournemouth Road, Chandlers Ford, Eastleigh, Hampshire, SO53 3ZG
tel: 02380 271 600
fax: 02380 271 700
email: cfrd.hire@hendy-group.com
web: www.hendy-hire.com
info: Must be at least 23 years old and have been driving for 2 years or more to hire any of the wide range of vans. All self drive. Hendy have several branches throughout the South East and South West. See listings for details.

Hendy Hire (Fareham)
Newgate Lane, Fareham, Hampshire, PO14 1TU
tel: 01329 825 874
fax: 01329 281 356
email: fare.hire@hendy-group.com
web: www.hendy-hire.com
info: Must be at least 23 years old and have been driving for 2 years or more to hire any of the wide range of vans. All self drive. Hendy have several branches throughout the South East and South West. See listings for details.

Hendy Hire (Hastings)
105 Battle Road, St. Leonards on Sea, Hastings, East Sussex, TN37 7AD
tel: 01424 428 121
fax: 01424 461 505
web: www.hendy-hire.com
info: Must be at least 23 years old and have been driving for 2 years or more to hire any of the wide range of vans. All self drive. Hendy have several branches throughout the South East and South West. See listings for details.

Hendy Hire (Portsmouth)
Southampton Road, Cosham, Portsmouth, Hampshire, PO6 4RW
tel: 02392 371 600
fax: 02392 322 922
email: cosh.hire@hendy-group.com
web: www.hendy-hire.com
info: Must be at least 23 years old and have been driving for 2 years or more to hire any of the wide range of vans. All self drive. Hendy have several branches throughout the South East and South West. See listings for details.

Hertz
25 Boulton Road, Rose Kiln Lane, Reading, Berkshire, RG2 0NH
tel: 0118 986 1313
web: www.hertz.co.uk
info: Self drive car and van hire available. Hertz is a worldwide chain with branches throughout the South East, and the rest of the UK. See website above to locate your nearest branch.

Kendall Car Hire Ltd. (Aldershot)
Ash Station, Guildford Road, Ash, GU12 6LX
tel: 01252 333 598
fax: 01252 338 722
web: www.kendallcars.com
info: Escort vans, short wheelbase Transits are available for self drive hire to those aged 21 years and over. Long wheelbase Transits and Lutons are available to those 25 years and over. Kendall Car Hire have several branches based in the South East of England. Refer to relevant listings.

Kendall Car Hire Ltd. (Camberley)
4 Doman Road, Camberley, Surrey, GU15 3DF
tel: 01276 691 972
fax: 01276 682 847
web: www.kendallcars.com
info: Escort vans, short wheelbase Transits are available for self drive hire to those aged 21 years and over. Long wheelbase Transits and Lutons are available to those 25 years and over. Kendall Car Hire have several branches based in the South East of England. Refer to relevant listings.

Kendall Car Hire Ltd. (Canterbury)
Canterbury East Railway Station, Station Road East, Canterbury, Kent, CT1 2RB
tel: 01227 781 180
web: www.kendallcars.com
info: Escort vans, short wheelbase Transits are available for self drive hire to those aged 21 years and over. Long wheelbase Transits and Lutons are available to those 25 years and over. Kendall Car Hire have several branches based in the South East of England. Refer to relevant listings.

Kendall Car Hire Ltd. (Chertsey)
Downside, Guildford Street, Chertsey, Surrey, KT16 9DS
tel: 01932 571 133
fax: 01932 570 132
web: www.kendallcars.com
info: Escort vans, short wheelbase Transits are available for self drive hire to those aged 21 years and over. Long wheelbase Transits and Lutons are available to those 25 years and over. Kendall Car Hire have several branches based in the South East of England. Refer to relevant listings.

Kendall Car Hire Ltd. (Guildford)
34 Aldershot Road, Guildford, Surrey, GU2 8AF
tel: 01483 574 434
fax: 01483 534 781
web: www.kendallcars.com
info: Escort vans, short wheelbase Transits are available for self drive hire to those aged 21 years and over. Long wheelbase Transits and Lutons are available to those 25 years and over. Kendall Car Hire have several branches based in the South East of England. Refer to relevant listings.

Kendall Car Hire Ltd. (Leatherhead/Gatwick Airport)
Kingslea Works, Kingston Road, Leatherhead, Surrey, KT22 7LE
tel: 01372 376 655
fax: 01372 377 799
web: www.kendallcars.com
info: Escort vans, short wheelbase Transits are available for self drive hire to those aged 21 years and over. Long wheelbase Transits and Lutons are available to those 25 years and over. Kendall Car Hire have several branches based in the South East of England. Refer to relevant listings.

Lee Hire
7 Church Place, Brighton, BN2 5JN
tel: 01273 680 044
email: sales@leehire.co.uk
web: www.leehire.co.uk
info: Minimum age for hiring vans over 1.4L is 25 years with a clean driving licence. All drivers must be over 21 years with 2 years driving experience. Drivers under 25 years must have a clean driving licence. Forms of identification required upon hiring any vehicle are driving licence, 10 year passport or credit card with 2 utility bills. £50 deposit returnable on completion of a clean, undamaged, vehicle full of fuel.

Lipscomb Volvo
Central House, Ashford Road, Chartham, Kent, CT4 7HH
tel: 01227 732 250
web: www.lipscomb.co.uk
info: No vans but do have a 7 seat XC90 people carrier for rent. The back seats fold down for kit storage.

Locost Car & Van Hire Sales & Services Ltd.
South Woodham Garage, Old Wickford Road, South Woodham Ferrers, Chelmsford, CM3 5QS
tel: 01245 324 101
info: Ford vehicles including Escort vans, Transits and more. Call for a quote.

Long Marsh Ltd. (Bedford)
Elstow Road, Bedford, MK42 9LE
tel: 01234 217 833
web: www.longmarshltd.co.uk
info: Wide range of vans. Must be aged between 25 and 70 years and have held a driving licence for over 1 year. No more than 6 points on licence in 5 years. See also listing for outlets located in Corby and Wellingborough.

Marshall's
Firbank Way, Leighton Buzzard, Bedfordshire, LU7 4YP
tel: 01525 376 077/01525 381 145
fax: 01525 850 967
email: info@marshalls-coaches.co.uk
web: www.marshalls.co.uk
info: 20 to 80 passenger coaches with driver. Also have branches in Hemel Hempstead and Milton Keynes. See website for details.

Motor World
19 Rossini Place, Old Farm, Milton Keynes, MK3 7QT
tel: 0800 731 7444
info: Self drive van hire. All kinds of vehicles available.

Myles Hire
108-112 Fairfax Drive, Westcliff-On-Sea, Essex, SS0 9BH
tel: 01702 301 111
web: www.myleshire.co.uk
info: Vans and trucks available to those aged 22 years and above. Must have been driving for at least 3 years.

Oxford Vehicle Rentals
18 Pony Road, Horspath Industrial Estate, Cowley, Oxford, OX4 2RD
tel: 01865 748 811
email: ollie@oxvan.co.uk
web: www.oxvan.co.uk
info: Wide range of vans including Nissan Kubistar and Primastar. Also short and long wheelbase vehicles.

Peter Waugh Self Drive Hire
2 Queens Road, Guildford, Surrey, GU1 4JJ
tel: 01483 576 362
fax: 01483 576 603
email: peter@peter-waugh.co.uk
web: www.peter-waugh.co.uk
info: Various people carriers and Transit vans. Drivers should be aged between 23 and 69 years, and have held a driving license for at least 1 year.

Practical Car & Van Rental
Unit D4, St. George's Business Park, Sittingbourne, Kent, ME10 3TB
tel: 01795 436 456
email: enquiry@practical.co.uk
web: www.practical.co.uk
info: Whole fleet of vehicles available for hire. Cars, vans, people carriers and minibuses. All self drive. Practical has several branches in the South East, as well as branches all over the UK. See website for details.

RGR Garages (Cranfield)
High Street, Cranfield, Bedford, Bedfordshire, MK43 0DG
tel: 01234 750 207
info: Latest Ford vans available for self drive hire.

Robertson Self Drive
26 Magdalen Street, Colchester, Essex, C01 2LD
tel: 0800 374 652
info: Escorts, Transits, full range of Ford vans. Must be 25 years and have at least 12 months driving experience

Sigma Self Drive
Longreach Road, Barking, IG11 0JR
tel: 020 8507 8900
email: hiredesk@sigmaselfdrive.co.uk
web: www.sigmaselfdrive.co.uk
info: Must hold a clean licence, have over 2 years driving experience, and be 25 years or over to rent any of the vans. Cash hire requires a £500 deposit.

Silvergray
Atlas Industrial Park, Rye Harbour Road, Rye, East Sussex, TN31 7TE
tel: 01797 226 296
fax: 01797 229 603
email: enquiries@silvergray.co.uk
web: www.silvergray.co.uk
info: Provide sleeper buses ranging from 10-16 berths. For splitter and general car hire see entry for sister company Civilised Car Company in Greater London section.

Steve's Self Drive
Bentalls Close, Southend-On-Sea, SS2 5PS
tel: 01702 612 047
email: info@steves-selfdrive.com
web: www.steves-selfdrive.com
info: Vans and people carriers available. Must be 23 years to hire vans, 25 years for people carrier.

Target Vehicle Rental
7-8 Hinksey Business Centre, North Hinksey Lane, Oxford, OX3 0EJ
tel: 01865 244 477
email: enquiries@targetrental.co.uk
web: www.targetrental.co.uk
info: Wide range of small, medium and large vans. Must be over 25 years and have been driving for 2 years.

Tavern Garage
10 The Causeway, Heybridge, Maldon, CM9 4LJ
tel: 01621 858 773
email: contact@tavernhire.co.uk
web: www.tavernhire.co.uk
info: Vans, Lutons, pickups and dropsides. Must be 21 years and have been driving for over 1 year.

Thames Valley Rentals
Water Eaton, Oxford, Oxfordshire, OX2 8HA
tel: 01865 310 888
email: enquiries@tvr-selfdrive.co.uk
web: www.tvr-selfdrive.co.uk
info: All self drive. Transits available, as well as people carriers and a wide range of other suitable vehicles. Must be 21 years to rent.

Thrifty Car & Van Rental
South East
tel: 01494 751 600
fax: 01494 751 601
email: thrifty@thrifty.co.uk
web: www.thrifty.co.uk
info: Self drive vehicles. Must be at least 23 years old to hire a van and have held a licence for 1 year. Vans available include Mercedes Sprinters, Transits, VW Transporters and other long and short wheel based vans. Thrifty has branches throughout the UK. See website for details.

Toomey Vehicles Rentals Ltd.
West Mayne, Basildon, SS15 6RW
tel: 01268 546 484
web: www.toomey-vauxhall.com
info: Astra, Combo, short wheel based Vivaro, medium wheel based Movano. Must be 25 years, have clean licence with 12 months driving experience.

United Rental Group
South East
tel: 01246 506 100
fax: 01246 506 256
email: enquiries@urg.co.uk
web: www.unitedrentalsystem.co.uk
info: Extensive range of cars and vans for self drive hire. United Rental Group have branches located throughout the UK. See the website for further details.

Victoria Hire
22 St. Dunstan's Street, Canterbury, Kent, CT2 8BU
tel: 01227 455 001
web: www.victoriahire.co.uk
info: Connects, Transits, Berlingos and Lutons. All available for self drive.

Wayside Car & Van Rental
Lyon Road, Denbigh West Industrial Estate, Milton Keynes,
Buckinghamshire, MK1 1EX
tel: 01908 271 272
web: www.waysidegroup.co.uk
info: Self drive van hire. Must be 25 years and have at least 1
year driving experience.

SOUTHWEST

1st Call Auto Rentals
Unit 138, Stroud Space Centre, Chestnut Lane, Stroud, Gloucestershire,
GL5 3EW
tel: 01453 763 302
fax: 01453 767 640
info: Small vans and Lutons available. Self drive. Drivers
available if needed.

1van1.com
Suite 6, Innsworth Technology Park, Innsworth Lane, Gloucester,
GL3 1DL
tel: 0113 387 5559
email: sales@1van1.com
web: www.1van1.com
info: Self drive minibus, car, van and MVP. Other branches in
the South West include Southampton, Bristol, Plymouth and Swindon.
All contactable on the above number. Also branches across rest of the
UK. See listings in other regions.

A1 Self Drive Hire
379 Wellsway, Bath, BA2 5RN
tel: 01225 830 630
contact: Al Kennedy
info: Transits, Sprinters and Lutons all available on self drive
basis. Insurance subject to status.

Arriva Vehicle Rental
5 Leigham Business Units, Silverton Road, Matford Park, Exeter,
EX2 8HY
tel: 01392 822 000
email: centralres@arriva.co.uk
web: www.arrivarental.co.uk
info: Wide range of vans from Astra to Luton. All self drive.
Arriva have branches throughout England. See website for details of all
locations.

Avis Rent A Car
Tregolls Road, Truro, Cornwall, TR1 1SB
tel: 01872 262 226
web: www.avis.co.uk
info: Renault vans available on self drive basis. Hire available
to those aged 23 years and above, but those under 25 years may face
a higher insurance premium. Avis has outlets throughout the UK. See
website for locations.

Beech Motors
Albert Road, St. Austell, Cornwall, PL25 4TZ
tel: 01726 747 743
email: emmalusk@beechmotors.demon.co.uk
info: Self drive hire.

Blights Motors
Clovelly Road, Handy Cross, Bideford, EX39 3ET
tel: 01237 472 282
web: www.blightsmotors.co.uk
info: Transit vans available for hire. Must be 21 years or over,
and have been driving for at least 12 months.

Bristol & West Vehicle Hire Ltd.
Unit 3a, Kingsditch Lane, Cheltenham, GL51 9NE
tel: 01452 307 777
email: hiredesk@bristolandwestvehiclehire.co.uk
web: www.bristolandwestvehiclehire.co.uk
contact: Paul McCarthy
info: All kinds of vans available. Self drive. Must be 21 years
or over, and have held a driving licence for minimum of 2 years.

Bristol Street Motors
South West
tel: 0870 444 0506
email: enquiries@bristolstreet.co.uk
web: www.bristolstreet.co.uk
contact: David Holland
info: Self drive hire. Vans and people carriers available
through a variety of dealers. Bristol Street have several branches in
England. See website above for locations.

Budget
South West
tel: 0870 153 9170
fax: 0870 010 2391
email: via website
web: www.budget.co.uk
info: Budget operates around 80 locations across the UK.
Check website for details. Each location has a range of vehicles
available including people carriers, minibuses of varying sizes, trucks
and vans, and cars. All locations offer self drive rentals. Rentals can be
made for any length of time. Bookings can be made online or through
the call centre number above.

Chief Vehicle Rentals
Paignton Railway Station, Paignton, Devon, TQ1 1LW
tel: 01803 520 494
contact: Sean Cunningham
info: Vans and minibuses available for hire. Self drive. Must
be at least 21 years and have 2 years driving experience.

Cleeve Hill Garage
Cleeve Hill, Cheltenham, GL52 3PX
tel: 01242 672 026
contact: Terry Harris
info: 7 and 8 seater people carriers, and minibuses up to 15
seaters. Self drive. No vans.

Elgin Car & Van Rental
Elgin Drive, Swindon, Wiltshire, SN2 8DP
tel: 01793 485 542
fax: 01793 614 875
email: alb@fish-bros.co.uk
web: www.fish-bros.co.uk
info: Wide range of vehicles, from compact to executive and
commercial. Also specialise in 7 to 12 seater vehicles.

Enterprise Rent-A-Van
Unit 4 Great Western Parade, Old Station Road, Barnstaple, EX32 8PB
tel: 01271 852 900
web: www.enterprise.co.uk
info: Self drive. Range of cars (including estates), 7 seater
MPVs and Transit vans available. Enterprise also has other branches
in the South West, as well as throughout the UK. See website for
locations.

Eurodrive Van Rental
South West
tel: 0870 160 9060
email: mail@eurodrive.com
web: www.eurodrive.com
info: Range of vehicles available include cars, vans and
MPVs. Self drive. Vehicle hire for the UK and worldwide. Eurodrive
have several branches located across the South West, check website for
details.

Europcar
South West
tel: 0870 607 5000
web: www.europcar.co.uk
info: Extensive car hire service. Obtain a quote either online
or by contacting the above number. Europcar have branches throughout
the UK and worldwide. See website for full list of locations.

Fish Brothers (Peugeot Swindon)
Great Western Way, Swindon, Wiltshire, SN5 7YQ
tel: 01793 401 118
fax: 01793 512 817
email: jrp@fish-bros.co.uk
web: www.fish-bros.co.uk
info: Self drive only. Wide range of cars and vans.

George Hartwell Ltd.
The Quay, Poole, BH15 1HB
tel: 01202 338 400
email: contact@georgehartwell.co.uk
web: www.georgehartwell.co.uk
contact: Sharon Skinner
info: Wide range of Peugeot vans. Minimum age for self drive
hire is 21 years.

Hendy Hire (Bournemouth)
Yeomans Way, Bournemouth, Dorset, BH8 0BJ
tel: 01202 547 700
fax: 01202 546 154
email: yeom.hire@hendy-group.com
web: www.hendy-hire.com
info: Must be at least 23 years old and have been driving for
2 years or more to hire any of the wide range of vans. All self drive.
Hendy have several branches throughout the South East and South
West. See listings for details.

Trathens Star Riders

Walkham Park
Burrington Way
Plymouth, Devon, England
PL5 3LS

Suppliers of Sleeper Coaches.

Recent Clients:
Stereophonics, Coldplay, Robbie Williams, Kasabian

**Serving the United Kingdom and Europe
Established in 1981**

(JB) - John Bettinson Manager 44 1752 772 000
www.trathensstarriders.com
jb1@trathensstarriders.com
Tel 44 1752 772 000
Fax 44 1752 769 629

Hendy Hire (Cheltenham)
Kingsville Road, Kingsditch Industrial Estate, Cheltenham,
Gloucestershire, GL51 9NZ
tel: 01242 526 734
fax: 01242 224 084
web: www.hendy-hire.com
info: Must be at least 23 years old and have been driving for
2 years or more to hire any of the wide range of vans. All self drive.
Hendy have several branches throughout the South East and South
West. See listings for details.

Hendy Hire (Exeter)
Grace Road, Marsh Barton Trading Estate, Marsh Barton, Exeter, Devon,
EX2 8QB
tel: 01392 275 136
fax: 01392 275 152
web: www.hendy-hire.com
info: Must be at least 23 years old and have been driving for
2 years or more to hire any of the wide range of vans. All self drive.
Hendy have several branches throughout the South East and South
West. See listings for details.

Hendy Hire (Gloucester)
7 Hucclecote Road, Hucclecote, Gloucester, Gloucestershire, GL3 3TQ
tel: 01452 610 736
fax: 01452 616 980
web: www.hendy-hire.com
info: Must be at least 23 years old and have been driving for
2 years or more to hire any of the wide range of vans. All self drive.
Hendy have several branches throughout the South East and South
West. See listings for details.

Hendy Hire (Salisbury)
Telford Road, Churchfields Industrial Estate, Salisbury, Wiltshire,
SP2 7PH
tel: 01722 326 444
fax: 01722 421 270
email: sali.hire@hendy-group.com
web: www.hendy-hire.com
info: Must be at least 23 years old and have been driving for
2 years or more to hire any of the wide range of vans. All self drive.
Hendy have several branches throughout the South East and South
West. See listings for details.

Hertz
Sutton Road, Coxside, Plymouth, PL4 0HN
tel: 01752 207 207
web: www.hertz.co.uk
info: Self drive car and van hire available. Hertz is a
worldwide chain with branches throughout the South West, and the
rest of the UK. See website above to locate your nearest branch.

Jumbo Cruiser Ltd.
Tweed Road, Clevedon, Bristol, BS21 6RR
tel: 07768 211 612
email: steve@jumbocruiser.com
web: www.jumbocruiser.com
contact: Stephen Lee
info: 8 to 16 berth sleeper coaches. Splitters and Single-
deckers. Driver provided. Charter in Europe and UK. TV, VCR,
Playstation and printer on board. Fully air conditioned. Contact
Stephen for price enquiries and booking.

Pinhoe Garage Ltd.
Main Road, Pinhoe, Exeter, EX4 8HR
tel: 01392 466 448
email: hire@pinhoegarage.co.uk
web: www.pinhoegarage.co.uk
contact: Andy Pearce
info: Transit, Connect and long wheel based high top roof
vans available for self drive hire. Must be 25 years. Insurance subject to
status.

Practical Car & Van Rental
Salisbury Road, Shaftesbury, Dorset, SP7 8BU
tel: 01747 852 726
email: enquiry@practical.co.uk
web: www.practical.co.uk
info: Whole fleet of vehicles available for hire. Cars, vans,
people carriers and minibuses. All self drive. Practical has several
branches in the South West, as well as branches all over the UK. See
website for details.

Teign Vehicle Rentals
Jetty Marsh Road, Newton Abbot, TQ12 2SW
tel: 01626 369 111
email: teignrentals@aol.com
info: Wide range of vans including long and short wheel
based varieties. Must be 25 years or over. Self drive.

Thornbury Self Drive Hire
Cooper Road, Thornbury Industrial Estate, Thornbury, Bristol,
BS35 3UY
tel: 01454 414 111
fax: 01454 412 679
contact: Stephen McCarthy
info: Lutons, box vans, Sprinters and Transits are all available
for self drive to those aged 21 years and over. No problem hiring
vehicles to musicians. Band friendly.

Thrifty Car & Van Rental
South West
tel: 01494 751 600
fax: 01494 751 601
email: thrifty@thrifty.co.uk
web: www.thrifty.co.uk
contact: Leon Antone
info: Self drive vehicles. Must be at least 23 years old to hire a
van and have held a licence for 1 year. Vans available include Mercedes
Sprinters, Transits, VW Transporters and other long and short wheel
based vans. Thrifty has branches throughout the UK. See website for
details.

Trathens Travel Services Ltd.
Walkham Business Park, Burrington Way, Plymouth, Devon, PL5 3LS
tel: 01752 772 000
fax: 01752 769 629
email: jb1@trathensstarriders.com
web: www.trathensstarriders.com
contact: JB
info: Supplier of sleeper coaches to the music industry.

United Rental Group
South West
tel: 01246 506 100
fax: 01246 506 256
email: enquiries@urg.co.uk
web: www.unitedrentalsystem.co.uk
info: Extensive range of cars and vans for self drive hire.
United Rental Group have branches located throughout the UK. See the
website for further details.

Vospers
Trevenson Road, Poole, Redruth, TR15 3PN
tel: 01209 612 277
web: www.vospers.com
contact: Tony Odgers
info: Must be aged 21 years or over to hire, however those under 25 years may have to pay a higher insurance premium. Connects, Transits and more available on self drive.

Williams Self Drive Ltd.
Charlton Garage, Charlton Road, Shepton Mallet, BA4 5PB
tel: 01749 343 304
fax: 01749 343 441
web: www.williams-selfdrive.co.uk
contact: Neville Foster
info: Full range of long and short wheel based vans. Minimum age for hire is 25 years.

YORKSHIRE

1van1.com
71-73 Lister Street, Hull, HU1 2RZ
tel: 0113 387 5559
email: sales@1van1.com
web: www.1van1.com
info: Self drive minibus, car, van and MVP. Other branches in Yorkshire include Leeds, York and Sheffield. All contactable on the above number. Also branches across rest of the UK. See listings in other regions.

4Wheels
158 Manningham Lane, Bradford, BD8 7DT
tel: 01274 738 324
fax: 01274 744 445
email: bradford@4wheels.co.uk
web: www.4wheels.co.uk
contact: Kumar Zaman
info: Range of vans includes Combos, Astros, Transits and Boxers. Must be 21 years or over and held a licence for at least 1 year.

Anchor Self Drive Ltd. (Hunslet)
Low Road, Hunslet, Leeds, LS10 1QR
tel: 0113 277 9455
email: hunslet@anchorselfdrive.co.uk
web: www.anchorselfdrive.co.uk
info: Full range of vans. Mostly for businesses but will hire to personal callers over the weekend. Customers must provide their own insurance. See also listings for branches in Leeds and Keighley.

Anchor Self Drive Ltd. (Keighley)
Unit 4, Deal Street, off Dalton Lane, Keighley, BD21 4LA
tel: 01535 669 935
fax: 01535 681 690
email: hiredesk@keighley@anchorselfdrive.co.uk
web: www.anchorselfdrive.co.uk
info: Full range of vans. Mostly for businesses but will hire to personal callers over the weekend. Customers must provide their own insurance. See also listings for branches in Leeds and Hunslet.

Anchor Self Drive Ltd. (Leeds)
Richardshaw Road, Grangefield Industrial Estate, Pudsey, Leeds, LS28 6QW
tel: 0113 255 0441
fax: 0113 257 1116
email: hiredesk@anchorselfdrive.co.uk
web: www.anchorselfdrive.co.uk
info: Full range of vans. Mostly for businesses but will hire to personal callers over the weekend. Customers must provide their own insurance. See also listings for branches in Hunslet and Keighley.

ARD Hire Ltd.
Howdenshire Way, Knedlington Road Industrial Estate, Howden, Goole, DN14 7HZ
tel: 01430 431 155
fax: 01430 431 143
email: hire@ardlandrovers.co.uk
web: www.ardlandrovers.co.uk
info: Full range of vans for self drive hire. The age limits on insurance are 25 to 74 years. They can cover down to the age of 23 years on cars and vans, but drivers aged between 23 and 25 may be subject to a young driver surcharge.

Arrow Self Drive
224 Spring Bank, Hull, HU3 1LU
tel: 01482 329 067
email: team@arrowselfdrive.com
web: www.arrowselfdrive.com
contact: Brian Mattison
info: Full range of vans and minibuses available to over 23 years. Self drive.

Avis Rent A Car
3 Layerthorpe, York, YO31 7UZ
tel: 01904 610 460
web: www.avis.co.uk
info: Renault vans available on self drive basis. Hire available to those aged 23 years and above, but those under 25 years may face a higher insurance premium. Avis has outlets throughout the UK. See website for locations.

Barkers of Malton
York Road, Malton, North Yorkshire, YO17 6YB
tel: 01653 695 111
contact: Audrey Jackon
info: Full Peugeot range of vans available for self drive hire. Must be aged 25 or over.

Budget
Yorkshire
tel: 0870 153 9170
fax: 0870 010 2391
email: via website
web: www.budget.co.uk
info: Budget operates around 80 locations across the UK. Check website for details. Each location has a range of vehicles available including people carriers, minibuses of varying sizes, trucks and vans, and cars. All locations offer self drive rentals. Rentals can be made for any length of time. Bookings can be made online or through the call centre number above.

Carlite Vehicle Hire
East Parade, Ilkley, LS29 8JP
tel: 01943 433 418
info: Small vans including Transits available for self drive. Must be over 25 years.

Central Self Drive
Unit 1, Wholesale Market, Jacob Well Lane, Wakefield, WF1 3NN
tel: 01924 366 366
fax: 01924 366 343
email: sales@centralselfdrive.com
web: www.centralselfdrive.com
info: Various vans available for self drive. Must be over 25 years.

Dews Self Drive
Northgate, Halifax, HX1 1XJ
tel: 0800 277 9455
contact: Michael Porter
info: Vans and minibuses available for hire. Self drive. Please call for further details.

Dixon Ford
9-15 Manton Street, Sheffield, S2 4BA
tel: 0114 263 6234
fax: 0114 263 6201
email: steve.murfitt@dixonmotors.co.uk
web: www.dixonmotors.co.uk
contact: Steve Murfitt
info: Ford Connect and Transit vans available for self drive hire.

Easi-Rent
Low Road, Hunslet, Leeds, LS10 1QR
tel: 0113 276 5091
email: leeds@easirent.com
web: www.easirent.com
info: Self drive. Car, van, truck, motor home and limousine hire. Vans available in a range of sizes including splitters. Also have branches in Liverpool, Wigan, Preston and Rochdale. See website for details.

Easy Hire Self Drive
Baghill Lane, Pontefract, WF8 2HA
tel: 01977 599 500
contact: Mark Huby
info: Wide range of small and large vans available. Self drive to those aged 21 years and above.

Enterprise Rent-A-Van
Sunderland Street, Keighley, West Yorkshire, BD21 5LE
tel: 01535 609 900
web: www.enterprise.com
info: Self drive. Range of cars (including estates), 7 seater MPVs and Transit vans available. Enterprise also has other branches in Yorkshire, as well as throughout the UK. See website for locations.

Eurodrive Van Rental
Yorkshire
tel: 0870 160 9060
email: mail@eurodrive.com
web: www.eurodrive.com
info: Range of vehicles available include cars, vans and MPVs. Self drive. Vehicle hire for the UK and worldwide. Eurodrive have several branches located across Yorkshire, check website for details.

Europcar
Yorkshire
tel: 0870 607 5000
web: www.europcar.co.uk
info: Extensive car hire service. Obtain a quote either online or by contacting the above number. Europcar have branches throughout the UK and worldwide. See website for full list of locations.

GK Group (Sheffield)
Savile Street, Sheffield, South Yorkshire, S4 7UD
tel: 0114 279 8800
email: rental@gkford.co.uk
web: www.gkford.co.uk
info: Ford dealership. Available for self drive hire are Transits, minibuses and Tourneos. Must be 23 years or over to hire vans, although for a higher insurance premium 21 year olds and over may hire them. Must be 27 years or over to hire minibuses. In all cases anyone wanting to hire a vehicle must have been driving for at least 2 years and have no more that 6 points on their license. The GK Group cannot insure any professional musicians. Also branches at Lawrence Street, Attercliffe Common, Sheffield (tel. 0870 950 0096), as well as in Midlands, Scotland and Cumbria. See listings in relevant sections for details.

Headingley Car & Van Hire Ltd.
57 Queens Road, Leeds, LS6 1HY
tel: 0113 274 4222
fax: 0113 274 4759
info: Transit vans available for self drive hire.

Hertz
123 St. Sepulchre Gate West, Doncaster, South Yorkshire, DN1 3AH
tel: 01302 344 997
web: www.hertz.co.uk
info: Self drive car and van hire available. Hertz is a worldwide chain with branches throughout Yorkshire, and the rest of the UK. See website above to locate your nearest branch.

Lawtons of Tadcaster
York Road, Tadcaster, LS24 8EA
tel: 01937 833 997
fax: 01937 835 563
email: via website
web: www.lawtonsoftadcaster.co.uk
contact: Garry Cooke
info: Ford Transits available for self drive hire.

Mennell Motors
Showfield Lane Industrial Estate, Showfield Lane, Malton, YO17 6BT
tel: 01653 695 880
contact: Janine
info: Wide range of vans available. All self drive.

N. L. Commercial
Rouse Mill Lane, Batley, WF17 5QB
tel: 01924 442 709
email: info@nlcommercials.co.uk
contact: Nigel Lella
info: Wide range of vans including standard Transit vans. Must be over 21 years to hire self drive.

Peugeot Car & Van Rental
127 Eccleshall Road, Sheffield, S11 8HY
tel: 0114 272 8476
contact: Andy Chapman
info: Range of brand new Peugeot vans available for self drive hire. Must be aged over 25 years.

Polar Motors (Barnsley)
223 Dodworth Road, Barnsley, S70 6PA
tel: 01226 732 500/0870 050 5647
fax: 01226 205 993
email: ford@barnsley.polar-motor.co.uk
web: www.polar-motor.co.uk
contact: Phil Foster
info: Full range of long and short wheel vans. Must be 23 years old and held driving licence for at least 2 years. To hire the 17 seat minibus must be 25 years or over and held licence for 6 years. Polar have several branches throughout Yorkshire and North West. See listings in relevant regions for details.

Polar Motors (Castleford)
Park Road, Castleford, West Yorkshire, WF10 4RJ
tel: 0870 085 3667
email: via website
web: www.polar-motor.co.uk
info: Full range of long and short wheel vans. Must be 23 years old and held driving licence for at least 2 years. To hire the 17 seat minibus must be 25 years or over and held licence for 6 years. Polar have several branches throughout Yorkshire and North West. See listings in relevant regions for details.

Polar Motors (Scarborough)
Seamer Road, Scarborough, North Yorkshire, YO12 4DH
tel: 0870 085 3167
email: via website
web: www.polar-motor.co.uk
info: Full range of long and short wheel vans. Must be 23 years old and held driving licence for at least 2 years. To hire the 17 seat minibus must be 25 years or over and held licence for 6 years. Polar have several branches throughout Yorkshire and North West. See listings in relevant regions for details.

Polar Motors (Thirsk)
Station Road, Thirsk, North Yorkshire, YO7 1PZ
tel: 0870 085 3178
email: via website
web: www.polar-motor.co.uk
info: Full range of long and short wheel vans. Must be 23 years old and held driving licence for at least 2 years. To hire the 17 seat minibus must be 25 years or over and held licence for 6 years. Polar have several branches throughout Yorkshire and North West. See listings in relevant regions for details.

Polar Motors (Wakefield)
Barnsley Road, Wakefield, WF1 5JS
tel: 0870 085 3181
email: via website
web: www.polar-motor.co.uk
info: Full range of long and short wheel vans. Must be 23 years old and held driving licence for at least 2 years. To hire the 17 seat minibus must be 25 years or over and held licence for 6 years. Polar have several branches throughout Yorkshire and North West. See listings in relevant regions for details.

Polar Motors (York)
Jockey Lane, Monks Cross, York, YO32 9GY
tel: 0870 085 3185
email: via website
web: www.polar-motor.co.uk
info: Full range of long and short wheel vans. Must be 23 years old and held driving licence for at least 2 years. To hire the 17 seat minibus must be 25 years or over and held licence for 6 years. Polar have several branches throughout Yorkshire and North West. See listings in relevant regions for details.

Practical Car & Van Rental
A1 Approach, Great North Road, Woodlands, Doncaster, DN6 7SU
tel: 01302 727 777
fax: 01302 729 999
email: enquiry@practical.co.uk
web: www.practical.co.uk
contact: Graham Southern
info: Whole fleet of vehicles available for hire. Cars, vans, people carriers and minibuses. All self drive. Practical has several branches in Yorkshire, as well as branches all over the UK. See website for details.

Skipton Ford
Millennium Road, Airedale Business Centre, Skipton, BD23 2UB
tel: 01756 700 700
fax: 01756 693 740
email: sales@skipton-ford.co.uk
web: www.skipton-ford.co.uk
info: Ford Transit vans available for self drive hire.

Stardes
Ashes Buildings, Old Lane, Holbrook Industrial Estate, Halfway, Sheffield, S20 3GZ
tel: 0114 251 005
email: info@stardes.co.uk
web: www.stardes.co.uk
contact: Sara Steinburg
info: Self drive hire of MPVs (Chrysler Grand Voyager) or Splitters.

Sunwin Rentacar
103 Queens Road, Halifax, HX1 3XY
tel: 01422 348 003
contact: Andy
info: Peugeot Boxer vans available for self drive hire.

Swinton Car Service Centre
15 Church Street, Swinton, Mexborough, S64 0HG
tel: 01709 583 017
email: dave@swintonselfdrive.com
web: www.swintonselfdrive.com
contact: David Parry
info: Full range of vans and minibuses available for self drive hire.

Thrifty Car & Van Rental
Yorkshire
tel: 01494 751 600
fax: 01494 751 601
email: thrifty@thrifty.co.uk
web: www.thrifty.co.uk
info: Self drive vehicles. Must be at least 23 years old to hire a van and have held a licence for 1 year. Vans available include Mercedes Sprinters, Transits, VW Transporters and other long and short wheel based vans. Thrifty has branches throughout the UK. See website for details.

United Rental Group
Yorkshire
tel: 01246 506 100
fax: 01246 506 256
email: enquiries@urg.co.uk
web: www.unitedrentalsystem.co.uk
info: Extensive range of cars and vans for self drive hire. United Rental Group have branches located throughout the UK. See the website for further details.

NORTHERN IRELAND

Annagh Motors Ltd.
57a Church Street, Banbridge, County Down, BT32 4AA
tel: 028 4066 2495
info: Range of small, mid size and larger vans. Can be aged between 21 and 24 years to rent the smaller vans, but must be at least 25 years to hire the larger vehicles.

Avis Rent A Car
30 Hillsborough Road, Lisburn, County Antrim, BT28 1AP
tel: 028 9266 7400
web: www.avis.co.uk
info: Renault vans available on self drive basis. Hire available to those aged 23 years and above, but those under 25 years may face a higher insurance premium. Avis has outlets throughout the UK. See website for locations.

Ballykelly Car & Van Hire
22 Ballykelly Road, Banbridge, County Down, BT32 4PS
tel: 028 4062 4966
info: Self drive hire available for a range of suitable vans. Must be over 24 years.

Budget
Northern Ireland
tel: 0870 153 9170
fax: 0870 010 2391
email: via website
web: www.budget.co.uk
info: Budget operates around 80 locations across the UK. Check website for details. Each location has a range of vehicles available including people carriers, minibuses of varying sizes, trucks and vans, and cars. All locations offer self drive rentals. Rentals can be made for any length of time. Bookings can be made online or through the call centre number above.

Burnside Vehicle Rentals
Unit 3, Ivan Wilson Complex, 277 Dunhill Road, Coleraine, County Londonderry, BT51 3QJ
tel: 028 7034 4451
info: High roof Transits and other small, medium and large vans available. Self drive to those aged 25 years and over. Those aged 23 and 24 years may hire, but at a higher insurance premium.

Carrick Self Drive
Keeburn Industrial Estate, Carrickfergus, County Antrim, BT38 8HQ
tel: 028 9335 1113
info: Vans available for self drive hire. Must be aged 23 years or over, and have been driving for 3 years.

Corrigans
72 Old Caulfield Road, Dungannon, BT70 3NG
tel: 028 8776 1482
email: information@corrigansvehiclehire.co.uk
web: www.corrigansvehiclehire.co.uk
info: Wide range of vans and minibuses. Self drive.

Enterprise Rent-A-Van
Charles Hurst Vauxhall, 70 Belfast Road, Lisburn, BT22 4AU
tel: 028 9263 5970
web: www.enterprise.com
info: Self drive. Range of cars (including estates), 7 seater MPVs and Transit vans available. Enterprise also has other branches in Northern Ireland, as well as throughout the UK. See website for locations.

Eurodrive Van Rental
Northern Ireland
tel: 0870 160 9060
email: mail@eurodrive.com
web: www.eurodrive.com
info: Range of vehicles available include cars, vans and MPVs. Self drive. Vehicle hire for the UK and worldwide. Eurodrive have several branches located across Northern Ireland, check website for details.

Europcar
Northern Ireland
tel: 0870 607 5000
web: www.europcar.co.uk
info: Extensive car hire service. Obtain a quote either online or by contacting the above number. Europcar have branches throughout the UK and worldwide. See website for full list of locations.

Hertz
Arrivals Hall, Airport Road, Eglinton, Londonderry, County Londonderry, BT47 3GY
tel: 028 7181 1994
web: www.hertz.co.uk
info: Self drive car and van hire available. Hertz is a worldwide chain with branches throughout Northern Ireland, and the rest of the UK. See website above to locate your nearest branch.

Holmes Motors
2-20 Beersbridge Road, Belfast, County Antrim, BT5 4BF
tel: 028 9045 1850
info: Self drive van hire. Must be aged 25 years or over.

Kings Self Drive
96 Oldstone Road, Muckamore, Antrim, BT41 4QB
tel: 028 9446 6645
info: Vans and minibuses available for self drive. Must be 25 years or over.

Lindsay Ford (Ballymena)
Pennybridge Industrial Estate, Larne Road, Ballymena, BT42 3HB
tel: 028 2566 2238
web: www.lindsayford.co.uk
contact: Dymphna Dixon
info: All vans by Ford, including Tansits, Connects, other short and long wheel based vehicles, minibuses and people carriers. All hire is subject to status.

Lindsay Ford (Bangor)
3 Balloo Park, Balloo Industrial Estate, Bangor, BT19 7PP
tel: 028 9147 4700
contact: Clark Stanford
info: See listing above for information.

Lindsay Ford (Coleraine)
80-82 Bushmills Road, Coleraine, BT52 1BB
tel: 028 7035 5921
email: carhire.coleraine@lindsay-car.co.uk
contact: Claire Tinkler
info: Refer to above listing for Lindsay Ford in Ballymena for details.

Lindsay Ford (Lisburn)
20 Market Place, Lisburn, BT28 1AR
tel: 028 9267 3121
email: carhire.lisburn@lindsay-cars.com
info: Refer to Lindsay Ford Ballymena listing above for details.

Practical Car & Van Rental
10a Church Street, Banbridge, County Down, BT34 4AA
tel: 028 4066 2022
email: enquiry@practical.co.uk
web: www.practical.co.uk
info: Whole fleet of vehicles available for hire. Cars, vans, people carriers and minibuses. All self drive. Practical has several branches in Northern Ireland, as well as branches all over the UK. See website for details.

Red Cent Thrifty Vehicle Rental Ltd.
66a Killead Road, Aldergrove, Crumlin, County Antrim, BT29 4EW
tel: 028 9445 2777
info: Vans available. Self drive. Must be 24 years and over, and have held a driving licence for at least 1 year.

SJS Vehicle Hire
Loves Hill, Castledawson, Magherafelt, County Londonderry, BT45 8DP
tel: 028 7946 9889
email: info@sjsvehicles.com
web: www.sjsvehicles.com
info: Range of suitable vans available to those aged between 23 and 70 years, who have been driving for over 1 year.

Thrifty Car & Van Rental
Northern Ireland
tel: 01494 751 600
fax: 01494 751 601
email: thrifty@thrifty.co.uk
web: www.thrifty.co.uk
info: Self drive vehicles. Must be at least 23 years old to hire a van and have held a licence for 1 year. Vans available include Mercedes Sprinters, Transits, VW Transporters and other long and short wheel based vans. Thrifty has branches throughout the UK. See website for details.

United Rental Group
Northern Ireland
tel: 01246 506 100
fax: 01246 506 256
email: enquiries@urg.co.uk
web: www.unitedrentalsystem.co.uk
info: Extensive range of cars and vans for self drive hire. United Rental Group have branches located throughout the UK. See the website for further details.

SCOTLAND

1van1.com
16 College Street, Aberdeen, AB11 6JX
tel: 0113 387 5559
email: sales@1car1.com
web: www.1car1.com
info: Self drive minibus, car, van and MVP. Other branches in the Scotland include Edinburgh, Glasgow and Paisley. All contactable on the above number. Also branches across rest of the UK. See listings in other regions.

A2B
26 Poplar Road, Glenrothes, Fife, KY7 4AA
tel: 01592 610 101
email: sales@a2bvanhire.co.uk
web: www.a2bvanhire.co.uk
contact: Louise
info: Self drive cars, Luton's and vans for hire. 17 seater minibus is also available.

Ace Car & Van Hire
Ratcliffe Terrace, Edinburgh, EH9 1SU
tel: 0870 600 6630
info: Full range of self drive cars and vans available. Call for details

Avis Rent a Car
St. Andrew's Drive, Paisley, Renfrewshire, PA3 2TJ
tel: 0870 608 6338
web: www.avis.co.uk
info: Renault vans available on self drive basis. Hire available to those aged 23 years and above, but those under 25 years may face a higher insurance premium. Avis has outlets throughout the UK. See website for locations.

Bill Bird Rentals
Hawk Head Road, Paisley, PA2 7BA
tel: 0141 848 5445
email: info@billbirdrentals.co.uk
web: www.billbirdrentals.co.uk
info: Vans and minibuses for hire. Can offer rental for up to a month in needed. Call for details

Boulevard Self Drive Hire
Drumry Roundabout, Great Western Road, Glasgow, G15 8LW
tel: 0141 944 2999
fax: 0141 944 8860
info: A selection of vans, minibuses, cars and people carriers for hire. Self drive only. Call for details.

Budget
Scotland
tel: 0870 153 9170
fax: 0870 010 2391
email: via website
web: www.budget.co.uk
info: Budget operates around 80 locations across the UK. Check website for details. Each location has a range of vehicles available including people carriers, minibuses of varying sizes, trucks and vans, and cars. All locations offer self drive rentals. Rentals can be made for any length of time. Bookings can be made online or through the call centre number above.

Condor Self Drive
32 Eskbank Road, Dalkeith, EH22 3BQ
tel: 0131 660 1272
fax: 0131 654 2233
email: tom@condorselfdrive.co.uk
web: www.condorselfdrive.co.uk
contact: Tom
info: Edinburgh based hire company. Self Drive. Wide range of vehicles including cars, vans, pickups and MPVs.

Cook's Car & Van Hire
St. Boswells, Scottish Borders, TV6 0PJ
tel: 01835 823 483
fax: 01835 823 483
email: cooksvans@aol.com
web: www.cookscarandvanhire.co.uk
info: Van and car hire. Self drive only. See website for prices.

Enterprise Rent-A-Van
Milton Street, Glasgow, DD1 1QR
tel: 0141 331 4622
web: www.enterprise.com
info: Self drive. Range of cars (including estates), 7 seater MPVs and Transit vans available. Enterprise also has other branches in Scotland, as well as throughout the UK. See website for locations.

Eurodrive Van Rental
Scotland
tel: 0870 160 9060
email: mail@eurodrive.com
web: www.eurodrive.com
info: Range of vehicles available include cars, vans and MPVs. Self drive. Vehicle hire for the UK and worldwide. Eurodrive have several branches located across Scotland, check website for details.

Europcar
Scotland
tel: 0870 607 5000
web: www.europcar.co.uk
info: Extensive car hire service. Obtain a quote either online or by contacting the above number. Europcar have branches throughout the UK and worldwide. See website for full list of locations.

GK Group (Dumfries)
Main Road, Locharbriggs, Dumfries, Dumfriesshire, DG1 1RZ
tel: 01387 711 560
email: rental@gkford.co.uk
web: www.gkford.co.uk
info: Ford dealership. Available for self drive hire are Transits, minibuses and Tourneos. Must be 23 years or over to hire vans, although for a higher insurance premium 21 year olds and over may hire them. Must be 27 years or over to hire minibuses. In all cases anyone wanting to hire a vehicle must have been driving for at least 2 years and have no more that 6 points on their license. The GK Group cannot insure any professional musicians. Also branches in Midlands, Yorkshire and Cumbria. See listings in relevant sections for details.

GK Group (Stranraer)
Blacksparks Industrial Estate, Fountain Way, Stranraer, Wigtownshire, DG9 7BZ
tel: 01776 702 478
email: rental@gkford.co.uk
web: www.gkford.co.uk
info: See listing above for Dumfries branch for information. Also branches in Midlands, Yorkshire and Cumbria. See listings in relevant sections for details.

Hertz
18 West Marketgait, Dundee, Angus, DD1 1QR
tel: 01382 223 711
web: www.hertz.co.uk
info: Self drive car and van hire available. Hertz is a worldwide chain with branches throughout Scotland, and the rest of the UK. See website above to locate your nearest branch.

Kerrs of Arbroath
3-5 Hannah Street, Arbroath, Angus, DD11 1PT
tel: 01241 877 990
fax: 01241 871 259
email: dot.kerrs@btinternet.com
info: Car and van hire. Self drive.

Kyle Taxi Co.
7 Lochalsh Road, Kyle, IV40 8BP
tel: 01599 534 323
email: kyletaxi@aol.com
web: www.lochalsh.net/taxi
contact: Kenny
info: Minibus available to hire for up to a week. Driver included for one night, bands supply own driver thereafter.

Practical Car & Van Rental
South Road, Peterhead, AB42 6NH
tel: 01779 479 787
email: enquiry@practical.co.uk
web: www.practical.co.uk
info: Whole fleet of vehicles available for hire. Cars, vans, people carriers and minibuses. All self drive. Practical has several branches in Scotland, as well as branches all over the UK. See website for details.

Swift Vehicle Rental (Aberdeen)
Unit 3b, Tyseal Base, Craigshaw Crescent, West Tullos Industrial Estate, Aberdeen, AB12 3AW
tel: 01224 216 540
email: hiredesk.aberdeen@swiftvehiclerental.co.uk
web: www.swiftvehiclerental.co.uk
info: Wide variety of vehicles available for self drive. Also branches in Queenslie, Stirling and Glasgow. See listings for details.

Swift Vehicle Rental (Glasgow)
337-341 Bogmoor Road, Shieldhall, Glasgow, G51 4SJ
tel: 0870 606 0663
email: hiredesk@swiftvehiclerental.co.uk
web: www.swiftvehiclerental.co.uk
info: Wide variety of vehicles available for self drive. Also branches in Queenslie, Stirling and Aberdeen. See listings for details.

Swift Vehicle Rental (Queenslie)
6 Carmaben Road, Easter Queenslie, Glasgow, G33 4UN
tel: 0141 773 4545
email: hiredesk.glasgowj10@swiftvehiclerental.co.uk
web: www.swiftvehiclerental.co.uk
info: Wide varierty of vehicles available for self drive. Also branches in Glasgow, Stirling and Aberdeen. See listings for details.

Swift Vehicle Rental (Stirling)
Springkerse Road, Springkerse Industrial Estate, Stirling, FK7 7SN
tel: 01786 471 555
email: hiredesk.stirling@swiftvehiclerental.co.uk
web: www.swiftvehiclerental.co.uk
info: Wide variety of vehicles available for self drive. Also branches in Queenslie, Glasgow and Aberdeen. See listings for details.

Thrifty Car & Van Rental
Scotland
tel: 01494 751 600
email: thrifty@thrifty.co.uk
web: www.thrifty.co.uk
info: Self drive vehicles. Must be at least 23 years old to hire a van and have held a licence for 1 year. Vans available include Mercedes Sprinters, Transits, VW Transporters and other long and short wheel based vans. Thrifty has branches throughout the UK. See website for details.

Turner Hire Drive
59 Holland Street, Aberdeen, AB12 3AW
tel: 01224 630 730
email: aberdeen@turnerhiredrive.com
contact: Allison
info: Car, van and minibus hire for self drive.

United Rental Group
Scotland
tel: 01246 506 100
fax: 01246 506 256
email: enquiries@urg.co.uk
web: www.unitedrentalsystem.co.uk
info: Extensive range of cars and vans for self drive hire. United Rental Group have branches located throughout the UK. See the website for further details.

Vanman
13-15 Glebe Street, Dumfries, DG1 2LQ
tel: 01387 251 517
info: Specialise in van hire. Call to check availability and prices.

W & J Short
Bonnyrigg Road, Eskbank, Dalkeith, EH22 3HF
tel: 0113 387 5559
info: Wide range of self drive vehicles available. Call for details.

WALES

1van1.com
Unit M, St. Catherine's Park, Pengam Road, Cardiff, CF24 2RZ
tel: 0113 387 5559
email: sales@1van1.com
web: www.1van1.com
info: Self drive minibus, car, van and MVP. Also branches across rest of the UK. See listings in other regions.

AJ Motors
Neath Road, Tonna, Neath, SA11 3BZ
tel: 01639 639 917
info: Transit vans and cars available for self drive hire. Vehicle recovery and maintenance.

Avis Rent A Car
124 Rhosnesni, Wrexham, Clwyd, LL12 7NE
tel: 01978 351 747
web: www.avis.co.uk
info: Renault vans available on self drive basis. Hire available to those aged 23 years and above, but those under 25 years may face a higher insurance premium. Avis has outlets throughout the UK. See website for locations.

Beeee Practical Car & Van Rental
46 Bassett Terrace, Llanelli, SA15 4DY
tel: 01554 753 040
info: Car, vans, lorries, minibuses and people carriers. All self drive.

Bev's Minibus Hire
Unit 1a, Padfield Court Business Park, Tonyrefail, CF39 8HQ
tel: 01443 435 805
info: Minibus and coach hire with driver. 16 seater minibus with large boot and trailer if required. 49 seater coach or 53 seater coach with DVD player.

Budget
Wales
tel: 0870 153 9170
fax: 0870 010 2391
email: via website
web: www.budget.co.uk
info: Budget operates around 80 locations across the UK. Check website for details. Each location has a range of vehicles available including people carriers, minibuses of varying sizes, trucks and vans, and cars. All locations offer self drive rentals. Rentals can be made for any length of time. Bookings can be made online or through the call centre number above.

C.J. Rentals
15 Sway Road, Morriston, Swansea, SA6 6HT
tel: 01792 795 103
email: via website
info: Cars, vans and minibuses. All self drive. Drivers must be over 25, driving for a minimum of 2 years with a full clean licence.

Celtic Self Drive
1 Gwern Helyg, Gwynedd, Dolgellau, LL40 1PA
tel: 01341 421 422
email: info@celticselfdrive.com
web: www.celticselfdrive.com
info: 13, 15 and 17 seater minibuses. Transit and long wheel based vans. People carriers. All self drive.

Emma's Coaches
Baker Street Garage, Baker Street, Dolgellau, Gwynedd, LL40 1EL
tel: 01341 423 934
email: info@emmascoaches.co.uk
web: www.emmascoaches.co.uk
info: Range of vehicles available for hire with driver including an 8 seater wheelchair accessible minibus, and 51 to 73 seater executive coaches. International licence.

Enterprise Rent-A-Van
David Street, Bridgend Industrial Estate, Bridgend, Mid Glamorgan, CF31 3SA
tel: 01656 663 366
web: www.enterprise.com
info: Self drive. Range of cars (including estates), 7 seater MPVs and Transit vans available. Enterprise also has other branches in Wales, as well as throughout the UK. See website for locations.

Eurodrive Van Rental
Wales
tel: 0870 160 9060
email: mail@eurodrive.com
web: www.eurodrive.com
info: Range of vehicles available include cars, vans and MPVs. Self drive. Vehicle hire for the UK and worldwide. Eurodrive have several branches located across Wales, check website for details.

Europcar
Wales
tel: 0870 607 5000
web: www.europcar.co.uk
info: Extensive car hire service. Obtain a quote either online or by contacting the above number. Europcar have branches throughout the UK and worldwide. See website for full list of locations.

Herdman Coaches
The Old Station, Three Cocks, Brecon, Powys, LD3 0SD
tel: 01497 847 100
info: Minibus and coach hire, 6 - 53 seaters available. With driver only.

Hertz
Leeway Industrial Estate, Spytt Road, Newport, NP19 4SL
tel: 01633 273 090
web: www.hertz.co.uk
info: Self drive car and van hire available. Hertz is a worldwide chain with branches throughout Wales, and the rest of the UK. See website above to locate your nearest branch.

Padarn Bus
Padarn View, High Street, Llanberis, Caernarfon, LL55 4EN
tel: 01286 872 121
fax: 01286 871 347
email: info@padarnbus.co.uk
web: www.padarnbus.co.uk
info: 20 to 51 seater coaches. TV, video and radio available on some vehicles. All with driver.

Phil The Bus
21 Llys-y-Coed, Hengoed, Mid Glamorgan, CF82 7FD
tel: 01443 813 883
info: 16 seater minibus available, or 12 seater with large luggage space. With driver.

Practical Car & Van Rental
Kingsmoor Road, Kilgetty, Pembrokeshire, SA68 0QP
tel: 01834 813 233
email: enquiry@practical.co.uk
web: www.practical.co.uk
info: Whole fleet of vehicles available for hire. Cars, vans, people carriers and minibuses. All self drive. Practical has several branches in Wales, as well as branches all over the UK. See website for details.

Pronto Vehicle Rental
Sir Alfred Owen Way, Pontygwyndy, Caerphilly, CF83 3HU
tel: 02920 851 177
info: Cars, vans, trucks and minibuses. Self drive.

Thrifty Car & Van Rental
Wales
tel: 01494 751 600
fax: 01494 751 601
email: thrifty@thrifty.co.uk
web: www.thrifty.co.uk
info: Self drive vehicles. Must be at least 23 years old to hire a van and have held a licence for 1 year. Vans available include Mercedes Sprinters, Transits, VW Transporters and other long and short wheel based vans. Thrifty has branches throughout the UK. See website for details.

Top Cat Travel
CATS House, Old Newport Road, Bedwas, Caerphilly, CF83 8YB
tel: 02920 886 117
email: catswales@btclick.com
info: 8 to 51 seater executive coaches. Larger vehicles have TV and video facilities and air conditioning. All with driver.

United Rental Group
Wales
tel: 01246 506 100
fax: 01246 506 256
email: enquiries@urg.co.uk
web: www.unitedrentalsystem.co.uk
info: Extensive range of cars and vans for self drive hire. United Rental Group have branches located throughout the UK. See the website for further details.

Wheels Van Hire
The Old Bus Depot, Victoria Road, Holyhead, LL65 1UD
tel: 01407 765 397
email: wheelshire@aol.com
info: Vans (up to 7.5 tonnes), 8 to 17 seater minibuses and vans. All self drive.

Wrexham Car & Van Hire
Unit 2, Felin Puleston, Wrexham, LL13 7RF
tel: 01978 314 158
info: Transit, Luton box and Ford Iveco vans. Minibuses and cars. All self drive. Drivers must be over 25 years and have at least 5 years driving experience.

MUSIC SERVICES/RETAIL

EDUCATION/TRAINING

3.17 VIDEO PROMO SERVICES

EAST of ENGLAND 547 GREATER LONDON 547 MIDLANDS 552 NORTHEAST 554 NORTHWEST 554
SOUTHEAST 558 SOUTHWEST 559 YORKSHIRE 559 NORTHERN IRELAND 560 SCOTLAND 560 WALES 561

EAST of ENGLAND

Big Head Media
22 Covent Garden, Willingham, Cambridgeshire, CB4 5GE
tel: 07884 393 600
email: martin@bigheadmedia.co.uk
web: www.bigheadmedia.co.uk
contact: Martin Pickering
info: Has worked with variety of musicians in the past
ranging from Heavy Rock bands to Hip-Hop artists. Special effects.

Brand Mason Ltd.
Keepers Cottage, Wennington, Cambridgeshire, PE28 2LY
tel: 01487 773 255
email: adam@brandmason.co.ik
web: www.brandmason.co.uk
contact: Nadya Brand
info: Live, studio and location filming available on all
formats. Post production and editing facilities in-house.

Culture Code
6 Thellusson Road, Rendlesham, Woodbridge, Suffolk, IP12 2TD
tel: 01394 460 163
email: dv@culturecode.co.uk
web: www.culturecode.co.uk
contact: Robert Walker
info: Live gig, location, studio recording, music video
production and documentary/Electronic Press Kit production. Editing
facilities and DVD authoring/duplication. Can work to broadcast
quality.

IAM (Initiative for Arts & Music)
Near Cambridge
tel: 07976 399 848
email: stevelewis@yahoo.co.uk
contact: Steve Lewis
info: Offer variety of services including video production and
mobile recording. Contact Steve for further details.

Redbox Productions
RBX Studios, Cambridge Printing Park, Milton, Cambridge, CB4 6AZ
tel: 01223 438 186
email: unsigned@redbox.tv
web: www.redbox.tv
contact: Andrew Hawkes
info: Redbox Productions is a pre- and post-production house.
They offer filming and editing services to get your promotional video
together. Final production can be produced on VHS, DVD or an internet
format. Can offer deals on album presses - just provide the master and
copies will be made for you.

White Shuck
78 Constable Road, Ipswich, IP4 2UZ
tel: 01473 410 442
email: info@whiteshuck.co.uk
web: www.whiteshuck.co.uk
contact: Mike Vincent
info: Video production company staffed and crewed by
musicians and specialising in music related video. Live gig recording,
music video production and documentary/Electronic Press Kit
production. Editing facilities and DVD authoring/duplication. Can work
to broadcast quality.

GREATER LONDON

10th Planet
40-44 Newman Street, London, W1T 1QJ
tel: 020 7637 9500
email: studio@10thplanet.net
web: www.10thplanet.net
contact: Martin
info: 10th Planet are experienced post production technicians
in the music industry. Whilst they do not offer video production
services, they do offer a comprehensive range of video duplication and
mastering services.

AAG
66 Lomond Grove, Camberwell, London, SE5 7HN
tel: 07821 284 304
email: aag_montage@hotmail.com.
contact: Daniel Lambert
info: Live gig, location, studio recording, music video
production and documentary/EPK (Electronic Press Kit) production.
Editing and DVD authoring and duplication. Can work in broadcast
quality and stream online.

Absolutely Visual Video & Multimedia Production
22 Cavendish Road, Sutton, Surrey, SM2 5ER
tel: 020 8661 7703
email: info@absolutely-visual.co.uk
web: www.absolutely-visual.co.uk
contact: Noriko Brewster
info: Work with local unsigned acts, filming live gigs and
on location. Editing facilities available and can work up to broadcast
quality. Call for prices.

Acceber Films Ltd.
10 St. James Cottages, Richmond, Surrey, TW9 1SL
tel: 020 8334 0901
email: contact@acceberfilms.com
web: www.acceberfilms.com
contact: Rebecca Long
info: Acceber Films deliver innovative MTV broadcast quality
music videos for all budgets. Can provide additional services such as
music video promotion as well.

Amstore
Block J, 4th Floor, Tower Bridge Business Complex, 100 Clements Road,
London, SE16 4DG
tel: 020 7232 2779
email: enquires@amstore.co.uk
web: www.amstore.co.uk
info: Offer a range of video and film services, including
location work, live gig filming and studio work. Also have DVD and CD
duplication facilities.

Banana Split Productions Ltd.
11 Carlisle Road, London, NW9 0HD
tel: 020 8200 8200
fax: 020 8200 1414
email: kate@bananasplitprods.com
web: www.bananasplitprods.com
contact: Kate Walker
info: Full service production agency with 14 digital video
editing, graphics and sound suites. Experienced producers of weekly
television programmes, ads and specials, as well as infomercials,
concerts and longform videos. Can shoot, produce and edit everything
from DV to film, on location or in the studio. Extensive in-house
experience in the international music business, including making video
clips for Top 10 singles and best selling concert videos. Prices start from
£4000.

BLAISE

PRODUCTIONS

DIR: HARPS JOHAL

MUSIC PROMOS

MADE

DIR: DOUGLAS THOMSON

DIR: MAT SUNDERLAND

SIMPLE.

OFFICE: 02087970513
MOBILE: 07737967648
WEBSITE: WWW.BLAISE-INC.COM
EMAIL: INFO@BLAISE-INC.COM

Blaise Digital
6 Milford Road, Southall, Middlesex, UB1 3QQ
tel: 07949 038 218
email: info@blaise-inc.com
web: www.blaise-inc.com
contact: Harps Johal
info: High quality digital video services at affordable rates. Can accommodate live gig filming and location work up to broadcast quality. No studio available. Work with artists of all genres from all over UK.

Brandt Animation
11 D'Arblay Street, London, W1F 8DT
tel: 020 7734 0196
email: promos@brandtanim.co.uk
web: www.brandtanim.co.uk
contact: Finn Brandt
info: Cater for many types of production projects including corporate videos, online animations and music promos. Over 20 years experience.

Brickwall Films
24a Radley Mews, London, W8 6JP
tel: 020 7937 3042
email: info@brickwallfilms.co.uk
web: www.brickwallfilms.co.uk
contact: Jon Brichto
info: Brickwall Films is a young and dynamic production company offering a professional and affordable digital filming service for the music industry and new and unsigned bands. Based in a state-of-the-art music and video production studio in Central London and can offer a flexible service to suit all needs.

Capricorn Multimedia
49 Golders Gardens, London, NW11 9BS
tel: 020 8209 0948
email: info@capricorn-multimedia.co.uk
web: www.capricorn-multimedia.co.uk
contact: Ryan Lazarus
info: Music video production incorporating animation and visual effects. Also offer duplication services, as well as artwork and design. See listings in relevant sections for further information.

Chris Horton Films Ltd.
19b Aldensley Road, Brackenbury Village, Hammersmith, London, W6 0DH
tel: 020 8741 3337
fax: 020 8741 9996
email: info@chrishortonfilms.com
web: www.chrishortonfilms.com
contact: Chris Horton
info: Highly reputable company, awarded status as 'Approved Independent Choice' for Channel 4. Commercials and music videos. Represent a host of award winning directors.

Chrome Productions
9 Gondar Building, Mill Lane, London, NW6 1NU
tel: 020 7794 8855
fax: 020 7794 5995
email: info@chromeproductions.com
web: www.chromeproductions.com
contact: Joel Mishcon
info: Chrome Productions aim to produce punchy, intelligent, thought provoking promos. On location filming, studio work and full editing facilities. Call Joel to discuss your project.

Creation Video
The Barley Mow Centre, Barley Mow Passage, London, W4 4PH
tel: 020 8987 9363
fax: 0871 277 2981
email: mark@creationvideo.co.uk
web: www.creationvideo.co.uk
contact: Mark Slocombe
info: Gigs, location and studio shoots. Editing up to broadcast quality. Call for rates.

Curious Yellow Ltd.
17 Sugarhouse Lane, Stratford, London, E15 2QS
tel: 020 8534 0101
email: paul@curiousyellow.co.uk
web: www.curiousyellow.co.uk
contact: Paul Penny
info: Can work with existing material, or create brand new works, to provide a visual element to your music. Previous clients include Chicane, Agnelli & Nelson, Bryan Adams and Thunder.

CVS International
1 Berkeley Street, London, W1J 8DJ
tel: 020 7224 3342
email: info@cvsinternational.co.uk
web: www.cvsinternational.co.uk
info: Offer a range of video and film services, including location work, filming gigs and studio work. Also have DVD and CD duplication facilities.

Decode Digital
Unit 9a, Walpole Court, Ealing Studios, Ealing Green, London, W5 5EP
tel: 020 8758 8432
email: decode@decodedigital.co.uk
web: www.decodedigital.co.uk
info: Provide editing and post-production facilities as well as mastering to DVD. Cater for all types of projects.

Exceeda Films
110-116 Elmore Street, London, N1 3AH
tel: 020 7249 0433
fax: 020 7288 0735
email: contact@exceeda.co.uk
web: www.exceeda.co.uk
contact: Yoshie Narahara, Xadaer Perkins
info: Offer live, location and studio filming as well as stage-show visuals. Post-production and editing services also available.

Fiction Factory
14 Greenwich Church Street, London, SE10 9BJ
tel: 020 8853 5100
email: radio@fictionfactory.co.uk
web: www.fictionfactory.co.uk
contact: John Taylor
info: Film gigs, on location and in a small studio suitable for lower budgets. Call John to discuss your project.

Focus Point Films
Unit 10, 70-72 Old Street, London, EC1V 9AN
tel: 020 7689 4202
email: nick@focuspointfilms.co.uk
web: www.focuspointfilms.co.uk
contact: Nick Clinch
info: Cater for live gig, studio, location work and music video recording, as well as documentaries and Electronic Press Kits. Editing facilities and authoring/duplication to DVD. Can work in broadcast quality.

Great Guns Ltd.
43-45 Camden Road, London, NW1 9LR
tel: 020 7692 4444
fax: 020 7692 4422
email: greatguns@greatguns.com
web: www.greatguns.com
info: Music videos and documentaries made to broadcast quality, edited and mastered to DVD in-house.

Green Bandana Productions
7 Ironbridge House, Bridge Approach, London, NW1 8BD
tel: 020 7722 1081
email: info@jameshymen.com
web: www.jameshyman.com
contact: James Hymen
info: DJ services, music supervision and video production.

Groovy Badger
PO Box 39002, London, E2 9YP
tel: 07831 431 019
email: info@groovybadger.com
web: www.groovybadger.com
contact: Sebastian Smith
info: Specialise in low budget promo videos, covering location and gig work.

Hector Films
Unit 6, Stirling Court, Marshall Court, London, W1F 9BP
tel: 020 7734 8330
email: info@hectorfilms.co.uk
web: www.hectorfilms.co.uk
contact: Piers Thompson
info: Hector Films have worked with unsigned bands in the past and film on location, in the studio or at live gigs. They use high definition format, but depending on budget will offer DVD, both finished to broadcast quality.

Highrise Media
Studio A116, Faircharm Trading Estate, 8-12 Creekside, London, SE8 3DX
tel: 020 8469 9300
fax: 020 8469 2442
email: mail@highrisemedia.com
web: www.highrisemedia.com
info: Studio recording, music video production and documentary/Electronic Press Kit production. Editing and DVD authoring and duplication. Can work to broadcast quality. Also offer web and graphic design services. See listing in Artwork & Design section for further details.

Illegal Inc
64 Hanbury Street, London, E1 5JP
tel: 020 8981 4300
email: info@illegalinc.com
web: www.i-inc.co.uk
contact: V.G. Biebuyck
info: Offer broadcasting and video production services. Contact for further details. Also run a promotions and PR company. See relevant section for details.

Illumina
8 Canham Mews, Canham Road, London, W3 7SR
tel: 020 8600 9300
email: info@illumina.co.uk
web: www.illumina.co.uk
contact: Liz Brown
info: Live and studio filming available for bands with any budget. Small in-house studio with post production and editing facilities on any format. Full multimedia computer graphics facilities available.

Image 'n' Action Productions Ltd.
53 West Ham Lane, Stratford, London, E15 4PH
tel: 020 8555 6111
email: info@ina-productions.co.uk
web: www.ina-productions.co.uk
contact: D. Garcia
info: Services start at around £300. Provide a full video and film production service, and also have music/audio recording studio. Offer graphics services and can produce and develop websites. In addition, can provide a full promotional package including an Electronic Press Kit to compile and present all promotional material from a single disc.

iMagic Films Ltd.
Lygon House, 550 London Road, Bromley, BR1 3RA
tel: 020 7617 7599
fax: 07005 801 989
email: info@imagicfilms.com
web: www.imagicfilms.com
contact: Bernhard Kellerer
info: iMagic Films offers high-end music videos, DVD productions, commercials and corporate films at competitive prices. Based in London with offices in Los Angeles and across continental Europe. iMagic Films represents director Bernhard Kellerer worldwide.

IUC Entertainment
8 Meadowbank, Primrose Hill, London, NW3 3AY
tel: 07930 154 190/07770 594 313
email: harleyruben@yahoo.com
web: www.iucentertainment.com
info: Music and video production services. Also record, edit and produce footage from IUC events. IUC Entertainment also provide artist and event management services.

JJ Lacey
London, N13 6JG
tel: 07773 860 497
email: jasonjlacey@hotmail.com
contact: Jason Lacey
info: Offers music promotion services to artists and bands. 3 packages available including full video and video samples for promotional material, artwork and design services, styling and photography. See listings in relevant sections for further details.

Kyng Films
100 Lady Margaret Road, London, N19 5EX
tel: 020 7687 0380
fax: 020 7687 0380
email: mail@kyngfilms.com
web: www.kyngfilms.com
contact: Heather Clarke
info: Live gig, location, studio recording, music video production and documentary/Electronic Press Kit production. Editing facilities and DVD authoring/duplication. Can work in broadcast quality. Previous clients include Motorhead, Run DMC, Elvis Costello as well as many unsigned acts.

The Lantern Twins
1c Shacklewell Studios, 18 Shacklewell Lane, London, E8 2EZ
tel: 020 7275 9816
email: michael@lantern-twins.co.uk
web: www.lantern-twins.co.uk
info: Lantern Twins can help produce low budget promos. Shot, directed, edited and produced in-house.

Lunafish Productions
London
tel: 07949 274 703
email: info@lunafish.co.uk
web: www.lunafish.co.uk
contact: Laura Kidd
info: LunaFish will produce video promos on budget, filming on location, in the studio or at live gigs. They offer post-production facilities and create digital quality DVD and VHS. They also have photography facilities and design CD covers.

Metropolis Productions
The Power House, 70 Chiswick High Road, London, W4 1SY
tel: 020 8742 1111
fax: 020 8742 2626
email: reception@metropolis-group.co.uk
web: www.metropolis-group.co.uk
contact: Alex Sanders
info: Live gig, location, studio recording, music video production and documentary/Electronic Press Kit production. Editing facilities and DVD authoring. Can work in broadcast quality.

Ministry of Video
Northway, Latimer Road, Barnet, EN5 5NF
tel: 020 8440 0770
email: ministryofvideo@yahoo.co.uk
contact: Andrew Andrea
info: Ministry of Video offers unsigned bands a complete package of digital filming, production and editing. The final production can be transferred to tape or DVD. With vast experience in the video music industry, they are happy to work within a band's specific budget. Full recording facilities are available at the Music of the Spheres Studios. See the Recording Studios section for more information.

The Mob Film Company
10-11 Great Russell Street, London, WC1B 3NH
tel: 020 7580 8142
email: james@mobfilm.com
web: www.mobfilm.com
contact: James Guy
info: Can film live gigs, on location or in the studio. Will consider any interesting projects. Call James to discuss your ideas.

Mobius Production
London
email: alex@mobiusproduction.co.uk
web: www.mobiusproduction.co.uk
contact: Benjamin da Costa
info: Live gig, location, studio recording, music video production and documentary/Electronic Press Kit production. Editing and DVD authoring/duplication. Can work in broadcast quality. All budgets catered for.

Mosquito Media
PO Box 33790, 18 Chelsea Manor Street, London, SW3 6WF
email: mosquitomedia@aol.com
web: www.mosquito-media.co.uk
info: Special packages for music videos. Contact Mosquito for further information. Also offer PR services. See listing in relevant section for details.

Nodding Dog Productions
3 Austins Court, Peckham Rye, London, SE15 3NR
tel: 07944 316 166/07971 678 686
email: nodding.dog@hotmail.com
web: www.myspace.com/noddingdog
contact: Rik Jackson, Steve Ithell
info: Produce high quality DVDs, music promos and live videos for both signed and unsigned acts. Nodding Dog also offer DVD and editing services. Also offer web design services.

Nomadic Films
18 Howard Close, London, W3 0JY
tel: 020 7565 8238
email: info@nomadicfilms.com
web: www.nomadicfilms.com
contact: Sam Parsons
info: Live gig, location, studio recording, music video production and documentary/Electronic Press Kit production. Editing facilities and DVD authoring. Can work to broadcast quality.

Noughte Productions
45-46 Poland Street, London, W1F 7NA
tel: 020 7292 0900
fax: 020 7734 0758
email: athene.p@noughte.co.uk
web: www.noughte.co.uk
contact: Athene Parker
info: Music video and documentary/Electronic Press Kit production. Can do location or studio recording, and editing and DVD authoring to broadcast quality.

OVC Media Ltd.
88 Berkeley Court, Baker Street, London, NW1 5ND
tel: 020 7402 9111
email: elliot@ovcmedia.com
web: www.ovcmedia.com
contact: Elliot Cohen
info: OVC have their own DVD label, and will film in the studio or on location. All finished to broadcast quality using DVD or VHS format. Full editing facilities.

Peanut Films
London
tel: 07970 167 042
email: adam.jennings@peanutfilms.com
web: www.peanutfilms.com
contact: Adam Jennings
info: A dynamic new company with relevant experience, that aims to bring a fresh, entertaining and creative approach to your project.

Phoenix Film & Television Productions Ltd.
Unit D2, Sugar House Yard, Sugar House Lane, London, E15 2QS
tel: 020 8536 3690
email: info@phoenixmedia.co.uk
web: www.phoenixmedia.co.uk
contact: Nicola Woodroff
info: Full production facilities for cooperate film and television. See website for more details.

Picture Production Company
19-20 Poland Street, London, W1F 3DD
tel: 020 7439 4944
email: sales@theppc.com
web: www.theppc.com
info: Editing and post production facilities available for DVD and VHS. On location and live shoots only, no in-house studio.

Playaville Ltd.
Imperial House, 64 Willoughby Lane, Tottenham, London, N17 0SP
tel: 0870 766 8303
email: info@playaville.com
web: www.playaville.com
contact: Stevie Nash
info: Music video production service at a reasonable rate for unsigned artists. Playaville also run a record label. See entry in relevant section for further information.

Pop Productions
34 Hatherley Mews, Walthamstow, London, E17 4QP
tel: 020 8509 1655
fax: 020 8509 2911
email: mail@popproductionsuk.com
web: www.popproductionsuk.com
contact: Nick Healy
info: New media company looking to expand into the music video business. Very interested in working with unsigned bands. Can work on location or in the studio. Also have animation facilities.

Raw Audio Engineering
118 Emlyn Road, Chiswick, London, W12 9TA
tel: 07752 520 170
email: ryan@rawaudio.co.uk
web: www.rawaudio.co.uk
contact: Ryan Wilkins
info: Online record label shop handling sales of live DVD media. Cater for live gig, location, studio recording and music video production, as well as documentaries and Electronic Press Kits. Editing facilities and DVD authoring/duplication. Can work to broadcast quality. 32 Channel Location Pro Tools recording with 4 camera DV shoot and DVD authoring package for £999 inc VAT.

Reeltime
Unit 205, The Foundry, Morris Road, London, E14 6NJ
tel: 020 7515 8787
email: info@reeltime.co.uk
web: www.reeltime.co.uk
contact: Charles, David
info: Live gigs, location and studio shoots, including green screen capability. In-house post production. Can work with all formats, from Mini-DV to High Definition, depending on the budget. Have worked with unsigned bands in the past.

Retina Productions Ltd.
6 Mount Pleasant Crescent, London, N4 4HP
tel: 020 7272 4448
email: info@retina-productions.co.uk
web: www.retina-productions.co.uk
contact: Nisrine Imane
info: Studio work and location filming up to broadcast quality. Offer a friendly, flexible and highly competitive service.

Roast TV
Unit 18, 21 Wren Street, London, WC1X 0HF
tel: 020 7833 8988
fax: 020 7837 9836
email: info@roast.tv
web: www.roast.tv
contact: Tom Cordell
info: Experienced music video production company. Film on location or at their studio in Bethnal Green. Currently producing an urban music documentary, Roast TV have worked on various music video projects in the past. Interested in working with bands or artists from any genre.

Scorpio Productions
7 Molly Huggins Close, Weir Road, Balham, London, SW12 0LU
tel: 07931 874 232
contact: Desire
info: Scorpio Productions deal with all kinds of commissions, and are very interested in filming live gigs. Desire also runs a music production company by the same name.

Siab Studios
Greater London
tel: 07773 535 170
email: info@siabstudios.co.uk
web: www.siabstudios.co.uk
info: Siab offer a number of services for unsigned bands including affordable music video production, photography, logo design and CD cover and insert designs. See listings in relevant sections for details.

Single Minded Production
11 Cambridge Court, 210 Shepherds Bush Road, London, W6 7NJ
tel: 0870 011 3748
email: tony@singleminded.com
web: www.singleminded.com
contact: Tony Byrne
info: In-house studio available, post production and editing.

Smoking Pictures Productions
1 Lily Gardens, Wembley, London, HA0 1DL
tel: 020 7278 0222
fax: 0870 133 2055
email: abi@smokingpictures.co.uk
web: www.smokingpictures.co.uk
contact: Abi Sirokh, Martin Romanella
info: Services include music video production, website design, promotional kit and planning, visual image development and stills photography. Clients include Natasha Sohl and Mindlab Recording.

Soho Media
17 St. Anne's Court, Soho, London, W1F 0BQ
tel: 020 7479 7197
fax: 020 7479 7198
email: mail@sohomediagroup.co.uk
web: www.sohomediagroup.co.uk
contact: Guy Harrington
info: Soho Media represents producers and directors that have experience in all areas of film and video production. They cover everything from promos to live work, on all formats from DV to film. Prices start from £5000.

Some Think Media
28 Wadsworth Road, Perivale, UB6 7JZ
tel: 020 8998 8944
fax: 020 8991 2661
email: info@somethinkmedia.co.uk
web: www.somethinkmedia.co.uk
info: Specialists in 2D and 3D animation for broadcast and film. Video streaming and web animation. Graphic artists and story board development. Linked with Loz Vegas recording and rehearsal rooms, equipment hire service and music shop 'Vegas Sound House', promotions and booking agency 'Music Scene UK', 'Music Providers' management, as well as running the Drum Academy. See entries in relevant sections for further information.

Source Productions Ltd.
Number 6, 115 Broadhurst Gardens, West Hampstead, London, NW6 3BJ
tel: 07712 583 088
email: carlmproduction@aol.com
contact: Carl Martin
info: Carl has extensive music industry experience, particularly in location work and video promos. Filming, editing and mastering services for live gigs.

Stylorouge
6 Salem Road, London, W2 4BU
tel: 020 7729 1005
email: mail@stylorouge.co.uk
web: www.stylorouge.co.uk
info: Stylorouge is an independent creative consultancy with 25 years experience in commercial media. They produce work for a variety of industries, although their speciality is the music business. Check website for an up-to-date portfolio and show reel of their work.

Sync Films
London
tel: 0845 201 1235
fax: 020 7419 1631
email: leo@syncfilms.com
web: www.syncfilms.com
contact: Leo Butler
info: Sync Films is an independent digital film and video production company providing contemporary productions produced by a team of film, music, radio and advertising professionals.

Tomato Films
Unit 1.6, The Tea Building, 5-11 Bethnal Green Road, London, E1 6LA
tel: 020 7033 0455
fax: 020 7033 0456
email: abi@tomatofilms.com
web: www.tomato.co.uk
contact: Abi Hodson
info: Music video production company.

Universal Productions Ltd.
Tower Bridge Business Complex, Block J, Suite 401, 100 Clements Road, SE16 4DG
tel: 020 7232 0326
email: info@universalproductions.co.uk
web: www.universalproductions.co.uk
contact: Alex Piot
info: Music video and event production. Cater for live gigs, studio and location recording, documentaries and Electronic Press Kits. Authoring and duplication to DVD and editing facilities. Can work in broadcast quality.

Victory Video Productions
12 The Drive, Loughton, IG10 1HB
tel: 020 8923 6068
email: info@victoryvideo.co.uk
web: www.victoryvideo.co.uk
contact: Tony Manning
info: Facilities for filming on location, live gigs, music videos and editing. Can work in standard or broadcast quality depending on budget. DVD duplication also available.

Vidbiz
265 Archway Road, London, N6 5BS
tel: 07976 241 983
email: rosiewells81@hotmail.com
web: www.vidbiz.tk
contact: Rosie Wells
info: Music promotions company. Specialising in small budget videos and photography for unsigned bands.

Voytek
23 Great Queen Street, London, WC2B 5BB
tel: 020 7916 6996
email: info@voytek.co.uk
web: www.voytek.co.uk
info: Full production facilities at full production prices. Can cater for a low budget shoot or edit depending on workload. Contact to discuss in more detail.

W6 Studio
359 Lillie Road, Fulham, London, SW6 7PA
tel: 020 7385 2272
fax: 020 7381 5252
email: info@w6studio.co.uk
web: www.w6studio.co.uk
contact: Kaz
info: W6 Studios use Digibeta cameras to produce broadcast quality videos to suit your budget. Location and live gig filming, editing and small studio available. Guide price of £1000 for a one track music video.

Wired Video
49 Sancroft Street, London, SE11 5UG
tel: 020 7820 8380
email: info@wiredvideo.net
web: www.wiredvideo.net
contact: Raj
info: Offer creative solutions to all video needs at affordable rates. Wired has produced videos for an eclectic mix of bands. Call to discuss your requirements.

MIDLANDS

360 Red Productions
Emerson Close, Amstey Heights, Leicester, LE4 0PE
tel: 07890 450 987
email: info@360red.co.uk
web: www.360red.co.uk
contact: Sanjay Rajput
info: 360 Red offers DVD format, although will use VHS if required. Full post-production including editing, finishing to broadcast quality. Can also produce documentaries around the making of the video.

AJS & Associates
13 Cornhill Road, Nottingham, NG4 1GE
tel: 0870 0686 184
fax: 0871 210 1998
email: info@ajs-associates.com
web: www.ajs-associates.com
contact: Stevie-Leigh
info: Catering for unsigned live gigs, location, studio recording, music video production and documentary/Electronic Press Kit production. Editing and DVD authoring. Can work to broadcast quality.

Amberley Video Productions
Edwinstowe, Mansfield, Nottingham, NG21 9NX
tel: 07767 258 636
email: amberleyvideo@aol.com
web: www.amberleyvideoproductions.co.uk
info: Offer full video production. From basic live video recording to blue screen with video effects and graphics. Can also record live gigs to a 24 track digital hard disk recorder for post production if required. 3 man camera team. Will also transfer video into any required streaming format. DVD and CD duplication with on-body printing and artwork available.

Antidote Produxions
Studio 406, The Green House, The Custard Factory, Birmingham, B9 4AA
tel: 0121 224 7710
email: info@antidoteproduxions.com
web: www.antidoteproduxions.com
info: Antidote Produxions works with record labels across the UK and abroad. Committed to creating original and conceptual music videos.

Artworks Unlimited
Birmingham
tel: 07788 931 511/0121 453 5264
email: info@artworks-unlimited.co.uk
web: www.artworks-unlimited.co.uk
info: Mobile service, up to 3 cameras per shoot. Post-production and editing. All associated packaging artwork can be undertaken. See listing in Artwork & Design section for more details.

Aspect Ratio Productions
Harvest Studios, Chapel Place, Northampton, NN1 4AQ
tel: 01604 621 600
fax: 01604 620 110
email: musicvideo@aspectratioproductions.com
web: www.aspectratioproductions.com
contact: Robert
info: Live gig, location, studio recording, music video production and documentary/Electronic Press Kit production. Editing facilities and DVD authoring. Work to broadcast quality.

Atmospheres Production Ltd.
658 Aylestone Road, Leicester, LE2 8PR
tel: 0116 244 0041
email: info@atmospheres.co.uk
web: www.atmospheres.co.uk
contact: Clive Worden
info: Atmospheres offer a full production package, from developing a creative concept, to filming and editing the video, to adding graphics, special effects and voice-overs. Also offer a DVD authoring and design service.

Banned Produxions
Dreadnaught Media Development, PO Box 4322, Cannock, WS12 9AB
tel: 07818 455 587
email: ched@banned-produxions.co.uk
web: www.banned-produxions.co.uk
contact: Ched
info: Specialise in the production of high quality promotional DVD packages. Fully equipped digital video editing suite, DV cameras, audio recording facilities and cutting edge software.

BMP Recording
The Red House, Aswardby, Spilsby, Lincolnshire, PE23 4JU
tel: 01790 754 400
email: info@bmp-recording.co.uk
web: www.bmp-recording.co.uk
info: Involved with both music promotion videos, as well as music education. Mainly involved with Acoustic, Jazz and Classical music. BMP also have recording facilities. See entry in relevant section for further details.

Bradgate Films
19 Wallace Drive, Groby, Leicestershire, LE6 0GQ
tel: 01530 245 535
email: contact@bradgatefilms.com
web: www.bradgatefilms.com
contact: Maria Ellis
info: Bradgate Films produces broadcast quality music videos and promos at affordable prices. They have produced videos all around the world for musicians and bands with vastly diverse styles of music. In-house equipment and crew. Budgets start at less than £1,000. Visit website for examples of work.

Capelin Media
Shrewsbury
tel: 07973 625 665
email: simon.jones@capelinmedia.co.uk
web: www.capelinmedia.co.uk
contact: Simon Jones
info: Caters for live gig and location recording. Broadcast quality available. Documentaries and Electronic Press Kits also provided.

Elevator Productions
The Smithy, Crawley Lane, Kings Bromley, Burton On Trent, D13 7JF
tel: 01543 472 473
email: info@elevatorproductions.com
web: www.elevatorproductions.com
contact: Paul Skellett
info: Elevator is an all-encompassing one stop shop for audio-visual design and promotional media requirements for the music and entertainments industry from design photography to packaging and music videos.

Frontline AV
85 Far Gosford Street, Coventry, West Midlands, CV1 5DZ
tel: 02476 224 221
email: colin@frontlineav.com
web: www.frontlineav.com
contact: Colin
info: Gigs, location and studio shoots. Contact Colin for full details. Also put on gigs in Coventry. See listing in Promoters section for details.

Get Your Band On
Leicester
email: via website
web: www.getyourbandon.com
info: Offer range of services for bands and artists including video promotion, photography and artwork and design. See listings in relevant sections for details.

Hellfire Recording & Rehearsal Studios
158 Crankhall Lane, Friar Park, Wednesbury, Birmingham, WS10 0EB
tel: 0121 556 2559
email: enquires@hellfireproductions.com
web: www.hellfireproductions.com
info: Hellfire have links with individuals and companies that produce video promos for bands. Rehearsal and recording facilities. See relevant section for more details.

Hocus Focus Productions
A213 Leicester Creative Business Depot, Leicester, LE1 1RE
tel: 0116 261 6859
email: info@hocus-focus.co.uk
web: www.hocus-focus.co.uk
contact: Dylan Hunter
info: Live gig, location, studio recording, music video production and documentary/Electronic Press Kit production. Editing facilities and DVD authoring/duplication. Can work to broadcast quality. All budgets accounted for and tailor made to client specification.

Ignite Creative
32-42 East Street, Coventry, CV1 5LS
tel: 02476 225 226
email: info@ignitecreative.co.uk
web: www.ignitecreative.co.uk
contact: Steve Holdsworth
info: Live gig, location, studio recording, music video production and documentary/Electronic Press Kit production. Editing and DVD authoring. Can work to broadcast quality.

Imagecleaver
Studio 22, Canal Warehouse, Leicester Row, Coventry, CV1 4LH
tel: 02476 631 610
email: video@imagecleaver.com
web: www.imagecleaver.com
contact: Samuel Smith
info: Intently focused on producing original and quality music videos. Cater for live gig, location, studio recording, music video production and documentary/EPK production. Editing facilities and DVD authoring. Can work to broadcast quality.

Iris Production
The Hollymoor Centre, Manor Park Grove, Northfield, Birmingham, B31 5ER
tel: 07811 435 186
email: info@iris-production.co.uk
web: www.iris-production.co.uk
contact: Scott Vale
info: Full multimedia services available including projections. Iris Production also offer graphic and web design services, as well as CD duplication. See entries in relevant sections for further details.

Katapult Ltd.
Vernon House, Vernon Street, Derby, DE1 1FR
tel: 01332 294 416
email: info@katapult-studios.com
web: www.katapult-studios.com
contact: Dawn Lockett
info: Katapult is a team of producers, photographers, designers and musicians. Services provided include music video production, motion graphics, CD duplication, as well as graphic design and printing. See listings in relevant sections for further details.

Morrell Studio
61 Abbey Road, Enderby, Leicester, Leicestershire, LE19 2DB
tel: 0116 286 2565
email: leightonmorrell@btinternet.com
web: www.morrellstudio.tripod.com
contact: Leighton Morrell
info: Morrell offer video production and promo sevices. Please call for more info. Morrell also runs a recording studio. See listing in relevant section.

Paydirt Productions Ltd.
34 Headlands, Kettering, Northamptonshire, NN15 7HP
tel: 01536 415 347
email: info@paydirtproductions.tv
web: www.paydirtproductions.tv
contact: Steve Stapley
info: Full production packages available. In-house graphics, editing and mastering. Contact for more information.

Pink Angel Promotion
Leicester Creative Business Depot, 31 Rutland Street, Leicester, LE1 1RE
tel: 0116 261 6838
email: enquiries@pinkangels.co.uk
web: www.pinkangels.co.uk
contact: Trevor Locke
info: Offer video production services. Contact for further details. Also provide a variety of other promotional services. See entry in Press & PR section for further information.

Pink Cadillac Productions
Leicester
tel: 07713 258 550
email: philip@pinkcadillacproductions.com
web: www.pinkcadillacproductions.com
contact: philip
info: Pink Cadillac offer a full service, producing music videos, live videos and band documentaries. Can create band Electronic Press Kit, professionally edited and recorded to broadcast quality. As a student film maker the prices charged are lower than for professional companies but the quality of the work speaks for itself. See the website for sample videos or contact for a reel on DVD. Philip is based in both London and Leicester, and can carry out work in either of these locations.

Rainmaker-vf Ltd.
Creative Industries Centre, Glaisher Drive, Wolverhampton Science Park, West Midlands, WV10 9TG
tel: 01902 313 213
email: info@rainmaker-vf.com
web: www.rainmaker-vf.com
contact: Jaspal Virdee
info: Rainmaker-vf are an independent film, television and video production company that produce work for the broadcast sector, as well as for the producing music videos and covering live events.

Tunnel Vizion Media UK
Victoria Road, Fenton, Stoke on Trent, Staffordshire, ST4 2RR
tel: 0845 644 6749
email: info@tunnelvizion.co.uk
web: www.tunnelvizion.co.uk
contact: Gary Bannister
info: Cater for live gig, location, studio recording and music video production as well as documentaries and Electronic Press Kits. Editing facilities and DVD authoring and duplication. Can work to broadcast quality. Cater for all budgets.

Volcano Pictures
Birmingham
tel: 07976 140 888
email: nick@volcanopictures.co.uk
web: www.volcanopictures.co.uk
info: Specialise in short films, promotional films, theatrical projections and music videos. Cater for filming, direction and editing, as well as DVD cover design.

NORTHEAST

Automatic Films
7 Reeds Mouth Place, Fenham, Newcastle-Upon-Tyne, NE5 2HQ
tel: 0191 274 6512
email: clivejackson8@hotmail.com
info: Brand new company catering for local bands making music videos. All Sony digital cameras and full Final Cut Pro editing software.

Line-Up PMC
9a Tankerville Place, Jesmond, Newcastle, NE2 3AT
tel: 0191 281 6449
fax: 0191 212 0913
email: info@line-up.co.uk
web: www.line-up.co.uk
contact: Chris Murtagh
info: Line-Up provides promotional services to artists and bands. High quality audio-visual products can be tailor made to suit the needs of the individual client. Can provide cameramen, graphic artists and other specialists to create professional DVDs, videos and electronic press kits.

Puddle Productions
4 Finchale Court, West Rainton, Houghton Le Spring, Tyne & Wear, DH4 6SS
tel: 0191 584 9295
email: puddlefilms@aol.com
web: www.puddleproductions.co.uk
info: Small video production company, based near Durham. Currently building an in-house studio. Are happy to hear from any local bands who want to make a music video at reasonable cost.

Superkrush Productions
Newcastle-Upon-Tyne, Tyne & Wear, NE1 5DW
tel: 0191 233 2001
fax: 0191 261 5746
email: chris@superkrush.com
web: www.superkrush.com
info: All digital, shoot on HD, Digibeta. Reasonable rates and can work to any budget. Previously worked with Sound Exposions and Letrix.

Walken Productions
258b Buddle Art Centre, Station Road, Wallsend, Tyne & Wear, NE28 8RH
tel: 0191 262 6545/0191 200 1173
email: walkenproductions@hotmail.com
web: www.walkenproductions.com
info: A small and new video production company. Currently working with a band on a DVD. Quite happy to hear from other bands in the area.

NORTHWEST

3 Bears Animations
Unit 45, Hartley Fold, Kirkby Stephen, Cumbria, CA17 4JH
tel: 01768 371 114
fax: 01768 371 118
email: doodi@3bears.co.uk
web: www.3bears.co.uk
contact: Linnhe Catlow
info: Award winning 3 Bears specialise in animation. Shoot on film and will transfer to whatever format is required, finishing to broadcast quality.

3D Imaging
12 Woodside Road, Simonstone, Ribble Valley, BB12 7JG
tel: 0870 740 9016
email: contact@3d-imaging.co.uk
web: www.3d-imaging.co.uk
contact: Geoff Hodbod
info: Animated video promos. Computer animations, 3D animated characters, 3D modelling and titling.

A1 Philm Videos
13 Kennsington Avenue, Chadderton, Oldham, OL9 0NL
tel: 0161 652 5413
fax: 0161 652 5413
web: www.philmvideo.co.uk
contact: Alan Roach
info: Live gigs and location work. Competitive rates. Filmed on DV camera.

Abacam Digital Video Productions
Flat 1, Tower Mansions, 669 Lord Street, Southport, PR9 0BJ
tel: 07905 220 662
contact: Nigel Barton
info: Live gigs and promo shoots. Shot on DV camera. Unsigned musicians welcomed.

Activideo Communications Ltd.
Hotspur House, 2 Gloucester Street, Manchester, M1 5QR
tel: 0161 228 6324
email: brianbarnes@activideo.co.uk
web: www.activideo.co.uk
contact: Brian Barnes
info: Live performance, promo shoots and music videos. Call Activideo for advice and to discuss your ideas and rates.

Airtight Productions
Albany Road Trading Estate, Albany Road, Chorlton, Manchester, M21 0AZ
tel: 0161 881 5157
email: video@airtightproductions.co.uk
web: www.airtightproductions.co.uk
contact: Tom Grimshaw
info: Location, live and studio shoots. Can film bands playing in associated recording studio. Graphic design service for album covers and promotional material.

Anchor Video Productions
57 Hollands Road, Hindley Green, Wigan, WN2 4JZ
tel: 01942 523 493
email: dave@anchorvideoproductions.co.uk
web: www.anchorvideoproductions.co.uk
contact: Dave
info: Gigs and promo shoots. Digital capture and editing. Multi-camera shoots are available. Call Dave to discuss your ideas.

Andrew Brooks Photography
Flat 3, 29 Brundretts Road, Chorlton, Manchester, M21 9DA
tel: 07813 780 386
email: a_p_brooks@hotmail.com
web: www.andrewbrooksphotography.com
contact: Andrew Brooks
info: Films in high definition, and outputs on DVD or VHS. Andrew specialises in live stage visuals for bands and clubs.

Apple Video Facilities
The Studio, 821 Chorley Old Road, Bolton, BL1 5SL
tel: 01204 847 974
email: paul@applevideo.co.uk
web: www.applevideo.co.uk
contact: Paul Cragg
info: Apple Video are a fully fledged production company who will be able to meet any requirements for promos, gigs and Pop videos. Contact for further information.

Axis Creative Communication Ltd.
Cameron House, White Cross Industrial Estate, South Road, Lancaster, LA1 4XF
tel: 01524 849 010
email: production@axico.co.uk
web: www.axico.co.uk
contact: Andrew Daykin
info: Digital recording and editing. Studio, location and live performance footage.

Brooklands Video Services
23 Sedbury Close, Manchester, M23 7JW
tel: 0161 945 2363
email: info@brooklandsvideo.co.uk
web: www.brooklandsvideo.co.uk
contact: Peter McHugh
info: Brooklands offer a professional service to bands in the Manchester area. Call Peter to discuss your ideas and rates.

Captured Alive
tel: 07740 907 181
email: info@capturedalive.com
web: www.capturedalive.com
contact: Ash Tidball
info: Cater for live recording. Editing and DVD authoring/duplication. Can work broadcast quality. Prices start from £500 for filming, audio recording and grafing of a gig to DVD. Can also produce documentaries and Electronic Press Kits.

Cavalier Studios
280 Wellington Road South, Stockport, Cheshire, SK2 6ND
tel: 0161 480 6073
email: info@cavalierstudios.co.uk
web: www.cavalierstudios.co.uk
info: 3 fully air-conditioned, broadcast standard DV edit suites, 4 television broadcast SP Betacam crews and nine semi-broadcast S-VHS crews. All filming and production is carried out by experienced camera and lighting operators, producers and directors. Video duplication. Have recorded for major artists such as The Stone Roses, James and Toyah.

Chameleon Video
9 Sowcar Way, Bollington, Macclesfield, Cheshire, SK10 5QW
tel: 01625 576 072
email: chameleonvideoco@btconnect.com
contact: Bob Cooper
info: Call with an idea of what you'd like and Chameleon Video will see what they can do for you. Special effects, black & white footage and all other styles covered. Aslo can transfer footage from VHS to DVD.

Cheshire Video Ltd.
11 Cowhey Close, Westminster Park, Chester, CH4 7QT
tel: 01244 671 027
email: john@cheshirevideo2.freeserve.co.uk
contact: John
info: Live gig, location recording, music video production and documentary/Electronic Press Kit production. Editing facilities and DVD authoring/duplication. Can work to broadcast quality. £400 per day for filming, £200 per day for editing.

Chroma Video Productions
Spring Hill Road, Accrington, BB5 0EX
tel: 01254 393 683
fax: 01254 393 683
email: lee@chromavideo.co.uk
web: www.chromavideo.co.uk
contact: Lee Mannering
info: Gigs, location shoots and music promos. Shot on DV camera. Post production facilities as well as DVD duplication. Welcomes unsigned talent. 20% discount available for unsigned musicians.

Classic Video Productions
The Wedding House, 3-4 Great George Place, Liverpool, L1 7AG
tel: 0151 280 4893
email: andyambrose@blueyonder.co.uk
contact: Andy Ambrose
info: Promos, live shoots and location filming. 4 digital edit suites available.

Click AV
157 Stamford Street, Ashton-under-Lyme, Tameside, OL6 6XW
tel: 0161 344 1835
fax: 0161 344 1836
email: hire@clickav.co.uk
web: www.clickav.co.uk
contact: Kevin Orchard
info: Gig coverage, studio and location shoots. Can also supply sound and lighting equipment, as well as event management. Associated with Procom music shop.

CVT Broadcast
507 Parkgate Road, Woodbank, Chester, Cheshire, CH1 6EZ
tel: 0151 339 4000
email: info@cvtbroadcast.com
web: www.cvtbroadcast.com
contact: Graham White
info: Location and live gigs. Promo placed on to VHS, DVD, digital betacam or multimedia CD-Rom. All finished footage is of broadcast quality.

Dash Productions Ltd.
2c Essex Lodge, Essex Avenue, Didsbury, Manchester, M20 6AN
tel: 0161 614 9781
fax: 07092 282 612
email: info@dashproductions.co.uk
web: www.dashproductions.co.uk
contact: Paul Green
info: Dash Productions specialise in music DVD and live concert filming. Offer a complete start-to-finish filming service including multiple cameras, jib cranes, editing, 5:1 audio, menus and authoring. For bands working with a large or small budget.

Digi Film
Box 422, 15 Hatton Garden, Liverpool, L3 2HB
tel: 07765 783 606
email: digifilm@postmaster.co.uk
contact: Daniel O'Toole
info: Post production facilities and VHS/DVD showreels.

Dubious Films
113 Commercial Road, Hazel Grove, Stockport, Cheshire, SK7 4BP
tel: 0161 285 0375
email: dubiousfilms@gmail.com
web: www.dubiousfilms.com
contact: Ross Nickson
info: Live gig, location, studio recording, music video production and documentary/Electronic Press Kit production. Editing and DVD authoring/duplication. Can work to broadcast quality.

Elite Video Production
359 Chester Road, Little Sutton, Wirral, CH66 3RG
tel: 0151 339 8423
email: studio@elitevideo.co.uk
web: www.elitevideo.co.uk
contact: David Bladen
info: Offers full band package. Location, studio, live performance and interview footage on VHS, DVD or CD-Rom.

Encounter Video Productions
PO Box 28, Marple, Stockport, Cheshire, SK6 6FG
tel: 0161 427 0661/07754 393 714
email: encounter@vidtech.fsnet.co.uk
web: www.encountervideo.co.uk
contact: Dennis Cooper
info: Freelance cameraman, experienced in multi-camera shoots providing video support at live events. Very supportive of unsigned bands. Own cameras and editing facilities with DVD capability. Betacam SP, DV camera and VHS decks. Recent venues covered include Manchester Apollo, Manchester Arena, The Lowry and many more.

ESP Multimedia
33-45 Parr Street, Liverpool, L1 4JN
tel: 0151 708 5090
fax: 0151 708 6669
email: admin@espmultimedia.com
web: www.espmultimedia.com
info: DVD, CD-Rom authoring service. Also transfer from VHS to DVD and other multimedia formats, including web streaming.

Four 23
The Apex, 6 Southern Street, Castlefield, Manchester, M3 4NN
tel: 0161 835 9466
fax: 0161 835 9468
email: mailman@four23.net
web: www.four23.net
contact: Warren Bramley
info: Animation, studio and location work. Also film live gigs and offer graphic and web design.

Gary Bannon Sound
19 St. Michael's Court, Huyton, Knowsley, Merseyside
tel: 07940 172 275
email: icon@merseymail.com
web: http://maxpages.com/garybannon
contact: Gary Bannon
info: Live gig, location, studio recording, music video production and documentary/Electronic Press Kit production. Prices start from £300.

Glass Studios
Unit 22, Price Street Business Centre, Birkenhead, Wirral, CH41 4JQ
tel: 0151 651 1666
fax: 0151 651 1666
email: alan@glasstudios.com
web: www.glasstudios.com
contact: Alan Lewis
info: Digital quality recording and editing. Location and live recording. Can also film in associated recording studio. Footage on to VHS, DVD or CD-Rom. £30 per hour for filming and post production. Also have rehearsal rooms at £6 per hour.

Gringo Multimedia Ltd.
18 Honeys Green Lane, West Derby, Liverpool, L12 9EW
tel: 07986 969 921
email: mail@gringomultimedia.com
web: www.gringomultimedia.com
contact: Graham, Mandy
info: Gringo offer music video production, live performance filming, DVD mastering, show reel editing and promo videos.

MUSIC SERVICES/RETAIL

Horizon
1 The Parklands, Penrith, Cumbria, CA11 8TF
tel: 01768 899 936
email: horizon@telco4u.net
contact: Les White
info: Promotional videos for musicians on VHS, CD-Rom or DVD. Shoots on DV camera.

Hungry Dog
Byre End, Burgh By Sands, Carlisle, CA5 6AW
tel: 01228 576 267/07710 551 571
contact: Mike Hairsine
info: Hungry Dog produces in a variety of formats including 35mm, 16mm, Digital, High Definition and Digicam. Will film on location, in the studio or at live gigs. Also offer editing and other post production facilities. Partner of company is experienced music producer.

Hungry Fox
Rossendale, Lancashire
tel: 01706 217 882/07973 832 317
email: graham@hungryfox.biz
web: www.hungryfox.biz
contact: Graham Barnes
info: Gigs and promo shoots. Post production using Final Cut Pro on Mac for editing. Cost effective video production. Multi-camera shoots available. Shoots on Digital DV camera. 20 years experience. Hungry Fox's sound engineer Alan Parry is a musician himself and knows how best to capture your sound. Ring Graham for a quote.

Hurricane Films
3 Hazel Avenue, Manchester, M16 8DY
tel: 0161 881 9991
fax: 0161 881 9991
email: huricfilms@aol.com
contact: Matt Bloom
info: Offers innovative, ground breaking videos for unsigned and signed bands. Location or studio work, depending on the project. Hurricane's aim is to make bands as marketable as possible.

Inch Productions
23 New Mount Street, Manchester, M4 4DE
tel: 0161 953 4232
fax: 0161 953 4001
email: keir@inchstudio.com
web: www.inchstudio.com
contact: Keir Stewart
info: Location and live performance footage. Can also film band playing in associated recording studio. DVD, VCD, VHS and multimedia CD-ROM. Also does dialogue recording and music for adverts.

Influential Films
PO Box 306, Manchester, M14 6GX
tel: 07050 395 708
email: info@influentialfilms.co.uk
web: www.influentialfilms.co.uk
contact: Mike Swindells
info: Influential started life specialising in musician management and concert and club promotions. More recently filming and production have become the focus of the company and they have produced videos for bands such as Ash and Space, as well as various other projects for both Atlantic Records and BBC Television. See the website to download examples of their work.

InnerDark Studios
Manchester
tel: 07740 907 181
email: contact@innerdarkstudios.com
web: www.innerdarkstudios.com
contact: Ash Tidball
info: Produce live visuals, documentaries and profiles. From nightclub VJ designs and advertising, to documentaries and corporate video, InnerDark have catered for major companies in the industry. Media suite features industry standard hardware and software.

Insight Moving Images Ltd.
336a Woodchurch Road, Prenton, Wirral, CH42 8PQ
tel: 0151 200 5577
email: enquiries@insightmovingimages.com
web: www.insightmovingimages.com
contact: Lisa Roberts
info: Live gigs and promo shoots. Shot and edited digitally. Multi-camera shoots available.

JWG Creative Media Ltd.
Latham Close, Bredbury Industrial Park, Bredbury, Stockport, SK6 2SD
tel: 07939 213 427
email: jonathan.green@jwgcreativemedia.co.uk
web: www.jwgcreativemedia.co.uk
contact: Jonathan Green
info: Creative solutions for musicians and industry professionals. Services include videos, promos and stage visuals (produced in association with Menagerie). Also do web and print design. See Artwork and Design section for more details.

Kalton Video Facilities
808 Bury Road, Breightmet, Bolton, BL2 6PA
tel: 01204 393 957/01204 371 467
email: sales@kaltonvideo.co.uk
web: www.kaltonvideo.co.uk
contact: David Felton
info: Experienced in live show coverage. Also offer bulk duplication and packaging of VHS, DVD, VCD and CD-Rom.

Keylink Studios
Roughwood Drive, Kirby, Merseyside, L33 8XF
tel: 0151 549 2499
fax: 0151 549 0745
email: info@keylinkstudios.org.uk
web: www.keylinkstudios.org.uk
contact: Claire Watts
info: Keylink Studios offers professional sound recording and video production services under one roof. Keylink are keen to help new talent and will gladly listen to you, whatever your ideas are.

KLS Digital Media
2 Copperfield Close, Burnley, BB10 3RT
tel: 01282 414 073
email: ken-stott@ntlworld.com
web: www.klsmedia.com
contact: Ken Stott
info: Gigs and promotional videos. Shot on Mini-DV pro. Has worked with Peter Ebdon and Rumours of Fleetwood Mac (tribute act).

Loop Productions
3 East Albert Road, Liverpool, L17 3BH
tel: 0151 727 7270
email: barefoot2@mac.com
contact: John Scotland
info: Prices start from £125 for a 3 hour shoot on location for next day delivery on DVD. Also cater for documentaries and more advanced location shoots.

Loyal Media
South Eastern, Dock Road, Birkenhead, L15 4YX
tel: 0151 638 6700
email: info@loyalmedia.com
web: www.loyalmedia.com
contact: Geoff Loyal
info: Promotional videos for bands, singers and instrumentalists. Live performance, mime to a pre-recorded track, or produce an original Pop video. Call Loyal Media for more details.

Mack Video Services
2 Top o' th' Green, Chadderton, OL9 7HL
tel: 0161 665 3078
email: info@mackvideo.co.uk
web: www.mackvideo.co.uk
contact: John McCormack
info: Live gigs and video promos. Digital filming and online editing with special effects. Multi-camera shoots available. Full studio.

The Madhouse Studio
Unit 1, Henry Street, Crewe, CW1 4BH
tel: 01270 251 014
email: thunk@cd2.com
web: www.thunkrecords.com
contact: Steve Brookes
info: Multi-camera shoots and editing. Call for details.

Mediafour
Unit 3, Bailey Court, Green Street, Macclesfield, Cheshire, SK10 1JQ
tel: 01625 423 424
email: info@mediafour.co.uk
web: www.mediafour.co.uk
contact: Vicky Fagan
info: Full production and post-production facilities for bands working with a larger budget.

Merseysound Production and Staging
Studio 4, Liverpool Film Studios, Boundary Street, Liverpool, L5 9YJ
tel: 0151 482 5630
email: msp@merseysoundproductions.co.uk
web: www.merseysoundproductions.co.uk
contact: Colin Reader
info: Demo and promo video production available. Non-linear editing using M-PEG 2. Call in to have a look at examples of Merseysound Production's work. Sound, lighting and stage equipment. Also cater for recording studio facilities (Tonewood Studios).

Mitchell Productions
9 Ennerdale Road, Ewanrigg, Maryport, Cumbria, CA15 8HN
tel: 01900 819 343
email: via website
web: www.mitchellproductionsvideo.com
contact: John Mitchell
info: Fully equipped, broadcast quality. Non-linear editing. Very competitive prices.

North West Video
Studio House, Coleridge Avenue, Dentons Green, St. Helens, Merseyside, WA10 6RN
tel: 01744 299 76
email: northwestvideo@blueyonder.co.uk
web: www.northwestvideo.co.uk
contact: Ron Lee
info: Location work, live gigs, multi-camera shoots. Digital broadcast studio editing facilities.

Pete Blacker
61 Albany Road, Chorlton, Manchester, M21 0BH
tel: 07974 236 541
email: pete@peteblacker.com
web: www.peteblacker.com
contact: Pete Blacker
info: Pete is an inventive and resourceful independent film maker who has worked on commissions from bands and other projects. See the website for portfolio.

Pro II Video Productions
37 Cliffton Court, Ashfield, Workington, Cumbria, CA14 3HR
tel: 01900 666 11
email: ph@pro-cam.net
web: www.pro-cam.net
contact: Peter Hoskin
info: Promos and live shoots. Digital camera/DV Cam. Ideal for bands with small scale ideas/limited budgets.

PWT Productions
1 Castle View, Sedgwick, Kendal, Cumbria, LA8 0JL
tel: 01539 560 516
email: pwt.productions@virgin.net
contact: Peter Thompson
info: Live gigs, location and promo shoots. All shot on digital camera. Final edit can be dropped to VHS or DVD. Call Peter for prices.

Red Brick Productions
Office 4, Breightmetfold House, Red Bridge Works, Bolton, BL2 5PH
tel: 01204 407 871
email: info@redbrickproductions.co.uk
web: www.redbrickproductions.co.uk
contact: David Kay
info: A range of budgets to include unsigned bands. Will travel to any area. Live gig, location, studio recording, music video production and documentary/Electronic Press Kit production. Editing and DVD authoring/duplication. Can work in broadcast quality. Previous clients include Babyshambles, The Levellers, The Proclaimers and Nick Harper.

Rich Video
351 Reddish Road, Reddish, Stockport, Cheshire, SK5 7EN
tel: 0161 480 3389
email: sales@richstudios.co.uk
web: www.richstudios.co.uk
contact: Carylon or David
info: Promotional show reels on video or DVD and multimedia CD-Roms. Also offer CD and video replication. Duplication at 50p per CD. Contact for full details.

Riproar Productions
20 Linden Avenue, Salford, Manchester, M6 7HT
tel: 0161 950 1348
email: alison@riproar.org
web: www.riproar.org
contact: Alison Surtees
info: Promo videos and live projections. Ideal for bands on low budgets who want professional looking videos. Digital filming and editing.

RVP Digicom
44 Rhyl Avenue, Blackburn, Lancashire, BB1 8JE
tel: 01254 679 625
email: info@rvpdigicom.co.uk
web: www.rvpdigicom.co.uk
contact: Kaija Swindlehurst
info: Full production facilities. Footage on to VHS, DVD or CD-Rom. Create music videos, live gig recordings and documentaries.

Saxon Video
62 Scott Lane, Blackrod, Bolton, BL6 5SB
tel: 01942 832 817
email: saxonvideo@aol.com
contact: Mike Bailey
info: Professional, high standard broadcast quality video promos. Location, studio and live gigs.

Seal Films
Flash Green Acre, Jenny Lane, Wheelton, Chorley, PR6 8JE
tel: 01254 830 823
email: info@sealfilms.co.uk
web: www.sealfilms.co.uk
contact: Dave Barrow, Nick Farrimond
info: Gig coverage, location and music promo videos. Very reasonable rates.

Shot Organisation
4 St. Dunstans Grove, Liverpool, L30 2NH
tel: 07952 790 391
email: yoshotorganisation@hotmail.com
web: www.yo-shot.com
contact: Chris Welford
info: Live gig, location, studio recording, music video production and documentary/Electronic Press Kit production. Editing facilities and DVD authoring/duplication. Can work to broadcast quality.

Thirteen Films Ltd.
39 Moorecroft Road, Northern Moor, Manchester, M23 0NP
tel: 0161 902 0880
email: email@thirteenfilms.co.uk
contact: Nadia Montgomery
info: Will help promote bands to all their creative needs. Give Thirteen Films a ring for advice.

Tiger Productions
9 Egremont Promenade, Wallasey, Merseyside, CH44 8BG
tel: 0151 691 2368
email: tigerimages@aol.com
web: www.tigerproductions.co.uk
contact: Juli or David
info: Live gigs, promo shoots and location or rehearsal shoots. Capture and editing is all done digitally. Contact Tiger Productions to discuss what you have in mind.

T-Tech Digital Media Services
The Ranch House, Bambers Lane, Blackpool, FY4 5LH
tel: 01253 760 101
email: info@t-techmedia.com
web: www.t-techmedia.com
contact: Andy Torkington
info: Gigs, location and studio shoots. DSR 500 digital cameras, Jimmy Jib and Triangle. Multi-camera shoots (up to 5 if required). Plenty of band experience.

Velvet Skies Music Video & Film
Manchester
tel: 07799 125 502
email: markbristol@hotmail.co.uk
web: www.velvetskiesfilm.com
contact: Mark Bristol
info: Velvet Skies can bring your ideas and imagery to life. Blending photography, fine art, animation and DV Film. Specialise in promo videos, offering competitive rates and will continue working until the band or individual is happy with the end product.

VFS Business Videos
VFS House, 6 Abrams Green, Nr. Southport, West Lancashire, PR9 8DN
tel: 01704 225 767
email: sales@vfsvideos.co.uk
web: www.vfsvideos.co.uk
contact: Graham Clark
info: 10 minute high impact promotional videos. Location, studio or live gigs. Digital editing. Versatile service.

Vision4Dreams Productions
Office 1a, Hawphorne Business Park, Warrington, WA5 0BX
tel: 07939 950 111
email: enquiries@vision4dreams.com
web: www.vision4dreams.com
contact: Acacio Moreno
info: Promo music videos, live gigs. Shot digitally and edited on Avid Express for broadcast quality finish. All music styles considered. High quality output at affordable rates. Also offers web design service.

White Star Video
26 Windermere Road, Wistaston, Crewe, Cheshire, CW2 8RJ
tel: 01270 663 647
email: m-white@btconnect.com
contact: Michael White
info: Experienced promo produced. Full studio and digital editing facilities. Location shoots. Interactive CD-Rom and DVD production

Wildcat Films
Windy Hall, Alston, Cumbria, CA9 3NJ
tel: 01434 381 067
email: mail@wildcatfilms.com
web: www.wildcatfilms.com
info: Basic film production package from £1200 per day. Equipment specs on the website.

SOUTHEAST

11th Circle Films
Boundary Cottage, Biddenden Road, St. Michaels, Tenterden, Kent, TN30 6TA
tel: 01233 850 885
email: eleventh.circle@virgin.net
contact: Mark Turner
info: Can film multi-camera live gigs, location shoots and can arrange good deals on studios for unsigned bands. Equipment list includes 16mm, Super 8, Digibeta, HighDef and DV cameras. Shoots arranged around available budget. Previous clients include Ash, Cornershop and Suede.

42 Films
Kent
email: david@42films.com
web: www.42films.com
contact: David Knight
info: 42 Films cater towards making original and inventive music videos for any type of music. They make videos of all costs for all clients so get in touch. As a special offer to readers of The Unsigned Guide, 42 Films are offering 10% off normal production costs, just mention the Guide when you contact them!

Activelight Video Production Services
Unit 18, Stort Mill, Riverway, Harlow, Essex, CM20 2SN
tel: 01279 414 736
email: john@activelight.co.uk
web: www.activelight.co.uk
contact: John Culleton
info: Specialise in filming live gigs and making low budget promo DVDs. Studio facilities, CD and DVD duplication also available.

AngelicFilms
The Hollies, NashLee Lane, Wendover, HP22 6BG
tel: 01296 625 414
fax: 01296 696 323
email: info@angelicfilms.co.uk
web: www.angelicfilms.co.uk
contact: Adam Coop
info: AngelicFilms mainly film on location and in the studio, but will film live gigs as well. Offer a variety of formats, generally finishing with DVD. Also offer in-house final cut facilities.

BandBits
Prince Bros Site, Old Bath Road, Charvil, Reading, Berkshire, RG10 9QJ
tel: 0118 932 0032
fax: 0118 932 0016
email: nick@bandbits.com
web: www.bandbits.com
contact: Nick Lawson
info: Studio video filming, editing and production for DVDs or web. Fast, effective videos filmed in our studio, synced to audio and produced to high standard. From £99 for an average length track. Discounts for additional tracks.

Create Media
39 Telegraph Lane, Four Marks, Alton, Hampshire, GU34 5AX
tel: 01420 561 144
fax: 01420 560 020
email: info@create-media.co.uk
web: www.create-media.co.uk
contact: Chris Dixon
info: Cater for live gigs, location and music video recording. Editing and mastering to DVD facilities. Also provide documentary and Electronic Press Kit services.

Doin' OK Productions
PO Box 15, Swanley, Kent, BR8 7XJ
tel: 07941 663 943
email: musicvid@doinokproductions.co.uk
web: www.doinokproductions.co.uk
contact: Matt Mitchell
info: Specialising in creative, professional, broadcast quality music video production to your budget. Substantial discounts and offers to new or unsigned bands. DV and DV CAM digital recording, post production and editing. This can be presented on DV, VHS or DVD and duplicated if needed.

Filmscape Media
6 Stammerham Business Centre, Capel Road, Rusper, West Sussex, RH12 4PZ
tel: 07984 788 221
fax: 01306 710 102
email: info@filmscapemedia.com
web: www.filmscapemedia.com
contact: Kevin Harvey
info: Filmscape Media are experienced filmmakers who specialise in promos for recording artists. Cater for live gig, location, studio recording, music video and documentary/Electronic Press Kit production. Editing and DVD authoring/duplication. Can work to broadcast quality. Contact with your requirements and budgets.

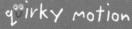

Image2Film
Studio 29-31, Stafford Road, Brighton, BN1 5PE
tel: 07958 272 333
email: info@image2film.com
web: www.image2film.com
contact: David Fenandes
info: Full production and editing facilities. Also offer photography services. See relevant section for details.

Lucky Airbag Productions
Flat 1, 18 Portland Place, Brighton, BN2 1DH
tel: 07917 135 049
email: info@luckyairbag.co.uk
web: www.luckyairbag.co.uk
contact: Wil Martin
info: Live gig, location, studio recording, music video production and documentary/Electronic Press Kit production. Can work to broadcast quality. Prices start from £500.

Nothing To See Here
Brighton
tel: 01273 626 274
email: steve@nothing-to-see-here.com
web: www.nothing-to-see-here.com
info: Nothing To See Here are a collective of design, video and new media specialists. Experienced in producing music promos, including shorts comprising of interviews and live gig footage. Also offer full design service. See listing in Artwork & Design for more details.

Panther Studios
5 Doods Road, Reigate, Surrey, RH2 0NT
tel: 01737 210 848
fax: 01737 210 848
email: studios@dial.pipex.com
web: http://ds.dial.pipex.com/sema/panther.htm
contact: Richard Coppen
info: A complete promotional video service for all budgets, all types of music and all levels of output quality. From first concept to finished promo. Storyboards, scripts, lights, special effects, camera crews, editing and audio enhancement.

Quirky Motion

Floor 5, The Amphenol Business Complex, Thanet Way, Whitstable, Kent, CT5 3WF
tel: 0870 787 4181
email: thechaps@quirkymotion.com
web: www.quirkymotion.com
contact: John Lumgair
info: Quirky Motion produces animation, illustration and video. Work with bands to create a unique video which suites their style and image. See website for some of examples of Quirky Motion's work. Also provide design services. See listing in relevant section.

Shoot Bamboo

63 Denmark Villas, Hove, East Sussex, BN3 3TD
tel: 01273 707 994
email: info@shootbamboo.com
web: www.shootbamboo.com
contact: Dax Device
info: Shoot Bamboo can produce in any format or medium required. Can also encode for the internet. Also do photography, see relevent section for details.

Shoot You Video Production

No.1 Victory Park Mews, Addlestone, Surrey, KT15 2AT
tel: 01932 853 696
email: quint@shootyou.co.uk
web: www.shootyou.co.uk
contact: Quint Boa
info: Shoot You Video Productions recently filmed a live band at the ICA and streamed it directly onto the 3G mobile network. Two of the editors are currently in unsigned bands themselves, and have produced various projects for unsigned bands. Prices are £750 a day for shooting and £75 an hour for editing.

Silk Purse Creations

Beckenham, Kent
tel: 07787 548 659
fax: 07787 548 659
email: rhughes@spcreations.tv
web: www.spcreations.tv
contact: Richard Hughes
info: In-house post production facilities with easy access to locations and studios across London and the South East. Specialise in music video and documentary production, and have a development programme to support unsigned bands. See website for more details.

Silvertip Films

Rosedene, Selhurst Common, Bramley, Surrey, GU5 0LS
tel: 07786 331 502
email: info@silvertipfilms.co.uk
web: www.silvertipfilms.co.uk
contact: Geof Cockwill
info: Specialise in live gig shoots. Able to burn DVDs of finished video with menus and extra features. QuickTime video facilities for Internet clips or for a demo CD. 3 camera live shoot starts from £600. 1 day music video shoot is £500. Also offer stills photography for websites or CDs. Email to find out whether Silvertip can cater for your project.

Stickmandoo Visuals

24 Buxton Road, Brighton, BN1 5DE
tel: 07789 547 098
email: anw@anwood.co.uk
web: www.anwood.co.uk
contact: Andrew Wood
info: Custom-made visual mixing and projections for gigs, stage shows or venue decoration. Static or video footage. No computer graphics. All original material with a bias towards graphics, text and animation. Urban and hard-hitting. See website for examples of style. Prices negotiable.

Viva Vancouver Productions

212 Ladyshot, Harlow, Essex, CM20 3ET
tel: 01279 439 189/07941 359 399
email: viva_vancouverproductions@hotmail.com
web: www.vivavancouver.co.uk
contact: John Sellings
info: Caters for music video/DVD production, live gig recording and short film production. Also has various editing facilities including studio or live recording and sound engineering.

Warren Films

One Commonside West, Mitcham, Surrey, CR4 4HA
tel: 020 8687 4432/07795 966 822
email: info@warrenfilm.com
web: www.warrenfilm.com
contact: Lee Warren
info: Live gig filming, location filming and studio work up to broadcast quality. Phone for details of rates.

Wild Productions

Randalls Farm House, Randalls Road, Leatherhead, Surrey, KT22 0AL
tel: 01372 379 069
fax: 01372 375 183
email: mail@wildproductions.co.uk
web: www.wildproductions.co.uk
contact: Simon Cowell
info: Live gig, location, studio recording, music video production and documentary/Electronic Press Kit production. Editing and DVD authoring/duplication. Can work to broadcast quality.

SOUTHWEST

Big Brush Films

Enterprise Pavillion, Poole, Dorset, BH12 5HH
tel: 01202 853 640
email: mark@bigbrushfilms.com
web: www.bigbrushfilms.com
contact: Mark Withers
info: Big Brush can produce in variety of formats - high definition, digital, 8mm. Based at Bournemouth University, they have full editing and production facilities

Cimitry Films

Creative Planet, Hackpen Lane, Wroughton, Wiltshire, SN4 9NS
tel: 01793 845 599
fax: 01793 845 455
email: info@cimitry.co.uk
web: www.cimitry.co.uk
contact: Tom Ward
info: Specialise in music promos, TV commercials and feature films. Facilities include film, HD, Digibeta and DVCAM shooting kits, full lighting and rig kits and on-site postproduction services.

Happy Hour Productions Ltd.

The Picture House, 4 Lower Park Row, Bristol, BS1 5BJ
tel: 0117 929 9797
fax: 0117 923 0862
email: info@hhour.co.uk
web: www.happyhourproductions.co.uk
info: Happy Hour provides a full production service, from an initial concept and its early development, through to the shoot itself. Happy Hour also provides a full post-production crew and facilities; from edit suites, editors, through to broadcast, duplication and delivery.

Laughing Cat Studio

Hyacinth Cottage, Cubert, Newquay, Cornwall, TR8 5EZ
tel: 01637 831 199/01637 830 989
email: mike@laughingcat-studio.co.uk
web: www.laughingcat-studio.co.uk
contact: Mike
info: Laughing Cat offer digital and audio production. Also offer video services and photography.

Omni Productions

Studio 47, Easton Business Centre, Felix Road, Easton, Bristol, BS5 0HE
tel: 0117 941 5820
email: creation@omniproductions.co.uk
web: www.omniproductions.co.uk
contact: Richard Penfold
info: Film production and multimedia company. Caters for location and studio recording and music video production. Can work in broadcast quality. Editing facilities and authoring to DVD. Produce documentaries and Electronic Press Kits.

YORKSHIRE

ABL

134 Archer Road, Sheffield, S8 0JZ
tel: 0114 255 6070
email: info@abl.gb.com
web: www.abl.gb.com
info: Will video gigs or rehearsals.

Aim For The Head

Leeds
tel: 07731 369 250
email: contact@aimforthehead.com
web: www.aimforthehead.com
contact: Alex
info: Creative film and video production collective based in the Leeds area. Cater for live gig, location, studio recording, music video production and documentary/Electronic Press Kit production. Editing facilities and DVD authoring/duplication. Can work to broadcast quality.

Altercentric
57 George Road, Horsforth, Leeds, LS18 5PY
tel: 01274 427 148
email: contact@altercentric.com
web: www.altercentric.com
contact: Andy Fox
info: Altercentric offer DVD, video, audio and CD-Rom production services. They also develop software and can create and build websites.

Classlane Media
Classlane Studios, 22 The Weir, Hessle, Hull, HU13 0RU
tel: 01482 640 093
fax: 01482 640 103
email: post@classlane.co.uk
web: www.classlane.co.uk
contact: Dave Beasley
info: Live gig, location, studio recording, music video production and documentary/Electronic Press Kit production. Editing facilities and DVD authoring/duplication. Can work in broadcast quality. Prices start from £1500.

Craven Image Studios
10 Myrtle Drive, Crossroads, Keighley, BD22 9AE
tel: 01535 646 444
email: ian@cravenimagestudios.freeserve.co.uk
web: www.cravenimagestudios.co.uk
contact: Ian Brown
info: Offer complete production promo packages to any bands, including live, location or studio shoots. Broadcast quality film/edit suites at realistic prices. Will cover West Yorkshire and Lancashire areas.

Creative Convergence Ltd.
Concept House, 2 Burley Road, Leeds, LS3 1NJ
tel: 0113 233 0001
fax: 0113 233 0016
email: general@converge.co.uk
web: www.converge.co.uk
info: Creative Convergence is a video production company making a variety of programmes and The Look is their post production facility, available to work on outside projects. Everything is produced to broadcast standards, with all the latest digital technology available. They have produced Pop promos in the past and the post production team have extensive experience in editing music videos (mostly retro compilations). Local musicians and composers are used for programme soundtracks.

Filmmakers
26 Elmete Avenue, Roundhay, Leeds, LS8 2QN
tel: 0113 273 1200
fax: 0113 273 1200
contact: Martin or Maggie Harris
info: Filmmakers have recorded some music promotional videos. Contact for further details.

Hardwired Video Productions
5 Marshall Street, Leeds, LS15 8DY
tel: 0113 226 6787
fax: 0113 260 9507
email: marcus@hardwired.freeserve.co.uk
contact: Marcus White
info: Hardwired can work on projects of varying budgets. Call to discuss your requirements. Full facilities are available, including a digital editing suite. Recent work includes a promo video for Leeds' band, Black Star Liner, as well as work shown at Leeds International Film Festival.

Leeds Animation Workshop
4 Bayswater Row, Leeds, LS8 5LF
tel: 0113 248 997
fax: 0113 248 997
email: law@leedsanimation.demon.co.uk
web: www.leedsanimation.demon.co.uk
info: Small animation company typically producing a 10 minute film each year. Opportunities for musicians are therefore very limited but they do commission work from local artists that they know and they would consider approaches to work on other people's projects.

Liquid Digital Media
16 Malham Way, Knaresborough, North Yorkshire, HG5 0HQ
tel: 07932 038 527
email: liquiddigitalmedia@hotmail.com
contact: Mark Graham
info: Liquis Digital Media specialises in video production and graphic design but they also have a range of other multimedia skills. Cost for music video production starts at £500 but Liquid Digital will discuss possibilities for lower budget videos. All work is up to broadcast standard.

West Yorkshire Media Service
Leeds Metropolitan University, 3 Queens Square, Leeds, LS2 8AF
tel: 0113 283 1906
email: m.spadafora@lmu.ac.uk
contact: Maria Spadafora
info: W.Y.M.S. run a training course in Film and Video Production aimed at people aged 25 and over who are in receipt of benefits (Certificate of Higher Education; 18 months; part-time; daytime). If you are looking for crew for your own project they could put you in touch with a number of appropriate people.

NORTHERN IRELAND

Best Cellars
Ballybean Activity Centre, Dundonald, County Down, BT16 2QE
tel: 028 9048 6290
fax: 028 9048 6290
email: dean@thecellars.org.uk
web: www.thecellars.org.uk
info: Part of Best Cellars music collective. Digital (mini DV) and S-VHS edit facility available. Best Cellars also provide recording and rehearsal facilities. See listing in relevant sections for details.

GraphXstudio
31 Regent Street, Newtownards, BT23 4AD
tel: 028 9180 0944
email: george@graphxstudio.co.uk
web: www.graphxstudio.co.uk
info: Creation and filming of video or DVD based media. Have previous experience of working with unsigned artists. Also provide artwork and design services. See listing in relevant section for details.

Inferno
16 Donegall Square South, Belfast, County Antrim, BT1 5JA
tel: 028 9033 1220
email: info@inferno.tv
web: www.inferno.tv
info: Inferno is a full service production house specialising in the concept generation, storyboarding, scripting, 3D and 2D animation, film, edit, motion design and sound design. Call for a no obligation quote.

Novatech AV
122 Hydepark Road, Newtownabbey, BT36 4PZ
tel: 028 9083 8981
fax: 028 9084 4299
email: info@www.novatechstudios.com
web: www.novatechstudios.com
contact: Dale
info: Live gig, location, studio recording, music video production and documentary/Electronic Press Kit production. Editing facilities and DVD authoring/duplication. Can work to broadcast quality.

Red Box Media Productions
3 Ardrigh Court, 737c Antrim Road, Belfast, County Antrim, BT15 4EL
tel: 028 9077 3854
email: liam@redboxmedia.co.uk
web: www.redboxmedia.co.uk
info: Can produce music videos and promos using DVC Pro, Digibeta and DV Cam. Two Avid editing suites available. Have worked with bands before, quite happy to hear from any local bands.

Red Label Records
7 Eglantine Avenue, Belfast, BT9 6DW
tel: 028 9066 8667
email: info@redlabelrecords.com
web: www.redlablerecords.com
info: Independent film company, very much interested in working with bands from the area. Call Gawain for an informal chat about what Red Label can offer.

SCOTLAND

Brever Studios
60a Craigour Drive, Edinburgh, EH17 7NT
tel: 0845 129 8534
email: via website
web: www.breverstudios.com
contact: Colin Myers
info: Live gig, location, studio recording and music video production. Editing facilities and DVD authoring/duplication. Can work in broadcast quality. Also offer web design and audio recording. See relevant sections for more details.

Cagoule Productions
2 Commercial Street, Edinburgh, EH6 6JA
tel: 0131 555 5414
email: info@cagoule.tv
web: www.cagoule.tv
contact: Lewis Gourlay
info: Live gig, location and studio recording. Editing and authoring to DVD/CD-Rom. Can work in broadcast quality. Documentaries and Electronic Press Kits catered for.

EchoBeach Video Productions
Glasgow
tel: 0141 570 1312
email: linda@echobeachvideo.co.uk
web: www.echobeachvideo.co.uk
contact: Linda McCallum
info: Music videos for artists and bands.

Go Go Studios
6 Great George Street, Westend, Glasgow, G12 8PD
tel: 07811 438 468
email: info@gogostudios.com
web: www.gogostudios.com
info: Can produce music videos and promos, as well as carrying out location filming and footage editing.

The Hold
20 Craigs Park, Edinburgh, EH12 8UL
tel: 0131 339 0164
email: info@thehold.co.uk
web: www.thehold.co.uk
contact: Kerry Mullaney
info: A cutting-edge independent music video production and live event recording company, serving the Edinburgh and Glasgow scenes. Authoring, streaming, design. Caters for live gig, location, studio recording and music video production. Editing, DVD authoring and duplication. Can work in broadcast quality. Can produce documentaries and Electronic Press Kits.

nuArts Productions
14 King Street, Glasgow, G1 5QP
tel: 0141 552 8641/07788 446 201
email: graham@nuarts.co.uk
web: www.nuarts.co.uk
info: Offer video production services to suit all budgets. nuArts Productions can provide a variety of packages to assist unsigned artists including photography, artwork and design, and assistance with compiling of EPKs. See listings in relevant sections for details.

Pro Create
PO Box 2800, Glasgow, G64 3DP
tel: 0141 587 1609
email: info@pro-create.co.uk
web: www.pro-create.co.uk
contact: Kit Cunnings
info: Video production service incorporating scripting, filming, lighting, editing, post production, effects and titling. Also offer duplication and video streaming for the web, as well as DVD menu creation, inlays and stickering.

Small Majority
Old Town Jail, Stirling, FK8 1EA
tel: 01786 465 225
email: info@smallmajority.co.uk
web: www.smallmajority.co.uk
contact: Alan
info: Offer broadcast quality video production specialising in live events, webcasting and music videos. Location, studio and live music filming and full editing facilities. DVD authoring with audio tracks, live performance and biography.

Sonic Lizard
10 Canmore Street, Dunfermline, Fife, KY12 7NT
tel: 01383 741 500
email: info@soniclizard.com
web: www.soniclizard.com
contact: Jamie Gleday
info: Sonic Lizard will film live gigs, on location or in the studio and offer full post-production services. They use DVD, CD and VHS format and finish to broadcast quality. Also have practice, recording and multimedia facilities. Check their website for further info.

Soundsmove
93 New Trows Road, Lesmahagow, ML11 0ER
tel: 01555 894 678
email: dg@soundsmove.com
web: www.soundsmove.com
contact: David Goodall
info: Soundsmove offer audio and video post production. Also offer project recording.

Walrus & Carpenter Ltd.
Unit 0/2, 216 Main Street, Glasgow, G40 1JU
tel: 0141 554 9945
fax: 0141 554 9945
email: info@wnc.uk.net
web: www.walrusandcarpenter.net
contact: Cavan McLaughlin
info: Live gig, location, studio recording, music video production. Editing facilities and DVD authoring. Can work in broadcast quality. Also provide web and graphic design service. Refer to listing in Artwork & Design section.

Zombie Works
1/1 The Angel Building, 12 Paislay Road West, Glasgow, G51 1LE
email: gareth@zombie-works.co.uk
web: www.zombie-works.co.uk
contact: Gillian, Gareth
info: Professional, broadcast quality, live music video production. Specialise in producing video footage from live events such as product launches, presentation/awards evenings and live performances/concerts. Cover everything from filming an event to converting video footage into broadcast quality film.

WALES

Camerusa Productions
6 Lon Tarw, Bull Bay, Amlwch, Gwynedd, LL68 9SS
tel: 01407 832 899
email: eddie@camerusa.freeserve.co.uk
info: Can work within any specified budget. Broadcast quality results.

Crash Editing
Office 13, Bankside Enterprise Park, Coverack Road, Newport, NP19 0DS
tel: 01633 840 480
email: crashediting@yahoo.co.uk
web: www.crashediting.co.uk
info: Crash Editing offer post-production services on footage provided by your band. Can also author multimedia DVD which can include images, songs and video.

Dart Film & Video Services
196 Whitchurch Road, Cardiff, CF14 3NB
tel: 02920 693 100
email: dart@ukgateway.net
web: www.dartvideo.co.uk
info: Experienced film and television directors and camera crews. Post-production. Reasonable rates.

Dinamo Productions Ltd.
Chapter Arts Centre, Market Road, Canton, Cardiff
tel: 02920 384 800
email: info@dinamo.co.uk
web: www.dinamo.co.uk
info: Digital media company producing animation for television productions, title sequences, interstitials and web designs. Produce series, features, short films and adverts for international television and film. Produce animation (2D and 3D) and live action.

Garage Door Productions
59 Ferry Road, Cardiff, CF11 7DX
email: info@garagedoorproductions.co.uk
web: www.garagedoorproductions.co.uk
info: Music videos and documentary films.

Knew Productions
The Place In The Park Studios, Bellvue Road, Wrexham, LL13 2JG
tel: 01978 358 522
email: studio@knewproductions.co.uk
web: www.knewproductions.co.uk
info: Full service video production company, specialising in corporate videos and DVDs. Provide broadcast quality filming and editing and a full script to screen service. Can also do location filming and duplication.

NikJaw
3 Ffordd Elfed, Wrexham, LL12 7LU
tel: 07961 486 969
email: nikjaw@lycos.com
web: www.nikjaw.com
info: NikJaw Productions was established in 2001. Since then the have produced a wide range of projects including music videos. Able to provide a complete digital service to any musician, from developing concepts to a final edit.

The Picture Works Ltd.
Llwyndrssi Ty Mawr, Carmarthenshire, SA40 9RB
tel: 0845 310 8321
email: info@pictureworks.co.uk
web: www.pictureworks.co.uk
info: Specialise in low budget work. All formats. Location, live gig and studio works. Editing services provided. Broadcast quality finished product.

The Pop Factory
Welsh Hills Works, Jenkin Street, Porth, Rhondda, CF39 9PP
tel: 01443 688 500
email: Via website
web: www.thepopfactory.com
info: Experienced music video producers. In-house post production. Live performance recording including showcase performances and studio shows. The Pop Factory comprises a number of studio spaces, sound recording facilities, record label (TPF Records) and venue as well as video production facilities. See relevant sections for more details.

Proactive Video
Bridgend
tel: 01656 667 843/07974 000 857
email: info@proactivevideo.co.uk
web: www.proactivevideo.co.uk
info: Proactive Video also offer media transfer and duplication. See Mastering & Duplication listings for more details.

R.T. Parker
Rheola Cottage, Llanharry, Pontyclun, Mid Glamorgan, CF72 9LH
tel: 01443 227 528
email: raytparker@mac.com
info: Professional sound recorder and mixer for broadcasts.

Red 90
The Edit Suite, 4 Llanthewy Road, Newport, NP20 4JR
tel: 01633 267 052
email: via website
web: www.red90.co.uk
info: Red 90 have over 30 years experience in the video production industry, including working on music promos.

Riddle Hallucinations Video Production
PO Box 5, Whitland, SA34 0WA
tel: 01994 484 466
email: cadillacranch@telco4u.net
web: www.nikturner.com
info: Also run 2 record labels (Riddle Records and Nikt Records), Money Talks Management, Money Talks Agency, and Cadillac Ranch Recording Studios. See entries in relevant sections for further details.

Sean James Cameron
South Wales
tel: 07952 245 967
email: sean_james_cameron@hotmail.com
info: Live, location and studio shoots. Broadcast quality end product. DVD authoring. Graphic design available for CD and DVD covers.

Select Video & Photography
68 Llanelli, Carmarthenshire, SA15 1AN
tel: 01554 777 902
web: www.select-video.com
info: Will cover all of Wales and England although there will be additional expenses to cover travel costs for long distances.

Square Edge Media
41 Winifred Road, Skewen, Neath, West Glamorgan, SA10 6HW
tel: 01792 818 085
email: squareedgemedia@aol.com
info: Lots of experience working with bands. In-house post-production.

Stiwdio Eglwys
48 Brynffynnon Road, Y Felinheli, Gwynedd, LL56 4SJ
tel: 01248 671 663
email: george@stiwdioeglwys.fsnet.co.uk
web: www.stiwdioeglwys.co.uk
contact: George Kempson
info: Audio visual production and training facility. Cater for location and studio recording and music video production. Editing facilities and authoring to DVD, as well as duplication services. Can work to broadcast quality. Can provide documentaries/Electronic Press Kits.

Sunshine Studios
Llantrisant, Mid Glamorgan, Cardiff
tel: 07876 340 172
email: sunshine_studio@hotmail.com
info: Location, live and in the studio. Broadcast quality productions on DVD. Also run a recording studio. See relevant section for details.

Tall Man Productions
106a Llanaff Road, Cardiff, CF11 9NN
tel: 07941 590 049
email: mike@tallmanproductions.co.uk
web: www.tallmanproductions.co.uk
info: Live and location shoots, can record on any format. Post-production facilities. Tall Man Productions are happy to work within a band's specified budget. Call to discuss your ideas.

TVPS
Television Studio, Morriston Hospital, Morriston, Swansea, SA6 6NL
tel: 01792 703 437
email: info@tvps-online.co.uk
web: www.tvps-online.co.uk
info: All productions filmed on DV Cam with digital editing. Can arrange single camera shoots, and multi camera events. Contact for more information.

Section 4
Live Performance

the|unsigned|guide

4.1 Live Performance Foreword

This section of The Unsigned Guide includes information regarding venues across the UK that will accept demos from unsigned and non-local bands and therefore most of the venues listed have capacities of between 100 and 500. You should also look out for the Musicians' Union information regarding Live Performance later in this foreword.

Where sending demos to the right contacts in respect of A&R/Recording and Publishing contacts, the same is true of venues and promoters. In the early stages, you should use this section to contact venues and promoters who are most likely to book you. We have made sure the listings don't include any obviously unsuitable venues and you should still check for the venues locally which you may have already heard of (or your contacts can recommend), before venturing further afield.

> **Live performance is one of the best ways to promote your band and increase your profile and awareness to the point where you begin to generate a wider public/industry interest.**

As part of your ongoing marketing/promotional campaign, live performance is one of the best ways to promote your band and increase your profile and awareness to the point where you may begin to generate a wider public/industry interest. Before you embark on a live campaign it is obviously necessary for you to plan a period of extensive rehearsals, developing your sound to the point where you are ready to gig.

Before you even book your first rehearsal with a view to playing live, it is advisable to discuss the various aspirations and levels of commitment of the musicians in your band. This is hugely important as you will not want to find yourself in the position where you are having to turn down the offer of a national tour support because some musicians in the band are unable, or unwilling, to hit the road for a month of gigs. There is obviously nothing wrong in forming a band as a hobby as long as everybody understands that it is just a hobby. Problems will inevitably arise when half the band want to make music a career and the other half don't. The Unsigned Guide operates on the assumption that you, or all members of your band aspire to a career as professional musicians.

First Rehearsals

A common mistake that bands make in the early days is failing to stick with one rehearsal room. If you chop and change your rehearsal rooms, by the nature of the acoustics in different rooms, your band will sound different each time you rehearse. This is bound to hinder the essential process of identifying your band 'sound'. It is much better to look around, test a few rehearsal facilities and then decide on one room that suits your needs and your budget - book the room on a weekly basis and rehearse there exclusively. Alternatively, in an ideal world you should hunt down a secure 'lock-out' facility which gives you 24-hour rehearsal access. This will obviously also save you hours of time transporting and setting up equipment.

Your first rehearsals should be spent experimenting with sound levels, position of the amps, drums, keyboards etc., until you find the combination of levels and equipment positions that allow everyone to hear clearly exactly what they, and (equally importantly) what everyone else is doing. Once you achieve this optimum state, it is advisable to draw diagrams and make notes of levels etc., so that when you come back to rehearse you will know exactly how to set-up to achieve the same clarity of sound. By doing this it will enable you, over the weeks and months, to identify the strengths and weaknesses of your band and to routine and write accordingly.

Getting A Sound Engineer

When you do your first gigs, you will need a sound engineer. Most unsigned venues will supply an engineer on the night but in order to develop your out-front/monitor sound it is advisable to recruit your own engineer who can get to know the band's sound and give you the best possible sound each time you play. This will also make sound checking significantly easier because you will be working with the same engineer each time, rather than someone who hasn't engineered your sound or even heard you play before. Bear in mind that a working engineer will charge anywhere upwards of £75 per show. It is always worth asking other bands and local promoters who they would recommend. Some engineers may even agree to work for free if they like your sound and on the understanding that you will employ their services if you secure a deal or go out on tour in the future - an investment on their part if you like.

When you start rehearsing you should ensure that either someone from the band or a friend or colleague with access to a portable studio is available to record your rehearsals and that copies of tapes/CDs/MDs are distributed the following day to each member of the band so that they can listen to, and make a personal judgment on, the strengths and weaknesses of the previous rehearsal. In this way the band will become familiar to the 'band sound' and give individuals the chance to consider changes and/or improvements to songs and ultimately the set, in plenty of time for the next rehearsal.

Your First Gigs

When you first start gigging, there are several important issues you must bear in mind. Early gigs should be used to develop your set, changes in songs and running orders for example - almost as an extension of your rehearsal sessions. The idea is to perfect your performance and settle on a basic stage set-up that you feel comfortable with and that will maintain the attention of people in the venue.

The most essential thing to remember at this early stage is that when mistakes happen, and they inevitably will, is to not make obvious the fact that they have. You will find yourself at the bottom of the bill, or playing without a sound check, but don't let it get you down, it's all part of getting 'gig-fit', be professional and show your support when other bands on the bill play - it is likely they will be in the same position as you, so watch their show in the hope that they (and their fans) will do the same for you.

Developing Your Fan Base

As an unsigned band, when you embark on a campaign of more serious gigs, you must remember that if you rely solely on a local promoter to attract audience, you will inevitably be disappointed with the turn out.

At first, you must approach your local venues and promoters and set to work on building your local fan base, even if it just consists of family and friends to start with. On a commercial basis, promoting unsigned bands can be a risky business. Promoters should always be willing to book you once, but if you do not attract at least 20-30 people, it is unlikely that you will be re-booked - harsh but true!

> **Make the effort to get people you know down to your gigs, it really is a crucial factor in developing your fan base and your working relationship with local venues and promoters.**

If word spreads amongst local promoters that your audience turnout is poor, it will be less likely that other venues will book you. Similarly, if you do attract a fair audience, promoters will be keen to book you again and again and also book you at different venues. So, make the effort to get people you know down to your gigs, it really is a crucial factor in developing your fan base and your working relationship with local venues and promoters.

Print & Promotion

As we have already mentioned, as an unsigned band early into a career, the role of promotion often falls squarely at the feet of the band itself. Make sure you are enthusiastic about your gigs when you tell your friends/fans and after gigs hand out flyers so you keep people informed of future dates. Use the Music Services/Retail section of The Unsigned Guide to source recommended designers and printers in your area. Black & white/mono printing can be just as effective as full colour and a great deal cheaper. If you book a series of gigs it makes good sense to advertise all the shows on one leaflet, plus any other information such as your web site, an e-mail address and contact information including a contact name and telephone number. Additionally, if you are selling CDs you should also include outlet information and the selling price.

You should also build your public awareness by displaying posters at the venue and around the area where you live at least a couple of weeks before you play. You should avoid road-side billboard/flyposter sites, they are operated by private organisations who will not take kindly to you putting posters over those that have been paid for by record company clients and other promoters.

Many bars, shops and fast-food outlets will let you put a small (A3) poster up, so use these sites in preference to illegal ones - council penalties for flyposting can run to thousands of pounds - so unless you can afford to pay the fines, stick to the permitted, private sites.

Mailing Lists
At each gig you do, try and collect contact information (name/address/e-mail/telephone etc.) from those people who make the effort to attend your shows. These names will form the basis for your mailing list. Add these to all the relevant journalists and reporters from the local press, music magazines, listings guides and internet sites, and before too long you will have a reasonable list of people to mail your gig and release information to each time you gig or produce a demo/CD.

During the run up to your gigs, make sure you submit listings to the local media. Your promoter should be submitting listings on a regular basis anyway, but to be sure, send your own listing with details of any recent, significant band developments such as news of new releases, gig dates etc. Use the Media section of The Unsigned Guide to identify those publications which carry gig listings and begin to develop your own working relationships with journalists at each of the listings publications and magazines. Additionally, keep your own records of who has received what in terms of your gig/press information. By being professional and keeping journalists regularly informed, you will be more likely to see the press attend your gigs and therefore more likely to see your shows written up in the live music columns.

Building Your Audience
It is highly unlikely that any artists or bands have sealed a deal, recording or otherwise, without generating a good degree of interest from a local audience. Apart from practicing your live performance, the main reason for gigging is to widen your local audience and for unsigned acts, in principle, the theory works like this: If you bring say 20

friends to your first gig, of which 10 tell another 2 or 3 of their friends how good your show was, at the next gig you may have an extra 15 or so people turn up giving you an audience of 30 or 40. If then another 10 people tell another 2 or 3 of their friends, you may have an extra 15 or 20 turn up at the next gig and a total audience of around 60 or 70 in just 4 or 5 gigs - providing people think your music is as good as you do! The more people recognise the band's name, the more likely they are to pick up on it in the gig listings and on posters, and come and see you when the band play next. Additionally, by pre-selling tickets to your gigs, you at least have the financial commitment from people as well as them being more likely to turn up on the night than had you simply given them flyers.

Another key piece of advice is to not play live too often. In the early stages, you will be relying heavily on support from friends and family so by gigging every week, for example, it is unlikely that the same group of people will turn out religiously to see you play. Pick your gigs at the rate of say one every six weeks and use different venues to keep the 'night out' varied for your audience. By keeping audience numbers up, you will keep your promoters happy and they will be more willing to book you for further gigs and possible support slots which may arise with smaller touring bands.

In this section you will find a list of independent promoters who book some larger events and festivals. Some will have an unsigned tent or stage that you may be able to play, others may be booking regional unsigned festivals or have support slots available. Make your calls selectively and be straight to the point when giving details of the size and type of audience you normally attract. If you have secured any recent press, tell the promoter, but don't exaggerate your claims - the promoter will find out on the night how many people actually pay to see your gig and if you have misled them, word will spread and other promoters will be even less likely to deal with you - if indeed at all.

Finally, in the Web Resources section you will find details of other useful sources of 'live' information, such as routing and mapping web sites (e.g. www.multimap.com) which you can use to plan your routing if you put a small tour together.
Don't forget, if there are any other venues, promoters or unsigned events that aren't listed in the Live section, please use the Feedback forms to let us know. It is the firm belief of many, including the Musicians Union, that without a healthy grass root scene the music and record industries will stagnate and suffer in the long term. There are many MU

branches around the country and the best way to ensure a vibrant local launch pad for new bands is to get along to regular Branch meetings and use them as a way of developing strategies to persuade local venue and club owners to promote more live music with fair play and conditions.

This information has been kindly provided (in part) by Musicians' Union.

For more information, please contact:

Musicians' Union - London Office
60-62 Clapham Road
London
SW9 0JJ

email: dp1@musiciansunion.org.uk
tel: 020 7582 5566

Visit **www.musiciansunion.org.uk** for more information.

GIG * TALK * PARTY
3 Nights * 10 Venues * 150 bands

BRIGHTON
18th - 20th May 2006

www.escapegreat.com

"... events like this offer the opportunity to musicians to be exposed to the reality, good a bad, of the music industry. This kind of experience is an important part of the armour Barfly are soldiers for new music, I for one have faith that this event will be very worth while"

Zane Lowe

"Any forum providing a focal point on new talent should be applauded. The barfly gang ha a great track record so I'm looking forward to seeing what happens."

Phil Alexander
Editor-In-Chiefs, MoJo, Kerrang!, & Q

Artist applications:
F.a.o. Chris Rice,
Barfly - The Great Escape,
59-61, Farringdon Rd,
EC1M 3JB
London
Email: chris@escapegreat.com
www.myspace.com/escape__great

LIVE PERFORMANCE

4.2 VENUES

EAST of ENGLAND 569 GREATER LONDON 570 MIDLANDS 585 NORTHEAST 590 NORTHWEST 592
SOUTHEAST 602 SOUTHWEST 607 YORKSHIRE 609 NORTHERN IRELAND 612 SCOTLAND 613 WALES 616

EAST of ENGLAND

Acoustic Routes/CB2
CB2, 5 Norfolk Street, Cambridge, CB1 2LD
tel: 07971 299 659
email: bernard@acousticroutes.co.uk
web: www.acousticroutes.co.uk
contact: Bernard Hoskin
capacity: 50
info: Acoustic Routes is a venue in Cambridge run by singer-songwriter Bernard Hoskin, which presents a wide range of non-mainstream music in a small concert setting. The concerts take place in the intimate surroundings of the cellar at CB2, usually on a Saturday night, and present some of the finest local, national and international performers around. Music that has been featured includes Singer-Songwriter, Acoustic guitarists, Traditional Folk, Blues, African, Jazz and Americana. Send demos FAO Bernard, 16 Apple Tree Grove, Burwell, Cambridge, CB5 0BF.

The Bay Horse
61-65 Melford Road, Sudbury, Suffolk, CO10 1JS
tel: 01787 377 450
email: micaela.andrews@btconnect.com
web: www.bayhorsesudbury.co.uk
contact: Chris Drake
capacity: 80
info: Live music every Saturday. All music styles welcome. Bands must supply own PA. Send demos FAO Chris Drake direct to the venue.

The Brickmakers
496 Sprowston Road, Norwich, Norfolk, NR3 4DY
tel: 01603 441 118
email: charley@thebrickmakers.com
web: www.thebrickmakers.com
contact: Charley
capacity: 300
info: Bands play 5 times a week. Have weekly jam night and karaoke and quiz night. In-house PA. Technical specification can be found on website. Send demos FAO Charley to the venue, or contact her on the above number or email address.

Broadway Theatre
46 Broadway, Peterborough, PE1 1RT
tel: 01733 316 109
email: dave@thebroadwaytheatre.co.uk
web: www.thebroadwaytheatre.co.uk
contact: Dave King
capacity: 1168
info: The Broadway Theatre is available for hire. The large capacity venue has full lighting and in-house PA provided. For full booking details contact Dave King on the above number.

The Cherry Tree
9 Oundle Road, Peterborough, Cambridgeshire, PE2 9PB
tel: 01733 703 495
email: acaprio@cherrytreeinn.co.uk
web: www.cherrytreeinn.co.uk
contact: Ann Caprio
capacity: 50
info: Live music every Friday and Saturday with 2-3 bands playing each night. Rock and Pop welcome but no Indie. Bands must provide PA. Send demo direct to the venue.

Clown's Café
54 King Street, Cambridge, CB1 1LN
tel: 01223 355 711
info: Café hosting occasional live music. Songs In The Dark is an event encompassing live music, poetry and comedy held at Clown's every other week. See listing in Promoter section for details of demo submission.

Ferry Boat Inn
191 King Street, Norwich, Norfolk, NR1 2DF
tel: 01603 613 553
capacity: 120
info: Live music most nights of the week, and unsigned events organised regularly through local promoters. Need to provide own PA. Send demo to the venue address.

George & Dragon
Hall Street, Long Melford, Suffolk, CO10 9JA
tel: 01787 371 285
email: geodrg@msn.com
web: www.longmelford.com
contact: Shannon Lewis
capacity: 200
info: Live music throughout the week with bands nights held on Wednesday and Friday. All music styles welcome. Send demos FAO Shannon Lewis at the venue address. In-house PA and sound engineer available.

Ipswich Corn Exchange
King Street, Ipswich, Suffolk, IP1 1DH
tel: 01473 433 465
email: hannah.stephenson@ipswich.gov.uk
web: www.ipswichcornexchange.com
contact: Hannah Stephenson
capacity: 800-1000 (Main Room), 200 (Second Room)
info: Rooms available for hire. In-house PA. Contact Hannah for full booking details.

The Junction
Clifton Road, Cambridge, CB1 7GX
tel: 01223 578 000
fax: 01223 565 600
email: bookings@junction.co.uk
web: www.junction.co.uk
contact: Rob Sinclair
capacity: 850 (Main Room), 250 (Second Room)
info: Unsigned night once a month, featuring 5 bands, mainly local acts. In-house PA. Full technical specification can be found on website. Send demos FAO Richard Brown at the venue. The venue hosts more unsigned events in the smaller 250 capacity room.

Man On The Moon
2 Norfolk Street, Cambridge, CB1 2LF
tel: 01223 474 144
email: moon.music@ntlworld.com
web: www.manonthemoon.freeserve.co.uk
contact: Steve
info: Band room at back of venue with in-house PA and lighting rig. Regular unsigned nights. Contact Steve to email MP3, or alternatively send demo to the above address.

LIVE PERFORMANCE

Milestone Beer House
5 Woodbridge End, Ipswich, IP4 2EA
tel: 01473 252 425
web: www.milestonebeerhouse.co.uk
contact: Tim
capacity: 150
info: 'Suffolk Songwriters Night' is an Acoustic talent showcase held twice a month. The first Thursday of the month is an open night, where songwriters can turn up to take part on a first come first served basis. The third Thursday of the month is a showcase of the best performers from the event. See website www.suffolksongwriters.co.uk for further details. Bands play every Friday and Saturday night, mainly Rock and Blues music. Need to provide own PA. Stage lighting available for use. Send demo and gig list FAO Tim at the venue, and he will try to attend a local gig. Bands without demos can ring and arrange a gig for the second and fourth Thursdays of the month.

Norwich Arts Centre
Norwich Arts Centre, St. Bennedicts, Norfolk, NR2 4PG
tel: 01603 660 387
fax: 01603 664 806
email: ian@norwichartscentre.co.uk
web: www.norwichartscentre.co.uk
contact: Ian Carrell
capacity: 250
info: Send demos to the venue FAO Ian. Venue is also available for hire. In-house PA. Full technical specification can be found on website. Monthly band night, 'WombatWombat' is held at Norwich Arts Centre. See entry in Promoters section for details of demo submission.

Portland Arms
129 Chesterton Road, Cambridge, CB4 3BA
tel: 01223 357 268
web: www.theportland.co.uk
capacity: 100
info: Live music 6 nights a week. Send demos of original music only to the venue, mark FAO 'Promotions'.

Prior's Inn
1 Priors Avenue, Bury St. Edmunds, IP33 3LT
tel: 01284 748 941
contact: JT
capacity: 200
info: Venue have live music from unsigned bands. For more info on getting a gig here, contact JT on the above number.

Reeds Club
27-28 Tombland, Norwich, NR3 1RE
tel: 01603 218 362
email: ashley.moon@targetfollow.com
web: www.reeds-club.co.uk
contact: Ashley Moon
capacity: 140
info: Reeds Club specialises in Jazz and Soul and runs a number of nights throughout the week. For full details of current programmes visit their website. Send demos FAO Ashley Moon to the venue. In-house PA.

St. Andrew's Hall
St. Andrew's Plain, Norwich, NR3 1AU
tel: 01603 628 477
email: richardsapiano@norwich.gov.uk
web: www.norwich.gov.uk
contact: Richard Sapiano
capacity: 900
info: Large capacity venue which is available for hire. For full details regarding demo submission contact Richard Sapiano directly at the venue.

Steamboat Tavern
78 New Cut West, Ipswich, Suffolk, IP2 8HW
tel: 01473 601 902
contact: Val Bint
capacity: 130 (Indoors), 280 (with use of outdoors area)
info: Bands play 2 or 3 times per week. Mainly Indie and Alternative original music. Need to provide own PA. Send demos FAO Val to the venue.

The Waterfront
139-141 King Street, Norwich, Norfolk, NR1 1QH
tel: 01603 632 717
fax: 01603 615 463
email: p.ingleby@uea.ac.uk
web: www.ueaticketbookings.co.uk
contact: Paul Ingleby
capacity: 700
info: Live music throughout the week with local band nights. 3-4 bands play each night. Send demos FAO Paul Ingleby at the venue address. In-house PA.

GREATER LONDON

100 Club
100 Oxford Street, London, W1D 1LL
⊖ Tottenham Court Road/Oxford Circus
tel: 020 7636 0933
email: info@the100club.co.uk
web: www.the100club.co.uk
contact: Jeff Horton
capacity: 300
info: Full technical specification can be found on website. Gigs are usually booked by outside promoters.

12 Bar
22-23 Denmark Place, off Denmark Street, London, WC2H 8NL
⊖ Tottenham Court Road
tel: 020 7240 2120
email: 12barclub@btconnect.com
web: www.12barclub.com
contact: Andy Lowe
capacity: 120
info: Live music 7 nights a week, up to 4 acts per night with focus on local acts. Send demo and biog plus any press releases to the venue FAO Andy Lowe. Audio recording of band performances available.

291 Arts Centre
291 Hackney Road, London, E2 8NA
⊖ Bethnal Green
tel: 020 7613 5676
info: Venue available to external promoters.

333 Club
333 Old Street, London, EC1V 9LE
⊖ Old Street
tel: 020 7739 1800
fax: 020 7613 0469
email: promotions@333mother.com
web: www.333mother.com
contact: Sarah
capacity: 200 (Basement)
info: 333 Club has hosted nights in the past at which The Libertines and The Zutons have played. Please contact the venue before sending a demo. The venue can potentially have live music every night and has weekly Wednesday band nights with in-house PA and lighting.

606 Club
90 Lots Road, London, SW10 0QD
⊖ Fulham Broadway
tel: 020 7352 5953
fax: 020 7349 0655
email: jazz@606club.co.uk
web: www.606club.co.uk
contact: Tammy
capacity: 120 seated
info: Late night candle-lit basement club/restaurant, reminiscent of the Jazz clubs and bars of Paris and New York. Jazz, Blues and Soul acts that wish to play should send demo to Tammy at the venue.

93 Feet East
150 Brick Lane, London, E1 6QN
⊖ Aldgate East/Liverpool Street
tel: 020 7247 3293
fax: 020 7247 5980
email: sean@93feeteast.co.uk
web: www.93feeteast.co.uk
contact: Sean Hitchins
capacity: 240 (Main Hall)
info: Venue consists of 4 rooms: the Pink Bar, the Members Bar, the Gallery Bar and the Main Hall (which is used for gigs). All available for hire, in pretty much any combination. Monday nights host mainly new bands, free to get in. Stage can hold up to 14 people. Large dressing rooms. All sound crew supplied by venue. Tuesday through to Thursday feature more innovative acts from Indie, Rock, Leftfield, Classical and Contemporary styles. Artist to have played 93 Feet East include The White Stripes, Clinic, Scratch Perverts, Coldcut, Peaches, Blak Twang and Roots Manuva. Send demo FAO Sean at the venue.

The Ace Café
Ace Corner, North Circular Road, Stonebridge, London, NW10 7UD
⊖ Stonebridge Park
tel: 020 8961 1000
fax: 020 8965 0161
email: acecafe2@aol.com
web: www.ace-café-london.com
contact: Kitty
capacity: 360
info: The Ace Café regularly puts on live music of all genres. See website for more details. Venue has in-house PA. To get a gig contact Kitty via email, or send a demo to the venue.

"The place to glimpse the stars of the future"
Time Out Magazine

"One of the top venues for emerging new rock,
indie and alternative talent"
Steve Lamacq - BBC Radio 1 & 6 Music

Over the past years the Barfly team have booked
and promoted some complete unknowns:

COLDPLAY, MUSE, OASIS, THE STROKES,
TRAVIS, ASH, BADLY DRAWN BOY,
STEREOPHONICS, THE VINES,
THE DARKNESS, FRANZ FERDINAND,
THE KILLERS, THE BRAVERY,
JULIETTE & THE LICKS, THE LIBERTINES,
RAZORLIGHT, KAISER CHIEFS,
BLOC PARTY, ARCTIC MONKEYS, EDITORS -

and put them on stage.

The Place to View
The Next Big Thing

The Barfly Group incorporates the following 6 live music venues:

barfly	barfly	(York logo)	barfly	barfly	barfly
GLASGOW	LIVERPOOL	YORK	CARDIFF	LONDON	BIRMINGHAM

WWW.BARFLYCLUB.COM

bull and gate

389 kentish town rd kentish town nw5

london's legendary live music venue

coldplay - muse - keane - the darkness
british sea power - the cooper temple clause
ash - the country teasers - blur - the libertines

p j harvey - razorlight - suede - pulp
the manic street preachers - oceansize

for bookings and information
contact andy or phil 020 7093 4820
e-mail info@bullandgate.co.uk
web site www.bullandgate.co.uk

demos to
bull and gate promotions
building a
trinity buoy wharf
64 orchard place
e14 0jw

The Acoustic Lounge
100 Clapham Park Road, Clapham Common, London, SW4 7BZ
⊖ Tooting Broadway
tel: 020 7720 8902
email: info@acousticlounge.co.uk
web: www.acousticlounge.co.uk
contact: Craig Mitchell
capacity: 80
info: The Acoustic Lounge puts on bands and singer songwriters of any genre, as long as the music is ground breaking and innovative. Chilled out atmosphere. Regular haunt for A&R in London. Open mic night every Monday. The Acoustic Lounge has a live music event held every Tuesday. Also run all day summer sessions every other Sunday from May to September. Excellent 1k in-house PA. Internationally acclaimed artists to have played at Acoustic Lounge include Tom Baxter (Sony), Guy Chambers (Songwriter for Robbie Williams) and Amrit Sond (Grammy award winner). External PA hire and music tuition services available. Enquire for further details.

Ain't Nothin' But Blues Bar
20 Kingly Street, Soho, London, W1B 5PZ
⊖ Oxford Circus
tel: 020 7287 0514
web: www.aintnothinbut.co.uk
capacity: 100
info: Ain't Nothin But is a Blues, R&B and Rock'n'Roll venue. Live music every night with a jam night on Mondays. Saturday features an open mic event from 3pm until 7pm weekly. In-house PA. Acts are generally booked 2-3 months in advance. Send demo to the venue. Will generally try to attend a gig in London before booking.

Albany
Douglas Way, Deptford, London, SE8 4AG
⊖ New Cross
tel: 020 8692 0231
fax: 020 8469 2253
email: reception@thealbany.org.uk
web: www.thealbany.org.uk
contact: Bridget Abengowe
capacity: 400-600
info: Live music throughout the week, mainly Thursday to Sunday. Check website for full details. Live music nights often incorporated into a club night.

The Amersham Arms
388 New Cross Road, New Cross, London, SE14 6TY
⊖ New Cross
tel: 020 8692 2047
contact: Titch Turner
capacity: 280
info: Every Friday and Saturday play host to the 'Catapult Club', a multimedia event with 2 stages featuring unsigned acts. Tuesday is Roots Night, and Thursday nights are dedicated to Jazz. 10kW in-house PA. Unsigned band nights are Wednesday, Friday and Saturdays featuring 3-4 bands per event. Once booked your band is given plenty of promotional help and can also access percentage of door takings should you draw a big audience. To play at any of these nights, refer to entry for 'Catapult Club' in Promoters section for details of demo submission. Amersham Arms also plays host to 'The Glue Rooms' on a monthly basis. See entry in Promoters section for information.

Archway Tavern
The Live Room, Archway Roundabout, Archway, London, N19 3TD
⊖ Archway
tel: 020 7272 2840
contact: Irene
capacity: 250
info: Live music 7 nights a week with 4 or 5 bands. In-house PA and sound engineers. 'Subculture' is a unsigned band night every Monday to Thursday are nights hosted by external promoters. The rest of the week live music is organised by the venue. Send demo and biog FAO Irene at the venue, she is very keen to receive more material.

Asylum
1A Percy Street, Soho, London, W1T 1DB
⊖ Tottenham Court Road
tel: 020 7636 8228
contact: Mark
capacity: 100
info: Bands or promoters can hire venue. Contact Mark for full booking details.

Bar Colour
22 Inverness Street, Camden, London, NW1 7HJ
⊖ Camden Town
tel: 020 7428 9771
email: adrianhunter@hotmail.com
contact: Adrian Hunter
capacity: 150
info: Bar Colour has the potential for live music every night of all genres. 3-4 bands play each night. If you are interested in a gig, please email Adrian, or send demo FAO Adrian at the venue.

Bar Latino/The Suite
48 Park Street, Croydon, London, CR0 1YF
⊖ South Croydon (Rail)
tel: 020 8688 0934
email: wonderwbb@homechoice.co.uk
web: www.barlatino.com
contact: Ellie
capacity: 150
info: The Suite has a weekly Rock Night every Thursday with 4 bands playing. In-house PA. The night is organised by Fairy Tale Promotions, see listings.

Barfly London @ The Monarch
49 Chalk Farm Road, London, NW1 8AN
⊖ Chalk Farm
tel: 020 7691 4244
fax: 020 7961 4245
email: info@barflyclub.com
web: www.barflyclub.com
capacity: 200
info: Send demos on CD or cassette (maximum 3 tracks) to Barfly Bookings, 59-61 Faraden Road, London, EC1M 3JB. Please allow 5 weeks for a response, then if you want to call for a reaction to your demo, you should phone on Tuesdays or Thursdays between midday and 6pm.

The Battersea Barge
Nine Elms Lane, Tideway Walk, London, SW8 5BP
⊖ Battersea Park (Rail)
tel: 020 7498 0004
email: peterlw@aol.com
web: www.batterseabarge.com
contact: Peter Lewis
capacity: 70
info: Live music 3 or 4 nights of the week. Music includes Jazz, Cabaret, Singer-Songwriter. In-house PA, stage and lights. To play, telephone Peter on the above number.

The Bedford
77 Bedford Hill, London, SW12 9HD
⊖ Balham
tel: 020 8682 8940
fax: 020 8682 8959
email: info@thebedford.co.uk
web: www.thebedford.co.uk
contact: Tony
capacity: 150-200
info: The Bedford hosts a Jam session every Monday in The Tavistock. Just turn up to take part. A mixture of signed and unsigned bands feature every Monday, Tuesday and Thursday in the Globe. Promotion for the bands is covered in an extensive newsletter, and listings can also be checked via the website. Please send demos FAO 'Booking' at the venue.

The Bell Inn
617 Forest Road, Walthamstow, London, E17 4NE
⊖ Wood Street (Rail)
tel: 020 8531 2779
email: darvies@yahoo.com
web: www.walcotstreet.com
contact: Yvonne, Sonny
capacity: 250
info: Blues and Rock on Saturday nights. Live music twice weekly. In-house PA. Send demos FAO Yvonne or Sonny at the venue.

The Betsey Trotwood
56 Farringdon Road, London, EC1R 3BL
⊖ Farringdon
tel: 020 7253 4285
email: plum.general@virgin.net
web: www.plummusic.com
contact: Allan North
capacity: 60
info: The Betsey Trotwood is one of the smallest venues in London. Live music 6 nights a week, usually with 3 acts playing. Send demos FAO Sarah at Mathew at Plum Promotions, 56b Farringdon Road, London, EC1R 3BL. The Betsey Trotwood also hosts demo workshops, check website for further information. Demo to gig turnaround is between 4 and 8 weeks. Plum Promotions will help support bands with flyers and posters, and a percentage split of door takings can be arranged in most circumstances.

Black Sheep Bar
68 High Street, Croydon, Surrey, CR0 1NA
East Croydon (Rail)

tel:	020 8680 2233
email:	steph@blacksheepbar.com
web:	www.blacksheepbar.com
contact:	Stephanie Darkes
capacity:	240
info:	Unsigned bands play every Wednesday, with 3 acts

playing per night. Send demo FAO Steph to the venue. 'Expose Yourself' open mic event is held first Sunday of every month, just turn up to take part. In-house PA. The website includes an online form, which acts interested in playing at Black Sheep Bar can complete. There is also a reviews section of the bands which have played the venue.

Blag Club
68 Notting Hill Gate, London, W11 3HT
Notting Hill Gate

tel:	020 7243 0123
email:	blag@blagclub.com
web:	www.blagclub.com
contact:	Kam
capacity:	100
info:	Acoustic duos play every Sunday night. Up to 5

acts play each time. Venue has in-house PA. To get a gig send demo addressed to Kam at the venue, or call for more information.

The Blue Belly @ The Purple Turtle
61-65 Crowndale Road, Camden Town, London, NW1 1TN
Mornington Crescent

tel:	020 7383 4976
email:	camden@purpleturtlebar.com
web:	www.purpleturtlebar.com
contact:	Helen
capacity:	400
info:	Open mic and band night every Monday and

Tuesday. Open mic sessions (maximum of 2 songs per person) between band sets. Original material only. For details of where to send demos, contact Helen.

The Boom Boom Club
Sutton United Football Club, Gander Green Lane, Borough Sports Ground, Sutton, Surrey, SM1 2EY
West Sutton (Rail)

tel:	01784 460 094
web:	www.boomboomlive.co.uk
contact:	Pete Feenstra
capacity:	300
info:	Bands put on by Pete Feenstra and George McFall.

See entry in Promoters section for details of demo submission.

The Borderline
16 Manette Street, London, W1D 4JB
Tottenham Court Road

tel:	020 7434 4592
fax:	020 7395 0766
email:	barry.borderline@virgin.net
web:	www.borderline.co.uk
contact:	Barry Everitt
capacity:	275
info:	Live music every night. An unsigned showcase takes

place every Sunday featuring around 4 acts. This event attracts a lot of A&R interest. Borderline can assist with publicity by providing unlimited flyers for bands to distribute. Send demos FAO Alexes Rogers at the venue. Acts that are well received at the unsigned night may have the opportunity of a support slot for larger bands playing the venue during the week. In-house PA, backline to be supplied by band.

The Boston Arms
178 Junction Road, Tufnell Park, London, N19 5QQ
Tufnell Park

tel:	020 7272 8153
email:	info@dirtywaterclub.com
web:	www.dirtywaterclub.com
contact:	PJ
capacity:	400
info:	'Dirty Water Club' is held every Friday night, with

3 bands playing. See entry in Promoters section for details of demo submission. In-house PA. Also room available for hire, call PJ for details.

Brave New World
21-26 Berrylands Road, Surbiton, Surrey, KT5 8QX

tel:	020 8399 0200
contact:	Jeff Gibson
info:	Brave New World host a live music night every

Thursday featuring all genres of music. There is also an open mic night every Sunday where you can just turn up to play. If an artist wants a gig on a Thursday, it is advised to play at the open mic night first. Contact Jeff for more information.

BRB The Arc
1 Torrens Street, Islington, London, EC1V 1NQ
Angel

tel:	020 7837 9421
email:	brb.arc@thespiritgroup.com
web:	www.barroombar.com
contact:	Patrick
info:	Live music is organised by the venue, although there

is no set schedule. Contact Sam regarding any possible dates. Band must supply PA.

The Bridge House Tavern
2 High Street, Penge, London, SE20 8RZ
Penge West (Rail)

tel:	020 8659 6928
contact:	Carol Hawks
capacity:	150
info:	Live music on weekends. Need to provide own PA.

Send demos FAO Carol at the venue.

Brixton Jamm
261 Brixton Road, London, SW9 5PR
Brixton

tel:	07740 175 585
email:	mike@brixtonjamm.com
web:	www.brixtonjamm.com
contact:	Mike Weller
info:	Unsigned nights held at least twice a week. Up to

4 bands play each night. Send demos marked 'Demos' to the above address.

The Buffalo Bar
259 Upper Street, Islington, London, N1 1RU
Highbury & Islington

tel:	020 7359 6191
email:	info@buffalobar.co.uk
web:	www.buffalobar.co.uk
capacity:	150
info:	All live music organised through external promoters.

Band night every Wednesday organised by Goo Music, with 3 or 4 bands playing Alternative, Indie, Punk, Garage Rock. Other unsigned events arranged by Dead Or Alive and ArtRocker. See entries in Promoters section for details of demo submission. In-house PA. Alternatively, check the website for details of nights.

The Bull
292-294 St. John's Street, Angel, London, EC1V 4PA
Angel

tel:	020 7278 8405
web:	www.badh-thebull.com
contact:	Rob or Dinah
capacity:	300
info:	There are no set nights for live music but The Bull

will accept all genres. For details of possible dates contact Rob or Dinah. In-house PA. Bar snacks are also available.

Bull & Gate
389 Kentish Town Road, London, NW5 2TJ
Kentish Town

tel:	020 7093 4820
fax:	020 7093 4821
email:	info@bullandgate.co.uk
web:	www.bullandgate.co.uk
contact:	Andy Clarke, Phil Avey
capacity:	150
info:	Live original music 7 nights a week. In-house PA.

Send demos to Andy or Phil at Bull & Gate Promotions, Building A, Trinity Bouy Wharf, 64 Orchard Place, London, E14 OJW.

The Cabbage Patch
67 London Road, Twickenham, Middlesex, TW1 3SZ
Twickenham (Rail)

tel:	020 8892 3874
email:	info@cabbagepatch.co.uk
web:	www.cabbagepatch.co.uk
contact:	Stuart Green
capacity:	250
info:	Live music 2 nights a week, Sundays are Folk nights,

Wednesdays are dedicated to R&B. There is an unsigned night the first Tuesday of every month called 'Patch Works' with 3-4 bands playing. In-house PA. To get a gig send a demo to the venue FAO Stuart.

Caernarvon Castle
7-8 Chalk Farm Road, Camden, London, NW1 8AA
Camden Town

tel:	020 7284 0219
web:	www.clubfabulous.co.uk
contact:	Max
info:	'Electric Nights' organised by Club Fabulous held

every Thursday night. Mainly Indie, Rock and Dance music. Pogo Music also put on 'Acoustic Trip' and 'The Beat Route' every week. Refer to entries in Promoters section for further details.

Academy Music Group Ltd
www.academy-music-group.co.uk
T. 020 7787 3131
F. 020 7787 3136
E. enquiries@academy-music-group.co.uk

Carling Academy Brixton

Address:	211 Stockwell Road, London, SW9 9SL
Tel:	020 7771 3000
Fax:	020 7738 4427
Web:	www.brixton-academy.co.uk
Contact:	mail@brixton-academy.co.uk
Capacity:	4,921
Box Office:	Open for personal callers on show days only 5pm - 9.30pm.

This box office also sells tickets for events at Carling Academy Islington & Shepherds Bush Empire

NME: 10 times winner Best Live Venue including 2005
TIME OUT: Live Venue of the Year 2004
TOTAL PRODUCTION INTERNATIONAL: Favourite Venue 2004
TRANSPORT FOR LONDON: Vote London Cool Clubs & Music Winner 2003

SHEPHERDS BUSH EMPIRE

Address:	Shepherds Bush Green, London, W12 8TT
Tel:	020 8354 3000
Fax:	020 8743 3218
Web:	www.shepherds-bush-empire.co.uk
Contact:	mail@shepherds-bush-empire.co.uk
Capacity:	2,000 (max)
Box Office:	Open for personal callers on show days only: 4pm - 6pm; 6.30pm - 9.30pm.

This box office also sells tickets for events at Carling Academy Brixton & Carling Academy Islington.

MUSIC WEEK AWARDS: Best Venue 2005

All tickets can be purchased 24 hours 7 days at
www.ticketweb.co.uk / 0870 771 2000.
Ticketweb is an internet based system that offers venues & promoters the option to sell ticket allocations as well as a ticket distribution service. For further information, please contact venue management.

academyevents

Carling Academy Islington

Address:	N1 Centre, 16 Parkfield Street, London, N1 0PS
Tel:	020 7288 4400
Fax:	020 7288 4401
Web:	www.islington-academy.co.uk
Contact:	mail@islington-academy.co.uk
Capacity:	250
Box Office:	Open for personal callers Monday - Saturday 12pm - 4pm.

This box office also sells tickets for events at Carling Academy Brixton & Shepherds Bush Empire.

BAR@ACADEMY

Address:	N1 Centre, 16 Parkfield Street, London, N1 0PS
Tel:	020 7288 4400
Fax:	020 7288 4401
Web:	www.islington-academy.co.uk
Contact:	mail@islington-academy.co.uk
Capacity:	800
Box Office:	Open for personal callers Monday - Saturday 12pm - 4pm.

This box office also sells tickets for events at Carling Academy Brixton & Shepherds Bush Empire.

Carling Academy Glasgow

Address:	121 Eglinton Street, Glasgow, G5 9NT
Tel:	0141 418 3000
Fax:	0141 418 3001
Web:	www.glasgow-academy.co.uk
Contact:	mail@glasgow-academy.co.uk
Capacity:	2,500 (max)
Box Office:	Open for personal callers Monday - Saturday 12pm - 2pm

Academy Events is the promoting division of Academy Music Group (AMG), owners and operators of Carling Academy venues across the country and promotes gigs of all sizes and genres, established acts, as well as unsigned bands to support the rising talent of the future.

The range of different sized AMG venues allows Academy Events to promote artists throughout varying stages of their careers, with many acts starting off at AMG's Bar Academy venues, the perfect stage for fresh, up and coming talent in an intimate setting. Just to prove it, The Libertines started out with an Academy Events show at Bar Academy in Birmingham well before they hit the big time as well as the likes of Scissor Sisters, Keane, Kasabian and many more, all of whom have gone on to enormous success, selling out AMG's largest and flagship venue, Carling Academy Brixton.

Academy Events online – www.academy-events.co.uk – is not only the destination for information and listings of what Academy Events shows are taking place and where, but also the place for budding artists and new and unsigned acts to find out how to get a gig at an Academy venue, where to send a demo, through to supplying information to music fans on how to work for our street teams.

Send your demo pack to:
Academy Events c/o Carling Academy Islington, N1 Centre, 16 Parkfield Street, London, N1 0PS

CARLING ACADEMY

Carling Academy Liverpool

Address: 11-13 Hotham Street, Liverpool, L3 5UF
Tel: 0151 707 3200
Fax: 0151 707 3201
Web: www.liverpool-academy.co.uk
Contact: mail@liverpool-academy.co.uk
Capacity: 1,200 (max)
Box Office: Open for personal callers
Monday - Saturday 12pm - 4pm

Carling Academy 2 Liverpool

Address: 11-13 Hotham Street, Liverpool, L3 5UF
Tel: 0151 707 3200
Fax: 0151 707 3201
Web: www.liverpool-academy.co.uk
Contact: mail@liverpool-academy.co.uk
Capacity: 250 / 500
Box Office: Open for personal callers
Monday - Saturday 12pm - 4pm

Carling Academy Bristol

Address: Frogmore Street, Bristol, NS1 5NA
Tel: 0117 927 9227
Fax: 0117 927 9295
Web: www.bristol-academy.co.uk
Contact: mail@bristol-academy.co.uk
Capacity: 1,600 (Gigs) / 1,900 (Clubs)
Box Office: Open for personal callers
Mon - Sat 12pm - 4pm

Carling Academy Newcastle

Address: Westgate Road, Newcastle-upon-Tyne, NE1 1SW
Tel: 0191 260 2020
Fax: 0191 260 4650
Web: www.newcastle-academy.co.uk
Contact: mail@newcastle-academy.co.uk
Capacity: 2,000
Box Office: Open for personal callers
Mon - Fri 12pm - 4pm

Carling Academy 2 Newcastle

Address: Westgate Road, Newcastle-upon-Tyne, NE1 1SW
Tel: 0191 260 2020
Fax: 0191 260 4650
Web: www.newcastle-academy.co.uk
Contact: mail@newcastle-academy.co.uk
Capacity: 400
Box Office: Open for personal callers
Mon - Fri 12pm - 4pm

Carling Academy Birmingham

Address: 52-54 Dale End, Birmingham, B4 7LS
Tel: 0121 262 3000
Fax: 0121 236 2241
Web: www.birmingham-academy.co.uk
Contact: mail@birmingham-academy.co.uk
Capacity: 1,250 – 2,700
Box Office: Open for personal callers
Mon - Fri 11am - 5pm & Sat 11am - 3.30pm

Carling Academy 2 Birmingham

Address: 52-54 Dale End, Birmingham, B4 7LS
Tel: 0121 262 3000
Fax: 0121 236 2241
Web: www.birmingham-academy.co.uk
Contact: mail@birmingham-academy.co.uk
Capacity: 400 / 600
Box Office: Open for personal callers
Mon - Fri 11am - 5pm & Sat 11am - 3.30pm

BAR ACADEMY

Address: 51 Dale End, Birmingham, B4 7LS
Tel: 0121 262 3000
Fax: 0121 236 2241
Web: www.birmingham-academy.co.uk
Contact: mail@birmingham-academy.co.uk
Capacity: 200
Box Office: Open for personal callers
Mon - Fri 11am - 5pm & Sat 11am - 3.30pm

LIVE PERFORMANCE

Café Boheme
13-17 Old Compton Road, London, W1D 5JQ
⊖ Tottenham Court Road/Oxford Circus
tel: 020 7734 0623
fax: 020 7434 3775
email: info@cafeboheme.co.uk
web: www.cafeboheme.co.uk
contact: Jose Gonzalez
capacity: 125
info: Bar and restaurant with live music on Thursdays and Sundays. Mainly Jazz and laid-back music. In-house PA. Send demo FAO Jose Gonzalez to the venue.

Café De Paris
3-4 Coventry Street, London, W1V 7FL
⊖ Piccadilly Circus
tel: 0207 734 7700
web: www.cafedeparis.com
contact: Stefane
capacity: 600
info: Café De Paris do organise live music but on no set basis. For enquiries about getting a gig contact Stefane at the venue.

Camden Centre
Euston Road, London, WC1H 9JE
⊖ Kings Cross
tel: 020 7974 5633
fax: 020 7974 6433
email: camdencentre@camden.gov.uk
web: www.camden.gov.uk/camdencentre
contact: Nicky Ezer, Kim Lau
capacity: 850
info: Venue available for hire. Helpful management team who can offer marketing strategies. In-house PA, lights and large stage. Postal address for demos is c/o Camden Centre, Town Hall, Judd Street, London, WC1H 9JE.

Cargo
Kingsland Viaduct, 83 Rivington Street, Shoreditch, London, EC2A 3AY
⊖ Old Street/Liverpool Street
tel: 020 7613 7743
fax: 020 7739 3441
email: ben.r@cargo-london.com
web: www.cargo-london.com
contact: Joe Roberts
capacity: 500
info: Unsigned night, 'Demo City' held every other Tuesday featuring 3 bands. Send demos direct to the venue FAO Keith. In-house PA and engineer available.

Carling Academy 2 Islington
16 Parkfield Street, Islington, London, N1 0PS
⊖ Angel
tel: 020 7288 4400
web: www.islington-academy.co.uk
contact: Jon Wing
capacity: 250
info: In order to get a gig or support slot contact Jon at the venue or send a demo for his attention marking the pack 'Academy Events'. Venue has in-house lighting and PA.

The Cartoon
179-183 London Road, Croydon, Surrey, CR0 2RJ
⊖ East Croydon (Rail)
tel: 020 8239 1616
email: mat@thecartoon.co.uk
web: www.thecartoon.co.uk
contact: Mat
capacity: 220
info: Live music most nights of the week. Bands must be 18 +, although do host some under 18 nights. Check website or enquire when these are held. 12kW PA with engineer. Full technical specification can be found on website. Send demos FAO Mat to the above address. Also put on Acoustic nights. To play contact Ray on 07951 834 230 or email acoustic.ray@hotmail.com.

Catch 22
22 Kingsland Road, London, E2 8DA
⊖ Old Street/Liverpool Street
tel: 020 7729 6097
email: bookings@thecatchbar.com
contact: Dianne
capacity: 150
info: Contact venue for full details on hire. In-house PA.

Cha Cha Cha Café
3 Cassiobury Park, Watford, London, WD18 7HY
⊖ Watford (Metropolitan Line)
tel: 07957 214 938
contact: Barney
capacity: 100
info: Cha Cha Cha is an intimate café bar that hold an Acoustic night every Thursday. 2 acts play each week. For details on demo submission contact Barney.

The Clapham Grand
21-25 St. John's Hill, Clapham Junction, London, SW11 1TT
⊖ Clapham Junction (Rail)
tel: 020 7223 6523
email: ian@claphamgrand.com
web: www.claphamgrand.com
contact: Ian Thatcher
capacity: 1000 (split over 2 levels)
info: Unsigned nights are held every night of the week, 4 bands play each night. In-house PA. All genres of music accepted. Contact Ian Thatcher for more information.

The Comedy
7 Oxenden Street, Piccadilly, London, SW1Y 4EE
⊖ Piccadilly Circus
info: In-house PA, stage and lights. Unsigned gigs organised regularly by Dead Or Alive Promotions. See listing in Promoters section for details.

Dirty South
162 Lee High Road, Lewisham, London, SE13 5PR
⊖ Lewisham (Rail)
tel: 020 8852 1267
contact: Michael Weller
info: Dirty South puts on signed and unsigned acts. Criminal Records host a once monthly night. Every Saturday is 'Dirty Bingo' featuring live bands and DJs. Fridays also play host to live bands and DJs. Only venue in Lewisham with a 5kW rig. All types of music considered, but mainly Indie Rock.

Dover Street Wine Bar
8-10 Dover Street, Mayfair, London, W1S 4LQ
⊖ Green Park
tel: 020 7491 7509
fax: 020 7491 2958
email: bookings@doverstreet.co.uk
web: www.doverst.co.uk
contact: Larry Price
capacity: 340 seated
info: Dover Street is a bar and restaurant which has different styles of live music every night. Monday is Jazz night. Acts must be at least 7 piece. Send demo, biog and photo FAO Larry at the venue. Larry will need to see an act perform live before booking.

Drayton Court Hotel
2 The Avenue, West Ealing, London, W13 8PH
⊖ West Ealing (Rail)
tel: 020 8997 1019
web: www.citypublife.co.uk
contact: Theo
capacity: 100 downstairs
info: Live music occasionally, about once per month. Mainly Easy Listening, Contemporary or Jazz music. In-house PA. Demos to be sent FAO Theo at the venue. Also enclose a covering letter detailing your act and previous gig and event listings.

Dublin Castle
94 Parkway, Camden Town, London, NW1 7AN
⊖ Camden Town
tel: 020 7485 1773
fax: 020 7485 1773
email: info@bugbear18.freeserve.co.uk
web: www.bugbearbookings.com
contact: Tony Gleed, Jim Mattison
capacity: 120
info: Live music every night. Demos can be sent to the venue but will be dealt with more efficiently if sent direct to Bugbear Bookings. See listing in relevant section for demo submission details.

The Elbow Room
89-91 Chapel Market, Islington, London, N1 9EX
⊖ Angel
tel: 020 7278 3244
fax: 020 7278 3266
email: islington@elbowroom.co.uk
web: www.theelbowroom.co.uk
contact: Andy Peyton
capacity: 600
info: Band nights featuring newly signed and unsigned Funk and Rock acts. Ring Andy at the venue for more information.

The Electric Ballroom
184 Camden High Street, Camden Town, London, NW1 8QP
⊖ Camden Town
tel: 020 7485 9006
fax: 020 7284 0745
email: info@electricballroom.co.uk
web: www.electricballroom.co.uk
contact: Mags, Brian
capacity: 1200
info: Venue available to promoters for hire Monday through to Thursday.

The Fiddler's Elbow
1 Morden Road, Kentish Town, London, NW5 3HS
⊖ Chalk Farm
tel: 020 7485 3269
email: kathrynatthefiddlerselbow@yahoo.co.uk
contact: Kathryn
capacity: 100-125
info: Put on 'Camden Jam' every Wednesday featuring unsigned bands. To get a gig send demos FAO Kathryn to the venue. In-house PA.

The Fighting Cocks
56 London Road, Kingston Upon Thames, Surrey, KT2 6QA
⊖ Richmond
tel: 020 8546 5174
email: jimbo66@blueyonder.co.uk
web: www.the-fighting-cocks.co.uk
contact: Jamie
info: Live music 3 to 7 nights a week, no definite schedule. All Alternative music styles welcome. In-house PA. Send demo FAO Jamie to the venue.

The Fountain
125 West Green Road, Seven Sisters, London, N15 5DE
⊖ Seven Sisters
tel: 020 8802 0433
email: alerollm@hotmail.com
contact: Luba
capacity: 200
info: Live music every Thursday and Saturday. Send demo direct to the venue FAO Luba. In-house PA.

The Fox & Firkin
316 Lewisham High Street, London, SE13 6JZ
⊖ Lewisham (Rail)
tel: 020 8690 8925
info: Unsigned gigs organised by 2bob, including occasional all day events. See listing in Promoter section for further details.

The Fridge
Town Hall Parade, Brixton Hill, London, SW2 1RJ
⊖ Brixton
tel: 020 7326 5100
email: info@fridgelondon.com
web: www.fridgelondon.com
contact: Management, Jim Mattison
capacity: 1500
info: Very occasional live music. Mainly have club nights. Call the venue manager for more information on playing at the venue.

The Globe
Morning Lane, Hackney, London, E9 6NA
⊖ Hackney Central (Rail)
tel: 020 8985 6455
fax: 020 8985 7211
email: globepube9@aol.com
contact: Steve Powell
capacity: 100
info: Monday night is Blues jam, just turn up to take part. Sunday afternoons are dedicated to Jazz. Need to provide own PA. Send demo FAO Steve to the venue.

The Grey Horse
46 Richmond Road, Kingston, London, KT2 5EE
⊖ Kingston (Rail)
tel: 020 8541 4328/07944 839 768
email: kt2promotions@blueyonder.co.uk
web: www.grey-horse.co.uk
contact: Katy Fletcher
capacity: 250
info: Live music every night, free all day Sunday. Full in-house PA. Monday is original acts night, Tuesday night is Blues and R&B jam, just bring an instrument along and join in! Wednesday is Acoustic night featuring up to 6 acts. Thursday is original bands night featuring up to 3 bands. Fridays and Saturdays, best of local, national and international acts, including tribute and cover bands. Contact Katy on the above mobile number. Demos can be sent FAO Richard at the venue. There is also a separate venue adjoining the Grey Horse called The Ramjam which serves Southern American soul food as well as live Jazz and Blues bands 5 nights a week. Forward demos to Richard.

The Grove Tavern
2 Morden Road, South Wimbledon, London, SW19 3BH
⊖ South Wimbledon
tel: 020 8543 2023
contact: Lee or Libby Harwood
capacity: 225
info: Live music every Thursday, Friday and Saturday. Every other Wednesday is a jam night where you can just turn up to take part. Need to provide own PA, although hoping to install PA shortly. If not Libby will hire one for you. Covers or original material welcome. To play, either phone Lee or Libby, or send demo for their attention to the venue.

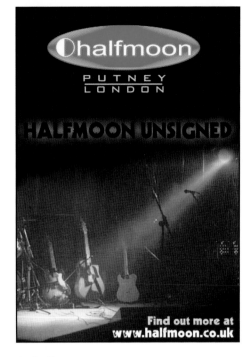

The Gun Tavern
83 Church Street, Old Town, Croydon, Surrey, CR0 1RN
tel: 020 8667 1472
contact: Julie Watson
info: One band plays every Friday & Saturday night. Monday nights are dedicated to jazz. Need to provide own PA. Send demo FAO Andy at the venue.

The Hackney Empire Theatre
291 Mare Street, London, E8 1EJ
⊖ Hackney Central (Rail)
email: hadrian.garrard@hackneyempire.co.uk
web: www.hackneyempire.co.uk
contact: Hadrian Garrard
info: 'Signed-Unsigned' is a night held every Wednesday with between 8 and 10 acts playing. Send demos FAO Hadrian Garrard at the above address.

Half Moon Herne Hill
10 Half Moon Lane, Herne Hill, London, SE24 9HU
⊖ Herne Hill (Rail)
tel: 020 7274 2733
contact: Lydia
capacity: 250
info: Live bands every Friday and Saturday, and occasionally on other nights. 2 or 3 bands playing. In-house PA. Send demo FAO Lydia at the venue.

Halfmoon Putney
93 Lower Richmond Road, Putney, London, SW15 1EU
⊖ Putney Bridge
tel: 020 8780 9383
email: office@halfmoon.co.uk
web: www.halfmoon.co.uk
contact: Carrie Davies
capacity: 200
info: The Halfmoon, Putney, has hosted live music full time since 1963, with occasional performances dating back as far as the 1920s. From The Rolling Stones to Kasabian, Kate Bush to Natasha Bedingfield the venue is steeped in music heritage. Before submitting material it is recommended that you check the website for full demo submission policy. Send demo FAO Carrie Davies to above address. Follow up with phone call after a week.

LIVE PERFORMANCE

The Harp Rock Bar
Parsons Mead, Croydon, Surrey, CR0 3SP
West Croydon (Rail)
tel: 020 8686 7995
email: jono@theharprockbar.co.uk
web: www.theharprockbar.co.uk
contact: John
capacity: 130
info: The Harp Rock Bar is Croydon's only Rock bar dedicated to Alternative, Rock, Metal, Goth, Punk and Rock'n'Roll music. No Indie or Emo bands need apply. Live bands twice a week, although this should be increasing in the near future. First Sunday of the month is a jam session, just turn up to take part. Acts which perform well at the jam session may be asked to play on other nights of the week. In-house PA, 4kW rig, dressing rooms and 100% dedicated Rock jukebox.

HMS President
Victoria Embankment, London, EC40HJ
Temple
tel: 020 7583 1918
email: enquiries@hmspresident.com
web: www.hmspresident.com
contact: Shaun
capacity: 350
info: Live music on a monthly basis. Often put on signed acts from all over country, as well as Europe and the USA. The venue is available to hire for unsigned bands. In-house PA.

Hope & Anchor
207 Upper Street, Islington, London, N1 1RL
Highbury & Islington
tel: 020 7354 1312
email: info@bugbearbookings.com
web: www.bugbearbookings.com
contact: Tony Gleed, Jim Mattison
capacity: 100
info: Live music every night. Demos can be sent to the venue but will be dealt with more efficiently if sent direct to Bugbear Promotions. See listing in Promoters section for contact details.

Inigo
642 Wandsworth Road, London, SW8 3JW
Wandsworth Road (Rail)
tel: 020 7622 4884
email: info@inigobar.com
web: www.inigobar.com
contact: Dave Minns
capacity: 165
info: Live music on first Wednesday and last Monday of each month. Will put on all genres of music from Electro and Breakbeat to Acoustic Singer-Songwriter music. Contact Dave by email to obtain details for demo submission. Inigo also run recording studios and a record label. See entries in relevant sections for details.

Jazz After Dark
9 Greek Street, Soho, London, W1V 5LE
Tottenham Court Road
tel: 020 7734 0545
email: jazzafterdark@btconnect.com
web: www.jazzafterdark.co.uk
capacity: 50
info: Restaurant with live Jazz and Blues music every night. In-house PA and Drum kit. Best way to play is to phone or call in to speak to manager at the venue.

Jazz Café
5 Parkway, Camden Town, London, NW1 7PG
Camden Town
tel: 020 7916 6060
fax: 020 7267 9219
email: andy@jazzcafe.co.uk
web: www.jazzcafe.co.uk
contact: Adrian Gibson
capacity: 340
info: Jazz Café hosts new talent nights occasionally which often take place at short notice during the week. Send demos with contact information and biog FAO Adrian to the venue.

King's Head
2 Crouch End Hill, London, N8 8AA
Harringay (Rail)
tel: 020 8340 1028
contact: Peter Graham
capacity: 120
info: In-house PA. Telephone between 9am and 11am weekdays to discuss bookings or demo submission.

King's Head
115 Upper Street, London, N1 1QM
Angel
tel: 020 7226 0364
email: kevin@kingsheadtheatre.demon.co.uk
web: www.kingsheadtheatre.org
contact: Alan Villiers
capacity: 120
info: Live music 7 nights a week. Need to supply own PA. Send demos FAO Alan at the venue.

King's Head
214 High Street, Acton, London, W3 9NX
Acton Town
tel: 020 8992 0282
email: kings.head@fullers.co.uk
contact: Dave Connell
capacity: 100
info: Live jam session every Thursday, just show up. In-house PA. The second Wednesday of every month is Folk night, which is free entry. There is also live Jazz on Sunday afternoons.

Klinker @ The Sussex Pub
107a Culford Road, London, N1
Dalston Kingsland (Rail)
tel: 020 8806 8216
email: theklinker@tesco.net
web: www.klinkerclub.info
contact: Hugh Metcalfe
capacity: 60
info: 'Klinker' takes place every Tuesday and Thursday. The event includes live Rock, Blues, Improvised and Experimental music, as well as poetry, comedy, film and performance art. No covers bands. Door takings are split between the performers on the evening. In-house PA. Contact Hugh by email or send demo for his attention to the venue.

Koko
1a Camden High Street, Camden, London, NW1 7JE
Camden Town
tel: 0870 432 5527
email: info@koko.uk.com
web: www.koko.uk.com
contact: Mark Johnson
capacity: 1500
info: Club NME runs every Friday night with 1 or 2 bands playing each week. This showcase night is a mixture of Indie and Rock styles, and has served as platform for a number of up and coming bands. Send demos FAO 'Booker' at the venue.

Lark In The Park
60 Copenhagen Street, Islington, London, N1 0JW
Angel
tel: 020 7278 5781
fax: 020 7278 5781
email: thelark@tiscali.co.uk
web: www.larkinthepark.co.uk
contact: Sammy
capacity: 175
info: Live music every night of the week apart from Mondays. These nights feature mainly Rock and Acoustic acts with various numbers of bands playing per night. To get a gig send a demo FAO Sammy at the venue. Venue has in-house PA. Gigs also promoted by Club Fabulous. See listing in relevant section for details.

Le Quecum Bar
42-44 Battersea High Street, London, SW11 3HX
Clapham Common
tel: 020 7787 2227
fax: 020 7787 2225
email: info@quecumbar.co.uk
web: www.quecumbar.co.uk
contact: Sylvia Rushbrooke
info: Specialises in Acoustic Jazz, Hot Club and Gypsy Swing music. Contact Sylvia by telephone or email. As all music is Acoustic, she will organise an audition for any acts wanting to play. Electric baby grand piano, double bass and 2 AER amps available for acts to use.

The Lincoln Lounge
52 York Way, London, N1 9AB
Kings Cross
tel: 020 7837 9339
email: info@.lincolnlounge.co.uk
web: www.lincolnlounge.co.uk
contact: Adrian Clark
capacity: 130
info: The Lincoln Lounge is an artsy, bohemian venue which features live music at least 2-3 times a week. Music is anything Leftfield including Funk, Jazz, Folk, Roots, Singer-Songwriter, Acoustic, Skiffle, as well as recitals. Basic in-house PA, but some acts prefer to bring their own PA. Send demos FAO Adrian to the venue.

The Loaded Dog
485 High Road, Leytonstone, London, E11 4PG
⊖ Leyton
tel: 020 8556 6695
email: theloadeddog@hotmail.co.uk
web: www.theloadeddog.co.uk
contact: Bernie
info: Accept all styles of music. Send demo to the venue. Include information on your style of music, a bit about the band members and their history. Also include details of upcoming gigs and how long the band has been together. As much information as possible, including website addresses, is preferred.

Lord Napier
521 Green Lane, Goodmayes, Ilford, Essex, IG3 9RH
⊖ Newbury Park
tel: 020 8599 2662
contact: Thomas
info: Live music 3 or 4 times per week, usually Tuesday, Friday, Saturday and Sunday nights. In-house PA. Send demo FAO Thomas at the venue.

Madame Jo Jo's
8-10 Brewer Street, London, W1F 0SP
⊖ Piccadilly Circus
tel: 020 7734 3040
email: events@madamejojos.com
web: www.madamejojos.com or www.electrogogo.com
contact: Paris, Paajoe
capacity: 180
info: Electrogogo held fortnightly features unsigned and signed bands of an Electro Rock style every Thursday. In-house PA. Send demos to venue address, marked FAO 'The Tin'. Venue is available for promoters to organise events, contact Paris or Paajoe on the above number for further details.

Marquee Club
1 Leicester Square, London, WC2H 7NA
⊖ Leicester Square
tel: 020 7909 0000
web: www.plummusic.com
info: Live music organised by Plum Promotions. See website above for details. Unsigned gigs are also organised through other external promoters. See listing for Curious Generation in Promoter section for details of gigs and demo submission.

Metro Club
19-23 Oxford Street, London, W1 1RF
⊖ Tottenham Court Road
tel: 020 7437 0964
email: bookings@blowupmetro.com
web: www.blowupmetro.com
contact: Paul
capacity: 250
info: Nights put on by Dead Or Alive, see entry in Promoters section for further information. Full details of upcoming gigs and venue information can be found on the website. Demos should be sent to PO Box 4961, London, W1A 7ZX.

Montague Arms
289 Queens Road, New Cross, London, SE15 2PA
⊖ Queens Road (Rail)
tel: 020 7639 4923
contact: Martin
capacity: 250
info: Live bands but no regular schedule. All music accepted, except Punk. In-house PA. Bands usually run the door and are entitled to all door takings. Send demo FAO Martin to the venue.

Moonbow Jake's
325 Brockley Road, London, SE4 2QZ
⊖ Crofton Park (Rail)
tel: 0208 694 9128
email: info@moonbowjakes.com
web: www.moonbowjakes.com
contact: Billy
capacity: 40
info: Moonbow Jake's is a café and wine bar which has live duos and singer-songwriters playing every Tuesday and Sunday. In-house PA. To play contact Billy for details.

Nambucca
596 Holloway Road, London, N7 6LB
⊖ Archway
tel: 020 7263 6939
email: info@hollowayroad.co.uk
contact: Jay
capacity: 350
info: Live music every Wednesday, Friday and Saturday organised by Sensible Promotions. All gigs are free. In-house vocal PA. For details of demo submission see entry for Sensible Promotions in relevant section.

Notting Hill Arts Club
21 Notting Hill Gate, London, W11 3JQ
⊖ Notting Hill Gate
tel: 020 7598 5226
email: info@nottinghillartsclub.com
web: www.nottinghillartsclub.com
contact: David
capacity: 218
info: Live music most nights of the week. 'One World Live' is an Urban night held every Thursday with Hip-Hop, World, Funk and Electronica music. 'RoTa' is an Indie and Electronica event held every Saturday afternoon. Contact Matt by email at courtesanx@yahoo.com to play. 'Beachclub' is held every Monday night, each with a different theme. Contact David by email at david@nottinghillarts.co.uk. It is important to check the demo page of the website to check contact information is up to date.

Old Tiger's Head
351 Lee High Road, Lee Green, London, SE12 8RU
⊖ Lee (Rail)
tel: 020 8244 2014
email: adrian.straatman@ntlworld.com
web: www.barrymags.com or
contact: Adrian
capacity: 100
info: One unsigned band plays every Thursday. In-house PA. Band is entitled to door takings. If Thursday gig is successful, there may be opportunity to play on Friday and Saturday nights. Contact Adrian on above number or email address to play.

On The Rocks
25 Kingsland Road, Shoreditch, London, E2 8AA
⊖ Old Street/Liverpool Street
tel: 020 7688 0339
contact: John Evans
capacity: 170
info: Live music every Wednesday and Thursday, 'The Future Of Rock & Roll Club', presented by Bugbear Bookings and Sonic Mook Experiment respectively. Please refer to Promoters section for contact details and demo submission information. On The Rocks are also opening a recording and rehearsal facility in winter 2005-06. Contact venue manager, John, on the above number for details.

The Peel
160 Cambridge Road, Kingston, Surrey, KT1 3HH
⊖ Wimbledon
tel: 020 8546 3516
email: info@peelmuzik.com
web: www.peelmuzik.com
contact: Jon Patrick
capacity: 250
info: Live music 4 or 5 nights a week. Strictly over 18 venue. Full in-house PA and lighting. Send demos on CD or cassette format to the venue, marked FAO Peelmuzik Promotions. Please include full contact postal address with your demo. No restrictions on type of music. Bands that have played Peel can have own biog page on website. Once a band is booked, venue promotes the gig; including designing flyers and posting details on website. Peel also has rehearsal rooms for hire. See listing in relevant section for further information.

The Pelton Arms
23-25 Pelton Road, Greenwich, London, SE10 9PQ
⊖ Maze Hill (Rail)
tel: 020 8858 0572
contact: Tony/Pauline Lock
capacity: 100
info: Live music, mainly duet styles, every Saturday night. Need to provide own PA. Send demo FAO Tony or Pauline to the venue.

The Pleasure Unit
359 Bethnal Green Road, London, E2 6LG
⊖ Bethnal Green
tel: 020 7729 0167
email: bands@pleasureunitbar.com
web: www.pleasureunitbar.com
contact: Nick
capacity: 150
info: Unsigned night 'Don't Forget Yer Bass Amp' is held every Tuesday, Wednesday and Thursday. In-house PA. Every Monday 'Sawdust Caesars' provides the best in raw Rock & Roll, Punk, New Wave and Indie. The main act is always a signed band supported by solid unsigned supports (no Metal, Hard Thrash Rock please). To play at either event, contact Nick or email band biog to the above address. Any demos should be submitted FAO Nick to the venue address.

Plough Inn
173 Wood Street, London, E17 3SU
⊖ Wood Street (Rail)
tel: 020 8503 7419
email: ploughinn@tiscali.co.uk
web: www.theploughinne17.co.uk
contact: Bill Hodgson
capacity: 100
info: The Plough Inn hosts an open mic night on Mondays. The venue puts on 5 nights of live music featuring all genres throughout the week. The venue also puts on regular Jazz and comedy nights. For more information on all live music events contact Bill at the venue, or send a demo to the venue for his attention. In-house PA provided.

Pop
14 Soho Street, Soho, London, W1D 3DN
⊖ Tottenham Court Road
tel: 020 7734 4004
fax: 020 7734 4006
email: pop@thebreakfastgroup.co.uk
web: www.thebreakfastgroup.co.uk
contact: Micky P.
capacity: 290
info: Hosts 'Wild' every Monday featuring a live jam session, show up to take part. 'Eyelash' every Wednesday features 2 of the most exciting unsigned bands every week. Contact Micky P. to play or send demo to 18 Lenora House, Lanark Road, London, W9 1DG.

Progress Bar
162 Tufnell Park Road, Tufnell Park, London, N7 0EE
⊖ Tufnell Park
tel: 020 7272 2078
web: www.progress-bar.co.uk
contact: Paul and Anthony Avogadri
capacity: 130 (Function Room), 450 (Overall)
info: Virtually Acoustic Club open mic night is held every Tuesday and Wednesday. Just turn up to take part. Participants can perform 2 songs. A baby grand piano is also available for use. See listing in Promoter section for further details regarding Virtually Acoustic Club. For details of other live music events contact the venue. In-house PA provided.

The Purple Turtle
65 Crowndale Road, Camden, London, NW1 1TN
⊖ Mornington Crescent
tel: 020 7383 4976
email: camden@purpleturtlebar.com
web: www.purpleturtlebar.com
contact: Rachelle
capacity: 285
info: Unsigned night every Monday with up to 4 bands playing. Any style of music welcome. In-house PA and sound engineer. Send demos to the above address.

The Puzzle Pub
175-177 Fulham Palace Road, Hammersmith, London, W6 8QT
⊖ Barons Court
tel: 020 7381 8682
email: fulham@puzzlepubco.com
web: www.puzzlepub.co.uk
contact: Travis
capacity: 450
info: Mainly puts on cover bands but they do host Battle Of The Bands event once a year. Contact Travis at the venue for more information.

Rayner's Hotel
Village Way East, Rayners Lane, Harrow, Middlesex, HA2 7LX

⊖ Rayners Lane
tel: 020 8866 1666
web: www.raynerslive.co.uk
contact: Pete Feenstra
info: Live music every night of the week. Bands put on by Pete Feenstra. See entry in Promoters section for details of demo submission.

The Red Lion
166 Heath Road, Twickenham, London, TW1 4BN
⊖ Strawberry Hill (Rail)
tel: 020 8892 5074
contact: Rick, Tom
capacity: 250
info: Jazz Club on Thursdays, unsigned nights on Fridays and Saturdays. Blues jam from 4pm until 8pm on Sundays. In-house PA.

The Rhythm Factory
16-18 Whitechapel Road, London, E1 1EW
⊖ Aldgate East
tel: 020 7375 3774
fax: 020 7375 2771
email: info@rhythmfactory.co.uk
web: www.rhythmfactory.co.uk
contact: Spoon
capacity: 300
info: Live music every Tuesday and Thursday night, and occasionally on other nights. 3 or 4 bands playing. In-house PA and engineer. Venue will promote all events with posters and flyers in-house. Bands are entitled to cut of the door takings. Send demos FAO Jonny or Spoon to the venue. Also host open mic night every second and fourth Monday, 'Spoon Full of Poison'. Just turn up to take part.

River Bar
206-208 Tower Bridge Road, London, SE1 2UP
⊖ Tower Hill
tel: 020 7407 0968
email: riverbar@hotmail.com
contact: Kat, Emma
capacity: 150 (Overall), 60 (Downstairs)
info: Live music downstairs on Thursday and Friday night with between 2 and 5 bands playing. Jazz upstairs on Thursdays and open mic on Wednesdays. In-house PA. Send demo FAO Kat or Emma to the venue.

Roadhouse
The Piazza, Covent Garden, London, WC2E 8BE
⊖ Covent Garden
tel: 020 7240 6001
fax: 020 7379 5035
email: tug@roadhouse.co.uk
web: www.roadhouse.co.uk
contact: Tug
capacity: 585
info: Every Monday features a open mic event. Unsigned night, 'Raw' featuring 3 bands, is held on the first, second and third Sundays of every month. In-house PA and full backline provided. Send demo FAO Tug at 9 King Street, Covent Garden, London WC2E 8HN.

The Rock Garden/Gardening Club
6-7 The Piazza, Covent Garden, London, WC2E 8HA
⊖ Covent Garden
tel: 020 7836 4052
fax: 020 7379 4793
email: info@rockgarden.co.uk
web: www.rockgarden.co.uk
contact: Alex Clarke
capacity: 150 (Seated), 250 (Standing)
info: Live music event called 'Platform' is held every Sunday between 2pm and 7pm in The Gardening Club for unsigned bands, followed by 'Old School' battle of the bands from 7pm til 10pm. Rock Garden is London's oldest small live music venue, and hosted U2's first London gig. For more information about how to play, please visit the website.

The Rocket Complex @ University of North London
166-220 Holloway Road, London, N7 8DB
⊖ Holloway Road
tel: 020 7133 4312
email: info.rocket@londonmet.ac,uk
web: www.rocketcomplex.co.uk
contact: Lucy Lyall
capacity: 1150
info: Night called 'Radio LolliPop' takes place the last Friday of every month featuring 3-4 unsigned artists of any genre. Call Lucy at the venue for more information.

Ronnie Scott's
47 Frith Street, London, W1D 4HT
⊖ Leicester Square
tel: 020 7439 0747
fax: 020 7437 5081
email: ronniescotts@ronniescotts.co.uk
web: www.ronniescotts.co.uk
contact: Sally Greene
capacity: 250 (Seated), 50 (Standing)
info: Live music Monday to Saturday. Send demos to the venue. Jazz only.

Ryan's Bar
181 Church Street, Stoke Newington, London, N16 0UL
⊖ Rectory Road (Rail)
tel: 020 7275 7807
contact: Giovanni
capacity: 100 (Standing), 60 (Seated)
info: Every Monday features an open mic night. Every third and fourth Wednesday of the month is 'Flim Flam', an Acoustic, free improvisation night in which 2 acts play per night. In-house PA. Contact Giovanni by telephone to play.

Sahara Nights

257 Pentonville Road, Kings Cross, London, N1 9NL
🚇 Kings Cross
tel: 020 7278 7223
email: info@saharanights.co.uk
web: www.saharanights.co.uk
contact: Vanessa
capacity: 500
info: 'United Diversity' is a live event which takes place on the first Thursday of every month. Bands also play regularly at Sahara Nights, although there is no definite schedule. All types of music considered. Send demos FAO Vanessa.

The Shrine @ The Rifleman

50 Hanworth Road, Hounslow, Middlesex, TW3 1UF
🚇 Hounsow
tel: 020 8570 1487
email: theriflemanuk@aol.com
web: www.therifleman.org.uk
contact: Mr Duxbury
capacity: 100-150
info: The Shrine is a music venue, adjoining The Rifleman pub. Live music at least twice a week. In-house PA. Send demos FAO Mr Duxbury at the venue.

Six Bells

148 High Street, Brentford, Middlesex, TW8 8EW
🚇 Kew Gardens
tel: 020 8560 8804
contact: Joyce
info: Live music Friday, Saturday and Sunday nights. Mainly Rock and Blues. Also hoping to start a Country & Western night. Need to provide own PA. Send demos FAO Joyce at the venue.

The Social

5 Little Portland Street, Oxford Circus, London, W1N 5AG
🚇 Oxford Circus
tel: 020 7494 2998
fax: 020 7636 4993
email: carl@thesocial.com
web: www.thesocial.com
contact: Danny Mitchel
capacity: 100
info: Send demo FAO Danny to Heavenly Recordings, 47 Frith Street, London, W1D 4SE. Also host open deck nights.

Sound

Swiss Centre, 10 Wardour Street, Leicester Square, London, W1D 6QF
🚇 Leicester Square
tel: 020 7287 1010
fax: 020 7437 1029
email: info@soundlondon.com
web: www.soundlondon.com
capacity: Main venue 500, Café Bar 100
info: Live bands play most nights, either in the main venue or Sound Café Bar. Gigs are organised through The Talent Scout. Also host all day events. For full details of various nights promoted and demo submission policy, see listing for The Talent Scout in Promoters section.

Spice of Life

6 Moor Street, London, W1V 5LJ
🚇 Tottenham Court Road
tel: 020 7437 7013
email: paulpace@tiscali.co.uk
web: www.spicejazz.co.uk or
www.spiceoflifesoho.com
contact: Paul Pace
capacity: 110
info: Live Jazz on Wednesday and Thursday nights. Contact Phil Pace or send demos for his attention to the venue. Up All Night Music organise live music on Monday, Tuesday and Friday nights. Monday is Anti-Folk open mic night, featuring Alternative styles of music. This event is one of the most Popular open mic nights in London. Acts should turn up by 6pm at the latest to take part. Tuesday is Blues jam, run in association with Blues in Britain magazine. Turn up by 7pm to participate. Friday night is an Acoustic showcase, featuring the best acts from Monday and Tuesday nights, plus acts selected through demo submission. In-house PA and backline provided. See Up All Night Music entry in Promoters section for further details.

The Spitz

109 Commercial Street, Old Spitalfields Market, London, E1 6BG
🚇 Liverpool Street
tel: 020 7392 9032
fax: 020 7377 8915
email: mail@spitz.co.uk
web: www.spitz.co.uk
contact: Martin, Andy
capacity: 250 (Standing), 180 (Seated & Standing)
info: Live music 7 nights a week. In-house PA. Full technical specification can be found on website. Any style of music considered. Send demo on CD with biog FAO Martin to venue.

Standard Music Venue

1 Blackhorse Lane, Walthamstow, London, E17 6DS
🚇 Blackhorse Road
tel: 020 8503 2523
email: standardtryst@btinternet.com
web: www.standardmusicvenue.co.uk
contact: Paul White
capacity: 350
info: Live music 4 nights a week. Support slots available. Full PA. Send demos FAO Paul at the venue. Bands can post photos of themselves playing the venue on the Standard Music Venue website.

The Strongroom Bar

120-124 Curtain Road, London, EC2A 3SQ
🚇 Old Street
tel: 020 7426 5103
fax: 020 7426 5102
web: www.strongroom.com
contact: Sean Parson
capacity: 200
info: Promotes live music from Thursday to Sunday, Mainly Acoustic music. Outside promoters also use the venue featuring genres such as Folk, World Music and Indie. Sean will forward your demo on to the appropriate promoter if interested in playing one of these nights. Send demo FAO Sean Parson to the venue. The bar is situated within the Strongroom complex, including other establishments such as the renowned Strongroom recording studios. For details regarding the studio, see listing in relevant section.

The Swan

215 Clapman Road, London, SW9 9BE
🚇 Stockwell
tel: 020 7738 3065
fax: 020 7738 6722
email: info@theswanstockwell.co.uk
web: www.theswanstockwell.co.uk
contact: Hannah Preen
capacity: 750
info: Live music on Fridays, Saturdays and Sundays. Send demos FAO Hannah at the venue. In-house PA and sound engineers. Promotional help is normally given.

The Telegraph

228 Brixton Hill, Brixton, London, SW2 1HE
🚇 Brixton
tel: 020 8678 0777
fax: 020 8678 9066
email: alex@thebrixtontelegraph.co.uk
web: www.thebrixtontelegraph.co.uk
contact: Alex
capacity: 600
info: The Telegraph is known for playing host to The Clash several times during the height of their fame. Unsigned bands play most nights, with exception of Fridays and Saturdays. 11kW PA with sound engineers. Full technical specification can be found on website. Occasionally promote showcases where record labels are invited. The Telegraph also has a rehearsal room. See entry in relevant section for details.

The Three Kings

42 Heath Road, Twickenham, Middlesex, TW1 4BZ
🚇 Richmond
tel: 020 8296 0983
email: via website
web: www.the3kingstwickenham.co.uk
contact: Larry
info: Live music every weekend. Mainly Contemporary music. Need to provide PA. Contact Larry on above number to play, or send demo to venue for his attention.

The Troubadour Club

263-167 Old Brompton Road, Earls Court, London, SW5 9JA
🚇 Earls Court
tel: 020 7370 1434
fax: 020 7341 6329
email: amanda@troubadour.co.uk
web: www.troubadour.co.uk
contact: Amanda Glyn
capacity: 120
info: Singer-songwriter and new bands night every Wednesday. For the rest of the week, there is live music with 3 bands performing on the bill. Most genres considered apart from Hard Rock and Metal. In-house PA and sound engineer. Send demos FAO Amanda at the venue.

NOW IT IS YOUR TURN

the garage & upstairs at the garage

www.myspace.com/upstairsatthegarage

ULU (University of London Union)
Manning Hall, Malet Street, London, WC1E 7HY
Goodge Street

tel:	020 7664 2000
email:	l.pegg@ulu.lon.ac.uk
web:	www.ulu.co.uk/ululive
contact:	Laurie Pegg
capacity:	800 (Main Room), 200 (Small Venue)
info:	'ULU Live' takes place every Friday night. The bill

varies between newly signed and unsigned acts. In-house PA. Send demo marked Demos to the venue.

Underbelly
11 Hoxton Street, London, N1 6NU
Old Street/Liverpool Street

tel:	020 7613 3105
email:	omar@zigfrid.com
web:	www.underbellylondon.com
contact:	Omar
capacity:	300
info:	Live music 6-7 nights a week. 4 bands play each

night, as well as a DJ. In-house PA. Send demos FAO Omar, Zig Frid Bar, 11 Hoxton Street, London, N1 6NU.

The Underworld
174 Camden High Street, London, NW1 0NE
Camden Town

tel:	020 7267 3939
fax:	020 7482 1955
email:	info@theunderworldcamden.co.uk
web:	www.theunderworldcamden.co.uk
capacity:	500
info:	Unsigned nights at least once a week. Upload demos

to www.wildplumnetwork.com. Full technical specification can be found on website.

Upstairs @ The Garage
20-22 Highbury Corner, London, N5 1RD
Highbury & Islington

tel:	020 7607 1818
fax:	020 8961 9238
email:	carina@meanfiddler.co.uk
web:	www.meanfiddler.co.uk or
	www.myspace.com/upstairsatthegarage
contact:	Carina Jirsch
capacity:	500 (Downstairs), 150 (Upstairs)
info:	A variety of nights are held Upstairs at the Garage.

The venue now mainly deals with touring, signed bands but there are a small amount of opportunities for unsigned bands to play. The venue is also used by external promoters. For more information or to get a gig email Carina and send her link to your website or music. Live music also organised by Club Fabulous. See listing in Promoter section for further details.

The Water Rat's Theatre
328 Grays Inn Road, Kings Cross, London, WC1X 8BZ
Kings Cross

tel:	020 7837 7269
email:	plum.general@virgin.net
web:	www.plummusic.com
contact:	Allan North
capacity:	200
info:	Timeout described The Water Rats Theatre as 'The

best of London's small Indie venues'. Send demos FAO Sarah at Plum Promotions, 56b Farringdon Road, London, EC1R 3BL. Online demo feedback service. Full technical specification can be found on website. Plum Promotions also organise gigs at The Betsey Trotwood.

Waxy O'Connor's
14-16 Rupert Street, Leicester Square, London, W1D 6DD
Piccadilly Circus

tel:	020 7287 0255
fax:	020 7287 3962
email:	saleslondon@waxyoconnors.co.uk
web:	www.waxyconnors.co.uk
contact:	Tara Cronin
capacity:	400 (Music Room)
info:	Live music on a weekend. Folk, Roots and

Traditional but with a strict Irish theme. Need to provide own PA. Send demos FAO Tara at the venue.

West One Four
3 North End Crescent, North End Road, West Kensington, London, W14 8TG
West Kensington

tel:	020 7603 7006
email:	livegigs@mail.com
web:	www.orangepromotions.com or
	www.westonefour.co.uk
contact:	Phil Brydon
capacity:	300
info:	Live music 5 or 6 nights a week. Monday is

Songwriters night, where the house band play your songs. Remaining nights are band nights with 4 or 5 bands per evening. Bands should have a following in London, or bring their own crowd. In-house PA. Call Phil to arrange a gig. See also Orange Promotions entry in Promoters section.

The White Hart
1-3 Mile End Road, Whitechapel, London, E1 4TP
Whitechapel

tel:	020 7790 2894
email:	enquiries@whitehartwhitechapel.com
web:	www.whitehartwhitechapel.com
contact:	Jane Malone
capacity:	170
info:	Live music on Saturday night with 1 band playing

every week. There is a function room for hire. Thursday, Friday and Saturday the venue has a late licence. Send demo to Jane at the venue.

The Windmill
22 Blenheim Gardens, Brixton, London, SW2 5BZ
Brixton

tel:	020 8671 0700
email:	windmillbrixton@yahoo.co.uk
web:	www.windmillbrixton.co.uk
contact:	Tim
capacity:	150
info:	Live music 6 nights a week from newly signed and

unsigned bands. Mainly Guitar-based music. In-house PA and sound engineer. Band entitled to share of door takings, so worthwhile bringing a large crowd. The Windmill are inundated with demos, so must send demo and biog plus details of previous gigs to Tim at the venue. Do not chase for reply, Tim will be in touch if they want to make a booking.

The Windsor Castle
378 Carshalton Road, Carshalton, Surrey, SM5 3PT
Morden

tel:	020 8669 1191
web:	www.windsorcastlepub.com
contact:	Pam Clarke
info:	The Windsor Castle has been featured in the 'Good

Pub Guide'. There is live music at the venue every Saturday evening featuring 1 band. There is also a jam night on the first Monday of every month. The venue has a separate function room that is available for hire. To get a gig contact Sarah at the venue.

MIDLANDS

The Actress & Bishop
36 Ludgate Hill, St. Paul's Square, Birmingham, B3 1EH

tel:	0121 707 8504
email:	scott@solarcreations.net
web:	www.solarcreations.net
contact:	Scott Roe, Mark Badger
capacity:	150
info:	Live music every night, spanning melodic Indie Rock

and Punk, Edgy New Wave to Hip-Hop and Jazz. See entry for Solar Creations in Promoter section for demo submission details.

The Annexe @ The Black Swan
12 New Road, Spalding, Lincolnshire, PE11 1DQ

tel:	01775 713 522
email:	jamestoynton@hotmail.com
web:	www.blackswanspalding.co.uk
contact:	James
capacity:	90
info:	2 or 3 bands play once a week, mainly Rock and

Guitar-based music. Bands from all over the country welcome. In-house PA. Send demo to James at the venue.

Aston Student's Guild
The Triangle, Birmingham, West Midlands, B4 7ES

tel:	0121 204 4855
fax:	0121 204 4910
email:	l.b.cook@astonguild.org.uk
web:	www.astonguild.org.uk
contact:	Larry Cook
capacity:	200-800 (depending on venue)
info:	Unsigned band night held once a week. To play

contact for details.

LIVE PERFORMANCE

The Attik
15 Free Lane, Leicester, LE1 1JX
tel: 0116 222 3800
email: mail@the-attik.co.uk
web: www.the-attik.co.uk
contact: Paul, Dave
capacity: 70
info: Live music nearly every night of the week. Underground, Experimental acts and DJs. In-house PA and Drum kit. Send demo FAO Paul or Dave to the venue.

Bar Academy @ Birmingham Academy
52-54 Dale End, Birmingham, B4 7LS
tel: 0121 262 3000
fax: 0121 236 2241
email: baracademy@birmingham-academy.co.uk
web: www.birmingham-academy.co.uk
contact: Stuart Strong
capacity: 292
info: Band night held every Thursday and Friday organised by Catapult Club. Regular unsigned nights also run by Cold Rice. See listings in Promoter section for details of demo submission.

Bivouac @ The Duke of Wellington
37 Broadgate, Lincoln, LN2 5AE
tel: 01522 527 069
email: lindsey@thedukeofwellington.fsnet.co.uk
web: www.bivouac.uk.com
contact: Steve Hawkins
capacity: 100
info: Unsigned bands play every Friday night, with at least 3 acts performing. In-house PA and sound engineer provided. Send demos FAO Steve to the venue.

Blue Note
14a Sadler Gate, Derby, DE1 3NF
tel: 01332 295 155
email: ros@thebluenotederby.wanadoo.co.uk
contact: Ros Fletcher
capacity: 250
info: A relaxed venue open 5 nights a week with live music once a month. 3-4 bands play each month. Mainly Rock and Indie but all styles will be considered. Send demos FAO Ros Fletcher direct to the venue.

Brunswick Inn
1 Railway Terrace, Derby, DE1 2RU
tel: 01332 290 677
contact: Marie McArthur
capacity: 100
info: Traditional pub with upstairs music room. Room is available to hire free of charge with the option of a door charge. Specialise in Jazz, with live music every Thursday. Contact Marie at the venue for information on demo submission and available gigs.

Bunkers Hill Inn
36-38 Hockley, Nottingham, NG1 1FP
tel: 0115 910 0114
web: www.pubpeople.com
contact: Andy, Charlotte
capacity: 100
info: Live band nights take place on a Fridays and occasional Saturdays. Bands can hire room out for £50, and are then entitled to the door takings. Need to provide own PA. Contact on the above number to make booking.

The Cabaret
22 Fletcher Gate, Nottingham, NG1 2FZ
tel: 0115 941 3111
web: www.cabaretnottingham.com
contact: Andy Fox
capacity: 350
info: Put on live music from unsigned bands. Hosts 'Hot Renault Traffic Nights' on regular basis. See listing for Hot Renault Traffic Club in Promoter section for further details.

The Charlotte
8 Oxford Street, Leicester, LE1 5XZ
tel: 0116 255 3956
email: charlotte@stayfree.co.uk
web: www.thecharlotte.co.uk
contact: Andy Wright
capacity: 390
info: Live venue, with in-house PA, dedicated to Alternative music. Tuesday nights are showcase nights. Acts wanting a gig should email Andy at the above address. Door percentage and rider optional.

The Colosseum
Primrose Hill Street, Coventry, West Midlands, CV1 5LY
tel: 02476 554 473
email: richelms@tiscali.co.uk or the.colosseum@excite.com
web: www.coventrycolosseum.co.uk
contact: Richard Elms
capacity: 1100
info: Live music held several nights a week, including touring bands. In-house PA. Send demo for attention for Richard at the venue.

Dogma Bar
Priory Place, Fairfax Street, Coventry, CV1 5RZ
tel: 02476 230 088
email: dogmacoventry@eversosensible.com
web: www.dogmabars.com
info: First Friday of every month organised by Frontline AV. See listing in Promoter section for details of demo submission.

Edwards No. 8
Lower Severn Street, Birmingham, B1 1PU
tel: 0121 643 5835
email: edwardsno8@hotmail.com
web: www.edwardsno.8m.com
info: Live music organised by MaxRock. See listing in Promoter section for details of gigs and demo submission.

The Farm
Anderby Road, Chapel St. Leonards, Skegness, Lincolnshire, PE24 5YD
tel: 01754 871 445
email: bandbookings@thefarm-online.co.uk
web: www.thefarm-online.co.uk
contact: Kate, Martin, Andy
capacity: 85 (Seated), 190 (Standing), 190 (Bar 2)
info: The Farm hosts live music across all genres at least twice a week, with up to 8 acts playing per session (some sessions run from midday to close). A regular jam night takes place every Tuesday. Along with 2 separate bar areas, The Farm has a large outdoor stage (capacity 1000) which has in the past been used for Blues & Rock Weekend and a Rock Weekend. Further similar events are planned for the future, as well as a community arts project utilising the stage. The Real Food Cafe at The Farm uses fresh local/organic produce wherever possible and has a GM free and fair-trade policy. To play The Farm, send a demo to the venue, email the address above, or call and speak to either Martin, Kate or Andy.

Firefly
1 Millstone Lane, Leicester, LE1 5JN
tel: 0116 255 1228
fax: 0116 254 7213
email: info@barfirefly.co.uk
web: www.barfirefly.co.uk
contact: Kat Frater
capacity: 400
info: Late night bar and live music venue. Contact the venue for more information.

The Fishpond
204 South Parade, Matlock Bath, Derbyshire, DE4 3NR
tel: 01629 581 000
fax: 01629 581 000
email: info@fishpond.co.uk
web: www.fishpond.co.uk
contact: John Gill
capacity: 200
info: Local singers and musicians play 'The Session' on Sundays. Every first Wednesday of the month is dedicated to Jazz. The first Sunday of every month is 'Candle Lit Cabaret'.

Flapper & Firkin
Kingston Row, Birmingham, West Midlands, B1 2NU
tel: 0121 236 2421
info: Band nights held on a regular basis organised through various external promoters.

Flowerpot
25 King Street, Derby, DE1 3DZ
tel: 01332 834 438
email: rawpromo@aol.com
web: www.rawpromo.co.uk
contact: Alan Wooley
capacity: 250
info: Live music Thursday to Saturday with 1 band playing each night. All styles considered. See listing for Raw Promotions in relevant section for details of demo submission.

Junktion 7 has become respected as one of Nottingham's leading live music venues, catering for all genres of music. Over the past 4 years such names as Ginger (Wildhearts), Mike Peters (The Alarm), 22-20s and hundreds more have graced our stage.

Vital Specs:
3K Full Logic purpose built PA system, Allen & Heath GL2200 channel mixing desk. Fully air conditioned. For full PA spec see our website.

Junktion 7 6 Ilkeston Road, Canning Circus, Nottingham NG7 3GE.
T/F: 0115 911 6959 email: info@junktion7.co.uk

www.junktion7.co.uk

LIVE PERFORMANCE

The Glee Club
The Arcadian Centre, Hurst Street, Birmingham, B5 4TD
tel:	0870 241 5093
email:	markus_sargeant@yahoo.com
web:	www.glee.co.uk
contact:	Markus Sargeant
capacity:	350 (Main Room), 150 (Studio Theatre)
info:	International and local bands, specialising in Singer-

Songwriters, Acoustic, Soul, Jazz, Folk and Roots. In-house PA. Contact Markus for full gig details. The venue has 2 rooms including a studio theatre. Artists that have played include Damien Rice, KT Tunstall, The Magic Numbers, Gemma Hayes, Anthony & The Johnsons, Ed Harcourt and Supergrass. Glee Club also have another venue in Cardiff. See listing for details.

The Globe/The Lift
144 High Street, Glossop, Derbyshire, SK13 8HJ
tel:	01457 852 417
email:	info@theglobepub.org
web:	www.globemusic.org
contact:	Ron Brookes
capacity:	80
info:	Live music every Monday, Thursday, Friday,

Saturday and Sunday. Bands keep the door taking minus the cost of a sound engineer. Full PA and lighting plus some backline including bass amp and Drum kit. There is a resident band on every Thursday. Send demos and biog to Ron Brookes at the venue. Venue also has its own recording studio. Enquire for details.

Hare & Hounds
High Street, Kings Heath, Birmingham, B14 7JZ
tel:	0121 444 2081
contact:	Solar Creations
capacity:	230
info:	Live music on Friday and Saturday nights, organised

through Solar Creations. 3 bands play per night. In-house PA. See entry in Promoters section for details of demo submission.

Jailhouse

118 Much Park Street, Coventry, CV1 2LU
tel:	02476 221 274
email:	paulf126@aol.com
web:	http://the-jailhouse.cjb.net
contact:	Paul
capacity:	300
info:	Live music Tuesday, Thursday, Friday, Saturday and

Sunday nights. 6kW PA, lights, in-house engineer. Send demos FAO Paul at the venue.

The Jam House
1 St. Paul's Square, Birmingham, B3 1QU
tel:	0121 200 3030
fax:	0121 200 3044
email:	info@thejamhouse.com
web:	www.jamhouse.com
capacity:	600
info:	Blues and Jazz venue. Jools Holland is musical

director. Unsigned bands play Tuesday to Saturday. Need to provide own PA.

JB's Club
15 Castle Hill, Dudley, DY1 4QF
tel:	01384 253 597
fax:	01384 456 525
email:	sam@jbsdudley.co.uk
web:	www.jbsdudley.co.uk
contact:	Sam Jukes
capacity:	1000/500 (Main Room), 150 (Downstairs)
info:	Live music 5 or 6 nights a week. Thursday night

dedicated to unsigned acts. Send demos to Sam at the venue. In-house PA, lights and engineer.

The Jug of Ale
43 Alcester Road, Moseley, Birmingham, B13 8AA
tel:	0121 449 1082
email:	gigenquiries@jugofale.com
web:	www.jugofale.com
contact:	Anna or Arthur
capacity:	80
info:	The Catapult Club is an unsigned showcase for

local talent which takes place 2 times a week. 3 or 4 bands play per night. In-house PA. See entry in Promoters section for details of demo submission.

Junktion 7
6 Ilkeston Road, Canning Circus, Nottingham, NG7 3GE
tel:	0115 911 659
email:	info@junktion7.co.uk
web:	www.junktion7.co.uk
capacity:	200
info:	Regular unsigned nights throughout each month,

although no definite schedule. 3 bands play per night during week, and 4 play on weekends. All music styles considered. May take up to 2 months to sort demos and match suitable acts for a gig, so please be patient. If necessary to follow up demo, contact via above email address.

Karn's Café Bar
17-19 New Buildings, Hinckley, Leicester, LE10 1HN
tel:	01455 618439
contact:	Heidi Ellis
capacity:	75
info:	A lively café bar with live music twice a week.

Mondays are acoustic open mic nights, turn up and play. Thursday is unsigned night with 1 band playing. All styles welcome. Send demos to the venue or call for gig details. In-house PA.

King Billy
2 Commercial Street, Northampton, NN1 1PJ
tel:	01604 621 325
contact:	Rachel Morgan
capacity:	280
info:	Live music every Thursday, Friday and Saturday.

Band should supply their own PA. Also have outdoor garden stage. Mostly local bands, but well known touring bands will be considered. Send demos to Rachel at the venue.

Little Civic
North Street, Wolverhampton, West Midlands, WV1 1RQ
tel:	01902 552 121
fax:	01902 556 713
email:	richard@wolvescivic.co.uk
web:	www.wolvescivic.co.uk
contact:	Richard Taylor
capacity:	140
info:	Live music every night. Support slots are available.

Full PA and backline. Technical specification and stage plan can be found on website. Contact Richard or Phil to arrange a gig. Will accept demos in MP3 format. Richard also books bands for Wulfrun Hall, capacity 1134. National Battle of the Bands competition runs throughout the year with a first prize of £3000 cash and studio time. For full details and application form see the Little Civic website or alternatively, contact Cliff on 01902 552 122 or cliff@wolvescivic.co.uk

Marr's Bar
12 Pierpoint Street, Worcester, WR1 1TA
tel:	01905 613 336
email:	brian@marrsbar.co.uk
web:	www.marrsbar.co.uk
contact:	Brian Marr
capacity:	276
info:	Live music 6 nights a week. Wednesday is jam night.

Friday is dedicated to local acts and Saturday nights are touring bands. Sunday is Acoustic night. 5kW in-house PA. Recording studio upstairs, facilities to record live from stage at cost to the band. Send demos to Brian Marr at the venue. 'Free Bands Three Quid' is held 3 Thursdays per month.

Medicine Bar @ Custard Factory
Custard Factory, Digbeth, Birmingham, B9 4AA
tel:	0121 693 6333
info:	Hosts several unsigned nights including Club NME,

and showcases organised by Angel Promotions. See listing in Promoter section for details of demo submission.

Midlands Arts Centre (MAC)
Cannon Hill Park, Birmingham, B12 9QH
tel:	0121 440 4221
fax:	0121 446 4372
email:	info@macarts.co.uk
web:	www.macarts.co.uk
contact:	Louisa Davies
capacity:	200 (Large Theatre), 88 (Studio Theatre)
info:	Live music on a regular basis, but no definite

schedule. In-house PA. Send demos and biogs to Louisa Davies at MAC. The venue is also available for hire, speak to Linda Jones, also at MAC.

The Mill
Bridge Street, Mansfield, Nottinghamshire, NG18 1AN
tel:	01623 632 451
email:	themill@postmaster.co.uk
web:	www.townmill.com
contact:	Kev, Dave
capacity:	275
info:	Unsigned night every Friday with 3 bands playing.

Live music also during the week, up to 5 nights. In-house PA. Send demo and biog FAO Dave or Kev at the venue.

The Music Room @ Cox's Yard
Bridgefoot, Stratford Upon Avon, Warwickshire, CV37 6YY
tel: 01789 404 600
email: info@coxsyard.co.uk
web: www.coxsyard.co.uk
contact: Katie Beswick
capacity: 252
info: Various nights of live music take place throughout the week apart from Sundays. Different nights take place featuring different genres of music. Venue has in-house lights, PA and engineer. To get a gig send demo FAO Katie at the venue.

The Musician
Clyde Street, Leicester, LE1 2DE
tel: 0116 251 0080
email: rideout@stayfree.co.uk
web: www.themusicianpub.co.uk
contact: Darren Knuckles
capacity: 220
info: Open mic night held every Monday, which has been running for 15 years. Just turn up to take part. Mainly Blues, R&B, World, Americana, Folk and Roots music. Acts may also have the opportunity to support touring acts who appear at the venue. In-house PA, lighting and sound engineer. Demos also accepted, send to Darren at the venue.

Nottingham Boat Club
Middle of Three, West Bridgford, Trent Side North, Nottingham, NG2 5FA
tel: 0115 981 1251
email: info@theboatclubnottingham.co.uk
web: www.theboatclubnottingham.co.uk
contact: Jim Waller
capacity: 250
info: Put on gigs a couple of times a month and occasionally hire out venue to external promoters. Need to provide own PA. Send demo FAO Jim Waller to the venue.

Obsessions
10 Thurland Street, Nottingham, NG1 3DR
tel: 0115 941 7709
fax: 0115 941 5604
email: obsessions@barracudagroup.co.uk
contact: Andy or Phil
capacity: 450 (Upstairs), 150 (Downstairs)
info: Venue available for hire on Tuesdays and Wednesdays. Monday night is Rock night with the occasional live band. Large stage, dressing room, fixed video camera for recording.

The Old Angel Inn
7 Stoney Street, Nottingham, NG1 1LG
tel: 0115 950 2303
contact: Sara or Richard
capacity: 100
info: Live music on Friday and Saturday, call the above number and ask for Sara or Richard to book a gig. In-house PA.

Perspective Lounge Bar
5 Saltergate, Lincoln, LN2 1DH
tel: 01522 513 888
email: info@perspectiveloungebar.com
web: www.perspectiveloungebar.com
contact: Phil Hughes
capacity: 100
info: Live Jazz bar open Thursday, Friday and Saturday. Jazz bands can send demos to the above address or email MP3s to the Perspective email address.

The Planet
Thornley Street, Wolverhampton, West Midlands, WV1 1JP
tel: 01902 711 301
email: steveneon@hotmail.com
web: www.clubhell.co.uk
contact: Steve Harrington
capacity: 300 downstairs, 450 upstairs
info: Band nights put on by external promoters, Neon Empire Marketing. Promote 'Electric Chair' most Fridays, and also organise a club night called 'After Dark'. See listing in Promoters section for details of demo submission.

Plumber's Arms
76 Wylds Lane, Worcester, WR5 1DS
tel: 01905 767 592
email: johnambler@aol.com
contact: John Ambler
capacity: 75
info: Put on live music. For more information contact John at the venue.

Rescue Rooms
Masonic Place, Goldsmith Street, Nottingham, NG1 5JT
tel: 0115 988 1889
email: info@rescuerooms.com
web: www.rescuerooms.com
contact: Anton Lockwood
capacity: 500
info: Occasional support slots available for unsigned bands. All music types considered except Metal, Hard Rock and Nu Metal. In-house PA. Please refer to Getting A Gig page on the website for guidelines on playing at the venue. Do not send demos via post. Email Anton at the above address attaching biog, reviews and MP3s. Occasional events organised through Cosmic American Music, see entry in Promoters section for details of demo submission.

The Roadmender
1 Lady's Lane, Northampton, Northamptonshire, NN1 3AH
tel: 01604 604 603
fax: 01604 603 166
email: enquiries@roadmender.org
web: www.roadmender.org
capacity: 850
info: Regular newly signed and unsigned band nights. Send demos to the venue.

Robbin's Well
2 Victoria Terrace, Leamington Spa, Warwickshire, CV31 3AB
tel: 01926 453 881
contact: Ooffii Hardwick
capacity: 100-150
info: Every Thursday there is a night called 'Alive and Well' which features Indie, Punk and Alternative bands. In order to play contact Ooffii on the above email address. PA will be provided. There is also once monthly Punk night on the first Thursday of every month. For more information on the Punk night contact Ooffii at the venue.

The Robin R&B Club
28 Mount Pleasant, Merry Hill, Bilston, Wolverhampton, WV14 7LJ
tel: 01902 401 211
email: music@therobin.co.uk
web: www.therobin.co.uk
contact: Mike Hamblett
capacity: 700
info: Live music most nights from signed and unsigned acts. Send demos to Leisure Factory booking office at 20-22 Mount Pleasant, Bilston, West Midlands, WV14 7LJ.

Rock Café 2000
Unit 1, Block L, Mill Race Lane, Stourbridge, West Midlands, DY8 1JN
tel: 01384 390 918/01384 833 556
fax: 01384 836 387
email: info@rockcafe2000.co.uk
web: www.rockcafe2000.fsnet.co.uk
capacity: 70 (Seated), 230 (Standing)
info: Live music 7 nights a week. Wednesday is Nu-Metal club night, 'Noise Pollution' plus 1 live band. All other nights are dedicated to live bands. To play Rock Café 2000 contact on the above numbers.

Royal George
1 Park Street, Aston, Birmingham, B6 5SH
tel: 0121 688 1964
contact: Rees
capacity: 150
info: Live music every week, Wednesday to Saturday. Bands are put on by Loop Promotions on a Wednesday night. 'I Bring You Courtesy of...' is an unsigned night held every Thursday. See entries in Promoters section for details of demo submission. Unsigned bands play on a Friday and Saturday nights, with smaller, local acts playing on a Friday, and larger local bands or acts from outside Birmingham playing on a Saturday. No need to send demo, just contact Rees on the above number.

The Rugeley Rose Theatre
Taylor's Lane, Rugeley, Staffordshire, WS15 2AA
tel: 01785 226 868
email: gasworksonline@hotmail.com
web: www.rugeleyrose.net
contact: Simon Broadhurst, Gavin McCaughey
capacity: 300
info: Live music once a week, usually a signed act with unsigned support. Send demos (CD or cassette format), biographies and press to 'I Want A Gig', The Gasworks, 24 Salter Street, Stafford, ST16 2JU. Full technical specification can be found on website.

LIVE PERFORMANCE

The Running Horse
16 Alfreton Road, Canning Circus, Nottingham, NG7 3NG
tel: 0115 978 7398
email: middletonbarry@hotmail.com
web: www.therunninghorse.ukpub.net
contact: Barry Middleton
capacity: 160
info: Live music every night. In-house PA and fitted stage lights. Open mic on Monday, everybody welcome. Tuesday night is 'Folk, Blues and Beyond' featuring Acoustic music. Wednesday night is a Blues jam, student bands on Thursday night. Friday, Saturday and Sunday nights are Blues, Rock and R&B. Call or email Barry to arrange a gig.

The Shed
5 Yeoman Street, Leicester, LE1 1UT
tel: 0116 262 2255
email: shedvenue@hotmail.com
web: www.shedvenue.co.uk
contact: Kevin Hollyland, Darren Nockles
capacity: 300
info: Venue open Monday to Saturday. Live music most nights, 4 or 5 bands a night. 'Saturday Matinee' is a Popular showcase held every Saturday between 2pm and 7pm for bands aged up to 16 years. 5K PA, sound engineer and 24 channel mixing desk. Send demos FAO Val or Darren at the venue. Alternatively email, or call between 2pm and 6pm.

The Social
23 Pelham Street, Nottingham, NG1 2ED
tel: 0115 950 5078
fax: 0115 950 5088
email: socialnottingham@thebreakfastgroup.co.uk
contact: Daniel
capacity: 190
info: Live music all week. Send demos FAO Daniel at the venue. The Social can be available to hire. In-house PA. Contact Daniel at the venue for further information. Bands will be required to pay a deposit which is returnable provided an agreed bar-take is reached. Bands also need to organise an engineer and door staff.

Soundhaus
Great Russell Street, Northampton, NN1 3BU
tel: 01604 250 898
fax: 01604 250 927
web: www.thesoundhaus.com
info: Regular gigs put on by external promoters. Soundhaus also run rehearsal rooms, as well as an equipment hire service (Xcel PA0). See listings in relevant sections for details.

The Sugarmill
Brunswick Street, Stoke On Trent, ST1 1DR
tel: 01782 214 991
fax: 01782 214 991
web: www.thesugarmill.co.uk
contact: In-house Promoter
capacity: 400-500
info: Regular unsigned band nights. Local bands (those who are based within 30 minute drive from Stoke) can send demos and biog to the venue. Other acts should contact the venue through an agent or manager. Friday and Saturday nights host Stoke's biggest Indie and Rock nights, respectively. Bands to have played The Sugarmill include Muse, Coldplay and Kaiser Chiefs.

Sumo
54 Braunstone Gate, Leicester, LE3 5LG
tel: 0116 285 6536
fax: 0116 285 6536
contact: Sam
capacity: 490
info: Live music every Thursday and Saturday. Send demos FAO Sam at the venue.

The Underground
Morley Street, Hanley, Stoke On Trent, ST1 4EZ
tel: 01782 219 944
info: Contact The Underground for information on how to play.

University of Warwick Student Union
Gibbet Hill Road, Coventry, West Midlands, CV4 7AL
tel: 02476 523 523
web: www.sunion.warwick.ac.uk
contact: Darren Walter
capacity: 1250
info: Occasional band nights organised by S.Punk, the University's Punk Society. Also host a night called 'Crash' at which 1 signed band plays every other Friday. Unsigned bands have the opportunity for support slots. For more information call Darren at the venue.

Victoria Inn
12 Midland Place, Derby, DE1 2RR
tel: 01332 740 091
fax: 01332 740 091
email: thevicinn@hotmail.com
web: www.thevicinn.co.uk
contact: Andy Sewell, Michael Sheehan
capacity: 150
info: Any band, any night. In-house PA. Sends demos (no MP3s) with day and evening contact numbers FAO Andy or Michael to the venue. Allow 2 weeks for reply.

Victoria Pub
Whitwick Road, Coalville, Leicestershire, LE67 3FA
tel: 01530 814 718
email: emblempromotions@aol.com
web: www.vicbikerspub.co.uk
contact: John Commons
capacity: 200
info: Biker pub with regular live music. Well known on national level. Covers bands every Friday and Saturday night. Tuesday night jam session (Classic Rock, Blues, Guitar Solo), Wednesday night Jam sessions (recent Metal and Punk). Unsigned acts play every Thursday and Sunday. Victoria Pub also hosts all day events in marquee holding 100 people with up to 10 unsigned bands playing. Venue supplies Drum kit and PA. All gigs heavily promoted on local radio (Oak FM), Victoria's own gig guide (6000 produced bi monthly), biker's mag covering central England, teletext plus all free listing guides (Kerrang!, Metal Hammer etc). Pub has outdoor jungle bar, midnight barbeques and camping facilities for bikers. Send demos to John at the venue, follow with a phone call.

Zanzibar
Cavendish Street, Chesterfield, Derbyshire, S40 1UY
tel: 01246 551 414
fax: 01246 555 766
web: www.zanzibar.co.uk
contact: Simone Johnston
capacity: 3000
info: A large venue with music throughout the week. There is no set live music nights but contact Zanzibar for possible dates. All styles considered. In-house PA. Send demos to the venue address.

NORTHEAST

Alnwick Playhouse
Bondgate Without, Alnwick, Northumberland, NE66 1PQ
tel: 01665 510 785
email: info@alnwickplayhouse.co.uk
web: www.alnwickplayhouse.co.uk
contact: Steve Cowton
capacity: 262
info: Alnwick Playhouse is available for hire. Programming is arranged months in advance, so contact the venue for full details of available slots.

The Barrels Alehouse
59-61 Bridge Street, Berwick Upon Tweed, Northumberland, TD15 1ES
tel: 01289 308 013
email: mark@thebarrelsalehouse.com
web: www.thebarrelsalehouse.com
contact: Mark Dixon
capacity: 70
info: Live music on Fridays, 3-4 bands play each night. Send demos FAO Mark to the venue address.

Bebside Inn
2A Front Street, Bebside, Blyth, Northumberland, NE24 4HT
tel: 01670 828 883
email: tony@bebsideinn.co.uk
web: www.bebsideinn.co.uk
contact: Anthony Fitch
capacity: 120
info: Live music every Saturday with 1 band playing. Send demos FAO Tony at the venue. Mainly Rock but other genres considered. Bands must provide own PA.

The Black Bull
Bridge Street, Morpeth, NE61 1PE
tel: 01670 512 089
contact: Danny Ostridge
capacity: 200
info: Live music every Friday with 1 band playing each week. The band must provide their own PA. Send demos FAO Danny Ostridge at the venue.

Caroline
Caroline Street, Hetton le Hole, Tyne & Wear, DH5 9DB
tel: 0191 526 6603
contact: Patrick Rouse
capacity: 150
info: Live music Friday and Saturday. Friday is Rock only and Saturday is open to any genre. The band most supply own PA. Send demos FAO Patrick at the venue.

The Centurion
Grand Central Station, Neville Street, Newcastle, NE1 5DG
tel: 0191 261 6611
info: Unsigned band nights promoted by Insangel13. See listing in Promoter section for details of demo submission.

The Cluny
36 Lime Street, Ouseburn, Newcastle Upon Tyne, NE1 2PQ
tel: 0191 230 4474
web: www.theheadofsteam.co.uk
contact: Dave Campbell
capacity: 300
info: Live music 7 nights per week, with 3 bands playing on average. In-house PA. Will put on local and touring acts. Contact Dave on the above number to play.

The Cooperage
33 The Close, Quayside, Newcastle upon Tyne, NE1 3RS
tel: 0191 233 2940
fax: 0191 233 2942
email: latinbeat@hotmail.co.uk
web: www.thecooperagenewcastle.co.uk
contact: Peter Ferry
capacity: 370 (over 3 floors)
info: Live music Monday and Thursday. Support slots available each Monday at 'Ignition' and Thursday nights are 'Live Band Showcase'. 3-4 bands play each night. The venue is also available for hire. Send demos FAO Julian Lee at the venue.

Derwentside
101 Durham Road, Blackhill, Conselt, County Durham, DH8 8RR
tel: 01207 502 562
contact: Angela Gowland
capacity: 120
info: Live music on Saturdays and occasionally Fridays. Acts should telephone Angela or send a demo to the venue.

Dog & Parrot
52 Clayton Street West, Newcastle Upon Tyne, NE1 4EX
tel: 0191 261 6998
contact: Jay
capacity: 100
info: Live music every night. Bands pay room hire £20, and extra £30 if they require PA. It is then up to the bands if they wish to charge on the door, they are entitled to all door takings if so. Contact any member of staff on above number for bookings. To speak in detail about equipment requirements, ask for Jay.

Egypt Cottage
117 City Road, Newcastle Upon Tyne, NE1 2AN
tel: 0191 232 0218
email: egypt_cottage@yahoo.com
web: members.lycos.co.uk/egypt_cottage/
contact: Paul Porter, Neil Adams
capacity: 100
info: Egypt Cottage puts on live music 7 nights a week. Will accept all genres of music and cover bands. 1-4 bands play per night. Contact Paul Porter on the venue phone number to get a gig. In-house PA and sound engineer.

The Empire
Corporation Road, Middlesbrough, Cleveland, TS1 2RT
tel: 01642 253 553
email: ted@tenfeettall.co.uk
web: www.theempire.co.uk
contact: Ted, Ashley
capacity: 1000
info: Ten Feet Tall put on bands every Saturday at The Empire. Mainly Rock genre. See listing for Ten Feet Tall in Promoter section for contact details. The Empire also host their own band night every Monday. Send demo to the venue FAO Ashley.

Fat Ox
278 Whitley Road, Whitley Bay, Tyne & Wear, NE26 2TG
tel: 0191 251 3852
contact: Jackie Cowings
capacity: 200
info: Live music Fridays and Saturdays. In-house PA. Bands need to play a mixture of covers and originals. Send demos to the above address.

The Fish Tank
29-33 Neville Street, Durham City, County Durham, DH1 4EY
tel: 07966 174 932
fax: 0191 384 5015
email: hatsandjackets@hotmail.com
web: www.fishtankdurham.co.uk
contact: Sam
capacity: 50
info: Venue has various live music and club nights. All music types considered. In-house PA. Send demos FAO Sam to the venue or call the mobile number given.

Flying Horse
78 Waterloo Road, Blyth, Northumberland, NE24 1DG
tel: 01670 353 314
email: flying.horse@virgin.net
web: www.flying-horse-blyth.co.uk
contact: Ian Young
capacity: 75
info: Live music Saturdays and Sundays. 3-4 bands play each night. Bands must provide own PA. All styles suitable.

The Gold Medal
Chowdene Bank, Low Fell, Gateshead, Tyne & Wear, NE9 6JP
tel: 0191 482 1549
contact: Tom Palmer
capacity: 400
info: Live music once a week. All styles suitable, 1 band plays each week. To play contact venue on the above number.

The Head of Steam (Newcastle)
2 Neville Street, Newcastle Upon Tyne, NE1 5EN
tel: 0191 232 4379
email: thosnewcastlens@theheadofsteam.co.uk
web: www.theheadofsteam.co.uk
contact: Steve Coulker
capacity: 100
info: Outside promoters 'Too Far North' and 'Rattled By The Rush' host nights on Wednesday and Thursday. See Promoter section for details of 'Too Far North'. To contact 'Rattled By The Rush', make contact through the venue first. For the rest of the week Steve Coulker arranges the gigs, featuring 3 or 4 bands a night. In-house PA. For more information or to get a gig call Steve at the venue, or send a demo for his attention.

Ivy House
Worcester Terrace, Sunderland, Tyne & Wear, SR2 7AW
tel: 0191 567 3399
info: Unsigned bands play regularly. See listing for Too Far North in Promoter section for further details.

Jax
Stockton Road, Hartlepool
info: Gigs promoted by Ten Feet Tall. Refer to listing in Promoter section for details of demo submission.

The Jug
83 Claypath, Durham, County Durham, DH1 1RG
tel: 0191 384 8354
contact: Gary Dobson
capacity: 150
info: Live music on Wednesdays and Sundays. Soul and Acoustic music. In-house PA.

Keelboat Inn
Stockfold, Washington, Tyne & Wear, NE38 8RU
tel: 0191 416 0406
contact: Dave Welsh
capacity: 120
info: Unsigned music every Friday with 1 band. Tuesday nights are informal solo performances by professional club artists from the area. Call Dave to play. All listings for the venue are submitted to www.onethecasemusic.com, an online music listings resource for the North East. See relevant listing in Web Resources section for details.

Ku.bar
Regent House, Prince Regent Street, Stockton On Tees, TS18 1DB
tel: 07812 989 537
email: kubar_events@hotmail.com
web: www.kubar.co.uk
contact: Jimmy Beck
capacity: 300
info: Mainly Indie venue, with Alternative night once a month. Put on unsigned bands from all over the country on Fridays, Saturdays and 2 Sundays a month. To play, either email Jimmy at the above address, or send demo for his attention to Shine Like Stars, 212 Bishopton Road West, Stockton On Tees, Fairfield, Cleveland, TS19 7HA.

LIVE PERFORMANCE

The Meadow House
North Road, Berwick-on-Tweed, Northumberland, TD15 1UR
tel: 01289 304 173
email: david@meadow-house.co.uk
web: www.meadow-house.co.uk
contact: David Hearn
capacity: 70
info: Live music once every 2 weeks. Mainly Rock, Blues and Soul music. In-house PA. Send demo FAO David at the venue.

Moby Grape
Calverts Lane, Stockton On Tees, Cleveland, TS18 1SW
tel: 01642 611 311
info: Gigs put on by Ten Feet Tall. See listing in Promoter section for details of demo submission.

The Office
78 Victoria Road, South Shields, Tyne & Wear, NE33 4NQ
tel: 0191 455 6083
fax: 0191 455 0355
email: mail@office-pub.com
web: www.office-pub.com
capacity: 200
info: Live bands every Friday and Saturday night. Need to provide own PA.

Red Rooms
Nelson Street, Newcastle
email: insangel13@aol.com
web: www.insangel13.co.uk
contact: Phil Hughes
capacity: 300
info: Unsigned bands play at Red Rooms every Monday night. To play, contact Phil at Insangel13.co.uk, refer to entry in Promoters section for details.

The Ropery
Websters Bank, Sunderland, SR4 6DJ
tel: 0191 514 7171
contact: Jonathan Graham
capacity: 200 (over 2 bars)
info: Live Rock music on Fridays. Need to provide own PA. Buskers night on Wednesday and Jazz music on a Thursday. Send demos to the above address.

The Royal Tavern
Beaconsfield Street, Blyth, Northumberland, NE24 2DS
tel: 01670 351 708
email: enquiries@royaltavern.co.uk
web: www.royaltavern.co.uk
contact: Bob Kilpatrick
capacity: 100
info: Live music on Fridays and Saturdays dedicated to Acoustic and Rock music respectively. Bands must provide PA. Send demos to the venue.

The Studio
Tower Street, Hartlepool, TS24 7HQ
tel: 01429 424 440
fax: 01429 424 441
email: thestudiohartlepool@btconnect.com
web: www.studiohartlepool.com
contact: Liz Carter
capacity: 200
info: The Studio is a live music venue with bands playing 7 nights a week. Full PA, 6kW rig and lights. Full technical specification can be found on website. Also have recording studio and rehearsal rooms. Facility to record live from stage. Send demo and biog FAO Liz at the venue.

The Three Tuns
92 Sheriffs Highway, Gateshead, Tyne & Wear, NE9 5SD
tel: 0191 487 0666
web: www.thethreetuns.com
contact: Paul Smith
capacity: 120
info: Live music 3-4 times a week, any style accepted. Performances from singer-songwriters to full bands. Send demos FAO Paul Smith at the venue. In-house PA.

Times Inn
Stockton Road, Dalton Le Dale, Seaham, County Durham, SR7 8QA
tel: 0191 581 6606
contact: David, Mary
capacity: 100
info: Live music every Sunday night. One band plays, usually Rock, Blues or Punk music. There is an Acoustic jam night on Tuesday evening where you can just turn up to play. Contact David or Mary on the above number and they will try to come along to a gig.

Trillian's Rock Bar
Princess Square, Newcastle, NE1 8DE
tel: 0191 232 1619
email: info@trilliansrockbar.com
web: www.trilliansrockbar.com
contact: Stuart Davidson, Steve Jones
capacity: 440
info: Pub dedicated to Rock music. Live bands play 2 or 3 times per week. In-house PA and sound engineer. The stage is visible from most areas of the venue, and where it is not, the gig seen via monitors all round the walls. Send demo FAO Steve at the venue.

The Tyne Bar
1 Maling Street, Ouseburn, Newcastle Upon Tyne, NE6 1LP
tel: 0191 265 2550
email: fred@thetyne.com
web: www.thetyne.com
contact: Ben
capacity: 150 (Indoors), 100 (Outdoors)
info: Live music every Sunday and also various nights during the week. Mainly original music of all genres ranging from Electronic to Folk. In-house PA. Venue also has an outdoor stage for use during summer. To play send demo FAO Ben to the venue.

The Vane Arms
Vane Street, Silksworth, Sunderland, SR3 1EJ
tel: 0191 521 0261
contact: Bill Calvert
capacity: 200
info: Live music Friday and Saturday nights, and Sunday afternoons. Usually a mixture of original and covers. Rock, Blues and Country & Western music. Need to provide own PA. Send details of your band and any gig listings to Bill at the venue and he will try to attend a local gig.

Voodoo Rooms @ Bar Pure
15 Olive Street, Sunderland, SR1 3PE
tel: 0191 565 5521
info: Bands play on regular basis organised through external promoters. Receptive Promotions organise gigs around once a month. See listing in Promoter section for details of demo submission.

NORTHWEST

3345
33-45 Parr Street, Liverpool, L1 4JN
tel: 0151 708 6345
email: info@3345parrst.com
web: www.3345parrst.com
contact: Mandy Quarless
capacity: 150
info: DJs from Friday to Sunday nights, and live music on various nights. Every other Thursday there is an Acoustic night. Check the website for details. 3345 also have a recording studio, enquire for details. There is also a room available for hire with plasma screen. For more information contact the venue.

Abbey Inn
77 West Street, Oldham, Lancashire, OL9 6EJ
tel: 0161 624 0888
contact: Natalie
capacity: 150
info: Bands play at least once a week, usually on a Friday or Saturday. Occasional all day events as well. All music types considered. Need to provide own PA, although will hopefully have in-house PA in near future. To play, contact on the above number or send demo to Natalie at the venue. Promotional help given.

The Acoustic Tearoom
39-41 Market Street, Kirkby Stephen, Cumbria, CA17 4QN
tel: 01768 372 123
fax: 01768 372 132
email: acoustictearoom@aol.com
web: www.acoustictearoom.co.uk
contact: Penny, Paul
capacity: 60
info: Soloists and duos. To play contact Penny on the above number or email address. Full promotional support is given, although word of mouth and reputation generally supercedes any press coverage.

Adelphi
43 Fylde Street, Preston, Preston, Lancashire, PR1 7DP
tel: 01772 897 961
contact: Sarah Woodthorpe
capacity: 100
info: Venue for hire. £25 deposit payable, which is returnable at the end of the night if 40 people attend. The Adelphi holds various live music nights on a monthly basis. Demos are not necessary as anyone is welcome. Phone the venue for more information.

THE BRICKYARD

PROMOTERS WELCOME
VENUE RENTAL POSSIBLE

CARLISLE'S LIVE MUSIC VENUE
NO NONSENSE
ORIGINAL ONLY MUSIC POLICY

FULL TIME PROFESSIONAL
PA & LIGHTING SYSTYEM

PRODUCTION & PROMOTIONAL TRAINING

**LIVE SOUND & LIGHTING ENGINEER TRAINING
& PROMOTIONAL TRAINING COURSES**

FOR MORE: INFO@BRICK-YARD.COM

WHEN SENDING DEMOS PLEASE ADDRESS AS FOLLOWS:

THE BRICKYARD
BAND DEMO (PLEASE STATE MUSIC STYLE)
14 FISHER STREET
CARLISLE
CA3 8RN

**PLEASE DO NOT CONTACT US REGARDING DEMOS
OTHER THAN BY POST!**

FOR MORE INFO ON GIGS, BANDS AND MORE. VISIT THE WEBSITE
WWW.BRICK-YARD.COM

LIVE PERFORMANCE

Alexander's Jazz Theatre
Rufus Court, Chester, CH1 2JW
tel:	01244 340 005
email:	info@alexandersjazz.com
web:	www.alexandersjazz.com
info:	Blues, Soul, R&B and Acoustic live music organised
by Northgate Music Promotions. See listing in relevant section for
details of demo submission.

The Alma Inn
152-154 Bradshawgate, Bolton, Lancashire, BL2 1BA
tel:	01204 364 113
email:	trevor.crook@virgin.net
web:	www.almainnlive.co.uk
contact:	Trevor Crook
capacity:	130
info:	Live bands play once a week, often signed acts with
unsigned support. Thursday night hosts unsigned local bands. In-house
PA. Send demos FAO Trevor to the venue with a contact number.

Barfly
90 Seel Street, Liverpool, L1 4BH
tel:	0151 707 6171
fax:	0151 707 9885
email:	eli@barflyclub.com
web:	www.barflyclub.com
contact:	Jez Couldwell, Tony Carter
capacity:	500 (Theatre), 350 (The Loft)
info:	Live bands play 7 nights per week. Original music
only, usually between 2 and 4 bands play per night. Venue also hosts
half day events once every couple of months with up to 8 bands
playing. In-house PA. Send demos to Jez at the venue. Follow up with a
phone call.

Barley Mow
29 Old Market Place, Golden Square, Warrington, Cheshire, WA1 1QB
tel:	01925 651 182
contact:	Helen Wynn
capacity:	100
info:	Live music every Saturday night, all music styles
considered. Open mic event is held every Wednesday, just turn up to
take part. In-house PA, although most acts prefer to bring their own PA.
Send demo FAO Leigh to the venue.

The Bierkeller
77 Piccadilly, Manchester, M1 2BU
tel:	0161 236 1807
fax:	0161 236 0368
email:	info@manchesterbierkeller.co.uk
web:	www.bierkeller.co.uk
contact:	Graham
capacity:	360
info:	Live music 3 or 4 times a week. In-house PA. Send
demo FAO Graham to the venue.

Black Horse Pub
80 Wallasey Village, Wallasey, Merseyside, CH45 3LQ
tel:	0151 638 1440
web:	www.blackhorse-wallasey.co.uk
contact:	Steve Fowlds
capacity:	100-150
info:	Live music Thursday, Friday and Monday nights,
as well as Sunday afternoons. Monday is jam night, and first Friday of
every month is Acoustic jam night. Everybody welcome to both. First
Sunday afternoon of every month is dedicated to original material,
mainly Acoustic Singer-Songwriter soloists or duos. Need to supply
own PA. Website includes gig guide and forum. Send demos to Steve
Fowlds at the venue to play the Sunday afternoon sessions, or Pop
along to the jam nights.

Blue Cat Café
Shaw Road, Heaton Moor, Stockport, Lancashire, SK4 4AG
tel:	0161 432 2117
email:	danny@bluecatcafe.co.uk
web:	www.bluecatcafe.co.uk
contact:	Danny
capacity:	100
info:	Monday night is 'Blue Monday', an Acoustic
songwriters night. To take part bring instrument, arrive by 8pm and
sign up at the bar. Minimum of 2 songs (no covers). In-house PA.
Unsigned nights on every other night. Contact Danny to play.

Bootleggers Music Bar
24 Finkle Street, Kendal, Cumbria, LA9 4AB
tel:	01539 723 824
email:	bar@bootleggersbar.com
web:	www.bootleggersbar.com
contact:	Penny Miller
capacity:	250
info:	Bootlegger's put on 4 nights of live music per week,
with 1 band playing each night. Venue has in-house PA, stage and
lighting. For more informarion on how to play contact Penny at the
venue, or send demos to the above address.

The Brickyard
14 Fisher Street, Carlisle, CA3 8RN
tel:	01228 512 220
web:	www.brick-yard.com
contact:	Andy McCormack
capacity:	250
info:	Live bands play on Friday and Saturday nights, and
occasionally during the week. 3 or 4 bands play per night. All music
types considered, The Brickyard promote a diverse range of music and
events, including comedy acts and plays. 6k PA and engineer supplied.
Large stage which can accommodate up to 11 piece band. Also
occasionally hold 'Acoustic Circus' open mic night, just turn up to take
part. Send demo and biog FAO Andy to the venue. No follow up phone
calls, as The Brickyard is often inundated with bands chasing feedback
on demos, Andy will contact you.

Briton's Protection
50 Great Bridgewater Street, Manchester, Lancashire, M1 5LE
tel:	0161 236 5895
email:	markusbp@aol.com
contact:	Markus Stevens
capacity:	60
info:	Room available for bands to hire from £30. In-house
PA. Contact Markus on the above number to make a booking.

Bruin's Bar
Moseley Road, Fallowfield, Manchester, M14 6ND
tel:	0161 256 1992
email:	bruins.bar@ntlworld.com
contact:	Mark
capacity:	250
info:	Open mic night every Tuesday, just turn up to take
part. Live music also on Thursday and Sunday nights. To play, send a
demo FAO Mark at the venue. Alternatively, go to the open mic night
and the best acts will be asked to come back and perform. In-house PA.

Carlton Hotel
33-37 Standish Street, Burnley, Lancashire, BB11 1AP
tel:	01282 835 763
email:	jacquelinelayfield@hotmail.com
contact:	Jacqueline Layfield
capacity:	150
info:	Live music every Friday and over weekend at
Christmas and bank holidays. Need to provide own PA. To play, contact
Jacqueline on the above number.

The Castle
38 Union Street, Oldham, Lancashire, OL1 1DJ
tel:	01706 882 759/07969 884 868
email:	thecastle@rock.com
web:	www.castlelive.com
contact:	Steve Jones
capacity:	300
info:	Live music every Thursday, Friday, Saturday and
some Sundays. Indie, Rock, Punk, Alternative music. 10kW PA, full
lighting rig. Every gig has a club night afterwards. The venue also hosts
Club NME every Saturday which has the opportunity for support slots.
Contact Steve for more information or send a demo for Steve's attention
to the venue.

The Cavern
Matthew Street, Liverpool, L2 6RE
tel:	0151 236 9091
fax:	0151 236 8081
email:	cavernnow@gmail.com
web:	www.cavern-liverpool.co.uk
contact:	Ged Ryan
capacity:	350
info:	Unsigned nights Thursday to Sunday. Send demos
FAO Ged Ryan to the venue. Promotional material provided. Door
percentage available, along with rider at the bar.

The Citadel
Waterloo Street, St. Helens, Merseyside, WA10 1PX
email:	mmurchison@citadel.org.uk
web:	www.citadel.org.uk
contact:	Morag Murchison, Gareth
info:	Send demos to Morag Murchison (Events
Programmer) at the venue, follow with a phone call 2 weeks later. See
also listing for St. Helens Musicians' Collective in relevant section, who
promote regular nights at the venue.

Club Academy
Basement of Student's Union, Manchester University, Oxford Road,
Manchester
tel:	0161 275 2930
fax:	0161 275 2980
email:	maximum@umu.man.ac.uk
info:	'Replay' is a band and club night held every Friday
at Club Academy. 4 bands play each week. To submit your demo, see
listing for mcr:music in Promoter section.

LIVE PERFORMANCE

The Cornerhouse
Ridgeway Street, Douglas, Isle of Man, IM1 1EW
email: gigs@itsonthecorner.com
web: www.itsonthecorner.com
info: Live music on Thursdays and Sundays. Send demo to the above address or email links to tracks online.

The Crypt
75 Market Street, Lancaster, Lancashire, LA1 1JG
tel: 01524 324 51
contact: Michael
capacity: 100
info: The Crypt hosts various unsigned nights featuring all genres of music. In order to get a gig or for more information contact Michael at the venue. When calling the venue, ask to be put through to The Crypt.

Cuban Knights
45 Pickford Street, Macclesfield, Cheshire, SK11 6HB
tel: 01625 669 300
email: bands@cuban-knights.co.uk
web: www.cuban-knights.co.uk
contact: Alistair Gaskell, Neil
capacity: 350
info: Wednesday is a showcase night for unsigned bands to play original material. In-house PA. Send demo clearly marked with contact details to Alistair or Neil at the venue.

De.Bees Music Bar
17-19 Market Place, Winsford, Cheshire, CW7 3DA
tel: 01606 558 596
email: info@debees.com
web: www.debees.com
contact: Damon Horrell
capacity: 400
info: Original live music takes place every Sunday and Monday at the venue. Mainly Indie and Rock based music. Every Wednesday there is an Acoustic and Jazz night. Tribute acts play on Thursday. To get a gig contact Damon with your MP3s via email. The venue has an in-house recording studio and they will provide live recordings of your set for free. In-house PA, lights and engineer. For more information on the recording studios contact the venue.

Dickie Doodle's
Yard 2, Stricklandgate, Kendal, Cumbria, LA9 4ND
tel: 01539 738 480
web: www.dickiedoodles.co.uk
contact: Tony
capacity: 120
info: Live music most nights with 1 or 2 bands playing. Mixture of covers and original songs. Mondays and Tuesdays are Acoustic jam and Electric jam nights respectively. Wednesday is an Acoustic Folk night. Need to provide own PA. To play, contact Tony by telephone on the above number.

Dry Bar
28 Oldham Street, Manchester, M1 1JN
tel: 0161 236 9840
email: mildred_hubble@hotmail.com
web: www.drybar.co.uk
contact: Rachel
capacity: 500 (Upstairs), 100 (Downstairs)
info: Dry Bar has live music most nights of the week with various different themes. There are club nights which feature live Electronic or Drum&Bass artists. Venue is also used by outside promoters such as Vman, Glasswerk and Carpe Diem Present. For more information see Promoters section for Vman Events listing, or contact Rachel who can pass you on to the appropriate promoter. Alternatively check the website for more details.

Farmer's Arms
86-88 Chorley Street, Bolton, Lancashire, BL1 4AL
tel: 01204 525 834
fax: 01204 525 834
web: www.thefarmersbolton.co.uk
contact: Steve, Linda
capacity: 150
info: Live music every Saturday night. Mainly Rock and Indie music. Bands can play covers or original songs. Popular bands may be offered repeat bookings. Need to provide own PA. Send demo FAO Steve or Linda to the venue.

Font Bar
7-9 New Wakefield Street, Manchester, M1 5NP
tel: 0161 236 0944
email: fontbar@tiscali.co.uk
web: www.fontbar.com
contact: Anna Scott
capacity: 300
info: Font Bar put on music of all genres. Please send demo to Anna at the venue or call for more information.

Fuel Café Bar
448 Wilmslow Road, Withington, Manchester, M20 3BW
tel: 0161 448 9702
web: www.fuelcafebar.co.uk
contact: Karen
capacity: 80
info: Fuel has open mic nights most Wednesdays, just turn up to play. The venue is available for hire free of charge for band and club nights. Fuel also put on signed Folk artists.

FX Club/Friar's Court Inn
2b Ryland Street, Warrington, Cheshire, WA1 1EN
tel: 01925 232 291
fax: 01925 232250
email: reynoldsnorthwest@hotmail.com
contact: Joe Coyle
capacity: 320 (FX Club), 230 (Friar's Court)
info: The FX Club and Friar's Court Inn are next door to each other. 'The Music Lounge' is held every Sunday in Friar's Court Inn. All music styles considered, although nothing too heavy. Open mic night every Monday at Friar's Court Inn. Tuesdays at Friar's Court hosts an Indie band night with £1 drinks. Various club nights take place at the venues featuring DJs. Contact Joe at the venue for more information.

Golden Lion
Main Street, Keswick, Cumbria, CA12 5JD
tel: 01768 772 347
email: mariongolden@aol.com
contact: Terry
capacity: 180
info: Unsigned acts play every other Thursday. During summer live music increases to every Thursday and Sunday. Need to provide own PA. Send demo FAO Terry at the venue.

Hanover Hotel
62 Hanover Street, Liverpool, L1 4AF
tel: 0151 709 6223
contact: Michael Cox
capacity: 250
info: Local unsigned bands play every Friday and Saturday, 1 band per night. In-house PA. To get a gig send demo FAO Michael to the venue. There is also a karaoke night every Thursday.

Hark to Towler
43 Market Street, Tottington, Bury, Lancashire, BL8 4AA
tel: 01204 883 856
email: hark2towler@aol.com
web: www.hark2towler.co.uk
contact: John Hanson
capacity: 150
info: Live music every Thursday, Friday and Saturday nights. All genres of music accepted. Venue has stage, lighting and PA. To play contact John on the above number, or send demos to the venue.

Heebie Jeebie's
80-82 Seel Street, Liverpool, L1 4BH
tel: 0151 708 7001
fax: 0151 708 6700
email: info@heebie-jeebies.com
web: www.heebie-jeebies.com
contact: Tracy Morgan
capacity: 375
info: Bands play at least 3 times per week. Live music organised by Black Sheep Productions. 'Mixed Bag' is a band night held every Thursday featuring a mixture of genres including Indie, Alternative, Pop, Soul, Rock, Punk, Rap, Funk, 60s, 70s and 80s. Full technical specification can be found on website. Send demos FAO Black Sheep Productions to the venue. Black Sheep also promote various events, as well as running a record label and management company. Refer to entries in relevant sections for further details.

The High Cross Inn
Broughton In Furness, Cumbria, LA20 6ES
tel: 01229 716 272
fax: 01229 716 555
email: info@highcrossinn.com
web: www.highcrossinn.com
contact: Dale Jarvis
capacity: 150 (Function Room), 100 (Bar)
info: Live music around 5 or 6 times a month, usually on a weekend. Mainly Blues, Folk, Singer-Songwriter. Need to provide own PA. Acoustic acts occasionally play in the bar area on a Sunday afternoon. Send demo FAO Dale at the venue, or alternatively send him an email to the above address.

Hornblowers
22 Market Street, Birkenhead, CH41 5ER
tel: 0151 647 6019
contact: Alec
capacity: 240
info: Live music every Thursday night. Hornblowers tend to book bands from their existing roster, although occasionally put on new acts. Need to provide own PA. Send demo FAO Alec to the venue.

Iguana Bar
115-117 Manchester Road, Chorlton, Manchester, Lancashire, M21 9PG
tel: 0161 881 9338
email: info@iguanabar.co.uk
web: www.iguanabar.co.uk
contact: Pascal
capacity: 200
info: Open mic night every Tuesday, just turn up to take part at 8:30pm and speak to a compere. Acts that impress on a Tuesday, will be asked to play on the acoustic night every Thursday.

Iron Door Club
60-64 Argyle Street, Birkenhead, Wirral, CH41 6AF
tel: 0151 647 2772
email: irondoor@wirrallive.com
contact: Jenny
capacity: 240
info: Live music every Wednesday, Thursday, Friday and Saturday nights, 10pm til 2am. Monthly band showcases (5 bands per show). Best of the showcase bands may get support slots later, and those that really impress will be invited to headline. Full 6.5K rig. Also have an Indie band night twice a month on a Thursday. Send demo FAO Jenny to the venue.

Jabez Clegg
2 Portsmouth Street, Manchester, M13 9GB
tel: 0161 272 8612
email: info@freakflag-music.com
contact: Paul O' Donaghue
capacity: 400
info: Unsigned band night once a month, with 3 or 4 bands per night. Organised by Paul O'Donaghue, he will also provide PA. Email Paul with details of your band and your music, and he will be in touch with further contact information. On the first Sunday of the month, Vman Events presents Manchester's new music festival, 'Twelve', at Jabez Clegg. Also hosts 'Vman:records showcase' on the last Thursday of the month featuring 4 bands. PA hire arranged. See entry for Vman Events in Promoters section for details of demo submission.

The Jacaranda
21-23 Slater Street, Liverpool, L1 4BW
tel: 0151 707 8281
email: jacaranda@jacaranda.u-net.com
contact: Peter Antonio
capacity: 255
info: Open mic night every Thursday, everybody welcome. Just turn up to take part. The Jacaranda is famous worldwide for hosting early Beatles shows, and murals painted by John Lennon and Stuart Sutcliffe in the late 1950s are still visible behind the stage.

Jim's Acoustic Café
New Market Street, Colne, Lancashire, BB8 9BJ
tel: 01282 868 828
contact: Adrian Melling
capacity: 65
info: Jim's Acoustic Café is a vegetarian restaurant. Live music is organised once a month through Planet Records. Mainly Folk and Roots with singer-songwriters and duos performing. In-house PA. See entry for Planet Records in Record Companies section for details of demo submission.

The Krazyhouse
16 Wood Street, Liverpool, L1 4AQ
tel: 0151 708 5016
fax: 0151 709 3273
email: info@thekrazyhouse.co.uk
web: www.thekrazyhouse.co.uk
contact: Chris Morrison
info: Live music at least once a month, likely to increase in the near future. PA supplied. Voted best music club in Liverpool by NME. Call, email or send demos to Chris Morrison at the venue.

The Late Room
23 Peter Street, Manchester, M2 5QR
tel: 0161 833 3000
fax: 0161 833 4000
capacity: 300
info: Regular unsigned band nights organised by mcr: music and Charabanc Promotions, including HMV Showcase every Friday, and Plastic Surgery band and club night every Saturday. Refer to entries in Promoters section for further details.

The Limelight
Hightown, Crewe, CW1 3BP
tel: 01270 251 929
fax: 01270 251 929
email: band.bookings@amserve.net
web: www.crewe-limelight.co.uk
contact: Martin Bentley
capacity: 400 (Main Room), 130 (2nd Room), 100 (3rd Room)
info: Live music 7 nights a week. Monday, Tuesday and Friday are dedicated unsigned nights. Will accommodate touring bands, who can share line up with local acts. Occasional support slots also available. Also put on tribute bands. Full PA, see website for specifications. Send demos to the venue FAO Martin. Details of local accommodation suitable for out of town bands can also be found on the website.

Liverpool Academy 2/3
160 Mount Pleasant, Liverpool, Merseyside, L69 7BR
tel: 0151 709 9108
email: ents@liv.ac.uk
web: www.liverpoolacademy.co.uk
contact: Ents Office
capacity: 480/250
info: Book an Academy Unsigned night through Glasswork, check relevant entry for more details.

The Magnet
45 Hardman Street, Liverpool, L1 9AS
tel: 0151 709 3654
email: magnetliverpool@btopenworld.com
contact: Kevin
capacity: 350
info: Unsigned bands play live every week, usually on Tuesdays. In-house PA and sound engineer. Send demos FAO Kevin to the office address: 48 Ampthill Road, Liverpool, L17 9QW. Also host jam night, 'Gumbo', in association with local music colleges every Monday. For further information, contact Kevin on the office number 0151 726 0705.

Malt & Hops
1 Barton Street, Blackburn, Lancashire, BB2 1LJ
tel: 01254 699 453
contact: Lisa Morris
capacity: 150
info: Local bands play every Thursday night. Usually Rock and Indie music. Need to provide own PA. Prefer local bands to be able to bring an audience of their own. Send demo FAO Lisa to the venue.

Manchester Metropolitan University Student Union
99 Oxford Road, Manchester, M1 7EL
tel: 0161 247 1162
email: s.u.entweb@mmu.ac.uk
web: www.mmu.ac.uk
contact: Simon
capacity: 550
info: Manchester Met often puts on up and coming signed bands. There is an opportunity for support slots for established Manchester bands. There is occasionally battle of the bands for unsigned acts but at present there are no set unsigned nights. Call Simon for more information on playing.

Manchester University Students' Union - Academy 3
Oxford Road, Manchester, M13 9PR
tel: 0161 275 2930
fax: 0161 275 2980
email: maximum@umu.man.ac.uk
web: www.manchesteracademy.net
contact: Sarah Bennett
capacity: 400
info: 'Academy Unsigned' is a regular unsigned night run by mcr:music, giving bands an opportunity to play a venue normally reserved for touring bands. Excellent facilities including dressing room, rider, lighting and monitor engineers, and chance to earn excellent performance fees from ticket sales. For details regarding these gigs and demo submission, see mcr:music in the Promoters section.

Matt & Phred's
64 Tib Street, Northern Quarter, Manchester, M4 1LW
tel: 0161 831 7002
email: club@mattandphreds.com
web: www.mattandphreds.com
contact: Matt
capacity: 250
info: Live music 6 nights a week. Jazz, Latin, Acoustic acts and musicians. 2.5K PA, full technical specification can be found on website. Send demo FAO Matt to 85 Oldham Street, Manchester, M4 1LW.

HOME TO
LIVE ROCK'N'ROLL
IN MANCHESTER

city life bar of the year

For the purpose of arranging a
performance or in order to pertain
information about an event speak to a
gentleman by the name of Jay

office ~ 0161 236 1822
venue ~ 0161 236 4597
jay@nightnday.org
www.nightnday.org

Nº 26 Oldham Street, Northern Quarter, Manchester, M1 1JN

Design: www.a-to-m.com | www.myspace.com/jaytaylor

NIGHT & DAY

*Now with
air-conditioning

Mersey Clipper
Prenton Road West, Birkenhead, Merseyside, CH42 9PY
tel: 0151 608 3446
contact: Jimmy
capacity: 350
info: Local bands play every Friday to Monday. Usually 1 band per night. Need to provide own PA. Send details of your band and gig listings to Jimmy at the venue. He will try and go to see a band perform before booking them.

The Met Theatre
Market Street, Bury, Lancashire, BL9 0BL
tel: 0161 761 7107
email: post@themet.biz
web: www.themet.biz
contact: Dave Naylor,
capacity: 300 (Standing), 225 (Seated), plus Separate 100 capacity space
info: Regular live band nights, The Big Rock Saturdays, held bi-monthly comprises of 4 to 6 bands playing Rock, Punk, Old Skool Metal, Nu-Metal, Emo, Ska-Punk, Stoner and Hardcore. To play on a Saturday, send demo to the venue and mark FAO Dave Naylor. In-house PA, lighting and engineer.

Middleton Civic Centre
Fountain Street, Middleton, Manchester, M24 1AF
tel: 0161 643 2470
fax: 0161 654 0221
web: www.nx.rocks.it
contact: Rick Garlack
capacity: 800 (Standing), 550 (Seated), 595 (Cabaret Seating)
info: There are 2 or 3 unsigned nights a month. 8K rig, with in-house intelligent lighting. Speak to Rick Garlack, follow by sending demo to the venue. Support slots are available for bands that impress.

The Mill
Aqueduct Street, Preston, Lancashire, PR1 7JN
tel: 01772 883 617
email: ruff@themillpreston.com
web: www.themillpreston.com
contact: Ruff
capacity: 600
info: 'Showcase Fuzzy' takes place every Friday evening in association with Action Records. This is a night specifically for unsigned artists. The Mill put on a lot of up and coming signed bands as well, and there may be the opportunity for support slots for bands that do well on the unsigned night. In-house PA provided.

The Mitre Tavern
90-91 Moor Lane, Preston, Lancashire, PR1 1JQ
tel: 01772 251 918
email: cmolyneux@hotmail.com
contact: Chris
info: Live music most Tuesday, Thursday, Friday, Saturday and Sunday nights. Bands are entitled to a percentage of bar takings, and an entry fee if applicable. To play contact Chris on the above email address.

Mulligan's Café Bar
Lord Street, Southport, Merseyside, PR9 0QE
tel: 01704 544 417
contact: Nicki Brindle
capacity: 180
info: Live music on Friday and Saturday nights. Covers only of any genre. Need to provide own PA. Send demo FAO Nicki at the venue, or call the venue for more information.

Music Box
65a Oxford Rd, Manchester, M1 6FS
tel: 0161 273 3435
fax: 0161 273 3695
capacity: 400
info: Regular Thursday nights run by High Voltage Refer to listing in the Promoter section for details.

New Central Club
St. Mary's Street North, Preston, Lancashire, PR1 5LG
tel: 01772 251 911
contact: Mr Patel
capacity: 250
info: Function room available for hire to bands. Contact Mr Patel on the above number for further details.

Night & Day Café
26 Oldham Street, Manchester, M1 1JN
tel: 0161 236 4597
fax: 0161 236 4597
email: jay@nightnday.org
web: www.nightnday.org
contact: Jay Taylor
capacity: 200
info: Local slots available most days of week, possible support slots also available. Send demos to Jay at the venue. Night and Day also hosts 'Club Fandango Manchester' on the last Friday of every month. Refer to entry in Promoters section for details of demo submission. Night and Day has gallery space and accepts film submissions, which are occasionally combined with live music and are shown on screen between bands. Contact Jay Taylor for further information about this.

Old Market Tavern
Old Market Place, Altrincham, Cheshire, WA14 4DN
tel: 0161 927 7062
contact: Ann-Marie
capacity: 220
info: Live Rock and Blues every Sunday night with 1 band playing. Send demo FAO Ann-Marie at the venue.

The Palace
Farmside Place, Levenshulme, Manchester, M19 3BF
tel: 0161 257 2484
fax: 0161 257 2362
email: palacenightclub@btclick.com
web: www.levenshulme.com/palace or
www.24rockfest.com
contact: Tony Hennigan
capacity: 830
info: Regular unsigned band nights, email your details to the address above. The Palace also host the YGG Unsigned competition, for unsigned bands with Irish roots (at least 1 member of the band must have Irish grandparents or parents). To apply, send demo and biog to the address above. Also run new band showcase, '24 Rock Fest', one Friday per month. Send demo FAO Tony to the venue.

The Platform
Old Station Building, Central Promenade, Morecambe, Lancashire, LA4 4DB
tel: 01524 582 803
email: jharris@lancaster.gov.uk
contact: John Harris
capacity: 350 (Seated), 1000 (Standing)
info: Support slots for signed acts become available 6 or 7 times per year. Headlining acts in the past have included Nitin Sawhney, Lee Scratch Perry and national tribute bands. The Platform also host a main stage every year in August dedicated to local unsigned bands. In-house PA. Send demo FAO John to the above address.

Pleasure
489 Wilmslow Road, Withington, Manchester, M20 4AN
tel: 0161 434 4300
email: pleasurelounge@btconnect.com
contact: Louis (outside promoter)
capacity: 75
info: Open mic night every Monday from 7pm. The final hour is a live jam, just turn up to take part.

Po Na Na Souk Bar
42 Charles Street, Manchester, Lancashire, M1 7DB
tel: 0161 272 6044
email: manchesterpnn@ponana.com
web: www.ponana.com/manchester
contact: Kieran Harkin
capacity: 320 (over 2 floors)
info: Po Na Na hosts 'Fret Noise' which has 4-5 acts on stage every Monday night. Acts range from 2 piece Acoustic acts to 10 piece Funk acts. Venue provides the PA. There is also a once monthly live music night on Saturday which features 1 band.

Porters Ale House
78 Butter Market Street, Warrington, Cheshire, WA1 2NN
tel: 01925 632 885
email: sinead.dooley@ntlworld.com
contact: Sinead
capacity: 99
info: Live music once a week. Mainly Rock acts playing covers and original songs. In-house PA. Send demo FAO Sinead to the venue.

The Red Herring
Mill Lane, Coppull, Lancashire, PR7 5AN
tel: 01257 470 130
contact: Mary
capacity: 150 (downstairs)
info: Live music every Saturday night. Acts play covers or original songs. No Heavy Rock or Metal music. Need to provide own PA. Contact Mary on the above number to play.

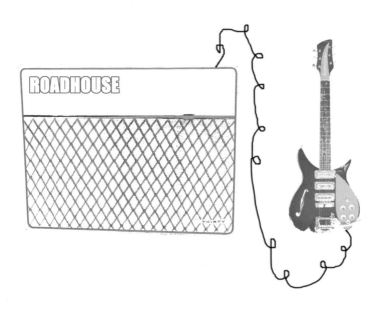

THE ROADHOUSE 8 NEWTON STREET PICCADILLY MANCHESTER M1 2AN

OFFICE T.0161 237 9789   FAX 0161 236 0789   VENUE T. 0161228 1789

E-MAIL: INFO@THEROADHOUSELIVE.CO.UK

WWW.THEROADHOUSELIVE.CO.UK

SEND YOUR DEMO TO KRIS or KARA

Retro Bar
78 Sackville Street, Manchester, M1 3NJ
tel: 0161 274 4892
email: andy@retrobarmanchester.com
web: www.retrobarmanchester.com
contact: Andy
capacity: 150
info: Host regular unsigned band nights. Speak to Andy about your band playing. Venue will help with press promotion of your gig. 500W PA system in-house.

The Roadhouse
8 Newton Street, Piccadilly, Manchester, M1 2AN
tel: 0161 237 9789
fax: 0161 236 9289
email: theroadhouse@btconnect.com
web: www.theroadhouselive.co.uk
contact: Kris Reid, Kara
capacity: 200
info: Unsigned nights 3-4 nights per week. Full technical specification can be found on website. Send demos to Kris Reid at the venue.

Rose & Crown
22 King Street, Ulverston, Cumbria, LA12 7DZ
tel: 01229 583 094
contact: Andy Woods
capacity: 100
info: Live music every Wednesday night, covers only. Need to provide own PA. To play, call Andy on the above number.

The Royal Hotel
2 Station Road, Great Harwood, Lancashire, BB6 7BA
tel: 01254 883 541
fax: 01254 877 375
email: beer@rosebrewery.co.uk
contact: Pete, Janice
capacity: 120 (Music Room)
info: Live bands play every Friday and Saturday night. Mainly Blues, Rock and Bluegrass music, original songs or covers. Contact Pete or Janice at the venue for more information on how to play. The Royal Hotel also brew their own beer tasty beer!

Royal Oak Hotel
Breck Road, Poulton-Le-Fylde, Lancashire, FY6 7AQ
tel: 01253 882 198
email: info@holidaysinthesun.net
contact: James
capacity: 160-200
info: Live music every Sunday. Punk night held every 5 or 6 weeks, organised by Carl and Paul, who are also behind the 'Holidays In The Sun' Punk festival held in Blackpool. Contact James on the above number to play.

Satan's Hollow
101 Princess Street, Manchester, M1 6DD
tel: 0161 236 0666
web: www.satanshollow.net
capacity: 360
info: Regular live music, both during the week and on weekends. Variety of nights organised by external promoters including Say It To My Face. See entry in Promoters section for further details. Mainly Punk, Ska and Metal bands. Send demos to the venue.

Slaughterhouse
13-15 Fenwick Street, Liverpool, L2 7LS
tel: 0151 231 6881
contact: Declan
capacity: 134
info: Live music every Friday, Saturday and Sunday, up to 4 bands per night. Slaughterhouse is an ideal venue for unsigned bands (a square room with low ceilings and exposed original beams). Contact Declan with details of your act on the above number. Follow with demo on request. Band friendly.

Slim Jim's Jazz Restaurant
2 St. Helen's Road, Ormskirk, Lancashire, L39 4QR
tel: 01695 571 888
contact: Matthew
capacity: 60
info: Live Jazz and Blues every weekend. In-house PA. Send demo FAO Mathew to the venue.

The Southern
Mauldeth Road West, Chorlton, Manchester, M21 7SP
tel: 0161 881 7048
fax: 0161 881 7048
email: grantpaull@msn.co.uk
contact: Grant Paull
capacity: 600 (over 2 levels)
info: The venue has 2 rooms available for hire holding between 50 and 300 people. If bands are interested in getting a gig, send demo to Grant Paull at the venue or ring for more information. In-house PA provided.

Stamps
4 Crown Buildings, Coronation Road, Crosby, Liverpool, L23 5SR
tel: 0151 286 2662
email: stampswinebar@hotmail.com
contact: Jackie
capacity: 120
info: 'Off the Record' Acoustic showcase night every Tuesday. Thursdays are dedicated to bands performing covers. Every Saturday and Sunday Stamps feature live, original music. In-house PA and backline provided. To play either telephone, email or send demos to Jackie at the venue.

Star & Garter
18-20 Fairfield Street, Manchester, M1 2QF
tel: 0161 273 6726
email: staff@starandgarter.co.uk
web: www.starandgarter.co.uk
contact: Derm
capacity: 100 on each floor
info: Live music most nights, organised through external promoters. 'Anti-Hoot' is an open mic night which is held downstairs on the third Saturday of every month. Just turn up to take part.

The Strawberry
228 Abbey Road, Barrow-in-Furness, Cumbria, LA14 5LD
tel: 01229 825 321
contact: Dave Calvert
capacity: 150
info: Live music every Sunday night. Need to provide own PA. Ring the venue for more information or send demo FAO Dave to the venue.

Strettles
53 Fylde Road, Preston, Lancashire, PR1 2QL
tel: 01772 827 007
contact: Terry Farnworth
capacity: 150
info: Live bands can book the upstairs room in Strettles at no cost. Bands play most weekends. In-house PA. Contact Terry by telephone to make a booking.

Sun Café
25 Sun Street, Lancaster, Lancashire, LA1 1EW
tel: 01524 845 599
capacity: 50
info: Jazz and Easy Listening musicians and duos play every Saturday night. In-house PA. For information on how to play call the venue on the above number

The Tache
Exchange Buildings, 12 Cookson Street, Blackpool, FY1 3EH
tel: 01253 628 732
email: ron@thetache.co.uk
web: www.thetache.co.uk
contact: Ron
capacity: 400
info: Dedicated Rock club with regular unsigned band nights. In-house PA, large stage and changing room. Send demo and biog to Ron at the venue.

The Tavern
37 Mesnes Street, Wigan, Lancashire, WN1 1QP
tel: 01942 243 871
web: www.wiganmusic.com
contact: Mark Briscoe
capacity: 175-200
info: Band showcase every Saturday night organised by The Wigan Music Collective. 3 or 4 bands usually play. In-house PA and engineer. Also arrange under-16 nights on occasional Sunday afternoons. To get a gig contact Wigan Music Collective on the email address above or contact the venue.

Telford's Warehouse
Tower Wharf, Chester, Cheshire, CH1 4EZ
tel: 01244 390 090
fax: 01244 370 071
email: info@telfordswarehouse.com
web: www.telfordswarehouse.com
contact: Jeremy Horral
capacity: 200
info: Unsigned nights throughout the week. Send demos to the address above. If need to contact Jeremy by phone, call between 5pm-6pm.

The Thirsty Scholar/The Attic
50 New Wakefield Street, Manchester, M1 5NP
tel: 0161 236 6071
email: enquiries@thirstyscholar.co.uk
web: www.thirstyscholar.co.uk
contact: Rory McKee
capacity: 165 (Thirsty Scholar), 210 (The Attic)
info: Adjoining venues, with The Thirsty Scholar downstairs hosting regular live music, and The Attic upstairs availablle for hire. Monday night is 'The Shooting Gallery' run by Rory McKee, a blend of the best new bands. Tuesday Tony presents live unsigned bands and Acoustic acts every Tuesday from 9pm. Thursday is open mic night called 'The Happening'. First Wednesday of the month at 'The Attic' is 'Wood' which is an Acoustic showcase night, also run by Rory, email or telephone Rory to book a slot. Contact venue for details of other nights held each week.

Transport Club
Baron Street, Rochdale, Lancashire, OL16 1SJ
tel: 01706 632 087
email: bookings@jlc-rock-promotions.com
web: www.jlc-rock-promotions.com
contact: Barry Cozens
capacity: 200
info: Live music every Friday. Mainly cover bands although do have occasional act playing original songs. Need to provide own PA. Send demo FAO Barry to the venue, or contact Barry by telephone or email.

The View Two Gallery
23 Mathew Street, Liverpool, L2 6RE
tel: 0151 236 9555
fax: 0151 236 9444
email: info@viewtwogallery.co.uk
web: www.viewtwogallery.co.uk
contact: Ken Martin
capacity: 70
info: The View Two Gallery is an independent gallery supporting local and international artists. Live music at least weekly, acts just need to contact Ken by phone or email to book the venue. In-house PA, grand piano and bar. Details of all gigs will be posted on the View Two Gallery website.

The Vines
81 Lime Street, Liverpool, L4 8SX
tel: 0151 709 3977
email: stephenmahoney78@yahoo.co.uk
contact: Stephen Mahoney
capacity: 200
info: Unsigned bands play in The Vines Ballroom, the 19th century Gothic ballroom at the back of The Vines pub. To get a gig contact Stephen at the venue, or send demo for his attention to the venue.

The Warehouse
43 Burrowgate, Penrith, Cumbria, CA11 7TA
tel: 01768 868 984
contact: Mark
capacity: 270
info: Live music every Friday night. Mainly covers of Pop, Easy Listening and Rock music. Need to provide own PA. Send demo FAO Mark to the venue.

Wellington Inn
Prescott Inn, Ditton, Widnes, Cheshire, WA8 7PD
tel: 0151 420 5634
fax: 0151 420 0996
contact: Debbie Beyga
capacity: 150
info: Live Acoustic jam session every Tuesday. Wednesday night is new bands night. Need to provide own PA. To play telephone Debbie Beyga or send demo to the venue. Competition running each year with £1000 cash prize, contact Debbie for more details.

The Witchwood
152 Old Street, Ashton-Under-Lyne, Lancashire, OL6 7SF
tel: 0161 344 0321
email: pod@arcmusic.freeserve.co.uk
web: www.arcsounds.com
contact: Pod
capacity: 200
info: Live music 7 nights a week. Send demos to Pod at the venue. The Witchwood also run a rehearsal centre with CD duplication facilities (Arc Sounds). Refer to entries in relevant sections for further details.

The Witton Chimes
122 Witton Street, Northwich, Cheshire, CW9 5NW
tel: 01606 479 04
email: whittonchimes@btconnect.com
web: www.thewittonchimes.com
contact: Michelle Partington
capacity: 200
info: Open mic night called 'Acoustic Moods' every Tuesday, just turn up to take part. Whitton Chimes also host 'A Song From The Heart Of Cheshire' which is an annual singer-songwriter competition in which studio time can be won. Call Michelle at the venue for more information about this. The venue also has a Rock club night on Friday nights, 'Rock Gods', and 'Soul-ution' on Saturdays which is a Soul club night. Live music also takes place every Saturday night. Call Michelle at the venue to get a gig.

Ye Olde John O'Gaunt
55 Market Street, Lancaster, Lancashire, LA1 1JG
tel: 01524 653 56
email: yeoldejohnogaunt@tiscali.co.uk
contact: Robin Edmundson
capacity: 200
info: Live music 6 nights a week from local acts. Traditional and Modern Jazz, Blues, Folk. Need to provide own PA. Send demos FAO Robin at the above address.

Yorkshire House
Parliament Street, Lancaster, LA11 1DB
tel: 01524 646 79
web: www.yorkshirehouse.enta.net
contact: Kev, Ali Baxter
capacity: 100
info: Live music every night with 2 or more bands playing per night. All original songs, mainly Guitar-based music. In-house PA. Full technical specification can be found on website. Send demo FAO Kev at the venue.

The Zanzibar Club
43 Seel Street, Liverpool, L1 4AZ
tel: 0151 707 0633
fax: 0151 707 0633
email: info@thezanzibarclub.com
web: www.thezanzibarclub.com
contact: Antony Butler
capacity: 300
info: Live music around 4 nights a week. In-house PA and engineer. Send demos to Antony at the address above.

SOUTHEAST

3 B's Bar and Café
Blagrave Street, Reading, Berkshire, RG1 1QH
tel: 0118 939 9803
fax: 0118 056 6719
email: gary.forshaw@reading.gov.uk
contact: Gary Forshaw
capacity: 150
info: Live music 3-4 nights a week. There is a mixture of open mic and live band nights. All styles welcome. Send demos to Gary at the venue. In-house PA.

The Abrook Arms
Harefield Road, Uxbridge, UB8 1PW
tel: 01895 234 360
email: www.abrookarms.co.uk
web: donn.burke@btinternet.com
contact: Margret
capacity: 150
info: Open mic night fortnightly on Sunday. To take part just turn up by 8:30pm as the night gets extremely busy.

The Agincourt
London Road, Camberley, Surrey, GU15 3UU
tel: 01276 65078
email: info@clubagincourt.co.uk
web: www.clubagincourt.co.uk
contact: Sam Prentice
info: Venue dedicated to Rock music with live bands playing regularly. Available for hire to external promoters. Send demo FAO Sam Prentice to the above address. Gigs also organised by Rubberband Promotions. See listing in relevant section for further information.

The Alma Arms
193 Highland Road, Southsea, Portsmouth, Hampshire, PO4 9EZ
tel: 02392 826 200
contact: Lisa Bendon
capacity: 70
info: Live music every Saturday with 1 band playing. Contact venue directly for details. Send demos FAO Lisa Bendon.

The Anvil
Churchill Way, Basingstoke, Hampshire, RG21 7QR
tel:	01256 819 797
fax:	01256 331 733
email:	ann.dickson@theanvil.org.uk
web:	www.theanvil.org.uk
contact:	Ann Dickson
capacity:	1500
info:	Venue staging performances including Classical, Opera, Rock and Pop, as well as comedy, dance and children's shows. The Anvil is also available to hire.

The Arches Club
63-65 Caversham Road, Reading, Berkshire, RG1 8AD
tel:	0118 950 0950
email:	via website
web:	www.thearchesclub.co.uk
contact:	Mr Gill
capacity:	260
info:	The Arches is a Jazz and Funk club with live music every Thursday, Friday and Saturday. Contact the venue or send demos FAO Mr Gill. Gigs only available for local bands and musicians. In-house PA and sound engineer available.

The Beacon Court Tavern
128 Canterbury Street, Gillingham, Kent, ME7 5TP
tel:	01634 853 186
web:	www.beaconcourttavern.com
contact:	Simon
capacity:	150 (Music Bar), can extend to 300
info:	The Beacon Court Tavern hosts a Battle of the Bands competition every year. Also live bands play 4 times a week. In-house PA. Send demo FAO Simon to the venue.

The Beercart Arms
15 Beer Cart Lane, Canterbury, Kent, CT1 2NY
tel:	01227 826 901
email:	mark@2tonepromotions.com
contact:	Mark
capacity:	245
info:	Punk and Ska band night every second Tuesday featuring an international signed act headlining, plus support from local unsigned bands. Alternate Tuesdays are an unsigned night, Death Metal through to Folk welcome. 2kW in-house PA. Send demo FAO Mark or Ruth to the venue.

Bertie's Bar
47 Church Street, Wolverton, Milton Keynes, MK12 5JW
tel:	01908 315 447
web:	www.qvmk.com
contact:	John
capacity:	200
info:	Part of the new Queen Victoria complex. Live music every weekend. All styles of music, a mixture of original and covers acts. In-house PA. Send demo to the venue address.

Brittania
Fort Hill, Margate, CT9 1HH
tel:	01843 223 269
contact:	Jonathan Wood
capacity:	180
info:	Live music Wednesday, Thursday, Friday and Saturday nights. Every second Thursday of the month is a jam night with drum kit provided. Acts who perform well on a Thursday night may be booked for weekend shows. Alternatively, send Mick Solly a demo and email with details of upcoming live gigs. Can often be booked up to a year in advance. Full in-house PA.

The Bullingdon
162 Cowley Road, Oxford, OX4 1UE
tel:	01865 244 516
email:	gigs@thebully.co.uk
contact:	Arron
capacity:	280
info:	Unsigned acts play 2 or 3 times per week. All music types considered. In-house PA. To play contact Arron by telephone or email.

The Carlisle
24 Pelham Street, Hastings, TN34 1PE
tel:	01424 420 193
fax:	01424 420 193
email:	info@the-carlisle.co.uk
web:	www.the-carlisle.co.uk
contact:	Sid Davis
capacity:	300
info:	Rock and biker pub. Live music every Friday and Saturday. Bands need to supply own PA. Send demos to Savage at the venue. Bands that play The Carlisle can include a link to their website from the venue's website.

Cella @ Sanctuary Café
51-55 Brunswick Street East, Hove, East Sussex, BN3 1AU
tel:	01273 770 006
email:	cella@sanctuarycafe.co.uk
web:	www.sanctuarycafe.co.uk
contact:	Sarah Whitaker
capacity:	60
info:	Cella hosts a packed programme of live music and arts every night of the week. All genres of music welcome. Venue has in-house PA. In order to get a gig send demo FAO Sarah to the venue. Room can also be hired subject to availability.

The Cellar
Frewin Court, Cornmarket, Oxford, OX1 3HZ
tel:	01865 244 761
email:	tim@cellarmusic.co.uk
web:	www.cellarmusic.co.uk
contact:	Tim or Jimmy
capacity:	150
info:	Live music every Saturday. Funk, Reggae, Ska and Dance music. Check regularly on website as have more live music on during week, depending on time of year. In-house PA and stage. To play either contact Tim or send demo for his attention to the venue.

Central Studio
Cliddesden Road, Basingstoke, RG21 3HF
tel:	01256 417 511
email:	phil.pennington@gmc.ac.uk
web:	www.centralstudio.co.uk
contact:	Phil Pennington
capacity:	150-200
info:	A small theatre and music venue based at Queen Mary's College. Live music Fridays and Saturdays. Send demos FAO Phil at the venue. In-house PA and sound engineer. There is also a recording studio in the college. For more information about this call and speak to Shane.

Chinnery's
21-22 Marine Parade, Southend-on-Sea, Essex, SS1 2EJ
tel:	01702 467 305
web:	www.chinnerys.co.uk
contact:	Glyn Morgan
capacity:	250
info:	Local bands play up to 3 times per week. In-house PA. Send demo to the venue.

Club 85
74 Whinbush Road, Hitchin, Hertfordshire, SG5 1PZ
tel:	01462 432 767
email:	bob@club-85.co.uk
web:	www.club-85.co.uk
contact:	Bob Mardon, Matt
capacity:	225
info:	Live music every Friday, Saturday and Sunday night. First Sunday of the month (and fifth where applicable) is Acoustic night. Second Sunday of the month hosts an eclectic mix of live music with 4 bands playing 30 minute sets. The third Sunday of the month is a funky jam session featuring the house band and participants from the audience. The focus on live music on fourth Sunday of the month is Psychedelia and is open to bands of this genre. Acts should contact Bob or Matt by email or telephone. Those with a recommendation from another band or an audience are preferred.

Colchester Arts Centre
Church Street, Colchester, Essex, CO1 1NF
tel:	01206 500 900
email:	info@colchesterartscentre.com
web:	www.colchesterartscentre.com
contact:	Staff
capacity:	400
info:	Support slots occasionally become available but nothing regular. Also host all day events for unsigned bands twice a year. Send demos FAO Staff at the address above.

Concorde II
Madeira Drive, Brighton, BN2 1EN
tel:	01273 697 888
fax:	01273 730 468
email:	trevor@concorde2.co.uk
web:	www.concorde2.co.uk
contact:	Trevor
capacity:	540
info:	Venue hosts variety of unsigned nights. 'Brighton Rocks' presented by Lout Promotions, is held one Sunday per month and features Indie and Rock bands from Brighton and the surrounding area. For details of demo submission, please see Lout Promotions entry in relevant section. Brighton Ska and Punk Festival takes place at the venue every 3 months. Send demos FAO Trevor at the venue and he will do best to accommodate unsigned talent. In-house PA. Full technical specification can be found on website.

Corn Exchange
Market Place, Newbury, Berkshire, RG1 5BD
tel:	01635 582 666
email:	tonyj@cornexchangenew.co.uk
web:	www.cornexchangenew.com
contact:	Tony Jones
capacity:	568
info:	The Corn Exchange organises gigs throughout the

year and works alongside Water Side Music Club. For details of current event programme visit the website. All styles welcome. Send demos FAO Tony Jones. In-house PA and sound engineer available.

The Crypt
53 Robertson Street, Hastings, East Sussex, TN34 1HY
tel:	01424 443 075
email:	info@hastingslive.com
web:	www.hastingslive.com
contact:	Peter
capacity:	300
info:	Live music organised about once a week by Peter,

mainly Rock and Indie acts. Sometimes require local bands to support touring acts. Send demo FAO Peter to the venue. Peter also uses The Brass Monkey venue, situated down the road from The Crypt, which is available for hire and hosts various nights.

Elbert Wurling's
Pegs Lane, Hertford, Hertfordshire, SG13 8EG
tel:	01992 509 153
email:	info@elberts.co.uk
web:	www.elberts.co.uk
info:	Bar and restaurant which also plays host to regular

live music, including open mic nights and showcase events organised by Insomnia Music. See entry in Promoters section for details of demo submission.

Extra Time Bar
Broadbridge Heath Leisure Centre, Wickhurst Lane, Horsham, West Sussex, RH12 3YS
tel:	01403 211 311
info:	Regular live music organised by Highgain

Promotions. See listing in relevant section for details of gigs and demo submission.

Face Bar
Ambrose Place, Chatham Street, Reading, RG1 7RB
tel:	0118 956 8188
email:	info@thefacebar.com
web:	www.thefacebar.com
info:	Live music organised by Bukandskit Promotions. See

listing in relevant section for demo submission details.

The Fez
5-6 Gun Street, Reading, Berkshire, RG1 2JR
tel:	0118 958 6839
email:	info@readingfez.com
web:	www.readingfez.com
capacity:	400/560
info:	Unsigned nights on Wednesdays put on by local

promoters. Check website for details. The Fez has its own in-house PA.

The Forum
The Common, Tunbridge Wells, Kent, TN1 1EB
tel:	01892 545 792
fax:	01892 512 427
email:	twforum@globalnet.co.uk
web:	www.twforum.co.uk
contact:	Mark Randall
capacity:	200
info:	'The Stable' is a project consisting of 70 selected

unsigned acts from the South East region. Bands that form 'The Stable' vary in style, quality and ambition. Every Monday 3 bands from the roster play a gig at the Forum and a track from their set is selected to be part of a compilation CD. The CD is then sent to major industry figures for them to pick their favourite bands. The fans also vote on their favourite bands each week, Scores on the Doors. This results in 2 grand finals featuring top 6 bands, The Fan's Choice and The Man's Choice. The prize to the winner of each of these finals is 2 days in a recording studio plus 500 CDs. Support slots for touring bands are also occasionally allocated to members of 'The Stable'. Send demo FAO Mark Randall to 35 Chandos Road, Tunbridge Wells, TN1 2NY. If you require further information please contact Mark who will forward a copy of the manifesto to you. 'The Stable' runs from September to July, a new crop of bands will be selected each year.

Fountain's Mill Youth Centre
81 High Street, Uxbridge, Middlesex, UB8 1JR
tel:	01895 231 192
contact:	Julie
capacity:	180
info:	Rock, Indie, Punk and Ska music will take place

every Friday evening from Christmas 2005. Must be aged 13 to 19 years to play at the venue, as it is part of a young person's centre. In-house PA.

Free Butt
1 Phoenix Place, Brighton, BN2 9ND
tel:	01273 603 974
email:	freebutt@zelnet.com
web:	www.zelnet.com
contact:	Jack or Rob
capacity:	150
info:	Live music up to 7 nights a week, including monthly

Hip-Hop, Punk and Electronica nights. Send demos and biog to at the venue. In-house PA and engineer. The Free Butt played host to live UK debuts of both The Vines and Yeah Yeah Yeahs.

The Gaiety/The Albert
South Parade Pier, Southsea, Portsmouth, Hampshire, PO4 0SP
tel:	02392 732 283
email:	sarahcooper@leisureparcs.co.uk
web:	www.southparadepier.co.uk
contact:	Sarah Cooper
capacity:	800/400
info:	The venue specialises in events and banqueting.

There is various live music nights put on by outside promoters. For more information about this contact Sarah at the venue. Every Thursday there is a live Blues night called 'Bulldog Blues', and on Saturdays there is an Alternative club night called 'Chaos'.

Gardner Arts Centre
University Of Sussex, Falmer, Brighton, East Sussex, BN1 9RA
tel:	01273 685 447
fax:	01273 678 551
email:	claire.soper@gardnerarts.co.uk
web:	www.gardnerarts.co.uk
contact:	Clair Soper
info:	Contact before sending demo. See website for more

details.

The Greys
105 Southover Street, Brighton, East Sussex, BN2 2UA
tel:	01273 680 734
email:	mike@greyspub.com
web:	www.greyspub.com
info:	Regular live music organised through Barn d'Or

Music. See entry in Promoter section for details of demo submission.

The Hall
Cliddesden Road, Basingstoke, RG21 3HF
tel:	01256 417511
email:	phil.pennington@gmc.ac.uk
web:	www.centralstudio.co.uk
contact:	Phil Pennington
capacity:	500 (Standing)
info:	A venue based at Queen Mary's College. Live music

mainly on Saturdays, see the website for monthly programmes. Send demos FAO Shane at the venue. In-house PA and sound engineer.

The Hobgoblin
26-28 High Street, Bedford, Bedfordshire, MK40 1SP
tel:	01234 356 391
contact:	Alex Scutt
capacity:	210
info:	Unsigned nights on Tuesdays and Sundays. From 1

to 3 bands per night, ranging from Acoustic acts to Indie bands. Need to provide own PA. To get a gig call Alex on the above number for more information.

Holly Tree
25 High Street, Addlestone, Surrey, KT15 1TT
tel:	01932 844 700
contact:	John
capacity:	200
info:	Live music takes place about twice a month. To get a

gig send demo FAO John at the venue. All genres of music accepted.

Holmer Green Sports Association
The Pavilion, Watchet Lane, Holmer Green, Buckinghamshire, HP15 6UF
tel:	01494 711 485
email:	info@hgsa.co.uk
web:	www.hgsa.co.uk
contact:	John
capacity:	130
info:	Live music every other Wednesday, 1-2 bands

perform each night. All styles from Jazz, Blues, Rock, Folk and Acoustic. Send demos FAO at the venue.

The Horn
Victoria Street, St. Albans, AL1 3TE
tel:	01727 844 627
email:	info@thehorn.co.uk
web:	www.thehorn.co.uk
contact:	Matt
capacity:	250
info:	Live music every night. In-house PA. Full technical

specification can be found on website. Send demos and biog to Matt at the venue.

The Jazz Café
Madejski Stadium, Bennet Road, Reading, Berkshire, RG2 0FL
tel: 0118 968 1442
fax: 0118 968 1443
email: info@thejazzcafe.co.uk
web: www.thejazzcafe.co.uk
contact: David Simpson
capacity: 300
info: Live music Friday and Saturdays but additional nights can be arranged if needs be. Mainly caters for Soul, R&B and Funk but the style of music is very relaxed. Send demos FAO David Simpson at the venue. In-house PA.

La Havana
3 Little London, Chichester, PO19 1PH
tel: 07788 481 163
email: pourangb@yahoo.co.uk
web: www.lahavana.co.uk
contact: Pourang Entertainment Manager
capacity: 120
info: Live music from Tuesday to Saturday. A combination of touring and unsigned bands. In-house PA, original music only.

Leo's The Red Lion
Crete Hall Road, Gravesend, Kent, DA11 9AA
tel: 01474 566 127
fax: 01474 334 445
web: www.leosredlion.com
contact: Terry Lee
capacity: 400
info: Established band night every Saturday, followed by an Indie and Rock club. In-house PA. Acts to have played the venue include Iron Maiden, Hawkwind and Marillion. Bands receive a percentage of the door, and are very much encouraged to bring along a crowd. Contact Terry at the venue for more information on getting a gig.

The Lion Brewery
104 Guildford Road, Ash Surray, Hampshire, GU12 6BT
tel: 01252 650 486
email: michaelj.armitage@ntlworld.com
contact: Michael Armitage
capacity: 120
info: Musician's jam night every Thursday, 3 or 4 songs per act. Just turn up to take part. Backline and PA provided. Local bands play every Friday and Saturday night, but need to provide own PA on these nights. Contact Michael if interested in playing and he will arrange a brief audition. There is also an audition night on Sunday evenings for up and coming bands or college bands.

The Mick Jagger Centre
Shepherds Lane, Dartford, Kent, DA1 2JZ
tel: 01322 291101 (enquiries)/01322 291 100 (box office)
fax: 01322 291 144
email: mail@themickjaggercentre.com
web: www.themickjaggercentre.com
contact: Nichola Bowden
capacity: Room 1 - 144 (Seated) 200 (Standing),
Room 2 - 350 (Seated) 600 (Standing)
info: 2 performance spaces available. Contact Peter Conway on 020 8378 1012 be considered for one of The Mick Jagger Centre's programmes or see the website for details of hiring the venue for your own gig. Rehearsal facilities available. See relevant section for more details.

Mill Arts Centre
Spiceball Park, Mill Lane, Banbury, Oxfordshire, OX16 5QE
tel: 01295 252 050
email: liz.reed@oxfordshire.gov.uk
web: www.millartscentre.org.uk
contact: Liz Reed
capacity: Theatre : 200/250 seating/standing, The Millers Bar 100 mixed seating and standing
info: Incorporates a theatre with resident sound and lighting technicians and in-house PA and a smaller bar venue (The Millers Bar). These rooms can be used on either a door-split basis or as a straight room hire, dependent on negotiation between the artist and venue. Practice rooms also available to hire.

Old Fire Station
40 George Street, Oxford, OX1 2AQ
tel: 01865 297 170
fax: 01865 297 199
email: julie.sturgess@clearchannel.co.uk
web: www.getlive.co.uk/ofs
contact: Julie Sturgess
capacity: 550
info: The venue will be hosting live music from early 2006 onwards featuring unsigned bands. To be considered for a gig contact Julie or send a demo to the venue.

The Orange Tree
Norton Road, Letchworth, SG7 5AW
tel: 0845 123 2658
email: alan@questor-cp.cp.uk
web: www.madnanny.co.uk
contact: Alan Hudson
capacity: 50
info: Live Folk music every Wednesday. Contact Alan on the above number for details of demo submission.

Phats Bar
50 Queen Street, Maidenhead, Berkshire, SL6 1HY
tel: 01628 770 777
contact: Andrew/Karl
capacity: 250
info: Unsigned nights organised by Bukandskit Promotions. See listing in relevant section for details of demo submission.

Pitz @ Woughton Centre
Rainbow Drive, Leadenhall, Milton Keynes, Buckinghamshire, MK6 5EJ
tel: 01908 660 392
fax: 01908 696 146
email: p.rivers@btconnect.com
web: www.thepitzmk.com
contact: Paul Rivers
capacity: 400
info: Live music every Thursday, Friday and some Saturdays. Average of 3 bands per night. Touring bands will share line up with local band. In-house PA, lights, sound and lighting engineers. Email Paul Rivers with details of band, send demo to the venue.

The Point @ Zodiac
190 Cowley Road, Oxford, Oxfordshire, OX4 1UE
tel: 07711 628 021
email: mac@planet57.freeserve.co.uk
web: www.the-zodiac.co.uk
contact: Mac
capacity: 300
info: Regular unsigned band nights. In-house PA. Send demos FAO Mac to The Point.

Pressure Point
33 Richmond Close, Brighton, BN2 9NA
tel: 01273 684 501
email: pressurepointpromos@hotmail.com
web: www.pressurepoint.me.uk
contact: Gareth Gwynne-Smith, Simon Parker
capacity: 210
info: Live music 3 times a week, with 3 or 4 bands playing. All music types considered. No covers, all original songs. In-house PA. Send demo FAO Gareth at the venue.

Pumphouse
Local Board Road, Watford, Hertfordshire, WD1 2JP
tel: 01923 241 362
info: Venue plays host to live Jazz events. Gigs are put on occasionally by Last Chance Records. See listing in Promoter section for details of demo submission.

The Railway Inn
3 St. Paul's Hill, Winchester, Hampshire, SO22 5AE
tel: 01962 867 795
fax: 01962 867 795
email: ben@liveattherailway.co.uk
web: www.liveattherailway.co.uk
contact: Ben
capacity: 120
info: Live music all week. Monday night is a dedicated Roots night, the remaining evenings play host to acts from any genre. To play, contact Ben at The Railway Inn office. Follow with demo on request.

Roebuck Hotel
Oxford Road, Tilehurst, Reading, Berkshire, RG31 6TG
tel: 0118 942 7517
contact: Brian
capacity: 200
info: Live music on Friday and Saturday nights. Need to provide own PA. Send demo FAO Brian to the venue.

Roger Courtney's Open Mic Club
The Barn, Milton Arms, 174-176 Milton Road, Southsea, Hampshire, PO4 8PR
tel: 02392 837 730/ 07952 967 948
email: vinylrecordsuk@aol.com
web: www.thursdaymusic.co.uk
capacity: 150
info: Hour long guest spot available to bands, plus open mic session on Thursdays only from 7pm to 12pm. PA and mics supplied. Send demo if interested in special guest spot from 8pm-9pm.

LIVE PERFORMANCE

South Street
21 South Street, Reading, Berkshire, RG1 4QU
tel: 0118 901 5234
fax: 0118 901 5235
email: 21southstreet@reading.gov.uk
web: www.readingarts.com
contact: Rob Sowden, Jess Clausen
capacity: 220 (Standing), 125 (Seated)
info: Unsigned band night, 'Pop Toys', held every second Saturday night. See entry for Pop Toys in Promoters section for details of demo submission. Promotional help given. Room also available for hire, contact Jess for further details at the venue.

The Square
Fouth Avenue, Harlow, Essex, CN20 1DW
tel: 01279 305 000
fax: 01279 866 151
email: adam@harlowsquare.com
web: www.harlowsquare.com
contact: Adam
capacity: 250
info: Between January and June, Thursday nights are devoted to a 'Battle of the Bands'. 27 acts take part, entry forms are available from The Square. Contact Adam for further information. Thursdays from July to December play host to new band showcases. 3 bands play per night, for 30 to 35 minutes each. Band must be located within 30 mile radius of venue and members must be under 25 years. Each band receives flyers for their gig and gets paid for every flyer through the door. Contact Adam on the above number or email to play at showcase nights. Blur, Oasis, Ride and The Cooper Temple Clause all made their Square debut on a showcase night. The Square has in-house PA and full video and audio recording facilities, including recording live from the stage.

The Star
2 Quarry Street, Guildford, Surrey, GU1 3TY
tel: 01483 532 887
email: thestarinn@hotmail.com
contact: Charlotte
capacity: 100
info: Live music every night, mostly unsigned bands and musicians. All styles of music. In-house PA. To play send a demo FAO Charlotte at the above address.

The Swan Inn
The Street, Hatfield Peverel, Chelmsford, Essex, CM3 2DW
tel: 01245 380 238
contact: Chris Ward, Jane
capacity: 150
info: Live music every Friday and Sunday. Thursday is Jam night, just turn up to take part. Bands also play every 6 weeks on a Saturday night. Need to provide own PA, except at Jam night. Send demo FAO Chris to the venue.

The Tumbledown Dick
227 Farnbourgh Road, Farnborough, Hampshire, GU14 7JT
tel: 01252 542 055
fax: 01252 541 858
email: simon.gerring@the-tumbley.com
web: www.quarantineclub.co.uk
contact: Simon Gerring
capacity: 280
info: Showcase night every Thursday and live music from local talent and tribute bands every Saturday. In-house PA and sound engineer. Send demos to Simon at the venue. Tumbledown Dicks also hosts weekly Rock night on Fridays called 'Quarantine Club'.

The Twist
25 Millitary Road, Colchester, Essex, CO1 2AD
tel: 01206 562 453
fax: 01206 545 566
email: info@thetwist.co.uk
web: www.thetwist.co.uk
contact: Max or Niel
capacity: 150
info: Wednesday nights is an Acoustic night. On Thursday, there is a showcase called 'Plug and Play', where bands can book to play without the promoter listening to your demo. If bands do well on this night then they will be asked back to play on the Friday or Saturday night where 3-4 bands play. Venue accept all genres of music. In-house PA, sound engineer and lights. To get a gig phone or email the venue.

Waterside Centre
Northbrook Street, Newbury, Berkshire, RG14 1DS
tel: 01635 412 69
email: watersidecentre@westberks.gov.uk
contact: Sharon Harrods
capacity: 200
info: Waterside Centre is part of a youth development programme for Newbury and the surrounding area, aimed at 13-19 year olds. Bands play every other Saturday night, and band practices are available on Thursday evenings and Sunday afternoons. Also organise gigs through external promoters, at which bands from all over the county can play. Send demos FAO Sharon Harrods and she will pass demo onto suitable promoter.

The Wedgewood Rooms
147b Albert Road, Southsea, Portsmouth, PO4 0JW
tel: 02392 293 301
fax: 02392 851 326
email: info@wedgewood-rooms.co.uk
web: www.wedgewood-rooms.co.uk
contact: Geoff Priestly
capacity: 400
info: Live music 7 nights a weeks. 2 unsigned nights a month, 'Stay True' (Metal and Punk) and 'Unplugged' (Acoustic). An annual battle of the bands is run through the summer. In-house PA. Send demos FAO Geoff at the venue.

West End Centre
Queens Road, Aldershot, Hampshire, GU11 3JD
tel: 01252 408 040
fax: 01252 408 041
email: barney.jeavons@hants.gov.uk
web: www.westendcentre.co.uk
contact: Barney Jeavons, Chris Shepherd
capacity: 200 (Standing), 100-150 (Seated)
info: Live bands once a week on a Friday or Saturday night, and an Acoustic night on the second Wednesday of every month. In-house PA. Send demos to Barney at the venue.

Western Front
11 Cranbourne Street, Brighton, BN1 2RD
tel: 01273 725 656
info: Badger Music promote regular unsigned nights. See listing in Promoter section for further details.

White Horse
95 West Wycombe Road, High Wycombe, HP11 2LR
tel: 01494 527 672
fax: 01494 439 782
email: thewandegroup@btinternet.com
web: www.whitehorse-rocks.co.uk
contact: James Everest
capacity: 250
info: Live music every Tuesday, Thursday, Friday and Saturday night. Acoustic nights on Sundays. Full PA, sound engineer and lighting engineer. Support slots available. Send demos FAO James Everest at the venue. Gigs also put on regularly by Alternator Promotions, see entry in Promoters section for further details.

Windsor Arts Centre
St. Leonard's Road, Windsor, Berkshire, SL4 3BL
tel: 01753 859 421
fax: 01753 621 527
email: graham@windsorartscentre.org
web: www.windsorartscentre.org
contact: Graham Steel
capacity: 100
info: Monthly band nights. Send demos FAO Graham at the venue. 2 annual band competitions for over 18s and under 18s. In-house PA.

Zodiac
190 Cowley Road, Oxford, OX4 1UE
tel: 01865 420 042
email: info@the-zodiac.co.uk
web: www.the-zodiac.co.uk
contact: Nick Moorbath
capacity: 450 (Upstairs), 250 (Downstairs)
info: Unsigned music up to 4 or 5 times a week. Support slots can become available for local bands. Full in-house PA. Send demos to Nick Moorbath at the venue. Also hosts monthly showcase event organised by Gappy Tooth Industries for musicians, artists and poets. See entry for Gappy Tooth Industries in Promoters section for further details.

SOUTHWEST

AR2
Students' Union, Queens Road, Clifton, Bristol, BS8 1LN
tel: 0117 954 5830
email: ents-ubu@bristol.ac.uk
web: www.ansonrooms.co.uk
contact: Kay Lowrie
capacity: 250
info: AR2 is the sister venue to Anson Rooms in Bristol University Student's Union. Anson Rooms 2 will this year be home to 'Live On 1', a free regular live music night featuring some of the country's best unsigned talent. Accept all genres of music and have in-house PA.

The Bear
261 Hotwell Road, Hotwells, Bristol, BS8 4SF
tel: 0117 987 7796
info: Jazz club held every Friday night called 'The Bebop Club'. See listing in Promoter section for details of demo submission.

Bell
103 Walcot Street, Bath, BA1 5BW
tel: 01225 460 426
web: www.walcotstreet.com
contact: Steve Henwood
capacity: 100
info: Live music on Monday and Wednesday nights, and Sunday afternoons. Jazz, World, Ethnic, Folk, Acoustic, Country Blues, Americana, Bluegrass, Cajun, Experimental music. 2 acts play 45 minute sets each. In-house PA and engineer. Send demo to the above address FAO Steve.

Black Cat Club @ Riverside Inn
49 St. Margaret's Street, Bradford-on-Avon, Wiltshire, BA15 1DE
tel: 01225 863 526
email: blackcat@riversideboa.co.uk
web: www.riversideboa.co.uk
contact: Peter Eveleigh
capacity: 180
info: Unsigned acts play on Thursday and Friday nights. Thursdays are dedicated to Acoustic and Blues. Fridays are mainly Rock and Indie bands. These nights are often attended by A&R. Plenty of promotional help provided including listings in the national press. In-house PA. Send demo and biog FAO Peter to the venue.

The Brook
446 Portswood Road, Portswood, Southampton, SO17 3SD
tel: 02380 555 366
email: bryn@the-brook.com
web: www.the-brook.com
contact: Bryn Lewis
capacity: 550
info: The Brook is only open when live music is booked so can vary from 2 to 6 nights per week. Only put on local bands, all music styles considered. In-house PA. Send demo FAO Bryn to the venue.

Bunch Of Grapes
Denmark Street, Bristol, BS1 5DQ
tel: 0117 987 0500
fax: 0117 929 1076
web: www.bunchofgrapes.net
contact: Lorraine Higginson
capacity: 80
info: Live music 5 nights a week. Blues night on Tuesdays. Wednesday is new bands night open mic. Friday is dedicated to Rock and Punk bands. Send demos on cassette or CD with biog to Lorraine at the venue. Need to provide own PA. Promotional help given.

The Cavern Club
83-84 Queen Street, Exeter, EX4 3RP
tel: 01392 495 370
email: exetercavern@hotmail.com
web: www.cavernclub.co.uk
contact: Dave Goodchild, Pippa Wragg
capacity: 220
info: Live band 4 or 5 nights a week, local and touring bands. In-house PA and lighting. Send demos to Dave or Pippa at the venue.

The Central Hotel
81 Commerical Road, Lower Parkstone, Poole, Dorset, BH14 0JB
tel: 01202 743 970
contact: Adam
capacity: 100 - Music Room
info: There is an open mic night on Monday where you can just turn up and play. Wednesday night features Acoustic artists. Thursday is a music quiz with live music in another room, as well as Folk club taking place. On Friday and Saturday night live music of all genres takes place. Venue has PA and sound engineer.

The Croft
117-119 Stokes Croft, Bristol, BS1 3RW
tel: 0117 987 4144
email: info@the-croft.com
web: www.the-croft.com
contact: Matt Otridge
capacity: 170
info: Live music every night of the week. 3 or 4 bands play per night. In-house PA. In order to get a gig, send an email to the above address.

Exeter Phoenix Arts & Media
Bradninch Place, Gandy Street, Exeter, Devon, EX4 3LS
tel: 01392 667 080
fax: 01392 667 599
email: boxoffice@exeterphoenix.org.uk
web: www.exeterphoenix.org.uk
contact: Patrick Cunningham
capacity: 450 (Standing), 216 (Seated)
info: Established bands in the main venue but support slots for unsigned bands. 'Phoenix Song Nights' takes place in the smaller bar where artists can turn up and play. Gigs also put on by Future Sound of Exeter. See listing in Promoter section for details of demo submission.

Fiddler's Club
Willway Street, Bedminster, Bristol, BS3 4BG
tel: 0117 987 3403
fax: 0117 987 3369
email: info@fiddlers.co.uk
web: www.fiddlers.co.uk
contact: Daniel
capacity: 450
info: Live music venue, open between 3 and 7 nights a week. In-house PA, 10kW rig. Send demos to Daniel at the venue.

Finns
26 Westham Road, Weymouth, DT4 8NU
tel: 01305 778 098
fax: 01305 839 723
contact: Steve Perry
capacity: 150
info: Live music 3 nights a week. Bands need to supply own PA. Call Steve at the venue with details of band and music before sending any demos.

Fleece & Firkin
12 St. Thomas' Street, Bristol, BS1 6JJ
tel: 0117 945 0996
email: via website
web: www.fleecegigs.co.uk
contact: Dave Brayley
capacity: 400
info: 10K PA, 32 channel mixing desk, lighting, in-house engineers. Send a demo with biography if possible to Dave Brayley, 1st Floor, 30a College Green, Bristol, BS1 5TB.

The Furnace
73 Commercial Road, Swindon, SN1 5NX
tel: 01793 534 238
email: info@thefurnace.org.uk
web: www.thefurnace.org.uk
capacity: 400
info: Live music regularly, check website for details. In-house PA. Send demos FAO Promoter to the venue.

The Gander on the Green
2 Holdenhurst Road, Bournemouth, Dorset, BH8 8AD
tel: 01202 290 294
contact: Shorty or John
capacity: 150
info: Live music every Thursday, Friday and Saturday night. In-house PA. To enquire about a gig call the venue on the above number, or send a demo addressed to Shorty or John.

Green Park Tavern
Lower Bristol Road, Old Field Park, Bath, BA2 3BD
tel: 01225 400 050
email: greenparktavern@aol.com
web: www.greenparktavern.co.uk
contact: Richard
capacity: 150 (Colony Rooms)
info: Green Park Tavern hosts an open decks night every Monday where DJs can bring 5 of their records and play them to the audience. Every Tuesday is a open mic night where people can just turn up to play. Both nights are free entry.

LIVE PERFORMANCE

The Hub
9 Bath Street, Plymouth, PL1 3LT
tel:	01752 222 664
fax:	01752 222 664
email:	annie@plymouthhub.com
web:	www.plymouthhub.com
contact:	Annie
capacity:	300-400
info:	An interactive entertainment venue hosting nights

including Dance music, gigs and open mics slots. For demo submission and gig details contact Annie at the venue.

The Joiners
141 St. Mary's Street, Southampton, SO14 1NS
tel:	02380 225 612
email:	info@joinerslive.co.uk
web:	www.joinerslive.co.uk
contact:	Kai Harris
capacity:	200
info:	Live music 5-6 nights a week. Full PA and in-house

sound engineer. Indie, Rock, Metal, Acoustic and Dance music. Send demos with biog to the venue, or register at the website where you can upload MP3s.

The Koola Club
12 Beach Road, Newquay, TR7 1ES
tel:	01637 873 415
email:	the.koola@virgin.net
web:	www.thekoola.com
contact:	Ian Whittaker
capacity:	390
info:	Live music occasionally, but Ian is willing to put on

any acts that interest him. In the past live Hip-Hop and Dance acts have performed, although open to all types of music. Venue will provide PA. Send demo FAO Ian to the venue.

Lennon's Nightclub
27-29 Onslow Road, Southampton, SO14 0JD
capacity:	200
info:	Hosts 'Long Live Rock & Roll' band and club night

every Saturday. See entry in Promoters section for details of demo submission.

The Louisiana
Wapping Road, Bathurst Terrace, Bristol, BS1 6UA
tel:	0117 966 3615 (office)
email:	popbox001@aol.com
web:	www.myspace.com/thelouisiana
contact:	Mig Shollace
capacity:	120
info:	Live music 7 nights a week. Full PA. Send demos

FAO Mig or Tim Bailey to The Louisiana.

Mister Smith's
49 Poole Hill Road, Bournemouth, Dorset, BH2 5PW
tel:	01202 291 617
email:	mrsmithsvenue@fsmail.net
contact:	Jay Dyson
capacity:	100
info:	Unsigned bands play every night a week. Send

a demo and biog to Jay at the venue. Follow up with phone call a week later. Between 2 and 4 bands per night. Acoustic night every Wednesday. The rest of the week has bands from a wide cross section of genres. In-house PA.

Moles
14 George Street, Bath, BA1 2EN
tel:	01225 404 445
fax:	01225 404 447
email:	steve@moles.co.uk
web:	www.moles.co.uk
contact:	Steve
capacity:	175
info:	Monday night is local band night. Send demos on

CD with photo and biog to Kath and Sarah at the venue. 'Go Ape' and 'Pulp' are unsigned nights held on alternate Thursdays. To play, send demo marked accordingly. In-house PA and engineer. Full technical specification can be found on website. Feel free to call the venue to chase a response if you have not heard from Moles after a few weeks. See also listing for associated venue, The Porter Cellar Bar. Moles also has a recording studio, refer to website and entry in Recording Studios section.

Mono Bar
3-4 Vernon Walk, Southampton, SO15 2EJ
tel:	02380 233 323
web:	www.monobar.com
info:	'Stripped' is an unsigned Acoustic night promoted

by Long Live Rock & Roll. Held every month on the second Sunday. For demo submission details refer to entry for Long Live Rock & Roll in Promoters section.

Mr Kyp's
8a Parr Street, Ashley Cross, Lower Parkstone, Poole, Dorset, BH14 0JY
tel:	01202 748 945
email:	info@mrkyps.net
web:	www.mrkyps.net
contact:	Romin
capacity:	200
info:	Support slots available for local bands. Gigs also

available for bands across the country, check contact page of website for details. In-house PA. To play send demo FAO Romin to the venue, or alternatively Pop in to speak to him.

The Phoenix
Phoenix Street, Plymouth, Devon, PL1 3NW
tel:	01752 253 334
email:	phil@plymouthphoenix.co.uk
web:	www.plymouthphoenix.co.uk
contact:	Matt Couch, Phil Baker
capacity:	150
info:	The Phoenix try to put on bands every night of the

week. For Rock, Punk and Metal genres contact Matt at the venue. For other genres such as Folk and Jazz, contact Phil at the venue. Local bands can get in contact via phone or email. Travelling bands should send demo to appropriate person at the venue. Venue has in-house PA.

The Platform Tavern
Town Quay, Southampton, Hampshire, SO14 2NY
tel:	02380 337 232
email:	stewart@platformtavern.com
web:	www.platformtavern.com
contact:	Stewart
capacity:	100
info:	Sunday afternoons for Jazz, Sunday evenings for

Blues. Tuesday and Thursday nights anything goes. Need to provide own PA. Send demos to Stewart at the venue.

The Porter Cellar Bar
14 George Street, Bath, BA1 2EN
tel:	01225 404 445
fax:	01225 404 447
email:	michelle@moles.co.uk
web:	www.moles.co.uk/porter/index.ihtml
contact:	Steve
capacity:	100
info:	Monday is open mic night, just turn up to take part.

Soundtracks to Tuesday, Wednesday and Thursday nights are provided by laid-back Funk or Jazz bands. No Rock please. Full technical specification can be found on website. Send demos on CD with photo and biog to Steve at the venue. See also listing for Moles venue.

Talking Heads
320 Portswood Road, Southampton, SO17 2TD
tel:	02380 678 446
email:	info@thetalkingheads.co.uk
web:	www.thetalkingheads.co.uk
contact:	Simon Bell
capacity:	260
info:	Live music 5 to 7 nights a week. Monday is open

mic night, Roots night and Jazz night held on alternate Tuesdays. In-house PA. Venue also available for hire (full specification can be found on website). Send demos FAO Simon at the venue.

Three Fat Fish
1 Mary Archer's Street, Exeter, EX4 3BA
tel:	01392 424 628
email:	info@threefatfish.co.uk
web:	www.threefatfish.co.uk
contact:	Terry Ankers
capacity:	260
info:	Three Fat Fish is a bar dedicated to bringing together

the very best in international, national and local talent. Monday is open mic and Wednesday is band night with 2-3 bands playing. In house PA and sound engineer. Send demos FAO Terry Ankers.

Tramps
Breton Side, Plymouth, Devon, PL4 0BG
tel:	01752 224 441
email:	steve.tramps@supanet.co.uk
contact:	Steve
capacity:	240
info:	Live music about twice a week, 3 bands play per

night. Mainly Punk and Rock music but will consider all types. Venue can assist with organising PA. Send demo FAO Steve to the venue.

Trout
46 Temple Street, Keynsham, BS31 1EH
tel:	0117 986 2754
fax:	0117 986 2754
contact:	Jim McCarthy
capacity:	80-100
info:	Live music every Friday and Saturday night, plus the

last Sunday of every month. 1 band per night. Band must supply own PA. Send demo with contact details to Jim McCarthy at the venue.

University of Plymouth Students' Union
Drake Circus, Plymouth, Devon, PL4 8AA
tel: 01752 238 500
email: chris.pike@su.plymouth.ac.uk
web: www.upsu.com
contact: Chris Pike
capacity: 300/600
info: Put on unsigned bands on several times per month. 2 separate venues within the SU. In-house PA. To play, send an email to Chris at the above address, or post demo for his attention to the venue.

The Victoria
88 Victoria Road, Swindon, Wiltshire, SN1 3BD
tel: 01793 535 713
email: thevicswindon@aol.com
web: www.thevicswindon.com
contact: Dave Young
capacity: 150-300
info: Live music 3 or 4 nights a week. In-house PA. Send demos on CD or cassette along with biog to Dave Young at the venue.

The Villa
142 Holdenhurst Road, Bournemouth, Dorset, BH8 8AS
tel: 01202 551 802
email: contact@villanightclub.com
web: www.villanightclub.com
contact: Danny
capacity: 400
info: Put on bands on a weekly basis, support slots available. Mainly Rock or Alternative music but are open to other styles. Also organise Battle of the Bands competition. In-house PA. Send demo FAO Danny to the venue.

YORKSHIRE

The 1 in 12 Club
21-23 Albion Street, Bradford, West Yorkshire, BD1 2LY
tel: 01274 734 160
web: www.1in12.com
contact: Pete
capacity: 100
info: Members only club. Unsigned bands play at least twice a week. Occasional all day events also. 2k in-house PA. Send demo FAO Pete to the venue. Bands pay £50 for venue and PA hire and then keep all the door money. Facility to record live performances as the club also owns a recording studio and rehearsal room. Enquire for further details.

The Adelphi
89 De Grey Street, Hull, East Yorkshire, HU5 2RU
tel: 01482 348 216
fax: 01482 348 216
email: paul@theadelphiclub.karoo.co.uk
web: www.theadelphi.com
contact: Paul Jackson
capacity: 200
info: Live music 6-7 nights a week. In-house PA. Send demos to Paul Jackson at the venue. All styles considered.

Adelphi
Vicarage Road, Sheffield, S9 3RH
tel: 0114 244 9428
fax: 0114 243 1609
email: dom@clubaldelphi.com
web: www.clubadelphi.com
contact: Dominic Maloney
capacity: 600-650
info: Live nights twice a week. Book nights rather than single acts, so get together with a few other acts and contact Dominic with a package. Acts must at least have a following and a solid biography.

Bar Phono
Merrion Centre, Leeds, LS2 8NG
tel: 0113 242 9222
info: Alternative club. Venue available for hire. Bar Phono have a flyer team promoting their events, who will be able to help with promotion of nights organised through external promoters if requested. Gigs organised by Raw Nerve Promotions. See listing in relevant section for details.

Boardwalk
Snig Hill, Sheffield, S3 8NA
tel: 0114 279 9090
fax: 0114 276 9292
email: chris@theboardwalklive.co.uk
web: www.theboardwalklive.co.uk
contact: Chris Wilson
info: Purely live music venue, open 7 nights. In-house PA, lighting and 6kW rig. Sunday nights, and occasionally others, dedicated to unsigned acts. Contact Chris or send demo and biog for his attention at the venue.

Brudenell Social Club
33 Queens Road, Leeds, LS6 1NY
tel: 0113 275 2411
info: Regular live events organised by V3ctor. See listing in Promoter section for information regarding gigs and demo submission.

Carpe Diem
Civic Court Basement, Calverley Street, Leeds, West Yorkshire, LS1 1BA
tel: 0113 243 6264
web: www.cdmlive.net
capacity: 350-400
info: Carpe Diem hosts an open mic night on Mondays. On Wednesdays there is a night called 'Midweek Mixer' which features Acoustic acts and Singer-Songwriters. Thursdays play host to a regular Indie Rock night called 'weareyou'. Also live music every Saturday. To book a gig send demo to the venue or call the venue.

The Casbah
1 Wellington Street, Sheffield, S1 4HF
tel: 0114 275 6077
fax: 0114 279 7974
email: howniceitversus@hotmail.com
web: www.sheffieldcasbah.com
contact: Haydn Britland
capacity: 360
info: Live music Monday to Saturdays. Headline band with local support acts. In-house PA. Send demos to Haydn Britland at the venue.

Certificate 18
54 Gillygate, York, YO31 7EQ
tel: 01904 627 679
email: cert18@fsmail.net
web: www.certificate18.co.uk
contact: David Jones
capacity: 250
info: Venue dedicated to non-mainstream music, in particular Rock and Metal. Bands and DJs play regularly. Punk, Hardcore, Emo, Goth, Industrial music. Live Rock music every weekend, and regular DJs during the week. In-house PA and sound engineer available for hire at £50.

City Varieties
Swan Street, Leeds, LS1 6LW
tel: 0113 391 7777
fax: 0113 234 1800
email: info@cityvarieties.co.uk
web: www.cityvarieties.co.uk
contact: Peter Sandeman
capacity: 531
info: Venue is available to hire. Bands must book via an external promoter. The venue can recommend local contacts. In-house PA.

The Cockpit
Swinegate, Leeds, LS1 4G
tel: 0113 244 3446/07714 752 823
email: colin@thecockpit.co.uk
web: www.thecockpit.co.uk
contact: John Truman, Colin Oliver
capacity: 250/500
info: Live music for unsigned acts during the week in the 250 capacity room. Unsigned showcases occasionally on Friday and Saturday nights. Send demos to Colin or John at the venue address, Alternatively, John can be contacted on the above mobile number. Support slots may become available in the 500 capacity room.

The Corporation
Milton Street, Sheffield, S1 4JU
tel: 0114 276 0262
fax: 0114 275 0771
email: slomo@corporation.org.uk
web: www.corporation.org.uk
contact: Iain, Mark Hobson
capacity: 200/550/1000
info: Occasional unsigned support slots for larger touring bands playing the venue. Contact Iain for further details. Alternative, Skate-Punk and Metal. The Corporation has 3 main rooms. A recent Kerrang! Readers' poll said The Corporation was "one of the top 10 Rock clubs in the country".

LIVE PERFORMANCE

Doctor Wu's
35 Call Lane, Leeds, West Yorkshire, LS1 7BT
tel: 0113 242 7629
email: mail@drwus.co.uk
web: www.drwus.co.uk
contact: Ben
capacity: 110
info: Doctor Wu's hosts a live music night every Monday featuring 3 bands. All genres are accepted. On Tuesday there is a open mic night in which you can just turn up to take part. In order to book a gig contact Ben at the venue or send a demo to the above address. On Saturday afternoons there is live Acoustic music organised by Acoustic Revolution. See Promoter section for details. In-house PA.

Duck & Drake
43 Kirkgate, Leeds, West Yorkshire, LS2 7DR
tel: 0113 245 9728
email: info@duckanddrakeleeds.co.uk
contact: Tracey Valentine
capacity: 100
info: Live music every Monday and Thursday night. All music types considered, a mixture of covers and original songs. Need to provide own PA. Send demo FAO Tracey to the venue.

The Faversham
1-5 Springfield Mount, Leeds, LS2 9NG
tel: 0113 243 1481
fax: 0113 243 3993
email: info@thefaversham.com
web: www.thefaversham.com
contact: Lucy Espinoza
capacity: 500
info: Live music 2-4 times a week. 3 or 4 bands play each night. Support slots may be available for touring bands. Send demos FAO Promotions Manager. In-house PA.

The Fenton
161 Woodhouse Lane, Leeds, LS2 3ED
tel: 0113 245 3908
web: www.leedsgigs.co.uk
capacity: 110
info: A room is available for hire on Thursday, Friday and Saturday nights. Room hire is £20, the band keep door takings. Need to provide own PA. Speak to anyone behind the bar about bookings.

The Fez Club
40 Charter Square, Sheffield, South Yorkshire, S1 4HS
tel: 0114 276 6082
web: www.ponana.co.uk
contact: Karen Wosskow
capacity: 250
info: Opportunity for unsigned bands to support signed acts. See entry for Pink Pandemonium Promotions in relevant section for further details.

Fibbers
8-10 Stonebow House, The Stonebow, York, YO1 7NP
tel: 01904 651 250
email: fibbers@fibbers.co.uk
web: www.fibbers.co.uk
contact: Tim
capacity: 200
info: Live music 7 nights a week, maximum of 6 acts per night. In-house PA. Email Tim with brief details of your act and a website address.

Fox & Newt
9-11 Burley Street, Leeds, LS3 1LD
tel: 0113 243 2612
contact: Roy Cadman
capacity: 60
info: Live Acoustic duos or solo acts on a Friday. In-house PA. Send demos to Roy Cadman at the venue, or call the venue for more information.

The George
67-69 Great George Street, Leeds, LS1 3BB
tel: 0113 245 3232
fax: 0113 245 3232
email: thegeorge@greatgeorgestreet.fsnet.co.uk
contact: Martin Glover
capacity: 90
info: Bands can hire the venue free of charge and take the door cover. Need to supply own PA. Venue can help with promotion if necessary.

The Grapes
80-82 Trippet Lane, Sheffield, S1 4EL
tel: 0114 249 0909
contact: Michael Ash
capacity: 80
info: Live music 6-7 nights a week. In-house PA. Bands receive all the money taken on the door but must pay for room hire, PA and sound engineer. Send demos to the venue FAO Michael. Venue also hosts events organised by Real Promotions. See entry in Promoters section for further details.

The Green Dragon Inn
Hardraw Rawes, North Yorkshire, DL8 3LZ
tel: 01969 667 392
web: www.greendragonmusic.com
contact: Mark or Yvonne Thompson
capacity: 150-200
info: The Green Dragon run a number of events throughout the year such as a 3 day festival of Traditional music, song and dance. For full details visit the website. Regular live music is on Fridays and Saturdays. Acts featured include Irish and Folk music, Rock, Blues, Jazz and R&B bands, as well as solo artists and instrumentalists. Send demos to the venue.

The Grove Inn
Back Row, Holbeck, Leeds, LS11 5PL
tel: 0113 243 9224
email: rachel@thegroveinn.go-legend.net
contact: Rachel Scordof
capacity: 80
info: 'Stormy Monday Blues' is held every first and fourth Monday. Jam sessions on Tuesdays. 'Leeds Unplugged' night at 9pm every Wednesday with Acoustic music and open mic, just turn up to take part. Folk night is every Friday except during July and August. Every second Sunday is Jazz Club. Live bands on Thursday and Saturday nights and Sunday afternoons, which are often selected from the Unplugged night on Wednesday. Contact Rachel to play.

The HiFi Club
2 Central Road, Leeds, LS1 6DE
tel: 0113 242 7353
email: info@thehificlub.co.uk
web: www.thehificlub.co.uk
contact: Andy Smith
capacity: 300
info: In the Leeds Bar & Club Awards 2003-2005. The HiFi Club has won Best Club and Best Live Music Venue. Offers a range of DJ led and live music nights based around Jazz, Funk, Soul and Hip-Hop. Send demos FAO Andy Smith to the venue.

Jockey
65 Northgate, Wakefield, WF1 3BP
tel: 01924 376 302
fax: 01924 376 302
email: jackie@thejockey.fsnet.co.uk
contact: Jackie
capacity: 200
info: Live music every Saturday night. Rock, Punk and Alternative music. Need to provide own PA. Phone Jackie at the venue to arrange a slot. Usually 1 band per session, but will try to accommodate bands that want to play together.

Joseph's Well
Chorley Lane, Leeds, LS2 9NW
tel: 0113 203 1861
email: mail@josephswell.co.uk
web: www.josephswell.co.uk
contact: Dave Bunn
capacity: 350
info: Live music every night, mainly small local acts, but will take bands from further afield. In-house PA. Full technical specification can be found on website. Send demos to Dave at the venue. See also Black Market Music in Promoters section.

The Junction
44 Bondgate, Otley, West Yorkshire, LS21 1AD
tel: 01943 463 233
contact: Jude
capacity: 100
info: Unplugged jam sessions every Monday, just turn up to take part. Live band plays every Tuesday. Need to provide own PA. Send demo and listings of any nearby gigs to Jude at the venue. Jude will try to attend a local gig.

Leadmill
6 Leadmill Road, Sheffield, S1 4SE
tel: 0114 221 2828
fax: 0114 221 2848
email: rupert@leadmill.co.uk
web: www.leadmill.co.uk
contact: Rupert Dell
capacity: 900/250
info: Regular unsigned nights. Send demo FAO Rupert at the venue. 13K PA, intelligent lighting. New stage for unsigned bands in the 250 capacity room.

Leopard
1 West Street, Doncaster, DN13AA
tel:	01302 363 054
fax:	01302 563 652
email:	alanmchugh@blueyonder.co.uk
web:	www.thegigguide.co.uk
contact:	Heather Brown
capacity:	200
info:	Live music every Thursday, Friday, Saturday and occasional Sundays. Full PA, 8.5K rig and sound engineer. Send demos FAO Heather at the venue.

Lincoln Imp
Gloucester Avenue, Scunthorpe, DN16 2DN
tel:	01724 840 891
contact:	Jan Price
capacity:	70
info:	Live music every week, usually weekends although occasional weeknights. 4 or 5 bands play per night. No minimum age limit. Bands welcome from all over the country. Venue will provide PA system. Facility to record live performances and burn onto CD. Send demo to Jan at the venue, or contact her on above telephone number.

The Linnet & Lark
30-32 Princes Avenue, Hull, HU5 3QA
tel:	01482 441 126
email:	maks33onions@yahoo.co.uk
contact:	Mark Page
capacity:	300
info:	Unsigned nights every week. Hosts 'The Sesh' on Tuesdays and Sundays. In order to get a gig email the above address, or send a demo to the venue for Mark's attention.

The Lion Inn
Blakey Ridge, Kirbymoorside, North Yorkshire, YO62 7LQ
tel:	01751 417 320
fax:	01751 417 717
email:	info@blakeymusic.com
web:	www.lionblakey.co.uk or www.blakeymusic.com
contact:	Paul Crossland
capacity:	150
info:	Live music once a fortnight with 1 or 2 bands playing. In-house PA. Send demo and press pack, including website details, reviews to Paul at the venue.

Love Apple Café
34 Great Horton Road, Bradford, West Yorkshire, BD7 1AL
tel:	01274 744 075
email:	info@loveapplecafe.co.uk
web:	www.loveapplecafe.co.uk
contact:	Pav
capacity:	150
info:	Live bands once a week during term time, and around once every 3 weeks during holidays. Between 1 and 3 bands play each night. Mainly Indie and Rock music. In-house PA and sound engineer. Send demo FAO Pav to the venue.

Market Tavern
78 Godwin Street, Kirkgate, Bradford, West Yorkshire, BD1 3PT
tel:	01274 722 215
email:	joe@bradfordrio.com
web:	www.bradfordrio.com/thetav
contact:	Joe
capacity:	150
info:	Room downstairs available for hire on Thursdays, Fridays and Saturdays. Bands pay small fee to cover room hire and engineer, they are then entitled to all money taken on the door. Full in-house PA. Market Tavern will help with publicity for the gig. Contact Joe for further information.

Mixing Tin
9a Albion Street, Leeds, LS1 5AA
tel:	0113 2468 899
info:	Unsigned gigs organised by Black Market Music. See listing in Promoter section for details of demo submission.

Murray's Music Bar
Murray's Pavillion House, Westborough, Scarborough, North Yorkshire, YO11 1UN
tel:	01723 503 170
email:	dropdis@hotmail.com
web:	www.murraysmusicbar.com
contact:	Paul Murray
capacity:	240
info:	Murray's Music Bar mainly deals with tribute bands but there are occasional gigs available for original music. Contact the venue or visit the website for full details. Send demos FAO Paul Murray at the venue.

New Roscoe
Bristol Street, Sheepscar, Leeds, LS7 1DH
tel:	0113 246 0778
email:	jfk@liveinleeds.com
web:	www.newroscoe.co.uk
contact:	John Keenan
capacity:	300
info:	Promoter John Keenan runs 'Springboard' on Wednesday nights, a chance for new bands in the local region to play live. 'Acoustic Springboard' for singers and songwriters takes place on Monday night. John supplies PA for these events. Size of audience will relate directly to size of payment - the more people there to see your band, the more money you'll earn from your performance. Contact John by email to play.

Norman's
36 Call Lane, Leeds, LS1 6DT
tel:	0113 234 3988
fax:	0113 234 1918
contact:	Mark Cliff
capacity:	250
info:	Live bands every night. In-house PA. Contact the venue if interested in playing.

Old Bar
Leeds University, Students' Union, PO Box 157, Leeds, LS1 1UH
tel:	0113 380 1280
email:	info@lsrfm.com
web:	www.lsrfm.com
contact:	Steve Darke
capacity:	300
info:	Old Bar is part of Leeds University campus. Band night every Saturday, 'New Slang', with 2 bands playing. Send demos FAO Rory Cheevers, LSR FM, PO Box 157, Leeds, LS1 1UH. Also see listing for The Terrace, another venue located within the campus. For information on when LSR FM airs, refer to entry in Student Media section.

The Packhorse
208 Woodhouse Lane, Leeds, West Yorkshire, LS2 9DX
tel:	0113 245 3980
contact:	Paul McIntyre
capacity:	60
info:	Live music 4 or 5 times per week. Upstairs room available for bands to use. £25 deposit payable for any damages, but this is returnable. Band are entitled to any door takings. Need to provide own PA. Contact Chantal Haynes or Paul McIntyre to make booking.

Rio
Thorn House, Woodhead Road, Bradford, BD7 1PD
tel:	01274 735 549
fax:	01274 414 090
email:	info@bradfordrio.com
web:	www.bradfordrio.com
contact:	Martin
capacity:	1000
info:	Live unsigned music Wednesday, Friday and Saturday. In-house PA. Full technical specification can be found on website. Call Martin at the venue for a chat about your music and details of how to play the Rio.

Royal Park Cellars
39 Queen's Road, Hyde Park, Leeds, LS6 1AA
tel:	0113 275 7494
email:	royalparkcellars@gmail.com
web:	www.royalparkcellars.co.uk
contact:	Ben
capacity:	100
info:	3 bands each on Thursday, Friday and Saturday nights. Tickets are priced between £2 and £4. The first £60 taken is used to cover the gig and venue expenses, the band get 80% of the takings after that. In-house PA, lights and sound engineer. Post any demos to the venue marked FAO Ben, or call him at the venue.

The Sands
Lord Street, Gainsborough, DN21 2DB
tel:	01427 811 118
email:	info@the-sands.co.uk
web:	www.the-sands.co.uk
contact:	Gee Labanca
capacity:	212
info:	Music venue hosting signed and unsigned musicians and acts. In-house PA and lights. Contact Gee on the above email address or send a demo to the venue address for his attention.

LIVE PERFORMANCE

The Shed
Brawby, Malton, North Yorkshire, YO17 6PY
tel: 01653 668 494
email: newmail@theshed.co.uk
web: www.theshed.co.uk
contact: Simon Thackray
capacity: 70-200
info: Venue dedicated to live music and poetry. Mainly Contemporary Jazz, Blues and World. Contact Simon Thackray for details of music programmes.

Silhouette
29 Park Street, Hull, Humberside, HU2 8RR
tel: 01482 320 584
email: zipwain@hotmail.com
contact: Raymond
capacity: 600
info: Put on 1 live band every Wednesday and Saturday night. Mainly Indie music. Friday evenings are dedicated to Rock, featuring heavier music. In-house PA. Contact Raymond by telephone or email to play.

The Snooty Fox
Brunswick Street, Kirkgate, Wakefield, West Yorkshire, WF1 4PW
tel: 01924 374 455
email: enquiries@snootyfoxlive.com
web: www.snootyfoxlive.com
contact: Malc
capacity: 150
info: Live music 5 nights a week. In-house PA, stage and lighting, as well as facilities for live audio and video recording. Full technical specifications can be found on the website. Website also includes details of payment for acts, dependent on size of crowd they can draw. To play send demo to the above address. Wednesday is open mic night, just turn up to take part.

Springhead Pub
Aston Road, Willerby, East Yorkshire, HU10 6QT
tel: 01482 650 924
fax: 01482 653 919
email: enquiries@springheadpub.co.uk
web: www.springheadpub.co.uk
contact: Terry
capacity: 300
info: Live music 7 nights a week. 18 piece orchestra every Monday, as well as tribute bands and unsigned acts during the week. Also the very best unsigned bands play a special event every February called Best Original Band.

The Terrace
Leeds University, Students' Union, PO Box 157, Leeds, LS1 1UH
tel: 0113 3801 280
email: info@lsrfm.com
web: www.lsrfm.com
contact: Steve Darke
capacity: 250-300
info: The Terrace is situated within the Leeds University Students' Union. Short live Acoustic every Friday afternoon organised by student radio station, LSR FM. In-house PA. Send demos FAO Rory Cheevers, LSR FM, PO Box 157, Leeds, LS1 1UH. Also see listing for Old Bar, another venue located within Leeds University. For details of when LSR FM airs, see listing in Student Media section.

The Trades Club
Holme Street, Hebden Bridge, HX7 8EE
tel: 01422 845 265
fax: 01422 845 599
email: info@tradesclub.info
web: www.tradesclub.info
contact: David Boardman
capacity: 140 (Seated), 180 (Standing)
info: Live music Thursday, Friday and Saturday nights. Also occasional Sunday nights. In-house PA, lights and sound engineers. Send demos FAO David Boardman at the venue.

The Vine
The Headrow, Leeds, LS1 6PU
tel: 0113 203 1821
email: neil@thevineleeds.com
web: www.thevineleeds.com
contact: Neil
capacity: 200
info: Run 'incoming' nights for unsigned acts 7 nights a week. 3 or 4 bands usually play. Bands need to attract a minimum audience of 10 to help cover costs. Acts which impress may be invited to play 'Transmission', a regular gig and club night which features signed acts. Contact Neil at the above email address and he will advise of demo submission details. 5K rig provided, operated and maintained by in-house engineers, Audible Science. Venue also boats new stage and lighting rig, as well as spacious dressing room areas for bands. Previous acts to have played The Vine include 10,000 Things, Kinesis, Four Day Hombre, Dogs Die In Hot Cars, les Flames!, The Yards and Lapsus Lingae.

Vivaz
Huntries Row, Scarborough, YO11 2EF
tel: 01723 368 222
email: dropdis@hotmail.com
web: www.vivaz.co.uk
contact: Paul Murray
capacity: 400
info: Vivaz is an original music bar. There is the potential for live music every night of the week featuring music of all genres. Recently hosted gig for Maximo Park. Local bands that do well on unsigned nights, have the opportunity for support slots. To get a gig send demo FAO Paul Murray at the venue.

The Wardrobe
No. 6, St. Peter's Building, St. Peter's Square, Leeds, LS9 8AH
tel: 0113 383 8800
email: music@thewardrobe.co.uk
web: www.thewardrobe.co.uk
contact: Martin Hudson
capacity: 460 (Basement), 380 (Café Bar)
info: Live music in the basement at least 3 nights a week. Wednesdays are run by Leeds Jazz Society, Fridays are dedicated to Nu-Skool Funk and Beats, and Saturdays are Jazz, Funk, Soul and Latin music. Occasionally live music on Tuesdays and Thursdays. In-house PA. Send demos FAO Martin at the venue.

The Woodhouse Liberal Club
Woodhouse Street, Leeds, LS6 2PY
info: 4K PA and lighting rig. Regular gigs promoted by Leedsoundsix. See listing in relevant section for details.

NORTHERN IRELAND

The Anchorage Inn
87-89 The Promenade, Portstewart, BT55 7AJ
tel: 028 7083 4401/028 7083 2003
fax: 028 7083 4508
email: anchorbar@btconnect.com
web: www.anchorbar.biz
contact: Danny Coyles
capacity: 700 (including night club)
info: Live music 3 or 4 times per week, 1 band plays each night. In-house PA. Send demos FAO Danny to the venue.

Auntie Annie's Porter House
44 Dublin Road, Belfast, BT2 7HN
tel: 028 9050 1660
contact: Mark Hutchinson, Declan Smyth
capacity: 200 (Downstairs)
info: In-house PA. Send demos FAO Mark or Declan at the venue. The upstairs room is available for hire from Sunday to Wednesday. Enquire directly with any member of staff at the venue. All bands must be over 18 years.

Bar 7
78 The Promenade, Portstewart, BT55 7AF
tel: 028 7083 6000 (ask for Bar 7)
web: www.shenanigascomplex.com
contact: Paul, Mike
capacity: 450 (over 2 levels)
info: Live music 5 times a week. Monday to Thursday are band nights with alternate Fridays dedicated to either a band or DJ. Bands need to supply PA. Send demos FAO Paul or Mike at the venue address.

Bound For Boston
31 Waterloo Street, Derry, BT48 6HA
tel: 028 7127 1315
email: enquiries@boundforboston.com
web: www.boundforboston.com
contact: Les
capacity: 250
info: Live music between 3 and 4 nights a week. 1 or 2 bands play each night. All styles considers. Send demos FAO Les at the venue. In-house PA.

The Duke of York
7-11 Commercial Court, Belfast, Antrim, BT1 2MB
tel: 0289024 1062
contact: Johnny Hero
capacity: 350
info: Live music 3 nights a week with 4 or 5 bands playing each night. Send demos FAO Johnny at the venue. In-house PA.

The Empire Bar & Music Hall
40-42 Botanic Avenue, County Antrim, Belfast, BT7 1FQ
tel: 028 9024 9276
email: info@thebelfastempire.com
web: www.thebelfastempire.com
contact: Mike Gatt
capacity: 500
info: Live music every night. All styles of music accepted. In-house PA. Send demos to the venue address.

Errigle Inn
320 Ormeau Road, Belfast, County Antrim, BT7 2GE
tel: 028 9064 1410
email: philip@errigle.com
web: www.errigle.com
contact: Philip McGurran
capacity: 250
info: Venue hosts live music around 3 or 4 times a week. Styles ranging from Traditional Irish music to Jazz. In-house PA. Send demos FAO Philip at the venue.

The Front Page
106-110 Donegal Street, Belfast, County Antrim, BT1 2GX
tel: 028 9032 4924
web: www.thefrontpagebar.com
contact: Ian
capacity: 250
info: Every Wednesday night The Front Page showcases local bands of varying ability and performance, giving them a platform to gain experience, confidence and an opportunity to air their music to the general public. Live music also organised on other nights throughout the week. In-house PA provided. Send demos to the venue.

Island Arts Centre
Lagan Valley Island, Lisburn, County Antrim, BT27 4RL
tel: 028 9250 9509
email: enquiries@lisburn.gov.uk
web: www.lisburncity.gov.uk
capacity: 150
info: Island Arts Centre runs a programme of events throughout the year. Visit the website for full details on how to get involved. The venue is also available for hire.

The John Hewitt
51 Donegall Street, Belfast, BT15 4EL
tel: 028 9023 3768
email: pedro@johnhewitt.com
web: www.thejohnhewitt.com
contact: Pedro Donald
capacity: 100
info: Bands play most nights of the week. Monday nights are Acoustic, Tuesday and Wednesday cover Traditional Irish music. Fridays are dedicated to Jazz. In-house PA. Send demos FAO Pedro at the venue.

The Limelight/Katy Daly's
17 Ormeau Avenue, Belfast, BT2 8HD
tel: 028 9032 5942
fax: 028 9031 3131
email: theoffice@the-limelight.com
web: www.the-limelight.co.uk
contact: Terry Lavery
capacity: Limelight 500, Katy Daly's 150
info: The Limelight and Katy Daly's are 2 adjoining venues. 'Stagefright' is an unsigned night held every Wednesday in Katy Daly's. Mainly Indie and Guitar-based music. Once a month the best bands from 'Stagefright' play the larger stage in The Limelight. In-house PA and sound engineer. Send demos FAO Terry to the venue. Terry also runs a record label, 'No Dancing', which hosts showcase club nights on Sundays. See entry in Record Companies section for further details.

The Nerve Centre
7-8 Magazine Street, Derry, Northern Ireland, BT48 6HJ
tel: 028 7126 0562
fax: 028 7137 1738
email: tonyd@nerve-centre.org.uk
web: www.nerve-centre.org.uk
contact: Tony Docherty
capacity: 650
info: Unsigned bands play once a week. All styles of music from Singer-Songwriter to Punk. In-house PA. Send demo FAO Tony to the venue.

Nucleus
13 Pump Street, Derry, BT48 6JG
tel: 028 7129 7777
email: nucleuscentre@yahoo.com
contact: Eamonn
capacity: 200
info: Venue has a no alcohol policy. Unsigned bands every Friday night, and occasional Saturdays. In-house PA. Send demo to the venue or contact Eamonn to play.

Rosetta Bar
73-75 Rosetta Road, Belfast, BT6 0LR
tel: 028 9064 9297
email: inforosetta@btconnect.com
web: www.rosettabar.com
contact: Mr A. Allen
capacity: 400
info: Venue is available 7 nights a week to put on unsigned bands. First class PA system, sound engineer and full lighting facilities. All genres of music accepted, but is renowned for Rock and Metal. Send demos to the venue FAO Mr Allen. Alternatively, contact him by telephone or email.

Sandino's
Water Street, Derry City, County Londonderry, BT48 2BQ
tel: 028 7130 9297
fax: 028 7127 1246
email: info@sandinos.com
web: www.sandinos.com
contact: Anne Harley
capacity: 500
info: Live music Tuesdays to Thursdays with up to 4 bands playing each night. Send demos to the venue. Visit the website for up to date events programme. In-house PA provided.

Spring & Airbrake
17 Ormeau Avenue, Belfast, BT2 8HD
tel: 028 9032 5942
fax: 028 9031 3131
email: theoffice@the-limelight.co.uk
web: www.the-limelight.co.uk
contact: David
info: Spring & Airbrake is an adjoining venue with Limelight and Katy Daly's. See separate listing for further details. Support slots are available alongside touring bands. In-house PA and sound engineer. Send demos FAO Terry to the venue. Terry also runs a record label, 'No Dancing', which hosts showcase club nights on Sundays. See entry in Record Companies section for further details.

SCOTLAND

The 13th Note Café
50-60 King Street, Glasgow, G1 5QT
tel: 0141 553 1638
fax: 0141 553 1883
email: brendan.ohare@ntlworld.com
web: www.13thnote.co.uk
contact: Brendan O' Hare
capacity: 100
info: Live music every night. In-house PA. Send demos to venue address FAO Brendan. Promotional support provided.

The Arches
253 Argyle Street, Glasgow, G2 8DL
tel: 0141 565 1035
email: info@thearches.co.uk
web: www.thearches.co.uk
info: Showcases organised by Kingsonic Promotions. See listing in relevant section for demo submission policy.

Bannerman's Bar
55 Niddry Street, Edinburgh, EH1 1LG
tel: 0131 556 3254
email: paul_hastie@hotmail.com
web: www.bannermansgigs.co.uk
contact: Paul Hastie
capacity: 200
info: Live music 6 nights a week. All music types considered, although no Country or Jazz. Maximum of 3 bands play per night. In-house PA. Send demo FAO Paul at the venue. Promotional support provided. Door percentage available.

Barfly Glasgow
260 Clyde Street, Glasgow, G1 4JH
tel: 0141 204 5700
fax: 0141 204 5711
email: glasgow.info@barflyclub.com
web: www.barflyclub.com
contact: Brian Reynolds
capacity: 300
info: Unsigned bands play 3 nights of the week. Send demos and biog FAO Brian to the address above.

LIVE PERFORMANCE

The Bongo Club
37 Holyrood Road, Edinburgh, EH8 8BA
tel: 0131 558 7604
fax: 0131 558 7604
email: ally@thebongoclub.co.uk
web: www.thebongoclub.co.uk
contact: Ally Hill
capacity: 450
info: As Edinburgh's busiest live venue, there is music most nights. In June 2005 alone The Bongo Club played host to 50 bands. The Bongo Club is housed in the Out of the Blue Arts Centre. Unsigned bands generally (but not exclusively) play week nights. Venue consists of 2 rooms: the main performance room (capacity 250) and an attached Chillout room, with a bar in between. Full PA, monitors, lights and video projector. Facilities to record live from the stage. A group of3 bands can hire out the venue at a minimal cost, then keep the door takings. The Bongo Club will help out with publicity by featuring the night on posters, flyers, the website and mail outs. Contact Ally Hill by either telephone or email.

Café Drummond
1 Belmont Street, Aberdeen, AB10 1JR
tel: 01224 619 931
email: eric@cafedrummond.com
web: www.cafedrummond.co.uk
contact: Eric McMillen
capacity: 300
info: Live music most nights. Battle of The Bands is held for 12 weeks at a time, several times throughout the year. Send demo FAO Eric. Past bands to have played the venue include Shed Seven and Supergrass. In-house PA, full backline, sound and lighting engineers provided.

Cathouse
15 Union Street, Glasgow, G1 3RB
tel: 0141 248 6606
web: www.cathouseglasgow.co.uk or ww.cplweb.com
contact: Keith Gainham
info: Kingsonic Promotions present Stepping Stone at Cathouse, a showcase for unsigned acts regularly attended by A&R from Sony and Polydor. Showcases take place on regular Thursday and Sunday nights (depending on venue availability). Five bands per night, each with a 30 minute set. Full backline is provided. Check Kingsonic website for full details of showcases including tickets, fees, equipment and times. For demo submission policy, see listing for Kingsonic in the Promoter section.

Citrus Club
40 Grindlay Street, Edinburgh, EH3 9AP
tel: 0131 622 7086
fax: 0131 622 7086
email: citrus@citrusclub.co.uk
web: www.citrusclub.co.uk
contact: Brian Charro
capacity: 250
info: Bands play quite regularly, but no definite schedule. Support slots can also become available. In-house PA. Send demo FAO Brian at the venue.

The Doghouse
13 Brown Street, Dundee, DD1 5ET
tel: 01382 206 812
web: www.lemuria.co.uk
contact: John
capacity: 400
info: Puts on a wide variety of music including a lot of unsigned bands. Host Battle of The Band nights. Bands get treated well and are given free beer. Always on the lookout for new acts, send a demo to the address above.

Dr. Drake's
62 Shiprow, Aberdeen
tel: 01224 569 999
email: info@drdrakesbar.co.uk
web: www.drdrakesbar.co.uk
contact: Sharon Young
capacity: 110
info: Live music 7 nights a week, all original, no cover bands. Dr. Drake's is Popular with touring bands who are usually supported by a local act. Tuesday is open mic night. In-house PA. Send demos FAO Sharon at the venue, or alternatively email with details of a website if applicable.

East Grange Loft
East Grange, Kinloss, Forres, Morayshire, IV36 2UD
tel: 01343 850 078
email: admin@eastgrange.co.uk
web: www.eastgrange.co.uk or www.lbpromo.co.uk
contact: Grigor
capacity: 150
info: Live music at least once a week. All music styles welcome. In-house PA. Send demo and biog FAO Grigor to the venue.

Ego
14 Picardy Place, Edinburgh, EH1 3JT
tel: 0131 478 7434
email: egoandout@hotmail.com
contact: Alan Gibb
capacity: 600 (over 2 levels)
info: Ego hosts band nights weekly on a Thursday. The Venue welcome demos of all genres from local acts. In-house PA. Sound and light technicians. Send demos FAO Alan to the above address.

The Exchange
55 Grove Street, Edinburgh, EH3 8AB
email: david@arpconcerts.co.uk
web: www.livemusicx.com
contact: David Lawson
capacity: 460
info: The Exchange offers a unique service to bands. Unsigned gigs can be recorded to a high quality and band can take home a DVD of their gig the same night. The gigs are also streamed on the above website. 5 bands play on these nights, which take place every week. Bands are asked to sell 40 tickets which will cover the cost of the recording. For further details about video production nights please contact David Lawson. Demos should be submitted FAO David at above address. See also listing for linked video promo company, The Hold.

Fat Sam's
31 South Ward Road, Dundee, Angus, DD1 1PU
tel: 01382 228 181
web: www.fatsams.co.uk
contact: Sarah Linton
capacity: 600
info: Mainly put on Indie and Rock bands, but are also interested in Ska, Jazz and Blues groups. Will accept demos and book unsigned bands. In-house PA.

Funhouse
Alloa Leisure Bowl, Parkway, Alloa, FK1 2AF
tel: 01259 723 527
email: alan.ziff@virgin.net
web: www.freewebs.com/theziff
contact: Alan Johnson
capacity: 180
info: Live music at least once every 2 weeks. Has played host to Travis, The Damned and Ocean Colour Scene, amongst others. Full in-house PA. Call or email Alan Johnson of Ziff Promotions to arrange gig. See also Ziff Promotions entry in Promoters section.

Fury Murry's
96 Maxwell Street, Glasgow, G1 4EQ
tel: 0141 221 6511
fax: 0141 221 6511
email: gigs@furyslive.co.uk
web: www.furyslive.co.uk
contact: R&A Music
capacity: 530
info: Live music on Friday nights, 3 bands per night. 4kW rig and Pearl Export Drum kit supplied. Full technical specification can be found on website. CD recordings of gigs available. Send demos to R&A Music, PO Box 3728, Glasgow, G41 2QY.

G2
474 Sauchiehall Street, Glasgow, G2 3LW
tel: 0141 353 3111
info: Unsigned events put on by Kingsonic Promotions. See listing in Promoter section for details of where to send demos.

The Garage
490 Sauchiehall Street, Glasgow, G2 3LW
tel: 0141 332 1120
web: www.cplweb.com
info: Unsigned nights organised by both Kingsonic Promotions and Cathouse Promotions. Technical specification for the venue can be found on website above. See listings in Promoters section for details of demo submission.

Kef
9 Belmont Street, Aberdeen, AB10 1JR
tel: 01224 639 546
email: paulstewart500@hotmail.com
contact: Paul Stewart
capacity: 300
info: Live music 5 to 6 nights a week. Support slots available for signed, touring acts. In-house PA, stage and lighting. Send demo FAO Paul to the venue.

King Tut's Wah Wah Hut
272a St. Vincent's Street, Glasgow, G2 5RL
tel: 0141 221 5279
email: kingtuts@dfconcerts.co.uk
web: www.kingtuts.co.uk
contact: Dave McGeachan
capacity: 300
info: Legendary Glasgow venue where Alan McGee first saw Oasis play live. Regular unsigned nights. Send demos and biog to the venue address. May have to wait a few weeks for a response.

The Lemon Tree
5 West North Street, Aberdeen, AB24 5AT
tel: 01224 647 999
email: music@lemontree.org
web: www.lemontree.org
contact: Andy Shearer
capacity: 550
info: Live music 4 or 5 times a week with 4 bands playing each night. Support slots available and gigs for bands involved with the Music Development Programme. See website for full details. In-house PA.

Links Hotel
Midlinks, Montrose, Angus, DD10 8RL
tel: 01674 671 000
email: cninteman@linkshotelmusic.com or info@linkshotelmusic.com
web: www.linkshotelmusic.com
contact: Casper Ninteman
capacity: 100
info: Hotel and live music venue hosting Jazz, Folk, Classical and Blues. Folk jam night takes place every second Tuesday. To play a gig, contact Casper by email or via the website, or send a demo to the above address for his attention.

Liquid Rooms
9c Victoria Street, Edinburgh, EH1 2HE
tel: 0131 225 2564
fax: 0131 225 2574
email: kath@liquidroom.com
web: www.liquidroom.com
contact: Kath MacKenzie
capacity: 800
info: Larger venue for signed bands, although support slots do become available about once a month. Send demo FAO Kath at the venue.

The Maltmill
82 Holburn Street, Aberdeen, AB10 6BY
tel: 01224 573 830
contact: Graham Gibb
capacity: 150
info: Live music Thursday to Sunday. Send demos FAO Graham. Will accept most musical styles.

Ma's Nightclub
23-29 Royal Exchange Square, Glasgow, G1 5NT
tel: 0141 221 8099
email: info@masglasgow.co.uk
web: www.masglasgow.co.uk
info: Regular gigs organised by Eleven Promotions. See listing in relevant section for details.

McPhail's
North Street, Leven, Fife, KY8 4LY
tel: 01333 423 662
email: info@mcphails.co.uk
web: www.mcphails.co.uk
contact: Lee Murray
capacity: 150
info: Local act plays around once a month. Need to provide own PA. Send demo FAO Lee to the venue.

The Moorings Bar
2 Trinity Quay, Aberdeen, AB11 5AA
tel: 01224 587 602
email: flash@themooringsbar.net
contact: Craig Adams
capacity: 100
info: Live music every Saturday night. Stage lighting, drum riser, sound proofed drapes. Send demos to Craig at the venue.

Moshulu
Windmill Brae, Aberdeen, AB11 6HU
tel: 01224 572 876
email: info@moshulu.net
web: www.moshulu.net
contact: James Bruce
capacity: 650
info: Moshulu is a 650 capacity live music venue and nightclub in the heart of Aberdeen. If supplied in advance, posters and flyers can be arranged to be handed out during all events in both the venues for up to 1 month prior to the show. Also have the facility to advertise the event on in-house TV and plasma screens throughout both venues.

Nice & Sleazy
421 Sauchiehall Street, Glasgow, G2 3LG
tel: 0141 333 9637
fax: 0141 333 0900
email: sleazys@hotmail.com
web: www.nicensleazy.com
contact: Mig
capacity: 180
info: Live music every night, a combination of touring and unsigned bands. In-house PA. Send demo and biog FAO Mig at the venue. Biffy Clyro and Mogwai are amongst some of the signed artists that have played this venue.

QMU (Queen Margaret Union @ Glasgow University)
22 University Gardens, Glasgow, G12 8QN
tel: 0141 339 9784
email: k.mckean@qmu.org.uk
web: www.qmu.org.uk
contact: Keren McKean
capacity: 900
info: 'Raw' is held every Thursday night, featuring 4 acts. Bands need to have a decent following if they want a gig, as the venue is so large. Send demos FAO Keren to the venue. 'Unplugged' is an open mic Acoustic night held every Sunday, just turn up to take part.

The Soundhaus
47 Hydepark Street, Anderston, Glasgow, G3 8BW
tel: 0141 221 4659
email: music@soundhaus.co.uk
web: www.soundhaus.co.uk
capacity: 250
info: Contact the venue for details on how to play, or send demo to the venue marked 'Entertainment'. Also comprises a rehearsal room and PA hire company (Xcel PAs). See relevant sections for more details.

Stereo
14 Kelvinhaugh Street, Glasgow, G3 8NU
tel: 0141 576 5018
web: www.stereomono.info
contact: Drew
capacity: 150
info: Live music most nights during the week. In-house PA and sound engineer. Send demos FAO Drew or Rob at the venue.

Strawberry Fields Nightclub
56 Oswald Street, Glasgow, G1 4PL
tel: 08450 539 289
email: strawberryfields.nightclub@vurgun.net
contact: Adrian, Neil
capacity: 300
info: Friday and Saturday nights for live bands. Early shows with 3 bands (doors at 7.30pm), followed by a club night. Send demos FAO Adrian or Neil at the venue.

Studio 4
Grahams Road, Falkirk, FK2 9BB
tel: 07886 527 464
email: audiograffiti1@yahoo.co.uk
capacity: 150
info: Audio Graffiti is a band night held every Friday. 6K PA with engineer. For demo submission policy see listing for Audio Graffiti in relevant section.

Subway Cowgate
69 Cowgate, Edinburgh, EH1 1JW
tel: 0131 225 6766
email: info@subwayclubs.co.uk
web: www.subwayclubs.co.uk
capacity: 350
info: Unsigned night every Thursday, 'Magdas Very Best of Scottish Unsigned Talent'. All genres welcome. Demos should be sent to Paul at the above address.

Tron
63 Trongate, Merchant City, Glasgow, G1 5HB
tel: 0141 552 4267
web: www.tron.co.uk
info: Events organised by PM Music. See listing in Promoter section for further details.

LIVE PERFORMANCE

The Tunnels
Carnegies Brae, Aberdeen, AB10 1BF
tel: 01224 211 121
email: henthetunnels@btconnect.com
web: www.thetunnels.co.uk
contact: Hen Beverly
capacity: 300
info: Send demos FAO Hen Beverly. Unsigned gigs are held 3 to 4 nights a week with 4 bands playing each night. Cover all styles. In-house PA.

Twa Tams
79-81 Scott Street, Perth, PH2 8JR
tel: 01738 634 500
email: thetwatams@yahoo.co.uk
contact: Stuart Hutton
capacity: 150
info: Live music every Friday and Saturday night, and occasional Thursday and Sunday nights. Support slots also available for signed touring bands. Any style of music considered. Bands to have played at Twa Tams in the past include Travis and Ocean Colour Scene. Contact Stuart by telephone or email to play.

The Universal
57-59 Sauciehall Street, Glasgow, G2 4AB
tel: 0141 332 8899
info: Live music organised through Joy Promotions. See listing in relevant section for details of gigs and demo submission.

The Venue
15-21 Calton Road, Edinburgh, EH8 8DL
tel: 0131 557 3073
fax: 0131 558 8528
email: jaq@edinvenue.com
web: www.edinvenue.com
contact: Jaq Findlayson, Lloyd McDermott
capacity: 350
info: Regular live band nights. In-house PA. Call or send demos to Jaq at the venue.

The Waverley Bar
3-5 St Mary's Street, Edinburgh, EH1 1TA
tel: 0131 556 8855
info: Open mic events run regularly by Out Of The Bedroom. See listing in Promoter section for details.

Westport Bar
64-66 North Lindsay Street, Dundee, DD1 1PS
tel: 01382 200 008
contact: Douglas Dow
capacity: 150
info: Regular band nights. In-house PA. Send demos and biog FAO Douglas at the venue.

Whistlebinkies
4-6 South Bridge, Edinburgh, EH1 1LL
tel: 0131 557 5114
fax: 0131 557 5114
email: info@whistlebinkies.com
web: www.whistlebinkies.com
contact: Gaz Long
capacity: 300
info: Live music 7 nights a week, with at least 2 acts playing. 'Turn On' is an unsigned showcase which is held every Tuesday night, featuring 5 bands. Backline and sound engineer are provided on Tuesday night. In-house PA. To play, contact Gaz by telephone or email.

WALES

Aberystwyth Arts Centre
University College of Wales, Peglais, Aberystwyth, Dyfed, SY23 3DE
tel: 01970 622 882
fax: 01970 622 883
email: aeh@aber.ac.uk
web: www.aber.ac.uk/artscentre
info: Deal with African, Big Band, Modern-Be Bop, Experimental, Latin, R&B, Soul, Traditional, World, Dixieland, Acid Jazz and Funk music. Contact before sending demo. See website for more details.

The Aberystwyth University Students' Union
Penglais Campus, Ceredigion, Penglais, SY23 3DX
tel: 01970 621 700
fax: 01970 621 701
email: stp@aber.ac.uk
web: www.aberguild.co.uk
contact: Steve Pickup
capacity: 980
info: Unsigned nights every 2 weeks on Sundays. Bigger and more regular nights planned for 2006.

Acedemi
Students' Union, University of Wales, Deiniol Road, Bangor, Gwynedd, LL57 2TH
contact: Adam Isbell
capacity: 500
info: Acedemi is one of the University of Wales Student Union venues. Live music or DJs 6 nights a week. In-house PA and sound engineer available. Send demos FAO Adam Isbell at the venue address. All styles welcome.

Bar Blu
92 High Street, Pen-y-cae, Rhyl, LL18 1UB
tel: 01745 356 600
fax: 01745 355 571
email: info@barblu.co.uk
web: www.barblu.co.uk
contact: Tony, Steve
capacity: 350
info: Unsigned bands play upstairs every Wednesday night. Wide range of musical styles from Acoustic to Punk. In-house PA. Send demos FAO Steve at 'Blood and Lipstick', 20 Walford Avenue, Rhyl, Denbighshire, LL18 2HL.

Barfly Cardiff
Kingsway, Cardiff, CF10 3FD
tel: 02920 396 589
email: cardiff.info@barflyclub.com
web: www.barflyclub.com
contact: Mark Walker
capacity: 200
info: Unsigned bands of all genres play most nights. Send demos, preferably on cassette or CD (maximum 3 tracks) to the address above. Include contact details. If you would like a reaction to your demo, you should phone on Tuesdays or Thursday on above number.

Blaengarw Workmen's Hall
Blaengarw, Bridgend, CF32 8AW
tel: 01656 871 911
email: creationdev@hotmail.com
web: www.creation.me.uk
contact: Jamie Warlow
capacity: 250
info: Band nights organised about twice a month by Black River Arts, a voluntary youth organisation. In-house PA and backline provided. Send demos marked Black River Arts to the venue.

Cardiff Coal Exchange
Mount Stuart Square, Cardiff, CF10 6EB
tel: 02920 494 917
fax: 02920 494 927
email: admin@coalexchange.co.uk
web: www.coalexchange.co.uk
capacity: 1000
info: The Cardiff Coal Exchange is available for hire only. For costs and booking details contact the venue direct. Visit the website for full programme listings.

Cathays Community Centre
36 Cathays Terrace, Cathays, Cardiff, CA24 4HX
tel: 02920 373 144
email: studio@soundsceneuk.com
web: www.soundsceneuk.com
info: Live music night once a month featuring 3 or 4 bands. Send demo to the address above. Cathays Community Centre houses Cardiff Sound Scene which incorporates a recording studio, rehearsal rooms and music tuition workshops. See relevant sections for details.

The Chattery
59 Uplands Crescent, Uplands, Swansea, SA2 0EZ
tel: 01792 473 276
email: thechattery@hotmail.com
web: http://homepage.ntlworld.com/thechattery
contact: Alex
capacity: 61
info: Restaurant which puts on live music about once a week. Often have touring artists from UK and USA playing, and give local Acoustic singers-songwriters the opportunity to support. Can be solo artist, duo or trio. In-house PA. Send demo FAO Alex to the venue.

The Claude Hotel
140 Albany Road, Cardiff, CF24 3RW
tel: 02920 418 741
email: openmic@jimjamsound.co.uk
web: www.jimjamsound.co.uk
contact: Jim
capacity: 200
info: Jim Jam hosts Acoustic and Electric nights every Thursday. Contact Jim for more information. PA will be provided by Jim.

Clwb Ifor Bach
Stryd Womanby, Cardiff, CF10 1BR
tel: 02920 232 199
fax: 02920 301 113
email: post@clwb.net
web: www.clwb.net
contact: Richard Hawkins
capacity: 380
info: Live music on a regular basis, but no definite schedule. All genres accepted, although no cover or tribute bands. In-house PA. To play send demo to the venue.

The Coopers Arms
Northgate Street, Aberystwyth, Dyfed, SY23 2JT
tel: 01970 624 050
email: somers3@hotmail.com
web: www.ycwps.co.uk
contact: Glynis, Brendan
capacity: 85
info: Unsigned bands play approximately twice a week. Bands are entitled to door takings. In-house PA. To play, contact Glynis or Brendan on the above number. Coopers Arms now hosts an open mic night on Mondays. A courtesy call to the venue is required to let them know you are turning up to play.

The Glee Club
Mermaid Quay, Cardiff Bay, CF10 5BU
tel: 0870 241 5093
web: www.glee.co.uk
contact: Markus Sargeant
capacity: 450
info: International and local bands. Specialises in Singer-Songwriters, Acoustic, Soul, Jazz, Folk and Roots. In-house PA. Contact Markus for full gig details. Glee Club have another venue based in Birmingham. See listing for further details.

Le Pub
1 Caxton Place, Newport, Gwent, NP20 4BN
tel: 01633 221 477
email: daninski@lepub-online.com
capacity: 220
info: Music venue used by Power of One Promotions, Deadsouls Promotions and Fact Fans Promotions. Call the venue for more information.

Meze Lounge
6 Market Street, Newport, NP20 1FU
tel: 01633 211 432
email: mezelounge@hotmail.com
web: www.mezelounge.com
contact: Steve
capacity: 200
info: On Mondays, there is 'Alternative Twist' night which feature Alternative artists. Meze Lounge also host a Rock night 'Over the Edge' in association with Planet Red Promo every Tuesday. Thursday is called 'Listening Post' which features Jazz and Funk music. On Sundays there is a also a showcase of live music. In-house PA provided. Call Steve for more information on getting a gig.

Monkey Café Bar
13 Castle Street, Swansea, SA1 1JF
tel: 01792 480 822
email: emmadavey@hotmail.co.uk
web: www.monkeycafe.co.uk
contact: Kate
capacity: 400
info: Live music 2 or 3 times per week. Broad range of musical styles. Bands can use live room upstairs if they want to put on their own gig. Otherwise, the venue pay bands they like to play downstairs. In-house PA. Send demo FAO Amanda or Kate to the address above.

The Point
Mount Stuart Square, Cardiff Bay, Cardiff
tel: 02920 499 979
email: the.point@clara.co.uk
web: www.thepointcardiffbay.com
contact: Ceri Whitehead
capacity: 400
info: Live music organised through Algee Promotions approximately twice a week. See entry in Promoters section for further details.

Pop Factory
Welsh Hills Works, Jenkin Street, Porth, Rhondda, CF39 9PP
tel: 01443 688 500
email: info@thepopfactory.com
web: www.thepopfactory.com
contact: Dave Driscoll
capacity: 300
info: The Pop Factory offers sound recording and production. Comprises a number of studio spaces, sound recording facilities, record label and video production facilities. See relevant sections for more details. The venue has live music 2-3 nights a week. In-house PA and sound engineer. Send demos to the venue.

Swansea University
Entertainments Office, Swansea Students Union, Fulton House, Singleton Park, Swansea, SA2 8PP
tel: 01792 295 485
email: russellwade@swansea-union.co.uk
web: www.ents.swansea-union.co.uk
contact: Ben Lucas, Russell Wade
capacity: 700/445/390
info: Unsigned bands play approximately once a week during the first term and beginning of second term. The rest of academic year is taken up with Battle of The Bands for Swansea University based acts. PA provided. Send demo FAO Ben to above address.

The Talbot Bar
2 Queen Street, Wrexham, LL11 1AP
tel: 01978 358 780
email: office@yales.fsbusiness.co.uk
web: www.thetalbotbar.co.uk
contact: Niel Thompson
capacity: 120
info: The Talbot Bar hosts HMV showcase night on Wednesdays featuring up and coming unsigned bands. Also have live Rock bands on Friday evenings. The venue also hosts various club nights. In-house PA, lights and sound engineer. Call for more information.

Theatr Brycheiniog
Canal Wharf, Brecon, Powys, Wales, LD3 7EW
tel: 01874 622 838
web: www.theatrbrycheiniog.co.uk
contact: Andy Eagle
capacity: 490
info: Theatre Brycheiniog organises music, drama, exhibitions, conferences, touring and local amateur productions. The venue is available for hire. Visit the website for current programme listings.

Time
Students' Union, University of Wales, Bangor, Bangor, Deiniol Road, Gwynedd, LL54
tel: 01286 760 69
email: info@timebangor.co.uk
web: www.timebangor.co.uk
contact: Adam Isbell
capacity: 500
info: Time is situated in the Students' Union, also see listing for Acedemi. Live music twice a month on the third and third Saturdays, with up to 7 bands may playing each night. In-house PA and sound engineer available. Send demos FAO Adam Isbell at the venue address. All styles welcome.

TJ's
14-16 Clarence Place, Newport, NP19 0AE
tel: 01633 216 608
email: sam@tjs-newport.demon.co.uk
web: www.tjs-newport.demon.co.uk
contact: Sam Bidmead
capacity: 500
info: Live music 2-7 nights per week. Send demos to Sam at the venue. Cheap Sweaty Fun Promotions organise unsigned band nights. See listing in Promoters section for further details.

Toucan Club
95 St. Mary Street, Cardiff, CF10 1DX
tel: 02920 372 212
email: simon@toucanclub.co.uk or helen@toucanclub.co.uk
web: www.toucanclub.co.uk
contact: Simon Kingman, Helen Kitchen
capacity: 300 (Club), 200 (Chill Out Bar)
info: Venue voted 'Best Alternative Venue in Wales' in 2001 and 2002. Artists who have performed at the Toucan Club in the past include Thea Gilmore, Damien Rice, Afrika Bambaataa and Super Furry Animals amongst others. Unsigned acts play most nights at Toucan Club. In-house PA and engineer. Open mic sessions held on Sunday and Tuesday nights in the Chill Out Bar, just turn up to take part. Contact Simon by email to play. Occasional gigs also organised through Dragon Bands, see entry in Promoters section.

Waterside Club
Coracle Way, The Quay, Carmarthen, SA31 3JR
tel: 01267 223 727
info: Live music once a month hosted by Tangled Parrot. See listing in Independent Promoters for more details.

Wyeside Arts Centre
Castle Street, Builth Wells, Powys, LD2 3BN
tel: 01982 553 668
email: filmwyeside@powys.org.uk
web: www.wyeside.co.uk
contact: Guy Roderick
capacity: 250 (Sated), 300 (Standing)
info: Unsigned showcases around 6 times per year. In-house PA. Send demo FAO Guy to the venue.

LIVE PERFORMANCE

Yales & Central Station
15-17 Hill Street, Wrexham, LL11 1SN
tel: 01978 311 857
fax: 01978 311 884
email: office@yales.fsbusiness.co.uk
web: www.centralstation-yales.co.uk
contact: Neil Thompson
capacity: 235 (Downstairs), 500 (Upstairs)
info: Live music on a regular basis. Live broadcasts of
unsigned bands on BBC Radio Wales occasionally take place at the
venue. Full PA and lighting. Send demos FAO Neil at the venue. Central
Station also hosts showcase nights 'The Redi Nights' and 'The Deck
Side'. See entry in Promoters section for further details.

LIVE PERFORMANCE

4.2 PROMOTERS

EAST of ENGLAND 619 GREATER LONDON 620 MIDLANDS 624 NORTHEAST 626 NORTHWEST 629
SOUTHEAST 631 SOUTHWEST 634 YORKSHIRE 635 NORTHERN IRELAND 636 SCOTLAND 636 WALES 638

EAST of ENGLAND

Acoustic Routes
16 Apple Tree Grove, Burwell, Cambridge, CB5 0BF
tel: 07971 299 659
email: bernard@acousticroutes.co.uk
web: www.acousticroutes.co.uk
contact: Bernard Hoskin
venues used: CB2
info: Acoustic night held on Saturdays in the basement at CB2. See website for demo submission policy. Bernard asks that musicians interested in playing get in touch before sending a demo.

Arts Development in East Cambridgeshire (ADEC)
Babylon Gallery, Waterside, Ely, Cambridgeshire, CB7 4AU
tel: 01353 669 022
fax: 01353 669 052
email: info@adec.org.uk
web: www.adec.org.uk
venues used: Various
info: Promote showcases for unsigned acts in East Cambridgeshire region, although will accept demos and book bands from any area. Contact the above number for further information. See listing in Useful Regional Organisations section for details of other services provided by ADEC.

The Band Agency
34 Dennis Road, Cambridge, CB5 8TT
email: gig@thebandagency.com
web: www.thebandagency.com
contact: Dave
venues used: Various
info: The Band Agency is a not-for-profit organisation that hosts numerous gigs and tours across the UK, as well as running festival stages, and hosting Break In The City. Send demo to the above address. See also listing in Regional Music Organisations section.

Blank Generation Collective
3 Cullingham Road, Ipswich, IP1 2EG
tel: 01473 404 038
email: info@blankgeneration.org.uk
web: www.blankgeneration.org.uk
venues used: Steamboat Tavern and others
info: Promote signed and unsigned bands at various venues in Ipswich. Music styles vary from Indie and Rock to Acoustic and Folk singer-songwriters. Send demos marked 'Blank Generation Collective' to the above address. Demos which are not suitable for Blank Generation will be passed onto more appropriate promoters in Ipswich.

Corkatronic Promotions
Utopia, Manningtree Road, Stutton, Ipswich, IP9 2SW
tel: 07709 600 050
email: corkatronica@therollocks.com
web: www.corkatronicpromotions.tk
contact: Tom
venues used: Various
info: Organise gigs at various venues in Ipswich and the surrounding area at least once a month. Mainly Rock and Alternative bands. Send demo FAO Tom to the above address.

Fiddler Crab Music
Ipswich
email: info@fiddlercrabmusic.co.uk
web: www.fiddlercrabmusic.co.uk
contact: Sam Clodd
venues used: Steamboat Tavern, Ipswich Vagabonds Coffee Shop
info: Band nights on average twice monthly, usually one in Colchester and one in Ipswich. Electric and Acoustic gigs. Email details of your act to the above address and send demo upon request. Fiddler Crab also run a record label. See listing in relevant section for details.

Foothold Promotions
3 Cullingham Road, Ipswich, IP1 2EG
tel: 01473 404 038
email: henry@footholdpromotions.co.uk
web: www.footholdpromotions.co.uk
contact: Dave, Henry
venues used: Steamboat Tavern and others
info: Promoters of signed and unsigned Punk, Metal and Ska bands at various venues in Ipswich. Links to MP3s welcome.

Metal Queen Promotions
63 Pembroke Road, Norwich, NR2 3HD
email: diego@mqprojects.co.uk
web: www.mqprojects.co.uk
contact: Diego
venues used: The Ferry Boat Inn
info: Metal Queen Promotions run the annual Norwich Pop Underground Convention (NPUC) every June. For more information on NPUC, see the website. Send demos to the address above. Also run a record label, see listing in relevant section for details.

One Bad Apple
1 Bradfield Road, North Waplsham, Norfolk, NR28 0HF
tel: 07736 323 501
email: inprintband@hotmail.com
web: www.onebadapple.tk
contact: Mike
info: Email before sending demo to above address. Interested in unique music. See website for more details.

Planet Beet
43 College Street, Bury St. Edmunds, Suffolk, IP33 1NL
email: info@planetbeet.tk
web: www.planetbeet.tk
contact: Jason
venues used: The Priors Inn
info: 'Planet Beet' takes place every Thursday night at The Priors Inn in Bury St. Edmunds. Wide variety of music including Indie, Alternative, Rock, Metal, Punk, Hardcore, Ska, Electronica and Jazz. 3 bands play every week, plus a DJ. Mainly book local acts playing their own songs, as well as good national bands looking to expand their fanbase. Send demo, biog and, if possible, picture to the above address. Alternatively, email a link to your website, and links to MP3s (do not send actual MP3s).

R*E*P*E*A*T
PO Box 438, Cambridge, CB4 1FX
email: rosey@repeatfanzine.co.uk
web: www.repeatfanzine.co.uk
contact: Richard Rose
venues used: Portland Arms
info: Website contains detailed section regarding band booking policy. Bands are requested to refer to this before contacting Richard about a gig.

Lambton & Varsani Communications
21-22 The Old Steyne, Brighton, BN1 1EL
tel: 01273 648 373
email: hash@lvcommunications.org
web: www.lvcommunications.org
contact: Hash Varsani
radio plugger: Yes
national coverage: Yes
info: Radio and press coverage on either national or regional basis, depending on requirements of the client. Specialist contact with music journalists, radio presenters and copywriters. See also listing for photography services in relevant section.

Uncollected Promotions
52 Merton Road, Norwich, NR2 3TT
tel: 0845 201 1240
email: james@uncollected.net
web: www.uncollected.net
contact: James
venues used: The Waterfront, Sonic, Norwich Arts Centre
info: Electronica promoters. Send demos FAO James. See website for more details.

wombatwombat
PO Box 24, Norwich, NR2 2WA
email: wombatwombatmouth.mortalwombat@ntlworld.com
web: www.wombatwombat.co.uk
venues used: Norwich Arts Centre
info: Primarily promote guitar based indie music, ranging from Punk to Alternative Country, once a month on Fridays at Norwich Arts Centre. 3 band bill featuring a mixture of new, established and cult indie bands from the UK and abroad, and almost always includes 1 local band. Books up to 6 months in advance, and there are a limited number of slots available. Unfortunately, it's not possible to provide feedback on demos but wombatwombat will contact you if able to offer a gig. Please send demo with contact details on the CD, cassette or MD. Alternatively email a link to your website and/or MP3s.

GREATER LONDON

2bob
284a Lewisham High Street, London, SE13 6JZ
email: info@2bob.co.uk
web: www.2bob.co.uk
contact: Ian Galloway, Carl
venues used: Fox & Firkin, Rose of Lee
info: 2bob Live is held at The Fox & Firkin in Lewisham every Thursday. Indie, Rock, Garage and Punk music. 3 bands play with 2bob DJs before, after and between sets. Also occasional nights in and around New Cross, Lewisham and Greenwich. Ideally, nights are kept free of charge so bands will be paid a percentage of bar takings. The more people you bring, the more you will be paid. To get a gig email with links to MP3s on website, or alternatively send a demo to the above address marked '2bob Demos'.

Artrocker
3a Highbury Crescent, London, N5 1RN
tel: 020 7609 7431
email: info@artrocker.com
web: www.artrocker.com
contact: Paul Cox, Tom Fawcett
venues used: Various
info: Run 'ArtRocker Club' at Buffalo Bar in London every Tuesday night. Usually feature newly signed headlining band and unsigned support act. Also occasionally promote unsigned bands at The Buzzard in Camden and The Garage in London. Send demo to the above address. ArtRocker also publish a weekly magazine. See entry in relevant section for details.

Automatic Promotion
1st Floor, 16-24 Underwood Street, London, N1 7JQ
tel: 020 7490 0666
fax: 020 7490 0660
email: enquiries@automaticpromotion.co.uk
web: www.clubautomatic.co.uk
contact: Genyia Davy
info: Specialise in promoting club nights especially for unsigned and new bands in London. Deal with all kinds of music but mostly Guitar based. Also offer marketing and distribution of flyers and posters. Clients include Nude Records and Polydor.

Bandnet
RA4 Bermondsey Trading Estate, Rotherhithe New Road, London, SE16 3LL
tel: 07957 551 724
email: df@bandnet.co.uk
web: www.bandnet.co.uk
contact: Dave
info: Organise live music. Mainly Guitar based. Contact for details of up and coming events. Send demos to above address.

The Basement Club
c/o rockfeedback.com, PO Box 704, High Wycombe, HP15 7GL
email: thebasement@rockfeedback.com
web: www.rockfeedback.com
venues used: The Buffalo Bar
info: 'The Basement Club' is a co-promotion between Rockfeedback.com and record producer Gordon Raphael (The Strokes). Held on fourth Thursday of every month at The Buffalo Bar, London. Line up is a mix of signed and unsigned acts, with 4 bands playing. Send demo to above address.

Black Clarion Entertainment
122-126 Kilburn High Road, London, NW6 4HY
tel: 020 7692 0597
email: teetime@37.com
contact: Tee
info: Promoter and manager of African musicians and actors.

Blow The Fuse
76 Hawksley Road, Stoke Newington, London, N16 0TJ
tel: 020 7254 8935
email: info@blowthefuse.com
web: www.blowthefuse.com
contact: Alison Raynor
venues used: Barracuda Jazz Cellar
info: Run Blow The Fuse Jazz Club held every other Friday at the Barracuda Jazz Cellar. Contact before sending demo to above address.

Bugbear Bookings
3a Highbury Crescent, London, N5 1RN
tel: 020 7700 0550
email: bugbear@btconnect.com
web: www.bugbearbookings.com
contact: Tony Gleed, Jim Mattison
venues used: Dublin Castle, Hope & Anchor, On The Rocks, Fridge
info: Refer to venue entries for further details. Send demos to Tony or Jim at the above address.

Catapult Club
London
tel: 020 8690 8980
web: www.catapultclub.co.uk
contact: Titch Turner
venues used: Amersham Arms
info: Catapult Club is a multimedia event held on the first Friday of every month at the Amersham Arms. Set up in style of 'Later with Jools Holland' with an Acoustic stage, main stage, presenter and 3 large screens. The event is filmed and recorded live. 3 bands play on the main stage, performing 2 sets each. In-house duo and guest act play 2 sets each on the Acoustic stage. Send demos marked The Catapult Club, c/o The Amersham Arms, 388 New Cross Road, London, SE14 6TY.

Club Fabulous
43 Northwold Road, London, N16 7DH
tel: 020 8806 1343
fax: 020 8806 1343
email: mark@clubfabulous.co.uk
web: www.clubfabulous.co.uk
contact: Mark
venues used: Caernarvon Castle, Lark In The Park, Upstairs at The Garage, The Garage
info: Runs 'Acoustic electric' nights on Tuesday, Wednesday, Thursday and Friday nights at the Lark In The Park. Also promote 'Electric Nights' at Caernarvon Castle every Wednesday and Thursday. Host an unsigned night on the last Thursday of the month upstairs at The Garage, and occasionally downstairs. Send demo FAO Mark to the above address.

Club Fandango (London)
London
email: antonio@clubfandango.co.uk
web: www.clubfandango.co.uk
contact: Antonio
venues used: Dublin Castle, Bull & Gate, Water Rats Theatre, Borderline
info: Eclectic band night founded by the owners of Fierce Panda Records and Pointy Records. To play contact Antonio on the above email address. Also held at various venues around the UK. See listings in other sections for booking details.

Club Hedonistic
The Old Fire House, 19 Sandringham Gardens, Barkingside, Ilford, Essex, 1G6 1NT
email: play@clubhedonistic.com
web: www.clubhedonistic.com
contact: Andrew Future
venues used: Islington Academy
info: Hedonistic promote free band nights once a month. Indie and Rock but all music types considered. Contact Andrew Future on the email address above.

CITY SHOWCASE
SPOTLIGHT LONDON

City Showcase – Spotlight London
The capital's leading festival for new
music and fashion

**SPOTLIGHTING SOME OF TODAY'S HOTTEST NEW
TALENT IN MUSIC AND FASHION**

**CITY SHOWCASE AIMS TO FIND TOMORROW'S
TALENT TODAY.**

Razorlight, Keane, Rooster, Amy Winehouse, Jay
Sean, Rishi Rich, Tyler James, The Rifles, Easy Kill,
David Ford, Sway and Pure Reason Revolution all
unveiled their musical wares at City Showcase
before going on to success. Designers who have
made their debut at City Showcase have also
gone on to shine at London Fashion Week.

Launched in 2003, City Showcase has already
established itself as a key date in the music and
fashion industry calendars. City Showcase is a
not-for-profit company that was launched with
one aim in mind: to help tomorrow's creative
talent make it in the cut-throat commercial world
of today.

The annual festival is free to the public in
London's West End and features new and
emerging musical talent dressed by up-and-
coming designers. This is a unique showcasing
opportunity for new designers and musicians.
City Showcase has gained the support of the
music and fashion industries with major label
A&Rs and fashion officionados looking to
discover the next big thing.

Through its website, www.cityshowcase.co.uk,
City Showcase also helps develop and support
talent through the creation of new networks,
relationships and promotional opportunities
culminating in the annual week-long London
festival which comprises workshops and
surgeries delivering essential industry advice
from industry experts.

You can watch out for our auditions which will
be advertised on our website
(www.cityshowcase.co.uk) or you can 'do a
Keane'…..

www.cityshowcase.co.uk

LIVE PERFORMANCE

Culture
12 Kingsley Road, Ilford, Essex, IG6 2LL
tel: 020 8262 3708
email: adrclegg@excite.com
web: www.culturepromotions.co.uk
contact: Mr. Chipps
venues used: The Garage, Purple Turtle
info: Promotes various venues around London.

Curious Generation
Bedford Chambers, Covent Gardens, London, WC2E 8H8
tel: 07719 140 848
email: info@curiousgeneration.com
web: www.curiousgeneration.com
contact: Alex Martin
venues used: Marquee Club
info: Promotion and consultancy aimed at discovering and developing emerging bands. Promote series of monthly showcase events, 'One Night At…' which are often attended by music industry professionals.

Damn You!
PO Box 3904, Clacton, Essex, CO15 5TF
email: scanlon@icr.ac.uk or chris.summerlin@btinternet.com or savegringo@aol.com
web: http://drink.to/damnyou
contact: Chris, Tom, Matt, Ian
venues used: Various
info: Promoters who have previously played in bands, and are dedicated to putting on quality music. Can arrange one off gigs to whole tours. Have lots of reliable contacts in venues. Regularly put on nights in London, Brighton and Nottingham.

Dead Or Alive Promotions
PO Box 34204, London, NW5 1FS
email: gigs@deadoralive.org.uk
web: www.deadoralive.org.uk
contact: Nicholas Barnett
venues used: The Metro Club, The Comedy, The Buffalo Bar, On The Rocks
info: Dead Or Alive host live music most nights of the week with 3 or 4 bands playing at various venues in London. Send demo FAO Nicholas to the above address.

Dirty Sound Promotions
107-109 Blackheath Road, Greenwich, London, SE10 8PD
tel: 07761 207 532
email: dirty_sounds@hotmail.com
contact: Wayne
venues used: Barfly, Infinity, Metro and various others around London
info: Dirty Sound Promotions organise signed and unsigned nights 3 to 4 nights a week . Send demos FAO Wayne at the above address.

Dirty Water Club
4 Woodlands Park Road, London, N15 3RT
tel: 020 7833 8868
email: info@dirtywaterclub.com
web: www.dirtywaterclub.com
contact: PJ
venues used: The Boston Music Room @ The Boston Arms
info: 'Dirty Water Club' is held every Friday night. 3 bands play each week. Before submitting demo visit website and click on Band Info link, to ensure your type of music is suitable. Send demo marked 'Dirty Water Club' to the above address.

Edyum Promotions
PO Box 47489, London, N13 4YS
tel: 07960 538 910
email: mail@edyum.co.uk
web: www.edyum.co.uk
contact: Caitlin Evens
venues used: Upstairs at The Garage
info: All music genres accepted. All proceeds from shows are donated to various charities.

Fairy Tale Promotions
59a High Street, South Norwood, London, SE25 6EF
tel: 020 8771 6956
email: wonderwbb@homechoice.co.uk
contact: Ellie
venues used: Bar Latino The Suite
info: Fairy Tale Promotions organise a night at Bar Latino The Suite in Corydon. Every Thursday is Rock Night with 4 bands playing each night. Send demos FAO Ellie to the above address.

Flag Promotions
PO Box 181, Wembley, London, HA0 4BE
tel: 020 8450 4506/07930 655 209
fax: 020 8450 4506
email: frank@flagpromotions.com
web: www.flagpromotions.com
contact: Frank
venues used: Astoria, Mean Fiddler venues, Madame Jo Jo's, Koko, Underworld
info: Promote unsigned bands 2 or 3 times per week at various venues in London. Industrial, Alternative Rock and some Indie and Goth. Send well presented demos FAO Frank to the above address. If you need to contact Frank, he prefers to speak by telephone, rather than via emails!

The Glue Rooms
25 Erlanger Road, New Cross, London, SE14 5TF
email: gluerooms@fsmail.net
web: www.gluerooms.com
contact: Patrick Thursby
venues used: Amersham Arms
info: Promote Experimental night on the last Wednesday of every month. Also linked with the Open Arts Platform, a community project based in South East London. Send demos on all formats to the above address.

Goo Music
Flat 4, 6 Glading Terrace, Stoke Newington, London, N16 7NR
tel: 07949 851 898
email: ben@goomusic.co.uk
web: www.goomusic.co.uk
contact: Ben Kirby
venues used: Buffalo Bar, Upstairs At The Garage
info: Promote gigs at various venues, including monthly band and club night 'Take Me To The Other Side' at The Garage. Also run management division. See listing in relevant section for details.

IUC Entertainment
8 Meadowbank, Primrose Hill, London, NW3 3AY
tel: 07930 154 190/07770 594 313
email: harleyruben@hotmail.com or internationalurbanchain@hotmail.com
web: www.iucentertainment.com
contact: Harley Ruben
venues used: Various
info: Event organisation from talent showcases for the music industry to commercial monthly club events. Mainly Hip-Hop, R&B and Drum&Bass music. Send MP3 tracks to either of the above email addresses.

Ken Carter
13 Rectory Grove, Croydon, Surrey, CR0 4AJ
tel: 020 8686 1521
email: kcjazz@blueyonder.co.uk
contact: Ken Carter
venues used: Grouse & Claret, The Eagle
info: Ken promotes Contemporary and Modern Jazz. Organises live Jazz every Thursday night at Grouse & Claret in Croydon and every Sunday lunchtime at The Eagle, Croydon. Send demo by cassette or CD format FAO Ken at the above address.

Leyline Promotions
Studio 24, Westbourne Studios, 242 Acklem Road, London, W10 5JJ
tel: 020 7575 3285
email: info@leylinepromotions.com
web: www.leylinepromotions.com
info: Leyline Promotions hold regular club nights, festivals and events at various venues around the country. Send demos to the address above.

Micky P
14 Soho Street, London, W1D 3DN
tel: 07789 456 526
email: mickyp@cafedeparis.com
contact: Micky
venues used: Pop, Cargo
info: Micky organises 'Eyelash' every Wednesday at Pop featuring 2 unsigned bands. He also puts on unsigned night 'Blink' at Cargo on the first and third Monday of every month. Send demos FAO Micky at the address above.

Mojo Boogie
c/o 3 Ireland Place, London, N22 8YY
tel: 020 8829 0919
web: www.mojoboogie.com
contact: Robert
info: Mojo Boogie organise occasional gigs at various venues in London. They specialise in Authentic Roots Music and Americana, Blues, Swing, Rhythm & Blues and Rock 'n' Roll. Send demos FAO Mojo Boogie to the above address.

Monsta Entertainments
1 Wadham House, 12 College Close, London, N18 2XT
tel: 07765 145 944
email: mick@monstaents.com
web: www.monstaents.com
contact: Mick Wood
venues used: Purple Turtle, Borderline and others
info: Promote band nights around London, no-pay-to-play or minimum audience policy. Essentially booking Rock, Metal and Alternative. Mick Wood has 20 years experience working with signed acts, but none chooses to favour up and coming talent. Vast industry and media contacts.

Music Scene UK
Unit 39, Silicon Business Centre, 28 Wadsworth Road, Perivale, UB6 7JZ
tel: 020 8998 9122
email: loz@vegassoundhouse.com or matt@vegassoundhouse.com
web: www.musicsceneuk.com
contact: Matt, Lawrence
venues used: Various
info: Promote unsigned nights regularly on a seasonal basis at various venues in London. Send demo to the above address. Music Scene also runs a booking agency under the same name, recording and rehearsal studios ' Loz Vegas Studios', equipment hire service and music shop 'Vegas Sound House', promotions and booking agency 'Music Scene UK', 'Music Providers' management, 'Some Think Media' media design company, as well as running the Drum Academy. See entries in relevant sections for further information.

MusicZombie
PO Box 180, Letchworth Garden City, Hertfordshire, SG6 3ZN
tel: 07961 985 959
email: richu@musiczombie.com
web: www.musiczombie.com
contact: Rich Underwood
venues used: Club 85, Hitchin Football Club, Purple Turtle and many more
info: Music Zombie organise gigs in various venues around Hertfordshire, Bedfordshire, Cambridgeshire and London (expanding to nationwide very soon). Usually 3 bands play, all music types considered including Rock, Punk, Metal, Pop, Dance and Rap. Also organise all day events. To get a gig or for help with getting gigs around the country, either send demo by post to the above address, marked for 'Gigs Department' or 'Agency Department' for the agency. Alternatively, email MP3 links to above email address. MusicZombie also runs a record label. See entries in relevant sections for details. Also have an online store selling unsigned band merchandise such as t-shirts, CDs, badges, posters and gig tickets. Go to www.mzstore.com.

Nefarious Promotions Ltd.
29 Littlebourne Road, Maidstone, Kent, ME14 5QP
tel: 07969 327 079
email: info@nefarious-promotions.co.uk
web: www.nefarious-promotions.co.uk
contact: Anthony
venues used: The Fox & Firkin, Underworld
info: Live Metal promoters. Organise band nights every Friday at The Fox & Firkin in Lewisham. Send demos for attention of Anthony to the above address.

Orange Promotions
3 Charter Court, Linden Grove, New Malden, K23 3BL
tel: 020 8942 7722
email: livegigs@mail.com
web: www.orangepromotions.com
contact: Phil Brydon
venues used: West OneFour
info: See The Orange @ West OneFour in venue listings for more details of individual nights. They also arrange unsigned nights at various other venues around London. Contact Phil to organise a gig.

Pete Feenstra - Real Music
c/o Mystic Records, 3rd Floor, Compass House, Bromley, Kent, BR1 1QU
tel: 020 8460 4907
email: pete@feenstra.co.uk
web: www.feenstra.co.uk
contact: Pete Feenstra
venues used: Rayners Hotel and various others
info: Put on gigs at various venues in the region. Send demos FAO Pete at the above address.

Phil's Acoustic Club
The Nineteenth Hole, Trent Park Golf Club, Bramley Road, Southgate, London, N14
tel: 020 8364 6620
email: phil@philsacousticclub.co.uk
web: www.philsacousticclub.co.uk
venues used: The Nineteenth Hole
info: Original live music on second Tuesday of every month. Call Phil at the number above to play.

RoaR Showcase
PO Box 44215, London, E3 5WE
tel: 07961 583 076
web: www.twylyte.co.uk
contact: Cal or Donna
info: RoaR Showcase brings together talented signed and unsigned urban artists in the UK. Mainly takes place in London every 2 or 3 months. The team also promote occasional club nights in London. To be considered for the showcase send demo with biog and photo to the address above.

RockStock Promotions
30 Beacon Grove, Carshalton High Street, Carshalton, Surrey, SM5 3BA
tel: 020 8767 3100
email: rockstock@tiscali.co.uk
web: www.rockstockpromotions.com
contact: Dave Clarke, Garry
venues used: Charles Cryer Theatre
info: Organise band nights at above venue at least once a month. Rockstock provide PA, monitors and lights. All ages and all styles of music. Bands will need to sell at least 25 tickets at £5 each. £2 per ticket sold is kept by the band. Send demo, biog and photos to the above address.

Sensible Promotions
596 Holloway Road, London, N7 6LB
tel: 020 7263 6939
email: sensiblepromotions@tiscali.co.uk
web: www.sensiblepromotions.co.uk
contact: Jay
venues used: Nambucca
info: Promote band nights 3 times a week. Send demos FAO Jay to the above address.

Sonic Mook Experiment
London
email: seanmclusky@aol.com
web: www.sonicmook.co.uk
contact: Sean McLusky
venues used: On The Rocks
info: Band promoter currently promoting an unsigned night, The Future Rock & Roll Club, every Thursday at On the Rocks, London. Email Sean for details of where to send demo and information on other unsigned nights he arranges.

Squid Ink
45 Twyford Avenue, London, N2 9NU
tel: 07890 595 653
email: squid@squidsound.com
web: www.squidsound.com
contact: Anna Goss
venues used: Buffalo Bar
info: Squid Ink is an unsigned night held on the first Sunday of every month. Demos to be sent to Anna Goss at the above postal address, or alternatively contact by email or telephone.

The Talent League
9 Douglas Square, Green Way, Norten, London, SM4 5MP
tel: 020 8685 0870
email: sam@thetalentleague.co.uk
web: www.thetalentleague.co.uk
contact: Samantha Crompton
venues used: Various
info: Organise showcases for artists. Also offer management and distribution services. See listings in relevant sections for details.

The Talent Scout
c/o Sound, PO Box 10349, London, NW1 9WJ
email: info@thetalentscout.co.uk
web: www.thetalentscout.co.uk
venues used: Sound
info: Promote variety of unsigned band nights at Sound. Every Wednesday 5 unsigned Indie, Rock and Pop bands play at 'Chu-bu'. 'Sound:Unplugged' is an Acoustic event for 5 acts, held every Tuesday in the Sound Café Bar. Every other Tuesday a showcase for 5 Alternative and Rock bands. Also organise all day events 'X-Treme Live' and 'FUNK:UK' featuring 8 bands at each. 'X-Treme Live' showcases Nu Metal and Hardcore on the first Saturday of every month and is open to all ages. 'FUNK:UK' is held on the third Saturday of every month and features Acid Jazz, Funk and Rare Groove acts. Send demos to the above address.

Tug
9 King Street, Covent Garden, London, WC2E 8HN
tel: 020 7379 6132 (Ext 159)
contact: Stefane Tug
venues used: Roadhouse, Café De Paris
info: Organise several nights in Central London. All styles of music considered. Send demos FAO Stefane to the above address.

LIVE PERFORMANCE

UK Unsigned
Bethnal Green Training Centre, Hanbury Street, London, E1 5HZ
tel: 07958 535 994/020 7377 8545
email: leavesofmusic@aol.com
web: www.ukunsigned.net or www.gigsonline.co.uk
contact: Sherry Nichols
venues used: Various
info: UK Unsigned is an event held nationwide for established unsigned bands. The event provides opportunities for successful bands to perform nationally. They also sponsor festivals giving bands the chance to support headlining acts. Send MP3s to the address above.

Up All Night Music
Top Floor, 20 Denmark Street, London, WC2H 8NA
tel: 020 7419 4696/020 7419 4697
email: info@upallnightmusic.com
web: www.upallnightmusic.com
venues used: Buffalo Bar, Spice of Life, The Cockpit, The Freebutt
info: Up All Night organise nights for newly signed and unsigned bands and musicians at various venues in London, as well as The Freebutt in Brighton. See individual venue entries for further details of specific nights. Send demos marked 'Bookings' to above address. Up All Night also provide a PA hire service, as well as artist and tour management.

Virtually Acoustic Club
50 Liden Close, London, E17 8HQ
tel: 07885 600 165
email: david@thevac.co.uk
web: www.thevac.co.uk
contact: David Sherwood
venues used: Progress Bar
info: 'Virtually Acoustic Club' is an open mic event held every Tuesday and Wednesday at the Progress Bar. See venue entries for further details. Acts which perform at these nights may have the opportunity to play at other events organised by Virtually Acoustic Club, held at Tinderbox and Borders Bookshop.

Whatever Club
London
email: whatever-club@hotmail.com
web: www.hotelmotel.co.uk
contact: Marika, Suzanne
venues used: The Underbelly
info: A night put on by members of the band Hotel Motel, who also organise the successful Computer Blue club night. Email to play.

XK8 Organisation
1st Floor, 16-24 Underwood, London, N1 7JQ
tel: 020 7490 0666
fax: 020 7253 8692
email: info@xk8organisation.com
web: www.xk8organisation.com
contact: Genia Davy
venues used: Barfly @ The Monarch
info: Run club nights at The Barfly in Camden. Alternative music of all genres; Pop, Funk, Rock. To play, either contact Genia on the above email address or telephone number. Alternatively send a demo to the above address. XK8 Organisation also leaflet distribute and bands should visit www.xk8organisation.com for more information

Zarathustras.com
St Mathews Church, Brixton, SW2 1JF
tel: 07974 500 019
email: zaid@zarathustras.com
web: www.zarathustras.com
contact: Zaid Joseph
venues used: Various
info: Mixture of Singer-Songwriters and up and coming bands from Indie, Funk, Rock to Soul, Reggae, Hip-Hop, Drum&Bass, as well as DJs. For full details of demo submission visit the website which also includes a 'bands wanted' section.

MIDLANDS

Angel Promotions
10 Duncroft Road, Yeardley, D26 2HY
tel: 07930 987 193
email: rebeccathompson_9@hotmail.com
web: www.angelpromotions.tk
contact: Becky Thompson
venues used: Medicine Bar, Glee Club, Scruffy Murphy's, The Royal George
info: Angel Promotions deal with most types of Alternative music. Send demos to the address above along with contact details.

Birmingham Jazz
19 Selwyn Road, Edgbaston, Birmingham, B16 0SH
tel: 0121 454 2371
fax: 0121 456 2351
email: dudley.evans@virgin.net
web: www.birminghamjazz.co.uk
contact: Tony Dudley-Evans
info: Promote variety of music including African, Big Band, Contemporary, Modern-Be Bop, Fusion, Free-Improvised and Latin. Contact Tony Dudley-Evans before sending demo to above address. See website for more details.

Bloodstock
30 Russell Avenue, Wollaton, Nottingham, NG8 2BN
tel: 0115 985 5251
email: info@bloodstock.uk.com
web: www.bloodstock.uk.com
contact: Vince Brotheridge
venues used: Various
info: Organise annual Bloodstock Festival held at end of August at The Assembly Rooms in Derby. Two day Rock and Metal festival featuring headliners from Europe and approximately 12 national unsigned bands. Attracted approximately 2,500 people last year and is expanding year by year. Bloodstock accept submissions all year round for bands interested in playing the festival. They also promote other related tours and details of these events can be found at www.nbobm.com. Send demo, biog and photo FAO Vince to the above address.

Brass Button Promotions
54 Rufford Avenue, Rainworth, Nottingham, NG9 3JH 10lg
tel: 01623 461 691
email: info@brassbutton.co.uk
web: www.brassbutton.co.uk
contact: Rebecca, Helena
venues used: Various
info: Acoustic music promoters Brass Button are holding regular live music events in and around Nottingham to promote the acoustic music scene.

Campbell Promotions
122 Gosford Street, Coventry, CV1 5DL
tel: 02476 234 830/07870 246 643
email: djkipuk@btinternet.com
contact: Kip, Jim, Stevo
venues used: The Phoenix
info: Send a full press pack including demo on either CD or MP3 format, discography and photos to the address above. All genres considered. Promote band night every Tuesday at The Phoenix.

Catapult Club
140b Alcester Road, Moseley, Birmingham, B13 8HT
tel: 0121 449 8601
email: arthur@catapultclub.freeserve.co.uk
web: www.catapultclub.freeserve.co.uk
contact: Arthur Tapp
venues used: Jug of Ale, Bar Academy and Birmingham Acadamy 2
info: Catapult Club is an unsigned showcase for local talent held at Jug of Ale in Birmingham 3 nights a week (Wednesday, Friday and Saturday). It is also held twice a week at Bar Academy, as well as occasional gigs at Academy 2. Send demo FAO Arthur at the address above or email with details of where your music is available for download.

Club Fandango (Birmingham)
Birmingham
tel: 07865 047 354
email: butchershook@tiscali.co.uk
web: www.clubfandango.co.uk
contact: Rob
venues used: Actress & Bishop
info: Eclectic band night founded by the owners of Fierce Panda Records and Pointy Records. To play contact Rob on the above email address. Also held at various venues around the UK. See listings in other sections for booking details.

Club Fandango (Nottingham)
Nottingham
email: rethm4@aol.com
web: www.clubfandango.co.uk
contact: Tom
venues used: Rescue Rooms
info: Eclectic band night founded by the owners of Fierce Panda Records and Pointy Records. To play contact Tom of Hot Renault Traffic Club on the above email address. Also held at various venues around the UK. See listings in other sections for booking details.

Cold Rice
Studio 315, The GreenHouse, 9 Gibb Square, Birmingham, B9 4AA
tel: 0121 224 7707
email: mastercomputer@coldrice.com
web: www.coldrice.com
venues used: Bar Academy
info: Cold Rice run a successful, eclectic night at
Birmingham Bar Academy on Saturday nights. Send a demo before
calling Cold Rice.

Cosmic American Music
44 Davies Road, West Bridgford, Nottingham, NG2 5JD
email: james@cosmicamerican.com
web: www.cosmicamerican.com or
                   www.cabaret-nottingham.com
contact: James Windsor
venues used: Rescue Rooms
info: Organise live music at Rescue Rooms in Nottingham.
Folk, Roots, Country Rock, Americana and Blues music. Usually
promote signed American acts, but have support slots available for
unsigned acts. Send demos FAO James to the above address

Friends of the Upton Jazz Festival
Court Cottage, Lockeridge Lane, Upton-upon-Severn, Worcestershire,
WR8 0RP
tel: 01684 593 794
contact: Paul Lawrence
venues used: Various
info: Promote Mainstream, New Orleans and Traditional
genres. Contact before sending demo to above address.

Frontline AV
85 Far Gosford Street, Coventry, West Midlands, CV1 5DZ
tel: 02476 224 221
email: colin@frontlineav.com
contact: Colin
venues used: Dogma Bar and various others
info: Specialise in Urban music. Organise live music
events for new talent in various clubs and outdoor venues in Coventry.
Also provide video promo service. See relevant section for further
details. Send demos to the above address.

Groundfloor Promotions
Birmingham
tel: 07816 480 672
email: xen@groundfloorobservatory.com
web: www.groundfloorobservatory.com
contact: Xenia Randle
venues used: Royal George, Flapper & Firkin, Birmingham
info: Occasionally puts on bands at venues above.
Can also pass demos onto other suitable promoters as well. Xenia is
also a photographer. See listing in relevant section for Groundfloor
Observatory.

Hot Renault Traffic Club
22a King Street, Southwell, Nottinghamshire, NG25 0EN
tel: 01636 819 093/07957 666 640
email: rethm4@aol.com
web: www.hotclubnight.com
contact: Thomas Reed, Reedy
venues used: The Cabaret, The Social & The Rescue Room. All
                   in Nottingham
info: Hot Renault Traffic Club is part of Awd Promotions.
Promote all the major venues in Nottingham and also run 'Club
Fandango Nottingham'.

Lee Fewkes
10 Charnwood Grove, Mansfield Woodhouse, Nottinghamshire,
NG19 8NZ
tel: 07944 850 575
email: info@leefewkes.co.uk
web: www.leefewkes.co.uk
contact: Lee Fewkes
venues used: Town Mill in Mansfield
info: Gig promoter, band manager, booking agent,
musician, designer and music all-rounder. Always looking for
interesting bands of any genre for gigs, recordings and exciting
ventures. Send demo to the address above.

Left of Center
11a Clark Road, Wolverhampton, WV3 9NP
tel: 07956 424 093
email: leftofcenter_uk@hotmail.com
contact: Spence Cater
venues used: The Planet
info: Left of Center promote live music at venues in
Wolverhampton and the West Midlands on a regular basis. Spence
Cater presents 'Naked Ambition', an internet radio show broadcast
on www.wcr1350.co.uk from 2pm to 5pm on Sunday afternoons and
is also an A&R scout for Kerrang! 105.2FM unsigned show. For more
information on Kerrang!'s unsigned show see the radio station listings.

Loop Promotions
PO Box 11815, Birmingham, B33 8WL
tel: 07939 851 422
email: tonyloop@blueyonder.co.uk
contact: Tony
venues used: Various
info: Loop Promotions organise band and acoustic nights
at venues in Birmingham, including occasional all day events. Contact
Tony by email or telephone to play.

Maxrock
c/o Edward's No.8, Low Severn Street, Birmingham, B1 1BL
tel: 07801 562 801
email: via website
web: www.maxrock.co.uk
contact: Robert Smith
venues used: Edward's No.8
info: MaxRock promotes Rock and Metal at Edward's No.8
which is a Popular dedicated Rock venue.

Neon Empire Marketing
61 Bowling Green Lane, Albrighton, Shropshire, WV7 3HL
tel: 07718 047 225
email: steveneon@hotmail.com
contact: Steve Harrington
venues used: The Planet
info: Promote unsigned night, Electric Chair, most Friday
nights. 3 or 4 bands play, occasionally with signed headline act. Send
demos FAO Sean Meredith to the above address. Also promote club
night at Club Hell called After Dark.

Parked
12 Hobby Close, Broughton Astley, Leicester, LE9 6RP
tel: 07989 937 976
email: parkedmusic@hotmail.com
web: www.parked-music.co.uk
contact: Paul Fogerty
venues used: The Shed, The Toucan
info: Organise gigs once a month at The Shed in Leicester
and The Toucan, Cardiff. Mainly Indie and Rock. Send demos FAO Paul
to the above address.

Pink Angel Promotions
LCB Depot, 31 Rutland Street, Leicester, LE1 1RE
tel: 0116 261 6837
email: trevor@pinkangels.co.uk
web: www.pinkangels.co.uk or
                   www.getyourbandon.co.uk
contact: Trevor Locke
venues used: The Attik, The Shed, The Charlotte
info: Promotes all types of Rock music including Punk,
Nu Rock, Ska Punk, Metal, Alternative, Emo and Indie. Also offers full
band promotion service, see the websites for further information.

Public-i
The Cottage, Slade Hill Farm, Staden Lane, Buxton, Derbyshire,
SK17 9SZ
tel: 07817 767 843/07005 963 263
email: events@public-i.org.uk
web: www.public-i.org.uk
contact: Clive Leighton
venues used: Various - capacities ranging from 50 to 950
info: Public-i organises events at venues all over the High
Peak and Derbyshire, providing entertainment for council, charity,
corporate, commerce, university, industry showcases and festivals. All
music types considered. PA and backline provided. Public-i create a
performer friendly atmosphere. In-house media arm offers performers
publicity packages. Also open to suggestions and collaborations from
all areas of the music industry such as designers, photographers and so
on. Contact Clive by telephone or email for further details.

Punk Soc
University of Warwick, Coventry
tel: 07766 008 765
email: su165c@sunion.warwick.ac.uk
web: www.punksoc.co.uk
contact: Martin
venues used: Robbins Well, Dog & Trumpet and
                   Warwick University SU
info: Organise monthly night 'No Logo' at Robbins Well in
Leamington Spa featuring DJs and 2 or 3 bands. PA and mics supplied,
amps and drum kits to be arranged by band. Also organise occasional
events at various venues including The Dog & Trumpet in Coventry and
University of Warwick SU. To play, email above address with details of
your act, or call Martin.

LIVE PERFORMANCE

Raw Promotions
PO Box 5718, Derby, DE21 2YU
tel:	01332 834 438
email:	rawpromo@aol.com
web:	www.rawpromo.co.uk
contact:	Alan Wooley
venues used:	Flowerpot and various
info:	Currently organise gigs at various venues across

Derby, Flowerpot being a regular venue. See listing in venue section. All music styles considered. Send demos the above address FAO Alan.

Red Revolution
Flat 39, Room 2, Shackleton Hall, Edgbaston, B15 3SZ
tel:	07733 027 671
email:	contact@redrevolution.org
web:	www.redrevolution.org
contact:	Nic Bowler
venues used:	Various
info:	Promotes Alternative, Rock and Guitar based acts.

Contact before sending demos and biographies.

Richard Elms
c/o The Coliseum Night Club, Primrose Hill Street, Coventry, CV1 5LY
tel:	02476 228 459
email:	richelms@tiscali.co.uk
venues used:	The Coliseum, The Sanctuary
info:	Organises gigs at various venues around the

Midlands, covers most styles of music. Contact Richard or Ashley for demo submission details.

SD Enterprises
1 Tilewright, Kidsgrove, Stoke On Trent, Staffordshire, ST7 4TR
tel:	07967 579 666
email:	sociald@btinternet.com
contact:	Martin Bentley
venues used:	Limelight
info:	Organise live music twice a week at The Limelight in

Crewe. Also put on gigs at various pubs in the local area. Send demos FAO Martin to the above address or c/o The Limelight, Hightown, Crewe, CW1 3BP.

Solar Creations
PO Box 9691, Birmingham, B27 7ED
tel:	0121 707 8504
email:	scott@solarcreations.net
web:	www.solarcreations.net
contact:	Scott Roe
venues used:	The Actress & The Bishop
info:	Organise bands every night at The Actress & The

Bishop, Birmingham and gigs at various other venues in Birmingham and across the country. Send demos to the above address. Solar Creations also have a record label and provide PR and management services. See entries in appropriate sections.

Solid Entertainments
4-6 Wellowgate, Grimsby, North East Lincolnshire, DN23 0RA
tel:	01472 349 222
email:	tickets@solidentertainments.freeserve.co.uk
web:	www.solidentertainments.com
contact:	Stephen Stanley
venues used:	Various
info:	Solid Entertainments book signed and unsigned

bands in venues throughout the country 52 weeks a year. Support slots are available. Send demos with biog to the address above, mark FAO Stephen Stanley. For a list of venues see Solid Entertainments' website.

Teddy Fullick
Flat 10, Windsor House, Redcliffe Gardens, Mapperley Park, Nottingham, NG3 5AX
tel:	0115 960 3450
contact:	Teddy Fullick
venues used:	The Lion, The Malt Shovel
info:	Regular band nights. Contact Teddy before sending

demo to above address.

Zoot Promotions
PO Box 3932, Birmingham, B30 2EQ
tel:	07958 340 162
email:	jackie@zootmusic.net
web:	www.zootmusic.net
contact:	Jackie, Rob
info:	Zoot Promotions mainly promote Indie and

Alternative music. See website for details.

NORTHEAST

Acoustic Circus
Newcastle
email:	simm@acousticcircus.co.uk
web:	www.acousticcircus.co.uk
contact:	Simma
venues used:	The Bridge Hotel
info:	Showcase for new musical talent based in the region.

Organise gigs approximately once a month at The Bridge Hotel. Firstly, refer to the information for performers page on the website, then email Simma at the above address with details of your act, as well as a contact telephone number.

Bunker
29 Stockton Road, Sunderland, SR2 7AQ
tel:	0191 567 1777
email:	info@bunkeruk.com
web:	www.bunkeruk.com
contact:	Kenny Sanger
venues used:	Various
info:	Bunker promote live music in various venues around

Sunderland. Visit the website for regularly updated information. Also see rehearsal rooms and recording studio sections.

Gateshead Council
Caedmon Hall, Central Library, Prince Consort Road, Gateshead, Tyne & Wear, NE8 4LN
tel:	0191 477 5380
email:	suehurrell@gateshead.gov.uk
web:	www.gateshead.gov.uk
contact:	Sue Hurrell
venues used:	Caedmon Hall
info:	Contact before sending demo to above address. See

website for more details.

Insangel.co.uk
61-62 Thornton Street, Newcastle Upon Tyne, NA1 4AN
tel:	07901 616 185
email:	phil@insangel.co.uk
web:	www.insangel.co.uk
contact:	Phil Hughes
venues used:	Various
info:	Insangel runs and promotes live music 7 nights a

week at The Archer in Newcastle, as well as promoting and developing the local scene on a Wednesday at The Telegraph. Insangel are booking for Legends on a national touring level. Out of town unsigned bands should send demos FAO Phil to the above address, but please send an email first. Gig swaps are preferred where possible. Can also assist with tour booking and management, as well as PA hire services.

Receptive Promotions
7 Gloucester Avenue, Fulwell, Sunderland, SR6 9ED
tel:	0191 549 5964/07910 461 705
email:	receptivepromotions@hotmail.com
web:	www.myspace.com/receptivepromotions
contact:	Jamie Common
venues used:	Pure Voodoo Room
info:	Promotes gigs around once a month. Alternative,

Metal, Screamo, Hardcore and Post Hardcore. Send demo FAO Jamie Common to the above address.

Rock Bottom Punk
11 Second Street, Blackhall, Hartlepool, Cleveland, TS27 4EN
tel:	07747 804 629
email:	rockbottompunk@aol.com
contact:	Chris
venues used:	The Clarendon Hotel
info:	Mainly promote gigs for touring bands, unsigned

bands can be included on bill. Also organise occasional nights at The Clarendon Hotel, Hartlepool with 5 or 6 bands. Touring bands will need to provide backline. Contact Chris by phone or email. Alternatively send demo FAO Chris to above address.

Ten Feet Tall
The Old Chaple, 70 Corporation Road, Middlesbrough, TS1 2RG
tel:	01642 247 755
fax:	01642 247 727
email:	info@tenfeettall.co.uk
web:	www.tenfeettall.co.uk
contact:	Phil Saunders
venues used:	Empire, Moby Gray, Jax
info:	Live music across the North East, signed and

unsigned bands. See website for information regarding demo submission.

UNSIGNED?
SEND US YOUR DEMO'S...
DETAILS AT WWW.INTHECITY.CO.UK
THE PREMIER NEW MUSIC EVENT IN THE WORLD
IN THE CITY™

Too Far North
1 Hodgeson Buildings, Sunderland
tel: 07712 001 685
email: music2fn@yahoo.co.uk
web: www.toofarnorth.co.uk
contact: Adam Offord
venues used: The Head of Steam, Ivy House,
    The Bridge Hotel, The Tyne
info: Organise unsigned showcases twice a month at The
Head of Steam. Usually 3 local bands plus 1 out of town band playing.
Send demo FAO Adam to the above address. Please contact Adam by
phone or email before sending demo.

Travelled Music
The Tile Works, Paxton, Berwick Upon Tweed, TD15 1TJ
tel: 01289 386 737
email: info@travelledmusic.co.uk
web: www.travelledmusic.co.uk
contact: Alan Thompson
venues used: Various
info: Promote unsigned nights every fortnight at various
venues around Berwick, Glasgow and Edinburgh. Mainly Indie,
Rock and Pop. Send demo to above address. Travelled Music also
offer management, equipment hire, merchandise and CD duplication
services.

NORTHWEST

A3H Promotion Ltd.
19 Thirlmere Drive, Withnell, Chorley, PR6 8AY
tel: 07812 577 987
email: a3hpromotion@aol.com
web: www.a3hpromotion.co.uk
contact: John Winstanley
venues used: Cellar Bar, The Attic
info: Organise band nights every Friday and Saturday
at The Attic, and has a monthly slot at Cellar Bar. Mainly Indie,
Alternative and Rock. John also writes for the UK's leading Punk Rock
fanzine, 'Pogo til I Die' and is happy to review band demos. Contact
John by email or via contact form on website.

Akoustik Anarkhy (aA)
Manchester
email: hello@akoustikanarkhy.co.uk
web: www.akoustikanarkhy.co.uk
venues used: Piccadilly Gardens Hotel
info: Promote regular gigs at Piccadilly Gardens Hotel,
as well as other venues around Manchester. Mainly Leftfield Guitar
Based music. See also listing for the Akoustik Anarkhy label in relevant
section. Contact with details of your act via email.

Alectro Ecoustic
115 Blackfriar Court, St. Simon Street, Salford, Greater Manchester,
M3 7FS
email: alectroecoustic@ntlworld.com
web: www.alectroecoustic.co.uk
contact: Daniel Weaver
venues used: Various
info: Mostly Jazz events - Contemporary, Experimental,
Free-Improvised, World. Email before sending demo. Will put on gigs at
various, unexpected venues. See website for more details.

Aurora Borealis Music
Gostin Building, 32-36 Hanover Street, Liverpool, L1 4LN
tel: 0151 709 1299
email: kaya@aurora-borealis.info
web: www.aurora-borealis.info
contact: Kaya Herstad
venues used: Liverpool Barfly and others.
info: Artist development company who can assist
unsigned bands with songwriting support, improving promo packs and
image consultation. Have numerous contacts to put bands in touch
with such as studios, photographers, vocal coaches. Also run monthly
showcase called 'Northern Lights' which acts they are currently
developing can perform at. For further information contact Kaya on the
above number for a chat, or alternatively send in a demo and existing
promo pack with covering letter detailing areas requiring assistance and
advice.

Banned! Network
c/o DAN, The Library, Witton Street, Northwich, Cheshire, CW9 5DR
tel: 01606 415 97
fax: 01606 415 97
email: banned@danarts.demon.co.uk
web: www.banned.org.uk
contact: Nick Hughes
venues used: Winnington Rec
info: Promote gigs in Northwich. Send demos to the above
address.

Blowout
Manchester
email: blowout@elvis.org.uk
web: www.blowout.org
contact: Graham Thomas
venues used: Bierkeller
info: Blowout is regular live music event for signed and
unsigned bands held every Friday at The Bierkeller. Always looking for
new bands, DJs and VJs to get involved. Email Blowout at the address
above for more information.

Charabanc Management & Promotions
18 Sparkle Street, Manchester, M1 2NA
tel: 0161 273 5554
fax: 0161 273 5554
email: charabanc@btconnect.com
contact: Richard Lynch
venues used: Late Room, Roadhouse, Night & Day
info: Charabanc Promotions organise 'The HMV
Showcase' for unsigned and signed bands. The CDs then go on sale in
HMV Manchester. Charabanc also promotes other unsigned and signed
nights at various venues. Send demo to the above address.

Club Fandango (Blackpool)
Blackpool
tel: 07876 588 864
email: david.b@muse-ltd.com
web: www.clubfandango.co.uk
contact: Dave Blundell
venues used: Beat Club
info: Eclectic band night founded by the owners of Fierce
Panda Records and Pointy Records. To play contact Dave on the above
email address. Also held at various venues around the UK. See listings
in other sections for booking details.

Club Fandango (Manchester)
Manchester
tel: 07811 449 529
email: matt@tcb-management.co.uk
web: www.clubfandango.co.uk
contact: Matt Johnson
venues used: Night & Day
info: Eclectic band night founded by the owners of Fierce
Panda Records and Pointy Records. 'Club Fandango' is held on the last
Friday of every month at Night & Day. To play contact Matt at TCB
Management by email. Also held at various venues around the UK. See
listings in other sections for booking details.

Cotton City
506 Bolton Road West, Ramsbottom, Bury, Lancashire, BL0 9RU
tel: 01204 882 930
email: barry@cottoncity.com
web: www.cottoncity.com
contact: Barry Aldous
venues used: Various
info: Recent artists include Cotton City Jazz Band,
Society Promenaders and Dave Donohoe Jazz Band. Barry has played
Traditional Jazz for 50 years with several local bands. He also continues
to lead the Cotton City jazz band established in 1954, and currently
develops websites and publicity material for local bands.

The Cotton Club
1a Bold Street, Liverpool, L1 4DJ
tel: 0151 707 2333
email: liverpool@thebarandgrill.co.uk
web: www.thebarandgrill.uk.com
contact: Chris
venues used: The Bar & Grill, Liverpool
info: Unsigned bands play around twice a month. The
Cotton Club occasionally puts on bands in association with local record
labels. In-house PA. Send demos FAO Chris to the above address.

Dirty Pink & Blue
Barcroft. Carr Lane, Blackburn, BB2 6QG
email: pendelm@hotmail.com
web: www.dirtypinkandblue.com
contact: Fran Marshall
venues used: Attic
info: Organise regular Punk nights at the Attic. Send
demos marked Dirty Pink & Blue to the above address.

djCOLpromotions
JukeBox Breakdown, The Castle, Union Street, Oldham, OL1 1DJ
tel: 07795 201 558
email: djCOLmusic@hotmail.co.uk
web: www.djcolmusic.co.uk
contact: Colin Campbell
venues used: The Castle
info: Promoter of Alternative music nights every
Thursday. Send demo to the above address.

LIVE PERFORMANCE

Glasswerk
Liverpool
tel:	0151 707 9044
email:	ar@glasswerk.co.uk
web:	www.glasswerk.co.uk
contact:	Mat Ong
venues used:	Various
info:	Glasswerk organize regular unsigned nights at

venues across the UK. Check the website for events currently being held, and details of demo submission.

High Voltage
Manchester
email:	rich@highvoltage.org.uk
web:	www.highvoltage.org.uk
contact:	Richard Cheetham
venues used:	Various
info:	Unsigned nights held at various venues in

Manchester. 3 or 4 bands play. Headline slot by out of town band, so far have had acts from Bristol, Leeds, Derby, Birmingham, Liverpool, London and Edinburgh. Mainly Guitar based Indie and Rock music. To play contact Richard with details of your act, or check the website. No MP3s please.

IdENTITY
26 Hulme Street, Manchester, M1 5GL
tel:	0161 247 7733
email:	info@idmusic.biz or
	rocco@armstronglearning.co.uk
web:	www.idmusic.biz
contact:	Bex Phillips
venues used:	Various
info:	IdENTITY was set up by managers, promoters and

artists involved with New Deal for Musicians. Organise showcases at various venues in Manchester. For further information contact Rocco or Bex on the above number.

In The City
8 Brewery Yard, Deva Centre, Trinity Way, Salford, M3 7BB
tel:	0161 839 3930
fax:	0161 839 3940
email:	info@inthecity.co.uk
web:	www.inthecity.co.uk
contact:	Tom Clarke
info:	In The City is the UK's annual international music

convention. To be considered for an 'In The City Unsigned', which have in the past has featured amongst others, Muse, Oasis and The Darkness. Check website for demo submission details.

Lancashire Music Collective (LMC)
40 Sefton Gardens, Aughton, Ormskirk, Lancashire, L39 6RZ
email:	peteguy3@hotmail.com
web:	www.lancashiremusiccollective.com
contact:	Pete Guy
venues used:	Ormskirk Civic Hall, Ormskirk Comrades Club
info:	Organise monthly gigs, alternating between venues

listed above on Friday or Saturday night. Between 4 and 6 acts play, one of which is usually a guest band from outside of Lancashire. 8k PA provided with 2 sound engineers. All music types considered. In the future LMC will be holding 2 gigs per month, plus an additional Acoustic gig. To play at LMC, send demo FAO Pete at the above address. Alternatively, complete the online band form which can be found on the website.

Loose Music Collective
PO Box 67, Runcorn, WA7 4NL
tel:	01928 566 261
email:	jaki.florek@virgin.net
web:	www.loosemusic.org
contact:	Jaki Florek
venues used:	Various
info:	Put on various nights in the Widnes and Runcorn

areas in venues ranging from pubs to arts centres. Put on 'Fused' gigs for under 19 year olds. Also organise Acoustic night for songwriters. Loose Music Collective will try to cover the bands' expenses and supply a good PA. To play a 'Fused' gig, no need to send a demo, but just some information about your band. For all other gigs send demo and biog to the above address. Will consider all styles of music, and are particularly interested in non-mainstream, fun and experimental music. Also see listing in Useful Regional Organisations section for other services provided by the collective.

Manchester Unsigned
219 Bolton Road, Bury, Lancashire, BL8 2NR
email:	info@manchesterunsigned.com
web:	www.manchesterunsigned.com
contact:	Rik Brundrit
venues used:	Late Room, Matt & Phreds, The Printworks
info:	Manchester Unsigned host 4 live events per

year, usually with 4 acts ranging from Jazz acts, guitar bands and Soundscapes. Events often held at Matt & Phreds and The Late Room in Manchester. To play, either send demo to the above address or an MP3 to the above email address. Also send a short biog and photo.

mcr:music
3rd Floor, 24-26 Lever Street, Manchester, M1 1DZ
tel:	0161 234 6814
email:	lee@mcrmusic.co.uk
web:	www.theunsignedguide.com
contact:	Jeni Chan
venues used:	The Late Room, Club Academy, Academy 3
info:	Booking a variety of Manchester venues. Run

'Academy Unsigned' at the University's Academy 3, offering unsigned bands an excellent opportunity to play a tour standard venue with professional lighting, excellent PA and monitor engineer. Also book gigs at The Late Room during the week and before 'Plastic Surgery' club night every Saturday. Also promote a band and club night held at Club Academy every Friday. mcr:music also programme the music for 'Ragtime', an online student recruitment agency that has its own music streaming. To be considered for the playlist send demos marked 'Ragtime' to the address above. See also www.ragtime.com.

Music & Mystic
5-7 Harrison Street, Barrow-in-Furness, Cumbria, LA14 1JF
tel:	01229 877 253
email:	brian@musicmystic.co.uk
web:	www.musicmystic.co.uk
contact:	Brian
venues used:	Railway Mens Club
info:	Organise nights 3 or 4 times a month held at The

Railway Mens Club in Barrow-in-Furness. Mainly Metal, Punk, Goth and Rock. Email Brian with MP3s and biog, or alternatively post a demo and biog to the address above. Also run a music shop. See listing in relevant section for details.

Nemo Records
25 Grosvenor Road, Heaton Moor, Stockport, SK4 4EE
email:	benphuzz@hotmail.com
contact:	Ben Taylor, Tony Pinkham
venues used:	Night & Day Café
info:	Nemo Records host a monthly showcase featuring 3

bands and a DJ per night. Send demos to the address above. See also record company and management company listings. Send an email to the address above.

Northgate Music Promotions
1 City Walls, Chester, CH1 2JG
tel:	01244 400 414
fax:	01244 400 414
email:	info@alexandersjazz.com
web:	www.alexandersjazz.com
contact:	Ian
venues used:	Alexander's Jazz Theatre
info:	Acoustic, Blues, Soul and R&B. Contact Ian on

either Wednesday or Friday. Also has facilities for booking bands for weddings and similar events. See website for more details.

Panic Promotions Ltd.
24 Mount Pleasant, Chester, CH4 8BW
tel:	01244 680 680
email:	admin@panic-promotions.com
web:	www.panic-promotions.com
contact:	Dave Mounter
venues used:	Various
info:	Always on the lookout for local bands who can play.

For more information contact Dave Mounter via email.

Quarantine
4 Aldwych Road, West Derby, Liverpool, L12 8QL
tel:	07720 839 843
email:	quarantine_1@hotmail.com
contact:	Mark Langshaw, Lucy
venues used:	Barfly
info:	Organise monthly or bi-monthly all day events,

usually on a Sunday. Held at Barfly in Liverpool featuring between 8 and 11 bands, mainly Punk and Metal. Send demos FAO Mark at the above address, or alternatively telephone Mark or Lucy.

Ready Made Promotions
20 Tweedle Hill Road, Blackley, Manchester, M9 8LP
tel:	07963 552 794
email:	sarahlouiseunwin@yahoo.com
contact:	Stuart Lawler, Sarah Unwin
venues used:	Various
info:	Promote nights at wide variety of venues across

the UK. Work regularly with venues, media sponsors, labels and event agencies in Manchester. Send demo with biog to the above address.

Redbrick Music
Office 4, Breightmet Fold House, Redbridge Works, Bolton, BL2 5PH
tel:	01204 407 871
email:	info@redbrickproductions.co.uk
web:	www.redbrickproductions.co.uk
contact:	Dave Kay
info:	Use a range of venues in and around Manchester.

Call Redbrick Productions for details on how to play.

Say It To My Face
Manchester
email: sayittomyface88@hotmail.com
web: www.sayittomyface.net
contact: Marios Sozos, Emma Doran
venues used: Satans Hollow, Music Box, Jilly's Rockworld
info: Deal with Punk, Hardcore, Post Hardcore, Noise core, Metal, but no Ska. Promote variety of gigs at various venues in Manchester. Contact via the above email address. Marios will try and come to a gig where possible.

Shot Organisation
4 St. Dunstan's Grove, Liverpool, L30 2NH
tel: 07929 521 484
email: yoshotorganisation@hotmail.com
web: www.yo-shot.com
contact: Chris Welford
venues used: Baby Blue, Barfly
info: Promote band night 'The New Movement' every month in Baby Blue. Also promote gigs in Barfly as well as DJ events. All music types accepted. Run the Shot Organisation Band Exchange where bands from the UK tour all over Europe, and bands from outside the UK come over to play. Send demos FAO Chris to the address above.

Sinsinattic Promotions
The Garage, 38 Car Bank Street, Atherton, Manchester, M46 9NJ
tel: 07969 459 120
email: sinsinattic@yahoo.co.uk
contact: Garry
info: Promote unsigned bands. For more contact Garry and send demos to the above address.

Smart Casual Events
35 Wood Lane, Greasby, Wirral, CH49 2PT
tel: 07884 472 732
email: info@smartcasualevents.co.uk
web: www.smartcasualevents.co.uk
contact: Chris Williamson
venues used: Barfly, Zanzibar, Magnet, Carling Academy, Manchester Academy
info: Promote variety of events mainly in Liverpool, but also in Leeds and Manchester. Promote all types of musical styles including vocalists, pianists, Jazz bands, Rock and Indie bands and male and female vocal groups. Organise weekly showcase in Liverpool every Friday night. Also organise regular gigs featuring some of the biggest and best unsigned bands from all over the country around 6 times per month. To get a gig, acts need to submit a band registration form (contact Chris for form) and demo to the above address.

St. Helens Musicians' Collective
c/o Citadel Arts Centre, Waterloo Street, St. Helens, Merseyside, WA10 1PX
tel: 01744 735 436
fax: 01744 762 309
email: info@citadel.org.uk
web: www.citadel.org.uk
contact: Tom Elwood
venues used: Citadel Arts Centre
info: Promote live band night every third Friday (over 18 year olds only now, due to licensing laws), an open mic night on Wednesdays, as well as an under 18s night on second Friday of each month. Send demos to the above address.

Steve Cato
34 Hulme Court, Linby Street, Manchester, M15 5AR
tel: 0161 226 3749
email: steve.cato@talk21.com
info: Steve books bands for venues in and around Manchester, and also runs regular 'Band and Bingo' nights. Send demos to the address above.

Transmission Manchester
c/o Retro Bar, 78 Sackville Street, Manchester, M1 3NJ
tel: 07849 453 776
email: info@transmissionmanchester.co.uk
web: www.transmissionmanchester.co.uk
venues used: Retro Bar
info: Originally started as a live music, club night at The Vine in Leeds. Now running regularly at Retro Bar. Send demos to the above address.

Unity Promotions
St. Helens
tel: 07854 077 654
email: andy@unitysoundsystem.co.uk
web: www.unitysoundsystem.co.uk
contact: Andy Duncan
venues used: The Rifle
info: Promoting live music nights in Manchester and Liverpool. Contact Andy for up to date demo submission address.

VmanEvents.co.uk
Brij House, Bankhall Lane, Altrincham, Cheshire, WA15 0LN
tel: 0161 980 7914/07970 821 270
email: thevman@vmanevents.co.uk
web: www.vmanevents.co.uk
contact: Vuz
venues used: Jabez Clegg, Late Room, Satans Hollow, Dry Bar, Jilly's Rockworld, Cuba Café
info: Currently promoting at least 15 shows a month. Work mainly in Manchester. Have booked national tours for 65daysofstatic, amongst others, and have worked with Pete Doherty, Babyshambles, Pitchshifter, SIkTh, Kaiser Chiefs, The Others and more.

Warm Gun Promotions
28 Russell Street, Liverpool, L3 5LJ
tel: 07903 586 629
email: tonycosgrove79@hotmail.com
web: www.fridayskive.co.uk
contact: Tony Cosgrove
info: Promote free Acoustic event, 'The Friday Skive'. The event is aimed at local musicians, students and the unemployed, and is an excellent opportunity for local artists to network with other people in the music industry. Send demo and short biog to the above address.

The Wigan Music Collective
19 Castlehouse Lane, Adlington, Lancashire, PR7 4DL
tel: 07902 376 067
email: charlie@wiganmusic.com
web: www.wiganmusic.com
contact: Charlie
venues used: The Tavern
info: Organise an unsigned showcase every Saturday night for performers of original music. Also arrange under 16 music events on occasional Sunday afternoons, and coordinate an annual all day, open air festival in June. Send demo to the above address. For information about other services the collective provide, see listing in Useful Regional Organisations section.

Xpo Music
c/o Middleton Civic Centre, Fountain Street, Middleton, Manchester, M24 1AF
tel: 0161 345 8256
email: xpomusic@mail.com
contact: Rick Garlack
venues used: Middleton Civic Centre
info: Regular unsigned nights. Support slots available up and down the country. Contact Rick for further details.

Zoom Events
39 St. Andrew Street, Liverpool, L3 5XZ
tel: 07816 604 279
email: ste_allan@hotmail.com
web: www.themojavecollective.co.uk or www.the-quarter.com
contact: Stephen Allan
venues used: The Vines Ballroom
info: Promotes 2 showcase nights at The Vines Ballroom in Liverpool. Both nights are hosted by bands, who also have local up and coming bands on the bill. The last Friday of the month is hosted by Dance tinged Rock band 'The Quarter'. First Saturday of the month is 'The Medicine Show' hosted by 'The Mojave Collective', an Americana/BritRock act. Send demos FAO Stephen Allan to the above address.

SOUTHEAST

Alternator Promotions
High Wycombe, Buckinghamshire
tel: 01494 441 081
email: alternativepromos@hotmail.com
web: www.alternatorpromotions.tk
contact: Neil
venues used: White Horse
info: Alternator Promotions put on gigs at The White Horse in High Wycombe around once a week. Deal with Rock, Emo, Punk, Ska, Metal and Hardcore bands. To play, send Neil an email and he will provide address to send demos.

The Arches
The Railway Arches, Caversham Road, Reading, Berkshire
tel: 0118 950 0950
fax: 0118 950 0951
email: mail@archesrecords.com
web: www.archesrecords.com
venues used: The Arches
info: Contact before sending demo. Soul, R&B and Jazz. See website for more details.

LIVE PERFORMANCE

Badger Music
1st Floor Flat, 1 St. Aubyns, Hove, BN3 2TG
tel: 01273 229 948
email: kevin@badgermusic.co.uk
web: www.badgermusic.co.uk
contact: Kevin McCann
venues used: Western Front
info: Promotes bands, musicians, singer-songwriters and open mic nights at various venues.

Barn d'Or Music
105 Southover Street, Brighton, BN2 9UA
tel: 01273 383 569
email: mike@greyspub.com
web: www.greyspub.com
contact: Mike Lance, Chris Beaumont
venues used: The Greys and various others
info: Live music event held at The Greys. The best way to get a gig is to make initial contact via email with link to band website if possible.

Bedford Jazz (at The Shed)
10 Putnoe Heights, Bedford, Bedfordshire, MK41 8EB
tel: 01234 353 522
email: jefkay@btinternet.com
web: www.bedfordjazz.org.uk
contact: Jeff Kaighin
venues used: Gordon Arms
info: Monthly Jazz night at the Gordon Arms showcasing Modern, Post-bop Jazz. Contact before sending demos to above address FAO Jeff Kaighin.

Ben Ward
c/o The Railway Inn, 3 St. Paul's Hill, Winchester, Hampshire, SO22 5AE
tel: 01962 867 795
email: ben@liveattherailway.co.uk
web: www.liveattherailway.co.uk
contact: Ben Ward
venues used: The Railway Inn
info: Ben mainly works with The Railway Inn, Winchester but also organises other unsigned nights at different venues. Contact by telephone or email for further details.

Boogaloo Promotions
Boogaloo House, Forest Glade, Rowledge, Farnham, Surrey, GU10 4DG
email: info@boogaloopromotions.com
web: www.boogaloopromotions.com
contact: Monica
venues used: Various
info: Boogaloo organise regular Blues weekends at various venues across the country. They also run a regular club night at Farnham Maltings in Surrey. Blues and R&B music. See website for more information. Send demos to the address above.

Bukandskit Promotions
email: info@bukandskit.com
web: www.bukandskit.com
venues used: Face Bar, Phats
info: Bukandskit organise unsigned band nights at various venues. Contact via email with details of your band.

CurlyGig
21 Crown Gardens, Brighton, BN1 3LD
tel: 07793 609 600
email: eddie@curlygig.com or laura@curlygig.com or suzi@curlygig.com
web: www.curlygig.com
contact: Eddie, Laura, Suzi
venues used: Various
info: Promotes gigs in Brighton for signed and unsigned acts. See website for list of venues used. Send demo, biog and photo to the above address.

Denial Records
Medina, Pimlico, Hemel Hempstead, Hertfordshire, HP3 8SH
email: info@denialrecords.com
web: www.denialrecords.com
contact: Dan Geraghty
venues used: Various
info: Promote Alternative Rock, Electronica and Indie across various venues in High Wycombe and Cambridge.

Devcaster Promotions
5 Neville Gardens, Emsworth, Hants, PO10 7XZ
tel: 01243 372 092
fax: 01243 379 819
email: devcaster@tiscali.co.uk
web: www.devcaster.co.uk
contact: Shaun Moncaster
info: Enthusiastically promote Jazz, Big Band and Swing events. Organise and stage their own events and also promote the bands used at these events. Recent artists include The Gershwin Years, The Hayling Island Jazz Festival, Big Band Night, Anything Goes - The Cole Porter Songbook, Tony Jacobs and The Cream Crackers, Bob Kerr and the Whoopee Band. Send demos to above address or see website for more details.

Explosion Entertainments
111 Woodland Way, Ongar, Essex, CM5 9ET
tel: 07789 377 405
email: policeartist@msn.com
web: www.explosionentertainments.com
contact: Peter George
venues used: Various
info: Charities and good causes contact Explosion Entertainments to book artists for their events. This is a good opportunity for acts to raise their profile, whilst helping raise money for a good cause.

Fresh Sounds
PO Box 2760, Caterham, CR3 6WW
email: contact@fresh-sounds.co.uk
web: www.fresh-sounds.co.uk or www.fresh-sounds.tv
contact: Andy Mead
venues used: Meanfiddler Group venues, Mr Smith's
info: Fresh Sounds Music organise some of the UK's largest up and coming band showcases. They utilise some of the most prestigious venues on offer including Mean Fiddler's London Astoria 2, Shepherds Bush Empire, Birmingham Academy 2 and Islington Academy. Acts that impress may have the chance to support major acts and/or play in front of key industry A&R and managers. The Fresh Rock Showcases run regularly around the country, please see the website for up to date information. Accept demos from all genres, please send all material to the above address or send links to your online music by email. Please do not sent MP3 file attachments.

Gappy Tooth Industries
52 Henley Street, Oxford, OX4 1ES
tel: 01865 793 307
email: info@gappytooth.com
web: www.gappytooth.com
contact: Rob Randell
venues used: The Zodiac
info: Organise live showcase events once a month at The Zodiac in Oxford. Gappy Tooth Industries aim to provide an outlet for people to perform or exhibit their material. They endeavour to present an event as varied as possible, usually including bands and acts of all genres, poets and artists. Anything is up for consideration provided it falls within the boundaries of time, space and the law! Send demos FAO Rob to the above address.

Glitch
Brighton
tel: 07946 734 836
email: underground@ygdmedia.co.uk
web: www.ygdmedia.co.uk
contact: Robin Coward
venues used: Bath Arms, London Unity
info: A successful open mic night with a good variety of musical styles. See the website for details.

Highgain Promotions
18 Brockhurst Close, Horsham, West Sussex, RH12 1UY
tel: 0845 174 3595
email: gigs@highgainlive.co.uk
web: www.highgainlive.co.uk
contact: Sam Albrow
venues used: Extra Time Bar, The Coot Pub
info: See listings on website for selection of gigs promoted by Highgain. Send demo to above address, or alternatively contact via telephone or email with details of gigs.

Insomnia Music UK Ltd.
PO Box 91, Hertford, Hertfordshire, SG13 7YZ
tel: 01992 587 719
email: matt@insomniamusic.co.uk
web: www.insomniamusic.co.uk
contact: Matt Chambers
venues used: Castle Hall, Elbert Wurlings
info: Collective working with a variety of musical styles and performers. Run Insomnia Music Showcase nights. Will also help run and promote club gigs and charity events.

Last Chance Records

44 Moor Lane, Rickmansworth, Hertfordshire, WD3 1LG
tel: 07817 005 978
email: watfordslastchance@hotmail.com
web: www.watfordslastchance.com
contact: Haggy
venues used: The Pumphouse, Wembley Rugby Club,
Hatch End, Barfly
info: Last Chance organise a couple of nights every month
at various venues. 3 or 4 bands play per night. Send demos FAO Haggy
to the above address.

Lightbug

Aintree Close, Horton Heath, Eastleigh, Hampshire, SO50 7PU
tel: 02380 696 034/07050 089 165
email: mail@lightbug.co.uk
web: www.lightbug.co.uk
contact: Kelly White
venues used: Various
info: Interested in Pop solo artists, duos and trios for
performances in pubs, clubs and private venues in all over the South.

Liquid State

PO Box 567, Rickmansworth, WD3 4ZN
tel: 07949 825 449
email: chey@liquid-state.net
web: www.liquid-state.net
contact: Chey
venues used: Various
info: Liquid State was set up to progress and push new
talent from the UK forward on a professional platform. Promotes artists
on all levels ranging from weekly and monthly club nights in London,
to getting involved with major festivals and shows throughout Europe.
Liquid State is also involved in school and council projects, keeping
an eye on developing, younger artists. For more information and event
listings see website above.

Lout Promotions

The Metway, 55 Canning Street, Brighton, BN2 0EF
tel: 01273 623 200
email: brightonrocks@rock.com
web: www.myspace.com/loutpromotions
contact: Lisa Lout
venues used: Concorde II
info: Lout Promotions organise 'Brighton Rocks' for Indie
and Rock unsigned bands from Brighton and the surrounding area.
Held one Sunday every month at Concorde II. Send demo FAO Lisa to
the above address.

Missing In Action (MIA)

18 Faraday Road, Slough, Berkshire, SL2 1RU
tel: 07812 432 766
email: dlangshaw@porthale.co.uk
contact: Darren Langshaw
venues used: Various
info: Organise gigs for unsigned original bands regularly
in Slough. All music types considered including Rap, Metal, Pop,
Electronic, Glam, Goth, Bhangra. Contact Darren before sending demo.

Music Mann Promotions

18 Mackay Close, Fords Farm, Reading, Berkshire, RG31 7XN,
RG31 7XW
email: tom.manning@music-mann.co.uk
web: www.music-mann.co.uk
contact: Tom Manning
info: Promotions company concerned with raising the
profile of live music, organising live events and promoting local up and
coming bands. Contact Tom on the above email address for further
details.

One Night Stand Acoustic

tel: 01252 622 297/07721 397 211
email: dav@davtrav.fsnet.co.uk
web: www.onenightstandacoustic.co.uk
contact: Mark
venues used: Various in North East Hampshire and Berkshire
info: An opportunity for musicians and singer-songwriters
to perform in a cosy well-organised and supportive atmosphere.
Approximately 10 acts are on the bill and perform 3 songs each. Turn
up on the night.

Phoenix Promotions

Portsmouth
email: phoenix@cinderrock.co.uk
web: www.cinderrock.co.uk
contact: Rachel Miller, Ben Humphrey
venues used: The Gaiety
info: Organise unsigned night, 'Alcatraz', which takes
place at The Gaiety in Southsea every fortnight on a Tuesday. The
event features 3 local bands who play a 40 minute slot each, as well as
special guests. A&R are often invited to attend. Bands appearing will be
sent 50 tickets in advance (or more if required) and are encouraged to
sell as many as possible. The band makes back £2 for every ticket sold.
'Alcatraz' is fully promoted with flyers and posters. To play contact
Phoenix Promotions via the above email address.

PopToys

Reading
tel: 07714 102 250
email: robsowden@supanet.com
web: www.bohemiannight.com
contact: Rob Sowden
venues used: South Street, 3B's
info: 'PopToys' is an unsigned night held monthly at
21 South Street in Reading. Also put on local bands every Saturday
night at 3B's, Reading. Contact Rob by telephone or email to play.
'The Bohemian Night' open mic event every Thursday at 3B's features
all kinds of acts including singers, performers, stand up, poetry and
jugglers. Just turn up to take part.

Prison Promotions

c/o Flat 2, 372 Nelson Road, Hounslow, Middlesex, TW3 3UW
tel: 07734 922 966
email: lydia@letsgotoprison.co.uk or
lydia.butler@gmail.com or
becky@letsgotoprison.co.uk
web: www.letsgotoprison.co.uk
contact: Lydia Butler, Becky Thistlethwaite, Ian Heydon
venues used: The Purple Turtle, Camden/Infinity, Mayfair
info: Send demos or MP3 links to one of the email
addresses above and they will get a response. No Emo, Goth, Metal
or BritPop, its more Indie, Electro, Punk, Post Punk, No Wave, Arts
School.

Raven Black Music

Oxford Innovation Centre, Mill Street, Oxford, OX2 0JX
tel: 01989 767 868
email: raven@tourdates.co.uk or
info@tourdates.co.uk or
dean@tourdates.co.uk
web: www.tourdates.co.uk
contact: Dean G Hill
venues used: Various
info: Raven Black Music put on concept tours such as the
'M4 Tour 2004' around 2 to 3 times each year. Use various venues in
the South of England and Wales. Submit demos FAO Dean G. Hill at
the above address. Contact by email to follow up responses to demos.
Raven Black Music run publishing and management companies, and
maintain the above listings website. See entries in relevant sections for
details.

Rock 'n' Rant

111 Otterham Quay Lane, Rainham, Kent, ME8 8NF
tel: 01634 398 814
email: enquiries@rocknrant.net
web: www.rocknrant.net
contact: Brad Harmer
venues used: Various
info: Organisation set up to help both young and unsigned
bands, as well as comedians to get their first gigs in Medway, Swale
and the surrounding area. Send demos FAO Brad Harmer to the above
address. If you do not have a demo, then contact Brad and he will
arrange for someone to attend a gig or rehearsal.

Rubberband Promotions

PO Box 5027, Reading, RG6 7ZN
tel: 0118 926 1440
email: kevin@rubberbandpromotions.co.uk
web: www.rubberbandpromotions.co.uk
contact: Kevin Harrington
venues used: The Agincourt, Drakes Bar, Rhu Bar
info: Rubberband Promotions put on gigs at several
venues in Hampshire and Berkshire including The Agincourt in
Camberley, Drakes Bar and Rhu Bar in Basingstoke. Deal with any local
acts from Folk to Metal. To play, send demo FAO Kevin at the above
address.

Starline Promotions

PO Box 13, Chinnor, Oxon, OX39 4WD
tel: 01844 353 154 (ext 2)
email: info@starlinepromotions.co.uk
web: www.crash-records.co.uk
venues used: Various
info: Organise Rock, Punk, Funk and Indie nights in the
Oxfordshire and Buckinghamshire area, as well as helping bands get
gig in other areas.

thewhitelabel.com Ltd.
c/o DLEO Ltd., 16 Basepoint, Metcalf Way, Crawley, RH1 7XX
tel:	07730 496 597
email:	tug@thewhitelabel.com
web:	www.thewhitelabel.com
contact:	Robin Scott, Simon Morley, Nic Vine
venues used:	Concorde 2
info:	thewhitelabel.com helps venues such as Concorde2

in Brighton to identify new, unsigned acts that could be invited to perform at monthly new music nights. Unsigned acts submit their tracks and feedback from fans, regulars to the site, and anyone interested in new music submitted. Each month, the 3 or 4 acts that generate the most positive feedback are invited to perform at the next new music night. Send demos to the above address.

Vandalism Begins @ Home
38 Tavistock Street, Luton, Bedfordshire, LU1 3UT
tel:	01582 611 230
email:	vandalismathome@hotmail.co.uk
web:	www.vbah.com
contact:	Chris
venues used:	The Exchange, The Hat Factory, The Sub-Club
info:	Promoting bands in the Luton Alternative music

scene.

SOUTHWEST

BB Promotions
3 Roberts Road, Bournemouth, BH7 6LN
tel:	07749 768 904/07969 443 516
email:	info@bb-promotions.co.uk
web:	www.bb-promotions.co.uk
contact:	Robert Burnell / Robert Fletcher
venues used:	Gander On The Gree
info:	Organise Acoustic night every Tuesday, and Rock

showcase on Saturdays. Also have a stage at Earth Wise Festival.

The Bebop Club
tel:	0117 966 9344
fax:	0117 963 6011
email:	andy@musicsender.com
web:	www.musicsender.com
contact:	Andy Hague
venues used:	The Bear
info:	Modern Jazz club on a Friday night at The Bear.

Contact Andy Hague on above email address.

Blazing Guitar Promotions
44 Beckington Road, Lower Knowle, Bristol, BS3 5EB
tel:	07944 735 723
email:	jeffdart@aol.com
contact:	Jeffrey Sparkes
venues used:	Various
info:	Currently organise gigs at various venues in Bristol

about once a month. Send demo FAO Jeffrey Sparkes to the above address.

Clevedon Jazz Club
c/o Walton Park Hotel, Wellington Terrace, Clevedon, BS21 7BL
tel:	01275 343 210
fax:	01275 880 803
email:	trevor@clevedonjazzclub.co.uk
web:	www.clevedonjazzclub.co.uk
contact:	Trevor Tomasin
venues used:	Walton Park Hotel
info:	Mainly Traditional Jazz. Contact before sending

demo, or see website for more details.

Club Fandango (Southampton)
Southampton
email:	ally_longliverockandroll@yahoo.co.uk
web:	www.clubfandango.co.uk
venues used:	Lennon's
info:	Eclectic band night founded by the owners of Fierce

Panda Records and Pointy Records. To play contact the above email address. Also held at various venues around the UK. See listings in other sections for booking details.

Future Entertainments
38 Holmefield, Yate, Bristol, BS37 5US
tel:	01454 325 681
fax:	01454 857 452
email:	cvh@blueyonder.co.uk
contact:	Charles Hart
venues used:	Various
info:	All demos welcome. Work with full spectrum of

venues. Contact before sending demo to above address.

Future Sound of Exeter
c/o Exeter Phoenix Arts, Bradninch Place, Gandy Street, Exeter, EX4 3LS
tel:	01392 676 550
email:	info@fsoe.org
web:	www.fsoe.org
contact:	Paul Giblin
venues used:	Exeter Phoenix
info:	Put on gigs for innovative local artists, particularly

those involved with exotic and Electronic sounds. Send demo FAO Future Sound of Exeter to the above address.

Glass Tone Productions Ltd.
Glass House, Unit 3a, Riverside Business Park, Bath, BA2 3DW
tel:	01225 487 700
email:	info@glasstone.co.uk
web:	www.glasstone.co.uk
contact:	Greg Brooker
venues used:	Various
info:	Generally organise signed, touring act and unsigned

support slots in order to raise profile. Arrange nights at venues in Bristol and Bath. Send demo FAO Greg to the above address. Glass Tone also provide recording, rehearsal, management, PA hire, mastering and design services. Refer to entries in appropriate sections.

Long Live Rock & Roll
27-29 Onslow Road, Southampton, SO14 0JD
email:	ally@longliverockandroll.com
web:	www.longliverockandroll.com
contact:	Ally
venues used:	Lennon's Nightclub, Mono Bar
info:	Promote 'Long Live Rock & Roll' band and club night

every Saturday at Lennon's Nightclub. Indie, Punk and Alternative music. 2 bands play up to midnight, and club night runs from then until 2am. Also run monthly unsigned Acoustic event at Mono Bar on second Sunday of every month. Send demo FAO Ally to the above address.

Purr Promotions
70 The Hollow, Southdown, Bath, BA2 1LZ
email:	info@purr.org.uk
web:	www.purr.org.uk
contact:	Dave
venues used:	Moles
info:	Purr Promotions organise live music on Thursday

nights featuring at least 3 bands at Moles, Bath. The genres of music that Purr deal with includes Off-Kilter, Post Rock, Indie, Punk, Kitsch, Noise, Garage Rock New Wave, No Wave, Lo-Fi, Bubblegum and Pop. Refer to website for further details. Send demo to the above address. Purr also run a record label.

Rookie Promotions
85 Cornbrash Rise, Hilperton, Trowbridge, Wiltshire, BA14 7TS
tel:	07974 956 228
email:	mail@rookiepromotions.co.uk
web:	www.rookiepromotions.co.uk
contact:	Ben Hawkes
venues used:	Various
info:	Established since early 2004, putting on shows

in Trowbridge, Devizes, Gloucester and Bath. Previous acts include Midasuno, Sparks Lights and Flames, Next Nine Years and many more. The music is Post-Hardcore, Emo and Rock. Always looking for new acts who have had some national exposure, and usually had a release. Rookie Promotions is a live promotions strand operated by Secret Tree, an online record store. See www.secrettree.net.

South Scene
Flat 1a, The Parade, Southampton Road, Southampton, SO40 2NG
tel:	02380 812 732
email:	mail@southscene.freeserve.co.uk
web:	www.southscene.net
contact:	Mike Spall
venues used:	Various
info:	Put on gigs across the South of England. Also run an

online webzine for the music scene across Southampton, Bournemouth, Portsmouth and Brighton. See website above.

Torch The House Promotions
3 Godfrey Avenue, Preston, Paignton, Devon, TQ3 1EY
tel:	07751 503 600
email:	torch_the_house@hotmail.com
contact:	Glen Poyner
venues used:	The Townhouse
info:	Promote Rock gigs a couple of times a month at The

Townhouse in Torquay. Contact Glen by email if you are interested in playing. Glen will accept demos from all over the country, and is willing to cover petrol costs.

Trowbands Promotions
BA14 7LN
email: simon@trowbands.com
web: www.trowbands.com
contact: Simon Moore
venues used: Terry's Nightspot
info: Trowbridge based band promotion organisation which aims to bring new bands to the local scene and support them as much as possible. Put on regular live music events featuring local up and coming talent, as well as more established bands.

YORKSHIRE

The Acoustic Revolution
Call Lane, Leeds, LS1 7BT
tel: 07713 635 049
email: acousticrevolution@hotmail.com
web: www.acousticrevolution.cjb.net
contact: Jon Gomm
venues used: Doctor Wu's
info: Organise well attended gigs every Saturday afternoon at Doctor Wu's in Leeds. Acoustic and unplugged Rock, Pop, Blues and Indie. Between 1 and 3 bands and artists play, can be local or out of town acts. To play, contact Jon at the above email address. Also arrange open mic event, 'The Limelight', every Tuesday night at Doctor Wu's. Just turn up to take part, up to 20 performers a night.

Barnsley Jazz Club
24 Kensington Road, Barnsley, South Yorkshire, S75 2TU
tel: 01226 281 805
contact: Stuart Currie
venues used: Silkstone Lodge
info: Traditional Jazz on a Monday night. Contact Stuart Currie before sending demo to above address.

Beat Promotions
37 Highfield Drive, Garforth, Leeds, LS25 1JY
tel: 07793 551 162
email: janeww1@aol.com
web: www.nocodemusic.co.uk
contact: Phil Sibson
venues used: Dry Bar (Manchester), Adelphi (Hull), Certificate 18 (York), Rugeley Rose Theatre (Rugeley)
info: Beat Promotions organise unsigned gigs at several venues in Yorkshire, Manchester and Staffordshire.

Black Market Music
PO Box 147, Leeds, West Yorkshire, LS15 7XX
email: dave@blackmarketmusic.net
web: www.blackmarketmusic.net
contact: Dave Bunn, Jack Simpson
venues used: Joseph's Well, The Mixing Tin, The Vine
info: Black Market Music organise HMV Showcase weekly event in Leeds at Joseph's Well. Also put on unsigned gigs at various other venues. Bands can book a gig by completing the online application form on the Black Market Music website. Option of electric gig or 'Naked Bar Guitar' - Acoustic performance. Full listings and photos of gigs are uploaded onto the website. They put on gigs every night and are always looking for new bands for showcases.

Clarence Park Festival
The Gatehouse, Tootal Street, Wakefield, WF1 5JN
tel: 01924 290 315
email: info@themusiccollective.co.uk
web: www.themusiccollective.co.uk
info: 2 stages of free unsigned music held over 2 days on the last weekend in July. Attracts around 5000 visitors each day. Unsigned bands and musicians from all over UK and worldwide can apply from January to April.

Creative Arts Promotions
Highfield, The Square, Yapham, York, North Yorkshire, YO42 1PJ
tel: 01759 303 454
fax: 01759 303 624
email: david@creativeartspromotion.org
web: www.hulljazzfestival.co.uk or www.jnight.org
contact: David Porter
venues used: Hull Truck Theatre
info: Bookings made up to 6 months in advance. Musical styles including African, Big Band, Fusion, Latin, New Orleans, Hip-Hop, Rhythm&Blues, Soul, World, Acid Jazz and Funk. Contact or see website for more details.

Cultural Foundation
Hollin Bush, Dale Head, Rosedale, North Yorkshire, YO18 8RL
tel: 01751 417 147
fax: 01751 417 804
email: info@cultfound.org
web: www.cultfound.org
contact: Peter Bell
venues used: Various
info: Put on events at a variety of venues across North Yorkshire. Music promoted includes African, Contemporary, Modern-Be Bop, Experimental, Fusion, Free-Improvised, Rhythm&Blues and World. Contact before sending demo to above address.

Jagged Entertainment
Leeds
tel: 07745 543 008
email: crew@jaggedentertainment.com
web: www.JaggedEntertainment.com
venues used: Various
info: Promotes R&B and Hip-Hop in Leeds and Manchester areas. Send MP3 tracks via the website.

Leedsoundsix
11 Stainbeck Gardens, Leeds, LS7 2EY
tel: 07900 568 840
email: leedsoundsix@hotmail.com
web: www.leedsoundsix.co.uk
contact: Jason
venues used: Woodhouse Liberal Club
info: Promote band night on the first Friday of every month. PA and lighting rig provided.

Panama Promotions
Vinery House, 1 Vinery Road, Leeds, LS4 2LB
tel: 0113 274 1758
email: gigs@royalparkcellars.co.uk
web: www.royalparkcellars.co.uk
contact: Steve Kind
venues used: Royal Park Cellars
info: Panama Promotions are in-house promoters for Royal Park Cellars in Leeds. Promote music of all genres from Underground Emo and Punk to Classic Rock and Indie. Send demo FAO Steve at the above address.

Pink Pandemonium Promotions
17-21 Charter Square, Sheffield, S1 4HS
tel: 07941 701 255
email: info@pandemoniumpromotions.com
web: www.pandemoniumpromotions.com
contact: Karen Wosskow
venues used: The Room a.k.a. Fez Club
info: Pink Pandemonium offer unsigned bands the opportunity to support national touring acts at The Fez Club in Sheffield. Past artists and bands have included Biffy Clyro, Stellastarr, Franz Ferdinand, Snow Patrol and The Thrills amongst others. Bands for which upcoming support slots are available are listed on the website. This is only applicable to bands within a 100 mile radius of Sheffield. Otherwise bands from all over the country are welcome to send demos if they would like a full live gig or any assistance such as demos to be passed onto record labels. All demos to the above address FAO Karen. Also organise acoustic nights, check website for details.

Raw Nerve Promotions
22 Eastdean Grange, Leeds, LS14 1HA
email: paulrawnerve@ntlworld.com
web: www.rawnervepromotions.co.uk
contact: Paul Priest
venues used: Bassment, Joseph's Well, Bar Phono
info: Put on bands at venues around Leeds, as well as recommending bands for supports slots at bigger shows. Can also assist with setting up shows or planning tours for particularly good and original acts. Mainly Metal music.

REAL Promotions
140 Cross Lane, Crookes, Sheffield, S10 1WP
email: mark@realpromo.co.uk
web: www.realpromo.co.uk
contact: Mark Roberts
venues used: The Grapes
info: Organises events at The Grapes, Sheffield. They run an acoustic night, 'Broken Strings', constituting the best of Sheffield's acoustic performers. It takes place every Wednesday at the Green Room. A local band and an invited out of town band can play at 'Sheffield Vs…' night. Also host night for 3 local bands, 'Loud and Live'. Send demos FAO Mark at the above address.

LIVE PERFORMANCE

Revolver Promotions
19 St. Jame's Close, Sutton on Hull, Hull, HU7 4XF
tel:	01482 473 367
email:	u_theinfluence@hotmail.com
contact:	Dean Shakespeare
venues used:	The Adelphi
info:	'Under the Influence', a weekly showcase at the Hull

Adelphi, alternates between Wednesday and Saturday nights featuring signed and unsigned bands. Bands who have appeared over the last year include Art Brut, The Ordinary Boys, The Subways, The Bluetones and Towers of London. Submit demo to the above address. Follow up with an email.

RM-Promotions
13 Lichfield Grove, Harrogate, North Yorkshire, HG3 2UA
tel:	01423 500 398/07876 443 722
email:	info@rm-promotions.co.uk
web:	www.rm-promotions.co.uk
contact:	Richard Sadler
info:	Will assist bands with gig bookings and promotions.

Also organise a festival in Harrogate.

Scholars Notes
c/o Scholars Bar, Somerset Terrace, Scarborough, North Yorkshire, YO11 2PW
tel:	01723 376 618
email:	mark@scholarsnotes.co.uk
web:	www.scholarsnotes.co.uk
contact:	Mark Gordon
venues used:	Scholars Bar
info:	Acoustic live music sessions on a Wednesday night.

Send demos to the bar itself. See website for more details.

The Sesh
30-32 Princes Avenue, Hull, HU5 3QA
tel:	01482 679 057
email:	maks33onions@yahoo.co.uk
contact:	Mark Page
venues used:	Linnet & Lark
info:	The Sesh started 2 years ago and has become a

popular weekly event. On Tuesday nights 2 or 3 unsigned acts play. They are then invited back the same week to play an acoustic set at the Sunday Sesh Unplugged. Local and out of town bands welcome. All styles of music. Send demos FAO Mark Page to the above address. The Sesh have also produced 2 compilation CDs showcasing some of the best local acts who have performed in the past.

V3ctor
21 Christopher Road, Woodhouse, Leeds, LS6 2JX
tel:	0113 246 0491
email:	ed_vector@hotmail.com
web:	www.v3ctor.com
contact:	Ed V3ctor
venues used:	Brudenell Social and various venues
info:	V3ctor is a new music and Electronic arts collective

established in 1998. Promote Experimental, Digital and Electronic music, plus anything Leftfield from any genre. Gigs are at least once a month, held at various venues in Leeds. Send demos FAO Ed to the above address.

Wafty Crank
24 Lime Tree Avenue, York, North Yorkshire, YO32 4BE
tel:	07753 327 826
email:	tim.johnson@waftycrank.co.uk
web:	www.waftycrank.co.uk
contact:	Tim Johnson
venues used:	Various
info:	Organise monthly gigs at various venues in York.

Wafty Crank also run a record label, and design service for bands and musicians. See entries in relevant sections for further details.

NORTHERN IRELAND

Belfast Jazz Society
2 Lenmore Park, Jordanstown, County Antrim, BT37 0PD
tel:	028 9086 5613
contact:	George Chambers
info:	Promote Big Band, Mainstream, New Orleans,

Traditional and Dixieland. Contact before sending demo to above address, marked FAO George Chambers.

Bruised Fruit Promotions
18 Rushfield Avenue, Belfast, BT7 3FP
tel:	07761 291 706
email:	jennie@airhead.co.uk
web:	www.bruisedfruitpromotions.co.uk
contact:	Jennie McCullough
venues used:	Auntie Annie's
info:	'Up In The Attic' is a band night held fortnightly

at Auntie Annie's for both new bands, and Belfast's best known local talent. Also organise other events including CD launches, and currently looks after the promotion of musical 'Hippos In The Shower'. Send demo FAO Jennie to the above address.

Karma Productions
Old Firestation, Georges Place, Dun Laoghaire, County Dublin, Rebublic of Ireland
tel:	00 3531 230 3880/00 3531 230 3881
email:	info@karmaproductions.ie
web:	www.karmaproductions.ie
contact:	Ciaran Conroy
info:	Organise a series of Irish tours for emerging artists

every year. The event features the best emerging acts in international music, and allows them the chance to play tours of Ireland's best known music venues, alongside established Irish and international acts. Check out their website for testimonials of artists who have toured in the past.

Komodo
79 Magheraconluce Road, Hillsborough, County Down, BT26 6PR
tel:	028 9268 8285
email:	info@komodorecordings.com
web:	www.komodorecordings.com
contact:	Darrell
venues used:	Various
info:	Put on gigs at various venues every 2 to 3 weeks.

Mainly Rock music. Send demos FAO Darrell to the above address. Komodo also offer recording facilities, mastering and duplication, drum tuition, graphic design and printing services, as well as promotional merchandise. See entries in relevant sections for further details.

Sean Paul Curry
10 Hollyhill View, Enniskillen, County Fermanagh
email:	greenshampy@yahoo.co.uk
info:	Promotes all ages gigs in the area. To play submit

your demo either via email or post to the above address. Also manages local band. See listing in relevant section for details.

SCOTLAND

Arp Concerts Ltd.
55 Grove Street, Edinburgh, EH3 8AB
tel:	0131 228 9393/07779 297 928
email:	david@arpconcerts.co.uk
web:	www.livemusicx.com
contact:	David
venues used:	The Exchange
info:	Arp Concerts organise nights at The Exchange. Will

consider local and touring bands of any music genre. To play contact David by email or visit the website for more information.

Assembly Direct Ltd.
89 Giles Street, Edinburgh, EH6 6BZ
tel:	0131 553 4000
fax:	0131 554 0454
email:	fiona@assemblydirect.ednet.co.uk
web:	www.jazzmusic.co.uk
contact:	Fiona Alexander
venues used:	Henry's Jazz Cellar
info:	Run a number of Jazz festivals, and also promote a

night at Henry's Jazz Cellar. Contact before sending demo. See website for more details.

AUBL
98 Spital, Aberdeen, AB24 3JU
email:	gigs@aubl.net
web:	www.aubl.net
contact:	Rico
venues used:	Moorings Bar, Kef
info:	AUBL host regular night on the fourth Saturday

of every month and book for other weekends too. Occasionally hold events at Kef in Aberdeen. Also available to help bands book gigs all over Scotland (including Glasgow, Edinburgh, Perth and Dundee). For more details check the website above.

Audio Graffiti
34 Thornbridge Gardens, Falkirk, FK2 9BB
tel: 07886 527 464
email: audiograffit1@yahoo.co.uk
contact: Anne-Marie McGregor
venues used: Studio 4
info: Weekly band night each Friday. To play send demo FAO Anne-Marie to the above address.

Aye Yer Maw
3F1 324 Easter Road, Edinburgh, EH6 8JT
email: info@ayeyermaw.freeserve.co.uk
web: www.ayeyermaw.freeserve.co.uk
contact: Neil
venues used: Various
info: Deal mainly with Punk and all its various offshoots: Hardcore, Ska, Oi!, as well as Rock and Metal music. Send demos to the above address.

Cathouse Promotions Ltd.
21 Sandyford Place, Glasgow, G3 7NG
tel: 0141 572 1120
email: craig@cplweb.com
web: www.cplweb.com
contact: Craig Wiley
venues used: Various
info: Promote a variety of music events and club nights. Put on hundreds of bands every year. Send a demo with information to the address above

Cromerty Arts Society
The Old Store, Ferryton Point, Balblair, IV7 8LJ
tel: 01381 610 309
fax: 01381 610 309
email: jennygunn@btopenworld.com
contact: Jenny Gunn
venues used: Victoria Hall, The Stables
info: Promote variety of musical styles including African, Big Band, Contemporary, Experimental, Fusion, Latin, Rhythm&Blues, World, Dixieland and Blues. Contact before sending demo.

DF Concerts
PO Box 25241, Glasgow, G2 5XS
email: via website
web: www.dfconcerts.co.uk
venues used: King Tuts and various others
info: A very well established promoter organising large events and smaller concerts from unsigned bands to household names.

Dicelines Promotions
Studio 2, 1st Floor, Argyle House, 1103 Argyle Street, Glasgow, G3 8ND
email: gigs@dicelines.com
web: www.dicelines.com
contact: Ally Gray
venues used: Glasgow Barfly, Nice N Sleazy, The Arches, 13th Note
info: Dicelines uses various small to mid sized capacity (100-500) venues in Glasgow. Mainly Rock music but will consider any genres. Some bands they have promoted in the past include Maximo Park, Arctic Monkeys, Special Needs, Pure Reason Revolution and Selfish C***.

Edinburgh Jazz 'n' Jive Club
46 Barnton Park Avenue, Edinburgh, Lothian, EH4 6HA
tel: 0131 312 8243
email: jnt@blueyonder.co.uk
contact: Norrie Thomas
venues used: Fairmile Inn
info: Host night every Friday at the Fairmile Inn. Mainly local bands with visiting bands once a month. Musical styles include New Orleans, Traditional and Dixieland. Send demos to above address.

Eleven Promotions
20 Elliot Street, 12 Minerva Court, Finnieston, Glasgow, G3 8EB
tel: 07904 379 154
email: www.elevenpromotions.com
web: www.elevenpromotions.com
contact: Derek McCann
venues used: Mas, Nice n Sleazy, the 13th note, Stereo
info: Promote gigs in and around the Glasgow area. Accept demos from signed and unsigned bands. Mainly Indie, Punk, Rock and Metal, but welcome demos from across the board. Send to above address.

Gable End Theatre
The Storehouse, Longhope, Aukney, AW16 3PQ
tel: 01856 701 301
fax: 01856 701 347
email: edorcades@btopenworld.com
contact: Peter Ford
venues used: Gable End Theatre
info: Hold monthly nights, currently Folk but looking to put on more Jazz in the new year. Contact before sending demo to above address.

Glasgow Jazz Services
5 Balfour Court, 12 Lethington Avenue, Glasgow, Lanarkshire, G41
tel: 0141 649 4044
fax: 0141 649 4044
contact: Ziggy Zigman
venues used: Café Source
info: Involved with many different events around Glasgow. Musical styles promoted include Big Band, Latin, New Orleans, Traditional and Dixieland. Contact for more details.

Good for Nothing?
4 Gilcomstoun Land, Aberdeen, AB10 1TA
email: goodfornothing_punk@yahoo.com
web: www.myspace.com/gfnrecords
contact: Kirk Burton
venues used: Moorings Bar, Tunnels, Cafe Drummonds, Moshulu, Malt Mill
info: Contact before sending demo. Punk, Hardcore, Ska, Psychobilly, Oi and occasionally a bit of Metal, Reggae and Hip-Hop. See website for more details.

Joy Promotions
35 Cressland Drive, Glasgow, G45 9HR
tel: 07966 683 748
email: graeme@joypromotions.com
web: www.joypromotions.com
contact: Graeme McAuslane
venues used: Stereo, Barfly, The Universal, 13th Note Café
info: Promote gigs at various venues in Glasgow including Stereo, Barfly and G2. Specialise in Post Punk, Rock, Acoustic, Garage. No Metal. Also organise an Electronic night at 13th Note Café which also incorporates artwork and short films. Send demos FAO Graeme to the above address.

Kingsonic
c/o 253 Argyle Street, Glasgow, G2 8DL
tel: 0141 221 1739 (11am-7pm)/07951 727 963 (Up to 9pm)
email: info@kingsonic.net
web: www.kingsonic.net
venues used: Cathouse, G2 The Arches, The Garage
info: Promote a variety of unsigned nights at least once a week across various venues in Glasgow. 4 or 5 bands play. 'Stepping Stone' covers Rock, Indie and Pop music. 'Stepping Stone: Central Metal' is a night dedicated to Metal, 'Stepping Stone: The Alternative Route' is for heavy Alternative acts, and 'Stepping Stone: Skate Punk Special' is a showcase for Pop, Skate and Ska Punk sounds. To play at any of the above nights, send demo to the above address.

MusicWorks
125-129 High Street, Glasgow, G1 1PH
tel: 0141 552 6027
fax: 0141 552 6048
email: contact@musicworksuk.com
web: www.musicworksuk.com
info: MusicWorks is an international cross-media convention held annually in Glasgow. It brings together the music and creative industries for seminars, exhibitions and live music across the city. 'Nightworks' also runs during the 3 day conference, featuring emerging local and international talent in showcases, gigs and club nights. Check website for details of showcase applications.

Out Of The Bedroom
The Waverley, 3-5 St. Mary's Street, Edinburgh, EH1 1TA
tel: 0131 556 8855
email: site@outofthebedroom.co.uk
web: www.outofthebedroom.co.uk
contact: Tommy Mackay
venues used: The Waverley
info: Open mic event for original Singer-Songwriters held every Thursday night. House guitars and PA available.

PM Music
Suite 226/228, 3rd Floor, Central Chambers, 109 Hope Street, Glasgow, G2 6LW
tel: 0141 334 4277
email: promotor@petermaccalman.co.uk
web: www.petermaccalman.co.uk or www.acousticaffair.co.uk
contact: Peter Maccalman
venues used: Tron, Arches, Stereo and others.
info: Promotes variety of styles of music and levels of act from beginner through to touring acts. If interested, please send demo with information to the address above.

LIVE PERFORMANCE

Triptych
Better Days Ltd., 15 North Claremont Street, Glasgow, G3 7NR
tel: 0141 332 6886
fax: 0141 331 2068
email: feedback@triptych04.com
web: www.triptych05.com
contact: Paul, Neil
venues used: Various venues in Aberdeen, Glasgow and Edinburgh
info: Triptych organise unsigned band showcases, as well as band support slots for more established artists. Gigs are hosted by a number of well-known venues across Scotland. See website for details of venues. All music types accepted. Send demos for attention of Paul or Neil to the address above.

Twisted Ape
G/2 624 Pollockshaws Road, Glasgow, G41 2PJ
tel: 07861 656 947
email: booking@twistedape.couk
web: www.twistedape.co.uk
contact: Kelvin
venues used: Cathouse, Barfly, 13th Note Café, Nice & Sleazy
info: Promote gigs at least 3 times a week at various venues in Glasgow including Cathouse, Barfly, 13th Note Café and Nice & Sleazy. Open to all musical genres but particularly specialise in Hardcore, Punk and Metal. Twisted Ape also deal with signed national and international bands such as The Exploited, The Meteors, GBH, The Misfits, Nile and Exodus. Every 2 or 3 months Twisted Ape organise a large showcase of the best bands which they have promoted over the past months. They also supply support bands for CPL Promotions. Send demos to Kelvin at the above address.

Wiseguys Promotions
1/1 The Angel Building, 12 Paisley Road West, Glasgow, G51 1LE
email: gillian@wiseguys.plus.com
web: www.wiseguys.plus.com
contact: Gillian
venues used: 13th Note, Barfly
info: Wiseguys Promotions is an ethical promotions company who work predominately with Extreme Metal and Hardcore signed and unsigned acts.

Ziff Promotions
16 Smithfield Loan, Alloa, FT10 1NJ
tel: 01259 211 244
email: alan.ziff@virgin.net
contact: Alan Johnson
venues used: Funhouse, Tollbooth, Loch Gelly Centre
info: Alan organises live music for Funhouse, Alloa. He also arranges other unsigned events throughout the year. No restrictions on type of music, will deal with unsigned or larger bands. Call or email Alan to arrange a gig. Alan is an agent for NU2, a U2 tribute band, who play at venues all over Scotland.

WALES

Alternative Swansea
Twisted, 220 Oxford Street, Swansea, SA1 3BP
tel: 07976 136 194
email: bookings@alternativeswansea.com
web: www.alternativeswansea.com
contact: Steve Lewis
venues used: Escape and various others
info: Promote 'Face/Off', the biggest Alternative night in South Wales every Friday night at Escape. Room 1 is Indie, Alternative, Metal and live touring bands. Also run student night, Envy, also at Escape on Mondays.

Cheap Sweaty Fun Promotions
Rockaway Records, Newport Provisions Market, Newport, Gwent
tel: 01633 257 244
email: dave@cheapsweatyfun.co.uk
web: www.cheapsweatyfun.co.uk
contact: Simon Phillips, Dave
venues used: TJ's
info: Cheap Sweaty Fun Promotions organise live music at T.J.'s in Newport, although there is no definite schedule. Send demos FAO Simon at the above address.

Dragon Bands
PO Box 55, Pontypool, NP4 7WZ
tel: 07793 552 357
email: angieoby@hotmail.com
web: www.dragonbands.com
contact: Angela Byrne
venues used: Various
info: Dragon Bands promote gigs throughout South Wales. They also take part in an exchange scheme between bands in South Wales, Leeds, Northampton, Cornwall, Holland and Dublin, allowing selected acts to play at the local venues of the band with which they have exchanged. Contact Angela by email or telephone to play at any of the above events.

Grand Pacific
PO Box 18, Porth, CF39 9YX
tel: 07775 558 548
email: darren@grandpacific.info
contact: Darren Jones
venues used: The Malthouse
info: 'Abergavenny Hi-Fi' is an Acoustic night held every Sunday at The Malthouse in Abergavenny. 3 acts play. All original music considered. To play, complete the online form on website and send MP3s. Alternatively, post a demo FAO Darren at the above address.

JimJam
Cardiff
email: openmic@jimjamsound.co.uk
web: www.jimjamsound.co.uk
venues used: Claude Hotel, bSb Bar
info: The Jim Jam Open Mic Jam takes place at the Claude Hotel, Cardiff every Thursday evening. Same event also takes place at the bSb Bar in Cardiff every Wednesday evening. Also provide PA hire. See relevant section for more details.

The Music Press
South Wales
tel: 07775 558 548
email: editor@themusicpress.com
web: www.themusicpress.com
contact: Darren Jones
info: Organise night for unsigned bands, 'The News Room'. Do not have set venue, host the night at variety of venues throughout South Wales. Usually takes place on a Friday, with 3 bands playing. All music types considered. Full PA provided. To play complete online 'I Want A Gig!' form on The Music Press website.

North Wales Jazz Society
54 Mytton Park, Denbigh, Denbighshire, LL16 3HR
tel: 01745 812 260
email: nwjsc@aol.com
web: www.northwalesjazz.org.uk
contact: Maureen Hopkins
venues used: Crown Inn, Lodge Inn, Victoria Hall
info: Expertise covering both performance and workshops and have numerous contacts in the art form of Jazz. Organise around 75 events throughout the year including weekly and monthly nights and The North Wales International Jazz Guitar Festival & Summer School. Contact Maureen for details of demo submission. See website for full events programme.

Northgate Music Promotions (Jazz)
6 Westminster Close, Wrexham, LL12 7AY
tel: 07812 833 068
contact: Louis Noble
venues used: Alexandre's Jazz Theatre
info: Put on Jazz nights each Sunday. Send demo to the above address.

The Point Cardiff Bay Ltd.
Mount Stuart Square, Cardiff Bay
tel: 02920 464 440
email: ceri.whitehead@btconnect.com
web: www.thepointcardiffbay.com
contact: Ceri Whitehead
venues used: The Point, Cardiff Coal Exchange, Bridgend Recreation Centre
info: Organise live music at The Point approximately twice a week. In-house PA. All music types considered. Have also put on gigs at Cardiff Coal Exchange and Bridgend Recreation Centre. To play, contact Mike Johnson directly 02920494917 or send demo to the above address.

The Redi Nights
PO Box 2199, Wrexham, LL13 8ZR
tel: 07951 620 913
email: adowen@freeola.com
web: www.theredi.co.uk
contact: Andy Owen
venues used: Central Station
info: 'The Redi Nights' is the longest running band showcase held every month at Central Station in Wrexham. 4 bands play, signed or unsigned. All music types considered. Also run showcase events for DJs and Electronic acts, 'The Deck Side', also at Central Station. Send demos to the above address.

Shockwave Entertainments
20 Bancyddraenen, Capel Hendre, Ammarford, Carmarthenshire, SA18 3SR
tel: 07903 392 864
email: mattward@fsmail.net
contact: Matt Ward
venues used: Various
info: Put on gigs at several venues around Carmarthenshire. Send demos to the above address and contact Matt for more details.

Tangled Parrot
15 Bridge Street, Carmarthen, SA31 3JS
tel: 01267 235 511
email: matt@tangledparrot.co.uk
web: www.tangledparrot.co.uk
contact: Matt Davies
venues used: The Waterside
info: Promotes band nights at The Waterside Club in
Carmarthen. All music types considered. 2 or 3 bands play per night.
Send demo FAO Matt to the address above. Tangled Parrot also run a
record shop. See listing in relevant section.

Tunetown
1 The Kingsway, Swansea, SA1 5JQ
tel: 01792 473 960
email: john.bevan@tunetown.org.uk
web: www.tunetown.org.uk
contact: John Bevan
venues used: Various
info: Tunetown put on showcases in local pubs in
Swansea. To play send a demo to John or Chris at the above address.
Castle Square Festival in June/July is a music festival for local bands
that Tunetown has previously worked with. August Bank Holiday
weekend is the Uplands Swansea Festival held in various venues in the
Uplands area of the city over 4 days. Tunetown also publish a listings
magazine, as well as running tuition workshops. See entries in relevant
sections for details.

Welsh Gigs
8 Fothergill Street, Treforest, Pontyrpidd, CF37 1SG
email: tom@welshgigs.co.uk
web: www.welshgigs.com
contact: Tom Naylor
venues used: Various
info: Promote gigs once or twice a month at various
venues in Swansea, Cardiff and Newport. Send demo FAO Tom Naylor
to the above address. Welsh Gigs also run a website focusing on the
Welsh music scene, as well as an equipment hire service. See listings in
relevant sections for details.

Welsh Jazz Society
26 The Balcony, Castle Arcade, Cardiff, South Glamorgan, CF10 1BY
tel: 02920 340 591
fax: 02920 665 160
email: welshjazz@btconnect.com
web: www.jazzwales.org.uk
contact: Brian Hennessey
venues used: Café Jazz
info: Contact before sending demo to the above address.

LIVE PERFORMANCE

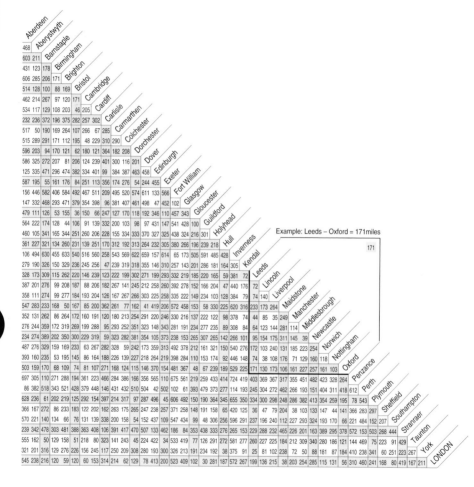

Example: Leeds – Oxford = 171miles

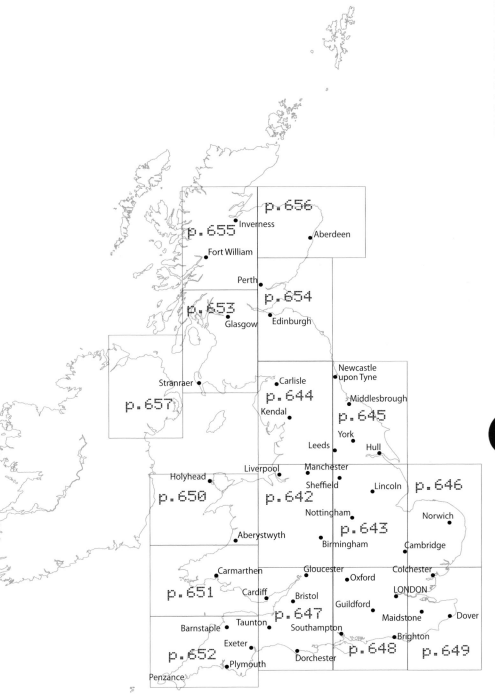

p.656

p.655
• Inverness

Fort William
•

Aberdeen
•

Perth
•

p.654

p.653

Glasgow
•

Edinburgh
•

Stranraer
•

p.657

Newcastle
upon Tyne
•

Carlisle
•

p.644

Kendal
•

Middlesbrough
•

p.645

York
•

Leeds
•

Hull
•

Liverpool
•

Manchester
•

Holyhead
•

p.650

Sheffield
•

Lincoln
•

p.646

p.642

Nottingham
•

Norwich
•

p.643

Aberystwyth
•

Birmingham
•

Cambridge
•

Carmarthen
•

Gloucester
•

Colchester
•

p.651

Cardiff
•

Oxford
•

LONDON
•

Bristol
•

Guildford
•

p.647

Maidstone
•

Dover
•

Barnstaple
•

Taunton
•

Southampton
•

Brighton
•

Exeter
•

Dorchester
•

p.648

p.649

p.652

Plymouth
•

Penzance

LIVE PERFORMANCE

Continues on page 644

Continues on page 650

Continues on page 643

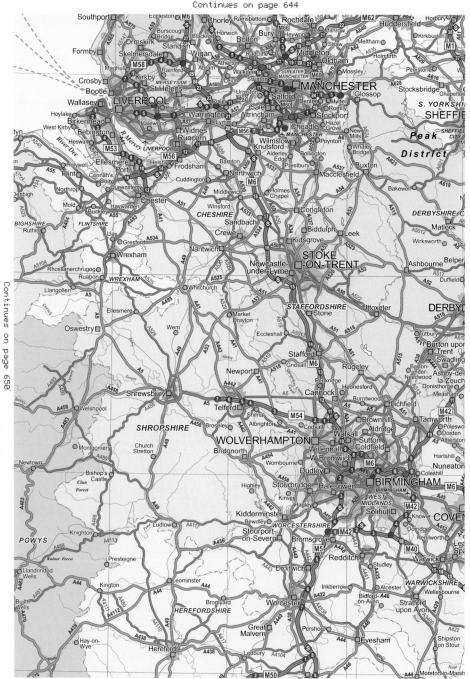

Continues on page 647

the | unsigned | guide

LIVE PERFORMANCE

Continues on page 645

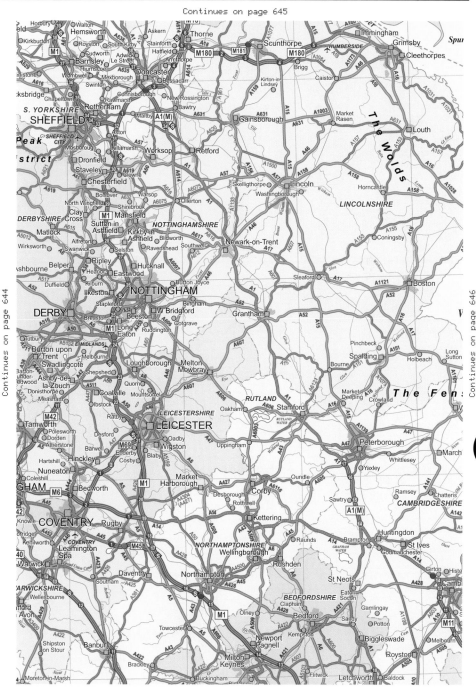

Continues on page 644

Continues on page 646

Continues on page 648

the|unsigned|guide

Continues on page 654

LIVE PERFORMANCE

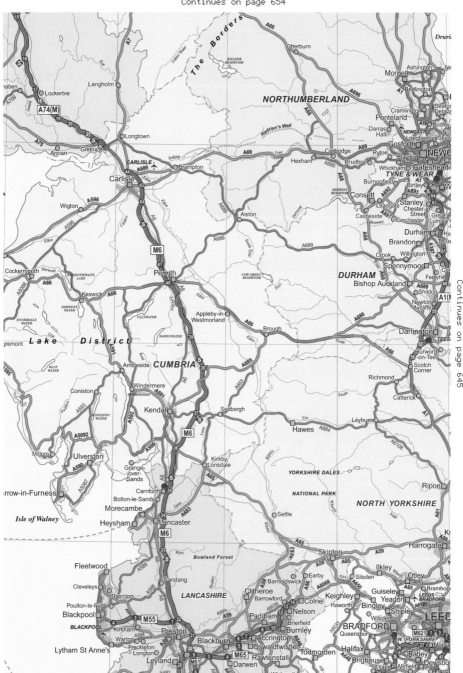

Continues on page 645

© MAPS IN MINUTES ™ 2005.
HMSO Ordnance Survey Permit No.GB399221 © Crown Copyright, Ordnance Survey & Ordnance Survey Northern Ireland 2003 Permit No. NI 1675 & © Government of Ireland, Ordnance Survey Ireland.

the|unsigned|guide
The Unsigned Guide/UK/2006. Material published in this directory may not be reproduced [in any form] without written consent.

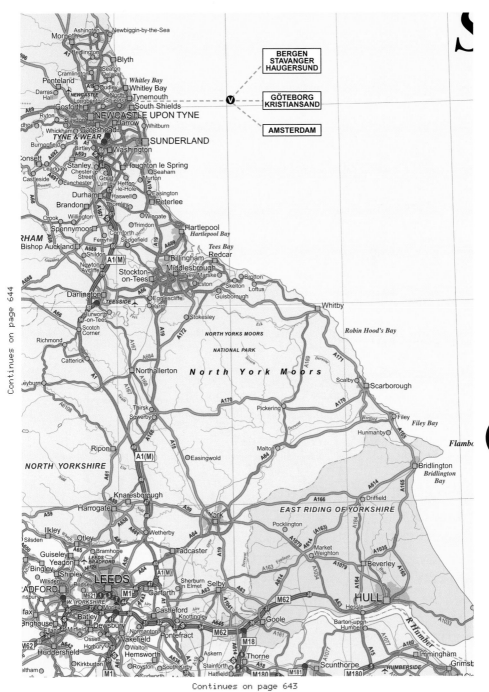

Continues on page 644

Continues on page 643

Continues on page 643

Continues on page 642

LIVE PERFORMANCE

Continues on page 651/652

Continues on page 648

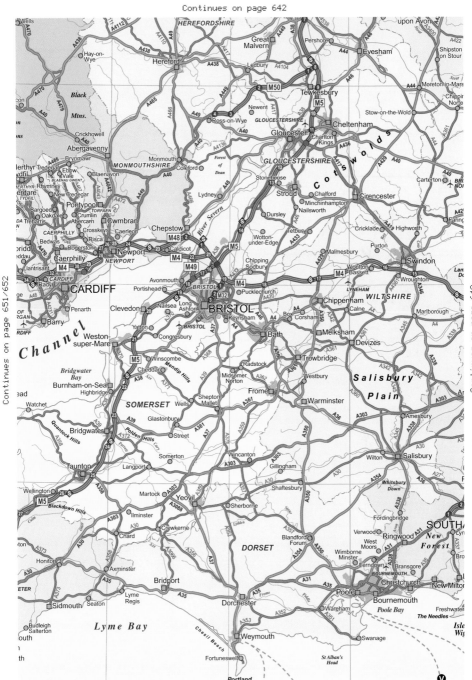

the|unsigned|guide

LIVE PERFORMANCE

Continues on page 643

Continues on page 647

Continues on page 649

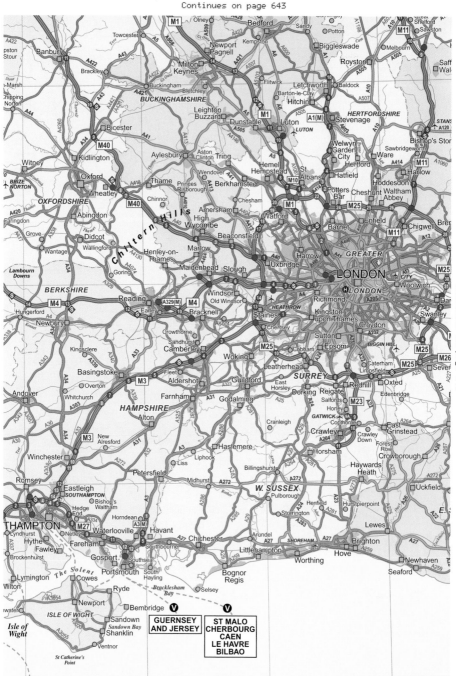

ST MALO
CHERBOURG
CAEN
LE HAVRE
BILBAO

GUERNSEY
AND JERSEY

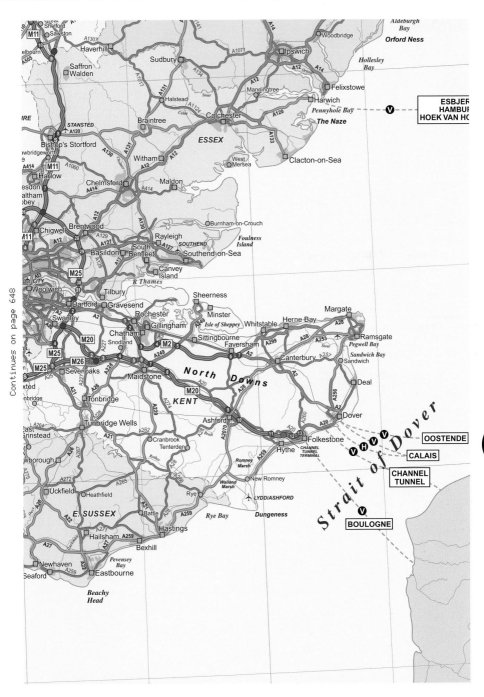

Continues on page 648

© MAPS IN MINUTES ™ 2005.

Continues on page 642

LIVE PERFORMANCE

Continues on page 651

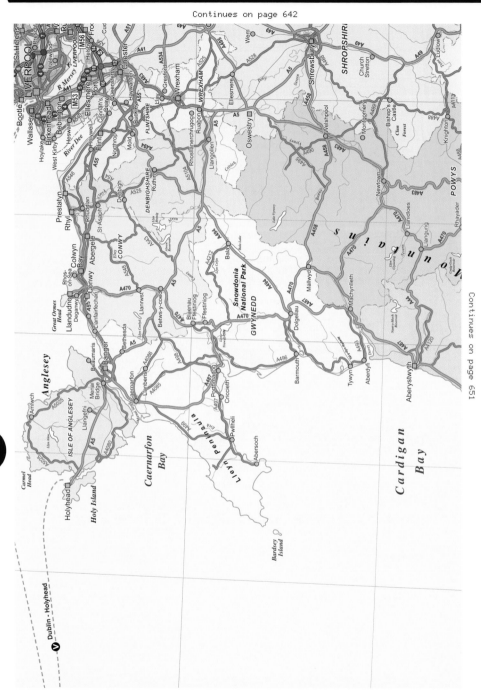

the | unsigned | guide

LIVE PERFORMANCE

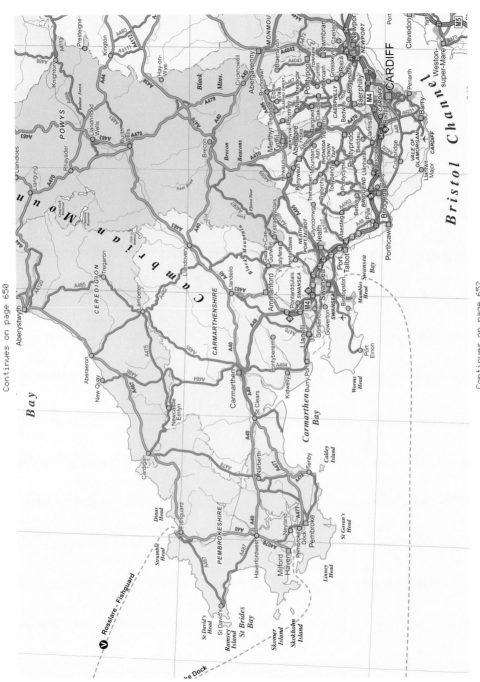

Continues on page 650

Continues on page 652

the|unsigned|guide

LIVE PERFORMANCE

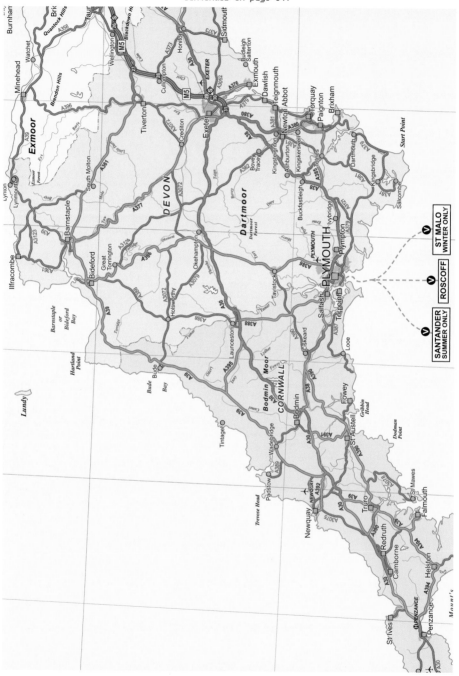

LIVE PERFORMANCE

Continues on page 655

Continues on page 657

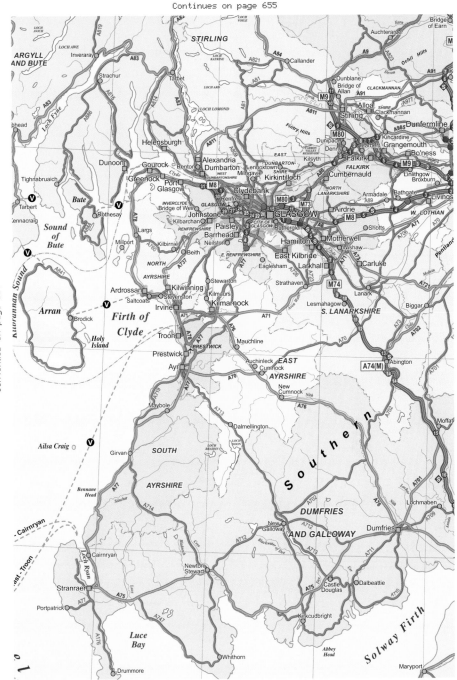

© MAPS IN MINUTES ™ 2005.

the | unsigned | guide

LIVE PERFORMANCE

Continues on page 656

Continues on page 653

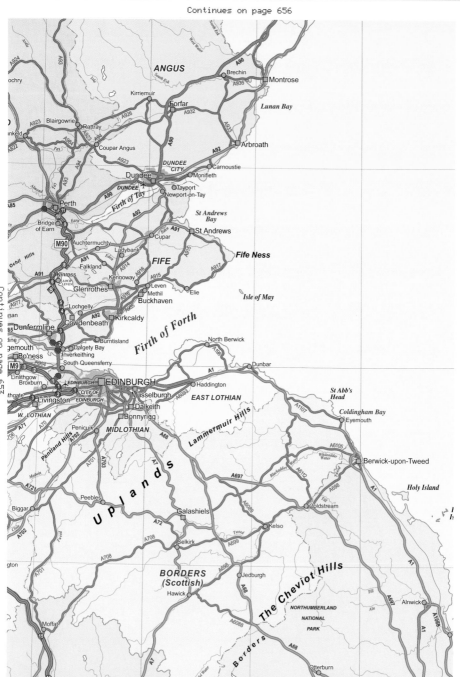

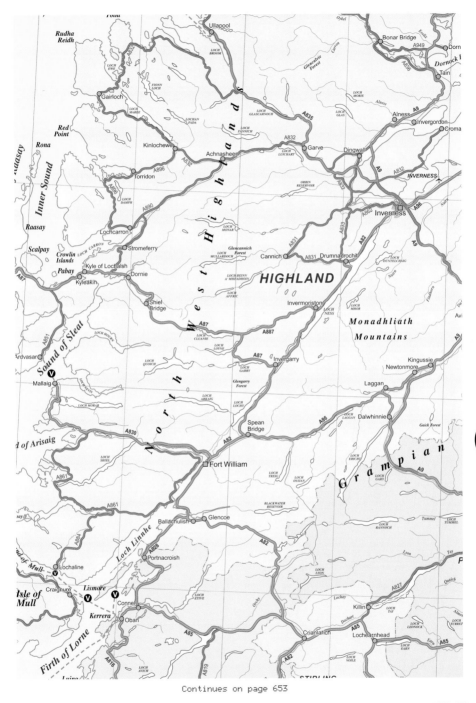

Continues on page 653

the|unsigned|guide

LIVE PERFORMANCE

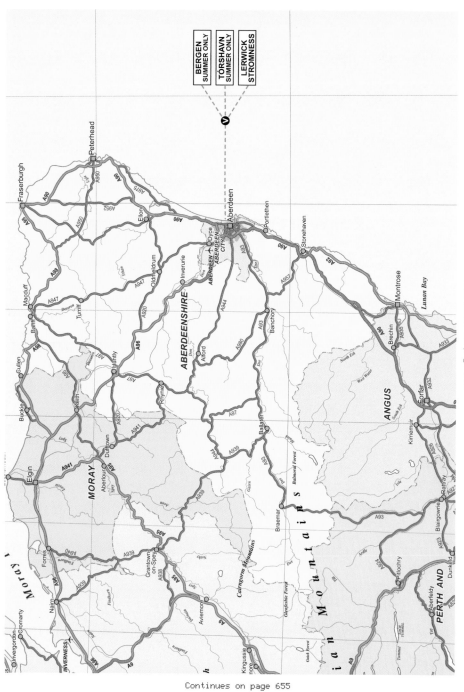

BERGEN SUMMER ONLY
TÓRSHAVN SUMMER ONLY
LERWICK STROMNESS

Continues on page 645

Continues on page 655

the|unsigned|guide

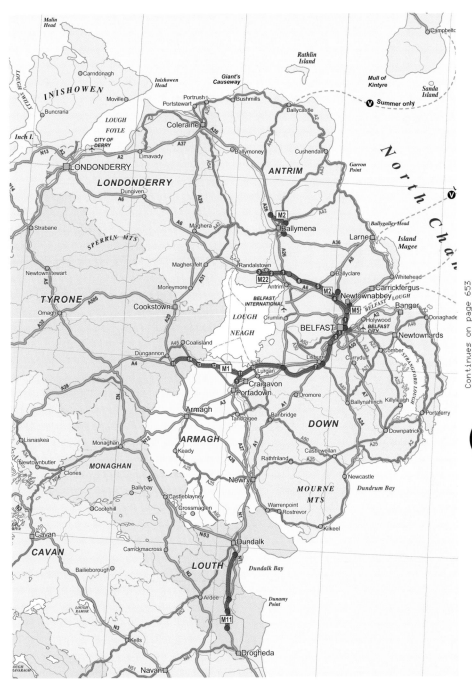

Continues on page 653

© MAPS IN MINUTES ™ 2005.

HMSO Ordnance Survey Permit No.GB399221 © Crown Copyright, Ordnance Survey & Ordnance Survey Northern Ireland 2003 Permit No. NI 1675 & © Government of Ireland, Ordnance Survey Ireland.

LIVE PERFORMANCE

Section 5
Management Companies

the|unsigned|guide

MANAGEMENT COMPANIES

5.1 Management Companies Foreword

The right choice of manager will be one of the most important business decisions your band will have to make. You must be 100% confident that you have chosen the right person to represent you. Never take on a manager out of laziness or flattery. Always bear in mind a recommendation or word of mouth is usually the best criterion when choosing someone. Also remember that there is no such thing as a 'standard' contract and don't be afraid to dispute clauses in a draft agreement. If the management company has a representative ensure his/her name is specifically mentioned in the agreement and not just the company name.

Commission
A commission rate of 20% is perhaps more common than 15% nowadays, but this is obviously negotiable. The manager should not take commission on recording costs, promotional video costs or tour support (money advanced to a band by the record company towards the cost of touring). Commission from live performances should be awarded after the costs of agents' commission and the production costs etc. have been deducted.

> **Always bear in mind a recommendation or word of mouth is usually the best criterion when choosing a manager.**

Length of Contract
A one year contract with two options to extend the deal for a further year (i.e. three years in total) would seem fair, but some managers try to secure a five year term. If the manager is known to be reputable and successful, then perhaps a less dogmatic approach to the issue of length of contract could be suggested. What the Musicians' Union does recommend though is the inclusion of a 'performance clause' which will state that if the manager has not secured within one year a recording or publishing deal to the artist's satisfaction, then the artist will be entitled to terminate the contract.

Territory
Artists or bands in a very strong position can sometimes limit a manager to specific territories so that someone else can represent in, for example, the highly important market of North America. Most new bands will probably have to settle for worldwide representation by the same manager unless they are willing to share their commission with another territory co-manager.

How comprehensive is the agreement?
The answer to this is usually more than you would think. Once again your bargaining power is important here. If you are already an in-demand session player, for example, you may want to try and exclude these activities from the management contract. Only ever allow the manager to sign individual live appearance contracts on the band's behalf. All recording, publishing and merchandising contracts should be signed by you.

Expenses
Attention to detail is very important where expenses are concerned. The manager has to be allowed to spend small amounts of money on behalf of the artist, but a figure should be agreed beforehand. Any additional expenses incurred should require your express permission. Only travelling and accommodation costs incurred by the manager whilst working for the band should come out of band funds. A manager should pay their own office expenses including phone costs etc.

Accounting

Ideally the Musicians' Union suggest all monies should be paid directly to the band's accountant who would then pay the manager commission and expenses that are due. If for any reason the manager will not agree to this then they should present their operating accounts to the band at least four times a year (monthly would be even better) and large sums of money such as advances from a recording or publishing company, should be paid to you within seven days of the manager receiving them.

Right of Audit Clause

This is an essential clause that allows you to look at the manager's books if you feel the need. It should be in any music business contract.

After the agreement is over

The position nowadays is usually that the manager should continue to be paid commission on records released or copyrights published during their term of office but not on future records or songs, even if they fall under a record or publishing agreement they helped to negotiate. Such 'after the term' commission should decrease over a period of time and eventually end completely. This leaves you at liberty to do an uncomplicated deal with a new manager if you wish.

This information is not a substitute for individual specialist advice. If you are a Musicians Union member and have been presented with a management agreement, you should send a copy to:

Musicians' Union
London Office
60-62 Clapham Road
London
SW9 0JJ

email: dp1@musiciansunion.org.uk
tel: 020 7582 5566

Visit **www.musiciansunion.org.uk** for more information.

(An experienced music business solicitor will look over your agreement and offer advice and any amendments Musicians Union feel might be suitable.)

MANAGEMENT COMPANIES

5.2 MANAGEMENT COMPANIES

EAST of ENGLAND

Amber Music Production
PO Box 12, Cromer, Norfolk, NR27 9NL
tel: 01263 510 989
email: ambermuzik@aol.com
web: www.ambermusicproductions.co.uk
contact: Andtreas Yiasimi
genre: All Music Types Accepted
info: Send demos to the above address. See website for full details of all services.

Clear Talent Media
53 Corbet Avenue, Sprowston, Norwich, NR7 8HS
tel: 01603 444 859
email: info@cleartalentmedia.com
contact: Kingsley Harris
genre: Guitar Based/Indie
info: Send demo FAO Kingsley Harris to the above address. Clear Talent Media is also linked with Norwich record labels, B2 Records and NR One Records. See listings in relevant section for further details.

Disco Disco Records
115 Sparrowhawk Way, Hartford, Huntingdon, Cambridgeshire, PE29 1XY
tel: 01480 353 646/07921 460 169
email: info@discodisco.net
web: www.discodisco.net
contact: James
genre: Indie/Singer-Songwriter
info: Send demo to the address above. Alternatively send an MP3 link via email.

Steve Allen Entertainments
60 Broadway, Peterborough, PE1 1SU
tel: 01733 569 589
fax: 01733 561 854
email: steve@sallenent.co.uk
web: www.sallenent.co.uk
contact: Steve Allen
genre: All Music Types Accepted
info: Specialise in the management of bands for corporate events and weddings. Steve Allen Entertainment are constantly looking for new talent. Send any promotional material to the address above.

GREATER LONDON

19 Management
Unit 33, Ransomes Dock, 35-37 Park Gate Road, London, SW11 4NP
tel: 020 7801 1919
fax: 020 7801 1920
web: www.19.co.uk
contact: Simon Fuller
genre: All Pop Genres Accepted
info: 19 Management look after artists such as Rachel Stevens and Wiil Young. Please call before sending your demo.

7Hz Management
Unit 29, Cygnus Business Centre, Dalmeyer Road, Willesden, London, NW10 2XA
tel: 020 8830 4466
fax: 020 8830 0220
email: barry@7Hz.co.uk
web: www.7Hz.co.uk
contact: Barry Campbell
genre: Rock/Indie/Singer-Songwriter
info: Call Barry with details of your act. Send demo on request. 7Hz currently manage Breed 77 and Red Top Matches.

A Crosse The World Management
PO Box 23066, London, W11 3FR
tel: 07956 311 810
web: www.morrighan.com
contact: Jon X
genre: All Music Types Accepted
info: Call before sending demo. Everything except Indie and Rock.

Adage Music
22 Gravesend Road, London, W12 0SZ
tel: 07973 295 113
email: dobs@adagemusic.co.uk
web: www.adagemusic.co.uk
contact: Dobs Vye
genre: All Music Types Accepted
info: Send demo to address above.

Alan Robinson Management
PO Box 177, New Malden, Surrey, KT3 3YT
tel: 020 8949 8885
fax: 020 8949 3558
email: arm5043@aol.com
contact: Alan Robinson
genre: Singer-Songwriter
info: Call or email Alan with details of your act. Send demo on request.

Alan Seifert Management
Flat 1, Winterton House, 24 Park Walk, London, SW10 0AQ
tel: 020 7795 0321
fax: 020 7795 0321
email: alanseifert@lineone.net
contact: Alan Seifert
genre: All Music Types Accepted
info: Call Alan with details of your act. Send demo on request.

All Star Management
PO Box 52, Ilford, Essex, IG1 3JT
tel: 020 8252 1007
fax: 020 8252 1007
email: xsquad_uk@yahoo.co.uk
contact: Ramesh Kansara
genre: Dance/World
info: Send demo with biography and photos to address above.

Ambush Management
32 Ransomes Dock, 35-37 Parkgate Road, London, SW11 4NP
tel: 020 7801 1919
fax: 020 7738 1819
email: info@ambushgroup.co.uk
web: www.ambushgroup.co.uk
contact: Alistair Jamieson
genre: Dance
info: Send demo to Alistair Jamieson at address above.

Andrew Miller Promotions Int. Ltd.
7 Hazelburgh Road, Fulham, London, SW6 2NA
tel: 020 74714 775
fax: 020 7371 5545
email: info@ampi.co.uk
web: www.ampi.co.uk
contact: Faye Miller
genre: All Music Types Accepted
info: Send demo to address above.

Arts Connection
Unit 26, 101 Amies Street, The Village, London, SW11 2JW
tel: 020 7978 5151
fax: 020 7978 5171
email: serge@artsconnection.net
web: www.artsconnection.net or www.puggyband.com
contact: Serge Sabahi
genre: Acoustic/Rock
info: Send demo to the address above. Arts Connection look after artists from France and Belgium, as well as the UK.

ASM
42 City Business Centre, Lower Road, Rotherhide, London, SE16 2XB
tel: 020 7740 1600
fax: 020 7740 1700
email: asm@missioncontrol.net
web: www.asmanagement.co.uk
contact: Albert Samuel
genre: All Music Types Accepted
info: Send demo and photo to address above. ASM welcome demo submissions from all genres.

Automatic Management
13 Cotswold Mews, 30 Battersea Square, London, SW11 3RA
tel: 020 7978 7888
fax: 020 7978 7808
email: auto@automan.co.uk
contact: Jerry Smith
genre: Alternative Guitar Based
info: Send demo (preferably on CD) to address above. Follow with phone call.

Big Blue Music Management
Windyridge, 39-41 Buck Lane, London, NW9 0AP
tel: 020 8205 2990
email: info@bigbluemusic.biz
web: www.bigbluemusic.biz
contact: Steve Ancliffe
genre: All Music Types Accepted
info: Send demo to address above.

Black & White Indians
PO Box 706, Ilford, Essex, IG2 6ED
tel: 07973 676 160
fax: 020 8373 1614
email: bij@btinternet.com
contact: Bij Dodhia
genre: Indie/Alternative Rock
info: Send demo to address above.

Black Clarion Entertainment
122-126 Kilburn High Road, London, NW6 4HY
tel: 020 7692 0597
email: teetime@37.com
genre: African
info: Manage and promote African musicians. Send demo to the above address.

Black Magic Management
296 Earls Court Road, London, SW5 9BA
tel: 020 7565 0806
email: blackmagicrecords@talk21.com
web: www.blackmagicrecords.com
contact: Mataya Clifford
genre: All Music Types Accepted
info: Send demo to address above.

Brian Reza Management
416 High Road, Harrow Weald, Middlesex, HA3 6HJ
tel: 020 8954 3428
fax: 020 8954 3239
contact: Brian Reza
genre: All Music Types Accepted
info: Deal with artists, producers, writers, engineers and programmers. Send CD with biography FAO Brian Reza to the address above. Follow with a phone call after 2 weeks. Do not contact Brian before sending any material.

Bulldozer Media Ltd.
8 Roland Mews, Stepney Green, London, E1 3JT
tel: 020 7929 3333
fax: 020 7929 3222
email: info@bulldozermedia.com
web: www.bulldozermedia.com
contact: Oliver Brown
genre: All Music Types Accepted
info: Artist management company interested in all types of music.

Cigale Entertainment
PO Box 38115, London, W10 6XG
tel: 020 8932 2860
email: info@cigale-entertainment.com
web: www.cigale-ent.com
genre: Hip-Hop/Rock
info: Send demo with full details to the above address.

CMO Management (International) Ltd.
Studio 2.6, 35-37 Parkgate Road, Shepherds East, Richmond Way, 242 Acklam Road, London, W14 0DQ
tel: 020 7316 6969
fax: 020 7316 6970
email: reception@cmomanagement.co.uk
web: www.cmomanagement.co.uk
contact: Charley Hutchings
genre: All Music Types Accepted
info: Send demo with biog and photos to address above.

Coalition Management
Devonshire House, 12 Barley Mow Passage, London, W4 4PH
tel: 020 8987 0123
fax: 020 8987 0345
email: management@coalitiongroup.co.uk
web: www.coalitiongroup.co.uk
contact: Jo
genre: All Music Types Accepted
info: Coalition currently look after artists such as The Streets, The Music, The Zutons, Bloc Party and Embrace. Send demo to Jo at address above. Also provide press and PR services. See listing in relevant section.

Crown Music Management
Matrix Complex, 91 Peterborough Road, London, SW6 3BU
tel: 020 7371 5444
fax: 020 7371 5454
email: mark@crownmusic.co.uk
contact: Mark Hargreaves
genre: Pop/Indie/Commercial
info: Email Mark with details of your act. Send demo on request.

DBBM
PO Box 738, Bunhill Row, London, EC1Y 8HN
tel: 020 7490 7744
fax: 020 7490 5593
email: danny@dbbm.co.uk
web: www.dbbm.co.uk
contact: Danny Brittain
genre: All Music Types Accepted
info: Call or email Danny with details of your act. Send demo on request.

DEF
PO Box 2477, London, NW6 6NQ
tel: 020 7328 2922
fax: 020 7328 2322
email: info@d-e-f.com
web: www.d-e-f.com
genre: All Music Types Accepted
info: Will listen to music of all types but mainly deal with Electronic Dance. Send demos to address above.

Deluxxe Management
PO Box 373, Teddington, TW11 8ZQ
tel: 020 8755 3630
fax: 020 8404 7771
email: info@deluxxe.co.uk
web: ww.deluxxe.co.uk
contact: Diane Wagg
genre: All Music Types Accepted
info: Send demo to address above.

Dune Management
First Floor, 73 Canning Road, Harrow, Middlesex, HA3 7SP
tel: 020 8424 2807
fax: 020 8861 5371
email: info@dune-music.com
web: www.dune-music.com
contact: Janine Irons
genre: Jazz
info: Send demo to address above. Jazz artists only please.

Equator Music Ltd.
17 Hereford Mansions, Hereford Road, London, W2 5BA
tel: 020 7727 5858
fax: 020 7229 5934
contact: Ralph Baker
genre: All Music Types Accepted
info: Send demo with biog and pictures to address above.
Follow with a phone call (allow at least a week for your material to be listened to).

Evolution Management
email: evomgt@aol.com
contact: John Brice
genre: All Music Types Accepted
info: Email John at the above address with details of your act.
Send demo on request.

Eye Industries
Rear of 71a Masbro Road, London, W14 0LS
tel: 020 7471 3205
fax: 020 7471 3206
email: info@eyeindustries.com
web: www.eyeindustries.com
contact: Marco
genre: All Music Types Accepted
info: Send demo on CD to the address above (maximum of 4 tracks please), or send an MP3 to the above email address. Eye Industries also run a record label. See listing in relevant section.

F&G Management
Unit A105, Saga Centre, 326 Kensal Road, London, W10 5BZ
tel: 020 8964 1917
fax: 020 8960 9971
email: info@prolifica.net
web: www.fgmusica.com
contact: Gavino Prunas
genre: All Music Types Accepted
info: Interested in anything eclectic, quirky or different. Send demo to address above.

Full On Entertainment Ltd.
4 Wilton Place, London, SW1X 8RH
tel: 020 7838 9470
fax: 020 7838 9473
email: alki@fullonentertainment.com
web: www.fullonentertainment.com
contact: Amy Bell
genre: Pop/Rock
info: Send demo to address above.

Gerry Bron Management
17 Priory Road, London, NW6 4NN
tel: 020 7209 2766
fax: 020 7813 2766
email: gerrybron@bronzerecords.co.uk
web: www.bronzerecords.co.uk
contact: Gerry Bron
genre: All Music Types Accepted
info: Send demo with contact email address. Bronze Records will listen to all material they receive.

Gold Apple Soul
34 Grasshaven Way, Thamesmead, London, SE28 8TJ
tel: 07985 105 916
email: goldapplesoul@hotmail.com
contact: Junior
genre: R&B/Soul/Gospel
info: Contact Junior either via email or telephone with details of your act. Send demo on request.

Goo Music Management
41 Prince George, Stoke Newington, London, N16 8DL
email: ben@goomusic.net
web: www.goomusic.net
contact: Ben Kirby
genre: Indie/Rock/Alternative
info: Presently manage The Subways. Send demos to the above address. Also promote gigs in London. See listing in Promoters section for further details.

Grand Union Management
93b Scrubs Lane, London, NW10 6QU
tel: 020 8968 7788
email: info@granduniongroup.com
web: www.granduniongroup.com
contact: David Bianchi
genre: All Music Types Accepted
info: Grand Union currently manage Raging Speedhorn and Boy Kill Boy. Send demos to the above address.

Greenlofts Promotions
10-12 Islington Green, London, N1 2XH
tel: 020 7359 6007/07788 755 581
email: greenlofts@fsmail.net
contact: Kelly Venables
genre: Indie/Rock
info: Offer free promotional services for unsigned bands and musicians including production and distribution of flyers, copying and distribution of CDs, compiling press packs, website management, and organising gigs and slots through contacting venues and independent promoters. Send CD, cassette to Kelly, along with brief biog, photo and details of upcoming and previous gigs played. If you wish to submit an MP3, email Kelly at the above address.

Hal Carter Organisation
101 Hazelwood Lane, Palmers Green, London, N13 5HQ
tel: 020 8886 2801
fax: 020 8882 7380
email: artistes@halcarterorg.com
web: www.halcarterorg.com
contact: Abbie Carter
genre: All Music Types Accepted
info: Send demo and biog to address above.

Higrade Music Productions Ltd.
97-103 Font Hill Road, London, N4 3JH
tel: 07931 869 772
fax: 020 8986 5527
email: higrademusic46@aol.com
web: www.hi-grademusic.co.uk
contact: Dego
genre: Hip-Hop/Pop/R&B/Garage
info: Send demo to address above.

Home
The Dairy Studios, 43-45 Tunstall Road, London, SW9 8BZ
tel: 020 7738 7777
fax: 020 7738 7007
email: emailus@takemehome.co.uk
contact: Emily Taylor
genre: All Music Types Accepted
info: Send demo to address above.

ie:music Ltd.
111 Frithville Gardens, London, W12 7JQ
tel: 020 8600 3400
fax: 020 8600 3401
email: info@iemusic.co.uk
web: www.iemusic.co.uk
contact: Ari Millar
genre: All Music Types Accepted
info: Send demo to address above.

Impro Management
35 Britannia Row, London, N1 8QH
tel: 07775 934 408
fax: 020 7704 1616
email: info@impromanagement.com
contact: Steve Baker
genre: All Music Types Accepted
info: Send demo to address above.

Interceptor
PO Box 46572, London, N1 9YL
tel: 020 7278 8001
fax: 020 7713 6298
email: info@interceptor.co.uk
contact: Charlie Charlton
genre: Alternative Guitar Based/Electronic
info: Will listen to any Guitar or Electronic based bands of a high standard. Send demo to Charlie at address above.

IUC Entertainment
8 Meadowbank, Primrose Hill, London, NW3 3AY
tel: 07930 154 190/07770 594 313
email: harleyruben@hotmail.com
web: www.iucentertainment.com
contact: Harley Ruben
genre: UK Grime/Drum&Bass/R&B/Hip-Hop
info: Send MP3 tracks to the above email address. IUC Entertainment also offer music and video production services, as well as events management and club promotions.

developing_the_artists of_the_future.

publishing
management
productions
commercial_sponsorship
public_relations
media_marketing
events_consultation
promotion

JAR

225_regent_street
london_w1_2bq

www.jarmusicgroup.com
tel._0207_5442804

Jackie Davidson Management
The Business Village, Gardiner House, 3-9 Broomhill Road, London, SW18 4JQ
tel: 020 8870 8744
fax: 020 8874 1578
email: seb@jdmanagement.co.uk
web: www.jdmanagment.co.uk
contact: Seb Monks
genre: All Music Types Accepted
info: Send demo via post, or email MP3s to above address.

Jack'n'Jill Artiste Management
F3, 60 West End Lane, London, NW6 2NE
tel: 07050 056 175/07860 232 527
fax: 020 7372 3088
email: jnj@mgmt.fsbusiness.co.uk
contact: Joycelyn Philips
genre: Pop/R&B
info: Send demo to address above.

Jamdown Ltd.
PO Box 45992, London, W3 7YL
tel: 020 8930 1073
email: othman@jamdown-music.com
web: www.jamdown-music.com
contact: Othman Mukhilis
genre: All Music Types Accepted
info: Send demo to address above. Also see listing in Publishing Companies section.

James Joseph Music Management
85 Cicada Road, Wandsworth, London, SW18 2PA
tel: 020 8874 8647
fax: 020 8877 1678
email: info@jamesjoseph.co.uk
web: www.jamesjoseph.co.uk
contact: James Joseph
genre: R&B/Rock/Jazz
info: Send demo to address above.

JAR Music Group
225 Regent Street, London, W1 2BQ
tel: 020 7544 2804
web: www.jarmusicgroup.com
info: JAR can assist unsigned artists across a variety of fields including management, promotion, marketing, publishing and public relations. Contact for further details. Send demo to the above address.

John Waller Management & Marketing
The Old Truman Brewery, 91 Brick Lane, London, E1 6QL
tel: 020 7247 1057
fax: 020 7377 0732
email: john.waller@dial.pipex.com
contact: John Waller
genre: All Music Types Accepted
info: Send demo to address above.

Jonny Paul Management
2 Downsbury Studios, 40 Steeles Road, London, NW3 4SA
tel: 020 7586 3005
fax: 020 7586 3005
email: jonny@paul66.fsworld.co.uk
contact: Jonny Paul
genre: Guitar Based
info: Send demo, biog and photo to address above. Include SAE so your material can be returned.

Jude Street Management
15 St. Jude Street, London, N16 8JU
tel: 020 7923 1362
fax: 020 7503 2431
email: info@judestreet.com
web: www.judestreet.com
contact: Paul Devaney
genre: Alternative/Indie
info: Call or email Paul with details of your act. Send demo on request.

Jungle Management
8 Bedford Hill, London, SW12 9RG
tel: 07970 270 630
email: will@junglemanagement.com
contact: Will Williams
genre: Singer-Songwriter/Guitar Based
info: Contact Will with details of your act. Send demo on request.

Justice Entertainment Ltd.
PO Box 4377, London, W1A 7SX
tel: 020 7499 4708
fax: 020 7409 0550
email: info@timwestwood.com
web: www.timwestwood.com
contact: Alex Wiffen
genre: Hip-Hop/R&B/Dancehall
info: Justice Entertainment Ltd. manage Radio 1 DJ, Tim Westwood. Although they are not looking to manage any new artists, demos are welcome from any R&B/Hip-Hop artists that are looking for possible exposure on Tim Westwood's Radio 1 show.

Justin Perry Management
PO Box 20242, London, NW1 7FL
tel: 020 7485 1113
email: info@proofsongs.co.uk
contact: Justin Perry
genre: All Music Types Accepted
info: Send demo containing 3 tracks to the address above. Include SAE if you would like material returned.

KAL Management
95 Gloucester Road, Hampton, Middlesex, TW12 2UW
tel: 020 8783 0039
fax: 020 8979 6487
email: kaplan222@aol.com
web: www.kaplan-kaye.co.uk
contact: Kaplan Kaye
genre: All Music Types Accepted
info: Send demo to address above.

The Klub International Management Company
UK Office, 10 Barnes Court, Ridgewell Road, Custom House, London, E16 3LW
tel: 07831 128 707
email: info@theklubman.com
contact: Lekan Olujimi
genre: All Music Types Accepted
info: Looking for any music with chart appeal. Send demos to the address above. Do not send music files via email.

L25 Group
17 Parkhill Road, London, London, NW3 2YH
tel: 07973 624 443
fax: 020 7209 4064
email: darren.michaelson@L25entertainment.co.uk
contact: Darren Michaelson
genre: Pop/Indie/Alternative/Rock
info: Darren currently represents Mark Joseph and The Sundays and is always looking for exciting new acts. Ideally send a 4-5 track demo along with picture and biog to the address above. Unfortunately demos cannot be returned, unless accompanied with SAE.

LH Management
1 Lonsdale Road, London, NW6 6RA
tel: 020 76249 220
email: lisa@lhmanagement.com
web: www.lhmanagement.com
contact: Lisa Horan, Jean Coffey
genre: Eclectic
info: Send demo to the address above. LH Management currently represent Roots Manuva, Nightmares on Wax, Black Strobe and Steve Dub.

Liquid Management
1st Floor 139 Sutherland Avenue, Maida Vale, London, W9 1ES
tel: 020 7286 6463
fax: 07092 389 779
email: david@liquidmanagement.net
contact: David Manders
genre: Singer-Songwriter/Rock
info: Email David with details of your act. Send demo on request.

Lokation
Unit 67, Pall Mall Deposits, 124-128 Barlby Road, London, W10 6BL
tel: 020 7274 3155
email: info@lokationco.com
contact: John Ducke
genre: Heavy Metal/R&B/Urban
info: Send demos to the above address.

LTM
Unit 3, 24 Tudor Grove, London, E9 7QL
email: ed.millet@ricall.com
web: www.agirlcalleddeddy.com or www.dibidim.com
contact: Ed Millett
genre: All Music Types Accepted
info: Send demo to the address above.

Marsupial Management Ltd.
Unit 5, 16-18 Empress Place, West Brompton, London, SW6 1TT
tel:	020 7385 1985
email:	info@marsupialmanagement.com
web:	www.marsupialmanagement.com
contact:	Sophie
genre:	Pop/Rock
info:	Send demo CD, photo and biography to the address above.

Masterpaul Entertainment
1st Floor, 79 Dean Street, London, W1D 3SJ
tel:	020 7734 1020
email:	info@masterpaul.co.uk
web:	www.masterpaul.co.uk
contact:	Christine
genre:	All Music Types Accepted
info:	Support, guidance and advice relating to the music industry. Services offered include demo review and talent clinic. See website for further details.

Media Records Ltd.
Units 1-2, Pepys Court, 84-86 The Chase, Clapham Common, London, SW4 0NF
tel:	020 7720 7266
fax:	020 7720 7255
email:	info@mediarec.co.uk
web:	www.mediarec.co.uk or www.nucleus.com
contact:	Peter Pritchard
genre:	Hard House/Trance/House
info:	Send demo to address above.

Mental Music Management
PO Box 20750, London, E3 2YU
email:	mentalmusicmgt@aol.com
contact:	Gary Heath
genre:	All Music Types Accepted
info:	Email with details of your act. Send demo on request. Mental currently look after a diverse range of artists such as Kenny Thomas, Jay Harvey, Pleasurebeach, and Descendants of Cain.

Michael McDonagh Music Management Ltd.
The Studio, c/o 63 Station Road, Winchmore Hill, London, N21 3NB
tel:	020 8364 3121
fax:	020 8364 3090
email:	caramusicltd@dial.pipex.com
contact:	Michael McDonagh
genre:	All Music Types Accepted
info:	Call Michael on number above with details of your act. Send demo on request.

Midnight To Six Management
33 Newman Street, London, W1T 1PY
tel:	020 7462 0026
fax:	020 7462 0012
email:	info@midnighttosix.com
contact:	Dave Harper
genre:	All Music Types Accepted
info:	Manage Goldfrapp, Ladytron and The Shortwave Set. Send demos to address above.

Mighty Music Management
2 Stucley Place, Camden, London, NW1 8NS
tel:	020 7482 6660
fax:	020 7482 6606
email:	art@mainartery.co.uk
contact:	Jo Mirowski
genre:	Commercial/Pop/Rock
info:	Send 3-4 track CD demo to the address above. Ideally include photos and a 1 page biography.

Modest Entertainment
Matrix Complex, 91 Peterborough Road, London, SW6 3BU
tel:	020 7384 6410
fax:	020 7384 6411
email:	firstname@modestentertainment.com
web:	www.modestentertainment.com
contact:	Jane Skillin
genre:	All Music Types Accepted
info:	Send demo to address above.

the | unsigned | guide

MANAGEMENT COMPANIES

Moksha Management
PO Box 102, London, E15 2HH
tel:	020 8555 5423
fax:	020 8519 6834
email:	info@moksha.co.uk
web:	www.moksha.co.uk
contact:	Charles Cosh
genre:	Dance/Hip-Hop/Urban
info:	Send demo with photo and brief biography to Charles Cosh at the address above.

Mumbo Jumbo Management Ltd.
2a-6a Southam Street, London, W10 5PH
tel:	020 8960 3253
fax:	020 8968 5111
email:	ian@mumbojumbo.co.uk
web:	www.mumbojumbo.co.uk
contact:	Ian Clifford
genre:	All Music Types Accepted
info:	Send a demo to the address above. Will deal with artists and producers from any genre.

Music Promotion Media Ltd
PO BOX 2423, Chigwell, IG6 1BN
email:	info@musicpromotionmedia.co.uk
web:	www.musicpromotionmedia.co.uk
genre:	All Music Types Accepted
info:	Specialising purely in the marketing of unsigned acts, Music Promotion Media is focused on using your demo to secure that elusive contract with an established record or publishing company. Visit the website above to download a submission form, which must accompany all demos.

Music Providers
28 Wadsworth Road, Perivale, UB6 7JZ
tel:	020 8998 8944
email:	matt@musicproviders.co.uk or loz@musicproviders.co.uk
web:	www.musicproviders.co.uk
genre:	All Music Types Accepted
info:	Artist management for signed and unsigned bands and booking agency for cover acts and other entertainment. Linked with Loz Vegas recording and rehearsal studios, equipment hire service and music shop 'Vegas Sound House', promotions and booking agency 'Music Scene UK', 'Music Providers' management, 'Some Think Media' media design company, as well as running the Drum Academy. See entries in relevant sections for further information.

N2 Records
Unit B, The Courtyard, 42 Colwith Road, London, W6 9EY
tel:	07900 431 131
fax:	020 8741 3289
email:	oliversmallman@aol.com
contact:	Oliver Smallman
genre:	All Music Types Accepted
info:	Send demo with SAE to address above. Follow with a phone call.

Nettwerk Management UK
Clearwater Yard, 35 Inverness Sreet, London, NW1 7HB
tel:	020 7424 7500
fax:	020 7424 7501
email:	mireille@nettwerk.com
contact:	Mireille Handover
genre:	All Music Types Accepted
info:	Send demo to address above.

Oceanic Music
PO Box 32697, London, W14 OYH
tel:	020 8746 0656
fax:	020 8746 0656
email:	a&r@omusic.org
web:	www.omusic.org
contact:	Dennis Stratford
genre:	Pop/Rock/Indie
info:	Send demo to address above.

One Fifteen
1 Prince of Orange Lane, London, SE10 8JQ
tel:	020 8293 0999
fax:	020 8293 9525
email:	paul@onefifteen.com
web:	www.onefifteen.com
contact:	Paul Loasby
genre:	All Music Types Accepted
info:	Send demo to the address above

OPL Management Ltd.
4 The Limes, North End Way, London, NW3 7HG
tel:	020 8209 0025
email:	oplmanagement@aol.com
contact:	Sabrina
genre:	Rock/Pop-Rock
info:	Call Sabrina with details of your act. Send demo on request.

Optimum Music
Unit 1, Suffolk Studios, 127-129 Great Suffolk Street, London, SE1 1PP
tel:	020 7407 2215
fax:	020 7407 2216
email:	reegs@btinternet.com
contact:	David Regan
genre:	Guitar Based
info:	Call or email David with details of your act. Send demo on request.

Orgasmatron Ltd.
4 Bourlec Close, off Riding House Street, London, W1W 7BJ
tel:	020 7580 4170
fax:	020 7 900 6244
email:	info@orgasmatron.co.uk
web:	www.orgasmatron.co.uk
contact:	Dylan Chambers
genre:	Pop/Rock/Commercial
info:	Send demo to address above.

OW Management
44c Lordship Park, London, N16 5UD
tel:	020 8800 4519
email:	o_kaddison@yahoo.co.uk
contact:	Oliver Wilkinson
genre:	Soul/Pop/Rock/R&B
info:	Send demos to the above address.

Pitt Buhl
21 Ruckholt Close, London, E10 5NX
tel:	07875 162 525
email:	info@pittbuhl.com
web:	www.pittbuhl.com
contact:	Mette Buhl
genre:	Electronica/Pop
info:	Pitt Buhl also offer a music consultancy service. See website for details.

Plus Music Management
36 Follingham Court, Drysdale Place, London, N1 6LZ
tel:	020 7684 8594
email:	deschisholm@hotmail.com
contact:	Desmond Chisholm
genre:	R&B/Funk/Soul/Pop
info:	Send demo to address above along with a recent photo. Include a SAE if you would like your material returned.

Program Music Ltd.
197 Queens Crescent, London, NW5 4DS
tel:	020 7482 5080
fax:	020 7424 0631
email:	info@program-music.co.uk
web:	www.program-music.co.uk
contact:	Pete Whelan
genre:	All Music Types Accepted
info:	Send demo to the address above. Program Music are currently booking for MJ Cole, Addictive TV, Narco, Kiosk and Warren Suicide.

Qdos
8 King Street, Covent Garen, London, WC2E 8HN
tel:	020 7836 2795
fax:	020 7716 3401
email:	info@qdosentertainment.plc.uk
web:	www.qdosentertainment.com
contact:	Phil Dale
genre:	All Music Types Accepted
info:	Send demo with SAE to address above.

MANAGEMENT COMPANIES

Quest Management
34 Trinity Crescent, London, SW17 7AE
tel: 020 8772 7888
fax: 020 7716 3401
email: info@quest-management.com
contact: Scott Rodger, Stuart Green, Giaco Bridgett
genre: Everything except mainstream Pop
info: Send demo, and follow up with a call to Scott or Stuart.

Represents Artist Management
Office 3, Bannon Court, 54-58 Michael Road, London, SW6 2EF
tel: 020 7384 2080
fax: 020 7384 2055
email: info@represents.co.uk
contact: Ben King
genre: Dance
info: Send demo to address above.

Riot Club Management
Unit 4, 27a Spring Grove Road, Hounslow, Middlesex, TW3 4BE
tel: 020 8572 8809
email: riot@riotclub.co.uk
web: www.riotclub.co.uk
contact: Lee Farrow
genre: Rock/Punk
info: Send demo to address above. Riot Club also run a rehearsal studio and record label. See listings for details.

RLM (Richard Law Management)
58 Marylands Road, Maida Vale, London, W9 2DR
tel: 020 7286 1706
fax: 020 7266 1293
email: richard@rlmanagement.co.uk
contact: Richard Law
genre: Rock/Rap/Pop/R&B/Electronic
info: Send 4 track demo to the address above, along with a recent photo and biog. Include SAE envelope if you would like your demo returned. No Hardcore Rock or Techno.

Rocket Music Management Ltd.
10 Thames Point, Imperial Wharf, Townmead Road, London, SW6 2SX
tel: 07711 148 562
email: info@rocket-music.co.uk
web: www.rocket-music.co.uk
contact: James Craven
genre: All Music Types Accepted
info: Management for music, TV and fashion. Send demo to the address above.

Roll Over Productions
29 Beethoven Street, London, W10 4LJ
tel: 020 8969 0299
fax: 020 8968 1047
email: music.studios@rollover.co.uk
web: www.rollover.co.uk
contact: Phillip Jacobs
genre: All Music Types Accepted
info: Call Phillip with details of your act. Send demo on request.

RPM Management Ltd.
Pierce House, London Apollo Complex, Queen Caroline Street, London, W6 9QU
tel: 020 8563 1234
fax: 020 8563 1337
email: marlene-rpm@pierce-entertainment.com
web: www.pierce-entertainment.com
contact: Marlene Gaynor
genre: R&B/Pop
info: Call Marlene with details of your act. Send demo on request.

Sanctuary Music Management Ltd.
Sanctuary House, 45-53 Sinclair Road, London, W14 0NS
tel: 020 7602 6351
fax: 020 7603 5941
email: info@sanctuarygroup.com
web: www.sanctuarygroup.com
contact: Paul Jones, Hannah Butler
genre: All Music Types Accepted

Serious Artist Management
PO Box 13143, London, N6 5BG
tel: 020 8815 5550
fax: 020 8815 5559
email: sam@seriousworld.com
web: www.seriousworld.com
contact: Sam O'Riordan
genre: Dance
info: Send demos to Sam O'Riordan at the address above.

The Session Connection
110-112 Disraeli Road, London, SW15 2DX
tel: 020 8871 1212
fax: 020 8682 1772
email: sessionconnection@mac.com
web: www.thesessionconnection.com
contact: Tina Hamilton
genre: Session musicians
info: The Session Connection provide session musicians for signed artists. Recent clients include Simply Red and Daniel Bedingfield. See website for further details.

Shalit Entertainment & Management
7 Moor Street, Soho, London, W1D 5NB
tel: 020 7851 9155
fax: 020 7851 9156
email: info@shalitglobal.com
web: www.shalitglobal.com
contact: Jonathan Shalit
genre: Urban/Alternative Rock/Pop
info: Send a well-packaged 3 track demo with biog and photo to the above address. First contact should be via post.

Shamrock Music Ltd.
9 Thornton Place, London, W1H 1FG
tel: 020 7935 9719
fax: 020 7935 0241
email: lindy@celtus.demon.co.uk
contact: Lindy McManus
genre: All Music Types Accepted
info: Email Lindy with details of your act. ShamRock are currently looking for artists based in Central London only.

SJ Promotions
London
tel: 07940 149 609
email: sales@sjpromotions.com
web: www.sjpromotions.com
contact: Steve Johnston
genre: All Music Types Accepted
info: Manage bands, artists and DJs. Submit your material by uploading to the website in MP3 format.

Slice DJ & Artist Management
2 Exmoor Street, London, W10 6QY
tel: 020 8964 0064
fax: 020 8964 0101
email: suzanne@slice.co.uk
web: www.slice.co.uk
contact: Suzanne
genre: House/Hip-Hop/Garage/R&B
info: Send demo to address above.

Social Misfit Entertainment
Suite 17, Hunter House, Woodfarrs, London, SE5 8HA
tel: 020 7924 0565
email: socialmisfits@hotmail.com
web: www.social-misfit.com
contact: Patrick Waweru
genre: Hip-Hop
info: Social Misfit is a production company specialising in producing, developing and marketing young upcoming international Hip-Hop talent. See website for artist roster and further details.

Societas
London, W1U 1DX
tel: 0870 910 4904/07976 971 080
email: info@societas.ltd.uk
web: www.societas.ltd.uk
contact: Melissa Sterry
genre: Pop/Pop-Rock/Rock
info: Contact Melissa with details of your act. Societas are interested in any fresh new act with commercial potential. See website for further details.

Spirit Music & Media Ltd.
PO Box 30884, London, W12 9AX
tel: 020 8746 7461
fax: 020 8749 7441
email: info@spiritmm.com
contact: Tom Haxell, David Jaymes
genre: All Music Types Accepted
info: Send demo to address above.

Step 2 Management Europe Ltd.
Basement Flat, 14a Gunterstone Road, West Kensington, London, W14 9BU
tel: 020 7371 4180
fax: 020 8400 1853
email: jon@step2management.co.uk
contact: Jon White, Shyla Hassan, Gregg Donovan
genre: Rock
info: Send demo to the address above. Step 2 currently look after Grinspoon, The Hitchers and Computerman.

Stereophonic Management
PO Box 3787, London, SE22 9DZ
tel: 020 8299 1650
fax: 020 8693 5514
email: duophonic@btopenworld.com
contact: Martin Pike
genre: Alternative/Electronic
info: Send demo to address above.

Strike 3 Management
11 Lambourne Avenue, London, SW19 7DW
tel: 07787 507 787
email: toby@strikeiii.com
web: www.strikeiii.com
contact: Toby Harris
genre: All Music Types Accepted
info: Send demo to the address above.

Strike Back Records
271 Royal College Street, Camden Town, London, NW1 9LU
tel: 020 7482 0115
fax: 020 7267 1169
email: maurice@baconempire.com
contact: Maurice Bacon
genre: Eclectic
info: Email Maurice with details of your act. Send demo on request.

Strongroom Management
120-124 Curtain Road, London, EC2A 3SQ
tel: 020 7426 5130
fax: 020 7426 5102
email: coral@strongroom.com
web: www.strongroom.com
contact: Coral Worman
genre: All Music Types Accepted
info: Send demo to Coral at the address above. Include SAE if you would like your demo returned.

SuperVision Management
Zepplin Building, 59-61 Farringdon Road, London, EC1M 3JB
tel: 020 7916 2146
fax: 020 7691 4666
email: info@supervisionmgt.com
web: www.supervisionmgt.com
contact: Paul Craig, James Sandom
genre: All Music Types Accepted
info: Contact before sending demo to above address.

The Talent League
9 Douglas Square, Green Way, Norten, London, SM4 5MP
tel: 020 8685 0870
email: sam@thetalentleague.co.uk
web: www.thetalentleague.co.uk
contact: Samantha Crompton
genre: All Music Types Accepted
info: Contact Samantha for further details of demo submission. The Talent League also provides promotion and distribution services. See entries in relevant sections for further information.

Tforce
Concorde House, 101 Sheperds Bush Road, London, W6 7LP
tel: 020 7602 8822
email: rich@tforce.com
web: www.tforce.com
contact: Richard Jones
genre: All Music Types Accepted
info: Contact Tforce with details of your act. Send demo on request. See website for further details.

Theo Music Management
27 Anson Road, London, N7 0RB
tel: 07765 640 964
email: daniel@theomanagement.com
contact: Daniel Theo
genre: Pop/Electronic/Rock
info: Prefer to receive demos via MP3 to the above email address, but you can also send CDs via post. Please include photo and biog.

TK1 Management Ltd.
11 Telford Yards, 6-8 The Highway, London, E1W 2BS
tel: 020 7481 1411
fax: 020 7481 1411
email: info@tk1management.com
web: www.tk1management.com
contact: Trina Torpey, Kathryn Nash
genre: All Music Types Accepted
info: Send demo to the address above. Please include SAE if you would like your material returned. Also represent writers and producers. TK1 Management guarantee they will listen to all material they receive.

TLS Management Ltd.
Unit 32-33, Ransomes Dock, 35-37 Parkgate Road, London, SW11 4NP
tel: 020 7801 1956
fax: 020 7738 1819
email: tracey@tlsmanagement.com
web: www.tlsmanagement.com
contact: Tracy Slater
genre: All Music Types Accepted
info: Send demo to address above.

Tony Hall Group Of Companies
Sweet Seven, 54 Broadwick Street, London, W1F 7AH
tel: 020 7434 7286
email: tonyhall@btconnect.com
contact: Tony Hall
genre: Soul/R&B
info: Send demo to Tony at address above. Include SAE for reply.

Tony Smith Personal Management
55 Fulham High Street, London, SW6 3JJ
tel: 020 7384 8990
fax: 020 7384 8994
email: carol@ts-pm.com
contact: Carol Willis
genre: Rock/Progressive Rock
info: Send demo to the address above. Tony Smith Management look after Genesis, Phil Collins and Mike & The Mechanics. Will endeavour to reply to every demo they receive.

Top Banana Management Ltd.
Monomark House, 27 Old Gloucester Street, London, WC1N 3XX
tel: 020 7419 5026
email: info@topbananaman.com
contact: Nino Pires
genre: Pop/Indie/R&B/Rock
info: Send demo to the address above FAO Nino Pires. See website for artist roster.

Top Draw Music Management
PO Box 21469, Highgate, London, N6 4ZG
tel: 020 8340 5151
fax: 020 8340 5159
email: info@topdrawmusic.biz
web: www.topdrawmusic.biz
contact: James Hamilton
genre: Dance
info: Specialise in DJ management.

Trinifold Management
3rd Floor, 12 Oval Road, London, NW1 7DH
tel: 020 7419 4300
fax: 020 7419 4325
email: nicola@trinifold.co.uk
web: www.trinifold.co.uk
contact: Nicola Powell
genre: All Music Types Accepted
info: Call Nicola with details of your act. Send demo on request.

Unique Corp Ltd.
1 Pennine Parade, Pennine Drive, London, NW2 1NT
tel: 020 8458 6006
fax: 020 8458 6660
email: richard@uniquecorp.co.uk
web: www.uniquecorp.co.uk
contact: Richard Mays
genre: Pop/Urban/Hip-Hop
info: Send demo to Richard Mays at address above.

Up All Night Music
Top Floor, 20 Denmark Street, London, WC2H 8NA
tel: 020 7419 4696
email: info@upallnightmusic.com
web: www.upallnightmusic.com
contact: Phil Taylor
genre: All Music Types Accepted
info: Mainly Guitar based bands, Indie and Garage Rock, as well as Singer-Songwriter. Send demo to the above address. Up All Night Music also organise gigs at several venues in London, as well as offering an equipment, PA and crew hire service. Refer to relevant sections for details.

War Zones & Associates
33 Kersley Road, London, N16 0NT
tel: 020 7249 2894
fax: 020 7254 3729
email: wz33@aol.com
contact: Richard Hermitage
genre: All Music Types Accepted
info: Call or email Richard with details of your act. Send demo on request.

MANAGEMENT COMPANIES

West
Unit 119, Westborn, 242 Acklam Road London, W10 5JJ
tel: 020 7524 7595
fax: 020 7524 7595
email: info@westorg.com
contact: Marc Picken
genre: All Music Types Accepted
info: Send demo to address above.

White Tiger Management
55 Fawcett Close, London, SW16 2QJ
tel: 020 8677 5199/5399
fax: 020 8769 5795
email: wtm@whitetigermanagement.co.uk
contact: Paul or Corinne White
genre: Rock/Indie/Singer-Songwriter
info: Send demo to the address above. White Tiger currently represent Carina Round, Assassins and Headlands. See artists' websites for more details.

Whoop! Management
1 East Hill, Marcilly Road, Wandsworth, London, SW18 2HT
tel: 020 8875 0381
fax: 020 8875 0385
email: contact@whoop.co.uk
web: www.whoop.co.uk
contact: Joel Xavier
genre: House/Funky House
info: Email Whoop! Management with an introduction to your act. Follow with demo on request. See also Record Company listings.

Wildlife Entertainment
Unit F, 21 Heathmans Road, Parsons Green, London, SW6 4TJ
tel: 020 7371 7008
fax: 020 7371 7708
contact: Ian McAndrew
genre: All Music Types Accepted
info: Send demo to the address above and follow up with a phone call.

The Yukon Management
91 Saffron Hill, London, EC1N 8PT
tel: 020 7242 8408
fax: 020 7242 8408
email: music@theyukonmusic.com
web: www.searchtheyukon.com
contact: Andrew Maurice
genre: All Music Types Accepted
info: Send demo to address above.

Z Management
The Palm House, PO Box 19734, London, SW15 2WU
tel: 020 8874 3337
fax: 020 8874 3599
email: office@zman.co.uk
web: www.zman.co.uk
contact: Zita Wadwa-mcq
genre: Indie Pop/Dance/R&B
info: Send demo to address above.

ZodoA
Flat 11, Mulberry Court, 99 Ashmore Road, London, W9 3DP
tel: 07880 726 544
email: tommy@deadsexy.co.uk
web: www.zodoa.co.uk
contact: Tommy Kennedy
genre: All Music Types Accepted
info: Contact ZodoA with details of your act. Send demo on request to Inn The Green, 3 Thorpe Close, Ladbroke Grove, LW11.

MIDLANDS

Aroia Music UK
Newark
tel: 01636 679 577/07903 743 581
email: aroiamusicuk@yahoo.co.uk
web: www.freewebs.com/aroiamusicuk04
contact: Mat, Gareth
genre: All Music Types Accepted
info: Contact Mat for details of demo submission. Aroia Music UK is set up to support local acts and deals with promotion, design and production.

BHX Management
Suite 306F, The Big Peg, 120 Vyse Street, Birmingham, B18 6NF
tel: 0121 251 5544
fax: 0870 127 5120
email: musicmgmt@hotmail.com
web: www.bhxmanagement.com
contact: Steve Hughes
genre: All Music Types Accepted
info: Send demo to the address above. BHX currently manage Apache Indian, Pato Banton, Reggae Revolution, Pharcyde, Tinkka and Emma Leigh, and are always looking for exciting new talent from any genre.

Big Bear Music
PO Box 944, Edgbaston, Birmingham, West Midlands, B16 8UT
tel: 0121 454 7020
fax: 0121 454 9996
email: admin@bigbearmusic.com
web: www.bigbearmusic.com
contact: Jim Simpson
genre: Jazz/Blues/Swing
info: Mostly manage Jazz, Swing and Blues artists. Email Jim with details of your act. Send demo on request.

Big Help Management
Pride Rock Studios, Deppers Bridge Farm, Deppers Bridge, Southam, Warwickshire, CV47 2SZ
tel: 01926 614 640/07782 172 101
email: dutch@bighelpmusic.com or helen@bighelp.biz
web: www.bighelp.biz
contact: Dutch Van Spall, Helen Wild
genre: Indie/Singer-Songwriter/Pop-Rock
info: Send demo to address above. Provide a full service (management including record production) for up and coming bands, as well as a training scheme for performers. Associated with Teen Idol (www.teenidol.biz), an organisation that seeks to support, encourage and inspire young musicians through training and performance opportunities.

Brian Yeates Associates
Home Farm House, Camwell, Sutton Coldfield, West Midlands, B75 5SH
tel: 0121 323 2200
fax: 0121 232 2313
email: brian@brianyeates.co.uk
web: www.brianyeates.co.uk
contact: Ashley Yeates
genre: All Music Types Accepted
info: Send demo to Ashley at address above.

Clever Cherry Ltd.
PO Box 1060, Birmingham, West Midlands, B1 3PQ
tel: 0121 236 1060
email: info@clevercherry.com
contact: Ian Allen
genre: Pop
info: Send demo to address above.

Copey J. Management
Wolds Cottage, Tealby, Lincolnshire, LN8 3XT
tel: 07792 336 967
email: queen_churchy@hotmail.com
contact: Emily Churchill
genre: Punk/Indie/Electroclash/Folk
info: Send demos to address above on CD or vinyl, include photos and biog if possible. Please telephone before emailing. Do not accept MP3s via email.

Creative World Entertainments Ltd.
The Croft, Deanslade Farm, Claypit Lane, Lichfield, Staffordshire, WS14 0AG
tel: 01543 253 576
fax: 01543 255 184
email: mail@creative-world-entertainment.co.uk
web: www.creative-world-entertainment.co.uk
contact: Mervyn Spence
genre: All Music Types Accepted
info: Send demo to address above. No returns.

Edition One
2, 77 Musters Road, Nottingham, NG2 7PY
tel: 07789 005 868
email: edition.one@hotmail.co.uk
contact: David Evans
genre: All Music Types Accepted
info: Management and freelance A&R company, looking for all kinds of bands. Get in touch via email, or send a demo to the above address.

Escape Committee
1 Bedford Street, Derby, DE22 3PB
tel:	01332 365 587
email:	escapecom@lineone.net
contact:	Dave McNicholas
genre:	All Music Types Accepted
info:	Associate of The Band Agency (www.thebandagency. com). Email Dave with details of your band, or with a link to a website containing MP3s of your music.

The Forge Management
The Old Smithy, Church Street, Oswestry, Shropshire, SY11 2SP
tel:	01691 658 550
fax:	01691 658 549
email:	sales@systemsworkshop.com
web:	www.forgestudio.com
contact:	Phil Beaumont
genre:	Alternative Guitar Based
info:	Send demos, photo and biography to the address above. The Forge Management guarantee they will listen to all material sent.

GC Entertainments
3 Davis Close, Leamington Spa, Warwickshire, CV32 6RT
tel:	01926 886 848
fax:	01926 886 433
email:	music@gcents.com
web:	www.gcents.com
contact:	Mark Stickley
genre:	All Music Types Accepted
info:	Email Mark with details of your act. Send demo on request.

Gloria Butler Management
PO Box 2686, Solihull, West Midlands, B94 5NQ
tel:	0156 478 2341
fax:	0156 478 3996
email:	gloria@gbmgt.com
contact:	Gloria Butler
genre:	Rock
info:	Send demo to address above.

Holier Than Thou Management
46 Rother Street, Stratford Upon Avon, Warwickshire, CV37 6LT
tel:	01789 268 661
email:	httrecords@aol.com
web:	www.holierthanthourecords.com
contact:	David Begg
genre:	Industrial/Rock/Alternative/Metal
info:	Send quality recordings on CD to the address above. Holier Than Thou also deal with distribution. For full details of all services visit the website.

Horus Music
PO Box 12780, Birmingham, B42 9AX
tel:	07814 050 007
email:	info@horusmusic.co.uk
web:	www.horusmusic.co.uk
contact:	Nick Dunn
genre:	All Music Types Accepted
info:	Will work with artists and bands at no cost to assist them in raising their profile. Send demo FAO Nick Dunn to the address above. See also listing in Publishing Companies section.

Impulse Reaction Management
48 John Rhodes Way, Stoke On Trent, ST6 5XA
tel:	01782 818 718/07814 014 614
email:	laura200522@yahoo.com
contact:	Laura
genre:	Rock
info:	Send demo to the address above.

PVA Management
Hallow Park, Worcester, WR2 6PG
tel:	01905 640 663
fax:	01905 641 842
email:	post@pva.co.uk
web:	www.pva.co.uk
contact:	Nick Harris
genre:	All Music Types Accepted
info:	Send demo to Nick at the address above.

STICKY LICKY
Management UK

Band Management - Promotions - label

Professionals Working with Professionals
Experienced & Enthusiastic Team
Artist Development
Promotion
Record label

Bands now required for Management and label 2006 Roster

Please send your Demo Press Pack
(to include Biog, Photos, Gigs)

STICKYLICKY MUSIC UK
PO Box 4234
Wolverhampton
WV6 8WZ

Websites: stickylicky.com — stickylickyrecords.com
band-idol.com

Sempre Entertainments Ltd.
36 Birches Park Road, Codsall, Wolverhampton, WV8 2DT
tel: 01902 842 720
fax: 01902 842 720
email: scmsempre@aol.com
contact: Stephen Markham
genre: Country Rock/Rhythm & Blues/Jazz/Funk/Fusion
info: Send demo, biog and picture to address above.
Represent musicians with a view to getting them studio or session
work. Sempre are not interested in receiving material from Rap or
modern R&B artists.

Solar Creations
PO Box 9691, Birmingham, B27 7ED
tel: 0121 707 8504
email: scott@solarcreations.net
web: www.solarcreations.net
contact: Scott Roe
genre: All Music Types Accepted
info: Send demos FAO Scott to the address above. Solar
Creations also have a record label and provide PR services, as well as
promoting live music at The Actress & The Bishop, Birmingham.

Split Music
13 Sandys Road, Worcester, WR1 3HE
tel: 01905 29809
fax: 01905 613 023
email: split.music@virgin.net
contact: Chris Warren
genre: All Music Types Accepted
info: Send demo to address above. Associated with Prison
Records.

StickyLicky Management UK
51 Pendleford Avenue, Tettenhall, Wolverhampton, WV6 9EH
tel: 01902 834 777
email: admin@stickylicky.com
web: www.stickylicky.com
contact: Roland Stow
genre: Pop/Indie/Rock/Punk/Punk Rock/Commercial
info: Send press pack including demo, biography, photo and
gig listings to the above address. StickyLicky are looking for talented,
original UK bands who are genuinely committed and able to take
advice and direction. They have an experienced team of professional
personnel who can help develop your music career. Visit website for
further details.

Three Ones Music Ltd.
Unit 111, The Custard Factory, Gibb Street, Birmingham, B9 4AA
tel: 0121 693 0013
email: info@saffa.co.uk
contact: Geoff Pearce
genre: All Music Types Accepted
info: Send demo to the address above.

What Management
Birmingham
email: whatmanagement@blueyonder.co.uk
genre: All Music Types Accepted
info: What Management are based in both Birmingham and
London. Send an email to the address above with details of your act.
Send demo on request.

Wizard Management
PO Box 6779, Birmingham, B13 9RZ
tel: 0121 778 2218
fax: 0121 778 1856
email: pk.sharma@ukonline.co.uk
contact: Mambo Sharma
genre: Reggae/World/Pop/R&B
info: Send demo to address above.

NORTHEAST

10xBetter
7 St. Nicholas' Church Yard, Newcastle Upon Tyne, NE1 1PS
tel: 0191 260 3377
email: info@10xbetter.com
web: www.10xbetter.com
contact: Terry Hollingsworth
genre: All Music Types Accepted
info: Artist management and booking agency. 10xBetter also
offers PR services. See listing in relevant section for further information.
Linked with label Subversive Records and Global Entertainment, who
offer music industry courses. For details refer to entries in appropriate
sections.

OFFBEAT management

Representing:
Lee Rogers
Undergroove
Steve Lee and The Soulutions
White and Hunter

23 Store Street
Newcastle Upon Tyne
England
NE15 8DY
Email: info@offbeat-management.co.uk

THE HOME OF GOOD MUSIC

Line-Up PMC
9a Tankerville Place, Jesmond, Newcastle, NE2 3AT
tel: 0191 281 6449
fax: 0191 212 0913
email: info@line-up.co.uk
web: www.line-up.co.uk
contact: Chris Murtagh
genre: All Music Types Accepted
info: Line up do not necessarily deal with unsigned demos,
but if they like it they can pass on your name. Its defintely worth
getting in touch for advice and feedback. Also` offer tour mnagement
services and audio and visual solutions.

Off Beat Management
23 Store Street, Lemington, Newcastle-upon-Tyne, Tyne & Wear,
NE15 8DY
tel: 0191 2640 601
fax: 0191 264 0601
email: soulman@madasafish.com
contact: Barry Skeels
genre: All Music Types Accepted
info: Send demo and biog to Barry at the address above. Off
Beat manage 2 recently signed artists, Lee Rogers and Bangstick.

Travelled Music
The Tile Works, Paxton, Berwick Upon Tweed, TD15 1TJ
tel: 01289 386 737
email: info@travelledmusic.co.uk
web: www.travelledmusic.co.uk
contact: Alan Thompson
genre: Indie/Pop/Rock
info: Work with acts based in Edinburgh, Glasgow, Newcastle
or Berwick. Also involved in event management. Have previously
worked with Ordinary Son, Eastern Lane and Wire Daisies. Send
demo to the above address. Travelled Music also offer equipment hire,
duplication and merchandise services, as well as promoting gigs. See
listings in relevant sections for details.

NORTHWEST

Alive Management
PO Box 114, Bury, Lancashire, BL9 8FG
tel: 0161 280 0908
fax: 0161 280 0908
email: info@alive.org.uk
web: www.alive.org.uk
contact: Peter Ross
genre: All Music Types Accepted
info: Send demo with full contact details to address above. Follow with phone call.

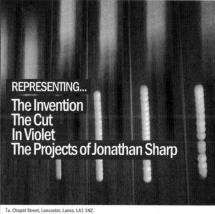

Arketek Management
53 Edge Street, Nut Grove, St. Helens, Merseyside, WA9 5JX
tel: 0151 430 6290
email: alan@arketek.com
web: www.arketek.com
contact: Alan Ferreira
genre: Indie/Pop/Dance
info: Arketek Management have a direct hand in helping unsigned artists reach the next stage of their development. Demos on CD only please. No returns.

BeMy
Apartment 10, 12 Palatine Road, Manchester, M20 3JA
tel: 07976 134 617
email: info@bemy.co.uk
web: www.bemy.co.uk
contact: Dave Fox
genre: Electronic/Alternative/Guitar Based
info: Manchester based. Alternative Guitar Based and Electronica. Send CD demos to the above address. No MP3 demos.

Creeme Entertainments
East Lynne, Harper Green Road, Farnworth, Bolton, BL4 7HT
tel: 01204 793 441
fax: 01204 792 655
email: info@creeme.co.uk
web: www.creeme.co.uk
contact: Tom Ivers, Anthony Ivers, Lynne Ivers
genre: All Music Types Accepted
info: Manage acts for the pubs and club circuits, as well as corporate events. Send demo to address above.

Highblue
13 Lenthall Street, Liverpool, L4 5TN
tel: 0151 222 5262/07740 365 898
email: management@highbue.co.uk
web: www.highblue.co.uk
contact: D.P. Ryan
genre: All Music Types Accepted
info: Send demos either via email or post to the above addresses.

Integral Management
51-55 Highfield Street, Liverpool, L3 6AA
tel: 0151 227 4447/07791 120 894
fax: 0151 283 3649
email: martin@integralrpm.com
contact: Kathy Walsh
genre: All Music Types Accepted
info: Send demo, biography and photos to address above. Integral guarantee to listen to all material they receive, and will get in touch if they are interested.

Jamcat Music
Bolton Enterprise Centre, Washington Street, Bolton, BL3 5EY
tel: 01204 364 555
email: mike@jamcat.co.uk
web: www.jamcat.co.uk
contact: Mike Welsh
genre: All Music Types Accepted/Tribute artists
info: Complete artist production service. Send demo to the address above.

Key Music Management
Edenhurst, 87 Station Road, Marple, Cheshire, SK6 6NY
tel: 0161 221 3681
fax: 0161 221 3682
email: keymusicmgmt@aol.com
contact: Richard Jones
genre: All Music Types Accepted
info: Contact Richard with details of your act. Send demo on request. Key Music Management's clients currently include Pixies and Jim Noir.

Landstar Management ●
7a Chapel Street, Lancaster, Lancashire, LA1 1NZ
tel: 01524 843 499/07957 626 297
fax: 01524 843 499
email: turnbuis@hotmail.com or sylviajthomas@hotmail.com
contact: Stuart Turnbull, Syliva Thomas
genre: Rock/Metal/Electronica/Indie
info: Send email with contact detail and an idea of your music to Stuart, or send demo directly. Stuart is also A&R director for Neurotic Records.

Liberty City Music
PO Box 451, Macclesfield, Cheshire, SK10 3FR
tel: 07921 626 900
email: darren@libertycity.biz
web: www.libertycity.biz
contact: Darren Eager
genre: All Music Types Accepted
info: Manage artists, promotion and events. Send demos FAO Darren Eager to the above address.

Maine Loft Management
Manchester
tel: 0161 434 1405/07779 171 570/07973 345 287
fax: 0161 434 1405
email: maineloft@hotmail.com
contact: Simon Ashby, Dave Alton
genre: All Music Types Accepted
info: Call or email Simon or Dave with details of your act. Send demo, biog (max 1 page) and photo on request. No MP3s please.

MAP Management
208 Huyton Lane, Huyton, Liverpool, Merseyside, L36 1TQ
tel: 0151 489 6142
email: mike@2dogsrecords.com
contact: Mike Walker
genre: Alternative/Classic Rock/Rock
info: Call Mike on the number above. Send demo on request.

MAXAR ARTISTS AND EVENTS
70a Kingswood Road, Manchester, M14 6RX
0161 256 4738
Artist & Event Management - from indie to urban.
www.idmusic.biz
maxarevents@aol.com
www.maxar.co.uk

Mat Ong Management
Liverpool
tel: 0151 707 9044
email: info@matongmanagement.co.uk
web: www.matongmanagement.co.uk
contact: Tom Ward
genre: All Music Types Accepted
info: Management and agency for UK bands and DJs. Development and production for UK and international artists. Current band roster includes Cadium, Day With Mary, and Kite (Norway). DJ roster includes Mat Tang, Ricky Zhang and Cesar. Demos on CD only with press pack, biog and gig dates. Contact by email or telephone initially.

Maxar Artists & Events
70a Kingswood Road, Ladybarn, Manchester, M14 6RX
tel: 0161 256 4738/07707 701050
email: maxarevents@aol.com
web: www.maxar.co.uk
contact: Max Sharif
info: Artist and event management from Indie to Urban. Also an independent promoter, putting on various nights in Manchester venues. Previous clients include The Arctic Monkeys, Kano, Pete Doherty, Wu Tang Clan.

Melancholic Music Management
Manchester
tel: 07748 706 961
email: melancholicmusic@gmail.com
web: www.52tng.com
contact: Chris Dart
genre: Alternative
info: Send tracks on MP3 to the above email address, with a photo, biog and any weblinks.

Memnon Entertainment UK Ltd.
3rd Floor, Habib House, 9 Stevenson Square, Manchester, M1 1DB
tel: 0161 238 8516
fax: 0161 236 6717
email: memnon@btconnect.com
genre: Urban/R&B
info: Send demo to address above.

Mercenary Music
Ashtons Farm, Cobbs Brow Lane, Latham, Lancashire, L40 6JJ
tel: 01695 724 064
fax: 01695 555 504
email: mms558@aol.com
contact: Paul Naylor
genre: Alternative Guitar Based/Rock
info: Ring Paul with details of your act. Send demo, biog and details of previous gigs on request.

Nemo Records
25 Grosvenor Road, Heaton Moor, Stockport, Cheshire, SK4 4EE
email: benphuzz@hotmail.com
contact: Ben Taylor, Tony Pinkham
genre: Rock/Beats/Funk
info: Nemo Records has a substantial A&R contact network and PR and promotions team (ex Sony). The label hosts monthly showcase nights and can offer studio sessions with a Wiiija Records producer. Send demos to the address above. See also Record Company and Promoter sections.

Northstar Artist Management
PO Box South 238, Egerton Road, Fallowfield, M14 6QF
tel: 07867 837 756
email: northstarartist@aol.com
contact: Tony Lovell
genre: Rock/R&B/Pop
info: Call or email Mick with details of your act. Send demo on request.

Pannone & Partners
123 Deansgate, Manchester, M3 2BU
tel: 0161 909 3000
email: charlotte.wigham@pannone.co.uk
web: www.pannone.com
contact: Charlotte Wigham
genre: All Music Types Accepted
info: Manage bands, DJs and producers. Send demo FAO Charlotte Wigham to the above address. Also offer legal advice. See listing in relevant section for details.

Phil Jones Presents
4th floor, 24-26 Lever Street, Manchester, M1 1DZ
tel: 0161 244 5795
fax: 0161 228 2277
email: phil@philjonespresents.com
web: www.cmplive.com
contact: Phil Jones
genre: Pop/Singer-Songwriter
info: Manages The Durutti Column. Especially interested in Pop and Commercial artists, as well as extremely talented songwriters. Introduce yourself via email and send demo on request. No MP3s please.

Poz Music
Manchester
tel: 0798 573 3956
contact: David Posner
genre: All Music Types Accepted
info: Call David with details of your act. Send demo on request.

Red Alert
Sun House, 2-4 Little Peter Street, Manchester, M15 4PS
tel: 0161 834 7434
fax: 0161 834 8545
email: info@redalert.co.uk
web: www.redalert.co.uk
contact: Liam Walsh
genre: All Music Types Accepted
info: Send demo to the above address with details of any press coverage received, and a covering letter.

Roger Boden Management
2 Gawsworth Road, Macclesfield, Cheshire, SK11 8UE
tel: 01625 420 163
fax: 01625 420 168
email: rbm@cottagegroup.co.uk
contact: Roger Boden
genre: All Music Types Accepted
info: Send demo to address above.

SDM Artist Management
9 Glynn Gardens, West Didsbury, Manchester, M20 2YP
tel: 07832 145 285
email: ottilia1@yahoo.co.uk
contact: Ottilia
genre: All Music Types Accepted
info: Artists currently being represented include RAW-T and Backdraft. Artist management and promotion available. Send demo to the above address.

SH Management ●
Lodge Road, Sandbach, Cheshire, CW11 3HP
tel: 01270 750 448
fax: 01270 750 449
email: info@shmanagement.co.uk
web: www.shmanagement.co.uk
contact: Steve Harrison, Jane
genre: All Music Types Accepted
info: Clients include Alfie and The Charlatans. Send demo FAO Jane at the address above.

Silk Studios
23 New Mount Street, Manchester, M4 4DE
tel: 0161 953 4045
email: leestanley@silkstudios.co.uk
web: www.silkstudios.co.uk
contact: Danny
genre: Indie/Singer-Songwriter/Soul/Urban
info: Have strong industry links, especially with advertising agencies. Send demos FAO of Danny to the above address.

Sound Image
Unit 2b, Bankquay Trading Estates, Slutchers Lane, Warrington, Cheshire, WA1 1PJ
tel: 01925 445 742
contact: Steve Millington, Steve Oates
genre: All Music Types Accepted
info: Send demo to the address above. Any style of music considered. Also run Publishing Company and Recording Studio (Frog Studios). See entries in relevant sections for further details.

Sparkle Street HQ Ltd.
18 Sparkle Street, Manchester, M1 2NA
tel: 0161 273 3435/07798 766 861
fax: 0161 273 3695
email: mailbox@pd-uk.com
contact: Gary McClarnan
genre: All Music Types Accepted
info: Post or email Gary details of your act. Send demo on request. No MP3s via email. Current roster includes Mr Scruff and Fingathing

Steve Draper Entertainments
2 The Coppice, Beardswood Manor, Blackburn, Lancashire, BB2 7BQ
tel: 01254 679 005
fax: 01254 679 005
email: steve@stevedraperents.co.uk
web: www.stevedraperents.org.uk
contact: Steve Draper
genre: All Music Types Accepted
info: Send demo to address above.

TCB Management ●
Manchester
tel: 07811 449 529
email: matt@tcb-management.co.uk
web: www.tcb-management.co.uk or www.tcblive.co.uk
contact: Matt Johnson
genre: Indie/Rock
info: TCB Management currently looks after Stoke band Centrifuge. Also looking for a North West act to work with. Call or email Matt with details of your act. Send demo on request. TCB Management co-runs the monthly Club Fandango and XFM X-posure band nights at Night and Day in Manchester, in conjunction with Fierce Panda Records and www.drownedinsound.com respectively.

TM Music
34 Lincoln Road, Earby, Barnoldswick, Lancashire, BB18 6QE
tel: 07914 946 175
email: See website for contact list
web: www.tmmusic.co.uk
contact: James Jackman
genre: Rock/Punk/Pop
info: Independent booking agency and management company. Looking to expand it's roster, with particular intrest in representing an act from the North West. Send a demo to James or invite an agency representative to a live show.

A Lovesick Dragon
35 Goldcroft, Bennett's End, Hemel Hempstead, Hertfordshire, HP3 8EY
tel: 07050 211 206
fax: 01442 261 154
email: leelorenc@hotmail.com
contact: Lee Lorenc
genre: Alternative Guitar Based
info: Mellow guitar based music. Send demos to the address above.

ABC Music
85 High Street, Esher, Surrey, KT10 9QA
tel: 01372 466 195
contact: Merv Joseph
genre: Rock/Pop
info: Send demos to the above address. ABC Music also run musical instrument stores in the surrounding area. See entry in relevant section.

Adventures in Music Management
PO Box 261, Wallingford, Oxfordshire, OX10 0ZY
tel: 01491 832 183
email: info@adventuresin-music.com
web: www.adventuresin-music.com
contact: Paul Conroy
genre: All Music Types Accepted
info: Send demo to address above.

Amber
PO Box 1, Ongar, Essex, CM5 9HZ
tel: 01277 362 916
email: paultage@amberartists.com
web: www.amberartists.com
contact: Paul Tage
genre: Adult Contemporary
info: Call Amber to introduce yourself and your music. Follow with demo on request.

Band-X
19 Barden Road, Speldhurst, Kent, TN3 0PZ
tel: 07707 574 534/07811 939 518
email: band-x@bluebottle.com
web: www.band-x.org.uk
contact: Matt Burgess
genre: Rock
info: Dedicated to helping unsigned bands in reaching their goals. Send demo to the above address. Also offer equipment hire service. See listing in relevant section.

Barry Collings Entertainments
21a Clifftown Road, Southend-on-Sea, Essex, SS1 1AB
tel: 01702 330 005
fax: 01702 333 309
email: bcollent@aol.com
web: www.barrycollings.co.uk
genre: Commercial
info: Clients include Boney M and Chaz'n'Dave. Also operate as a publishing company. See relevant section for details.

Crash Management
PO Box 13, Chinnor, Oxon, OX39 4WD
tel: 01844 353 154 (ext 2)
email: info@crash-records.co.uk
web: www.crash-records.co.uk
genre: All Music Types Accepted
info: Manage several bands and solo artists. Members of the Music Managers Forum. All genres accepted on CD format

David Morgan Management
Weybridge, Surrey
email: davidmanagement@aol.com
contact: David Morgan
genre: All Music Types Accepted
info: Email information to the address above. Send demo on request.

Duroc Media
Riverside House, 10-12 Victoria Road, Uxbridge, Middlesex, UB8 2TW
tel: 01895 810 831
fax: 01895 231 499
email: info@durocmedia.com
web: www.durocmedia.com
contact: Simon Porter
genre: All Music Types Accepted
info: Send demo to address above.

First Column Management Ltd.
34 West Street, Brighton, BN1 2RE
tel: 01273 724 710
fax: 01273 736 004
email: fcm@firstcolumn.co.uk
contact: Phil Nelson
genre: All Music Types Accepted
info: Send demo to address above.

Fox Management
62 Lake Rise, Romford, Essex, RM1 4EE
tel: 01708 760 544
fax: 01708 760 563
email: foxrecords@talk21.com
contact: Colin Brewer
genre: Dance/Pop-Rock/R&B
info: Send demo, biog and photo to the address above. Fox Management is interested in representing artists who show chart and commercial potential. See also Record Company listings.

Fresh Management
PO Box 4075, Pangbourne, Berkshire, RG8 7FU
tel: 0118 984 3468
fax: 0118 984 3463
email: info@freshmusic.co.uk
web: www.freshmusic.co.uk
contact: Dave Morgan
genre: All Music Types Accepted
info: Send demo to address above.

Friars Management Ltd.
33 Alexander Road, Aylesbury, Buckinghamshire, HP20 2NR
tel: 01296 434 731
fax: 01296 422 530
email: info@fmlmusic.com
web: www.fmlmusic.com
contact: Joe Stopps
genre: All Music Types Accepted/Dance/Indie
info: Send demo to address above.

Impact Management
PO Box 2106, Rayleigh, Essex, SS6 7YT
tel: 07958 746 764
email: paul@maniczone.com
contact: Paul Maynard
genre: All Music Types Accepted
info: Send an email to introduce yourself and your music. Follow with demo on request.

Joe Bangay Enterprises
River House, Riverwoods, Marlow, Buckinghamshire, SL7 1QY
tel: 01628 486 193
fax: 01628 890 239
email: joebangay@joebangay.com
web: www.joebangay.com
contact: Joe Bangay
genre: Pop/Rock
info: Joe has been involved in the music industry for many years. He has had 2 big hits with female fronted pop and rock bands. Joe is now looking for a similar project to take on. Send demo to the address above. Joe is also a photographer, see listing in relevant section.

Killin Time
PO Box 121, Stevenage, Hertfordshire, SG2 8XG
tel: 01438 232 195
email: keith@killintimerecords.co.uk
web: www.killintime.co.uk
contact: Keith
genre: Metal/New Metal/Emo/Thrash Metal/Neo-Folk
info: Send demos to the above address FAO Keith. Also see listing for Killin Time Records. For full details visit the website.

ModernWood Management
Cambridge House, Card Hill, Forest Row, East Sussex, RH18 5BA
tel: 01342 822 619/01342 826 914
email: mickey.modernwood@virgin.net
web: www.modernwoodmanagement.co.uk
contact: Mickey Modern, Mark Wood
genre: Indie Rock/Pop/Singer-Songwriter
info: Contact ModernWood with details of yourself and your act. Send demo on request. Current acts on the roster include Dum Dums, Rags, The Decipers, Imogen Heat and Nick Kershaw.

Multiplay Music Management
19 Eagle Way, Harrold, Bedfordshire, MK43 7EW
tel: 01234 720 785
fax: 01234 720 664
email: info@multiplaymusic.com
web: www.multiplaymusic.com
contact: Kevin White
genre: Singer-Songwriter/Pop
info: Will represent pop music songwriters, producers and artists from any genre. Send demo with SAE to the address above.

Natural State
PO Box 2614, Eastbourne, BN21 7DQ
tel: 01323 721 603
email: info@obedientbone.com
web: www.obedientbone.com
contact: Simon Vieler
genre: All Music Types Accepted
info: Currently manage award winning act Obedient Bone. Send demo to the above address. Natural State also run a publishing company. See entry in relevant section for further information.

Park Promotions
PO Box 651, Oxford, OX2 9AZ
tel: 01865 241 717
fax: 01865 204 556
email: info@parkrecords.com
web: www.parkrecords.com
contact: John Dagnell
genre: Folk/Singer-Songwriter
info: Send demo to address above accompanied by photograph. Currently looking for female singer-songwriter.

Psycho Management Co.
Sollys Mill, Wimbledon, Mill Lane, Godalming, Surrey, GU7 1EY
tel: 01483 419 429
fax: 01483 419 504
email: agents@psycho.co.uk
web: www.psycho.co.uk
contact: Patrick Haveron
genre: Tribute artists
info: Call or email Patrick with details of your act. Send demo on request.

Raven Black Music
Oxford Centre for Innovation, Mill Street, Oxford, OX2 0JX
tel: 01989 767 868
email: raven@tourdates.co.uk
web: www.tourdates.co.uk
contact: Dean G. Hill
genre: Rock
info: Submit demos FAO Dean G. Hill at the above address. Contact by email to follow up response to demo. Raven Black Music also run a publishing company, promote unsigned bands, and run the above listings website. See entries in relevant sections for details.

RM Music Management
73 Downsway, Springfield, Chelmsford, Essex, CM1 6TT
tel: 01245 614 118/07763 763 221
email: rmmusicmanagement@blueyonder.co.uk
web: www.rmmusicmanagement.co.uk
contact: Richard Martin
genre: All Music Types Accepted
info: Artist and band management. Send demo, biog and photo to the above address.

Safe Management
St. Ann's House, Guildford Road, Lightwater, Surrey, GU18 5RA
tel: 01276 476 676
fax: 01276 451 109
email: daryl@safemanagement.co.uk
web: www.safemanagement.co.uk
contact: Daryl Costello
genre: All Music Types Accepted
info: Send demo to address above. Daryl will contact you if he is interested in your act.

South Star Music
PO Box 1350, Southampton, SO15 5WX
tel: 07789 882 368
email: admin@southstarmusic.co.uk
web: www.southstarmusic.co.uk
contact: Stewart Dugdale
genre: R&B/Pop/Rock/Soul
info: Send 3 track demo with biog, picture and any press coverage to the above address.

Starfisch Records Ltd.
Barco House, 15 Bessemer Road, Welwyn Garden City, Hertfordshire, AL7 1HB
tel: 01707 387 938
fax: 01707 372 621
email: starfisch@barco.net
contact: Steve Peacocks
genre: All Music Types Accepted
info: Send demo to address above.

Sublime Music
77 Preston Drove, Brighton, East Sussex, BN1 6LD
tel: 01273 560 605
fax: 01273 560 606
email: info@sublimemusic.co.uk
web: www.sublimemusic.co.uk
contact: Patrick Spinks
genre: All Music Types Accepted
info: Send 3 track CD to address above. Include contact
telephone number and email address only.

Tsunami Sounds
Muscott House, Meadrow, Goldalming, Surrey, GU7 3HN
tel: 01483 410 100
email: info@tsunami.co.uk
web: www.tsunami.co.uk
genre: All Music Types Accepted
info: Send demo to address above.

Violation Management
26 Mill Street, Gamlingay, Sandy, Bedfordshire, SG19 3JW
tel: 01767 651 552
fax: 01767 651 228
email: dicky_boy@msn.com
contact: Dick Meredith
genre: Alternative/Indie
info: Send demo to address above.

Yellow Balloon Productions Ltd.
Freshwater House, Outdowns, Effingham, Surrey, KT24 5QR
tel: 01483 281 500
fax: 01483 281 502
email: yellowbal@aol.com
contact: Mike Smith
genre: All Music Types Accepted
info: Send demo to address above. Include SAE if you would
like your demo returned. Mike will contact you if interested.

SOUTHWEST

ACA Music Management
7 North Parade, Bath, Somerset, BA2 4DD
tel: 01225 428 284
fax: 01225 400 090
email: aca_aba@freenet.co.uk
contact: Harry Finegold
genre: All Music Types Accepted
info: Send demo to address above.

Bionic Monkey Management
Pine Tree Farm, Cranborne, Wimbone, Dorset, BH21 5RR
tel: 01725 517 204
email: carl@bionicmonkeymanagement.com
web: www.bionicmonkeymanagement.com
contact: Carl Pratt
genre: All Music Types Accepted
info: Professional artist management. Send demos to the
above address. Visit the website for full details.

Caravan Music Promotions
PO Box 3674, Somerset, BA5 3ZR
tel: 07739 126 794
email: caravanmusic@hotmail.com
web: www.caravanmusicpromotions.com
contact: JJ Kane
genre: All Music Types Accepted
info: Currently working with platinum selling artist, as well
as new talents just starting out. Accept all genres of music and have no
age limits. Caravan Music Promotions also offer Press and PR services.
See listing in relevant section for further details.

Charles Salt Management
Leacroft, Cheriton Cross, Cheriton Bishop, Exeter, Devon, EX6 6JH
tel: 01647 245 02
email: charlie35@supanet.com
contact: Charles Salt
genre: All Music Types Accepted
info: Send demo to address above.

First Time Management
Sovereign House, 12 Trewartha Road, Praa Sands, Penzance, Cornwall,
TR20 9ST
tel: 01736 762 826/07721 449 477
fax: 01736 763 328
email: panamus@aol.com
web: www.songwriters-guild.co.uk or www.panamamusic.
co.uk
contact: Roderick Jones
genre: All Music Types Accepted
info: Send demo to address above.

Glass Tone Productions Ltd.
Unit 3a, Riverside Business Park, Bath, BA2 3DW
tel: 01225 487 700
email: management@glasstone.co.uk
web: www.glasstone.co.uk
contact: Greg Brooker
genre: All Music Types Accepted
info: Send biog and gig listings via email to above address.
Glass Tone will reply with address details to send a demo package,
if they feel they can help a band or musician in any way. Quality of
music is the main consideration. In the past have worked with Metal,
Rock, Drum&Bass and Pop acts. Glass Tone also provide recording and
rehearsal facilities, PA hire, mastering and design services, as well as
organising live events in Bath and Bristol, and occasionally further
afield. Refer to entries in appropriate sections for further information.

Hope Artist Management
Loft 5, The Tobacco Factory, Raleigh Road, Southville, Bristol, BS3 1TFA
tel: 0117 953 5566
fax: 0117 953 7733
email: info@hoperecordings.com
web: www.hoperecordings.com
contact: Matt Rickard
genre: All Music Types Accepted
info: Send demos to the address above. Part of the Hope
Music Group.

Madrigal Music
Guy Hall, Awre, Gloucester, GL14 1EL
tel: 01594 510 512
fax: 01594 510 512
email: artists@madrigalmusic.co.uk
web: www.madrigalmusic.co.uk
contact: Nick Ford
genre: Singer-Songwriter/Rock/Indie
info: Send demo to address above. Madrigal do accept
unsolicited material and will listen to everything sent to them. Release-
quality finished masters preferred. Material can be returned if an SAE
is included. No MP3s via email. Madrigal attend all international music
conferences and are constantly seeking new and exciting acts.

MWM Music Management
11 Great George Street, Bristol, BS1 5RR
tel: 0117 929 2393
fax: 0177 929 2696
email: office@mwmuk.com
contact: Craig Williams
genre: All Music Types Accepted
info: Send demos, biography and press to the address above.
Follow with a phone call.

PVA Ltd.
2 High Street, Westbury On Trym, Bristol, BS9 3DU
tel: 0117 950 4504
fax: 0117 959 1786
email: enquiries@pva.ltd.uk
web: www.pva.ltd.uk
contact: Pat Vincent
genre: All Music Types Accepted
info: Call or email Pat with details of your act. Send demo on
request.

Soundcity UK Artiste Agency
Somerset
tel: 07888 776 831
email: joseph@scukagency.co.uk
web: www.scukagency.co.uk
contact: Joseph Wicks
genre: Urban
info: Artist agency and management company. Send MP3
demos via email to the above address.

Sprint Music Ltd.
High Jarmany Farm, Jarmany Hill, Barton St. David, Somerton,
Somerset, TA11 6DA
tel: 01458 851 010
fax: 01458 851 029
email: info@sprintmusic.co.uk
web: www.sprintmusic.co.uk
contact: John Ratcliff
genre: All Music Types Accepted
info: Email John at the address above with details of your act.
Send demo on request.

Sugar Shack Management
PO Box 73, Fishponds, Bristol, BS16 7EZ
tel: 0117 985 5092
fax: 0117 985 5092
email: mike@sugarshackrecords.co.uk
web: www.sugarshackrecords.co.uk
contact: Mike Darby
genre: Rock/Guitar Based
info: Send 3 track CD to the address above. See also listing for
Sugar Shack Records in the relevant section.

the|unsigned|guide

House Music has a new home

Player Management are proud to present their **EXCLUSIVE** talent rosta for 2005

Artists . Jamie Lewis . DJ Disciple . Audiowhores
Paul Farris . Joey Musaphia . Soul Avengerz
Richard Earnshaw . SUMO

Record Label Tours
Refunkt Records
Look At You Records
Purple Music
Player Records

Non-exclusive Vocalists
Lisa Millett
Michelle Weeks
Shena
Tanya Dankner

Round Foundry Media Centre
Foundry Street . Leeds . LS11 5QP
www.player-management.com

tel . +44 870 4202360
fax . +44 870 4202370
ben@player-management.com

player management

Visible Underground Ltd.
85 Cornbraish Rise, Hilperton, Trowbridge, BA14 7TS
tel: 07974 956 228
email: ben@visibleunderground.co.uk
web: www.visibleunderground.co.uk
contact: Ben Hawkes
genre: Rock/Post Hardcore/Folk
info: Artist management company formed in 2002 to look
after Rock act Decora. Currently manage Decora and The Panic, as
well as advising The Smears and Mea Culpa. Only take submissions
from acts who are well developed (at least 3 years experience, over
100 shows played). Also looking for talented Singer-Songwriters. Offer
honest feedback. Visible Underground are also part of Secret Tree, an
online retailer of Alternative music who are looking to release unsigned
artists under the Visible Noise banner.

Xtreme Music Production
4-7 Forewoods Common, Holt, Wiltshire, BA14 6PJ
tel: 01225 782 984/07909 995 011
email: info@xtrememusic.co.uk
web: www.xtrememusic.co.uk
contact: George Allen
genre: Rock/Singer-Songwriter/Pop-Rock
info: Artist and tour management services for Rock music.
Clients during 2004-05 include The Magic Numbers, The Operation,
The Mission, Chikinki and Iain Archer. Send CD, biography and
pictures to above address.

YORKSHIRE

Adastra
2 Star Row, North Dalton, Driffield, East Yorkshire, YO25 9UX
tel: 01377 217 662
fax: 01377 217 754
email: adastra@adastra-music.co.uk
web: www.adastra-music.co.uk
contact: Chris Wade
genre: Folk/Roots/World
info: Send demo to address above. Adastra will send a letter
to confirm receipt of material.

Cultural Foundation
Dalehead, Rosedale, North Yorkshire, YO18 8RL
tel: 01751 417 147
fax: 01751 417804
email: info@cultsound.org
web: www.cultfound.org
contact: Peter Bell
genre: All Music Types Accepted
info: The Cultural Foundation is a music collective offering
music performance, production, promotion, record company and
distribution, management, publishing, workshop, film and video
production, equipment resource and advice services.

Full 36ixty
PO Box 902, Suite 306, Bradford, BD1 9AH
tel: 07792 499 198
email: info@full360ltd.com
web: www.full360ltd.com
contact: Katherine Canoville
genre: All Music Types Accepted
info: Full 360 manage Serotonin and Ko-d-Fy. Call Katherine
with details of your act. Send demo on request.

Krack Music Management
East Cowick, East Yorkshire
tel: 01405 861 124
email: info@krack.prestel.co.uk
web: www.jonlacey.co.uk
contact: Alan
genre: All Music Types Accepted
info: Contact Alan with details of your act. Send demo on
request.

Mal Spence Management
Cherry Tree Lodge, Copmanthorpe, York, Yorkshire, YO23 3SH
tel: 01904 703 764
fax: 01904 702 312
email: sspence@aol.com
web: www.sugarstar.com
contact: Mal Spence
genre: All Music Types Accepted
info: Send email to Mal at the address above with details of
your act. Send demo on request.

Moneypenny Management

The Stables, Westwood House, Main Street, North Dalton, Driffield, East Yorkshire, YO25 9XA
tel:	01377 217 815
fax:	01377 217 754
email:	nigel@adastra-music.co.uk
web:	www.adastra-music.co.uk/moneypenny
contact:	Nigel Morton
genre:	Rock/Americana/Folk/Classic Rock/World
info:	Contact Nigel with details of your act. Send demo on request. Moneypenny currently look after Eliza Carthy and also run a booking agency with a comprehensive list of clients. See website for details.

Northern Music Company

Cheapside Chambers, 43 Cheapside, Bradford, Yorkshire, BD1 4HP
tel:	01274 306 361
fax:	01274 730 097
email:	info@northernmusic.co.uk
web:	www.northernmusic.co.uk
contact:	Andy Farrow
genre:	Rock
info:	Send demo on CD or cassette with biog. Mainly interested in Rock orientated material.

Player Records & Management

Round Foundry Media Centre, Foundry Street, Leeds, LS11 5QP
tel:	0870 420 2360
fax:	0870 420 2380
email:	info@player-management.com
web:	www.player-management.com
contact:	Andy Benge
genre:	House
info:	Artists and DJs can send demos on DAT, MD or CD to the address above. Remixes can also be submitted.

Zoof Management

6 Hollins Close, Stannington, Sheffield, S6 5GN
tel:	07891 184 267
email:	simon@zoofmanagement.com
web:	www.zoofmanagement.com
contact:	Simon Pursehouse
genre:	Alternative/Acoustic/Rock/Indie
info:	Management and promotions company. Run 'Quids In' night in Liverpool showcasing new music. Send demo to the above address.

Badger Management

Belfast
email:	steve@badger-management.com
web:	www.badger-management.com
info:	Currently manage Duke Special, Edgeweather and The Amazing Pilots.

Bigjolly Management

30 Irish Street, Downpatrick, County Down, BT30 6BP
tel:	02844 615 613
fax:	02844 617 411
email:	damian@bigjolly.co.uk
web:	www.bigjolly.co.uk
contact:	Damian McKee
genre:	Metal
info:	Send 3 tracks, a photo and biography to Damian. Inclusion of any DVD footage would also be useful.

Sean Paul Curry

10 Holyhill View, Enniskillen, County Fermanagh
email:	greenshampy@yahoo.com
genre:	Rock
info:	Currently manages local act. Also promotes gigs in the area. See listing in Promoters section for further details. Send demo via email or post to the above address.

Dead Anyway

4 Springfield Gardens, Aberdeen, AB15 7RX
tel:	07959 595 845
email:	info@deadanyway.com
contact:	Greig Robertson
genre:	Alternative Rock/Indie/Metal
info:	Contact Dead Anyway with details of your act. Send demo on request. They also run a promotion company and are always looking for exciting talent for gigs in the area.

Freedag Artist Management
39 Palmerston Place, Edinburgh, EH12 5AU
tel:	0131 202 6236
fax:	0131 202 6238
email:	talent@freedagmusicgroup.com
contact:	David Murray
genre:	Alternative/Indie/Acoustic
info:	Send demos,maximum of 5 tracks, to the above address.

Alternatively, email MP3s with a biog and a photo. Freedag would prefer bands who are based in Scotland, but are willing to listen to anyone in the UK. All demos will be listened too.

GR Management Ltd.
974 Pollokshaws Road, Glasgow, G41 2HA
tel:	0141 632 1111
email:	info@grmanagement.co.uk
contact:	Rab Andrews
genre:	All Music Types Accepted
info:	Send demo, picture and biography (maximum 1 page) to address above.

Hot Rock Productions
29 Echline Drive, South Queensferry, Edinburgh, EH30 9UX
tel:	07960 344 276
email:	louise@hotrockproductions.co.uk
web:	www.hotrockproductions.co.uk
contact:	Louise Holland
genre:	Indie/Rock
info:	Run live music events at venues across central Scotland and manage a wide range of DJs and Indie Rock bands. Send a 3 track demo with biog and photo to the above address.

No Half Measures Ltd.
Studio 19, St. George's Studios, 93-97 St. George's Road, Glasgow, G3 6JA
tel:	0141 331 9888
fax:	0141 331 9889
email:	info@nohalfmeasures.com
web:	www.nohalfmeasures.com
contact:	Suzanne Lochhead
genre:	Rock/Pop
info:	Send demo to address above.

Page 6 Music
Rustic Cottage, Culbokie, By Dingwall, IV7 8JY
tel:	01349 877 449
email:	cara@page6music.com
web:	www.page6music.com
contact:	Cara Anderson
genre:	All Music Types Accepted
info:	Currently represent both signed and unsigned bands from Dundee, Glasgow, Edinburgh and the Highlands. Send demo FAO Cara Anderson to the above address. Page 6 Music also offer PR services. See entry in relevant section for further details.

Urban Promotions (East)
Dundee
tel:	07986 151 006
email:	angie@urbanpromotions.co.uk
web:	www.urbanpromotions.co.uk
contact:	Angie
genre:	Hip-Hop/R&B/Dancehall
info:	Represent Urban artists, DJs, rappers and dancers. Call or email the above address for details of demo submission. Also put on showcase event 'Make It Rough'.

WALES

Angst Management Ltd.
104a Cowbridge Road East, Canton, Cardiff, CF11 9DX
tel:	02920 394 200
fax:	02920 372 703
email:	allwyd@aol.com
contact:	Alun Llwyd
genre:	All Music Types Accepted
info:	Send demo to address above.

Bastard Management
Cefn Coch Gwyllt, Cemmaes Road, Machynlleth, Powys, SY20 8LU
email:	bastardmgt@hotmail.com
contact:	Alex Holland
genre:	Dub/Urban
info:	Specialise in Dub and Urban music. Send demo to address above. Bastard Management also manage the new Roots Stage at Glastonbury.

Fried Egg Studios
6 Blandy Terrace, Nantymoel, Bridgend, CF32 7NR
tel: 07970 277 035/01656 841 885
email: chris@friedeggstudios.com
web: www.friedeggstudios.com
contact: Chris Williams
genre: Rock
info: Send demos on CD to the address above. Fried Egg Studios also provide recording, mastering and songwriting services as well as practise rooms. See the Recording Studios listings for more details.

MJM Agency
6 Bryn Coed, St. Asaph, Denbighshire, North Wales, L117 0DQ
email: mike@mjmagency.co.uk
web: www.mjmagency.co.uk
contact: Mike Jones
genre: All Music Types Accepted
info: Contact Mike with details of your act. Send demo on request. MJM also run successful unsigned band nights in the local area, see website for details.

Money Talks Management Co
PO Box 5, Cwmbach, Whitland, SA34 0WA
tel: 01994 484 466
email: cadillacranch@telco4u.net
web: www.nikturner.com
contact: Sid Money
genre: Hip-Hop/Funk/World/Jazz/Latin/Fusion
info: Call or email with details of your act. Send demo on request. Also run 2 record labels (Riddle Records and Nikt Records), Money Talks Agency, Riddle Hallucinations Video Productions, and Cadillac Ranch Recording Studios. See entries in relevant sections for further details.

Rhys Mwyn Management
Uned 19, Galeri, Doc Victoria, Gwynedd, LL55 1SQ
tel: 01286 685 215
fax: 01286 671 553
email: rhys@rhysmwyn.com
web: www.rhysmwyn.com
contact: Rhys Mwyn
info: Successful music manager. Deals with Welsh and English language acts. Current roster includes Phil Bates (ELO 2) TNT, Lisa Pedrick and Cyffro.

Rock'n'Roll Enterprises
21 Grove Terrace, Penarth, South Glamorgan, CF64 2NG
tel: 02920 704 279
fax: 02920 709 989
email: barrettrocknroll@amserve.com
contact: Paul Barrett
genre: Rock 'n' Roll
info: Specialises in 50s and early 60s style bands.

Silverword Music Group: Kevin King Management
16 Limetrees, Llandattock, Crickhowell, Powys, NP8 1LB
tel: 01873 810 142
fax: 01873 811 557
email: silverwordgroup@aol.com
web: www.silverword.co.uk
contact: Kevin King
genre: MOR/Pop/Hip-Hop/Jazz/Rock
info: Send demo to the address above. Artist representation from the Silverwood Music Group also incorporates a record company, see relevant section for details. They also run a distribution company (SMG Distributions). See website for details.

Smooch Management
2 Seabank Road, Colwyn Bay, LL28 4BT
tel: 07788 181 750
email: geoffpburke@yahoo.com
contact: Geoff Burke
genre: Pop/Dance/Jazz/Funk/Soul/R&B
info: Email Geoff with details of your act. Follow with demo upon request. Any music with commercial potential considered. Looking for acts from London, North Wales and North West regions. Smooch also run a record label. See entry in relevant section for details.

Section 6
Industry Organisations

the|unsigned|guide

INDUSTRY ORGANISATIONS

6.1 Industry Organisations Foreword

The Industry Organisations section of this directory includes relevant contact details for some of the more general music industry enquiries you may have. From AIM to The MCPS-PRS Alliance, each organisation has a listing which as well as providing an address, telephone number, website and email details, contains basic information on the type of the services each organisation provides.

Musicians' Union

The MU was founded over 100 years ago in 1893 and has a proud history of service to musicians of all types. The music profession and the music industry have seen constant evolution and change over the years and the Musicians' Union has evolved and changed with them, with one aim in view - to offer you the musician a better service and a democratic organisation. You can help to shape its policies but only if you are a member.

The Rock and Pop world is not just about records and videos. The most successful bands in the long term are still those who excel in a live situation and record companies are all too aware of this. In order to polish up your act you need as many of those vital early local gigs as possible. It's a sad fact that many young bands just starting up fail to get themselves a fair deal in the pubs and clubs. By joining the Musicians' Union you can actively campaign from within our ranks to change this situation.

The MU believe that without a healthy grass roots scene the music and record industries will stagnate and suffer in the long term. We have 100 branches throughout the country, and the best way to ensure that your town or city provides a vibrant local launch pad for new bands is to get along to regular branch meetings and use them as a way of developing strategies to persuade local publicans and club owners to promote more live music with fair pay and conditions.

Visit **www.musiciansunion.org.uk**

Releasing Your Own Product

The Musicians' Union have compiled the following information with regards to releasing your own product. It is an ideal example of how this section can be applied in a wider industry context.

Increasingly, bands and artists are recognising the promotional value of releasing their own product. This section is designed to give some basic advice on how to go about it, and who to contact. The following industry organisations exist to control the distribution of monies to the relevant parties.

Mechanical Copyright Protection Society (MCPS)

Acting on behalf of its composer, songwriter and music publisher members, MCPS negotiates agreements with those who wish to record music, ensuring the copyright owners are rewarded for the use of their music. The Society collects and then distributes the "mechanical" royalties generated from the recording of music onto many different formats, including CDs, cassettes, videos, audio visual and broadcast material, including online.

Every time a musical work is copied, or a copy of the work is issued to the public, a mechanical royalty is generated. This includes not only the recording of a song for sale on a sound carrier (e.g. CD, cassette etc) but also where music is copied into TV and radio programmes, feature films, TV and radio commercials, videos, the internet, retail multimedia, premium products (e.g. a free CD with a newspaper) and mobile phone ring-tones.

MCPS levies a variety of commission fees, depending on the source of the royalties and the administration necessary to process the royalties.

Visit **www.mcps.co.uk**

Performing Right Society (PRS)
PRS works for its songwriter, composer, and music publisher members, to license the public performance and broadcast of their copyright works. The Society collects the license fees, assembles information about the usage of works and then distributes royalties to members.

As well as licensing all terrestrial, cable and satellite broadcasters, and the use of music online, PRS also has about 40 different tariffs for the live or recorded public performance of music in venues including concert halls, pubs, clubs, factories, shops, offices and even aircraft and zoos.

PRS is a non-profit making organisation with over 40,000 members. Through affiliation with other rights societies overseas it represents approaching a million copyright owners around the world and about 10 million registered musical works.

Visit **www.prs.co.uk**

Although remaining separate in terms of income, constitution, membership and guardianship of separate rights, MCPS and PRS are now working together as an operational alliance; The MCPS-PRS Alliance.

Visit **www.mcps-prs-alliance.co.uk**

 MCPS and PRS: Frequently Asked Questions

Q. I'm in the process of sending my songs to various record labels. Do I need to be a member of PRS or MCPS at this stage?

A. No. The time to consider PRS membership is when one of your songs has been broadcast, performed live, or played in public. Similarly you should consider MCPS membership when one of your songs has been released by a record company (other than your own) and not assigned to a publisher.

Q. I've just produced some tracks for my friend's band. Should I join either MCPS or PRS?

A. No. Membership of both societies is only relevant to the composers and songwriters of the music. However, if a writer agrees that your production work justifies a writing credit on their songs, then you should consider applying.

Q. As a PRS member can I get any money for all the gigs my band play in small pubs?

A. Yes. Under the PRS' Gigs and Clubs scheme if you perform a core set of songs at 10 or more gigs in any 12 month period you could be eligible for a payment.
For more info simply visit www.prs.co.uk/gigs-clubsscheme or tel: 020 7306 4822

Q. Someone has released a cover of my song on their album; am I likely to receive a royalty?

A. If it's a commercial release, mechanical royalties will be due for the use of work. You will need to have the work published by an MCPS member or become a writer member of MCPS in order to receive these royalties.

Q. What sort of permission do I need if I want to sample someone else's song on my recording?

A. Before sampling another songwriter's work you must obtain permission from both the copyright owner (either the publisher or the actual song writer) and the sound recording owner (usually the record company).

Q. I'm putting out my own 4 track single but don't know where I stand with regard to the MCPS?

A. You will need to submit an application for license (AFL) to the MCPS. This is necessary since pressing plants only manufacture once they have seen an MCPS license. Provided the songs are not written or published by a MCPS member you will be issued with a notification of no claim.

Q. I've just joined a covers band which has been offered a monthly residency at our local pub. Can we earn any money by becoming PRS members?

A. No. Any royalties generated by these performances would be distributed to the original songwriters/ publishers of the works being played.

Q. All the members of my band contribute to the writing of our songs. Is it possible for us to join as a group, or must we join individually?

A. In respect of both MCPS and PRS, each song-writer within a band needs to apply for individual membership.

Q. How much does it cost to join MCPS and PRS?

A. Current admission fees are:
- MCPS: £50 for writer membership/£50 for publisher membership.
- PRS: £100 for writer membership/£400 for publisher membership.

Q. Is there an annual fee?

A. Neither society charges an annual membership fee.

For more information about either society, telephone 020 7306 4805 or visit www.prs.co.uk or www.mcps.co.uk.

PAMRA
(Performing Artists' Media Rights Association)
PAMRA is the performers' collecting society which was set up to administer the new statutory right of performers to receive equitable remuneration for the exploitation of their commercially published sound recordings. Broadcasters and venue operators pay when they use recordings in their broadcasts or in public performances and P@MRA collects and distributes this money to performers whose recordings have been used. Performers who wish to join P@MRA should have contributed to a recorded performance and need to complete a membership application form. Membership is free, although a minimal charge will be made on all payments distributed to performers in order to cover the cost of P@MRA's administration.

P.P.L (Phonographic Performance Ltd.)
P.P.L. is a membership organisation representing record companies and issues licenses for the broadcast of commercial audio recordings.

In the Mastering & Duplication section (Music Services/Retail) of The Unsigned Guide there are a list of companies which may be able to offer you either all or any of the various stages involved in product manufacture. This enables you to decide whether or not you wish to have the whole process handled by one company or to shop around for the best deal available for each stage. Timing is very important, remember that the preparation of the art-work and the printing of sleeves and labels can take at least a couple of weeks so allow plenty of time for this stage. You should aim to have your product available to journalists, DJs (and anyone else who may be able to help promote your releases) at least

four weeks before the release date so as to create a healthy demand on its week of release. The release should coincide with some live shows to maximise the exposure and hopefully allow the journalists who like the product a chance to review the band live.

Distribution
Unless you or your band have already established a substantial market for your music you will find it hard to secure a national distribution deal. However, if your promotional campaign starts to take off you may interest one of the smaller distribution companies in placing the product in the shops. On average the charge for this service is between 25% and 30% of the dealer price. If you are unable to interest a distribution company then consider another mail-out to key record shops around the country, sending them a couple of free copies and a contact phone number for obtaining more. This way you are operating your own distribution.

When preparing the budget for product release, remember that the success of the product very much depends on the level and efficiency of your promotion. You will need to plan a mail-out to at least 200 DJs and journalists and the cost of packaging and postage for this mail-out needs to be calculated in advance. If you can afford to hire a plugger to plug your release to the radio stations or a press officer to push for press reviews and interviews, shop around, as the costs and the results can vary greatly.

6.3 INDUSTRY ORGANISATIONS

Agents' Association
54 Keyes House, Dolphin Square, London, SW1V 3NA
tel: 020 7834 0515
fax: 020 7821 0261
email: association@agents-uk.com
web: www.agents-uk.com
info: Represents the interest of entertainment agents in the UK. The Agents' Association has a detailed code of conduct to which all its members must adhere.

Arts Council England (ACE)
14 Great Peter Street, London, SW1P 3NQ
tel: 0845 300 6200
fax: 020 7973 6950
email: enquiries@artscouncil.org.uk
web: www.artscouncil.org.uk
info: Arts Council England is the national development agency for the arts, investing in and funding projects run by individuals and groups. Information sheets regarding different services provided by the Arts Council England are available on the website above. The Arts Council national office is at 14 Great Peter Street, London, SW1P 3NQ or phone the above number.

Association of Festival Organisers
PO Box 296, Matlock, Derbyshire, DE4 3XU
tel: 01629 827 014
fax: 01629 821 874
email: info@folkarts-england.org
web: www.afouk.org
info: Folk Arts England is a national development agency for Folk, Roots, Traditional and Acoustic music in England. It is funded by the Arts Council and incorporates the Association of Festival Organisers, Folk Arts Network, Shooting Roots (youth project) and Direct Roots directory, the guide to Folk, Roots and related music and arts in the British Isles. Folk Arts England provides a voice for Folk art, promoting their growth, accessibility and development in England through provision of services in information, publishing, education, training, communications and marketing.

Association of Independent Music (AIM)
Lamb House, Church Street, Chiswick, London, W4 2PD
tel: 020 8994 5599
fax: 020 8994 5222
email: info@musicindie.com
web: www.musicindie.com
info: AIM promotes the interests of British independent record labels. Offers information, advice, representation and education to its members.

Association of Professional Recording Services (APRS)
PO Box 22, Totnes, TQ9 7YZ
tel: 01803 868 600
fax: 01803 868 444
email: info@aprs.co.uk
web: www.aprs.co.uk
info: APRS members include recording studios, post-production houses, mastering, replication, pressing and duplicating facilities, providers of education and training, audio engineers, manufacturers, suppliers and consultants. The aim of the society is to promote high standards in the audio industry and help professionals work together.

Association of United Recording Artists (AURA)
1 York Street, London, W1 6PA
tel: 0870 850 5200
fax: 0870 850 5201
email: office@aurauk.com
web: www.aurauk.com
info: AURA represents professional recording artists, performers and studio producers by acting as a collection society and working to maximise its members' income.

British Academy of Composers & Songwriters (BACS)
British Music House, 26 Berners Street, London, W1T 3LR
tel: 020 7636 2929
fax: 020 7636 2212
email: info@britishacademy.com
web: www.britishacademy.com
info: The British Academy of Composers & Songwriters is the recognised trade association for UK music writers. Their aim is to protect and increase the value of copyright, provide members with a range of services and benefits, campaign to raise the profile of composers and songwriters with key decision makers and with the public as a whole, and to provide support for those embarking upon their careers. The Academy runs the Ivor Novello Awards, the Gold Badge and the British Composer Awards.

Bwwritish Music Rights (BMR)
British Music House, 26 Berners Street, London, W1T 3LR
tel: 020 7306 4446
fax: 020 7306 4449
email: britishmusic@bmr.org
web: www.bmr.org
info: Promotes the interests of British music composers, songwriters and publishers through lobbying to UK government and EU institutions, education, PR and events.

British Phonographic Industry (BPI)
Riverside Building, County Hall, Westminster Bridge Road, London, SE1 7JA
tel: 020 7803 1300
fax: 020 7803 1310
email: general@bpi.co.uk
web: www.bpi.co.uk
info: The aim of the BPI is to promote and protect the British music industry by targeting piracy, ensuring their members' legal rights are upheld, and researching and publishing key statistics on the value of the UK record business.

Concert Promoters' Association (CPA)
6 St. Mark's Road, Henley On Thames, Oxon, RG9 1LJ
tel: 01491 575 060
fax: 01491 414 082
email: carolesmith.cpa@virgin.net
info: Organisation representing the interests of concert promoters of contemporary music. The association actively lobbies the Government and other industry bodies over issues relating to ticketing procedures, event security, e-touting, work permits, Health and Safety regulations, and licensing.

Department For Culture, Media & Sport
2-4 Cockspur Street, London, SW1Y 5DH
tel: 020 7211 6200
email: enquiries@culture.gov.uk
web: www.culture.gov.uk
info: UK government department responsible for museums, galleries and libraries, the built heritage, the arts, sport, education, broadcasting and the media and tourism, as well as the creative industries and the National Lottery. DCMS have also established the Live Music Forum, chaired by Feargal Sharkey, which aims to promote live music and evaluate the impact Licensing Act 2003 on the performance of live music. See above website for further details.

ASSOCIATION OF
INDEPENDENT MUSIC

The source of collective strength enabling independent music businesses to flourish.

- The Association of Independent Music is a non-profit-making trade organisation for independent record companies and distributors in the UK.
- AIM has over 750 members, representing 25% of the UK market, across all musical genres and all sizes of company.
- AIM collectively promotes the use of its members' music on the best commercial terms.
- AIM offers support, advice, information and resources to help you run, fund and sustain your business and trade internationally.

AIM ensures that independent record companies have a voice – your issues represented to UK government, EU decision makers and the music industry establishment.

AIM Members receive lots of benefits, including:

- **Regular email updates:** on essential issues and diary dates and an information packed website
- **E-Book:** with comprehensive advice on running an independent label: The 'AIM guide to Survival and Success in the Music Business' free to members - or available to buy for £10.00.
- **Free online email advice:** Dr John's legal surgery, Dr Geek technical tips & Dr Bean for accountancy.
- **Access to private E-mail rings**: ask questions on international and marketing issues - other record companies will reply and AIM will share the responses.
- **Introductory meeting:** when you join: to help you make the most of AIM.
- **Monthly seminars and networking events**: "Big Wednesday's" in London on topics including licensing, new media, contracts, design, studios, distribution fair, radio – and events around the UK free to members or £20.00 per meeting to non-members.
- **Introductions to key service providers:** CD pressing, legal, financial, travel, pensions and more.
  Discounts on UK and international trade fairs: including Midem, Popkomm, In The City, Musicworks & SXSW – we also offer advice on travel grants and how to work these events.
- **Musicindie's collectively negotiated licenses for new media deals**: you can opt in to deals with O2, OD2, Sonet and others to get your music on mobile and internet platforms and earn revenue.
- **Representation of your company's business issues:** to PPL, MCPS, MU, Equity, Radio and TV music users, and the UK and EU government to ensure a level playing field of access and fair deals for the independents.
- **Mentoring scheme** to help support your development, and a **work experience scheme** that brings music business students into independent labels.
- **International market access**: through trade fairs, sales trips, market research and international collaboration – target territories include USA and the Far East.

Want to access the UK independent record sector but not a label or distributor?

Our **'Friends of AIM'** scheme enables manufacturers, printers, e-commerce companies and other music business services to access the independent sector and expand their business.

TO JOIN AIM
Please go to our website http://www.musicindie.org to download membership application forms, or to read more about the costs and benefits of joining AIM.

Association of Independent Music Ltd
Lamb House, Church Street, Chiswick, London W4 2PD
T 020 8994 5599   **F** 020 8994 5222   **E** info@musicindie.com **W** www.musicindie.org
Registered in England and Wales Company number: 3685877 Registered office: Second Floor, Quadrant House (Air Street Entrance), 80-82 Regent Street, London W1B 5RP

Drake Music Project
Deptford Albany, Douglas Way, Deptford, London, SE8 4AG
tel: 020 8692 9000
fax: 020 8692 3110
email: info@drakemusicproject.org
web: www.drakemusicproject.org
info: Works with disabled musicians through assistive technology and enables anyone who wishes to perform music through a variety of means.

EQ
Suite E229, Dean Clough, Halifax, HX3 5AX
tel: 01422 381 618
email: hello@thinkeq.org.uk
web: www.thinkeq.org.uk
info: EQ strive to increase diversity and equality within the creative industry. Check the website for details of their current projects.

The Guild Of International Songwriters & Composers
Sovereign House, 12 Trewartha Road, Praa Sands, Penzance, Cornwall, TR20 9ST
tel: 01736 762 826
email: songmag@aol.com
web: www.songwriters-guild.co.uk
contact: Carol Jones
info: The Guild Of International Songwriters & Composers offers advice, guidance, assistance, copyright protection, information and services to its members. Members include songwriters, composers, lyricists, poets, independent record companies, music publishers and studio owners. Also associated with many publishing and record companies. The Guild has been publishing 'Songwriting and Composing' magazine since 1986.

Incorporated Society Of Musicians
10 Stratford Place, London, W1C 1AA
tel: 020 7629 4413
fax: 020 7408 1538
email: membership@ism.org
web: www.ism.org
info: The UK's professional association for musicians. Aims to promote the art of music, protect the interests of professional musicians, and raise standards within the industry. The association provides advice on law, tax and career issues. Members are eligible for discounts on a range of instruments and equipment.

International Association of Entertainment Lawyers
3 Nobel Street, London, EC2V 7EE
email: info@iael.org
web: www.iael.org
contact: Duncan Calow
info: IAEL represents for lawyers involved in the music industry. Provides a specialist, international forum for the sharing of knowledge and experience of legal and commercial issues.

International Federation for the Phonographic Industry
5th Floor, 54-62 Regent Street, London, W1B 5RE
tel: 0207 878 7900
fax: 0207 878 7950
email: info@ifpi.org
web: www.ifpi.org
info: Represents the recording industry world wide. The priorities of the IFPI are to fight music piracy, promote fair market access and adequate copyright laws, develop the legal conditions and technologies for the industry to prosper in the digital era, and to promote the value of music to all sectors of the population.

International Festivals & Events Association
c/o Unit 7, Science Park, Howard Street, Sheffield, S1 1WB
tel: 0114 225 3434
fax: 0114 225 4038
email: office@ifeaeurope.com
web: www.ifeaeurope.com
info: Organisation created to bring together all those that are active in the cultural festival and event sector. Encourage the sharing of ideas and best practice to facilitate continued development and promote networking and international exchange.

Making Music
2-4 Great Eastern Street, London, EC2A 3NW
tel: 0870 903 3780
fax: 0870 903 3785
email: info@makingmusic.org.uk
web: www.makingmusic.org.uk
info: Making Music represents and supports amateur and semi-professional music groups of all genres throughout the United Kingdom. Provide a comprehensive range of artistic and administrative services and development and training opportunities. Making Music also lobbies on behalf of its members to national and local government and other agencies.

Mechnical Copyright Protection Society (MCPS)
29-33 Berners Street, London, W1T 3AB
tel: 020 7580 5544
fax: 020 7306 4455
email: info@mcps.co.uk
web: www.mcps.co.uk
info: The MCPS is concerned with collecting and distributing mechanical royalties (those from music recorded onto any physical format) to its music publisher and composer members. The MCPS and PRS have formed an alliance to make best use of their individual strengths. (MCPS-PRS Alliance).

Music For Youth
102 Point Pleasant, London, SW18 1PP
tel: 020 8870 9624
fax: 020 8870 9935
email: mfy@mfy.org.uk
web: www.mfy.org.uk
info: Educational charity for helping young individuals perform music at concerts and festivals. No specific courses but the opportunity to perform to a wide audience.

Music Industries Association
Ivy Cottage Offices, Finch's Yard, Eastwick Road, Great Bookham, Surrey, KT23 4BA
tel: 01372 750 600
fax: 01372 750 515
email: office@mia.org.uk
web: www.mia.org.uk
info: UK trade organisation that represents businesses selling musical instruments and associated products including retailers, manufacturers, publishers and importers.

Music Managers' Forum (MMF)
1 York Street, London, W1U 6PA
tel: 0870 850 7800
fax: 0870 850 7801
email: info@ukmmf.net
web: www.ukmmf.net
info: Promotes communication between music managers and other industry bodies and the government, as well as between managers themselves. The MMF is particularly concerned with manager and artist contracts, and redressing the balance between the artist and the music industry.

The Music Producers Guild
PO Box 32, Harrow, HA2 7ZX
tel: 020 7371 8888
fax: 020 7373 8887
email: office@mpg.org.uk
web: www.mpg.org.uk
info: The Music Producers Guild promotes and represents all individuals in the music production and recording professions, including producers, engineers, mixers, re-mixers and programmers.

Music Publishers Association (MPA)
6th Floor, British Music House, 26 Berner Street, London, W1T 3LR
tel: 020 7839 7779
fax: 020 7839 7776
email: info@mpaonline.org.uk
web: www.mpaonline.org.uk
info: The MPA site contains information on publishing, copyright infringement, sampling and careers in the music publishing sector. There is also a directory of members and information on how to join the MPA online.

Musicians' Union
60-62 Clapham Road, London, SW9 0JJ
tel: 020 7840 5534
fax: 020 7840 5599
email: see website for regional email addresses
web: www.musiciansunion.org.uk
info: Trade union representing interests of musicians. Members' benefits include free contract advice, careers service, legal service and competitive insurance rates. The National Office is at 60-62 Clapham Road, London, SW9 0JJ, telephone 0207 582 5566, fax 0207 582 9805, email info@musiciansunion.org.uk.

New Deal For Musicians
UK
tel: 0845 606 2626
web: www.scottishculture.co.uk or www.newdeal.gov.uk
info: New Deal gives people claiming benefits the help and support they need to look for work within the music industry, including training and job preparation. Offers one to one meetings with a Music Industry Consultant (MIC), chosen from a group of successful professionals currently working in the music industry, musicians and songwriters, artist managers, A&R executives, promoters, label owners, press and PR specialists, DJs, and producers. Provide support, practical help and up to date information, and will advise the best way to go about achieving your career ambitions.

Record labels - why you should join the BPI

We are the British record industry's trade association.

In addition to the work we do on behalf of the whole industry there are many benefits to membership, including:

Representation

- A seat at our table. From committee membership to standing for council, the BPI is your opportunity to influence your industry

- Direct access to the anti-piracy and legal teams for advice on piracy problems

- Access to blanket industry agreements, negotiated by the BPI on your behalf

- Greater industry involvement via events such as the BPI Annual Conference for Members and regular networking events

- Entry in BPI membership directory distributed to thousands of music business contacts domestically and worldwide

- Membership of BRIT Awards voting academy

Services

- BPI mailings to keep you in touch with current industry issues, developments, events and trade fairs

- Access to key international contacts at trade fairs and on bespoke organised events such as our Japan and SXSW programmes

- Regular seminars designed to help members do better business, such as the successful Getting Your Music Online series

- A copy of the BPI Statistical Handbook, access to market information report and information and assistance from the research department

- Significant savings on chart data

- Free use of BPI conference rooms for meetings and interviews

Any music company in the UK can take advantage of our services regardless of size. Membership starts at a mere £50 + 5% of PPL income. **Find out more at www.bpi.co.uk or call Jon Webster on 020 7803 1300**

Licensing sound recordings on behalf of 3,000 record company members and 30,000 performers

www.ppluk.com

The Official UK Charts Company
4th Floor, 58-59 Great Marlborough Street, London, W1F 7JY
tel: 020 7478 8500
fax: 020 7478 8519
email: info@theofficialcharts.com
web: www.theofficialcharts.com
info: Compiles the official UK music and retail charts including album and singles sales.

Performing Artists Media Rights Association (PAMRA)
3rd Floor, 161 Borough High Street, London, SE1 1HR
tel: 020 7940 0413
fax: 020 7407 2008
email: office@pamra.org.uk
web: www.pamra.org.uk
info: PAMRA distribute monies to qualifying performers for the broadcast of their recorded performances. The site contains details on membership criteria, information on how to claim royalties, and a section which links performers to recordings.

Performing Right Society (PRS)
29-33 Berners Street, London, W1T 3AB
tel: 020 7580 5544
fax: 020 7306 4455
email: info@prs.co.uk
web: www.prs.co.uk
info: The PRS collects revenue accrued from the public performance and broadcast of musical works in the UK and overseas. The money is distributed to the society's members who are the writers and publishers of music. The MCPS and PRS have formed an alliance to make best use of their individual strengths (MCPS-PRS Alliance).

Performing Right Society Foundation
29-33 Berners Street, London, W1T 3AB
tel: 020 7306 4044
fax: 020 7306 4814
email: info@prsf.co.uk
web: www.prsf.co.uk
info: The PRSF is a registered charity offering financial awards to organisations that encourage, promote and sustain music creation and its performance.

Phonographic Performance Ltd. (PPL)
1 Upper James Street, London, W1F 9DE
tel: 020 7534 1000
fax: 020 7534 1111
email: team@ukperformerservices.com
web: www.ppluk.com
info: Music industry organisation collecting and distributing airplay and public performance royalties in the UK on behalf of over 3,000 record companies and 30,000 performers.

Producers & Composers Of Applied Music
email: bobfromer@onetel.com
web: www.pcam.co.uk
info: Represents the writers and producers whose music is used in advertising, television programmes and other audio-visual media.

Production Services Association (PSA)
PO Box 2709, Bath, BA1 3YS
tel: 01225 332 668
email: via website
web: www.psa.org.uk
contact: Andy Lenthall
info: Represent freelance technical production personnel and service companies working in the entertainment industry.

Royalties Reunited
c/o PPL, 1 Upper James Street, London, W1F 9DE
tel: 020 7534 1166
email: team@royaltiesreunited.co.uk
web: www.royaltiesreunited.co.uk
info: Royalties Reunited aims to award airplay royalties to the recording artists, session musicians and backing vocalists who have earned it. If you have ever performed on a track that received airplay, you could be owed money. Check online at the address above. Royalties Reunited is a joint initiative of AURA, Equity, MPG, the Musicians' Union, PAMRA and PPL.

Society For The Promotion Of New Music
4th Floor, 18–20 Southwark Street, London, SE1 1TJ
tel: 020 7407 1640
email: spnm@spnm.org.uk
web: www.spnm.org.uk
info: SPNM aims to promote and advance the development of new music composed in the UK. The society is involved in presenting concerts, seminars, lectures and creative workshops. Also coordinate the 'New Adventures In Composition' programme for 16-19 year olds and selecting new works and composers for performance and promotion.

Youth Music
1 America Street, London, SE1 0NE
tel: 020 7902 1060
fax: 020 7902 1061
email: info@youthmusic.org.uk
web: www.youthmusic.org.uk
info: Nationwide charity set up in 1999 to provide high quality and diverse music making opportunities for up to 18 year olds. It targets young people living in areas of social and economic need who might otherwise lack opportunity, and predominantly supports activities which are held outside school hours.

6.4 REGIONAL ORGANISATIONS

EAST of ENGLAND

Amplifier
Amplifier Office, CSV Media Clubhouse, 120 Princes Street, Ipswich, IP1 1RS
tel:	01473 418 025
email:	info@amplifiersuffolk.co.uk
web:	www.amplifiersuffolk.co.uk
contact:	Richard Brown
info:	Amplifier has been set up to help young musicians in

the Suffolk area to learn about music, from playing, recording and stage technique to the actualities of working within the music industry. They run a wide range of workshops from songwriting and MCing to digital music composition.

Arts Development in East Cambridgeshire
Babylon Gallery, Waterside, Ely, Cambridgeshire, CB7 4AU
tel:	01353 669 022
fax:	01353 669 052
email:	info@adec.org.uk
web:	www.adec.org.uk
contact:	Jane Wilson
info:	ADEC organise and promote showcase gigs in the East

Cambridgeshire area, although they will accept demos and book bands from any location. They offer an equipment hire service and can also provide grants for instruments, specialised software and travel to and from gigs. Welcome grant applications from unsigned acts, although applicants for funding must live in the East Cambridgeshire area.

Community Music East
189 King Street, Norwich, NR1 2BR
tel:	01603 628 367
fax:	01603 767 863
email:	enquiries@cme.org.uk
web:	www.cme.org.uk
contact:	Sophie Brown
info:	Established in 1985, CME was developed to run music

workshops for a wide range of people within the community. They now run a variety of courses including songwriting, singing and music technology, many of which are free.

East Anglian Music Archive
53 Corbet Avenue, Sprowston, Norwich, NR7 8HS
tel:	01603 444 859/07941 957 541
email:	eama@eastzone.co.uk
contact:	Kingsley Harris
info:	Organisation established in 1982, dedicated to collecting

and preserving all music made in East Anglia from 1955 to current day. Bands can submit their work along with accompanying details, which will be published as part of 3 books cataloguing music from the region. Material is promoted to local magazines and venues. Currently have over 4,500 entries. £20 lifetime membership available which includes subscription to Eastzone magazine. Contact Kingsley for further information. See also listing for NR One Records in relevant section.

IAM (Initiative for Arts & Music)
tel:	07976 399 848
email:	stevelewis@yahoo.co.uk
contact:	Steve Lewis
info:	Based on a farm near Cambridge, IAM offer a wide

variety of services including mobile recording, video production services and tour buses for unsigned bands. Are particularly keen to hear from unsigned bands.

GREATER LONDON

The Band Agency
UK
email:	info@thebandagency.com
web:	www.bandagency.com/
info:	The Band Agency is a not-for-profit organisation created

with the aim of helping new music thrive, and generating opportunities for unsigned musicians through touring, education, record releases, industry interaction and media exposure. See entry in Promoters section for details of showcases and events organised by The Band Agency throughout the UK.

London Musicians' Collective
3.6 Lafone House, 11-13 Leathermarket Street, London, SE1 3HN
tel:	020 7403 1922
fax:	020 7403 1922
web:	www.l-m-c.org.uk
contact:	Ben Drew
info:	Charity and membership organisation devoted to

contemporary music. The collective organise tours, gigs, festivals, workshops and publish a magazine. They have equipment and a recording studio available to hire. For details of London Musicians' Collective radio station, Resonance FM, see listing in relevant section.

Making Music (The National Federation Of Music Societies)
2-4 Great Eastern Street, London, EC2A 3NW
tel:	0870 903 3780
fax:	0870 903 3785
email:	info@makingmusic.org.uk
web:	www.makingmusic.org.uk
contact:	Robin Osterley
info:	Not itself a collective, but an umbrella organisation that

represents, supports and lobbies on behalf of non-professional musician groups. The federation is accountable for some 150,000 music makers. They can inform members of opportunities, undertake fund raising, work with young people and much more.

Music Tank
University of Westminster, 115 New Cavendish Street, London, W1W 6UW
tel:	020 7915 5412
fax:	020 7911 5812
email:	info@musictank.co.uk
web:	www.musictank.co.uk
info:	Network run by the University of Westminster's Business

Development Unit and Commercial Music Department in collaboration with 14 industry bodies including Music Managers Forum, Music Publishers' Association and the Musicians' Union. Its aim is to create and sustain a 'knowledge network' that encourages adaptation of best practice, circulation of innovative ideas, new collaborations and evolution of creative ventures into professional success. Lots of good advice available on website.

Music Tree/Tribal Tree Music
66 Chalk Farm Road, London, NW1 8AN
tel:	020 7482 6945
email:	info@musictree.net
web:	www.musictree.net or www.tribaltreemusic.co.uk
info:	Camden based charities providing various programmes

and training courses, as well as forums, work experience, events, studio time, equipment, advice and funding. See also listing for Tribal Songs in Publishing Companies section.

OverTones
14 Lambs Conduit Passage, London, WC1R 4RH
tel: 020 7404 6006
fax: 020 7404 6060
email: lesley@overtones.co.uk
web: www.overtones.co.uk
contact: Lesley Wood, Lesley Willis
info: Overtones is one half music charity and one half
commercial studio. The two concerns overlap, enabling up and coming
musicians to record cheaply. They also offer a range of services,
information and advice, as well as working in conjunction with other
music organisations.

Sonic Arts Network
The Jerwood Space, 171 Union Street, London, SE1 0LN
tel: 020 7928 7337
email: info@sonicartsnetwork.org
web: www.sonicartsnetwork.org
contact: David Rogerson
info: Events, education and information resource aimed at
people with a 'sound as art' approach. Members can sell their work
through the website. They also work on commissions with visual artists
(including sound installations for galleries).

Vampire Music
20 Tanners Hill, Deptford, London, SE8 4JP
tel: 020 8691 6666
fax: 020 8692 9999
email: info@vampiremusic.co.uk
web: www.vampiremusic.co.uk
info: A music co-operative that provides high quality
affordable recording and rehearsal facilities. They have recently
relocated to a brand new purpose built music complex hosting a large
variety of up to date equipment and training facilities. Vampire Music
also incorporates music shop, mastering and duplication services,
as well as record label (MCL Records). There is a full programme of
training courses available at the centre. See entries in relevant sections
for details.

Birmingham Music Network
Project 1, Unit 502, The Greenhouse, Gibb Street, Birmingham, B9 4AA
tel: 0871 226 2725
email: info@birminghammusicnetwork.com
web: www.birminghammusicnetwork.co.uk
info: Set up to help musicians in the Birmingham area, with
a good list of resources on website including labels, management,
publishers, recording studios and booking agents. Also list of venues
and classified adverts including musicians wanted and available.

East Midlands Music Network (EMMNET)
Suite 2, Newton House, 38 Grantham Street, Lincoln, LN2 1LW
tel: 01522 510 073
fax: 01522 510 076
email: shelley@soundlincs.org
web: www.emmnet.org
contact: Shelley
info: EMMNET are a council funded body who exist to
support Contemporary Popular music and musicians in the East
Midlands. They provide an objective, supportive network between
unsigned bands and the music industry.

Fleet Arts
The Fleet, Belper, Derbyshire, DE56 1NU
tel: 01773 820 484
fax: 01773 820 484
email: julian@fleet-arts.org
web: www.fleet-arts.org
contact: Julian
info: Fleet Arts are a locally based and managed arts
organisation in the Derbyshire area, with 20 years of experience and
charitable status. They offer support and resources such as portable
lighting rigs and rehearsal spaces. Turn It Up, their music development
project works with young musicians by running workshops, recording
sessions and putting on gigs.

SoundLINCS
Suite 2, Newton House, 38 Grantham Street, Lincoln, LN2 1LW
tel: 01522 510 073
fax: 01522 510 076
email: info@soundlincs.org
web: www.soundlincs.org
contact: Shelley
info: SoundLINCS was formed to enhance, enable and
encourage music making throughout the county of Lincolnshire.
SoundLINCS have an equipment resource including instruments,
mainly percussion, a vocal PA and instrument amplifiers. These are all
available for hire when not being used in workshops. Can also assist
with funding and advice.

From Teeside with Love
Calvin House, Green Dragon Yard, Stockton, TS18 1AE
tel: 01642 633 817
email: info@ftwl.co.uk
web: www.ftwl.co.uk
info: FTwL is a not-for-profit organisation set up in 2000
to assist emerging musicians in the Teesside area. It aims to help
musicians to engage more efficiently with the industry. They also
organise showcases, CD releases, build websites and hold workshops
and seminars.

Generator
2nd Floor, Black Swan Court, 69 Westgate Road, Newcastle, NE1 1SG
tel: 0191 245 0099
email: mail@generator.org.uk
web: www.generator.org.uk or www.metamusic.org.uk
info: Generator, based in the North East of England, aims
to help small business projects to develop through the provision of
ongoing support, advice, events, activities and educational work. With
the Meta project, Generator has been given the role of helping other
regions develop their own organisations. It runs the first subsidised
promoter development scheme, in view of strengthening opportunities
for unsigned artists. Generator represents the grassroots music
sector on government bodies such as the Live Music and the Music
Education Forums. See the website for more information on Generator's
programme of work.

North East Music Network (NEMNET)
North East
email: info@northwestmusic.net
web: www.northeastmusic.net
contact: Russ Conway
info: NEMNET is a guide to the North East music industry,
with details of all the music-based activities and businesses in the
region. If you want to be more involved in the North-East regional
music scene, NEMNET is the place to find out about the help,
information and facilities which are available.

Studio 64
90 Corporation Road, Middlesbrough, TS1 2RE
tel: 01642 860 006
fax: 01642 860 006
email: info@studio64.org.uk
web: www.studio64.org.uk
info: Studio 64 is a not-for-profit organisation providing
many different services such as recording and rehearsal studios, CD
duplication, equipment hire and workshops in variety of music related
skills. They also put on events and have a music consultancy service
for advice on any part of the industry.

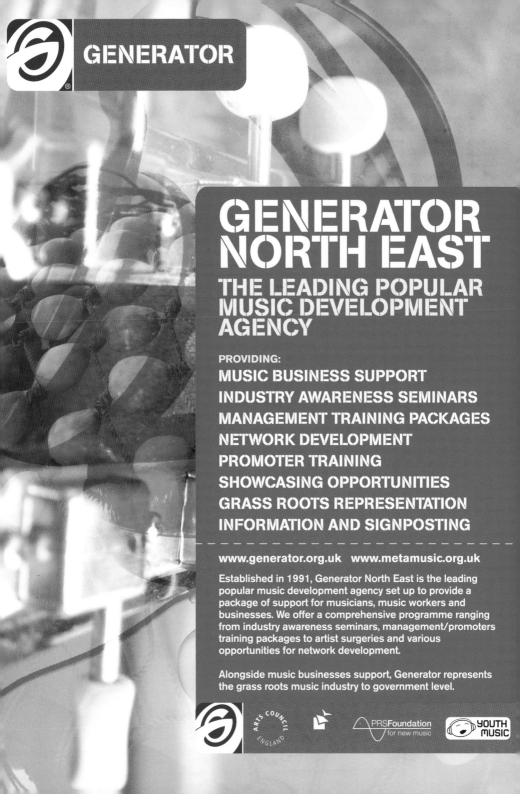

GENERATOR

GENERATOR NORTH EAST
THE LEADING POPULAR MUSIC DEVELOPMENT AGENCY

PROVIDING:

MUSIC BUSINESS SUPPORT

INDUSTRY AWARENESS SEMINARS

MANAGEMENT TRAINING PACKAGES

NETWORK DEVELOPMENT

PROMOTER TRAINING

SHOWCASING OPPORTUNITIES

GRASS ROOTS REPRESENTATION

INFORMATION AND SIGNPOSTING

www.generator.org.uk   www.metamusic.org.uk

Established in 1991, Generator North East is the leading popular music development agency set up to provide a package of support for musicians, music workers and businesses. We offer a comprehensive programme ranging from industry awareness seminars, management/promoters training packages to artist surgeries and various opportunities for network development.

Alongside music businesses support, Generator represents the grass roots music industry to government level.

ARTS COUNCIL ENGLAND   PRSFoundation for new music   YOUTH MUSIC

NORTHWEST

Banned Network
c/o DAN, The Library, Witton Street, Northwich, Cheshire, CW9 5DR
tel: 01606 415 97
fax: 01606 415 97
email: banned@danarts.demon.co.uk
web: www.banned.org.uk
contact: Nick
info: Established in 1993, Banned are part of DAN (Development of Arts in Northwich) and are involved in many aspects of the music scene including local gigs, battle of the bands, festivals, compilation CDs, guide books, music workshops and recording sessions.

Bolton Music Collective
Bolton, Lancashire
email: info@boltonmusic.co.uk
web: www.boltonmusic.co.uk
contact: Martin Marsell
info: Bolton Music Collective provide a message board for organising and promoting gigs in the local area, as well as a gig list for all live music in Bolton. They also have contact details on their website for bands, venues, music shops and recording and rehearsal places in the Bolton area, and have recently received a grant allowing them to stage regular live music every Saturday.

The Collective Circus
20 Camp Street, Maryport, Cumbria, CA15 6HP
tel: 01900 817 768
contact: David Millward
info: Formerly the 'Cumbri', they put on rural music workshops, gigs in village halls with young, up and coming bands. Also organise one day music festivals.

Denton Music Project
Tameside Young Peoples Centre, Duke Street, Denton, M34 2AN
tel: 0161 336 6615
email: musicmediaproject@yahoo.co.uk
web: www.tameside.gov.uk
contact: Dave Crawford
info: The project can provide rehearsal space, recording, tuition, information, advice and performance opportunities for young people.

EPN Live
Community Unit, Council Offices, 4 Civic Way, Ellesmere Port, CH65 0BE
tel: 0151 356 6704
fax: 0151 355 0508
email: samantha.lee@epnbc.gov.uk
web: www.epnbc.gov
contact: Samantha Lee
info: Covering the Ellesmere Port and Neston area. EPN Live organise band nights, provide equipment hire for under 19's, host workshops and seminars, open mic nights and live poetry.

Greater Manchester Music Action Zone (GMMAZ)
Sun House, 2-4 Little Peter Street, Knotts Mill, Manchester, M15 4PS
tel: 0161 834 2723
email: info@gmmaz.org.uk
web: www.gmmaz.org.uk
contact: Karen Jupp
info: GMMAZ was founded in 2001 with funding from Youth Music. Its remit is to deliver music workshops to socially excluded young people across the 10 boroughs of Greater Manchester. Workshops are diverse music styles from Hip-Hop to Chinese music and everything inbetween. In addition to the core workshop programmes, GMMAZ is committed to the continued professional, creative, personal and educational development of artists and young people. Also provide regular performance opportunities for artists and emerging artists, giving them the chance to showcase their musical talents.

The Hive Collective
The Hive, 12 Imperial Chambers, 62 Dale Street, Liverpool, L2 5SX
email: thehivecollective@hotmail.com
web: www.thehivecollective.co.uk
contact: Alex Spiers, Matthew Smith
info: The Hive Collective host a monthly evening called 'Hive' which comprises performed and recorded new Electronic music. They try to put on at least 2 live acts on each night, as well as the wide variety of recorded Electronic and Experimental music. It is run by DJs, producers and new music promoters and allows bedroom producers a chance to air their material. They meet in 'The Box' at the Film Art and Creative Technology (FACT) centre in Liverpool. Hive want to establish a community of like minded people through the collective. Check the website for more details.

The Joe Strummer Foundation For New Music (Strummerville)
Strummerville, PO Box 376, Salford, Manchester, M6 8WJ
tel: 0161 736 8817
fax: 0870 124 7254
email: info@strummerville.com
web: www.strummerville.com
info: The main aim of Strummerville is to provide rehearsal space and studio time to individuals, groups and organisations to enable the production of music by creative young people who would otherwise be prevented from doing so simply because they lack the necessary funds. See the website for details of news and events and to find out how to donate to Strummerville.

Lancashire Music Collective (LMC)
40 Sefton Gardens, Aughton, Ormskirk, Lancashire, L39 6RZ
email: peteguy3@hotmail.com
web: www.lancashiremusiccollective.com
contact: Pete Guy
info: Organise monthly gigs for members, and feature profile pages of local acts on the website. Have also released compilation 'Unsigned Magic Vol. 1'. For details of gigs and demo submission, see listing in Promoters section.

Lancaster Musicians' Co-operative
1 Lodge Street, Lancaster, LA1 1QW
tel: 01524 388 544
email: musiccoop@musiccoop.co.uk
web: www.musiccoop.co.uk
contact: Ian Dicken
info: A long established music collective who offer a variety of help to bands and musicians in the area. They provide such services as CD production, rehearsal and recording facilities and PA hire, as well as supporting the area's music scene in general.

Loose Music Collective
PO Box 67, Runcorn, WA7 4NL
tel: 01928 566 261
email: jaki.florek@virgin.net
web: www.loosemusic.org
contact: Jaki Florek
info: Put on various nights in the Widnes and Runcorn areas at venues ranging from pubs to arts centres. Loose Music Collective also run a recording studio and a magazine collective which publishes 'Feedback' magazine. Contact Jaki for details of meetings. See entries in relevant sections for further information on studios and gigs.

Manchester City Music Network (MNCN)
2nd Floor, Fourways House East, 57 Hilton Street, Manchester, M1 2EJ
tel: 0161 228 6160
fax: 0161 228 3773
email: network@manchester-music.org.uk
web: www.manchester-music.org.uk
info: MCMN aims to strengthen and develop the infrastructure of the independent music industry in Manchester, with the focus on economic rather than creative or artistic issues. The network offers free training via industry master classes, business support and advice. MCMN provides information on funding opportunities and holds a large database of Manchester music businesses, plus music industry directories and publications.

Music Development Agency (MDA)
70 Hope Street, Liverpool, L1 9EB
tel: 0151 709 2202
fax: 0151 709 2005
email: info@mmda.org.uk
web: www.mmda.org.uk
info: Organisation dedicated to maximising the contribution of the music sector to economic, cultural and social prosperity on Merseyside. MMDA publish a music business directory, and run several music programmes for the community. See website for details of current projects.

More Music In Morecambe
The Hothouse, 13-17 Devonshire Road, Morecambe, Lancashire, LA3 1QS
tel: 01524 831 997
fax: 01524 419 653
email: geoff@mormusic.net
web: www.mormusic.net
contact: Geoff Dixon, Pete Moser, Kathryn McDonald
info: A community music project with workshops for a broad range of people including a regular Thursday night, 'Stages' for young musicians. The group also have plans for forming a label to help those involved to release their own material.

The Realsounds Music Collective
336 Hungerford Road, Crewe, CW1 6HD
tel: 01270 583 426
contact: Fluffy
info: Formed by musicians in the Crewe and Nantwich areas. Dedicated to supporting local acts. Realsounds promote a variety of gigs and also liaise with other collectives.

INDUSTRY ORGANISATIONS

St. Helens Musicians' Collective
Citadel Arts Centre, Waterloo Street, St. Helens, Merseyside, WA10 1PX
tel: 01744 735 436
fax: 01744 762 309
email: info@citadel.org.uk
web: www.citadel.org.uk
contact: Tom Elwood
info: A collective operating out of the Citadel Arts Centre in St. Helens. They meet once every fortnight and put on various nights of musical entertainment at the venue. See listing in Promoters section for details of demo submission.

The Wigan Music Collective
19 Castlehouse Lane, Adlington, Lancashire, PR7 4DL
tel: 07092 376 067
email: charlie@wiganmusic.com
web: www.wiganmusic.com
contact: Charlie
info: Voluntary organisation dedicated to developing a healthy live music scene in the Wigan area. Promote various gigs, as well as coordinating an annual all day, open-air festival in June. Can provide a mobile recording service for local under-18 acts, which is available for hire with engineer, plus another PA available for hire. Contact Charlie by email or telephone about any of the above services. See listing in Promoters section for further details.

SOUTHEAST

MAP (Multi Arts Programme)
Witney Youth Centre, Witan Way, Witney, Oxton, OX28 4YA
tel: 01993 706 487
email: emma.titcomb@oxfordshire.gov.uk
web: www.map-project.co.uk
contact: Emma Titcomb
info: Multi Arts Programme offer music technology sessions plus other music based workshops. Facilities are for the use of 16 to 25 year olds who are out of education.

Music Fusion
Floor U2, Guildhall, Guildhall Square, Portsmouth, PO1 2AL
tel: 02392 834 144
fax: 02392 834 159
email: ymaz@portsmouthcc.gov.uk
web: www.musicfusion.org.uk
contact: Richard Wright
info: Set up for under-18's based in Fareham, Gosport, Havant and Portsmouth. Organise music making activities and training days.

SoundArt
SoundArt Studio, Unit E1, St. George's Business Park, Sittingbourne, ME10 3TB
tel: 07961 177 013
email: viv_soundart@hotmail.com
web: www.soundart.co.uk
contact: Viv
info: SoundArt promote live music and events and to create economic opportunity for musicians. They offer recording and rehearsal facilities, as well as promotional services. They also offer an 'all in' demo package including a band biog and 30 CD copies of a demo.

SOUTHWEST

The Basement Studio
2 Trenchard Street, Bristol, BS1 5AN
tel: 0117 934 9013
email: basementstudio@ukonline.co.uk
web: www.basementstudio.co.uk
contact: Troy
info: Charity working with young people aged between 13 and 19 years who are interested in music. Drop in to the studio or join up as a member. Activities include learning and rehearsing instruments and organising live events. Also run free courses. See listing in relevant section for details.

Black Heart Studios
30a Ashley Road, St. Pauls, Bristol, BS5 5NP
tel: 0117 924 6454
email: info@blackheartstudios.co.uk
web: www.blackheartstudios.co.uk
contact: Marcus Dahl
info: Black Heart Studios is an independent cooperative of musicians, artists and filmmakers, operating in the Bristol area. They aim to make original and interesting music, their philosophy being, 'Make it new, make it brave'.

CRAMP (Crediton Rural Arts & Music Project)
21 Redhills Close, Exeter, Devon, EX4 1SD
tel: 01392 668 824
email: info@crampdevon.org
web: www.crampdevon.org
contact: Marie Belsten
info: Community project for the Devon area. Organise workshops and seminars, as well as gigs and events in Crediton and surrounding areas approximately once a month. Resources on website including an online musicians directory. CRAMP also have a record label. See entry in relevant section for further details.

Future Sound of Exeter
c/o Exeter Phoenix Arts, Bradninch Place, Gandy Street, Exeter, EX4 3LS
tel: 01392 676 550
email: info@fsoe.org
web: www.fsoe.org
contact: Paul Gilblin
info: Created to promote innovative local music, particularly the exotic and electronic. They are particularly keen on the promotion of live music. For details to support local acts or demo submission, see listing in Promoters section. Also release compilations featuring local talent through their own label, SAS Records. Contact Paul for further details.

The Music Zone
Raglan Road, Brickfields, Plymouth, PL1 4NQ
tel: 01752 213 690
fax: 01752 509 888
email: info@themusiczone.org.uk
web: www.themusiczone.org.uk
contact: Ben Ballard
info: The Music Zone provide workshops, tuition and training to young people. They have a well equipped music centre with instruments, PAs and computers. They also have a multi track recording studio.

Platform One
48a Dodnor Lane, Newport, Isle of Wight, PO30 5XD
tel: 01983 537 550
fax: 01983 241 700
email: info@platformone.org
web: www.platformone.org
contact: David Pontin
info: Platform One is a not-for-profit organisation set up to create opportunities for young people (mainly 16 years and over) and the wider community in arts initiatives, with an emphasis on new technology. Run a selection of courses and workshops. See listing in Music Tuition and Training section for further details. Also have 3 professional recording studios, fully equipped rehearsal space and a specialist music technology suite.

The Soundhouse
Estover Community College, Miller Way, Estover, Plymouth, Devon, PL6 8UN
tel: 01752 207 920
fax: 01752 707 921
email: info@soundhouse.co.uk
web: www.soundhouse.co.uk
contact: Phil
info: The Soundhouse is a community music and arts project. Aims to open up opportunities for young people interested in music. Variety of courses.

YORKSHIRE

Cloth Cat Studio
127 Woodhouse Street, Charing Cross Shopping Centre, Leeds, LS6 2PY
tel: 0113 244 2773
email: mike@clothcatleeds.org.uk
web: www.clothcatleeds.org.uk
contact: Mike Jolly
info: Created to provide education and facilities to promote those who are involved in, or want to be involved in music and are on low incomes. For further information regarding courses, see listing in Music Tuition and Training section. Can offer advice on any aspects of the industry. Also run a weekly open mic night at the Primrose Pub in Leeds. Contact for details.

Cultural Foundation
Rosedale, North Yorkshire, YO18 8RL
tel: 0845 458 4699
fax: 01751 417 804
email: info@cultfound.org
web: www.cultfound.org
contact: Peter Bell
info: Organisation run by musicians, for musicians. Give local bands and artists a platform to promote their music. There is a lot of information and advice on the website which bands from any region should find useful.

Music Port
The Porthole, 16 Skinner Street, Whitby, YO21 3AJ
tel: 01947 603 475
email: info@whitbymusicport.com
web: www.musicport.fsnet.co.uk
contact: Jim Mclaughlin
info: Not-for-profit community organisation. Promoter the World Music Festival every October aswell as regular concerts at the Resolution Hotel in Whitby. Organise the Link listings for the North magazine in collaboration with Cultural Foundation. If you would like to play or want to be listed in the Link, send demos or details to the above address.

Wakefield Music Collective
The Gatehouse, Tootal Street, Wakefield, West Yorkshire, WF1 5JN
tel: 01924 290 315
email: info@themusiccollective.co.uk
web: www.themusiccollective.co.uk
contact: Helen
info: Voluntary organisation which exists to support live music in the Wakefield district and beyond. Organise the Clarence Park Festival; 2 days of free unsigned music held annually over last weekend in July. Encourage gig swaps between bands from all over UK. The website is a resource for all promoters, venues and bands in the Wakefield area. Friendly collective who are willing to assist with anything musical in the region. Feel free to contact by email.

NORTHERN IRELAND

The Cellars
Ballybean Activity Centre, Dundonald, County Down, BT16 2QEtel: 028 9048 6290
email: via website
fax: 028 9048 6290
web: www.thecellars.org.uk
info: Established in 1992, The Cellars have been involved with promoting music and media throughout the local community. It provides facilities for musicians of all ages including recording and video studios, as well as training in Sound Recording and Video Production, plus instrument tuition services.

Northern Ireland Music Industry Commission (NIMIC)
Unit 2, Northern Whig House, Bridge Street, Belfast, BT1 1LU
tel: 028 9092 3488
email: info@nimusic.com
web: www.nimusic.com
contact: Ross Graham
info: NIMIC supports artists, bands, technicians and business people working in any music genre at any level. It offers organisational and financial support for musicians and music events throughout Northern Ireland. NIMIC also offers free consultancy for anyone involved in any area of the music business.

SCOTLAND

Castlemilk Youth Complex
39 Arden Craig Road, Glasgow, Scotland, G45 0EQ
tel: 0141 630 0000
fax: 0141 630 0066
email: castleyouthcom@talk21.com
web: www.castlemilkyouthcomplex.co.uk
contact: Fraser Howat
info: An organisation run by young people for young people. Deal with all aspects of performing arts and promote lifelong learning. Music features heavily on the agenda and the complex provides a forum, rehearsal, recording and performance opportunities. Also provide tuition and resources for the area's youth. Facilities include an 80 seater theatre, digital recording and broadcasting. Run own label (Burning Haggis) and radio station (Cyclone FM). Contact for further details.

Dumfries & Galloway Arts Association
Gracefield, 28 Edinburgh Road, Dumfries, DG1 1JQ
tel: 01387 253 383
fax: 01387 253 303
email: info@dgaa.net
web: www.dgaa.net
contact: Jennifer Wilson
info: Independent arts development serving South West Scotland. A resource for information on regional arts and artists, organisations and contacts, and on fund-sourcing for regional arts activities.

Edinburgh Contemporary Arts Trust (ECAT)
16 Clerwood Gardens, Edinburgh, EH12 8PT
tel: 0131 539 8877
fax: 0131 539 2211
email: hazelsheppard@blueyonder.co.uk
web: www.edinburgh.gov.uk
contact: Hannah Sheppard
info: Presents a series of contemporary music concerts in Scotland. It supports emerging and established Scottish composers and presents their work in an international context. Details are available from the number above.

Foyer Music
Aberdeen Foyer, Marywell Street, Aberdeen, AB11 6JF
tel: 01224 252 894
fax: 01224 252 899
email: daves@aberdeenfoyer.com
web: www.foyerlive.com
contact: Dave Stewart
info: Foyer Music is the music department of a charity based in North East Scotland. Range of facilities available to under 25 year olds including newly furnished DJ room with both record and CD decks, a live room and a recording room. Run music related crash courses and can give advice on getting airplay and gigs.

HAIL Music
Hi Arts, Ballantyne House, 84 Academy Street, Inverness, IV1 1LU
tel: 07974 245 348
email: shaunarnold@hailmusic.com
web: www.hailmusic.com
contact: Shaun Arnold
info: HAIL (Highlands And Islands Labels) began in 2000 as a trade group representing the area's record labels but now works with a wide variety of artists, labels, promoters, distributors and those involved in the training and development of new talent. See the website for all the events and projects that they are involved with, including opportunities for unsigned bands and musicians.

Hi~Arts (Highland & Islands Arts)
Ballantyne House, 84 Academy Street, Inverness, IV1 1LU
tel: 01463 717 091
fax: 01463 720 895
email: info@hi-arts.co.uk
web: www.hi-arts.co.uk
info: Independent company established in 1990 to promote and develop the arts in the Highlands and Islands of Scotland.

New Music In Scotland (NEMIS)
2nd Floor, 22 Jamaica Street, Glasgow, G1 4QD
tel: 0141 221 6660
email: alec@nemis.org
web: www.nemis.org
contact: Alec Downie
info: NEMIS was established in 2001 as a music network for Scottish artists, labels, music businesses, media, recording studios, venues, radio, creatives and professional services within the industry in order to bring together those with a strong interest in the promotion and development of new music in Scotland.

South West Arts & Music Project Glasgow (SWAMP)
Swamp Creative Media Centre, 1 Barnbeth Road, Pollock, Glasgow, G53 5YR
tel: 0141 891 5564
fax: 0141 000 0000
email: info@swampglasgow.co.uk
web: www.swampglasgow.co.uk
contact: Andy Poline
info: Swamp deliver a range of musical education and leisure activities, including courses in sound engineering and tuition in a wide variety of musical instruments. They also offer access to recording and rehearsal facilities for up and coming bands and talented individuals.

WALES

Promo
Coal Exchange, Mount Stuart Square, Cardiff, CF10 5EB
tel: 02920 462 222
fax: 02920 450 475
email: info@promo-cymru.org
web: www.promo-cymru.org
contact: Marco Gil-Cervantes
info: Training, advice, business skills and funding for young people involved in the creative industries including visual artists, DJ collectives, event organisers and promoters, or just someone who feels that they have an idea that will bring something back into the Welsh social economy. Also have recording facilities. See entry in relevant section for details.

INDUSTRY ORGANISATIONS

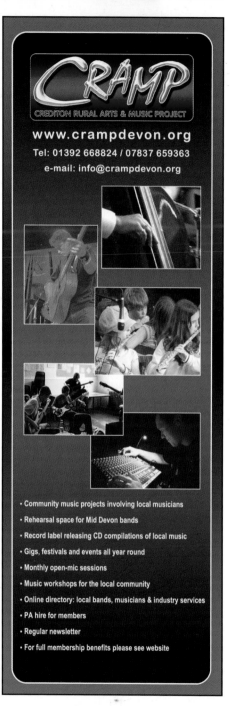

www.crampdevon.org

Tel: 01392 668824 / 07837 659363

e-mail: info@crampdevon.org

- Community music projects involving local musicians
- Rehearsal space for Mid Devon bands
- Record label releasing CD compilations of local music
- Gigs, festivals and events all year round
- Monthly open-mic sessions
- Music workshops for the local community
- Online directory: local bands, musicians & industry services
- PA hire for members
- Regular newsletter
- For full membership benefits please see website

Soundscape
tel:	01792 230 115
email:	info@sound-scape.org.uk
web:	www.sound-scape.org.uk
contact:	Boyd
info:	Soundscape is an organisation based in Swansea, Neath

and Port Talbot areas. Aims to support local unsigned acts and people wanting to get involved in music. Offers free advice and information on all aspects of the music industry. Can also assist with website design and have launched free scheme to host websites for unsigned acts. Soundscape website provides free publicity, comprehensive local links and news service. Also organise showcase events. Currently working with a South Wales arts organisation to organise 'The Gathering', a combined battle of the bands and industry training project which involves unsigned bands from South Wales.

Steer Multimedia Studios
New Road, Tairgwaith, Ammanford, SA18 1UP
tel:	01269 823 815
fax:	01269 825 687
email:	info@steerstudios.net
web:	www.steerstudios.net
contact:	Alud Owen-Jones
info:	An exciting and innovative community project which

has been developed in response to the needs of local young people. Steer consists of a community recording and design studio which offers training, recording and design services, location recording, alongside community music and multimedia projects with all types of groups and organisations.

TMPL Consultants
26 Mortimer Road, Pontcanna, Cardiff, CF11 9JZ
tel:	02920 256 350
fax:	02920 256 352
email:	pdcox@tmpl-oline.co.uk
web:	www.tmpl-online.co.uk
contact:	Peter Cox
info:	A Welsh based national management and training

organisation with offices in both Wales and England. A development and training company skilled in developing music and arts.

Tunetown
1 The Kings Way, Swansea, SA1 5JQ
tel:	01792 473 960
email:	enquiries@tunetown.org.uk
web:	www.tunetown.org.uk
contact:	Chris Woodman
info:	Established to create opportunities in music for the

people of Swansea and South West Wales. They organise events such as the Swansea Fringe Festival and run workshops in a variety of subjects such as guitar playing and drumming. Also publish a local listings magazine. See listings in relevant sections for all of the above services.

Welsh Music Foundation
Ty Cefn, Rectory Road, Canton, Cardiff, CF5 1QL
tel:	02920 668 127
fax:	02920 341 622
email:	enquiries@welshmusicfoundation.com
web:	www.welshmusicfoundation.com
info:	The Welsh Music Foundation aims to assist the

development of the music industry infrastructure in Wales. They exist to provide support to businesses and also act as advisers to those who have public money to spend on music business related projects. Their directory is published annually, as well as being available online.

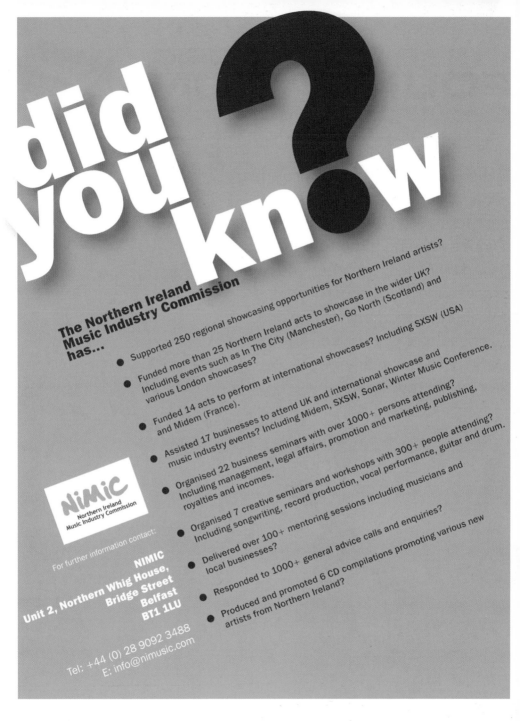

did you know?

The Northern Ireland Music Industry Commission has...

- Supported 250 regional showcasing opportunities for Northern Ireland artists?

- Funded more than 25 Northern Ireland acts to showcase in the wider UK? Including events such as In The City (Manchester), Go North (Scotland) and various London showcases?

- Funded 14 acts to perform at international showcases? Including SXSW (USA) and Midem (France).

- Assisted 17 businesses to attend UK and international showcase and music industry events? Including Midem, SXSW, Sonar, Winter Music Conference.

- Organised 22 business seminars with over 1000+ persons attending? Including management, legal affairs, promotion and marketing, publishing, royalties and incomes.

- Organised 7 creative seminars and workshops with 300+ people attending? Including songwriting, record production, vocal performance, guitar and drum.

- Delivered over 100+ mentoring sessions including musicians and local businesses?

- Responded to 1000+ general advice calls and enquiries?

- Produced and promoted 6 CD compilations promoting various new artists from Northern Ireland?

NiMiC
Northern Ireland
Music Industry Commission

For further information contact:

NIMIC
Unit 2, Northern Whig House,
Bridge Street
Belfast
BT1 1LU

Tel: +44 (0) 28 9092 3488
E: info@nimusic.com

NIMIC gratefully acknowledges the support of

PRS**Foundation** for new music

Invest Northern Ireland

arts council

BRITISH COUNCIL

EU Programme for Peace and Reconciliation

WELSH MUSIC
FOUNDATION

www.welshmusicfoundation.com

Welsh Music Foundation provides support, advice, information and contacts to the Welsh music industry. If you're running a music business based in Wales - whether you're an artist manager, a record label, a distribution company or any other business that is involved with the world of music in any way - then we're here to help!

Head Office:
Ty Cefn
Rectory Road
Canton
Cardiff
CF5 1QL

T: 029 2066 8127
F: 029 2034 1622

enquiries@welshmusicfoundation.com

Section 7
Media

the|unsigned|guide

7.1 Media Foreword

Increasingly it is the case that your marketing and promotional activity will rely heavily on all forms of the media. In this section we have listed details of conventional media such as regional newspapers, magazines (consumer, specialist and industry titles), plus radio stations and student media as well as internet sites and other useful web resources.

It is crucial that you build and maintain a database of local, regional, national and internet media contacts and journalists. In the same way that record companies, their associated media agencies and pluggers will plan marketing and promotional campaigns for their releases, promoters will also advertise gigs and tours using similar marketing techniques and sectors of the media.

The principle is exactly the same for unsigned bands. However, with so many unsigned bands writing and producing material or gigging at any one time, competition for column space and airtime is fierce. It is essential that you stay well informed of different and new magazines, newspapers, radio shows and internet sites which you feel you may be able to exploit in order to promote your music.

It goes without saying that the larger and more recognised media titles you would expect to see in a directory such as this are listed, but perhaps more importantly for unsigned artists we have also included a wider cross-section of media to cover community radio stations, internet radio, student media (including press, radio and television), fanzines, lower circulation regional and specialist magazines as well free listings guides and music supplements.

Most bands and artists will already have compiled a biography and circulated it to various press and media titles in the hope that they will be quoted or featured in an article or radio show. The truth is that this rarely happens. Like any form of commercial media, the sales of advertising are directly proportional to readership/audience size and audience composition. The more readers, listeners or viewers, the higher the value of its advertising. For this reason, content or editorial has to meet the tastes and requirements of its target audience to ensure readers keep reading and listeners keep listening.

> **No magazine is going to dedicate column space to your band simply because you exist, you must have something that is newsworthy and of interest to their audience.**

A high percentage of any editorial or programme content where the music industry is concerned, will be product driven, be it Radio 1's playlists, NME's album reviews or Q's artist/band features. Almost exclusively, they will be playing/reviewing newly available releases (unless the radio station's Promise of Performance or the press title's editorial remit is not to that format). It is a simple fact that commercial projects will use the media wherever and whenever they can and this stands to reason. If you have product to sell, be it a single, album or gig ticket, it needs marketing to drive sales and it is far more effective (both in terms of cost and impact) to have a journalist or presenter recommend your single or album to an existing audience of readers or listeners than it is to merely rely on generic advertising and other methods of 'blanket' promotion. Although advertising will usually feature in a record company's overall marketing mix, as an unsigned band you should research the field of media planning/buying before committing any spend to advertising. Advertising can be very expensive and not always as effective as you might think, so make your decisions very carefully even if you feel your budget runs to it.

In terms of editorial, as an unsigned band you must have a reason (just as signed band does) for the media to be interested in giving you coverage - for example a new string of gig dates or a new album release. No magazine is going to dedicate column space to your band simply because you exist, you must have something that is newsworthy and of interest to their audience. The types of magazines and other media that you approach must at least have a proportion of its audience that will be interested in the fact that you are gigging, have a new demo or that you have just signed a recording deal.

If you are planning to gig in other parts of the country, you should also use the relevant media listings from this section to promote your shows and/or releases. Regional media titles will only usually be interested in you as an artist or band if you are locally based, gigging at a local venue or have product for sale in the area, so plan which media titles are appropriate to contact and identify the relevant journalists. Make sure your new contacts are also recorded in your media database.

You must also update your press releases regularly and make them as media friendly as possible. Work in the same delivery formats as the media titles you are contacting. Ask the journalists you may already know how they normally like biographies, press packs, pictures, logos and music actually delivered (for example email or post). You should also make the necessary media information available on your website, for example as downloadable files. This will mean that journalists can quickly and easily access your music and media information from any geographical location. It will also mean that you do not unnecessarily clog email servers with large electronic files such as MP3s and graphics files.

Finally, keep your press releases short and to the point and always include the your best press cuttings and details of any other recent media coverage. A media campaign should also run in conjunction with other promotional and marketing activity. Assuming you have the budget, use the Music Services/Retail section of this directory to produce and distribute leaflets, posters and other publicity as part of a planned and organised marketing campaign.

Remember where your marketing is concerned, it is always the sum of the parts that counts. Ensure that you have a good database of media contacts, a well structured and functional website, some inventive design work, good flyers & posters, targeted print distribution, some well written press releases and a touch of luck here and there (don't forget the dogged determination!) and you will eventually begin to see some progress in terms of marketing your music.

7.2 RADIO STATIONS

EAST of ENGLAND

102.7 Hereward FM
PO Box 225, Queensgate Centre, Peterborough, PE1 1XJ
tel:			01733 460 460
fax:			01733 281 379
email:			paul.green@musicradio.com
web:			http://herewardfm.musicradio.com
contact:		Matt Jarvis
take demos:		Yes
info:			Do not accept demos for airtime or feedback, but
local bands can send demo and biography marked for attention of Matt
Jarvis with a view to being chosen to play local live events.

103.4 FM The Beach
PO Box 1034, Lowestoft, Suffolk, NR32 4QP
tel:			01502 565 639
fax:			0845 345 1036
email:			reception@thebeach.co.uk
web:			www.thebeach.co.uk
contact:		Paul Carter
take demos:		Yes
info:			Every Monday at 7.45pm an unsigned band's track
is played as part of 'The Evening Show'. Send demos to the address
above.

106.8 Lite FM
5 Church Street, Peterborough, PE1 1XB
tel:			01733 898 106
fax:			01733 898 107
email:			admin@lite1068.co.uk
web:			www.lite1068.com
take demos:		No

BBC Radio Cambridgeshire (96 & 95.7 FM)
PO Box 96, 104 Hills Road, Cambridge, CB2 1LD
tel:			01223 259 696
email:			cambs@bbc.co.uk
web:			www.bbc.co.uk/england/radiocambridgeshire/
take demos:		Yes
info:			The target audience of BBC Radio Camdridgeshire
is the over 45s. This is reflected in the playlist so only a very limited
number of demos that fit a particular style of music will be considered
for air-time.

BBC Radio Norfolk (95.1 & 104.4 FM)
The Forum, Millennium Plain, Norwich, NR2 1BH
tel:			01603 617 411
email:			radionorfolk@bbc.co.uk
web:			www.bbc.co.uk/england/radionorfolk/
contact:		Roy Waller
take demos:		Yes
info:			Email Roy Waller with details of your band and
your music. Follow with demo on request. Roy's show is aired every
weekday between 9am to noon. Graham Barnard also has an afternoon
show from 2pm to 5pm that will play new music.

BBC Radio Suffolk (95.5, 103.9 & 104.6 FM)
Broadcasting House, St. Matthew's Street, Ipswich, Suffolk, IP1 3EP
email:			radiosuffolk@bbc.co.uk
web:			www.bbc.co.uk/england/radiosuffolk/
contact:		Stephen Foster
take demos:		No
info:			Stephen Foster is Head of Music.

Broadland 102 FM
St. George's Plain, 47-49 Colegate, Norwich, NR3 1DB
tel:			01603 630 621
web:			http://broadland102.musicradio.com
contact:		Steve Martin
take demos:		Yes
info:			The station is playlisted by Head Office, but demos
can be sent to the address above for consideration.

Fen Radio 107.5 FM
5 Church Mews, Wisbech, Cambridgeshire, PE13 1HL
tel:			01945 467 107
fax:			01945 467 464
email:			studio@fenradio.co.uk
web:			www.fenradio.co.uk
contact:		Andy B.
take demos:		Yes
info:			On Thursday nights between 9pm and midnight, Andy
B. showcases new music and local bands. Send demo and biog to the
address above.

KLFM 96.7
18 Blackfriars Street, King's Lynn, Norfolk, PE30 1NN
tel:			01553 772 777
fax:			01553 766 453
email:			info@klfmradio.co.uk
web:			www.klfm967.co.uk
contact:		Mark Pryke
take demos:		Yes
info:			Send demo and biog to Mark Pryke for consideration.

North Norfolk Radio
PO Box 962, Norfolk, NR24 2ER
email:			info@northnorfolkradio.com
web:			www.northnorfolkradio.com
take demos:		Yes
info:			Accept demos. Played at Programme Director's
discretion.

Q103 FM
Enterprise House, The Vision Park, Chivers Way, Histon,
Cambridgeshire, CB4 9WW
tel:			01223 235 255
email:			paul.green@musicradio.co.uk
web:			www.q103.co.uk
contact:		Chris, Paul
take demos:		Yes
info:			Contact Paul Green at the email address listed for more
details or send demo to Chris at above address.

SGR-FM 97.1FM
Alpha Business Park, 6-12 White House Road, Ipswich, Suffolk, IP1 5LT
tel:			01473 461 000
fax:			01473 741 200
email:			editor@musicradio.co.uk
web:			www.musicradio.com
contact:		Tracey Cooper, Paul Morris
take demos:		Yes
info:			Send demos to Paul Morris (Head of Music) at the
address above.

MEDIA

Star 107 FM
Radio House, Sturton Street, Cambridge, CB1 2QS
tel: 01223 722 300
fax: 01223 577 686
email: studio@star107.co.uk
web: www.star107.co.uk
contact: Freddy Shearer, Matthew Rowe
take demos: Yes
info: No dedicated unsigned slots but do accept demos for consideration. Send to the contacts above. There is a weekend 'Rock Show' presented by Neil Jones. Contact Neil Jones for details.

Vibe FM (105 - 108 FM)
Reflection House, Olding Road, Bury St. Edmunds, Suffolk, IP33 3TA
tel: 01284 715 300
email: glen.white@vibefm.co.uk
web: www.vibefm.co.uk
contact: Glen White
take demos: Yes
info: Vibe will accept Dance and R&B demos for consideration. Send demos to the address above.

GREATER LONDON

102.2 Smooth FM
26-27 Castlereagh Street, London, W1H 6DJ
tel: 020 7706 4100
fax: 020 7723 9742
email: info@smoothfm.com
web: www.smoothfm.com
take demos: Yes
info: The station does not generally accept demos for airplay. However, Jazz FM runs an enterprise department, record label and live events board (contact information as above), where demos may be forwarded. Mark FAO Horace Macdonald.

95.8 Capital FM
PO Box 1049, London, WC2H 7LA
tel: 020 7766 6000
fax: 020 7766 6100
email: info@capitalradio.co.uk
web: www.capitalfm.com
take demos: Yes
info: Send demos to the above address.

BBC Radio 1 (97-99 FM)
Yalding House, 152-156 Great Portland Street, London, W1W 6AJ
tel: 020 7580 4468
email: onemusic@bbc.co.uk
web: www.bbc.co.uk/radio1/onemusic
take demos: Yes
info: 'OneMusic' gives unsigned bands and musicians from all genres the chance to feature on the BBC Radio 1 playlist. Submit your demo with a completed entry form (available from the OneMusic website) to OneMusic, PO Box 111, London, W1A 7WW. The best demos received will be posted on the OneMusic website, where users rate the featured tracks. Those with the best reactions will be considered for the Unsigned Playlist.

BBC Radio London (94.9 FM)
PO Box 94.9, London, W1A 6FL
tel: 020 7224 2424
email: yourlondon@bbc.co.uk
web: www.bbc.co.uk/london
contact: Jim Lahat
take demos: No
info: Speech based station with some specialist music programmes at the weekend. Mainly Jazz, Classical and World based.

BBC Three Counties Radio (95.5, 104.5 & 103.8 FM)
1 Hastings Street, Luton, LU1 5XL
tel: 01582 637 400
email: 3cr@bbc.co.uk
web: www.bbc.co.uk/england/threecounties/
contact: Gareth Lloyd
take demos: Yes
info: Some unsigned material may be aired on weekend shows, including Sunday morning and Sunday evening slots. Good quality demos should be sent to the address above, marked for the attention of Gareth Lloyd.

Capital Gold (London 1548 AM)
30 Leicester Square, London, WC2H 7LA
tel: 020 7766 6000
email: mario.vella@capitalinteractive.co.uk
web: www.capitalgold.com
take demos: No
info: Frequencies vary for different areas in the UK. Check website for details.

Choice FM (107.1 & 96.9 FM)
PO Box 969, London, WC2H 7BB
tel: 020 7378 3969
fax: 020 7378 3911
email: info@choicefm.com
web: www.choicefm.com
contact: Ivor Ettienne
take demos: Yes
info: Send demos to the address above, mark FAO The Library or Ivor Ettienne (Programme Controller).

Classic Gold
50 Lisson Street, London, NW1 5DF
tel: 01582 676 200
email: admin@classicgolddigital.com
web: www.classicgolddigital.com
take demos: Yes
info: Covers all areas of the UK. See website for local frequencies. Send demos to Stuart Davis.

Club Asia (963 & 972 AM)
Asia House, 227-247 Gascoigne Road, Barking, IG11 7LN
tel: 020 8594 6662
email: veena.virahfammy@clubasiaonline.com
web: www.clubasiaonline.com
take demos: Yes
info: Encourage new Asian music. Send demo along with photo and biog. New music is selected every Monday.

Desi Radio (1602 AM)
The Punjabi Centre, 30 Sussex Road, Southall, Middlesex, UB2 5EG
tel: 020 8574 9591
fax: 020 8574 9850
email: info@desiradio.org.uk
web: www.desiradio.org.uk
take demos: Yes
info: Desi Radio represents the Asian and Punjabi community, demos played will reflect this. Part of an organisation, The Punjabi Centre, which houses the station and also provides media and production training.

Easy Radio London DAB
Radio House, Merrick Road, Southall, UB2 4AU
tel: 020 8843 5341
email: info@easy1035.com
web: www.easy1035.com
contact: Paul Owen, Ron Brown
take demos: Yes
info: Easy Radio broadcasts 24-hours a day throughout London and the South East digital radio (DAB). Send demo and biog to the address above. Although there is no dedicated unsigned airtime, all submissions will be considered.

Heart 106.2 FM
The Chrysalis Building, 13 Bramley Road, London, W10 6SP
tel: 020 7468 1062
fax: 020 7470 1095
email: programming.enquiries@heart1062.co.uk
web: www.heart1062.co.uk

Kismat Radio
Radio House, Merrick Road, Southall, Middlesex, UB2 4AU
tel: 020 8843 5330
email: info@kismatradio.com
web: www.kismatradio.com
contact: Surekha Abbas
take demos: Yes
info: Welcome demos but strictly Asian music. Looking to start new music show in near future.

Kiss 100 FM
Mappin House, 4 Winsley Street, London, W1W 8HF
tel: 020 7436 1515
fax: 020 7975 8150
email: studio@kiss100.com
web: www.kiss100.com
take demos: Yes
info: Several evening slots which will air new music and will accept material for consideration. See website for further details and send demos to the address above.

London Greek Radio
LGR House, 437 High Road, North Finchley, London, N12 0AP
tel: 0871 288 1000
email: info@lgr.co.uk
web: www.lgr.co.uk
contact: Mr. Panayi
take demos: Yes
info: Greek music radio. Will accept demos. New music played at DJ's discretion.

AIR • ARCADE FIRE • ARCTIC MONKEYS • ASH • RICHARD ASHCROFT • ATHLETE • BABYSHAMBLES • BEASTIE BOYS • BECK • THE BEES • BELLE & SEBASTIAN • BLOC PARTY • BLUR • THE BRAVERY • IAN BROWN • THE CHARLATANS • THE CHEMICAL BROTHERS • CLOR • COLDPLAY • THE CORAL • GRAHAM COXON • THE CRIBS • THE CURE • THE DANDY WARHOLS • THE DARKNESS • THE DEAD 60S • DOVES • DOGS • EDITORS • ELBOW • EL PRESIDENTE • EMBRACE • FEEDER • THE FLAMING LIPS • FOO FIGHTERS • FRANZ FERDINAND • THE FUTUREHEADS • GARBAGE • GOLDFRAPP • GORILLAZ • GRANDADDY • GREEN DAY • HARD-FI • THE HIVES • HOT HOT HEAT • INTERPOL • JET • JACK JOHNSON • KAISER CHIEFS • KASABIAN • KEANE • THE KILLERS • KINGS OF LEON • LCD SOUNDSYSTEM • THE LIBERTINES • LONG-VIEW • THE MAGIC NUMBERS • MANIC STREET PREACHERS • MAXIMO PARK • MORRISSEY • MUSE • THE MUSIC • NEW ORDER • NIRVANA • OASIS • THE OFFSPRING • THE ORDINARY BOYS • THE PADDINGTONS • PIXIES • PLACEBO • PRIMAL SCREAM • PRODIGY • PULP • QUEENS OF THE STONE AGE • RADIOHEAD • THE RAPTURE • RAZORLIGHT • RED HOT CHILI PEPPERS • THE RAKES • R.E.M. • DAMIEN RICE • SCISSOR SISTERS • SECRET MACHINES • SMASHING PUMPKINS • THE SMITHS • SNOW PATROL • SOULWAX • STARSAILOR • STEREOPHONICS • THE STONE ROSES • THE STREETS • THE STROKES • SUEDE • SUPER FURRY ANIMALS • SUPERGRASS • THE TEARS • THE THRILLS • TRAVIS • TURIN BRAKES • U2 • THE VERVE • THE VINES • WEEZER • PAUL WELLER • THE WHITE STRIPES • YEAH YEAH YEAHS • THE ZUTONS

YOU CAN HEAR XFM ON 104.9FM IN LONDON, ONLINE AT XFM.CO.UK, ON SKY, NTL AND TELEWEST AND ON DAB DIGITAL RADIO COMING SOON ON 97.7FM IN MANCHESTER

MEDIA

London Turkish Radio
185b High Road, Wood Green, London, N22 6BA
tel: 020 8881 0606
email: info@londonturkishradio.org
web: www.londonturkishradio.org
contact: Akin Pastirmaciogle
take demos: Yes
info: Accept demos. Send to Akin Pastirmaciogle.

Radio Jackie (107.8 FM)
110 Tolworth Broadway, Tolworth, Surrey, KT6 7JD
tel: 020 8288 1300
fax: 020 8288 1312
email: dave.owen@radiojackie.com
web: www.radiojackie.com
contact: Dave Owen
take demos: Yes
info: Send demo and biog marked FAO Dave Owen. There is no dedicated unsigned airtime but material submitted will be considered.

Resonance 104.4 FM
c/o LMC, 3.6 Lafone House, 11-13 Leathermarket Street, London, SE12 3HN
tel: 020 7836 3664
fax: 020 7403 1922
email: info@resonancefm.com
web: www.resonancefm.com
take demos: No
info: Resonance features programmes made by musicians, artists and critics who represent the diversity of London's arts scenes, with regular weekly contributions from nearly 200 musicians, artists, thinkers, critics, activists and instigators, plus numerous unique broadcasts by artists on the weekday 'Clear Spot'. Station created by London Musicians' Collective. See listing in Useful Regional Organisations section for details of other services they provide.

Spectrum International Radio (558 AM & DAB)
4 Ingate Place, London, SW8 3NS
tel: 020 7627 4433
fax: 020 7627 3409
email: enquiries@spectrumradio.net
web: www.spectrumradio.net
take demos: Yes
info: Spectrum International is a commercial radio station purely dedicated to serving London's ethnic communities. Send demos to address above, marked FAO The Music Library.

Time FM 106.8 & 107.3
2-6 Basildon Road, Abbey Wood, London, SE2 0EW
tel: 020 8311 3112
email: info@timefm.com
web: www.timefm.com
contact: Gary Mulligan
take demos: Yes
info: Commercial radio station. Demos can be sent for attention of Gary Mulligan.

Total Rock
1 Denmark Place, London, WC2H 8NL
tel: 020 7240 6665
email: info@totalrock.com
web: www.totalrock.com
take demos: Yes
info: Play Rock and Metal music and get involved with local events. Welcome information about unsigned bands. Demos should be sent to the address above.

Virgin Radio (105.8 FM & 1197, 1215, 1233, 1242, 1260 AM)
1 Golden Square, London, W1S 4DJ
tel: 020 7434 1215
fax: 020 7434 1197
email: reception@virginradio.co.uk
web: www.virginradio.co.uk
contact: Pete Mitchell
take demos: Yes
info: Pete Mitchell has played unsigned material on his 'Razor Cuts' show, broadcast every Sunday night between 8pm and 10pm. Email him at the show directly via the website. Send demos FAO Pete Mitchell to the address above.

XFM 104.9FM
30 Leicester Square, London, WC2H 7LA
tel: 020 7766 6000
fax: 020 7766 6100
email: claire.sturgess@xfm.co.uk
web: www.xfm.co.uk
contact: Claire Sturgess
take demos: Yes
info: Claire Sturgess hosts 'X-posure Part 1' Monday to Friday from 9pm to 11pm. During the show she will play music from her favourite unsigned bands from that week. Demos should be sent on CD to Claire at the address above, minimum of three tracks. Include biog, details of upcoming gigs, web address and photo (preferably a 250px x 180px digital image).

MIDLANDS

102.8 RAM FM
35-36 Irongate, Derby, DE1 3GA
tel: 01332 205 599
fax: 01332 324 009
email: ramfm@musicradio.com
web: http://ramfm.musicradio.com
take demos: No

103.1 Beacon FM
Winchester House, 9 St. Mary's Court, St. Mary's Street, Shrewsbury, SY1 1EG
tel: 01743 266 800
web: www.musicradio.com
contact: Nigel Freshman
take demos: Yes
info: Local bands can send in demos for consideration. Also arrange local events. Contact the Programme Controller, Nigel Freshman, for details.

106 Century FM
City Link, Nottingham, NG2 4NG
tel: 0115 910 6100
fax: 0115 910 6107
web: www.106fm.co.uk
contact: Anna Riggs, Jim Davis
take demos: Yes
info: Send demo and biog to the address above. Mark FAO Jim Davis (Head of Music) or Anna Riggs (Programme Director).

107.1 Rugby FM
Suite 4-6, Dunsmore Business Centre, Spring Street, Rugby, CV21 3HH
tel: 01788 541 100
email: mail@rugbyfm.co.uk
web: www.rubgyfm.co.uk
contact: Dale Collins
take demos: No
info: Do not accept demos but do organise local community events that allow new bands to perform.

107.4 Telford FM
Shropshire Star Building, Waterloo Road, Ketley, Telford, TF1 5HU
tel: 01952 280 011
fax: 01592 280 010
email: info@telfordfm.co.uk
web: www.telfordfm.co.uk
contact: Rob James
take demos: Yes
info: Currently no specific shows for unsigned bands but information can be sent to Rob James at news@telfordfm.co.uk.

107.7 The Wolf
10th Floor, Mander House, Wolverhampton, WV1 3NB
tel: 01400 822 21
fax: 01400 821 76
email: steve@foreverbroadcasting.com
web: www.thewolf.co.uk
contact: Steve King
take demos: Yes
info: There is no dedicated unsigned air time, but Pop and Mainstream demos can be sent to the address above for consideration. Include any other relevant information and mark FAO Steve King (Group Programme Director).

96 Trent FM
29-31 Castle Gate, Nottingham, Nottinghamshire, NG1 7AP
tel: 0115 873 1500
fax: 0115 873 1509
email: trentreceptionusers@musicradio.com
web: www.musicradio.com
contact: Lewis Clark
take demos: No
info: Do not give air time to unsigned bands, however they do run events during the summer period where unsigned bands are able to perform. For details contact Lewis Clark on the number above.

96.4 FM BRMB
9 Brindleyplace, 4 Oozells Square, Birmingham, B1 2DJ
tel: 0121 245 5000
fax: 0121 245 5245
email: nick.ralph@brmb.co.uk
web: www.brmb.co.uk
contact: Nick Ralph
take demos: Yes
info: Send biog and demo to Nick Ralph at the address above.

97.2 Beacon FM
267 Tettenhall Road, Wolverhampton, WV6 0DE
tel: 01902 461 300
fax: 01902 461 299
web: http://beaconfm.musicradio.com
take demos: Yes
info: Send demos to above address.

BBC Coventry and Warwickshire (103.7, 104.0, 94.8 FM)
Holt Court, 1 Greyfriars Road, Coventry, CV1 2WR
tel: 02476 551 000
email: coventry.warwickshire@bbc.co.uk
web: www.bbc.co.uk/coventry/local_radio/
take demos: Yes
info: Local artists only should send demos to Anita.miah@bbc.co.uk, who runs the evening show from 7pm to10pm.

BBC Radio Derby (95.3, 96, 104.5 FM & 1116 AM)
PO Box 104.5, Derby, DE1 3HL
tel: 01332 361 111
email: radio.derby@bbc.co.uk
web: www.bbc.co.uk/england/radioderby
contact: Bev Pickles
take demos: Yes
info: Gig listings and details of local events can be emailed to the station at the address above. The BBC Derby website (www.bbc.co.uk/derby) features information about the local music scene. Email derby@bbc.co.uk for more details. Demos should be forwarded to Bev Pickles.

BBC Radio Hereford & Worcester (94.7, 104 & 104.6 FM)
Hylton Road, Worcester, Worcestershire, WR2 5WW
tel: 01905 748 485
fax: 01905 748 006
email: max.thomas@bbc.co.uk
web: www.bbc.co.uk/england/herefordworcester/
contact: Max Thomas
take demos: Yes
info: No specific unsigned slots but some specialist shows will play suitable demos. Send CD and biog to the address above. Mark FAO Max Thomas.

BBC Radio Leicester (104.9 FM)
9 St. Nichol's Place, Leicester, LE1 5LB
tel: 0116 251 6688
fax: 0116 251 1463
email: radioleicester@bbc.co.uk
web: www.bbc.co.uk/england/radioleicester/
contact: Trish Dolman
take demos: Yes
info: The afternoon show, broadcast between 12 noon and 3pm, occasionally plays unsigned local talent. Send demos and biog to the address above.

BBC Radio Lincolnshire (94.9, 104.7 FM & 1368 AM)
PO Box 219, Newport, Lincoln, Lincolnshire, LN1 3XY
tel: 01522 511 411
fax: 01522 511 058
email: radio.lincolnshire@bbc.co.uk
web: www.bbc.co.uk/england/radiolincolnshire/
contact: Nick Wilmhurst
take demos: Yes
info: The 'Youth Issues' show broadcast every Friday between 7pm and 9pm, regularly plays music by unsigned bands who are from or playing in Lincolnshire. Send demos to the address above. Mark FAO show producer Nick Wilmhurst.

BBC Radio Northampton (103.6 & 104.2 FM)
Broadcasting House, Abington Street, Northampton, NN1 2BH
tel: 01604 239 100
fax: 01604 667 949
email: bob.castleton@bbc.co.uk
web: www.bbc.co.uk/england/radionorthampton/
contact: Iain Griffin
take demos: Yes
info: Send demos to the above address marked FAO Iain Griffin.

BBC Radio Nottingham (95.5 & 103.8 FM)
London Road, Nottingham, NG2 4UU
tel: 0115 955 0500
fax: 0115 902 1955
email: radio.nottingham@bbc.co.uk
web: www.bbc.co.uk/england/radionottingham/
contact: Dean Jackson
take demos: No
info: Although the station does not generally play demos, the local music scene is extensively covered on the BBC Nottingham website at www.bbc.co.uk/nottingham/music/. Email nottingham@bbc.co.uk with details of your band and upcoming gigs in the Nottingham area.

BBC Radio Shropshire (96 FM)
PO Box 96, Shrewsbury, SY1 3TT
tel: 01743 248 484
fax: 01743 271 702
email: radio.shropshire@bbc.co.uk
web: www.bbc.co.uk/england/radioshropshire
contact: Tim Pemberton
take demos: Yes
info: No dedicated unsigned air-time but do accept demos for consideration. Send demo, biog and any other relevant information to the address above.

BBC Radio Stoke (94.6 & 104.1 FM)
Cheapside, Hanley, Stoke on Trent, ST1 1JJ
tel: 01782 208 080
email: radio.stoke@bbc.co.uk
web: www.bbc.co.uk/england/radiostoke/
contact: Mary Fox
take demos: Yes
info: Demos and biogs are accepted, but in the main are considered for the station's website content, rather than for airplay.

BBC WM
The Mailbox, Birmingham, B1 1RF
tel: 0845 300 9956
email: radio.wm@bbc.co.uk
web: www.bbc.co.uk/radiowm
take demos: Yes
info: Send demos to Fiona Dye, presenter of The Late Show, which regularly showcases unsigned artists.

The Bear 102 FM
Guard House Studios, Banbury Road, Stratford Upon Avon, CV37 7HX
tel: 01789 262 636
fax: 01789 263 102
email: steve.heiden@thebear.co.uk
web: www.thebear.co.uk
contact: Steve Heiden
take demos: Yes
info: Send demos marked FAO Steve Heiden, email the address above for more details.

Centre 101.6 FM
5-6 Aldergate, Tamworth, Staffordshire, B79 7DJ
tel: 01827 318 000
fax: 01827 318 002
email: studio@centrefm.com
web: www.centrefm.com
contact: Jason Moss
take demos: Yes
info: Jason Moss hosts a show that promotes unsigned Staffordshire bands. Send demos to address above, FAO Jason Moss.

Connect 97.2 & 107.4 FM
Unit 1, Centre 2000, Robinson Close, Telford Way Industrial Estate, Kettering, Northamptonshire, NN16 8PU
tel: 01536 412 413
fax: 01536 517 390
email: info@connectfm.com
web: www.connectfm.com
contact: Danny Gibson
take demos: Yes
info: Send demo and biog to the address above. Mark FAO Danny Gibson. Also organise local events where bands can perform.

Fosseway 107.9 FM
PO Box 107, Hinckley, Leicestershire, LE10 1WR
tel: 01455 614 151
fax: 01455 616 888
email: enquiries@fossewayradio.co.uk
web: www.fossewayradio.co.uk
contact: Ian Ison
take demos: Yes
info: Demos are welcome for consideration, although there are no specific unsigned slots. Mark FAO Ian Ison. Will also promote local events.

MEDIA

Galaxy 102.2 FM
1 The Square, 111 Broad Street, Birmingham, B15 1AS
tel: 0121 695 0000
fax: 0121 696 1007
email: galaxy1022@galaxy1022.co.uk
web: www.galaxybirmingham.co.uk
take demos: No

Heart 100.7 FM
1 The Square, 111 Broad Street, Birmingham, B15 1AS
tel: 0121 695 0000
fax: 0121 696 1007
email: heartfm@heartfm.co.uk
web: www.heartfm.co.uk
take demos: No
info: Does not accept demos from unsigned bands.

Heart 106 FM
City Link, Nottingham, Nottinghamshire, NG2 4NG
tel: 0115 910 6100
email: anna@heart106.com
web: www.heart106.com
contact: Anna Riggs, Jim Davis
take demos: Yes
info: Jim Davis presents an evening show which features CD of the week.

High Peak Radio 103.3 & 106.6 FM
PO Box 106, Chapel-en-le-Frith, Derbyshire, SK23 0QD
tel: 01298 813 144
email: info@highpeakradio.co.uk
web: www.highpeakradio.co.uk
take demos: Yes
info: Run a show called High Peak Performance which showcases local artists live. Contact Katie at the above email address.

Kerrang! 105.2 FM
20 Lionel Street, Birmingham, B3 1AQ
tel: 0845 053 1052
email: kerrangradio@kerrangradio.co.uk
web: www.kerrangradio.co.uk
take demos: Yes
info: Welcome new music. Have a showcase programme on a Sunday evening 9pm to 10pm. Contact Laurence Guest who is Head of Unsigned Music.

Kix 96.2 FM
Watch Close, Spon Street, Coventry, CV1 3LN
tel: 02476 525 656
fax: 02476 525 656
email: alzira.slater@cnradio.co.uk
web: www.kix.fm
contact: Steffan La Touche
take demos: Yes
info: Tend not to include unsigned music for their playlist, but have hosted several local roadshows which have featured local bands. Demos should be sent to the address above.

Leicester Sound 105.4 FM
6 Dominus Way, Leicester, Leicestershire, LE19 1RR
tel: 0116 256 1300
email: dave.campbell@musicradio.com
web: www.leicestersound.com
contact: Dave Campbell
take demos: Yes
info: Welcome demos. Send them to Dave at above address.

Lincs 102.2 FM
Witham Park, Waterside, South Lincoln, LN5 7JN
tel: 01522 549 900
fax: 01522 549 911
email: enquiries@lincsfm.co.uk
web: www.lincsfm.co.uk
contact: Eddie Shaw
take demos: Yes
info: Send demos to the address above. They will advertise charity and non-profit making events in their 'What's On' guide.

Mansfield 103.2 FM
Samuel Brunts Way, Mansfield, Nottingham, NG18 2AH
tel: 01623 646 666
fax: 01623 660 606
email: studio@mansfield103.co.uk
web: www.mansfield103.co.uk
contact: Joe Sentence
take demos: Yes
info: Send an email FAO Joe Sentence at the address above. Follow with a demo on request. Also get involved with live music events. Contact Joe for details.

Mercia 97.0 FM
Hertford Place, Coventry, CV1 3TT
tel: 02476 868 200
email: russ.williams@creation.com
web: www.merciafm.co.uk
contact: Russ Williams
take demos: Yes
info: Send demos to the address above, FAO Russ Williams.

Northants 96.6 FM
19-21 St. Edmund's Road, Northampton, NN1 5DY
tel: 01604 795 600
fax: 01604 795 601
email: chris.rick@musicradio.com
web: www.musicradio.com
contact: Chris Rick
take demos: Yes
info: No specific unsigned band airtime, but demos can be sent for consideration. Mark all submissions FAO Chris Rick.

Oak 107 FM
7 Waldron Court, Prince William Road, Loughborough, LE11 5GD
tel: 01509 211 711
fax: 01509 246 107
email: info@oak107fm.co.uk
web: www.oak107fm.co.uk
contact: Dave James
take demos: Yes
info: Demos will be considered. There is airtime dedicated to unsigned music and Oak do get involved with local (mainly charity) events. Contact Dave James for further information.

Peak FM
Radio House, Foxwood Road, Chesterfield, Derbyshire, S41 9RF
tel: 01246 269 107
fax: 01246 269 933
email: info@peak107.com
web: www.peak107.com
contact: Craig Pattison
take demos: No

Radio XL (1296 AM)
KMS House, Bradford Street, Birmingham, B12 0JD
tel: 0121 753 5353
fax: 0121 753 3111
email: sukhjinder@radioxl.net
web: www.radioxl.net
take demos: Yes
info: Radio XL is aimed primarily, but not exclusively, at the Asian community. Send demos to the address above.

Rutland Radio (97.4 & 107.2 FM)
40 Melton Road, Oakham, Rutland, LE15 6AY
tel: 01572 757 868
fax: 01572 757 744
email: enquiries@rutlandradio.co.uk
web: www.rutlandradio.co.uk
contact: Rob Persani
take demos: Yes
info: Take a particular interest in local bands. Send demos to the address above.

Sabras Radio (1260 AM)
Radio House, 63 Melton Road, Leicester, LE4 6PN
tel: 0116 261 0666
fax: 0116 266 7776
email: enq@sabrasradio.com
web: www.sabrasradio.com
contact: Mark Spokes
take demos: Yes
info: There is an affiliated digital station which has more dedicated unsigned band airtime. All demos sent FAO Mark Spokes.

Signal 1 (102.6 FM)
Stoke Road, Stoke On Trent, Staffordshire, ST4 2SR
tel: 01782 861 026
email: info@signalradio.com
web: www.signal1.co.uk
contact: Sam Plank
take demos: Yes
info: Send demos to Sam Plank.

Signal 2 (1170 AM & DAB)
Stoke Road, Stoke On Trent, Staffordshire, ST4 2SR
tel: 01782 861 170
email: sam@signal2.co.uk
web: www.signal2.co.uk
contact: Sam Plank
take demos: Yes
info: Send demos to Sam Plank.

Sunrise 855 AM
Unit 11, Burway Trading Estate, Bromfield Road, Ludlow, Shropshire, SY8 1EN
tel: 01584 873 795
fax: 01584 875 900
email: info@sunshine855.com or frontdesk@sunshine855.com
web: www.sunshine855.com
contact: Simon Doe
take demos: Yes
info: Send demos to the address above. All airplay enquiries and demos should be marked FAO Simon Doe.

Trax 107.9 FM
PO Box 444, Worksop, Nottinghamshire, S80 1GP
tel: 01909 532 333
fax: 01909 500 445
email: enquiries@traxfm.co.uk
web: www.traxfm.co.uk
contact: Mike Bargh
take demos: Yes
info: All demos for this radio station are sent to the Doncaster address above. Refer to relevant entry for details.

Wyvern FM (102.8, 96.7 & 97.6 FM)
5-6 Barbourne Terrace, Worcester, WR1 3JZ
tel: 01905 612 212
fax: 01905 746 637
email: richard.clarke@musicradio.com
web: www.wyvernfm.co.uk
contact: Richard Clarke
take demos: Yes
info: Although there are no shows with a dedicated unsigned slot, the station will consider giving airtime to local bands who impress. Send demos to the address above.

NORTHEAST

103.4 Sun FM
PO Box 1034, Sunderland, Tyne & Wear, SR5 2YL
tel: 0191 548 1034
email: progs@sun-fm.com
web: www.sun-fm.com
contact: Simon Grundy
take demos: Yes
info: Unsigned bands are not included in the playlists but bands may send demos to be considered for local events organised by the station. Please mark for attention of Peter Clough.

Alpha 103.2
Radio House, 11 Woodland Road, Darlington, DL3 7BJ
tel: 01325 255 552
fax: 01325 255 551
email: via website
web: www.alphafm.co.uk
contact: Steve Philips
take demos: Yes
info: Send demos to Steve Philips.

BBC Radio Cleveland (95 FM)
PO Box 95FM, Broadcasting House, Newport Road, Middlesbrough, Cleveland, TS1 5DG
tel: 01642 225 211
email: bbcradiocleveland@bbc.co.uk
web: www.bbc.co.uk/england/radiocleveland/
contact: David Macmillan
take demos: Yes
info: Every Friday night between 7pm and 10pm, David Macmillan presents PURE, giving local unsigned bands airplay. Send demos to David at the station. The BBC Tees website has a large section dedicated to unsigned bands called 'The Future Sound of Teeside'. To feature on the site, send a full biog, photo (JPEG preferably) and one track demo on CD to the address above, marked FAO Future Sound of Teeside c/o Natalie Boxall. You will also need to sign a release form that is available to print from the website at www.bbc.co.uk/tees/music/.

BBC Radio Newcastle (95.4 FM)
Broadcasting Centre, Barrack Road, Fenham, Newcastle Upon Tyne, NE99 1RN
tel: 0191 232 4141
fax: 0191 232 5082
email: kate.slater@bbc.co.uk
web: www.bbc.co.uk/england/radionewcastle/
contact: Jamie Wilkinson
take demos: Yes
info: Send demos to Jamie Wilkinson, Music Manager.

Century Radio (100 - 102 FM)
Century House, PO Box 100, Gateshead, NE8 2YY
tel: 0191 477 6666
fax: 0191 477 5660
email: info100-102@centuryfm.co.uk
web: www.centuryfm.co.uk
contact: Tim Rumboll
take demos: Yes
info: Accept demos, which should be sent to the programme controller. No specific shows dedicated to unsigned bands but will occasionally produce outside broadcasts. For details please contact Tim Rumboll at the above address.

Galaxy 105 - 106FM
Kingfisher Way, Silverlink Business Park, Tyne & Wear, NE28 9NX
tel: 0191 206 8000
fax: 0191 206 8080
email: mail@galaxy1056.co.uk
web: www.galaxy1056.co.uk
contact: Dan Archer
take demos: Yes
info: Send Dance and R&B demos to the address above. Mark FAO Dan Archer (Programme Controller)

Magic 1152 AM - Tyne & Wear
Radio House, Newcastle Upon Tyne, Tyne & Wear, NE99 1BB
tel: 0191 420 0971
web: www.magic1152.co.uk
take demos: No
info: Only play published music.

Magic 1170 AM
Radio House, Yale Cresent, Thornby, Stockton On Tees, TS17 6AA
tel: 01642 888 222
web: www.magic1170.co.uk
take demos: No
info: Magic 1170 AM is dedicated to playing 'Golden Oldies'.

Metro Radio (97.1, 102.6 & 103 FM)
55 Degrees North, Pilgrim Street, Newcastle Upon Tyne, NE1 6BF
tel: 0191 230 6100
email: news@metroandmagic.com
web: www.metroradio.co.uk
contact: Alex Roland
take demos: Yes
info: Demos should be sent FAO Alex Roland. Alan Robson hosts a show where unsigned bands can feature, aired from 10pm to 2am. For details contact Alan Robson.

TFM (96.6 FM)
Radio House, Yale Crescent, Thornaby, Stockton on Tees, TS17 6AA
tel: 01642 888 222
fax: 01642 868 288
email: rob.knight@tfmradio.co.uk
web: www.tfmradio.co.uk
contact: Rob Knight
take demos: No

NORTHWEST

102.4 Wish FM
Orrell Lodge, Orrell Road, Orrell, Wigan, WN5 8HJ
tel: 01942 761 024
fax: 01942 777 694
email: studio@wish-fm.com
web: www.wishfm.net
contact: Jo Heuston
take demos: Yes
info: There is no dedicated airtime for unsigned bands, but demos are accepted for consideration. Pop and Commercial tracks only please. Mark for attention of Jo Heuston.

105.4 Century FM
Laser House, Salford Quays, Waterfront Quays, Manchester, M50 3XW
tel: 0161 400 0105
fax: 0161 400 1105
email: ande.macpherson@centuryfm.co.uk
web: www.1054centuryfm.com
contact: Ande Macpherson
take demos: No

106.7 The Rocket
The Studios, Cables Retail Park, Prescot, Knowsley, L34 5SW
tel: 0151 290 1501
web: www.1067therocket.com
take demos: Yes
info: Send demo CD to address listed, marked for attention of Andi Macvey.

MEDIA

E RNB LIVE BANDS WORLD
L JAZZ MANCHESTER'S
NGRA REGGAE IRISH AFRI
CE ALTERNATIVE RNB LIVE
IC LATIN FUNK SOUL JAZZ

(allfm)96.9
...all yours

The community radio station that has captured the imagination of the people of Ardwick, Longsight, Levenshulme ...and beyond.

A radio station with a difference; broadcasting the views, the opinions and the music of the community.

www.allfm.org

Call us now 0161 248 6888

106.9 Silk FM
Radio House, Bridge Street, Macclesfield, Cheshire, SK11 6DJ
tel: 01625 268 000
fax: 01625 269 010
email: mail@silkfm.com
web: www.silkfm.com
contact: Andy Bailey
take demos: No

107.2 Wire FM
Warrington Business Park, Link Lane, Warrington, WA2 8TX
tel: 01925 445 545
fax: 01925 657 705
email: firstname@wirefm.com
web: www.wirefm.com
contact: Pete Pinnington
take demos: Yes
info: Send demos and biog to Pete Pinnington at the address above.

107.4 Tower FM
The Mill, Brownlow Way, Bolton, BL1 2RA
tel: 01204 387 000
fax: 01204 534 065
email: info@towerfm.co.uk
web: www.towerfm.co.uk
contact: Kev McLean
take demos: Yes
info: There is no dedicated airtime for unsigned bands, but demos can be send for consideration to the address above.

107.9 Dune FM
The Power Station, Victoria Way, Southport, Merseyside, PR8 1RR
tel: 01704 502 500
fax: 01704 502 540
email: info@dunefm.co.uk
web: www.dunefm.co.uk
contact: Jon Jessop
take demos: No
info: Do not include unsigned bands in the station playlist.

2BR
Imex Lomeshaye Business Village, Nelson, Lancashire, BB9 7DR
tel: 01282 690 000
fax: 01282 690 001
email: tony@2br.co.uk
web: www.2br.co.uk
contact: Andrew Turner
take demos: Yes
info: Send demos to Andrew Turner at the address above. The station is particularly interested in hearing from local bands.

3FM 104.2
45 Victoria Street, Douglas, Isle of Man, IM1 2LD
tel: 01624 616 333
email: moremusic@three.fm
web: www.three.fm
take demos: Yes
info: Welcome demos. Send to Managing Director and he will pass onto correct department.

96.2 The Revolution
PO Box 962, Oldham, OL1 3JF
tel: 0161 621 6500
fax: 0161 621 6521
email: info@therevolution.uk.com
web: www.revolutiononline.co.uk
contact: Clint Boon
take demos: Yes
info: Clint Boon presents Radio Rescue, a show playing 'the best records ever made, no matter who made them or when'. Any band or artist with an upcoming live show in the area can send demo and details to the address above.

97.4 Rock FM
St. Paul's Square, Preston, PR1 1IE
tel: 01772 477 700
email: brian.paige@rockfm.co.uk
web: www.rockfm.co.uk
contact: Brian Paige, Martin Greenwood
take demos: Yes
info: Will accept demos and also get involved with local events. For further details contact Brian Paige.

ALL FM 96.9
19 Albert Road, Levenshulme, Manchester, M19 2EQ
tel: 0161 248 6888
email: info@allfm.org
web: www.allfm.org
contact: Alex Green, Danielle Porter
take demos: Yes
info: ALL FM is a community radio station that is broadcast over the South Manchester area. Bands and musicians can submit demos to the address above. Demos to Gavin White, publicity Danielle Porter. There are regular unsigned live sessions and some unsigned material on the playlist. ALL FM is part of the Radio Regen community radio initiative. See www.radioregen.org for more information.

Asian Sounds Radio (1377 & 963 AM)
Globe House, Southall Street, Manchester, M3 1LG
tel: 0161 288 1000
email: mitto@asiansoundradio.co.uk
web: www.asiansoundradio.co.uk
take demos: Yes
info: Accept demos. Most DJs will play unsigned band tracks if they like them.

The Bay 96.9 FM
26 St. George's Quay, Lancaster, LA1 3LD
tel: 01524 848 747
fax: 01524 848 787
web: www.thebay.fm
contact: Sarah Graham
take demos: Yes
info: Accept demos for consideration. Send with a biog marked FAO Sarah Graham.

BBC GMR (95.1 & 104.6 FM)
Box 951, Oxford Road, Manchester, M60 1SD
tel: 0161 244 3054
fax: 0161 228 6110
email: gmr@bbc.co.uk
web: www.bbc.co.uk/gmr/
contact: Conrad Murray, Helen Brown
take demos: Yes
info: Terry Christian and Conrad Murray present 'Terry Christian's Manchester Music Show' every Wednesday between 7pm and 10pm. The show is dedicated to local music and regularly plays unsigned material. Send demos to Helen Brown at the address above. There is a live acoustic session every week day night for signed and unsigned bands.

BBC Radio Cumbria (95.6, 96.1 & 104.1 FM)
Annetwell Street, Carlisle, Cumbria, CA3 8BB
tel: 01228 592 444
fax: 01228 640 079
email: radio.cumbria@bbc.co.uk
web: www.bbc.co.uk/radiocumbria/
contact: Pat Graham
take demos: Yes
info: No dedicated unsigned slots but do accept demos for consideration. Mark any submissions FAO Pat Graham.

BBC Radio Lancashire (95.5, 103.9 & 104.5 FM)
26 Darwen Street, Blackburn, Lancashire, BB2 2EA
tel: 01254 262 411
fax: 01254 680 821
email: radio.lancashire@bbc.co.uk
web: www.bbc.co.uk/england/radiolancashire/
contact: Steve Barker
take demos: Yes
info: 'On The Wire' is BBC Radio Lancashire's Indie and Alternative show. Broadcast every Saturday night from 10pm. Submit demos to the address above. Mark FAO presenter Steve Barker.

BBC Radio Merseyside (95.8 FM)
55 Paradise Street, Liverpool, L1 3BP
tel: 0151 708 5500
fax: 0151 794 0988
email: radio.merseyside@bbc.co.uk
web: www.bbc.co.uk/liverpool
contact: Eric Wise
take demos: Yes
info: Billy Butler's show is broadcast on Fridays from 3pm to 4pm, and has a regular 'Stars In Your Ears' slot to highlight local talent. Send demo and biog to Billy at the address above. There is also a 'What's On' spot presented by Nickie Mackay where bands can perform. Contact nickie.mackay@bbc.co.uk for details.

The Bee (107 FM)
8 Dalton Street, Darwin, Lancashire, BB3 0DG
tel: 01254 778 000
email: info@thebee.co.uk
web: www.thebee.co.uk
take demos: Yes
info: New station. Very eager to receive any unsigned material and open to idea of having a show dedicated to new music.

The Buzz 97.1
Pacific Arts Centre, Pacific Road, Birkenhead, CH41 1LJ
tel: 0151 650 1700
email: steve.farrell@musicradio.com
web: www.wirralsbuzz.com
contact: Steve Farell
take demos: Yes
info: Send demos for consideration FAO Steve Farell.

CFM 96.4 FM
Brunel Way, Durranhill Industrial Estate, Carlisle, CA1 3NG
tel: 01228 818 964
fax: 01228 819 444
email: david.bane@cfmradio.com
web: www.cfmradio.com
contact: David Bane
take demos: Yes
info: Although there is no dedicated unsigned airtime, demos are accepted for consideration. Send material to the address above, mark FAO David Bane (Programme Controller).

Dee 106.3 FM
Chantry Court, Chester, CH1 4QN
tel: 01244 391 000
email: studio@dee1063.com
web: www.dee1063.com
take demos: Yes
info: Willing to listen to demos. Most likely to be played on Sunday night request show.

Energy FM (98.6 FM)
100 Market Street, Douglas, Isle of Man, IM1 2PH
tel: 01624 611 936
email: mail@energyfm.net
web: www.energyfm.net
take demos: Yes
info: 'The Blackroom' is a show broadcast on Monday at 10pm to 1am that focuses on unsigned new music. Contact Cristie DeHaven for details.

Galaxy 102 FM
5th Floor, The Triangle, Hanging Ditch, Manchester, M4 3TR
tel: 0161 279 0300
fax: 0161 279 0303
web: www.galaxymanchester.co.uk
take demos: No

Imagine 104.9 FM
1st Floor, Regent House, Heaton Lane, Stockport, SK4 1BX
tel: 0161 609 1400
fax: 0161 609 1401
email: reception@imaginefm.net
web: www.imaginefm.net
contact: Steve Howarth, Paul Willett, Simon Walkington
take demos: Yes
info: No dedicated unsigned airtime but do accept demos for consideration. Send demo, biog and any other relevant information to the address above, marked FAO Paul Willett or Simon Walkington.

Juice 107.6 FM
27 Fleet Street, Liverpool, L1 4AR
tel: 0151 707 3107
fax: 0871 200 7006
email: mail@juiceliverpool.com
web: www.juiceliverpool.com
take demos: Yes
info: Send demos to the address above. From November 2005, Richard Morris will be running a competition called 'The Next Big Thing' as part of his 'Large Portion' show. For further details, contact via the above details.

Key 103
Castle Quay, Castlefield, Manchester, M15 4PR
tel: 0161 288 5000
email: news@key103.co.uk
web: www.key103.co.uk
contact: Ewen McMurrow
take demos: Yes
info: All demos will be considered. Please send to Ewen McMurrow or Programme Director Anthony Gay at the address above.

Lakeland Radio (100.1 & 100.8 FM)
Plumgarths, Kendal, Cumbria, LA8 8QJ
tel: 01539 737 380
fax: 01539 737390
email: studio@lakelandradio.co.uk
web: www.lakelandradio.co.uk
contact: Colin Yare
take demos: Yes
info: Weekday evening magazine show between 7pm and 10pm showcasing local talent and unsigned bands. Regularly play acoustic sets from the studio. The radio station is heavily involved with the Kirkland Festival. For details of either contact Colin Yare.

MEDIA

Magic 1152 AM
Castle Quay, Castlefield, Manchester, M15 4PR
tel: 0161 288 5000
web: www.manchestersmagic.co.uk
take demos: No
info: Don't accept demos.

Magic 1548 AM
St. John's Beacon, 1 Haughton Street, Liverpool, L1 1RL
tel: 0151 472 6800
fax: 0151 472 6821
email: richard.maddock@magic1548.co.uk
web: www.magic1548.co.uk
contact: Richard Maddock
take demos: Yes
info: Send demos to Richard Maddock (Programme Director) at the address above.

Magic 999 AM
St. Paul's Square, Preston, PR1 1YE
tel: 01772 477 700
fax: 01772 477 701
email: brian.paige@rockfm.co.uk
web: www.magic999.com
contact: Brian
take demos: Yes
info: Often get involved in and organise local events. Contact Brian Paige for details. Send demos to the above address.

Manx Radio (89, 97.2 & 103.7 FM)
Broadcasting House, Douglas Head, Douglas, Isle Of Man, IM99 1SW
tel: 01624 682 600
fax: 01624 682 604
email: postbox@manxradio.com
web: www.manxradio.com
contact: Chris Williams
take demos: Yes
info: Send demos to the address above.

Merseyside 106.7 The Rocket
The Studios, Cables Retail Park, Prescot, Merseyside, L34 5SW
tel: 0151 290 1501
fax: 0151 290 1505
web: www.1067therocket.com
contact: Dave Monks
take demos: Yes
info: 'The Pool', presented by Dave Monks, is Merseyside's only dedicated new local music show, broadcast every Sunday night between 8pm and 10pm. The show offers a platform to local bands with session and interview time for more established local acts. Send demos on CD to the address above.

Radio City (96.7 FM)
St. John's Beacon, 1 Houghton Street, Liverpool, L1 1RL
tel: 0151 472 6800
fax: 0151 472 6801
web: www.radiocity.co.uk
contact: Caroline Roberts, Kevin Seed
take demos: No
info: Do not accept any demos from unsigned bands or artists as the playlist is largely commercial and compiled centrally, not individual presenters.

Radio Regen
12 Hilton Street, Manchester, M1 1JF
tel: 0161 237 5012
fax: 0161 237 9139
email: info@radioregen.org
web: www.radioregen.org
contact: Phil Korbel
take demos: Yes
info: Send all demos to Phil Korbel at the above address. Radio Regen guarantee to listen to all demos sent in to them, and tracks that impress will receive airtime.

Radio Wave 96.5 FM
965 Mowbray Drive, Blackpool, FY3 7JR
tel: 01253 304 965
fax: 01253 301 965
email: info@thewavefm.co.uk
web: www.wave965.com
contact: Helen Bowden
take demos: Yes
info: No dedicated unsigned airtime but do accept demos for consideration. Send demo, biog and any other relevant information to Head of Programming, Helen Bowden, at the address above.

Smooth FM (100.4 FM)
8 Exchange Quay, Manchester, M5 E3J
tel: 0161 877 1004
fax: 0161 877 1005
email: steve.collins@smoothfm.com
web: www.smoothfm.com
contact: Steve Collins
take demos: No

Wave 96.5 FM
965 Mowbray Drive, Blackpool, FY3 7JR
tel: 01253 304 965
email: info@thewavefm.co.uk
web: www.wave965.com
contact: Roy Lynch, Helen Bowden
take demos: Yes
info: Send demos to the address above.

Wythenshawe FM (97.2 FM)
Suite A4, Alderman Gatley House, Hale Top, Wythenshawe, Manchester, M22 5RG
tel: 0161 499 0222 (Studio) 0161 499 7982 (Office)
fax: 0161 499 7442
email: info@wfmradio.org
web: www.wfmradio.org
contact: Jason Kenyon, Hadyn Insley, James Murphy
take demos: Yes
info: Happy to receive demos from local bands and will do their best to help out with airplay and interviews. Every now and then, bands will be called in to perform sessions live on air. Presenters who may be worth contacting regarding live plugs are Jason Kenyon, Haydn Insley, James Murphy, Mike Dawson, Mike George and Phil Novak. Wythenshawe FM is part of the Radio Regen community radio initiative. See www.radioregen.org for more information.

XFM Manchester 97.7FM
Laser House, Waterfront Quay, Salford Quays, Manchester, M50 3XW
web: www.xfm.co.uk
info: XFM Manchester plays the best in new music, Indie Rock and guitar music with some Alternative Dance, and covers the best of the Manchester music scene. Launches in April 2006.

SOUTHEAST

102.7 Mercury FM
9 The Stanley Centre, Kelvin Way, Crawley, West Sussex, RH10 9SE
tel: 01293 519 161
web: http://mercuryfm.musicradio.com
take demos: No

103.2 Power FM
Radio House, Whittle Avenue, Segensworth West, Fareham, PO15 5SH
tel: 01489 589 911
fax: 01489 587 754
email: info@powerfm.com
web: www.powerfm.com
contact: Craig Morris
take demos: Yes
info: Demos should be addressed to Craig Morris.

107.4 The Quay FM
PO Box 1074, Portsmouth, Hampshire, PO2 8YG
tel: 02392 364 141
email: info@quayradio.com
web: www.quayradio.com
contact: Matt McIlroy
take demos: Yes
info: To enter 107.4 The Quay FM's 'Battle Of The Bands,' send a demo to the address above for attention of Matt McIlroy.

107.5 Sovereign Radio
14 St. Mary's Walk, Hailsham, East Sussex, BN27 1AF
tel: 01323 442 700
fax: 01323 442 866
email: info@1075sovereignradio.co.uk
web: www.1075sovereignradio.co.uk
contact: Nigel Ansell
take demos: Yes
info: Local bands can send demos to the address above FAO Nigel Ansell. There is no dedicated unsigned airtime, but material submitted will be considered.

107.6 Kestral FM
2nd Floor, Paddington House, Festival Place, Basingstoke, Hampshire, RG21 7LJ
tel: 01256 694 000
email: studio@kestralfm.com
web: www.kestralfm.com
contact: Mandy O'Neill
take demos: Yes
info: Send demos to the address above.

107.7 Splash FM
Guildbourne Centre, Worthing, Sussex, BN11 1LZ
tel: 01903 233 005
email: studio@splashfm.com
web: www.splashfm.com
take demos: Yes
info: Welcome demos from unsigned artists, which receive
play on evening show from 4pm to 8pm. Submit to Pete Macintosh at
above address.

107.8 Arrow FM
Priory Meadow Centre, Hasting, East Sussex, TN34 1PJ
tel: 01424 461 177
fax: 01424 422 662
email: info@arrowfm.co.uk
web: www.arrowfm.co.uk
contact: Vickie Jones
take demos: Yes
info: The daily magazine show, aired between 1pm and
1:15pm, occasionally runs features on bands with relevance to the area.
Send demo and biog to the address above.

2-Ten 97.0 FM
The Chase, Calcot, Reading, Berkshire, RG31 7RB
tel: 0118 945 4400
fax: 0118 928 8566
email: sophie.dobbs@musicradio.com
web: www.musicradio.com
contact: Sophie Dobbs
take demos: Yes
info: Demos should be sent to the address FAO Tim Parker
or Sophie Dobbs. 2-Ten hold a local radio event called Summer XS for
approx. 1500 people. Contact for further details.

96.4 The Eagle FM
Dolphin House, North Street, Guildford, GU1 4AA
tel: 01483 300 964
email: onair@964eagle.co.uk
web: www.964eagle.co.uk
take demos: Yes
info: Eagle FM air 'The Gig Guide' each weekday evening
at 7:30pm and 8:30pm. Email to be included. Also showcase local
bands each Tuesday night during the evening show. Send demo CD and
information to Roy The Boy. You must be based in or near Surrey or
Hampshire to be included.

97.6 Chiltern FM
Chiltern Road, Dunstable, LU6 1HQ
tel: 01582 676 200
fax: 01582 676 201
email: info@musicradio.com
web: http://chilternfm.musicradio.com
contact: Stuart Davis
take demos: No

BBC Radio Berkshire (104.1, 104.4, 95.4 & 94.6 FM)
PO Box 104.4, Reading, RG4 8TZ
tel: 0118 946 4200
fax: 0118 946 4555
email: berkshire.online@bbc.co.uk
web: http://www.bbc.co.uk/england/radioberkshire/
contact: Linda Serke
take demos: Yes
info: Linda Serke takes an active interest in the local
music scene, and regularly attends and reviews gigs for the BBC Radio
Berkshire website (as above). Email or phone with details of your band
and upcoming live dates. The website also features numerous local
band profiles and a gig guide.

BBC Radio Essex (103.5 & 95.3 FM)
PO Box 765, Chelmsford, Essex, CM2 9XB
tel: 01245 616 000
email: essex@bbc.co.uk
web: www.bbc.co.uk/england/essex/
contact: Tim Gillett, Steve Scruton
take demos: Yes
info: Ray Clark will occasionally play unsigned material
on his 'Drivetime' show. Send demos to Steve Scruton to the address
above, or to Tim Gillett (Programme Controller). Will publicise local
events. Details should be sent to the address above.

BBC Radio Kent
(96.7, 104.2, 96.7 FM & 774, 1062 AM)
The Great Hall, Mount Pleasant Road, Tunbridge Wells, Kent, TN1 1QQ
tel: 01892 670 000
fax: 01892 675 644
email: radio.kent@bbc.co.uk
web: www.bbc.co.uk/england/radiokent/
take demos: No

BBC Radio Oxford (95.2 FM)
269 Banbury Road, Oxford, OX2 7DW
tel: 0845 931 1444
email: radio.oxford@bbc.co.uk
web: www.bbc.co.uk/england/radiooxford/
contact: Tim Bearder
take demos: Yes
info: To be considered for features on the BBC Radio Oxford
website and for airplay on the station, send demos to Tim Bearder at
the address above.

BBC Southern Counties Radio (95 - 104.8 FM)
Broadcasting House, 40-42 Queens Road, Brighton, BN1 3XB
tel: 01483 306 306
fax: 01483 304 952
email: phil.jackson@bbc.co.uk
web: www.bbc.co.uk/southerncounties/
contact: Phil Jackson
take demos: Yes
info: Phil Jackson broadcasts 'South Live' from Brighton
every Sunday evening between 7pm and 9pm. The show covers
unsigned bands and musicians. Send demos and biographies to the
above address for consideration.

Bright 106.4 FM
Unit 34, The Market Place Shopping Centre, Burgess Hill, West Sussex,
RH15 9NP
tel: 01444 248 127
email: info@bright1064.com
web: www.bright1064.com
contact: Matt Collison
take demos: Yes
info: Accept demos but are unlikely to play them live on
air as there is not a programme dedicated to new music on the station.
Will get involved with local events that include live music. For queries
contact Matt Collison.

Chiltern FM (96.9 FM)
5 Abbey Court, Fraser Road, Priory Business Park, MK44 3WH
tel: 01234 272 400
email: via website
web: www.bedfordschilternfm.com
take demos: Yes
info: Send demos to Jono Woodward who will play at his
discretion.

County Sound (1566 AM)
Dolphin House, 3 North Street, Guildford, Surrey, GU1 4AA
tel: 01483 300 964
fax: 01483 531 612
email: studio@countysound.co.uk
web: www.countysound.co.uk
contact: Dave Johns
take demos: Yes
info: Local radio that covers and publicises local events.
Send demo to address above.

CTR 105.6 FM
6-8 Mill Street, Maidstone, Kent, ME15 6XH
tel: 01622 662 500
email: studio@ctrfm.com
web: www.ctrfm.com
contact: Jo Dyer
take demos: Yes
info: Accept demos from local bands. Most likely to get
airplay on Sunday morning show 'County Town in Focus.' Send FAO Jo
Dyer at above address.

Delta FM 102
Haslemere Studio Centre, 65 Weyhill, Haslemere, Surrey, GU27 1HN
tel: 01428 651 971
fax: 01428 658 971
email: mail@deltaradio.co.uk
web: www.deltaradio.co.uk
contact: Keith Woodhouse
take demos: Yes
info: Keith Woodhouse presents 'The New Music Show'. For
a chance to be included in the regular unsigned slots, submit demo and
biog to Keith at the address above.

Dream 100
Northgate House, St. Peter's Street, Colchester, Essex, CO1 1HT
tel: 01206 764 466
email: info@dream100.com
web: www.dream100.com
take demos: No

MEDIA

Dream 107.7 FM
Cater House, High Street, Chelmsford, Essex, CM1 1AL
tel: 01245 259 400
fax: 01245 259 558
email: reception@dream107.com
web: www.dream107.com
contact: Nick Hull
take demos: Yes
info: Send demos to Nick Hull at the address above.

Essex FM (96.3, 97.5 & 102.6 FM)
Radio House, 31 Glebe Road, Chelmsford, Essex, CM1 1QG
tel: 01245 524 500
email: james.bassam@creation.com
web: www.musicradio.com
contact: James Bassam
take demos: Yes
info: Demos are accepted for consideration. These should be addressed to James Bassam along with a band biography to the above address.

Fox FM (97.4 & 102.6 FM)
Brush House, Pony Road, Oxford, OX4 2XR
tel: 01865 871 000
fax: 01865 871 038
email: reception@foxfm.co.uk
web: www.foxfm.co.uk
contact: Sam Walker
take demos: Yes
info: Send demos on CD to Sam Walker (Programme Director) at the address above.

Hertbeat FM (106.7 & 106.9 FM)
Knebworth Park, Hertfordshire, SG3 6HQ
tel: 01438 810 900
fax: 01438 815 100
email: info@hertbeat.com
web: www.hertbeat.com
contact: Russell Obsorne
take demos: Yes
info: There is an unsigned bands feature on a Wednesday called, 'Battle of the Bands'. Presented by Russell Osborne, who accepts local demos. Contact Russell for details via the email address above. Occasionally organise local band nights featuring unsigned acts.

Horizon FM 103
14 Vincent Avenue, Crowhill, Milton Keynes, Buckinghamshire, MK8 0AB
tel: 01908 269 111
fax: 01908 564 893
email: trevor.marshall@creation.com
web: www.musicradio.com
contact: Trevor Marshall
take demos: Yes
info: Local bands can send in demos for consideration. Mark FAO Trevor Marshall. Also arrange local events.

Invicta FM
Radio House, John Wilson Business Park, Whitstable, Kent, CT5 3QX
tel: 01227 772 004
fax: 01227 774 450
email: max.hailey@invictafm.com
web: www.invictafm.com
contact: Max Hailey
take demos: Yes
info: No dedicated unsigned slots but will accept demos for consideration. Send CDs or MDs to the address above. Run the Kent Essential Guide, which can include any local events, and will also publicise it on the website. For details email reception@invictaradio.co.uk.

Isle Of Wight Radio (102.0 & 107.0 FM)
Dodnor Park, Newport, Isle of Wight, PO30 5XE
tel: 01983 822 557
fax: 01983 822 109
email: studio@iwradio.co.uk
web: www.iwradio.co.uk
contact: Tom Stroud
take demos: Yes
info: Accept demos, though mainly from local bands. Airplay of new music at the presenter's discretion. Organise and get involved with local events. Contact Tom Stroud or the Station Director, Andy Shier, at andy.shier@iwradio.co.uk

Juice 107.2
170 North Street, Brighton, BN1 1EA
tel: 01273 386 107
fax: 01273 273 107
email: studio@juicebrighton.com
web: www.juicebrighton.com
contact: Marcus O'Dair
take demos: Yes
info: Every Sunday Marcus O'Dair hosts 'Totally Wired' between 8pm and 10pm. Features new music and unsigned bands. Juice is also involved with several local events, email enquiries to info@juicebrigton.com.

Kick FM 105.6 & 107.4 FM
The Studios, 42 Bone Lane, Newbury, RG14 5SD
tel: 01635 841 600
fax: 01635 841 010
email: markwatson@kickfm.com
web: www.kickfm.co.uk
contact: Mark Watson
take demos: Yes
info: No specific time dedicated to unsigned bands, but do get involved with and organise local events where bands can perform. Contact Mark Watson for details.

KM-FM 106 FM
9 St. George's Place, Canterbury, CT1 1UU
tel: 01227 475 950
fax: 01227 785 106
email: kmfmstudio@kmradio.co.uk
web: www.kmradio.co.uk
contact: Toby Mackenzie
take demos: Yes
info: Broadcast over Canterbury, Whitstable and Herne Bay. Demos will be considered. May cover local events. For details contact Toby Mackenzie.

KM-FM 107.2 FM
8 Northdown Road, Cliftonville, Margate, CT9 2PA
tel: 01843 223 344
fax: 01843 299 666
email: kmfmstudio@kmradio.co.uk
web: www.kmradio.co.uk
contact: Toby Mackenzie
take demos: Yes
info: Broadcast locally over Thanet. Demos will be considered. May cover local events. For details contact Toby Mackenzie.

KM-FM 107.9 & 100.4 FM
Medway House, Sir Thomas Longly Road, Medway City Estate, Strood, Rochester, ME2 4DU
tel: 01634 227 808
fax: 01634 297 272
email: kmfmstudio@kmradio.co.uk
web: www.kmradio.co.uk
contact: Toby Mackenzie
take demos: Yes
info: Broadcast over Medway. Demos will be considered and bands may be asked to play at local events. For details contact Toby Mackenzie.

KM-FM 96.2 & 101.6 FM
1 East Street, Tonbridge, Kent, TN9 1AR
tel: 01732 369 200
fax: 01732 369 201
email: kmfmstudio@kmradio.co.uk
web: www.kmradio.co.uk
contact: Toby Mackenzie
take demos: Yes
info: Broadcast across West Kent. Demos will be considered. For details contact Toby Mackenzie.

KM-FM 96.4 & 106.8 FM
93-95 Sandgate Road, Folkstone, Kent, CT20 2BQ
tel: 01303 220 303
fax: 01303 246 659
email: kmfmstudio@kmradio.co.uk
web: www.kmradio.co.uk
contact: Toby Mackenzie
take demos: No
info: Broadcast over Shepway and White Cliffs Country. Demos will be considered and the station covers local events from time to time. For details contact Toby Mackenzie.

Mercury 96.6 FM
Unit 5, The Metro Centre, Dwight Road, Watford, WD18 9UD
tel: 01923 205 470
email: tank.montana@musicradio.com
web: www.hertsmercury.co.uk
contact: Tank Montana
take demos: Yes
info: Welcome demos. Send to Programmer Tank Montana via above email address.

Mix 107 FM
PO Box 1107, High Wycombe, Buckinghamshire, HP13 6WQ
tel: 01494 446 611
email: studio@mix107.co.uk
web: www.mix107.co.uk
contact: Kate Beveridge
take demos: Yes
info: Demos can be sent to the address above, although there are no dedicated unsigned slots. Mark submissions FAO Kate Beveridge.

Mix 96 FM
Friars Square Studios, 11 Bourbon Street, Aylesbury, HP20 2PZ
tel: 01296 399 396
fax: 01296 398 988
email: mix@mix96.co.uk
web: www.mix96.co.uk
contact: James O'Neill
take demos: Yes
info: Local bands can send demos to the address above, although there is no dedicated unsigned air time.

Ocean FM (96.7 & 97.5 FM)
Radio House, Whittle Avenue, Segensworth, West Fareham, PO15 5SH
tel: 01489 589 911
fax: 01489 589 453
email: via website
web: www.oceanfm.com
contact: Stuart Ellis
take demos: Yes
info: Send demos to Stuart Ellis at the address above. For information about local events contact Neil Wyatt.

Passion 107.9 FM
270 Woodstock Road, Oxford, OX2 7NW
tel: 01865 315 980
fax: 01865 315 981
email: via website
web: www.passion1079.com
contact: Susie
take demos: Yes
info: There is no dedicated unsigned airtime, but Susie has played demos in the past on her Sunday evening show. Send demos to the address above.

Reading 107 FM
Radio House, Madejski Stadium, Reading, RG2 0FN
tel: 0118 986 2555
fax: 0118 945 0809
email: warren or tim@reading107fm.com
web: www.reading107fm.com
contact: Tim Grundy, Warren Lee
take demos: Yes
info: Contact Warren or Tim at the email address above. Follow with demo on request.

SGR Colchester (96.1 FM)
Abbeygate Two, 9 Whitwell Road, Colchester, CO2 7DE
tel: 01206 575 859
fax: 01206 216 149
email: jonathan.hemmings@musicradio.com
web: www.sgrfm.co.uk
contact: Natasha Sims, Jonathan Hemmings
take demos: Yes
info: Send demos to Jonathan Hemmings (Programme Controller) at the address above.

Southern FM (102.4 - 103.5 FM)
Radio House, PO Box 2000, Brighton, BN41 2SS
tel: 01273 430 111
fax: 01273 430 098
email: info@southernfm.com
web: www.southernfm.com
contact: Tony Aldridge
take demos: No
info: Playlist is compiled centrally and not by individual presenters.

Spirit FM (96.6 & 102.3 FM)
9 Dukes Court, Bognor Road, Chichester, West Sussex, PO19 2FX
tel: 01243 539 000
fax: 01243 786 464
email: info@spiritfm.net
web: www.spiritfm.net
contact: Ian Meadows
take demos: Yes
info: Every Wednesday night Ian Meadows presents 'The Unsigned'. Send demos to the address above.

Star 106.6 FM
The Observatory, High Street, Slough, Berkshire, SL1 1LH
tel: 01753 551 066
email: info@star1066.co.uk
web: www.star1066.co.uk
contact: Paul Allen
take demos: No
info: Do not accept demos but will get involved with local events. Contact Paul Allen for details.

Ten-17 (101.7 FM)
Latton Bush Business Centre, Southern Way, Harlow, Essex, CM18 7BU
tel: 01279 431 017
fax: 01279 236 659
email: jack.cayler@musicradio.com
web: http://ten17.musicradio.com
contact: Jack Cayler
take demos: No

Time 107.5 FM
7th Floor, Lambourne House, Weston Road, Romford, RM1 3LD
tel: 01708 731 643
fax: 01708 730 383
email: onair@timefm.com
web: www.timefm.com
contact: Mark Dover
take demos: Yes
info: Demos sent FAO Mark Dover to the address above. Commercial radio station but will consider all material sent to them.

Wave 105.2 FM
5 Manor Court, Barnes Willis Road, Segensworth East, Fareham, Hampshire, PO15 5TH
tel: 01489 481 057
email: studio@wave105.com
web: www.wave105.com
contact: Michelle Horn
take demos: Yes
info: Michelle Horn presents the weekday night time show from 8pm. Occasionally play unsigned material. Send demos to the address above.

Win 107.2 FM
PO Box 107.2, The Brooks, Winchester, SO23 8FT
tel: 01962 841 071
email: webmaster@winfm.co.uk
web: www.winfm.co.uk
take demos: Yes
info: Send demos to the above address. There is no specific show to promote unsigned artists but selected demos from local bands are sometimes broadcast during the afternoon.

SOUTHWEST

102 Spire FM
City Hall Studios, Malthouse Lane, Salisbury, Wiltshire, SP2 7QQ
tel: 01722 416 644
email: studio@spirefm.co.uk
web: www.spirefm.co.uk
contact: Ceri Jones
take demos: Yes
info: Send demos to the address above.

102.4 FM Severn Sound
Bridge Studios, Eastgate Centre, Gloucester, GL1 1SS
tel: 01452 572 400
fax: 01452 313 213
email: marcus.langreiter@musicradio.co.uk
web: http://severnsound.musicradio.com
contact: Marcus Langreiter
take demos: Yes
info: Demos can be sent directly to the station, from where they will be forwarded to the GWR Group in Bristol who compile playlists centrally.

104.7 Island FM
12 Westerbrook, St. Sampsons, Guernsey, GY2 4QQ
tel: 01481 242 000
fax: 01481 241 120
email: studio@islandfm.guernsey.net
web: www.islandfm.com
contact: Simon Charlwood
take demos: Yes
info: 'The Edge' is aired on Mondays between 8pm and 10pm and regularly features live Acoustic sets and Alternative music. Send demos to Simon Charlwood at the address above. Mike Campbell, who presents the Saturday night Rock Show between 10pm and 1am, also plays unsigned material.

MEDIA

107.4 BCR FM
PO Box 1074, Bridgwater, Somerset, TA6 4WE
tel: 01278 727 700
email: info@bcrfm.co.uk
web: www.bcrfm.co.uk
contact: Adrian Fraser
take demos: Yes
info: 'The Sunday Alternative' is presented by Adrian Fraser and is broadcast every Sunday night between 7pm and 9pm. Features local unsigned talent. Send demos to the address above.

107.9 Bath FM
Station House, Ashley Avenue, Lower Weston, Bath, BA1 3DS
tel: 01225 483 344
fax: 01225 471 681
email: steve.collins@bathfm.com
web: www.bathfm.com
contact: Geoff Barker
take demos: Yes
info: Geoff Barker's evening show, broadcast Monday to Friday between 7pm and 11pm, features local unsigned bands. Submit demos and biog to the address above.

2CR 102.3 FM
5-7 Southcote Road, Bournemouth, Dorset, BH1 3LR
tel: 01202 234 900
email: martin.lee@creation.com
web: http://2crfm.musicradio.com
contact: Martyn Lee
take demos: Yes
info: Accept demos for consideration, mark FAO Martyn Lee.

3TR 107.5 FM
Riverside Studios, Warminster, Wiltshire, BA12 9HQ
tel: 01985 211 111
email: admin@3trfm.com
web: www.3trfm.com
take demos: No

97 FM Plymouth Sound
Earls Acre, Plymouth, PL3 4HX
tel: 01752 275 600
fax: 01752 275 605
email: dave.england@creation.com
web: www.musicradio.com
contact: Dave England
take demos: Yes
info: Do accept demos but there is a very clear programming policy. Plymouth Sound are happy to try and publicise local events and can do outside broadcasts. For further information contact the Programming Department.

97.4 Vale FM
Longmead, Shaftesbury, Dorset, SP7 8QQ
tel: 01747 855 711
email: studio@valefm.co.uk
web: www.valefm.co.uk
contact: Stewart Smith
take demos: Yes
info: Local bands can submit demos to the address above.

BBC Radio Bristol (95.5, 94.9 FM & 1548 AM)
Po Box 194, Bristol, BS99 7QT
tel: 0117 974 1111
email: radio.bristol@bbc.co.uk
web: www.bbc.co.uk/england/radiobristol/
contact: Keith Warmington
take demos: Yes
info: Local Singer-Songwriter and Acoustic acts may get some airplay on Keith Warmington's Evening Show between 4pm and 7pm. Submit demo and biog to the address above. May publicise unsigned events. Send details to 'What's On' department at the address given.

BBC Radio Cornwall (103.9 & 95.2 FM)
Phoenix Wharf, Truro, Cornwall, TR1 1UA
tel: 01872 275 421
email: radio.cornwall@bbc.co.uk
web: www.bbc.co.uk/england/radiocornwall/
contact: David White
take demos: Yes
info: There are no dedicated unsigned slots, but demos are welcome for consideration. Mark FAO David White.

BBC Radio Devon
(103.4, 104.3, 95.8, 94.8, 96 FM & 801, 1458 AM)
Broadcasting House, Seymour Road, Mannamead, Plymouth, PL3 5BD
tel: 01752 260 323
email: radio.devon@bbc.co.uk
web: www.bbc.co.uk/england/radiodevon/
take demos: No
info: Do not accept demos.

BBC Radio Gloucestershire (104.7 FM & 1413 AM)
London Road, Gloucester, GL1 1SW
tel: 01452 308 585
email: radio.gloucestershire@bbc.co.uk
web: www.bbc.co.uk/england/radiogloucestershire/
take demos: No
info: Does not accept demos but the BBC Gloucestershire website does have a large section dedicated to local new music (www.bbc.co.uk/gloucestershire/music). Email gloucestershire@bbc.co.uk with details of your band and upcoming live dates.

BBC Radio Guernsey (93.2 FM & 1116 AM)
Broadcasting House, Bulwer Avenue, St. Sampsons, GY2 4LA
tel: 01481 200 600
email: radio.guernsey@bbc.co.uk
web: www.bbc.co.uk/england/radioguernsey/
contact: John Randall
take demos: Yes
info: John Randall will occasionally play unsigned material. Send demos to the address above.

BBC Radio Jersey (88.8 FM & 1026 AM)
18 Parade Road, St. Helier, Jersey, JE2 3PL
tel: 01534 870 000
email: ryan.morrison@bbc.co.uk
web: www.bbc.co.uk/england/radiojersey/
contact: Ryan Morrison
take demos: Yes
info: The station's playlist is typically MOR, Singer-Songwriter and Classical music, so demos for airplay are generally not considered. However, the BBC Radio Jersey website has a large section dedicated to the local music scene (www.bbc.co.uk/jersey/music). The site features a full A to Z directory of local bands and musicians and details of gigs on the island. May run features on any Jersey based band or bands with a Jersey connection. Email Ryan Morrison at the address above. Follow with demo and details of any upcoming Jersey gigs.

BBC Radio Swindon
PO Box 1234, Swindon, Wiltshire, SN1 3RW
tel: 01793 513 626
email: radio.swindon@bbc.co.uk
web: www.bbc.co.uk/england/radioswindon
take demos: Yes
info: Accept demos. Send to the address above.

BBC Radio Wiltshire & Radio Swindon
(103.5, 104.3 & 104.9 FM)
PO Box 1234, Trowbridge, Wiltshire, SN1 3RW
tel: 01793 513 626
email: radio.wiltshire@bbc.co.uk
web: www.bbc.co.uk/england/radiowiltshire/
contact: Mark Seaman, James Harrison, Kelly Stooke
take demos: Yes
info: Demos submitted will need to appeal to the target audience of the station, 45 + , for any chance of airplay. Please send all demos FAO Mark Seaman.

BBC Somerset Sound (1566 AM)
Broadcasting House, Park Street, Taunton, Somerset, TA1 4DA
tel: 01823 348 920
fax: 01823 332 539
web: www.bbc.co.uk/england/somersetsound
contact: Jo Philips
take demos: Yes
info: Jo Philips hosts a show every Fridays that showcases local Somerset bands. Send demo to the above address.

Channel 103.7 FM
6 Tunnell Street, St. Helier, Jersey, JE2 4LU
tel: 01534 888 103
fax: 01534 887 799
email: steve.ross@channel103.com
web: www.channel103.com
contact: Spencer Davis
take demos: Yes
info: Demos can be sent to the address above, although the station does not have any dedicated unsigned airtime.

Fire 107.6 FM
Quadrant Studios, Old Christchurch Road, Bournemouth, BH1 2AD
tel: 01202 318 100
fax: 01202 318 110
email: paul@fire1076.com
web: www.fire1076.com
contact: Paul Gerrard
take demos: Yes
info: The Sunday evening show may play unsigned material. Send demos and biog to Paul Gerard (Head Of Music) at the above address. Will also get involved with live events. See website for details.

Gemini FM (97 & 103 FM)
Hawthorne House, Exeter Business Park, Exeter, Devon, EX1 3QS
tel: 01392 444 444
fax: 01392 354 209
email: info@musicradio.com
web: www.musicradio.com
contact: Gavin Marshall
take demos: Yes
info: Send demos to Gavin Marshall (Programme Controller) at the address above. Will organise some local events where local bands can play. Contact Gavin for details.

GWR 96.3 FM
PO Box 2000, 1 Passage Street, Bristol, BS99 7SN
tel: 0117 984 3200
fax: 0117 984 3202
email: reception@gwrfm.musicradio.com
web: www.musicradio.com
contact: Paul Andrew, Caroline Muphy
take demos: Yes
info: Send demos and biog to Paul Andrew (Programme Controller) at the address above. Although there are no specific unsigned slots, material submitted will be considered.

GWR FM (102.2, 96.5 & 97.2 FM)
PO Box 2000, Swindon, SN4 7EX
tel: 01793 842 600
fax: 01793 842 602
email: wiltshire.news@musicradio.com
web: www.musicradio.com
contact: Shaun Skinner
take demos: Yes
info: No dedicated unsigned airtime, but demo submissions will be considered. Send material to the address above, mark FAO Shaun Skinner. Will consider coverage of local events. For information contact eve.reynolds@musicradio.com.

Ivel FM 105.6
The Studios, Middle Street, Yeovil, Somerset, BA20 1DJ
tel: 01935 848 488
email: info@ivelfm.com
web: www.ivelfm.com
take demos: No
info: Don't accept demos.

Lantern FM (96.2 & 97.3 FM)
2b Lauder Lane, Roundswell Business Park, Barnstaple, EX31 3TA
tel: 01271 340 340
fax: 01271 340 345
email: lanternfm@koko.com
web: www.musicradio.com
contact: Paul Hopper
take demos: Yes
info: There is no dedicated unsigned airtime, but demos are accepted for consideration.

Orchard FM (96.5, 97.1 & 102.5 FM)
Haygrove House, Taunton, Somerset, TA3 7BT
tel: 01823 338 448
fax: 01823 368 318
email: orchardfm@koko.com
web: http://orchardfm.musicradio.com
contact: Steve Bulley
take demos: Yes
info: Send demos to the address above.

Pirate FM 102
Wilson Way, Redruth, Cornwall, TR15 3XX
tel: 0870 800 0007
fax: 01209 315 250
email: neil@piratefm.co.uk
web: www.piratefm.co.uk
contact: Bob McCreadie, Neil Caddy
take demos: Yes
info: Neil Caddy will air new and unsigned music. Demos should be sent to the address above.

Quaywest Radio (102.4 & 100.8 FM)
The Harbour Studios, The Esplanade, Watchet, Somerset, TA23 0AJ
tel: 01984 634 900
fax: 01984 634 811
email: studio@quaywest.fm
web: www.quaywestradio.com
contact: David Mortimer
take demos: Yes
info: There are no dedicated unsigned slots but demos can be sent to the address above.

Queywest FM 100.8 FM
The Harbour Studios, The Esplanade, Watchet, Somerset, TA23 0AJ
tel: 01984 634 900
email: studio@queywest.fm
web: www.queywest.fm
take demos: Yes
info: Send demos to Scott Temple - may play occasional unsigned songs.

The Saint 107.8 FM
Friends Provident, St. Mary's Stadium, Britannia Road, Southampton, SO14 5FP
tel: 02380 330 300
email: thesaint@saintsfc.co.uk
web: www.saintsfc.co.uk
contact: Stewart Dennis, Robin Caddy
take demos: Yes
info: Southampton Football Club's own radio station. Unsigned demos can be submitted for airplay on the evening slot 'In Session'. All enquiries about unsigned airplay to Robin Caddy (Presenter).

South Hams Radio (100.5 FM)
Unit 1G, South Hams Business Park, Churchstow, South Devon, TQ7 3QR
tel: 01548 854 595
email: rob.wheeler@musicradio.com
contact: Rob Wheeler
take demos: Yes
info: Rob Wheeler will play unsigned material on his Sunday night show between 7pm and midnight. Send demos to the address above.

Star 107 (107.9 FM)
Brunel Mall, London Road, Stroud, Gloucestershire, GL5 2BP
tel: 01453 767 369
fax: 01453 757 107
email: programming@star1079.co.uk
web: www.star1079.co.uk
take demos: Yes
info: Send demos marked FAO Head of Programming.

Star 107.2 FM
Temple Way, Bristol, BS99 7HD
tel: 0117 910 6600
fax: 0117 925 0941
email: studio@star1072.co.uk
web: www.star1072.co.uk
contact: Dave Coull
take demos: Yes
info: Demos will be considered.

Star 107.5 FM
Cheltenham Film Studios, 1st Floor, West Suite, Arle Court, Hatherley Lane, Cheltenham, GL51 6PN
tel: 01242 699 555
fax: 01242 699 666
email: junie@star1075.co.uk
web: www.star1075.co.uk
contact: Brodie Slain
take demos: Yes
info: Send demo to the address above. Mark FAO Brodie Slain.

Star 107.7 FM
11 Beaconsfield Road, Weston Super Mare, Somerset, BS23 1YE
tel: 01934 624 455
email: reception@star1077.co.uk
web: www.star1077.co.uk
contact: Ian Downs
take demos: Yes
info: Send demos to the address above, FAO Ian Downs.

Vibe 101 FM
Millennium House, 26 Baldwin Street, Bristol, BS1 1SE
tel: 0117 901 0101
fax: 0117 930 9149
email: via website
web: www.vibe101.co.uk
take demos: Yes
info: Vibe is a specialist Dance and R&B station. Demos from those genres are accepted, although there is no dedicated unsigned slots.

Wessex 96 FM
Trinity Street, Dorcester, Dorset, DT1 1DJ
tel: 01305 250 333
fax: 01305 250 052
email: via website or jason.herbert@wessexfm.co.uk
web: www.wessexfm.com
contact: Jason Herbert
take demos: No

MEDIA

YORKSHIRE

104.7 Minster FM
Chessingham House, Chessingham Park, Common Road, York,
YO19 5SE
tel: 01904 488 888
email: ed@minsterfm.com
web: www.minsterfm.com
contact: Ed Bretten
take demos: Yes
info: Local bands can send demos to the address above.

96.3 Radio Aire FM
51 Burley Road, Leeds, LS3 1LR
tel: 0113 283 5500
fax: 0113 283 5501
email: stuart.baldwin@radioaire.com
web: www.radioaire.co.uk
contact: Stuart Baldwin, Dan Wood
take demos: Yes
info: Send demos to Stuart Baldwin (Programme Director)
at the address above. Dan Wood presents a late night show which
features local new music.

96.9 Viking FM
Commercial Road, Hull, HU1 2SG
tel: 01482 325 141
fax: 08454 585 969
email: reception@vikingfm.co.uk
web: www.vikingfm.co.uk
contact: Jim Coulson
take demos: Yes
info: The Sunday Session airs music by new bands. Send
your demos to Jim Coulson at the above address.

97.2 Stray FM
The Hamlet, Hornbeam Park Avenue, Harrogate, HG2 8RE
tel: 01423 522 972
email: mail@strayfm.com
web: www.strayfm.com
contact: Ray Stroud
take demos: Yes
info: Send demos to Ray Stroud, the station's Head Of
Music, at the address above.

BBC Radio Humberside (95.9 FM & 1485 AM)
Queens Court, Queens Gardens, Hull, HU1 3RH
tel: 01482 323 232
email: radio.humberside@bbc.co.uk
web: www.bbc.co.uk/england/radiohumberside/
contact: Alan Raw
take demos: Yes
info: Every Thursday night between 7pm and 10pm, Alan
Raw presents 'Raw Talent', a show dedicated to unsigned bands. Send
demos to the address above. 'Raw Talent' is also aired on BBC Radio
Leeds, BBC Radio Sheffield and BBC Radio York.

BBC Radio Leeds (92.4, 95.3 FM & 774 AM)
2 St. Peter's Square, Leeds, LS9 8AH
tel: 0113 224 7300
email: radio.leeds@bbc.co.uk
web: www.bbc.co.uk/england/radioleeds/
contact: Alan Raw
take demos: Yes
info: Every Thursday night between 7pm and 10pm, Alan
Raw presents 'Raw Talent', a show dedicated completely to unsigned
music. Send demo to Alan Raw at the BBC Radio Humberside address.

BBC Radio Sheffield (88.6, 94.7 & 104.1 FM)
54 Shoreham Street, Sheffield, S1 4RS
tel: 0114 273 1177
fax: 0114 267 5454
email: radio.sheffield@bbc.co.uk
web: www.bbc.co.uk/england/radiosheffield/
contact: Ony Bright, Cynthia Brookes
take demos: Yes
info: No dedicated unsigned airtime but do accept demos
for consideration.

BBC Radio York (103.7, 104.3 & 95.5 FM)
20 Bootham Row, York, YO30 7BR
tel: 01904 641 351
email: northyorkshire.radio@bbc.co.uk
web: www.bbc.co.uk/england/radioyork/
contact: Matt Seymour
take demos: Yes
info: Every Thursday night from 7pm to 10pm Alan Raw
presents 'Raw Talent', a show dedicated completely to unsigned music.
Send a demo to Alan Raw at the BBC Radio Newcastle address. There
is also a weekly local Folk programme aired at Radio York. For details
please Michael Brothwell at michael.brothwell@bbc.co.uk.

BCB 96.7 FM
11 Rawson Road, Bradford, BD1 3SH
tel: 01274 771 677
email: info@bcb.yorks.com
web: www.bcb.yorks.com
contact: John Gill
take demos: Yes
info: Send demos to Head of Music, John Gill.

Dearne FM (97.1 & 102 FM)
Unit 7, Network Centre, Zenith Park, Whaley Road, Barnsley, S75 1HT
tel: 01226 321 733
fax: 01226 321 755
email: studio@dearnefm.co.uk
web: www.dearnefm.co.uk
contact: Matt Jones
take demos: Yes
info: Send demos to the address above. Mark FAO Matt
Jones.

Fresh Radio (936, 1413 & 1431 AM)
Firth Mill, Firth Street, Skipton, BD23 2PT
tel: 01756 799 991
fax: 01756 799 771
email: info@freshradio.co.uk
web: www.freshradio.co.uk
contact: Laurence Budd
take demos: Yes
info: Weekly local unsigned show. Send demo on MD,
DAT or CD to Laurence Budd at the address above. Fresh Radio covers
Lancashire and Yorkshire. Encourages all bands from this area to send
in material for possible inclusion.

Galaxy 105 FM
2a Joseph's Well, Hanover Way, Park Lane, Leeds, LS3 1AB
tel: 0113 213 0105
fax: 0113 213 1054
email: andi.durrant@galaxy105.co.uk
web: www.galaxy105.co.uk
contact: Andi Durrant
take demos: Yes
info: Send demos on CD, vinyl, MD or DAT to Andi Durrant,
who presents 'The Big Night In' every Friday from 11pm. Dance Music
only please.

Hallam FM
Radio House, 900 Herries Road, Sheffield, S6 1RH
tel: 0114 209 1000
fax: 0114 285 3159
email: programmes@hallamfm.co.uk
web: www.hallamfm.co.uk
contact: Chris Straw
take demos: Yes
info: Send demos to the address above. Air-time dedicated
to new music, presented by The Foam Boy. Will also get involved with
local events where unsigned bands can perform. For details contact
Head of Music, Chris Straw.

Home 107.9 FM
Lockwood Park, Huddersfield, West Yorkshire, HD1 3UR
tel: 01484 321 107
email: info@home1079.com
web: www.home1079.com
contact: Ritchie Clark
take demos: Yes
info: Direct demos to Ritchie Clark.

Magic 1161
Commercial Road, Hull, HU1 2SG
tel: 01482 325 141
web: www.magic1161.co.uk
contact: Dan Morfitt
take demos: Yes
info: Have show called the Sunday Session aired 10pm to
midnight, playing new music. Send demos to Dan Morfitt.

Magic 828 AM
51 Burley Road, Leeds, LS3 1LR
tel: 0113 283 5500
web: www.magic828.co.uk
contact: Andy Siddell
take demos: Yes
info: Willing to listen to demos. Send to Andy Siddell.

Magic AM (Sheffield 1548 AM)
Radio House, 900 Herries Road, Sheffield, S6 1RH
tel: 0114 209 1000
web: www.magicam.co.uk
info: Don't accept demos..

The Pulse of West Yorkshire (97.5 & 102.5 FM)
Forster Square, Bradford, BD1 5NE
tel: 01274 203 040
fax: 01274 203 120
email: general@pulse.co.uk
web: www.pulse.co.uk
contact: Mark Brow
take demos: Yes
info: Send demos to the address above. For details about airplay contact Mark Brow.

Real Radio Yorkshire (106-108 FM)
1 Sterling Court, Capitol Business Park, Tingley, WF3 1EL
tel: 0113 238 1114
fax: 0113 252 7102
email: via website
web: http://yorkshire.realradiofm.com
contact: Terry Underhill
take demos: Yes
info: Send demos to Terry Underhill, Programme Director.

Ridings FM (106.8 FM)
PO Box 333, Wakefield, WF2 7YQ
tel: 01924 367 177
fax: 01924 367133
email: enquiries@ridingsfm.co.uk
web: www.ridingsfm.co.uk
contact: John Tolson
take demos: Yes
info: Demos are accepted for consideration with an emphasis on local unsigned music. Send all demos to John Tolson (Station Manager) at the address above.

Sunrise FM (103.2 FM)
Sunrise House, 30 Chapel Street, Little Germany, Bradford, BD1 5DN
tel: 01274 735 043
fax: 01274 728 534
email: info@sunriseradio.fm
web: www.sunriseradio.fm
contact: Raj Parmer
take demos: Yes
info: Send demos to the address above.

Trax 107.1 FM
5 Sidings Court, White Rose Way, Doncaster, DN4 5NU
tel: 01302 341 166
fax: 01302 326 104
email: enquiries@traxfm.co.uk
web: www.traxfm.co.uk
contact: Mike Bargh, Rob Wagstaff
take demos: Yes
info: Showcase local unsigned talent every Wednesday night. Send demos for attention of Mike Bargh to the above address.

Yorkshire Coast Radio (103.1 FM)
PO Box 962, Scarborough, North Yorkshire, YO12 3ZP
tel: 01723 581 700
email: info@yorkshirecoastradio.com
web: www.yorkshirecoastradio.com
take demos: No

Yorkshire Coast Radio (Bridlington 102.4fm)
Old Harbour Master's Office, Harbour Road, Bridlington, East Yorkshire, YO15 2NR
tel: 01262 404 400
email: studio@yorkshirecoastradio.com
web: www.yorkshirecoastradio.com
take demos: Yes
info: Accept demos. Send to Ben Fry at the address above.

NORTHERN IRELAND

BBC Radio Foyle (93.1 FM & 792 MW)
8 Northland Road, Derry, Londonderry, BT48 7GD
tel: 028 7137 8600
email: mark.patterson@bbc.co.uk
web: www.bbc.co.uk/northernireland/radiofoyle/
contact: Mark Patterson
info: Send demos to Mark Patterson at the address above.

BBC Radio Ulster (92.7 - 95.4 FM & 873, 1341 AM)
Broadcasting House, Ormeau Avenue, Belfast, BT2 8HQ
tel: 028 9033 8000
fax: 028 9033 8800
web: www.bbc.co.uk/northernireland/radio/
contact: Donna Legge
take demos: Yes
info: 'Across The Line' is BBC Radio Ulster's Alternative music show. Broadcast Monday to Thursday, 8pm to 10pm. Send demos to the show's producer, Donna Legge, at to the address above.

Belfast City Beat (96.7 FM)
Lamont Buildings, 46 Stranmillis Embankment, Belfast, BT9 5FN
tel: 028 9020 5967
email: info@citybeat.co.uk
web: www.citybeat.co.uk
take demos: Yes
info: Send demos to the address above.

City Beat 96.7 FM
Lamont Buildings, Strandmillis Road, Belfast, BT9 5FN
tel: 028 9020 5967
fax: 028 9020 0023
email: stuart.robinson@cnradio.co.uk
web: www.citybeat.co.uk
contact: Stuart Robinson
take demos: Yes
info: No dedicated unsigned airtime, but demos and biogs can be sent to the address above. Mark FAO Stuart Robinson.

Cool FM (97.4 FM)
PO Box 974, Belfast, BT1 1RT
tel: 028 9181 7181
email: music@coolfm.co.uk
web: www.coolfm.co.uk
take demos: Yes
info: Demos accepted. Send to address above.

Downtown Radio (96.4 - 103 FM)
Newtownards, County Down, Northern Ireland, BT23 4ES
tel: 028 9181 5555
fax: 028 9181 8913
email: programmes@downtown.co.uk
web: www.downtown.co.uk
contact: Lisa Flavell
take demos: Yes
info: Lisa Flavell presents the weekday afternoon show, and will occasionally feature local unsigned bands. Send demos to Lisa at the address above.

Mid FM 106-7 FM
2c Park Avenue, Burn Road, Cookstown, BT80 8AH
tel: 028 8675 8696
email: studio@midfm.co.uk
web: www.midfm.co.uk
contact: James Delvin
take demos: Yes
info: Send demos for attention of James Delvin, Programme Controller.

Q101 West
42a Market Street, Omagh, BT74 6AA
tel: 028 6632 0777
email: stewart@q101west.fm
web: www.q101west.fm
contact: Paddy Hunter, Nick Davidson
take demos: Yes
info: Paddy Hunter is happy to receive demos from unsigned bands and musicians of all genres. He presents the station's Sunday night show between 6pm and 10pm, and regularly broadcasts unsigned material. Send CDs or MDs to the address above.

Q102.9 FM
The Riverview Suite, 87 Rossdowney Road, Old Waterside Railway Station, Derry, BT47 5SU
tel: 028 7134 4449
fax: 028 7131 1177
email: manager@q102.fm
web: www.q102.fm
contact: Steve Kirk
take demos: Yes
info: Send demos to Steve Kirk at the address above.

Q97.2 Causeway Coast Radio
24 Cloyfin Road, Coleraine, BT52 2NU
tel: 028 7035 9100
fax: 028 7032 6666
email: requests@q972.fm
web: www.q972.fm
contact: Nick Davidson
take demos: Yes
info: Send demos to the address above. Nick Davidson will air new and unsigned music on his show and demos should be sent to him at the address above.

MEDIA

SCOTLAND

103.1 Central FM
201-203 High Street, Falkirk, FK1 1DU
tel: 01324 611 164
email: mail@centralfm.co.uk
web: www.centralfm.co.uk
contact: Tom Bell
take demos: Yes
info: Send demos to Tom Bell at the address above.

107 The Edge
Radio House, Rowantree Avenue, Newhouse Industrial Estate, Newhouse, Lanarkshire, ML1 5RX
tel: 01698 733 107
email: dan@107theedge.com
web: www.107theedge.com
contact: Dan Stenhouse
take demos: Yes
info: Send demos to Dan Stenhouse at the address above. Contact Brian Wilson at brian@107theedge.com with details of any new music. The Edge are also involved with a festival at Strathclyde Country Park where bands can perform. For further details contact Brian Wilson.

1548 AM Forth 2
Forth Street, Edinburgh, EH1 3LF
tel: 0131 556 9255
email: info@forth2.com
web: www.forth2.com
take demos: No
info: Only play Top 40 hits.

97.3 Forth One
Forth House, Forth Street, Edinburgh, EH1 3LE
tel: 0131 556 9255
fax: 0131 558 3277
email: info@forthone.com
web: www.forthone.com
info: Do not accept demos.

97.4 MFR FM
Scorguie Place, Inverness, IV3 6SF
tel: 01463 224 433
email: danny.gallagher@mfr.co.uk
web: www.mfr.co.uk
contact: Danny Gallagher
take demos: Yes
info: Send demos for the attention of Danny.

Argyll 106.5, 107.1 & 107.7 FM
27-29 Longrow, Campbeltown, Argyll, PA28 6ER
tel: 01586 551 800
fax: 01586 551 888
email: argyllradio@hotmail.com
web: www.argyllfm.co.uk
contact: Colin Middleton
take demos: Yes
info: Airplay is varied and spans several genres. Demos should be sent to Colin Middleton for consideration.

BBC Radio Scotland (92 - 95 FM & 810 MW)
Queen Margaret Drive, Glasgow, G12 8DG
tel: 0141 338 2000
fax: 0141 338 2346
email: air@bbc.co.uk
web: www.bbc.co.uk/scotland/radioscotland/
take demos: Yes
info: Play demos from new bands via web vote. Send your demos to the above address.

Beat 106 FM
Four Winds Pavilion, Pacific Quay, Glasgow, G51 1EB
tel: 0141 566 6106
fax: 0141 566 6110
email: reception@beat106.com
web: www.beat106.com
contact: Jim Gellatly
take demos: Yes
info: Demos can be sent to the programme controller, with band demos can be sent to Jim Gellatly. Jim Gellatly also presents 'The Beat Scene' which plays unsigned music. To participate in any local events, contact Karen Woodrow, Station Co-ordinator.

Caithness FM (102.5 FM)
Neil Gunn Drive, Thurso, Highland, KW14 7QU
tel: 01847 890 000
email: studio@caithnessfm.co.uk
web: www.caithnessfm.co.uk
take demos: Yes
info: Caithness FM broadcast times are 7pm to midnight from Sunday to Friday. Saturday transmissions are from 2pm to 4pm and 8pm to midnight.

Clyde 1 (102 FM)
Clydebank Business Park, Clydebank, Glasgow, G81 2RX
tel: 0141 565 2300
fax: 0141 565 2265
email: billy.sloan@clyde1.com
web: www.clyde1.com
contact: Billy Sloan
take demos: Yes
info: Billy Sloan will occasionally play unsigned music on his Sunday evening show, broadcast between 7pm and 10pm. Send demos and biog to the address above.

Clyde 2 (1152 AM)
Clydebank Business Park, Clydebank, Glasgow, G81 2RF
tel: 0141 565 2200
email: info@clyde2.com
web: www.clyde2.com
take demos: Yes
info: Send CDs and information to Billy Sloan who runs an unsigned music show 7pm to 10pm every Sunday.

Cuillin FM 106.2 FM
Tigh Lisigarry, Bridge Road, Portree, Isle of Skye, IV51 9ER
tel: 01478 612 921
email: info@cuillinfm.co.uk
web: www.cuillinfm.co.uk
take demos: Yes
info: Run by volunteers. Send demos to Nick Wakeham.

Heartland 97.5 FM
Lower Oakfield, Pitlochry, Highland Perthshire, PH16 5HQ
tel: 01796 474 040
fax: 01796 474 007
email: mailbox@heartlandfm.co.uk
web: www.heartlandfm.co.uk
contact: Pete Ramsden, Marion McDonald
take demos: Yes
info: Pete Ramsden will play some unsigned material on his Saturday night show, which airs between 7pm and 10pm. Send demos to the address above. Will happily publicise any local events in their 'What's On' section. Also organise events where bands can perform. Contact Marion McDonald for details.

Isles 103 FM
PO Box 333, Stornaway, Isle of Lewis, Western Isles, HS1 2PU
tel: 01851 703 333
fax: 01851 703 322
email: admin@isles.fm
web: www.isles.fm
contact: Kenny Macloed, Innes Morrison
take demos: Yes
info: The station is happy to receive demos from local unsigned bands, along with details of up and coming gigs. Bands that receive airplay may also be invited into the studio for interviews. Contact Innes Morrison for details of local events.

Kingdom 95.2 FM & 96.1 FM
Haig House, Haig Business Park, Markinch, Fife, KY7 6AQ
tel: 01592 753 753
fax: 01592 612 022
email: kevin@kingdomfm.co.uk
web: www.kingdomfm.co.uk
contact: Kevin Brady
take demos: Yes
info: No dedicated unsigned air-time but do accept demos for consideration. Send CDs to the address above, mark FAO Kevin Brady.

Lochbroom FM 102.2 & 96.8 FM
Radio House, Mill Street, Ullapool, IV26 2UN
tel: 01854 613 131
email: lochbroomfm@ecosse.net
web: www.lochbroomfm.co.uk
contact: Stephen Murphy
take demos: Yes
info: Accept demos. Stephen Murphy plays Murphy's Monday Mix 7pm to 8pm and is very open to new music.

Moray Firth Radio (1107 AM)
PO Box 271, Scorguie Place, Inverness, IV3 8UJ
tel: 01463 224 433
fax: 01463 243 224
email: danny@mfr.co.uk
web: www.mfr.co.uk
contact: Titch McCooey
take demos: Yes
info: No dedicated unsigned slots but will accept demos for consideration. Mark FAO Titch McCooey. Organise lots of local events for bands to perform. For further details contact kyle.taylor@mfr.co.uk.

NECR (97.1 - 106.4 FM)
The Shed, School Road, Kintore, Inverurie, Aberdeenshire, AB51 0UX
tel: 01467 632 909
fax: 01467 632 969
email: enquiries@necrfm.co.uk
web: www.necrfm.co.uk
contact: John Dean
take demos: Yes
info: Demos are accepted for consideration. Airtime is available for unsigned acts particularly 'The Album Programme', which is broadcast every Saturday and Sunday between 10pm and 12pm. There are also limited slots for more pop orientated demos on 'The Hit Factor' which is broadcast between 10pm and 12pm, Monday to Friday. Send CD and biog to John Dean at the address above.

Nevis Radio (96.6, 97, 102.3 & 102.4 FM)
Ben Nevis Industrial Estate, Fort William, PH33 6PR
tel: 01397 700 007
fax: 01397 701 007
email: onair@nevisradio.co.uk
web: www.nevisradio.co.uk
contact: Michael Mcrae
take demos: Yes
info: Send demos addressed to Michael McRae, Head of Music.

Northsound 1 (96.9 97.6 & 103 FM)
Abbotswell Road, West Tullis, Aberdeen, AB15 4EL
tel: 01224 337 000
fax: 01224 636 282
email: chris.thomson@northsound1.co.uk
web: www.northsound1.com
contact: Chris Thomson
take demos: Yes
info: There are night slots where new music will be played. For further information and to send demos, contact Chris Thomson at the address above.

Northsound 2
Abbotswell Road, West Tullos, Aberdeen, Aberdeenshire, AB12 3AJ
tel: 01224 337 000
email: chris.thomson@northsound2.co.uk
web: www.northsound2.co.uk
contact: Chris Thomson
take demos: Yes
info: Send CDs to Chris at above address

Oban FM 103.3
132 George Street, Oban, Argyll, PA34 5NT
tel: 01631 570 057
fax: 01631 570 530
email: obanfmradio@btconnect.com
contact: Ian Simmonds, Laura Johnston
take demos: Yes
info: Local bands can send demos to the address above. Rock and Pop only please. Send demos to Ian Simmonds or Laura Johnston.

Q96
65 Sussex Street, Glasgow, G41 1DX
tel: 0141 429 9430
fax: 0141 429 9431
email: studio@q-fm.com
web: www.q96.net
contact: Mike Richardson
take demos: Yes
info: No dedicated unsigned airtime but demos are accepted for consideration. Send demos and requests for details of local events and shows to the address above. Mark FAO Mike Richardson.

Radio Borders (96.8 - 103.4 FM)
Tweedside Park, Galashiels, TD1 3TD
tel: 01896 759 444
fax: 0848 345 7080
email: stuart.mcculloch@radioborders.com
web: www.radioborders.com
contact: Stuart McCulloch
take demos: Yes
info: Demo submissions are accepted for consideration. Mark FAO Stuart McCulloch (Head of Music).

Real Radio Scotland (100 - 101 FM)
Glasgow Business Park, Glasgow, G69 6GA
tel: 0141 781 1011
fax: 0141 781 1112
email: jay.crawford@realradiofm.com
web: http://scotland.realradiofm.com/
contact: Jay Crawford
take demos: Yes
info: Demos are considered. Submit to the address above, marked FAO Jay Crawford (Programme Manager).

River FM 103.4 FM
Stadium House, Alderstone Road, Livingston, West Lothian, EH54 7DN
tel: 01506 410 411
email: donny.hughes@riverfm.co.uk
web: www.river-fm.com
contact: Donny Hughes
take demos: Yes
info: Send demos into Donny at above address.

SIBC 96.2 FM
Market Street, Lerwick, Shetland Islands, ZE1 0JN
tel: 01595 695 299
email: info@sibc.co.uk
web: www.sibc.co.uk
take demos: Yes
info: Very supportive of local bands. Three local bands currently on high rotation. Unsigned bands are consider for the playlist. Demos must be from local bands only.

South West Sound Radio (96.5, 97 & 103 FM)
The Loreburne Centre, High Street, Dumfries, DG1 2BD
tel: 01387 250 999
fax: 01387 265 629
email: robin.dalgleish@southwestsound.co.uk
web: www.southwestsound.co.uk
contact: Robin Dalgliesh
take demos: Yes
info: South West Sound Radio run an annual 'Battle of The Bands' competition for local acts, which takes place during summer. Visit the website for similar unsigned opportunities throughout the year. The station accepts demos marked FAO Robin Dalgliesh. Robin often plays unsigned material on his lunchtime shows.

Tay FM (96.4 & 102.8 FM)
6 North Isla Street, Dundee, DD3 7JQ
tel: 01382 200 800
email: tayfm@radiotay.co.uk
web: www.tayfm.co.uk
contact: Graeme Ogden
take demos: Yes
info: Graeme Ogden presents 'Weekender', every Sunday night between 7pm and 8pm. Graeme does broadcast selected unsigned material. Send demos to the address above.

Two Lochs Radio
Gairloch, IV21 2LR
tel: 0870 741 4657
web: www.2lr.co.uk
take demos: Yes
info: Community-based radio station, run mainly by volunteers.

Wave 102 FM
8 South Tay Street, Dundee, DD1 1PA
tel: 01382 901 000
email: studio@wave102.co.uk
web: www.wave102.co.uk
contact: Peter Mac
take demos: No

Waves Radio (101.2 FM)
7 Blackhouse Circle, Blackhouse Industrial Estate, Peterhead, Aberdeenshire, AB42 1BN
tel: 01779 491 012
email: waves@wavesfm.com
web: www.wavesfm.com
contact: Norman Spence
take demos: Yes
info: Send demos to the address above.

West 96.7 FM
Radio House, 54A Holmston Road, Ayr, KA7 3BE
tel: 01292 283 662
fax: 01292 283 665
email: alan.toomey@westfm.co.uk
web: www.westfm.co.uk
contact: Alan Toomey
take demos: Yes
info: No dedicated unsigned slots but will accept demos for consideration.

Westsound 1035 AM
Radio House, 54a Holmston Road, Ayr, KA7 3BE
tel: 01292 283 662
email: westsound@srh.co.uk
web: www.westsound.co.uk
contact: Lisbeth Simmons, Innes Young
take demos: Yes
info: There is no dedicated airtime but unsigned bands should see the entry for Westsound's sister station West FM, which accepts demo material.

MEDIA

Your Radio
Pioneer Park Studios, Unit 3, 80 Castlegreen Street, Dumbarton, G82 1JB
tel: 01389 734 422
email: info@yourradiofm.com
web: www.yourradiofm.com
take demos: No
info: Station playing commercial hits, as well as news and sports coverage. Do not accept demos.

WALES

102.5 FM Radio Pembrokeshire
14 Old School Terrace, Station Road, Narbeth, SA67 7DE
tel: 01834 869 384
email: enquiries@radiopembrokeshire.com
web: www.radiopembrokeshire.com
contact: BB Skone
take demos: Yes
info: BB Skone presents a local music show every week, with unsigned bands in session. Send demos to the address above. Radio Pembrokeshire also owns and operates 97.1 Radio Carmarthenshire and 97.5 Scarlet FM. See listings for further details or visit www.radiocarmarthenshire.com

106.3 Bridge FM
Bridge FM Radio Limited, PO Box 1063, Bridgend, Mid Glamorgan, CF35 6WF
tel: 0845 890 4000
fax: 0845 890 5000
email: chris.bull@bridge.fm
web: www.bridge.fm
contact: Chris Bull
take demos: Yes
info: 'Bridge Alternative' is aired every Sunday night between 7pm and 9pm and regularly plays unsigned material. Send demo and biog to Chris Bull at the address above.

96.4 The Wave FM
Radio House, Victoria Road, Gowerton, Swansea, SA4 3AB
tel: 01792 511 964
web: www.thewave.co.uk
contact: Andy Miles
take demos: Yes
info: Send demos with a short biog to Andy Miles at the address above.

97.5 Scarlet FM
Stebonheath Studios, The Foothold Centre, Stebonheath Terrace, Llanelli, Carmarthenshire, SA15 1NE
tel: 01834 869 384
web: www.scarletfm.com
take demos: No
info: Do not accept demos.

Ceredigion Radio (96.6, 97.4 & 103.3 FM)
The Old Welsh School, Alexandra Road, Aberwystwyth, Ceredigion, SY23 1LF
tel: 01970 627 999
fax: 01970 627 206
email: admin@ceredigionradio.co.uk
web: www.ceredigionradio.co.uk
contact: Phil Olyott
take demos: Yes
info: Phil Olyott presents 'The Other Side' every Monday, Wednesday, Thursday and Friday night between 9pm and 10pm. He is happy to give airtime to local and touring bands, as well as mentioning forthcoming gigs in the area. Send demos, details of live dates and any other relevant information to the address above. Sarah Bowen presents a similar show on a Tuesday night. The radio station also gets involved with local events where unsigned bands can play. For details contact the address above.

Champion 103 FM
Llys y Dderwen, Parc Menai, Bangor, LL57 4BN
tel: 01248 671 888
fax: 01248 671 971
email: admin@champion.musicradio.com
web: www.musicradio.com
contact: Steve Simms
take demos: Yes
info: No dedicated unsigned slots but do accept demos for consideration. Also organise events where unsigned bands can perform. Submit material and requests for any further information to Steve Simms.

Coast 96.3 FM
PO Box 963, Bangor, LL57 4ZR
tel: 01248 673 272
email: steve.simms@musicradio.com
web: http://coastfm.musicradio.com
contact: Steve Simms
take demos: Yes
info: Send demos to the address above. Also organise various shows and events where unsigned bands can perform. For further information please contact Steve Simms.

MFM 103.4
The Studio, Mold Road, Gwersyllt, North Wrexham, LL11 4AF
tel: 01978 752 202
fax: 01978 722 209
email: admin@mfm.musicradio.com
web: www.musicradio.com
contact: Andy Parry
take demos: Yes
info: No dedicated unsigned slots but will accept demos for consideration.

Radio Carmarthenshire (91.7 FM)
Unit 14, The Old School Estate, Station Road, Narberth, Pembrokeshire, SA67 7DU
tel: 0845 351 1971
email: studio@radiocarmarthenshire.com
web: www.radiocarmarthenshire.com
take demos: Yes
info: Welcome CDs from local unsigned artists. Will preview albums and have slots for playing unsigned songs.

Radio Maldwyn 756 AM
The Studios, The Park, Newtown, Powys, SY16 2NZ
tel: 01686 623 555
email: radio.maldwyn@ukonline.co.uk
web: www.magic756.net
take demos: Yes
info: Have specialist programme on Tuesday from 6pm to 10pm playing new music. Contact presenter Chris Lewis.

Real Radio Wales (105 - 106 FM)
Ty-Nant Court, Morganstown, Cardiff, CF15 8LW
tel: 02920 315 100
fax: 02920 315 150
email: info@realradiofm.com
web: http://wales.realradiofm.com/
contact: Ricky Durkin
take demos: No
info: Contact Ricky Durkin to find out about any current opportunities for unsigned bands.

Red Dragon (97.4 & 103.2 FM)
Atlantic Wharf, Cardiff Bay, CF10 4DJ
tel: 02920 662 066
fax: 02920 662 060
email: studio@reddragonfm.co.uk
web: www.reddragonfm.co.uk
contact: Ben Evans
take demos: Yes
info: Send demos to the address above. New music show called 'The Playlist'. For further information regarding the show contact Ben Evans at ben.evans@reddragonfm.co.uk.

Swansea Sound (1170 AM)
Radio House, Victoria Road, Gowerton, Swansea, SA4 3AB
tel: 01792 511 170
fax: 01792 511 171
email: info@swanseasound.co.uk
web: www.swanseasound.co.uk
contact: Andy Miles
take demos: Yes
info: Send demos to the address above. For details about unsigned airtime contact Andy Miles.

Valleys Radio 1116 AM
PO Box 116, Ebbw Vale, NP23 8XW
tel: 01495 301 116
email: admin@valleysradio.co.uk
web: www.valleysradio.co.uk
contact: Symon John
take demos: Yes
info: Symon John presents the evening show Monday to Friday between 6pm and 10pm. He will occasionally play unsigned material. Send demos to Symon at the address above.

7.3 NATIONAL PRESS & MAGAZINES

Acoustic
Oyster House Media Ltd., Oyster House, Hunter's Lodge, Kentisbeare, Devon, EX15 2DY
tel: 01884 266 100
fax: 01884 266 101
email: info@acousticmagazine.com
web: www.acousticmagazine.com
info: UK's only acoustic guitar magazine, containing interviews and profiles of players, reviews of products, as well as instructional features.

Alive
80 New North Road, Huddersfield, HD1 5NE
tel: 01484 451 730
fax: 01484 451 729
email: ents@alive.co.uk
web: www.alive.co.uk
info: Magazine covering live music, clubs and theatre, as well as features on artists and cultural news. Distributed nationwide but listings are regional.

ATM Magazine
PO Box 5307, Southend-on-Sea, Essex, SS1 1TW
tel: 01702 540 043
fax: 01702 540 053
email: info@atm-mag.co.uk
web: www.atm-mag.co.uk
info: ATM Magazine has been running since 1992. Dedicated to Drum&Bass. News, reviews and features.

Audience
Miracle Publishing Ltd., 1 York Street, London, W1U 6PA
tel: 020 7486 7007
fax: 020 7486 2002
email: info@audience.uk.com
web: www.audience.uk.com
contact: Gordon Masson
info: Monthly news, features and information title, covering all aspects of the live music business. International production, equipment and festival news. Every issue features a Tour Guide detailing artists, agents and their tour schedule. Audience.uk is a free supplement for UK readers that contains local news information and features. Which concentrates on emerging and unsigned talent in the UK.

B&S
153 Praed Street, London, W2 1RL
email: editorial@bluesandsoul.com
web: www.bluesandsoul.com
info: Urban music magazine that has features and news on Urban music and lifestyle. Reviews singles, albums, compilations and re-issues. Please contact for demo submissions.

Bass Guitar Magazine
Bass Media Ltd., Oyster House, Hunter's Lodge, Kentisbeare, Devon, EX15 2DY
tel: 01884 266 100
fax: 01884 266 101
email: info@bassguitarmagazine.com
web: www.bassguitarmagazine.com
info: Covers all aspects of bass playing over several genres, with interviews and reviews.

Big Cheese
Unit 7, 26 Horsell Road, London, N5 1XL
tel: 020 7607 0303
email: info@bigcheesemagazine.com
web: www.bigcheesemagazine.com
info: Specialist coverage of Rock music and the related scene. Album, single and live reviews. Welcomes information about new music and unsigned bands, including demos. Worldwide distribution.

Blag
email: blag@blagmagazine.com
web: www.blagmagazine.com
info: US magazine dedicated to 'hip, intelligent culture'. Contains features on artists and reviews. See website for further details. Global distribution.

Blowback
107 The Custard Factory, Gibb Street, Digbeth, Birmingham, B9 4AA
tel: 0121 245 6667
email: info@blowback.co.uk
web: www.blowback.co.uk
info: Free national counter culture title featuring interviews and articles. Focuses on cutting edge art, music, visuals, film and design. Will consider coverage of unsigned bands for articles, reviews and listings. Send any information to the address above.

Blues in Britain
10 Messaline Avenue, London, W3 6JX
tel: 020 8723 7376
fax: 020 8723 7380
email: info@bluesinbritain.org
web: www.blueprint-blues.co.uk
info: Magazine covering the British Blues scene. Reviews on the latest releases and gigs. Full national gig listings.

Blues Matters!
PO Box 18, Bridgend, CF33 6YW
tel: 01656 743 406
email: info@bluesmatters.com
web: www.bluesmatters.com
info: Magazine promoting the Blues music scene. Covers the whole genre with features, interviews, news and reviews as well as comprehensive gig listings and news on releases.

Breakthru Music Magazine
Sequel Publications, PO Box 723, Windsor, Berkshire, SL4 1GP
tel: 020 7900 3101
fax: 020 8688 7678
email: all@breakthru-magazine.com
web: www.breakthru-online.com
info: Entertainment guide and informative journal. Contains features on unsigned and newly signed artists. Also highlights industry services and contacts available, as well as information to help get a foothold in the music industry. Free advert section for songwriters and musicians.

Clash
143c Nethergate, Dundee, DD1 4DP
tel: 01382 870 870
email: info@clashmagazine.com
web: www.clashmagazine.com
info: Bi-monthly publication with music and fashion coverage. Live gig reviews.

Classic Rock
99 Baker Street, London, W1U 6FP
tel: 020 7317 2600
email: classicrock@futurenet.co.uk
web: www.classicrockmagazine.com
info: Magazine dedicated to Rock music - past, present and future. Each monthly edition includes in-depth features, interviews, as well as an exhaustive reviews and gig listings section.

Computer Music
30 Monmouth Street, Bath, BA1 2BW
tel: 01225 442 244
fax: 01225 732 353
email: ronan.macdonald@futurenet.co.uk
web: www.computermusic.co.uk
info: UK's biggest selling music technology magazine. Reader demos can be submitted for review, and MP3s are posted online. Complete entry form either from magazine or online, send to above address marked 'Reader Demos'. Comes with free DVD-ROM each issue with free full software, demos, samples, videos and interactive tutorials.

Dazed & Confused
112-116 Old Street, London, EC1V 9BG
tel: 020 7336 0766
email: see website for email addresses
web: www.confused.co.uk
info: Lifestyle magazine featuring music, fashion, film, literature, theatre and any original ideas. Music reviews, as well as extensive coverage of new music.

DJ
Highgate Studios, 53-79 Highgate Road, Kentish Town, London, NW5 1TW
tel: 020 7331 1000
email: info@djmag.com
web: www.djmag.com
info: Dance music and club news. DJ, artist and producer profiles, charts, club listings, equipment and extensive reviews. Hardware reviews. See the website for demo submission details.

Don't Panic
Record-Play, Studio 203, 45-46 Charlotte Road, London, EC2A 3PD
email: info@record-play.com
web: www.dontpanicmedia.com
info: Music and lifestyle magazine with selected distribution at various venues and independent outlets. See website for more details. Send demo and biog to address above.

Drummer
MB Media Ltd., Alexander House, Forehill, Ely, Cambridgeshire, CB7 4ZA
tel: 01353 665 577
fax: 01353 662 489
email: info@drummer-mag.com
web: www.drummer-mag.com
info: Interviews and features on drumming and drummers. Tuition and reviews. Occasional features unsigned and new music. Contact for demo submission policy.

Flux Magazine
42 Edge Street, Manchester, Lancashire, M4 1HN
tel: 0161 832 0300
fax: 0161 832 0311
email: editorial@fluxmagazine.com
web: www.fluxmagazine.com
contact: Lee Xander
info: National bi-monthly style magazine. Will run features and gig previews on unsigned bands. Send demos with biog to Lee Xander at Flux. Flux will also run features on bands that the team have heard good things about and have seen live, so contacting them first might not be necessary if you're already making waves on the local scene.

The Fly
59-61 Farringdon Road, London, EC1M 3JB
tel: 020 7691 4555
fax: 020 7691 4666
email: listings@channelfly.com
web: www.the-fly.co.uk
info: Free monthly magazine available in selected venues and outlets. Covers all the latest indie and alternative music, with interviews, reviews and news. For a free gig listing, send dates to above email address.

Fused
Studio 315, The Greenhouse, Gibb Square, Birmingham, B9 4AA
tel: 0121 246 1946
email: enquiries@fusedmagazine.com
web: www.fusedmagazine.com
info: Music, fashion, art and lifestyle magazine. The music section includes features on artists, many of them up and coming.

Future Music
30 Monmouth Street, Bath, BA1 2BW
tel: 01225 442 244
fax: 01225 732 353
email: futuremusic@futurenet.co.uk
web: www.futuremusic.co.uk
info: Music technology title. Hardware and software news and reviews, as well as album reviews. Free readers' classified ads. Future Music also has a demo review section. DVD supplied with every edition featuring audio samples, effects and related video footage. Also contains a manufacturers contacts directory. Worldwide distribution.

Guitar & Bass
IPC Focus Network, Leon House, 223 High Street, Croydon, CR9 1HZ
tel: 020 8726 8000
fax: 020 8726 8399
email: guitar@ipcmedia.com
web: www.guitarmagazine.co.uk
info: Covers every aspect of guitar and bass playing. Equipment reviews, artist profiles and workshops on playing and guitar maintenance.

Guitar Buyer
PVD Innovation Centre, Broad Lane Industrial Estate, Cambridge, CB4 8SW
fax: 01954 252 984
email: info@guitarbuyermag.com
info: Monthly magazine with news and reviews on guitars (electric, acoustic and bass) and amps. Features on technique and news. Free reader adverts for instrument and equipment sales, swaps and musicians wanted. See the publication for a form or email ads@guitarbuyermag.com. Also contains contact numbers and website listings for retailers and manufacturers nationwide.

Guitar Techniques
30 Monmouth Street, Bath, BA1 2BW
tel: 01225 442 244
fax: 01225 732 353
email: guitar.tech@futurenet.co.uk
web: www.guitartechniques.co.uk
info: Regarded as the world's leading guitar tuition magazine. Contains full song transcriptions and lessons, as well as interactive CDs. Distributes globally.

Guitarist
Future Publishing, 30 Monmouth Street, Bath, BA1 2BW
tel: 01225 442 244
fax: 01225 732 398
email: guitarist@futurenet.co.uk
web: www.guitarist.co.uk
info: Interviews and features, as well as instrument and equipment reviews, techniques and product demos. Free readers ads to be submitted either by email to guitarist.readerads@futurenet.co.uk, or by completing the form in the magazine. Free interactive CD with every issue.

Hip Hop Connection
email: via website
web: www.hiphop.co.uk
info: Dedicated to Hip-Hop music and culture. Large news section, music reviews, interviews, profiles and features related to all aspects of the scene. Have recently teamed up with Diesel for Diesel-U-Music competition for unsigned artists. Issued monthly.

Hitsheet
31 The Birches, London, N21 1NJ
tel: 020 8360 4088
fax: 020 8360 4088
email: info@hitsheet.co.uk
web: www.hitsheet.co.uk
info: Weekly music industry magazine featuring news, statistics and charts. The 'Tip Sheet' section highlights new releases from established, breaking and unsigned artists, as chosen by industry professionals. Each issue includes a free CD.

Hot Press
Osnovina Ltd., 13 Trinity Street, Dublin, Republic Of Ireland
email: info@hotpress.com
web: www.hotpress.com
info: Published fortnightly in the Republic of Ireland, Hot Press features interviews, news, reviews and event listings from all genres of modern music. Section called 'First Cuts' that reviews demos. Current affairs, cinema, sport, humour, books, fashion and politics are also covered.

International DJ
7th Floor, Tower House, Fairfax Street, Bristol, BS1 3BN
tel: 0117 945 1913
fax: 0117 927 7984
email: idj@i-dj.co.uk
web: www.i-dj.co.uk
info: Magazine for aspiring DJs including equipment reviews, best buys and technique. Interviews and features with Dance acts. Readers can send their mix tapes on cassette, CD or MD to above address, marked 'Reader Mixes'. The best 7 or 8 tapes received each month will be featured in the magazine.

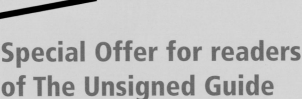

Jazzwise
2b Gleneagle Mews, Ambleside Avenue, London, SW16 6AE
tel: 020 8664 7222
fax: 020 8677 7128
email: jon@jazzwise.com
web: www.jazzwise.com
contact: Jon Newey
info: Leading Jazz monthly in the UK published by the Jazzwise group. Includes news, features, reviews and gig guide. Spans Jazz genres from Contemporary to Fusion to World. Contains editorials and welcomes coverage of unsigned bands and musicians. Distributes worldwide. Jazzwise also run a summer school. See listing in Training and Tuition section for details.

Kerrang!
Mappin House, 4 Winsley Street, London, W1W 8HF
tel: 020 7436 1515
fax: 020 7436 1515
email: kerrang@emap.com
web: www.kerrang.com
info: Weekly magazine dedicated to Alternative Rock and Metal. Send details of gigs (date, venue, contact telephone number, headline band and support bands) to listings@kerrang.com for inclusion in The Gig Guide. Deadline is 110 days previous to Kerrang! publication date. Classified listings cost £30 for 25 words and include bands and musicians' wanted adverts. Send details to Bob Soper, Kerrang! Small Ads, Endeavour House, 2nd Floor, 189 Shaftsbury Avenue, London, WC2H 8JG. Promos can be sent to the Reviews Editor at the address above.

Knowledge
Vision Publishing, 1 Trafalgar Mews, Eastway, London, E9 5JG
tel: 020 8533 9300
fax: 020 8533 9320
email: editor@knowledgemag.co.uk
web: www.knowledgemag.co.uk
info: Established in 1994, Knowledge is one of the UK's longest running British Urban music specialist magazines, covering Drum&Bass, Hip-Hop, Leftfield and Breaks&Beats. Design led music and street culture. Contains reviews on singles, albums, clubs, art exhibitions as well as studio and DJ equipment.

M8
Music (Scotland) Ltd., Trojan House, Phoenix Business Park, Paisley, PA1 2BH
tel: 0141 840 5980
fax: 0141 840 5995
email: kevin@m8magazine.com
web: www.m8magazine.com
contact: Kevin McFarlane
info: Monthly clubbing and Dance music magazine. Music reviews, DJ and label profiles. Club listings.

Metal Hammer
Future Publishing, 4th Floor, 99 Baker Street, London, W1U 6FP
email: chris.ingham@futurenet.co.uk
web: www.metalhammer.co.uk
info: Mainstream Hard Rock monthly. Demos can be sent to be reviewed, along with brief biog and photo, to the above address marked Demo Reviews.

Mixmag
Emap Metro Ltd., 5th Floor, Mappin House, 4 Winsley Street, London, W1W 8HF
tel: 020 7817 8805
fax: 020 7817 8101
email: mixmag@emap.com
web: www.mixmag.net
info: All genres of Dance music covered including Techno, House, Hard House, Drum&Bass, Trance, Breaks, Garage, Electro and Chillout. News, reviews and club listings. Published monthly. There is a 'next best thing' section where new talent is reviewed.

Modern Drummer
email: moreinfo@moderndrummer.com
web: www.moderndrummer.com
info: US magazine for drummers which contains features, lessons, advertisements, reviews and articles. Includes features on techniques and artists. Contact via email for details of back-issues and reprints.

MEDIA

Get 30% off a subscription to RHYTHM magazine

1 year UK subscription is £40.95 - a saving of 30% off shop prices.* Why not spread the cost by Direct Debit and pay just £10.00 every 3 months?

Why subscribe?

- Save 30% - that's a saving of £17.55!
- Never miss an issue!
- FREE delivery to any UK address
- Money-back guarantee – we'll refund un-mailed issues if not entirely satisfied with the magazine
- Exclusive Rhythm CD with every issue

SAVE UP TO 30%

To take advantage of this special Rhythm subscription offer log on to:
www.myfavouritemagazines.co.uk/rhy/x029
Alternatively, call our hotline on **0870 837 4722** and quote the code X029
(lines are open 8.00am to 9:30pm Monday to Friday and 8:00am to 4.00pm Saturdays)

*This offer is based on 13 full price issues. You will receive 13 issues per year This is a UK offer only. Your subscription will start with the next available issue. Closing date is 31/12/06.

Mojo
Mappin House, 4 Winsley Street, London, W1W 8HF
tel: 020 7436 1515
fax: 020 7436 1515
email: mojo@emap.com
web: www.mojo4music.com
info: Monthly specialist music title containing features on current artists. Also has an online radio station, Mojo Radio.

Music & Vision Daily
Flat D, 25 Oxford Road, Ealing, London, W5 3SP
tel: 020 8840 1564
email: contact via the website
web: www.mvdaily.com
contact: Keith Bramich
info: Classical music magazine including book, CD, concert and opera reviews, plus downloadable music, interviews, editorials and international news from the music community. Also contains concert listings from around the world. Daily publication.

Music Mart
1st Floor, Edward House, Tindal Bridge, Edward Street, Birmingham, B1 2RA
tel: 0121 233 8730
fax: 0121 233 8711
email: john.moore@musicmartonline.co.uk
web: www.musicmartonline.co.uk
info: Long established music magazine for people buying and selling instruments and equipment. Guitars, drums, keyboards, PA, studio and DJ equipment reviews. Large classified section with free private lineage adverts (up to 40 words). Registered users of the website can place adverts via email, as well as submitting gig listings.

Music Tech
Anthem Publishing Ltd., Suite 6, Piccadilly House, London Road, Bath, BA1 6PL
tel: 01225 489 984
fax: 01225 489 980
email: See website for contact list
web: www.musictechmag.co.uk
info: Magazine aimed at engineers, producers and recording musicians. Music Tech provides extensive and comprehensive reviews on equipment and technology.

Music Week
CMP Information, United Business Media, 8th Floor, Ludgate House, 245 Blackfriars Road, London, SE1 9UR
tel: 020 7921 8349
fax: 020 7921 8326
email: via website
web: www.musicweek.com
info: Weekly industry magazine. Focuses on industry sales, news, airplay and charts, as well as new release information. Recruitment pages. Subscription to the website allows access to directories, charts, releases and other resources.

New Musical Express
25th Floor, King's Reach Tower, Stamford Street, London, SE1 9LS
tel: 0870 444 5000
fax: 020 7261 7605
web: www.nme.com
info: Weekly music newspaper. News, singles, album and live reviews, features and interviews. Text adverts for musicians are free. Also offer free gig listings. To submit details visit www.nme.com/gigs. Listings must be sent at least 3 weeks before the gig.

Notion
2nd Floor, 57 Hatton Garden, London, EC1N 8HP
tel: 0870 046 6622
email: info@notionmag.com
web: www.notionmag.com
info: Music, culture and lifestyle magazine. The music section covers many current bands and provides features and reviews.

The Observer Music Monthly
3-7 Herbal Hill, London, EC1R 5EJ
tel: 020 7713 4797
email: omm@observer.co.uk
web: http://observer.guardian.co.uk/omm/
info: Free monthly supplement published with The Observer on the last Sunday of every month. Contains features, interviews, news and music reviews across a range of musical genres.

spill
new music. real artists
new music. real artists.
spill
GAY FOR JOHNNY DEPP
SPILL GOES STATESIDE
STORY ONE
SOUL MEKANIK
napster...unveiled
SCENE
YAMAHA
THE independent music magazine
Spill live!
Music Promotions
www.spillonline.com

SUBSCRIPTION OFFERS

Get up to 24% off a subscription to Total Guitar and Guitarist magazines

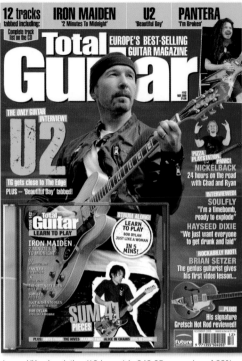

1 year UK subscription (13 issues) is £49.95 – a saving of 23%
Spread the cost by Direct Debit at just £12.25 every 3 months
– a saving of 24%*

Why Subscribe?

- Save up to 24%
- Never miss an issue!
- FREE delivery to any UK address
- Money-back guarantee – we'll refund un-mailed issues if not entirely satisfied
- CD with every issue

1 year UK subscription (13 issues) is £54.95 – a saving of 19%
Spread the cost by Direct Debit at just £13 every 3 months
– a saving of 24%*

Guitarist

To take advantage of this special Guitarist subscription offer log on to:
www.myfavouritemagazines.co.uk/gui/x029

Total Guitar

To take advantage of the Total Guitar subscription offer log on to:
www.myfavouritemagazines.co.uk/tgr/x029

Alternatively, call our hotline on **0870 837 4722** and quote the code X029
(lines are open 8.00am to 9:30pm Monday to Friday and 8:00am to 4.00pm Saturdays)

*These are UK offers only. Your subscription will start with the next available issue. Closing date is 31/12/06.

Play Music
Acquiro House, 3 Station Road, Borough Green, Kent, TN15 8ER
tel: 01732 884 554
email: barney@just-play.com
web: www.just-play.com
contact: Barney Jameson
info: Monthly music title covering both signed and unsigned bands, with an emphasis on live music. News, features and music reviews (including an extensive unsigned gig review section). Hardware and instrument reviews. Play Music is very happy to hear from unsigned bands and is especially supportive of the new music scene. Send demo FAO Holly Hernandez, as well as gig listings to the address above. Distributed nationally.

Powerplay
PO Box 159, York, YO24 3WT
email: see website for contact details
web: www.powerplaymagazine.co.uk
info: Rock and Metal magazine. Interviews and features, as well as extensive live gig reviews. Contact for demo submission policy.

Q
Mappin House, 4 Winsley Street, London, W1W 8HF
tel: 020 7182 8000
fax: 020 7182 8547
email: q@emap.com
web: www.Q4music.com
info: Britain's biggest selling monthly music magazine. Features and interviews. Live, album, book and film reviews. Worldwide distribution.

Record Collector
Room 101, 140 Wales Farm Road, London, W3 6UG
tel: 0870 732 8080
info: Monthly magazine for collectors of CDs, vinyl and memorabilia. Contains section dedicated to new and unsigned music. Though the content is primarily based upon re-issues, it does review new singles (mainly vinyl format). 'In the Pipeline' section which notes up and coming events. Submissions should be sent to Jake Kennedy, Reviews Editor to the address above.

Rhythm
Future Publishing, 30 Monmouth Street, Bath, BA1 2BW
tel: 01225 442 244
fax: 01225 732 353
email: rhythm@futurenet.co.uk
web: www.rhythm.co.uk
contact: Louise King
info: Rhythm is the UK's leading Drum Magazine and comes complete with the educational 'Play Drums' CD to help readers improve their playing. Packed with exclusive interviews with the hottest players in the world, features, news, reviews, gigs and gossip.

Rock Sound
Unit 22, Jack's Place, 6 Corbet Place, London, E1 6NN
tel: 020 7877 8770
email: see website for contact list .
web: www.rock-sound.net
contact: Darren Sadler
info: Monthly Rock music magazine featuring news and interviews plus listings for gigs, tours and rock club nights. Accept demos, which may be featured in the demo review section. Send to the above address.

RWD
Unit 2.1, Lafone House, 11-13 Leathermarket Street, London, SE1 3HN
tel: 0870 774 5619
fax: 020 8367 6184
email: editor@rwdmag.com
web: www.rwdmag.com
info: Coverage of UK Garage, Hip-Hop, R&B, Drum&Bass and US House music and lifestyle. Published monthly. 'Future Artists' section that provides features on up and coming artists. Records can be sent for review to the above address.

Songwriting & Composing Magazine
Sovereign House, 12 Trewartha Road, Praa Sands, Penzance, Cornwall, TR20 9ST
tel: 01736 762 826
email: songmag@aol.com
web: www.songwriters-guild.co.uk
contact: Roderick Jones
info: Magazine for members of the Guild containing reviews and articles about recording and publishing companies, and other industry items. Outlet for composers and songwriters containing member profiles and artist contact details. Membership is open to all for an annual fee. See website for further details.

Sound On Sound
Media House, Trafalgar Way, Bar Hill, Cambridge, CB3 8SQ
tel: 01954 789 888
fax: 01954 789 895
email: sos@soundonsound.com
web: www.soundonsound.com
info: Monthly music recording magazine. Techniques, features and reviews. Demos can be submitted to be reviewed by either the resident Demo Doctor, or by a panel of producers, songwriters, musicians and managers, as part of the Business End feature. To submit your material to the Demo Doctor, send CD, DAT, MD or cassette with band/artist photo and demo artwork to above address, marked 'Demo Doctor'. To have your demo reviewed for the Business End, send for attention of Business End to above address and write on outside of package the style that best describes your music. Free readers' ads to sell equipment can be placed via a coupon in the magazine, or directly on to the Sound on Sound website.

Spill Magazine
Global House, Bridge Street, Guilford, Surrey, GU1 4SB
tel: 01483 501216/7
fax: 01483 501201
email: info@spillonline.com
web: www.spillonline.com
info: Publication offering exposure to established, newly signed and unsigned bands and artists. Articles, features and reviews of new releases and gigs.

Terrorizer
Dark Arts Ltd., Unit 36, 10-50 Willow Street, London, EC2A 4BH
tel: 020 7729 7666
fax: 020 7739 0544
email: via website
web: www.terrorizer.com
info: Publication for Extreme music of any kind. Interviews and features covering Metal, Hardcore and Industrial genres. Worldwide distribution.

Total Guitar
Future Publishing, 30 Monmouth Street, Bath, BA1 2BW
tel: 01225 442 244
fax: 01225 732 353
email: totalguitar@futurenet.co.uk
web: www.totalguitar.co.uk
info: Published monthly. Guitar related features and equipment reviews. A CD of backing tracks accompanies every issue. Interviews, tips and techniques from famous guitarists. Readers demo reviews. Also issue Total Guitar Bass edition quarterly.

Total Production
19 Prince's Street, Southend On Sea, Essex, SS1 1QA
tel: 01702 333 003
email: m.cunningham@mondiale.co.uk
web: www.mondiale.co.uk/tpi
info: Magazine aimed at the international live event production industry. Distributed worldwide to a professional readership across 90 countries. Covers applications of sound, lighting, video and staging technology in concert touring, theatre and special events.

Uncut
IPC Media, 24th Floor, King's Reach Tower, Stamford Street, London, SE1 9LS
tel: 020 7261 6992
fax: 020 7261 5573
web: www.uncut.co.uk
info: Music and film magazine with new and re-release music news and reviews. Movies, DVDs and books. Published monthly.

The Wire
2nd Floor East, 88-94 Wentworth Street, London, E1 7SA
tel: 020 7422 5010
fax: 020 7422 5011
email: chris@thewire.co.uk
web: www.thewire.co.uk
info: Independent monthly magazine for non-mainstream music including Electronica, Avant Rock, Breakbeat, Jazz, Modern Classical and Global music. News, features and reviews. Demos can be submitted to the address above. The Wire listen to all submissions but cannot guarantee a response. Involved with several international events such as Sonar and MUTEK. Worldwide distribution.

Word
Development Hell Ltd., 90-92 Pentonville Road, London, N1 9HS
tel: 020 7520 8625
fax: 020 7833 9900
email: mail@wordmagazine.co.uk
web: www.wordmagazine.co.uk
info: Music and entertainment publication issued monthly. Film, music, book, DVD and games reviews. Every month there is a CD included showcasing new talent.

MEDIA

Zero Tolerance
PO Box 3958, Rugby, CV21 9AJ
email: radar@ztmag.com
web: www.ztmag.com
info: Covering a whole spectrum of Rock music. Features and reviews on bands, as well as technical information and advice such as producing and recording tips. There is also a section called 'Insider Knowledge' citing new music and talent. Submit news and gig listings to the above email address.

7.4 Regional Press/Magazines

In the Regional Press section of The Unsigned Guide we have outlined a cross section of key publications in your area. There are thousands of newspapers in the United Kingdom and it would be hugely impractical to list them all here. However, we have listed most of the major press groups and the newspapers they publish. This puts the onus on you to identify newspapers in your area and get in touch with them if they are not listed in The Unsigned Guide. Check for any mentions of the press group they are published by, an email address or a telephone number. Local newspapers should not be particularly difficult to contact. Have a read through your local newspaper's entertainment pages and see what they may be able to offer you. If you do decide to contact them, ask for the Newsdesk or Entertainments Editor when you call, and unless instructed otherwise, mark any emails 'FAO Newsdesk', introduce yourself and make sure you have something newsworthy to tell them. Whilst most newspapers will not have space simply to review a demo, it's always worth sending one to the journalists who write gig reviews/previews in your area. Eventually, you may well secure a feature on one of your forthcoming gigs. At very least make sure you always submit your gig listings to as many press contacts as you can. This aspect of self-promotion is covered in more detail in both the Live Performance and Media forewords.

Use local press to connect with people in your town or city in a bid to build your local audience. If you can do this and establish a good relationship with the local press and journalists, you should be able to maintain and develop this audience. Keep the link with yourselves and the press strong and keep them informed of all your news and gigs.

Finally, you know which newspaper lands on your doorstep every week, so if it's not listed in The Unsigned Guide, follow these simple steps and get in touch with them. Good luck!

7.4 REGIONAL PRESS/MAGAZINES

EAST of ENGLAND

Archant (Anglia)
8 Bevan Street, Lowestoft, Suffolk, NR32 2AA
tel: 01502 582 318
fax: 01502 516 581
email: enquiries@archant.co.uk
web: www.archant.co.uk
take demos: Yes
info: Archant Anglia publish the following titles:
Cambridgeshire Times, Dunmow Broadcast & Recorder, Ely Standard, Essex Advertiser Great Yarmouth & Gorleston Advertiser, The Hunts Post, Ipswich, Felixstowe and Stowmarket Advertiser, Norfolk Advertiser, Norfolk South Advertiser, North Essex Advertiser, Norwich Advertiser, Royston & Buntingford Crow, Saffron Walden Reporter, Suffolk Advertiser, Waveney Advertiser and Wisbech Standard.

Archant (Norfolk)
Prospect House, Rouen Road, Norwich, NR1 1RE
tel: 01603 628 311
fax: 01603 612 930
email: enquiries@archant.co.uk
web: www.archant.co.uk
take demos: Yes
info: Norwich - Eastern Daily Press, Norwich - Evening News, Beccles & Bungay Journal Buchan Observer, Dereham & Fakenham Times, Diss Mercury, Ellon Times & East Gordon Advertiser, Fraserburgh Herald, Great Yarmouth Mercury, Lowestoft Journal, Norfolk North News, Thetford & Watton Times, Wymondham & Attleborough Mercury.

Cambridge Newspapers Ltd.
Winship Road, Milton, Cambridge, CB4 6PP
tel: 01223 434 434
fax: 01223 434 321
email: editorial@cambridge-news.co.uk
web: www.cambridge-news.co.uk
take demos: No
info: Cambridge Evening News, Cambridge Town Crier, Cambridge Weekly News, Ely Weekly News, Haverhill Weekly News, Huntingdon Weekly News, Newmarket Weekly News Royston Weekly News, Saffron Walden Weekly News, St Ives Weekly News, St Neots Weekly News.

Dereham & Fakenham Times
Prospect House, Rouen Road, Norwich, NR1 1RE
tel: 01603 628 311
fax: 01603 615 903
email: terry.redhead@archant.co.uk
web: www.archant.co.uk
contact: Terry Redhead
take demos: No
info: What's on section, 'The Guide', features local bands whenever possible. They also cover the local Battle of the Bands held annually.

Diss Express
Norfolk & Suffolk House, Mere Street, Diss, Norfolk, IP22 4AE
tel: 01379 642 264
fax: 01379 650 110
email: frasermckay@dissexpress.co.uk
contact: Fraser McKay
take demos: No
info: Gig listings published on a Friday. Submit any gig details by Tuesday 5pm. Happy to cover local unsigned bands. Send demo marked FAO Fraser McKay.

East Anglian Daily Press
30 Lower Brook Street, Ipswich, Suffolk, IP4 1AN
tel: 01473 324 788
fax: 01473 324 840
email: joanne.macdonald@eveningstar.co.uk
contact: Joanne MacDonald
take demos: No
info: The paper features a weekly music supplement, 'Ticket on a Friday', edited by Joanne MacDonald. She will review demos, and features a new local unsigned band every week. Send any information via email at the above addresst.

IP1 Magazine
1 Cornhill, Ipswich, IP1 1DD
tel: 01473 420 545
email: chris@ip1zine.com
web: www.ip1zine.com
contact: Howard Freeman
take demos: No
info: Bands can submit their demos via the magazine if they are seeking a review or feature. Alternatively, artists and bands can post sample tracks on the website for visitors to listen to. Prefer submissions from local bands based around Ipswich and Suffolk. However, they will consider submissions from artists and bands who are not from the region if it is relatable to the local area e.g. those who will be performing locally or those who derive from the local area.

Red Pages
Cambridge
tel: 07712 414 762
email: info@red-pages.co.uk
web: www.red-pages.co.uk
take demos: Yes
info: Red Pages is a listings guide for the Cambridge area. Published fortnightly it also features articles on local bands. Also available online.

GREATER LONDON

Archant (London)
Recorder House, Ilford, Essex, IG1 1UD
tel: 020 8478 4444
web: www.archant.com
take demos: Yes
info: Archant London publish: Barking & Dagenham Post, Barking & Dagenham Post Weekender, Bexley & Elthan Express, Bexleyheath & Welling Times, Bromley & Beckenham Times, Bromley & Orpington Express, Camden Chronicle, Dartford Express, Dartford Times, East London Advertiser, Gravesend Express, Gravesend Reporter, Hackney Gazette, Ham & High Series, Hammersmith Times, Harlow & Bishop's Stortford Herald, Havering Herald, Hornsey & Crouch End Journal, Ilford & Redbridge Free Post, Ilford & Redbridge Post, Ilford Recorder, Islington Gazette, Kensingtom Times, Kilburn Times, Newham Recorder, North London Weekly Herald, Paddington Times, Romford & Havering Free Post, Romford Recorder Series, Stoke Newington, Shoreditch, Hoxton & Stamford Hill Express (incorporating Stoke Newington & Stamford Hill Express, Hoxton & Shoreditch Express), Stratford, Newham & Docklands Express (incorporating Stratford & Newham Express, Docklands Express), Thurrock & Grays Post and finally, Wembley & Kingsbury Chronicle

Fulham Chronicle Series
93 Staines Road, Hounslow, Middlesex, TW3 3JB
tel: 020 8538 2202
fax: 020 8741 1973
email: newshammersmith@trinitysouth.co.uk
contact: Jo McDermott
take demos: No
info: 'The Hitlist', an entertainment guide including previews, reviews and gig listings, is published in the newspaper once a week. Contact Jo if you would like to be considered for inclusion. The Fulham Chronicle series includes the press titles Hounslow, Hounslow & Fulham Chronicles, Kensington & Chelsea News, Marylebone & Paddington Mercury, and Westminster & Pimlico News, all published weekly on a Wednesday.

Newsquest (North London)
Guardian House, 480-500 Larkshall Road, Highams Park, London, E4 9GD
tel: 020 8498 3400
fax: 020 8531 2499
email: name@londonnews.co.uk
web: www.thisislocallondon.co.uk
take demos: Yes
info: London Newsquest publishes the Enfield Independent, Epping Forest & Redbridge Independent, Haringey Independent, Harlow Citizen, Hendon & Finchley Times, Redbridge & West Essex Gazette, Hillingdon & Uxbridge Times, Waltham Forest Guardian and Waltham Forest Independent.

The Press Association
292 Vauxhall Bridge Road, London, SW1V 1AE
tel: 020 7963 7000
email: gigs@pa.press.net
web: www.pa.press.net
contact: Joss Hutton
take demos: Yes
info: National news agency of the UK and Ireland. Gig listings can be submitted via the email address above. They are then available for publication to every national and regional daily newspaper, as well as major broadcasters, online publishers and a wide range of commercial organisations.

Artrocker
3a Highbury Crescent, London, N5 1RN
tel: 020 7609 7431
email: info@artrocker.com
web: www.artrocker.com
take demos: No
info: Weekly music paper available in record stores and sold at gigs in the London area. Interviews, news, CD and gig reviews, plus gig listings. Subscriptions can be made online. Very keen to cover the unsigned scene and also run weekly night featuring signed and unsigned bands.

Camden Gazette
North London Newspapers, 161 Tottenham, London, N8 9BU
tel: 020 8342 5777
fax: 020 8540 6577
email: nlnews@archant.co.uk
contact: Gemma Briggs
take demos: No
info: Published weekly. Includes gig listings, and occasionally features on local unsigned acts. Send as much relevant information as possible about yourself or your band to the email address above.

Camden New Journal
40 Camden Road, London, NW1 9DR
tel: 020 7419 9000
fax: 020 7482 7317
email: cnj@blueyonder.co.uk
web: www.camdennewjournal.com
contact: Richard Osley
take demos: No
info: Published weekly on Thursday, with a circulation of 64,841. Reviews of events in the area and demos by local bands. Contact Richard to be considered.

Croydon Guardian
10 Pegasus Road, Croydon, Surrey, CR0 4RN
tel: 020 8774 6583
fax: 020 8774 6551
email: leisure@croydonguardian.co.uk
web: www.croydonguardian.co.uk
contact: Christine Van Emst
take demos: Yes
info: Published weekly every Wednesday, with a circulation of 120,000. Entertainment section includes a music page and 'What's On' guide. Contact Christine to be listed.

East London & West Essex Guardian
Guardian House, 480-500 Larkshall Road, Highams Park, London, E4 9GD
tel: 020 8498 3400
fax: 020 8531 2924
email: stotten@london.newsquest.co.uk
contact: Simon Totten
take demos: No
info: Published weekly every Friday, with a circulation of 32,000. Includes 'Staying In' supplement featuring CD reviews and a 'What's On' section with local gig listings. Contact Simon to be considered.

East London Advertiser
138 Cambridge Heath Road, Bethnal Green, London, E1 5QJ
tel: 020 7790 8822
fax: 020 7790 0646
email: ela.editoral@archant.co.uk
contact: Lucy Teagle
take demos: No
info: Published weekly every Thursday, with a circulation of 15,730. Includes local gig listings, and occasional reviews of local acts. Use the email address above for first contact.

Enfield Advertiser
North London & Herts Newspapers, 3rd Floor, Refuge House, Enfield, Midddlesex, EN1 3SZ
tel: 020 8367 2345
email: leisureenfield@trinitysouth.co.uk
contact: Johnathon Lovett
take demos: No
info: Published weekly every Wednesday, with a circulation of 94,617. Regular reviews of local unsigned acts, mainly live. Contact Jonathon to be considered for a review or preview.

Ham & High
Archant North London, 100a Avenue Road, Hampstead, NW3 3HF
tel: 020 7433 0000
email: andrew.brightwell@hamhigh.co.uk or editorial@hamhigh.co.uk
web: www.hamhigh.co.uk
contact: Andrew Brightwell
take demos: No
info: Published weekly every Friday. The paper is hoping to expand its coverage of the local music scene, and is keen to hear from unsigned acts playing gigs in the area. Contact Andrew to be considered.

Harrow & Wembley Observer Series
Harrow Observer Series, 362 Station Road, Harrow, Middlesex, HA1 2DR
tel: 01895 451 035
fax: 020 8863 1727
email: victoriaprewer@trinitysouth.co.uk
contact: Victoria Prewer
take demos: No
info: Will occasionally run features on local bands. Send demo, biog and any other relevant information to Victoria at the address above. The Harrow & Wembley Observer Series includes Harrow, Stanmore, Pinner, Wembley and Wilsden Observer titles. All titles are published weekly every Thursday.

Islington Gazette
North London Newspapers, 161 Tottenham Lane, London, N8 9BU
tel: 020 8342 5777
fax: 020 8342 5730
email: nlnews@archant.co.uk
take demos: Yes
info: Published weekly every Thursday, with a circulation of 13,000. Gig listings and occasional reviews of gigs. Contact the news desk for information on getting listed.

Lewisham & Greenwich Mercury
South London Press, 2-4 Leigham Court Road, Streatham, London, SW16 2PD
tel: 020 8769 4444
fax: 020 8664 7247
email: pulse@slp.co.uk
contact: Zoe Walker
take demos: No
info: Published weekly every Wednesday, with a circulation of 96,689. 'The Pulse' entertainment supplement includes local gig listings. Previews and interviews with local unsigned acts may also be included in this section. Call or email Zoe.

London Evening Standard
Northcliffe House, 2 Derry Street, London, W8 5TT
tel: 020 7938 7586
email: art@pa.press.net
web: www.standard.co.uk
contact: Amelia Pinsent
take demos: Yes
info: Gig listings featured in the Metro Life supplement. Send details 3 weeks in advance of gig to Amelia at the address above.

Metro (London)
1 Surrey Quays Road, Rotherhithe, London, SE16 7ND
tel: 020 7651 5242
fax: 020 7651 5342
email: claire.allfree@ukmetro.co.uk
web: www.metro.co.uk
contact: Claire Allfree
take demos: Yes
info: Published daily. To be included in the gig listings, contact PA Arts & Leisure on 020 7963 7707. To be considered for a review or preview, contact Claire Allfree by email.

South London Press
South London Press, 2-4 Leigham Court Road, Streatham, London, SW16 2PD
tel: 020 8769 4444
fax: 020 8664 7247
email: pulse@slp.co.uk
web: www.icsouthlondon.co.uk
contact: Zoe Walker
take demos: No
info: Published bi-weekly on Friday (circulation 28,429) and Tuesday (circulation 23,400). 'The Pulse' entertainment supplement is published every Friday, and includes local gig listings. Previews and interviews with local unsigned acts may run in this section. Contact Zoe to be considered.

Southwark News
Unit A 302, Tower Bridge Business Complex, Clements Road, London, SE16 4DG
tel: 020 7232 1639
fax: 020 7237 1578
email: kevin@southwarknews.org
contact: Kevin Quinn
take demos: No
info: Published twice weekly every Thursday, with a circulation of 60,000. Southwark News also produce the 'Weekender'. Published every Friday, it contains local gig listings, and regularly features or reviews about local unsigned acts. Contact Kevin to be considered.

Time Out
Universal House, 251 Tottenham Court Road, London, W1T 7AB
tel: 020 7813 3000
fax: 020 7813 6158
email: chrissalmon@timeout.com
web: www.timeout.com/london
contact: Chris Salmon, Sharon O'Connell
take demos: No
info: Published weekly every Wednesday. Offers listings and review coverage of art, music, film, theatre and nightlife. To submit music listings contact with details at least 9 days prior to publication. This can be done by sending by fax to the above number, or via the website by completing the online form found in the feedback section. Can also contact by email to one of the following addresses, depending on musical style: Rocklistings@timeout.com, rootslistings@timeout.com, or jazzlistings@timeout.com.

West London Times Group
Cumberland House, 80 Scrubs Lane, Willesden, London, NW10 6RF
tel: 020 8962 6868
fax: 020 8692 6897
email: peter.kennedy@archant.co.uk
web: www.independentregionals.co.uk
contact: Peter Kennedy
take demos: Yes
info: Include local gig listings. Occasionally review unsigned gigs or demos. Contact Peter to get listed or to be considered for review.

Westminster Times
North West London Newspapers, Cumberland House, 80 Scrubs Lane, London, NW10 6RF
tel: 020 8962 6868
fax: 020 8962 6897
email: peter.kennedy@archant.co.uk
web: www.independentregionals.co.uk
contact: Peter Kennedy
take demos: No
info: Published every Wednesday. Includes local gig listings and will occasionally review unsigned gigs or demos. Contact Peter to get listed or to be considered for review.

The Wharf
1 Canada Square, Canary Wharf, London, E14 5AP
tel: 020 7510 6055
fax: 020 7293 2264
email: advertising@wharf.co.uk
web: www.wharf.co.uk
take demos: Yes
info: Published weekly every Thursday. For local gig listings, contact Advertising at the paper if you would like to be included.

What's On In London
180 Pentonville Road, London, N1 9LB
tel: 020 7278 4393
fax: 020 7837 5838
email: jcoleman@whatsoninlondon.co.uk
web: www.whatsoninlondon.co.uk
contact: John Coleman
take demos: No
info: Weekly magazine published every Wednesday as a comprehensive guide to events in the capital. Includes gig listings, previews of gigs and reviews of CDs, with occasional demo reviews. Contact John with details of your act to be considered.

MIDLANDS

Birmingham Post & Mail Ltd.
Weaman Street, Birmingham, B4 6AY
tel: 0121 236 3366
fax: 0121 233 0678
web: www.icbirmingham.ic24.com
take demos: Yes
info: Birmingham Evening Mail, Birmingham Post, Birmingham News North, Birmingham News South, Sunday Mercury.

Coventry Newspapers Ltd.
Corporation Street, Coventry, CV1 1FP
tel: 01203 633 633
fax: 01203 550 868
web: www.iccoventry.co.uk
take demos: Yes
info: Coventry Evening Telegraph, Bedworth Echo, Coventry Citizen, Hinckley Herald & Journal, Hinckley Times, Nuneaton Weekly Tribune.

Leicester Mercury Group
St. George Street, Leicester, LE1 9FQ
tel: 0116 251 2512
fax: 0116 262 4687
email: enquiries@leicestermercury.co.uk
web: www.thisisleicestershire.co.uk
take demos: Yes
info: Leicester Mercury, Ashby & Coalville Mail, Leicester Mail, Loughborough Mail, Oadby & Wigston Mail.

Lincolnshire Publishing Co.
Brayford Wharf East, Lincoln, Lincolnshire, LN5 7AT
tel: 01522 820 000
fax: 01522 804 492
email: editor@thisislincolnshire.co.uk
web: www.thisislincolnshire.co.uk
take demos: No
info: Lincoln - Lincolnshire Echo, Boston Target, East Lindsey Target, Gainsborough Target, Lincoln Target, Retford, Gainsborough & Worksop Times, Sleaford Target, Spalding Target, Wolds Target Series.

Newsquest Midlands South
Berrows House, Hylton Road, Worcester, WR2 7JX
tel: 01905 748200
fax: 01905 429605
email: name@newsquestmidlands.co.uk
web: www.thisisherefordshire.co.uk
take demos: Yes
info: Worcester News, Berrow's Worcester Journal, Bromsgrove/Droitwich Advertiser, Dudley News, Evesham Admag, Evesham Cotswold & Stratford Journal, Halesowen News, Hereford Times, Kidderminster Shuttle Ludlow Advertiser, Malvern Gazette/Ledbury Reporter, Redditch Advertiser & Alcester Chronicle, Stourbridge News & County Express and Tewkesbury Admag

Nottingham Post Group
Castle Wharf House, Nottingham, NG1 7EU
tel: 0115 948 2000
fax: 0115 964 4098
web: www.thisisnottingham.co.uk
take demos: Yes
info: Nottingham Evening Post, Mansfield & Ashfield Recorder, Long Eaton Recorder, Nottingham Recorder.

Black Velvet
336 Birchfield Road, Webheath, Redditch, Worcestershire, B97 4NG
email: shari@blackvelvetmagazine.com
web: www.blackvelvetmagazine.com
contact: Shari
take demos: No
info: Black Velvet prefer bands to send CDs rather than email first, no MP3 reviews. Bands should preferably buy a copy of Black Velvet first, to check out what it's like and if they think they would fit in with the music covered. If so, forward a CD and press kit.

MEDIA

Blank Stares & Cricket Claps
Northampton
email: cricketclaps@yahoo.co.uk
web: www.bsacc.co.uk
take demos: Yes
info: Free music fanzine which can also be viewed online. Features, live and CD reviews. To receive a copy contact via the above email address.

Burntwood Post
103-106 High Green Court, Newhall Street, Cannock, Staffordshire, WS11 1AB
tel: 01543 501 700
fax: 01543 501 793
email: mike_lockley@mrn.co.uk
web: www.iccannock.co.uk
contact: Mike Lockley
take demos: No
info: Janet Leigh writes a dedicated Rock music page every week. Demos biogs and news can be sent for her attention, or to Mike Lockley, to be considered for inclusion. To have any gigs listed, submission is preferred by Monday for the upcoming week's events. The area has a large following of Heavy Metal bands, so the paper is keen to cover any bands from this genre.

Derby Evening Telegraph
Derby Express Newspapers, Northcliffe House, Derby, DE1 2DW
tel: 01332 291 111
fax: 01332 253 027
email: newsdesk@derbytelegraph.co.uk
web: www.thisisderbyshire.co.uk
contact: Nigel Powlson
take demos: No
info: Local bands can send any gig listings for a possiblity of a live review. Send any information to the Newsdesk. The paper features 'QT', an entertainment section published every Friday. Contact the Newsdesk for consideration.

Derby Express
Derby Express Newspapers, Northcliffe House, Derby, DE1 2DW
tel: 01332 291 111
fax: 01332 253 027
email: newsdesk@derbytelegraph.co.uk
web: www.thisisderbyshire.co.uk
take demos: Yes
info: Local bands can send any gig listings for a possiblity of a live review. Send any information to the Newsdesk. The paper features 'QT', an entertainment section published every Friday. Contact the Newsdesk for consideration.

Derbyshire Times
Station Road, Chesterfield, Derbyshire, S41 7XD
tel: 01246 504 500
fax: 01246 504 557
email: phil.bramley@derbyshiretimes.co.uk
web: www.chesterfieldtoday.co.uk
contact: Phil Bramley
take demos: No
info: Every Thursday the paper features a full page of local music, with gig guide, album reviews and live reviews. Submit demos or gig details by noon on Mondays. Once a year the paper runs Battle of the Bands competition. Contact Phil Bramley for more information.

Metro (Midlands)
tel: 0121 236 2975
email: listings@metromidlands.co.uk
web: www.metro.co.uk
take demos: Yes
info: Free paper distributed in Nottingham and Birmingham. Submit gig details to the above email address.

Sandman Nottingham
PO Box 8451, Nottingham, NG2 7YY
tel: 0114 278 6727
email: nottingham@sandmanmagazine.co.uk
web: www.sandmanmagazine.co.uk
contact: Sam Metcalf
take demos: No
info: Sandman Magazine will concentrate on unsigned acts from each edition of the magazine's locality. They will run features, reviews and profile new releases. Any bands touring in the area may get gig previews in the listings section. See also listing for Sandman Yorkshire.

TrashPit
95 Flamstead Avenue, Loscoe, Heanor, Derbyshire, DE75 7RP
email: rob@trashpit.co.uk
web: www.trashpit.co.uk or
www.myspace.com/trashpit
take demos: No
info: TrashPit reviews full albums by unsigned artists. Request bands to send full press kit including biog. Unfortunately they do not have room to review CD singles and demo samplers, but are always willing to listen to music by new bands. The magazine is mainly interested in Hard Rock, Glam Rock and Power Pop.

What's On Magazine Group
5-6 Shoplatch, Shrewsbury, SY1 1HF
tel: 01743 281 777
fax: 01743 248 256
email: davina@whatsonmag.com
contact: Davina Evans
take demos: No
info: Free monthly magazine available in theatres, music venues, tourist information centres and various other outlets. Will include gigs in entertainment listings but cannot guarantee entry for every band they receive information from. Will very occasionally run features on unsigned acts. Send biography and details of live dates (preferably via email) to Davina. Deadline for entries is 2 weeks before the first of the month.

NORTHEAST

Gazette Media Company Ltd.
Gazette Buildings, Borough Road, Middlesbrough, Cleveland, TS1 3AZ
tel: 01642 245 401
fax: 01642 210 565
email: alastair.maccoll@eveninggazette.co.uk
web: www.icteesside.co.uk
take demos: No
info: Middlesbrough - Evening Gazette, Darlington Herald & Post, East Cleveland & North Yorkshire Herald & Post, Middlesbrough Herald & Post, North Yorkshire Herald & Post, South Durham Herald & Post, Stockton & Billingham Herald & Post.

Newcastle Chronicle & Journal Ltd.
Thomson House, Groat Market, Newcastle Upon Tyne, NE1 1ED
tel: 0191 232 7500
fax: 0191 230 4144
email: callcentre@ncjmedia.co.uk
web: www.icnewcastle.co.uk
take demos: Yes
info: Newcastle-upon-Tyne - Evening Chronicle, Newcastle-upon-Tyne - The Journal, Gateshead Herald & Post, Newcastle Herald & Post, Newcastle-upon-Tyne - Sunday Sun, North Tyneside Herald & Post, Northumberland Herald & Post, South Tyneside Herald & Post.

Newsquest (North East)
PO Box 14, Priestgate, Darlington, County Durham, DL1 1NF
tel: 01325 381 313
fax: 01325 360 756
web: www.thisisthenortheast.co.uk
take demos: Yes
info: Newsquest in the North East publish the following newspapers: Darlington - The Northern Echo, Chester-Le-Street Advertiser, Consett & Stanley Advertiser, Darlington & Aycliffe Advertiser, Darlington & Stockton Times, Durham Advertiser, East Cleveland Advertiser, North Yorkshire Advertiser and Wear Valley Advertiser.

Northeast Press Ltd.
Echo House, Pennywell, Sunderland, SR4 9ER
tel: 0191 501 5800
fax: 0191 534 3807
email: echo@npress.demon.co.uk
web: www.sunderland.com
take demos: Yes
info: Hartlepool - The Mail, South Shields - The Gazette, Sunderland Echo, Hartlepool Star, Houghton Star, Morpeth Herald, North Tyneside & Whitley Bay News Guardian, Northumberland Gazette, Northumberland News Post Leader, Peterlee Star, Seaham Star, South Tyne Star, Sunderland Star, Washington Star.

Berwick Advertiser
90 Marygate, Berwick-upon-Tweed, Northumberland, TD15 1BW
tel: 01289 306 677
fax: 01289 307 377
email: mail@tweeddalepress.co.uk
web: www.berwicktoday.co.uk
contact: Janet Wakenshaw
take demos: No
info: The paper will sometimes feature write ups on local bands. The 'What's On' section would include local gigs. Contact the Editor Janet Wakenshaw, or the Newsdesk to be considered.

The Crack Magazine
1 Pink Lane, Newcastle Upon Tyne, Tyne & Wear, NE1 1DW
tel: 0191 230 3038
fax: 0191 230 4484
email: rob@thecrackmagazine.com
web: www.thecrackmagazine.com
contact: Rob Meddes
take demos: No
info: Published at the beginning of every month. The deadline for inclusion is 6 weeks in advance. The Crack mainly deals with Pop, Rock and Indie music but can cover more diverse genres such as Jazz or world music. There is a dedicated North East band section which will feature profiles and demo reviews each month of 2 or 3 bands. Any gigs in the area will be listed. Touring bands may request a review or preview.

Darlington Herald & Post
Royal Oak Yard, Bondgate, Darlington, County Durham, DL3 7JD
tel: 01325 262 000
fax: 01325 380 348
email: kathy.marshall@gazettemedia.co.uk
contact: Kathy Marshall
take demos: No
info: The paper will cover any bands playing in the area. They are happy to feature profiles on local bands. Send demos to the above address. Submit any gig details a week in advance for Thursdays' edition.

The Evening Gazette
Borough Road, Middlesborough, Teeside, TS1 3AZ
tel: 01642 245 401
fax: 01642 232 014
email: andrew.pain@eveninggazette.co.uk
web: www.icteeside.co.uk
contact: Andew Pain
take demos: No
info: Friday's edition of the Gazette includes a 'What's On' section featuring 2 pages of unsigned band news, reviews and previews. Music Editor Andrew Pain also endeavours to put any newsworthy stories on local bands into the main body of the paper. Contact Andrew for more details.

Generator Magazine
2nd Floor, Black Swan Court, 69 Westgate Road, Newcastle, Tyne & Wear, NE1 1SG
tel: 0191 245 0099
fax: 0191 245 0144
email: colin@generator.org.uk
web: www.generator.org.uk
contact: Colin Davies
take demos: Yes
info: The magazine is published quarterly. It is mainly used as a portal to advertise Generator's projects but will occasionally publish features on great new bands, so do get in touch. No demo reviews or listings as such. Generator magazine is sent to over 6,000 readers in the music industry. Worth picking up a copy for advice.

The Informer Magazine
Wingrove House, Ponteland Road, Newcastle Upon Tyne, Tyne & Wear, NE5 3DP
tel: 0191 286 5020
email: informer.magazine@btinternet.com
contact: Peter Dixon
take demos: No
info: Monthly listings magazine for the North East, concerning live shows from Morpeth to Cleveland. The deadline to submit your gig is the 19th of the month. Send a demo marked FAO Peter Dixon, and space permitting, your gig may get a preview. 30,000 copies of each edition are circulated around the North East's venues.

Metro (North East)
195 High Street, Gateshead, NE8 1AS
tel: 0191 477 8200
email: ray.clark@ukmetro.co.uk
web: www.metro.co.uk
contact: Deane Hodgson
take demos: Yes
info: Free paper distributed in Newcastle and Sunderland. Submit any gig listings to Ray Clark at the above email address.

Newcastle Herald & Post
Groat Market, Newcastle upon Tyne, Tyne & Wear, NE1 1ED
tel: 0191 232 7500
fax: 0191 230 4144
email: hp.newsdesk@ncjmedia.co.uk
web: www.icnewcastle.co.uk
contact: Zoe Burn
take demos: Yes
info: The Herald & Post will include listings of local gigs. Published on Wednesdays so listings must be submitted by Monday to Zoe via the above email address. No demo reviews or profiles.

NORTHWEST

Liverpool Daily Post & Echo Ltd.
PO Box 48, Old Hall Street, Liverpool, L69 3EB
tel: 0151 227 2000
fax: 0151 285 8483
web: www.icliverpool.co.uk
take demos: Yes
info: Publish: Liverpool - Daily Post, Anfield & Walton Star, Bebbington & Bromborough News, Birkenhead News, Bootle Times, Crosby Herald, Formby Times, Heswall News, Hoylake & West Kirby News, Huyton & Roby Star, Maghull & Aintree Star, Midweek Advertiser/Village Visiter, Neston News, Ormskirk Advertiser, Ormskirk Midweek Advertiser, South Liverpool Merseymart, Southport Midweek Visitor, Southport Visitor, Village Visitor, Wallasey News, and West Derby & Tuebrook Merseymart.

Newsquest (Bolton/Bury)
Newspaper House, Churchgate, Bolton, Lancashire, BL1 1DE
tel: 01204 522 345
fax: 01204 361 237
web: www.thisislancashire.co.uk
take demos: Yes
info: Newsquest Bolton/Bury publish the following titles: Blackburn/Lancashire Evening Telegraph, Bolton Evening News, Blackburn Citizen, Blackpool & Fylde Citizen, Bolton Journal, Burnley Citizen, Bury Journal, Chorley Citizen, Lancaster & Morecambe Citizen, Leigh Journal Midweek, Preston & Leyland Citizen, Prestwich & Whitefield Guide and Radcliffe Times.

Rochdale Observer Group
Drake Street, Rochdale, Lancashire, OL16 1PH
tel: 01706 354 321
fax: 01706 522 927
email: rochdaleobserver@gmwn.co.uk
web: www.rochdaleobserver.co.uk
take demos: Yes
info: The Rochdale Observer Group publish the following titles: Accrington Observer & Times, The Advertiser North & East Manchester, Heywood Advertiser, Middleton & North Manchester Guardian, Oldham Advertiser, Prestwich & Whitefield Advertiser, Rochdale & Heywood Express, Rochdale Observer (Sat), Rochdale Observer (Wed), Rossendale Free Press and The Salford Advertiser.

Apna News
Washington House, 259 Derby Street, Bolton, BL3 6LA
tel: 07973 168 857
fax: 01204 437 384
email: apna@zen.co.uk
web: www.apnaonline.net
contact: BC Patel
take demos: No
info: Free Magazine is published monthly and distributed door to door. Will run features on local bands and review demos. Apna prefer that you send an email describing the band and if interested, they will take it from there. Send demos and biog to Apna News office. Submit by the 15th of the month.

Asian News
82 Drake Street, Rochdale, Lancashire, OL16 1PH
tel: 01706 357 086
fax: 01706 341 595
email: asiannews@gmwn.co.uk
web: www.theasiannews.co.uk
contact: Shelina Begum
take demos: No
info: Monthly magazine distributed to 20,000. Publication date varies but usually towards the end of the month. Will run features on up and coming Asian bands. Does not usually list gigs, but if details are submitted Asian News may list local events. Deadline is a couple of days before publication.

Big Issue in the North (Manchester & Liverpool)
135-141 Oldham Street, Manchester, M4 1LN
tel: 0161 834 6300
email: editorial@bigissueinthenorth.com
web: www.bigissueinthenorth.com
contact: Ray Bullpit
take demos: No
info: The Big Issue has 4 'Gig of the Week' spots every week and will occasionally dedicate one of these to an unsigned act or, more likely, an unsigned band showcase featuring a number of acts. If your band has a gig coming up, send a demo and biography to Ally Fogg at the magazine. The Big Issue may run a gig preview, but will not normally review demos or gigs.

MEDIA

Bolton Evening News
Newspaper House, Churchgate, Bolton, BL1 1DE
tel: 01204 537 270
fax: 01204 365 068
email: bennewsdesk@boltoneveningnews.co.uk
web: www.boltoneveningnews.co.uk
contact: David Crookes
take demos: No
info: Will review demos and run features on local bands
in the weekly entertainment section, '24/7'. Deadline for gig listing
submissions is the Tuesday before. Send demo, biog, photos and details
of forthcoming local dates to David Crookes.

The Buz Magazine
3rd Floor, 2a Price Street, Birkenhead, CH41 7JN
tel: 0151 649 9449
fax: 0151 649 9229
email: thebuz@thebuz.org
web: www.thebuz.org
take demos: No
info: Monthly free entertainment magazine with a
distribution of 40,000 around the Wirral. Bands can place quarter-page
gig guides for £35.25 (including VAT) that list all up and coming live
dates. Entry into the artist directory, which lists band name and contact
details, costs £5. For gig guides and inclusion in the artist directory
contact The Buz office on details above. The Buz run band profiles
every month, plus an artist profile and a newcomer profile. There are
also 4 demo reviews per edition. Profiles and demo reviews are free.
Send biog and demo to the office. For details of showcase events run by
The Buz in The Wirral, call the office on the number above.

Flux Magazine
2nd Floor, 42 Edge Street, Manchester, M4 1HN
tel: 0161 832 0300
fax: 0161 819 1196
email: editorial@fluxmagazine.com
web: www.fluxmagazine.com
contact: Xander Cook
take demos: No
info: International magazine on sale on the 12th of every
other month. They are not looking to cover unsigned bands, but keep
an eye on any Leftfield acts that they are impressed with. Will feature
a specific event such as a gig or festival appearance. Do not generally
review demos but are always looking for the next good artist. Send all
biogs, demos, photos and gig listings to Xander Cook, no later than the
20th of the month.

FreeStyle
Clare House, 166 Lord Street, Southport, PR9 0QA
tel: 01704 392 336
fax: 01704 501 678
email: erica.dillon@freestyleguide.com
web: www.freestyleguide.com
contact: Erica Dillon
take demos: No
info: Monthly lifestyle and leisure magazine covering the
Sefton and Liverpool area. On sale on the first Friday and circulated
to 70,000. Keen to expand music section. Send demo, biog, photos
and details of live dates to Erica Dillon at the magazine. Deadline
for submission is a week before publication. Part of the Champion
Newspaper Group.

Inaudible Music
Unit F, Wordsworth Trading Estate, Wordsworth Street, Halliwell,
Bolton, BL1 3ND
tel: 01204 846 333
email: paul@inaudiblemusic.co.uk
web: www.inaudiblemusic.co.uk
contact: Paul Dean
take demos: No
info: 5,500 copies of the magazine are distributed around
every venue and record shop in Manchester every month. Contact Paul
Dean at the magazine with your demo. They are very keen to feature
unsigned Manchester based bands, as well as bands based further
afield in the North West, such as Wigan and Chester.

Live Magazine
Suite 215, Queens Dock Commercial Centre, Norfolk Street, Liverpool,
L1 0BG
tel: 0151 709 1667
fax: 0151 708 9264
email: music@livemagazine.co.uk
web: www.livemagazine.co.uk
contact: Tony de Costa
take demos: No
info: Weekly publication, covering arts and culture in
Merseyside. There is a section dedicated to local music, featuring gig
and demo reviews, listings and profiles. Send demo, biographies and
upcoming gig dates to the address above.

Liverpool Daily Post
PO Box 48, Old Hall Street, Liverpool, L69 3EB
tel: 0151 227 2000
fax: 0151 472 2474
email: chrisbrown@dailypost.co.uk
web: www.icliverpool.co.uk
contact: Chris Brown
take demos: No
info: There is a weekly column '…On Rock', that appears
every Friday. Circulated to 20,000, it contains profiles of local bands
and up and coming gigs, with the possibility of demo reviews if space
allows. Send demos, biography and details of local live dates to Chris
Brown at the paper. Deadline for submission is Tuesday.

Liverpool Echo
PO Box 48, Old Hall Street, Liverpool, L69 3EB
tel: 0151 227 2000
fax: 0151 285 8483
email: gillianguilfoyle@icliverpool.net
web: www.icliverpool.co.uk
contact: Gillian Guilfoyle, Kate Mansey
take demos: No
info: Supplement runs each Friday with gig details included
in the daily entertainment guide. Contact Gillian Guilfoyle for any
website features or Kate Mansey for any newspaper features. Pop page
every Friday always features some local music scene news, and a larger
editorial piece each month profiles 1 unsigned band (with an interview
and photo). Send demo, biography and photo to Kate Mansey. Deadline
for submission is Tuesday morning. If you would like the feature to
coincide with a gig, Kate will need a few weeks notice.

Living Edge Magazine Ltd.
14a Bath Street, Hale, WA14 2EJ
tel: 0161 928 0333
email: matt.livingedge@btinternet.com
contact: Matthew Stansfield
take demos: No
info: Monthly lifestyle publication. There is no dedicated
local music scene coverage but the title does accept demos and biogs
for consideration. Gig details can be submitted for inclusion in the
'What's On' listings.

Loot the Free Ads Paper
Manchester Loot, 11th Floor, Alberton House, St. Mary's Parsonage,
Manchester, M3 2WJ
tel: 0870 043 4343
email: freeads.manchester@loot.com
web: www.loot.com
take demos: Yes
info: Place free ads to Loot magazine to buy or sell
instruments and other equipment. Also a good way to find band
members and like minded musicians in your area. Prices do vary
from area to area, basic ads which appear for 1 day are usually free
of charge. You can place up to 5 of these ads. Black boxed ads are £12
for 1 week or £18 for 2 weeks, red boxed ads are £15. All ads will also
appear on the Loot website. Phone, fax, email or post your ad into
Loot.

Manchester Evening News
164 Deansgate, Manchester, M3 3RN
tel: 0161 832 7200
fax: 0161 839 0968
web: www.manchesteronline.co.uk
contact: David Sue
take demos: No
info: The 'Go' section is published every Friday and
distributed to 300,000. Regularly features an unsigned band profile.
Send demos, biography, photo and details of upcoming gigs to David
Sue at the address above. For inclusion in the gig guide email details to
David 10 days in advance.

Manchester Metro News
164 Deansgate, Manchester, M3 3RN
tel: 0161 834 9677
fax: 0161 834 0556
email: news@metro-news.co.uk
web: www.metronews.co.uk
contact: Rachel Broady
take demos: Yes
info: Weekly publication issued every Friday that circulates
to over 300,000. No demo reviews or gig listings but will run features
on up and coming bands and preview or review gigs in it's 16
page supplement. Deadline for submission is Tuesday for Friday's
publication.

Messenger Newspapers
Brindley House, 25 Ashton Lane, Sale, Cheshire, M33 6TP
tel: 0161 908 3380
fax: 0161 908 3403
email: sam.editorial@messengergrp.co.uk
web: www.messengernewspapers.co.uk
contact: Rick Bowen
take demos: No
info: Weekly publication coming out on Thursday's with a deadline for all submissions on Tuesday. Will consider listing gigs and reviewing demos from unsigned bands from the Trafford area. Address all correspondence for the attention of 'Music Matters', the music section of the website. Publish the Sale and Altrincham Messenger and the Stretford and Urmston Messenger.

Metro (Manchester)
Acresfield, 8-10 Exchange Street, Manchester, M2 7HA
tel: 0161 836 5168
fax: 0161 836 5161
email: ben.east@ukmetro.co.uk
web: www.metro.co.uk
contact: Ben East
take demos: No
info: Daily free newspaper circulated to 110,000 readers. Extensive listing guide covering Greater Manchester. Will sometimes profile local bands with up and coming gigs, but do not have specific demo review section. Send details of live dates, demos, biog, photos and any other relevant information to Ben East. Part of Associated Newspapers.

North & East Manchester Advertiser
17 Chaddesley Walk, Beswick, Manchester, M11 3SW
tel: 0161 223 9199
fax: 0161 223 5447
email: beswick.news@gmwn.co.uk
web: www.nemadvertiser.co.uk
contact: Chris Humphries
take demos: No
info: Free weekly newspaper covering North and East Manchester. Features on local bands and gig listing are included in the 'Weekender' sections. Submit demos and other relevant information to Chris Humphries at the address above.

SOUTHEAST

Archant (Hertfordshire)
16-18 Market Square, Hitchin, Hertfordshire, SG5 1DS
tel: 01462 423 423
fax: 01462 420 804
web: www.archant.co.uk
take demos: Yes
info: Archant Hertfordshire publish the following newspapers: Herts Advertiser, Hitchin Comet, Hoddesdon Herald, Letchworth & Baldock Comet, Stevenage & Letchworth Herald, Stevenage Comet and the Welwyn & Hatfield Times.

Berkshire Regional Newspapers
50-56 Portman Road, Reading, RG30 1BA
tel: 0118 950 3030
fax: 0118 939 1619
email: trudyparsons@rnc.co.uk
web: www.icberkshire.co.uk
take demos: Yes
info: Bracknell Midweek News, Bracknell News Extra, Newbury & Thatcham Chronicle, Reading Chronicle, Reading Chronicle Midweek, Slough Windsor & Ascot Informer, Slough Windsor Eton Express.

The Ealing Gazette Series
28 Bakers Road, Uxbridge, Middlesex, UB8 1RG
tel: 01895 451 035
take demos: Yes
info: The Ealing Gazette Series includes the Ealing & Acton, Hammersmith & Shepherds Bush, Southall, Greenford & Northolts, and Fulham Gazette titles, all published weekly on a Friday.

Milestone Group Plc
20 Marcham Road, Abingdon, Oxfordshire, OX14 1AA
tel: 01235 553 444
fax: 01235 554 465
email: enquiries@courier-newspapers-oxford.co.uk
web: www.courier-newspapers-oxford.co.uk
take demos: Yes
info: Publish Oxford Courier, Oxford Journal, South Oxfordshire Courier.

Newsquest (Oxfordshire)
Osney Mead, Oxford, Oxfordshire, OX2 OEJ
tel: 01865 425 262
fax: 01865 425 557
email: enquiries@nqo.com
web: www.thisisoxfordhire.co.uk
take demos: Yes
info: Publish the following newspapers: Banbury Cake (see separate entry), Bicester Advertiser, Oxford Star, Oxford Times, Oxfordshire Herald and Witney & West Oxfordshire Gazette.

Newsquest (Sussex)
Crowhurst Road, Hollingbury, BN1 8AR
tel: 01273 544 544
fax: 01273 566 114
web: www.thisisbrightonandhove.co.uk
take demos: Yes
info: Newsquest (Sussex) publish: Brighton & Hove Leader, Mid Sussex Leader and South Coast Leader.

Banbury Cake
62-63 High Street, Banbury, Oxfordshire, OX16 5JP
tel: 01295 256 111
fax: 01295 268 544
email: juliandancer@nqo.com
web: www.thisisoxfordshire.co.uk
contact: Julian Dancer
take demos: Yes
info: Keen to feature local talent when space allows. Send any information in to Julian Dancer, or call the Mill Arts Centre's Deep Space Club on 01295 252 050, who work closely with Julian.

Blah Blah Magazine
PO Box 2622, Reading, RG1 9DJ
tel: 0118 975 3577
fax: 0118 975 3559
email: marc@blahblah.co.uk
web: www.blahblah.co.uk
contact: Marc or Luisa
take demos: No
info: Blah Blah Magazine is the leading listings and entertainment monthly for the Reading area. Currently read by more than 40,000 people every month, the magazine includes previews, reviews and record reviews, alongside the listings. To submit your listings send details (including name of event, times, prices, dates and venue details) to listings@blahblah.co.uk. The deadline for publication is the 17th of the month.

Brighton - The Argus
Argus House, Crowhurst Road, Hollingbury, BN1 8AR
tel: 01273 544 544
fax: 01273 566 114
email: news@theargus.co.uk
web: www.thisisbrightonandhove.co.uk
contact: Jakki Phillips
take demos: No
info: The Argus will feature write ups and listings for local bands. Mark any demos FAO Jakki Phillips.

Bubblegum Slut
27 Stores Lane, Tiptree, Essex, CO5 OLH
tel: 07751 595 710
email: bubblegumslutzine@gmail.com
web: www.bubblegumslutfanzine.1hwy.com.
contact: Alison Bateman
take demos: Yes
info: Bubblegum Slut is a 60 A5 page quarterly zine covering a mix of Glam, Sleaze, Goth, DeathRock, Rockabilly and other big-haired, over made-up music. Does not contain gig listings but will always consider any material sent to them.

Canterbury Adscene
Newspaper House, Wincheap, Canterbury, CT1 3YR
tel: 01227 767 321
fax: 01227 456 444
email: lizmcdonagh@kentregionalnewspapers.co.uk
web: www.trinitymirrorsouthern.co.uk
take demos: Yes
info: Local bands can send any gig details to the above email address for a listing request. Alternatively, send a demo to the Newsdesk with any biogs or pictures for consideration.

Dartford Times
Kentish Times Newspapers, Roxby House, Station Road, Sidcup, Kent, DA15 7EJ
tel: 01474 320 749
fax: 01474 320 316
email: eric.randalph@archant.co.uk
web: www.dartfordtimes.com
contact: Eric Randalph
take demos: No
info: Eric Randalph writes a music column. Contact him with details of your band for consideration.

MEDIA

Ealing Gazette
28 Bakers Road, Uxbridge, Middlesex, UB8 1RG
tel: 01895 451 035
email: victoriaprewer@trinitysouth.co.uk
contact: Victoria Prewer
take demos: No
info: Will occasionally run features on local bands. Send demo, biog and any other relevant information to Victoria at the address above.

Essex Chronicle
Westway, Chelmsford, CM1 3BE
tel: 01245 603 428
fax: 01277 219 172
email: go@essexchronicle.co.uk
web: www.thisisessex.com
contact: Darryl Webber
take demos: No
info: The 'Go' supplement will feature local bands extensively. They have a 'Meet the Band' article focusing on a new local band each week. The Go section will also print any upcoming gigs. Contact Darryl for consideration.

Harrow Times
Times and Observer Newspapers, Observer House, Caxton Way, Watford Business Park, Watford, WD18 8RJ
tel: 01923 216 216
fax: 01923 243 738
email: j.brockett@london.newsquest.co.uk
contact: James Brockett
take demos: No
info: Published weekly every Thursday. Includes gig listings and reviews of gigs and demos. Local unsigned acts should send as much relevant information about themselves as possible to James at the address above.

Hillingdon Times
Loudwater Mill, Station Road, Loudwater, High Wycombe, Buckinghamshire, HP10 9TY
tel: 01494 755 000
fax: 01494 441 977
email: rwakefield@london.newsquest.co.uk
web: www.hillingdontimes.co.uk
contact: Rachael Wakefield
take demos: No
info: Published weekly every Thursday. To be included in the local gig listings, email Rachael at the address above. The paper will also occasionally include features on local bands.

Kent on Sunday
Apple Barn, Hythe Road, Smeeth, Ashford, Kent, TN25 6SR
tel: 01303 817 000
fax: 01303 817 001
email: editorial@kosmedia.co.uk
web: www.kentonsunday.co.uk
contact: Charlotte Wilson
take demos: Yes
info: Published every Sunday with a circulation of 120,637. Includes local gig listings. If you would like your gig to be listed, email the paper at least 2 weeks in advance.

Oxford Mail
Newsquest (Oxfordshire) Ltd., Osney Mead, Oxford, Oxfordshire, OX2 0EJ
tel: 01865 425 262
fax: 01865 425 557
email: enquiries@nqo.com
web: www.thisisoxfordshire.co.uk
contact: Tim Hughes
take demos: No
info: Tim Hughes writes the music section on a freelance basis. Contact him on 07941 183 834 for consideration of inclusion in the paper.

Southend Echo
Newspaper House, Chester Hall Lane, Basildon, Essex, SS14 3BL
tel: 01268 522 792
fax: 01268 469 281
email: paul.offord@nqe.com
web: www.thisisessex.co.uk/echo
take demos: No
info: Very happy to feature unsigned bands from the vicinity. For listings contact Charlotte Potter. Paul Offord writes a music column every Wednesday, for which the submission deadline is Monday. The column focuses on gig previews rather than reviews, but will review demos. The column goes out to over 40,000 people.

Spill Magazine
Global House, Bridge Street, Guildford, Surrey, GU1 4SB
tel: 01483 501 216
email: chris.dempsey@spillonline.com
web: www.spillonline.com
contact: Chris Dempsey
take demos: No
info: SPILL is an independent monthly music magazine with a circulation of 10,000 copies across London and the South East, devoting 5 pages per month to unsigned artists from every genre. Very keen to support unsigned bands with dedicated coverage including features and reviews. Contact Chris with demos, biogs and live dates for consideration.

SOUTHWEST

Archant (South West)
32 Waterloo Road, Weston Super Mare, Somerset, BS23 1LW
tel: 01934 422522
web: www.archant.co.uk
contact: Mr Bernard Driscoll
take demos: Yes
info: Archant South West publish the following array of publications: Exmouth Herald, Exmouth Journal, Midweek Herald, North Devon Gazette & Advertiser, North Somerset Times, Sidmouth Herald, Weston & Somerset Mercury and the Weston Super Mare Admag.

Bath Newspaper Publishers
Windsor House, Windsor Bridge, Bath, BA2 3AU
tel: 01225 322 322
fax: 01225 322 296
web: www.thisisbath.co.uk
take demos: Yes
info: Publish: Bath Chronicle, Somerset & Avon Guardian, Somerset Standard, and West Wiltshire Advertiser, and Bath Times.

Bristol Evening Post & Press Ltd.
Temple Way, Bristol, Avon, BS99 7HD
tel: 0117 934 3339
web: www.thisisbristol.co.uk
take demos: Yes
info: Bristol Evening Post & Press Ltd publish the following titles: Bristol - Western Daily Press, Bristol Observer (East Bristol), Bristol Observer (Keynsham), Bristol Observer (Kingswood), Bristol Observer (North West Bristol), Bristol Observer (South Bristol) and Bristol Observer (South Gloucestershire).

Newsquest (Wiltshire)
100 Victoria Road, Swindon, Wiltshire, SN1 3BE
tel: 01793 528 144
fax: 01793 542 434
email: msuddaby@newswilts.co.uk
web: www.thisiswiltshire.co.uk
take demos: Yes
info: Newsquest Wiltshire publish Devizes Melksham & Vale of Pewsey News, Swindon Evening Advertiser, Swindon Star, West & North Wilts Star and Wiltshire Gazette & Herald.

Southern Daily Echo
Newspaper House, Test Lane, Redbridge, SO16 9JX
tel: 023 8042 4777
fax: 023 8042 4770
web: www.thisishampshire.net
take demos: Yes
info: Southampton - Southern Daily Echo, New Forest Post, Southampton Advertiser.

Westcountry Publications Ltd.
17 Brest Road, Derriford Business Park, Plymouth, Devon, PL6 5AA
tel: 01752 765 500
fax: 01752 765 555
web: www.thisissouthdevon.co.uk or www.thisisplymouth.co.uk or www.thisisexeter.co.uk
take demos: Yes
info: Exeter - Express & Echo, Plymouth - Evening Herald, Plymouth - Western Morning News, Torquay - Herald Express, Exeter Leader, Newton Abbot & District Weekender, Plymouth Extra.

24-7
24-7 Demo Reviews, Unit 29, Scott Business Park, Beacon Park Road, Plymouth, PL2 2PB
tel: 01752 294 130
fax: 01752 564 010
email: editorial@afterdarkmedia.com
web: www.twenty4-seven.co.uk
contact: Lucy Griffiths
take demos: No
info: 24-7 tend to feature bands from the South West region only, as opposed to elsewhere in the UK. Any genre of music is accepted.

And Magazine
The Rose Bowl, Botley Road, West End, Southampton, SO30 3XN
tel: 02380 473 000
email: info@and-magazine.co.uk
web: www.and-magazine.co.uk
contact: Martin
take demos: No
info: Often include a free cover CD. No charge for inclusion but must be unsigned and original material.

Bath Times
Windsor House, Windsor Bridge, Bath, BA2 3AU
tel: 01225 322 322
fax: 01225 322 296
email: features@bathchron.co.uk
web: www.thisisbath.co.uk
contact: Charley Dunlap
take demos: No
info: Every Friday a gig guide is published in a supplement entitled 'Bathtime'. Any musical features on local unsigned bands will be written by Charley Dunlap. Send any demos, biogs, gig listings and other info marked for her attention.

Bristol Evening Post
Temple Way, Bristol, Avon, BS99 7HD
tel: 0117 934 3339
email: k.clark@bepp.co.uk
web: www.thisisbristol.co.uk
contact: Keith Clark
take demos: No
info: Weekly supplement '24/7' published every Thursday, which features listings, articles, interviews, reviews and previews of local bands. Deadline for submission is the previous Friday. The paper is very keen to cover unsigned talent. Each week a panel cast their eye over a new band in 'Bristol Sound'. Bands featured in this section can then go on to play at 'The Fleece' in conjunction with the paper at 'Bristol Sounds Live'. Keith Clark is the man to speak to about all these opportunities on his direct line or via email.

The Cornishman
30 Fore Street, Bodmin, Cornwall, PL31 2HQ
tel: 01208 781 33
fax: 01208 733 74
email: cgleisure@c-dm.co.uk
web: www.thisiscornwall.co.uk
take demos: No
info: Happy to cover local bands. Send details of any gigs by Monday for Thursday's edition.

Metro (South West)
Bristol Evening Post and Press Limited, Temple Way, Bristol, BS99 7HD
tel: 0117 934 3726
email: southwestlife@ukmetro.co.uk
web: www.metro.co.uk
take demos: Yes
info: Gig previews and listings. Send all information to the above email address FAO Clare.

Splinter
PO Box 2482, Bristol, BS5 5AB
tel: 01179 020 031
email: enquiries@splintermag.com
web: www.splintermag.com
contact: Giles Turnbull
take demos: No
info: Splinter has national and international coverage from bands to readership and stockists. No genre is excluded.

Venue Magazine
64-65 North Road, St. Andrews, Bristol, BS6 5AQ
tel: 0117 942 8491
fax: 0117 942 0369
email: music@venue.co.uk
web: www.venue.co.uk
contact: Julian Owen
take demos: No
info: Bristol and Bath's leisure magazine. Happy to feature local bands in the features and listings sections. Send demos to the above address.

Western Daily Press
Temple Way, Bristol, Avon, BS99 7HD
tel: 0117 934 3339
fax: 0117 934 3571
email: k.clark@bepp.co.uk
web: www.thisisbristol.co.uk
contact: Keith Clark
take demos: No
info: Weekly supplement '24/7' published every Thursday, which features listings, articles, interviews, reviews and previews of local bands. Deadline for submission is the previous Friday. The paper is very keen to cover unsigned talent. Each week a panel cast their eye over a new band in 'Bristol Sound'. Bands featured in this sectin can go on to play at 'The Fleece' in conjunction with the paper at 'Bristol Sounds Live'. Keith Clark is the man to speak to about all these opportunities on his direct line or via email.

YORKSHIRE

The Halifax Courier Ltd
Courier Building, King Cross Street, Halifax, HX1 2SF
tel: 01422 260 200
fax: 01422 260 341
take demos: Yes
info: Publish the Halifax - Evening Courier, Brighouse Echo, Calderdale News, Hebden Bridge Times and Todmorden News.

Newsquest (Bradford)
Hall Ings, Bradford, West Yorkshire, BD1 1JR
tel: 01274 729 511
fax: 01274 724 907
web: www.telegraph-and-argus.co.uk
take demos: Yes
info: Newsquest Bradford also publish Bradford Telegraph & Argus, Craven Herald & Pioneer, Ilkley Gazette, Keighley News, Keighley Craven Target, Target Series (North Yorkshire), The Town Crier and Wharfedale & Airedale Observer.

Hull Daily Mail Publications
PO Box 34, Blundells Corner, Beverley Road, Hull, HU3 1XS
tel: 01482 327 111
fax: 01482 599 452
web: www.thisishull.co.uk
take demos: Yes
info: Hull Daily Mail, Beverley Advertiser, East Riding Advertiser, Haltenprice Advertiser, Holderness Advertiser, Hull Advertiser (East Hull), Hull Advertiser (West Hull).

Newsquest (York)
PO Box 29, 76-86 Walmgate, York, YO1 9YN
tel: 01904 653 051
fax: 01904 626 388
email: yorkads@york.newsquest.co.uk
web: www.thisisyork.co.uk
take demos: Yes
info: Publish Yorkshire Evening Press, Selby Star, York Star, Yorkshire Gazette & Herald.

Sheffield Newspapers Ltd.
York Street, Sheffield, South Yorkshire, S1 1PU
tel: 0114 276 7676
fax: 0114 275 3551
email: david.edmondson@rim.co.uk
take demos: No
info: Sheffield - The Star, Doncaster Star, Sheffield Journal, Sheffield Telegraph, Sheffield Weekly Gazette.

Yorkshire Post Newspapers Ltd.
PO Box 168, Wellington Street, Leeds, LS1 1RF
tel: 0113 243 2701
fax: 0113 244 3430
email: eped@ypn.co.uk
web: www.thisisleeds.co.uk
take demos: Yes
info: Leeds - Yorkshire Evening Post, Yorkshire Post.

Beverley Guardian
Times House, Mill Street, Driffield, East Yorkshire, YO25 6TN
tel: 01377 241 414
fax: 01377 241 507
email: marc.meneuad@yrnltd.co.uk
web: www.driffieldtoday.co.uk
contact: Marc Meneaud
take demos: No
info: The paper will run demo reviews, band profiles and features. A gig guide appears in the 'What's On' supplement. Get in touch with Marc Meneaud, who is keen to support the local music scene.

Bradford Target
Newsquest Bradford Ltd, Hall Ings, Bradford, West Yorkshire, BD1 1JR
tel: 01274 729 511
fax: 01274 724 907
email: editorial@bradford.newsquest.co.uk
contact: David Barnett
take demos: No
info: The paper's 'What's On' section may feature local bands, space allowing. Send any demos marked FAO David Barnett.

Calderdale News
Halifax Courier Ltd., PO Box 19, Kings Cross Street, Halifax, West Yorkshire, HX1 2SF
tel: 01422 260 200
fax: 01422 260 282
email: newsdesk@halifaxcourier.co.uk
web: www.halifaxtoday.co.uk
contact: Suzanne Rutter
take demos: No
info: Large coverage of bands based in the immediate area. Bands meeting this criteria can turn to the paper for any help they need. Weekly local band column featuring news, reviews, interviews, gig previews and profiles. Also features separate gig listings. Submit details by Tuesday for the Friday edition. Happy to hear from musicians of any genre.

Dewsbury & District Press
1 Oates St, Dewsbury, West Yorkshire, WF13 1BB
tel: 01924 439 498
fax: 01924 457 994
email: info@dewspr.co.uk
contact: Martin Shaw
take demos: No
info: The Press is published on a Friday. Deadline for submissions is Thursday morning. Gig guide, colloquially titled 'Aat and Abaht', will run comprehensive listings in the area, and feature local unsigned band profiles.

Doncaster Advertiser
Sunny Bar, Doncaster, South Yorkshire, DN1 1NB
tel: 01302 347 211
fax: 01302 348 521
email: jheppenstall@doncastertoday.co.uk
contact: John Heppenstall
take demos: No
info: Local bands will be considered for a demo review. The paper include a magazine called 'The Entertainer' on a Thursday which may feature local unsigned Rock bands. Please submit any gig details at least 10 days in advance. Mark any demos FAO John Heppenstall.

Goole Howden Thorne Courier
8 Pasture Road, Goole, North Humberside, DN14 6EZ
tel: 01405 720 888
email: jbright@gooletoday.co.uk
web: www.gooletoday.co.uk
contact: James Bright
take demos: No
info: 3 pages of leisure news each week, and a 'Youth' page which features previews and reviews of breaking local acts. The Courier are happy to be leading experts on the local area's Punk scene.

Leeds Guide
30-34 Aire Street, Leeds, West Yorkshire, LS1 4HT
tel: 0113 244 1007
fax: 0113 244 1002
email: editor@leedsguide.co.uk
web: www.leedsguide.co.uk
contact: Abi Bliss
take demos: No
info: Fortnightly listings magazine. Submit your listings as far in advance as possible. Deadline is 3 weeks before publication. Send demos to Abi at the above address.

Metro (Yorkshire)
PO Box 168, Wellington Street, Leeds, LS1 1RF
tel: 0113 238 8062
email: yorkshire.listings@ukmetro.co.uk
web: www.metro.co.uk
take demos: Yes
info: Free newspaper distributed daily in Leeds and Sheffield. Gig listings should be submitted at least 3 days before the event, preferably 2 weeks if they intend to write a preview.

Sandman Yorkshire
PO Box 684, York, YO31 7WT
tel: 0114 278 6727
email: york@sandmanmagazine.co.uk
web: www.sandmanmagazine.co.uk
contact: Jan Webster
take demos: No
info: Sandman Magazine will concentrate on unsigned acts from each edition of the magazine's locality; Sheffield, York, Hull and Leeds. They will run features, reviews and profile new releases. Any bands touring in the area may get gig previews in the listings section. To submit information for Sandman York edition, use details above. See website for submission email and postal addresses for Hull, Sheffield and Leeds Sandman. Also refer to listing for Sandman Nottingham in relevant section.

Belfast Telegraph Newspapers Ltd.
124-144 Royal Avenue, Belfast, BT1 1EB
tel: 028 9026 4000
fax: 028 9033 1332
email: editor@belfasttelegraph.co.uk
web: www.belfasttelegraph.co.uk
take demos: Yes
info: The publishing group includes Belfast Telegraph, Belfast - Sunday Life, East Belfast Community Telegraph, North Down Community Telegraph, North & Newtownabbey Community Telegraph and South Belfast Community Telegraph.

Derry Journal Ltd.
Buncrana Road, Derry, BT48 8AA
tel: 028 7127 2200
fax: 028 7127 2218
email: editorial@derryjournal.com
web: www.derryjournal.com
take demos: Yes
info: Publish Derry Journal (Fri & Tues), Derry Journal Extra, Foyle News.

Alternative Ulster
58 Wellington Place, Belfast, BT1 6GF
tel: 028 9027 8627
email: info@alternativeulster.com
web: www.alternativeulster.com
contact: Jonny Tiernan
take demos: No
info: Alternative Ulster provide blanket coverage of unsigned bands, providing information about gigs, demos and news. Send demo to Jonny to be considered. The magazine runs gig nights for mostly local bands, but may offer coverage to bands further afield.

The Belfast Beat
Adman Publishing, 5 University Street, Belfast, BT7 1FY
tel: 028 9024 6624
email: natalie@admanpublishing.com
web: www.admanpublishing.com
contact: Natalie Brolly
take demos: No
info: The 'Almost Famous' section is a springboard for unsigned bands, dedicating plenty of space to unsigned acts from Belfast, as well as everywhere else in the UK. Natalie also runs an unsigned band night. Send demo, biog and anything else useful to be considered.

Belfast Telegraph
124-144 Royal Avenue, Belfast, BT1 1EB
tel: 028 9026 4000
fax: 028 9055 4517
email: ubradley@belfasttelegraph.co.uk
web: www.belfasttelegraph.co.uk
contact: Una Bradley
take demos: No
info: Dedicated 'Going Out' section published in the Telegraph every Friday called 'Twentyfourseven' which features gig listings and previews. Get in touch with Una if you would like to be considered for inclusion.

The Big Buzz Magazine
96 Duncairn Gardens, Belfast, BT15 2GJ
tel: 028 9075 7000
fax: 028 9075 7641
email: barry@bigbuzzireland.com
web: www.bigbuzzireland.com
contact: Barry O'Kane
take demos: No
info: Keen to support local bands as much as possible. Send demos to the above address.

Derry Journal
Derry Journal, Buncrana Road, Derry, BT48 8AA
tel:	028 7127 2200
fax:	028 7127 2218
email:	editorial@derryjournal.com
web:	www.derryjournal.com
contact:	Caroline Morrif
take demos:	No
info:	Entertainment section will cover local bands, send any
information to Caroline Morrif.

Irish News (Belfast)
113-117 Donegall Street, Belfast, BT1 2GE
tel:	028 9032 2226
fax:	028 9033 7508
email:	d.roy@irishnews.com
web:	www.irishnews.com
contact:	David Roy
take demos:	No
info:	'Noise Annoys' is a unsigned band column published
on Friday written David Roy. To be considered for inclusion send a 1 sheet press release and a CD along with any high resolution photos you may have to David by Wednesday. Any Irish bands may apply.

Sunday Journal
Derry Journal, Buncrana Road, Derry, BT48 8AA
tel:	028 7127 2200
fax:	028 7127 2218
email:	editorial@derryjournal.com
web:	www.derryjournal.com
contact:	Caroline Morrif
take demos:	No
info:	Published on a Sunday. Submit gig details by Friday
at 3pm. Entertainment section will cover local bands, send any information to Caroline Morris.

SCOTLAND

Aberdeen Journals Ltd.
PO Box 43, Lang Stracht, Maastrick, Aberdeen, AB15 6DF
tel:	01224 690 222
fax:	01224 694 613
email:	editor@pg.ajl.co.uk
web:	www.thisisnorthscotland.co.uk
take demos:	Yes
info:	Publish the Aberdeen Evening Express, Aberdeen
Press & Journal and the Aberdeen Citizen

Archant (Scotland)
Park House, Gower Street, Glasgow, G51 1PT
tel:	0141 427 7878
fax:	0141 427 0519
email:	editor@glasgowextra.demon.co.uk
web:	www.archant.co.uk
contact:	Neville Keithley
take demos:	Yes
info:	Archant Scotland publish the following newspapers:
Ayr & District Extra, Bearsde Milngavie & Glasgow Extra, Glasgow South & Eastwood Extra, Hamilton People, Irvine & North Ayrshire Extra, Kilmarnock & District Extra, Motherwell Extra and finally the Paisley, Renfrewshire & Gryffe Extra.

Daily Record & Sunday Mail Ltd.
One Central Quay, Glasgow, G3 8DA
tel:	0141 309 3000
fax:	0141 309 3340
web:	www.dailyrecord.co.uk
take demos:	Yes
info:	Daily Record & Sunday Mail Ltd publish The Sunday
Mail, The Daily Record and The Glaswegian.

DC Thomson & Co. Ltd.
2 Albert Square, Dundee, DD1 9QJ
tel:	01382 223 131
fax:	01382 225 511
web:	www.dcthomson.co.uk
take demos:	Yes
info:	Publish: The Dundee Courier & Advertiser, The
Dundee Evening Telegraph and The Sunday Post Scotland

Highland Printing & Publishing Ltd.
Henderson Road, Inverness, IV1 1SP
tel:	01463 713 700
fax:	01463 221 251
email:	adv-highlandnews@zetnet.co.uk
take demos:	Yes
info:	Publish the Caithness Courier, Highland News,
Inverness & Nairnshire Herald, The Inverness North Star, John O'Groats Journal and Lochaber News

Tweeddale Press Ltd.
90 Marygate, Berwick-upon-Tweed, Northumberland, TD15 1BW
tel:	01289 306 677
fax:	01289 307 377
email:	mail@tweeddalepress.co.uk
web:	www.tweeddalepress.co.uk
take demos:	Yes
info:	Publish Berwick Advertiser, Berwick
Gazette, Berwickshire News & East Lothian Herald, East Lothian News, East Lothian Times, Hawick News, Midlothian Advertiser, Musselburgh News, Peebles Times, Selkirk Weekend Advertiser and Selkirk - Southern Reporter

Daily Record
One Central Quay, Glasgow, G3 8DA
tel:	0141 309 3000
fax:	0141 309 3340
email:	r.fulton@dailyrecord.co.uk
web:	www.dailyrecord.co.uk
contact:	Rick Fulton
take demos:	No
info:	Every Friday the Daily Record has a column called
'Sound Check' featuring Scottish unsigned bands. Send gig details at least two weeks in advance. Any demos should be marked FAO Rick Fulton.

The Extra
5000 Academy, Gower Street, Pollokshields, G51 1PT
tel:	0141 427 7878
fax:	0141 427 0519
email:	rhona.sweeting@archant.co.uk
web:	www.theextra24.co.uk
contact:	Rhona Sweeting
take demos:	No
info:	Monthly paper covering the whole of Glasgow. Part
of 'The Extra' series. The paper has an arts page which previews and profiles local arts issues and events with a 'What's On' listings column. Also includes feature, 'Downtime', which previews forthcoming arts-related events.

Glasgow South Extra
5000 Academy, Gower Street, Pollokshields, G51 1PT
tel:	0141 419 4245
fax:	0141 427 0519
email:	nadia.anwer@archant.co.uk
web:	www.theextra24.co.uk
contact:	Nadia Anwer
take demos:	No
info:	The paper has an area-specific arts page which
previews and profiles local arts issues and events with a 'What's On' listings column. Covers the following areas: Eaglesham, Busby, Newton Mearns, Clarkston, Giffnock, Shawlands, Pollokshields, Hillpark, Cathcart, Battlefield, Newlands and Eastwood. There is also a feature called 'Downtime', which previews forthcoming arts-related events.

Glasgow West Extra
5000 Academy, Gower St, Pollokshields, G51 1PT
tel:	0141 419 4247
fax:	0141 427 0519
email:	rhona.sweeting@archant.co.uk
web:	www.theextra24.co.uk
contact:	Rhona Sweeting
take demos:	No
info:	The paper has an area-specific arts page which
previews/profiles local arts issues and events with a 'What's On' listings column. There's also a feature, 'Downtime', which previews forthcoming arts-related events. Rhona is very keen to support the thriving local music scene so get in touch with her via email.

Is This Music?
PO Box 13516, Linlithgow, EH49 6AS
email:	editor@isthismusic.com
web:	www.isthismusic.com
contact:	Miles O'Toole
take demos:	No
info:	Is This Music? is a bi-monthly publication with
unsigned band coverage of half a page dedicated to demo reviews in each issue. Send demos marked FAO of Miles O'Toole.

M8 Magazine
Music (Scotland) Ltd., Trojan House, Phoenix Business Park, Paisley, PA1 2BH
tel:	0141 840 5980
fax:	0141 840 5995
email:	kevin@m8magazine.com
web:	www.m8magazine.com
contact:	Kevin McFarlane
take demos:	No
info:	M8 focuses mainly on Dance music, and generally
does not accept demos from unsigned artists. However, if someone sends a track that they like, they will be able to assign it some coverage.l: Fax:

Metro (Scotland)
7th Floor, 144 St. Vincents Street, Glasgow, G2 5LQ
tel: 0141 225 3336
email: gaynor.mackay@ukmetro.co.uk
web: www.metro.co.uk
contact: Gaynor MacKay
take demos: Yes
info: Metro Scotland is distributed in the central belt. They will list and preview gigs if you send a listing request to the above email address.

Newsquest Scotland
200 Renfield Street, Glasgow, G2 3PR
tel: 0141 300 3300
web: www.newsquestmedia.co.uk
take demos: Yes
info: Newsquest Scotland publish The Evening Times in Glasgow and The Herald daily and the Sunday Herald.

Paisley & Renfrewshire Extra
5000 Academy, Gower Street, Pollokshields, G51 1PT
tel: 0141 419 4247
fax: 0141 427 0519
email: lesley.brown@archant.co.uk
web: www.theextra24.co.uk
contact: Lesley Brown
take demos: No
info: The paper has an area-specific arts page which previews and profiles local arts issues and events with a 'What's On' listings column. Areas covered include Paisley, Neilston, Uplawmoor, Renfrew, Erskine, Bishopton, Inchinnan, Houston, Bridge of Weir, Linwood and Kilbarchan. There is also a feature, 'Downtime', which previews forthcoming arts-related events.

Perthshire Advertiser
58 Watergate, Perth, PH1 5TF
tel: 01738 626 211
fax: 01738 493 277
email: preoch@s-un.co.uk
web: www.icscotland.co.uk
contact: Paul Reoch
take demos: No
info: The Advertiser runs a dedicated local music column. Any bands from the area should get in touch with Paul Reoch to be considered for gig listings, live reviews and profiles. Paul will listen to demos from any local bands.

The Sunday Mail
One Central Quay, Glasgow, G3 8DA
tel: 0141 309 3000
fax: 0141 309 3340
email: b.sloan@dailyrecord.co.uk
web: www.dailyrecord.co.uk
contact: Billy Sloan
take demos: No
info: Send a demo to Billy Sloan for a review, space allowing. Billy also has a radio show on Clyde FM.

WALES

Newsquest (Wales & Western)
Cardiff Road, Newport, NP20 3QN
tel: 01633 810 000
web: www.thisisgwent.co.uk
take demos: Yes
info: Newsquest Wales & Western publish the following newspapers: South Wales Argus - Newport, Abergavenny Free Press, Barry & District News, Penarth Times, Campaign Blackwood/Risca/Newbridge, Campaign Caerphilly/Ystrad Mynach/Bargoed, Campaign Pontypridd/Porth/Mountain Ash/Llantrisant, Campaign Tredegar/Ebbw Vale/Brynmawr/Abertillery, Cardigan & Tivyside Advertiser, Cheltenham Independent, Chepstow Free Press, Cwmbran Free Press, Dusley - County Independent, Gloucestershire & Avon Gazette, Milford Mercury, Monmouth Free Press, Penarth Times, Pontypool Free Press, South Wales Guardian, Stroud News & Journal, The Gazette Series Gloucester, Weekly Argus Newport & Cwmbran, Western Telegraph Dyfed and Wiltshire & Gloucestershire Standard.

North Wales Newspapers Ltd.
Mold Business Park, Wrexham Road, Mold, Flintshire, CH7 1XY
tel: 01352 707 707
fax: 01352 700 048
email: nwnfd@netwales.co.uk
web: www.nwn.co.uk
take demos: Yes
info: Wrexham - Evening Leader, Bangor - North Wales Chronicle, Chester & District Standard, Denbighshire Free Press, Ellesmere Port Standard, Flintshire Leader & Standard, Mold - Y Cymro, Montgomeryshire Tribune, North Wales - The Pioneer, Oswestry & Border Counties Advertiser, Rhyl, Prestatyn & Abergele Journal, Welshpool - County Times & Express and the Wrexham Leader.

South West Wales Publications Ltd.
PO Box 14, Adelaide Street, Swansea, SA1 1QT
tel: 01792 510 000
fax: 01792 472 208
web: www.thisissouthwales.co.uk
take demos: Yes
info: Swansea - South Wales Evening Post, Carmarthen Herald, Carmarthen Journal, Llanelli Star, Neath Courier, Port Talbot Courier, Swansea - Herald of Wales.

Western Mail & Echo Ltd.
Thomson House, Havelock St, Cardiff, CF10 1XR
tel: 02920 223 333
web: www.totalwales.com
take demos: Yes
info: Western Mail & Echo Ltd publish: Cardiff - South Wales Echo, Cardiff - The Western Mail, Barry Post, Bridgend & Ogwr Post, Cardiff - Wales On Sunday, Cynon Valley Leader, Glamorgan Gazette, Gwent Gazette, Llantwit Major & Cowbridge Post, Merthyr Express, Neath & Port Talbot Guardian, Pontypridd Observer Series and the Rhondda Leader.

Buzz
12-14 The Balcony, Castle Arcade, Cardiff, CF10 2BU
tel: 02920 256 883
fax: 02920 256 885
email: editorial@buzzmag.co.uk
web: www.buzzmag.co.uk
contact: Noel Gardener
take demos: No
info: Buzz has been a leading entertainment magazine for 9 years. Free monthly 'Entertainments and What's on Guide' for Cardiff and South East Wales, including Newport, Swansea, the Valleys, Gwent and West Glamorgan. Buzz contains a gig guide in which unsigned bands can be listed. Deadline is the 18th of the month. The magazine is published on the 1st of the month. Any genre is accepted, but they would prefer to hear from bands from the local area. Contact Noel for more information.

Cardiff Post
Thomson House, Havelock Street, Cardiff, CF10 1XR
tel: 02920 223 333
email: cardiff.post@wme.co.uk
web: www.totalwales.com
take demos: No
info: Cardiff Post does not have a gig guide, but may detail individual local gigs of interest. Send demo to the above address or email with details of upcoming dates.

South Wales Echo
Thomson House, Havelock Street, Cardiff, CF10 1XR
tel: 02920 223 333
fax: 02920 583 624
email: ecadmin@wme.co.uk
contact: Alison Stokes
take demos: No
info: The Echo contains a 'What's On' section that will feature local bands. It also includes a gig guide, deadline for submission is 1pm 2 days prior to the event you would like listed. Mark material FAO Alison Stokes.

Tunetown
1 The Kingsway, Swansea, SA1 5JQ
tel: 01792 473 960
email: john.bevan@tunetown.org.uk
web: www.tunetown.org.uk
contact: John Bevan
take demos: No
info: Started as a reaction to the lack of opportunities for original musicians in Swansea and South West Wales. Organise a festival every summer in Swansea for local bands. The magazine will list local gigs, review demos and feature profiles. If you are based in South West Wales please contact John or Chris as they may be able help you. Send demo or email to start communication. To contact John by telephone, try ringing before 1:30pm on a weekday. Also promote gigs and offer music tuition. See listings in relevant sections for details.

The Western Mail
Thomson House, Havelock Street, Cardiff, CF10 1XR
tel: 02920 223 333
fax: 02920 583 553
email: hannah.jones@wme.co.uk
web: www.icwales.co.uk
contact: Hannah Jones
take demos: No
info: The Mail features the 'Box Office' supplement on a Friday which includes listings, demo reviews and gig previews of any local bands playing in the area. Contact Hannah Jones to be considered for inclusion.

7.5 STUDENT MEDIA

EAST of ENGLAND

Anglia Polytechnic University
East Road, Cambridge, CB1 1PT
tel:	01223 363 271
fax:	01223 352 973
email:	apex@apusu.ac.uk
web:	www.apusu.com
contact:	Simon
media:	Newspaper
info:	Anglia Polytechnic run a monthly newspaper, The Apex.

They are also planning to start an internet radio station.

Cambridge University
11-12 Trumpington Street, Cambridge, CB2 1QA
tel:	01223 273 929
fax:	01223 323 244
email:	tcs@cusu.cam.ac.uk or
	radio@cusu.cam.ac.uk
web:	www.cambridgestudent.com or
	www.cur.co.uk
contact:	Pamela Welsh, Beth McAvoy
media:	Newspaper/Radio Station
info:	Cambridge University has both a weekly newspaper,

The Cambridge Student, who will review CDs and a radio station, CUR 1350.

University Of East Anglia
The Union House, Norwich, Norfolk, NR4 7TJ
tel:	01603 593 272
email:	su.comms@uea.ac.uk
web:	www.stu.uea.ac.uk or
	www.livewire1350.com
contact:	Ian, Alan
media:	Newspaper/Radio Station
info:	Radio Livewire 1350 broadcasts during term time. The

Rabbit is published once a week.

GREATER LONDON

City University
Northampton Square, London, EC1V 0HB
tel:	020 7040 5060
web:	www.massivelonline.co.uk
contact:	Galia
media:	Newspaper/Radio Station
info:	Massive magazine is published monthly. City University

also have a radio station, Divercity radio.

Goldsmith's College
Dixon Road, New Cross, London, SE14 6NW
tel:	020 8692 1406
email:	smiths@gold.ac.uk or wired@gold.ac.uk
web:	www.goldsmiths.ac.uk
contact:	Claire Ratoina
media:	Newspaper/Radio Station
info:	Smiths is a monthly magazine. Wired Radio broadcasts

during term time.

Imperial College London
Prince Consult Road, South Kensington, London, SW7 2BB
tel:	020 7594 8060
web:	www.union.ic.ac.uk/media
media:	Newspaper/TV Station/Radio Station
info:	Felix newspaper is published weekly. STOIC TV and IC

Radio broadcast throughout the university term, and will accept demos.

King's College London
Students' Union, Surrey Street, London, WC2R 2NS
tel:	020 7836 7132
email:	roar@kclsu.org
web:	www.kclsu.org
contact:	Ed Drummond
media:	Newspaper
info:	King's College publish a magazine, Roar, every 3 weeks,

and occasionally features local unsigned bands. Will accept demos.

Kingston University
Students' Union, Penrhyn Road, Kingston Upon Thames, Surrey, KT1 2EE
tel:	020 8547 7884
email:	media@kingston.ac.uk
web:	www.kingstonsu.com
contact:	Paul Stephen
media:	Newspaper
info:	Sublime is published fortnightly.

London Metropolitan University
Students' Union, 2 Goulston Street, London, E1 7TP
tel:	020 7320 2233
email:	media.su@londonmet.ac.uk
web:	www.londonmetsu.org.uk
contact:	Maria Ginelli
media:	Newspaper/Radio Station
info:	The Student Metro is published once a month and is

also available online. A radio station is currently being planned.

London School of Economics
East Building, Houghton Street, London, WC2A 2AE
tel:	020 7955 7158
email:	thebeaver@lse.ac.uk
web:	www.pulsefm.co.uk
contact:	Neshy Boukhari
media:	Newspaper/Radio Station
info:	LSE produce both a weekly magazine, The Beaver, and

a radio station, Pulse Radio. The station broadcasts over the internet. Both accept demos.

Middlesex University
Cat Hill, Barnet, Hertfordshire, EN4 8HT
tel:	020 8411 6473
web:	www.musu.mdx.ac.uk
contact:	Prince Maxwell Uzochukwu
media:	Newspaper
info:	MUD is published regularly during the university term.

Queen Mary University of London
432 Bencroft Road, London, E1 4DH
tel:	020 7882 7670
email:	vpmeida@qmsu.org
web:	www.qmsu.org
contact:	Bryoni Hewer
media:	Newspaper
info:	Cub is a student magazine published once a month.

Roehampton Institute
Roehampton Lane, London, SW15 5PH
tel:	020 8392 3738
email:	fresh@roehamptonstudent.com
web:	www.roehamptonstudent.com
contact:	Ben Matthews
media:	Newspaper
info:	Fresh is published once a month and would be

interested in receiving demos from unsigned artists. Looking to start a radio station in 2006.

MEDIA

Royal Holloway (University of London)
Egham, Surrey, TW20 0EX
tel: 01784 486 300
email: orbital@su.rhul.ac.uk
web: www.rhul.ac.uk
contact: Matt
media: Newspaper/Radio Station
info: Royal Holloway publish a newspaper, The Orbital. Insanity (1287AM) is broadcast all year round.

South Bank University
Keyworth Street, London, SE1 6NG
tel: 020 7815 6060
email: vpcomms@lsbu.ac.uk
web: www.sbu.ac.uk or www.lsbsu.org
media: Newspaper
info: Magazine published several times during the year. Newspaper published fortnightly and contains listings for local events.

Thames Valley University
St. Mary's Road, Ealing, London, W5 5RF
tel: 020 8579 5000
email: frankiewedge@gmail.com
web: www.tvu.ac.uk
contact: Frankie Wedge
media: Newspaper
info: Magazine published throughout term time.

University Of East London
Student Union Office, 4-6 University Way, Dagenham, E16 2RD
tel: 020 8223 7026
email: sucom@uel.ac.uk
web: www.uelsu.net
contact: Patrick Link
media: Newspaper
info: University of East London publish re:fuel magazine monthly. Contact via the website.

University Of London
Malet Street, London, WC1E 7HY
tel: 020 7664 2000
email: londonstudent@ulu.lon.ac.uk
web: www.london-student.net
contact: Patrick Ward
media: Newspaper
info: The London Student is published fortnightly.

University of the Arts
Students' Union, 2-6 Catton Street, London, WC1R 4AA
tel: 020 7514 6274
email: info@su.arts.ac.uk
web: www.suarts.org
contact: Steven Pigott
media: Newspaper
info: The London Institute produce a quarterly magazine, Less Common More Sense . The magazine was awarded Best Student Magazine and Best Production by The Guardian this year. They do not accept demos but the university run a regular unsigned band night on Thursdays and a DJ night on Fridays. Both take place at the London College of Communication. If you would like to play get in touch with Steven Pigott.

University Of Westminster
32-38 Wells Street, London, WIT 3UW
tel: 020 7911 5000
email: supubs@wmin.ac.uk
web: www.uwsu.com
contact: Rob Watson
media: Newspaper
info: The Smoke is published monthly and will feature unsigned acts, but only from the Westminster area. They will accept demos.

MIDLANDS

Aston University
The Triangle, Birmingham, B4 7ES
tel: 0121 359 6531
fax: 0121 359 6350
email: guild.editor@aston.ac.uk
web: www.aston.ac.uk
media: Newspaper
info: The Aston Times is published once a month. Weekly newsletter available.

Coventry University
Priory Street, Coventry, CV1 5FJ
tel: 02476 571 224
email: suexec@coventry.ac.uk
web: www.coventry.ac.uk
media: Newspaper/Radio Station
info: Coventry University have a monthly magazine, Source, and radio station, Source FM.

De Montfort (Bedford)
Students' Union, 1st Campus Centre Building, Mill Lane, Leicester, LE2 7DR
tel: 01234 211 688
web: www.mydsu.com
contact: Jo Leese, Maddy Cormrie
media: Newspaper/TV Station/Radio Station
info: The Voice is published regularly during term time. Demon FM broadcasts for 1 month periods throughout the university term and has a show, 'Plugged', which is dedicated to unsigned musicians. Also broadcast Demon TV which has a show dedicated to unsigned musicians, 'Uncouth'. Both are available at De Montfort campuses.

De Montfort (Leicester)
Campus Centre Building, South Floor, Mill Lane, Leicester, LE2 7DR
tel: 0116 255 5576
web: www.mydsu.com
contact: Jo Leese
media: Newspaper/Radio Station
info: See listing for De Montfort (Bedford).

Harper Adams University College
Newport, Shropshire, TF10 8NB
tel: 01952 820 280
email: su@harper-adams.ac.uk
web: www.harper-adams.ac.uk

Keele University
Students' Union, Keele, Staffordshire, ST5 5BJ
tel: 01782 711 411
web: www.kusu.net
contact: Kate Johnson
media: Newspaper/Radio Station
info: Keele University publish a fortnightly magazine and broadcast Kube radio online.

Leicester University
Students' Union, Mayor's Walk, University Road, Leicester, Leicestershire, LE1 7RH
tel: 0116 223 1111
email: lush@le.ac.uk
web: www.lushradio.co.uk
media: Newspaper/Radio Station
info: Leicester University publish The Ripple fortnightly and have a radio station during term time called Lush. The newspaper can be contacted via the website.

Loughborough University
Ashby Road, Loughborough, Leicester, LE11 3TT
tel: 01509 217 766
email: media@lborosu.org.uk
web: www.lufbra.net
contact: Kelly Tarrant
media: Newspaper/TV Station/Radio Station
info: Label is a weekly magazine produced by Loughborough students. It has a music section and will include articles on unsigned bands and musicians. Loughborough Campus Radio and LSUTV operate throughout term time.

Newmans College
Genners Lane, Bartley Green, Birmingham, B32 3NT
tel: 0121 475 6714
email: ncsu@newman.ac.uk
web: www.newman.ac.uk

Nottingham Trent University
Platform Magazine, Nottingham Trent Students' Union, Cliffton Campus, Nottingham, NG11 8NS
tel: 0115 848 6200
email: platform@su.ntu.ac.uk
web: www.trentstudents.org
contact: Luke Eldridge, Charlie Goldthorpe
media: Newspaper/Radio Station
info: 107.6 Fly FM broadcasts twice a year to the whole of Nottingham, and all year round in the Glo Bar. Platform is published fortnightly on Mondays throughout the university term and will accept demos.

Nottingham University
Students' Union, University Park, Nottingham, NG7 2RD
tel: 0115 846 8722
email: studentsunion@nottingham.ac.uk
web: www.urn1350.net
contact: Ed Ackerman
media: Newspaper/Radio Station
info: Impact Magazine is published regularly during the university term. Urn 1350 AM broadcasts throughout term time.

University College, Worcester
Students' Union, Henwick Grove, Worcester, WR2 6AJ
tel: 01905 740 800
web: www.worcsu.com
contact: Anna Hodgeson
media: Newspaper
info: The Voice is published 3 times a year.

University of Birmingham
Edgbaston Park Road, Birmingham, B15 2TU
tel: 0121 472 1841
email: enquiires@bugs.bham.ac.uk
web: www.bugs.bham.ac.uk
contact: Matthew Williams, Ben Ziman-Bright, Alex White
media: Newspaper/TV Station/Radio Station
info: Birmingham University's radio station, BurnFM, runs for approximately half of the university semester. Their newspaper, Redbrick, is published once a week. They also run a TV station, Guildtelevision.

University of Central England
Union of Students, Ranchise Street, Perry Bar, Birmingham, B42 2SU
tel: 0121 331 6801
email: studio@scratchradio.co.uk
web: www.scratchradio.co.uk
contact: Sarah Porter
media: Newspaper/Radio Station
info: SCRatch Radio is a student and community station. It broadcasts during term time on campus and for 1 month per year on the FM dial. Will accept demos and are interested in local musical talent. Spaghetti Junction, the University's magazine, is published monthly and often features CD and live reviews of local bands and musicians.

University of Derby
Kedleston Road, Derby, DE22 1GB
tel: 01332 622 222
email: vpcomms@derby.ac.uk
web: www.udsu-online.co.uk
contact: Shaun Jepson, Ali Paterson
media: Newspaper/Radio Station
info: Derby University's new TV channel should be broadcasting from November 2005. Dusted magazine is published monthly.

University of Wolverhampton
Wulfruna Street, Wolverhampton, WV1 1LY
tel: 01902 322 021
email: crywolf@wolvesunion.org
web: www.wolvesunion.org
contact: Anita Smith
media: Newspaper
info: Crywolf magazine is published 6 times a year. There is a music page where unsigned bands can be featured.

Warwick University
University of Warwick Students' Union, Gibbert Hill Road, Coventry, CV4 7AL
tel: 02476 572 777
email: sunion@sunion.warwick.ac.uk
web: www.sunion.warwick.ac.uk or radio.warwick.ac.uk
media: Newspaper/TV Station/Radio Station
info: The Word is published once a month. Raw 1251 AM and WTV broadcast during the university semester.

NORTHEAST

Durham University
Dunelm House, New Elvet, Durham, DH1 3AN
tel: 0191 374 3310
email: student.platinate@durham.ac.uk
web: www.du.ac.uk/platinate or www.durham21.co.uk
contact: Ed Rose
media: Newspaper/Radio Station
info: Platinate magazine is published fortnightly. Purple radio broadcasts from September to October. Durham21, the universities online newspaper, has been voted NUS Website of the Year for the past 3 years.

Newcastle University
Kings Walk, Newcastle Upon Tyne, NE1 8QW
tel: 0191 239 3900
email: union@ncl.ac.uk
web: www.unionsociety.co.uk or www.nsrfm.com
contact: Stewart Vose
media: Newspaper/Radio Station
info: The Courier is published weekly. NSR radio broadcasts to Newcastle and Northumbria Universities over 2 periods of 1 month during term time. Both will accept demos.

Northumberland College
College Road, Ashington, Northumberland, NE63 0PH
tel: 01670 841 200
email: advice.centre@northland.ac.uk
web: www.northland.ac.uk

Sunderland University
Wearmouth Hall, Chester Road, SR1 3SD
tel: 0191 514 5512
email: dnmagazine@sunderland.ac.uk
web: www.sunderlandsu.co.uk
contact: Cielje Boyum
media: Newspaper
info: DNMagazine is published bi-monthly.

University of Northumbria
2 Sandyford Road, Newcastle, NE1 8SB
tel: 0191 227 4991
email: incite@stop-press.co.uk
web: www.unsu.org.uk
media: Newspaper
info: Incite magazine and Northumbria Student are published throughout the university term.

University of Teeside
Southfield Road, Middlesbourgh, TS1 3BA
tel: 0164 234 2234
email: enquiries@utsu.org.uk
web: www.utsu.org.uk
contact: Anne-Marie Wadsworth
media: Newspaper
info: Student newspaper published once a month.

NORTHWEST

Edge Hill University College
St. Helen's Road, Ormskirk, Lancashire, L39 4QP
tel: 01695 575 457
email: enquiries@edgehill.ac.uk
web: www.edgehill.ac.uk
media:

Lancaster University
Students' Union, Slaidburn House, Lancaster University, Bailrigg, LA1 4YT
tel: 01524 652 01
email: scan@lusu.co.uk
web: scan.lusu.co.uk
contact: Jody D'Souza, Victoria Kirby
media: Newspaper/Radio Station
info: Bailrigg FM is broadcast during term time. Published fortnightly, Scan Paper occasionally features live reviews of unsigned bands playing in the Lancaster area.

LIPA (Liverpool Institute of Performing Arts)
Mount Street, Liverpool, L1 9HF
tel: 07891 184 267
email: s.pursehouse@lipa.ac.uk
web: www.liparadio.com
media: Radio Station
info: Student radio station broadcasting from January to April every year. LIPA Radio has a diverse range of shows with all genres of music covered. There are weekly unsigned shows. Contact for details of how to submit your material.

Liverpool Community College
Old Swan Site, Broadgreen Road, Liverpool, L13 5SQ
tel: 0151 252 1515
web: www.liv-coll.ac.uk
media: Newspaper
info: Liverpool Community College produce a weekly newsletter, Student's Eye.

MEDIA

Liverpool Hope University
Derwent House, Taggart Avenue, Liverpool, L16 9LA
tel: 0151 291 3063
email: union@hope.ac.uk
web: www.hope.ac.uk
media: Newspaper/Radio Station
info: Liverpool Hope run a radio station and are also involved with production of newspaper, Liverpool Student.

Liverpool John Moore's University
The Haigh Building, Maryland Street, Liverpool, L1 9DE
tel: 0151 231 4900
fax: 0151 231 4931
email: studentsunion@livjm.ac.uk
web: www.l-s-u.com
contact: Jodie McDermot
media: Newspaper/Radio Station
info: Havoc magazine is produced and distributed to the students of Liverpool John Moore's University. Shout FM is an internet-based station that regularly airs unsigned material from bands across the UK. Liverpool Student News is also distributed to students of Liverpool John Moore's, as well as University of Liverpool and Liverpool Hope.

Manchester Metropolitan University
99 Oxford Road, All Saints, Manchester, M1 7EL
tel: 0161 247 1162
email: s.u.pubs@mmu.ac.uk
web: www.mmsu.com
contact: Roy Gibsen
media: Newspaper
info: Pulp Magazine is published fortnightly. Includes music based features, although the emphasis is on signed rather than unsigned bands.

Manchester University
University of Manchester Union, Oxford Road, Manchester, M13 9PR
tel: 0161 275 2943
email: union@umu.man.ac.uk
web: www.umu.manchester.ac.uk or www.student-direct.co.uk
contact: Catherine Bolsover
media: Newspaper/Radio Station
info: Student Direct is published weekly and distributed to Manchester University, Manchester Metropolitan University, Bolton and Salford. Fuse FM will broadcast unsigned material. See www.fusefm.co.uk for more information.

Salford University
University House, The Crescent, Salford, M5 4WT
tel: 0161 736 7811
email: salfordstudent@salford.ac.uk or info@channelm.co.uk
web: www.susu.salford.ac.uk or www.shockradio.co.uk
contact: Evelyn Downing
media: Newspaper/TV Station/Radio Station
info: Salford University has close links with Manchester based television station Channel M (www.channelm.co.uk). Channel M is broadcast throughout the Manchester area 16 hours a day, all year round, and has a potential audience of 600,000. 'Bring The Noise', a weekly half-hour programme, aims to grant exposure to Manchester's unsigned bands. See the website for details of how to send in your demo. Shock Radio (97.6FM) broadcasts for 1 month during term time. Student Direct is also distributed weekly to Salford University students. See also listing for Manchester University.

Staffordshire University
College Road, Stoke-on-Trent, ST4 2DE
tel: 01782 294 629
email: communications@staffs.ac.uk
web: www.staffunion.com
contact: Kavinder Tomar
media: Newspaper/Radio Station
info: GK Radio is broadcast between 10am and 6pm every weekday. GK newspaper comes out every month.

Trinity & All Saints College
Brownberrie Lane, Horsforth, Leeds, LS18 5HD
tel: 0113 283 7100
email: enquiries@leedstrinity.ac.uk
web: www.tasc.ac.uk
media:

University College of St. Martins
Boweham Road, Lancaster, Lancashire, LA1 3JD
tel: 01524 384 384
email: sulancaster@ucsm.ac.uk
web: www.thestudentsunion.org.uk
contact: Jeff Tweddle
media: Newspaper
info: The Saint is published fortnightly and reviews local bands and gigs.

University of Bolton
Students' Union, Deane Annex, Derby Street, BL3 5AB
tel: 01204 900 850
email: info@ubsu.org.uk
web: www.ubsu.org.uk
contact: Mark Ashworth
media: Newspaper
info: Student Direct is published fortnightly. See listing for Manchester University for further details.

University of Central Lancashire
Students' Union, Fylde Road, Preston, PR1 2TQ
tel: 01772 893 000
email: suinformation@uclan.ac.uk
web: www.yourunion.co.uk
media: Newspaper/Radio Station
info: Student magazine, Pluto, is keen to hear from unsigned bands in the area. Email the editor with details of your band including upcoming live dates. The students run radio station, Frequency 1350AM, regularly featuring unsigned bands. Send a demo and biog to Frequency 1350AM, Students Union, University of Central Lancashire, Preston, PR1 2HE.

University of Liverpool
Liverpool Student News, PO Box 146, 160 Mount Pleasant, Liverpool, L69 7BR
tel: 0151 794 2000
email: lsmusic@liv.ac.uk
web: www.liverpoolstudentpaper.com or www.liverpoolguild.com/student
media: Newspaper/Radio Station
info: Liverpool Student News is produced by and distributed to the students of University of Liverpool, Liverpool John Moore's University and Liverpool Hope University. Send your demos FAO Music Editor at the address above.

University of Manchester
Students' Union, Oxford Road, Manchester, M13 9PR
tel: 01612 752 943
email: Contact form on website
web: www.student-direct.co.uk or www.fusefm.co.uk
contact: Catherine Bolsover
media: Newspaper/Radio Station
info: Grip magazine is currently undergoing changes and is out of print at the moment. Student Direct (see listing for Manchester University) is published weekly on Mondays. Fuse FM (87.9) is broadcast for 8 weeks of the year.

SOUTHEAST

Brighton University SU
Steamhouse, Pelham Terrace, Lewes Raod, Brighton, BN2 4AF
tel: 01273 642 870
email: ubsu@brighton.ac.uk
web: www.ubsu.net
contact: Caroline Lewis
media: Newspaper
info: Fastlikesquirrel magazine is run independently by students of Brighton University.

Brunel University
Cleveland Road, Uxbridge, Middlesex, UB8 3PH
tel: 01895 462 200
email: lenurb@brunelstudents.com
web: www.brunelstudents.com
contact: Elliot Ross
media: Newspaper/Radio Station
info: Le Nurb magazine is published weekly. Contact using the above email address. Radio station B1000 is broadcast all year round on both the radio and the internet.

Buckinghamshire Chilterns
Queen Alexander Road, High Wycombe, HP11 2JZ
tel: 01494 605 188
email: tristan.tipping@bcuc.ac.uk
web: www.bcsu.net
contact: Laura Knight
media: Newspaper
info: The Noise newspaper is published 8 times a year and occasionally reviews gigs and demos by unsigned bands.

Canterbury Christ Church University
North Holmes Road, Canterbury, Kent, CT1 1QU
tel: 01227 782 416
web: www.c4online.net
contact: Gary Devlin, Alex Davies, Ozzy
media: Newspaper/TV Station/Radio Station
info: Canterbury College produce Bluebeard magazine. Canterbury Student Radio is also broadcast over the internet, and C4 TV is now all year round.

Colchester Institute
Students' Union, Sheppen Road, Colchester, CO3 3LL
tel: 01206 518 705
email: students.union@colchester.ac.uk
web: www.colchester.ac.uk
media: Newspaper
info: Colchester Institute produce a monthly newspaper, SUN (Student Union News). Plans for a radio station are currently under review.

Cranfield University
Silsoe Campus, Barton Road, Silsoe, Bedfordshire, MK45 4DT
tel: 01234 750 111
web: www.cranfield.ac.uk

De Montfort (Lincoln)
Hammerwood Gate, Kents Hill, Milton Keynes, Buckinghamshire, LN2 1NP
tel: 01908 834 984
web: www.mydsu.com
media: Newspaper/Radio Station
info: See listing for De Montfort (Bedford).

East Surrey College
Gatton Point North, Claremount Road, Redhill, Surrey, RH1 2JX
tel: 01737 772 611
email: studentservices@esc.ac.uk
web: www.esc.ac.uk
media:

Essex University
Wivenhoe Park, Colchester, CO4 3SQ
tel: 01206 863 236
email: ents@essex.ac.uk
web: www.essex.ac.uk
media: Newspaper/Radio Station
info: The Rabbit is published fortnightly. RED 1404AM broadcasts during term time.

Farnborough College
Boundary Road, Farnborough, Hampshire, GU14 3SB
tel: 01252 407 140
email: sun@farn-ct.ac.uk
web: www.farn-ct.ac.uk
contact: Andrew Isaac
media: Newspaper/Radio Station
info: Student magazine called ID will review CDs sent to them. Student radio which runs for 1 month per year will also accept demos.

King Alfred's College
Students' Union, Sparkford Road, Winchester, Hampshire, SO22 4NR
tel: 01962 827 414
email: su-entertainments@winchester.ac.uk or suwhatson@winchester.ac.uk
web: www.winchester students.co.uk
contact: Gemma Durt
media: Newspaper/Radio Station
info: What's On is a weekly listings magazine. The Voice broadcasts in the university campus during the week.

Milton Keynes College
Chaffron Way, Leadenhall, Milton Keynes, MK6 5LP
tel: 01908 684 444
email: info@mkcollege.ac.uk
web: www.mkcollege.ac.uk

Oxford Brooke's University
Helena Kennedy Students' Centre, Headington Hill Campus, Oxford, Oxfordshire, OX3 0BP
tel: 01865 484 750
email: obsu@brookes.ac.uk
web: www.thesu.com
contact: Laurna Morris
media: Newspaper/Radio Station
info: OBScene is published throughout the university term. Obsession Radio broadcasts occasionally in the students' union.

Oxford University
Thomas Hull House, New Inn Hall Street, Oxford, OX1 2DH
tel: 01865 288 450
email: enquiries@ousu.org
web: www.ousu.org or www.oxfordstudent.com
contact: Rob Lewis
media: Newspaper
info: The Oxford Student is published weekly.

Portsmouth University
Portsmouth Students Centre, Cambridge Road, Portsmouth, Hampshire, PO1 2EF
tel: 02392 843 679
web: www.upsu.net or www.purefm.com
contact: Adrian Fraguela,
media: Newspaper/Radio Station
info: Pugwash Magazine is published monthly. Pure FM broadcasts throughout term time on campus only.

Reading University
PO Box 230, Whiteknights, Reading, RG6 6AZ
tel: 0118 986 0222
email: spark@rdg.ac.uk
web: www.1287am.com/popup.php
contact: Francesca Bingley
media: Newspaper/Radio Station
info: Spark is published weekly. Junction11 (1287 AM) broadcasts across the campus and online, and can be contacted via the website.

Southampton Solent University
East Park Terrace, Southampton, SO14 0YN
tel: 02380 232 154
email: suvpcomm@solent.ac.uk
web: www.solentsu.co.uk or www.sinradio.co.uk
contact: Hollie Moore
media: Newspaper/Radio Station
info: SIN Radio (1431 AM) is broadcast all year round. Resus is published 7 times a year.

Sussex University
Falmer House, Falmer, Brighton, BN1 9QF
tel: 01273 678 152
email: communications@ussu.sussex.ac.uk
web: www.ussu.net or www.urfonline.com
contact: Tom Harle
media: Newspaper/Radio Station
info: University Radio Falmer (URF) broadcasts throughout term time. The Pulse magazine is published termly. The Badger newspaper is published weekly.

University College for the Creative Arts
Farnham Site, Falkner Road, The Hart, Farnham, GU9 7DS
tel: 01252 710 263
email: sketchmag@hotmail.com
web: www.uccasu.com
contact: Rob Adlam
media: Newspaper
info: University College are in the process of relaunching their magazine which, as yet, remains unnamed. Its aim will be to showcase student arts and therefore, they will take interest in unsigned musicians.

University Of Hertfordshire
College Lane, Hatfield, Hertfordshire, AL10 9AB
tel: 01707 284 000
email: uhsu.comms@herts.ac.uk
web: www.uhsu.herts.ac.uk
contact: Marek Nusl
media: Newspaper/Radio Station
info: University of Hertfordshire publish a newspaper, Universe. Crush 1278AM is broadcast all year round.

University oof Kent
Mandela Buildings, Canterbury, CT2 7NW
tel: 01227 823 301
email: mail@ukcradio.co.uk
web: www.kentunion.co.uk or www.ukcradio.co.uk
contact: Matt Mendell
media: Newspaper/Radio Station
info: UKC Radio broadcasts 24 hours a day. KRED magazine is published monthly.

University of Surrey
Union House, University of Surrey, Guildford, GU2 7XH
tel: 01483 683 928
email: comms@ussu.org
web: www.ussu.co.uk or www.gu2.co.uk
contact: Neil Bolton, Matt Badcock, Phil Brown
media: Newspaper/Radio Station
info: Barefacts is published once every 2 weeks. Award winning GU2 Radio broadcasts throughout the university term.

SOUTHWEST

Bath Spa University College
Newton Park, Newton Street Loe, Bath, BA2 9BN
tel: 01225 875 588
email: h2o@bathspa.ac.uk
web: www.bathspasu.co.uk
contact: David James
media: Newspaper
info: Bath Spa's student newspaper, H2O, is published once a fortnight.

MEDIA

Bournemouth University
Fern Barrow, Poole, Dorset, BH12 5BB
tel: 01202 524 111
email: suup.comms@bournemouth.ac.uk
web: www.subu.org.uk or www.nervemedia.net
media: Newspaper/TV Station/Radio Station
info: Bournemouth University run a radio station, Nerve Radio, as well as a television station, Nerve Television. Nerve Television is broadcast every Wednesday from 6pm during term time. Also publish magazine once a month.

Bristol University
Students' Union, Queens Road, Clifton, Bristol, BS8 1LN
tel: 0117 954 5815
email: communications-ubu@bristol.ac.uk
web: www.ubu.org.uk
contact: Kate Quilton
media: Newspaper/Radio Station
info: Bristol University produces Epigram, a bi-weekly newspaper. Also run radio station, Burst.

Exeter University
Student Media Department, Cornwall House, Stocker Road, Exeter, EX4 4PZ
tel: 01392 263 546
email: g.j.oughton@ex.ac.uk
web: www.ex.ac.uk
contact: Gareth Oughton, Sam Ball, Andy Kench
media: Newspaper/TV Station/Radio Station
info: Exeter University produces a weekly newspaper, Expose. Both their radio station, Xpression FM, and TV station, XTV, broadcast throughout term time. Demos can be sent to the newspaper and radio section.

University College of Falmouth
Woodlane, Falmouth, Cornwall, TR11 4RH
tel: 01326 211 077
web: www.falmouth.ac.uk

University Of Bath
Claverton Down, Bath, BAS 7AY
tel: 01225 386 612
email: sabbs@bath.ac.uk
web: www.bathstudent.com
media: Newspaper/TV Station/Radio Station
info: URB radio broadcasts during term time. CTV is shown in the Students' Union all year round. Impact is published fortnightly.

University of Gloucestershire
UGSU, The Park, Cheltenham, GL50 2RH
tel: 01242 532 848
email: pksu@glos.ac.uk
web: www.ugsu.org
contact: Dom Williams
media: Newspaper
info: Space newspaper is produced throughout the university term. There are roughly 14 issues per term with an estimated circulation of 7800 readers. They will gladly accept demos and often feature unsigned bands in their culture section.

University of Plymouth
Drake Circus, Plymouth, Devon, PL4 8AA
tel: 01752 238 500
email: suenquiries@su.plymouth.ac.uk
web: www.upsu.com/
contact: Chris Pike
media: Newspaper
info: Student magazine, Fly is published weekly. Currently in the process of developing a radio station. Contact Chris Pike for details.

University of The West of England
Frenchay Site, Coldharbour Lane, Frenchay, Bristol, BS16 1QY
tel: 0117 965 6261
email: publications@uwesu.net or hub.management@uwe.ac.uk
web: www.uwesu.net
contact: Kal Wright
media: Newspaper/Radio Station
info: Western Eye newspaper is published fortnightly and Westworld magazine is published monthly. They regularly feature local unsigned talent. The Hub radio is broadcast throughout the university term.

Bradford University SU
The Communal Building, Longside Lane, Richmond Road, Bradford, BD7 1DP
tel: 01274 232 323
email: editor@kineticmag.com
web: www.bradford.ac.uk or www.kineticmag.com
media: Newspaper/Radio Station
info: Bradford's radio station, Ram Air, broadcasts throughout term time. Its magazine, Kinetic, is published monthly, and can be contacted via the website.

Sheffield Hallam University
The Hubs, Paternoster Row, Sheffield, S1 2QQ
tel: 0114 225 4111
web: www.hallamunion.com or www.rushradio.fm
media: Newspaper/Radio Station
info: Stu-print is published monthly. Rushradio FM broadcasts during term time and live from the SU bar during peak hours.

University of Huddersfield
Queensgate, Huddersfield, HD1 3DH
tel: 01484 538 156
email: STUN-newspapereditor@hud.ac.uk
web: www.huddersfieldstudent.com
contact: Amy Farnworth
media: Newspaper
info: The University of Huddersfield publish the Huddersfield Student newspaper once a month.

University of Hull
University House, Cottingham Road, Hull, HU6 7RX
tel: 01482 445 361
email: hullfire@hotmail.com
web: www.hullstudent.com or www.jam1575.com
contact: Sian Hyden
media: Newspaper/Radio Station
info: HullFire is a monthly newspaper. Radio JAM 1575 broadcasts all year round.

Leeds Metropolitan University
LMUSU, Calverley Street, Leeds, LS1 3HE
tel: 0113 209 8400
email: enquiries@leedsmet.org.uk
web: www.leedsmetsu.org.uk or www.leedsstudent.org.uk
contact: Sam/Richard Corbett/Crisp
media: Newspaper
info: Leeds Student is published once a week, and distributed in both Leeds Met and Leeds University. Demos are accepted with possibility of review.

Leeds University
Students' Union, PO Box 157, Leeds, LS1 1UH
tel: 0113 380 1234
email: leedsstudentmusic@hotmail.com
web: www.leedsstudent.org.uk or www.lsrfm.com
contact: Sam Corbett, Mark Powell, Richard Crisp
media: Newspaper/Radio Station
info: See listing for Leeds Met for details of Leeds Student Newspaper. LSR FM broadcasts for 2 months of the university term. Local band nights organised by LSR FM, check website for further details, or see listings for venues based on Leeds University campus, Old Bar and The Terrace.

University of Sheffield
The Union, Western Bank, Sheffield, S10 2TG
tel: 0114 222 8500
email: steel@sheffield.ac.uk
web: www.shef.ac.uk
contact: Simon Osbourne
media: Newspaper
info: The Steel Press is published fortnightly. Another separate music publication called Stainless is also released fortnightly.

University of York
Student' Centre, Godriche College, Heslington, York, YO10 5DD
tel: 0190 443 3724
email: su-president@york.ac.uk
web: www.york.ac.uk or www.ystv.york.ac.uk
contact: Chris Havergal, Andy
media: Newspaper/TV Station/Radio Station
info: York Student Television broadcasts all year round via their website. URY 1350 FM broadcasts 24 hours a day during term time and will play unsigned local bands. YU Magazine is published 3 times a year.

NORTHERN IRELAND

Queens University, Belfast
Students' Union, University Road, Belfast, BT7 1NF
tel: 028 9097 3106
email: s.union@qub.ac.uk
web: www.qubsu.org
contact: Peter Quinn
media: Newspaper/Radio Station
info: Queens University publish a newspaper, The Edge, several times during the course of the university term. Queens radio broadcasts full time.

SCOTLAND

Dundee University
Airlie Place, Dundee, DD1 4HP
tel: 01382 386 060
email: admin@dusa.co.uk
web: www.dusa.dundee.ac.uk
contact: Sarah Hoine
media: Newspaper/Radio Station
info: Vertigo FM broadcasts for short periods of the university term. Blunt Instrument is published once a semester.

Edinburgh University
Bristol Square, Edinburgh, EH8 9AL
tel: 0131 650 2656
web: www.eusa.ed.ac.uk
contact: Tony Foster
media: Newspaper/Radio Station
info: Edinburgh University produce fortnightly magazine, Hype, and a listings magazine, The Guide. Freshair FM broadcasts during term time.

Forth Valley College
Grangemouth Road, Falkirk, FK2 9AD
tel: 01324 403 290
web: www.forthvalley.ac.uk

Glasgow Caledonian University
70 Cowcaddens Road, Glasgow, G4 0BA
tel: 0141 332 0681
email: reunion@gcal.ac.uk
web: www.caledonianstudent.com
media: Newspaper
info: Re:union is published throughout the university term.

Glasgow School of Art
Assembly Buildings, 168 Renfrew Street, Glasgow, G3 6RT
tel: 0141 353 4500
email: sa-president@gsa.ac.uk
web: www.gsa.ac.uk

Glasgow University
John MacIntyre Building, University Avenue, Glasgow, G12 8QQ
tel: 0141 341 6215
web: www.guu.co.uk/ www.src.gla.ac.uk
contact: Stef MacBeth, Robin Davies, Chris Hall, Gordon Kennedy
media: Newspaper/TV Station/Radio Station
info: Glasgow University Guardian is published fortnightly. GUM Magazine is published regularly during term time. SubcityFM and Gust TV broadcast throughout term time. Glasgow University also run a weekly unsigned night called Bandwagon. Contact Gregor Young through the Glasgow University Union website if you would like to take part.

Herriot Watt University
The Union, Riccarton Campus, Edinburgh, EH14 4AS
tel: 0131 451 5333
email: watts_on@hwusa.org
web: www.hwusa.org
contact: Helen Pierce
media: Newspaper
info: Watt's On is a colour magazine published twice a term.

Napier University
Verites, Room 345, Craighouse Campus, Craighouse Road, Edinbrough, EH10 5LG
tel: 0131 229 8791
email: verites@napier.ac.uk
web: www.napier.ac.uk
contact: Laura Brown
media: Newspaper
info: Verites is published monthly, and has 4 pages dedicated to music with emphasis on unsigned and local musicians. Also looking to start 'podcasting' in the near future.

North Glasgow College
110 Flemington Street, Glasgow, G21 4BX
tel: 0141 558 9001
email: all@ngc.u-net.com
web: www.north-gla.ac.uk
media:

Queen Margaret College
36 Clerwood Terrace, Corstorphine, Edinburgh, EH12 8TS
tel: 0131 317 3400
email: union@qmuc.ac.uk
web: www.qmucsu.org.uk
contact: Jo Carauna
media: Newspaper
info: The Echo newspaper is published monthly and has a music section.

Robert Gordon University
60 School Hill, Aberdeen, AB10 1JQ
tel: 01224 262 262
email: cogno@hotmail.com
web: www.rgunion.co.uk
contact: Katie Board
media: Newspaper
info: Cogno is published bi-monthly throughout term time.

Stirling University
Students Association, Robbins Centre, Stirling, FK9 4LA
tel: 01786 467 166
email: ukbrig@netscape.net
web: www.susaonline.org.uk
contact: Graham Naiel, Matt Ludlow
media: Newspaper/TV Station/Radio Station
info: Stirling University publish a newspaper, Brig. Air TV and Air3 (1350 FM) broadcast throughout the university term.

University of St. Andrews
St. Mary's Place, St. Andrews, Fife, KY16 9UZ
tel: 0133 447 7355
email: thesaint@st-andrews.ac.uk
web: www.yourunion.net or
www.saintonline.co.uk
media: Newspaper
info: The Saint is an independent newspaper, published fortnightly.

University of Strathclyde
90 John Street, Glasgow, G1 1JH
tel: 0141 567 5054
email: fusion@theunion.strath.ac.uk
web: www.strathstudents.com or
www.sur.strath.ac.uk
contact: Amy Mackay
media: Newspaper/Radio Station
info: Strathclyde Telegraph is published throughout the university term. SUR is an online radio station which can be heard via the above website.

WALES

Cardiff University
University Union, Ark Place, Cardiff, CF1 3QN
tel: 02920 781 400
email: studentsunion@cardiff.ac.uk
web: www.cardiffstudents.com
contact: Tom Wellingham
media: Newspaper/Radio Station
info: Gair Rhydd is published weekly and distributed throughout the university. Xpress Radio broadcasts for 2 months of the university semester. It also broadcasts all year round on the internet.

Swansea Institute
Mount Pleasant Campus, Mount Pleasant, Swansea, SA1 6ED
tel: 01792 481 000
email: president@sihe.co.uk
web: www.susistudent.co.uk

Swansea University
Union House, Singleton Park, Swansea, SA2 8PP
tel: 01792 295 466
email: editor@swansea-union.co.uk
web: www.swansea-union.co.uk
contact: Rachel Howells
media: Newspaper/TV Station/Radio Station
info: Waterfront newspaper is published weekly throughout the university term. Front magazine is published monthly and has a music section with features on up and coming acts. Xtreme1431 FM is broadcast during term time.

MEDIA

University of Glamorgan
SU Building, Treeforest, Pontypridd, Mid Glamorgan, CF37 1UF
tel: 01443 483 500
email: leek1@glam.ac.uk
web: www.glamsu.com
contact: Matt Wood
media: Newspaper/Radio Station
info: The university runs GTFM in conjunction with local volunteers, and can be contacted via their website. They have a show dedicated to unsigned local musicians. Leek newspaper is published once a week and also focuses on unsigned musicians.

University of Wales (Aberystwyth)
Penglais, Aberystwyth, SY23 3DX
tel: 01970 621 700
email: courier@aber.ac.uk or bayradio@aber.ac.uk
web: www.thecourier.org.uk
contact: Dave Allen
media: Newspaper/Radio Station
info: Bay Radio broadcasts during term time. The Courier is published 5 times a year and would like to hear from local bands.

University of Wales (Bangor)
Deinol Road, Bangor, LL57 2TH
tel: 01248 388 000
email: undeb@undeb.bangor.ac.uk
web: www.undeb.bangor.ac.uk or
www.seren.bangor.ac.uk
media: Newspaper/Radio Station
info: Seren is published once a month. Y Ddraenen, a Welsh magazine, is published several times during term time. Storm FM can be contacted via the union website.

University of Wales (Lampeter)
Ty Ceredig, Lampeter, Ceredigion, SA48 7ED
tel: 01570 422 619
email: union@lamp.ac.uk
web: www.lamp.ac.uk
contact: Saad
media: Newspaper
info: 1822 is published throughout term time.

University of Wales Institute
Students' Union, Cyncoed Campus, Cyncoed Road, Cardiff, CF23 6XD
tel: 02920 416 070
web: www.uwic.ac.uk
contact: Hannah
media: Newspaper
info: Retro newspaper is published once a month. Will review and promote unsigned bands and musicians.

120 Years Of Modern Music
web: www.obsolete.com/120_years
info: This site charts the development of electronic musical instruments from 1870 to 1990 and instruments that synthesise sounds from an Electronic source. A condensed history of modern music. Also has a wide selection of links to other electronic music sites.

3BTV
The Forum, 277 London Road, Burgess Hill, West Sussex, RH15 9QU
email: phil@3btv.com
web: www.3btv.com
info: 3BTV is an online channel promoting new work by producers, writers, directors, animators and musicians who want to showcase their work to the widest possible audience. New footage is always welcome. To have your work shown on 3BTV, submit to the above address.

9th Circle
email: paul@9thweb.org
web: www.9thweb.org
info: Online magazine for Northampton including reviews of gigs, pubs, CD releases and unsigned demos. Contributions are welcome, contact at the above email address.

A&R Online
email: info@aandronline.com
web: www.aandronline.com
info: US based professional music industry tip sheet for record labels, publishers and supervisors. Artists can submit demos and copyright songs online. Also has the opportunity to sign up for a fortnightly email newsletter, as well as their online band directory.

Aberdeen Music
email: Via website
web: www.aberdeen-music.com
info: Community dedicated to the music scene in Aberdeen. Gig calendar, online radio station, forum, and useful links directory for bands and music related services.

Aberdeen Ultimate Band List
tel: 01224 638 543
email: aubl@aubl.net
web: www.aubl.net
info: Lists details of venues, industry contacts and band showcases in Aberdeen. All bands from Aberdeen and surrounding area are entitled to a free page in the bands section. Also contains reviews and gig listings. AUBL have been organising gigs and events in Aberdeen since 2000, see entry in Promoters section for further details.

About The Music
tel: 07974 438 833
email: info@aboutthemusic.co.uk
web: www.aboutthemusic.co.uk
info: Interviews with and reviews of unsigned bands. Fill out the online form before sending a demo.

Access To Music
Lionel House, 35 Millstone Lane, Leicester, LE1 5JN
tel: 0800 281 842
fax: 0116 242 6868
email: info@access-to-music.co.uk
web: www.accesstomusic.co.uk
info: Access to Music is dedicated to increasing the number of people making a living from music, preparing young musicians for a career in the industry and teacher training for more experienced musicians. Website features news on open days and courses, musicians' notice board, gig guide and news. There is also a section dedicated to job vacancies in the music industry.

Acid Planet
email: Use online contact form
web: www.acidplanet.com
info: An online community of 100,000 digital musicians and videographers. Create and upload your own music or listen to music by others, as well as looking at videos. Enter contests and remix music by major artists.

Acoustic Sussex
web: www.acousticsussex.org.uk
info: What's on guide for singer-songwriters and Acoustic musicians based in the Sussex area.

ActionTab
email: Use online contact form
web: www.actiontab.com
info: Macromedia Flash Player is used to provide site users with an audio-visual method of learning guitar.

All About Jazz
web: www.allaboutjazz.com
info: Comprehensive jazz site. Includes a forum, reviews, interviews, global jazz listings and an online shop.

All Music
web: www.allmusic.com
info: All genres and styles of music are covered on the website, ranging from the most commercially Popular to the most obscure. Navigate the website by searching for artist, genre, mood, instrument or country.

All Music Guide
email: See website for list of contacts
web: www.allmusic.com
info: Details the origins of a huge amount of musical genres, highlighting significant artists and releases from each particular movement. Large musical glossary. Album reviews including user feedback section. Buy titles online. At time of print only accept professionally published CD releases.

All Record Labels
email: scott@lights.com
web: www.allrecordlabels.com
info: Canadian based international record label database listing over 17,000 companies. Search for labels by genre, format, country or city.

Aloud
tel: 0115 912 9189
web: www.aloud.com
info: Online ticket agency with full listings of events and venues, tour dates for all main acts and bands in the UK as well as a shop for T-shirts and ringtones. Buy tickets online or call 0870 998 8888.

AlternationMusic
email: officeboy@alternationmusic.com
web: www.alternationmusic.com
info: Guide to the live music scene in Cambridge with event listings, as well as video and audio streams of signed artists and bands.

Alternative Addiction
email: webmaster@alternativeaddiction.com
web: www.alternativeaddiction.com
info: Independently owned and operated, Alternative Addiction is a resource for lovers of Alternative music. Includes an online radio station. Also a section dedicated to unsigned bands, where details can be submitted if a band wishes to feature on the site.

Alternative Devon
web: www.alternativedevon.co.uk
info: MP3 streaming for bands and musicians in the South West. Create your own user login to upload and access material, as well as post gig details.

Alternative Nation
web: www.alternativenation.net
info: Online community for anyone involved with or interested in Alternative music. Information on bands, venues, as well as reviews, forum and articles.

Alternative Swansea
email: bands@alternativeswansea.co.uk
web: www.alternativeswansea.co.uk
info: Devoted to the Alternative music scene in Swansea, this site includes news, gig and club night listings, as well as discussion forum. Currently compiling a local band list. To be included send your details to the above email address.

Amnesty International
The Human Rights Action Centre, 17-25 New Inn Yard, London, EC2A 3EA
tel: 020 7033 1500
fax: 020 7033 1503
email: sct@amnesty.org.uk
web: www.amnesty.org.uk
info: Amnesty International is a worldwide movement that campaigns for internationally recognised human rights.

Amplifeye
5 Pendarves Road, Camborne, Cornwall, TR14 7QB
email: dan@amplifeye.com
web: www.amplifeye.net
info: Independent music community based in the South West with the intention of supporting and promoting unsigned artists and bands. Interviews, reviews, unsigned downloads, charts, auctioning, web hosting and much more. Site also has access to useful industry directory.

Amplifier
email: See website for list of contacts
web: www.amplifiermagazine.com
info: US based music publication specialising in Pop, Melodic, Roots and Rock music. Includes interviews, reviews, listing, subscription and back issues.

Anatid
email: projektmaehem@yahoo.com
web: www.anatid.net
info: Site providing free promotional opportunities for bands, venues and event promoters. Submit profiles and listings

Anime Music Videos
email: admin@animemusicvideos.org
web: www.animemusicvideos.org
info: Dedicated to the creation, discussion and general enjoyment of fan-made anime music videos where contributors can share ideas and learn from one another.

Applause
email: Use online contact form
web: www.cnvi.com/applause/
info: Tips, tricks and secrets to assist your band's career.

Arena-list
web: www.arena-list.co.uk
info: The aim of Arena-list is to provide a platform for unsigned bands and new artists in the UK. Add your band to the directory, post your gig listings and upload MP3s online.

ARTISTdirect
email: See website for list of contacts
web: www.artistdirect.com
info: US based umbrella website incorporating new, artists information, music dowloads and online shopping. Also links to Ulimate Band List, or UBL (www.ubl.com), a site dedicated to unsigned bands.

Arts Journal
email: mclennan@artsjournal.com
web: www.artsjournal.com
info: Daily digest of arts and cultural journalism from around the world.

Association of Professional Recording Services (APRS)
PO Box 22, Totnes, TQ9 7YZ
tel: 01803 868 600
email: info@aprs.co.uk
web: www.aprs.co.uk
info: Extensive music industry news, details on APRS education and training in the recording services industry, directory of APRS members.

The South West's premier music culture network

Amplifeye

COMMUNITY CULTURE NETWORK

In association with Concerts South West Ltd.

Unsigned artists, community forums, web hosting & services, internet radio, online shopping, live events & listings, reviews, interviews, news & community articles, competitions, and much more!

w: www.amplifeye.com / e: helpdesk@amplifeye.net

Amplifeye.com
INDEPENDENT MUSIC COMMUNITY ONLINE

AmplifeyeForums
COMMUNITY DISCUSSION BOARDS
www.amplifeyeforums.com

AmplifeyeSolutions
WEBHOSTING AND INTERNET SERVICES
www.amplifeyesolutions.com

AmplifeyeShop
INDEPENDENT ONLINE RETAIL
www.amplifeyeshop.com

Amplifeye Studio
RECORDING AND MASTERING SUITE
www.amplifeyestudio.com

Atomicduster
web: www.atomicduster.com
info: Music site featuring single, album and live reviews, interviews and articles. Unsigned Spotlight is an area of the website dedicated to showcasing unsigned artists.

Attenshun
email: Via online form
web: www.attenshun.co.uk
info: Website for music, arts and street culture in Coventry and the surrounding area. Forum and listing for gigs and bands.

Audio Courses Online School
Tredeague, Meadowbank Road, Falmouth, Cornwall, TR11 2ND
tel: 020 7871 4760
email: use online form
web: www.audiocourses.com
info: Audio Courses is the world's largest distance learning school for Sound Engineering and Music Production. Students get to study from their own home in their own time and can earn an internationally recognised City & Guilds qualification in Sound Engineering.

Audio Masterclass
114 High Street, Tetsworth, Thame, Oxfordshire, OX9 7AE
tel: 01844 281 878
email: david.mellor@audiomasterclass.com
web: www.audiomasterclass.com
info: 24 week sound engineering course that you can study from home. Accredited by City & Guilds of London Institute. Start the course at any time and study at your own pace.

Audio Recording Centre
web: www.audio-recording.co.uk
info: Online tutorials covering mastering, stereo recording and 4 track recording. Also details of events, jobs, as well as discussion forum.

Audiojunkies
email: jed@audiojunkies.net
web: www.audiojunkies.net
contact: Jed Shepherd, Chris Dart
info: Music webzine, with news, reviews, interviews, features and downloads. Audiojunkies.net will cover anything from anywhere if they like it, and have championed unsigned bands to success in the past. Active forum and large online music community with members from all over the music world including DJs, band members, journalists and promoters. Also featuring a dedicated unsigned band forum with hints, tips and feedback. Contact Jed Shepherd or Chris Dart with any information or register on the forum.

Audiomastermind
email: webmaster@audiomastermind.com
web: www.audiomastermind.com
info: Large links directory for all things pro audio, from studios and producers to licensing and distribution.

Audioscope
email: audioscope@audioscope.co.uk
web: www.audioscope.co.uk
info: Audioscope is an organisation committed to raising money through music for the national homelessness charity Shelter. Since 2001 Audioscope has raised nearly £10,000 for Shelter, whilst presenting the best in local, national and international independent music in the process. Sign up to mailing list for further details on upcoming events.

Audioset
email: tracks@audioset.co.uk
web: www.audioset.co.uk
info: Online mastering service. Upload your tracks or forward via CD. Quality guaranteed. If you are not satisfied with your completed master then you pay nothing.

Auralgasms
email: szumberg or mfoster@auralgasms.com
web: www.auralgasms.com
info: A venue for discovering new artists. Categorised into genres including Alternative Rock, Brit Pop, Dream Pop, and Singer-Songwriters. Also features an online radio.

Auto Transposer
email: Use online form
web: www.autotransposer.com
info: An online gadget that allows you to transpose chord sequences to different keys.

Axes All Areas
tel: 01904 659 911
email: contact@axes-all-areas.co.uk
web: www.axes-all-areas.co.uk
info: Online music store selling wide selection of guitars and related accessories.

Backstage World
email: backstage@backstageworld.com
web: www.backstageworld.com
info: Resource for the latest sound and light equipment. Featuring companies providing rent sound, light and stage equipment. Also includes information regarding booking agents, crew and a sound & light technician pool.

Badger Promotions
web: www.badgerpromotions.co.uk
info: Birmingham based promoters with useful website. Resources section lists music-related services for the region. Also includes information on local venues. See entry for Badger Music in Promoters section for details of unsigned gigs organised through Badger Promotions.

Band Family Tree
web: www.bandfamilytree.com
info: Portal for musicians throughout the world to record their playing history, experiences and details. As a current or ex-band member you can add your own details to the family tree of bands and musicians. Free registration. Site also contains forum, musical resources and classified ads.

www.
audiojunkies
.NET

Audiojunkies*

Band It A&R Newsletter
PO Box 22, Newport, PO30 1LZ
tel: 01983 524 110
email: bandit@banditnewsletter.com
web: www.banditnewsletter.com
info: Subscribe to the Band It A&R Newsletter to receive details of labels, publishers, management companies and production companies looking for new artists. The website contains a guide to demo submission, A&R message board and details of subscription rates and offers, including a request form for a free back issue.

Band Promote
email: leo@bandpromote.com
web: www.bandpromote.com
info: US website. Submit your music for inclusion on the Band Promote CD sampler, which is distributed to music industry professionals. See website for further information about demo submission.

Band Radio
email: Use online contact form
web: www.bandradio.com
info: US based band resource with news and articles from the music industry. The site contains an extensive glossary and library plus a 'Tip of the Day' section, giving you practical advice on managing band issues.

The Band Register
PO Box 594, Richmond, Surrey, TW10 6YT
tel: 020 8940 7518
email: peter@bandreg.com
web: www.thebandregister2.co.uk
info: From this site you can search the world's largest database of band and artist names, email addresses, music links for streaming and / or downloading and general information. Find out if your band name is in use, and if not, register it to help protect from other bands using it.

Bandmad
web: www.bandmad.com
info: Online store for music merchandise including t-shirts, posters, calendars and tour programmes, amongst many other items.

The Bandmaker
web: www.thebandmaker.co.uk
info: Run by musicians for musicians, The Bandmaker allows venues and event organisers to book artists. Database of musicians wanted and available of all ages, all abilities and all UK locations. Also database of unsigned bands from garage bands to wedding bands. Free registration.

Bandname.com
email: information@bandname.com
web: www.bandname.com
info: Worldwide band name registry. Your band/artist name and date of registration will be recorded in the online archive and featured in the World Wide Band and Artists Directory, the leading industry publication of name usage and official websites. The directory is distributed to legal affairs departments of major record labels and lodged with the Library of Congress in Washington and British Reference Library as a guide to global name activity.

Band-Space Sites
99 Eggbuckland Road, Higher Compton, Plymouth, PL3 5JR
tel: 07762 661615
email: paul@band-space.com
web: www.band-space.com
contact: Paul Springett
info: Get your complete personal site including band info, bio, photos, MP3s, news, gigs and contact pages for just £99.

The Barking Spiders
email: newartists@barkingspiders.co.uk
web: www.barkingspiders.co.uk
info: Downloads, gig reviews, links and related articles. Unsigned bands looking for promotion should email a link to their MP3 download to the email address above. For gig reviews contact gigreviews@barkingspiders.co.uk.

Bass Tab Archive
web: www.basstabarchive.com
info: This free archive creates a central repository for bass tablature found on the internet.

Bassplaza.com
web: www.bassplaza.com
info: Online community created for, and by, bass players around the world. Information about all bass-related matters, plus tabs and discussion forum.

Bassworld
web: www.bassworld.co.uk
info: Community for Bass players with discussion boards for Bass tuition, equipment, repairs and items sold or wanted.

BBC 1Xtra
email: 1Xtra.online@bbc.co.uk
web: www.bbc.co.uk/1xtra/
info: Focusing on Urban, R&B, Hip-Hop, Garage, DanceHall, Drum&Bass and more, 1Xtra publish content including reviews, audio clips, interviews and What's On information. Another hugely informative and well structured feature of the extensive BBC website.

BBC OneMusic
email: Via website
web: www.bbc.co.uk/radio1/onemusic/
info: OneMusic is a extensive site from the BBC which includes a huge range of useful and informative features on all subjects including how to get into the music industry, how to submit demos to the industry, unsigned audio clips, in-depth help and advice on all areas of music making as well as links to various other very useful websites. Essential browsing.

BBC Where I Live
email: See contact page for your region
web: www.bbc.co.uk/whereilive/
info: Regional mini-sites covering the UK. Offers information on the music scene in your particular area, such as reviews, A to Z of local bands, news, interviews and gig guide.

The Beat Surrender
77 Smithy Lane, Tingley Wakefield, West Yorks, WF3 1QB
email: Via website
web: www.thebeatsurrender.co.uk
contact: Johnny Ratcliffe
info: Online music magazine offering features, interviews and reviews. Linked to Massive Media, see Artwork and Design section for more details.

Beatsketching
email: alcwsy@hotmail.com
web: www.beatsketching.tk
info: Illustrated music website featuring record and live reviews plus articles.

Bedford Metal
email: bedfordmetal@hotmail.com
web: www.bedfordmetal.co.uk
info: Interactive community devoted to the Metal scene in Bedford. Includes interviews, news, gig dates and reviews. Bands can upload their tracks onto the site by contacting the email address above.

Bedford Unplugged
email: music@bedfordunplugged.co.uk
web: www.bedfordunplugged.co.uk
info: Live music in and around Bedford. Post your gig and event listings on the site. Video and audio clips available online.

Big Gig Guide
email: Via online form
web: www.big-gig.co.uk
info: Gig guide for Taunton and surrounding areas. List your gigs and classified ads online.

Big Noise
email: artists@bignoisenow.com
web: www.bignoisenow.com
info: Award-winning international music promotion firm. Website showcases a range of independently released music. For information on submitting a demo, email algomes@bignoisenow.com.

Bigmouth
email: info@bigmouth.co.uk
web: www.bigmouth.co.uk
info: Comprehensive tour details for artists and bands. Featuring online ticket sales, UK festival dates and links to UK bands' official websites. Subscribe to have gig and festival news emailed directly to you.

BIRDpages
Knighton Music Group, 14 Heddington Way, West Knighton, Leicester, LE2 6HF
tel: 0116 288 5788
fax: 0116 288 7549
email: info@birdpages.co.uk
web: www.birdpages.co.uk
info: Directory of British independent record dealers, shops, and record collectors. Search for outlets by location, category or alphabetically.

Birmingham Music
email: Via website
web: www.birminghammusic.com
info: Platform for promotion of the music scene in Birmingham. Online resource database containing contacts for management, labels, music courses and services. Online unsigned radio and charts, plus discussion forum.

Blackpool Bands
email: skell@blackpoolbands.co.uk
web: www.blackpoolbands.co.uk
info: Details of Blackpool bands, venues and gig listings. Also reviews, message board, downloads and online shop.

Blurb
Artwork, Fairways House, Mount Pleasant Road, Southampton, SO14 0QB
email: editor@blurb.org.uk
web: www.blurb.org.uk
info: Gigs, news and reviews for the South of England. Band of the month feature for local acts. Submit music, photo, any press reviews to the above postal or email addresses. Blurb also has an online directory listing local music services.

Boogaloo Promotions
email: info@boogaloopromotions.com
web: www.boogaloopromotions.com
info: News updates about Blues and Boogie events located in the South East of England. Boogaloo also organise their own events and run a booking agency. Contact on the above email address for further details.

Boro Bands
email: nick@boro-bands.co.uk
web: www.boro-bands.co.uk
info: Site for unsigned Peterborough bands, with Showcase section where artists can set up their own feature page. Just send details to the above email address. Online gig listings and forum.

Bravenet
web: www.bravenet.com
info: A website of free tools for webmasters of all skill levels to help you build your own (band) website.

Bristol Bands
email: contact@bristolbands.co.uk
web: www.bristolbands.co.uk
info: Directory for band and artists based in Bristol. Add your profile, or search the website for musicians in the area.

British Academy of Composers and Songwriters
British Music House, 25-27 Berners Street, London, W1T 3LR
tel: 020 7636 2929
fax: 020 7636 2212
email: info@britishacademy.com
web: www.britishacademy.com
info: Music industry news and details of opportunities, workshops and competitions for songwriters of all genres. Register of BACS members.

British Hit Singles
Guinness World Records, 338 Euston Road, London, NW1 3BD
email: editor@bibleofpop.com
web: www.britishhitsingles.com
info: Chart news and trivia from the Guinness Book of British Hit Singles. Weekly 'Pop Genius' quiz, discussion board, shop and links to related sites.

British Music Rights (BMR)
British Music House, 26 Berners Street, London, W1T 3LR
tel: 020 7306 4446
fax: 020 7306 4449
email: britishmusic@bmr.org
web: www.bmr.org
info: Information for songwriters on copyright, royalties, sampling, recording and publishing contracts. Links to advisory and support organisations. Details on the 'Respect the Value of Music' campaign. The site also contains a 'Guide to the Music Industry' with industry events and updates for writers and performers.

British Phonographic Industry (BPI)
Riverside Building, County Hall, Westminster Bridge Road, London, SE1 7JA
tel: 020 7803 1300
fax: 020 7803 1310
email: general@bpi.co.uk
web: www.bpi.co.uk
info: Large section on the legal issues surrounding piracy, copy control, MP3s and CDRs. Sales and trade statistics. Detailed UK music charts information. Advice on careers and education in the music industry. Updates on BPI and other industry events.

Broadjam
email: Via website contact form
web: www.broadjam.com
info: US based site. Musicians can sign up as a member to Broadjam to post photos, biogs, press releases and gig schedule, as well as host songs in multiple streaming formats and sell CDs.

Brum Punk Scene
25 Staplehurst Road, Hall Green, Birmingham, B28 9AR
email: james@brumpunkscene.co.uk
web: www.brumpunkscene.co.uk
contact: James Davison
info: Everything you need to know about the Punk scene in Birmingham. Submit your gig and event details, and a link to your band website.

Bucks Bands
email: via website
web: www.bucksbands.com
info: Band directory for the Buckinghamshire area. Gig listings, forum, classified ads and band directory for out of town bands and artists.

Build A Rock Star
email: info@buildarockstar.com
web: www.buildarockstar.com
info: Fun website where you can direct your own animated Rock video. Vote for your favourite video, or post yours online for chance to win competition prizes.

BURBs
PO Box 5213, Milton Keynes, MK9 4AZ
email: via website
web: www.burbs.org.uk
info: UK unsigned band directory with links to the BURBs radio station and artist websites. Bands can sell CDs online via the site. Includes an 'Artists of the Month' profile.

Cakewalk
email: Via website
web: www.cakewalk.com
info: Providers of software for creating music and sound on the desktop. For such applications as music CD creation, post-production, editing, film and video soundtracks, the integration of sound with computer games, multimedia applications and the internet.

Cambridge Bands
web: www.cambridgebands.com
info: Cambridge Bands was created as a drop-in centre for Cambridge bands and their fans. Contains band profiles and discussion forum.

Cambridge Music Directory
PO Box 445, Cambridge, CB1 2ZG
tel: 01223 316 351
email: lizzie@cambridge-music-directory.co.uk
web: www.cambridge-music-directory.co.uk
info: Online information about music in and around Cambridge including gig listings and directory of local music services.

Camden Guide
web: www.camdenguide.co.uk
info: Offers comprehensive guide to everything happening in Camden, from information about Camden markets and shops to entertainment. Contains Camden gig guide with a summary of the venues in the area where bands can play.

Campaign Against Living Miserably (C.A.L.M.)
tel: 0800 585 858
email: See website for list of contacts
web: www.thecalmzone.co.uk
info: News and information on the C.A.L.M. campaign that aims to raise awareness about the problem of depression affecting young men in the North West. The site also features online games, regional 'What's On' guide and links to music and lifestyle related websites. Telephone line open 5.00pm-3.00am.

Cardiff Soundscene
tel: 02920 373 144
email: via online form
web: www.soundsceneuk.com
info: Large online community of Cardiff bands and musicians. Forum, classified ads and links to local recording studios and practice rooms which can be booked online.

Cardiff Underground
email: info@cardiffunderground.com
web: www.cardiffunderground.com
info: Message board for gigs, events and cool stuff around Cardiff.

CD Baby
email: cdbaby@cdbaby.com
web: www.cdbaby.com
info: US based online record shop that sells CDs by independent musicians, sourced directly from them.

CD Pimp
web: www.cdpimp.com
info: US website. Unsigned bands and artists of all genres can sell their material via the site. Sign up for membership and get your CDs distributed through the CD Pimp network, and receive payments for downloads.

CREATIVE
INDUSTRIES
DEVELOPMENT
SERVICE

Fashion Designer needs to network

Concept and art direction: Dinosaur | Photography: Antony Crook

Creative Industries Development Service, CIDS, is here to help all 'creative' businesses or ideas people, whether you're involved in anything from art to gaming and craft to performing arts. If you live or work in and around Manchester and you're looking for workspace, training or want to know who's who and what's what in your industry, we're here to get your ideas out in the open.

Call Freephone **0800 169 1143** Visit **www.cids.co.uk/hello** Email **hello@cids.co.uk**
Write **CIDS, The Department Store, 5 Oak Street, Manchester, M4 5JD**

 northwest
development agency

 Project Part-Financed
by the European Union
European Regional
Development Fund

 NWDATrust/Fund
Fund wud UK

MEDIA

CD Unsigned
Dotcom Allsorts, PO Box 4462, Worthing, West Sussex, BN11 YF
email: Via online form
web: www.cdunsigned.com
info: Online CD retailer and music website, specialising in CDs by new and emerging bands. Independent artists and bands can create an artist page and stock their CDs in the online store, as well as on linked website www.getmemusic.com. All transactions and shipping will be handled by CD Unsigned.

Channel 4 Music
web: www.channel4.com/music
info: Comprehensive music site with features on current bands and artists, details of music on TV and online community. Making Music section of the website is dedicated to new music.

The Cheesepress
email: See contact list on website
web: www.cheesepress.co.uk
info: Online resource for bands and musicians in the North West of England. Submit your band and gig details.

Citizen Advice Bureau
email: Use online contact form
web: www.nacab.org.uk
info: The Citizens Advice Bureau helps to solve problems that are central to people's lives including debt and consumer issues, benefits, housing, legal matters, employment and immigration.

Classic Trax
PO Box 35, West Molesey, Surrey, KT8 2XF
tel: 0870 747 1299
email: Use online contact form
web: www.classictrax.co.uk
info: Classic Trax is a specialist supplier of Underground Dance music. They have an extensive selection of hard to find titles and have been supplying collectors worldwide for many years.

Clish
web: www.clish.tk
info: Site for Alternative music in Scotland. Well used forum with threads for local bands and general music discussion.

CMJ
email: See website for contacts
web: www.cmj.com/marathon/
info: Annual music and film conference held in New York. Includes performances, panel discussions, exhibits and showcases. Check website for updates on upcoming events and registration details.

CMU Online
web: www.cmumusicnetwork.co.uk
info: Music information service including artist interviews, industry features and a daily news mailing list.

CODE Interactive
email: via website
web: www.code-mag.com
info: Site dedicated to showcasing Urban talent including Hip-Hop, Asian and Drum&Bass. Unsigned artists can register for free, and upload their tracks

Comfort Comes
email: info@comfortcomes.com
web: www.comfortcomes.com
info: Music webzine with news updates, reviews, features and message board. If you would like to be reviewed on the site, or contribute to it, contact the above email address.

Commerial Breaks & Beats
web: www.commercialbreaksandbeats.co.uk
info: The UK Television Advert Music Database. Contains full search tools to find the artist and song title that features in a specific commercial. If you are unable to find the appropriate commercial, use the online link to find out the artist and song title.

The Creative Handbook
email: See contact list on website
web: www.chb.com
info: Website listing businesses that provide various creative services including photography, picture libraries, sound and design.

Creative Industries Development Service
1st Floor, The Department Store, 5 Oak Street, Manchester, M4 5JD
tel: 0800 169 1143
email: info@cids.co.uk
web: www.cids.co.uk
info: CIDS is a Manchester based economic development agency for cultural and creative enterprises. The website contains details of funding opportunities, support networks and available workspace. Different cultural sectors including music, film, art and photography are profiled with links to relevant websites.

Creative Launchpad
tel: 0121 224 7375
email: d.roberts@creativelaunchpad.co.uk
web: www.creativelaunchpad.co.uk
info: Free service for people in the creative industries based in the West Midlands. Information about organisations, business support agencies, funding sources, plus training and advice.

Culture Northern Ireland
web: www.culturenorthernireland.org
info: Website devoted to Performing Arts, Music, Film and TV, Literature, Visual Arts and Sport in Northern Ireland. Sign up for free newsletter updates.

d.i.y.h.t.m.l.
email: arianne@siljadesign.com
web: www.indiepages.com/diyhtml
info: Learn how to make your own Indie web page from scratch so you can create your own online music publication.

Damn Pest
email: via online form
web: www.damnpest.com
info: Music news, record and gig reviews plus discussion forum.

Daydreamer Music Reviews
email: info@daydreamer-music-reviews.com
web: www.daydreamer-music-reviews.com
info: Independent review service. Offer quality, in-depth appraisals of your music compiled by enthusiastic and honest reviewers. Refer to demo submission policy on the website before sending any material.

Designer Magazine
web: http://designermagazine.tripod.com/
info: Manchester webzine created as an alternative to the music and entertainment press. Reviews and interviews, as well as What's On guide.

Diesel-U-Music
web: www.diesel-u-music.com
info: Diesel-U-Music run an annual talent competition which aims to find the most exciting and unique music being created today. Competition open to unsigned artists in UK, Belgium, Italy, Japan and USA. See website for further details.

DirtyZine
email: dirtyzine@dirtyzine.co.uk
web: www.dirtyzine.co.uk
info: Music interviews and reviews, including demo reviews. DirtyZine have also released a compilation of the independent and unsigned talent which they have come across. If you would to contribute to DirtyZine, contact the above email address.

Diskant
email: See contact list on website
web: www.diskant.net
info: Music reviews. The Talentspotter section aims to profile the best bands, labels and fanzines.

DJ Peanuts
web: www.djpeanuts.co.uk
info: UK music database and directory with huge list of links to music-related topics including sound files, computer software, lyrics and music courses.

DL Music Consultants
33 Colomb Street, London, SE10 9HA
tel: 020 8305 2448
email: info@dlmusicconsultants.com
web: www.dlmusicconsultants.com
contact: Dean Hart, Laurence Hobbs
info: Online music consultancy for anyone wishing to get involved in the music industry.

Do Something Pretty
email: dosomethingpretty@hotmail.com
web: www.dosomethingpretty.com
info: Independent music news and articles. Contains single, album and demo reviews. See site for details on how to submit an article.

Don't Lose The Music
c/o RNID Campaign Team, 19-23 Featherstone Street, London, EC1Y 8SL
tel: 020 7296 8142
email: dontlosethemusic@rnid.org.uk
web: www.dontlosethemusic.com
info: A campaign run by the Royal National Institute of the Deaf to protect musicians, clubbers and festival goers from irreversible hearing damage. Contains useful advice about how to enjoy music safely.

GET SIGNED!
www.extraplay.com
enough said...

Downhill Battle
email: contact@downhillbattle.org
web: www.downhillbattle.org
info: US based music activism site that promotes the freedom of artistic expression through the media and to develop awareness of corporate interests.

Download.com
email: Use online contact form
web: www.download.com
info: Freeware and shareware downloads including design and multimedia, MP3 and audio, games and internet tools for Windows, Mac, Linux, Palm and Handhelds. Site includes features, reviews and new release news.

Drawer B
email: Use online contact form
web: www.drawerb.com
info: Music review web page that welcomes unsolicited demo submissions from unsigned bands.

Drowned In Sound
c/o Silentway, 61b Pall Mall Deposit, 124-128 Barlby Road, London, W10 6BL
email: sean.adams@drownedinsound.com or see contact list
web: www.drownedinsound.com
contact: Sean Adams
info: Drowned In Sound boasts an array of features including gig and event browser, single and album reviews, online forum, downloads page and artist/label search facility.

DrummerGirl
web: www.drummergirl.com
info: Site dedicated to female drummers with details of workshops, classified ads, articles and message boards.

Drummin' Men
email: webmaster@drumminmen.com
web: www.drumminmen.com
info: US based online Drummers' resource with over 1300 links to Drum related websites. Includes Drum directories, manufacturers, instruction, events, organisations and publications. Subscribe to receive the Drummin' Men newsletter by email.

Duckworth Square
web: www.duckworthsquare.com
info: Forum aimed at Derby musicians including board where MP3s can be posted and listened to.

East Anglia Web
web: www.eaweb.co.uk
info: Online community of forums with specific board dedicated to music. Other forums include cinema, local news, pubs and clubs, as well as sports and leisure for the region.

East Mids Music
email: via website
web: www.eastmidsmusic.co.uk
info: News and reviews of unsigned bands and artists in the East Midlands.

Eat This Music
PO Box 8479, Prestwick, Ayrshire, Scotland, KA9 2YR
email: admin@eatthismusic.com
web: www.eatthismusic.com
info: Eat This Music provides an interactive advertising site for unsigned artists and bands. Not exclusively for bands, it is also a marketing and management area for companies associated with promotion, support and management.

Ebay
web: www.ebay.co.uk
info: One of the most popular sales/auction sites on the internet. Ebay is a good way to buy and sell music related items and has a large amount of recorded music, instruments, sheet music, music memorabilia and more for competitive bidders.

Eerie Powers
email: andrewk@eeriepowers.co.uk
web: www.eeriepowers.co.uk
info: Guide to the Doncaster music scene. Area for local artists on the site, with a monthly spotlight feature on one chosen band.

eFestivals
email: webmaster@efestivals.co.uk
web: www.efestivals.co.uk
info: eFestivals covers a range of UK based music events with festival news, chat rooms, listings, line up rumours, photo galleries and online ticket sales.

Egigs
email: gigs@egigs.co.uk
web: www.egigs.co.uk
info: Check details of upcoming gigs and purchase tickets online. Website also includes live reviews and photos.

Electric Blues Club
email: Via website
web: www.electricbluesclub.co.uk
contact: Tracey Howard-Barker
info: Electric Blues Club is a not-for-profit voluntary group made up of musicians. Website contains listings, resources, information and links for all things musical.

Emagic
web: www.emagic.de
info: US based site for the manufacturers of Logic Audio. Includes product information and free downloads.

EmuBands
Studio 2, 1st Floor, Argyle House, 1103 Argyle Street, Glasgow, G3 8ND
email: info@emubands.com
web: www.emubands.com
contact: Ally Gray
info: EmuBands is a service for unsigned bands offering web hosting and design, digital distribution into the leading download services (e.g. iTunes, Napster etc), online merchandise design and retailing and much more. Open to submissions from any band or musicians.

Ents24.com
email: events@ents24.com
web: www.ents24.com
info: What's on guide for live music, clubs, theatre and cinema. Venue directory available online. Post event listings free of charge either by using online form or contacting email address shown above.

Epitonic
email: Use online contact form
web: www.epitonic.com
info: Provides music with the express permission of the record labels and artists including MP3 downloads from unsigned bands.

Europunk
email: vai website
web: www.europunk.net
info: Highly regarded Punk webzine dealing mainly with Punk, but also Alternative bands throughout Europe. Contact the team for reviews.

Evil Twin Promotions
tel: 07863 352 539
email: eviltwins@tiscali.co.uk
web: www.eviltwinpromotions.com
contact: Alex Darbyshire
info: Promotional service for unsigned bands and musicians. Acts as an agency to help publicise artists to various sectors of the music industry. Bands can submit their details on website and upload their tracks.

Extraplay.com
Cheshire
email: info@extraplay.com
web: www.extraplay.com
info: ExtraPlay.com promote and broadcast unsigned band music worldwide, 24 hours a day. Songs from unsigned bands and artists from around the world. To make your tracks available and broadcast on the radio, register online at the above website.

EzFolk
web: www.ezfolk.com
info: Popular Folk music resource. Unlimited MP3 hosting for Folk and Acoustic musicians, free tablature for guitar, banjo, ukulele and harmonica, as well as over 3000 links to other web resources. Online store selling instruments, books, CDs and DVDs.

Fairplay Music
email: contact@fairplaymusic.com
web: www.fairplaymusic.com
info: Promotion for unsigned bands and musicians. Sign up and post your profile, gig details and MP3s.

Fastfude
web: www.fastfude.com
info: Website dedicated to the music scene in Northern Ireland. It operates on a not-for-profit making basis and encourages everyone from any musical genre or background to take part, contribute and learn.

The Federation of Music Collectives
web: www.fmc-ireland.com
info: The FMC aims to promote, encourage and develop the work of music collectives. Useful website with information about starting a music collective, as well as fact sheets on subjects such as approaching A&R, Copyright Basics and Music Law.

Fender
tel: 01342 331 700
fax: 01342 331 746
email: Use online contact form
web: www.fender.co.uk
info: Online store for Fender guitars, amplifiers and basses. With news and local dealer information.

Figure of Eight
email: contact@figure-of-eight.com
web: www.figure-of-eight.com
info: Online music magazine including band related reviews, features and interviews.

Find Midis
web: www.findmidis.com
info: A free database containing Chart, recent and vintage music in MIDI format. No registration or log-in required.

Find Videos
email: eric@bored.com
web: www.findvideos.com
info: Record companies put their artists' videos online to promote CD sales. This site searches the internet to find these videos so you can watch them free of charge from their website.

Five Miles High
web: www.fivemileshigh.com
info: UK band resource with Band of the Month feature, gig listings and band directory. Join to receive regular band and live updates.

Floppyswop
web: www.floppyswop.co.uk
info: A website for sharing any files small enough to fit on a conventional floppy disc (1.44Mb HD) including art, media, sound or noise.

Folk & Roots
web: www.folkandroots.co.uk
info: Guide to the Folk and Acoustic scene with information about gigs, releases, festivals and venues.

Forming Bands
web: www.formingbands.co.uk
info: Created by musicians, this website is designed to help those who are looking to get a band together. Get in touch with other musicians who play your type of music at your level. Caters for wide range of areas and music genres.

Freemuse
email: freemuse@humanrights.dk
web: www.freemuse.org
info: Independent international organisation advocating freedom of expression for musicians and composers worldwide.

Freesheetmusic.net
email: Use online contact form
web: www.freesheetmusic.net
info: Search for sheet music by instrument, genre or alphabetically, and purchase it online.

Front Room Music
email: danpeel@frontroommusic.co.uk
web: www.frontroommusic.co.uk
info: Website devoted to showcasing new, unsigned musical talent. To be featured on the site free of charge, contact the above email address.

FrozenUK
web: www.frozenuk.com
info: Frozen UK is an online Dance music collective created for musicians, producers, DJs and promoters. They have an online DJ agency in which you can advertise yourself and accept demos. Also have two functioning studios.

F-Sharp
email: sales@f-sharp.co.uk
web: www.f-sharp.co.uk
info: Online retailer selling Fender Footwear. Also sponsors of the YourBand project (see listing in this section). Check website for products and more information.

Funk Network UK
web: www.fnuk.com
info: Funk Network UK is a free worldwide database of live Funk bands and musicians. Also provide services to the music industry including PA and sound engineering, tour management, booking agency, function bands, events and promotion.

Furness Music
email: admin@furnessmusicpromotions.tk
web: www.furnessmusic.co.uk
info: Site devoted to live music in and around the Furness Peninsula. Bands from the area can post their tracks and profiles online.

Fused
Studio 315, The Greenhouse, Gibb Square, Birmingham, B9 4AA
tel: 0121 246 1946
email: enquiries@fusedmagazine.com
web: www.fusedmagazine.com
info: Birmingham-based online publication that features local media news and artist profiles.

Gamefoe
16 Common Lane, Thundersley, Essex, SS7 3TD
web: www.gamefoe.co.uk
info: Webzine for South East of England. News, reviews and features on bands from the area. Submit your material for review at the above address.

GarageBand
web: www.garageband.com
info: GarageBand offers a range of free and paid services to unsigned musicians such as gig promotion and advice from industry experts.

Bringing Music To Your EARS

webzine and UK promoters since 2000
www.glasswerk.co.uk

Gemm
email: inquiry@gemm.com
web: www.gemm.com
info: Online search engine for music, video and books. Linked to online record stores worldwide and allows small businesses to sell their music directly and with no setup charge.

Get A Gig
email: via online form
web: www.getagig.ie
info: Live entertainment resource for Ireland. Music news, gig listings, downloads, classified ads, as well as online directory of music services.

Get Live
web: www.getlive.co.uk
info: The latest gigs, festivals, art and theatre events. Purchase tickets and music merchandise.

Get Me Music
email: via online form
web: www.getmemusic.com
info: Get Me Music is an innovative online CD retailer and music website specialising in music by new and emerging bands.

Get Signed
email: editor@getsigned.com
web: www.getsigned.com
info: Extensive US based band resource containing music industry news and features, artist and A&R interviews, plus forum. Site also includes a large article database giving advice on touring, recording, compiling press kits and promotion.

Get The Gig
email: info@getthegig.co.uk
web: www.getthegig.co.uk
info: Unsigned band promotion site featuring artist profiles. Get The Gig are always looking for demos to be played on their streamed radio show each week. Email the above address for more details.

Gig Guide
42 Kirby Drive, Luton, Bedfordshire, LU3 4AW
tel: 01582 583 823
fax: 01582 491 384
email: gigmaster1@gig-guide.co.uk
web: www.gig-guide.co.uk
info: Free national gig listings. Dates can be added online by registered users. The site also features musicians' forums, classified ads, band reviews and a message board.

The Gig Guide
web: www.gigguide.co.uk
info: Useful resource for Scotland containing gig listings, as well as details of recording and rehearsal studios, music tuition and venues. Scottish bands can submit their details free of charge to the website via the online form.

Gig Listings
web: www.giglistings.co.uk
info: Listings for the North East region including gigs, band profiles, music reviews, photo gallery and discussion forum. Gig and band details can be submitted using online forms.

Gig Pro
web: www.gigsoftwarez.com
info: Freeware applications tailored to assist professional sound mixers.

Gigged
179 Farnborough Road, Nottingham, NG1 8HP
email: gigguide@giggedweb.co.uk
web: www.giggedweb.co.uk
info: Reviews of local bands and venues in Nottingham and the surrounding areas. News, gig guide and message board also available on the site. Visitors to the site can contribute their own reviews and submit their listings to email address above. Visitors can also vote for, play and download demos. Demos can be forwarded to the above postal address.

Gighit
email: listings@gighit.com
web: www.gighit.com
info: One stop for bands, promoters, DJs, clubbers and gig-goers in the South of England. Band profiles and listings can be submitted to the site by using the online form or contacting the email address above.

GigNetwork
email: newcontact@gignetwork.co.uk
web: www.gignetwork.co.uk
info: Directory for aspiring bands planning their foray onto the live circuit. Provides details on music policies, payment arrangements and any specifications unique to particular venues or promoters. See sample listings on the website. Contact the above email address if you would like to be listed.

Gigs in Scotland
web: www.gigsinscotland.com
info: Guide and online ticket outlet for gigs, events and festivals in Scotland. Contains travel and venue information. Register for regular updates.

Gigs Unlimited
17 Cromford Avenue, Stretford, Manchester, M32 9RQ
email: info@gigs-unlimited.co.uk
web: www.gigs-unlimited.co.uk
info: Both unsigned and signed bands' gigs are promoted regardless of genre. Website also contains database of thousands of artists, bands, gigs and venues.

Gigwise
email: via online form
web: www.gigwise.com
info: Music webzine for signed and unsigned music in the UK. Reviews, features, interviews, gig listings, artist profiles and shop selling tickets, CDs and merchandise. Gigwise also has an extensive online directory for services such as photography, CD duplication and studios.

Gigzter.com
email: info@gigzter.com
web: www.gigzter.com
info: Canadian website offering online promotion for unsigned and independent artists.

Girl Player
email: info@girlplayer.com (general information)
web: www.girlplayer.com
info: US based online resource for female musicians including artist photo galleries, reviews, articles, musician classifieds, gig swapping and advice.

Glasgow Music
email: craig@glasgowmusic.co.uk
web: www.glasgowmusic.co.uk
info: Features single and album reviews, interviews, as well as guide to the music scene in Glasgow.

GlasJazz
email: info@glasjazz.co.uk
web: www.glasjazz.co.uk
info: Online resource and community for Jazz music in Glasgow. Find information about Jazz musicians, venues, concerts and CD releases in the area.

Glasswerk.co.uk
email: See website for list of contacts
web: www.glasswerk.co.uk
info: Online resource for unsigned bands in Liverpool, Glasgow, Leeds, London, Manchester, Nottingham, Southeast and Wales. Online distribution of unsigned material, artist database (including links to band websites and MP3 music samples), music news and reviews. 'Band Tips' section offering artists advice on success in the music industry.

Glastonbury Festival
email: office@glastonburyfestivals.co.uk
web: www.glastonburyfestivals.co.uk
info: News and information on Glastonbury Festival. The site also contains links to the charities supported by the event, including Oxfam, Water Aid and Drop The Debt.

God Is In The TV
email: godisinthetv2003@yahoo.co.uk
web: www.godisinthetvzine.co.uk
info: Online cultural fanzine featuring unsigned reviews, as well as music interviews and discussion forum.

Gods Of Music
email: Use online contact form
web: www.godsofmusic.com
info: A resource to access quality original music on the internet. Each review contains a link to the artist's website where you will be able to download the full MP3 song file.

Gojangle
email: simon@gojangle.com
web: www.gojangle.com
info: Website designed for both musicians who want to advertise their music and fans of music who want a single source for all new music and record companies on the lookout for talent. Send your music either on CD or MP3 format. A section of the website will be dedicated to your act, and tracks will be uploaded and can be listened to via the site.

gomusicstore
web: www.gomusicstore.com
info: Huge selection of music available from both unsigned and independent artists. Songs available to buy from as little as 50p. Browse artist details and listen to full length LoFi samples of artist tracks before you buy.

Grassroots Xchange

email: via website
web: www.grassrootsx.com
info: Grassroots Xchange aims to aid creative talent in the music industry. Registered members will receive access to an industry directory and can upload their own MP3s.

The Great Unsigned

web: www.thegreatunsigned.com
info: Forum for Lowestoft's independent music network. Contains discussion threads on local events and bands, as well as classifieds and general information about musical instruments.

The Guardian Jobs

web: www.guardian.co.uk/jobs
info: One of the most comprehensive search facilities for media and creative industry jobs in the UK including employer listings and links to media recruitment agencies. Post your CV online.

Guitar Noise

web: www.guitarnoise.com
info: Free online guitar lessons, tablature, interviews, as well as advice on careers and songwriting. Website also features shop and message boards.

Guitar Tabs Universe

web: www.guitartabs.cc
info: Browse by artist and then by song to access both lyrics and tabs. Guitar lessons also available online.

Guitargeek

email: guitargeek@guitargeek.com
web: www.guitargeek.com
info: Guitar rig database. Browse by artist, instrument, style and manufacturer.

Gutta World

web: www.guttaworld.com
info: Website for Gutta World Magazine - the voice of the independent Rap industry. Demo reviews, articles, classified ads, online forum and careers section.

Handle

Handle Recruitment, 4 Gees Court, London, W1U 1JD
tel: 020 7569 9999
email: info@handle.co.uk
web: www.handle.co.uk
info: Handle is a recruitment agency specialising in roles for the creative industries including music, entertainment and media. Mainly London based.

Hard To Find Records

Vinyl House, 10 Upper Gough Street, Birmingham, B1 1JG
tel: 0121 687 7777
fax: 0121 687 7774
email: Use online contact form
web: www.htfr.com
info: Hard To Find specialise in supplying all types of new and deleted House, Garage, Techno, Electro, Disco, Funk, Soul and Hip-Hop vinyl. They also offer a record finding service and will try to locate any record released.

Helter Skelter Books

Southbank House, Black Prince Road, London, WC2H 8LL
tel: 020 7463 2204
email: sales@helterskelterbooks.com
web: www.helterskelterbooks.com
info: Helter Skelter is a book publishing company dedicated to music and the music industry. Website allows users to browse the extensive catalogue by genre and to buy online.

Highland Ultimate Bands List

email: email@hubl.co.uk
web: www.hubl.co.uk
info: Created to promote the music scenes in Moray and The Highlands. Submit your band details with picture to the email address above. Also contact this address to submit reviews. Online form on website for posting gig dates.

Hip-Hop Directory

web: www.hiphop-directory.com
info: Web portal with extensive links directory for everything Hip-Hop related, from record labels to Beatbox events.

The Hip-Hop List

web: www.thehiphoplist.co.uk
info: Dedicated to Hip-Hop and Urban music culture in Cambridge. Online forum, ticket giveaways and email updates of local gigs and club nights.

Hit Quarters

email: info@hitquarters.com
web: www.hitquarters.com
info: Directory of the world's top record company A&R contacts, managers, publishers and producers including their contact information and track records.

Hitheads

web: www.hitheads.com
info: Industry database for the UK, US and Europe. Hitheads aim is to assist musicians in the development and advancement of their careers. They liaise directly with various leading industry figures and organisations and offer a headhunting service for labels, managers and publishers who are seeking to source new acts or new material.

The Holy Toilet

email: mail@holytoilet.com
web: www.holytoilet.com
info: Online community linked with The Forum venue in Tunbridge Wells. Website features local band directory, reviews, message board and general news relating to the music scene in the area.

Homespun Collective

email: info@hspun.com
web: www.hspun.com
info: Web-based collective bringing together many aspects of Glasgow's Electronic music scene. Features, information and listings. Also offer free, no spam email accounts.

Huddersfield Music Scene

email: info@huddsmusicscene.co.uk
web: www.huddsmusicscene.co.uk
info: Links to bands, venues, studios and music shops in and around Huddersfield. Also details of local gigs and events.

Hull & Yorkshire Rockers

web: www.hullrockers.co.uk
info: Network of forums for Rock music lovers in Hull and Yorkshire. Boards for all specific genres of Rock music, as well as local band and gig information threads.

Hull Scene

email: hullscene@gmail.com
web: www.hullscene.com
info: News, gigs, reviews, classified ads, discussion forum and local band A to Z list.

Hull Spotlight

web: www.hull-spotlight.tk
info: Dedicated to promoting up and coming bands and musicians from Hull. Forum, band and gig lists, pictures, reviews and classified ads online.

The Hunger Site

email: customerservice@thehungersite.com
web: www.thehungersite.com
info: 24,000 people die of hunger each day. Click on the 'Give Free Food' button and 100% of collected revenue from the site goes to hunger relief efforts.

Ideas Factory

email: editor@ideasfactory.com
web: www.ideasfactory.com
info: Ideas Factory is dedicated to helping people get ahead within the creative industries across the UK. Individual areas of the site containing features, information, forums and details of opportunities for art and design, performance, film and TV, writing and new media. Useful information is also available about funding and awards, careers, and training and courses.

I'm Gifted

web: www.imgifted.co.uk
info: Online music promotions. Create your own profile, upload photos, tracks and videos, and sell your music online.

In The City

8 Brewery Yard, Deva Centre, Trinity Way, Salford, M3 7BB
tel: 0161 839 3930
fax: 0161 839 3940
email: info@inthecity.co.uk
web: www.inthecity.co.uk
info: Updates and information on the UK's annual international music convention. The site contains details on how to apply for the In The City Unsigned showcase events, attended by UK/International A&R representatives.

Indie Centre

email: Via website
web: www.indiecentre.co.uk
info: Website created to provide independent labels with vital information about getting their music to the masses. Advice and tips covering everything from setting up a label to promotion and touring.

INDIEgo

email: Via website
web: www.indiego.com
info: INDIEgo is a US based promotions and distribution company for independent artists and labels. Provides commercial and non-commercial radio promotion, press and publicity, retail promotion, tour support and national distribution.

MEDIA

Indigo Flow
email: Use online contact form
web: www.indigoflow.co.uk
info: News, gigs, reviews and interviews. Register to receive the monthly e-zine and download music and video from the website. Site also has links to record labels.

IndyReview
email: info@indyreview.net
web: www.indyreview.net
info: The aim of IndyReview is to create a global community of original independent artists. Artists and bands can sign up and create a profile, upload original music and merchandise and post articles and news on their page.

Insound
web: www.insound.com
info: US based website for fans of underground music and film.

Intellectual Property
The Patent Office, Cardiff Road, Newport, South Wales, NP10 8QQ
tel: 0845 950 0505
fax: 01633 813 600
email: enquiries@patent.gov.uk
web: www.intellectual-property.gov.uk
info: Introduction to and advice on intellectual property (IP) such as how to enforce your IP rights, using other people's material, and protecting your own ideas. Links to websites concerned with copyright, patents and trademarks.

Internet Underground Music Archive
email: support@iuma.com
web: www.iuma.com
info: US based band database that offers bands free custom web pages where they can post information and MP3s, sell CDs, create message boards and receive emails. Get updates on latest additions to the site, charts and bulletin board. Users can search for bands by genre.

IntoMusic.co.uk
web: www.intomusic.co.uk
info: Independent music download site, selling both downloads and MP3 players. Musicians can subscribe free of charge and will receive 50% of download royalties.

Ipswich Gigs
web: www.ipswichgigs.co.uk
info: Site for gig listings in Ipswich. Also provides contact details for local venues, promoters and studios.

irLondon
web: www.irlondon.co.uk
info: London club and gig listings guide. Contains venue guide, photo gallery and features.

Isle of Wight Rock
email: see online contact list
web: www.iowrock.net
info: Details of local gigs and artists, plus news and reviews relating to the Isle of Wight music scene.

Isound
email: via online form
web: www.isound.com
info: Promote your music online via Isound. It is free to set up a basic artist account allowing you to create your own professional band or artist website, upload your MP3s and sell your music to fans.

Itchy City
Unit 2, Whitehorse Yard, 78 Liverpool Road, London, N1 0QD
tel: 020 7288 9810
email: wherearemymittens@itchymedia.co.uk
web: www.itchycity.co.uk
info: Individual online guides to 17 cities across the UK including Liverpool, Manchester, London, Cardiff, Glasgow and Edinburgh. Itchy City covers gigs, clubbing, accommodation, shopping, jobs and more. Subscribe to the site to receive news and offers to your inbox.

Jazz in Leeds
web: www.jazzinleeds.co.uk
info: Website is split into 2 areas: forums and the main site which has details of Jazz events and news for the area.

Jazz in Scotland
email: admin@jazz-in-scotland.co.uk
web: www.jazz-in-scotland.co.uk
info: Dedicated to the Jazz scene in Scotland. Contains band directory, listings, information about Jazz teachers and also Jazz radio programmes.

Jockrock
PO Box 13516, Linlithgow, EH49 6WB
email: jockrock@vacant.org.uk
web: www.vacant.org.uk/jockrock/
info: Information about the music scene in Scotland. Submit band and gig details to the email address above. Send demo for review to the postal address.

John Peel Music
web: www.johnpeelmusic.com
info: Website devoted to the memory of John Peel. The aim of the site is to encourage new musical talent to upload their music, whilst music fans will be asked to rate the music posted.

Josaka
email: via online form
web: www.josaka.com
info: Website devoted to live music in Berkshire. Contains news, reviews, gig guide, classified ads and band profiles. Also links to Berkshire Live discussion forum. Josaka contains resources section with details for music equipment suppliers, local promoters and rehearsal and recording facilities.

Joy
email: paul@joyzine.co.uk
web: www.joyzine.co.uk
info: Music webzine. If you would like your demo or gig reviewed by Joy, email link to MP3 to the above address. Also contact this address if you are interested in contributing to Joy.

KarmaDownload
email: info@karmadownload.com
web: www.karmadownload.com
info: Download site for unsigned bands and independent labels. Tracks can be searched for by genre and downloaded legally for a small price. When artists sign up to the site they are given their own updatable section for biog, gig dates and web links. KarmaDownload is committed to helping unsigned talent, and there is no charge to join. Tracks can also be submitted to the site's A&R team.

Kent Gigs
tel: 01303 893 472
email: chris@kentgigs.com
web: www.kentgigs.com
info: Gig guide for Kent and East Sussex. Also profiles of local bands and musicians. List your details by contacting Kent Gigs on the above number or email address.

Kent Indie
email: submit@kentindie.co.uk
web: www.kentindie.co.uk
info: Independent music and art scene in Kent. List your events and band details. Kent Indie also welcome story and review contributions for the website.

Knowhere
email: info@knowhere.co.uk
web: www.knowhere.co.uk
info: A compilation of unedited comments on towns and cities in the UK. This includes music related links specific to towns and cities around the country.

Kooba Radio
Studio 12, 37 Tanner Street, London, SE1 3LF
email: submissions@koobaradio.co.uk
web: www.koobaradio.co.uk
contact: Jonny Yeah
info: Internet radio station dedicated to playing unsigned bands. Email MP3s (no more than 2MB) to above email address. Alternatively, send demo and press pack to the address above.

L2SB
email: petel2sb@hotmail.co.uk
web: www.l2sb.co.uk
info: Site for music lovers based in Sheffield. News, reviews, links directory and online unsigned jukebox.

Last Sound
email: sach@lastsound.com
web: www.lastsound.com
info: Last Sound provides a means for producers and beatmakers to have their music heard. Also offers resources and articles for producers. Submit your material by contacting the above email address. Check the website for details of information to include with your submission.

LastMinuteMusicians.com
web: www.lastminutemusicians.com
info: Puts musicians and bands in touch with event organisers and party planners. Other services include music tuition and workshops, as well as contact information for other music service providers.

developing a stage for the **next** generation.

manchester's best
online resource for
unsigned independent bands...

mancpunkscene
.co.uk

LAUNCH
web: music.yahoo.com
info: Watch over 6,000 music videos via the online database and buy albums online.

The Laundrette
57 Meersbrook Avenue, Sheffield, S8 9ED
email: info@thelaundrette.co.uk
web: www.thelaundrette.co.uk
info: Online outlet for unsigned bands in Sheffield. Browse and order releases from local and national artists, both signed and unsigned.

Leeds Music Scene
tel: 07005 964 458
email: info@leedsmusicscene.co.uk
web: www.leedsmusicscene.co.uk
info: A collection of articles relating to the music scene in Leeds including a gig guide, reviews and interviews.

Leicester Music Scene
email: drew@leicestermusicscene.co.uk
web: www.leicestermusicscene.co.uk
info: Promoting bands and musicians in Leicester. The website also has sections dedicated to gigs, releases, reviews, MP3s, features and classified ads, plus forum.

Leicester Punk Scene
email: my_toilet@hotmail.com
web: www.leicesterpunkscene.co.uk
info: Add news, gigs, photos and links relating to the Punk scene in Leicester by contacting the email address above.

Lincoln Bands
email: see contact list online
web: www.lincolnbands.co.uk
info: Band A to Z. Submit your details using the form online. The website also has sections dedicated to gigs, releases, reviews, MP3s, features and classified ads, plus forum.

Link 2 Wales
PO Box 152, Rhyl, LL22 7ZA
web: www.link2wales.co.uk
info: Guide to the Alternative scene in Wales, and also stretching to Liverpool. Coverage of local bands, venues, fanzines, gigs and radio shows. Send demos to the address above.

Listen Up
email: listenupnorthwest@yahoo.co.uk
web: www.listenupnorthwest.org.uk
info: Platform for Preston's evolving music scene. Local news, reviews, artist and venue details, as well as discussion forum.

Live 365
email: Use online contact form
web: www.live365.com
info: Become the DJ of your own radio station with this US-based internet radio network. Stream your station to any internet listener, anywhere in the world. Requires a monthly payment agreement.

Live Club
email: Use online contact form
web: www.liveclub.co.uk
info: Dedicated to the UK's unsigned music scene. Band services, listings, gig guide, advice on how to promote your gigs (including getting online) and live reviews. Message board and classified ads. Live Club Radio is broadcast via the internet and Live Club also runs a stage at the annual Guildford Festival.

Live For Music
web: www.liveformusic.co.uk
info: News from the music world. Alphabetical index of artist interviews and articles. Gig guide and forum also available on the site.

Live Wire Listings
tel: 01202 433 258
email: feedback@livewirelistings.co.uk
web: www.livewirelistings.co.uk
info: Submit listings, news, reviews and articles to this website based in Bournemouth.

Livingston Music Scene
email: Via website
web: www.livims.co.uk
info: Site dedicated to live music in Livingston. Details of local bands, gigs and events, as well as message board.

Loopmasters
web: www.loopmasters.com
info: Professional sample libraries available for producers worldwide. Sign up for free newsletter. Preview samples and loops free of charge online, and request CD samplers.

Loud 1
web: www.loud1.net
info: Comprehensive Rock mail order website. Purchase albums, DVDs, merchandise, magazines and related accessories.

Love Music Hate Racism
Anti Nazi League, PO Box 2566, London, N4 1WJ
tel: 020 7924 0333
fax: 020 7924 0313
email: anl@anl.org.uk
web: www.lmhr.org.uk
info: Organised by the Anti Nazi League, Love Music Hate Racism aims to use the positive energy of the music scene to fight back against the racism being pushed by Nazi organisations such as the British National Party, National Front and Combat 18. The website has full information about high profile album releases and events that benefit the cause.

Low Wattage
email: lowwattage@hotmail.com
web: www.lowwattage.vze.com
info: Resource for unsigned bands in Ayrshire. Bands can upload their biog, tracks and photos. Site also features reviews, interviews and discussion forum.

M11 Music
email: via website
web: www.m11music.co.uk
info: M11 Music aims to promote and encourage growth of the music scene in the South East of England. Bands can set up their own forum, as well as posting gig dates on the calendar. Music classified ads sections and large community on message boards.

The Mag
141 Bramley Crescent, Southampton, SO19 9LG
email: gigs@the-mag.me.uk
web: www.the-mag.me.uk
info: Online music zine with features, reviews and news on local bands and gigs. To have your demo reviewed send CD, biog and website details to the above address. Gig listings can be submitted to the above email address.

Make Trade Fair
Oxfam House, John Smith Drive, Cowley, Oxford, OX4 2JY
tel: 0870 333 2700
email: Via website
web: www.maketradefair.com
info: Updates and reports on the Make Trade Fair campaign which aims to put an end to poverty in the developing world by ensuring farmers and labourers are paid a living wage.

Manchester Bands
web: www.manchester-bands.co.uk
info: A to Z database of bands from Manchester and the surrounding area. The site also contains a gig guide, message board and a section dedicated to keeping bands up to date with any unsigned opportunities.

Manchester Music
PO Box 1977, Manchester, M26 2YB
email: manchestermusic@gmail.com
web: www.manchestermusic.co.uk
contact: Dave Himelfield
info: Site dedicated to the music scene in Manchester and the North West. Live and new release reviews (both signed and unsigned), interviews and music news and noticeboard. Send demos to the above address.

Manchester Unsigned
219 Bolton Road, Bury, Lancashire, BL8 2NR
email: info@manchesterunsigned.com
web: www.manchesterunsigned.com
info: This community site provides a free platform for those involved in the arts, and enables them to showcase their creative skills at up and coming events.

MancPunkScene
12 Langford Road, Withington, Manchester, M20 1QA
tel: 07835 645 000
email: mackie@mancpunkscene.co.uk
web: www.mancpunkscene.co.uk
contact: Mackie
info: Dedicated to the Punk/Indie scene in Manchester, this website features news and reviews, interviews and thriving discussion forums to help promote yourself. MancPunkScene also release CD compilations and put on shows annually showcasing local talent. Contact Mackie for details of getting involved with the site, submitting your MP3 for possible inclusion, or more queries.

Manx Bands
web: www.manxbands.co.uk
info: Manx bands was created to enable any band from the Isle of Man to have web presence by offering free web hosting and design. Site also features news, reviews, gig dates and discussion forum.

The genre-free independent label with a Virtual Venue for unsigned artists. We sign artists on the basis of audience response.

You get:

- Full length track promotion – FREE
- Your music rated & reviewed on-line – FREE
- Listener feedback – FREE
- A global audience and new fans – FREE

Plus:

- 50% of revenue when you sell downloads
- A chance to be the next MVine signing

Visit the Virtual Venue for more info – we're on your side.

www.mvine.com

Marshall
web: www.marshallamps.com
info: Corporate website for Marshall Amplifiers. In addition to product information and an online shop you can download handbooks and instruction guides for all available models.

Masteringworld.com
email: sales@masteringworld.com
web: www.masteringworld.com
info: Online virtual mastering complex. Select from 3 studios, and 4 engineers. For further information or to upload your tracks, see the website.

Mean Fiddler
16 High Street, Harlesden, London, NW10 4LX
tel: 0208 961 5490/0870 150 0044 (ticket enquiries)
fax: 0208 961 9238
web: www.meanfiddler.com
info: Gig information, reviews and band information.
Contains links to associated music events with tickets available online.

Media UK
email: Use online contact form
web: www.mediauk.com
info: An internet directory of UK radio stations, magazines, newspapers and television channels. Also has online media related job vacancies and much more.

The Met Office
web: www.met-office.gov.uk
info: Useful in advance of outdoor gigs, this website offers full weather information with daily and seasonal forecasts.

Metal Ireland
email: ct@metalireland.com
web: www.metalireland.com
info: Webzine dedicated to Metal scene in Ireland. Provides platform for unsigned bands who can submit material for review and post gig dates and band news. Home to the Irish Metal forum.

Mi2N (Music Industry News Network)
web: www.mi2n.com
info: Excellent website with up to date news covering all aspects of the music industry.MI2N is a leading news publisher and CSP (Content Service Provider) in the digital entertainment market. Users of the website can register their email address and have up to the minute news letters about all aspects of the music industry delivered daily to their inbox.

Midem
web: www.midem.com
info: Midem is a music conference held yearly in the South of France. It attracts independent and major record companies, music publishers, online and traditional distributors, live music professionals, A&R executives, agents, producers and promoters, amongst others.

Milton Keynes Music Sessions
tel: 01908 562 736
email: lithop@lineone.net
web: www.session.musician.org.uk
info: Online facility for musicians and singers in the Milton Keynes area where they can view events at which they can air their talents. Details of venues and events can be submitted via email or telephone.

The Mod Pop Punk Archives
email: rgmod79@aol.com
web: http://punkmodpop.free.fr/
info: Site dedicated to Mod, Pop and Punk bands from the late 70s. Features band biographies, discographies, pictures, sounds and links.

mp3.com
web: www.mp3.com
info: Listen to and download MP3s from different genres. Watch music videos and excerpts from film and television.

Mr Gig
email: gigs@mrgig.com
web: www.mrgig.com
info: Live music listings for East Kent, Maidstone and Medway. Search by artist, gig or venue. Mr Gig recently produced a compilation CD of local unsigned acts which can be purchased via the website.

MEDIA

MTV
web: www.mtv.com
info: Multi-genre site including on-air schedules, band/artist features, videos, photos, radio, interviews, competitions downloads and more. Also includes link to MTV2 site which features Alternative and Urban content.

The Muse's Muse
email: jodi@musesmuse.com
web: www.musesmuse.com
info: Resource for songwriters and composers, with reference guides and articles. Subscribe for free monthly newsletter. Also online radio station, as well as chat rooms and classified ads.

Music Business Journal
email: info@musicjournal.org
web: www.musicjournal.org
info: Independent online resource developed to increase an understanding of all issues relating to the music industry. Articles, updates and industry insights. Comprehensive links section available.

Music Business Resources For Students
Nottignham, Nottinghamshire, NG2 4AB
tel: 0115 910 0843
email: dazsmith@proweb.co.uk
web: www.mustard-mg.com/musbiz
contact: Daz Smith
info: Great industry resource which outlines all areas of the business.

Music By Music
7 Stanley Street, Kinning Park, Glasgow, G41 1JA
email: info@musicbymusic.com
web: www.musicbymusic.com
info: This website is dedicated to offering free hosting of MP3s to unsigned artists. Bands and musicians can upload tracks, pictures, gig dates and contact information to give a complete profile.

Music Hound Dog
email: bandsites@musichounddog.com
web: www.musichounddog.com
info: Music Hound Dog was created to encourage live music in Birmingham. Useful band advice section which includes information and tips, as well as details of local music related contacts. Lists web links for local bands, submit your details to the above email address.

Music Hurts
email: hello@musichurts.com
web: www.musichurts.com
info: Cutting edge music magazine. All 93 pages can be viewed online. Read features and reviews whilst listening to the tracks at the same time.

Music Industry News Network
web: www.mi2n.com
info: MI2N is a leading news publisher and CSP (Content Service Provider) in the digital entertainment market. Users of the website can register their email address and have up to the minute news letters about all aspects of the music industry delivered daily to their inbox.

Music Scene UK
Unit 39, Silicone Business Centre, 28 Wadsworth Road, Perivale, Middlesex, UB6 7JZ
tel: 020 8998 8944
email: sales@vegassoundhouse.com
web: www.musicsceneuk.com
contact: Matt
info: Free service for bands who do not have the expertise or money to create their own website. Any band with material of a good standard can sign up to be included as part of the Music Scene UK site. They are then able to include a biog, pictures, MP3s and details of any gig dates. Contact Matt for further information.

Music Tank
University of Westminster, New Cavendish Street, London, W1W 6UW
tel: 020 7915 5412
fax: 020 7911 5812
email: info@musictank.co.uk
web: www.musictank.co.uk
info: A music industry business network that aims to give artists, managers, labels, publishers, promoters, audio professionals and the media the chance to share ideas, exchange information and forge new partnerships. Contains information on funding, legal, training and musical genres.

Music:vids
4 Sycamore Close, Lepton, Huddersfield, West Yorkshire, HD8 0EP
email: contact@musicvids.co.uk
web: www.musicvids.co.uk
info: Site offering coverage and promotion to local bands in the UK. Watch streamed videos from both major signed, and local unsigned artists. Send videos, promos and releases to the above address.

Musical Instrument Sales
web: www.musicalinstrumentsales.co.uk
info: Buy, sell and advertise all musical instruments, whether they be new or second hand.

Musician Seeks Musician
web: www.musicianseeksmusician.com
info: Website for musicians to post their classified ads. Musicians available and wanted, music tuition and other services are all advertised on the site. Also includes links directory for management companies and record labels.

The Musician's Benevolent Fund
16 Ogle Street, London, W1W 6JA
tel: 020 7636 4481
email: info@mbf.org.uk
web: www.mbf.org.uk
info: The Musicians Benevolent Fund is the music business's own charity. Provides help and support to musicians and their dependants and also to those in related occupations when illness, accident or old age bring stress or financial burdens.

Musicians In Your City
web: www.musicians-in-your-city.co.uk
info: Join for free and search for musicians in your area, or post your own details on the website.

Musician's Tech Central
email: jandd00@fastmail.fm
web: www.musicianstechcentral.com
info: Growing resource for music equipment, recording, MIDI, digital audio, and Indie how-to information. MTC search the internet for useful or cutting edge information for musicians.

Musicians' Web
web: www.musicians-web.com
info: Musicians can register for free to use this online resource. Contains classified ads for band members/musicians wanted, message boards, unsigned band profile pages, gig news and reviews plus guitar tab archive.

The Musicland
email: info@themusicland.co.uk
web: www.themusicland.co.uk
info: Online music education resource for students, teachers and other music professionals. Offers wide range of free resources and materials.

MusicMK
email: ndmweb@hotmail.com
web: www.musicmk.org.uk
info: Site for local music in Bedfordshire, Hertfordshire and Buckinghamshire. Lists local bands, venues and gigs. To add a listing contact by email at the address above.

musicOMH
web: www.musicomh.com
info: Features, interviews and reviews of albums, singles, gigs and music DVDs, together with music videos and downloads, film, theatre and cultural content from this London-based website. To get reviewed submit your details via the online form.

Musicroom
email: via website
web: www.musicroom.com
info: Online shop selling sheet music, songbooks, music software, instructional DVDs and videos, as well as a selection of instruments and accessories.

Muso's Guide
email: info@musosguide.com
web: www.musosguide.com
info: This site is supportive of new, unsigned and lesser-known acts. The Videodrome page features audio and video streams of new music from established, emerging and unsigned acts. Reviews of new music and artists, as well as 'The Unsigned Directory' which features tips on getting started, profiles of fresh talent, interviews with artists and industry professionals, links to other interesting sites. Also includes a database of label websites, gig guides and competitions.

Musoswire Networks
PO Box 100, Gainsborough, Lincolnshire, DN21 3XH
tel: 01427 628 826
email: info@musoswire.net
web: www.musoswire.net
info: A network of websites whose aim is to provide independent musicians with the services and support necessary to promote their music such as help with recording an album or EP, artwork design, duplication, distribution and promotion.

Muzikvoice

32 Wareham House, Brompton Pool Road, Hall Green, Birmingham, B28 0SL

tel:	0121 474 5228
email:	steve@muzikvoice.com
web:	www.muzikvoice.com
contact:	Steve Page
info:	Music promotion for unsigned bands offering free basic starter account, allowing musicians to upload tracks and gig listings, as well as sell their music and tickets over the site. To sign up complete online registration form.

MVine Ltd.

82 Chestnut Grove, New Malden, Surrey, KT3 3JS

tel:	0845 890 0521
email:	info@mvine.com
web:	www.mvine.com
contact:	Kerry Harvey-Piper
info:	Independent label with web-based virtual venue for original unsigned artists. Upload 3 songs for public A&R, receive feedback from the audience, expand your fan base and sell your tracks as downloads (proceeds are split 50/50). On the basis of audience approval, you may progress through to becoming a Featured Artist and a potential signing to the label. Visit the website for full details of all free services for artists.

Mxtabs.net

web:	www.mxtabs.net
info:	Directory of tabs for guitar, bass and drums. Website also includes forum and CD review section.

My Music Job

email:	Use online contact form
web:	www.mymusicjob.com
info:	Website created to provide assistance to people making their living in the music industry. All employers can post their music related jobs for free.

MyCokeMusic

web:	www.mycokemusic.com
info:	Legal music downloads. Search by artist or by song.

MySpace.com

web:	www.myspace.com
info:	Unsigned bands and artists can create their own profile page where they can post biog, gig listings and upload tracks.

N:Live Radio

email:	submissions@nlive.co.uk
web:	www.nlive.co.uk
info:	N:Live is a station for unsigned and underground bands, musicians and DJs. It also supports the many emerging and established small record labels. Send an email to above address if you would like your music played on the station.

Napster

web:	www.napster.co.uk
info:	Download music service with access to over 750,000 tracks from huge array of artists of all genres available for a monthly subscription fee.

National Gig Guide

web:	www.nationalgigguide.com
info:	Comprehensive guide for all music events in the UK. Add your band or venue details for free. Also information on single, album and demo releases, as well as musician's classified ads.

Native Instruments

email:	Register online using the contact form.
web:	www.nativeinstruments.com
info:	Native Instruments manufacture audio software including plug-in Synths, samplers and virtual instruments. The site contains product information, downloads, upgrades, FAQs and technical support contacts. User forums and library are featured in the Community section.

Nemo

email:	info@nemoboston.com
web:	www.nemoboston.com
info:	2 day festival and music conference held annually in Boston, USA. See website for details of performers, panellists and exhibitors.

Neon Plague

tel:	01932 821 082
email:	info@neonplague.co.uk
web:	www.neonplague.co.uk
info:	Viral marketing for your music event via interactive flyers. Check website for details of various packages available.

Ness MP3

email:	Contact via website
web:	www.nessmp3.com
info:	Bands and artists can host their music, promote themselves via online artist pages, and airplay on free internet radio station, Ness MP3.

New Deal For Musicians

tel:	0845 606 2626
web:	www.newdeal.gov.uk/musicians
info:	New Deal for Musicians is available to people of all ages on certain New Deals wanting to make a career as a musician. New Deal for Musicians covers all types of music for instrumentalists, vocalists, composers and songwriters, as well as performing DJs. Contact the above number for further information and to see if you qualify.

New Found Sounds

web:	www.newfoundsounds.co.uk
info:	Site dedicated to the diverse music scene for the North East. Up to date gig, club and event listings. Submit your demos and gig details for review.

New Strings

email:	sales@newstrings.co.uk
web:	www.newstrings.co.uk
info:	Mail order for Acoustic and electric guitar and bass strings, as well as guitar picks and other accessories.

New-Noise.net

web:	www.new-noise.net
info:	Music website featuring reviews, downloads and video streams for artists and bands from the UK and beyond.

NIDJ

email:	Via website
web:	www.nidj.com
info:	Website for all DJs based in Northern Ireland to create their own profile, whether club, mobile or radio. The purpose of the site is to help local DJs promote themselves for bookings across the internet.

Nightshift

web:	http://nightshift.oxfordmusic.net/
info:	Message boards for discussion of local music in Oxford.

No Ordinary Music

email:	team@no-ordinarymusic.com
web:	www.no-ordinarymusic.com
info:	Website dedicated to the Alternative music scene with an emphasis on UK bands. Includes reviews and 'Upcoming Talent' section.

No Ripcord

email:	mail@noripcord.com
web:	www.noripcord.com
info:	This UK based website specialises in independent music. Submit reviews to the email address above.

NoiseHub.com

email:	Via website
web:	www.noisehub.com
info:	Artist A-Z directory, venue guides, information about charts and new releases. Section dedicated to new, upcoming bands. Submit your own reviews to the website.

NorfolkGigs

web:	www.norfolkgigs.co.uk
info:	Definitive guide to gigs, live music, bands and promotion in East Anglia. Submit your band or venue details via the online form.

NoRipcord.com

email:	mail@noripcord.com
web:	www.noripcord.com
info:	Webzine devoted to Indie music and film. News, reviews and features covering the latest releases.

Norman Records

Unit 1, Armley Park Court, Stanningley Road, Leeds, LS12 2AE

email:	phil@normanrecords.com
web:	www.normanrecords.com
info:	Mail order Indie, Electronic and Alternative music.

North By North East

email:	info@nxne.com
web:	www.nxne.com
info:	Held annually in Toronto, North By North East is a conference and festival for both the music and film industries. See the above website for further information about becoming involved with the event.

North East Music

email:	info@northeastmusic.co.uk
web:	www.northeastmusic.co.uk
info:	Information for bands and musicians in the North East of England. Gig listings, plus details of bands, studios and venues in the area. Also includes Musicians Wanted section, as well as reviews and interviews.

Northampton Bands
email: webmaster@northamptonbands.co.uk
web: www.northamptonbands.co.uk
info: Resource for artists and bands based in Northampton. Up to date news, gig listings and classifieds plus band and venue information.

NorthBands.co.uk
email: admin@northbands.co.uk
web: www.northbands.co.uk
info: North East bands webzine was created as a place to listen to local talent. Bands can create their own profile and upload tracks. Run online band chart for the most played songs.

NorthwestBands.co.uk
email: info@northwestbands.co.uk
web: www.northwestbands.co.uk
info: Provides a comprehensive gig listing service for bands and venues based in the North West. Submit details using the forms online.

Norwich Darkside
web: www.norwichdarkside.co.uk
info: Site covering local bands, music and gigs in Norwich. Once registered, bands can submit their details to the local band directory, upload videos, MP3s and photos, and contribute to the website by reviewing gigs or demos.

Norwich Gigs
email: mail@norwichgigs.co.uk
web: www.norwichgigs.co.uk
info: Website dedicated to band news and gigs in the Norwich area. Contains reviews, interviews and photos.

Nosher
email: Via website
web: www.nosher.co.uk
info: Website devoted to unsigned talent from Norwich. Bands from the area can promote themselves for free on the site. Site also features gig listings and reviews.

NotSoUnknown
4 Cowpark Terrace, Northam, Bideford, Devon, EX39 1EG
tel: 0870 286 1579
email: simon@notsounknown.co.uk
web: www.notsounknown.co.uk
info: MP3 download site for unsigned Alternative bands across the UK.

NUS
Nelson Mandela House, 461 Holloway Road, London, N7 6LJ
tel: 020 7272 8900
fax: 020 7263 5713
email: nusuk@nus.org.uk
web: www.nusonline.co.uk
info: Comprehensive regional guide for students. Offers advice on careers, drugs, disabilities, education, housing, money, sex and many other topics. Includes a campaign update and offers links to student discounts.

Off The Wall Online Music Promotion
8 Waldon Road, Macclesfield, Cheshire, SK11 7UQ
tel: 07815 078 311
email: info@otwonline.com
web: www.otwonline.com
contact: Christian D'Acuna, Kara James
info: OTW specialise in online promotion for both signed and unsigned artists. Can create and maintain a heavy online presence for any band by submitting your tracks to music sites, e-zines and blogs. Also create specific online campaigns for tours, gigs and releases. Phone or email for more information on the service and rates. Alternatively, check the website for details.

The Official Charts
4th Floor, 58/59 Great Marlborough Street, London, W1F 7JY
tel: 020 7478 8500
fax: 020 7478 8519
email: info@theofficialcharts.com
web: www.theofficialcharts.com
info: Provides a wide range of information about the national UK charts. Record companies can obtain fast, accurate information about how their artists are performing within hours of shops closing.

On The Case Music
email: jem@onthecasemusic.freeserve.co.uk
web: www.onthecasemusic.com
contact: Jem
info: On The Case Music provides an gig listings and advertising service for festivals, pubs, venues and bands in North East England.

On The Rocks
tel: 07811 449 529
email: matt@onthe-rocks.co.uk
web: www.onthe-rocks.co.uk
info: Community for people to write about music and entertainment. Always looking for new writers from all over the world, anyone is welcome to get involved. If you would like to contribute to the website, email the above address.

Onelouder Radio
89 Romanby Road, Northallerton, North Yorkshire, DL7 8FH
email: via online form
web: www.onelouderradio.co.uk
info: Internet station for unsigned artists. If you would like your material played send links to MP3s via the online submission form or, alternatively post demos to the above address.

Online Guitar Archive
email: questions@olga.net
web: www.olga.net
info: Complete online guitarists' resource. Guitar tab archive with over 20,000 songs. Lessons on technique and reading tablature. Chord dictionary. Articles on amps, customising, effects, pickups and sound effects. Users can submit tabs online.

Overplay
PO Box 11188, Sutton Coldfield, B76 1WX
tel: 0870 112 1382
email: service@overplay.co.uk
web: www.overplay.co.uk
info: Website dedicated to the development and exposure of unsigned bands. It aims to put unsigned bands on the map by giving them a platform to be seen and heard. The site aims to keep you in touch with like-minded bands and also offers the opportunity to sell your music online. Extensive directory available on website detailing venues, promoters, labels and musical services.

Overwater Basses
Atlas Works, Nelson Street, Carlisle, CA2 5ND
tel: 01228 590 591
fax: 01228 590 597
email: Use online contact form
web: www.overwaterbasses.com
info: Company website for Overwater, specialists in bass guitars. Includes custom design, construction, accessories, books and more.

Oxford Bands
email: See contact list on website
web: www.oxfordbands.com
info: Online music community for Oxfordshire. Band directory, reviews, features, gig listings and forum. Oxford Bands welcome reviews of live gigs and demos. Website also contains information for bands such as venue guide and local contacts list. Oxford Bands also promote their own unsigned nights.

Oxford Music
web: www.oxfordmusic.info
info: Local gig listings. Live, release and demo reviews. Useful online contact information for rehearsal and recording facilities, venues and record labels.

Oxford Underground
web: www.uoxford.com
info: Devoted to underground music and arts in Oxford. Submit your profile and audio files. Site also contains useful links directory for creative services in the vicinity.

Panhandle
email: heather@panhandle.co.uk
web: www.panhandle.co.uk
info: Forum for all kinds of artistic expression, not just music. Smaller acts can raise their profiles and network on a grander scale whilst larger acts can gain from the extra publicity. Submit news, listings, reviews, features, artwork and poetry for inclusion on the website. Contact the above email address.

Paper-Jam
email: Via website
web: www.paper-jam.co.uk
info: Music features and news plus gig, track and album reviews.

Peoplesound
20 Orange Street, London, WC2H 7NN
email: Via website
web: www.peoplesound.com
info: New music from signed and unsigned bands across all genres. Artists' pages include profiles and music tracks. Users can post reviews online.

Pineapster
Cuttlefish Digital Arts, Devonshire House, Devonshire Square, Loughborough, LE11 3DW
email: pineapster@cuttlefish.com
web: www.pineapster.co.uk
info: Online community for music makers in the East Midlands. Offers free self-managed web page with MP3 and video downloads. Site also features forum, gig guide and online radio station. Demos can be submitted to the above address.

Pitchfork
email: mail@pitchforkmedia.com
web: www.pitchforkmedia.com
info: US based music webzine with new music, recent reviews, features archive, release dates and breaking news.

Planet Loud
web: www.planet-loud.com
info: Audio and video streams, interviews, reviews, club and gig listings, as well as discussion forum.

The Plastic Ashtray
33 Junction Road, Stourbridge, West Midlands, DY8 1JU
email: theplasticashtray_info@yahoo.co.uk
web: www.theplasticashtray.tk
info: Independent music webzine created and maintained by music lovers. The Ashtray supports unsigned bands right up to major label talent.

Playing Out Loud
45 Roseland Gardens, Highfield, Southampton, SO17 1QG
email: reviews@playingoutloud.co.uk
web: www.playingoutloud.co.uk
contact: Peter Ashton
info: Music website for the South featuring gig guide, reviews and articles. Send your demo or press pack for review to the above address. If you wish to submit your own review, contact the above email address.

Playlouder
web: www.playlouder.com
info: Music website encompassing downloads, online radio, reviews and interviews, MP3 shop and live listings.

PlayRecord.net
web: www.playrecord.net
info: UK online musical store selling instruments, sound recording equipment and accessories.

Pogo Entertainment
tel: 0870 766 2446
email: via website
web: www.pogoentertainment.com
info: Promotional tool for unsigned bands and musicians. Sign up and you will receive 5 page website with MP3 player and online shop. Pogo Entertainment also offer duplication and T-shirt printing services. See listings in relevant sections for details.

Pontemusic
web: www.pontemusic.tk
info: Forums for Pontefract music. Post details of gigs, bands news, classifieds and your MP3s.

Pop Matters
web: www.popmatters.com
info: International magazine of cultural criticism. The scope is broad and covers most cultural products including music, television, films, books, video games, computer software, theatre, visual arts and the internet.

Popjustice
email: mail@popjustice.co.uk
web: www.popjustice.co.uk
info: Website devoted to Pop music with information about artists, charts, releases and news updates.

Popkomm
web: www.popkomm.de
info: Popkomm is the business platform for music and entertainment, attended by trade visitors and exhibitors from all over the world. The event is held in September each year in Berlin. See website for information on how to register for next years convention.

Post Everything
web: www.posteverything.com
info: Mail order website created to assist independent labels and artists of all genres. To send on your material, firstly refer to demo submission details on the website.

Power Tab Archive
web: www.powertabs.net
info: Large tablature archive, with specialist section including Classical guitar, movie and TV themes.

Pro-Music
web: www.pro-music.org/
info: Select your country and link to legal download websites from across the world.

Punk & Oi in the UK
email: rebecca@punkoiuk.co.uk
web: www.punkoiuk.co.uk
info: Information on the current Punk and Oi scene in the UK. Features links to bands, clothing, record labels, specialist websites, gigs, merchandise and mailing lists.

Punk In Scotland
email: punkinscotland@hotmail.com
web: www.punkinscotland.co.uk
info: Band and gig details covering the Punk scene in Scotland. Site also features interviews, reviews, photos and competitions.

Punknews.org
web: www.punknews.org
info: A hive of information for all things Punk. Contains release schedules, interviews, gigs, tours, an international spotlight and downloadable MP3s.

Punktastic
email: paul@punktastic.com
web: www.punktastic.com
info: Highly popular UK Punk website. Includes daily news, reviews, interviews and a thriving forum for music discussion.

Punky Hosting
email: via website
web: www.punkyhosting.com
info: Hosting company offering no-nonsense packages for band websites.

Purevolume
email: via online form
web: www.purevolume.com
info: US based music website for independent labels and unsigned artists to upload their music.

QT Radio
116 Tib Street, Northern Quarter, Manchester, M4 1LR
tel: 0161 839 9067
email: qtradio@hotmail.co.uk
web: www.superchannel.org
contact: steve
info: Internet radio station which broadcasts unsigned bands and musicians. Send demos to the above address.

R Labels
email: contact2@rlabels.com
web: www.rlabels.com
info: An international database of record label web pages with more than 5000 links. Search for label by genre or country.

Radio Gets Wild
17 London Road, King's Lynn, Norfolk, PE30 5PY
tel: 07796 565 918
email: tim@radiogetswild.com
web: www.radiogetswild.com
info: Online station with airplay for unsigned artists. Demos are welcome, send to the above address.

Radio2XS
email: Via website
web: www.radio2xs.com
info: Online Alternative radio station playing a mix of genres and styles. Also includes features, reviews, press cuttings, links, programme schedules, playlist information and competitions. Will play tracks from unsigned bands and artists.

The Raft
email: theraft@vmg.co.uk
web: www.the-raft.com
info: Website dedicated to the music and artists of all genres linked to Virgin Records. Watch and listen to tracks and videos online.

Rainsound
email: Via website
web: www.rainsound.net
info: Webzine for Scottish bands. News, reviews, stories and interviews.

Rate My Band
email: Use online contact form
web: www.ratemyband.co.uk
info: This site allows its visitors to rate tracks by unsigned bands. Register with the site and upload your demos and photographs.

Record Of The Day
PO Box 49554, London, E17 9WB
tel: 020 8520 2130
email: info@recordoftheday.com
web: www.recordoftheday.com
info: Up to date music and media news in a weekly magazine and a daily newsletter. There is a subscription for the newsletter at a monthly or yearly rate. Offers a 2 week free trial.

Record Scout
web: www.recordscout.com
info: Online directory for artists of all genres. Registration is free. Upload your MP3s for review. Record Scout list their Top 10 bands from the demos they receive.

RecordProduction.com
web: www.recordproduction.com
info: Website containing hundreds of streamed videos that can help you find the right producer, engineer and studio for your project.

Resident Advisor
web: www.residentadvisor.net
info: Independent source of information relating to the global Dance music scene. Features up to the minute news, vinyl and CD reviews, interviews with leading and emerging artists, event coverage and an online community.

Retford Music
email: band@retfordmusic.co.uk
web: www.retfordmusic.co.uk
info: Created for and run by musicians in Retford and the North Nottinghamshire region. Useful resources area with links for local music-related businesses. Submit your band or venue details using the email address above. Well used message board.

Revolution
The Northern Echo, PO Box 14, Priestgate, Darlington, DL1 1NF
email: revolution@nne.co.uk
web: www.thisisrevolution.co.uk
info: Comprehensive website for all things musical in the North East. Gig guide covering all genres of music, unsigned band profiles, features, reviews, forum and music industry advice. Area of site called 'Ones 2 Watch' which highlights the most talented artists from across the region. To be featured send demo, biog and good quality photos by email or post to details above for consideration.

Rhythm & Booze
32 Barnes Way, Worcester, WR5 3AP
email: see contact list on website
web: www.rhythmandbooze.net
info: Music webzine featuring news, reviews and features. Unsigned artist MP3 and media downloads. Site also contains useful venue list for Nottingham. Send your demos to the above address.

Rhythm Online
email: mick@rhythmonline.co.uk
web: www.rhythmonline.co.uk
info: Specialists in Alternative, rare and independent label music. Extensive catalogue listings of tracks, artists and labels.

Rock Beast
web: www.rockbeast.com
info: Site devoted to Rock music featuring CD reviews, interviews and news updates.

Rock Matrix
email: via website
web: www.rockmatrix.co.uk
info: Rock promotion website. Submit your band and gig details using the online forms. Site also features online shop and forums.

Rock Midgets
email: Use online contact form
web: www.rockmidgets.com
info: Rock and Alternative e-zine featuring new releases and live reviews, interviews, features and competitions. New bands showcased via the site radio, videos and MP3s, news and gig listings, plus more coverage of Hardcore, Metal, Punk and Emo.

Rock Pulse
email: editor@rockpulse.co.uk
web: www.rockpulse.co.uk
info: Webzine with area of the site dedicated to unsigned bands. Email details of your band to the above address. Also contact this address if you would like your material to be reviewed on the website.

Rock Review
email: See website for list of contacts
web: www.rockreview.co.uk
info: Website dedicated to the world of Rock and Metal.

Rock The Shires
web: www.rocktheshires.co.uk
info: Music webzine for Rock fans throughout Bedfordshire, Buckinghamshire, Oxfordshire, Hertfordshire and Milton Keynes. Registered users can post news, and band profiles, chat live on the forum and vote in online polls.

Rock3 Radio Network
email: info@rock3.co.uk
web: www.rock3.co.uk
info: Rock3 Radio Network is a collection of Rock internet radio stations that specialise in promoting new talent. Email your band details to the above address.

Rockfeedback.com
web: www.rockfeedback.com
info: Webzine focusing on new music. Features include Bandwatch, unsigned demo reviews and MP3 streaming. To submit information about your band, or to send an article or review for the site, use the online forms.

Room Thirteen
email: enquiries@roomthirteen.com
web: www.roomthirteen.com
info: Webzine dedicated to the Alternative scene with unsigned coverage. Daily updates regarding bands, CDs, tours, festivals, news and competitions.

RU Thinking About It?
tel: 0800 282 930
web: www.ruthinking.co.uk
info: Information resource for sexual health and specialist information for male and female queries, with features on emergency help, relationships and advice.

Rusty Snails
web: www.rustysnails.com
info: Online tool for tracking down rare and deleted tracks from wide variety of genres including Hip-Hop, Drum&Bass, Breakbeat, Dance and Jungle.

Saggy Pants
email: glynn@saggy-pants.com
web: www.saggy-pants.com
info: Saggy Pants is run by music fans in the Nottingham area and features news and reviews relating to the local scene. Artist page where band logos and links can be submitted. To do so, send your details to the above email address.

Save or Delete
email: info@uk.greenpeace.org
web: www.saveordelete.com
info: Site run by Greenpeace to increase awareness of the plight of the world's ancient forests. Information on how to get involved in the Save or Delete campaign and facts and figures on the diversity and destruction of our forest environments.

Scarborough Music Scene
web: www.scarboroughmusic.tk
info: Website for bands and musicians local to Scarborough, North Yorkshire. Gig and event listings, forum and venue details.

Scottish Bands
email: via website
web: www.scottishbands.co.uk
info: Directory aimed at bands looking for venues, rehearsal or recording studios, PA hire, music shops and promoters in every town and city throughout Scotland. Also offer online promotion for Scottish bands by providing 7 page website including email address, biog, gig listings and area to upload tracks.

Scottish Music Centre
email: info@scottishmusiccentre.com
web: www.scottishmusiccentre.com
info: The Scottish Music Centre maintains comprehensive directories, including a contact database of contributors towards music making in Scotland. Other directories include concert and event listings, and music publications including sheet music, recordings and books.

Scottish Music Network
email: Via website
web: www.scottishmusicnetwork.co.uk
info: Features music news, articles and discussion forum.

Scottish Underground Directory Service (SUDS)
email: info@sudsonline.co.uk
web: www.sudsonline.co.uk
info: Online resource for anyone interested or involved with the Scottish underground music scene. Search for studio, venue, merchandise, label, radio and press contacts.

Scottish Unsigned
email: Via website
web: www.scottishunsigned.com
info: Online promotion for unsigned bands in Scotland. Submit your details to the website and post gig dates.

Screaming Tarts
email: info@screamingtarts.com
web: www.screamingtarts.com
info: Music portal featuring interviews, reviews and discussion forum.

Sheffield Music Hub
email: Via online form
web: www.sheffieldmusic.com
info: If you are in a Sheffield band, or provide a music-related service, submit your details to Sheffield Music Hub. Site also includes reviews and message board.

Shetland Music Development
email: david.gardner@shetland-arts-trust.co.uk
web: www.shetland-music.com
info: Download and purchase music from Shetland bands and performers. Online contact directory for local musical services.

Shock Online
web: www.shockonline.net
info: Rock and Metal webzine featuring band information, interviews, downloads and photos.

Signet Music
tel: 0800 542 1566
email: via online form
web: www.signetmusic.com
info: Online store supplying musical instruments, accessories, DJ equipment and studio gear.

Silent Industry
email: via online form
web: www.silentindustry.com
info: Online agency for musicians, dancers, actors and models. Information about castings, auditions, jobs and parties.

Skye Live
email: bands@skyelive.com
web: www.skyelive.com
info: Celtic music gig guide for the Isle of Skye. Sort by type of music or by band. Submit listings to above email address.

Smash Music
email: info@smashmusic.co.uk
web: www.smashmusic.co.uk
info: Devoted to new music, Smash Music provides live and CD reviews and interviews. Sign up to the website to receive news updates.

The Smoking Gun
web: www.thesmokinggun.com
info: Great trivia site including obscure and outlandish rider and backstage requirements, trivia competitions, archived news stories and more.

Snickers Unsigned
web: www.snickersunsigned.co.uk
info: Bands can enter the Snickers Unsigned contest, and have a chance of winning the opportunity to headline the Snickers stage at Download Festival. See website for terms and conditions.

Solarise Records
email: info@solariserecords.com
web: www.solariserecords.com
info: Independent resource which showcases, promotes and distributes music of all genres by signed and unsigned artists. Refer to website for details of joining up.

Sold On Song
web: www.bbc.co.uk/radio2/soldonsong/
info: Part of the BBC Radio 2 website, dedicated to the art of songwriting. Search by genre, artist or song title. Songwriting guides, advice and tips available.

Songfacts
email: feedback@songfacts.com
web: www.songfacts.com
info: Database of song information compiled by radio professionals, music enthusiasts and visitors to the website. They provide the album title, year songs were released, highest US and UK chart position and "Songfacts" about each record.

Sonic Garden
email: info@sonicgarden.com
web: www.sonicgarden.com
info: A US based artist community website for independent artists and labels. Maintain an artist page on the website to receive a whole range of free tools and resources.

Sonictown
email: Via online form
web: www.sonictown.co.uk
info: Website bringing together the best original music in Newark. Dedicated band page and resource section. Register as a member to upload your details.

Sound Control
email: info@soundcontrol.co.uk
web: www.soundcontrol.co.uk
info: As the largest music equipment retailer in Europe with 25 stores across the UK, Sound Control has the most extensive range of guitars, basses, backline, PA, hi-tech, recording and percussion equipment available at the lowest prices around. Coupled with over 25 years experience and unrivalled staff training, shopping at Sound Control is the easiest step you will make on the road to being signed. Visit the above website to locate your nearest store, or to buy online and have your purchase delivered direct to your door.

Sound Generator
email: mail@soundgenerator.com
web: www.soundgenerator.com
info: Music information site including news, reviews, streamed music videos, as well as many other features. Also contains extensive directory listings useful for anyone involved in the music industry or with a serious interest in music.

Sound It Out
The Arch, Unit G9, 48-52 Floodgate Street, Birmingham, B5 5SL
tel: 0121 773 7322
fax: 0121 773 1117
email: enquiries@sounditout.co.uk
web: www.sounditout.co.uk
info: Sound It Out employs professional musicians with skills in all genres of music to work with people with any level of musical experience (or none at all) to create and perform music throughout Birmingham and the region.

Sound@45rpm
email: soundat45rpm@hotmail.com
web: www.soundat45rpm.i12.com
info: A non-for-profit organisation which offers a free hosting site for unsigned bands to design and create their own websites. Email files for uploading to above address.

Soundaloud
email: webmaster@soundaloud.com
web: www.soundaloud.com
info: Sheffield musicians and bands can register to Soundaloud for free and upload their details. Site features include 'MP3 of the Month' competition, gig listings, details of new releases, and links to local venues and studios.

Soundengineer.co.uk
email: general@soundengineer.co.uk
web: www.soundengineer.co.uk
info: Contains links to manufacturers' technical information, audio professionals' CVs, lighting links, a 'For Sale' board with classified advertisements, manufacturers' manuals, as well as templates for mixing desk control surfaces.

SoundsMusical
tel: 01992 716 000
email: Via website
web: www.soundsmusical.com
info: Search, review, compare and buy instruments at Soundsmusical. Large selection of musical instruments and music accessories.

SoundsXP
30 Somerville Road, London, SE20 7NA
web: www.soundsxp.com
info: Alternative music webzine. Review unsigned demos, plus albums, singles and gigs. Submit your material to the above address.

The Source
email: arts@leeds.gov.uk
web: lcc.wisshost.co.uk/theSource/
info: Advice service for Leeds musicians. The online resource guide provides a comprehensive directory of local music-related companies, services and contacts, as well as advice and information relating to all aspects of the music industry.

South By Southwest
web: www.sxsw.com
info: Large annual music convention in Austin, Texas. Established for 20 years, the event attracts music industry professionals, bands, musicians and music fans from all over the world. See website for information about past conventions, and details of registering for the next one.

South Coast HQ
web: www.southcoasthq.co.uk
info: Forum devoted to the DIY Punk scene based on the South Coast of England. Post details of upcoming gigs online.

South Wales Massive
web: www.southwalesmassive.com
info: Portal for discussion forums in South Wales, including boards dedicated to music and related projects, as well as gigs.

South West Demos
PO Box 219, Plymouth, PL5 3WU
email: info@southwestdemos.com
web: www.southwestdemos.com
info: This website aims to promote some of the many talented unsigned musicians from Cornwall, Devon, Dorset, Somerset and the Channel Islands. Bands and artists can create their own page within the South West Demos site. Demos can also be forwarded for review to the above address.

South West Gig Guide
email: editor@lemonrock.com
web: www.lemonrock.com
info: Interactive music and gig guide. Section for band and artist profiles, classified ads, as well as venue information for the region. Upload MP3s to the site, or submit your own review.

Southscene
email: mail@southscene.freeserve.co.uk
web: www.southscene.net
info: Local music webzine for Southampton, Bournemouth, Brighton, Portsmouth and surrounding areas. Contains listings, news, reviews, classified ads, as well as useful music directory covering the area. To include any gig, band or other music related details on the site, contact via the above email address.

StageAccess.com
email: enquiries@stageaccess.com
web: www.stageaccess.com
info: StageAccess.com is an online resource aimed at all individuals and companies in the entertainment industry, providing a networking solution for the entertainment community. Register your details free of charge.

Starland
web: www.starland.co.uk
info: Online instrument store with extensive range of stock. Follow link on website to educational division of Starland which serves the needs of music teachers and educational professionals.

Starpolish
email: info@starpolish.com
web: www.starpolish.com
info: Contains invaluable information on everything you will need to know about the music industry. Includes insider tips, reviews, features, columns, community resources, news and artist services.

Steinberg
email: info@steinberg.net
web: www.steinberg.de
info: German based site of the manufacturers of Cubase software. Detailed product information available, as well as facility to buy products online. Services section contains tips on how to get the most from your software and an extensive samples library.

The Stereo Effect
web: www.thestereoeffect.com
info: TheStereoEffect is a fully independent music site with reviews, news, interviews and features about new music.

Stoke Gothic
email: via website
web: www.stokegothic.co.uk
info: Online community with gigs, reviews, band pages and forum for the Gothic scene based in Stoke.

Stoke Rock Scene
email: Via website
web: www.stokerockscene.co.uk
info: Register to take advantage of A to Z unsigned band listings, as well as video and MP3 downloads. Forum, gig dates, reviews and articles also available on the site.

Strings 4 Pleasure
1 Edingale Court, Bramcote, Nottingham, NG9 3LY
tel: 0870 754 1770
email: info@strings4pleasure.co.uk
web: www.strings4pleasure.co.uk
info: Strings4Pleasure deals exclusively in strings and related accessories for musical instruments including violin, viola, cello, double bass, acoustic guitar, electric guitar, bass guitar, classical guitar, banjo, tenor banjo, ukulele, bouzouki, mandolin and mandola.

Student Bands
email: broshnat@hotmail.com
web: www.studentbands.co.uk
contact: Bretski
info: Source for unsigned talent in the UK. Create band profiles on the site. Online chart of most downloaded tracks.

Subba Cultcha
47 Trinity Road, Wimbledon, London, SW19 8QS
tel: 07843 392 255
email: jeremy@subba-cultcha.com
web: www.subba-cultcha.com
contact: Jeremy Chick
info: Reviews albums, singles, demos and gigs. Lots of other interesting stuff including comical guest reviewers.

Subedition
email: roar@subedition.co.uk
web: www.subedition.co.uk
info: Online t-shirt community. Submit t-shirt designs and let others rate them. Highly rated designs will be printed. 10% profit goes to the designer. Will do special competitions for bands.

Suburban Sound Initiative
email: team@doncastermusic.org.uk
web: www.doncastermusic.org.uk
info: Local band profiles, gig listings and reviews for Doncaster and the surrounding area.

Surge Music
email: via website
web: www.surgemusic.co.uk
info: Music guide for Birmingham and the Black Country. Useful online directory of artists, venues, studios and music shops.

Taborama
email: Via website
web: www.taborama.com
info: Source for tabs and lyrics. Browse through archives for guitar, bass, drum, keyboard and power tabs. Also feature an unsigned band monthly on the site.

Talk Bass
web: www.talkbass.com
info: Website for bass players featuring gear reviews, articles, lessons, online store and forum.

Talk To Frank
tel: 0800 776 600
email: frank@talktofrank.com
web: www.talktofrank.com
info: Free confidential drugs information and advice available 24 hours a day. Calls from landlines are free and will not show up on the phone bill. In addition to comprehensive drug directory, there are also search facilities to guide you to your local advice centres for both children and adults.

Tasty Fanzine
email: info@tastyfanzine.org.uk
web: www.tastyfanzine.org.uk
info: Online magazine based in Leeds and Nottingham. Tasty strives to cover a wide range of music irrelevant of genre, as honestly as possible. To submit a demo, please contact Tasty Fanzine via the email address above.

Telford Rocks
email: submissions@telfordrocks.co.uk
web: www.telfordrocks.co.uk
info: Website devoted to Telford and its growing music scene. Bands can post their photo, biog, contact details and links to web page and MP3 tracks using the above email address.

Ten Feet Tall
web: www.tenfeettall.co.uk
info: Online magazine covering Rock 'n' Roll and art. Listings, reviews, merchandise and forums.

This Day In Music
email: editor@thisdayinmusic.com
web: www.thisdayinmusic.com
info: Music archive with details of artists' birthdays, charts, awards and more, all searchable by date. Users can find out who was at Number 1 in the Singles chart on the day they were born and what artists they share their birthday with. Chart facts, music related jokes and lots of music trivia.

This Is Ull
Suite 2, 161 High Street, Hull, HU1 1NQ
tel: 01482 329 451
email: See online contact list
web: www.thisisull.com
info: Website devoted to the Hull music scene, featuring band index, reviews of new releases and live gigs.

Thumped
web: www.thumped.com
info: Music portal covering both Northern and Republic of Ireland. Gig and event listings, news, discussion forum and reviews. Listen to tracks and view videos of local acts.

Ticket Web
tel: 08700 600 100
web: www.ticketweb.co.uk
info: Browse listings and buy gig tickets online .

Tiger Sushi
email: contact@tigersushi.com
web: www.tigersushi.com
info: Quirky online portal dedicated to a variety of musical genres. Includes a dealer page, downloadable songs, music news, site forum, discovery section, newsletters, radio and video links.

Top 40 Charts
web: www.top40-charts.com
info: Ultimate source for music news and charts from around the world, including album, single, ringtone and download sales.

Totally Radio
email: Via website
web: www.totallyradio.com
info: Internet streamed radio featuring shows of all genres. Listen to archived shows and sign up for playlist details and weekly newsletter.

Traffic
web: wwwtrafficonline.net
info: Traffic Online builds, maintains and coordinates street teams in the UK for bands and record labels, as well as for a whole host of other projects. If you would like to further information about joining a team visit the website.

Trust The DJ
White Horse Yard, 78 Liverpool Road, London, N1 0QD
tel: 020 7288 9814
fax: 020 7288 9817
email: contact@trustthedj.com
web: www.trustthedj.com
info: Specialist site for DJs including news, books, tickets, merchandise and musical equipment.

Tunetrader
web: www.tunetrader.com
info: Fresh, new, independent and unsigned music from a variety of talented artists. Create an account on the site to purchase or license tracks.

Tunetribe
web: www.tunetribe.com
info: Music download site for independent artists, labels and unsigned bands.

Tyne & Wear Music Scene
web: www.freewebs.com/tyneandwearmusicscene/
info: Guide to bands and gigs in the Newcastle and Sunderland areas. Bands can submit links to their websites.

UK Bands
email: Via website
web: www.ukbands.net
info: Large unsigned band database, searchable by name, genre and city. Individual band pages can contain biographies, photographs, contact details, MP3s, website links and gig listings. Live reviews, news and UK Gig Guide. Bands can post advertisements and announcements on the forum message board.

The UK Copyright Service
email: Via website
web: www.copyrightservice.co.uk
info: Provides copyright registration for original works by writers, musicians, artists, designers, software providers, authors, companies, organisations and individuals. Offer secured back up and archive management for your work, meaning there will always be evidence to support you in any future disputes. For further information and registration details, refer to the website.

UK Guitars
email: enquiries@ukguitars.com
web: www.ukguitars.com
info: Website features great offers on guitars and accessories, as well as tuition books, software and sheet music. Also includes profiles of well known guitarists, as well as forums, interviews, reviews and competitions.

UK Mix
email: webmaster@ukmix.net
web: www.ukmix.org
info: Over 2,500 music related links, including artist sites, music resources and news and media. Reviews, features and interviews.

The UK Songwriting Contest
web: www.songwritingcontest.co.uk
info: UK competition held annually. Each year many finalists and winners are featured on national and international radio, TV and press and are offered recording, management and publishing deals. See website for terms and conditions.

ukhh.com
email: info@ukhh.com
web: www.ukhh.com
info: Hip-hop webzine with news, reviews and features. Listen to tracks online.

UKMIX
email: via website
web: www.ukmix.org
info: Website run entirely by fans, covering the UK music scene. Links directory to artist websites, reviews, forums and articles.

Ultimate Band List
email: See website for list of contacts
web: www.ubl.com
info: US based site with extensive links to music related websites. Search for artists by genre, year or alphabetically. Free MP3 downloads. View music videos online. Album and record label databases plus music guide by genre.

Ultimate Guitar
web: www.ultimate-guitar.com
info: Tabs and lessons plus reviews and columns. Visitors to the site can also submit their own tabs, articles or reviews.

Under The Radar
web: www.undertheradarmag.com
info: Website for music based US magazine containing lots of news, features, reviews, photos and more. Plenty of UK bands and artists featured.

Underground Scene
email: forums@undergroundscene.co.uk
web: www.undergroundscene.co.uk
info: Online community for Underground British music. WAP-enabled for mobile phone users.

Unsigned Band Aid
email: via website
web: www.unsignedbandaid.co.uk
info: The aim of Unsigned Band Aid is to encourage people to download MP3s free of charge from the website, and donate the money they would have spent purchasing the songs elsewhere to a charity of their choice. For further information, visit the website.

Unsigned Band Web
email: via online form
web: www.unsignedbandweb.com
info: Music community featuring unsigned artists and music of all genres.

Unsigned FM
PO Box 20182, London, W10 6US
email: See website for list of contacts
web: www.unsignedfm.com
info: An internet based station with label, studio and venue connections, dedicated to providing quality services and resources to unsigned musicians. Demos selected will make up part of the Unsigned FM playlist and be used to create programs for the many UK regional stations. Musicians can submit demos, biographies and photographs (make sure you include your full address) to the address above.

The Unsigned Guide
3rd Floor, 24-26 Lever Street, Manchester, M1 1DZ
tel: 0161 907 0029
email: info@theunsignedguide.com
web: www.theunsignedguide.com
info: Creators of this very book. Website includes information on The Unsigned Guide, with a virtual tour and sample pages. Purchases and free trials can be attained via the site through an online form, as well as adding your own band to the band database.

Unsigned Promotions
Po Box 18, Milford Haven, Pembrokeshire, SA73 2XB
tel: 07879 457487
email: Via online form
web: www.unsignedpromotions.co.uk
info: Promotional services for unsigned bands. Linked to related sites Scottish Unsigned, English Unsigned and Welsh Unsigned. Register your details into the artist database and submit gig details.

Unsigned-UK
email: Via website
web: www.unsigneduk.co.uk
info: Submit demos to Unsigned UK, where they will be reviewed by a panel of industry professionals. Band profiles, gig guide and advice for unsigned artists.

UP210
email: info@up210.co.uk
web: www.up210.co.uk
info: Used musical instruments for sale in the West Midlands region. Create an account and place your advert online.

NEW MUSIC IS THE FUTURE

YOUR MUSIC.
YOUR STAGE.

in association with

YOURBAND

UR Talented
web: www.urtalented.com
info: Specialise in promotion of new music. Offer free promotional space for your band. Website also contains music forum, local music reviews, local gig reviews, MP3s and news updates.

Urban Mags
email: info@urbanmags.net
web: www.urbanmags.co.uk
info: Website supplying variety of US and UK Urban magazines under one roof. Will ship all magazines worldwide.

Use Your Ears
email: via online form
web: www.useyourears.co.uk/music-resources/
info: Internet resource for musicians including directory of services, classified listings, plus news and concert details.

VH1
web: www.vh1.com
info: Portal for the VH1 music channel which includes artist A-Z directory, news, tour dates, message boards, ringtones and shop.

Violence at Bus Stops
email: toearst@lycos.co.uk
web: www.violenceatbusstops.tk
info: Music website for Northerners with prime objective of providing exposure to unsigned bands and musicians. If you would like to be featured on the website, or are interested in contributing photography or reviews, then contact the above email address.

Virtual Festivals
email: See online contact page
web: www.virtualfestivals.com
info: Music festival portal providing comprehensive and frequently updated coverage of UK and global music festivals. News, backstage gossip, reviews, artist interviews, photos and online community for festival-goers, music fans and clubbers. Purchase tickets online.

The Virtually Acoustic Club
email: david@thevac.co.uk
web: www.thevac.co.uk
info: Website for the longest established open mic night in London. Also lists open mic events across the UK, as well as classified ads, useful tips and venue details.

Vitaminic
email: info@vitaminic.com
web: www.vitaminic.com
info: Platform for the promotion and distribution of digital music over the Internet and other digital networks.

Vocalist
email: via website
web: www.vocalist.org.uk
info: Resource for singers, vocalists and singing tutors. Free online singing lessons for singers of all ages, styles and levels. Exercises on breathing, pitch and posture, online scales, information, books, links to dedicated vocal sites and related resources for vocalists. Useful database of musician services.

The Volts Show
20 St. Govan's Place, Waunarlwldd, Swansea, SA5 4QZ
web: www.thevoltsshow.com
info: Online radio station dedicated to the propagation of new talent. All bands guaranteed airplay. Submit your material to the address above, along with form found on website.

VSO
tel: 020 8780 7200
email: infoservices@vso.org.uk
web: www.vso.org.uk
info: VSO sends qualified and experienced volunteers to work alongside communities in some of the world's poorest countries and focuses on sustainable development rather than short-term disaster relief.

War Child Music
5-7 Anglers Lane, London, NW5 3DG
email: info@warchildmusic.com
web: www.warchildmusic.com
info: War Child is a network of independent organisations working across the world to help children affected by war. The War Child Music site offers exclusive downloads, with all download costs going towards the charity.

Wejamming.com
email: jay@wejamming.com
web: www.wejamming.com
info: Guide to clubbing, gigging and new music in London. Submit details of any events to the above email address.

Welsh Gigs
28 Queen Street, Treforest, Pontypridd, CF37 1RN
tel: 07967 341 112
email: tom@welshgigs.com
web: www.welshgigs.com
contact: Tom Naylor
info: Developed to help Welsh bands gain exposure using various methods including live gigs, radio exposure, online databases, polls, gig listings and much more.

Welsh Unsigned
Unsigned Promotions, PO Box 18, Milford Haven, Pembrokeshire, SA73 2XB
tel: 07879 457 487
email: via website
web: www.welshunsigned.com
info: Site offering free promotional services for unsigned Welsh artists. Acts can create profile including biog and MP3s, and post gig dates.

Wharfedale Pro
email: dean@iaguk.com
web: www.wharfedalepro.com
info: Manufacturers of professional loudspeakers. Run the Adopt A Band competition, a series of regional events across the UK for unsigned bands. See website for further information of competition and application details.

Whisperin & Hollerin
email: james@whisperinandhollerin.com
web: www.whisperinandhollerin.com
info: Webzine covering all genres of music. Register to receive a regular newsletter and also to add your own reviews, comments and join the forums.

Wildplum Network
email: info@wildplum.co.uk
web: www.wildplum.co.uk
info: Wildplum was created to assist bands, musicians and businesses around the world to network. Upload your details for free and create your own mini-site.

Winter Music Conference
email: Via website
web: www.wmcon.com
info: Annual convention aimed at the Dance music community, which takes place in Miami. Every aspect of the industry is represented including the top technological innovators, artists, DJs, producers, radio and video programmers, retailers, distributors, audio manufacturers and many more. Check website for details on registration for future events.

Wippit
email: info@wippit.com
web: www.wippit.com
info: Download MP3s from a large range of musical genres of both old and new music.

Wolves Rocks
web: www.wolvesrocks.co.uk
info: Network of forums set up to support live music in Wolverhampton.

Yamaha
web: www.yamaha.co.uk
info: Website for Yamaha instruments, audio, computer related equipment and accessories. Soundcard drivers and manuals can be downloaded. Also contains links to related music schools and relevant educational sites.

YorkPunkScene
email: addme@yorkpunkscene.co.uk
web: www.yorkpunkscene.co.uk
info: Website and forum dedicated to Punk and Ska in York and the surrounding area. Submit your band details to be listed on the site via the email address above.

Yo-Shot Organisation
email: yoshotorganisation@hotmail.com
web: www.yo-shot.com
contact: Chris Welford
info: Website of Yo-Shot unsigned promotion and management company. Offer 'Band Exchange' where bands from the UK tour all over Europe, and bands from outside the UK come over to play. Also see Independent Promoters section.

YourBand
email: yourband@f-sharp.co.uk
web: www.f-sharp.co.uk/yourband
contact: Paul
info: An interactive website giving bands/artists a free platform to showcase themselves online, including a self-written biography, weblinks and even tracks on the YourBand mp3 jukebox. Genuinely parades the next generation of artists and bands wanting to make that breakthrough into the bigtime.

Zombie Works

1/1 The Angel Building, 12 Paisley Road West, Glasgow, G51 1LE
email: gillian@wiseguys.plus.com
web: www.wiseguys.plus.com
contact: Gillian, Gareth
info: Zombie Works is an online musicians' resource, producing high quality promotional material for bands and musicians. Provides bands and musicians with everything they need to get noticed and ensures that the right image is presented when they do. Services include photography, promo packs, video duplication and web design.

Zonicweb

email: zon@zonicweb.net
web: www.zonicweb.net
info: Zonicweb is a an online music and arts centre. Free music downloads and streaming videos. Website also contains Museum of Bad Album Covers.

Section 8
Tuition/Training

8.1 TUITION/TRAINING

EAST of ENGLAND

Ace Tones Music
1 Goodmans Business Park, Ramsey Road, Whittlesey, Peterborough, PE7 1DR
tel:	01733 206 605
email:	enquiry@acetonemusic.com
web:	www.acetonemusic.com
contact:	Lewis Slack
instrument(s):	Guitar, Saxophone, Piano, Drums, Strings, Woodwind
info:	Working with a number of tutors, Ace Tones Music can offer lessons in a wide variety of musical instruments. Lessons are usually offered at student's own home and can be individual or group sessions.

Alan Morris FTCL Piano and Organ
Cantor, Topps Hill Road, Thorpe Market, Norwich, Norfolk, NR11 8TR
tel:	01263 833 652
contact:	Alan Morris
instrument(s):	Piano, Organ
info:	Teaches ABRSM exam syllabus to Grade 8 in both piano and pipe organ. Mainly Classical styles.

And Then Strum
2 Osier Place, Downs Crescent, Haverhill, Suffolk, CB9 9LQ
tel:	07984 794 143
email:	gill@andthenstrum.co.uk
web:	www.andthenstrum.co.uk
contact:	Gill Matthews
instrument(s):	Guitar
info:	Offering guitar lessons to all ages and abilities, as well as music workshops in songwriting, rhythm and percussion and home recording.

Any Subject Ltd.
Unit 4, Carlton House, Stamford, PE9 1XP
tel:	0870 777 0420
email:	enquiries@anysubject.com
web:	www.anysubject.com
instrument(s):	All instruments
info:	An agency that can provide music tutors for any instrument. If you are interested in becoming a tutor yourself, call 01780 753 313.

Bob Parslow Guitar Tuition
72 Gloucester Street, Norwich, Norfolk, NR2 2DY
tel:	01603 620 261
email:	bob@parslowguitar.freeserve.co.uk
contact:	Bob Parslow
instrument(s):	Guitar
info:	Teach range of styles including Rock, Jazz, Blues, Acoustic and Classical. Caters for a range of exam syllabuses.

Brian Coupe
19 Northwold, Ely, Cambridgeshire, CB6 1BG
tel:	01353 663 007
email:	briancoupe@aol.com
contact:	Brian Coupe
instrument(s):	Double Bass
info:	Classical teacher. Experienced working with young and mature students. Follows ABRSM syllabus to Grade 6 standard. As well as teaching from his own premises, can also travel to students based in surrounding area.

Bruce Cameron Guitar & Saxophone
2 Thornbury, Comberton, Cambridge, CB3 7AP
tel:	07905 376 046
email:	jazzambi@aol.com
web:	www.jazzambience.co.uk
contact:	Bruce Cameron
instrument(s):	Saxophone, Guitar
info:	Specialises in Jazz saxophone. All styles covered in guitar including Rockschool examinations. Teaches from beginner to advanced levels.

Chandra James Tutti ALCM Piano
236 High Road, Trimley St. Martin, Felixstowe, Suffolk, IP11 0RG
tel:	01394 215 877
email:	chandra.james@ntlworld.com
web:	www.tuttimusicschool.co.uk
contact:	Chandra James
instrument(s):	Piano, Clarinet
info:	Teaches up to diploma level including exam tutoring if students wish. Styles range from Classical to Jazz to Contemporary. Lessons held from tutor's home studio. Member of the Incorporated Society of Musicians.

Claire Powlson
15 Townsfield Court, Barnton, Norfolk, CW8 4UT
tel:	07970 984 486
email:	clairepowlson@hotmail.co.uk
instrument(s):	Brass
info:	Teaches all brass excluding French horn. All styles and levels welcome.

Daniela McDermott
1 Fletcher Terrace, Cambridge, CB1 3LU
tel:	01223 476 771/07881 960 259
email:	danmcdrum@hotmail.com
web:	www.danmcdrum.supanet.com
contact:	Daniela McDermott
instrument(s):	Percussion
info:	Primary school to university level. Specialises in West African, Brazilian and Cuban drumming. Will travel to students, as well as teaching from home.

David Earl
19 Newmarket Road, Cambridge, CB5 8EG
tel:	01223 303 857
email:	david@davidearl-pianist.net
web:	www.davidearl-pianist.net
contact:	David Earl
instrument(s):	Piano
info:	Pianist and composer who also teaches classical piano at all levels. Lessons mostly held at tutor's premises. Tuition starts at £25 per hour (or £12.50 per half hour for children or beginner lessons). Follows the ABRSM syllabus.

David Irving
80 Beaumont Road, Cambridge, CB1 8PZ
tel:	07729 064 551
email:	daveirving1@ntlworld.com
web:	www.daveirving.net
contact:	David Irving
instrument(s):	Acoustic Guitar
info:	Teaches Acoustic guitar. Best suited to pupils of any age who wish to learn chords and rhythm in the style of artists such as Oasis, David Gray, Cat Stevens and Radiohead. Will travel within the Cambridge area.

Dorothy F. Morris
6 Colvile, Wisbeck, Cambridgeshire, PE13 2EL
tel:	01945 463 723
instrument(s):	Pianoforte
info:	Teach Grades 1 to 8 Associated Board, practical theory and musicianship. Private practice. Member of the ALCM.

Drum & Guitar Lessons
25 Sutton Road, Witchford, Ely, Cambridgeshire, CB6 2HX
tel: 01353 669 854
email: info@drumandguitarlessons.co.uk
web: www.drumandguitarlessons.co.uk
contact: Stuart Braybrooke
instrument(s): Drums, Guitar, Bass
info: Teaches mainly beginner to intermediate levels,
as well as advanced drums. Covers range of styles and techniques
including Rockschool exams. Lessons are taught in well equipped
recording studios.

Emily Ward
4 Scotland Farm Cottages, Scotland Road, Dry Drayton, Cambridgeshire,
CB3 8BN
tel: 07789 394 493
email: emilycward@yahoo.co.uk
contact: Emily Ward
instrument(s): Flute, Piano
info: Prepared students for concerts and ABRSM exams.
Teaches flute to Grade 8 and piano to Grade 5. While mainly sticking
to Classical repertoire, Emily is willing to explore different styles if
requested.

Fredrick Franklin Piano & Keyboard Tuition
6 Meadowvale, New Costessey, Norwich, Norfolk, NR5 0NJ
tel: 01603 740 559
contact: Fredrick Franklin
instrument(s): Piano, Keyboard
info: Offering a variety of musical styles to students who
want to play for leisure. From beginner to advanced levels.

Gillian Ruddick
Trumpington, Cambridge
tel: 01223 844 364
contact: Gillian Ruddick
instrument(s): Violin, Viola
info: Will teach all ages and standards from beginner to
post diploma. Students can be entered into exams if it will help them
progress. Open to all styles and genres of music. Teaches from home.

Glenn Povey Guitar Tuition
22 Geneva Road, Ipswich, IP1 3NP
tel: 01473 410 269
email: mail@glennpovey.com
web: www.glennpovey.com
contact: Glenn Povey
instrument(s): Guitar, Bass
info: Specialising in Rock, Metal and Blues. All ages
welcome for practical and theory guidance.

Ian Dyball Guitar
71 St. Peter's Road, Great Yarmouth, Norfolk, NR30 3BQ
tel: 01493 843 874
email: sonnydaez@aol.com
contact: Ian Dyball
instrument(s): Guitar
info: Teaches all styles and ages. Offers London College
of Music exam tuition up to Grade 8. Teaches from own premises.

Jean Fairbairn
15 Trent Close, St. Ives, Cambridgeshire, PE27 3FH
tel: 07801 978 798
email: fairbairnjean@hotmail.com
contact: Jean Fairbairn
instrument(s): Flute, Saxophone
info: Teaches ABRSM for flute and saxophone at all
levels. Willing to explore different genres of music on each instrument.
Takes lessons from home.

Jeff Gordon Bass Guitar
8 Queens Crescent, Gorleston, Great Yarmouth, Norfolk, NR31 7NN
tel: 01493 445 484
email: jgbassgui@hotmail.com
contact: Jeff Gordon
instrument(s): Bass
info: Teaches all levels and ages including various
exams syllabuses. Styles and techniques are developed according to
individuals requirements.

Jenny Roche School of Music
Grove Cottage, Mellis Road, Yaxley, Eye, Suffolk, IP23 8DB
tel: 01379 788 212
email: nick@nroche.net
web: www.nroche.net
instrument(s): Piano, Flute, Saxophone, Oboe, Violin, Classical
Guitar, Vocal Coaching, Music Theory
info: Teaches beginner to advanced including ABRSM
exam syllabus. Mainly Classical styles.

Jo Luckhurst
Cambridge
tel: 07870 605 533
contact: Jo Luckhurst
instrument(s): Saxophone, Clarinet, Oboe
info: Experienced musician and teacher. Specialises in
teaching saxophone beyond Grade 6, following the ABRSM, Guildhall
and Trinity syllabuses. Also equally able to teach beginners. Covers
Classical and Jazz syllabus. Will travel to students.

Joanne Rolph
7 St. Augustine Road, Ipswich, Suffolk, IP3 8PT
tel: 01473 717 290
email: joannerolph@hotmail.com
web: www.joanne-rolph.co.uk
contact: Joanne Rolph
instrument(s): Piano, Flute, Clarinet, Saxophone
info: All levels up to diploma taught. Mainly Classical
styles taught from tutor's own premises.

Joe Pearson
5 Starlock Close, Stretham, Cambridgeshire, CB6 3LZ
tel: 07743 918 004
email: joepearson87@gmail.com
contact: Joe Pearson
instrument(s): Percussion, Drums
info: Teaches beginner to intermediate level. Generally
follows the LCM syllabus and explores different styles of music. Keen
interest in Jazz. Will teach from home or travel to students.

John Hogger Drum Tuition
Ardel, 2 Wellington Gardens, Spring Road, Ipswich, Suffolk, IP4 5LX
tel: 01473 728 146
email: hogger@totalise.co.uk
web: www.johnhogger.co.uk
contact: John Hogger
instrument(s): Drums
info: Teaches all standards from beginner to advanced.
Offers London College of Music exam tuition and covers a wide variety
of styles. Full time teacher since 1990.

Judith Chalkley Piano (CTABRSM)
35 Beachampstead Road, Great Staughton, St. Neots, Cambridgeshire,
PE19 5DX
tel: 01480 860 278
contact: Judith Chalkley
instrument(s): Piano, Music Theory
info: Teaches beginner to Grade 8 standard, including
theory. Mainly Classical styles taught from tutor's home.

Julie York
Cambridge
tel: 01223 711 795
email: juliann.yorke@ntlworld.com
contact: Julie York
instrument(s): Piano
info: ABRSM teacher with experience working with
children and adult beginners. Interests in Jazz and composition.

Keith Day
204 Queen Ediths Way, Cambridge, CB2 2NL
tel: 01223 247 639
email: keithday@ntlworld.com
contact: Keith Day
instrument(s): Guitar, Bass
info: Teaches all genres at all levels from his home.

Ken & Chris Fisher
Hill Farm, Clay Hills Road, Kelsale, Saxmundham, Suffolk, IP17 2PR
tel: 01728 604 056/07813 350 582
email: treblecleff_music@yahoo.com
instrument(s): Piano, Keyboard, Organ
info: Teach all levels from beginner to advanced
including exams. Can make home visits or teach from home.

Linda Purdy Music Tuition
Tinkers Rest, Staithe Road, Repps With Bastwick, Great Yarmouth,
Norfolk, NR29 5JU
tel: 01692 670 397
contact: Linda Purdy
instrument(s): Brass, Woodwind, Piano, Music Theory
info: Teaches to advanced level for all instruments
listed, particularly brass. Covers a variety of styles in lessons including
exam syllabuses, which are taught from the tutor's home.

Linton School of Music
63 Finchams Close, Linton, Cambridge, CB1 6ND
tel: 01223 893 941
instrument(s): Piano, Organ, Music Theory
info: Teaches beginner to advanced level covering a
range of styles. Offers exam tuition if required.

Lisa Taylor
63 Thorpe Way, Cambridge, CB5 8UJ
tel: 01223 521 770
email: curly141@hotmail.com
contact: Lisa Taylor
instrument(s): Flute, Piano, Keyboard, Recorder, Clarinet
info: Teaches up to Grade 5 standard from home or the local school. As well as Classical repertoire, can explore different musical styles such as Jazz.

Marion Bell Piano & Singing
The Annex, 21 Rampton Road, Willingham, Cambridge, Cambridgeshire, CB4 5JG
tel: 01954 261 116
contact: Marion Bell
instrument(s): Piano, Vocal Coaching
info: Teaches ABRSM syllabus Grades 1 to 8, including Music Theory. Mainly Classical styles. Lessons are taught at the student's home.

Maurice Clarke Organ & Keyboard
5 The Green, Martham, Great Yarmouth, Norfolk, NR29 4AH
tel: 01493 748 126
contact: Maurice Clarke
instrument(s): Organ, Keyboard
info: Teaches double manual and single keyboard to adults for leisure. Teaches in student's own home (local area only). Covers a wide ranges of styles as requested.

Max Delderfield
163 Hills Road, Cambridge, CB2 2RJ
tel: 07841 423 259
email: maxdelderfield@hotmail.com
contact: Max Delderfield
instrument(s): Guitar
info: Teaches students at any age from beginner to intermediate standard. Specialises in Rock, Pop, Modern and Blues. Prefers to teach lessons from home, but this can be negotiated.

Meg Turpin Piano, Theory & Singing
87 Portersfield Road, Norwich, Norfolk, NR2 3JU
tel: 01603 495 062
contact: Meg Turpin
instrument(s): Piano, Music Theory
info: Teaches all levels up to Grade 8, including exam preparation. Covers all styles including Classical, Jazz, Blues and Pop. Also holds concert parties with students as an informal opportunity for performances.

Michael Anderson
8 Davidbull Way, Milton, Cambridge, CB4 6DP
tel: 01223 361 271
email: micjanderson@aol.com
contact: Michael Anderson
instrument(s): Electric Guitar
info: Specialises in electric guitar. Teaches against the Thames Valley Syllabus from beginner up to Grade 8.

Michael Roca-Terry
23 Martingale Close, Cambridge, CB4 3SA
tel: 07764 743 852
email: bluefrets@yahoo.co.uk
contact: Michael Roca-Terry
instrument(s): Guitar
info: Teaches beginner to advanced on electric, Rock and Classical guitar following the relevant syllabuses. Mostly teaches from home but will travel within the Cambridge area.

Michael Williams Guitar
22 Cowley Road, Felixstowe, Suffolk, IP11 7BU
tel: 01394 282 084
contact: Michael Williams
instrument(s): Guitar, Bass
info: Teaches beginner to advanced level in all styles from Jazz to Heavy Rock to Folk. Acoustic and electric guitar. Teaches from own studio with recording facilities.

Mr David G. Tibbits Piano
12 Honey Hill, Bury St Edmunds, Suffolk, IP33 1RT
tel: 01284 725 479
contact: David Tibbits
instrument(s): Piano, Music Theory
info: Classically trained teacher who can teach student to Grade 8 and further. Will teach a range of styles as requested. Can visit students locally if necessary.

Ms J. Middleton Piano Tuition
13 Burrells Cottages, Post Office Road, Knodishall, Saxmundham, Suffolk, IP17 1UF
tel: 01728 832 426
contact: J Middleton
instrument(s): Piano
info: Mainly concentrating on Classical tuition. Particularly interested in adult beginners.

Natasha Free Piano & Clarinet Teacher
282 Ravenswood Avenue, Ipswich, Suffolk, IP3 9TQ
tel: 01473 680 648
email: learnpiano@ntlworld.com
contact: Natasha Free
instrument(s): Piano, Clarinet, Music Theory
info: Mainly Classical tuition but happy to cover any other styles student might want to play. Can prepare for exams or playing just for fun. Lessons taught at tutor's home.

Neil Jackman
8 Anchor Court, Great Yarmouth, Norfolk, NR31 0QJ
tel: 01493 300 485
email: neilhjackman@yahoo.com
contact: Neil Jackman
instrument(s): Guitar, Bass
info: Teaches beginner to advanced level, including exam tuition (Rockschool syllabus). Covers all styles of music. Teaches students in their own homes.

Norwich Drum Academy
Unit 1, W2 Scotts Yard, Ber Street, Norwich, NR1 3HA
tel: 01603 443 313
email: tuition@norwichdrumacademy.com
web: www.norwichdrumacademy.com
contact: Matt Goom
instrument(s): Drums
info: Experience and knowledge of the music industry. Lessons are structured to individual's needs. Complete beginners to advanced players,. No age restrictions. All aspects and styles are covered including Rock, Pop Jazz, Metal, Fusion, Reggae, Latin, sight reading, studio and live work and performance. Incorporates the Rockschool syllabus.

Peter Davies
The Hollies, Withersdale Road, Mendham, Harleston, IP20 0JB
tel: 01379 854 439
email: ddavarm@aol.com
contact: Peter Davies
instrument(s): Drums
info: Professional musician teaching students for fun or to work on performance technique. Teaches to all levels, covering any style. Teach from own premises but will visit local students.

Peter Sawski Guitar Tuition
19 Cockcroft Place, Cambridge, Cambridgeshire, CB3 0HF
tel: 01223 360 226
contact: Peter Sawski
instrument(s): Guitar, Mandolin
info: Specialises in Acoustic guitar. Folk, Blues and Rock but not Classical. Also traditional mandolin. Teaches beginner to advanced level at tutor's home.

Peter Shepherd
17 Marsh Lane, Hemmingford Gray, Huntington, Cambridgeshire, PE28 9EN
tel: 01480 351 664
email: peter.shepherd999@ntlworld.com
web: www.lessons.jazzcreation.com
contact: Peter Shepherd
instrument(s): Piano
info: Specialist in Jazz piano and prefers students with some prior experience. Explores style without adhering to a strict syllabus.

R.J. Maynard Guitar Tuition
Westbury House, Chapel Road, Strumpshaw, Norwich, Norfolk, NR13 4PA
tel: 01603 712 172
contact: Bob Maynard
instrument(s): Guitar
info: Teaches a variety of styles on electric and Acoustic guitar. Beginners or improvers only.

Rebecca Applin
43 Chalmers Road, Cambridge, CB1 3SZ
tel: 01223 240 418
fax: 01223 410 561
email: rebeccaapplin@mail.com
contact: Rebecca Applin
instrument(s): Harp
info: Will teach ABRSM syllabus at any standard from her premises. Works primarily as a composer.

Richard Winch Singing Tutor
46 Ask Close, Swaffham, Norfolk, PE37 7NH
tel: 01760 722 724
email: rwinch4648@aol.com
contact: Richard Winch
instrument(s): Vocal Coaching
info: Professional singer teaching a variety of styles including Operatic, Classical, Pop and Music Theatre. All levels and ages taught from tutor's home.

Roger James Saxophone, Clarinet & Flute Tuition
Court Lodge, Quebec Road, Dereham, Norfolk, NR19 2DR
tel: 01362 698 301
contact: Roger James
instrument(s): Saxophone, Clarinet, Flute
info: Teaches all levels and styles including Jazz, Blues, Folk, Pop and anything else students would like to play. Also teaches improvisation techniques.

Roxane Houston
8 Hartington Road, Aldeburgh, Suffolk, IP15 5HD
tel: 01728 454 048
contact: Roxane Houston
instrument(s): Vocal Coaching
info: Teaches classical singing techniques and performance. Available to pupils of all levels and ages.

Spontin Studios
Chimneys, Woodlands Lane, Holbrook, Ipswich, Suffolk, IP9 2PW
tel: 07775 892 098
email: paul@spontinstudios.co.uk
web: www.spontinstudios.co.uk
contact: Paul Haley
instrument(s): Guitar, Bass, Keyboards, Drums
info: Teaches advanced guitar, and beginner and intermediate bass, keyboard and drums. Students are welcome to come to the recording studio and try different instruments out. 25 years experience.

Tom Eagle Drum Tuition
6 Jolly Gardeners Court, Norwich, Norfolk, NR3 3HD
tel: 01603 660 527
email: tomeagledrums@hotmail.co.uk
contact: Tom Eagle
instrument(s): Drums
info: Teaches all styles of drums from beginner to advanced level. Exam tuition also available.

Veronica Henderson
33 Romsey Road, Cambridge, CB1 3DD
tel: 01223 413 234
email: veronica.jc.henderson@talk21.com
contact: Veronica Henderson
instrument(s): Cello
info: Tutors beginners to post Grade 8 and adult beginners, as well as children and re-starters. Follows ABRSM syllabus, and teaches from home.

GREATER LONDON

1st Guitar Tuition
54 Bradfield Drive, Barking, IG11 9AR
tel: 020 8252 8688
contact: Glen Parish
instrument(s): Guitar
info: All levels, all styles.

Aarons Mignonette LRAM
2 Waltham Avenue, London, NW9 9SJ
tel: 020 8204 8778
email: mignonetteaarons@tiscali.co.uk
instrument(s): Piano, Vocal Coaching
info: Teaches Piano to all grades along with singing and voice training for all styles. Coaching for auditions, theory and accompanying. Sensitive approach. Sound-proof studio. Free consultation.

ABC Coaching
9a St. Mary Abbot's Place, London, W8 6LS
tel: 07905 933 227
email: info@evelynebrink.com
web: www.evelynebrink.com
contact: Evelyne Brink
instrument(s): Vocal Coaching, Performance Coaching
info: Performance coaching for singers, singer-songwriters and bands. Please see website for more information on Evelyne's professional background.

Accapella Vocal Tuition
Suite 1, 226 Court Farm Road, London, SE9 4JZ
tel: 07956 209 990/07956 417 479
email: info@accapella.net
web: www.accapella.net
contact: Jason
instrument(s): Vocal Coaching
info: Teaches all styles and levels. Offers individual and group tuition. Accapella's 'Artist Support Consultancy' aims to provide help with all aspects of the music industry. See the website for more information.

Al Pinches
143 Carshalton Park Road, Carshalton, SM5 3SF
tel: 020 8647 6376
email: alanpinches@hotmail.com
web: www.jazzguitarworld.co.uk
instrument(s): Guitar
info: All modern styles to all levels. Al has 36 years playing experience.

Alexandra Carr
London, NW2
email: alexjcarr@hotmail.com
instrument(s): Horn, Brass
info: Horn at all levels and general Brass from beginner to intermediate.

Annabel Williams
Flat 1, 84 Madeley Road, London, W5 2LX
tel: 07814 197 384
instrument(s): Vocal Coaching
info: Vocal tutor covering all aspects of singing styles. Teaches on own premises but will travel within the Ealing area.

Bad Science Records
Greenwich, London, SE3 7LH
tel: 020 8305 1499
email: nick@badsciencerecords.com
web: www.badsciencerecords.com
contact: Nick Rundall
instrument(s): Music Technology, Turntables, Guitar
info: Music Technology tuition, beginner to advanced. Vinyl and CD turntables and digital recording studio practices. Nick is an experienced producer and engineer. Please see website for more details.

Bill Collis Drum Tuition
36 Whellock Road, London, W4 1DZ
tel: 020 8994 5729
email: billcollis@supanet.com
instrument(s): Drums
info: Teaches all styles including Jazz, Latin and Rock. All ages welcome. Teaches from own premises in sound-proof studio. Covers Rockschool, Guildhall and Trinity syllabuses. Previous clients include Richie from Texas. Sponsored by Remo and Zildjan.

Blake Wilner Guitar Tuition
Flat 4, 29 Tierney Road, London, SW2 4QL
tel: 07880 637 715
email: info@blakewilnergroup.com
web: www.blakewilnergroup.com
instrument(s): Guitar
info: All styles to all levels (except Classical). Blake teaches from a modern studio on his own premises.

Bob Hooper
54 Further Green Road, Catford, London, SE6 1JH
tel: 020 8461 0330
instrument(s): Guitar
info: Rock, Pop, Folk, Blues, Ragtime, Classical, Latin American and Flamenco styles taught. Beginner to advanced levels. Teaches from own home.

BonaFideStudio
Burbage House, 83-85 Curtain Road, London, EC2A 3BS
tel: 020 7684 5350
email: info@bonafidestudio.co.uk
web: www.bonafidestudio.co.uk
instrument(s): Studio Skills
info: Courses available in recording, processing, Synth zone, sampling, monitoring, mastering, programming, editing and production. BonaFideStudios also have rehearsal and recording details. See the relevant sections for more details.

Bryan Evans
London
tel: 0208 575 3150
email: bryan@musicstudiohelp.com
web: www.musicstudiohelp.com
contact: Bryan Evans
info: Studio Consultation and Training Service. Drawing on his experience as a Recording Engineer/Producer and Music Technology Tutor, Bryan can help fellow music-making enthusiasts setting up or expanding their recording systems, learning how to use them effectively, and/or seeking to acquire the skills to achieve professional quality results.

Christopher Gordon
West Wimbledon, London, SW20 ODS
tel: 020 8879 7147
email: chris_gordon23@hotmail.com
instrument(s): Guitar
info: Over 20 years experience in private schools and studio teaching. All styles. Teaches from own premises.

Clive Jenner
25a Horn Lane, Acton, London, W3 9NJ
tel: 07919 094 286
email: clive.jenner1@btopenworld.com
contact: Clive Jenner
instrument(s): Drums, Percussion
info: Drum, percussion and vibes taught for all styles and all levels. Teaches to Rockschool grades if required. Lessons held at own home studio but can travel.

Concrete Productions
Greater London
tel: 07703 611 535
email: support@concreteworld.co.uk
web: www.concreteworld.co.uk
contact: Christian Huant
instrument(s): Production
info: Specialist advice, training, tuition and music production. Contact Christian for more information.

Craig Mitchell
London, SW4
tel: 07754 265 836
email: craigmitchell111@yahoo.com
web: www.acousticlounge.co.uk
instrument(s): Guitar, Saxophone, Didgeridoo
info: Beginner to intermediate. Teaches from own home or can travel. Fun and friendly lessons. Learn the songs you want.

Darren Galer
23 Woodside Court, The Common, London, W5 3JD
tel: 020 8567 9958
email: darrengaler@mac.com
instrument(s): Guitar
info: Teaches all styles to all levels. Lessons held at his own premises.

Darren Mason Drum Tuition
66 Salisbury Road, Harrow, Middlesex, HA1 1NZ
tel: 020 8861 2188
email: darren.nightowlers@virgin.net
instrument(s): Drums
info: All levels. Beginners especially welcome. Day and evening sessions available. Teaches in sound-proof studio on own premises. Rockschool syllabus covered. All styles taught.

David Bouet
566 Cable Street, Limehouse, London, E1W 3HB
tel: 07984 924 589
email: bouetdav@yahoo.com
web: www.davidbouet.co.uk
instrument(s): Drums
info: Teaches all styles to all levels. Lessons held from studio on own premises.

David Flynn
London, EC1Y 4SB
tel: 07970 299 561
email: dave@daveflynn.com
web: www.daveflynn.com
instrument(s): Guitar, Bass, Mandolin, Mandola, Banjo
info: Teaches intermediate to advanced only. Encourages composition and improvisation. First lesson is a free introductory session.

David Kelly
43a Vaughn Road, Harrow, Middlesex, HA1 4DP
tel: 0870 794 0060
email: kellys@sidneys1.freeserve.co.uk
web: www.davidkelly.net
instrument(s): Guitar
info: Teaches guitar to all ages, either one on one or in groups. Blues, Jazz, Rock, Classical and Acoustic styles. Electric and Acoustic guitar up to Grade 8, classical guitar up to Grade 5, bass up to Grade 5. Beginners are very welcome.

Dolls House Studio
Bell Lane, Hendon, London, NW4 2AD
tel: 020 8732 8511/07976 371 944
email: bongojoe50@hotmail.com
web: www.dollshousestudio.co.uk
contact: Joe
instrument(s): Guitar, Bass, Drums
info: The complex houses recording and rehearsal facilities. See entries in relevant sections for details.

Dominic Brown
75a Thrale Road, London, SW16 1NU
tel: 07801 234 399
email: mail@dombrown.com
web: www.dombrown.com
instrument(s): Guitar, Bass
info: Teaches guitar and bass to all levels. Dominic is an experienced session musician and has worked with many high profile artists including Elton John, Rod Stewart, and most recently Duran Duran. Covers Streatham and Tooting area.

The Drum Academy
Unit 39, Silicone Business Centre, 28 Wadsworth Road, Perivale, Middlesex, UB6 7JZ
tel: 020 8998 9122
fax: 020 8991 2661
email: loz@vegassoundhouse.com or matt@vegassoundhouse.com
web: www.lozvegasmusic.co.uk
contact: Lawrence
instrument(s): Drums
info: Lessons held every weekend between 9am and 11am with session drummer Tony. All levels. The Drum Academy is part of a music complex incorporating recording and rehearsal studios (Loz Vegas Studios), equipment hire service and musical instrument shop (Vegas Sound House), promotions and booking agency (Music Scene UK), artist management services (Music Providers) and a media design company (Some Think Media). See entries in relevant sections for further information.

Drum Sense
68-70 London Road, Croydon, Surrey, CR0 2TB
tel: 020 8288 0863
email: colin@drumsense.com
web: www.drumsense.com
contact: Colin Woolway
instrument(s): Drums
info: Drumsense is a drum tuition programme which uses a proven method based on books and play along material by contemporary players and teachers. All levels and styles catered for.

Drum Tuition
2 Preston Drive, Bexleyheath, DA7 4UQ
tel: 020 8304 2358
email: geoffisaacs@ntlworld.com
instrument(s): Drums
info: All levels and styles taught. One-to-one tuition in fully equipped studio.

Gary Subs
Islington, London, N19 4EH
tel: 020 7281 0720
email: subassa@hotmail.com
instrument(s): Bass
info: Beginner to intermediate. 17 years experience of playing, arranging and recording all styles of bass guitar. Can also teach Pro Tools on a Mac. Gary also plays improvised electronic music with various musicians in London, and is a member of the London Musician's Collective.

Gateway School of Recording
The School Of Music, Kingston Hill Centre, Kingston Upon Thames, Surrey, KT2 7LB
tel: 020 8549 0014
email: info@gsr.org.uk
web: www.gsr.org.uk
contact: Jennifer Goodwin
instrument(s): Recording Techniques
info: Courses available include BA (Hons) Audio Technology & Music Industry Studies and Pro Tools short courses. Tuition from fully equipped studio.

GCMP
Unit 5, Knight Properties, Brewery Road, Hoddesdon, EN11 8HF
tel: 01992 461 089
email: geoffcooper@btinternet.com
web: www.gcmp.co.uk
contact: Geoff Cooper
instrument(s): Drums
info: GCMP also have a recording studio. See entry in relevant section for details.

Geoff Coxon Drum Tuition
97 Percy Road, Hampton, Middlesex, TW12 2JS
tel: 020 8979 5716
email: geoffcoxon97@hotmail.com
instrument(s): Drums
info: Teaches to the Drumsense programme. All styles and levels catered for.

Harmonica Tuition
374c New Cross Road, London, SE14 6AG
tel: 020 8691 7509
email: joffharp@yahoo.com
contact: Joff Watkins
instrument(s): Harmonica
info: Beginner to advanced levels. All ages welcome. Any styles covered.

Harmony Works
61 Bollo Bridge Road, Acton, London, W3 8AX
tel: 07710 245 904
email: helen@harmonyworks.co.uk
web: www.harmonyworks.co.uk
contact: Helen Astrid
instrument(s): Vocal Coaching
info: Harmony Works is a singing workshop company. Tuition incorporates acting and general presentation skills. All levels.

Helen Webb
Flat 8, 15 Belsize Avenue, London, NW3 4BL
tel: 07966 513 954
email: helenwebb@mac.com
web: www.helenwebb.com
instrument(s): Vocal Coaching
info: Private vocal tuition. All genres of Popular music. Techniques covered include vocal, microphone, studio, performance, as well as demo recordings and presentation skills. Weekend courses available. Beginners welcome. Also see Venue section for details of nights Helen organises at 12 Bar Club.

Helena Shenel
Flat 80, Falkirk House, 165 Maida Vale, London, W9 1QX
tel: 020 7328 2921
instrument(s): Vocal Coaching
info: Promotes 'natural voice' coaching. Teaches from own home. Previous clients include Shirley Bassey, George Michael, Peter Gabriel, Lulu and Mike Oldfield.

James Anthony
22 John Campbell Road, Dalston, London, N16 8JZ
tel: 020 7275 8970
email: jamesanthony@blueyonder.co.uk
instrument(s): Vocal Coaching
info: All styles and all levels welcome.

James Stratton
Kilburn, London, NW6 7RT
tel: 020 7328 7858
email: james@sounds.demon.co.uk
instrument(s): Guitar, Bass
info: Electric, Acoustic and bass guitar. All styles and levels.

Jazzwise
2b Gleneagle Mews, London, SW16 6AE
tel: 0845 345 7027
fax: 020 8677 7128
email: admin@jazzwise.com
web: www.jazzwise.com
contact: Charles Alexandra
instrument(s): Jazz Techniques
info: Jazz summer school course held by an industry professional. See listing in relevant section for details of Jazzwise's monthly publication.

Jester Entertainment
Feltham, Middlesex, TW13 6LF
tel: 020 8894 9871
email: tracy.warner@freeuk.com
web: www.jesterentertainment.co.uk
contact: Tracy Warner
instrument(s): All Instruments
info: Jester Entertainment is an agency that can provide tuition in all instruments, as well as performing arts and stage school classes. Various workshops and a band-booking service.

Joe Betro
West Croydon, Surrey, CR0 3DL
tel: 020 8684 0126
contact: Joe Betro
instrument(s): Music Technology, Piano
info: Joe is a songwriter, performer and sound engineer. Tuition in all aspects of music technology and sound engineering, music production, Cubase, MIDI and sampling. Piano to Grade 5, including sight reading, music theory and improvisation. Beginner to intermediate levels.

Joe Pettitt
East Croydon, London, CR0 6UL
tel: 020 8686 8172
email: joe@joepettitt.com
web: www.joepettitt.com
contact: Joe Pettitt
instrument(s): Guitar, Bass, Double Bass
info: All styles to all levels. Please see website for further details.

Joe Read Cubase Tuition
North London
tel: 020 8341 7896
email: joe@joeread.fsnet.co.uk
web: www.cubasetuition.com
instrument(s): Cubase
info: One to one tuition in Cubase for creative musicians, producers and DJs.

John Crawford
36 Avignon Road, London, SE4 2JT
tel: 020 7635 4384/07837 291 188
email: john@vidanova.freeserve.co.uk
web: www.vidanova.freeserve.co.uk/jcweb.htm
instrument(s): Piano
info: Specialising in Jazz and Latin styles, including Brazilian and Cuban. Teaches from intermediate to advanced from Goldsmiths College. Also focuses on improvisation.

John Foward Guitar
63 Clinton Road, London, E3 4QY
tel: 020 8983 4442
email: jazzyjohn@foward.fsbuisness.co.uk
web: www.johnfoward.com
contact: John Forward
instrument(s): Guitar
info: Rock, Blues, Jazz and Fusion. Beginner to advanced. Teaches on one to one basis from own digital studio.

John Hills
1 Worslade Road, London, SW17 0BT
tel: 020 8672 0307
contact: John Hills
instrument(s): Bass, Jazz Techniques
info: Bass guitar tuition for all levels and all ages. Practical, reliable and inventive method offered by experienced professional. John has been gigging since the 60s and teaching since 1986. He also offers 'Blues Into Jazz' improvisation workshops for all instruments at all levels, as well as complete programmes on Jazz improvisation.

John Hudson
3 Wellington House, 148 Peckham Rye, London, SE22 9PQ
tel: 020 8693 4396
email: guitar@johnhudson.plus.com
instrument(s): Guitar
info: Teaches all styles to all levels. John is listed with the Registry of Guitar Tutors. Caters to all Popular styles from Rock to Jazz.

John Mizarolli
69 Fleetwood Road, Dollis Hill, London, NW10 1NR
tel: 020 8452 3176
web: www.guitarguru.co.uk
instrument(s): Guitar
info: New age approach to guitar tuition. Free information pack available. Visit the website for further details.

John Worthington
40 Bampton Road, Forest Hill, London, SE23 2BG
tel: 020 8291 1068
email: alljazzlive@onetel.com
web: www.alljazzlive.com
instrument(s): Saxophone
info: Live Jazz for all occasions. Teaches from own premises. All styles and levels.

Johnny Querke
48 Hopner Road, Hayes, Middlesex, UB4 8PZ
tel: 020 8845 3828
instrument(s): Guitar
info: Teaches all styles except Jazz. Classical and Rock guitar taught to the London College of Music syllabus.

Jorge Cortesao
57a Temple Road, London, NW2 6PN
tel: 020 8208 1309
web: www.bridgesto.com
instrument(s): All Latin and Brazilian Percussion
info: Teaches beginner to intermediate. Has also published 8 videos and DVDs about Brazilian and Latin percussion. For further details see the above website.

Katherine Stagg
66 Salisbury Road, Harrow, Middlesex, HA1 1NZ
tel: 020 8861 2188
instrument(s): Saxophone, Clarinet
info: Teaches Saxophone and Clarinet in sound-proof studio on own premises. Day and evening sessions available.

Kelvin Christiane
33 Mill Road, Twickenham, Middlesex, TW2 5HA
tel: 020 8286 3242
email: kelvin@kcmusic.co.uk
web: www.kcmusic.co.uk
contact: Kelvin Christiane
instrument(s): Flute, Clarinet, Saxophone
info: Professional session musician. Works with top industry names. Teaches at all ages and standards according to ABRSM and Guildhall Jazz and Classical syllabuses. Specialises in Jazz and Blues. Teaches solely from his own premises.

Kim Chandler
Brentford, London
tel: 07931 342 395
email: kim@kimchandler.net
web: www.kimchandler.net
instrument(s): Vocal Coaching
info: Pop vocal coach. Intermediate and advanced students only.

Latin Quarter
87 Hampstead Road, London, NW1 2PL
tel: 020 7383 0567/07765 878 078
email: enquiries@latinquarter.org.uk
web: www.latinquarter.org.uk
instrument(s): Vocal Coaching, Guitar
info: Centre for Latin and Flamenco music and dance. Tuition available in Flamenco singing and guitar, and Cajun percussion. Classes also include a wide variety of dancing styles such as Tango, Salsa, Flamenco and Belly Dancing.

Liberty Hall Music
Battle House, 1 East Barnet Road, New Barnet, Hertfordshire, EN4 8RR
tel: 020 8440 0011/07961 447 589
email: kristina@libertyhallmusic.com
web: www.libertyhallmusic.com
contact: Kristina
instrument(s): DJing, Mixing, Mastering, Sound Engineering & Music Production, Vocal Coaching
info: Established in 1993, Liberty Hall Music offer a wide range of services including studio recording, mastering and duplication services and various music training courses. See entries in relevant sections for more details.

LogicTraining.co.uk
tel: 07813 657 524
email: logictraining@mac.com
web: www.logictraining.co.uk
instrument(s): Logic, Logic Audio
info: One to one tuition in Logic and Logic Audio. Specialist advice on Apple Mac OS and hardware. Logic training CDs available to buy. Contact Peter Dudley for more information.

Lucinda Barry
London, W11
tel: 020 7229 2754
email: lucinda.barry@btopenworld.com
instrument(s): Vocal Coaching
info: Lucinda is a qualified vocal coach and experienced session performer, both live and in the studio. All students of all levels welcome. Specialise in Pop, R&B, Gospel, Jazz and Musical Theatre. Individually tailored lessons, encouraging a contemporary voice. Focus on breath control, relaxation, support and confidence building. Affordable prices.

Malcolm Morley Studio
268c St. Paul's Road, London, N1 2LJ
tel: 020 7354 0690
email: tuftytumpkins@hotmail.com
web: www.malcolm-morley.com
instrument(s): Vocal Coaching
info: Teaches from small studio. Voice development. All styles. Songwriting and demo services also available.

Marcella Puppini
Unit 10, 97-103 Fonthill Road, London, N4 3JH
tel: 07956 376 138
email: marcella@marcellapuppini.com
web: www.marcellapuppini.com
contact: Marcella
instrument(s): Vocal Coaching
info: Professional Jazz singer and teacher. Covers all aspects of technique and improvisation. Beginner to advanced. Pop, Jazz, Rock and R&B styles taught.

Mark Roberts
Panic Music Studios, Park Royal, London, NW10 7LU
tel: 020 8961 9540/020 8965 1122
email: mroberts.drums@virgin.net
instrument(s): Drums
info: Acoustic and electronic drums taught. All styles and levels. High quality studio. Credits include Massive Attack, Neneh Cherry and D:Ream.

The Midi Music Company
77 Watsons Street, Deptford, London, SE8 4AU
tel: 020 8694 6093
fax: 020 8694 6609
email: theteam@themidimusiccompany.co.uk
web: www.themidimusiccompany.co.uk
instrument(s): MIDI Technology and Multi Media
info: Established in 1995 to provide music education with specific reference to MIDI technology targeting children and young people with limited access to creative resources and facilities, particularly those who have disadvantaged backgrounds or those who just love music and performing.

Music Everything Ltd.
Parchmore Place, 1-6 The Mews, 92a Parchmore Road, London, CR7 8LX
tel: 020 8241 2277
email: info@musiceverything.com
web: www.musiceverything.com
info: Various music courses available. See website for further details.

Neil Findlay
London, N16
tel: 07941 011 257
email: sessiondrummer44@hotmail.com or neilfindlay@bravehost.com
instrument(s): Drums, Percussion, Sequencing, Timpani
info: Beginner to advanced. All styles. Teaches from own premises, but can also travel to student's premises if required. Active session drummer with extensive biography available. Neil is also available for session work.

Nicola Lawrence
74 Glen Wood Avenue, Westcliff, SSO 9DT
tel: 0845 456 8415
email: manic-pianic@uk2.net
instrument(s): Piano, Organ, Keyboard, Theory, Composition, Aural Practice, Flute
info: From beginner to advanced. All styles. Also cover GCSE and A level music, composition techniques, music recording and software, festival preparation, piano accompaniment, and practice for other instrumental and aural exams including violin, flute and electric guitar.

NTS Ltd.
National Works, Unit 27, Bath Road, Hounslow, TW4 7EA
tel: 020 8577 8572
fax: 020 8569 6430
email: benoconnor@nts-group.com
web: www.nts-group.com
contact: Ben O' Connor
info: Private training provider offering NVQ training in variety of general subjects. Also run government funded programme called Hands On Music, for young adults. Contact Ben for further details.

Oliver McKiernan
London, E1
tel: 07931 163 240
email: oli234@lycos.co.uk
instrument(s): Bass, Guitar
info: Experienced and qualified tutor. Teaches beginner to advanced levels. All styles. Guitar to intermediate level.

Panic Music
14 Trading Estate Road, London, NW10 7LU
tel: 020 8961 9540/020 8965 1122
fax: 020 8838 2194
email: mroberts.drums@virgin.net
web: www.panic-music.co.uk
contact: Mark Roberts
instrument(s): Drums
info: Drum tuition and various music courses available. Check website for details.

Pat Cotton
26 Lynde House, Gauden Road, Clapham, London, SW4 6LN
tel: 020 7498 8048
email: pat@patcotton.com
contact: Pat Cotton
instrument(s): Bass, Guitar
info: Teaches all styles to advanced level. Both beginners and experienced players welcome. Modern studio on own premises.

Patrick Zambonin
London, NW6 2BS
tel: 020 7328 6139/07944 546 397
email: pzambonin@beeb.net
instrument(s): Bass
info: Teaches4 and 5 string bass. Beginner to advanced. All styles and techniques, including fingerstyle, slapping, harmony, reading, ear-training, scales and transcribing.

Paul Abrahams
Flat 2, 355 Clapham Road, London, SW9 9BT
tel: 020 7207 9553
email: music@paulabrahams.com
web: www.paulabrahams.com
instrument(s): Piano, Keyboard, Vocal Coaching
info: Modern piano styles including Jazz, Blues and Pop. Coaching for confidence, presentation and audition preparation. Teaches from own premises. Tuition available for bands as well as individuals. See website for more information.

Paul Lennon LTCL
2 Downs Road, Beckenham, Kent, BR3 5JY
tel: 020 8650 2987
email: paul.lennon@eclipse.co.uk
instrument(s): Violin, Piano, Guitar, Bass, Vocal Coaching
info: Associated Board exams including Theory and Jazz Piano. Teaches from own premises. Tuition in all styles but specialises in Jazz and Classical.

Paul Todd
3 Rosehart Mews, London, W11 3JN
tel: 020 7229 9776
email: paultodd@talk221.com
instrument(s): Vocal Coaching
info: Mainly teaches musical theatre but has been known to coach full bands in stage presence and related subjects, as well as individual voice coaching. Teaches from own premises.

Phil Bell
18 Lady Somerset Road, London, NW5 1UP
tel: 020 7485 2960
email: pbellko@hotmail.com
contact: Phil Bell
instrument(s): Guitar
info: Teaches all styles to all levels. Will teach from own premises or visit as required. Can teach to Guildhall syllabus.

Phil Gostelow
London, E18
tel: 07740 195 446
email: phil@philgostelow.com
web: www.philgostelow.com
instrument(s): Trumpet, Cornet, Horn, Trombone, Euphonium, Baritone, Tuba. Vocal Coaching
info: Friendly and committed teacher. Studied at Guildhall School with Trombone as first study. Now works primarily as a Musical Director in Theatre. Has wide knowledge of musical styles. Willing to travel around London if required.

Phil Warren
25 Rivermead, Uxbridge Road, Kingston Upon Thames, KT1 2LR
tel: 020 8549 7397
contact: Phil Warren
instrument(s): Guitar
info: Rock and Pop styles taught. All levels and ages. Home visits only. Can also provide production facilities.

Philip Dawson
Fortis Green, East Finchley, London, N2 9HH
tel: 020 8444 7409/07941 257 470
email: philipdawson@onetel.com
instrument(s): Guitar, Piano, Keyboards, Music Technology, Production
info: Teaches all styles (including Jazz, R&B, Soul, Funk, Latin, Brazilian, African, Rock, Blues and Jazz) to all levels. 15 years teaching experience.

The Planet Drum
20 Castlehaven Road, Camden, London, NW1 8RA
tel: 020 7428 9012
email: info@theplanetdrum.co.uk
web: www.theplanetdrum.co.uk
contact: Alan Maureal
instrument(s): Percussion, Drums
info: Aim to help you get the necessary knowledge and inspiration to play drums to the best of your ability. Train a broad range of individuals, children and adults, amateur and professional drummers, music teachers, and total beginners. Scar Studios rehearsal facilities are also located at the same address. See listing in relevant section.

Rhythm 4 Life
Whitecross Street, Opposite Safeway, London, EC1Y 8JA
tel: 020 7628 9270
fax: 020 7628 9270
email: ec1musicproject@hotmail.com
contact: Zeynel Kasapodlglu
instrument(s): Music Technology, Guitar, Piano, Drums
info: Music lessons and opportunities to develop talent for young people aged between 8 and 21 years. Call for more details.

Robert Bicknell
London, SW2
tel: 020 7733 8669
email: mail@robertbicknell.co.uk
web: www.robertbicknell.co.uk
instrument(s): Vocal Coaching
info: Exercises and songs recorded to CD. Assistance for studio work. Masterclasses for university, theatre or drama school. Coach for television, film, musical theatre and Pop work. See Robert's website for more details, including a list of previous clients.

Robert Thompson Music
166 Gosforth Lane, Watford, WD19 7RD
tel: 020 8428 7512
email: rob@rtguitar.com
web: www.rtguitar.com
instrument(s): Guitar, Vocal Coaching
info: All styles of guitar up to Grade 8. Teaches from own premises.

School of Audio Engineering (SAE)
United House, North Road, London, N7 9DP
tel: 020 7609 2653
email: saelondon@sae.edu
web: www.saeuk.com
instrument(s): Variety
info: SAE offers a selection of courses covering Audio, Creative Media and Digital Film. Also have institutes based in Liverpool and Glasgow.

Sebastian Stear
East London
tel: 020 8989 6567
email: sebastian.stear@absolutemusicians.com
contact: Sebastian Stear
instrument(s): Piano
info: Teaches any age from beginner to advanced level. Follows a Classical repertoire, but will allow the student some choice within this. Take lessons from home.

Seven Studios
49-51 Leswin Road, London, N16 7NX
tel: 020 7923 9533
email: info@seventhmusic.co.uk
contact: Dan Chudley
instrument(s): Music Technology, Production
info: Seven Studios run courses in conjunction with Hackney and Haringey councils, including NVQ Music Technology courses and New Deal For Musicians. For more information on Seven Studio's rehearsal and recording facilities, see the relevant sections.

Simon Strong BA (Hons)
London, W3
tel: 07967 824 778
email: speakdrums@hotmail.com
instrument(s): Drums
info: Beginner to advanced. Simon has 20 years playing experience and 11 years teaching experience. Teaches from his own studio or will visit students. Grade 8 Rockschool and 1 year Drumtech Diploma available.

Singing Lessons
73 Woodville Road, Thornton Heath, Surrey, CR7 8LN
tel: 020 8653 0352
contact: Marianne
instrument(s): Vocal Coaching
info: All modern tracks and styles. Backing tracks, sheet music, showcases and microphone technique. One to one or couple bookings. Day, evening and weekend sessions available. Located a few minutes from Thornton Heath Station. Parking available nearby.

Singing Lessons Are Fun!
86 South Lambeth Road, London, SW8 IQU
tel: 020 7735 0532
email: sandrasinging@hotmail.com
contact: Sandra Scott
instrument(s): Vocal Coaching
info: Vocal Training, Vocal and Musical Coaching, Professional Performance Counsellor Dip. Couns

Southend Music School
9 South End, Croydon, Surrey, CR0 1BE
tel: 020 8256 6483
email: contact@southendschoolofmusic.com
web: www.southendmusicschool.com
instrument(s): Guitar, Keyboard, Piano, Vocal Coaching
info: Complete beginners welcome. All styles and abilities. Day, evening and weekend sessions available. Martin Phelps Music is an instrument store situated at the same address as Southend Music School. See listing in relevant section for details.

Spanish Guitar Centre
36 Cranbourn Street, London, WC2H 7AD
tel: 020 7240 0754/0800 371 339 (Freephone)
fax: 020 7240 0754
email: enquiries@spanishguitarcentre.com
web: www.spanishguitarcentre.com
instrument(s): Guitar
info: Classical and Flamenco styles taught. See entry in relevant section for details of the Spanish Guitar Centre instrument shop.

Steve Dell
Flat J, 10 Sutherland Road, West Ealing, London, W13 0DT
tel: 020 8621 1394
email: stevedell@ealing717.fsnet.co.uk
instrument(s): Guitar
info: Teaches Classical and Spanish up to Grade 8 and Rock guitar up to Grade 5 (Trinity Rockschool syllabus).

Talents Tuition
9 Brockley Rise, Forest Hill, London, SE23 1JG
tel: 020 8699 4216
email: info@talentsmusic.com
web: www.talentsmusic.com
instrument(s): All Instruments
info: All styles and levels. Also have practice rooms and provide instrument repair services. For more information, see the relevant sections.

Tim Williams
Chelsea, London, SW10
tel: 020 7352 4964
email: timwilliams@musician.net
instrument(s): Piano, Keyboard, MIDI
info: Teach to advanced levels. All styles. Tuition also available in computer skills, MIDI theory and practice, and Cubase to an advanced level.

Tugwell Guitar
Beckenham, Kent
tel: 020 8289 0946
email: tugwellguitar@yahoo.com
contact: Paul Tugwell
instrument(s): Guitar, Bass
info: Teaches all styles to all levels. Can cover Rock School syllabus if required. Paul is an experienced musician and has been teaching for 15 years.

Udit Pankhania
Hayes, Middlesex, UB4 9BE
tel: 020 8841 5739
instrument(s): TABLA, Rhythm coaching for all instruments
info: Professional Tabla player teaching at all levels. Students have passed with distinctions at official exams. Organised approach to teaching. Hold various diplomas in Indian Music.

UK Pianos Ltd.
83 Southbury Road, Enfield Town, Middlesex, EN1 1PJ
tel: 020 8367 2080
email: via website
web: www.ukpianos.co.uk
contact: Katrin Bellman
instrument(s): Piano, Guitar, Violin, Vocal Coaching, Theory
info: All levels. Cover syllabus for Associated Board of Royal School of Music. Will also be introducing tuition in drums, keyboard and saxophone. See entry in relevant section for details of the UK Pianos instrument shop.

Vampire Music
20 Tanners Hill, Deptford, London, SE8 4JP
tel: 020 8691 6666
fax: 020 8692 9999
email: info@vampiremusic.co.uk
web: www.vampiremusic.co.uk
instrument(s): Music Production
info: Professional training in all aspects of music production and sound engineering. Private courses, as well as LOCN accredited courses in partnership with Lewisham College. Vampire Music also incorporates recording studios, rehearsal rooms, duplication services, music shop, as well as equipment hire and design services. See entries in relevant sections for details.

The Vocal Academy
Carshalton, Surrey, SM5 2HH
tel: 020 8395 2655
email: via website
web: www.thevocalacademy.co.uk
contact: Sally Garozzo
instrument(s): Vocal Coaching
info: Beginner to intermediate. Popular styles covered. Lesson are generally on The Vocal Academy's own premises, but will visit student's home if necessary. See website for more information on workshops and assessment consultation.

Vocal Confidence
2-1a The Boulevard, London, SW17 7BW
tel: 07958 450 382
email: info@vocalconfidence.com
web: www.vocalconfidence.com
contact: Alix Longman
instrument(s): Vocal Coaching
info: Coaching seminars for all styles and levels of singing and speech. Contact Alex for further details.

VoxBox
164 Eversholt Street, Camden, London, NW1 1BL
tel: 020 7388 1799
email: info@vox-box.biz
web: www.vox-box.biz
instrument(s): Vocal Coaching
info: Teach all Popular styles of singing. Vocal foundation, development and performance. See the website for details of different lessons, courses, classes and events.

Walthamstow Music
2 Greenleaf Road, Walthamstow, London, E17 6QQ
tel: 020 8520 2163
email: info@walthamstowmusic.com
web: www.walthamstowmusic.com
contact: Aaron
info: Associated Board examination centre. Contact Aaron for details of enrolling. Walthamstow Music also have an instrument shop. See listing in relevant section for details.

The World Academy for Interdisciplinary Training
16 Balderston Street, London, W1K 6TN
tel: 020 7629 2927
email: wait_academy@btinternet.com
web: www.wait-academy.envy.nu
contact: Ziggy Agocsi
instrument(s): Vocal Coaching
info: Interdisciplinary voice coaching and singing lessons for performers from all backgrounds (including Pop, Rock, R&B, Jazz, Dance, Musical and Opera). Holistic voice therapy including voice confidence and stammering. Vocational certificate courses by the World Academy for Interdisciplinary Training. Combining holistic Western and Eastern approaches for coordination of the voice, body, posture, breathing and the stimulation of the brain. Clients include winners of MTV awards, Best Singer of the Year, Best Life Performance Acts and other national and international awards.

X-Treme Studios
Unit 10, Rose Hill Court, St. Helier Avenue, Morden, SM4 6JS
tel: 020 8687 5225
email: suttondistrict@aol.com
contact: George Panteli
instrument(s): Music Technology, DJing
info: X-Treme run courses for young people with problematic backgrounds. Call for more information.

MIDLANDS

7th Wave
Unit 8, Sheriff Street, Worcester, WR14 9AB
tel: 01905 617 177
instrument(s): Drums, Bass, Guitar
info: Teaches all styles and levels. 7th Wave also offer rehearsal space and recording. See relevant sections for more details.

Access To Music
Lionel House, 35 Millstone Lane, Leicester, LE1 5JN
tel: 0116 242 6888
fax: 0116 242 6868
email: amy.walshe@access-to-music.co.uk
web: www.accesstomusic.co.uk
contact: Amy Walshe
info: Access To Music are designers and providers of Popular Music education in the UK, offering courses from beginner level through to degree. It bridges the gap between education and the music industry by developing relevant skills and promoting music opportunity. In addition to its own centres, ATM also works in partnership with 10 colleges nationwide.

A Kind Of Jazz
2 Kings Walk, Leicester Forest East, Leicester, LE3 3JP
tel: 0116 224 9290
email: glenn.hughes@amserve.com
contact: Glenn Hughes
instrument(s): Piano
info: Teaches beginner to intermediate level. Exams up to Grade 5. Teaches a range of styles including Classical, Jazz, Blues and Pop. Lessons held wither at tutor's premises or can visit students locally.

Andrew Ellis
58 Earl Street, Earl Shilton, Leicester, Leicestershire, LE9 7AQ
tel: 01455 841 284/07976 719 856
email: andy@milnet.uk.net
instrument(s): Brass
info: CT ABRSM qualified. Andrew teaches all brass instruments and specialises in trombone. All levels and exams taught from his own home.

B. Barron
46 Merrivale Road, Stafford, Staffordshire, ST17 9EB
tel: 01785 603 020
email: barron@1tel.com
contact: Barbra
instrument(s): Keyboard, Brass, Woodwind
info: Teaches Classical and Jazz from her own home. All levels and all exams.

The Birmingham Drum Academy
14 Rea Street, South Digbeth, Birmingham, B5 6LB
tel: 0121 622 7110
email: info@muthersstudio.com
web: www.muthersstudio.com
instrument(s): Drums
info: Private tuition. Uses graded syllabus. £20 per hour. Part of Muthers rehearsal and recording Studio. See entries in relevant sections for further details.

C. Bushell Piano Teacher
9 Cherry Orchard, Lichfield, Staffordshire, WS14 9AN
tel: 01543 262 237
instrument(s): Piano, Theory
info: With emphasis on musicianship, C. Bushell teaches all ages and abilities including grades. Lessons held from his own premises.

Classical Guitar Tuition
23 Clent Road, Bear Wood, Oldbury, B68 9ES
tel: 0121 421 4275
web: www.classicalguitartuition.co.uk
contact: Roy Bull
instrument(s): Classical Guitar
info: Beginner to diploma level and exam preparation. 27 years experience. Teaches from home.

D.R. Drum Tuition
17 Cottage Close, Ratby, Leicester, LE6 0XY
tel: 0116 239 3038
instrument(s): Drums
info: All ages and all levels of ability. Exams available. Can teach from own premises or arrange home visits.

Die Hard Productions
The Music Village, 55 Great Hampton Street, Birmingham, B18 6EL
tel: 07947 405 393
email: diehardproduction@blueyonder.co.uk
contact: Ken White, Joel Farrell
instrument(s): Vocal Coaching
info: Die Hard Studios offer digital studio recording. See entry in relevant section for details.

DOV Productions
7 Richmond Aston Drive, Tipton, DY4 8GD
tel: 0121 557 0275/07908 723 128
email: dov.ab@btinternet.com
contact: Donovan Bailey
instrument(s): Vocal Coaching
info: Coaching available at premises, or mobile service within vicinity. DOV Productions also offer songwriting, arrangement and production services. Contact Donovan for further details.

E. Tomlinson
17 Ashford Rise, Sutton-In-Ashfield, Nottinghamshire, NG17 2BB
tel: 01623 510 353
email: ja.tomlinson@ntlworld.com
contact: Esther
instrument(s): Flute, Vocal Coaching, Keyboard
info: Teaches all levels and exams from her own home.

Fay Madeley Suzuki Piano Tuition
15 Luttrell Road, Sutton Coldfield, West Midlands, B74 2SP
tel: 0121 308 0409
instrument(s): Suzuki Piano
info: GRSM, ARCM and ABSM qualified. The only graduate Suzuki teacher in the West Midlands. Teaches all levels from home.

Fiona Duncan Peak Tuition
54 Wellington Street, Matlock, DE4 3GS
tel: 01629 583 643
instrument(s): Piano, Organ, Keyboard, Guitar, Recorder
info: Beginner to exam standard. Teaches from home. All age groups welcome.

Four Oaks School Of Music
217 Clarence Road, Sutton Coldfield, B74 4LE
tel: 0121 302 5410/07957 818 606
email: fouroaksmusic@btinternet.com
instrument(s): Violin, Guitar, Mandolin, Viola
info: Beginner to advanced. Teaches from home and makes visits to student's homes if required. Exam training available.

Freya Randle Singing Violin & Piano
12 Findon Street, Kidderminster, DY10 1PU
tel: 01562 744 139
instrument(s): Vocal Coaching, Violin, Piano
info: Teaches all levels and grades from home.

Graham Croft
tel: 07796 645 525
email: pianolessons@doubtwell.co.uk
instrument(s): Piano, Keyboard
info: Teaches all levels and grades from his own home.

Guitar & Bass Tuition
114 Goosemoor Lane, Birmingham, West Midlands, B23 5QD
tel: 0121 373 3462
contact: PJ Cartin
instrument(s): Guitar, Bass
info: Teaches all levels and all styles from home. 30 years of playing experience.

Hellfire Productions
158 Crankhill Lane, Wednesbury, Birmingham, WS10 0PB
tel: 0121 556 2559/07870 657 747
email: ajeet@hellfireproductions.com
web: www.hellfireproductions.com
contact: Ajeet Gill
instrument(s): Drums, Guitar, Bass
info: Hellfire offer a wide range of services. See entries in relevant sections for information on studio recording services and rehearsal spaces.

Hijack Music
5b The Basement, Millsborough House, Ipsley Street, Redditch, B98 78L
tel: 07855 271 834
email: info@hijackmusic.co.uk
web: www.hijackmusic.co.uk
contact: Nigel Clark
instrument(s): Drums, Guitar, Studio training including Cubase
info: Studio recording services also available. See entry in relevant section for details.

Hockley Music Academy
9-13 Hockley, Nottingham, NG1 1FH
tel: 0115 320 7802
web: www.hma.org.uk
instrument(s): Drums, Bass, Guitar, Vocal Coaching
info: Teach exams and lessons to all ages and abilities from their premises. The academy is a team of 10 professional teachers who teach in a purpose built facility consisting of 7 studios.

Hughie James
212 Blandford Avenue, Kettering, NN16 9AT, NN16 9AT
tel: 01536 312 395
web: www.hughiejames.com
instrument(s): Piano, Vocal Coaching, Orchestration
info: Preparation for exams. Teaches from home to all ages and levels.

Jane Morrey
Lichfield
tel: 01543 252 201
email: jane.morrey@btopenworld.com
web: www.janemorreymusic.com
contact: Jane Morrey
instrument(s): Keyboard, Electronic Organ
info: Will teach students of all ages, from absolute beginners to advanced levels. Lessons are customised to the individual students improvement, and cover a range of music styles. Teaches from local high school.

Jane Morris Piano Tuition
1 Parkland Close, Mansfield, Nottinghamshire, NG18 4PP
tel: 01623 658 780
instrument(s): Piano
info: Teaches all levels and exams from her own home.

Janet Murphy Singing Tuition
32 Beechwood Road, Northampton, NN5 6JT
tel: 01604 581 901/07789 147 258
fax: 0870 135 4376
email: jan@janmurphy.co.uk
web: www.janmurphy.co.uk
instrument(s): Vocal Coaching
info: First lesson free. Relaxed and fun approach. All ages and abilities. Teaches from own home.

Joe Dring Guitar Tuition
134 Lichfield Road, Stone, ST15 8PY
tel: 01785 811 544
email: joedring@hotmail.com
instrument(s): Guitar
info: Pop, Rock, Folk and Blues. All ages and abilities. Experienced teacher. Teaches Monday to Friday from his own home.

John Hancock
63 High Street, Croughton, Brackley, NN13 5LT
tel: 01869 810 790
email: hancockj@home28.freeserve.co.uk
web: www.johnhancockmusic.f2s.com
instrument(s): Piano, Keyboard
info: Near to Banbury, Bicester and Brackley. John is an experienced music professional teaching Classical or Jazz and Blues. Can teach at home or in student's home.

Judith Baxter
The Old School, Banbury Road, Moreton Pinkney, Daventry, NN11 3SQ
tel: 01295 768 257
instrument(s): Vocal, Theory
info: Teaches all levels and exams from home.

Judy Nicol - Big Band
6 Crosswood Close, Loughborough, Leicestershire, LE11 4BP
tel: 01509 561 116
email: t.nicol@ntlworld.com
contact: Judy Nicol
instrument(s): Saxophone, Clarinet, Flute
info: From absolute beginners up to Grade 8 level. Teaches ABRSM and Trinity Guildhall syllabuses. Covers range of styles but leans towards Swing, Jazz and Blues.

Kevin M. Fowkes
61 Lindon Drive, Alvaston, Derby, DE24 0LP
tel: 01332 751 623
email: ck@ckfowkes1.wanadoo.co.uk
contact: Kevin Fowkes
instrument(s): Piano, Keyboard, Organ, Music Theory
info: Teaches a broad range of styles including Classical, Jazz and Blues. Can provide support for exams up to diploma level. Teaches from home. 25 years experience.

Leon Haynes
82 Bermuda Village, Nuneaton, Warwickshire, CV10 7PN
tel: 07798 896 858
email: rockinbean@hotmail.com
instrument(s): Vocal Coaching
info: Professional performance experience. Teaches all standards at any age in Rock, Pop and Musical Theatre genres. Will travel to students. Focuses on the performance side in particular. Works along side Big Help Management. See listing in relevant section.

Leonard Rayner Piano School
183 Harborne Lane, Birmingham, B29 6SS
tel: 0121 471 2472
instrument(s): Piano, Vocal Coaching, Violin, Music Theory
info: Academic school with focus on exam progression and performance technique. From beginners to professionals.

Lesley Woodyer
20 Waterdale 20 Waterdale, Wombourne, Wolverhampton, WV5 0DH
tel: 01902 892 367
contact: Lesley Woodyer
instrument(s): Piano, Violin, Viola, Compositon
info: Teaches beginner to diploma level, covering ABRSM and Trinity College syllabuses. Classically based but likes to teach a range of styles to broaden students repertoire. Also offers short courses for other teachers.

Leslie Glaze
37 Meadowlea, Madeley, Telford, TF7 5BE
tel: 01952 582 656
instrument(s): Classical Spanish Guitar
info: Teaches exams from his own premises or
in student's homes. All abilities welcome. Friendly service and
competitive rates.

Lincoln Noel
90 Duston Wildes, Northampton, NN5 6NR
tel: 01604 756 266
email: lincoln@noel1965.fsnet.co.uk
contact: Lincoln Noel
instrument(s): Piano
info: Teaches beginner to advanced level. Exams covered
up to diploma level (including Jazz exam syllabus). Teach all types of
musical style from own premises.

Margaret Griffiths
39 Holbeche Road, Sutton Coldfield, B75 7LL
tel: 0121 329 3149
instrument(s): Vocal Coaching, Piano
info: Teach beginners only. Will cover exams up to
Grade 2. Teaches from own home.

Maria Bohdan Dip. LCM
18 Gatcombe Grove, Sandiacre, Nottingham, Nottinghamshire,
NG10 5PN
tel: 07931 704 408
instrument(s): Piano
info: Teaches all levels and exams from her own home.

Michael Clarke Studio
10 Hall Lane, Connah's Quay, Deeside, CH5 4LX
tel: 01244 822 535
email: michael@mclarke55.freeserve.co.uk
web: www.michaelclarkestudio.com
instrument(s): Guitar, Bass
info: Teaches all levels and exams from his own
premises.

Mike Holt
Lichfield
tel: 07808 182 123
email: mikeholt000@aol.com
contact: Mike Holt
instrument(s): Guitar, Drums
info: Teaches from beginner to advanced in a range
of musical styles following the Rockschool syllabus. Keen interest in
teaching Jazz. Lessons from his premises.

MTY Ltd.
1 Aversley Road, Birmingham, B38 8PD
tel: 0121 459 5382/07919 815 814
email: mtynotes@blueyonder.co.uk
contact: Tanya Cush
instrument(s): All instruments
info: Music workshops in schools. All levels and
abilities.

Music Maker
6 Hotel Street, Coalville, LE67 3EP
tel: 01530 831 633
email: sales@musicmaker4music.co.uk
web: www.musicmaker4music.co.uk
instrument(s): Organ, Keyboard, Piano, Music Theory
info: Music school with tuition aimed at all ages. Also
run an instrument store. See listing in relevant section for details.

Nathan Rose Music Tuition
1 Skinner Street, Wolverhampton, WV1 4LD
tel: 01902 311 655
email: info@nathanrosemusic.co.uk
web: www.nathanrosemusic.co.uk
contact: Nathan Rose
instrument(s): Piano, Keyboard, Guitar, Drums, Vocal Coaching,
Saxophone, Clarinet
info: Teaches all instruments from beginners up to
diploma level. Covers ABRSM and LCM syllabuses. Taught from own
studios. Small music shop on site. 1 free lesson if you bring this
Unsigned Guide listing along!

No Limitz Music Academy
56 Spencer Street, Hickley, Birmingham, B18 6DS
tel: 0121 236 1080/07796 340 802
email: info@nolimitzmusic.com
web: www.nolimitzmusic.com
contact: David Largie
instrument(s): Vocal Coaching
info: Singing school with individual and group lessons
held weekly. As well as providing professional singing tuition, No
Limitz is also dedicated to assisting in the artistic development of their
students.

The Oxygen Rooms
122 Barr Street, Hockley, Birmingham, B19 3DE
tel: 0121 551 7001
web: www.theoxygenrooms.com
contact: Nick Rendall
instrument(s): Drums, Vocals, DJing
info: All levels and styles welcome. Recording and
rehearsal space also available. See relevant entries for details.

Punch
Studio 112-113, The Greenhouse, Custard Factory, Gibb Street,
Birmingham, B9 4AA
tel: 0121 224 7444
fax: 0121 224 7411
email: info@punch-records.co.uk
web: www.punch-records.co.uk
contact: Ammo
instrument(s): Djing, MCing, Percussion
info: Specialise in educational music activities for young
people. Offer workshops covering DJing, MCing, percussion and music
production. Focus on Urban and Hip-Hop styles. Also involved in
promotion, production and marketing.

Richard Paul Singing Tuition ARCM, LTCL
5 Denmark Villas, Walsall Road, Pipe Hill, Lichfield, Staffordshire,
WS13 8JS
tel: 01543 252 372
email: richardsingteach@aol.com
contact: Richard Paul
instrument(s): Vocal Coaching
info: Teaches beginner to advanced level in singing, as
well as intermediate and advanced in drums. Can enter students for a
variety of exam syllabuses. Teaches from home.

Rob Grinsted
Rosemary House, Essington, Staffordshire, WV11 2RA
tel: 01922 710 601
email: robgrinsted@hotmail.com
contact: Rob Grinsted
instrument(s): Piano, Keyboard
info: Teaches any age to Grade 6 standard. Generally
follows ABRSM syllabus, but is flexible. Teaches mainly Classical
repertoire on the piano. Lessons held from his own home.

Rose Drum Studios
3 Hoggs Field, Eastwood, Nottingham, NG16 3HN
tel: 01773 710 927
email: drumstudio@btinternet.com
web: www.rose-studios.co.uk
contact: Duncan Rose
instrument(s): Drums
info: Beginner to intermediate level. Covers the Gigajam
syllabus which is graded. Lessons held both from studios, and also
from tutor's premises.

Sally Rivers
7 Hardwick Close, Trentham, Stoke On Trent, Staffordshire, ST4 8TU
tel: 01782 644 287/07957 127 348
email: thesessionsinger@tiscali.co.uk
web: www.my-vocalcoach.co.uk
instrument(s): Vocal Coaching
info: Professional session singer who aims to develop
modern vocal style covering Rock, Pop, R&B and Soul genres. Normally
coaches towards a particular event e.g. concert, gig and recording,
and so lessons are tailored to each student's individual needs. Tends
to teach from her studio, but will travel. Experience in working in the
music industry. Can offer support and guidance.

Simply Singing
79 Russell Road, Forest Fields, Nottingham, NG7 6HA
tel: 0115 912 1146/07790 454 622
email: info@simply-singing.com
web: www.simply-singing.com
contact: Sarah Simmonds
instrument(s): Vocal Coaching
info: Teaches students from 10 years. All styles and
levels.

Sly Arts
35 Lytham Road, Leicester, LE2 1YD
tel: 07815 051 632
email: jon@slyarts.co.uk
web: www.artsark.com/sly
contact: Jon Knight
instrument(s): Range of workshops
info: Series of youth workshops, although no strict age
limit. Studio or live performance recording of solo artists, bands, DJs
and all creative types. Composing and recording workshops where you
can create and record your own material. Record a pro-standard cover
version of your favourite tune.

TUITION/TRAINING

Still Water Music
22 Peveril Drive, Sutton-In-Ashfield, Nottinghamshire, NG17 2GT
tel: 01623 557 255
contact: Peter Smith
instrument(s): Guitar
info: Teach all ages and specialise in beginners. Lessons held from their own home.

Strings
5 Blackwell Street, Kidderminster, Worcestershire, DY10 2DP
tel: 01562 823 584
email: lawrencelynch@gmail.com
contact: Lawrence Lynch
instrument(s): Electric and Acoustic Guitar, Bass
info: 2 teachers providing lessons from their own premises.

Susan Lake Piano ALCM (TD)
47 Farm Road, Chilwell, Nottinghamshire, NG9 5DA
tel: 0115 913 3627
contact: Susan Lake
instrument(s): Piano
info: Classical tuition from beginner to Grade 8 level. Teaches from home.

NORTHEAST

Adrian Biddulph
3 Willbore Croft, School Aycliffe, Newton Aycliffe, County Durham, DL5 6TF
tel: 01325 320 398
email: adrian@bidfmusic.freeserve.co.uk
instrument(s): Piano, Theory
info: All levels taught. Teach from home.

Bev Crawley
63 Castle View, Amble, Morpeth, Northumberland, NE65 0NN
tel: 01665 711 196
instrument(s): Piano, Pipe Organ
info: Teaches all levels from her own home.

Billy Johnson Guitar Tuition
31 Exeter Road, North Tyneside, Tyne & Wear, NE28 9HG
tel: 07795 066 406
email: billy8998@msn.com
web: www.billyjohnson.co.uk
instrument(s): Guitar
info: Teaches all levels of guitar from his own premises.

Brian Arthur
1 Riverbank, Warkworth, Northumberland, NE65 0UZ
tel: 01665 712 532
instrument(s): Guitar and other stringed instruments
info: Speciality in Classical but also teaches Jazz and Rock. Follows the Associated Board. All ages and levels to an advanced level.

Cathy Edmunds
5 Waldron Street, Bishop Auckland, County Durham, DL14 7DS
tel: 01388 608 815/07939 533 471
email: cathyedmunds@msn.com
instrument(s): Violin, Viola, Piano
info: Teach all levels and all ages and will choose the syllabus to suit the pupil. Teaches from home.

Don Fraser ALCM
41 St. Alban's Cresent, Heaton, Newcastle Upon Tyne, Tyne & Wear, NE6 5UQ
tel: 0191 265 8108
instrument(s): Piano, Organ, Keyboard
info: Teaches all levels in pupils home.

Ebony & Ivory School Of Music
8 Caldley Gardens, Ingleby Barwick, Stockton On Tees, Northumberland, TS17 5HW
tel: 01642 761 017
email: fewebster@ntlworld.com
contact: Sue Webster
instrument(s): Piano, Keyboard
info: Group tuition. Associated Board and Guild Of Music examinations.

Emma Fisk
Peterlee, County Durham
tel: 07939 533 471
email: em@therye.demon.co.uk
instrument(s): Violin
info: Teaches a range of styles. All levels and ages. LTTL and MMUS qualification.

G. Keeler Guitar Tuition
30 Green Road, Skelton-In-Cleveland, Saltburn-By-The-Sea, Cleveland, TS12 2BQ
tel: 01287 654 393
email: geoffkeeler@hotmail.com
instrument(s): Guitar, Bass
info: Electric and Acoustic guitar. All levels and abilities. Teaches RGT exams. Works from his own premises.

G.A. Wood
Braeburn, Fair Hill, Haltwhistle, NE49 9ED
tel: 01434 322 472
instrument(s): Piano, Organ, Keyboard, Elocution
info: All levels and grades. Standard examinations, up to diploma and first degree. Will mostly teach in students own home, but has own premises if preferred.

Global Entertainment
Hawethorn House, Forth Banks, Newcastle Upon Tyne, NE1 3SG
tel: 0191 221 1666
fax: 0191 221 1777
email: info@globalmusicbiz.co.uk
web: www.globalmusicbiz.co.uk
contact: Terry Hollingsworth
instrument(s): Business training for Music and Media industries
info: Provide introduction courses to the music industry. See website or contact Terry for further details. Global Entertainment is linked to Subversive Records, 10xBetter management and PR company. See listings in relevant sections for further details.

Helen Barber
Brancepeth Castle, Brancepeth, Durham, County Durham, DH7 8DE
tel: 01913 782 988
instrument(s): Vocal Coaching
info: Teaches all levels from home.

Jane Ford Singing Tuition
Ormuz House, 11 North Green, Staindrop, Darlington, County Durham, DL2 3JN
tel: 01833 660 028
instrument(s): Classical Singing, Voice Production
info: Works from home and teaches all levels. Will cover Associated Board exams.

Jane Marie School Of Music
35 Danesmoor Cresent, Darlington, County Durham, DL3 8NJ
tel: 01325 460 506
email: a.chloe@ntlworld.com
instrument(s): Piano, Keyboard, Organ, Guitar
info: Teaches London College Of Music qualifications. All levels. Lessons held at tutor's premises.

Jeremy Hockin Guitar Tutoring
23 Watt Street, Merton, County Durham, SR7 9AT
tel: 0191 526 5580
contact: Jeremy Hockin
instrument(s): Guitar
info: Rock and Blues styles taught. All levels up to advanced. Lessons from tutor's premises.

John Rhodes Guitar Tuition
tel: 01642 616 618
web: www.king-of-chords.com
instrument(s): Guitar
info: John teaches from his own home. Was voted the best local guitar teacher by Cleveland Scene Magazine.

John Temple
35 North View Terrace, Colliery Row, Houghton-le-Spring, Tyne & Wear, DH4 5NN
tel: 07814 321 603/0191 385 4968
email: temjohn@hotmail.co.uk
instrument(s): Piano, Electronic Keyboard, Music Theory
info: Pupils are entered for Associated Board exams. All ages. Beginner to intermediate levels. Interest in Classical, Jazz and Blues.

Karin Carter
16 Priors Grange, High Tittington, Durham, DH6 1DA
tel: 0191 372 0953
email: adagioval@yahoo.co.uk
instrument(s): Vocal Coaching
info: Rockschool vocal syllabus. Covers and teaches all genres except Classical. All levels and ages.

Katherine Jones School Of Music
17 Forth Court, South Shields, Tyne & Wear, NE34 0NP
tel: 0191 456 5681
instrument(s): Claranet, Saxophone, Piano
info: Teaches Classical, Jazz and Pop music. All ages and abilities. Covers all major exam boards. Works from home.

Kevin Fairless
tel:	07778 277 597
email:	kevinfairless@tinyworld.co.uk
instrument(s):	Piano
info:	Teaches all genres, all ages and all levels. Also

teaches music appreciation and history of music.

Louise Howarth
2 Boyd Street, Consett, County Durham, DH8 7JY
tel:	01207 506 342
email:	nmlmusic@fairadsl.co.uk
instrument(s):	Clarinet, Saxophone, Flute
info:	Teaches up to diploma level for all levels and ages.

Follows the Associated Board syllabus.

Michael Woods Guitar Tuition
32 Fernwood Avenue, Newcastle Upon Tyne, Tyne & Wear, NE3 5DL
tel:	0191 284 8707
instrument(s):	Guitar
info:	Teaches all levels of guitar and will enter students

for exams. Lessons held at tutor's premises.

Miss Helen Inglis
8 Broom Hall Dive, Ushaw, Moor, Durham, DH7 7NU
tel:	07837 121 777
email:	heleninglis@hotmail.com
instrument(s):	Piano, Clarinet, Saxophone, Flute, Oboe, Recorder,

Music Theory
info:	Follows ABRSM, EDExcel and QA syllabus.

Teaches all levels and ages. Very experienced in taking rehearsals and accompanying. Prefers teaching students within the area.

Muriel Smith
Swinburne Lodge, 2A Swinburne Road, Darlington, DL3 7TB
tel:	07812 188 212
email:	muriel.smith3@btinternet.com
instrument(s):	Vocal Coaching
info:	Follows the Associated Board and Trinity Music

Theatre syllabus. All levels and all ages. Teaches up to Grade 8 and beyond.

Musicworks (Northern) Ltd.
25 Emerald Street, Saltburn-By-The-Sea, Cleveland, TS12 1EE
tel:	01287 209 023
email:	musicworks@ntlworld.com
contact:	Tony Adams
instrument(s):	All instruments
info:	Teaches students of all levels and ages. Works with

schools and teach at their premises or the student's home.

Newcastle Drum Centre Ltd.
10-12 Akenside Hill, Newcastle Upon Tyne, NE1 3XP
tel:	0191 221 0301
email:	team@newcastledrum.co.uk
web:	www.newcastledrum.co.uk
instrument(s):	Drums
info:	Full in-store drum kit tuition service, utilising

the latest electronic equipment in 2 purpose built booths. Suitable for absolute beginners through to accomplished players. Tuition tailored to suit individual requirements. Cover Guildhall School of Music and Drama examinations for drum kit and snare drum Grades 1 to 8. Also have an instrument store. See listing in relevant section for details.

Night Owl Music
43 The Riding, Newcastle Upon Tyne, Tyne & Wear, NE3 4LQ
tel:	0191 213 2422/07761 753 054
contact:	Dave Black
instrument(s):	Guitar, Bass, Keyboard
info:	Teach mainly Rock and Blues. Also repairs and

sells guitars. Will teach in your home or his premises. PA, amps and lights also available to hire.

North East Music Academy
19 Punstall Terrace, Sunderland, Tyne & Wear, SR2 7AG
tel:	0191 510 3628/07720 620 433
instrument(s):	Piano, Organ, Keyboard
info:	Teaches from home to all levels and ages. Exam

syllabus covered. Can teach either group or one to one sessions.

Paul Tilley
33 Hawkstone Close, Guisborough, Cleveland, TS14 7PE
tel:	01287 634 819
instrument(s):	Snare Drum, Drums
info:	Teaches Guildhall School Of Music and London

College Of Music grades. Paul teaches from home in his purpose built studio.

Peter J.L. Mason
Durham, SR8 3ST
tel:	07798 798 096
email:	pj23lm@aol.com
instrument(s):	Brass
info:	Specialise in euphonium and trombone tuition.

Beginner to advanced levels. 30 years experience in brass military band and orchestra, as well as brass quintet and woodwind quintet. Peter has also taught in primary and senior schools as a Peripatetic Brass Teacher.

Peter Tickell
70 Briddlestone Road, Heaton, Newcastle Upon Tyne, Tyne & Wear, NE6 5SL
tel:	07818 038 493
email:	petertickell@hotmail.com
instrument(s):	Violin
info:	Traditional Folk and Classical training. Peter will

teach the ABRSM syllabus. Lessons held from his own premises.

Robertson Guitar School
21 Shaftesbury Crescent, North Shields, Tyne & Wear, NE30 3LR
tel:	0191 252 7014
email:	acr.rgsuk@tiscali.co.uk
contact:	Alan Robertson
instrument(s):	Guitar
info:	From Rock to Classical, and beginner to degree

level. Will make home visits, or can travel to student's homes.

The Sage Academy Of Performing Arts
Potts Street, Newcastle Upon Tyne, Tyne & Wear, NE6 1ED
tel:	0191 224 5604
fax:	0191 224 5604
web:	www.sage-academy.co.uk
contact:	Lucy
instrument(s):	Performing Arts
info:	Teaches all levels of ability.

South Durham Drum Centre
17 Gladstone Terrace, Ferryhill, County Durham, DL17 0AA
tel:	07779 571 398
instrument(s):	Drums
info:	Enter for Guildhall examinations. All genres and all

ages.

Steve Blakeburn
46 Rockwell ave, Darlington, County Durham, DL1 2AX
tel:	07786 982 890
email:	steviebongo@hotmail.com
instrument(s):	Drums, Percussion
info:	Any ages from beginner to intermediate. Will teach

most styles.

Steve McGarvie
141 Lansdowne Street, Darlington, County Durham, DL3 0NH
tel:	01325 241 941
email:	stevemcgarvie@hotmail.com
instrument(s):	Clarinet, Saxophone, Piano, Music Technology
info:	Follows the Associated Board syllabus. Teaches all

levels and all ages up to diploma standard and also takes big band and percussion ensembles.

Studio 64
90 Corporation Road, Middlesbrough, TS1 2RE
tel:	01642 860 006
fax:	01642 860 006
email:	info@studio64.org.uk
web:	www.studio64.org.uk
instrument(s):	Variety of workshops
info:	Run workshops and courses including Sound

Recording Skills, DJ Skills, Music Technology and Songwriting Skills. Studio 64 also provide recording and rehearsal facilities, equipment hire and duplication services. See listings in relevant sections for further details.

T. Lawson Music Tuition
10 Westfields, School Aycliffe, Newton Aycliffe, County Durham, DL5 6PX
tel:	01325 312 883
email:	terrence@lawson7492.fsnet.co.uk
instrument(s):	Piano, Vocal Coaching, Theory
info:	Teaches pupils from beginner to diploma level

including Associated Board examinations. Teaches from home.

Wilfred Harker
Hawthorne House, Rumby Hill Bank, Howden Le Wear, Crook, County Durham, DL15 8AF
tel:	01388 765 258
instrument(s):	Piano, Keyboard

Yzen Eng - Piano Tuition
8 Hadleigh Court, Coxhoe, Durham, Tyne & Wear, DH6 4SJ
tel: 0191 377 8660
instrument(s): Piano, Keyboard, Bass
info: Classical, Jazz and Pop. Beginner to advanced levels of all ages. Teaches from student's homes, as well as his own premises.

NORTHWEST

A&C Hamilton Technics Music Academy
946-950 Blackpool Road, Lea, Preston, PR2 1XN
tel: 01772 722 468
email: info@achamilton.co.uk
web: www.achamilton.co.uk
instrument(s): Guitar, Keyboard, Piano, Drums, Saxophone, Flute, Clarinet
info: Large number of teachers available, offering both group or individual lessons. Tuition available throughout the day and evenings. Reasonable rates. Free trial lesson available.

A1 Guitar Tuition
36 Dakins Road, Leigh, Lancashire, WN7 3AU
tel: 01942 517 256
contact: Daniel
instrument(s): Guitar
info: Tuition in all styles of guitar from beginner to advanced. Mobile service available. Exam syllabus for Classical guitar can be covered if required.

Ad Lib Music
Sale, Manchester
tel: 0161 962 9183
contact: David Love
instrument(s): Guitar, Clarinet, Saxophone, Trumpet, Flute
info: Pop, Classical and Jazz from beginner to Grade 8. Teaches from own home.

Airtight Productions
Unit 16, Albany Road Trading Estate, Albany Road, Manchester, M21 0AZ
tel: 0161 881 5157
email: ant@airtightproductions.co.uk
web: www.airtightproductions.co.uk
contact: Antony Davie
instrument(s): Media Production training
info: Offer one to one tuition in areas of media production including setting up your own studio, studio engineering, music software and sound mixing.

Alan Worswick Piano Teacher
5 Tanyard Close, Coppull, PR7 5BT
tel: 01257 792 407
contact: Alan
instrument(s): Piano
info: Teach beginner to advanced standard following the ABRSM syllabus. Explores different styles of music. Lessons held from home.

Alison Skidmore LTCL
Hampden Househaw, Hampden Road, Shaw, Oldham, OL2 8QB
tel: 01706 663 811
contact: Alison Skidmore
instrument(s): Vocal Coaching
info: Mainly vocal training, although beginner keyboard tuition available. Songwriting skills development, music theory and microphone instruction also available. Recording facilities also available.

Andrew Norwood
108a Barlow Moor Road, Manchester, M20 2PN
tel: 0161 434 2407
email: andrewnorwood@hotmail.com
instrument(s): Guitar
info: Teaches beginner to intermediate.

Arabesque Music
34 Scargreen Avenue, Liverpool, L11 3BB
tel: 0151 226 8893
contact: Joanne Bolland
instrument(s): Guitar, Violin, Flute, Clarinet, Saxophone, Piano, Keyboards
info: Music tuition in your own home. All levels.

Armstrong Learning
Studio 1, Chorlton Mill, 26 Hulme Street, Manchester, M1 5GL
tel: 0161 247 7733
fax: 0161 247 7779
email: info@armstronglearning.co.uk
web: www.armstronglearning.co.uk
info: Jobs driven music industry training packages. See display ad.

Astin's
Fleetwood Music Academy, 52 Harris Street, Fleetwood, FY7 6QT
tel: 01253 777 556
contact: Hazel Astin
instrument(s): Electronic Keyboard, Vocal Coaching
info: All levels welcome. On contacting Hazel for lessons, she will carry out an initial assessment. London College of Music exam syllabus can be taught for keyboard.

Bandskool
PO Box 449, Altrincham, WA14 5WQ
tel: 0161 972 0862
email: bandskool@tiscali.co.uk
web: www.bandskool.co.uk
contact: Andrew Turnbull
info: Bandskool was created to help young musicians who are part of, or looking to form a band. Variety of musical genres covered such as Metal, Punk, Blues, Pop, Soul and Indie. Skills taught include writing your own music, playing together, arranging covers, and putting on a professional performance. Band exams offered. Recording sessions also available.

Barrie Owen Drum Tuition
Graceland, Long Lane, Heath Charnock, Chorley, Lancashire, PR6 9EQ
tel: 01257 474 407
contact: Barrie Owen
instrument(s): Drums, Percussion
info: Teach all styles and levels from music studio.

Blackburn School of Music
53 Preston New Road, Blackburn, Lancashire, BB2 6AY
tel: 01254 262 888
fax: 01254 690 258
email: pagbsm@aol.com
web: www.blackburnschoolofmusic.co.uk
contact: Paul Greenhalgh
info: Instrumental and vocal tuition on an individual basis. Instruments include guitars, percussion, keyboard, piano, brass and woodwind. All styles catered for. Creative learning environment.

Brian Costello Drum Tuition
23 Levens Grove, Blackpool, FY1 5PP
tel: 01253 314 545
email: bricostello@hotmail.com
instrument(s): Drums, Latin Percussion
info: Drums and percussion tuition in all styles including Rock, Jazz and Latin. Call Brian for more details.

Bridge Street Music School
Above Aardvark Music, 67 Bridge Street, Warrington, Cheshire, WA1 2HJ
tel: 01925 657 833
email: tuition@aardvark-music.co.uk
web: www.aardvark-music.co.uk
contact: Louise McColl
info: High quality musical tuition.

Broughton Music Academy
506-508 Garstang Road, Broughton, Preston, Lancashire, PR3 5HE
tel: 01772 864 300
email: bmamusic@yahoo.co.uk
instrument(s): Wide range of instruments
info: Tuition for all ages and levels in a variety of instruments including guitar, piano, keyboard, drums, flute, clarinet, saxophone, violin, brass, vocal, as well as Music Theory. ABRSM examination centre.

Burke's Guitar Tuition
20 Napier Street, Hazel Grove, Stockport, SK7 4EW
tel: 0161 355 6779
email: kevinburke.guitar@ntlworld.com
contact: Kevin
instrument(s): Guitar
info: One to one tuition for electric and Acoustic guitar. Teach all styles and all levels. Lessons held on tutor's premises. Will cover RGT exam syllabus if required.

C.M.V.C.
28 Withington Road, Manchester, M16 8BX
tel: 0161 226 3911
email: carolinemrrtt@hotmail.com
contact: Caroline Marriott
info: C.M.V.C. have a team of coaches across the North West who offer private vocal coaching, studio coaching, workshops, performance direction and corporate speech and training days. Contact Caroline Marriott, Director of Coaching.

Campbell Singing Tuition
31 Lyndon Park Road, Ewood Bridge, Rossendale, Lancashire, BB4 6LZ
tel: 01706 240 008
contact: Margo Campbell
instrument(s): Vocal
info: Teaches all styles from beginner to professional. 7 years old plus.

Carnegie Guitar & Drum Workshops
Carnegie Theatre, Finkle Street, Workington, Cumbria, CA14 2BD
tel: 01900 602 122
email: carnegie@allerdale.gov.uk
contact: Paul Shirwin, Jimmy Graham
instrument(s): Guitar, Drums
info: Workshops every Saturday for any age above 10 years. Aimed at all levels. Experienced tutors. 10 week course available costing £30.

Carol Jackson-Crook
38 Hawkshead Avenue, Euxton, Chorley, PR7 6NZ
tel: 01257 260 876
email: carol.crook@blueyonder.co.uk
contact: Carol
instrument(s): Organ, Keyboard
info: All levels taught. Can cover Victoria College of Music syllabus. Lessons held either at tutor's premises or in your own home.

Cheadle Hulme Music Academy
5 Langdale Road, Bramhall, Cheshire, SK7 1DH
tel: 0161 439 0091/07885 027 909
contact: Sheila Brammer
instrument(s): Range of instruments, Vocal Coaching
info: Individual and group lessons. Classical and contemporary styles. Preparation for music schools. GCSE and A Level work also undertaken. Regular concerts performed by students. Qualified teachers in safe environment with excellent facilities.

Cheryl Batkin
Greater Manchester
tel: 0161 483 9690/07931 387 281
instrument(s): Vocals
info: Vocal coaching for all ages and levels. Lessons held from premises based in either Hazel Grove or Droylsden.

Chetham's School of Music
Long Millgate, Manchester, M3 1SB
tel: 0161 834 9644
fax: 0161 839 3609
email: chets@chethams.com chets@chethms.com chets@chethms.com
web: www.chethams.com
instrument(s): Strings, Brass, Percussion, Woodwind, Keyboard, Vocal Coaching
info: Chetham's School of Music is a unique school and draws pupils from many different backgrounds, from all over the UK and abroad. The school sets out to educate boys and girls who are admitted solely on the basis of musical audition. Pupils develop a specialist interest to the highest level, which may be in an orchestral instrument, guitar, keyboard, voice, electronic music, jazz or composition, and all sing in choirs.

Chris Dumigan
14 Rochester Road, Urmston, Manchester, M41 0RL
tel: 0161 747 3851
email: c.dumigan@ntlworld.com
instrument(s): Guitar, Bass
info: Tuition in Classical and Acoustic guitar, and basic tuition for bass. Can cover exam syllabus if necessary. Mobile service available during the day. Evening lessons held from tutor's premises.

Armstrong Learning
Studio 1, Chorlton Mill, 26 Hulme Street, Manchester, M1 5GL
tel: 0161 247 7733
fax: 0161 247 7779
email: info@armstronglearning.co.uk
web: www.armstronglearning.co.uk
contact: Adrian Armstrong
info: Jobs driven music industry training packages. Training and consultancy targeted at the creative industries.

Christine Horton Piano Forte
Wallasey
tel: 0151 639 5340
instrument(s): Piano
info: Associated Board of Royal School of Music exams. Grades 1 to 8 for both practical and theory. Composition around lyrics. All ages and all levels welcome.

City College Manchester
City Campus, Whitworth Street, Manchester, M1 3HB
tel: 0800 013 0213/0161 614 8000
web: www.ccm.ac.uk
instrument(s): Variety
info: City College Manchester provide a number of music based courses ranging from performance based syllabuses to music business and technology. Several campuses located in Greater Manchester. Contact for further information.

Clarion 2000 West Coast School of Music
No.1, 2 St. George's Square, Lytham St. Annes, FY8 2NY
tel: 01253 721 903
contact: John Durrant
instrument(s): Brass, Woodwind, Piano
info: All levels taught. Lessons held at teaching studio. Exam syllabus by Associated Board of the Royal School of Music.

Cleveleys Keyboard School
29 Beryl Avenue, Cleveleys, FY5 3BW
tel: 01253 829 719
contact: Alan Dyson
instrument(s): Keyboard, Organ, Piano
info: All levels welcome, from beginner to advanced. Free trial lesson.

Creative Industries UK Ltd.
Offices 1 & 2, Tollbar Business Park, New Church Road, Stackstead, Bacup, OL13 0NA
tel: 01706 870 110
email: enquiries@creativeindustriesuk.com
contact: Sonia Ramsay
instrument(s): Range of workshops, Vocal Coaching
info: Complete artist development programme, including vocal coaching, demo production, choreography, portfolio and songwriting skills.

Crossroads Guitar Academy
7 Toronto Avenue, Fleetwood, FY7 8HB
tel: 01253 877 878
email: info@crossroadsguitaracademy.com
web: www.crossroadsguitaracademy.com
contact: Harold G. Jones
instrument(s): Range of stringed instruments
info: Acoustic, electric, resonator, bass, banjo, ukulele and mandolin tuition. Home lessons available. All ages and levels welcome.

D. Leatham Piano & Keyboard Tuition
34 Daleswood Avenue, Whitefield, Manchester, M45 7WP
tel: 0161 766 1410
contact: David Leatham
instrument(s): Piano, Keyboard
info: Teaches piano and keyboard. Jazz, Pop and Classical styles.

Dane Chalfin & Associates Vocal Studio
Liverpool Institute of Performing Arts, Mount Street, Liverpool, L1 9HF
tel: 01457 763 945
email: info@danechalfin.com
web: www.danechalfin.com
instrument(s): Vocal Coaching
info: Offer private or group master classes, workshops and consultations. Can teach from studio or location. Visit the website for full details of both Dane Chalfin and Associates. Offices based in Manchester also.

Darren Atkins Guitar Tuition
134 Ashworth Street, Baxingdon, Lancashire, BB5 2QB
tel: 01254 390 464
instrument(s): Guitar
info: All styles covered. Acoustic and electric guitar. Beginners welcome. Lessons taught from tutor's premises.

Dave Doherty
35 Chelmsford Place, Chorley, PR7 2PE
tel: 01257 274 299
instrument(s): Guitar and Music Theory
info: Guitar tuition including tablature and notation. Teaching hours between 3.30pm and 10pm.

David Fillingham
85 Gathurst Road, Orrel, Wigan, WN5 8QJ
tel: 01942 203 809
email: daxeguru@blueyonder.co.uk
instrument(s): Guitar, Bass
info: Electric, Acoustic and bass guitar. Any style catered for. Preparation for exams.

David Ireland
12 Barley Field, Bamber Bridge, Preston, PR5 8J2
tel: 01772 322 286
instrument(s): Keyboard, Organ
info: Enjoyable lessons in own home. Course designed to student's specifications. Can cover Classical to Chart music.

Dean Aldred
300 Greenside Lane, Manchester, M43 7SL
tel: 07709 784 279
email: docdread@yahoo.co.uk
contact: Dean Aldred
instrument(s): Music Technology
info: Mobile music technology teacher.

Denise Flanagan
Salford, Manchester
tel: 07989 074 748
instrument(s): Violin, Fiddle
info: Vibrant, versatile violin and feisty, fabulous fiddle. All styles covered including Jazz, Folk, Irish Traditional, Rock and Dance. Available for teaching, playing and studio work.

Des James Guitar Tuition
46 Park Road, Adlington, Chorley, PR7 4HZ
tel: 01257 483 540
email: desjames@hotmail.com
instrument(s): Guitar
info: Classical, Blues and Rock tuition available on both Acoustic and electric guitar. Music theory. Mobile service if required.

Folkus
55 The Strand, Fleetwood, FY7 8NP
tel: 01253 872 317/01254 548 77
fax: 01253 878 382
email: alanbell@fylde-folk-fest.demon.co.uk
contact: Alan Bell
instrument(s): Guitar, Melodeon, Penny Whistle, Fiddle, Bodhran, Vocal Coaching
info: Range of instruments and vocal tuition in Folk style. Call for details of workshops.

Graham Collier
43 Timperley Lane, Leigh, WN7 3DZ
tel: 01942 679 936
email: graham.collier4@btinternet.com
instrument(s): Piano, Keyboard
info: Grade exam tuition if required. All levels welcome.

GT Music
11 Sandringham Close, Blackburn, Lancashire, BB1 8QJ
tel: 01254 668 800/01254 664 202
contact: Gary Taylor
instrument(s): Piano, Keyboard, Guitar
info: Teach all levels and grades. Can teach to exam level - London College of Music, RGT and Rockschool.

The Guitar & Bass Studio
10 Hall Lane, Connahs Quay, Deeside, CH5 4LX
tel: 01244 822 535
email: michael@mclarke55.freeserve.co.uk
web: www.michaelclarkestudio.com
contact: Michael Clarke
instrument(s): Guitar, Bass
info: First lesson is free. Teaches from the studio. All levels welcome.

The Guitar Studio
54 Stanway Road, Whitefield, Manchester, M45 8FX
tel: 0161 272 1048
email: justin@theguitarstudio.co.uk
web: www.theguitarstudio.co.uk
contact: Justin Proudman
instrument(s): Guitar
info: Guitar lessons in all contemporary styles by a professionally trained, gigging musician.

Henshaws Guitar School
Office 5, 72-74 Topping Street, Blackpool, FY1 3AD
tel: 01253 751 450
contact: S. Henshaw
instrument(s): Guitar
info: FVCM, LVCM (Hons), AVCM (Hons) qualified. Classical guitar tuition. Theory, diplomas and grade exams. All levels welcome.

Heylings Music
Highfield House, 114 Park Road, Chorley, PR7 1QY
tel: 01257 267 264
contact: Mr. Bowden
instrument(s): Vocal Coaching, Piano, Keyboard, Violin, Flute, Guitar
info: Singing and instrumental, from beginner to diploma levels. All ages welcome. For performing, fun or exams. All styles of guitar and singing tuition available.

Hugh Macleod Guitar Tuition
181 Ashfield Road, Rochdale, OL11 1QH
tel: 01706 644 615
email: cloudy8511@yahoo.co.uk
contact: Hugh Macleod
instrument(s): Guitar
info: Classical, Country, Blues and Rags. Teaches at all levels.

Ian Hare
The Porch, Skiddaw Lodge, Crosthwaite Road, Keswick, Cumbria, CA12 5QA
tel: 01768 773 342
instrument(s): Piano, Organ, Vocal Coaching
info: Music theory tuition also available. Classical training.

Irene Smith
Heather Rise, Thurston Clough Road, Scouthead, Oldham, Lancashire, OL4 3RX
tel: 01457 874 509
instrument(s): Guitar, Piano, Keyboard, Theory, Vocal Coaching
info: All levels and all ages. Lessons held from tutor's premises.

John Forster
1 Lonsdale Gardens, Crosby Village, Maryport, Cumbria, CA15 6TH
tel: 01900 814 113
email: forsterguitarist@aol.com
web: www.johnforsterguitars.co.uk
instrument(s): Guitar, Bass
info: John has 42 years teaching experience and covers all contemporary styles. Repairs on all guitars also available.

John Miller
116 Elterwater Avenue, Moor Close, Workington, Cumbria, CA14 3LF
tel: 01900 608 483
instrument(s): Guitar, Bass and all fretted instruments
info: All levels and all styles welcome.

Jon Mills Guitar Tuition
23 New Mount Street, Manchester, M4 4DE
tel: 07817 559 634
email: jonmillsguitartuition@yahoo.co.uk
instrument(s): Guitar
info: Electric and Acoustic guitar. Lessons held at tutor's premises. Intermediate to advanced level.

Learn Music Co.
Holy Spirit Community Hall, East Prescot Road, Liverpool, L14 5NA
tel: 0151 475 0001
email: lessons@learnmusic.co.uk
web: www.learnmusic.co.uk
instrument(s): All
info: Teach a wide range of instruments from beginner to advanced. See the website for full details.

Little Notes Music School
12 Starworth Drive, Wirral, CH62 1HJ
tel: 0845 166 2475
email: littlenotes@littlenotes.co.uk
web: www.littlenotes.co.uk
instrument(s): Piano, Theory
info: Also provide tuition and assistance with song writing. All levels and ages catered for. Cover Associated Board of Royal School of Music syllabus and happy to enter students for other board examinations also. Music theory up to degree level. Lessons held at tutors premises.

Liverpool Yamaha Music School Ltd.
4th Floor, 42 Whitechapel, Liverpool, L1 6EF
tel: 0151 226 2515
email: stuart.monkcom@liverpool.gov.uk
web: www.yamaha-music.co.uk
contact: Stuart Monkcom
instrument(s): Range of instruments, Vocal Coaching
info: Keyboard, piano, guitar, flute, clarinet, saxophone, violin and vocal tuition. School houses 7 studios and employs 8 teachers. Courses run in 11 week terms, pay per term (hourly rate of £9.00). Introductory lesson at £5 with no obligation. Optional grade exams. Yamaha Music School also has branches in Stockport, Formby, Chester, Owestry, Altrincham, Bury, Macclesfield, Holmfirth, Blackburn, Blackpool and across the rest of the UK. Check website for individual branch contact details.

Manchester MIDI School
Bexley Chanbers, Bexley Square, M3 6DB
tel: 0161 8334 722
fax: 0161 839 3030
email: mail@midischool.com
web: www.midischool.com
info: Tuition in audio tools (including Cubase), editing, sampling and production. Courses available at MMS include diplomas in Music Construction and Production and Commercial Engineering, as well as intensive DJ training for beginners and intermediates. One to one training is offered on and off site. In-house studios. Free monthly taster sessions in DJing and Production.

Margin Music Tuition Centre
3 Market Place, Macclesfield, Cheshire, SK10 1EB
tel: 01625 619 013
fax: 01625 269 013
email: marginmusic@aol.com
web: www.marginmusic.co.uk
contact: Mary Kirkpatrick
instrument(s):   Guitar, Keyboard, Piano
info: All levels welcome.

Mark Bateson
88 Lynwood Avenue, Darwen, Lancashire, BB3 0HZ
tel: 07719 219 421
email: info@elitemusicservices.co.uk
web: www.elitemusicservicess.co.uk
instrument(s):   Guitar, V ocal Coaching
info: Run songwriter workshops. All levels welcome.
Teach from their studio. See website for full details.

Mark Spencer
Bolton
tel: 01204 405 709
email: spenny1972@hotmail.com
web: www.bigredfireengine.com
instrument(s):   Guitar
info: Teaches beginner to advanced. All styles apart from
Jazz.

Marsh Mill School of Music
17a Marsh Mill Village, Thornton, Lancashire
tel: 01253 822 046
email: accordions@btinternet.com
web: www.accordionsonline.nstemp.com/school.htm
instrument(s):   Piano, Keyboard, Accordion
info: Tuition for all ages and levels through Associated
Board.

Melanie Sellars-McDonagh
14 Apple Tree Way, Oswaldtwistle, Accrington, Lancashire, BB5 0FB
tel: 01254 392 560/07909 831 409
web: www.singlikeapopstar.co.uk
instrument(s):   Vocal Coaching
info: Teaches all ages in contemporary singing styles
such as Pop, Musical Theatre, Jazz, Country & Western and R&B.
Teaches primarily from home, but takes workshops in studio. Syllabus
is determined by assessing the students needs, generally follows
Rockschool repertoire. Check website for email address.

Memorable Music
9 Sylvan Avenue, Sale, Cheshire, M33 3NP
tel: 0161 969 7080
email: tamara_lepp@yahoo.com
web: www.memorable-music.com
instrument(s):   Piano, Keyboard, Guitar, Theory
info: Tuition for processional singers and musicians.
Highly qualified tutor with over 25 years experience. All levels catered
for. Will cover exam syllabuses if required. Recommended by Royal
Northern College of Music. See also Tamara Lepp Singing Tuition.

Music Links
Brewery Arts Centre, 122a Highgate, Kendal, Cumbria, LA9 4HE
tel: 01539 735 083
email: musiclinks1@yahoo.co.uk
contact: Andy Halsey
instrument(s):   Wide range of training
info: Provide a variety of workshops from instrument
tuition such as percussion to composition and IT based music classes.
Contact by email or telephone for details of current workshops. Some
workshops are held at Brewery Arts Centre, although the majority
are on the road as Music Links have a music bus which travels the
county. Music Links are always interested in hearing from new business
partners.

The Music Place
32-34 Railway Street, Altrincham, WA14 2RE
tel: 0161 928 3337
email: lucy@themusicplace.co.uk
web: www.themusicplace.co.uk
contact: Lucy Howells
instrument(s):   Most instruments, Vocal Coaching
info: All abilities and ages welcome. Music Place is also
an examination centre so instrumental examinations can be taken on-
site.

The Music Rooms
High Street, Newton-Le-Willows, Merseyside, WA12 9SQ
tel: 01925 290 620
instrument(s):   Range of instruments
info: Tuition for guitar, drums, keyboard, piano,
saxophone, violin, clarinet and singing. Rockschool exam syllabus for
drums. All other instruments covered by Associated Board of Royal
School of Music. All levels catered for.

The Music Tuition Centre
22 Pikes Lane, Glossop, Cheshire, SK13 8EA
tel: 01457 866 920/01457 860 541
email: judith@watson355.freeserve.co.uk
contact: Rob Wombell
instrument(s):   Piano, Guitar, Woodwind
info: All styles covered, from Classical to Contemporary.
Also teach Music Technology.

New Deal for Musicians - MIC Service
City College, City Campus, Chorton Road, Manchester, M1 3HB
tel: 0161 279 7302
fax: 0161 279 7342
email: p.ellis@ccm.ac.uk
web: www.citycol.com/ndfm
info: MIC - Music Industry Consultants. See website for
further information.

New Deal for Musicians - MOLP Service
Armstrong Learning, 26 Hulme Street, Manchester, M1 5GL
tel: 0161 247 7733
fax: 0161 247 7779
email: info@armstronglearning.co.uk
web: www.armstronglearning.co.uk
contact: Rocco
info: MOLP - Music Open Learning Provision. Visit
website for more information.

One to One Guitar Tuition
16 Alexandra Road, Ashton-in-Makerfield, Greater Manchester,
WN4 8LG
tel: 01942 717 658
email: paul@one2oneguitartuition.freeserve.co.uk
contact: Paul Bowers
info: Acoustic and electric guitar. Modern and Classical
styles. Beginners welcome.

Opus 1 Music (Tuition)
102 Winter Hey Lane, Horwich, Bolton, Lancashire, BL6 7PJ
tel: 01204 690 756
contact: Donna Morgan
instrument(s):   Piano, Keyboard, Brass, Woodwind, Guitar, Vocal
Coaching
info: Also tuition in music theatre, speech, drama and
communication. Teach all levels from beginner to diploma standard.
Associated Board of Royal School of Music and London College of
Music & Media exam syllabus. Lessons taught from Opus 1 Music
premises.

Paul Mackay
8b High Sand Lane, Cockermouth, Cumbria, CA13 9NA
tel: 01900 828 194
email: paul@mac-musica.freeserve.co.uk
instrument(s):   Guitar, Bass
info: Electric and classical guitar. Theory and exams
if required. Also run recording studio, Mac Musica. See entry in
Recording Studios section for further details.

Phil Armitage (BA)
9 St. Mary's Close, Preston, PR1 4XN
tel: 01772 490 579
email: phil@oldschoolslim.wanadoo.co.uk
instrument(s):   Guitar, Banjo
info: Teaches classical, electric and bass guitar, as well
as banjo. Popular music theory.

Phil Millar Piano & Keyboard Tuition
28 Oak Cottages, Styal, Wilmslow, Cheshire, SK9 4JQ
tel: 01625 537 696
instrument(s):   Piano, /keyboard
info: All styles and levels. Support for GCSE and A Level
Music. Mobile service in local area.

Philip Garvin ALCM
Above 194 Ormskirk Road, Newtown, Wigan
tel: 07879 463 794
instrument(s):   Piano, Keyboard, Guitar, Organ, Music Theory
info: All levels welcome. Rockschool syllabus covered.

Philip Quigley
Clayton-Le-Woods, Lancashire, PR6 7UH
tel: 01772 323 489
email: philip@lancashire-music-lessons.org.uk
web: www.lancashire-music-lessons.org.uk
instrument(s):   Guitar, Bass, Keyboard, Piano, Drums, Vocal
Coaching, Theory
info: Beginner to advanced guitar. All styles.

bandskool

For information and online applications go to the Bandskool website:

Web: www.bandskool.co.uk

Phone: 0161 972 0862

Email: bandskool@tiscali.co.uk

Pop Guitar Tuition
7 Davenhill Road, Manchester, M19 2JU
tel: 0161 256 2969
email: pop.guitar@ntlworld.com
web: www.popguitartuition.co.uk
contact: Simon Sparkes
instrument(s): Guitar
info: Pop guitar covering Beatles and Oasis. Rock and Blues tuition for all levels. Music software tuition. Songwriting skills. Professional mobile service.

Powerplay Guitar Tuition
8 Kendal Grove, Whitefield, Manchester, M45 6FE
tel: 0161 796 8169
contact: Martin
instrument(s): Guitar
info: Acoustic and electric guitar. One to one or group sessions. Over 20 years experience. Song writing assistance. Lessons held from tutor's premises.

Robert V. Yates
60 New Drake Green, West Houghton, Bolton, Lancashire, BL5 2RF
tel: 01942 819 408
instrument(s): Piano, Keyboard
info: Tuition for all levels and ages. Do not cover exam syllabuses. Lessons held from tutor's own premises.

Rochdale Guitar Tuition
181 Ashfield Road, Rochdale, OL11 1QH
tel: 01706 644 615
instrument(s): Guitar
info: Teach Classical, Country, Blues, Folk and Spanish Acoustic guitar. From beginner to advanced levels.

Ruth Jones
Apartment G13, Castlegate, 2 Chester Road, Manchester, M15 4QG
tel: 07787 125 303
email: ruthleahjones@hotmail.com
instrument(s): Oboe, Cor Anglais
info: Teaches beginner to advanced level following the ABRSM. Students learn a Classical repertoire. Will teach from home or travel.

Sale School of Music
7a Heywood Road, Sale, Manchester, M33 3WB
tel: 0161 976 1291
email: p.molner@ntlworld.com
contact: Paul Molner
instrument(s): Guitar, Keyboard
info: Guitar specialist. All styles from Classical to Modern. Keyboard at beginner level. Introductory offer of 5 lessons at £5.75 per lesson. Tuition in other instruments by arrangement.

School of Sound Recording
10 Tariff Street, Manchester, M1 2FF
tel: 0161 228 1830
fax: 0161 236 0078
email: enquiries@s-s-r.com
web: www.s-s-r.com
info: Tuition in Audio Engineering, Music Production and Development (including Dance Music Production), Computer Music Technology, DJ skills and Video Editing. Facilities include 8, 16, 24 and 32 track studios, Audio Visual Suite, PC room, DJ Booth and MIDI Suite.

Scott Bradley's Guitar Tuition Dip. TCL
128 Denton Street, Carlisle, Cumbria, CA2 5JP
tel: 01228 531 286
email: scott_bradley128@hotmail.com
instrument(s): Guitar, Piano, Accordion
info: Teaches from beginner to diploma levels. For further details contact Scott on the above number.

Sean Corker
21 Lichfield Road, Urmston, Manchester, M41 0RU
tel: 07736 836 163
instrument(s): Guitar
info: 10 years teaching experience. Acoustic and electric. Tuition in all contemporary styles. Instrument rental available.

Sense of Sound
Parr Street Studios, 33-45 Parr Street, Liverpool, L1 4JN
tel: 0151 707 1050
email: jenny@senseofsound.net
web: www.senseofsound.net
contact: Jennifer John
instrument(s): Vocal Coaching
info: Tuition for all ages held from Sense of Sound premises. Also teach for bigger projects organised through schools, universities, record labels or management companies.

Sheila Gott
Stockport
tel: 0161 477 4373/07769 822 202
instrument(s): Vocal Coaching
info: 'Gotta voice, Wanna know how to use it, Gotta choice, How to Rock, soul and blues it!' Vocal tuition for all levels. Sheila's previous clients have included Take That and Robbie Williams.

Simon Bennett
14 Thornley Street, Hyde, Cheshire, SK14 1SY
tel: 0161 367 7451
instrument(s): Guitar
info: Full time mobile guitar tuition for both electric and Acoustic. All styles covered, but specialises in Rock. Exams and grades covered if required. In the course of his 10 year career, Simon has taught over 1000 pupils.

Singing Tuition
The Crescent, Presall, Poulton-Le-Fylde, Lancashire, FY6 0EE
tel: 01253 811 438
contact: Jill Bradley
instrument(s): Vocal Coaching
info: Pop and chart styles covered. Lessons conducted with backing tracks. All ages and levels welcome. Also run Times Stage School at Clevelys Park Methodist Church every Saturday afternoon for ages up to 16 years. The afternoon involves dancing, singing and drama. Contact Jill on the above number for further details.

Sound Technique Music Centre
123 Runcorn Road, Barnton, Northwich, CW8 4EX
tel: 01606 872 474
email: enquiries@soundtechnique.com
web: www.soundtechnique.com
contact: Simon Walker
instrument(s): All Keyboard instruments, Guitar, Drums
info: Specialists in contemporary styles including Rock. Music exam tuition if required. All ages and levels welcome. Open 6 days a week. Associated with Sounds Great Music retail.

SPICE (Student & Graduate Placements in Creative Enterprises)
Manchester
email: via website
web: www.spiceplacements.com
info: The SPICE project is designed to help students (from the University of Manchester and UMIST) and graduates (from any university) to gain work within Manchester's creative sector. This may include arts administration, performing arts, music, community arts, film graphic design, new media, as well as many other fields of work.

St. Aubyn's Academy of Music
404 Marine Road, East Morecambe, LA4 5AR
tel: 01524 410 202
fax: 01524 410 802
email: staubyns@promenademusic.co.uk
web: www.promenademusic.co.uk/services
contact: David Wood
instrument(s): Guitar, Bass, Piano, Organ, Keyboard, Vocal Coaching
info: Music theory tuition also available. Can enter pupils for London College of Music, Associated Board of the Royal Schools of Music or Rockschool examinations. All ages and abilities welcome.

Stuart Dottridge
Red Oak, Castle View Road, Appleby, Cumbria, CA16 6HH
tel: 01768 353 648
info: Theory and music workshops offered. Sheet music library facilities available to students. Preparation for Grade exams. Lessons in Appleby and Penrith.

Tamara Lepp Singing Tuition
9 Sylvan Avenue, Sale, M33 3NP
tel: 0161 969 7080
email: tamara_lepp@yahoo.com
instrument(s): Piano, Guitar, Vocal Coaching, Keyboard
info: Tuition for all levels held at tutor's own premises. Tamara also runs another tuition business. See entry for Memorable Music.

Technics DJ Academy
10 Tariff Street, Manchester, M1 2FF
tel: 0161 228 1830
fax: 0161 236 0078
email: enquiries@dj-academy.com
web: www.dj-academy.com
info: DJ training and tuition in Dance music production. Courses available include Audio Engineering, Computer Music Technology, Contemporary Popular Music, Sound Engineering and Video Editing. DJ Training over 2 hours, a weekend or 6 months.

Tim Scott
PO Box 118, Hazel Grove, Stockport, Cheshire, SK7 6WX
tel: 01625 261 879
email: timscottmusic@hotmail.com
web: www.timscott.co.uk
instrument(s):   Guitar, Bass
info: Tuition by professional gigging and session
guitarist with diploma from Guitar Institute. Lessons from teaching
studio. All styles and all levels catered for. Can teach Rockschool
syllabus.

The True Art of Singing
21 North Drive, Wallasey, Merseyside, CH45 0LZ
tel: 0151 639 1999
email: enquiries@trueartmanagement.com
contact: Mr robinson
instrument(s):   Vocal Coaching
info: All levels and ages welcome. Offer free trial lesson.
Lessons held at tutor's premises.

The Voice Coach
Body Works, Charlotte Street, Burnley, BB11 1LZ
tel: 01282 702 839
email: voice.coach@ntlworld.com
contact: Chris Broughton
instrument(s):   Vocal Coaching
info: Extension of range, strengthening of voice and
development of style. Preparation for studio work. All Popular styles
covered. Any level and any age.

Wirral Academy of Performing Arts
3 Firs Hill, Village Road, West Kirby, Wirral, CH48 7HP
tel: 0151 625 1763
fax: 0151 625 1763
email: wapauk@aol.com
web: www.wapa.uk.com
contact: Sheila
instrument(s):   Vocals, Acting, Dance
info: Singing, acting, performance and dance.
Contemporary styles covered from Rock to Pop to R&B. Have in-house
recording studios. Also run artist management company called Respect.

Wirral Drum Studio
112 Liscard Road, Wallasey, CH44 0AA
tel: 0151 638 7628
email: brian@wirraldrumstudio.co.uk
web: www.wirraldrumstudio.co.uk
contact: Brian Evans
instrument(s):   Drums
info: Tuition in a range of styles including Rock, Blues,
Jazz and Latin. Guildhall exam if required. Recording facilities.

Wirral School of Music
43 Shrewsbury Road, Oxton, Birkenhead, CH43 2JB
tel: 0151 652 1963
email: info@wirralschoolofmusic.co.uk
web: www.wirralschoolofmusic.co.uk
contact: Peter Rainsford
instrument(s):   Range of instruments
info: Tuition in all woodwind and strings, bass, Drums,
keyboard, piano, voice and saxophone. Contemporary and Classical
styles. Hire outs available on most instruments. Free trial on instrument
of your choice. Associated with Tafelmusik Music Shop. See listing in
relevant section.

SOUTHEAST

Alison Townend
Burnaby, Triplow Road, Fowlmere, SG8 7QT
tel: 01763 209 377
email: musicians@onetel.com
contact: Alison Townend
instrument(s):   Flute, Piano
info: Experienced teaching all ages and abilities,
following the Classical ABRSM syllabus. Teaches from home.

Andrew Mullens Piano
104 Wheble Drive, Woodley, Reading, Berkshire, RG5 3DU
tel: 0118 962 8455
email: andrew_mullens@hotmail.com
contact: Andrew Mullens
instrument(s):   Piano
info: All ages and all levels, including ABRSM exam
preparation. Plays Classical and Pop music. Lessons held from tutor's
home.

Anthony Witt Singing Tuition
7 Windrush Court, Reading, RG30 2NF
tel: 0118 950 8369
email: enquiries@witt.uk.com
web: www.witt.uk.com
contact: Anthony Witt
instrument(s):   Vocal Coaching, Piano
info: All singing styles taught from Classical to Heavy
Rock. Focus is mainly on public performance and students are
encouraged to perform in concerts and shows. Teaches advanced piano
at Grade 8 level and above only.

Catriona Kelbie Piano & Flute
102 Creighton Avenue, St. Albans, Hertfordshire, AL1 2LQ
tel: 01727 839 151
email: catriona@chgeorge.fsnet.co.uk
contact: Catriona Kelbie
instrument(s):   Piano, Flute, Music Theory
info: Mainly Classical tuition but can cover other styles
at student's request. Provides exam preparation up to diploma level.
Teaches from home.

Chris Walter Guitar Tuition
3 Foster Clarke Drive, Boughton Monchelsea, Maidstone, Kent,
ME17 4SZ
tel: 07957 214 822
contact: Chris Walter
instrument(s):   Guitar, Bass
info: Teaches beginner to advanced level in all styles
from Classical to Jazz to Rock. Do not cover exams. Teaches students in
their own homes.

Christine Long Piano
18 Augustus Drive, Basingstoke, Hampshire, RG23 8HU
tel: 01256 363 406
email: dcsmlong@yahoo.co.uk
contact: Christine Long
instrument(s):   Piano, Electric Organ, Keyboard, Music Theory
info: From beginner to advanced students, covering
ABRSM and London College exams. Teaches Classical, Jazz and Pop. 15
years experience.

Circus Bizarre Guitar Tuition
84f Valley Road, Portslade, Brighton, BN41 2TQ
tel: 01273 430 090
email: info@circusbizarre.co.uk
web: www.circusbizarre.co.uk
contact: John
instrument(s):   Guitar
info: Specialist in Hard Rock and Metal guitar. From
beginner to advanced level. No exams. Teaches from own premises.

CNR School of Rock
Woking
tel: 01483 479 935/07957 577 145
contact: Ren
instrument(s):   Range of instruments
info: CNR School of Rock is located in an old barn
which has been converted into a fully equipped studio with 2 live
rooms. Clinics run by experienced musicians take place every weekend.
Students select songs that they wish to learn, rather than studying
any exam syllabus. One to one tuition available for beginners. Tuition
sessions end with a group jam, and all songs performed are recorded
live.

Colin Thompson
156 Brighton Road, Amstead, Surrey, SM7 1BT
tel: 01737 354 438
email: colin@mainlymusic.co.uk
web: www.mainlymusic.co.uk
instrument(s):   Piano, Electric Keyboard
info: Lessons for all levels and ages. Follows the LMC
syllabus for piano. Musical genre varies more for Keyboard music,
although willing to explore different music styles on both. Teaches from
home.

Copnor Music Centre
Railway Cottage, Copnor Bridge, Copnor Road, Copnor, Portsmouth,
PO3 5AA
tel: 02392 597 784
contact: Brian Walsh
instrument(s):   Most instuments
info: Broad range of styles and exams covered, including
performance preparations. Also have 2 other centres in Gosport and
Clanfield.

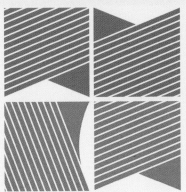

WOMEN IN MUSIC CREATIVE WOMEN

WMCW - A NETWORK FOR WOMEN IN MUSIC AND THE CREATIVE INDUSTRIES

ITS AIM IS TO JOIN UP CREATIVE WOMEN WHO MIGHT WISH TO SHARE IDEAS, GOOD PRACTICE, SERVICES AND BUSINESS OPPORTUNITIES!

WITH AN INTERNATIONAL PRESENCE AT MAJOR INDUSTRY EVENTS, WMCW WILL SUPPORT CREATIVE WOMEN WITH A WEBSITE *(WHICH HAS A GALLERY FOR CREATIVE WORK TO BE SHOWCASED)* A NEWSLETTER, NETWORK MEETINGS PLUS A MULTIMEDIA DVD RELEASE

BORN OUT OF CITY COLLEGE MANCHESTER, WMCW OFFERS A PORTAL TO THE MUSIC AND CREATIVE INDUSTRIES FOR WOMEN ON ITS MUSIC, DANCE, DRAMA, DESIGN AND MUSIC MANAGEMENT PROGRAMMES.

CALL JO HILDITCH ON 0161 279 7302 FOR FURTHER INFORMATION OR EMAIL AT JHILDITCH@WMCW.CO.UK OR VISIT OUR WEBSITE AT WWW.WMCW.CO.UK

SEND YOUR MUSIC AND CREATIVE WORK FOR CONSIDERATION FOR THE WEBSITE, NEWSLETTER AND DVD RELEASE NOW

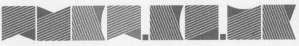

WOMEN IN MUSIC
CREATIVE WOMEN
CITY COLLEGE MANCHESTER
CHORLTON STREET
MANCHESTER M1 3HB.

Creative Studios
Unit 2a, Middleton Hall, Brentwood Road, West Horndon, Essex, CM13 3LX
tel: 01277 812 413/07779 108 629
email: creativestudios2000@yahoo.co.uk
web: www.creativestudios2000.com
contact: Mike
instrument(s): Drums, Vocals, Bass, Guitar
info: Creative Rehearsal Studio incorporates a purpose built music academy which provides professional tuition at affordable prices. All tutors are professional musicians.

Denny Enterprises
4 Beckenshaw Gardens, Barnstead, SM7 3NB
tel: 01737 851 145
email: soundsred@rdplus.net
web: www.dennyenterprises.co.uk
contact: Denny Terrell
instrument(s): Vocal Coaching
info: Pop, Soul and R&B styles taught. Advanced stage and recording skills tuition also available.

Drumsense
65 Holtye Crescent, Maidstone, Kent, ME15 7DD
tel: 01622 204 739
instrument(s): Drums
info: All ages, all styles and all standards. Teach Drumsense exams as well as Rockschool, Trinity and Guildhall syllabuses.

Erin Harte Violinist
7 Hayton Court, Chesnut Walk, Worthing, West Sussex, BN13 3QL
tel: 07736 468 740
email: erin_harte@hotmail.co.uk
contact: Erin Harte
instrument(s): Violin
info: Mainly Classical styles. Can do exams if students request to. Teaches from own premises.

Find Your Voice
19 Seymour Square, Brighton, BN2 1EP
tel: 01273 677 321
email: janjinkerson@fsmail.net
contact: Jan Jinkerson
instrument(s): Vocal Coaching, Piano
info: Teach wide range of styles including Pop, Jazz, Blues and Country. Piano taught at beginner level. Lessons are held at tutor's premises.

Flute, Recorder & Saxophone Tuition
27 Spring Avenue, Egham, Surrey, TW20 9PJ
tel: 01784 438 983
instrument(s): Flute, Recorder, Saxophone
info: All styles and levels. Graded examinations available.

Gareth Lloyd
Woodbury, 6 Royce Close, Dunstable, LU6 2NT
tel: 07764 745 202
email: info@garethlloyd.com
web: www.garethlloyd.com
instrument(s): Drums
info: Teach from beginner to advanced at any age. Repertoire is determined to suit the student, but generally follows GSMD syllabus. Also can teach orchestral percussion.

Gemma Denman
Aldershot, Hampshire
tel: 07929 760 092
email: gemmadenman@yahoo.co.uk
web: www.freewebs.com/gemmadenman
instrument(s): Vocal Coaching
info: Teacher of Contemporary singing. All ages and levels. Tuition on one to one basis from tutor's premises.

Geoff Moore
118 Plains Avenue, Maidstone, Kent, ME15 7AY
tel: 01622 675 825
email: geoff@premierbrass.co.uk
web: www.premierbrass.co.uk
instrument(s): Brass, Composition
info: Teaches all brass, as well as composition and music theory. All grades welcome.

Gill Keenan Piano Tuition
5 Linden Road, Redbourn, St. Albans, Hertfordshire, AL3 7PL
tel: 01582 793 727
email: gillkeenan@onetel.com
contact: Gill Keenan
instrument(s): Piano, Music Theory
info: Exam tuition up to Grade 8 standard and diploma level in music theory. Can teach a variety of musical styles according to the student's tastes. Teaches from home and can also visit students locally.

Guitar Workshop
5 Royal Sussex Crescent, Eastbourne, East Sussex, BN20 8PB
tel: 01323 724 594
email: jstocker@zoom.co.uk
contact: Jason Stocker
instrument(s): Guitar
info: Teaches electric and Acoustic guitar from beginner to advanced level. Mainly teaches Rock but all types of music can be catered for.

Hugh Turner Guitar Tuition
26b Brunswick Hill, Reading, Berkshire, RG1 7YU
tel: 07973 615 405
email: hughturner1@aol.com
contact: Hugh Turner
instrument(s): Guitar
info: Teach both electric and Acoustic guitar. All styles and all levels. Do not cover exam syllabuses.

Ian Stott
28 Rothes Road, Dorking, Surrey, RH4 1CD
tel: 07958 369 380
instrument(s): All Brass
info: Teaches beginner to advanced. Main focus on French horn. Extensive teaching experience including, horn teacher at Epsom College and brass teacher for Ealing and Kingston Music Services

James Allgrove Guitar, Keyboard & Accordian
24 Broomfield Road, Tilehurst, Reading, Berkshire, RG30 6AL
tel: 0118 967 6874
contact: James Allgrove
instrument(s): Guitar, Keyboard, Banjo, Mandolin, Accordian
info: One to one tuition for all ages, from Classical music to Rock. Has an enhanced disclosure certificate for tuition of young children.

James Knight PDC Guitar Tuition
118 Broad Street, Guildford, Surrey, GU3 3BE
tel: 07791 705 144
email: knight_oakes@hotmail.com
contact: James Knight
instrument(s): Guitar
info: Teaches Acoustic and electric guitar to all standards and in all styles. Includes sight reading and theory tuition.

Jerry Lamberth Guitar Tuition
19 Waghorn Street, Chatham, Kent, ME4 5LT
tel: 07766 343 866
email: jerryqcsl@hotmail.com
contact: Jerry Lamberth
instrument(s): Guitar, Bass
info: Specialises in 'finger style' guitar but covers all music styles from Classical to Rock. Teaches from own studio with recording facilities.

Jessie Nickell Piano, Voice & Flute
34 Park Street Lane, Park Street, St. Albans, Hertfordshire, AL2 2JB
tel: 01727 873 358
email: jessienickell@yahoo.co.uk
contact: Jessie Nickell
instrument(s): Piano, Vocal Coaching, Flute
info: Classical training including ABRSM exam tuition up to diploma level. Intermediate and advanced level students only. Teaches from tutor's own premises.

Jim Stewart Drum Tuition
1 Crooks Terrace, Wantage, Oxfordshire, OX12 7BL
tel: 07742 089 666
email: jim@gigajam.com
web: www.gigajam.com
contact: Jim Stewart
instrument(s): Drums
info: Jim Stewart is a local drummer with Oxfordshire based Metallers 'Outofinto' and Rythym & Blues band 'Dr Hexters Healers'. Also teaches drums from his purpose built sound-proof studio. Telephone or email for more information.

Jon Overton Guitar & Vocal
28 Silver Street, Reading, Berkshire, RG1 2ST
tel: 07743 897 688
email: preacher@preacherjohn.co.uk
contact: Jon Overton
instrument(s): Guitar, Vocal Coaching
info: From absolute beginners to advanced players for guitar and vocals. Covers all styles including Pop, Punk, Rock, Reggae, Blues and Folk. Teaches from home and has guitars available to borrow during lessons.

Jon Prentice Piano Teacher
Flat 62, Linkswood, Compton Place Road, Eastbourne, East Sussex, BN21 1EF
tel: 01323 724 182
contact: Jon Prentice
instrument(s): Piano, Music Theory
info: Teach range of musical styles and examination syllabuses if requested. Teaches from home or can visit students locally.

Julia Watkins
51 Chamberlain Avenue, Maidstone, Kent, ME16 8NT
tel: 01622 204 184
web: www.juliawatkins.com
contact: Julia Watkins
instrument(s): Piano, Keyboard, Guitar
info: All ages and all standards welcome. 3 tutors are available teaching a range of musical styles, including ABRSM exams syllabuses. Lessons are given in professionally equipped teaching studios.

K2 Music Ltd.
Unit 70, Fresh Wharf Estate, Fresh Wharf Road, Barking, Essex, IG11 7BW
email: info@k2musicltd.co.uk
web: www.k2musicltd.co.uk
contact: Steve Gee
instrument(s): Drums, Guitar, Bass
info: K2 also run rehearsal facilities and an instrument shop, as well as offering equipment hire and repair services. See listings in relevant sections for further details.

Louise Templer
58 Exton Road, Chichester, West Sussex, PO19 8DS
tel: 01243 780 224/07984 226 272
email: louise@lrmusic.freeserve.co.uk
contact: Lousie Templer
instrument(s): Piano, Vocal Coaching
info: Teaches from beginner to advanced level at any age. Mainly follows Classical syllabus but is willing to explore other musical styles. Also creates performance opportunities regionally and nationally. Will teach at home or travel.

Marina Lyon Piano Tuition
7 Cedarwood Drive, St. Albans, Hertfordshire, AL4 0DX
tel: 01727 811 751
email: marina@lyon4694.freeserve.co.uk
contact: Marina Lyon
instrument(s): Piano
info: Teaches beginner, intermediate and advanced level. Covers ABRSM and Guildhall exam syllabuses up to Grade 8 level. Mainly Classical styles but can cover other styles of music. Teaches at home but can visit students at an additional cost.

The Mayfair Studio
Mayfair Farm, Churt Road, Churt, Farnham, Surrey, GU10 2QS
tel: 01428 712 750/07831 333 502
email: rupert@themayfairstudio.com
web: www.themayfairstudio.com
contact: Rupert
instrument(s): Drums, Guitar
info: The Mayfair Studio offers studio and location recording, as well as rehearsal space. See entries in relevant sections for details.

Michael Finucane Piano
16 Westbere Lane, Westbere, Canterbury, Kent, CT2 0HH
tel: 01227 712 196
email: maf@kentwriters.fsnet.co.uk
contact: Michael Finucane
instrument(s): Piano, Keyboard
info: Lessons available to all ages and levels, covering a broad range of styles including Classical, Jazz and Pop. Can provide ABRSM exam tuition.

Musico
7 Barr Road, Potters Bar, EN6 5PG
tel: 01707 851 555
web: www.learnwithmusico.com
instrument(s): All Instruments
info: Provides a directory of professional music tutors for any instrument, as well as vocal coaching. Lessons available in own home (London area only).

Nicky Moore Singing Teacher
82 Hardy Street, Maidstone, Kent, ME14 2SJ
tel: 01622 208 633
email: nickymoorevoice@hotmail.com
web: www.nickymoore.com
contact: Nicky Moore
instrument(s): Vocal Coaching
info: Works with professional and 'hobby' singers, teaching from own fully equipped studio (including recording facilities). Covers all styles except Classical. Do not follow any exam syllabus.

Oli Baxendale Drum Tuition
38 Bishopstone Road, Stone, Aylesbury, Buckinghamshire, HP17 8QX
tel: 01296 748 644
email: oli.baxendale@gigajam.com
web: www.gigajam.com
contact: Oli Baxendale
instrument(s): Drums
info: Teach beginner to advanced level using the Gigajam school of teaching. A very interactive method, this involves lessons on an electric drum kit with software that monitors the student's performance. Lessons are centred on the types of music that the student wants to play but can cover a broad ranges of styles.

One to One Guitar Tuition
63 Sanderling Way, Iwade, Sittingbourne, Kent, ME9 8TE
tel: 01795 410 314
contact: Paul Clive
instrument(s): Guitar
info: Tuition for beginner to advanced level including music theory and improvisation. Can offer London College of Music exam tuition but covers all styles from Pop to Jazz to Rock.

Paul Tucker Guitar
23 Watsons Walk, St Albans, Hertfordshire, AL1 1PD
tel: 01727 837 172
contact: Paul Tucker
instrument(s): Electric and Acoustic Guitar
info: Teaches all standards of player, mainly concentrating on Blues, Rock and Popular styles. As students get more confident they can work on improvisation and composition. Travels to student's homes.

Peter Siegelstrang Guitar
16 Marconi Way, St. Albans, Hertfordshire, AL4 0JG
tel: 07771 665 872
contact: Peter Siegelstrang
instrument(s): Acoustic Guitar
info: Classical guitar tuition from beginner to advanced level. Can help with exams up to Grade 8 level. Will teach students in their own home.

Phil Craig
St. Albans
tel: 07791 101 395
email: pfgcraig@hotmail.com
instrument(s): Drums, percussion
info: Professional in music industry. Teaches from beginning to advanced level, in Rock, funk, blues, jazz and Latin styles. Follows the Rock School syllabus fro drum kit and the more classical ABRSM syllabus for percussion. Also works in studio production.

Phil Walker Guitar & Piano
1 Hill End Farm, Tyttenhanger Green, St. Albans, Hertfordshire, AL4 0RN
tel: 01727 838 973
contact: Phil Walker
instrument(s): Guitar, Drum Programming, Piano
info: Any age, any level. Can take students through music exams up to Grade 8 if they wish. Covers any musical styles you might want to play.

Philip Gates Piano Tuition
Woods Corner, Woods Lane, Cliddesden, Basingstoke, Hampshire, RG25 2JF
tel: 01256 466 854
contact: Philip Gates
instrument(s): Piano, Music Theory
info: Teaches all standards and ages. Covers ABRSM exam syllabus as well as a broad range of musical styles including Classical, Jazz, Popular and Blues.

POD Music
Phuture Tower, Barker Chambers, Barker Road, Maidstone, Kent, ME16 8SF
tel: 0870 200 0763
email: info@podmusic.co.uk
web: www.podmusic.co.uk
instrument(s): Vocal Coaching
info: Also offer vocal recording and rehearsal facilities. See relevant sections for more details.

Premier Brass
PO Box 958, Maidstone, Kent, ME15 7WZ
tel: 01622 675 825
email: info@premierbrass.co.uk
web: www.premierbrass.co.uk
contact: Geoff Moore
instrument(s): Brass, Music Theory
info: Teach all brass instruments and music theory.

Ronald Howe
22 Balcombe Road, Horley, Surrey, RH6 9AA
tel: 01293 783 452
email: rohow@globalnet.co.uk
instrument(s): Saxophone, Wind Synths
info: Beginner to advanced levels.

TUITION/TRAINING

Russell Scott
80 The Champions, Borehamwood, Hertfordshire, WD6 5QE
tel:	07970 953 489
email:	russ@russellscott.me.uk
web:	www.russellscott.me.uk
instrument(s):	Vocal Coaching
info:	Professional performer and teacher in Classical, Music Theatre and Pop. Coaches all elements of vocal technique such as performance and breathing.

Sera Golding Singing & Guitar
36 Guildford Park Road, Guildford, Surrey, GU2 7NF
tel:	01483 567 145
email:	enquiries@guildfordmusictuition.co.uk
web:	www.guildfordmusictuition.co.uk
contact:	Sera Golding
instrument(s):	Vocal Coaching, Guitar, Bass
info:	Teaches mainly modern styles ranging from Pop and Rock to Soul and R&B. Can give tuition in Contemporary Pop singing exams and Rockschool exams. Teaches from tutor's premises.

Sheila Henderson Piano Tuition
The Firs, Alton Road, Winslade, Basingstoke, Hampshire, RG25 2NQ
tel:	01256 321 272
email:	shenderson@amserve.com
contact:	Sheila Henderson
instrument(s):	Piano
info:	Teaches Grades 1 to 8 from own premises on a Bosendörfer piano. Mainly Classical tuition but also some Jazz and Blues.

The Silent Coup
Unit 3, Grange Farm Units, Nelsons Lane, Hurst, Berkshire, RG10 0RR
tel:	0118 934 0934/07094 601 059
email:	admin@the-silent-coup.org
web:	www.the-silent-coup.org
instrument(s):	Drums
info:	Lessons take place in studio complex with recording and rehearsal facilities, as well as design services. See relevant sections for more details.

Sing Confidently
18 Vernon Terrace, Brighton, East Sussex, BN1 3JG
tel:	01273 889 687
contact:	Zoe Pay
instrument(s):	Vocal Coaching
info:	Expert friendly tuition at affordable rates. All ages and levels welcome.

Singing Lessons Are Fun!
Ferry Road, Rye, East Sussex, TN31 7DN
tel:	020 7735 0532
email:	sandrasinging@hotmail.com
instrument(s):	Vocal Coaching
info:	Vocal development training and intensive coaching designed especially for performing artists.

Sound Foundation
Unit 23, Headley Park, 10 Headley Road, Woodling, Reading, RG5 4SW
tel:	0118 969 0900
fax:	0118 969 1397
email:	info@soundfoundation.com
web:	www.soundfoundation.com
contact:	Mark Payne
info:	Live sound engineer training programme. Intensive 1 day courses covering basic acoustics and mixing techniques. See website for more details.

Stephen Law
Ruislip Manor, Middlesex, HA4 0BT
tel:	01895 471 657
email:	stevejwlaw@hotmail.com
instrument(s):	Piano, Keyboard, Theory
info:	All styles to all levels.

Steve Dawson Trumpet
21 Berens Way, Chislehurst, Kent, BR7 6RH
tel:	01689 602 121
email:	stevedawson05@yahoo.co.uk
contact:	Steve Dawson
instrument(s):	Trumpet,Ccornet, Flugel Horn
info:	Qualified teacher with 25 years of experience. Teaches Jazz and Classical exams, as well as a range of styles including Blues and Latin. Teaches from home or can visit students locally.

Steve Ward
Sussex
email:	swsounds@tiscali.co.uk
web:	www.swsounds.co.uk
instrument(s):	Sound Engineering, Music Technology
info:	Studio system set up and music creation software advice and tuition (including Cubase, Reason, Logic and Digital Performer). Songwriting, arranging and production services.

Streetlights Contemporary Music School
Tally Ho, Sheepdown Drive, Petsworth, West Sussex, GU28 0BP
tel:	01798 343 388
email:	streetlights@btconnect.com
web:	www.streetlightsmusicschool.co.uk
contact:	Chris Mountford
instrument(s):	Vocal Coaching, Trumpet, Saxophone, Guitar, Keyboard, Bass Guitar, Drums
info:	Teach 10 to 20 year olds to an advanced standard. Cover a wide range of musical genres from Rock to Funk to Reggae in their own customised syllabus. Educate about related artists and musicians in the process. Classes are organised into termly calendar and take place at the music school.

Susan Beutler LGSM
25 Brook Street, Aston Clinton, Aylesbury, HP22 5ES
tel:	01296 631 165/07776 185 581
email:	susan@imagingbusiness.co.uk
contact:	Susan Beutler
instrument(s):	Piano, Clarinet, Saxophone, Music Theory
info:	All ages and abilities. Can provide exam tuition up to Grade 8 standard. Mainly Classical but can cover a variety of styles. Teaches from own premises.

Susan Greenham Piano Tuition
60 Upper Fant Road, Maidstone, Kent, ME16 8DN
tel:	01622 750 943
contact:	Susan Greenham
instrument(s):	Piano, Music Theory
info:	Teaches from beginner to advanced level, including exams. Can cater for any styles. Teaches from own premises.

The Academy of Contemporary Music
Rodboro Buildings, Bridge Street, Guildford, GU1 4SB
tel:	01483 500 800
fax:	01483 500 801
web:	www.acm.co.uk
instrument(s):	Variety
info:	Offers a wide range of full and part time courses ranging from Band skills covering instrument tuition, to BA (Hons) Contemporary Popular Music Degree. For further information see the above website or contact the Academy.

Tina Tracey Singing Teacher
91 Sandgate Road, Sandgate, Folkestone, Kent, CT20 2BQ
tel:	01303 814 983
email:	tinatraceys@aol.com
contact:	Tina Tracey
instrument(s):	Vocal Coaching
info:	Teaches beginner to advanced level in Pop and Musical Theatre singing. Covers Rockschool exam syllabus, taught from own premises.

Yamaha Music School Canterbury Ltd.
Simmonds Road, Wincheap Industrial Estate, Canterbury, Kent, CT1 3RA
tel:	01227 456 331
contact:	James Wilford
instrument(s):	All
info:	Teach a wide range of musical instruments, as well as music technology, to all standards with the option of exam tuition. Taught at fully equipped teaching and recording studios. Also have on-site music shop.

SOUTHWEST

Arthur Sigwick Piano & Keyboard
39 Cornmill Crescent, Exeter, Devon, EX2 8TL
tel:	01392 256 834
email:	r4@minimhouse.com
web:	www.minimhouse.com
instrument(s):	Piano, Keyboard, Theory, Music Technology
info:	Teaches all levels and exam support from his studio.

The Basement Studio
2 Trenchard Street, Bristol, BS1 5AN
tel:	0117 934 9013
email:	basementstudio@ukonline.co.uk
web:	www.basementstudio.co.uk
contact:	Troy
instrument(s):	Various courses
info:	Charity working with young people aged between 13 and 19 years. Run free courses in Music Technology, Radio Production, and MC and DJ skills.

Ben Travers
Unit 10, Block 2, Forme Hall Mill, Lodge Moor Lane, Stroud, Gloucestershire, G15 3EH
tel: 07950 859 866
contact: Ben Travers
instrument(s): Guitar
info: All styles taught at any levels. Teaches from the studio.

Ben Watson
Flat 23, 30 Park Row, Bristol, BS1 5LS
tel: 07779 795 989
email: ben@purplelight.com
contact: Ben Watson
instrument(s): Guitar
info: Professional session musician and teacher. Teaches from beginner to advanced at all ages. Lessons at his home or studio. Follow RGT syllabus for exams and explores different styles of music.

Bulrush Studios
Unit 5, Enterprise Park, Mart Road, Minehead, Somerset, TA24 5BJ
tel: 01643 707 277
email: info@bulrushstudios.co.uk
web: www.bulrushstudios.co.uk
instrument(s): Drums
info: Drum tuition on-site. Bulrush Studios also offer recording and rehearsal facilities, equipment hire and CD duplication services. See entries in relevant sections for details.

C. Gilmour
75 East Avenue, Bournemouth, Dorset, BH3 7BU
tel: 01202 761 462
contact: Chris
instrument(s): Piano
info: Teaches all levels, as well as exam preparation from his own home.

Christine Toothill LRAM LGSM
58 New Street, Honiton, Devon, EX14 1BZ
tel: 01404 442 36
email: christinetoothill@lineone.net
web: www.trulliland.co.uk/piano
instrument(s): Piano
info: Teaches all levels and exams from home.

Colin Aldridge Drum Tuition
51 Dominion Road, Fishponds, Bristol, BS16 3ES
tel: 0117 965 6612
email: colinaldridgedrumtuition@yahoo.co.uk
web: www.colinaldridgedrumtuition.co.uk
instrument(s): Drums
info: Teaches all levels from his studio. Also teaches exam syllabuses.

D.A.E. Crocker
Peace Heaven, 112 Broad Park Road, Bere Alston, Yelverton, Devon, PL20 7DX
tel: 01822 840 656
contact: David
instrument(s): Piano, Pipe Organ
info: Teaches all ages and abilities from beginner to advanced. Teaches exams, makes home visits and will also teach from own premises. He is also an accompanist.

Dave Easto Guitar Tutor
56 Beauley Road, Bedminster, Bristol, Avon, BS3 1QF
tel: 0117 963 4849
instrument(s): Guitar, Bass
info: Teaches all levels from his home.

David Barton
72 Courtfield Road, Quedgeley, Gloucester, GL2 4UG
tel: 01452 883 704
email: dcmbarton@blueyonder.co.uk
contact: David Barton
instrument(s): Piano, Vocal Coaching, Flute
info: Teaches beginner to advanced levels of all ages. Covers different genres of music. Lessons from home tailored to the student's needs.

David Guest Guitar Tuition
16 Byfield Close, Woodmancote, Cheltenham, Gloucestershire, GL52 9PZ
tel: 01242 675 985
email: david@play-guitar.biz
web: www.play-guitar.biz
instrument(s): Guitar, Bass
info: Teaches all levels and exams from home.

Des Henley Guitar Tuition
11b Milton Road, Weston Super Mare, Somerset, BS23 2SH
tel: 01934 629 126
email: bellvox@aol.com
web: www.fumbleontheweb.com
instrument(s): Guitar
info: Teaches all levels and exams on request. Makes home visits or teaches from own premises.

Diana Dickerson Flute Tuition
8 Bathwell Road, Totterdown, Bristol, BS4 3AN
tel: 0117 904 0863
email: totterdown@blueyonder.co.uk
instrument(s): Flute
info: Teaches all levels and exams from her own home.

Different Strings
15 Hungerberry Close, Shanklin, Isle of Wight, PO37 6LX
tel: 01983 866 859
instrument(s): Guitar
info: Teach all levels. Playing for 20 years. Harmony and practical theory. Will teach from own or student's premises.

Drum Bank Music Services
203 Gloucester Road, Bishopston, Bristol, BS7 8NN
tel: 0117 975 5366
email: paul@drumbankmusic.co.uk
web: www.drumbankmusic.co.uk
instrument(s): Drums, Guitar, Vocal Coaching, Keyboard
info: Tuition for anyone aged from 8 years upwards, and all levels. Rehearsal rooms available. Drum Bank also have an instrument shop, as well as hire service. See listings in relevant sections for details.

Drum Skills
36a St. James' Street, South Petherton, Somerset, TA13 5BW
tel: 01460 241 369
email: simon@drumskills.co.uk
web: www.drumskills.co.uk
contact: Simon Lomax
instrument(s): Drums
info: Teach all levels from home.

Guitar Tuition (T. Keefe)
6 Martins Close, Wells, BA5 2ES
tel: 01749 679 831
email: tracey_keefe@btopenworld.com
instrument(s): Guitar
info: All styles taught including Rock, Blues, Country and Jazz. 10 years experience. Teaches all levels and exams from his own home.

High C's Singing & Piano
23 Long Croft, Yate, Bristol, BS37 7YN
tel: 01454 321 766
email: viv_evans@blueyonder.co.uk
contact: Sian Walters
instrument(s): Vocal Coaching, Piano
info: Teaches all levels and exams from her own home.

Holmes Music
21-23 Faringdon Road, Swindon, SN1 5AR
tel: 01793 534 095
email: alan@holmesmusic.co.uk
web: www.holmesmusic.co.uk
instrument(s): Gutar, Drums, Keyboards, Digital Piano, Organ
info: Teaches all levels and exams from his studio.

Jane Riley
Vine House, Old Town, Chard, Somerset, TA20 2AS
tel: 01460 649 88/07732 807 744
instrument(s): Piano
info: Teaches all levels and exams from home. Specialises in working with children.

John Lyall
6 Stanley Avenue, Filton, Bristol, BS34 7NQ
tel: 0117 983 3141
email: johnlyall@blueyonder.co.uk
web: www.jldrumtuition.co.uk
contact: John Lyall
instrument(s): Drums
info: Teaches all standards from beginner to advanced in his home studio. Lessons are customised to the individual students needs, but will explore a variety of musical styles from Rock to Swing.

M. Barbey
46 Roman Road, Salisbury, Wiltshire, SP2 9BJ
tel: 01722 334 406
email: michel@barbey.org
contact: Michel
instrument(s): Piano, Keyboard, Clarinet, Saxophone, Drums, Guitar
info: Teach all levels and exams. Teach from home and make visits to students homes. Also teach children with learning difficulties.

The Music Zone
Raglan Road, Brickfields, Plymouth, PL1 4NQ
tel: 01752 213 690
email: info@themusiczone.org.uk
web: www.themusiczone.org.uk
contact: Ben Ballard
instrument(s): Various
info: Provide workshops, tuition and training to young people. Well equipped music centre with instruments, PA, computers and graphic reproduction equipment. Contact for further details.

Musical Originals
The Coach House, Clairvale Road, St. Helier, Jersey, JE2 3YQ
tel: 01534 732 374
instrument(s): Vocal Coaching
info: Singing and voice coaching school. Teaching over 200 students per week.

Nathan Williams Bmus (Hons)
21a Northload Street, Glastonbury, BA6 9JJ
tel: 01458 835 272
email: nathanvibration@yahoo.co.uk
instrument(s): Guitar, Keyboard, Bass, Mandolin, Bazzuki, Popular Music Theory
info: Teaches all levels from Glastonbury music shop.

Nina Lloyd Singing Tuition
1 Southernhay, Newton Abbot, Devon, TQ12 1AX
tel: 01626 207 875
instrument(s): Vocal Coaching
info: Teaches all levels from home.

Passmore Guitar Tuition
2 Nevada Close, Plymouth, PL3 6SY
tel: 07734 863 539
contact: Dave
instrument(s): All Guitar
info: Teaches all levels and styles from student's premises. Weekday and evening lessons. Will also cover exam syllabuses.

Paul Hinam Piano Tuition
Ground Floor Flat, 71 Somerset Road, Bristol, BS4 2HX
tel: 0117 300 5468/07906 288 199
email: info@paulhinam.co.uk
instrument(s): Piano, Guitar, Bass
info: All ages and abilities welcome. Teaches from home or can visit student's premises. Will cover exams on request.

Peter Bengry
2 Riseholme, Avenue Road, Lyme Regis, Dorset, DT7 3AE
tel: 07947 343 639
email: info@peterbengry.com
web: www.peterbengry.com
contact: Peter Bengry
instrument(s): Percussion
info: Peter regularly performs with Cornershop and has played alongside acts such as Beck, Oasis, Pulp, and Beastie Boys. Tuition is offered on a one to one or group basis. Studio recording is also available. Call for further details

Platform One
48a Dodnor Lane, Newport, Isle of Wight, PO30 5XD
tel: 01983 537 550
fax: 01983 241 700
email: info@platformone.org
web: www.platformone.org
contact: David Pontin
instrument(s): Various
info: Offer BTEC National Diploma in Music and Foundation Degree in Commercial Music, as well as running many other projects. Contact for further details.

R.P. Saunders Guitar Tuition
93 Bloomfield Road, Gloucester, GL1 5BP
tel: 01452 410 218
instrument(s): Guitar and Bass
info: Teaches all levels and exams from his own home. Also teaches Classical and Jazz theory.

Rachel Beale
41 Treninnick Hill, Newquay, Cornwall, TR7 2JU
tel: 01637 852 176
instrument(s): Violin, Recorder, Piano and Theory
info: Teach all levels and Associated Board exams from home.

Roger Seville Piano Tuition Dip. ABRSM
56 Holly Close, Threemilestone, Truro, Cornwall, TR3 6TX
tel: 01872 225 740/07817 439 287
email: roger.seville@virgin.net
web: www.rogerseville.co.uk
instrument(s): Piano, Musical Theatre Singing
info: Teaches all levels and exams from his purpose built studio.

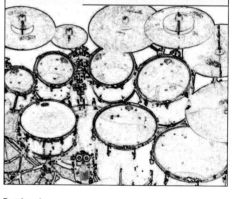

Ros Angel
2 Elliston Drive, Bath, Avon, BA2 1LU
tel: 01225 335 105/07871 868 477
instrument(s): Piano
info: Teaches all ages and abilities. Lessons held from tutor's premises. Will cover exams syllabuses on request.

Sallie Ranken Piano Tuition
Flat 2, 76 Exeter Road, Exmouth, Devon, EX8 1PZ
tel: 01395 263 708/07901 610 300
instrument(s): Piano, Recorder
info: Teaches mostly beginners. Exams up to Grade 3. Will make home visits.

Sally Barnett Cello Teacher
45 Eden Grove, Bristol, Avon, BS7 0PQ
tel: 0117 979 9564
email: sallybcelloteacher@yahoo.co.uk
instrument(s): Cello
info: Offers a free first lesson. Teaches all levels and exams from her own home.

The Soundhouse
Estover Community College, Miller Way, Estover, Plymouth, PL6 8UN
tel: 01752 207 920
fax: 01752 707 921
email: info@soundhouse.co.uk
web: www.soundhouse.co.uk
contact: Phil
instrument(s): Various
info: Run a variety of courses ranging from Indian Vocal and African Drumming workshops, to a Foundation Degree in Music and Sound Technology. Contact for details.

Sue Aston
Chy an Bryally, 15 Primrose Close, Goldsithney, Penzance, Cornwall, TR20 9JL
tel: 01736 719 342
email: sue.aston@geniusloci.co.uk
web: www.sueaston.com
instrument(s): Vocal Coaching
info: Composer, tutor and professional violinist.

Tracy Story
39 Causewayhead, Penzance, TR18 2ST
tel: 01736 754 967
email: tracy@tracystory.com
web: www.tracystory.com
instrument(s): Guitar, Bass
info: Teaches beginners to advanced in guitar and bass. Registry of Guitar Tutors exams taught if required.

W.T. Truran
Treweek, 21 New Street, Penryn, Cornwall, TR10 8EB
tel: 01326 372 326
instrument(s): Piano, Violin, Saxophone, Clarinet, Flute, Music Theory
info: Teaches all levels including Associated Board examinations. Classical, Jazz and Pop styles are taught from his own home.

Yamaha Music School
35 Orchard Street, Newport, Isle of Wight, PO30 1JZ
tel: 01983 523 900
web: http://website.lineone.net/~yamahamusicschool/
instrument(s): Keyboard, Organ.
info: Free trial lesson.

YORKSHIRE

Andrew Marshall Drum Tuition
24 Town Street, Guiseley, Leeds, West Yorkshire, LS20 9DT
tel: 01943 876 649
contact: Andrew Marshall
instrument(s): Drums
info: Teaches beginners to Grade 8 level. Wide variety of styles including Rock, Latin, Funk and Jazz. Reasonable rates. Can travel to student's home, although this will incur extra costs.

Anne E. Sheehan
25 Meadow Head, Sheffield, S8 7UA
tel: 0114 235 9524
instrument(s): Piano, Keyboard, Classical Guitar
info: Will teach beginners up to Grade 8. Covers syllabus from the London College of Music. Anne has her own music studio which lessons are conducted from.

The Art of Music
50 Eldon Court, Eldon Street, Sheffield, S1 4GY
tel: 0114 275 3201/07795 202 712
email: annegarner2002@yahoo.co.uk
contact: Anne Garner
instrument(s): Vocal, Songwriting, Piano, Flute
info: Taught in flexible and fun way to encourage creativity and confidence.

Basil Copley Piano
18 Fore Hill Avenue, Doncaster, South Yorkshire, DN4 7EX
tel: 01302 538 425
contact: Basil Copley
instrument(s): Piano, Music Theory
info: Classical and Jazz tuition for beginners through to Grade 8, and up to graduate level. Broad experience includes teaching members of the Doncaster Jazz Orchestra.

Cloth Cat Studio
127 Woodhouse Street, Charing Cross Shopping Centre, Leeds, LS6 2PY
tel: 0113 244 2773
email: mike@clothcatstudios.org.uk
web: www.clothcatstudios.org.uk
instrument(s): Range of courses
info: Run variety of courses and workshops including how to use Cubase, live sound systems and PAs, songwriting, and setting up a home studio. See website for full course listings. Also see listing in Useful Regional Organisations section for details of other services offered by Cloth Cat.

David Martin
178 Roughwood Road, Kimberworth Park, Rotherham, S61 3HW
tel: 01709 560 629
email: dmmusic@blueyonder.co.uk
contact: David Martin
instrument(s): Piano
info: Teach from beginner to advanced standard at all ages, following ABRSM or Trinity syllabus. Lessons take place from tutor's home. Interest in Gospel music. Teach a wide curriculum of piano studies including pedagogy, and has vast musical resources.

Derek Clutton
12 Meadowfields Drive, Crofton, Wakefield, WF4 1JE
tel: 01924 864 928
contact: Derek Clutton
instrument(s): Piano, Organ, Keyboard, Brass, Flute, Clarinet, Guitar
info: Teach all levels from beginner to diploma in keyboard, woodwind and brass instruments . Up to Grade 4 on guitar). ABRSM and LCM exam tuition.

Drum Therapy
23 Liberty Place, Stannington, Sheffield, S6 5QD
tel: 0114 234 8748/07966 751 978
email: info@drumtherapy.co.uk
web: ww.drumtherapy.co.uk
contact: Paul Hans Bennett
instrument(s): Drums, Percussion
info: Drum Therapy sessions are designed to promote a sense of well-being, relaxation and stimulation. Drums and percussion instruments are used in a group setting. No prior experience required. Participants are initially encouraged to explore the sounds and textures of the instruments. Basic technical instruction is given, and there is opportunity for creativity and spontaneity within the session.

Elaine Axon Guitar & Keyboard Tuition
Medina Avenue, Bridlington, North Humberside, YO16 4NA
tel: 01262 679 122
email: elaine.axon@btinternet.com
contact: Elaine Axon
instrument(s): Piano, Keyboard, Guitar, Accordion
info: Teaches all ages and styles. Exam tuition up to Grade 5 guitar (classical and plectrum) and Grade 8 piano.

Fastfingers Guitar Lessons
8 Carr Lane, Willerby, Hull, HU10 6JW
tel: 01482 657 556
email: see website
web: www.fastfingers.co.uk
contact: Steven Bray
instrument(s): Guitar
info: Mail order guitar tuition by CD and video. Free back up service. Lead guitar, rhythm guitar, Blues, Rock, Pop, riffs, chords. All main guitar styles are covered.

Freestyle Vocals
25 Headford Gardens, Sheffield, S3 7XB
tel: 0114 225 7018
contact: Jahfa
instrument(s): Vocal Coaching
info: Performance tuition. All styles from beginner to professional.

Gary Burt Organ & Piano
241 Stoops Lane, Doncaster, South Yorkshire, DN4 7HT
tel: 01302 531 326
contact: Gary Burt
instrument(s): Piano, Organ, Keyboard, Music Theory
info: Teaches beginner to diploma level. Variety of styles including Jazz.

Gordon Clayton Bass Guitar Tuition
68 Stainburn Crescent, Leeds, LS17 6NS
tel: 0113 228 9377
email: gjc_265@msn.com
instrument(s): Bass, Guitar
info: Guitar for beginner level. Teaches Rockschool and Registry of Guitar Tutors exam syllabus. Variety of styles covered from Motown to Slap Bass.

Helen Audley Clarinet, Piano & Theory Tuition
The Sycamores, South End, Roos, Hull, North Humberside, HU12 0HJ
tel: 01964 670 895
contact: Helen Audley
instrument(s): Clarinet, Music Theory, Piano
info: Classical tuition to all levels (piano up to Grade 5) including ABRSM exams. Will visit students at their own home. All ages welcome.

Jayne Perry Piano & Guitar
8a Church Lane, Esholt, Shipley, West Yorkshire, BD17 7RA
tel: 01274 583 313
contact: Jayne Perry
instrument(s): Piano, Music Theory, Electric Guitar
info: Tuition up to Grade 8 on the piano and beginner level on the guitar. All styles covered including LCM exam syllabuses.

Joanna Lewis Flute Specialist
1 Abbeydale Mount, Leeds, LS5 3RA
tel: 0113 258 2492
email: jo.lewis50@ntlworld.com
web: www.musicteacheryorkshire.co.uk
contact: Joanna Lewis
instrument(s): Flute, Saxophone, Clarinet, Violin, Music Theory
info: Teaches flute to advanced level, and saxophone, clarinet and violin at beginner to intermediate levels. Offers exam tuition. Mainly Classical styles. First lesson given free of charge.

John Little
37 Whiteways, Bolton, Bradford, BD2 4BD
tel: 01274 726 173
contact: John Little
instrument(s): Vocal Coaching, Guitar, Piano, Keyboard
info: Patient, friendly tuition from experienced teacher.
Exam preparation at all levels for piano and singing and up to Grade 5 on guitar.

Judy Day
Beech House, 15 Pickering, West Ayton, Scarborough, Yorkshire, YO13 9JE
tel: 01723 864 384
email: judyday@daymusic.co.uk
instrument(s): Orchestral Percussion, Timpani, Drums
info: All styles. Samba available for workshops. Teaches from beginner to advanced.

Kate James
South Yorkshire
email: kittyjames@hotmail.com
instrument(s): Piano, Saxophone, Clarinet, Theory
info: Teaches piano, saxophone, clarinet, theory and GCSE and A level booster classes. Beginner to advanced.

Kathy Nash Singing & Theory Tuition
3 Tudor Close, Pontefract, WF8 4NJ
tel: 01977 796 452
email: kathy@3tudor.freeserve.co.uk
contact: Kathy Nash
instrument(s): Vocal Coaching, Theory
info: Teaches all styles from Classical to Heavy Rock.
Performance tuition including exam preparation, auditions for music school, and festival performances. Home tuition.

Katy Neary
6 Stonecross Gardens, Canpley Acres, Doncaster, DN4 6UF
tel: 01302 537 961
email: katyneary@hotmail.com
contact: Katy Neary
instrument(s): Piano
info: Teach absolute beginners to Grade 8 following the ABRSM syllabus. Mainly focus on Classical repertoire and takes lessons from home.

Learning Made Easy for Piano & Keyboard
22 Carlton Approach, Wetherby, West Yorkshire, LS22 6XH
tel: 01937 587 186
instrument(s): Piano, Keyboard, Guitar
info: Teaches Grades 1 to 8 on piano, and beginner and intermediate guitar. All styles covered. Can visit students or teach from own premises as required.

Maureen Penfold Accordion Tuition
98 Whitethorn Close, York, North Yorkshire, YO31 9EU
tel: 01904 629 392
email: maureen.penfold@synergybroadband.co.uk
contact: Maureen Penfold
instrument(s): Piano, Accordion
info: Teaches up to advanced levels including exam tuition or just for fun. Styles include Classical, Folk, French and Tango. Instruments also available to hire for students without their own accordion.

Megajam Club
PO Box 534, York, YO32 9XE
tel: 01904 415 069
email: rob@megajamclub.com
web: www.megajamclub.com
info: Megajam Club gives 8 to 18 year olds from York the chance to join a band and perform at top venues in the area. All levels welcome. With support from experienced musicians, members are able to practice regularly and work in a professional recording studio. Also run workshops and masterclasses.

Mrs A. Kirkham Piano Tuition
11 Penn Road, Richmond, North Yorkshire, DL10 4BE
tel: 01748 824 027
email: kirki04@aol.com
contact: Mrs Kirkham
instrument(s): Piano, Recorder
info: Tuition for exams or just for fun. Wide variety of styles up to Grade 5 standard on the piano.

Mrs E.N. McClure
70 Upperwood Road, Darfield, Barnsley, South Yorkshire, S73 9RQ
tel: 01226 752 381
contact: Mrs McClure
instrument(s): Piano
info: ABRSM exam syllabus taught to Grade 8 and diploma level. Specialises in advanced level tuition including theory.

Murdoch School of Music
1 Glenholme Terrace, Ossett, Wakefield, WF5 9RN
tel: 01924 211 540
email: sm014x6425@blueyonder.co.uk
contact: Stephen
instrument(s): Vocal Coaching, Music Theory
info: A Levels and GCSE music support classes. Teaches using Sibelius. Will make home visits.

Oli Deakin Guitar
16 Norwood Road, Leeds, LS16 6AB
tel: 07779 029 226
email: hydeparkguitar@hotmail.com
contact: Oli Deakin
instrument(s): Guitar
info: Beginner to advanced. Covers all styles for students wishing to play for leisure.

Pamela Pritchard
26 Franklin Road, Harrogate, HG1 5EE
tel: 07885 615 030
contact: Pamela Pritchard
instrument(s): Vocal Coaching
info: Singing and voice coaching. From beginner to advanced level. Students must be over 18 years.

Peter Firmani Singing Tutor
35 Folder Lane, Sprotbrough, Doncaster, South Yorkshire, DN5 7PB
tel: 01302 852 869
email: peterandjackie@firmani.freeserve.co.uk
contact: Peter Firmani
instrument(s): Vocal Coaching
info: Member of the Association of Teachers of Singing (AOTOS). Teaches Grade 1 to diploma level. Offers Classical and Theatre music exam tuition, as well as covering Jazz and Pop styles. Fully equipped teaching studio.

Peter Lyth MA
29 Falcon Terrace, Whitby, North Yorkshire, YO21 1EH
tel: 01947 603 507
contact: Peter Lyth
instrument(s): Piano, Music Theory, Keyboard
info: Teaches piano, music theory and harmony. Can teach students from home if they live locally.

Quikstix Drum Tuition
240 Hough Lane, Wombwell, Barnsley, South Yorkshire, S73 0LL
tel: 07876 796 391
instrument(s): Drums
info: Teach beginner to professional levels, including exam tuition if desired. All styles covered. Can visit students at their own home or teach from own premises.

Rainbow Connection
73 Thorne Road, Doncaster, South Yorkshire, DN1 2EX
tel: 01302 360 330
email: rainbowconnection@mac.com
web: www.rainbowconnection.org.uk
instrument(s): Piano, Vocal Coaching, Msic Technology, Drama
info: A public centre for London College Of Music offering Classical, Jazz and Pop piano tuition and exams, as well as Musical Theatre and Pop vocal exams and Music Technology lessons. Demo recording in fully equipped digital studio. Private and group classes available. Conveniently located in Doncaster city centre.

Repercussion Music Academy
Beverley Road, Hull, HU5 1BA
tel: 01482 348 649
email: repercussion@yahoo.com
web: www.repercussionmusic.co.uk
instrument(s): Drums, Bass, Guitar, Keyboard, Music Technology
info: Private one to one tuition available. Repercussion also run an instrument store. See listing in relevant section for details.

Richard Francis Saxophone
9 Coldwell Lane, Sheffield, South Yorkshire, S10 5TJ
tel: 0114 263 0660
instrument(s): Saxophone, Music Theory
info: 40 years experience. Qualified to teach new ABRSM Jazz syllabus and Classical exam syllabus. Teaches from own sound-proof studios. Can source discounted saxophones for students.

Richard Michael Routh
23 Wigfull Road, Sheffield, S11 8RJ
tel: 0114 266 4830
email: michrou6@aol.com
contact: Richard Routh
instrument(s): Piano, Music Theory
info: Piano, theory and composition at all levels, including exam preparation (AB syllabus). Primarily Classical but also teaches Jazz from scratch. 25 years of experience.

Sheila Burman Piano Tuition
1 Watsons Houses, Skipton, North Yorkshire, BD23 1LD
tel: 01756 798 259
contact: Sheila Burman
instrument(s): Piano
info: Teaches all ages and all levels to Grade 8. Can offer a wide variety of styles including Jazz up to Grade 4.

Stuart Day
Beech House, 15 Pickering, West Eyton, Scarborough, YO13 9JE
tel: 01723 864 384
email: stuartday@daymusic.co.uk
instrument(s): Piano, Violin, Theory
info: Professional accompanist and arrangements.
Teaches piano, violin and music theory from beginner to advanced levels.

Stuart Hedington Saxophone
42 Conway Mount, Hare Hills, Leeds, LS8 5HZ
tel: 0113 368 4661
contact: Stuart Hedington
instrument(s): Saxophone
info: All styles and all levels including Jazz and Classical exam tuition. Very competitive rates.

Tim Brickel Drum Tuition
19 Hawthorn Grove, Rodley, Leeds, LS13 1NH
tel: 07989 951 561
email: timothy.brickel@ntlworld.com
contact: Tim Brickel
instrument(s): Drums
info: 20 years experience. All levels and styles. Teaches from own fully equipped studio.

Westside Guitar Studio
1 Steel Road, Hunters Bar, Sheffield, S11 8QP
tel: 0114 268 2342
instrument(s): Guitar
info: All ages. Beginner to advanced levels. Based at own premises. Teaches all styles including QCA exam preparation.

Zoe Carroll Cello & Violin
The Kings Head, 27 North Street, Silsden, Keighley, West Yorkshire, BD20 9PE
tel: 01535 656 434
email: zoevcarroll@breathemail.net
contact: Zoe Carroll
instrument(s): Cello, Violin
info: Teaches cello to advanced level and violin to intermediate standard. Mainly Classical styles. Teaches from home but may be able to visit students locally.

Zonia Binns Piano & Clarinet
71 Hollins Lane, Sowerby Bridge, West Yorkshire, HX6 2RW
tel: 01422 833 660
email: azbinns@aol.com
contact: Zonia Binns
instrument(s): Piano, Clarinet
info: Teaches all levels up to diploma standard. Classical and Jazz styles taught at tutor's premises.

NORTHERN IRELAND

Chantal Clifford
Apartment 3, Sandown Court, 82 Sandown Road, Belfast, BT5 6GU
tel: 07747 855 626
web: www.chantalcilfford.co.uk
instrument(s): Piano
info: Teaches up to Grade 7 standard using the Associated Board. Mostly Classical.

David Lurie
tel: 07732 089 466
instrument(s): Saxophone, Clarinet, Theory
info: Saxophone and theory to advanced standard and clarinet to intermediate standard. Teach both Jazz and Classical styles.

David McClurg
Maranatha, 7 Lennox Park, Carrickfergus, County Antrim, BT38 7HY
tel: 028 9336 4920
email: abrsmteacher@tiscali.co.uk
instrument(s): Music Theory
info: Teaches all levels and exams from home.

Denise Williamson Piano Tutor
6 Roslyn Avenue, Bangor, BT20 4UW
tel: 028 9145 4837
instrument(s): Piano, Music Theory
info: Teaches all levels, ages and styles up to Grade 8 piano and Grade 5 theory. Uses the Trinity College syllabus.

rossARDILL GUITARIST

Professional guitar teacher and session musician situated in Newtownabbey, Northern Ireland.

Call 02890 852 824

www.rossardill.com

TUITION/TRAINING

Guitar Tuition
30 Stranmillis Road, Belfast, County Antrim, BT9 5AA
tel: 07786 834 597
email: paddy@patrickmckeown.com
web: www.patrickmckeown.com
contact: Patrick McKeown
instrument(s): Guitar
info: Teaches all styles. Beginner to intermediate levels. Lessons taken from his own home.

JLG Guitar Tuition
81 Gilpins Manor, Lurgan, Craigavon, County Armagh, BT66 8AG
tel: 028 3834 9876/07871 879 780
email: jlgtuition@hotmail.com
web: www.jlgtuition.com
contact: Ledley
instrument(s): All Guitar
info: Teaches all levels and exams from home.

Joanne Muldrew ALCM
37 Ravenswood, Bambridge, County Down, BT32 3RD
tel: 028 4062 9448
instrument(s): Piano
info: Teach all ages and levels to diploma. Teaches London College and Trinity syllabuses.

Kathleen Hunter
North Down Music Academy, 22 South Street, Newtownards, Down, BT23 4JT
tel: 028 9182 6683/028 9044 8540
email: kateehunter@hotmail.com
web: www.ndma.co.uk
instrument(s): Piano, Guitar, Vocal Coaching, Drums, Trumpet, Violin
info: Beginner to advanced. All styles catered for by a range of teachers.

Kenny Briggs Piano Tutor
25 Springfort Lodge, Dollingstown, Craigavon, County Armagh, BT66 7BE
tel: 028 3832 1256
email: kbriggs@piano72.freeserve.co.uk
instrument(s): Piano
info: Kenny is the regional co-ordinator for the London College of Music & Media. Teaches all levels and exams from his own home.

Komodo
79 Magheraconluce Road, Hillsborough, Down, BT26 6PR
tel: 028 9268 8285
email: info@komodorecordings.com
web: www.komodorecordings.com
contact: Kyle
instrument(s): Drums
info: As well as drum tuition also offer studio recording, cover graphic design and printing, and duplication services. See entries in relevant sections for details.

Making Music Workshop Ltd.
Unit A204, Portview Trade Centre, 310 Newtownards Road, Belfast, County Antrim, BT4 1 HE
tel: 028 9045 6263
email: info@makingmusicworkshop.com
web: www.makingmusicworkshop.com
contact: Linley Hamilton
instrument(s): All Instruments
info: Music workshop teach all levels and abilities and teach all over the UK. They also have a mobile recording studio.

Mark Flanagan Guitar Tuition
Newtownards, County Down
tel: 028 9181 6996
instrument(s): Acoustic Guitar
info: All styles, ages and levels. Teach up to intermediate standard.

Morgan's House Of Music
73 Sweep Road, Cooks Town, CountyTyrone, BT80 8JT
tel: 028 8676 4432
instrument(s): Piano, Guitar, Tin Whistle, Accordian
info: All levels and ages up to diploma. Teach all styles. Also has classes for GCSE and A Level support. Registered with the ISM.

Mrs Margaret Nelson
12 Knocknarea Road, Lisburn, County Antrim, BT28 2TA
tel: 028 9262 1492
email: margaret.nelson@btinternet.com
instrument(s): Piano
info: Teaches from beginner up to Grade 5. Offers exams and teaches from home.

Music DC
14 Gloonan Hill, Ahoghill, Ballymena, County Antrim, BT4 3EA
tel: 028 2587 1151
email: enquiries@musicdc.co.uk
contact: Darren Cumberland
instrument(s): Guitar, Piano, Clarinet, Bodhran, Speech and Drama
info: Gold medallist AVCM Hons, LVCM Hons. Teaches all levels and grades from home.

Ossia Music
5A Sandown Road, Belfast, BT4 3EA
tel: 028 9047 3695
email: info@ossiamusicschool.com
web: www.ossiamusicschool.com
instrument(s): Guitar, Bass, Drums, Keyboard, DJ, Vocal Coaching, Kazoo
info: Rockschool and Trinity. All ages and all levels. Specialise in Contemporary music. Very friendly atmosphere.

Ross Ardill
tel: 028 9085 2824
email: rawziz@hotmail.com
web: www.rossardill.com
instrument(s): Guitar
info: Uses the Rockschool syllabus. Teaches all ages and levels up to advanced standard.

Ruby Colley Violin Teacher
tel: 07730 400 743
email: rubyvroom@yahoo.co.uk
instrument(s): Violin
info: Teaches all levels of Classical violin from her own home. Also offers exams.

Shirley Johnston
Culky, Enniskillen, County Fermanagh, BT92 2FP
tel: 028 6632 2138
instrument(s): Piano
info: Teaches all levels and exams from her own home.

Singing Lessons Are Fun!
Holywood, Belfast, BT18 9LX
tel: 020 7735 0232
email: sandrasinging@hotmail.com
instrument(s): Vocal Coaching
info: Vocal development training and intensive coaching designed especially for performing artists.

Steven 'Dakiz' Davis
16 William Street, Donaghadee, County Down, BT21 OHP
tel: 07759 529 279
email: dakiz@hotmail.com
web: www.dakiz.co.uk
instrument(s): Drums, Percussion
info: Teaches all styles but is Jazz specialist.

Violin Tuition
20 Laurel Grove, Lisburn, County Antrim, BT28 3EW
tel: 028 9262 8782
email: hayley.howe@ntlmorld.com
contact: Hayley Howe
instrument(s): Violin
info: Teaches all levels and exams from home.

Zara Kirkpatrick
41 Bushmills Road, Coleraine, Londonderry, BT52 2BT
tel: 028 7034 2395
email: zarakirkpatrick@hotmail.com
instrument(s): Piano
info: Teaches all ages and levels from beginner to intermediate piano. Teaches all styles.

SCOTLAND

Ainur Poulsen
19 Beech Court, Kemnay, Aberdeenshire, AB51 5PY
tel: 01467 642 878/07947 634 938
email: ainur@fsmail.net
instrument(s): Piano
info: Teaches from beginner to advanced level for all genres and ages. Specialist in Chamber music.

Andy Bell
Achmhor, Roseisle, Elgin, IV30 8XN
tel: 01343 831 078
email: andyandmalc@tesco.net
instrument(s): Woodwind, Piano
info: Teaches up to intermediate piano and Grade 8 woodwind following the Associated Board syllabus. Open to all genres.

Banana Row
47 Eyre Place, Edinburgh, EH3 5EY
tel: 0131 557 2088
email: info@bananarow.com
web: www.bananarow.com
instrument(s): Piano, drums, bass, guitar, vocal
info: Based in a studio complex providing rehearsal facilities and drum hire. See relevant section for details. Pro-shop on-site.

Barry Caulfield
213 Bonkle Road, Newmains, ML2 9AA
tel: 07917 605 931
email: barry.caulfield@strath.ac.uk
instrument(s): Electric Bass
info: Teaches at all standards, encompassing a wide range of styles. Lessons are customised to individual student requirements. Will travel to accommodate.

Bertie Fritsch
Park House, 2 Well Road, Moffat, Dumfriesshire, Scotland, DG10 9AS
tel: 01683 222 862
email: fritsch@zen.co.uk
web: www.soundsrage.org.uk
instrument(s): Drums, Percussion, Music Technology
info: Teach any level, genre or age, but with slightly more focus on the music technology side.

Bridget Kelly
Edinburgh
tel: 0131 228 5394
email: bridget.kelly@btinternet.com
contact: Bridget Kelly
instrument(s): Flute, Piano
info: All levels and ages welcome to study Classical piano and flute. Teaches from home.

CAPTAIN TOM MUSIC

www.captaintommusic.co.uk

Captain Tom
11-15 Ann Street, Aberdeen, AB25 3LH
tel: 01224 647 500
email: info@captaintommusic.co.uk
web: www.captaintommusic.co.uk
instrument(s): Drums, Guitar, Bass, Mandolin, Vocal Coaching
info: Lesson are taught in complex comprising recording and rehearsal facilities. See relevant sections for more details.

Central Music School
16 Aitchison Drive, Larbert, Falkirk, FK5 4PB
tel: 01324 579 947
email: centralmusicagency@fsmail.net
web: www.centralmusicschool.co.uk
instrument(s): Guitar, Drums
info: Offer group or individual lessons from beginner to advanced standard. Classes take place at the school or at another site.

Ceri Heaney
15 Thane Road, Knightswood, Glasgow, G13 3YG
tel: 07970 878 391
email: celticclarion@hotmail.co.uk
web: www.celticclarion.com
contact: Ceri Heaney
instrument(s): Piano, Trumpet
info: Will welcome players of all ages and standard. Teaches trumpet to any level, piano beginner to intermediate. Classically trained but can teach a variety of styles. Will travel to students, as well as teaching from home.

Dave Ford
2 Broonhills Cottages, 29 Frogsten Road, Edinburgh, EH17 8RT
tel: 0131 672 1983/07970 744 986
email: djf@davejford.co.uk
web: www.davejford.co.uk
contact: Dave Ford
instrument(s): Saxophone, Trumpet
info: Interested in developing musicianship by listening and analysing. Will teach all woodwind, guitar, piano and keyboard instruments, as well as some brass and strings. Specialises in tuition for those who want to restart an instrument without having classical repertoire forced upon them. See website for more details.

David Woollven
73 Mouberay Grove, South Queens Ferry, EH30 9PD
tel: 0131 331 1519
contact: David
instrument(s): Guitar, Bass
info: Music tuition for all levels. Home tuition.

Diane Henry
42 Kirkburn, Laurencekirk, Aberdeenshire, AB30 1LG
tel: 07752 443 230
email: diane.dhenry@btopenworld.com
contact: Diane Henry
instrument(s): Brass
info: LCM teaching diploma. All ages and levels taught on any brass instrument. Tailor repertoire to individual to help progression, and so covers many musical styles. Will teach at home or travel to students' premises.

Donald Macleod
31 Stoneyflatt Road, Dumbarton, West Dumbartonshire, G82 3HH
tel: 01389 606 481
email: beagletboo@yahoo.co.uk
contact: Donald Macleod
instrument(s): Guitar
info: Teaches all levels in all musical styles such as Jazz and Blues. Customises lessons to individual students requirements, covering practical to theoretical. Teaches from home mainly, but will travel to student at extra cost.

Douglas Watt
492 Holburn Street, Aberdeen, AB10 7LY
tel: 01224 586 451
email: doug@wheelofharmony.com
web: www.wheelofharmony.com
instrument(s): Piano, Keyboard
info: Teaching up to diploma level and currently working as an instrumental instructor in schools. Can also offer tuition in songwriting. Douglas is also involved with 'Wheel of Harmony', a company that teaches the importance of harmony.

FMK Guitars
11 Wallace Place, Culloden, Inverness, IV2 7NS
tel: 01463 792 661
instrument(s): Guitar, Bass
info: All levels, ages and genres. Follow RGT syllabus. Specialises in Jazz fingerstyle.

Fraser Maclean
32 West Keptie Street, Arbroath, DD11 2BB
tel: 07956 427 875
email: guitartutor@fsmail.net
web: www.guitartutor.0catch.com
instrument(s): Guitar
info: Teaches beginner to intermediate level. Lessons are customised to students preferences. Covers range of styles such as Rock and Blues. Will travel to students within the Arbroath and Angus area.

Gordon Callaghan
Lanarkshire
tel: 07733 116 074
instrument(s): Piano
info: All levels and ages taught. Exam syllabus can be covered if requested. Lessons held at student's home.

Iain Stephens
252/4 Canongate, Edinburgh, EH8 8AA
tel: 07963 594 376
email: iainss@yahoo.com
contact: Iain Stephens
instrument(s): Guitar
info: Over 20 years professional live and studio experience. All musical styles taught on electric, classical and Acoustic guitar, from beginner to advanced standard. Teaches from home.

Jon Jacobs
1 Stennis Gardens, Liberton, Edinburgh, EH17 7QW
tel: 07799 843 598
email: thefunk@blueyonder.co.uk
contact: Jon Jacobs
instrument(s): Guitar, Vocal Coaching
info: Teaching at all levels to all interested. Keen to explore different musical styles, and will teach from home or travel to students.

Kenny Robertson
Glasgow (Southside)
tel: 0141 571 8525
email: kgrobertson@ntlworld.com
contact: Kenny Robertson
instrument(s): Drums, Guitar, Bass
info: 30 years experience in all musical styles including Blues and Rock. Teaches drums from beginner to advanced, guitar and bass to intermediate. Concentrates on improvisation at all levels, with repertoire chosen to progress musicianship. Also teaches how to read drum music. Travels to students for lessons.

Lewis Cannon
13 Rulley View, Stirling, FK6 6QQ
tel: 01324 825 609/07821 925 604
email: lewis_cannon@hotmail.co.uk
web: www.lewiscannon.co.uk
contact: Lewis Cannon
instrument(s): Guitar
info: Teaches beginners to advanced including exam tuition up to Grade 8 if required. Covers a range of styles from Jazz and Classical to Rock and Funk. Teaches from own studio with recording facilities.

Lighthouse Studios
20-22 West Harbour Road, Edinburgh, EH5 1PN
tel: 0131 551 5788
fax: 0131 551 5787
email: via website
web: www.lighthousestudios.org
instrument(s): Drums
info: Lessons cover styles, technique, time keeping, reading and co-ordination. All ages and abilities welcome. The Lighthouse Studios complex incorporates recording and rehearsal facilities. See listings in relevant sections for more information.

Loch Lomond Studios
Unit 20, Block 1, Vale of Leven Industrial Estate, Dumbarton, G82 3PD
tel: 07812 746 985
email: llstudiosphil@yahoo.com
contact: Phil, Phil
instrument(s): Drums, Guitar, Bass, Keyboards, Vocal Coaching, Djing
info: Organisation affiliated with the Prince's Trust. Offers music tuition in various disciplines. Rehearsal studio with DJ equipment can also be hired out on Friday and Saturday nights. Sessions can be recorded. The studio also offers PA hire packages for around £60 per night.

Louise Dodds
14 Wardlaw Street, Edinburgh, EH11 1TR
tel: 07793 848 549
instrument(s): Vocal Coaching
info: All ages and levels catered for. Provide tuition in all aspects of singing including technique, performance, vocal care and repertoire. Covers all musical styles and genres. Teaches from home or local studio.

Marina Adamia
36 Howard Place, Edinburgh, EH3 5JY
tel: 0131 557 6681
email: marina@armazi.com
web: www.armazi.com/adamia
instrument(s): Piano, Composition
info: Also teaches music theory and harmony. Teach piano to advanced level.

Miss Christine Smith
92 Calder Street, Govanhill, Glasgow, G42 7RB
tel: 01866 804 651
instrument(s): French Horn
info: Teaches beginner to advanced level and will take Associated Board exams. Willing to travel.

Mrs Susan Smyth
56 High Street, Gatehouse of Fleet, Kirkcudbrightshire, DG7 2HP
tel: 01557 814 458
email: susansmyth@btopenworld.com
instrument(s): Piano, Violin
info: Follows the Associated Board syllabus and teaches at all levels.

The Music & Dance Academy
33 Clydesdale Street, Mossend, Bellshill, Lanarkshire, ML4 2RS
tel: 01698 734 703
fax: 01698 734 703
email: via website
web: www.the-music-academy.co.uk
instrument(s): Accordion, Bass, Clarinet, Drums, Flute, Guitar, Piano, Saxophone, Violin, Vocal Coaching
info: Run lessons in a variety of instruments from beginner to advanced levels. Repertoire is mix of both syllabus and what student wants to look at. All lessons take place at the Academy.

Pat Spence
Dochroyle Farm, Barrhill, Girvan, South Ayrshire, KA26 0QG
tel: 01465 821 377
email: patspence@piperpublications.co.uk
instrument(s): Flute
info: Teaches all levels and all ages, teaching up to diploma standard.

Paul Wilson
125 Blairbeth Road, Rutherglen, Glasgow, G73 5BT
tel: 0141 631 3197
email: wookieboy@tiscali.co.uk
contact: Paul Wilson
instrument(s): Guitar
info: Teaches Acoustic, electric and bass guitar in all musical styles, especially Modern. From absolute beginners to advanced standard. Lessons tailored around what the student wants to play. Teaches from home.

Paul's Halls
11 Glencryan Road, South Carbrain, Cumbernauld, G67 2UH
tel: 01236 722 228
email: practice@paulshalls.com
web: www.paulshalls.com
instrument(s): Guitar, Drums
info: Lessons take place every Monday evening. Classes for adults and children. Recording and rehearsal facilities. See entries in relevant sections for more details.

Peter Dyer
41 Albert Road, Falkirk, FK1 5LS
tel: 07845 800 303
email: fugee41@hotmail.com
instrument(s): Guitar
info: Teaches beginners from home. Interested in Jazz.

Reza Pervaiz
Glasgow
tel: 07776 487 369
email: rezapervaiz3@yahoo.co.uk
contact: Reza Pervaiz
instrument(s): Guitar
info: Teaches electric or acoustic guitar from beginner to intermediate level, in styles ranging from Rock to Pop. Reza is a songwriter and so explores the practical areas of musicianship such as chord progression and tuning. Teaches from home.

Rick Abel
16 Harvest Street, Wallace View, Stirling, FK9 5GE
tel: 01786 447 875
email: rickabel_uk@yahoo.co.uk
web: www.kiddomusic.co.uk
contact: Rick Abel
instrument(s): Drums, Percussion
info: Renowned teacher and musician, teaching absolute beginners to industry professionals. Covers all ages, abilities and music genres. Will travel to students, as well as teaching from home. Rick is in a band himself. See website for further information.

Ryan Gibson
41 Bendachin Drive, Dunfermline, Fife, KY12 7RZ
tel: 07939 434 882
email: gibbo1982@hotmail.com
contact: Ryan Gibson
instrument(s): Guitar
info: Graduate of the Guitar Institute London. Teaches Contemporary styles in lessons tailored to individual needs. Covers theory as well as practical music. Will teach at home or travel to students.

Scott Auldjo
30 John Humble Street, Mayfield, Dalkeith, Midlothian
tel: 07854 606 112
email: scottyguitar@hotmail.co.uk or scottauldjo@aol.com
web: www.nervosajazzfunk.co.uk or www.chordonblue.co.uk
contact: Scott Auldjo
instrument(s): Guitar
info: Teaches guitar from beginner to intermediate level, covering Blues, Metal, Rock, Jazz and Funk. Repertoire depends on what direction the student wants to take. Will travel to students as convenient. Scott is part of unsigned Jazz/Funk band and a Jazz trio.

Scott Young
Edinburgh
tel:	07970 916 556
email:	info@scottyoung.co.uk
web:	www.scottyoung.co.uk
contact:	Scott Young
instrument(s):	Drums
info:	Offers tuition at all standards and all ages. Follows

syllabus tailored to the individual, covering all musical styles. Will teach at home or travel to students.

Sophie Bancroft
Midlothian
email:	sbancroft@btinternet.com
web:	www.sophiebancroft.co.uk
instrument(s):	Vocal Coaching
info:	Jazz, Pop, Soul and Folk specialist. All levels.

Stage 2000
Taybridge Station, Riverside Drive, Tayside, Dundee, DD1 4DB
tel:	01382 223 332
email:	info@stage2000.co.uk
web:	www.stage2000.co.uk
instrument(s):	Bass, Guitar, Drums, Keyboard, Vocal Coaching
info:	Stage 2000 comprises 8 teaching rooms and 5

rehearsal rooms. For more details on rehearsal facilities see the relevant section.

Steve Haden
1 Crofthead, Kirriemuir, Angus, DD8 4ER
tel:	07971 535 099
email:	kshaden@lycos.com
web:	www.beats-working.com
contact:	Steve Haden
instrument(s):	Djembe African Drum
info:	Teaches traditional African drumming though

rhythms and songs at all levels. Able to travel to students.

Stuart Thomson
8 Newbiggin Road, Grangemouth, FK3 0LE
tel:	01324 871 578
email:	stuart.thomson6@btinternet.com
contact:	Stuart Thomson
instrument(s):	Drums
info:	Teaches electro or acoustic drums in any style.

Tuition for leisure, or can enter students for Rockschool exams if requested. Teaches all ages and levels. Will travel to student, as well as teaching from home.

Tom P. Morris
10 Den View, Blackburn, Aberdeenshire, AB21 0LD
tel:	01224 791 697/07742 943 259
email:	checkthecone@hotmail.co.uk
instrument(s):	Guitar
info:	Mainly focus on Rock guitar. Teaches from his

studio.

Wayan Carliner
Flat 3/4, 5 Wall Street, Glasgow, G1 1PA
tel:	07747 524 704
email:	kingwayan@hotmail.com
contact:	Wayan Carliner
instrument(s):	Bass, Drums, Guitar
info:	All styles, except Classical. Specialist in Jazz

performance and electronic production. Teaches guitar to advanced level, and bass and drums to intermediate. Repertoire is tailored around the student. Teaches from home.

WALES

A.M. Doran Piano Tuition Dip.LCM
18 Highfield Cresent, Abergavenny, Monmouthshire, NP7 6DA
tel:	01873 852 196
instrument(s):	Piano
info:	Teaches all levels and exams from her own home.

Amplified Music
Cross Hands Shopping Centre, Pontardulais Road, Cross Hands, Llanelli, Dyfed, SA14 6NT
tel:	01269 833 808
email:	amplifiedinfo@yahoo.co.uk
web:	www.amplifiedmusic.co.uk
contact:	Simon
instrument(s):	Guitar, Drums, Keyboard, Piano, Vocal Coaching
info:	Teach all levels from their own premises.

Baker School Of Guitar
171 Whitchurch Road, Cardiff, South Road, CF14 3JR
tel:	07730 344 237
instrument(s):	Guitar, Bass
info:	Teaches all levels from home. Exams on request.

Brian Swaddling Guitar Teacher
Aberystwyth
tel:	07984 115 362
email:	dirtybottom@hotmail.com
instrument(s):	Guitar
info:	Teaches all levels from his own home.

Cardiff Guitar School
45 Richard Street, Cardiff, South Glamorgan, CF24 4DB
tel:	02920 638 059
contact:	Brian Firkins
instrument(s):	Guitar, Bass
info:	Teach all levels and exams from their own

premises.

Cardiff Music Tuition
2 Heol Ifor, Whitchurch, Cardiff, CF14 1SZ
tel:	02920 623 422/07971 519 758
email:	cardiffmusictuition@hotmail.com
contact:	Mrs. Pasley
instrument(s):	Piano, Vocal Coaching
info:	Piano and vocal tuition for all ages and levels.

Also cover GCSE and A Level Music and Music Theory. Lessons held in music studio on-site.

Cardiff Sound Scene
36 Cathays Terrace, Cathays Terrace, Cathays, Cardiff, CF24 4HX
tel:	02920 373 144
email:	studio@soundsceneuk.com
web:	www.soundsceneuk.com
instrument(s):	Guitar, Drums, MCing, Djing
info:	Music workshops for young people are held every

Sunday. Entry is £1 and the workshops are open to 11 to 16 year olds. Cardiff Sound Scene also incorporates a recording studio, rehearsal rooms and live venue, Cathays Community Centre. See relevant sections for more details.

Clarke School Of Piano, Woodwind, Brass and Song
Rhydlydan, Nebo, Caernrarfon, Gwynedd, LL54 6EH
tel:	01286 881 556
email:	yvonne.clarke@members.v21.co.uk
contact:	Yvonne Clarke
instrument(s):	Piano, Woodwind, Brass, Vocal Coaching
info:	Teaches all levels from own premises. 3 different

tutors with a wealth of experience between them. Can offer exam tuition up to diploma level. Mainly Classical and Jazz styles and also Pop and Music Theatre in singing.

Classical Guitar
North Wales
tel:	01492 544 259
instrument(s):	Classical Guitar
info:	Teaches all levels from home. Exams on request.

Coleg Llandrillo Cymru
Llandudno Road, Rhos-on-Sea, Colwyn Bay, LL28 4HZ
tel:	01492 546 666
fax:	01492 543 052
email:	admissions@llandrillo.ac.uk
web:	www.llandrillo.ac.uk
instrument(s):	Music Technology, Djing

Colin Owens Drum Academy
3 Aber Crescent, Northop, Mold, Flintshire, CH7 6DB
tel:	01352 840 692/07974 197 009
instrument(s):	Drums
info:	Teaches all levels from his own premises. Exams

available on request.

Community Music Wales
Unit 8, 24 Norbury Road, Fairwater, Cardiff, CF5 3AU
tel:	02920 838 060
fax:	02920 566 573
email:	admin@communitymusicwales.org.uk
web:	www.communitymusicwales.org.uk
instrument(s):	Contact for details
info:	Training for 18 to 24 year old unemployed

musicians. Community Music Wales provides trained and experienced community tutors, equipment, advice and support to give people the opportunity to write, play, record or perform their own music.

Derek Morgan
5 Beili Bach, Rumney, Cardiff, South Glamorgan, CF3 3DR
tel: 02920 794 840
instrument(s): Guitar, Bass, Banjo
info: Teaches all levels and styles from home.

Drum Lessons
PO Box 51, Pontypridd, Mid Glamorgan, CF37 2YQ
tel: 07792 732 760
email: nic@drumlessons.info
web: www.drumlessons.info
contact: Nic Waulker
instrument(s): Drums
info: Teaches all levels and exams from home.

Duncan Bache Music Co. Ltd.
Ty Nant, Cae Capel, Llangurig, Llanidloes, SY18 6SB
tel: 01686 440 683/07876 233 818
email: bache@globalnet.co.uk
web: www.cedar-box.co.uk
instrument(s): Piano, Cello, Guitar
info: Experienced ALCM qualified teacher. Teaches all levels and exams from his home or student's home.

Easybeat Drum Tuition
5 Well Street, Brynmawr, Ebbw Vale, Gwent, NP23 4TP
tel: 01495 311 515
contact: Dave
instrument(s): Drums
info: Teaches all levels. Can teach from own premises or can make home visits.

Elaine Morgan
5 Beili Bach, Rumney, Cardiff, South Glamorgan, CF3 3DR
tel: 02920 794 840
email: elaine@elainemorgan.co.uk
web: www.elainemorgan.co.uk
instrument(s): Vocal Coaching
info: Teaches all levels and exams from home.

Elizabeth Hayes LRAM, ARCM, GRSM
Dragon Park, King Street, Laugharne, Carmerthen, Dyfed, SA33 4QE
tel: 01994 427 919
instrument(s): Cello, Piano
info: Teaches all levels and exams from home.

Emma Openshaw
8 Victoria Terrace, Crickhowell, Powys, NP8 1DN
tel: 01873 811 006
instrument(s): Piano, Vocal Coaching, Theory
info: Beginners to diploma and university level. Classical, Jazz and Contemporary genres.

Gigajam Guitar School
29 Islwyn Road, Wattsville, Newport, Gwent, NP11 7QH
tel: 01495 270 277
email: dan.lucas@btinternet.com
contact: Dan Lucas
instrument(s): Guitar
info: Use the Gigajam course and exam syllabus which is based on a computer that provides backing tracks to play along with. The course is modified according to what music the student wants to play. Beginners to advanced students are welcome.

Glennon Music Tuition
1 Hollybush Avenue, Malpas, Newport, NP20 6ES
tel: 01633 852 543
contact: Mrs Glennon
instrument(s): Piano, Vocal Coaching, Music Theory
info: Beginners up to advanced level tuition. Can help with exams up to diploma level. Teaches all musical styles from own home.

Grassroots
58 Charles Street, Cardiff, CF10 2GG
tel: 02920 231 700
fax: 02920 387 143
email: drivesalive@hotmail.com
web: www.cardiff.gov.uk/leisure/roots
contact: Suke Driver
info: Provides training, recording and rehearsal space for under 25 year olds. See relevant sections for full details.

Immtech
Unit C, Building 8, Curran Road, Butetown, Cardiff, CF10 5NB
tel: 02920 640 500
fax: 02920 640 600
email: immtech@immtech.co.uk
web: www.immtech.co.uk
contact: Jonny Lenny
instrument(s): Music & Multimedia
info: Immtech specialises in training young people in music industry and multimedia training. Courses available in music technology, radio production, DJing, songwriting, video production, rap and MCing, vocal tuition, web design and MIDI technology. PA hire available on request. See listing in Equipment Hire section for details.

Jasey Hall Piano & Brass
20 Garth Olwg, Cardiff, CF15 9HW
tel: 02920 811 448
email: jaseyhall@aol.com
contact: Jasey Hall
instrument(s): Piano, Brass
info: Teaches everyone from beginner to advanced level, including exams. Mainly Classical but covers Jazz and some Popular music as well. Teaches students in their own homes.

Jeff Harris Drum Tuition
106 Hereford Road, Monmouth, Gwent, NP25 3HH
tel: 01600 712 022
email: sunltd@aol.com
instrument(s): Drums
info: Teaches all levels and exams from home.

John Evans
5 Glanmor Terrace, Penclawdd, Swansea, West Glamorgan, SA4 3YL
tel: 01792 851 738
instrument(s): Vocal Coaching
info: Teaches all levels from home.

Louise Roberts Flute And Piano
29 Little Mountain Road, Buckley, Clwyd, CH7 3BY
tel: 01244 546 726/07989 632 999
email: stonycroft29@hotmail.com
instrument(s): Flute, Piano, Clarinet
info: Teaches all levels and exams from home.

Lucy Slane
Carmarthen
tel: 01267 222 112
instrument(s): Piano
info: Classical piano tuition for all levels and ages. Covers Associated Board syllabus. Lessons held at tutor's premises.

Martin Peel Modern Guitar Tuition
17 Rhodfa Lwyd, Colwyn Bay, Clwyd, LL29 8BH
tel: 01492 514 933
instrument(s): Guitar, Bass
info: Teaches all levels and makes home visits only.

Mays Music
St. Michael's House, St. Michael's Road, Abergavenny, NP7 5AY
tel: 01873 855 050
web: www.mayzmusik.co.uk
contact: May Williams
instrument(s): Guitar, Bass, Drums, Vocal Coaching, Saxophone, Flute, Clarinet, Piano, Keyboard
info: Teaches all levels from her own premises. Teaches exams and is also a Rockschool Centre. Also run music workshops and a small theatre production company.

Mr Laurence Talbot
41 Mountain Ash Road, Abercynon, Mid Glamorgan, CF45 4PY
tel: 01443 741 040
instrument(s): Piano, Theory
info: Teaches all levels and exams. Can teach from his own premises or make home visits.

The Music Studio
45a Cross Street, Cross Street, Abergavenny, Gwent, NP7 5ER
tel: 01873 859 966
instrument(s): Guitar, Bass, Piano, Clarinet, Flute, Saxophone, Vocal Coaching, Theory, Drums
info: Teaches all levels and exams from home.

Nigel Lantham LTCL
Penarth, South Wales
tel: 02920 654 776/07910 554 475
email: nigelplantham@hotmail.com
instrument(s): Vocal Coaching, Piano, Viola
info: Teaches all levels and exams. Teaches from own premises or can make home visits.

North Wales Music Tuition Centres
Bod Afon, Mill Street, Betws-Y-Coed, LL24 0BB
tel: 01690 710 364
fax: 01690 710 364
email: brendanwms@aol.com
contact: Brenda
instrument(s): Piano, Guitar, Bass, Saxophone, Clarinet, Flute, Violin, Drums, Vocal Coaching, Music Theory
info: Have 3 main centres in Queensferry, Rhuddlan and Colwyn Bay. Teach all levels and abilities at great rates. They are also a register charity and make donations from all lessons they teach from their own premises.

Paul Demarco Guitar
Amlwch, Anglesey, North Wales
tel: 01407 839 310
email: gumshaw@hotmail.com
instrument(s): Guitar
info: Mobile tuition service for all ages and levels. Can cover RGT training if required.

Pavlina Radoslavova
6 Haverford Road, Cardiff, CF5 5EL
tel: 02920 569 095
email: pavlina@radoslavova.com
web: www.radoslavova.com
contact: Pavlina Radoslavova
instrument(s): Piano
info: Accomplished performer, teaches at the Welsh
College of Music and Drama. Takes beginner to diploma level at
any age through ABRSM exams. Also coaches Chamber music and
ensembles.

Peter Smith African Hand Drumming
Canton, Cardiff
tel: 02920 640 538
email: petersmithcardiff@hotmail.com
contact: Peter Smith
instrument(s): African Percussion
info: Tuition in African percussion including jembe,
goumbe and bougarabou drums. Offers weekly evening classes in hand-
drumming using West African drums and rhythms at both beginner
and intermediate level, in a community hall in Canton, Cardiff. Also
one-off participatory workshops for schools, hospitals, celebrations and
corporate and team building events. Instruments are provided.

The Practice Pad Ltd.
Unit 5a, St. Margaret's Park, Pengam Road, Aberbargoed, CF81 9FW
tel: 01443 838 484
email: mail@practicepad.co.uk
web: www.practicepad.co.uk
instrument(s): Piano, Keyboard, Guitar, Bass, Drums
info: Teach all levels up to Grade 8. The Practice Pad
also offer recording and rehearsal facilities. See listings in relevant
sections for details.

Robert Kay
43 Holly Road, Elwater, Cardiff, CF5 3HH
tel: 07779 887 431
email: mail@robkay.co.uk
web: www.robkay.co.uk
contact: Robert Kay
instrument(s): Brass, Piano
info: Teaches from beginner to Grade 8 standard,
following ABRSM syllabus. Mainly teaches Classical repertoire. Will
travel to students.

Roger Fisher
The Old Chapel, Trelogan, Holywell, Clwyd, CH8 9BD
tel: 01745 561 072
email: rogerfisher@mac247.co.uk
web: www.rogerfisher.org.uk
instrument(s): Piano, Organ
info: Teaches all levels and exams from home.

Saxophone, Clarinet, Piano & Flute Lessons
112 Ropewalk Road, Llanelli, SA15 2AN
tel: 01554 772 380
email: misswoodwind@hotmail.com
instrument(s): Saxophone, Clarinet, Flute, Piano
info: Teaches beginner to advanced including exams up
to Grade 8. Teaches from home. Can also offer accompanist support.

Scout Enterprises
154 High Street, Bangor, Gwynedd, LL57 1NU
tel: 01248 361 846
fax: 01248 361 846
email: scouteuropean@scout-enterprises.co.uk
web: www.scout-enterprises.co.uk
contact: Sarah Roberts
info: Specialise in the provision of performance industry
programmers including free residential courses, workshops, New Deal
for Musicians and OCNs.

Simon Paul Guitar Tuition
56 Graig Nedd, Glynneath, Neath, West Glamorgan, SA11 5HG
tel: 01639 722 030
instrument(s): Electric and Acoustic Guitar
info: Teaches all levels and exams from home.

Stiwdio Eglwys
48 Brynffynnon Road, Y Felinheli, Gwynedd, LL56 4SJ
tel: 01248 671 663
email: george@stiwdioeglwys.fsnet.co.uk
web: www.stiwdioeglwys.fsnet.co.uk
contact: Goerge Kempson
info: Induction courses for understanding how a studio
works as a whole. Introduction to sequencing. Hybu Gwaith (New Deal
for Musicians) clients are welcome. Training is provided in a friendly
and comfortable environment. Also see publishing and recording
company sections.

Street Youth Project
The Wellfare Hall, Wind Street, Ammanford, Cardiff, SA18 3DN
tel: 01269 596 956
email: streets@btinternet.com
contact: Barry Roberts
instrument(s): Guitar, Drums, Bass, Vocal Coaching
info: Songwriting workshops, as well as guitar, bass,
drums, vocals and decks. Also run recording facilities. See listing in relevant section for details.

Tunetown Rock School
1 The Kingsway, Swansea, SA1 5JQ
tel: 01792 473 960
email: john.bevan@tunetown.org.uk
web: www.tunetown.org.uk
contact: John Bevan
instrument(s): Guitar, Bass, Drums, Keyboards, Vocals and DJ
skills.
info: Tunetown Rock School is held in youth clubs
and schools across Swansea. For ages 14 to 25. Deliver Open College
Network (OCN) qualifications. Teach instrumentation and performance
skills, and helps with confidence and team building skills. Also publish
listings magazine and promote gigs. See listings in relevant sections for
details.

Victoria Wright
24 Dinas Street, Cardiff, South Glamorgan, CF11 6QY
tel: 02920 396 035
email: v_wright@hotmail.com
instrument(s): Violin, Viola
info: Teaches all levels and exams from home.

100 Careers in the Music Business
Tanja Crouch
ISBN: 0-76411-577-4
price: £8.20
publisher: Barron's Educational Series Mellor

All You Need To Know About The Music Business
Donald S. Passman
ISBN: 0-14101-845-3
price: £18.99
publisher: Penguin Books Chester Road
web: www.penguin.com

The Art of Mixing
David Gibson
ISBN: 0-91837-117-1
price: £25.82
publisher: Music Sales Limited

The Band's Guide To Getting A Record Deal
Will Anshurst
ISBN: 1-86074-243-2
price: £11.95
publisher: Sanctuary Publishing

Behind The Glass: Top Record Producers Tell Us How They Craft The Hits
Howard Massey
ISBN: 0-87930-614-9
price: £16.95
publisher: Backbeat UK
web: www.backbeatuk.com

The Billboard Guide to Music Publicity: Techniques and Tools of the Professional Publicist for Musicians, Managers, Publicists, Promoters and Record Companies
Jim Pettigrew
ISBN: 0-82307-626-1
price: £12.97
publisher: Billboard Books
web: www.billboardbooks.com

The Business of Artist Management: A Practical Guide to Successful Strategies for Career Development in the Music Business for Musicians, Managers, Music Publishers and Record Companies
Xavier M. Frascogna, Lee. H Hetherington, Xavier M. Frascogna Jnr
ISBN: 0-82307-705-5
price: £13.95
publisher: Billboard Books
web: www.billboardbooks.com

The Business of Music Marketing and Promotion
Tad Lathrop
ISBN: 0-82307-729-2
price: £12.90
publisher: Watson-Guptill Publications/Billboard Books
web: www.billboardbooks.com

Creating A Music Website
Mike Simmons
ISBN: 1-87077-572-4
price: £9.95
publisher: PC Publishing
web: www.pc-publishing.com

The Cut The Crap Guide to the Music Business (Cut the Crap Guides)
Garry Marshall, Berni Georges
ISBN: 1-90441-106-1
price: £7.99
publisher: Artemis Music Wright Sreet
web: www.artemismusic.com

Getting Signed!: An Insider's Guide to the Record Industry
ISBN: 0-87639-045-9
price: £14.99
publisher: Berklee Press

The Guerilla Guide to the Music Business
Sarah Davis, David Laing
ISBN: 0-82644-700-7
price: £19.99
publisher: Continuum International 57 Northampton Road
web: www.continuumbooks.com

How to Be a Working Musician: A Practical Guide to Earning Money in the Music Business
Mike Levine
ISBN: 0-82308-329-2
price: £12.95
publisher: Billboard Books
web: www.billboardbooks.com

How to Get a Job in the Music and Recording Industry (Music Business)
Keith Hatschek
ISBN: 0-6340-186-8X
price: £13.99
publisher: Berklee Press Publications

How to Make It in the New Music Business
Robert Wolff, William. M Krasilovsky
ISBN: 0-82307-954-6
price: £10.99
publisher: Billboard Books Waterhead
web: www.billboardbooks.com

How To Succeed in the Music Business (Pocket Essentials S.)
Paul Charles
ISBN: 1-90404-806-4
price: £3.99
publisher: Pocket Essentials North Cheshire Trading Estate
web: www.pocketessentials.com

How To Write A Hit Song: The Complete Guide To Writing and Marketing Chart Topping Lyrics & Music
Molly-Ann Leikin
ISBN: 0-6340-280-9X
price: £7.95
publisher: International Music Publications

I.M.F.(International Managers Forum) Handbook: A Guide to Professional Music Management
Andy Allen
ISBN: 1-86074-257-2
price: £11.95
publisher: Sanctuary Publishing 40 Hospital Sreet
web: www.sanctuarypublishing.com

Inside the Music Business (Blueprint: Career Builders Guides)
Tony Barrow, Julian Newby
ISBN: 0-41513-660-1
price: £18.99
publisher: Routledge
web: www.routledge.com

Label Launch: A Guide to Independent Record Recording, Promotion, and Distribution
Veronika Kalmar
ISBN: 0-31226-350-3
price: £8.59
publisher: St Martins Press Pepper Road Haze
web: www.stmartins.com

Making It
Danny Praz
ISBN: 1-41340-201-1
price: £14.00
publisher: Xlibris Corporation
web: www.xlibris.com

Making It In The New Music Business
James Riordan
ISBN: 0-89879-458-7
price: £50.95
publisher: F&W Publications
web: www.fwpublications.com

Making Music Your Business
David Ellefson
ISBN: 0-8793-046-0X
price: £10.95
publisher: Backbeat UK
web: www.backbeatuk.com

The Mansion on the Hill: Dylan, Young, Geffen, Springsteen, and the Head-On Collision of Rock and Commerce
Fred Goodman
ISBN: 0-67974-377-4
price: £7.76
publisher: Vintage Books USA

The MMf Guide To Professional Music Management
MMF
ISBN: 1-86074-355-2
price: £30.00
publisher: Sanctuary Publishing

The Music Business
Dick Weissman
ISBN: 0-51788-784-3
price: £9.99
publisher: Three Rivers Press

The Music Deals: A Guide to Making Contracts in the UK Popular Music Industry
Tom Harrison
ISBN: 1-9018-881-0X
price: £7.95
publisher: Harrison Law Publishing 94 Talbot Road
web: www.banditnewsletter.com/books.htm

Music Genres and Corporate Cultures
ISBN: 0-41517-400-7
price: £17.99
publisher: Routledge
web: www.routledge.com

Music Industry Manual: 2004/5
ISBN: 0-95436-141-5
price: £24.95
publisher: Music Industry Manual

Music Industry Uncovered (CAREERS UNCOVERED)
Tania Shillam
ISBN: 0-8566-096-5X
price: £11.99
publisher: Trotman

The Music Management Bible
ISBN: 1-84492-025-9
price: £14.99
publisher: Sanctuary Publishing Littledales Lane

Music: The Business- The Esssential Guide to the Law and the Deals
Ann Harrison
ISBN: 1-85227-013-6
price: £22.50
publisher: Virgin Books
web: www.virginbooks.com

The Musician's Business and Legal Guide
Mark E. Halloran
ISBN: 0-13031-681-4
price: £20.29
publisher: Prentice Hall

New Perspectives: How To Survive & Succeed In The Music Industry: The Indispensable Guide For Budding Musicians & All Who Want To Work In The Music Industry
Teri Saccone, Roger Sproston
ISBN: 1-90390-925-2
price: £10.99
publisher: Emerald Publishing

Off the Charts
Bruce Harling
ISBN: 1-5597-2316-5
price: £6.99
publisher: Birch Lane Press

Playing Live
Paul Charles
ISBN: 0-71199-835-3
price: £12.95
publisher: Wise Publications

Popular Music and Society
ISBN: 0-74561-464-7
price: £19.99
publisher: Polity Press
web: Polity Press

Producing Pop: Culture and Conflict in the Popular Music Industry
ISBN: 0-34057-512-3
price: £16.99
publisher: Hodder Arnold
web: www.hodderheadline.co.uk

The Real Deal: How to Get Signed to a Record Label From A to Z
Daylle Deanna Schwartz
ISBN: 0-82308-405-1
price: £12.95
publisher: Billboard Books
web: www.billboardbooks.com

The Real Deal: How to Get Signed to a Record Label from A to Z
Daylle Deanna Schwartz
ISBN: 0-82307-611-3
price: £12.95
publisher: Billboard Books
web: www.billboardbooks.com

The Rock Band Handbook
Katheryn Lineberger
ISBN: 0-39952-237-9
price: £7.00
publisher: Time Warner International

Secrets of Performing Confidence
ISBN: 0-71366-288-3
price: £8.39
publisher: A&C Black
web: www.acblack.com

Sound Recording Practice
John Borwick
ISBN: 0-19816-608-7
price: £33.50
publisher: Oxford University Press Wincham
web: www.oup.co.uk

Successful Artist Management: Strategies for Career Development in the Music Business
Xavier M. Frascogna Jr, Lee Hetherington
ISBN: 0-8230-768-9X
price: £16.95
publisher: Billboard Books
web: www.billboardbooks.com

The Rock File: Making It In The Music Business
ISBN: 0-1981-619-3X
price: £37.84
publisher: Oxford University Press
web: www.oup.co.uk

This Business of Music Marketing & Promotion
Tad Lathrop
ISBN: 0-82307-729-2
price: £13.99
publisher: Billboard Books
web: www.billboardbooks.com

The Ultimate Survival Guide for the New Music Industry: A Handbook for Hell
Justin Goldberg
ISBN: 1-58065-048-1
price: £21.99
publisher: Lone Eagle Publishing Company
web: www.loneeagle.com

Understanding Popular Music
ISBN: 0-41523-510-3
price: £15.19
publisher: Routledge
web: www.routledge.com

What They'll Never Tell You About the Music Business: The Myths, the Secrets, the Lies (and a few truths)
Peter M. Thall
ISBN: 0-82308-439-6
price: £12.04
publisher: Billboard Books
web: www.billboardbooks.com

JANUARY

SUNDAY	1
MONDAY	2
TUESDAY	3
WEDNESDAY	4
THURSDAY	5
FRIDAY	6
SATURDAY	7
SUNDAY	8
MONDAY	9
TUESDAY	10
WEDNESDAY	11
THURSDAY	12
FRIDAY	13
SATURDAY	14
SUNDAY	15
MONDAY	16
TUESDAY	17
WEDNESDAY	18
THURSDAY	19
FRIDAY	20
SATURDAY	21
SUNDAY	22
MONDAY	23
TUESDAY	24
WEDNESDAY	25
THURSDAY	26
FRIDAY	27
SATURDAY	28
SUNDAY	29
MONDAY	30
TUESDAY	31

the | unsigned | guide

The Unsigned Guide/UK/2006. Material published in this directory may not be reproduced [in any form] without written consent.

TUITION/TRAINING

FEBRUARY

1	WEDNESDAY
2	THURSDAY
3	FRIDAY
4	SATURDAY
5	SUNDAY
6	MONDAY
7	TUESDAY
8	WEDNESDAY
9	THURSDAY - CHELTENHAM FOLK FESTIVAL 9th-12th
10	FRIDAY
11	SATURDAY
12	SUNDAY
13	MONDAY
14	TUESDAY
15	WEDNESDAY
16	THURSDAY
17	FRIDAY
18	SATURDAY
19	SUNDAY
20	MONDAY
21	TUESDAY
22	WEDNESDAY
23	THURSDAY
24	FRIDAY
25	SATURDAY
26	SUNDAY
27	MONDAY
28	TUESDAY

MARCH

WEDNESDAY	1
CWLWM CELTAIDD 3rd-5th - THURSDAY	2
FRIDAY	3
SATURDAY	4
SUNDAY	5
MONDAY	6
TUESDAY	7
WEDNESDAY	8
THURSDAY	9
FRIDAY	10
SATURDAY	11
SUNDAY	12
MONDAY	13
TUESDAY	14
WEDNESDAY	15
THURSDAY	16
FRIDAY	17
SATURDAY	18
SUNDAY	19
MONDAY	20
TUESDAY	21
WEDNESDAY	22
THURSDAY	23
FRIDAY	24
LIMELIGHT PRIVATE FUNCTION SATURDAY	25
SUNDAY	26
MONDAY	27
TUESDAY	28
WEDNESDAY	29
THURSDAY	30
FRIDAY	31

APRIL

1	SATURDAY
2	SUNDAY
3	MONDAY
4	TUESDAY
5	WEDNESDAY
6	THURSDAY
7	FRIDAY
8	SATURDAY
9	SUNDAY
10	MONDAY
11	TUESDAY
12	WEDNESDAY
13	THURSDAY - GOSPORT & FAREHAM EASTER FOLK FESTIVAL 13th-17th
14	FRIDAY
15	SATURDAY
16	SUNDAY
17	MONDAY
18	TUESDAY
19	WEDNESDAY
20	THURSDAY
21	FRIDAY
22	SATURDAY
23	SUNDAY
24	MONDAY
25	TUESDAY
26	WEDNESDAY
27	THURSDAY
28	FRIDAY
29	SATURDAY
30	SUNDAY

MAY

	MONDAY	1
	TUESDAY	2
	WEDNESDAY	3
	THURSDAY	4
	FRIDAY	5
	SATURDAY	6
HEADLING DEBEES	SUNDAY	7
	MONDAY	8
	TUESDAY	9
	WEDNESDAY	10
	THURSDAY	11
	ALL TOMORROWS PARTIES - WEEKEND ONE 12th-14th - FRIDAY	12
	SATURDAY	13
	SUNDAY	14
	MONDAY	15
	TUESDAY	16
	LLANTILIO CROSSENNY 17th-21st - WEDNESDAY	17
	THURSDAY	18
	ALL TOMORROWS PARTIES - WEEKEND TWO 19th-21st - FRIDAY	19
	SATURDAY	20
	SUNDAY	21
	MONDAY	22
	TUESDAY	23
	WEDNESDAY	24
	THURSDAY	25
	OFF THE TRACKS SPRING FESTIVAL 26th-28th - FRIDAY	26
	THE OTHER FESTIVAL 27th-28th / DIDJIN HAMPTON FESTIVAL 27th-28th / WE LOVE... HOMELANDS - SATURDAY	27
	SUNDAY	28
	KINGSTON GREEN FAIR - MONDAY	29
	TUESDAY	30
	WEDNESDAY	31

JUNE

1 THURSDAY

2 FRIDAY - WYCHWOOD MUSIC FESTIVAL 2nd-4th

3 SATURDAY - STRAWBERRY FAIR

4 SUNDAY

SUPPORTING DIRTY DC
SUPPORTING FREE ATLAST   LIMELIGHT

5 MONDAY

6 TUESDAY

7 WEDNESDAY

8 THURSDAY

9 FRIDAY - DOWNLOAD FESTIVAL 9th-11th / ISLE OF WIGHT FESTIVAL 9th-11th

10 SATURDAY - FRENZY FESTIVAL

11 SUNDAY

STUDIO

12 MONDAY

13 TUESDAY

14 WEDNESDAY

15 THURSDAY

16 FRIDAY - THE BIG SESSION FESTIVAL 16th-18th

17 SATURDAY

18 SUNDAY

19 MONDAY

20 TUESDAY

21 WEDNESDAY - STONEHENGE

22 THURSDAY - DEEPLY VALE 22nd-25th

23 FRIDAY

24 SATURDAY

25 SUNDAY

26 MONDAY

27 TUESDAY

28 WEDNESDAY

29 THURSDAY

30 FRIDAY

JULY

SATURDAY	**1**
SUNDAY	**2**
MONDAY	**3**
TUESDAY	**4**
WEDNESDAY	**5**
THURSDAY	**6**
FRIDAY	**7**
T IN THE PARK 8th-9th / OXEGEN 8th-9th - SATURDAY	**8**
SUNDAY	**9**
MONDAY	**10**
TUESDAY	**11**
WEDNESDAY	**12**
THURSDAY	**13**
GUILFEST 14th-16th / WAKESTOCK 14th-15th / BLOODSTOCK OPEN AIR 14th-15th - FRIDAY	**14**
SATURDAY	**15**
SUNDAY	**16**
MONDAY	**17**
TUESDAY	**18**
WEDNESDAY	**19**
THURSDAY	**20**
THE WICKERMAN FESTIVAL 21st-22nd - FRIDAY	**21**
LOVEBOX WEEKENDER 22nd-23rd - SATURDAY	**22**
SUNDAY	**23**
MONDAY	**24**
TUESDAY	**25**
WEDNESDAY	**26**
THURSDAY	**27**
WOMAD 28th-30th / GODSKITCHEN GLOBAL GATHERING 28th-29th - FRIDAY	**28**
NASS 29th-30th - SATURDAY	**29**
SUNDAY	**30**
MONDAY	**31**

TUITION/TRAINING

AUGUST

1	TUESDAY
2	WEDNESDAY
3	THURSDAY
4	FRIDAY - BIG CHILL @ EASTNOR CASTLE 4th-6th / DIDJEFEST 4th-6th / RHYTHM FESTIVAL 4th-6th / SIDMOUTH FOLK WEEK 4th-11th
5	SATURDAY - FENMUSE 5th-6th
6	SUNDAY
7	MONDAY
8	TUESDAY
9	WEDNESDAY
10	THURSDAY
11	FRIDAY - ENDORSE-IT IN-DORSET 11th-13th / SUMMER SUNDAE WEEKENDER 11th-13th
12	SATURDAY - BLOOM FESTIVAL 12th-15th
13	SUNDAY
14	MONDAY
15	TUESDAY
16	WEDNESDAY
17	THURSDAY
18	FRIDAY - BEAUTIFUL DAYS 18th-20th
19	SATURDAY - V FESTIVAL (CHELMSFORD) 19th-20th / V FESTIVAL (STAFFORDSHIRE) 19th-20th
20	SUNDAY
21	MONDAY
22	TUESDAY
23	WEDNESDAY
24	THURSDAY - TOWERSEY VILLAGE FESTIVAL 24th-28th
25	FRIDAY - LEEDS FESTIVAL 25th-27th / READING FESTIVAL 25th-27th
26	SATURDAY - CREAMFIELDS
27	SUNDAY *ANGLESEY MOTORBIKE SHOW*
28	MONDAY
29	TUESDAY
30	WEDNESDAY
31	THURSDAY

SEPTEMBER

OFF THE TRACKS LATE FESTIVAL 1st-3rd - FRIDAY	**1**
SATURDAY	**2**
SUNDAY	**3**
MONDAY	**4**
TUESDAY	**5**
WEDNESDAY	**6**
THURSDAY	**7**
BESTIVAL 8th-10th - FRIDAY	**8**
SATURDAY	**9**
SUNDAY	**10**
MONDAY	**11**
TUESDAY	**12**
WEDNESDAY	**13**
THURSDAY	**14**
FRIDAY	**15**
SATURDAY	**16**
CROWPOINT 17th-18th - SUNDAY	**17**
MONDAY	**18**
TUESDAY	**19**
WEDNESDAY	**20**
THURSDAY	**21**
FRIDAY	**22**
LOOPALLU 23rd-24th - SATURDAY	**23**
SUNDAY	**24**
MONDAY	**25**
TUESDAY	**26**
WEDNESDAY	**27**
THURSDAY	**28**
BLOODSTOCK 29th-30th - FRIDAY	**29**
SATURDAY	**30**

TUITION/TRAINING

OCTOBER

1	SUNDAY
2	MONDAY
3	TUESDAY
4	WEDNESDAY
5	THURSDAY
6	FRIDAY
7	SATURDAY
8	SUNDAY
9	MONDAY
10	TUESDAY
11	WEDNESDAY
12	THURSDAY
13	FRIDAY
14	SATURDAY
15	SUNDAY
16	MONDAY
17	TUESDAY
18	WEDNESDAY
19	THURSDAY
20	FRIDAY
21	SATURDAY
22	SUNDAY
23	MONDAY
24	TUESDAY
25	WEDNESDAY
26	THURSDAY
27	FRIDAY
28	SATURDAY
29	SUNDAY
30	MONDAY
31	TUESDAY

NOVEMBER

WEDNESDAY	1
THURSDAY	2
FRIDAY	3
SATURDAY	4
SUNDAY	5
MONDAY	6
TUESDAY	7
WEDNESDAY	8
THURSDAY	9
FRIDAY	10
SATURDAY	11
SUNDAY	12
MONDAY	13
TUESDAY	14
WEDNESDAY	15
THURSDAY	16
FRIDAY	17
SATURDAY	18
SUNDAY	19
MONDAY	20
TUESDAY	21
WEDNESDAY	22
THURSDAY	23
FRIDAY	24
SATURDAY	25
SUNDAY	26
MONDAY	27
TUESDAY	28
WEDNESDAY	29
THURSDAY	30

TUITION/TRAINING

DECEMBER

1	FRIDAY
2	SATURDAY
3	SUNDAY
4	MONDAY
5	TUESDAY
6	WEDNESDAY
7	THURSDAY
8	FRIDAY
9	SATURDAY
10	SUNDAY
11	MONDAY
12	TUESDAY
13	WEDNESDAY
14	THURSDAY
15	FRIDAY
16	SATURDAY
17	SUNDAY
18	MONDAY
19	TUESDAY
20	WEDNESDAY
21	THURSDAY
22	FRIDAY
23	SATURDAY
24	SUNDAY
25	MONDAY
26	TUESDAY
27	WEDNESDAY
28	THURSDAY
29	FRIDAY
30	SATURDAY
31	SUNDAY

Section 9
Index

Alex Flahive, 285
Alexander Accessories, 184
Alexander Graphics, 295
Alexander's Jazz Theatre, 594, 630
Alexandra Carr, 798
Alexandra Popoff, 270
Alexco, 335
Alfie Goodrich, 292
Alfred Premier Luxury Mini Coaches, 525
Alien Eye, 280
Alienistic Studios, 486
A-Line Audio Visual Services, 165
Alison Jane Print, 304
Alison Skidmore LTCL, 810
Alison Townend, 816
Alison Wonderland, 270
Alistair Hughes Studio, 270
Alive, 731
Alive Management, 676
Alive Recording, 447
All About Image, 348
All About Jazz, 763
All Ages Record Shop, 363
All Around The World, 28, 553
All Brass & Woodwind, 210
All Computer Solutions, 101
All Flutes Plus, 175
ALL FM 96.9, 719
All Music, 27-48, 50-52, 54-59, 61-67, 73-87, 324, 379, 382-383, 393, 452, 497, 557, 94, 135-139, 156, 569, 580-581, 588-589, 591-592, 594, 596, 603, 605, 607, 610, 613-614, 620, 622-623, 625-626, 630-631, 633, 638-639, 663-665, 667-673, 675-678, 680-682, 684-685, 697, 763, 781, 818
All Music Guide, 763
All Over Minibuses, 532
All Print & Design, 295
All Record Labels, 763
All Round Productions, 165
All Safe And Sound, 142
All Star Management, 663
All Things Print, 295
All You Need To Know About The Music Business, 234, 833
Allegro, 206
Allen & Heath, 419, 421, 423-424, 427, 429-433, 436, 439-447, 449, 451, 455-456, 461, 469, 472-473, 476-477, 479-481
Allen Ford, 528
Allen of Derby Ltd., 301
Alley Cat Car & Van Rental, 535
Alleycat Studios, 421
Alliance Multimedia, 264
Allianz Cornhill Musical Insurance, 225
Alligator Music, 195
All-Media Music Ltd., 73
The Alma Arms, 602
The Alma Inn, 594
Almega, 350
Alnwick Playhouse, 590
Aloud, 274, 279, 281, 763
ALP Print Services, 296
Alpha 103.2, 717
Alpha Colour, 296
Alpha Communications, 105
Alpha Duplication, 255
Alpha Dynamic Audio, 474
Alphagraphics, 318
Alphanet Media Ltd., 118
Alt. Vinyl, 37, 379, 192
Alt.Vinyl, 37, 379, 192
Alteariamotive Sound System, 482, 169
Altercentric, 560
Altered Media, 118
Altered States, 447
AlternationMusic, 763
Alternative Addiction, 763
Alternative Devon, 764
Alternative Nation, 764
Alternative Swansea, 638, 764
Alternative Ulster, 752
Alternator Promotions, 606, 631
Amadi Design, 95
Amarok Multimedia Ltd., 264
Amazon Sound, 142
Amber, 678
Amber Artists, 28
Amber Music Productions, 239, 663
Amber Sound & Light Ltd., 505
Amberley Video Productions, 552
Ambience Records Ltd., 28
Ambient Sound Hire, 165
Ambrow Ltd., 101
Ambush Management, 664
Amelia Dowsett, 270
Amelia Music, 480, 519
Amen Corner Music, 203
Ameritz Music Productions, 448

The Amersham Arms, 573, 620
Ami Barwell, 270, 289
AMI Music Photographer, 289
AML, 270
Amnesty International, 764
Ampec, 165
Amphonic Music Ltd., 73
Amplifeye, 462, 764
Amplified Music, 219, 829
Amplifier, 697, 764
Amplisound Studios, 448
AMS Music, 419
Amstore, 547, 240
Anamorphic, 93
Anatid, 764
Anchor Self Drive Ltd., 540
Anchor Video Productions, 554
The Anchorage Inn, 612
And Magazine, 751
And Then Strum, 795
Andante Percussion, 213
Andara Print Marketing, 296
Anders Jacobsen, 270
Anderson Print, 315
Andertons, 203
Andrew Brooks, 280, 554
Andrew Carruth, 269
Andrew Future, 287, 620
Andrew Holt Photography, 270
Andrew Marshall Drum Tuition, 823
Andrew Miller Promotions Int. Ltd., 764
Andrew Mullens Piano, 816
Andrew Norwood, 810
Andrew Photographic, 278
Andrew Powell Photography, 289
Andrew Rae, 271
Andrew Sound, 146
Andrew Spiers Photography, 287
Andrew Whittuck, 270
Andrew Wood Photography, 287
Andy Bell, 826
Andy Cash Music Ltd., 373
Andy Cash Records & Tapes, 373
Andy Espin Photography, 278
Andy Forman, 291
Andy Lee Woodwind, 192
Andy Simpson Audio, 146
Andy Simpson Music Centre, 216
Andy's Guitars, 175
Andy's Records, 373, 415
Angel & Co., 233
Angel Pianos, 175
Angel Promotions, 102, 279, 588, 624-625
AngelicFilms, 558
Anglia Music Company, 73
Anglia Polytechnic University, 755
Anglian Self Drive Ltd., 523
Anglo Plugging, 323
Angst Management Ltd., 684
Angus Publications, 73
The Animal Farm, 28, 422
Anime Music Videos, 764
Anna Bates Photography, 280
Annabel Williams, 798
Annagh Motors Ltd., 542
Anne E. Sheehan, 823
Anneset, 312
The Annexe @ The Black Swan, 585
Announcement Audio Services, 160
Ant Music, 210
Antenna Studios, 421, 486, 175, 240
Anthony Fisher, 437, 278
Anthony Jones, 271
Anthony Mosley Photographer, 289
Anthony Tomlinson Studio, 280
Anthony Witt Singing Tuition, 816
Antidote Produxions, 552
The Anvil, 603
Any Subject Ltd., 795
AOTN Sound & Lighting, 156
AP: Design Matters, 132
The Apartment Studios, 480
Ape Design, 132
Ape Music Publishing, 73
Apex Acoustics Sound Services Ltd., 165
APG T-Shirt Screen, 335
Apna News, 747
Apocalypse Studios, 500
Apogee Telecom, 153
Apparelize Custom Streetwear, 335
Applause, 764
Apple Screen Print, 342
Apple Video Facilities, 554
Applecroft, 318
Applegate Van Hire, 523
Appletree Studios, 456
APR Audio, 160
APR Radio, 259
APT, 532
Aquarius Acoustics, 153

Aquasonic, 255
Aquasonic Records, 29
Aquasonic Studio, 456
AR2, 607
Arabesque, 135
Arabesque Music, 810
ARC Recording Studio, 474
Arc Sound Studio, 421, 486
Arc Sounds, 251, 602
Archant, 743, 749, 753
The Arches, 613, 631
The Arches Club, 603
Archway Tavern, 573
Archway Travel, 532
Arclite Productions, 421
ARD Hire Ltd., 540
Ards Music, 213
Arena Entertainment Systems, 156
Arena Music Co Ltd., 74
Arena-list, 764
ArenaPAL, 271
Argiriadis Analogue Electronics, 177
Argraff, 359, 132
Argyll 106.5, 107.1 & 107.7 FM, 728
Ariel Music Centre, 462, 510
Aries Litho, 296
Arietta Music, 195
Ariwa Sounds Ltd., 29, 422
Ark Creative Ltd., 95
Arketek, 74, 676
Armstrong Learning, 810-811, 813
Army Of Cats, 124
Arnett Design To Print, 106
Aroia Music UK, 438, 672
AR-One, 438-439
Arp Concerts Ltd., 636
Arranpaul Audio, 153
Arriva Vehicle Rental, 523, 525, 528, 530, 532, 538
Arrival Vehicle Rental, 535
Arrow Embroidery Services, 348
Arrow Self Drive, 540
Art Lighting Services, 165
The Art of Mixing, 833
The Art of Music, 693, 823
Artees, 344
Artful, 29
Arthur Doodson (Brokers) Ltd., 225
Arthur Sigwick Piano & Keyboard, 820
Arti Promotions, 335
Artic King Music, 74
Artificial Bliss Recordings Ltd., 29
Artisan Audio, 438
Artisan Studio, 304
Artist Les Clark, 129
Artista, 129
ARTISTdirect, 764
Artistic Impressions Advertising, 355
Artrocker, 326, 574, 620, 744
Arts Connection, 664
Arts Council England (ACE), 691
Arts Development in East Cambridgeshire, 141, 619, 697
Arts Journal, 764
Artspec, 301
ArtWorks, 552, 101, 129
Artworks Unlimited, 552, 101
Arvo Studios, 456
ASAP Screen Printers & Embroidery, 340
Ascape Studios, 422
Ashley Press, 312
Ashton Instrument Repairs, 195
Ashwood Recording Studios, 419
Ashwood Studios, 239
Asian News, 747
Asian Sounds Radio (1377 & 963 AM), 719
Askey Graphics & Design, 312
ASM Pro Audio Solutions, 146
Aspect Design & Marketing, 124
Aspect Ratio Productions, 552
Assassination Music Promotions, 329
Association Of Independent Music (AIM), 691
Association Of Professional Recording Services (APRS), 455, 691, 764
Association Of United Recording Artists (AURA), 691
Astin's, 810
Astir Records, 29
Aston Student's Guild, 585
Aston University, 756
Astonishing Sounds, 382
Asylum, 573
AT Sound Hire, 142
ATG Records, 29
Atlantic Audio Ltd., 160
Atlantic Hire Services, 142
Atlantic Records UK, 29
Atlantis Minibuses, 532
Atlas Garage, 530
ATM Magazine, 731

ATM Studios, 510
Atmospheres Production Ltd., 552
Atomic Studios, 28, 422, 486
Atomicduster, 765
Atrium, 92
ATS Digital.com, 363
Attic Attack, 463
Attic Recordings, 474
Attic Studios, 502
The Attik, 586, 625
Atto, 128
AUBL, 636, 763
Audience, 731
Audigist Digital Distribution, 135
Audio & Acoustics, 142
Audio Alchemy, 162
Audio Copying Corporation, 251
Audio Courses Online School, 765
Audio Crafts PA Hire, 146
Audio Energy, 142
Audio Graffiti, 615, 637
The Audio Loft, 445
Audio Masterclass, 765
Audio Plus, 455, 156
Audio Print, 309
Audio Recording Centre, 765
Audio Repair Shop, 177
Audio Sorcery, 456
Audio Underground, 422, 486
Audio Village Ltd., 142
Audio Visual Machines, 142
Audio XL Location Recording, 438
Audio Zone Studios, 511
Audiobulb Records, 29
Audioforum Ltd., 160
Audiohire, 142
Audiojunkies, 765
Audiomaster, 259
AudioPlexus, 240
Audiorec Records, 30
Audioscope, 765
Audioset, 765
Audiotec, 153
Audiowax, 373
Audioworks, 153
Audixion, 474
Auntie Annie's Porter House, 612
Aura Studios, 438
Aura Surround Sound Ltd./Mo's Music Machine, 135
Auralgasms, 765
Aurora Borealis Music, 329, 629
Aurora Light & Sound, 150
Austin Rose Printers Ltd., 293
Authentic Music, 30
Auto Transposer, 765
Autodrome Van Hire, 525
Autography Sound Recording Ltd., 142
Automatic Films, 554
Automatic Management, 664
Automatic Promotion, 620
Autumn Road Studios, 480
Autumn Studios, 463, 259
Avalanche, 410
Avalanche Records, 410
Avalon, 511
Avalon Music Ltd., 203
Avelone, 468
Avid, 74, 455, 557, 560
Avis Rent A Car, 523, 525, 528, 530, 532, 535, 538, 540, 542-544
Avon Promotional Items, 351
AW Jazz, 415
AW Perry Printers Ltd., 306
Awal UK, 135
Award Records, 30
Axe Hire, 535
Axe Victims, 499
Axes All Areas, 765
Axis Audio Ltd., 249
Axis Creative Communication Ltd., 554
Axis Graphic Design Ltd., 109
Axis Recording Studios, 468
Aybul Design, 95
Aye Yer Maw, 637
Aztec Printware & Promotions, 342
Aztec Signs, 344

B

B&H Sound Services, 419, 141
B&B Hire & Sales Ltd., 525
B&S, 259, 602, 731
B. Barron, 805
B.E. Print, 315
B.J. McNally, 315
B.P.M. Records, 373
B.R.A. Records UK, 373
B.Z. Marketing & Design, 109
B-17 Design Publicity & Marketing, 124
B2 Records, 30, 663

the|unsigned|guide

The Unsigned Guide/UK/2006. Material published in this directory may not be reproduced in any form) without written consent

the|unsigned|guide

The Unsigned Guide/UK/2006. Material published in this directory may not be reproduced (in any form) without written consent

INDEX

the|unsigned|guide

The Unsigned Guide/UK/2006. Material published in this directory may not be reproduced (in any form) without written consent.

the|unsigned|guide

The Unsigned Guide/UK/2006. Material published in this directory may not be reproduced (in any form) without written consent.